Beginning & Intermediate Algebra

Beginning & Intermediate Algebra

Fifth Edition

JULIE MILLER

Professor Emerita, Daytona State College

MOLLY O'NEILL

Professor Emerita, Daytona State College

NANCY HYDE

Professor Emerita, Broward College

Mc Graw Hill Education

BEGINNING & INTERMEDIATE ALGEBRA, FIFTH EDITION

This book is printed on acid-free paper.

1 2 3 4 5 6 7 8 9 0 LWI 21 20 19 18 17

ISBN 978-1-259-61675-4
MHID 1-259-61675-4

ISBN 978-1-259-93649-4 (Annotated Instructor's Edition)
MHID 1-259-93649-X

Chief Product Officer, SVP Products & Markets: *G. Scott Virkler*
Vice President, General Manager, Products & Markets: *Marty Lange*
Vice President, Content Design & Delivery: *Betsy Whalen*
Managing Director: *Ryan Blankenship*
Brand Manager: *Amber Van Namee*
Director, Product Development: *Rose Koos*
Product Developer: *Luke Whalen*
Director of Marketing: *Sally Yagan*
Marketing Coordinator: *Annie Clarke*
Digital Product Analyst: *Ruth Czarnecki-Lichstein*
Digital Product Analyst: *Adam Fischer*
Director, Content Design & Delivery: *Linda Avenarius*
Program Manager: *Lora Neyens*
Content Project Manager: *Peggy J. Selle*
Assessment Project Manager: *Emily Windelborn*
Buyer: *Jennifer Pickel*
Design: *David W. Hash*
Content Licensing Specialists: *Carrie Burger, Melisa Seegmiller*
Cover Image: © *Juanmonino/iStock/Getty Images Plus/Getty Images*
Compositor: *SPi Global*
Typeface: *10/12 pt STIX MathJax Main*
Printer: *LSC Communications*

Library of Congress Cataloging-in-Publication Data

Names: Miller, Julie, 1962- | O'Neill, Molly, 1953- | Hyde, Nancy.
Title: Beginning & intermediate algebra/Julie Miller, professor emerita, Daytona State College, Molly O'Neill, professor emerita, Daytona State College, Nancy Hyde, professor emerita, Broward College.
Other titles: Beginning and intermediate algebra
Description: Fifth edition. | New York, NY : McGraw-Hill Education, [2018] | Includes index.
Identifiers: LCCN 2016049795 | ISBN 9781259616754 (alk. paper)
Subjects: LCSH: Algebra—Textbooks.
Classification: LCC QA152.3.M57 2018 | DDC 512.9—dc23
LC record available at https://lccn.loc.gov/2016049795

mheducation.com/highered

Letter from the Authors

Dear Colleagues,

Across the country, Developmental Math courses are in a state of flux and we as instructors are at the center of it all. As many of our institutions are grappling with the challenges of placement, retention, and graduation rates, we are on the front lines with our students—supporting each one of them in their educational journey.

Flexibility—No Matter Your Course Format!

The three of us each teach differently, as do many of our current users. The Miller/O'Neill/Hyde series is designed for successful use in a variety of different course formats, both traditional and modern—traditional classroom lecture settings, flipped classrooms, hybrid classes, and online-only classes.

Ease of Instructor Preparation

We've all had to fill in for a colleague, pick up a last-minute section, or find ourselves running across campus to yet a different course. The Miller/O'Neill/Hyde series is carefully designed to support instructors teaching in a variety of different settings and circumstances. Experienced, senior faculty members can draw from a massive library of static and algorithmic content found in ALEKS and Connect Hosted by ALEKS to meticulously build assignments and assessments sharply tailored to individual student needs. Newer, part-time adjunct professors, on the other hand, can lean for support on a wide range of digital resources and prebuilt assignments that are ready to go from Day 1, affording them an opportunity to facilitate successful student outcomes in spite of little or no time to prepare for class in advance.

Many instructors want to incorporate discovery-based learning and groupwork into their courses but don't have time to write or find quality materials. We have ready-made Group Activities that are found at the end of each chapter. Furthermore, each section of the text has numerous discovery-based activities that we have tested in our own classrooms. These are found in the Student Resource Manual along with other targeted worksheets for additional practice and materials for a student portfolio.

Student Success—Now and in the Future

Too often our math placement tests fail our students, which can lead to frustration, anxiety, and often withdrawal from their education journey. We encourage you to learn more about ALEKS Placement, Preparation, and Learning (ALEKS PPL), which uses adaptive learning technology to place students appropriately. No matter the skills they come in with, the Miller/O'Neill/Hyde series provides resources and support that uniquely positions them for success in that course and for their next course. Whether they need a brush-up on their basic skills, ADA supportive materials, or advanced topics to help bridge them into the next level, we've created a support system for them.

We hope you are as excited as we are about the series and the supporting resources and services that accompany it. Please reach out to any of us with any questions or comments you have about our texts.

Julie Miller
julie.miller.math@gmail.com

Molly O'Neill
molly.s.oneill@gmail.com

Nancy Hyde
nhyde@montanasky.com

About the Authors

Julie Miller is from Daytona State College, where she taught developmental and upper-level mathematics courses for 20 years. Prior to her work at Daytona State College, she worked as a software engineer for General Electric in the area of flight and radar simulation. Julie earned a bachelor of science in applied mathematics from Union College in Schenectady, New York, and a master of science in mathematics from the University of Florida. In addition to this textbook, she has authored textbooks for college algebra, trigonometry, and precalculus, as well as several short works of fiction and nonfiction for young readers.

"My father is a medical researcher, and I got hooked on math and science when I was young and would visit his laboratory. I can remember using graph paper to plot data points for his experiments and doing simple calculations. He would then tell me what the peaks and features in the graph meant in the context of his experiment. I think that applications and hands-on experience made math come alive for me and I'd like to see math come alive for my students."

—Julie Miller

Molly O'Neill is also from Daytona State College, where she taught for 22 years in the School of Mathematics. She has taught a variety of courses from developmental mathematics to calculus. Before she came to Florida, Molly taught as an adjunct instructor at the University of Michigan–Dearborn, Eastern Michigan University, Wayne State University, and Oakland Community College. Molly earned a bachelor of science in mathematics and a master of arts and teaching from Western Michigan University in Kalamazoo, Michigan. Besides this textbook, she has authored several course supplements for college algebra, trigonometry, and precalculus and has reviewed texts for developmental mathematics.

"I differ from many of my colleagues in that math was not always easy for me. But in seventh grade I had a teacher who taught me that if I follow the rules of mathematics, even I could solve math problems. Once I understood this, I enjoyed math to the point of choosing it for my career. I now have the greatest job because I get to do math every day and I have the opportunity to influence my students just as I was influenced. Authoring these texts has given me another avenue to reach even more students."

—Molly O'Neill

Nancy Hyde served as a full-time faculty member of the Mathematics Department at Broward College for 24 years. During this time she taught the full spectrum of courses from developmental math through differential equations. She received a bachelor of science degree in math education from Florida State University and a master's degree in math education from Florida Atlantic University. She has conducted workshops and seminars for both students and teachers on the use of technology in the classroom. In addition to this textbook, she has authored a graphing calculator supplement for *College Algebra.*

"I grew up in Brevard County, Florida, where my father worked at Cape Canaveral. I was always excited by mathematics and physics in relation to the space program. As I studied higher levels of mathematics I became more intrigued by its abstract nature and infinite possibilities. It is enjoyable and rewarding to convey this perspective to students while helping them to understand mathematics."

—Nancy Hyde

Dedication

To Our Students

Julie Miller ❧ Molly O'Neill ❧ Nancy Hyde

The Miller/O'Neill/Hyde Developmental Math Series

Julie Miller, Molly O'Neill, and Nancy Hyde originally wrote their developmental math series because students were entering their College Algebra course underprepared. The students were not mathematically mature enough to understand the concepts of math, nor were they fully engaged with the material. The authors began their developmental mathematics offerings with intermediate algebra to help bridge that gap. This in turn developed into several series of textbooks from Prealgebra through Precalculus to help students at all levels before Calculus.

What sets all of the Miller/O'Neill/Hyde series apart is that they address course issues through an author-created digital package that maintains a consistent voice and notation throughout the program. This consistency—in videos, PowerPoints, Lecture Notes, and Group Activities—coupled with the power of ALEKS and Connect Hosted by ALEKS, ensures that students master the skills necessary to be successful in Developmental Math through Precalculus and prepares them for the calculus sequence.

Developmental Math Series (Hardback)

The hardback series is the more traditional in approach, yet balanced in its treatment of skills and concepts development for success in subsequent courses.

Beginning Algebra, Fifth Edition
Beginning & Intermediate Algebra, Fifth Edition
Intermediate Algebra, Fifth Edition

Developmental Math Series (Softback)

The softback series includes a stronger emphasis on conceptual learning through Skill Practice features and Concept Connections, which are intended to help students with the conceptual meaning of the problems they are solving.

Basic College Mathematics, Third Edition
Prealgebra, Second Edition
Prealgebra & Introductory Algebra, First Edition
Introductory Algebra, Third Edition
Intermediate Algebra, Third Edition

College Algebra/Precalculus Series

The Precalculus series serves as the bridge from Developmental Math coursework to setting the stage for future courses, including the skills and concepts needed for Calculus.

College Algebra, Second Edition
College Algebra and Trigonometry, First Edition
Precalculus, First Edition

Acknowledgments

The author team most humbly would like to thank all the people who have contributed to this project.

Special thanks to our team of digital contributors for their thousands of hours of work: to Kelly Jackson, Andrea Hendricks, Jody Harris, Lizette Hernandez Foley, Lisa Rombes, Kelly Kohlmetz, and Leah Rineck for their devoted work on the integrated video and study guides. Thank you as well to Lisa Rombes, J.D. Herdlick, Adam Fischer, and Rob Brieler, the masters of ceremonies for SmartBook with Learning Resources. To Donna Gerken, Nathalie Vega-Rhodes, and Steve Toner: thank you for the countless grueling hours working through spreadsheets to ensure thorough coverage of Connect Math content. To our digital authors, Jody Harris, Linda Schott, Lizette Hernandez Foley, Michael Larkin, and Alina Coronel: thank you for spreading our content to the digital world of Connect Math. We also offer our sincerest appreciation to the outstanding video talent: Jody Harris, Alina Coronel, Didi Quesada, Tony Alfonso, and Brianna Kurtz. So many students have learned from you! To Hal Whipple, Carey Lange, and Julie Kennedy: thank you so much for ensuring accuracy in our manuscripts.

Finally, we greatly appreciate the many people behind the scenes at McGraw-Hill without whom we would still be on page 1. First and foremost, to Luke Whalen, our product developer and newest member of the team. Thanks for being our help desk. You've been a hero filling some big shoes in the day-to-day help on all things math, English, and editorial. To Amber Van Namee, our brand manager and team leader: thank you so much for leading us down this path. Your insight, creativity, and commitment to our project has made our job easier.

To the marketing team, Sally Yagan and Annie Clark: thank you for your creative ideas in making our books come to life in the market. Thank you as well to Mary Ellen Rahn for continuing to drive our long-term content vision through her market development efforts. To the digital content experts, Rob Brieler and Adam Fischer: we are most grateful for your long hours of work and innovation in a world that changes from day to day. And many thanks to the team at ALEKS for creating its spectacular adaptive technology and for overseeing the quality control in Connect Math.

To the production team: Peggy Selle, Carrie Burger, Emily Windelborn, Lora Neyens, and Lorraine Buczek—thank you for making the manuscript beautiful and for keeping the train on the track. You've been amazing. And finally, to Ryan Blankenship, Marty Lange, and Kurt Strand: thank you for supporting our projects for many years and for the confidence you've always shown in us.

Most importantly, we give special thanks to the students and instructors who use our series in their classes.

Julie Miller
Molly O'Neill
Nancy Hyde

Contents

Chapter 15 (Online)

To the Student

Take a deep breath and know that you aren't alone. Your instructor, fellow students, and we, your authors, are here to help you learn and master the material for this course and prepare you for future courses. You may feel like math just isn't your thing, or maybe it's been a long time since you've had a math class—that's okay!

We wrote the text and all the supporting materials with you in mind. Most of our students aren't really sure how to be successful in math, but we can help with that.

As you begin your class, we'd like to offer some specific suggestions:

1. **Attend class.** Arrive on time and be prepared. If your instructor has asked you to read prior to attending class—do it. How often have you sat in class and thought you understood the material, only to get home and realize you don't know how to get started? By reading and trying a couple of Skill Practice exercises, which follow each example, you will be able to ask questions and gain clarification from your instructor when needed.
2. **Be an *active* learner.** Whether you are at lecture, watching an author lecture or exercise video, or are reading the text, pick up a pencil and work out the examples given. Math is learned only by doing; we like to say, "Math is not a spectator sport." If you like a bit more guidance, we encourage you to use the Integrated Video and Study Guide. It was designed to provide structure and note-taking for lectures and while watching the accompanying videos.
3. **Schedule time to do some math every day.** Exercise, foreign language study, and math are three things that you must do every day to get the results you want. If you are used to cramming and doing all of your work in a few hours on a weekend, you should know that even mathematicians start making silly errors after an hour or so! Check your answers. Skill Practice exercises all have the answer at the bottom of that page. Odd-numbered exercises throughout the text have answers at the back of the text. If you didn't get it right, don't throw in the towel. Try again, revisit an example, or bring your questions to class for extra help.
4. **Prepare for quizzes and exams.** At the end of each chapter is a summary that highlights all the concepts and problem types you need to understand and know how to do. There are additional problem sets at the end of each chapter: a set of review exercises, a chapter test, and a cumulative review. Working through the cumulative review will help keep your skills fresh from previous chapters—one of the key ways to do well on your exams. If you use ALEKS or Connect Hosted by ALEKS, use all of the tools available within the program to test your understanding.
5. **Use your resources.** This text comes with numerous supporting resources designed to help you succeed in this class and your future classes. Additionally, your instructor can direct you to resources within your institution or community. Form a student study group. Teaching others is a great way to strengthen your own understanding and they might be able to return the favor if you get stuck.

We wish you all the best in this class and your educational journey!

Julie Miller
julie.miller.math@gmail.com

Molly O'Neill
molly.s.oneill@gmail.com

Nancy Hyde
nhyde@montanasky.com

Student Guide to the Text

Clear, Precise Writing

Learning from our own students, we have written this text in simple and accessible language. Our goal is to keep you engaged and supported throughout your coursework.

Callouts

Just as your instructor will share tips and math advice in class, we provide callouts throughout the text to offer tips and warn against common mistakes.

- Tip boxes offer additional insight to a concept or procedure.
- Avoiding Mistakes help fend off common student errors.

Examples

- Each example is step-by-step, with thorough annotation to the right explaining each step.
- Following each example is a similar **Skill Practice** exercise to give you a chance to test your understanding. You will find the answer at the bottom of the page—providing a quick check.
- When you see this Animation in an example, there is an online dynamic animation within your online materials. Sometimes an animation is worth a thousand words.

Exercise Sets

Each type of exercise is built for your success in learning the materials and showing your mastery on exams.

- **Study Skills Exercises** integrate your studies of math concepts with strategies for helping you grow as a student overall.
- **Vocabulary and Key Concept Exercises** check your understanding of the language and ideas presented within the section.
- **Review Exercises** keep fresh your knowledge of math content already learned by providing practice with concepts explored in previous sections.
- **Concept Exercises** assess your comprehension of the specific math concepts presented within the section.
- **Mixed Exercises** evaluate your ability to successfully complete exercises that combine multiple concepts presented within the section.
- **Expanding Your Skills** challenge you with advanced skills practice exercises around the concepts presented within the section.
- **Problem Recognition Exercises** appear in strategic locations in each chapter of the text. These will require you to distinguish between similar problem types and to determine what type of problem-solving technique to apply.

Calculator Connections

Throughout the text are materials highlighting how you can use a graphing calculator to enhance understanding through a visual approach. Your instructor will let you know if you will be using these in class.

End-of-Chapter Materials

The features at the end of each chapter are perfect for reviewing before test time.

- Section-by-section summaries provide references to key concepts, examples, and vocabulary.
- Chapter review exercises provide additional opportunities to practice material from the entire chapter.
- Chapter tests are an excellent way to test your complete understanding of the chapter concepts.
- Cumulative review exercises are the best preparation to maintain a strong foundation of skills to help you move forward into new material. These exercises cover concepts from all the material covered up to that point in the text and will help you study for your final exam.

Get Better Results

How Will Miller/O'Neill/Hyde Help Your Students *Get Better Results?*

Better Clarity, Quality, and Accuracy!

Julie Miller, Molly O'Neill, and Nancy Hyde know what students need to be successful in mathematics. Better results come from clarity in their exposition, quality of step-by-step worked examples, and accuracy of their exercises sets; but it takes more than just great authors to build a textbook series to help students achieve success in mathematics. Our authors worked with a strong mathematical team of instructors from around the country to ensure that the clarity, quality, and accuracy you expect from the Miller/O'Neill/Hyde series was included in this edition.

"The most complete text at this level in its thoroughness, accuracy, and pedagogical soundness. The best developmental mathematics text I have seen."
—Frederick Bakenhus, *Saint Phillips College*

Better Exercise Sets!

Comprehensive sets of exercises are available for every student level. Julie Miller, Molly O'Neill, and Nancy Hyde worked with a board of advisors from across the country to offer the appropriate depth and breadth of exercises for your students. **Problem Recognition Exercises** were created to improve student performance while testing.

Practice exercise sets help students progress from skill development to conceptual understanding. Student tested and instructor approved, the Miller/O'Neill/Hyde exercise sets will help your students *get better results.*

- **Problem Recognition Exercises**
- **Skill Practice Exercises**
- **Study Skills Exercises**
- **Mixed Exercises**
- **Expanding Your Skills Exercises**
- **Vocabulary and Key Concepts Exercises**

"This series was thoughtfully constructed with students' needs in mind. The Problem Recognition section was extremely well designed to focus on concepts that students often misinterpret."
—Christine V. Wetzel-Ulrich, *Northampton Community College*

Better Step-By-Step Pedagogy!

Beginning & Intermediate Algebra provides enhanced step-by-step learning tools to help students *get better results.*

- **Worked Examples** provide an "easy-to-understand" approach, clearly guiding each student through a step-by-step approach to master each practice exercise for better comprehension.
- **TIPs** offer students extra cautious direction to help improve understanding through hints and further insight.
- **Avoiding Mistakes** boxes alert students to common errors and provide practical ways to avoid them. All three learning aids will help students get better results by showing how to work through a problem using a clearly defined step-by-step methodology that has been class tested and student approved.

"The book is designed with both instructors and students in mind. I appreciate that great care was used in the placement of 'Tips' and 'Avoiding Mistakes' as it creates a lot of teachable moments in the classroom."
—Shannon Vinson, *Wake Tech Community College*

Get Better Results

Formula for Student Success

Step-by-Step Worked Examples

- Do you get the feeling that there is a disconnection between your students' class work and homework?
- Do your students have trouble finding worked examples that match the practice exercises?
- Do you prefer that your students see examples in the textbook that match the ones you use in class?

Miller/O'Neill/Hyde's *Worked Examples* offer a clear, concise methodology that replicates the mathematical processes used in the authors' classroom lectures!

Example 4 Solving an Application Involving Consecutive Integers

The sum of two consecutive odd integers is −188. Find the integers.

Solution:

In this example we have two unknown integers. We can let x represent either of the unknowns.

Step 1: Read the problem.

...presents the first odd integer. **Step 2:** Label the unknowns.

...sents the second odd integer.

$\begin{pmatrix}\text{second}\\ \text{integer}\end{pmatrix} = (\text{total})$ **Step 3:** Write a verbal model.

$(x + 2) \;=\; -188$ **Step 4:** Write a mathematical equation.

$x + (x + 2) = -188$

$2x + 2 = -188$ **Step 5:** S...

$2x + 2 - 2 = -188 - 2$

$2x = -190$

$\dfrac{2x}{2} = \dfrac{-190}{2}$

$x = -95$

The first integer is $x = -95$. **Step 6:** I... v...

The second integer is $x + 2 = -95 + 2 = -93$.

The two integers are −95 and −93.

"As always, MOH's Worked Examples are so clear and useful for the students. All steps have wonderfully detailed explanations written with wording that the students can understand. MOH is also excellent with arrows and labels making the Worked Examples extremely clear and understandable."

—Kelli Hammer, *Broward College–South*

"Easy to read step-by-step solutions to sample textbook problems. The 'why' is provided for students, which is invaluable when working exercises without available teacher/tutor assistance."

—Arcola Sullivan, *Copiah-Lincoln Community College*

Example 3 Solving a System of Linear Equations by Graphing

Solve the system by the graphing method.

$$x - 2y = -2$$
$$-3x + 2y = 6$$

30. $x + y = -1$
$2x - y = -5$

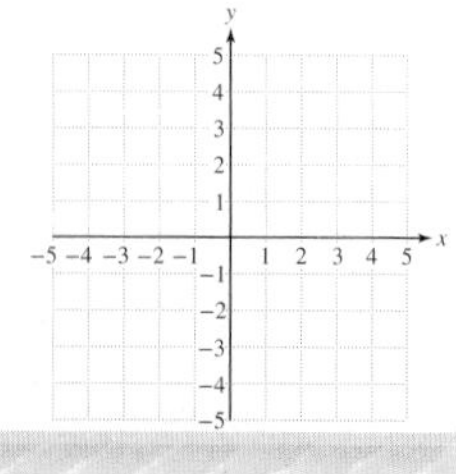

Classroom Examples

To ensure that the classroom experience also matches the examples in the text and the practice exercises, we have included references to even-numbered exercises to be used as Classroom Examples. These exercises are highlighted in the Practice Exercises at the end of each section.

Better Learning Tools

TIP and Avoiding Mistakes Boxes

TIP and **Avoiding Mistakes** boxes have been created based on the authors' classroom experiences—they have also been integrated into the **Worked Examples.** These pedagogical tools will help students get better results by learning how to work through a problem using a clearly defined step-by-step methodology.

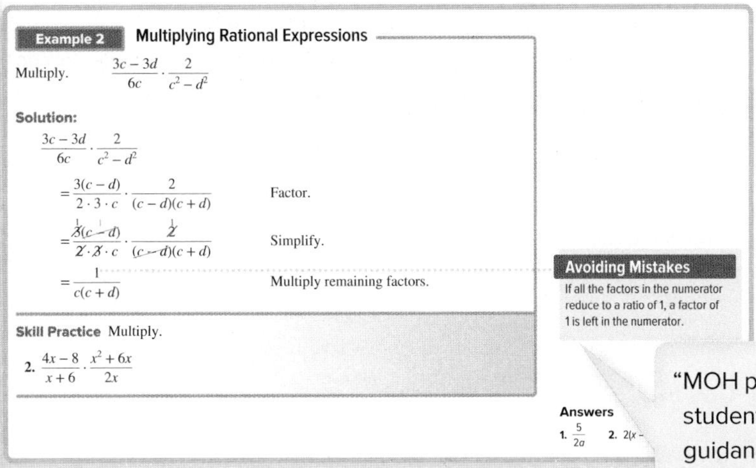

Example 2 Multiplying Rational Expressions

Multiply. $\frac{3c-3d}{6c}\cdot\frac{2}{c^2-d^2}$

Solution:

$\frac{3c-3d}{6c}\cdot\frac{2}{c^2-d^2}$

$=\frac{3(c-d)}{2\cdot 3\cdot c}\cdot\frac{2}{(c-d)(c+d)}$ Factor.

$=\frac{\cancel{3}(\cancel{c-d})}{\cancel{2}\cdot\cancel{3}\cdot c}\cdot\frac{\cancel{2}}{(\cancel{c-d})(c+d)}$ Simplify.

$=\frac{1}{c(c+d)}$ Multiply remaining factors.

Skill Practice Multiply.

2. $\frac{4x-8}{x+6}\cdot\frac{x^2+6x}{2x}$

Avoiding Mistakes

If all the factors in the numerator reduce to a ratio of 1, a factor of 1 is left in the numerator.

Answers

1. $\frac{5}{2a}$ 2. 2(x –

Avoiding Mistakes Boxes

Avoiding Mistakes boxes are integrated throughout the textbook to alert students to common errors and how to avoid them.

> "MOH presentation of reinforcement concepts builds students' confidence and provides easy to read guidance in developing basic skills and understanding concepts. I love the visual clue boxes 'Avoiding Mistakes.' Visual clue boxes provide tips and advice to assist students in avoiding common mistakes."
>
> —**Arcola Sullivan, *Copiah-Lincoln Community College***

TIP Boxes

Teaching tips are usually revealed only in the classroom. Not anymore! TIP boxes offer students helpful hints and extra direction to help improve understanding and provide further insight.

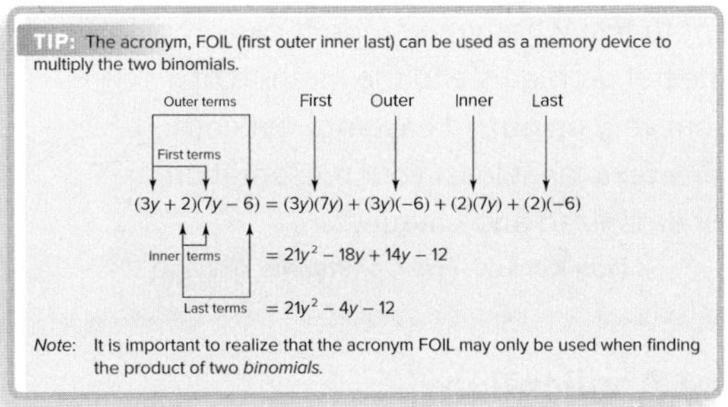

TIP: The acronym, FOIL (first outer inner last) can be used as a memory device to multiply the two binomials.

$(3y+2)(7y-6) = (3y)(7y) + (3y)(-6) + (2)(7y) + (2)(-6)$

$= 21y^2 - 18y + 14y - 12$

$= 21y^2 - 4y - 12$

Note: It is important to realize that the acronym FOIL may only be used when finding the product of two *binomials.*

Better Exercise Sets! Better Practice! Better Results!

- Do your students have trouble with problem solving?
- Do you want to help students overcome math anxiety?
- Do you want to help your students improve performance on math assessments?

Get Better Results

Problem Recognition Exercises

Problem Recognition Exercises present a collection of problems that look similar to a student upon first glance, but are actually quite different in the manner of their individual solutions. Students sharpen critical thinking skills and better develop their "solution recall" to help them distinguish the method needed to solve an exercise—an essential skill in developmental mathematics.

Problem Recognition Exercises were tested in the authors' developmental mathematics classes and were created to improve student performance on tests.

"The PREs are an excellent source of additional mixed problem sets. Frequently students have questions/comments like 'Where do I start?' or 'I know what to do once I get started, but I have trouble getting started.' Perhaps with these PREs, students will be able to overcome this obstacle."

—Erika Blanken, *Daytona State College*

Problem Recognition Exercises

Equations and Inequalities

For Exercises 1–24, identify the category for each equation or inequality (choose from the list here). Then solve the equation or inequality. Express the solution in interval notation where appropriate.

- Linear
- Quadratic
- Polynomial (degree greater than 2)
- Rational
- Absolute value

1. $z^2 + 10z + 9 > 0$ **2.** $5a - 2 = 6(a + 4)$ **3.** $\dfrac{x-4}{2x+4} \geq 1$

4. $4x^2 - 7x = 2$ **5.** $|3x - 1| + 4 < 6$ **6.** $2t^2 - t + 1 < 0$

7. $\frac{1}{2}p - \frac{2}{3} < \frac{1}{6}p - 4$ **8.** $p^2 + 3p \leq 4$ **9.** $3y^2 + y - 2 \geq 0$

10. $\dfrac{x+6}{x+4} = 7$ **11.** $3(2x - 4) \geq 1 - (x - 3)$ **12.** $|6x + 5| + 3 = 2$

13. $(x - 3)(2x + 1)(x + 5) > 0$ **14.** $-x^2 - x - 3 < 0$ **15.** $\dfrac{-6}{y-2} < 2$

18. $x^2 - 36 < 0$

21. $5b - 10 - 3b = 3(b - 2) - 4$

24. $4x(x - 5)^2(2x + 3) < 0$

"These are so important to test whether a student can recognize different types of problems and the method of solving each. They seem very unique—I have not noticed this feature in many other texts or at least your presentation of the problems is very organized and unique."

—Linda Kuroski, *Erie Community College*

Student-Centered Applications!

The Miller/O'Neill/Hyde Board of Advisors partnered with our authors to bring the *best applications* from every region in the country! These applications include real data and topics that are more relevant and interesting to today's student.

47. A boat in distress, 21 nautical miles from a marina, travels toward the marina at 3 knots (nautical miles per hour). A coast guard cruiser leaves the marina and travels toward the boat at 25 knots. How long will it take for the boats to reach each other?

48. An air traffic controller observes a plane heading from New York to San Francisco traveling at 450 mph. At the same time, another plane leaves San Francisco and travels 500 mph to New York. If the distance between the airports is 2850 mi, how long will it take for the planes to pass each other?

© Dennis MacDonald/Alamy RF

Group Activities!

Each chapter concludes with a Group Activity to promote classroom discussion and collaboration—helping students not only to solve problems but to explain their solutions for better mathematical mastery. Group Activities are great for both full-time and adjunct instructors—bringing a more interactive approach to teaching mathematics! All required materials, activity time, and suggested group sizes are provided in the end-of-chapter material.

Group Activity

Computing Monthly Mortgage Payments

Materials: A calculator

Estimated Time: 15–20 minutes

Group Size: 3

When a person borrows money to buy a house, the bank usually requires a down payment of between 0% and 20% of the cost of the house. The bank then issues a loan for the remaining balance on the house. The loan to buy a house is called a *mortgage*. Monthly payments are made to pay off the mortgage over a period of years.

A formula to calculate the monthly payment, P, for a loan is given by:

$$P = \frac{\frac{Ar}{12}}{1 - \frac{1}{\left(1 + \frac{r}{12}\right)^{12t}}}$$

where P is the monthly payment
A is the original amount of the mortgage
r is the annual interest rate written as a decimal
t is the term of the loan in years

Suppose a person wants to buy a $200,000 house. The bank requires a down payment of 20%, and the loan is issued for 30 years at 7.5% interest for 30 years.

1. Find the amount of the down payment. ____________
2. Find the amount of the mortgage. ____________
3. Find the monthly payment (to the nearest cent). ____________
4. Multiply the monthly payment found in question 3 by the total number of months in a 30-year period. Interpret ... blem.

... r the house? ____________

... clude the down payment). ____________

"This is one part of the book that would have me adopt the MOH book. I am very big on group work for *Beginning Algebra* and many times it is difficult to think of an activity. I would conclude the chapter doing the group activity in the class. Many books just have problems for this, but the MOH book provides an actual activity."
—**Sharon Giles, *Grossmont College***

"MOH's group activity involves true participation and interaction; fun with fractions!"
—**Monika Bender, *Central Texas College***

Get Better Results

Dynamic Math Animations

The Miller/O'Neill/Hyde author team has developed a series of animations to illustrate difficult concepts where static images and text fall short. The animations leverage the use of on-screen movement and morphing shapes to enhance conceptual learning.

Through their classroom experience, the authors recognize that such media assets are great teaching tools for the classroom and excellent for online learning. The Miller/O'Neill/Hyde animations are interactive and quite diverse in their use. Some provide a virtual laboratory for which an application is simulated and where students can collect data points for analysis and modeling. Others provide interactive question-and-answer sessions to test conceptual learning. For word problem applications, the animations ask students to estimate answers and practice "number sense."

The animations were created by the authors based on over 75 years of combined teaching experience! To facilitate the use of the animations, the authors have placed icons in the text to indicate where animations are available. Students and instructors can access these assets online in either the ALEKS 360 Course product or Connect Math Hosted by ALEKS.

Additional Supplements

SmartBook. . . NOW with Learning Resources!

SmartBook is the first and only adaptive reading experience available for the world of higher education, and facilitates the reading process by identifying what content a student knows and doesn't know. As a student reads, the material continuously adapts to ensure the student is focused on the content he or she needs the most to close specific knowledge gaps. Additionally, new interactive Learning Resources now allow students to explore connections between different representations of problems, and also serve as an added resource right at the moment when a student answers a probe incorrectly and needs help. These Learning Resources—such as videos, interactive activities, and kaleidoscopes—are available at all times to provide support for students, even when they are working late at night or over the weekend and therefore do not have access to an instructor.

NEW Integrated Video and Study Workbooks

The Integrated Video and Study Workbooks were built to be used in conjunction with the Miller/O'Neill/Hyde Developmental Math series online lecture videos. These new video guides allow students to consolidate their notes as they work through the material in the book, and provide students with an opportunity to focus their studies on particular topics that they are struggling with rather than entire chapters at a time. Each video guide contains written examples to reinforce the content students are watching in the corresponding lecture video, along with additional written exercises for extra practice. There is also space provided for students to take their own notes alongside the guided notes already provided. By the end of the academic term, the video guides will not only be a robust study resource for exams, but will serve as a portfolio showcasing the hard work of students throughout the term.

Student Resource Manual

The *Student Resource Manual (SRM),* created by the authors, is a printable, electronic supplement available to students through Connect Math Hosted by ALEKS Corp. Instructors can also choose to customize this manual and package with their course materials. With increasing demands on faculty schedules, this resource offers a convenient means for both full-time and adjunct faculty to promote active learning and success strategies in the classroom.

This manual supports the series in a variety of different ways:

- Discovery-based classroom activities written by the authors for each section
- Worksheets for extra practice written by the authors

- Excel activities that not only provide students with numerical insights into algebraic concepts, but also teach simple computer skills to manipulate data in a spreadsheet
- Additional fun group activities
- Lecture Notes designed to help students organize and take notes on key concepts
- Materials for a student portfolio

Lecture Videos Created by the Authors (Available in ALEKS and Connect Math Hosted by ALEKS Corp.)

Julie Miller began creating these lecture videos for her own students to use when they were absent from class. The student response was overwhelmingly positive, prompting the author team to create the lecture videos for their entire developmental math book series. In these new videos, the authors walk students through the learning objectives using the same language and procedures outlined in the book. Students learn and review right alongside the author! Students can also access the written notes that accompany the videos.

All videos are closed-captioned for the hearing-impaired, and meet the Americans with Disabilities Act Standards for Accessible Design. These videos are available online through Connect Math Hosted by ALEKS Corp. as well as in ALEKS 360.

Exercise Videos (Available in ALEKS and Connect Math Hosted by ALEKS Corp.)

The authors, along with a team of faculty who have used the Miller/O'Neill/Hyde textbooks for many years, have created new exercise videos for designated exercises in the textbook. These videos cover a representative sample of the main objectives in each section of the text. Each presenter works through selected problems, following the solution methodology employed in the text.

Annotated Instructor's Edition

In the *Annotated Instructor's Edition* (*AIE*), answers to all exercises appear adjacent to each exercise in a color used *only* for annotations. The *AIE* also contains Instructor Notes that appear in the margin. These notes offer instructors assistance with lecture preparation. In addition, there are Classroom Examples referenced in the text that are highlighted in the Practice Exercises. Also found in the *AIE* are icons within the Practice Exercises that serve to guide instructors in their preparation of homework assignments and lessons.

Powerpoints (Available in the Resources of Connect Math Hosted by ALEKS Corp.)

The Powerpoints present key concepts and definitions with fully editable slides that follow the textbook. An instructor may project the slides in class or post to a website in an online course.

McGraw-Hill Connect Math Hosted by ALEKS Corp.

Connect Math Hosted by ALEKS Corp. is an exciting new assignment and assessment ehomework platform. Instructors can assign an AI-driven ALEKS Asssessment to identify the strengths and weaknesses of each student at the beginning of the term rather than after the first exam. Assignment creation and navigation is efficient and intuitive. The gradebook, based on instructor feedback, has a straightforward design and allows flexibility to import and export additional grades.

ALEKS Prep for Developmental Mathematics

ALEKS Prep for Beginning & Intermediate Algebra focuses on prerequisite and introductory material for this text. The prep products can be used during the first 3 weeks of a traditional course or in a corequisite course where students need to quickly narrow the gap in their skill and concept base.

ALEKS Prep Course Products Feature:

- Artificial Intelligence Targeting Gaps in Individual Student's Knowledge
- Assessment and Learning Directed Toward Individual Student's Needs
- Open Response Environment with Realistic Input Tools
- Unlimited Online Access—PC and Mac Compatible

Free trial at www.aleks.com/free_trial/instructor

Get Better Results

Instructor's and Student's Solutions Manuals (Available in the Resources of Connect Math Hosted by ALEKS Corp., the Online Learning Center, and at www.mcgrawhillcreate.com, our print-on-demand book-building website)

The *Instructor's Solutions Manual* provides comprehensive, worked-out solutions to all exercises in the Chapter Openers, the Practice Exercises, the Problem Recognition Exercises, the end-of-chapter Review Exercises, the Chapter Tests, and the Cumulative Review Exercises. The *Student's Solutions Manual* provides answers to the odd-numbered exercises in the text.

Instructor's Test Bank (Available in the Resources of Connect Math Hosted by ALEKS Corp.)

Among the supplements is a computerized test bank utilizing algorithm-based testing software to create customized exams quickly. Hundreds of text-specific, open-ended, and multiple-choice questions are included in the question bank. Sample chapter tests are also provided.

Loose-Leaf Text

This three-hole punched version of the traditional printed text allows students to carry it lightly and comfortably in a binder, integrated with notes and workbook pages as desired.

Acknowledgments and Reviewers

Paramount to the development of *Beginning & Intermediate Algebra* was the invaluable feedback provided by the instructors from around the country that reviewed the manuscript or attended a market development event over the course of the several years the text was in development.

Reviewers of Miller/O'Neill/Hyde Developmental Mathematics Series

Maryann Faller, *Adirondack Community College*
Albert Miller, *Ball State University*
Debra Pearson, *Ball State University*
Patricia Parkison, *Ball State University*
Robin Rufatto, *Ball State University*
Melanie Walker, *Bergen Community College*
Robert Fusco, *Bergen Community College*
Latonya Ellis, *Bishop State Community College*
Ana Leon, *Bluegrass Community College & Technical College*
Kaye Black, *Bluegrass Community College & Technical College*
Barbara Elzey, *Bluegrass Community College & Technical College*
Cheryl Grant, *Bowling Green State University*
Beth Rountree, *Brevard College*
Juliet Carl, *Broward College*
Lizette Foley, *Broward College*
Angie Matthews, *Broward College*
Mitchel Levy, *Broward College*
Jody Harris, *Broward College*
Michelle Carmel, *Broward College*
Antonnette Gibbs, *Broward College*
Kelly Jackson, *Camden Community College*
Elizabeth Valentine, *Charleston Southern University*
Adedoyin Adeyiga, *Cheyney University of Pennsylvania*
Dot French, *Community College of Philadelphia*
Brad Berger, *Copper Mountain College*
Donna Troy, *Cuyamaca College*
Brianna Kurtz, *Daytona State College–Daytona Beach*
Jennifer Walsh, *Daytona State College–Daytona Beach*
Marc Campbell, *Daytona State College–Daytona Beach*
Richard Rupp, *Del Mar College*
Joseph Hernandez, *Delta College*
Randall Nichols, *Delta College*
Thomas Wells, *Delta College*
Paul Yun, *El Camino College*
Catherine Bliss, *Empire State College–Saratoga Springs*
Laurie Davis, *Erie Community College*
Linda Kuroski, *Erie Community College*
David Usinski, *Erie Community College*
Ron Bannon, *Essex County College*
David Platt, *Front Range Community College*
Alan Dinwiddie, *Front Range Community College*
Andrea Hendricks, *Georgia Perimeter College*
Shanna Goff, *Grand Rapids Community College*
Betsy McKinney, *Grand Rapids Community College*
Cathy Gardner, *Grand Valley State University*

Reviewers of the Miller/O'Neill/Hyde Developmental Mathematics Series

Jane Mays, *Grand Valley State University*
John Greene, *Henderson State University*
Fred Worth, *Henderson State University*
Ryan Baxter, *Illinois State University*
Angela Mccombs, *Illinois State University*
Elisha Van Meenen, *Illinois State University*
Teresa Hasenauer, *Indian River State College*
Tiffany Lewis, *Indian River State College*
Deanna Voehl, *Indian River State College*
Joe Jordan, *John Tyler Community College*
Sally Copeland, *Johnson County Community College*
Nancy Carpenter, *Johnson County Community College*
Susan Yellott, *Kilgore College*
Kim Miller, *Labette Community College*
Michelle Hempton, *Lansing Community College*
Michelle Whitmer, *Lansing Community College*
Nathalie Vega-Rhodes, *Lone Star College*
Kuen Lee, *Los Angeles Trade Tech*
Nic Lahue, *MCC-Longview Community College*
Jason Pallett, *MCC-Longview Community College*
Janet Wyatt, *MCC-Longview Community College*
Rene Barrientos, *Miami Dade College—Kendall*
Nelson De La Rosa, *Miami Dade College—Kendall*
Jody Balzer, *Milwaukee Area Technical College*
Shahla Razavi, *Mt. San Jacinto College*
Shawna Bynum, *Napa Valley College*
Tammy Ford, *North Carolina A & T University*
Ebrahim Ahmadizadeh, *Northampton Community College*
Christine Wetzel-Ulrich, *Northampton Community College*
Sharon Totten, *Northeast Alabama Community College*
Rodolfo Maglio, *Northeastern Illinios University*
Christine Copple, *Northwest State Community College*
Sumitana Chatterjee, *Nova Community College*
Charbel Fahed, *Nova Community College*
Ken Hirschel, *Orange County Community College*
Linda K. Schott, *Ozarks Technical Community College*
Matthew Harris, *Ozarks Technical Community College*
Daniel Kopsas, *Ozarks Technical Community College*
Andrew Aberle, *Ozarks Technical Community College*
Alan Papen, *Ozarks Technical Community College*
Angela Shreckhise, *Ozarks Technical Community College*
Jacob Lewellen, *Ozarks Technical Community College*
Marylynne Abbott, *Ozarks Technical Community College*
Jeffrey Gervasi, *Porterville College*
Stewart Hathaway, *Porterville College*
Lauran Johnson, *Richard Bland College*
Matthew Nickodemus, *Richard Bland College*
Cameron English, *Rio Hondo College*
Lydia Gonzalez, *Rio Hondo College*
Mark Littrell, *Rio Hondo College*
Matthew Pitassi, *Rio Hondo College*
Wayne Lee, *Saint Philips College*
Paula Looney, *Saint Philips College*
Fred Bakenhus, *Saint Philips College*
Lydia Casas, *Saint Philips College*
Gloria Guerra, *Saint Philips College*
Sounny Slitine, *Saint Philips College*
Jessica Lopez, *Saint Philips College*
Lorraine Lopez, *San Antonio College*
Peter Georgakis, *Santa Barbara City College*
Sandi Nieto-Navarro, *Santa Rosa Junior College*
Steve Drucker, *Santa Rosa Junior College*
Jean-Marie Magnier, *Springfield Tech Community College*
Dave Delrossi, *Tallahassee Community College*
Natalie Johnson, *Tarrant County College South*
Marilyn Peacock, *Tidewater Community College*
Yvonne Aucoin, *Tidewater Community College*
Cynthia Harris, *Triton College*
Jennifer Burkett, *Triton College*
Christyn Senese, *Triton College*
Jennifer Dale, *Triton College*
Patricia Hussey, *Triton College*
Glenn Jablonski, *Triton College*
Myrna La Rosa, *Triton College*
Michael Maltenfort, *Truman College*
Abdallah Shuaibi, *Truman College*
Marta Hidegkuti, *Truman College*
Sandra Wilder, *University of Akron*
Sandra Jovicic, *University of Akron*
Edward Migliore, *University of California–Santa Cruz*
Kelly Kohlmetz, *University of Wisconsin—Milwaukee*
Leah Rineck, *University of Wisconsin—Milwaukee*
Carolann Van Galder, *University of Wisconsin—Rock County*
Claudia Martinez, *Valencia College*
Stephen Toner, *Victor Valley Community College*
David Cooper, *Wake Tech Community College*
Karlata Elliott, *Wake Tech Community College*
Laura Kalbaugh, *Wake Tech Community College*
Kelly Vetter, *Wake Tech Community College*
Jacqui Fields, *Wake Tech Community College*
Jennifer Smeal, *Wake Tech Community College*
Shannon Vinson, *Wake Tech Community College*
Kim Walaski, *Wake Tech Community College*
Lisa Rombes, *Washtenaw Community College*
Maziar Ouliaeinia, *Western Iowa Tech Community College*
Keith McCoy, *Wilbur Wright College*

Also, a special thanks to all instructors who have reviewed previous editions of this series.

Our Commitment to Market Development and Accuracy

McGraw-Hill's Development Process is an ongoing, never-ending, market-oriented approach to building accurate and innovative print and digital products. We begin developing a series by partnering with authors that desire to make an impact within their discipline to help students succeed. Next, we share these ideas and manuscript with instructors for review for feedback and to ensure that the authors' ideas represent the needs within that discipline. Throughout multiple drafts, we help our authors adapt to incorporate ideas and suggestions from reviewers to ensure that the series carries the same pulse as today's classrooms. With any new series, we commit to accuracy across the series and its supplements. In addition to involving instructors as we develop our content, we also utilize accuracy checks through our various stages of development and production. With our commitment to this process, we are confident that our series has the most developed content the industry has to offer, thus pushing our desire for quality and accurate content that meets the needs of today's students and instructors.

New and Updated Content for Miller/O'Neill/Hyde Beginning & Intermediate Algebra, Fifth Edition:

- New Chapter Openers focused on contextualized learning that introduce the main idea of each chapter in an applied setting
- New SmartBook with Learning Resources digital resource added for students that includes over 1,400 student learning resources, over 500 learning objectives, and over 1,300 student activity probes
- New Integrated Video & Study Guide workbook to accompany the online lecture video series created by the Miller/O'Neill/Hyde author team
- Updated Applications to be timely in all instances where appropriate
- Modularized content for easier course customization and flexibility in a digital or traditional classroom environment
- Over 200 new algorithmic exercises added to Connect Math to better cover developmental math content for students
- New online chapter added to provide students with additional targeted instruction on transformations, piecewise-defined functions, and probability

How can ConnectMath + SmartBook help solve your students' math challenges?

I like to learn by __________.

Whether it's reading, watching, discovering, or doing, ConnectMath has something for everyone. Instructors can create assignments that accommodate different learning styles, and students aren't stuck with boring multiple-choice problems. Instead they have a myriad of motivational learning and media resources at their fingertips. SmartBook delivers an interactive reading and learning experience that provides personalized guidance and just-in-time remediation. This helps students to focus on what they need, right when they need it.

I still don't get it. Can you do that problem again?

Because the content in ConnectMath is author-developed and goes through a rigorous quality control process, students hear one voice, one style, and don't get lost moving from text to digital. The high-quality, author-developed videos provide students ample opportunities to master concepts and practice skills that they need extra help with . . . all of which are integrated in the ConnectMath platform and the eBook.

How can ConnectMath + SmartBook help solve your classroom challenges?

I need meaningful data to measure student success!

From helping the student in the back row to tracking learning trends for your entire course, ConnectMath + SmartBook delivers the data you need to make an impactful, meaningful learning experience for students. With easy-to-interpret, downloadable reports, you can analyze learning rates for each assignment, monitor time on task, and learn where students' strengths and weaknesses are in each course area.

We're going with the ________ (flipped classroom, corequisite model, hybrid, etc.) implementation.

ConnectMath + SmartBook is an intuitive digital solution that can be used in any course setup. Each course in ConnectMath comes complete with its own set of text-specific assignments, author-developed videos and learning resources, and an integrated eBook that cater to the needs of your specific course. The easy-to-navigate home page keeps the learning curve at a minimum, but offers an abundance of tutorials and videos to help get you and your colleagues started.

Let's Talk!

Ready to take the next step?

Let's talk. Whether you're looking to redesign your course, change technologies, or just explore, our team of dedicated faculty consultants, reps, and digital specialists are standing by.

http://shop.mheducation.com/store/paris/user/findltr.html

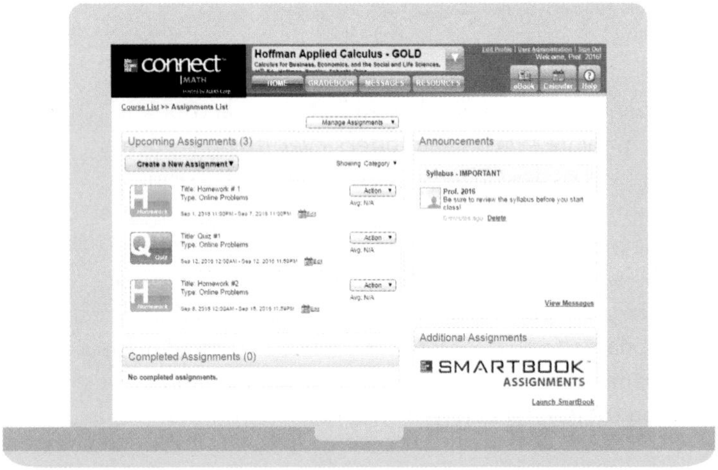

Looking for stable technology? Connect Math Hosted by ALEKS has an uptime of 99.97%.

Problem Solved!

How can ALEKS help solve your students' challenges?

I've never been good at math, so why should I try?

The perceived struggle with math is often too real for many students. ALEKS offers a chance to break from that struggle through its cycle of individualized assessment and learning. Students only work on topics they are ready to learn, which have a proven learning success rate of 93% or higher. Periodic assessments reinforce content mastery and provide targeted remediation. As students watch their progress in the ALEKS Pie grow, their confidence grows with it.

I did all my homework, so why am I failing my exams?

The purpose of homework is to ensure mastery and prepare students for exams. Yet how well do homework scores correlate to exam scores? ALEKS is the only adaptive learning system that ensures mastery through periodic reassessments and delivers just-in-time remediation to efficiently prepare students. Because of how ALEKS presents lessons and practice, students learn by understanding the core principle of a concept rather than just memorizing a process.

I'm too far behind to catch up. - OR - I've already done this, I'm bored.

No two students are alike. So why start everyone on the same page? ALEKS diagnoses what each student knows and doesn't know, and prescribes an optimized learning path through the curriculum you put forth. Students are only working on what they need, when they need it, rather than focusing on topics they already know or aren't ready for. The frustration of falling behind and the boredom from redundant review is virtually eliminated.

"ALEKS improved my math skills tremendously. What I love the most about it is that it makes sure you understand the material ... Thanks to ALEKS I got the job that I have now."
– Student, Broward College, FL

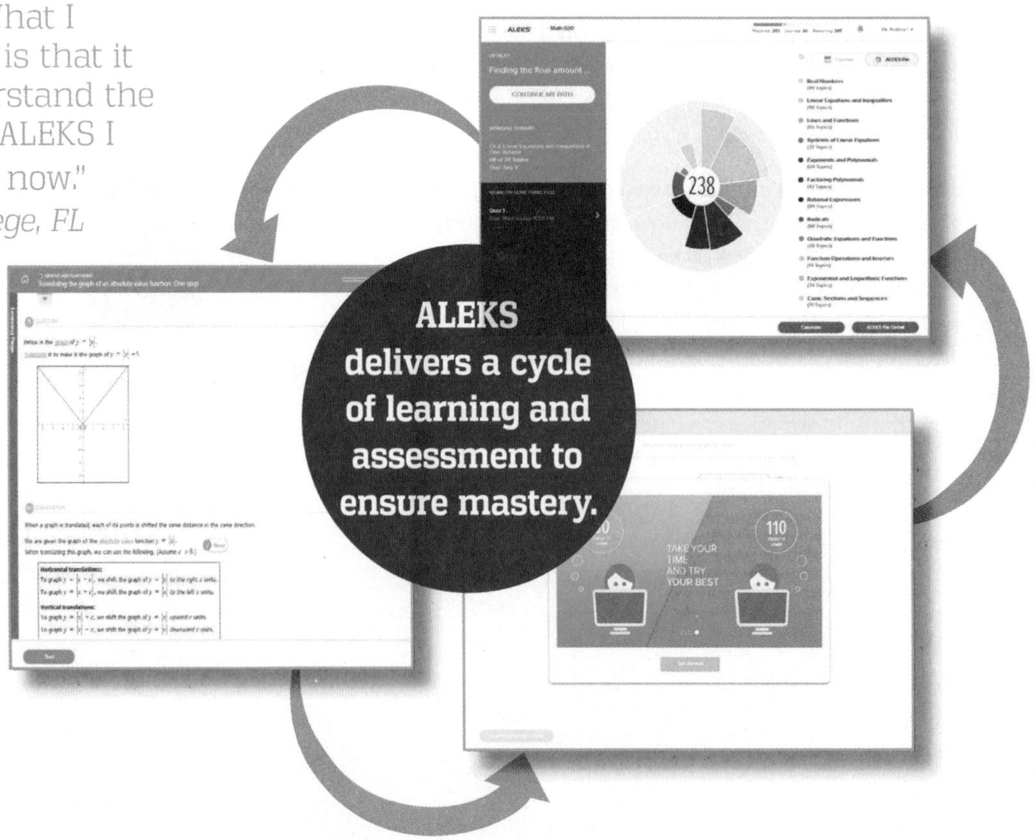

How can ALEKS help solve your classroom challenges?

I need something that solves the problem of cost, time to completion, and student preparedness.

ALEKS is the perfect solution to the trifecta of these problems. It provides an efficient path to mastery through its individualized cycle of learning and assessment that targets prerequisite gaps and focuses students on what they are ready to learn. Students move through their math requirements more quickly and are better prepared for subsequent courses. This saves both the institution and the student money.

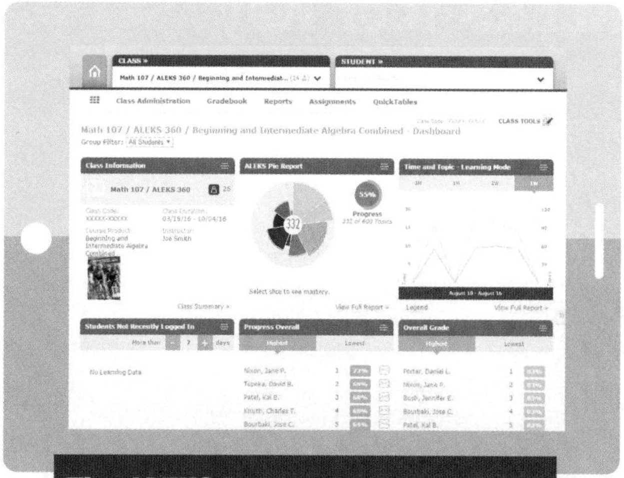

The ALEKS Instructor Module is an intuitive interface where you can easily manage courses and track student progress.

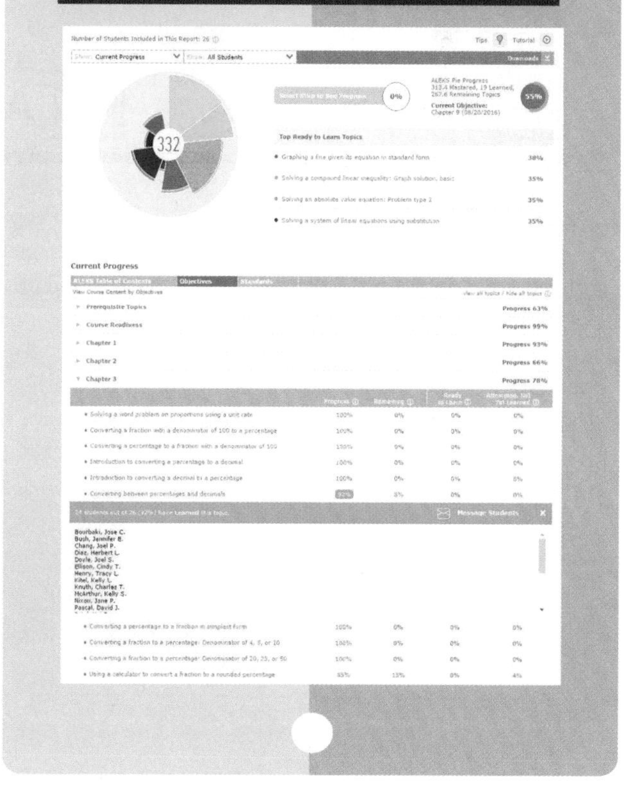

We're going with the ________ (flipped classroom, corequisite, accelerated, etc.) implementation.

No matter your course setup, ALEKS can handle it. ALEKS courses cover a broad curriculum, so that you can easily tailor it to cover just the topics that you need. ALEKS Objectives gives you control over when and in what order students move through the content so that the pacing matches that of the textbook and/or curriculum. The flexibility of ALEKS allows you to use it in conjunction with any textbook or set of resources that you want to use.

My administration and department measure success differently. How can we compare notes?

ALEKS offers the most comprehensive and detailed data analytics on the market. From helping the student in the back row to monitoring pass rates across the department and institution, ALEKS delivers the data needed at all levels. The customizable and intuitive reporting features allow you and your colleagues to easily gather, interpret, and share the data you need, when you need it.

"ALEKS is the only product that diagnoses and prescribes an individualized learning path. The ALEKS management system is intuitive and easy to use. The reports are easy to construct, read and interpret, allowing us to help students focus and succeed."

–Yoshi Yamato and Marie McClendon, Pasadena City College, CA

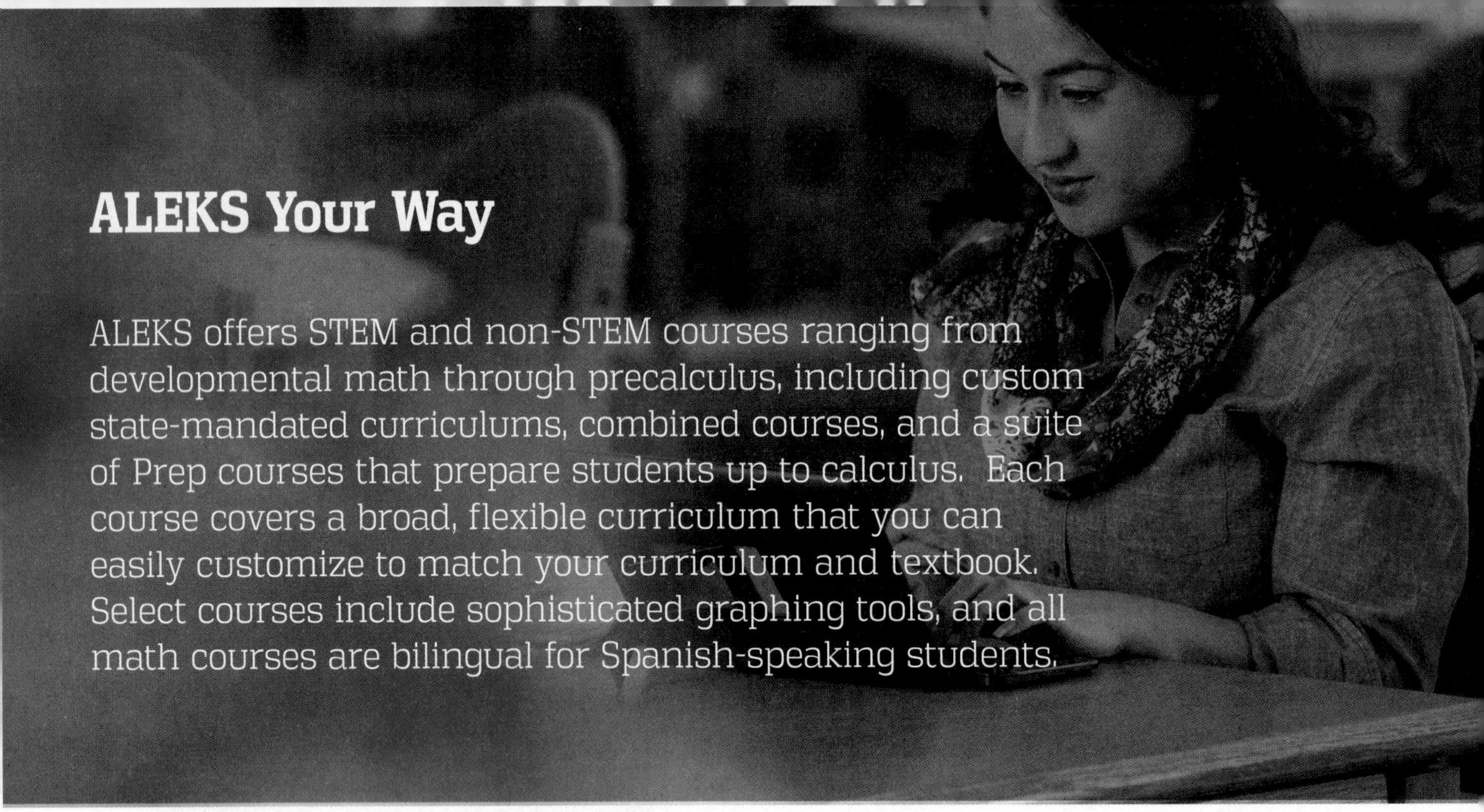

ALEKS Your Way

ALEKS offers STEM and non-STEM courses ranging from developmental math through precalculus, including custom state-mandated curriculums, combined courses, and a suite of Prep courses that prepare students up to calculus. Each course covers a broad, flexible curriculum that you can easily customize to match your curriculum and textbook. Select courses include sophisticated graphing tools, and all math courses are bilingual for Spanish-speaking students.

McGraw Hill Education ALEKS® 360

ALEKS 360 combines the power of ALEKS with an integrated, interactive McGraw-Hill eBook. Students have direct access to the text, lecture videos, supplementary resources, and practice examples right when they need it as they work each topic. ALEKS 360 is available with most ALEKS courses, and at an affordable price. For those students who still prefer to hold a page in their hand, they can order a loose-leaf version of the eBook for a significant discount.

McGraw Hill Education ALEKS® PREP

ALEKS Prep courses target students' prerequisite knowledge gaps and provide individualized learning and remediation to ensure students are ready to succeed in their math course. It is the perfect solution for the accelerated "bootcamp" program, instructors that need to get students up to speed during the first few weeks of a course, or as the remedial component of a corequisite course.

McGraw Hill Education ALEKS® PPL

PLACEMENT, PREPARATION, AND LEARNING

ALEKS Placement, Preparation, and Learning (ALEKS PPL) is the first and only institution-wide placement solution to both diagnose and remediate, all in one completely personalized program. The adaptive placement assessment places students from Basic Math through Calculus I. Then students get six months of personalized learning and remediation. ALEKS PPL gives institutions the tools to improve college preparedness, course performance, and retention.

"My students are much more prepared because of ALEKS Prep. I saw noticeably fewer errors on exams and fewer Algebra-related questions during class. I can now focus on Calculus material without having to review."
–Jeanette Martin, University of Washington

Study Tips

In taking a course in algebra, you are making a commitment to yourself, your instructor, and your classmates. Following some or all of the study tips presented here can help you be successful in this endeavor. The features of this text that will assist you are printed in blue.

Concepts

1. Before the Course
2. During the Course
3. Preparation for Exams
4. Where to Go for Help

© Blend Images/Getty Images RF

1. Before the Course

1. Purchase the necessary materials for the course before the course begins or on the first day.
2. Obtain a three-ring binder to keep and organize your notes, homework, tests, and any other materials acquired in the class. We call this type of notebook a portfolio.
3. Arrange your schedule so that you have enough time to attend class and to do homework. A common rule is to set aside at least 2 hours for homework for every hour spent in class. That is, if you are taking a 4-credit-hour course, plan on at least 8 hours a week for homework. A 6-credit-hour course will then take *at least* 12 hours each week—about the same as a part-time job. If you experience difficulty in mathematics, plan for more time.
4. Communicate with your employer and family members the importance of your success in this course so that they can support you.
5. Be sure to find out the type of calculator (if any) that your instructor requires.

2. During the Course

1. Read the section in the text *before* the lecture to familiarize yourself with the material and terminology. It is recommended that you read your math book with paper and pencil in hand. Write a one-sentence preview of what the section is about.
2. Attend every class and be on time. Be sure to bring any materials that are needed for class such as graph paper, a ruler, or a calculator.
3. Take notes in class. Write down all of the examples that the instructor presents. Read the notes after class, and add any comments to make your notes clearer to you. Use an audio recorder to record the lecture if the instructor permits the recording of lectures.
4. Ask questions in class.
5. Read the section in the text *after* the lecture, and pay special attention to the Tip boxes and Avoiding Mistakes boxes.
6. After you read an example, try the accompanying Skill Practice problem. The skill practice problem mirrors the example and tests your understanding of what you have read.
7. Do homework every day. Even if your class does not meet every day, you should still do some work every day to keep the material fresh in your mind.
8. Check your homework with the answers that are supplied in the back of this text. Correct the exercises that do not match, and circle or star those that you cannot correct yourself. This way you can easily find them and ask your instructor, tutor, online tutor, or math lab staff the next day.
9. Be sure to do the Vocabulary and Key Concepts exercises found at the beginning of the Practice Exercises.

10. The Problem Recognition Exercises are located in all chapters. These provide additional practice distinguishing among a variety of problem types. Sometimes the most difficult part of learning mathematics is retaining all that you learn. These exercises are excellent tools for retention of material.
11. Form a study group with fellow students in your class, and exchange phone numbers. You will be surprised by how much you can learn by talking about mathematics with other students.
12. If you use a calculator in your class, read the Calculator Connections boxes to learn how and when to use your calculator.
13. Ask your instructor where you might obtain extra help if necessary.

3. Preparation for Exams

1. Look over your homework. Pay special attention to the exercises you have circled or starred to be sure that you have learned that concept.
2. Begin preparations for exams on the first day of class. As you do each homework assignment, think about how you would recognize similar problems when they appear on a test.
3. Read through the Summary at the end of the chapter. Be sure that you understand each concept and example. If not, go to the section in the text and reread that section.
4. Give yourself enough time to take the Chapter Test uninterrupted. Then check the answers. For each problem you answered incorrectly, go to the Review Exercises and do all of the problems that are similar.
5. To prepare for the final exam, complete the Cumulative Review Exercises at the end of each chapter. If you complete the cumulative reviews after finishing each chapter, then you will be preparing for the final exam throughout the course. The Cumulative Review Exercises are another excellent tool for helping you retain material.

4. Where to Go for Help

1. At the first sign of trouble, see your instructor. Most instructors have specific office hours set aside to help students. Don't wait until after you have failed an exam to seek assistance.
2. Get a tutor. Most colleges and universities have free tutoring available. There may also be an online tutor available.
3. When your instructor and tutor are unavailable, use the Student Solutions Manual for step-by-step solutions to the odd-numbered problems in the exercise sets.
4. Work with another student from your class.
5. Work on the computer. Many mathematics tutorial programs and websites are available on the Internet, including the website that accompanies this text.

Group Activity

Becoming a Successful Student

Materials: Computer with Internet access

Estimated Time: 15 minutes

Group Size: 4

Good time management, good study skills, and good organization will help you be successful in this course. Answer the following questions and compare your answers with your group members.

Answers will vary.

1. To motivate yourself to complete a course, it is helpful to have clear reasons for taking the course. List your goals for taking this course and discuss them with your group.

2. For the following week, write down the times each day that you plan to study math.

Monday	Tuesday	Wednesday	Thursday	Friday	Saturday	Sunday

3. Write down the date of your next math test. ________________

4. Taking 12 credit-hours is the equivalent of a full-time job. Often students try to work too many hours while taking classes at school.

   a. Write down the number of hours you work per week and the number of credit-hours you are taking this term.

      Number of hours worked per week ________________

      Number of credit-hours this term ________________

   b. The table gives a recommended limit to the number of hours you should work for the number of credit-hours you are taking at school. (Keep in mind that other responsibilities in your life such as your family might also make it necessary to limit your hours at work even more.) How do your numbers from part (a) compare to those in the table? Are you working too many hours?

Number of Credit-Hours	Maximum Number of Hours of Work per Week
3	40
6	30
9	20
12	10
15	0

5. Discuss with your group members where you can go for extra help in math. Then write down three of the suggestions.

   ____

   ____

   ____

6. Do you keep an organized notebook for this class? Can you think of any suggestions that you can share with your group members to help them keep their materials organized?

7. Look through a chapter and find the page number corresponding to each feature in that chapter. Discuss with your group members how you might use each feature.

   Problem Recognition Exercises: page ________________

   Chapter Summary: page ________________

   Chapter Review Exercises: page ________________

   Chapter Test: page ________________

   Cumulative Review Exercises: page ________________

8. Look at the Skill Practice exercises. For example, find Skill Practice exercises 1 and 2 in the first section. Where are the answers to these exercises located? Discuss with your group members how you might use the Skill Practice exercises.

9. Do you think that you have math anxiety? Read the following list for some possible solutions. Check the activities that you can realistically try to help you overcome this problem.

   _____ Read a book on math anxiety.

   _____ Search the Web for tips on handling math anxiety.

   _____ See a counselor to discuss your anxiety.

   _____ Talk with your instructor to discuss strategies to manage math anxiety.

   _____ Evaluate your time management to see if you are trying to do too much. Then adjust your schedule accordingly.

10. Some students favor different methods of learning over others. For example, you might prefer:

    - Learning through listening and hearing.
    - Learning through seeing images, watching demonstrations, and visualizing diagrams and charts.
    - Learning by experience through a hands-on approach.
    - Learning through reading and writing.

    Most experts believe that the most effective learning comes when a student engages in *all* of these activities. However, each individual is different and may benefit from one activity more than another. You can visit a number of different websites to determine your "learning style." Try doing a search on the Internet with the key words "*learning styles assessment*." Once you have found a suitable website, answer the questionnaire and the site will give you feedback on what method of learning works best for you.

11. As you read through Chapter 1, try to become familiar with the features of this textbook. Then match the feature in column B with its description in column A.

    Column A

    1. Allows you to check your work as you do your homework e
    2. Shows you how to avoid common errors g
    3. Provides an online tutorial and exercise supplement b
    4. Outlines key concepts for each section in the chapter f
    5. Provides exercises that help you distinguish between different types of problems d
    6. Offers helpful hints and insight a
    7. Offers practice exercises that go along with each example c

    Column B

    a. Tips
    b. ConnectMath
    c. Skill Practice exercises
    d. Problem Recognition Exercises
    e. Answers to odd-numbered exercises
    f. Chapter Summary
    g. Avoiding Mistakes

The Set of Real Numbers

1

CHAPTER OUTLINE

Numbers in Our World

Imagine a world where the only numbers known are the counting or natural numbers (1, 2, 3, 4, . . .). Now imagine that you want to sell only a fraction of your land to another person, or that you owe twenty dollars and fifteen cents to your bank. How could these values be written without formal numerical symbols? Living in such a world would deter the growth of a complex society like ours.

© Zephyr_p/Shutterstock RF

It is difficult to fathom that the use of zero, fractions, and negative numbers was formally accepted only about a thousand years ago! Before that time, communicating about parts of items, the absence of value, and owing money to a lender was likely done in creative but arduous ways. When we talk about a *third* of a parcel of land, temperatures below *zero* such as *negative* 20 degrees, and the number π, we make use of the many subsets of the **set of real numbers**.

Real numbers enable us to talk about parts of things, to expand our thinking to explain phenomena in precise ways, and to operate with numbers in a consistent and predicable manner. In this chapter we will explore how real numbers are used, and the way they open the door to algebra.

Section 1.1 Fractions

Concepts

1. Basic Definitions
2. Prime Factorization
3. Simplifying Fractions to Lowest Terms
4. Multiplying Fractions
5. Dividing Fractions
6. Adding and Subtracting Fractions
7. Operations on Mixed Numbers

1. Basic Definitions

The study of algebra involves many of the operations and procedures used in arithmetic. Therefore, we begin this text by reviewing the basic operations of addition, subtraction, multiplication, and division on fractions and mixed numbers.

We begin with the numbers used for counting:

the **natural numbers:** 1, 2, 3, 4, . . .

and

the **whole numbers:** 0, 1, 2, 3, . . .

Whole numbers are used to count the number of whole units in a quantity. A fraction is used to express part of a whole unit. If a child gains $2\frac{1}{2}$ lb, the child has gained two whole pounds plus a portion of a pound. To express the additional half pound mathematically, we may use the fraction, $\frac{1}{2}$.

A Fraction and Its Parts

Fractions are numbers of the form $\frac{a}{b}$, where $\frac{a}{b} = a \div b$ and b does not equal zero.

In the fraction $\frac{a}{b}$, the **numerator** is a, and the **denominator** is b.

The denominator of a fraction indicates how many equal parts divide the whole. The numerator indicates how many parts are being represented. For instance, suppose Jack wants to plant carrots in $\frac{2}{5}$ of a rectangular garden. He can divide the garden into five equal parts and use two of the parts for carrots (Figure 1-1).

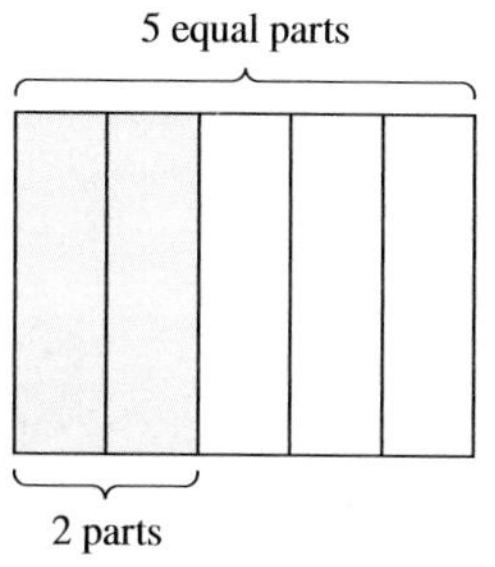

The shaded region represents $\frac{2}{5}$ of the garden.

Figure 1-1

Instructor Note: Tell the students that the word "improper" does not imply that there is anything wrong with a fraction.

Proper Fractions, Improper Fractions, and Mixed Numbers

1. If the numerator of a fraction is less than the denominator, the fraction is a **proper fraction**. A proper fraction represents a quantity that is less than a whole unit.
2. If the numerator of a fraction is greater than or equal to the denominator, then the fraction is an **improper fraction**. An improper fraction represents a quantity greater than or equal to a whole unit.
3. A **mixed number** is a whole number added to a proper fraction.

Proper Fractions: $\frac{3}{5}$ 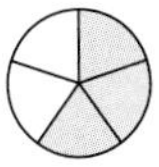 $\frac{1}{8}$ 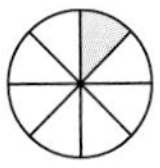

Improper Fractions: $\frac{7}{5}$ 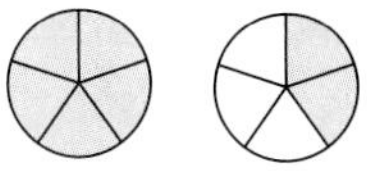 $\frac{8}{8}$ 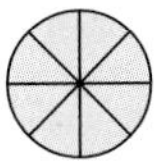

Mixed Numbers: $1\frac{1}{5}$ 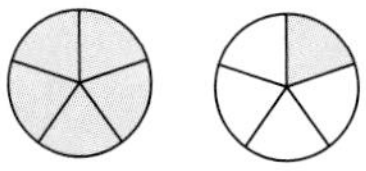 $2\frac{3}{8}$ 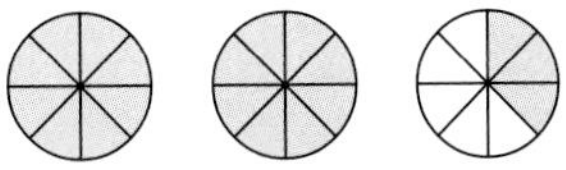

2. Prime Factorization

To perform operations on fractions it is important to understand the concept of a factor. For example, when the numbers 2 and 6 are multiplied, the result (called the **product**) is 12.

$$\underbrace{2 \times 6}_{\text{factors}} = \underbrace{12}_{\text{product}}$$

The numbers 2 and 6 are said to be **factors** of 12. (In this context, we refer only to natural number factors.) The number 12 is said to be factored when it is written as the product of two or more natural numbers. For example, 12 can be factored in several ways:

$$12 = 1 \times 12 \qquad 12 = 2 \times 6 \qquad 12 = 3 \times 4 \qquad 12 = 2 \times 2 \times 3$$

A natural number greater than 1 that has only two factors, 1 and itself, is called a **prime number**. The first several prime numbers are 2, 3, 5, 7, 11, and 13. A natural number greater than 1 that is not prime is called a **composite number**. That is, a composite number has factors other than itself and 1. The first several composite numbers are 4, 6, 8, 9, 10, 12, 14, 15, and 16.

Avoiding Mistakes

The number 1 is neither prime nor composite.

Example 1 **Writing a Natural Number as a Product of Prime Factors**

Classroom Example: p. 18, Exercise 36

Write each number as a product of prime factors.

a. 12 **b.** 30

Solution:

a. $12 = 2 \times 2 \times 3$ Divide 12 by prime numbers until the result is also a prime number.

2)12
2)6
3

Or use a factor tree

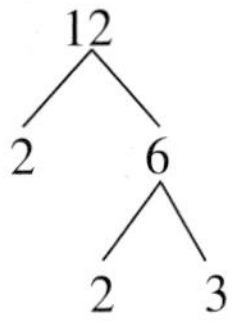

b. $30 = 2 \times 3 \times 5$

2)30
3)15
5

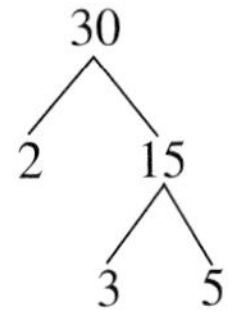

Skill Practice Write the number as a product of prime factors.

1. 40 **2.** 72

Answers

1. $2 \times 2 \times 2 \times 5$
2. $2 \times 2 \times 2 \times 3 \times 3$

3. Simplifying Fractions to Lowest Terms

The process of factoring numbers can be used to reduce or simplify fractions to lowest terms. A fractional portion of a whole can be represented by infinitely many fractions. For example, Figure 1-2 shows that $\frac{1}{2}$ is equivalent to $\frac{2}{4}$, $\frac{3}{6}$, $\frac{4}{8}$, and so on.

Animation

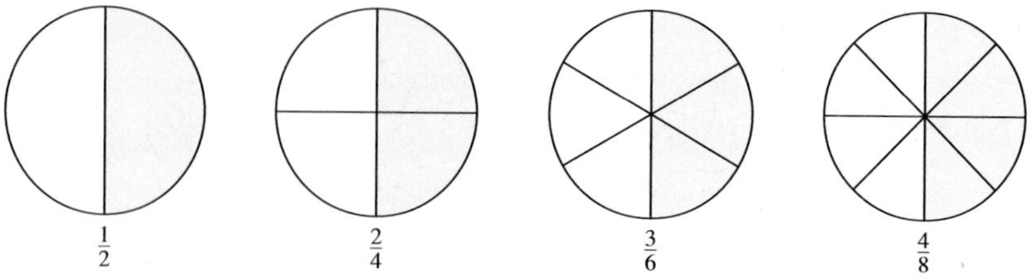

Figure 1-2

The fraction $\frac{1}{2}$ is said to be in **lowest terms** because the numerator and denominator share no common factor other than 1.

To simplify a fraction to lowest terms, we use the following important principle.

Fundamental Principle of Fractions

Suppose that a number, c, is a common factor in the numerator and denominator of a fraction. Then

$$\frac{a \times c}{b \times c} = \frac{a}{b} \times \frac{c}{c} = \frac{a}{b} \times 1 = \frac{a}{b}$$

To simplify a fraction, we begin by factoring the numerator and denominator into prime factors. This will help identify the common factors.

Classroom Example: p. 19, Exercise 44

Example 2 Simplifying a Fraction to Lowest Terms

Simplify $\frac{45}{30}$ to lowest terms.

Solution:

$\frac{45}{30} = \frac{3 \times 3 \times 5}{2 \times 3 \times 5}$	Factor the numerator and denominator.
$= \frac{3}{2} \times \frac{3}{3} \times \frac{5}{5}$	Apply the fundamental principle of fractions.
$= \frac{3}{2} \times 1 \times 1$	Any nonzero number divided by itself is 1.
$= \frac{3}{2}$	Any number multiplied by 1 is itself.

Instructor Note: Students often confuse writing a fraction in lowest terms with writing a mixed number. The fraction $\frac{3}{2}$ is in lowest terms.

Skill Practice Simplify to lowest terms.

3. $\frac{20}{50}$

Answer

3. $\frac{2}{5}$

In Example 2, we showed numerous steps to reduce fractions to lowest terms. However, the process is often simplified. Notice that the same result can be obtained by dividing out the greatest common factor from the numerator and denominator. (The **greatest common factor** is the largest factor that is common to both numerator and denominator.)

$\frac{45}{30} = \frac{3 \times 15}{2 \times 15}$ The greatest common factor of 45 and 30 is 15.

$= \frac{3 \times \overset{1}{\cancel{15}}}{2 \times \underset{1}{\cancel{15}}}$ The symbol / is often used to show that a common factor has been divided out.

$= \frac{3}{2}$ Notice that "dividing out" the common factor of 15 has the same effect as dividing the numerator and denominator by 15. This is often done mentally.

$\frac{\overset{3}{\cancel{45}}}{\underset{2}{\cancel{30}}} = \frac{3}{2}$ ← 45 divided by 15 equals 3. ← 30 divided by 15 equals 2.

Example 3 **Simplifying a Fraction to Lowest Terms**

Classroom Example: p. 19, Exercise 48

Simplify $\frac{14}{42}$ to lowest terms.

Solution:

$\frac{14}{42} = \frac{1 \times 14}{3 \times 14}$ The greatest common factor of 14 and 42 is 14.

$= \frac{1 \times \overset{1}{\cancel{14}}}{3 \times \underset{1}{\cancel{14}}}$

$= \frac{1}{3}$ $\frac{\overset{1}{\cancel{14}}}{\underset{3}{\cancel{42}}} = \frac{1}{3}$ ← 14 divided by 14 equals 1. ← 42 divided by 14 equals 3.

Avoiding Mistakes

In Example 3, the common factor 14 in the numerator and denominator simplifies to 1. It is important to remember to write the factor of 1 in the numerator. The simplified form of the fraction is $\frac{1}{3}$.

Skill Practice Simplify to lowest terms.

4. $\frac{32}{12}$

4. Multiplying Fractions

Multiplying Fractions

If b is not zero and d is not zero, then

$$\frac{a}{b} \times \frac{c}{d} = \frac{a \times c}{b \times d}$$

To multiply fractions, multiply the numerators and multiply the denominators.

Answer

4. $\frac{8}{3}$

Classroom Example: p. 19, Exercise 58

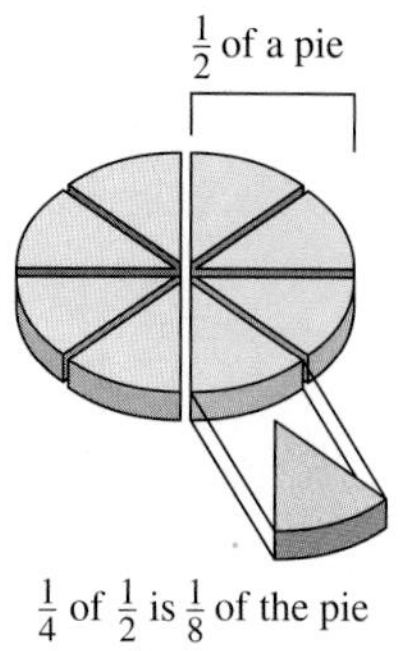

Figure 1-3

Example 4 Multiplying Fractions

Multiply the fractions: $\dfrac{1}{4} \times \dfrac{1}{2}$

Solution:

$$\frac{1}{4} \times \frac{1}{2} = \frac{1 \times 1}{4 \times 2} = \frac{1}{8}$$ Multiply the numerators. Multiply the denominators.

Notice that the product $\frac{1}{4} \times \frac{1}{2}$ represents a quantity that is $\frac{1}{4}$ of $\frac{1}{2}$. Taking $\frac{1}{4}$ of a quantity is equivalent to dividing the quantity by 4. One-half of a pie divided into four pieces leaves pieces that each represent $\frac{1}{8}$ of the pie (Figure 1-3).

Skill Practice Multiply.

5. $\dfrac{2}{7} \times \dfrac{3}{5}$

Classroom Example: p. 19, Exercise 62

Example 5 Multiplying Fractions

Multiply the fractions.

a. $\dfrac{7}{10} \times \dfrac{15}{14}$ **b.** $\dfrac{2}{13} \times \dfrac{13}{2}$ **c.** $5 \times \dfrac{1}{5}$

Solution:

a. $\dfrac{7}{10} \times \dfrac{15}{14} = \dfrac{7 \times 15}{10 \times 14}$ Multiply the numerators. Multiply the denominators.

$= \dfrac{\overset{1}{\cancel{7}} \times \overset{3}{\cancel{15}}}{\underset{2}{\cancel{10}} \times \underset{2}{\cancel{14}}}$ Divide out the common factors.

$= \dfrac{3}{4}$ Multiply.

b. $\dfrac{2}{13} \times \dfrac{13}{2} = \dfrac{2 \times 13}{13 \times 2} = \dfrac{\overset{1}{\cancel{2}} \times \overset{1}{\cancel{13}}}{\underset{1}{\cancel{13}} \times \underset{1}{\cancel{2}}} = \dfrac{1}{1} = 1$

Multiply $1 \times 1 = 1$. (numerator)

Multiply $1 \times 1 = 1$. (denominator)

c. $5 \times \dfrac{1}{5} = \dfrac{5}{1} \times \dfrac{1}{5}$ The whole number 5 can be written as $\frac{5}{1}$.

$= \dfrac{\overset{1}{\cancel{5}} \times 1}{1 \times \underset{1}{\cancel{5}}} = \dfrac{1}{1} = 1$ Divide out the common factors and multiply.

TIP: The same result can be obtained by dividing out common factors *before* multiplying.

$$\frac{\overset{1}{\cancel{7}}}{\underset{2}{\cancel{10}}} \times \frac{\overset{3}{\cancel{15}}}{\underset{2}{\cancel{14}}} = \frac{3}{4}$$

Instructor Note: You can also show multiplication of fractions using shading: The overlapped portion is the product.

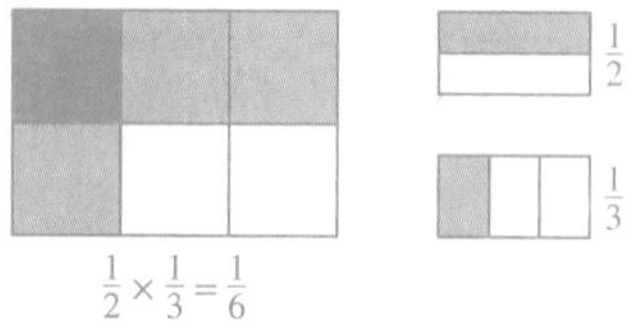

Skill Practice Multiply.

6. $\dfrac{8}{9} \times \dfrac{3}{4}$ **7.** $\dfrac{4}{5} \times \dfrac{5}{4}$ **8.** $10 \times \dfrac{1}{10}$

Answers

5. $\dfrac{6}{35}$ **6.** $\dfrac{2}{3}$ **7.** 1 **8.** 1

5. Dividing Fractions

Before we divide fractions, we need to know how to find the reciprocal of a fraction. Notice from Example 5 that $\frac{2}{13} \times \frac{13}{2} = 1$ and $5 \times \frac{1}{5} = 1$. The numbers $\frac{2}{13}$ and $\frac{13}{2}$ are said to be reciprocals because their product is 1. Likewise the numbers 5 and $\frac{1}{5}$ are reciprocals.

The Reciprocal of a Number

Two nonzero numbers are **reciprocals** of each other if their product is 1. Therefore, the reciprocal of the fraction

$$\frac{a}{b} \text{ is } \frac{b}{a} \qquad \text{because} \qquad \frac{a}{b} \times \frac{b}{a} = 1$$

Number	Reciprocal	Product
$\frac{2}{15}$	$\frac{15}{2}$	$\frac{2}{15} \times \frac{15}{2} = 1$
$\frac{1}{8}$	$\frac{8}{1}$ (or equivalently 8)	$\frac{1}{8} \times 8 = 1$
$6 \left(\text{or equivalently } \frac{6}{1}\right)$	$\frac{1}{6}$	$6 \times \frac{1}{6} = 1$

To understand the concept of dividing fractions, consider a pie that is half-eaten. Suppose the remaining half must be divided among three people, that is, $\frac{1}{2} \div 3$. However, dividing by 3 is equivalent to taking $\frac{1}{3}$ of the remaining $\frac{1}{2}$ of the pie (Figure 1-4).

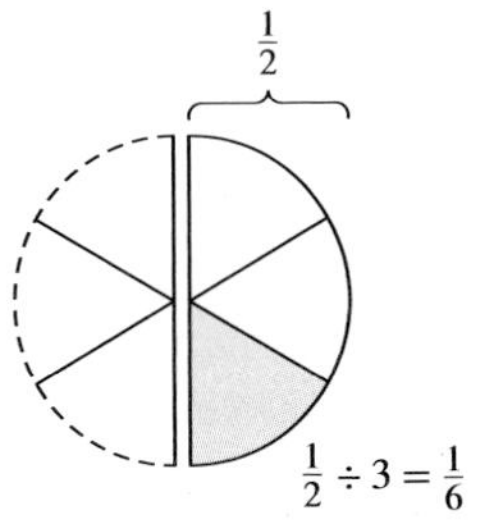

$$\frac{1}{2} \div 3 = \frac{1}{2} \cdot \frac{1}{3} = \frac{1}{6}$$

Figure 1-4

This example illustrates that dividing two numbers is equivalent to multiplying the first number by the reciprocal of the second number.

Dividing Fractions

Let a, b, c, and d be numbers such that b, c, and d are not zero. Then,

$$\frac{a}{b} \div \frac{c}{d} = \frac{a}{b} \times \frac{d}{c}$$

(multiply; reciprocal)

To divide fractions, multiply the first fraction by the reciprocal of the second fraction.

Classroom Examples: p. 19, Exercises 60 and 64

Example 6 Dividing Fractions

Divide the fractions.

a. $\frac{8}{5} \div \frac{3}{10}$ **b.** $\frac{12}{13} \div 6$

Solution:

a. $\frac{8}{5} \div \frac{3}{10} = \frac{8}{5} \times \frac{10}{3}$ Multiply by the reciprocal of $\frac{3}{10}$, which is $\frac{10}{3}$.

$= \frac{8 \times \overset{2}{\cancel{10}}}{\underset{1}{\cancel{5}} \times 3} = \frac{16}{3}$ Divide out the common factors and multiply.

b. $\frac{12}{13} \div 6 = \frac{12}{13} \div \frac{6}{1}$ Write the whole number 6 as $\frac{6}{1}$.

$= \frac{12}{13} \times \frac{1}{6}$ Multiply by the reciprocal of $\frac{6}{1}$, which is $\frac{1}{6}$.

$= \frac{\overset{2}{\cancel{12}} \times 1}{13 \times \underset{1}{\cancel{6}}} = \frac{2}{13}$ Divide out the common factors and multiply.

Avoiding Mistakes

Always check that the final answer is in lowest terms.

Skill Practice Divide.

9. $\frac{12}{25} \div \frac{8}{15}$ **10.** $\frac{1}{4} \div 2$

6. Adding and Subtracting Fractions

Adding and Subtracting Fractions

Two fractions can be added or subtracted if they have a common denominator. Let a, b, and c be numbers such that b does not equal zero. Then,

$$\frac{a}{b} + \frac{c}{b} = \frac{a+c}{b} \quad \text{and} \quad \frac{a}{b} - \frac{c}{b} = \frac{a-c}{b}$$

To add or subtract fractions with the same denominator, add or subtract the numerators and write the result over the common denominator.

Classroom Examples: p. 19, Exercises 78 and 80

Example 7 Adding and Subtracting Fractions with the Same Denominator

Add or subtract as indicated.

a. $\frac{1}{12} + \frac{7}{12}$ **b.** $\frac{13}{5} - \frac{3}{5}$

Answers

9. $\frac{9}{10}$ **10.** $\frac{1}{8}$

Solution:

a. $\dfrac{1}{12} + \dfrac{7}{12} = \dfrac{1+7}{12}$ Add the numerators.

$= \dfrac{8}{12}$

$= \dfrac{2}{3}$ Simplify to lowest terms.

b. $\dfrac{13}{5} - \dfrac{3}{5} = \dfrac{13-3}{5}$ Subtract the numerators.

$= \dfrac{10}{5}$ Simplify.

$= 2$ Simplify to lowest terms.

TIP: The sum $\frac{1}{12} + \frac{7}{12}$ can be visualized as the sum of the pink and blue sections of the figure.

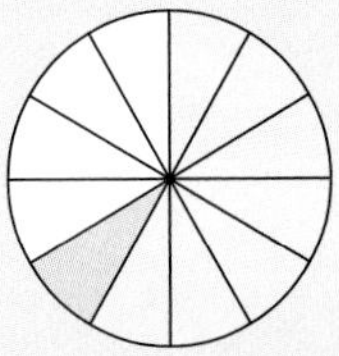

Skill Practice Add or subtract as indicated.

11. $\dfrac{2}{3} + \dfrac{5}{3}$ **12.** $\dfrac{5}{8} - \dfrac{1}{8}$

In Example 7, we added and subtracted fractions with the same denominators. To add or subtract fractions with different denominators, we must first become familiar with the idea of the least common multiple between two or more numbers. The **least common multiple (LCM)** of two numbers is the smallest whole number that is a multiple of each number. For example, the LCM of 6 and 9 is 18.

multiples of 6: 6, 12, 18, 24, 30, 36, . . .
multiples of 9: 9, 18, 27, 36, 45, 54, . . .

Listing the multiples of two or more given numbers can be a cumbersome way to find the LCM. Therefore, we offer the following method to find the LCM of two numbers.

Finding the LCM of Two Numbers

Step 1 Write each number as a product of prime factors.

Step 2 The LCM is the product of unique prime factors from *both* numbers. Use repeated factors the maximum number of times they appear in *either* factorization.

Example 8 Finding the LCM of Two Numbers

Classroom Example: p. 20, Exercise 82

Find the LCM of 9 and 15.

Solution:

	3's	5's
9 =	(3 × 3)	
15 =	3 ×	(5)

LCM = $3 \times 3 \times 5 = 45$

For the factors of 3 and 5, we circle the greatest number of times each occurs. The LCM is the product.

Skill Practice Find the LCM.

13. 10 and 25

Answers

11. $\frac{7}{3}$ or $2\frac{1}{3}$ **12.** $\frac{1}{2}$ **13.** 50

To add or subtract fractions with *different* denominators, we must first write each fraction as an equivalent fraction with a common denominator. A common denominator may be *any* common multiple of the denominators. However, we will use the least common denominator. The **least common denominator (LCD)** of two or more fractions is the LCM of the denominators of the fractions. The following example uses the fundamental principle of fractions to rewrite fractions with the desired denominator. *Note:* Multiplying the numerator and denominator by the *same* nonzero quantity will not change the value of the fraction.

Classroom Examples: p. 20, Exercises 86 and 90

Example 9 **Writing Equivalent Fractions and Subtracting Fractions**

a. Write each of the fractions $\frac{1}{9}$ and $\frac{1}{15}$ as an equivalent fraction with the LCD as its denominator.

b. Subtract $\dfrac{1}{9} - \dfrac{1}{15}$.

Solution:

From Example 8, we know that the LCM for 9 and 15 is 45. Therefore, the LCD of $\frac{1}{9}$ and $\frac{1}{15}$ is 45.

a. $\dfrac{1}{19} = \dfrac{}{45}$ $\dfrac{1 \times 5}{9 \times 5} = \dfrac{5}{45}$ So, $\dfrac{1}{9}$ is equivalent to $\dfrac{5}{45}$.

What number must we multiply 9 by to get 45? — Multiply numerator and denominator by 5.

$\dfrac{1}{15} = \dfrac{}{45}$ $\dfrac{1 \times 3}{15 \times 3} = \dfrac{3}{45}$ So, $\dfrac{1}{15}$ is equivalent to $\dfrac{3}{45}$.

What number must we multiply 15 by to get 45? — Multiply numerator and denominator by 3.

b. $\dfrac{1}{9} - \dfrac{1}{15}$

$= \dfrac{5}{45} - \dfrac{3}{45}$ Write $\frac{1}{9}$ and $\frac{1}{15}$ as equivalent fractions with the same denominator.

$= \dfrac{2}{45}$ Subtract.

Skill Practice

14. Write each of the fractions $\frac{5}{8}$ and $\frac{5}{12}$ as an equivalent fraction with the LCD as its denominator.

15. Subtract. $\dfrac{5}{8} - \dfrac{5}{12}$

Answers

14. $\dfrac{5}{8} = \dfrac{15}{24}$ and $\dfrac{5}{12} = \dfrac{10}{24}$ **15.** $\dfrac{5}{24}$

Classroom Example: p. 20, Exercise 98

Example 10 Adding and Subtracting Fractions

Simplify. $\frac{5}{12}+\frac{3}{4}-\frac{1}{2}$

Solution:

$\frac{5}{12}+\frac{3}{4}-\frac{1}{2}$

To find the LCD, we have:
LCD $= 2\times2\times3 = 12$

	2's	3's
12 =	(2×2)	(3)
4 =	2×2	
2 =	2	

$=\frac{5}{12}+\frac{3\times3}{4\times3}-\frac{1\times6}{2\times6}$ Write each fraction as an equivalent fraction with the LCD as its denominator.

$=\frac{5}{12}+\frac{9}{12}-\frac{6}{12}$

$=\frac{5+9-6}{12}$ Add and subtract the numerators.

$=\frac{8}{12}$ Simplify to lowest terms.

$=\frac{2}{3}$

Skill Practice Add.

16. $\frac{2}{3}+\frac{1}{2}+\frac{5}{6}$

7. Operations on Mixed Numbers

Recall that a mixed number is a whole number added to a fraction. The number $3\frac{1}{2}$ represents the sum of three wholes plus a half, that is, $3\frac{1}{2}=3+\frac{1}{2}$. For this reason, any mixed number can be converted to an improper fraction by using addition.

$$3\tfrac{1}{2}=3+\frac{1}{2}=\frac{6}{2}+\frac{1}{2}=\frac{7}{2}$$

TIP: A shortcut to writing a mixed number as an improper fraction is to multiply the whole number by the denominator of the fraction. Then add this value to the numerator of the fraction, and write the result over the denominator.

$3\frac{1}{2}$ ⟶ Multiply the whole number by the denominator: $3\times2=6$
Add the numerator: $6+1=7$
Write the result over the denominator: $\frac{7}{2}$

To add, subtract, multiply, or divide mixed numbers, we will first write the mixed number as an improper fraction.

Answer
16. 2

Classroom Example: p. 20, Exercise 114

Example 11 Operations on Mixed Numbers

Subtract. $5\frac{1}{3} - 2\frac{1}{4}$

Solution:

$5\frac{1}{3} - 2\frac{1}{4}$

$= \frac{16}{3} - \frac{9}{4}$ Write the mixed numbers as improper fractions.

$= \frac{16 \times 4}{3 \times 4} - \frac{9 \times 3}{4 \times 3}$ The LCD is 12. Multiply numerators and denominators by the missing factors from the denominators.

$= \frac{64}{12} - \frac{27}{12}$

$= \frac{37}{12}$ or $3\frac{1}{12}$ Subtract the fractions.

Skill Practice Subtract.

17. $2\frac{3}{4} - 1\frac{1}{3}$

TIP: An improper fraction can also be written as a mixed number. Both answers are acceptable. Note that

$$\frac{37}{12} = \frac{36}{12} + \frac{1}{12} = 3 + \frac{1}{12}, \text{ or } 3\frac{1}{12}$$

This can easily be found by dividing.

$$\frac{37}{12} \longrightarrow 12\overline{)37} \text{ quotient } 3,\quad -36,\quad \text{remainder } 1 \qquad 3\frac{1}{12}$$

quotient: 3; remainder: 1; divisor: 12

Classroom Example: p. 20, Exercise 110

Example 12 Operations on Mixed Numbers

Divide. $7\frac{1}{2} \div 3$

Solution:

$7\frac{1}{2} \div 3$

$= \frac{15}{2} \div \frac{3}{1}$ Write the mixed number and whole number as fractions.

$= \frac{\overset{5}{\cancel{15}}}{2} \times \frac{1}{\underset{1}{\cancel{3}}}$ Multiply by the reciprocal of $\frac{3}{1}$, which is $\frac{1}{3}$.

$= \frac{5}{2}$ or $2\frac{1}{2}$ The answer may be written as an improper fraction or as a mixed number.

Avoiding Mistakes

Remember that when dividing (or multiplying) fractions, a common denominator is not necessary.

Answer

17. $\frac{17}{12}$ or $1\frac{5}{12}$

Skill Practice Divide.

18. $5\frac{5}{6} \div 3\frac{2}{3}$

Answer

18. $\frac{35}{22}$ or $1\frac{13}{22}$

Section 1.1 Practice Exercises

For additional exercises, see Classroom Activities 1.1A–1.1E in the *Student's Resource Manual* at www.mhhe.com/moh.

Study Skills Exercise

To enhance your learning experience, we provide study skills that focus on eight areas: learning about your course, using your text, taking notes, doing homework, taking an exam (test and math anxiety), managing your time, recognizing your learning style, and studying for the final exam.

Each activity requires only a few minutes and will help you pass this course and become a better math student. Many of these skills can be carried over to other disciplines and help you become a model college student. To begin, write down the following information:

a. Instructor's name
b. Instructor's office number
c. Instructor's telephone number
d. Instructor's e-mail address
e. Instructor's office hours
f. Days of the week that the class meets
g. The room number in which the class meets
h. Is there a lab requirement for this course? How often must you attend lab and where is it located?

Vocabulary and Key Concepts

1. a. A ___product___ is the result of multiplying two or more numbers.

b. The numbers being multiplied in a product are called ___factors___.

c. Given a fraction $\frac{a}{b}$ with $b \neq 0$, the value a is the ___numerator___ and ___b___ is the denominator.

d. A fraction is said to be in ___lowest___ terms if the numerator and denominator share no common factor other than 1.

e. The fraction $\frac{4}{4}$ can also be written as the whole number ___1___, and the fraction $\frac{4}{1}$ can be written as the whole number ___4___.

f. Two nonzero numbers $\frac{a}{b}$ and $\frac{b}{a}$ are ___reciprocals___ because their product is 1.

g. The least common multiple (LCM) of two numbers is the smallest whole number that is a ___multiple___ of both numbers.

h. The ___least___ common denominator of two or more fractions is the LCM of their denominators.

Concept 1: Basic Definitions

For Exercises 2–10, identify the numerator and denominator of each fraction. Then determine if the fraction is a proper fraction or an improper fraction.

2. $\frac{7}{8}$ Numerator: 7; denominator: 8; proper

3. $\frac{2}{3}$ Numerator: 2; denominator: 3; proper

4. $\frac{9}{5}$ Numerator: 9; denominator: 5; improper

5. $\frac{5}{2}$ Numerator: 5; denominator: 2; improper

6. $\frac{6}{6}$ Numerator: 6; denominator: 6; improper

7. $\frac{4}{4}$ Numerator: 4; denominator: 4; improper

8. $\frac{12}{1}$ Numerator: 12; denominator: 1; improper

9. $\frac{5}{1}$ Numerator: 5; denominator: 1; improper

10. $\frac{6}{7}$ Numerator: 6; denominator: 7; proper

For Exercises 11–18, write a proper or improper fraction associated with the shaded region of each figure.

11. 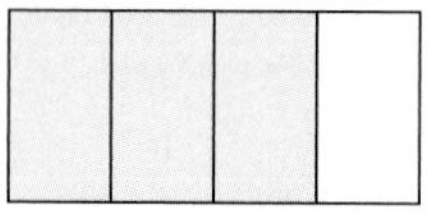 $\frac{3}{4}$

12. 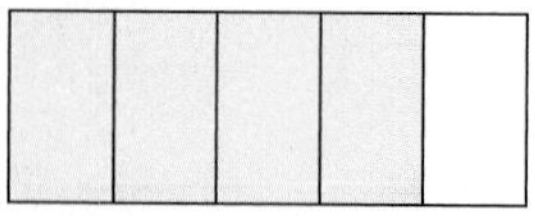 $\frac{4}{5}$

13. 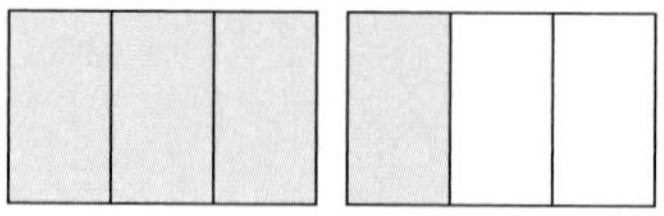 $\frac{4}{3}$

14. 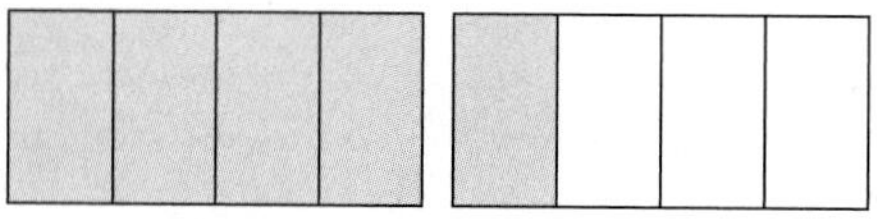 $\frac{5}{4}$

15. 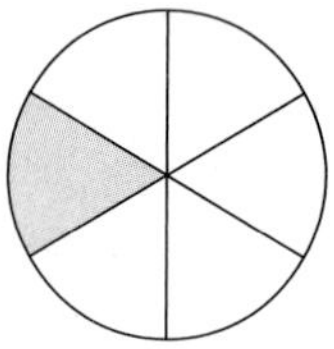 $\frac{1}{6}$

16. 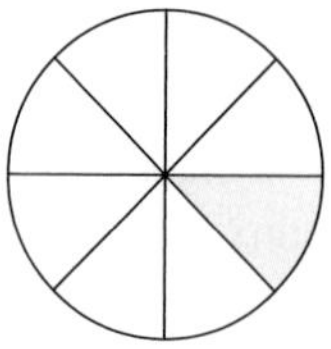 $\frac{1}{8}$

17. 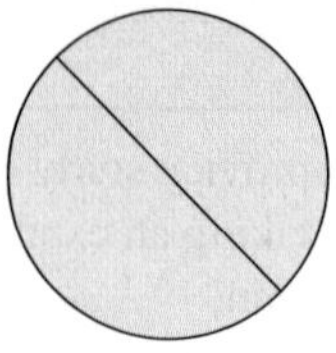 $\frac{2}{2}$

18. 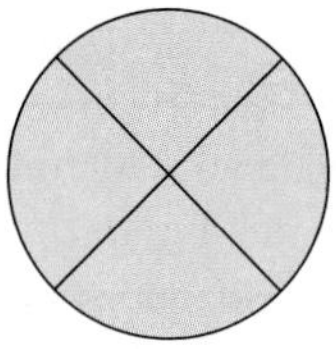 $\frac{4}{4}$

For Exercises 19–22, write both an improper fraction and a mixed number associated with the shaded region of each figure.

19. 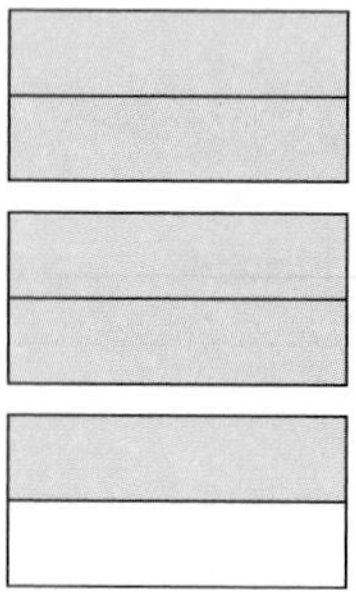 $\frac{5}{2}$ or $2\frac{1}{2}$

20. 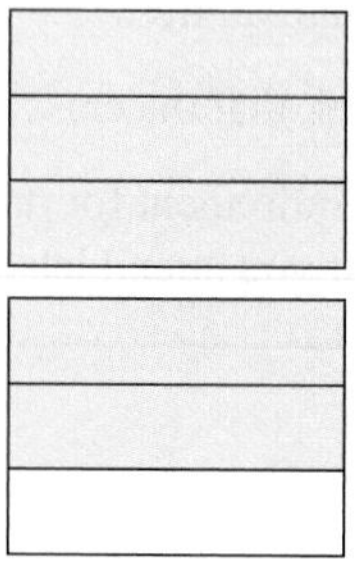 $\frac{5}{3}$ or $1\frac{2}{3}$

21. 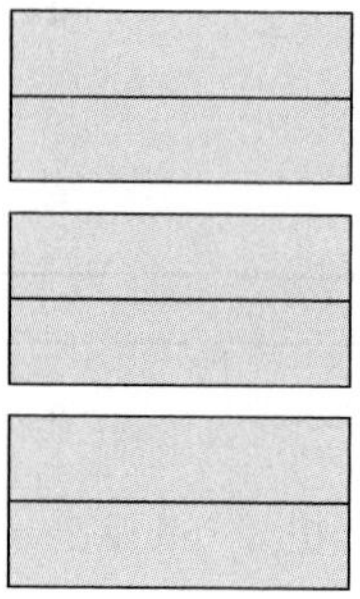 $\frac{6}{2}$ or 3

22. 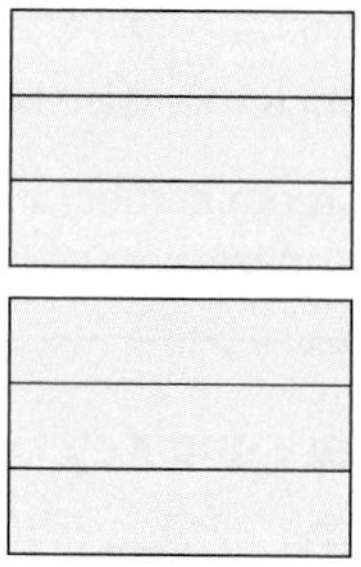 $\frac{6}{3}$ or 2

23. Explain the difference between the set of whole numbers and the set of natural numbers.
The set of whole numbers includes the number 0 and the set of natural numbers does not.

24. Explain the difference between a proper fraction and an improper fraction. A proper fraction represents a number less than one unit. An improper fraction represents a number greater than or equal to a whole unit.

25. Write a fraction that simplifies to $\frac{1}{2}$. (Answers may vary.) For example: $\frac{2}{4}$

26. Write a fraction that simplifies to $\frac{1}{3}$. (Answers may vary.) For example: $\frac{2}{6}$

Concept 2: Prime Factorization

For Exercises 27–34, identify each number as either a prime number or a composite number.

27. 5 Prime

28. 9 Composite

29. 4 Composite

30. 2 Prime

31. 39 Composite

32. 23 Prime

33. 53 Prime

34. 51 Composite

For Exercises 35–42, write each number as a product of prime factors. **(See Example 1.)**

35. 36 $2 \times 2 \times 3 \times 3$

36. 70 $2 \times 5 \times 7$

37. 42 $2 \times 3 \times 7$

38. 35 5×7

39. 110 $2 \times 5 \times 11$

40. 136 $2 \times 2 \times 2 \times 17$

41. 135 $3 \times 3 \times 3 \times 5$

42. 105 $3 \times 5 \times 7$

Concept 3: Simplifying Fractions to Lowest Terms

For Exercises 43–54, simplify each fraction to lowest terms. **(See Examples 2–3.)**

43. $\frac{3}{15}$ $\frac{1}{5}$

44. $\frac{8}{12}$ $\frac{2}{3}$

45. $\frac{16}{6}$ $\frac{8}{3}$ or $2\frac{2}{3}$

46. $\frac{20}{12}$ $\frac{5}{3}$ or $1\frac{2}{3}$

47. $\frac{42}{48}$ $\frac{7}{8}$

48. $\frac{35}{80}$ $\frac{7}{16}$

49. $\frac{48}{64}$ $\frac{3}{4}$

50. $\frac{32}{48}$ $\frac{2}{3}$

51. $\frac{110}{176}$ $\frac{5}{8}$

52. $\frac{70}{120}$ $\frac{7}{12}$

53. $\frac{200}{150}$ $\frac{4}{3}$ or $1\frac{1}{3}$

54. $\frac{210}{119}$ $\frac{30}{17}$ or $1\frac{13}{17}$

Concepts 4–5: Multiplying and Dividing Fractions

For Exercises 55–56, determine if the statement is true or false. If it is false, rewrite as a true statement.

55. When multiplying or dividing fractions, it is necessary to have a common denominator. False: When adding or subtracting fractions, it is necessary to have a common denominator.

56. When dividing two fractions, it is necessary to multiply the first fraction by the reciprocal of the second fraction. True

For Exercises 57–68, multiply or divide as indicated. **(See Examples 4–6.)**

57. $\frac{10}{13} \times \frac{26}{15}$ $\frac{4}{3}$ or $1\frac{1}{3}$

58. $\frac{15}{28} \times \frac{7}{9}$ $\frac{5}{12}$

59. $\frac{3}{7} \div \frac{9}{14}$ $\frac{2}{3}$

60. $\frac{7}{25} \div \frac{1}{5}$ $\frac{7}{5}$ or $1\frac{2}{5}$

61. $\frac{9}{10} \times 5$ $\frac{9}{2}$ or $4\frac{1}{2}$

62. $\frac{3}{7} \times 14$ 6

63. $\frac{12}{5} \div 4$ $\frac{3}{5}$

64. $\frac{20}{6} \div 5$ $\frac{2}{3}$

65. $\frac{5}{2} \times \frac{10}{21} \times \frac{7}{5}$ $\frac{5}{3}$ or $1\frac{2}{3}$

66. $\frac{55}{9} \times \frac{18}{32} \times \frac{24}{11}$ $\frac{15}{2}$ or $7\frac{1}{2}$

67. $\frac{9}{100} \div \frac{13}{1000}$ $\frac{90}{13}$ or $6\frac{12}{13}$

68. $\frac{1000}{17} \div \frac{10}{3}$ $\frac{300}{17}$ or $17\frac{11}{17}$

69. Gus decides to save $\frac{1}{3}$ of his pay each month. If his monthly pay is \$2112, how much will he save each month? \$704

70. Stephen's take-home pay is \$4200 a month. If he budgeted $\frac{1}{4}$ of his pay for rent, how much is his rent? \$1050

71. In Professor Foley's Beginning Algebra class, $\frac{5}{6}$ of the students passed the first test. If there are 42 students in the class, how many passed the test? 35 students

72. Shontell had only enough paper to print out $\frac{3}{5}$ of her book report before school. If the report is 10 pages long, how many pages did she print out? 6 pages

73. Marty will reinforce a concrete walkway by cutting a steel rod (called rebar) that is 4 yd long. How many pieces can he cut if each piece must be $\frac{1}{2}$ yd in length? 8 pieces

74. There are 4 cups of oatmeal in a box. If each serving is $\frac{1}{3}$ of a cup, how many servings are contained in the box? 12 servings

75. Anita buys 6 lb of mixed nuts to be divided into decorative jars that will each hold $\frac{3}{4}$ lb of nuts. How many jars will she be able to fill? 8 jars

76. Beth has a $\frac{7}{8}$-in. nail that she must hammer into a board. Each strike of the hammer moves the nail $\frac{1}{16}$ in. into the board. How many strikes of the hammer must she make to drive the nail completely into the board? Beth must make 14 strikes.

Concept 6: Adding and Subtracting Fractions

For Exercises 77–80, add or subtract as indicated. **(See Example 7.)**

77. $\frac{5}{14} + \frac{1}{14}$ $\frac{3}{7}$

78. $\frac{9}{5} + \frac{1}{5}$ 2

79. $\frac{17}{24} - \frac{5}{24}$ $\frac{1}{2}$

80. $\frac{11}{18} - \frac{5}{18}$ $\frac{1}{3}$

For Exercises 81–84, find the least common multiple for each list of numbers. **(See Example 8.)**

81. 6, 15 30

82. 12, 30 60

83. 20, 8, 4 40

84. 24, 40, 30 120

For Exercises 85–100, add or subtract as indicated. **(See Examples 9–10.)**

85. $\frac{1}{8}+\frac{3}{4}$ $\frac{7}{8}$

86. $\frac{3}{16}+\frac{1}{2}$ $\frac{11}{16}$

87. $\frac{11}{8}-\frac{3}{10}$ $\frac{43}{40}$ or $1\frac{3}{40}$

88. $\frac{12}{35}-\frac{1}{10}$ $\frac{17}{70}$

89. $\frac{7}{26}-\frac{2}{13}$ $\frac{3}{26}$

90. $\frac{25}{24}-\frac{5}{16}$ $\frac{35}{48}$

91. $\frac{7}{18}+\frac{5}{12}$ $\frac{29}{36}$

92. $\frac{3}{16}+\frac{9}{20}$ $\frac{51}{80}$

93. $\frac{5}{4}-\frac{1}{20}$ $\frac{6}{5}$ or $1\frac{1}{5}$

94. $\frac{7}{6}-\frac{1}{24}$ $\frac{9}{8}$ or $1\frac{1}{8}$

95. $\frac{5}{12}+\frac{5}{16}$ $\frac{35}{48}$

96. $\frac{3}{25}+\frac{8}{35}$ $\frac{61}{175}$

97. $\frac{1}{6}+\frac{3}{4}-\frac{5}{8}$ $\frac{7}{24}$

98. $\frac{1}{2}+\frac{2}{3}-\frac{5}{12}$ $\frac{3}{4}$

99. $\frac{4}{7}+\frac{1}{2}+\frac{3}{4}$ $\frac{51}{28}$ or $1\frac{23}{28}$

100. $\frac{9}{10}+\frac{4}{5}+\frac{3}{4}$ $\frac{49}{20}$ or $2\frac{9}{20}$

101. For his famous brownie recipe, Chef Alfonso combines $\frac{2}{3}$ cup granulated sugar with $\frac{1}{4}$ cup brown sugar. What is the total amount of sugar in his recipe? $\frac{11}{12}$ cup sugar

102. Chef Alfonso eats too many of his brownies and his waistline increased by $\frac{3}{4}$ in. during one month and $\frac{3}{8}$ in. the next month. What was his total increase for the 2-month period? $\frac{9}{8}$ in. or $1\frac{1}{8}$ in.

103. Currently the most popular smartphone has a thickness of $\frac{9}{25}$ in. The second most popular is $\frac{1}{2}$ in. thick. How much thicker is the second most popular smartphone? $\frac{7}{50}$ in.

104. The diameter of a penny is $\frac{3}{4}$ in. while the dime is $\frac{7}{10}$ in. How much larger is the penny than the dime? $\frac{1}{20}$ in.

Concept 7: Operations on Mixed Numbers

For Exercises 105–118, perform the indicated operations. **(See Examples 11–12.)**

105. $3\frac{1}{5}\times 2\frac{7}{8}$ $\frac{46}{5}$ or $9\frac{1}{5}$

106. $2\frac{1}{2}\times 1\frac{4}{5}$ $\frac{9}{2}$ or $4\frac{1}{2}$

107. $1\frac{2}{9}\div 7\frac{1}{3}$ $\frac{1}{6}$

108. $2\frac{2}{5}\div 1\frac{2}{7}$ $\frac{28}{15}$ or $1\frac{13}{15}$

109. $1\frac{2}{9}\div 6$ $\frac{11}{54}$

110. $2\frac{2}{5}\div 2$ $\frac{6}{5}$ or $1\frac{1}{5}$

111. $2\frac{1}{8}+1\frac{3}{8}$ $\frac{7}{2}$ or $3\frac{1}{2}$

112. $1\frac{3}{14}+1\frac{1}{14}$ $\frac{16}{7}$ or $2\frac{2}{7}$

113. $3\frac{1}{2}-1\frac{7}{8}$ $\frac{13}{8}$ or $1\frac{5}{8}$

114. $5\frac{1}{3}-2\frac{3}{4}$ $\frac{31}{12}$ or $2\frac{7}{12}$

115. $1\frac{1}{6}+3\frac{3}{4}$ $\frac{59}{12}$ or $4\frac{11}{12}$

116. $4\frac{1}{2}+2\frac{2}{3}$ $\frac{43}{6}$ or $7\frac{1}{6}$

117. $1-\frac{7}{8}$ $\frac{1}{8}$

118. $2-\frac{3}{7}$ $\frac{11}{7}$ or $1\frac{4}{7}$

119. A board $26\frac{3}{8}$ in. long must be cut into three pieces of equal length. Find the length of each piece. $8\frac{19}{24}$ in.

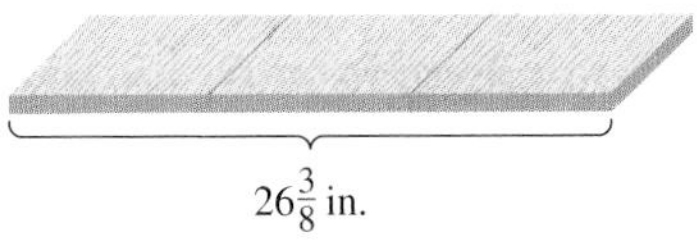

120. A futon, when set up as a sofa, measures $3\frac{5}{6}$ ft wide. When it is opened to be used as a bed, the width is increased by $1\frac{3}{4}$ ft. What is the total width of this bed? $5\frac{7}{12}$ ft

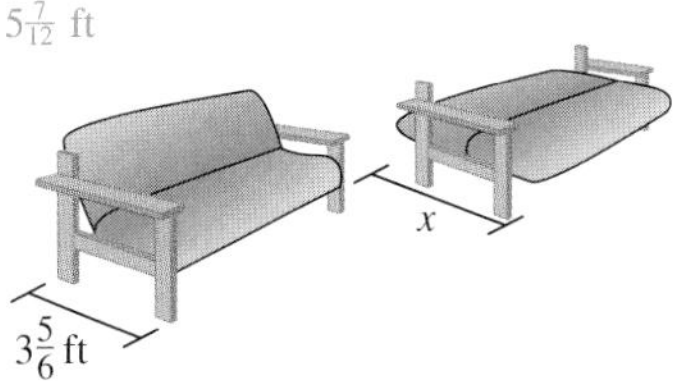

121. A plane trip from Orlando to Detroit takes $2\frac{3}{4}$ hr. If the plane traveled for $1\frac{1}{6}$ hr, how much time remains for the flight? $1\frac{7}{12}$ hr

122. Silvia manages a sub shop and needs to prepare smoked turkey sandwiches. She has $3\frac{3}{4}$ lb of turkey in the cooler, and each sandwich requires $\frac{3}{8}$ lb of turkey. How many sandwiches can she make? 10 sandwiches

123. José's catering company plans to prepare two different shrimp dishes for an upcoming event. One dish requires $1\frac{1}{2}$ lb of shrimp and the other requires $\frac{3}{4}$ lb of shrimp. How much shrimp should José order for the two dishes? $2\frac{1}{4}$ lb

124. Ayako took a trip to the store $5\frac{1}{2}$ mi away. If she rode the bus for $4\frac{5}{6}$ mi and walked the rest of the way, how far did she have to walk? $\frac{2}{3}$ mi

125. If Tampa, Florida, averages $6\frac{1}{4}$ in. of rain during each summer month, how much total rain would be expected in June, July, August, and September? 25 in.

126. Pete started working out and found that he lost approximately $\frac{3}{4}$ in. off his waistline every month. How much would he lose around his waist in 6 months? $\frac{9}{2}$ in. or $4\frac{1}{2}$ in.

Introduction to Algebra and the Set of Real Numbers — Section 1.2

Concepts

1. **Variables and Expressions**
2. **The Set of Real Numbers**
3. **Inequalities**
4. **Opposite of a Real Number**
5. **Absolute Value of a Real Number**

1. Variables and Expressions

Doctors promote daily exercise as part of a healthy lifestyle. Aerobic exercise is exercise for the heart. During aerobic exercise, the goal is to maintain a heart rate level between 65% and 85% of an individual's maximum recommended heart rate. The maximum recommended heart rate, in beats per minute, for an adult of age a is given by:

$$\text{Maximum recommended heart rate} = 220 - a$$

In this example, value a is called a **variable**. This is a symbol or letter, such as x, y, z, a, and the like, that is used to represent an unknown number that is subject to change. The number 220 is called a **constant**, because it does not vary. The quantity $220 - a$ is called an algebraic expression. An algebraic **expression** is a collection of variables and constants under algebraic operations. For example, $\frac{3}{x}$, $y + 7$, and $t - 1.4$ are algebraic expressions.

The symbols used in algebraic expressions to show the four basic operations are shown here:

Addition $a + b$

Subtraction $a - b$

Multiplication $a \times b$, $a \cdot b$, $(a)b$, $a(b)$, $(a)(b)$, ab
(*Note:* We rarely use the notation $a \times b$ because the symbol $\times$ may be confused with the variable x.)

Division $a \div b$, $\frac{a}{b}$, a/b, $b\overline{)a}$

The value of an algebraic expression depends on the values of the variables within the expression.

Classroom Example: p. 32, Exercise 16

Example 1 Evaluating an Algebraic Expression

The expression $220 - a$ represents the maximum recommended heart rate for an adult of age a. Determine the maximum heart rate for:

a. A 20-year-old **b.** A 45-year-old

Solution:

a. In the expression $220 - a$, the variable, a, represents the age of the individual. To calculate the maximum recommended heart rate for a 20-year-old, we substitute 20 for a in the expression.

$220 - a$

$220 - (\ \ )$	When substituting a number for a variable, use parentheses.
$= 220 - (20)$	Substitute $a = 20$.
$= 200$	Subtract.

The maximum recommended heart rate for a 20-year-old is 200 beats per minute.

b. $220 - a$

$220 - (\ \ )$	When substituting a number for a variable, use parentheses.
$= 220 - (45)$	Substitute $a = 45$.
$= 175$	Subtract.

The maximum recommended heart rate for a 45-year-old is 175 beats per minute.

Skill Practice

1. After dining out at a restaurant, the recommended minimum amount for tipping the server is 15% of the cost of the meal. This can be represented by the expression $0.15c$, where c is the cost of the meal. Compute the tip for a meal that costs:

a. \$18 **b.** \$46

Classroom Examples: p. 31, Exercises 8 and 10

Example 2 Evaluating Algebraic Expressions

Evaluate the algebraic expression when $p = 4$ and $q = \frac{3}{4}$.

a. $100 - p$ **b.** pq

Solution:

a. $100 - p$

$100 - (\ \ )$	When substituting a number for a variable, use parentheses.
$= 100 - (4)$	Substitute $p = 4$ in the parentheses.
$= 96$	Subtract.

Answers

1. a. \$2.70 **b.** \$6.90

b. pq

$= (\quad)(\quad)$	When substituting a number for a variable, use parentheses.
$= (4)\left(\frac{3}{4}\right)$	Substitute $p = 4$ and $q = \frac{3}{4}$.
$= \frac{\overset{1}{\cancel{4}}}{1} \cdot \frac{3}{\underset{1}{\cancel{4}}}$	Write the whole number as a fraction.
$= \frac{3}{1}$	Multiply fractions.
$= 3$	Simplify.

Skill Practice Evaluate the algebraic expressions when $x = 5$ and $y = 2$.

2. $20 - y$ **3.** xy

2. The Set of Real Numbers

Typically, the numbers represented by variables in an algebraic expression are all part of the set of **real numbers**. These are the numbers that we work with on a day-to-day basis. The real numbers encompass zero, all positive, and all negative numbers, including those represented by fractions and decimal numbers. The set of real numbers can be represented graphically on a horizontal number line with a point labeled as 0. Positive real numbers are graphed to the right of 0, and negative real numbers are graphed to the left of 0. Zero is neither positive nor negative. Each point on the number line corresponds to exactly one real number. For this reason, this number line is called the *real number line* (Figure 1-5).

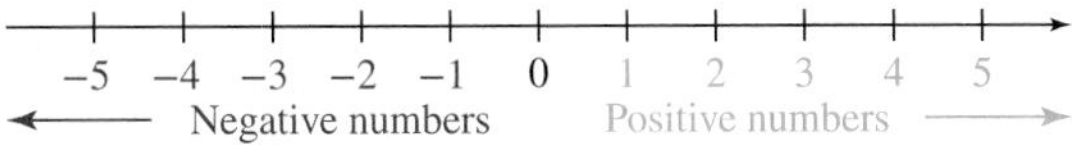

Figure 1-5

Example 3 Plotting Points on the Real Number Line

Classroom Example: p. 32, Exercise 20

Plot the numbers on the real number line.

a. -3 **b.** $\frac{3}{2}$ **c.** -4.7 **d.** $\frac{16}{5}$

Solution:

a. Because -3 is negative, it lies three units to the left of 0.

b. The fraction $\frac{3}{2}$ can be expressed as the mixed number $1\frac{1}{2}$ which lies halfway between 1 and 2 on the number line.

c. The negative number -4.7 lies $\frac{7}{10}$ unit to the left of -4 on the number line.

d. The fraction $\frac{16}{5}$ can be expressed as the mixed number $3\frac{1}{5}$, which lies $\frac{1}{5}$ unit to the right of 3 on the number line.

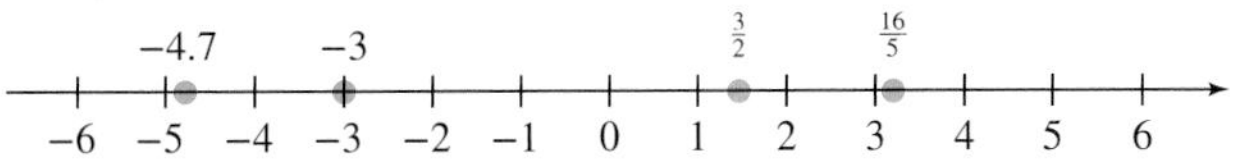

Answers

2. 18 **3.** 10

Skill Practice Plot the numbers on the real number line.

4. $\{-1, \frac{3}{4}, -2.5, \frac{10}{3}\}$

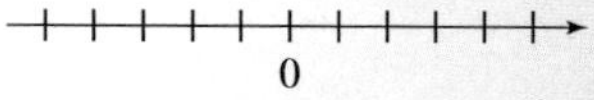

TIP: The natural numbers are used for counting. For this reason, they are sometimes called the "counting numbers."

In mathematics, a well-defined collection of elements is called a **set**. "Well-defined" means the set is described in such a way that it is clear whether an element is in the set. The symbols { } are used to enclose the elements of the set. For example, the set {A, B, C, D, E} represents the set of the first five letters of the alphabet.

Several sets of numbers are used extensively in algebra and are *subsets* (or part) of the set of real numbers.

Natural Numbers, Whole Numbers, and Integers

The set of **natural numbers** is $\{1, 2, 3, \ldots\}$

The set of **whole numbers** is $\{0, 1, 2, 3, \ldots\}$

The set of **integers** is $\{\ldots -3, -2, -1, 0, 1, 2, 3, \ldots\}$

Notice that the set of whole numbers includes the natural numbers. Therefore, every natural number is also a whole number. The set of integers includes the set of whole numbers. Therefore, every whole number is also an integer.

Fractions are also among the numbers we use frequently. A number that can be written as a fraction whose numerator is an integer and whose denominator is a nonzero integer is called a *rational number.*

Instructor Note: Memory Device: Rational = RATIO-nal can be written as a ratio of two integers

Rational Numbers

The set of **rational numbers** is the set of numbers that can be expressed in the form $\frac{p}{q}$, where both p and q are integers and q does not equal 0.

We also say that a rational number $\frac{p}{q}$ is a *ratio* of two integers, p and q, where q is not equal to zero.

Classroom Examples: p. 32, Exercises 22 and 24

Example 4 Identifying Rational Numbers

Show that the following numbers are rational numbers by finding an equivalent ratio of two integers.

a. $\dfrac{-2}{3}$ **b.** -12 **c.** 0.5 **d.** $0.\overline{6}$

Solution:

a. The fraction $\frac{-2}{3}$ is a rational number because it can be expressed as the ratio of -2 and 3.

b. The number -12 is a rational number because it can be expressed as the ratio of -12 and 1, that is, $-12 = \frac{-12}{1}$. In this example, we see that an integer is also a rational number.

Answer

4.

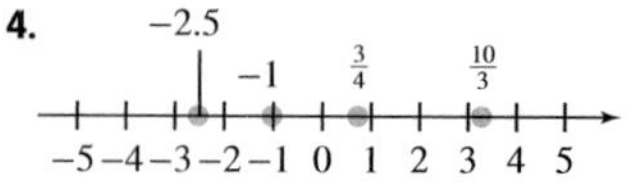

c. The terminating decimal 0.5 is a rational number because it can be expressed as the ratio of 5 and 10, that is, $0.5 = \frac{5}{10}$. In this example, we see that a terminating decimal is also a rational number.

d. The numeral $0.\overline{6}$ represents the nonterminating, repeating decimal 0.6666666 . . . . The number $0.\overline{6}$ is a rational number because it can be expressed as the ratio of 2 and 3, that is, $0.\overline{6} = \frac{2}{3}$. In this example, we see that a repeating decimal is also a rational number.

Skill Practice Show that each number is rational by finding an equivalent ratio of two integers.

5. $\frac{3}{7}$ **6.** -5 **7.** 0.3 **8.** $0.\overline{3}$

TIP: A rational number can be represented by a terminating decimal or by a repeating decimal.

Some real numbers, such as the number π, cannot be represented by the ratio of two integers. These numbers are called irrational numbers and in decimal form are nonterminating, nonrepeating decimals. The value of π, for example, can be approximated as $\pi \approx 3.1415926535897932$. However, the decimal digits continue forever with no repeated pattern. Another example of an irrational number is $\sqrt{3}$ (read as "the positive square root of 3"). The expression $\sqrt{3}$ is a number that when multiplied by itself is 3. There is no rational number that satisfies this condition. Thus, $\sqrt{3}$ is an irrational number.

Irrational Numbers

The set of **irrational numbers** is a subset of the real numbers whose elements cannot be written as a ratio of two integers.

Note: An irrational number cannot be written as a terminating decimal or as a repeating decimal.

The set of real numbers consists of both the rational and the irrational numbers. The relationship among these important sets of numbers is illustrated in Figure 1-6 along with numerical examples.

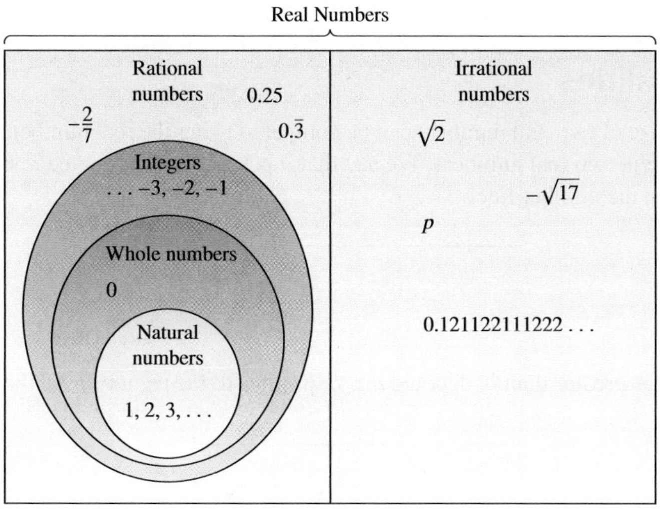

Figure 1-6

Answers

5. Ratio of 3 and 7
6. Ratio of −5 and 1
7. Ratio of 3 and 10
8. Ratio of 1 and 3

Classroom Examples: p. 33, Exercises 44 and 46

Example 5 Classifying Numbers by Set

Check the set(s) to which each number belongs. The numbers may belong to more than one set.

	Natural Numbers	Whole Numbers	Integers	Rational Numbers	Irrational Numbers	Real Numbers
5						
$\frac{-47}{3}$						
1.48						
$\sqrt{7}$						
0						

Solution:

	Natural Numbers	Whole Numbers	Integers	Rational Numbers	Irrational Numbers	Real Numbers
5	✓	✓	✓	✓ (ratio of 5 and 1)		✓
$\frac{-47}{3}$				✓ (ratio of −47 and 3)		✓
1.48				✓ (ratio of 148 and 100)		✓
$\sqrt{7}$					✓	✓
0		✓	✓	✓ (ratio of 0 and 1)		✓

Skill Practice Identify the sets to which each number belongs. Choose from: natural numbers, whole numbers, integers, rational numbers, irrational numbers, real numbers.

9. -4 **10.** $0.\overline{7}$ **11.** $\sqrt{13}$ **12.** 12 **13.** 1

3. Inequalities

The relative size of two real numbers can be compared using the real number line. Suppose a and b represent two real numbers. We say that a is less than b, denoted $a < b$, if a lies to the left of b on the number line.

$a < b$

We say that a is greater than b, denoted $a > b$, if a lies to the right of b on the number line.

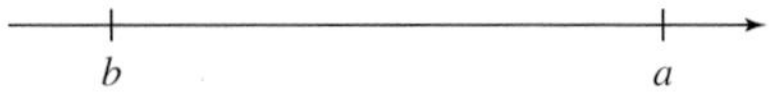

$a > b$

Answers

9. Integers, rational numbers, real numbers
10. Rational numbers, real numbers
11. Irrational numbers, real numbers
12. Natural numbers, whole numbers, integers, rational numbers, real numbers
13. Natural numbers, whole numbers, integers, rational numbers, real numbers

Table 1-1 summarizes the relational operators that compare two real numbers a and b.

Table 1-1

Mathematical Expression	Translation	Example
$a < b$	a is less than b.	$2 < 3$
$a > b$	a is greater than b.	$5 > 1$
$a \leq b$	a is less than or equal to b.	$4 \leq 4$
$a \geq b$	a is greater than or equal to b.	$10 \geq 9$
$a = b$	a is equal to b.	$6 = 6$
$a \neq b$	a is not equal to b.	$7 \neq 0$
$a \approx b$	a is approximately equal to b.	$2.3 \approx 2$

The symbols $<$, $>$, $\leq$, $\geq$, and $\neq$ are called *inequality signs*, and the statements $a < b$, $a > b$, $a \leq b$, $a \geq b$, and $a \neq b$ are called **inequalities**.

Example 6 Ordering Real Numbers

Classroom Example: p. 33, Exercise 50

The average temperatures (in degrees Celsius) for selected cities in the United States and Canada in January are shown in Table 1-2.

Table 1-2

City	Temp (°C)
Prince George, British Columbia	−12.5
Corpus Christi, Texas	13.4
Parkersburg, West Virginia	−0.9
San Jose, California	9.7
Juneau, Alaska	−5.7
New Bedford, Massachusetts	−0.2
Durham, North Carolina	4.2

Plot a point on the real number line representing the temperature of each city. Compare the temperatures between the following cities, and fill in the blank with the appropriate inequality sign: $<$ or $>$.

Solution:

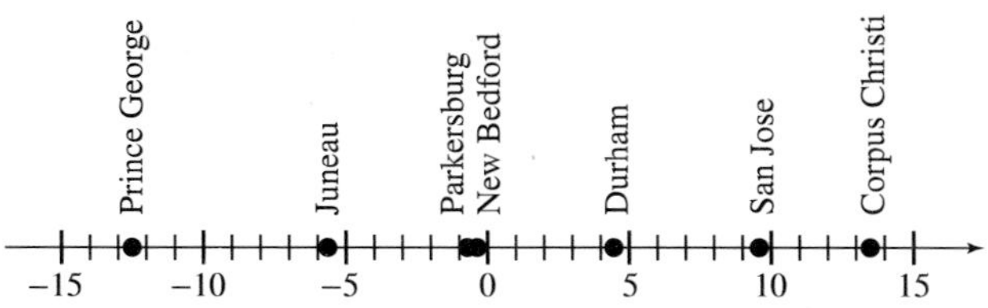

a. Temperature of San Jose [$<$] temperature of Corpus Christi

b. Temperature of Juneau [$>$] temperature of Prince George

c. Temperature of Parkersburg [$<$] temperature of New Bedford

d. Temperature of Parkersburg [$>$] temperature of Prince George

Skill Practice Fill in the blanks with the appropriate inequality sign: < or >.

14. -11 ________ 20 **15.** -3 ________ -6

16. 0 ________ -9 **17.** -6.2 ________ -1.8

4. Opposite of a Real Number

To gain mastery of any algebraic skill, it is necessary to know the meaning of key definitions and key symbols. Two important definitions are the *opposite* of a real number and the *absolute value* of a real number.

The Opposite of a Real Number

Two numbers that are the same distance from 0 but on opposite sides of 0 on the number line are called **opposites** of each other. Symbolically, we denote the opposite of a real number a as $-a$.

Classroom Examples: p. 33, Exercises 52 and 54

Example 7 Finding the Opposite of a Real Number

a. Find the opposite of 5. **b.** Find the opposite of $-\frac{4}{7}$.

Solution:

a. The opposite of 5 is -5. **b.** The opposite of $-\frac{4}{7}$ is $\frac{4}{7}$.

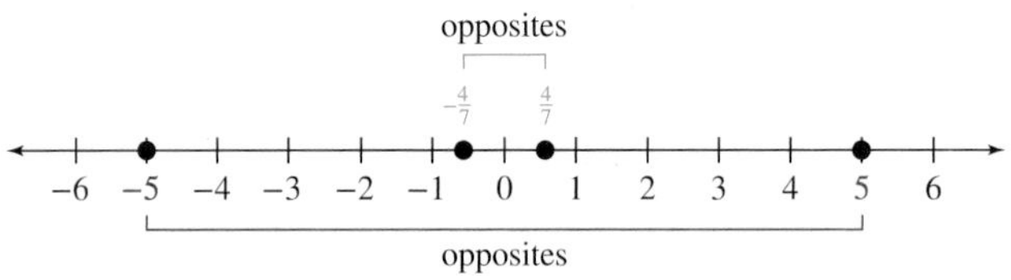

Skill Practice Find the opposite.

18. 224 **19.** -3.4

Classroom Example: p. 34, Exercise 62

Example 8 Finding the Opposite of a Real Number

Evaluate each expression.

a. $-(0.46)$ **b.** $-\left(-\frac{11}{3}\right)$

Solution:

a. $-(0.46) = -0.46$ The expression $-(0.46)$ represents the opposite of 0.46.

b. $-\left(-\frac{11}{3}\right) = \frac{11}{3}$ The expression $-\left(-\frac{11}{3}\right)$ represents the opposite of $-\frac{11}{3}$.

Skill Practice Evaluate.

20. $-(2.8)$ **21.** $-\left(-\frac{1}{5}\right)$

Answers

14. < **15.** > **16.** >
17. < **18.** -224 **19.** 3.4
20. -2.8 **21.** $\frac{1}{5}$

5. Absolute Value of a Real Number

To define the addition of real numbers, we use the concept of absolute value.

Informal Definition of the Absolute Value of a Real Number

The **absolute value** of a real number a, denoted $|a|$, is the distance between a and 0 on the number line.

Note: The absolute value of any real number is positive or zero.

Instructor Note: Remind students that because absolute value is a measure of *distance* it will always be nonnegative. We don't measure distance with negative numbers.

For example, $|3| = 3$ and $|-3| = 3$.

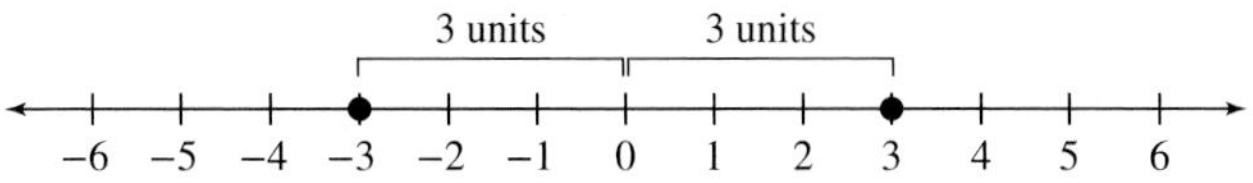

Example 9 **Finding the Absolute Value of a Real Number**

Classroom Examples: p. 34, Exercises 68 and 72

Evaluate the absolute value expressions.

a. $|-4|$ **b.** $\left|\frac{1}{2}\right|$ **c.** $|-6.2|$ **d.** $|0|$

Solution:

a. $|-4| = 4$ −4 is 4 units from 0 on the number line.

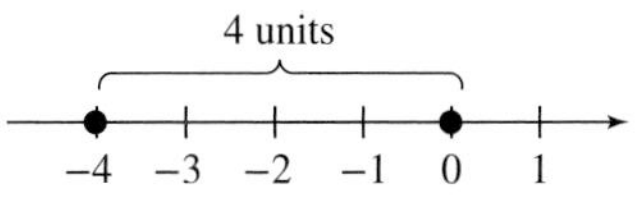

b. $\left|\frac{1}{2}\right| = \frac{1}{2}$ $\frac{1}{2}$ is $\frac{1}{2}$ unit from 0 on the number line.

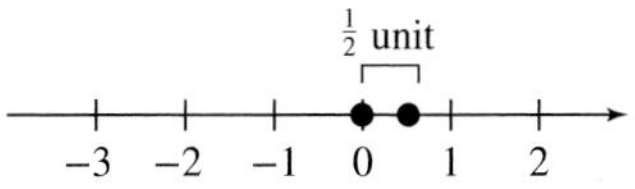

c. $|-6.2| = 6.2$ −6.2 is 6.2 units from 0 on the number line.

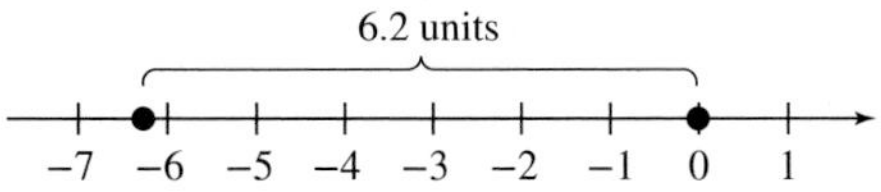

d. $|0| = 0$ 0 is 0 units from 0 on the number line.

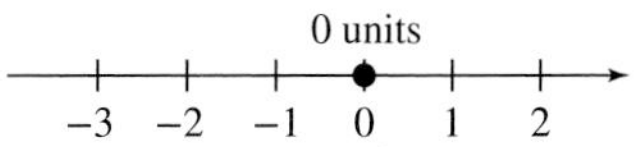

Skill Practice Evaluate.

22. $|-99|$ **23.** $\left|\frac{7}{8}\right|$ **24.** $|-1.4|$ **25.** $|1|$

Answers

22. 99 **23.** $\frac{7}{8}$

24. 1.4 **25.** 1

The absolute value of a number a is its distance from 0 on the number line. The definition of $|a|$ may also be given symbolically depending on whether a is negative or nonnegative.

Absolute Value of a Real Number

Let a be a real number. Then

1. If a is nonnegative (that is, $a \geq 0$), then $|a| = a$.
2. If a is negative (that is, $a < 0$), then $|a| = -a$.

This definition states that if a is a nonnegative number, then $|a|$ equals a itself. If a is a negative number, then $|a|$ equals the opposite of a. For example:

$\lvert 9\rvert = 9$	Because 9 is positive, then $\lvert 9\rvert$ equals the number 9 itself.
$\lvert -7\rvert = 7$	Because -7 is negative, then $\lvert -7\rvert$ equals the opposite of -7, which is 7.

Classroom Examples: p. 34, Exercises 94 and 100

Example 10 Comparing Absolute Value Expressions

Determine if the statements are true or false.

a. $|3| \leq 3$ **b.** $-|5| = |-5|$

Solution:

a. $\lvert 3\rvert \leq 3$	$\lvert 3\rvert \overset{?}{\leq} 3$	Simplify the absolute value.
	$3 \overset{?}{\leq} 3$	True
b. $-\lvert 5\rvert = \lvert -5\rvert$	$-\lvert 5\rvert \overset{?}{=} \lvert -5\rvert$	Simplify the absolute values.
	$-5 \overset{?}{=} 5$	False

Skill Practice Answer true or false.

26. $-|4| > |-4|$ **27.** $|-17| = 17$

Answers

26. False **27.** True

Calculator Connections

Topic: Approximating Irrational Numbers on a Calculator

Scientific and graphing calculators approximate irrational numbers by using rational numbers in the form of terminating decimals. For example, consider approximating π and $\sqrt{3}$.

Scientific Calculator:

Enter: [π] or [2nd] [π] **Result:** 3.141592654

Enter: 3 [√] **Result:** 1.732050808

Graphing Calculator:

Enter: [2nd] [π] [ENTER]

Enter: [2nd] [√] 3 [ENTER]

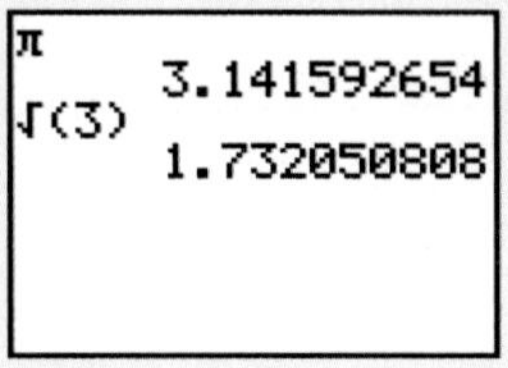

The symbol $\approx$ is read "is approximately equal to" and is used when writing approximations.

$$\pi \approx 3.141592654 \quad \text{and} \quad \sqrt{3} \approx 1.732050808$$

Calculator Exercises

Use a calculator to approximate the irrational numbers. Remember to use the appropriate symbol, $\approx$, when expressing answers.

1. $\sqrt{12}$ ≈ 3.464101615 **2.** $\sqrt{99}$ ≈ 9.949874371 **3.** 4π ≈ 12.56637061 **4.** $\sqrt{\pi}$ ≈ 1.772453851

Section 1.2 Practice Exercises

Study Skills Exercise

For additional exercises, see Classroom Activities 1.2A–1.2C in the *Student's Resource Manual* at www.mhhe.com/moh.

Look over the notes that you took today. Do you understand what you wrote? If there were any rules, definitions, or formulas, highlight them so that they can be easily found when studying for the test.

Vocabulary and Key Concepts

1. a. A variable is a symbol or letter used to represent an unknown number.

b. Values that do not vary are called constants.

c. In mathematics, a well-defined collection of elements is called a set.

d. The statements $a < b$, $a > b$, and $a \neq b$ are examples of inequalities.

e. The statement $a < b$ is read as "a is less than b."

f. The statement $c \geq d$ is read as "c is greater than or equal to d."

g. The statement $5 \neq 6$ is read as "5 is not equal to 6."

h. Two numbers that are the same distance from 0 but on opposite sides of 0 on the number line are called opposites.

i. The absolute value of a real number, a, is denoted by $|a|$ and is the distance between a and 0 on the number line.

Review Exercises

For Exercises 2–4, simplify.

2. $4\frac{1}{2} - 1\frac{5}{6}$ $2\frac{2}{3}$ or $\frac{8}{3}$ **3.** $4\frac{1}{2} \times 1\frac{5}{6}$ $8\frac{1}{4}$ or $\frac{33}{4}$ **4.** $4\frac{1}{2} \div 1\frac{5}{6}$ $2\frac{5}{11}$ or $\frac{27}{11}$

Concept 1: Variables and Expressions

For Exercises 5–14, evaluate the expressions for the given substitution. **(See Examples 1–2.)**

5. $y - 3$ when $y = 18$ 15

6. $3q$ when $q = 5$ 15

7. $\frac{15}{t}$ when $t = 5$ 3

8. $8 + w$ when $w = 12$ 20

9. $6d$ when $d = \frac{2}{3}$ 4

10. $\frac{6}{5}h$ when $h = 10$ 12

11. $c - 2 - d$ when $c = 15.4$, $d = 8.1$ 5.3

12. $1.1 + t + s$ when $t = 93.2$, $s = 11.5$ 105.8

13. abc when $a = \frac{1}{10}$, $b = \frac{1}{4}$, $c = \frac{1}{2}$ $\frac{1}{80}$

14. $x - y - z$ when $x = \frac{7}{8}$, $y = \frac{1}{2}$, $z = \frac{1}{4}$ $\frac{1}{8}$

15. The cost of downloading songs from the Internet can be represented by the expression $1.29s$, where s is the number of songs downloaded. Calculate the cost of downloading:

a. 3 songs $3.87 **b.** 8 songs $10.32 **c.** 10 songs $12.90

16. The number of calories burned by a 150-lb person by walking 2 mph can be represented by the expression $240h$, where h represents the number of hours spent walking. Calculate the number of calories burned by walking:

a. 4 hr 960 calories **b.** $2\frac{1}{2}$ hr 600 calories **c.** $1\frac{1}{4}$ hr 300 calories

17. Aly is trying to limit her total calorie intake for breakfast and lunch to 850 calories. The number of calories that she can consume for lunch is given by the expression $850 - b$, where b is the number of calories consumed for breakfast. Determine the number of calories allowed for lunch assuming that she had the following number of calories at breakfast:

a. 475 calories
375 calories

b. 220 calories
630 calories

c. 580 calories
270 calories

18. Lorenzo knows that the gas mileage on his car is about 25 miles per gallon. The number of gallons needed to travel a certain distance is given by the expression $\frac{d}{25}$, where d is the distance traveled. Find the number of gallons of fuel needed if Lorenzo drives:

a. 200 mi
8 gal

b. 450 mi
18 gal

c. 180 mi
7.2 gal

Concept 2: The Set of Real Numbers

19. Plot the numbers on the real number line: $\{1, -2, -\pi, 0, -\frac{5}{2}, 5.1\}$ **(See Example 3.)**

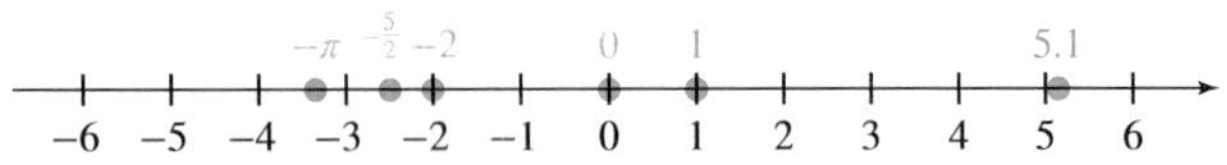

20. Plot the numbers on the real number line: $\{3, -4, \frac{1}{8}, -1.7, -\frac{4}{3}, 1.75\}$

For Exercises 21–36, describe each number as (a) a terminating decimal, (b) a repeating decimal, or (c) a nonterminating, nonrepeating decimal. Then classify the number as a rational number or as an irrational number. **(See Example 4.)**

21. 0.29 a; rational

22. 3.8 a; rational

23. $\frac{1}{9}$ b; rational

24. $\frac{1}{3}$ b; rational

25. $\frac{1}{8}$ a; rational

26. $\frac{1}{5}$ a; rational

27. 2π c; irrational

28. 3π c; irrational

29. -0.125 a; rational

30. -3.24 a; rational

31. -3 a; rational

32. -6 a; rational

33. $0.\overline{2}$ b; rational

34. $0.\overline{6}$ b; rational

35. $\sqrt{6}$ c; irrational

36. $\sqrt{10}$ c; irrational

37. List three numbers that are real numbers but not rational numbers. For example: $\pi, -\sqrt{2}, \sqrt{3}$

38. List three numbers that are real numbers but not irrational numbers. For example: $-\frac{1}{2}, 5, 0.\overline{3}$

39. List three numbers that are integers but not natural numbers. For example: $-4, -1, 0$

40. List three numbers that are integers but not whole numbers. For example: $-5, -2, -1$

41. List three numbers that are rational numbers but not integers. For example: $-\frac{3}{4}, \frac{1}{2}, 0.206$

For Exercises 42–48, let $A = \{-\frac{3}{2}, \sqrt{11}, -4, 0.\overline{6}, 0, \sqrt{7}, 1\}$ **(See Example 5.)** Animation

42. Are all of the numbers in set A real numbers? Yes

43. List all of the rational numbers in set A. $-\frac{3}{2}, -4, 0.\overline{6}, 0, 1$

44. List all of the whole numbers in set A. $0, 1$

45. List all of the natural numbers in set A. 1

46. List all of the irrational numbers in set A. $\sqrt{11}, \sqrt{7}$

47. List all of the integers in set A. $-4, 0, 1$

48. Plot the real numbers from set A on a number line. (*Hint:* $\sqrt{11} \approx 3.3$ and $\sqrt{7} \approx 2.6$)

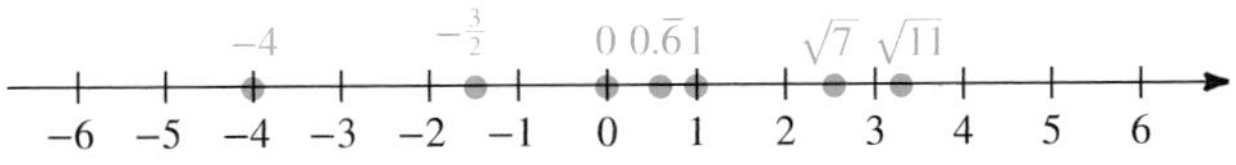

Concept 3: Inequalities

49. The women's golf scores for selected players at an LPGA event are given in the table. Compare the scores and fill in the blank with the appropriate inequality sign: $<$ or $>$. **(See Example 6.)**

a. Kane's score __$>$__ Pak's score.

b. Sorenstam's score __$>$__ Davies's score.

c. Pak's score __$<$__ McCurdy's score.

d. Kane's score __$>$__ Davies's score.

LPGA Golfers	Final Score with Respect to Par
Annika Sorenstam	7
Laura Davies	−4
Lorie Kane	0
Cindy McCurdy	3
Se Ri Pak	−8

50. The elevations of selected cities in the United States are shown in the figure. Compare the elevations and fill in the blank with the appropriate inequality sign: $<$ or $>$. (A negative number indicates that the city is below sea level.)

a. Elevation of Tucson __$>$__ elevation of Cincinnati.

b. Elevation of New Orleans __$<$__ elevation of Chicago.

c. Elevation of New Orleans __$<$__ elevation of Houston.

d. Elevation of Chicago __$>$__ elevation of Cincinnati.

Concept 4: Opposite of a Real Number

For Exercises 51–58, find the opposite of each number. **(See Example 7.)**

51. 18 -18

52. 2 -2

53. -6.1 6.1

54. -2.5 2.5

55. $-\frac{5}{8}$ $\frac{5}{8}$

56. $-\frac{1}{3}$ $\frac{1}{3}$

57. $\frac{7}{3}$ $-\frac{7}{3}$

58. $\frac{1}{9}$ $-\frac{1}{9}$

The opposite of a is denoted as $-a$. For Exercises 59–66, simplify. **(See Example 8.)**

59. $-(-3)$ 3 **60.** $-(-5.1)$ 5.1 **61.** $-\left(\frac{7}{3}\right)$ $-\frac{7}{3}$ **62.** $-(-7)$ 7

63. $-(-8)$ 8 **64.** $-(36)$ -36 **65.** $-(72.1)$ -72.1 **66.** $-\left(\frac{9}{10}\right)$ $-\frac{9}{10}$

Concept 5: Absolute Value of a Real Number

For Exercises 67–78, simplify. **(See Example 9.)**

67. $|-2|$ 2 **68.** $|-7|$ 7 **69.** $|-1.5|$ 1.5 **70.** $|-3.7|$ 3.7

71. $-|-1.5|$ -1.5 **72.** $-|-3.7|$ -3.7 **73.** $\left|\frac{3}{2}\right|$ $\frac{3}{2}$ **74.** $\left|\frac{7}{4}\right|$ $\frac{7}{4}$

75. $-|10|$ -10 **76.** $-|20|$ -20 **77.** $-\left|-\frac{1}{2}\right|$ $-\frac{1}{2}$ **78.** $-\left|-\frac{11}{3}\right|$ $-\frac{11}{3}$

For Exercises 79–80, answer true or false. If a statement is false, explain why.

79. If n is positive, then $|n|$ is negative.
False, $|n|$ is never negative.

80. If m is negative, then $|m|$ is negative.
False, $|m|$ is never negative.

For Exercises 81–104, determine if the statements are true or false. Use the real number line to justify the answer. **(See Example 10.)**

81. $5 > 2$ True **82.** $8 < 10$ True **83.** $6 < 6$ False **84.** $19 > 19$ False

85. $-7 \geq -7$ True **86.** $-1 \leq -1$ True **87.** $\frac{3}{2} \leq \frac{1}{6}$ False **88.** $-\frac{1}{4} \geq -\frac{7}{8}$ True

89. $-5 > -2$ False **90.** $6 < -10$ False **91.** $8 \neq 8$ False **92.** $10 \neq 10$ False

93. $|-2| \geq |-1|$ True **94.** $|3| \leq |-1|$ False **95.** $\left|-\frac{1}{9}\right| = \left|\frac{1}{9}\right|$ True **96.** $\left|-\frac{1}{3}\right| = \left|\frac{1}{3}\right|$ True

97. $|7| \neq |-7|$ False **98.** $|-13| \neq |13|$ False **99.** $-1 < |-1|$ True **100.** $-6 < |-6|$ True

101. $|-8| \geq |8|$ True **102.** $|-11| \geq |11|$ True **103.** $|-2| \leq |2|$ True **104.** $|-21| \leq |21|$ True

Expanding Your Skills

105. For what numbers, a, is $-a$ positive?
For all $a < 0$

106. For what numbers, a, is $|a| = a$?
For all $a \geq 0$

Exponents, Square Roots, and the Order of Operations

Section 1.3

Concepts

1. Exponential Expressions
2. Square Roots
3. Order of Operations
3. Translations

1. Exponential Expressions

In algebra, repeated multiplication can be expressed using exponents. The expression $4 \cdot 4 \cdot 4$ can be written as

exponent

$$4^3$$

base

In the expression 4^3, 4 is the base, and 3 is the exponent, or power. The exponent indicates how many factors of the base to multiply.

TIP: A number or variable with no exponent shown implies that there is an exponent of 1. That is, $b = b^1$.

Definition of b^n

Let b represent any real number and n represent a positive integer. Then,

$$b^n = \underbrace{b \cdot b \cdot b \cdot b \cdot \ldots b}_{n \text{ factors of } b}$$

b^n is read as "b to the nth power."

b is called the **base**, and n is called the **exponent,** or **power**.

b^2 is read as "b squared," and b^3 is read as "b cubed."

The exponent, n, is the number of times the base, b, is used as a factor.

Example 1 Evaluating Exponential Expressions

Translate the expression into words and then evaluate the expression.

a. 2^5 **b.** 5^2 **c.** $\left(\frac{3}{4}\right)^3$ **d.** 1^6

Classroom Examples: p. 43, Exercises 24 and 26

Solution:

a. The expression 2^5 is read as "two to the fifth power."
$2^5 = (2)(2)(2)(2)(2) = 32$

b. The expression 5^2 is read as "five to the second power" or "five, squared."
$5^2 = (5)(5) = 25$

c. The expression $(\frac{3}{4})^3$ is read as "three-fourths to the third power" or "three-fourths, cubed."

$$\left(\frac{3}{4}\right)^3 = \left(\frac{3}{4}\right)\left(\frac{3}{4}\right)\left(\frac{3}{4}\right) = \frac{27}{64}$$

d. The expression 1^6 is read as "one to the sixth power."
$1^6 = (1)(1)(1)(1)(1)(1) = 1$

Skill Practice Evaluate.

1. 4^3 **2.** 2^4 **3.** $\left(\frac{2}{3}\right)^2$ **4.** $(1)^7$

Answers

1. 64 **2.** 16 **3.** $\frac{4}{9}$ **4.** 1

2. Square Roots

If we reverse the process of squaring a number, we can find the square roots of the number. For example, finding a square root of 9 is equivalent to asking "what number(s) when squared equals 9?" The symbol, $\sqrt{\ }$ (called a **radical sign**), is used to find the *principal* square root of a number. By definition, the principal square root of a number is nonnegative. Therefore, $\sqrt{9}$ is the nonnegative number that when squared equals 9. Hence, $\sqrt{9} = 3$ because 3 is nonnegative and $(3)^2 = 9$.

Classroom Examples: p. 43, Exercises 34 and 42

Example 2 Evaluating Square Roots

Evaluate the square roots.

a. $\sqrt{64}$ **b.** $\sqrt{121}$ **c.** $\sqrt{0}$ **d.** $\sqrt{\dfrac{4}{9}}$

Solution:

a. $\sqrt{64} = 8$ Because $(8)^2 = 64$

b. $\sqrt{121} = 11$ Because $(11)^2 = 121$

c. $\sqrt{0} = 0$ Because $(0)^2 = 0$

d. $\sqrt{\dfrac{4}{9}} = \dfrac{2}{3}$ Because $\dfrac{2}{3} \cdot \dfrac{2}{3} = \dfrac{4}{9}$

Skill Practice Evaluate.

5. $\sqrt{81}$ **6.** $\sqrt{100}$ **7.** $\sqrt{1}$ **8.** $\sqrt{\dfrac{9}{25}}$

A perfect square is a number whose square root is a rational number. If a positive number is not a perfect square, its square root is an irrational number that can be approximated on a calculator.

TIP: To simplify square roots, it is advisable to become familiar with the following perfect squares and square roots.

$0^2 = 0 \longrightarrow \sqrt{0} = 0$ $7^2 = 49 \longrightarrow \sqrt{49} = 7$
$1^2 = 1 \longrightarrow \sqrt{1} = 1$ $8^2 = 64 \longrightarrow \sqrt{64} = 8$
$2^2 = 4 \longrightarrow \sqrt{4} = 2$ $9^2 = 81 \longrightarrow \sqrt{81} = 9$
$3^2 = 9 \longrightarrow \sqrt{9} = 3$ $10^2 = 100 \longrightarrow \sqrt{100} = 10$
$4^2 = 16 \longrightarrow \sqrt{16} = 4$ $11^2 = 121 \longrightarrow \sqrt{121} = 11$
$5^2 = 25 \longrightarrow \sqrt{25} = 5$ $12^2 = 144 \longrightarrow \sqrt{144} = 12$
$6^2 = 36 \longrightarrow \sqrt{36} = 6$ $13^2 = 169 \longrightarrow \sqrt{169} = 13$

3. Order of Operations

When algebraic expressions contain numerous operations, it is important to evaluate the operations in the proper order. Parentheses ( ), brackets [ ], and braces { } are used for grouping numbers and algebraic expressions. It is important to recognize that operations

Answers
5. 9 **6.** 10 **7.** 1 **8.** $\dfrac{3}{5}$

must be done within parentheses and other grouping symbols first. Other grouping symbols include absolute value bars, radical signs, and fraction bars.

Applying the Order of Operations

Step 1 Simplify expressions within parentheses and other grouping symbols first. These include absolute value bars, fraction bars, and radicals. If imbedded parentheses are present, start with the innermost parentheses.

Step 2 Evaluate expressions involving exponents, radicals, and absolute values.

Step 3 Perform multiplication or division in the order that they occur from left to right.

Step 4 Perform addition or subtraction in the order that they occur from left to right.

TIP: Radical signs act as grouping symbols.

$$\sqrt{16+9} = \sqrt{(16+9)}$$
$$= \sqrt{25}$$
$$= 5$$

Perform operations inside the radical first, then apply the square root.

Example 3 Applying the Order of Operations

Simplify the expressions.

a. $17 - 3 \cdot 2 + 2^2$ **b.** $\frac{1}{2}\left(\frac{5}{6} - \frac{3}{4}\right)$

Classroom Examples: p. 43, Exercises 48 and 54

Solution:

a. $17 - 3 \cdot 2 + 2^2$

$= 17 - 3 \cdot 2 + 4$ Simplify exponents.

$= 17 - 6 + 4$ Multiply before adding or subtracting.

$= 11 + 4$ Add or subtract from left to right.

$= 15$

b. $\frac{1}{2}\left(\frac{5}{6} - \frac{3}{4}\right)$ Subtract fractions within the parentheses.

$= \frac{1}{2}\left(\frac{10}{12} - \frac{9}{12}\right)$ The least common denominator is 12.

$= \frac{1}{2}\left(\frac{1}{12}\right)$

$= \frac{1}{24}$ Multiply fractions.

Skill Practice Simplify the expressions.

9. $14 - 3 \cdot 2 + 3^2$

10. $\frac{13}{4} - \frac{1}{4}(10 - 2)$

Answers

9. 17 **10.** $\frac{5}{4}$

Classroom Examples: pp. 43–44, Exercises 62 and 68

Example 4 Applying the Order of Operations

Simplify the expressions.

a. $25 - 12 \div 3 \cdot 4$

b. $6.2 - |-2.1| + \sqrt{16+9}$

c. $28 - 2[(6-3)^2 + 4]$

Avoiding Mistakes

In Example 4(a), division is performed before multiplication because it occurs first as we read from left to right.

Solution:

a. $25 - 12 \div 3 \cdot 4$	Multiply or divide in order from left to right.
$= 25 - 4 \cdot 4$	Notice that the operation $12 \div 3$ is performed first (not $4 \cdot 4$).
$= 25 - 16$	Multiply $4 \cdot 4$ before subtracting.
$= 9$	Subtract.
b. $6.2 - |-2.1| + \sqrt{16+9}$	
$= 6.2 - |-2.1| + \sqrt{25}$	Simplify within the square root.
$= 6.2 - (2.1) + 5$	Simplify the absolute value and square root.
$= 4.1 + 5$	Add or subtract from left to right.
$= 9.1$	Add.
c. $28 - 2[(6-3)^2 + 4]$	
$= 28 - 2[(3)^2 + 4]$	Simplify within the inner parentheses first.
$= 28 - 2[(9) + 4]$	Simplify exponents.
$= 28 - 2[13]$	Add within the square brackets.
$= 28 - 26$	Multiply before subtracting.
$= 2$	Subtract.

Skill Practice Simplify the expressions.

11. $1 + 2 \cdot 3^2 \div 6$ **12.** $|-20| - \sqrt{20-4}$ **13.** $60 - 5[(7-4) + 2^2]$

Classroom Example: p. 44, Exercise 72

Example 5 Applying the Order of Operations

Simplify the expression. $\dfrac{32 + 8 \div 2}{2 \cdot 3^2}$

Solution:

$\dfrac{32 + 8 \div 2}{2 \cdot 3^2}$	In this expression, the fraction bar acts as a grouping symbol.
$= \dfrac{32 + 4}{2 \cdot 9}$	First, simplify the expressions above and below the fraction bar using the order of operations.
$= \dfrac{36}{18}$	The last step is to simplify the fraction.
$= 2$	

Answers

11. 4 **12.** 16 **13.** 25

Skill Practice Simplify the expression.

14. $\dfrac{60 - 3^2 \cdot 2}{3 + 8 \div 2}$

4. Translations

Algebra is a powerful tool used in science, business, economics, and many day-to-day applications. To apply algebra to a real-world application, we need the important skill of translating an English phrase to a mathematical expression. Table 1-3 summarizes commonly used phrases and expressions.

Table 1-3

Operation	Symbols	Translation
Addition	$a + b$	**sum** of a and b a plus b b added to a b more than a a increased by b the total of a and b
Subtraction	$a - b$	**difference** of a and b a minus b b subtracted from a a decreased by b b less than a a less b
Multiplication	$a \times b$, $a \cdot b$, $a(b)$, $(a)b$, $(a)(b)$, ab (*Note:* From this point forward we will seldom use the notation $a \times b$ because the symbol, $\times$, might be confused with the variable, x.)	**product** of a and b a times b a multiplied by b
Division	$a \div b$, $\dfrac{a}{b}$, a/b, $b\overline{)a}$	**quotient** of a and b a divided by b b divided into a ratio of a and b a over b a per b

Example 6 **Writing an English Phrase as an Algebraic Expression**

Classroom Examples: p. 44, Exercises 82 and 92

Translate each English phrase to an algebraic expression.

a. The quotient of x and 5

b. The difference of p and the square root of q

c. Seven less than n

d. Seven less n

e. Eight more than the absolute value of w

f. x subtracted from 18

Answer

14. 6

Solution:

a. $\frac{x}{5}$ or $x \div 5$	The quotient of x and 5
b. $p - \sqrt{q}$	The difference of p and the square root of q
c. $n - 7$	Seven less than n
d. $7 - n$	Seven less n
e. $\lvert w \rvert + 8$	Eight more than the absolute value of w
f. $18 - x$	x subtracted from 18

Avoiding Mistakes

Recall that "a less than b" is translated as $b - a$. Therefore, the statement "seven less than n" must be translated as $n - 7$, not $7 - n$.

Instructor Note: Show students that 7 less than x would not be written $7 < x$. This expression would be worded as 7 is less than x.

Skill Practice Translate each English phrase to an algebraic expression.

15. The product of 6 and y

16. The difference of the square root of t and 7

17. Twelve less than x

18. Twelve less x

19. One more than two times x

20. Five subtracted from the absolute value of w

Classroom Examples: p. 45, Exercises 94 and 100

Example 7 Writing English Phrases as Algebraic Expressions

Translate each English phrase into an algebraic expression. Then evaluate the expression for $a = 6$, $b = 4$, and $c = 20$.

a. The product of a and the square root of b

b. Twice the sum of b and c

c. The difference of twice a and b

Solution:

a. The product of a and the square root of b

$a\sqrt{b}$	
$= (\ \ )\sqrt{(\ \ )}$	Use parentheses to substitute a number for a variable.
$= (6)\sqrt{(4)}$	Substitute $a = 6$ and $b = 4$.
$= 6 \cdot 2$	Simplify the radical first.
$= 12$	Multiply.

b. Twice the sum of b and c

$2(b + c)$	To compute "twice the sum of b and c," it is necessary to take the sum first and then multiply by 2. To ensure the proper order, the sum of b and c must be enclosed in parentheses. The proper translation is $2(b + c)$.
$= 2((\ \ ) + (\ \ ))$	Use parentheses to substitute a number for a variable.
$= 2((4) + (20))$	Substitute $b = 4$ and $c = 20$.
$= 2(24)$	Simplify within the parentheses first.
$= 48$	Multiply.

Answers

15. $6y$ **16.** $\sqrt{t} - 7$
17. $x - 12$ **18.** $12 - x$
19. $2x + 1$ **20.** $\lvert w \rvert - 5$

c. The difference of twice a and b

$2a - b$

$= 2(\quad) - (\quad)$	Use parentheses to substitute a number for a variable.
$= 2(6) - (4)$	Substitute $a = 6$ and $b = 4$.
$= 12 - 4$	Multiply first.
$= 8$	Subtract.

Skill Practice Translate each English phrase to an algebraic expression. Then evaluate the expression for $x = 3$, $y = 9$, $z = 10$.

21. The quotient of the square root of y and x

22. One-half the sum of x and y

23. The difference of z and twice x

Answers

21. $\frac{\sqrt{y}}{x}$; 1 **22.** $\frac{1}{2}(x + y)$; 6

23. $z - 2x$; 4

Calculator Connections

Topic: Evaluating Exponential Expressions on a Calculator

On a calculator, we enter exponents greater than the second power by using the key labeled [y^x] or [^]. For example, evaluate 2^4 and 10^6:

Scientific Calculator:

Enter: 2 [y^x] 4 [=] **Result:** 16

Enter: 10 [y^x] 6 [=] **Result:** 1000000

Graphing Calculator:

```
2^4
                16
10^6
           1000000
```

Topic: Applying the Order of Operations on a Calculator

Most calculators also have the capability to enter several operations at once. However, it is important to note that fraction bars and radicals require user-defined parentheses to ensure that the proper order of operations is followed. For example, evaluate the following expressions on a calculator:

a. $130 - 2(5 - 1)^3$ **b.** $\frac{18 - 2}{11 - 9}$ **c.** $\sqrt{25 - 9}$

Scientific Calculator:

Enter: 130 [−] 2 [×] [(] 5 [−] 1 [)] [y^x] 3 [=] **Result:** 2

Enter: [(] 18 [−] 2 [)] [÷] [(] 11 [−] 9 [)] [=] **Result:** 8

Enter: [(] 25 [−] 9 [)] [√] **Result:** 4

Graphing Calculator:

```
130-2*(5-1)^3
                2
(18-2)/(11-9)
                8
√(25-9)
                4
```

Calculator Exercises

Simplify each expression without the use of a calculator. Then enter the expression into the calculator to verify your answer.

1. $\dfrac{4+6}{8-3}$ 2
2. $110 - 5(2+1) - 4$ 91
3. $100 - 2(5-3)^3$ 84
4. $3 + (4-1)^2$ 12
5. $(12-6+1)^2$ 49
6. $3 \cdot 8 - \sqrt{32+2^2}$ 18
7. $\sqrt{18-2}$ 4
8. $(4 \cdot 3 - 3 \cdot 3)^3$ 27
9. $\dfrac{20-3^2}{26-2^2}$ 0.5

Section 1.3 Practice Exercises

For additional exercises, see Classroom Activities 1.3A–1.3C in the *Student's Resource Manual* at www.mhhe.com/moh.

Study Skills Exercise

Sometimes you may run into a problem with homework or you find that you are having trouble keeping up with the pace of the class. A tutor can be a good resource.

a. Does your college offer tutoring? **b.** Is it free? **c.** Where would you go to sign up for a tutor?

Vocabulary and Key Concepts

1. a. Fill in the blanks with the words *sum, difference, product,* or *quotient.*

The ___quotient___ of 10 and 2 is 5. The ___product___ of 10 and 2 is 20.

The ___sum___ of 10 and 2 is 12. The ___difference___ of 10 and 2 is 8.

b. In the expression b^n, the value b is called the ___base___ and n is called the ___exponent___ or ___power___.

c. The expression ___8^2___ is read as "8-squared."

d. The expression ___p^4___ is read as "p to the 4th power."

e. The symbol $\sqrt{\ }$ is called a ___radical___ sign and is used to find the principal ___square___ root of a nonnegative real number.

f. The set of rules that tell us the order in which to perform operations to simplify an algebraic expression is called the ___order of operations___.

Review Exercises

2. Which of the following are rational numbers? $-4,\ 5.\overline{6},\ \sqrt{29},\ 0,\ \pi,\ 4.02,\ \dfrac{7}{9}$ $-4, 5.\overline{6}, 0, 4.02, \dfrac{7}{9}$
3. Evaluate. $|-56|$ 56
4. Evaluate. $-|-14|$ −14
5. Find the opposite of 19. −19
6. Find the opposite of −34.2. 34.2

Concept 1: Exponential Expressions

For Exercises 7–12, write each product using exponents.

7. $\frac{1}{6}\cdot\frac{1}{6}\cdot\frac{1}{6}\cdot\frac{1}{6}$ $\left(\frac{1}{6}\right)^4$

8. $10\cdot10\cdot10\cdot10\cdot10\cdot10$ 10^6

9. $a\cdot a\cdot a\cdot b\cdot b$ a^3b^2

10. $7\cdot x\cdot x\cdot y\cdot y$ $7x^2y^2$

11. $5c\cdot5c\cdot5c\cdot5c\cdot5c$ $(5c)^5$

12. $3\cdot w\cdot z\cdot z\cdot z\cdot z$ $3wz^4$

13. **a.** For the expression $5x^3$, what is the base for the exponent 3? x

b. Does 5 have an exponent? If so, what is it? Yes, 1

14. **a.** For the expression $2y^4$, what is the base for the exponent 4? y

b. Does 2 have an exponent? If so, what is it? Yes, 1

For Exercises 15–22, write each expression in expanded form using the definition of an exponent.

15. x^3 $x\cdot x\cdot x$

16. y^4 $y\cdot y\cdot y\cdot y$

17. $(2b)^3$ $2b\cdot2b\cdot2b$

18. $(8c)^2$ $8c\cdot8c$

19. $10y^5$ $10\cdot y\cdot y\cdot y\cdot y\cdot y$

20. x^2y^3 $x\cdot x\cdot y\cdot y\cdot y$

21. $2wz^2$ $2\cdot w\cdot z\cdot z$

22. $3a^3b$ $3\cdot a\cdot a\cdot a\cdot b$

For Exercises 23–30, simplify each expression. **(See Example 1.)**

23. 6^2 36

24. 5^3 125

25. $\left(\frac{1}{7}\right)^2$ $\frac{1}{49}$

26. $\left(\frac{1}{2}\right)^5$ $\frac{1}{32}$

27. $(0.2)^3$ 0.008

28. $(0.8)^2$ 0.64

29. 2^6 64

30. 13^2 169

Concept 2: Square Roots

For Exercises 31–42, simplify the square roots. **(See Example 2.)**

31. $\sqrt{81}$ 9

32. $\sqrt{64}$ 8

33. $\sqrt{4}$ 2

34. $\sqrt{9}$ 3

35. $\sqrt{144}$ 12

36. $\sqrt{49}$ 7

37. $\sqrt{16}$ 4

38. $\sqrt{36}$ 6

39. $\sqrt{\frac{1}{9}}$ $\frac{1}{3}$

40. $\sqrt{\frac{1}{64}}$ $\frac{1}{8}$

41. $\sqrt{\frac{25}{81}}$ $\frac{5}{9}$

42. $\sqrt{\frac{49}{100}}$ $\frac{7}{10}$

Concept 3: Order of Operations

Animation

For Exercises 43–74, use the order of operations to simplify each expression. **(See Examples 3–5.)**

43. $8+2\cdot6$ 20

44. $7+3\cdot4$ 19

45. $(8+2)\cdot6$ 60

46. $(7+3)\cdot4$ 40

47. $4+2\div2\cdot3+1$ 8

48. $5+12\div2\cdot6-1$ 40

49. $81-4\cdot3+3^2$ 78

50. $100-25\cdot2-5^2$ 25

51. $\frac{1}{4}\cdot\frac{2}{3}-\frac{1}{6}$ 0

52. $\frac{3}{4}\cdot\frac{2}{3}+\frac{2}{3}$ $\frac{7}{6}$

53. $\left(\frac{11}{6}-\frac{3}{8}\right)\cdot\frac{4}{5}$ $\frac{7}{6}$

54. $\left(\frac{9}{8}-\frac{1}{3}\right)\cdot\frac{3}{4}$ $\frac{19}{32}$

55. $3[5+2(8-3)]$ 45

56. $2[4+3(6-4)]$ 20

57. $10+|-6|$ 16

58. $18+|-3|$ 21

59. $21-|8-2|$ 15

60. $12-|6-1|$ 7

61. $2^2+\sqrt{9}\cdot5$ 19

62. $3^2+\sqrt{16}\cdot2$ 17

63. $3\cdot5^2$ 75

64. $10\cdot2^3$ 80

65. $\sqrt{9+16}-2$ 3

66. $\sqrt{36+13}-5$ 2

67. $[4^2 \cdot (6-4) \div 8] + [7 \cdot (8-3)]$ 39

68. $(18 \div \sqrt{4}) \cdot \{[(9^2 - 1) \div 2] - 15\}$ 225

69. $48 - 13 \cdot 3 + [(50 - 7 \cdot 5) + 2]$ 26

70. $80 \div 16 \cdot 2 + (6^2 - |-2|)$ 44

71. $\dfrac{7 + 3(8-2)}{(7+3)(8-2)}$ $\frac{5}{12}$

72. $\dfrac{16 - 8 \div 4}{4 + 8 \div 4 - 2}$ $\frac{7}{2}$

73. $\dfrac{15 - 5(3 \cdot 2 - 4)}{10 - 2(4 \cdot 5 - 16)}$ $\frac{5}{2}$

74. $\dfrac{5(7-3) + 8(6-4)}{4[7 + 3(2 \cdot 9 - 8)]}$ $\frac{9}{37}$

75. A person's debt-to-income ratio is the sum of all monthly installment payments (credit cards, loans, etc.) divided by monthly take-home pay. This number is often considered when one is applying for a loan. Each month, Monica makes credit card payments of \$52 and \$20, a student loan payment of \$65, and a payment for furniture of \$43. Her monthly take-home pay is \$1500.

a. Determine Monica's debt-to-income ratio. 0.12

b. To obtain a car loan, Monica's debt-to-income ratio must be less than 0.20. Does she meet this criteria?
Yes. $0.12 < 0.20$

76. Each month, Jared makes credit card payments of \$115, \$63, and \$95. He also makes a student loan payment of \$77 and another loan payment of \$100. His monthly take-home pay is \$2000.

a. Use the definition given in Exercise 75 to determine Jared's debt-to-income ratio. 0.225

b. To obtain a loan for a new home theater system his debt-to-income ratio must be less than 0.15. Does he meet this criteria? No. $0.225 > 0.15$

77. The area of a rectangle is given by $A = lw$, where l is the length of the rectangle and w is the width. Find the area for the rectangle shown. 57,600 ft²

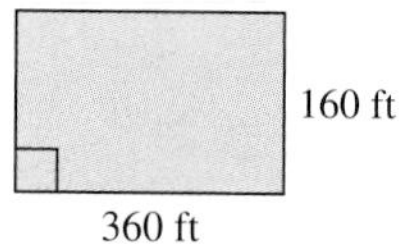

78. The perimeter of a rectangle is given by $P = 2l + 2w$. Find the perimeter for the rectangle shown. 1040 ft

79. The area of a trapezoid is given by $A = \frac{1}{2}(b_1 + b_2)h$, where b_1 and b_2 are the lengths of the two parallel sides and h is the height. A window is in the shape of a trapezoid. Find the area of the trapezoid with dimensions shown in the figure. 21 ft²

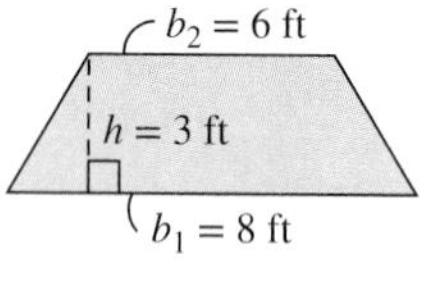

80. The volume of a rectangular solid is given by $V = lwh$, where l is the length of the box, w is the width, and h is the height. Find the volume of the box shown in the figure. 1000 yd³

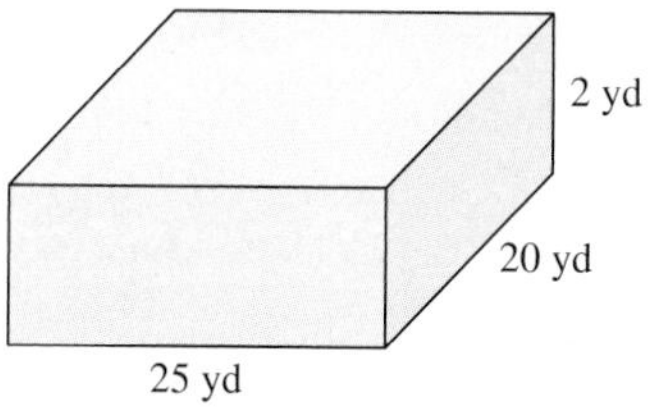

Concept 4: Translations

For Exercises 81–92, write each English phrase as an algebraic expression. **(See Example 6.)**

81. The product of 3 and x $3x$

82. The sum of b and 6 $b + 6$

83. The quotient of x and 7 $\frac{x}{7}$ or $x \div 7$

84. Four divided by k
$\frac{4}{k}$ or $4 \div k$

85. The difference of 2 and a
$2 - a$

86. Three subtracted from t
$t - 3$

87. x more than twice y
$2y + x$

88. Nine decreased by the product of 3 and p $9 - 3p$

89. Four times the sum of x and 12
$4(x + 12)$

90. Twice the difference of x and 3
$2(x - 3)$

91. Q less than 3
$3 - Q$

92. Fourteen less than t
$t - 14$

For Exercises 93–100, write the English phrase as an algebraic expression. Then evaluate each expression for $x = 4$, $y = 2$, and $z = 10$. **(See Example 7.)**

93. Two times y cubed $2y^3$; 16

94. Three times z squared $3z^2$; 300

95. The absolute value of the difference of z and 8
$|z - 8|$; 2

96. The absolute value of the difference of x and 3
$|x - 3|$; 1

97. The product of 5 and the square root of x
$5\sqrt{x}$; 10

98. The square root of the difference of z and 1
$\sqrt{z - 1}$; 3

99. The value x subtracted from the product of y and z
$yz - x$; 16

100. The difference of z and the product of x and y
$z - xy$; 2

Expanding Your Skills

For Exercises 101–104, use the order of operations to simplify each expression.

101. $\dfrac{\sqrt{\frac{1}{9}} + \frac{2}{3}}{\sqrt{\frac{4}{25}} + \frac{3}{5}}$ 1

102. $\dfrac{5 - \sqrt{9}}{\sqrt{\frac{4}{9}} + \frac{1}{3}}$ 2

103. $\dfrac{|-2|}{|-10| - |2|}$ $\frac{1}{4}$

104. $\dfrac{|-4|^2}{2^2 + \sqrt{144}}$ 1

105. Some students use the following common memorization device (mnemonic) to help them remember the order of operations: the acronym PEMDAS or **P**lease **E**xcuse **M**y **D**ear **A**unt **S**ally to remember **P**arentheses, **E**xponents, **M**ultiplication, **D**ivision, **A**ddition, and **S**ubtraction. The problem with this mnemonic is that it suggests that multiplication is done before division and similarly, it suggests that addition is performed before subtraction. Explain why following this acronym may give incorrect answers for the expressions:

a. $36 \div 4 \cdot 3$ $36 \div 4 \cdot 3 = 9 \cdot 3 = 27$ Division must be performed before multiplication.

b. $36 - 4 + 3$ $36 - 4 + 3 = 32 + 3 = 35$ Subtraction must be performed before addition.

106. If you use the acronym **P**lease **E**xcuse **M**y **D**ear **A**unt **S**ally to remember the order of operations, what must you keep in mind about the last four operations? Multiplication or division is performed in order from left to right. Addition or subtraction is performed in order from left to right.

107. Explain why the acronym **P**lease **E**xcuse **D**r. **M**ichael **S**mith's **A**unt could also be used as a memory device for the order of operations. This is acceptable, provided division and multiplication are performed in order from left to right, and subtraction and addition are performed in order from left to right.

Addition of Real Numbers

Section 1.4

Concepts

1. Addition of Real Numbers and the Number Line
2. Addition of Real Numbers
3. Translations
4. Applications Involving Addition of Real Numbers

1. Addition of Real Numbers and the Number Line

Adding real numbers can be visualized on the number line. To do so, locate the first addend on the number line. Then to add a positive number, move to the right on the number line. To add a negative number, move to the left on the number line. The following example may help to illustrate the process.

On a winter day in Detroit, suppose the temperature starts out at 5 degrees Fahrenheit (5°F) at noon, and then drops 12° two hours later when a cold front passes through. The resulting temperature can be represented by the expression $5° + (-12°)$. On the number line, start at 5 and count 12 units to the left (Figure 1-7). The resulting temperature at 2:00 P.M. is -7°F.

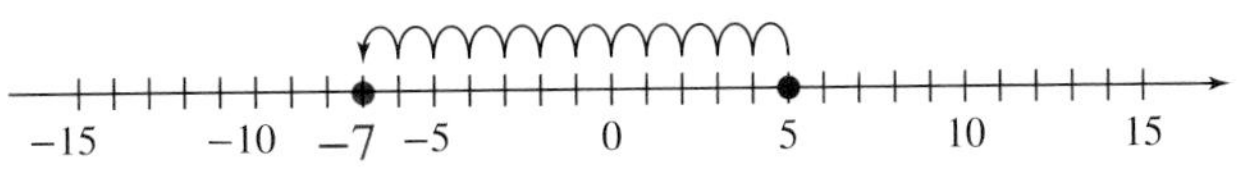

Figure 1-7

Classroom Examples: p. 51, Exercises 10 and 12

Example 1 **Using the Number Line to Add Real Numbers**

Use the number line to add the numbers.

a. $-5 + 2$ **b.** $-1 + (-4)$ **c.** $7 + (-4)$

Solution:

a. $-5 + 2 = -3$

Start at -5, and count 2 units to the right.

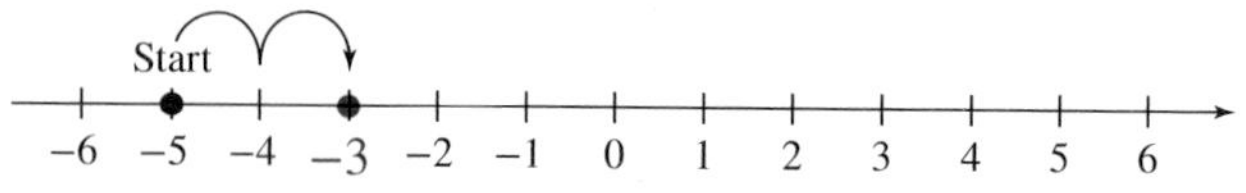

TIP: Note that we move to the left on the number line when we add a negative number. We move to the right when we add a positive number.

b. $-1 + (-4) = -5$

Start at -1, and count 4 units to the left.

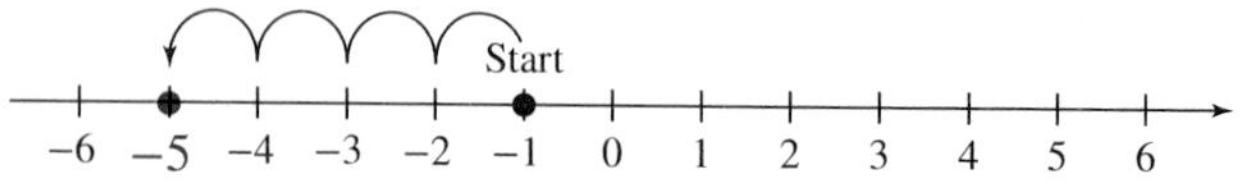

c. $7 + (-4) = 3$

Start at 7, and count 4 units to the left.

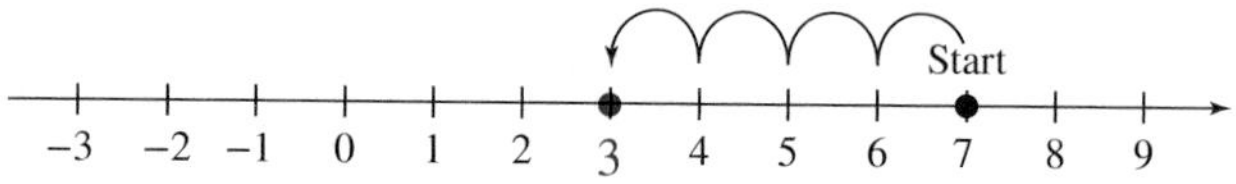

Skill Practice Use the number line to add the numbers.

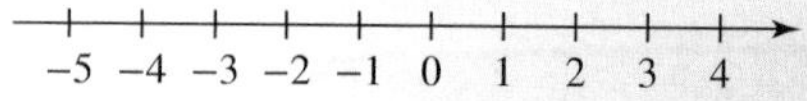

1. $-2 + 4$ **2.** $-2 + (-3)$ **3.** $5 + (-6)$

2. Addition of Real Numbers

When adding large numbers or numbers that involve fractions or decimals, counting units on the number line can be cumbersome. Study the following example to determine a pattern for adding two numbers with the *same* sign.

$1 + 4 = 5$

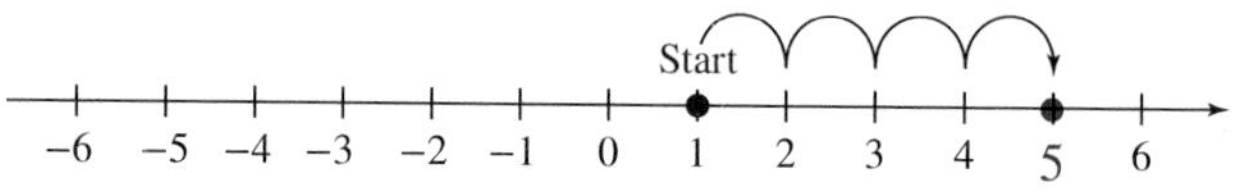

$-1 + (-4) = -5$

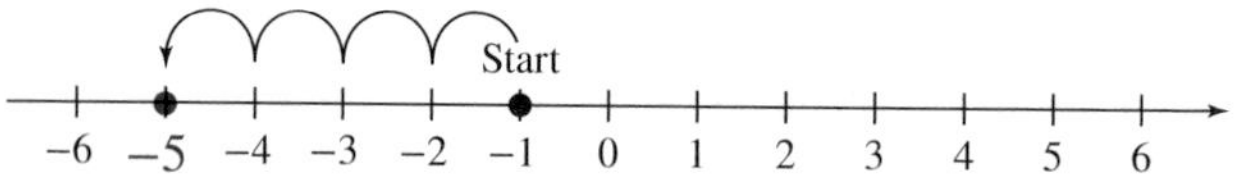

Adding Numbers with the *Same* Sign

To add two numbers with the *same* sign, add their absolute values and apply the common sign.

Classroom Examples: pp. 51–52, Exercises 22 and 52

Example 2 **Adding Real Numbers with the Same Sign**

Add.

a. $-12 + (-14)$ **b.** $-8.8 + (-3.7)$ **c.** $-\frac{4}{3} + \left(-\frac{6}{7}\right)$

Answers

1. 2 **2.** −5 **3.** −1

Solution:

a. $-12 + (-14)$ — First find the absolute value of the addends. $|-12| = 12$ and $|-14| = 14$.

$= -(12 + 14)$ — Add their absolute values and apply the common sign (in this case, the common sign is negative).

common sign is negative

$= -26$ — The sum is -26.

b. $-8.8 + (-3.7)$ — First find the absolute value of the addends. $|-8.8| = 8.8$ and $|-3.7| = 3.7$.

$= -(8.8 + 3.7)$ — Add their absolute values and apply the common sign (in this case, the common sign is negative).

common sign is negative

$= -12.5$ — The sum is -12.5.

c. $-\frac{4}{3} + \left(-\frac{6}{7}\right)$ — The least common denominator (LCD) is 21.

$= -\frac{4 \cdot 7}{3 \cdot 7} + \left(-\frac{6 \cdot 3}{7 \cdot 3}\right)$ — Write each fraction with the LCD.

$= -\frac{28}{21} + \left(-\frac{18}{21}\right)$ — Find the absolute value of the addends.

$\left|-\frac{28}{21}\right| = \frac{28}{21}$ and $\left|-\frac{18}{21}\right| = \frac{18}{21}$.

$= -\left(\frac{28}{21} + \frac{18}{21}\right)$ — Add their absolute values and apply the common sign (in this case, the common sign is negative).

common sign is negative

$= -\frac{46}{21}$ — The sum is $-\frac{46}{21}$.

Skill Practice Add.

4. $-5 + (-25)$ **5.** $-14.8 + (-9.7)$ **6.** $-\frac{1}{2} + \left(-\frac{5}{8}\right)$

Study the following example to determine a pattern for adding two numbers with *different* signs.

$1 + (-4) = -3$

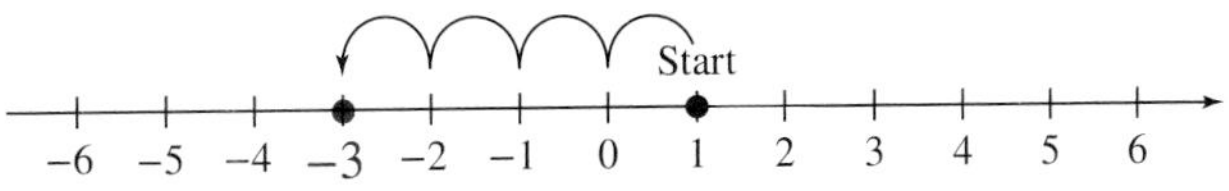

$-1 + 4 = 3$

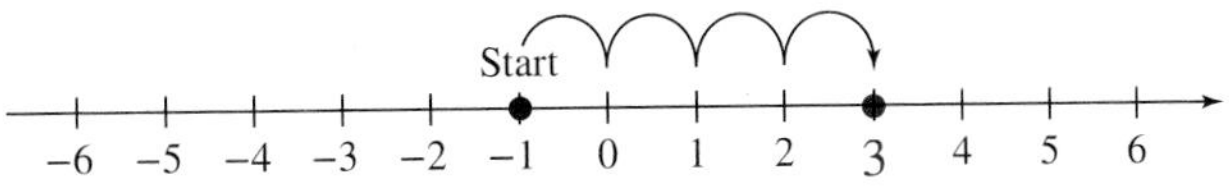

Instructor Note: Memory Device:
Same Sign ⇒ Sum
Different Sign ⇒ Difference

Answers

4. -30 **5.** -24.5 **6.** $-\frac{9}{8}$

Adding Numbers with *Different* Signs

To add two numbers with *different* signs, subtract the smaller absolute value from the larger absolute value. Then apply the sign of the number having the larger absolute value.

Classroom Examples: pp. 51–52, Exercises 20 and 32

Example 3 **Adding Real Numbers with Different Signs**

Add.

a. $12 + (-17)$ **b.** $-8 + 8$

Solution:

a. $12 + (-17)$ First find the absolute value of the addends. $|12| = 12$ and $|-17| = 17$.

The absolute value of -17 is greater than the absolute value of 12. Therefore, the sum is negative.

$= -(17 - 12)$ Next, subtract the smaller absolute value from the larger absolute value.

Apply the sign of the number with the larger absolute value.

$= -5$

b. $-8 + 8$ First find the absolute value of the addends. $|-8| = 8$ and $|8| = 8$.

$= 8 - 8$ The absolute values are equal. Therefore, their difference is 0. The number zero is neither positive nor negative.

$= 0$

Skill Practice Add.

7. $-15 + 16$ **8.** $6 + (-6)$

Classroom Examples: p. 52, Exercises 46 and 54

Example 4 **Adding Real Numbers with Different Signs**

Add.

a. $-10.6 + 20.4$ **b.** $\frac{2}{15} + \left(-\frac{4}{5}\right)$

Solution:

a. $-10.6 + 20.4$ First find the absolute value of the addends. $|-10.6| = 10.6$ and $|20.4| = 20.4$.

The absolute value of 20.4 is greater than the absolute value of -10.6. Therefore, the sum is positive.

$= +(20.4 - 10.6)$ Next, subtract the smaller absolute value from the larger absolute value.

Apply the sign of the number with the larger absolute value.

$= 9.8$

Answers

7. 1 **8.** 0

b. $\frac{2}{15}+\left(-\frac{4}{5}\right)$ The least common denominator is 15.

$= \frac{2}{15}+\left(-\frac{4 \cdot 3}{5 \cdot 3}\right)$ Write each fraction with the LCD.

$= \frac{2}{15}+\left(-\frac{12}{15}\right)$ Find the absolute value of the addends.

$\left|\frac{2}{15}\right| = \frac{2}{15}$ and $\left|-\frac{12}{15}\right| = \frac{12}{15}$.

The absolute value of $-\frac{12}{15}$ is greater than the absolute value of $\frac{2}{15}$. Therefore, the sum is negative.

$= -\left(\frac{12}{15}-\frac{2}{15}\right)$ Next, subtract the smaller absolute value from the larger absolute value.

Apply the sign of the number with the larger absolute value.

$= -\frac{10}{15}$ Subtract.

$= -\frac{2}{3}$ Simplify to lowest terms.

Skill Practice Add.

9. $27.3 + (-18.1)$ **10.** $-\frac{9}{10}+\frac{2}{5}$

3. Translations

Example 5 **Translating Expressions Involving the Addition of Real Numbers**

Classroom Examples: p. 53, Exercises 86 and 88

Write each English phrase as an algebraic expression. Then simplify the result.

a. The sum of $-12, -8, 9$, and -1 **b.** Negative three-tenths added to $-\frac{7}{8}$

c. The sum of -12 and its opposite

Solution:

a. The sum of $-12, -8, 9$, and -1

$\underbrace{-12+(-8)}+9+(-1)$

$= \underbrace{-20+9}+(-1)$

$= \underbrace{-11+(-1)}$ Apply the order of operations by adding from left to right.

$= -12$

b. Negative three-tenths added to $-\frac{7}{8}$

$-\frac{7}{8}+\left(-\frac{3}{10}\right)$

$= -\frac{35}{40}+\left(-\frac{12}{40}\right)$ The common denominator is 40.

$= -\frac{47}{40}$ The numbers have the same signs. Add their absolute values and keep the common sign. $-\left(\frac{35}{40}+\frac{12}{40}\right)$

Answers

9. 9.2 **10.** $-\frac{1}{2}$

TIP: The sum of any number and its opposite is 0.

c. The sum of −12 and its opposite

$-12 + (12)$

$= 0$ Add.

Skill Practice Write as an algebraic expression, and simplify the result.

11. The sum of −10, 4, and −6

12. Negative 2 added to $-\frac{1}{2}$

13. −60 added to its opposite

4. Applications Involving Addition of Real Numbers

Classroom Example: p. 53, Exercise 94

© Ryan McVay/Getty Images RF

Example 6 Adding Real Numbers in Applications

a. It is common for newborn infants to fluctuate in weight. Elise and Benjamin's baby lost 7 oz the first week after birth and gained 10 oz the second week. Write a mathematical expression to describe this situation and then simplify the result.

b. A student has $120 in her checking account. After depositing her paycheck of $215, she writes a check for $255 to cover her portion of the rent and another check for $294 to cover her car payment. Write a mathematical expression to describe this situation and then simplify the result.

Solution:

a. $-7 + 10$ A loss of 7 oz can be interpreted as −7 oz.

$= 3$ The infant had a net gain of 3 oz.

b. $\underbrace{120 + 215} + (-255) + (-294)$ Writing a check is equivalent to adding a negative amount to the bank account.

$= \underbrace{335 + (-255)} + (-294)$ Use the order of operations. Add from left to right.

$= 80 + (-294)$

$= -214$ The student has overdrawn her account by $214.

Skill Practice

14. A stock was priced at $32.00 per share at the beginning of the month. After the first week, the price went up $2.15 per share. At the end of the second week it went down $3.28 per share. Write a mathematical expression to describe the price of the stock and find the price of the stock at the end of the 2-week period.

Answers

11. $-10 + 4 + (-6)$; -12

12. $-\frac{1}{2} + (-2)$; $-\frac{5}{2}$

13. $60 + (-60)$; 0

14. $32.00 + 2.15 + (-3.28)$; $30.87 per share

Section 1.4 Practice Exercises

For additional exercises, see Classroom Activities 1.4A–1.4B in the *Student's Resource Manual* at www.mhhe.com/moh.

Study Skills Exercise

It is very important to attend class every day. Math is cumulative in nature, and you must master the material learned in the previous class to understand today's lesson. Because this is so important, many instructors have an attendance policy that may affect your final grade. Write down the attendance policy for your class.

Vocabulary and Key Concepts

1. a. If a and b are both negative, then $a + b$ will be (choose one: positive or negative). negative

b. If a and b have different signs, and if $|b| > |a|$, then the sum will have the same sign as (choose one: a or b). b

Review Exercises

Plot the points in set A on a number line. Then for Exercises 2–7 place the appropriate inequality (<, >) between the numbers.

$$A = \left\{-2, \frac{3}{4}, -\frac{5}{2}, 3, \frac{9}{2}, 1.6, 0\right\}$$

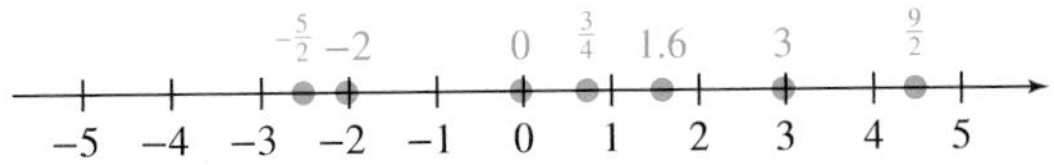

2. $-2 \square 0$ <

3. $\frac{9}{2} \square \frac{3}{4}$ >

4. $-2 \square -\frac{5}{2}$ >

5. $0 \square -\frac{5}{2}$ >

6. $\frac{3}{4} \square 1.6$ <

7. $\frac{3}{4} \square -\frac{5}{2}$ >

8. Evaluate the expressions.

a. $-(-8)$ 8

b. $-|-8|$ −8

Concept 1: Addition of Real Numbers and the Number Line

For Exercises 9–16, add the numbers using the number line. **(See Example 1.)**

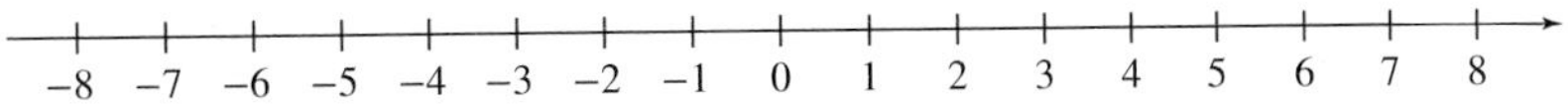

9. $-2 + (-4)$ −6

10. $-3 + (-5)$ −8

11. $-7 + 10$ 3

12. $-2 + 9$ 7

13. $6 + (-3)$ 3

14. $8 + (-2)$ 6

15. $2 + (-5)$ −3

16. $7 + (-3)$ 4

Concept 2: Addition of Real Numbers

Animation

For Exercises 17–70, add. **(See Examples 2–4.)**

17. $-19 + 2$ −17

18. $-25 + 18$ −17

19. $-4 + 11$ 7

20. $-3 + 9$ 6

21. $-16 + (-3)$ −19

22. $-12 + (-23)$ −35

23. $-2 + (-21)$ −23

24. $-13 + (-1)$ −14

25. $0+(-5)$ -5 **26.** $0+(-4)$ -4 **27.** $-3+0$ -3 **28.** $-8+0$ -8

29. $-16+16$ 0 **30.** $11+(-11)$ 0 **31.** $41+(-41)$ 0 **32.** $-15+15$ 0

33. $4+(-9)$ -5 **34.** $6+(-9)$ -3 **35.** $7+(-2)+(-8)$ -3 **36.** $2+(-3)+(-6)$ -7

37. $-17+(-3)+20$ 0 **38.** $-9+(-6)+15$ 0

39. $-3+(-8)+(-12)$ -23 **40.** $-8+(-2)+(-13)$ -23

41. $-42+(-3)+45+(-6)$ -6 **42.** $36+(-3)+(-8)+(-25)$ 0

43. $-5+(-3)+(-7)+4+8$ -3 **44.** $-13+(-1)+5+2+(-20)$ -27

45. $23.81+(-2.51)$ 21.3 **46.** $-9.23+10.53$ 1.3 **47.** $-\frac{2}{7}+\frac{1}{14}$ $-\frac{3}{14}$ **48.** $-\frac{1}{8}+\frac{5}{16}$ $\frac{3}{16}$

49. $\frac{2}{3}+\left(-\frac{5}{6}\right)$ $-\frac{1}{6}$ **50.** $\frac{1}{2}+\left(-\frac{3}{4}\right)$ $-\frac{1}{4}$ **51.** $-\frac{7}{8}+\left(-\frac{1}{16}\right)$ $-\frac{15}{16}$ **52.** $-\frac{1}{9}+\left(-\frac{4}{3}\right)$ $-\frac{13}{9}$

53. $-\frac{1}{4}+\frac{3}{10}$ $\frac{1}{20}$ **54.** $-\frac{7}{6}+\frac{7}{8}$ $-\frac{7}{24}$ **55.** $-2.1+\left(-\frac{3}{10}\right)$ -2.4 or $-\frac{12}{5}$ **56.** $-8.3+\left(-\frac{9}{10}\right)$ -9.2 or $-\frac{46}{5}$

57. $\frac{3}{4}+(-0.5)$ $\frac{1}{4}$ or 0.25 **58.** $-\frac{3}{2}+0.45$ $-\frac{21}{20}$ or -1.05 **59.** $8.23+(-8.23)$ 0 **60.** $-7.5+7.5$ 0

61. $-\frac{7}{8}+0$ $-\frac{7}{8}$ **62.** $0+\left(-\frac{21}{22}\right)$ $-\frac{21}{22}$ **63.** $-\frac{3}{2}+\left(-\frac{1}{3}\right)+\frac{5}{6}$ -1 **64.** $-\frac{7}{8}+\frac{7}{6}+\frac{7}{12}$ $\frac{7}{8}$

65. $-\frac{2}{3}+\left(-\frac{1}{9}\right)+2$ $\frac{11}{9}$ **66.** $-\frac{1}{4}+\left(-\frac{3}{2}\right)+2$ $\frac{1}{4}$ **67.** $-47.36+24.28$ -23.08 **68.** $-0.015+(0.0026)$ -0.0124

69. $-0.000617+(-0.0015)$ -0.002117 **70.** $-5315.26+(-314.89)$ -5630.15

71. State the rule for adding two numbers with different signs. To add two numbers with different signs, subtract the smaller absolute value from the larger absolute value and apply the sign of the number with the larger absolute value.

72. State the rule for adding two numbers with the same sign. To add two numbers with the same sign, add their absolute values and apply the common sign.

For Exercises 73–80, evaluate each expression for $x=-3, y=-2$, and $z=16$.

73. $x+y+\sqrt{z}$ -1 **74.** $2z+x+y$ 27 **75.** $y+3\sqrt{z}$ 10 **76.** $-\sqrt{z}+y$ -6

77. $|x|+|y|$ 5 **78.** $z+x+|y|$ 15 **79.** $-x+y$ 1 **80.** $x+(-y)+z$ 15

Concept 3: Translations

For Exercises 81–90, write each English phrase as an algebraic expression. Then simplify the result. **(See Example 5.)**

81. The sum of -6 and -10 $-6+(-10); -16$ **82.** The sum of -3 and 5 $-3+5; 2$

83. Negative three increased by 8 $-3+8; 5$ **84.** Twenty-one increased by 4 $21+4; 25$

85. Seventeen more than -21 $-21 + 17; -4$

86. Twenty-four more than -7 $-7 + 24; 17$

87. Three times the sum of -14 and 20 $3(-14 + 20); 18$

88. Two times the sum of 6 and -10 $2[6 + (-10)]; -8$

89. Five more than the sum of -7 and -2
$[-7 + (-2)] + 5; -4$

90. Negative six more than the sum of 4 and -1
$[4 + (-1)] + (-6); -3$

Concept 4: Applications Involving Addition of Real Numbers

91. The temperature in Minneapolis, Minnesota, began at $-5°$F (5° below zero) at 6:00 A.M. By noon, the temperature had risen 13°, and by the end of the day, the temperature had dropped 11° from its noontime high. Write an expression using addition that describes the change in temperatures during the day. Then evaluate the expression to give the temperature at the end of the day.
$-5 + 13 + (-11); -3°$F

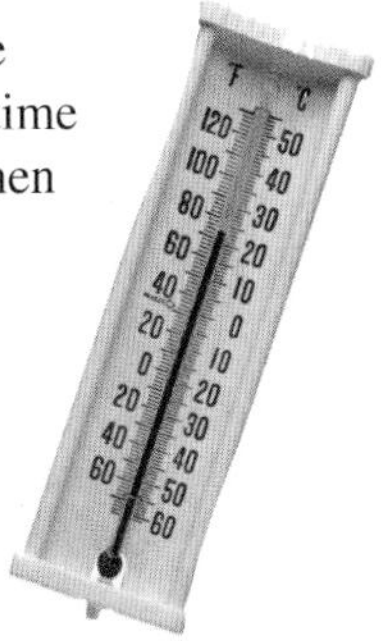

© Burke/Triolo/Brand X Pictures/Jupiterimages RF

92. The temperature in Toronto, Ontario, Canada, began at 4°F. A cold front went through at noon, and the temperature dropped 9°. By 4:00 P.M., the temperature had risen 2° from its noontime low. Write an expression using addition that describes the changes in temperature during the day. Then evaluate the expression to give the temperature at the end of the day. $4 + (-9) + 2; -3°$F

93. For 4 months, Amara monitored her weight loss or gain. Her records showed that she lost 8 lb, gained 1 lb, gained 2 lb, and lost 5 lb. Write an expression using addition that describes Amara's total loss or gain and evaluate the expression. Interpret the result. **(See Example 6.)**
$-8 + 1 + 2 + (-5) = -10$; Amara lost 10 lb.

94. Alan just started an online business. His profit/loss records for the past 5 months show that he had a profit of \$200, a profit of \$750, a loss of \$340, a loss of \$290, and a profit of \$900. Write an expression using addition that describes Alan's total profit or loss and evaluate the expression. Interpret the result.
$200 + 750 + (-340) + (-290) + 900 = 1220$; Alan had a profit of \$1220.

95. Yoshima has \$52.23 in her checking account. She writes a check for groceries for \$52.95. **(See Example 6.)**

a. Write an addition statement that expresses Yoshima's transaction. $52.23 + (-52.95)$

b. Is Yoshima's account overdrawn? Yes

96. Mohammad has \$40.02 in his checking account. He writes a check for a pair of shoes for \$40.96.

a. Write an addition statement that expresses Mohammad's transaction. $40.02 + (-40.96)$

b. Is Mohammad's account overdrawn? Yes

97. The table gives the golf scores for a top golfer for five rounds of the LPGA Final Qualifying Tournament. Find her total score. -6; She was 6 below par.

Score per Round	
Round 1	−5
Round 2	0
Round 3	−1
Round 4	−1
Round 5	+1

98. A company that has been in business for 5 years has the following profit and loss record.

a. Write an expression using addition to describe the company's profit/loss activity.
$-50{,}000 + (-32{,}000) + (-5000) + 13{,}000 + 26{,}000$

b. Evaluate the expression from part (a) to determine the company's net profit or loss.
$-48{,}000$; The company lost \$48,000.

Year	Profit/Loss (\$)
1	−50,000
2	−32,000
3	−5,000
4	13,000
5	26,000

Section 1.5 Subtraction of Real Numbers

Concepts

1. Subtraction of Real Numbers
2. Translations
3. Applications Involving Subtraction
4. Applying the Order of Operations

1. Subtraction of Real Numbers

We have learned the rules for adding real numbers. Subtraction of real numbers is defined in terms of the addition process. For example, consider the following subtraction problem and the corresponding addition problem:

$$6 - 4 = 2 \quad \Leftrightarrow \quad 6 + (-4) = 2$$

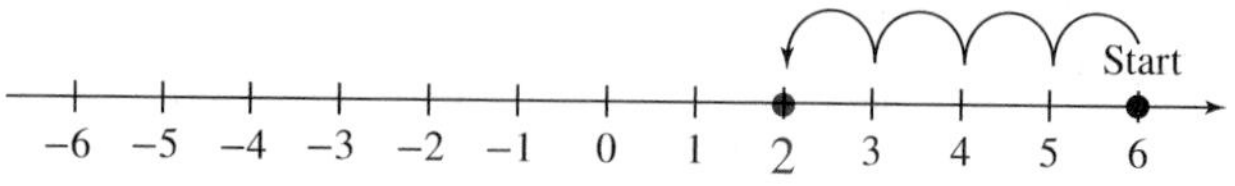

In each case, we start at 6 on the number line and move to the left 4 units. That is, adding the opposite of 4 produces the same result as subtracting 4. This is true in general. To subtract two real numbers, add the opposite of the second number to the first number.

Subtracting Real Numbers

If a and b are real numbers, then $a - b = a + (-b)$.

$$\left.\begin{aligned} 10 - 4 &= 10 + (-4) = 6 \\ -10 - 4 &= -10 + (-4) = -14 \end{aligned}\right\}$$ Subtracting 4 is the same as adding -4.

$$\left.\begin{aligned} 10 - (-4) &= 10 + (4) = 14 \\ -10 - (-4) &= -10 + (4) = -6 \end{aligned}\right\}$$ Subtracting -4 is the same as adding 4.

Classroom Examples: p. 60, Exercises 16, 18, and 20

Example 1 Subtracting Integers

Subtract the numbers.

a. $4 - (-9)$ **b.** $-6 - 9$ **c.** $-11 - (-5)$ **d.** $7 - 10$

Solution:

a. $4 - (-9)$

$= 4 + (9) = 13$

Take the opposite of −9.

Change subtraction to addition.

b. $-6 - 9$

$= -6 + (-9) = -15$

Take the opposite of 9.

Change subtraction to addition.

c. $-11 - (-5)$

$= -11 + (5) = -6$

Take the opposite of −5.

Change subtraction to addition.

d. $7 - 10$

$= 7 + (-10) = -3$

Take the opposite of 10.

Change subtraction to addition.

Skill Practice Subtract.

1. $1 - (-3)$ **2.** $-2 - 2$ **3.** $-6 - (-11)$ **4.** $8 - 15$

Answers

1. 4 **2.** −4 **3.** 5 **4.** −7

Example 2 Subtracting Real Numbers

Classroom Examples: p. 60, Exercises 46 and 48.

a. $\frac{3}{20} - \left(-\frac{4}{15}\right)$ **b.** $-2.3 - 6.04$

Solution:

a. $\frac{3}{20} - \left(-\frac{4}{15}\right)$ The least common denominator is 60.

$= \frac{9}{60} - \left(-\frac{16}{60}\right)$ Write equivalent fractions with the LCD.

$= \frac{9}{60} + \left(\frac{16}{60}\right)$ Rewrite subtraction in terms of addition.

$= \frac{25}{60}$ Add.

$= \frac{5}{12}$ Simplify by dividing the numerator and denominator by the GCF of 5.

b. $-2.3 - 6.04$

$-2.3 + (-6.04)$ Rewrite subtraction in terms of addition.

-8.34 Add.

Skill Practice Subtract.

5. $\frac{1}{6} - \left(-\frac{7}{12}\right)$ **6.** $-7.5 - 1.5$

2. Translations

Example 3 Translating Expressions Involving Subtraction

Classroom Examples: p. 60, Exercises 64 and 70.

Write an algebraic expression for each English phrase and then simplify the result.

a. The difference of -7 and -5

b. 12.4 subtracted from -4.7

c. -24 decreased by the sum of -10 and 13

d. Seven-fourths less than one-third

Solution:

a. The difference of -7 and -5

$-7 - (-5)$

$= -7 + (5)$ Rewrite subtraction in terms of addition.

$= -2$ Simplify.

Answers

5. $\frac{3}{4}$ **6.** -9

TIP: Recall that "b subtracted from a" is translated as $a - b$. In Example 3(b), −4.7 is written first and then 12.4.

b. 12.4 subtracted from −4.7

$-4.7 - 12.4$

$= -4.7 + (-12.4)$ Rewrite subtraction in terms of addition.

$= -17.1$ Simplify.

TIP: In Example 3(c), parentheses must be used around the sum of −10 and 13 so that −24 is decreased by the entire quantity (−10 + 13).

c. −24 decreased by the sum of −10 and 13

$-24 - (-10 + 13)$

$= -24 - (3)$ Simplify inside parentheses.

$= -24 + (-3)$ Rewrite subtraction in terms of addition.

$= -27$ Simplify.

d. Seven-fourths less than one-third

$\frac{1}{3} - \frac{7}{4}$

$= \frac{1}{3} + \left(-\frac{7}{4}\right)$ Rewrite subtraction in terms of addition.

$= \frac{4}{12} + \left(-\frac{21}{12}\right)$ The common denominator is 12.

$= -\frac{17}{12}$

Skill Practice Write an algebraic expression for each phrase and then simplify.

7. 8 less than −10

8. −7.2 subtracted from −8.2

9. 10 more than the difference of −2 and 3

10. Two-fifths decreased by four-thirds

3. Applications Involving Subtraction

Classroom Example: p. 61, Exercise 72

Example 4 **Using Subtraction of Real Numbers in an Application**

During one of his turns on *Jeopardy,* Harold selected the category "Show Tunes." He got the \$200, \$600, and \$1000 questions correct, but he got the \$400 and \$800 questions incorrect. Write an expression that determines Harold's score. Then simplify the expression to find his total winnings for that category.

Solution:

$200 + 600 + 1000 - 400 - 800$

$= 200 + 600 + 1000 + (-400) + (-800)$ Add the positive numbers.

$= 1800 + (-1200)$ Add the negative numbers.

$= 600$ Harold won \$600.

Skill Practice

11. During Harold's first round on *Jeopardy,* he got the \$100, \$200, and \$400 questions correct but he got the \$300 and \$500 questions incorrect. Determine Harold's score for this round.

Answers

7. $-10 - 8; -18$
8. $-8.2 - (-7.2); -1$
9. $(-2 - 3) + 10; 5$
10. $\frac{2}{5} - \frac{4}{3}; -\frac{14}{15}$
11. −100, Harold lost \$100.

Example 5 **Using Subtraction of Real Numbers in an Application**

The highest recorded temperature in North America was 134°F, recorded on July 10, 1913, in Death Valley, California. The lowest temperature of −81°F was recorded on February 3, 1947, in Snag, Yukon, Canada.

Find the difference between the highest and lowest recorded temperatures in North America.

Solution:

$134 - (-81)$

$= 134 + (81)$ Rewrite subtraction in terms of addition.

$= 215$ Add.

The difference between the highest and lowest temperatures is 215°F.

Skill Practice

12. The record high temperature for the state of Montana occurred in 1937 and was 117°F. The record low occurred in 1954 and was −70°F. Find the difference between the highest and lowest temperatures.

Classroom Example: p. 61, Exercise 74

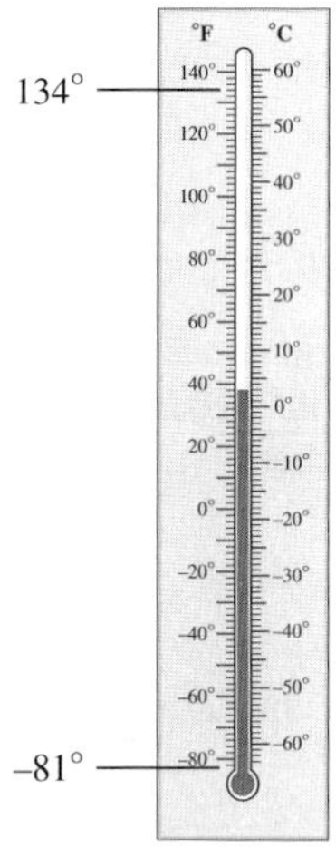

4. Applying the Order of Operations

Example 6 **Applying the Order of Operations**

Simplify the expressions.

a. $-6 + \{10 - [7 - (-4)]\}$ **b.** $5 - \sqrt{35 - (-14)} - 2$

Solution:

a. $-6 + \{10 - [7 - (-4)]\}$ Simplify inside the inner brackets first.

$= -6 + \{10 - [7 + (4)]\}$ Rewrite subtraction in terms of addition.

$= -6 + \{10 - (11)\}$ Simplify the expression inside brackets.

$= -6 + \{10 + (-11)\}$ Rewrite subtraction in terms of addition.

$= -6 + (-1)$ Add within the braces.

$= -7$ Add.

b. $5 - \sqrt{35 - (-14)} - 2$ Simplify inside the radical first.

$= 5 - \sqrt{35 + (14)} - 2$ Rewrite subtraction in terms of addition.

$= 5 - \sqrt{49} - 2$ Add within the radical sign.

$= 5 - 7 - 2$ Simplify the radical.

$= 5 + (-7) + (-2)$ Rewrite subtraction in terms of addition.

$= -2 + (-2)$ Add from left to right.

$= -4$

Skill Practice Simplify the expressions.

13. $-11 - \{8 - [2 - (-3)]\}$ **14.** $(12 - 5)^2 + \sqrt{4 - (-21)}$

Classroom Examples: p. 61–62, Exercises 86 and 92

Answers

12. 187°F **13.** −14 **14.** 54

Classroom Examples: p. 62, Exercises 90 and 94

Example 7 Applying the Order of Operations

Simplify the expressions.

a. $\left(-\frac{5}{8}-\frac{2}{3}\right)-\left(\frac{1}{8}+2\right)$ **b.** $-6-|7-11|+(-3+7)^2$

Solution:

a. $\left(-\frac{5}{8}-\frac{2}{3}\right)-\left(\frac{1}{8}+2\right)$ Simplify inside the parentheses first.

$=\left[-\frac{5}{8}+\left(-\frac{2}{3}\right)\right]-\left(\frac{1}{8}+2\right)$ Rewrite subtraction in terms of addition.

$=\left[-\frac{15}{24}+\left(-\frac{16}{24}\right)\right]-\left(\frac{1}{8}+\frac{16}{8}\right)$ Get a common denominator in each parentheses.

$=\left(-\frac{31}{24}\right)-\left(\frac{17}{8}\right)$ Add fractions in each parentheses.

$=\left(-\frac{31}{24}\right)+\left(-\frac{17}{8}\right)$ Rewrite subtraction in terms of addition.

$=-\frac{31}{24}+\left(-\frac{51}{24}\right)$ Get a common denominator.

$=-\frac{82}{24}$ Add.

$=-\frac{41}{12}$ Simplify to lowest terms.

b. $-6-|7-11|+(-3+7)^2$ Simplify within absolute value bars and parentheses first.

$=-6-|7+(-11)|+(-3+7)^2$ Rewrite subtraction in terms of addition.

$=-6-|-4|+(4)^2$

$=-6-(4)+16$ Simplify the absolute value and exponent.

$=-6+(-4)+16$ Rewrite subtraction in terms of addition.

$=-10+16$ Add from left to right.

$=6$

Skill Practice Simplify the expressions.

15. $\left(-1+\frac{1}{4}\right)-\left(\frac{3}{4}-\frac{1}{2}\right)$

16. $4-2|6+(-8)|+(4)^2$

Answers

15. −1 **16.** 16

Calculator Connections

Topic: Operations with Signed Numbers on a Calculator

Most calculators can add, subtract, multiply, and divide signed numbers. It is important to note, however, that the key used for the negative sign is different from the key used for subtraction. On a scientific calculator, the [+/-] key or [+○-] key is used to enter a negative number or to change the sign of an existing number. On a graphing calculator, the [(−)] key is used. These keys should not be confused with the [−] key which is used for subtraction. For example, try simplifying the following expressions.

a. $-7 + (-4) - 6$ **b.** $-3.1 - (-0.5) + 1.1$

Scientific Calculator:

Enter: 7 [+○-] [+] [(] 4 [+○-] [)] [−] 6 [=] **Result:** −17

Enter: 3.1 [+○-] [−] [(] 0.5 [+○-] [)] + 1.1 [=] **Result:** −1.5

Graphing Calculator:

```
-7+(-4)-6
              -17
-3.1-(-0.5)+1.1
             -1.5
```

Calculator Exercises

Simplify the expression without the use of a calculator. Then use the calculator to verify your answer.

1. $-8 + (-5)$ −13 **2.** $4 + (-5) + (-1)$ −2 **3.** $627 - (-84)$ 711 **4.** $-0.06 - 0.12$ −0.18

5. $-3.2 + (-14.5)$ −17.7 **6.** $-472 + (-518)$ −990 **7.** $-12 - 9 + 4$ −17 **8.** $209 - 108 + (-63)$ 38

Section 1.5 Practice Exercises

For additional exercises, see Classroom Activities 1.5A–1.5C in the *Student's Resource Manual* at www.mhhe.com/moh.

Study Skills Exercise

Some instructors allow the use of calculators. What is your instructor's policy regarding calculators in class, on the homework, and on tests?

Helpful Hint: If you are not permitted to use a calculator on tests, it is a good idea to do your homework in the same way, without a calculator.

Vocabulary and Key Concepts

1. a. The expression $a - b$ is equal to $a +$ ___$-b$___.

b. If a is positive and b is negative, then the difference $a - b$ will be (choose one: positive or negative). positive

Review Exercises

For Exercises 2–5, write each English phrase as an algebraic expression.

2. The square root of 6 $\sqrt{6}$ **3.** The square of x x^2

4. Negative seven increased by 10 $-7 + 10$ **5.** Two more than $-b$ $-b + 2$

For Exercises 6–8, simplify the expression.

6. $4^2 - 6 \div 2$ 13 **7.** $1 + 36 \div 9 \cdot 2$ 9 **8.** $14 - |10 - 6|$ 10

Concept 1: Subtraction of Real Numbers

For Exercises 9–14, fill in the blank to make each statement correct.

9. $5 - 3 = 5 +$ ___−3___ **10.** $8 - 7 = 8 +$ ___−7___ **11.** $-2 - 12 = -2 +$ ___−12___

12. $-4 - 9 = -4 +$ ___−9___ **13.** $7 - (-4) = 7 +$ ___4___ **14.** $13 - (-4) = 13 +$ ___4___

For Exercises 15–60, simplify. **(See Examples 1–2.)** Animation

15. $3 - 5$ −2 **16.** $9 - 12$ −3 **17.** $3 - (-5)$ 8 **18.** $9 - (-12)$ 21

19. $-3 - 5$ −8 **20.** $-9 - 12$ −21 **21.** $-3 - (-5)$ 2 **22.** $-9 - (-5)$ −4

23. $23 - 17$ 6 **24.** $14 - 2$ 12 **25.** $23 - (-17)$ 40 **26.** $14 - (-2)$ 16

27. $-23 - 17$ −40 **28.** $-14 - 2$ −16 **29.** $-23 - (-23)$ 0 **30.** $-14 - (-14)$ 0

31. $-6 - 14$ −20 **32.** $-9 - 12$ −21 **33.** $-7 - 17$ −24 **34.** $-8 - 21$ −29

35. $13 - (-12)$ 25 **36.** $20 - (-5)$ 25 **37.** $-14 - (-9)$ −5 **38.** $-21 - (-17)$ −4

39. $-\frac{6}{5} - \frac{3}{10}$ $-\frac{3}{2}$ **40.** $-\frac{2}{9} - \frac{5}{3}$ $-\frac{17}{9}$ **41.** $\frac{3}{8} - \left(-\frac{4}{3}\right)$ $\frac{41}{24}$ **42.** $\frac{7}{10} - \left(-\frac{5}{6}\right)$ $\frac{23}{15}$

43. $\frac{1}{2} - \frac{1}{10}$ $\frac{2}{5}$ **44.** $\frac{2}{7} - \frac{3}{14}$ $\frac{1}{14}$ **45.** $-\frac{11}{12} - \left(-\frac{1}{4}\right)$ $-\frac{2}{3}$ **46.** $-\frac{7}{8} - \left(-\frac{1}{6}\right)$ $-\frac{17}{24}$

47. $6.8 - (-2.4)$ 9.2 **48.** $7.2 - (-1.9)$ 9.1 **49.** $3.1 - 8.82$ −5.72 **50.** $1.8 - 9.59$ −7.79

51. $-4 - 3 - 2 - 1$ −10 **52.** $-10 - 9 - 8 - 7$ −34 **53.** $6 - 8 - 2 - 10$ −14 **54.** $20 - 50 - 10 - 5$ −45

55. $10 + (-14) + 6 - 22$ −20 **56.** $-3 - (-8) + (-11) - 6$ −12

57. $-112.846 + (-13.03) - 47.312$ −173.188 **58.** $-96.473 + (-36.02) - 16.617$ −149.11

59. $0.085 - (-3.14) + 0.018$ 3.243 **60.** $0.00061 - (-0.00057) + 0.0014$ 0.00258

Concept 2: Translations

For Exercises 61–70, write each English phrase as an algebraic expression. Then evaluate the expression. **(See Example 3.)**

61. Six minus −7 $6 - (-7)$; 13 **62.** Eighteen minus −1 $18 - (-1)$; 19

63. Eighteen subtracted from 3 $3 - 18$; −15 **64.** Twenty-one subtracted from 8 $8 - 21$; −13

65. The difference of −5 and −11 $-5 - (-11)$; 6 **66.** The difference of −2 and −18 $-2 - (-18)$; 16

67. Negative thirteen subtracted from −1 $-1 - (-13)$; 12 **68.** Negative thirty-one subtracted from −19 $-19 - (-31)$; 12

69. Twenty less than −32 $-32 - 20$; −52 **70.** Seven less than −3 $-3 - 7$; −10

Concept 3: Applications Involving Subtraction

71. On the game, *Jeopardy,* Jasper selected the category "The Last." He got the first four questions correct (worth \$200, \$400, \$600, and \$800) but then missed the last question (worth \$1000). Write an expression that determines Jasper's score. Then simplify the expression to find his total winnings for that category. **(See Example 4.)** 200 + 400 + 600 + 800 − 1000; \$1000

72. On Courtney's turn in *Jeopardy,* she chose the category "Birds of a Feather." She already had \$1200 when she selected a Double Jeopardy question. She wagered \$500 but guessed incorrectly (therefore she lost \$500). On her next turn, she got the \$800 question correct. Write an expression that determines Courtney's score. Then simplify the expression. 1200 − 500 + 800; \$1500

73. In Ohio, the highest temperature ever recorded was 113°F and the lowest was −39°F. Find the difference between the highest and lowest temperatures. (*Source: Information Please Almanac*) **(See Example 5.)** 152°F

74. On a recent winter day at the South Pole, the temperature was −52°F. On the same day in Springfield, Missouri, it was a pleasant summer temperature of 75°F. What was the difference in temperatures? The difference in the temperature was 127°F.

75. The highest mountain in the world is Mt. Everest, located in South Asia. Its height is 8848 meters (m). The lowest recorded depth in the ocean is located in the Marianas Trench in the Pacific Ocean. Its "height" relative to sea level is −11,033 m. Determine the difference in elevation, in meters, between the highest mountain in the world and the deepest ocean trench. (*Source: Information Please Almanac*) 19,881 m

© Daniel Prudek/iStockphoto/Getty Images RF

76. The lowest point in North America is located in Death Valley, California, at an elevation of −282 ft. The highest point in North America is Denali, Alaska, at an elevation of 20,320 ft. Find the difference in elevation, in feet, between the highest and lowest points in North America. (*Source: Information Please Almanac*) 20,602 ft

© Comstock Images/Alamy RF

Concept 4: Applying the Order of Operations

For Exercises 77–96, perform the indicated operations. **(See Examples 6–7.)**

77. $6 + 8 - (-2) - 4 + 1$ 13

78. $-3 - (-4) + 1 - 2 - 5$ −5

79. $-1 - 7 + (-3) - 8 + 10$ −9

80. $13 - 7 + 4 - 3 - (-1)$ 8

81. $2 - (-8) + 7 + 3 - 15$ 5

82. $8 - (-13) + 1 - 9$ 13

83. $-6 + (-1) + (-8) + (-10)$ −25

84. $-8 + (-3) + (-5) + (-2)$ −18

85. $-4 - \{11 - [4 - (-9)]\}$ −2

86. $15 - \{25 + 2[3 - (-1)]\}$ −18

87. $-\frac{13}{10} + \frac{8}{15} - \left(-\frac{2}{5}\right)$ $-\frac{11}{30}$

88. $\frac{11}{14} - \left(-\frac{9}{7}\right) - \frac{3}{2}$ $\frac{4}{7}$

89. $\left(\frac{2}{3}-\frac{5}{9}\right)-\left(\frac{4}{3}-(-2)\right)$ $-\frac{29}{9}$

90. $\left(-\frac{9}{8}-\frac{1}{4}\right)-\left(-\frac{5}{6}+\frac{1}{8}\right)$ $-\frac{2}{3}$

91. $\sqrt{29+(-4)}-7$ -2

92. $8-\sqrt{98+(-3)+5}$ -2

93. $|10+(-3)|-|-12+(-6)|$ -11

94. $|6-8|+|12-5|$ 9

95. $\dfrac{3-4+5}{4+(-2)}$ 2

96. $\dfrac{12-14+6}{6+(-2)}$ 1

For Exercises 97–104, evaluate each expression for $a=-2$, $b=-6$, and $c=-1$.

97. $(a+b)-c$ -7

98. $(a-b)+c$ 3

99. $a-(b+c)$ 5

100. $a+(b-c)$ -7

101. $(a-b)-c$ 5

102. $(a+b)+c$ -9

103. $a-(b-c)$ 3

104. $a+(b+c)$ -9

Problem Recognition Exercises

Addition and Subtraction of Real Numbers

1. State the rule for adding two negative numbers. Add their absolute values and apply a negative sign.

2. State the rule for adding a negative number to a positive number. Subtract the smaller absolute value from the larger absolute value. Apply the sign of the number with the larger absolute value.

For Exercises 3–10, perform the indicated operations.

3. **a.** $14+(-8)$ 6 **b.** $-14+8$ -6 **c.** $-14+(-8)$ -22 **d.** $14-(-8)$ 22 **e.** $-14-8$ -22

4. **a.** $-5-(-3)$ -2 **b.** $-5+(-3)$ -8 **c.** $-5-3$ -8 **d.** $-5+3$ -2 **e.** $5-(-3)$ 8

5. **a.** $-25+25$ 0 **b.** $25-25$ 0 **c.** $25-(-25)$ 50 **d.** $-25-(-25)$ 0 **e.** $-25+(-25)$ -50

6. **a.** $\frac{1}{2}+\left(-\frac{2}{3}\right)$ $-\frac{1}{6}$ **b.** $-\frac{1}{2}+\left(\frac{2}{3}\right)$ $\frac{1}{6}$ **c.** $-\frac{1}{2}+\left(-\frac{2}{3}\right)$ $-\frac{7}{6}$ **d.** $\frac{1}{2}-\left(-\frac{2}{3}\right)$ $\frac{7}{6}$ **e.** $-\frac{1}{2}-\frac{2}{3}$ $-\frac{7}{6}$

7. **a.** $3.5-7.1$ -3.6 **b.** $3.5-(-7.1)$ 10.6 **c.** $-3.5+7.1$ 3.6 **d.** $-3.5-(-7.1)$ 3.6 **e.** $-3.5+(-7.1)$ -10.6

8. **a.** $6-1+4-5$ 4 **b.** $6-(1+4)-5$ -4 **c.** $6-(1+4-5)$ 6 **d.** $(6-1)-(4-5)$ 6

9. **a.** $-100-90-80$ -270 **b.** $-100-(90-80)$ -110 **c.** $-100+(90-80)$ -90 **d.** $-100-(90+80)$ -270

10. **a.** $-8-(-10)+20^2$ 402 **b.** $-8-(-10+20)^2$ -108 **c.** $[-8-(-10)+20]^2$ 484 **d.** $[-8-(-10)]^2+20$ 24

Multiplication and Division of Real Numbers

Section 1.6

Concepts

1. **Multiplication of Real Numbers**
2. **Exponential Expressions**
3. **Division of Real Numbers**
4. **Order of Operations**

1. Multiplication of Real Numbers

Multiplication of real numbers can be interpreted as repeated addition. For example:

$$3(4) = 4 + 4 + 4 = 12 \qquad \text{Add 3 groups of 4.}$$

$$3(-4) = -4 + (-4) + (-4) = -12 \qquad \text{Add 3 groups of } -4.$$

These results suggest that the product of a positive number and a negative number is *negative.* Consider the following pattern of products.

$$\begin{aligned} 4 \cdot 3 &= 12 \\ 4 \cdot 2 &= 8 \\ 4 \cdot 1 &= 4 \\ 4 \cdot 0 &= 0 \\ 4 \cdot (-1) &= -4 \\ 4 \cdot (-2) &= -8 \\ 4 \cdot (-3) &= -12 \end{aligned}$$

The pattern decreases by 4 with each row.

Thus, the product of a positive number and a negative number must be *negative* for the pattern to continue.

Now suppose we have a product of two negative numbers. To determine the sign, consider the following pattern of products.

$$\begin{aligned} -4 \cdot 3 &= -12 \\ -4 \cdot 2 &= -8 \\ -4 \cdot 1 &= -4 \\ -4 \cdot 0 &= 0 \\ -4 \cdot (-1) &= 4 \\ -4 \cdot (-2) &= 8 \\ -4 \cdot (-3) &= 12 \end{aligned}$$

The pattern increases by 4 with each row.

Thus, the product of two negative numbers must be *positive* for the pattern to continue.

From the first four rows, we see that the product increases by 4 for each row. For the pattern to continue, it follows that the product of two negative numbers must be *positive.*

We now summarize the rules for multiplying real numbers.

Multiplying Real Numbers

- The product of two real numbers with the *same* sign is positive.

  Examples: $(5)(6) = 30$
  $(-4)(-10) = 40$
- The product of two real numbers with *different* signs is negative.

  Examples: $(-2)(5) = -10$
  $(4)(-9) = -36$
- The product of any real number and zero is zero.

  Examples: $(8)(0) = 0$
  $(0)(-6) = 0$

Classroom Examples: p. 71, Exercises 8 and 14

Example 1 **Multiplying Real Numbers**

Multiply the real numbers.

a. $-8(-4)$ **b.** $-2.5(-1.7)$ **c.** $-7(10)$

d. $\frac{1}{2}(-8)$ **e.** $0(-8.3)$ **f.** $-\frac{2}{7}\left(-\frac{7}{2}\right)$

Solution:

a. $-8(-4) = 32$ — *Same* signs. Product is positive.

b. $-2.5(-1.7) = 4.25$ — *Same* signs. Product is positive.

c. $-7(10) = -70$ — *Different* signs. Product is negative.

d. $\frac{1}{2}(-8) = -4$ — *Different* signs. Product is negative.

e. $0(-8.3) = 0$ — The product of any real number and zero is zero.

f. $-\frac{2}{7}\left(-\frac{7}{2}\right) = \frac{14}{14}$ — *Same* signs. Product is positive.

$=1$ — Simplify.

Skill Practice Multiply.

1. $-9(-3)$ **2.** $-1.5(-1.5)$ **3.** $-6(4)$

4. $\frac{1}{3}(-15)$ **5.** $0(-4.1)$ **6.** $-\frac{5}{9}\left(-\frac{9}{5}\right)$

Observe the pattern for repeated multiplications.

$(-1)(-1)$
$= 1$

$\underbrace{(-1)(-1)}(-1)$
$= (1)(-1)$
$= -1$

$\underbrace{(-1)(-1)}(-1)(-1)$
$= \underbrace{(1)(-1)}(-1)$
$= (-1)(-1)$
$= 1$

$\underbrace{(-1)(-1)}(-1)(-1)(-1)$
$= \underbrace{(1)(-1)}(-1)(-1)$
$= \underbrace{(-1)(-1)}(-1)$
$= (1)(-1)$
$= -1$

The pattern demonstrated in these examples indicates that

- The product of an even number of negative factors is positive.
- The product of an odd number of negative factors is negative.

2. Exponential Expressions

Recall that for any real number b and any positive integer, n:

$$b^n = \underbrace{b \cdot b \cdot b \cdot b \cdot \ldots b}_{n \text{ factors of } b}$$

Be particularly careful when evaluating exponential expressions involving negative numbers. An exponential expression with a negative base is written with parentheses around the base, such as $(-2)^4$.

Answers

1. 27 **2.** 2.25 **3.** −24
4. −5 **5.** 0 **6.** 1

To evaluate $(-2)^4$, the base -2 is used as a factor four times:

$$(-2)^4 = (-2)(-2)(-2)(-2) = 16$$

If parentheses are *not* used, the expression -2^4 has a different meaning:

- The expression -2^4 has a base of 2 (not -2) and can be interpreted as $-1 \cdot 2^4$.

$$-2^4 = -1(2)(2)(2)(2) = -16$$

- The expression -2^4 can also be interpreted as the opposite of 2^4.

$$-2^4 = -(2 \cdot 2 \cdot 2 \cdot 2) = -16$$

TIP: The following expressions are translated as:
$-(-3)$: opposite of negative 3
-3^2: opposite of 3 squared
$(-3)^2$: negative 3, squared

Example 2 **Evaluating Exponential Expressions**

Classroom Examples: p. 71, Exercises 16, 18, 20 and 22

Simplify.

a. $(-5)^2$ **b.** -5^2 **c.** $(-0.4)^3$ **d.** -0.4^3 **e.** $\left(-\frac{1}{2}\right)^3$

Solution:

a. $(-5)^2 = (-5)(-5) = 25$ Multiply two factors of -5.

b. $-5^2 = -1(5)(5) = -25$ Multiply -1 by two factors of 5.

c. $(-0.4)^3 = (-0.4)(-0.4)(-0.4) = -0.064$ Multiply three factors of -0.4.

d. $-0.4^3 = -1(0.4)(0.4)(0.4) = -0.064$ Multiply -1 by three factors of 0.4.

e. $\left(-\frac{1}{2}\right)^3 = \left(-\frac{1}{2}\right)\left(-\frac{1}{2}\right)\left(-\frac{1}{2}\right) = -\frac{1}{8}$ Multiply three factors of $-\frac{1}{2}$.

Avoiding Mistakes

The negative sign is not part of the base unless it is in parentheses with the base. Thus, in the expression -5^2, the exponent applies only to 5 and not to the negative sign.

Skill Practice Simplify.

7. $(-7)^2$ **8.** -7^2 **9.** $\left(-\frac{2}{3}\right)^3$ **10.** -0.2^3

3. Division of Real Numbers

Two numbers are *reciprocals* if their product is 1. For example, $-\frac{2}{7}$ and $-\frac{7}{2}$ are reciprocals because $-\frac{2}{7}(-\frac{7}{2}) = 1$. Symbolically, if a is a nonzero real number, then the reciprocal of a is $\frac{1}{a}$ because $a \cdot \frac{1}{a} = 1$. This definition also implies that a number and its reciprocal have the same sign.

The Reciprocal of a Real Number

Let a be a nonzero real number. Then, the **reciprocal** of a is $\frac{1}{a}$.

Recall that to subtract two real numbers, we add the opposite of the second number to the first number. In a similar way, division of real numbers is defined in terms of multiplication. To divide two real numbers, we multiply the first number by the reciprocal of the second number.

Answers

7. 49 **8.** -49
9. $-\frac{8}{27}$ **10.** -0.008

Division of Real Numbers

Let a and b be real numbers such that $b \neq 0$. Then, $a \div b = a \cdot \frac{1}{b}$.

Consider the quotient $10 \div 5$. The reciprocal of 5 is $\frac{1}{5}$, so we have

$$10 \div 5 = 2 \qquad \text{or equivalently,} \qquad 10 \cdot \frac{1}{5} = 2$$

(multiply: $\div$ becomes $\cdot$; reciprocal: 5 becomes $\frac{1}{5}$)

Because division of real numbers can be expressed in terms of multiplication, then the sign rules that apply to multiplication also apply to division.

Dividing Real Numbers

- The quotient of two real numbers with the *same* sign is positive.

  Examples: $24 \div 4 = 6$

  $-36 \div (-9) = 4$

- The quotient of two real numbers with *different* signs is negative.

  Examples: $100 \div (-5) = -20$

  $-12 \div 4 = -3$

Classroom Examples: p. 71, Exercises 24 and 26

Example 3 Dividing Real Numbers

Divide the real numbers.

a. $200 \div (-10)$ **b.** $\frac{-48}{16}$ **c.** $\frac{-6.25}{-1.25}$ **d.** $\frac{-9}{-5}$

Solution:

a. $200 \div (-10) = -20$ *Different* signs. Quotient is negative.

b. $\frac{-48}{16} = -3$ *Different* signs. Quotient is negative.

c. $\frac{-6.25}{-1.25} = 5$ *Same* signs. Quotient is positive.

d. $\frac{-9}{-5} = \frac{9}{5}$ *Same* signs. Quotient is positive.

Because 5 does not divide into 9 evenly the answer can be left as a fraction.

TIP: If the numerator and denominator of a fraction are both negative, then the quotient is positive. Therefore, $\frac{-9}{-5}$ can be simplified to $\frac{9}{5}$.

Skill Practice Divide.

11. $-14 \div 7$ **12.** $\frac{-18}{3}$ **13.** $\frac{-7.6}{-1.9}$ **14.** $\frac{-7}{-3}$

Answers

11. -2 **12.** -6 **13.** 4 **14.** $\frac{7}{3}$

Example 4 **Dividing Real Numbers**

Divide the real numbers.

a. $15 \div (-25)$ **b.** $-\frac{3}{14} \div \frac{9}{7}$

Solution:

a. $15 \div (-25)$ *Different* signs. Quotient is negative.

$= \frac{15}{-25}$

$= -\frac{3}{5}$

b. $-\frac{3}{14} \div \frac{9}{7}$ *Different* signs. Quotient is negative.

$= -\frac{3}{14} \cdot \frac{7}{9}$ Multiply by the reciprocal of $\frac{9}{7}$ which is $\frac{7}{9}$.

$= -\frac{\overset{1}{\cancel{3}}}{\underset{2}{\cancel{14}}} \cdot \frac{\overset{1}{\cancel{7}}}{\underset{3}{\cancel{9}}}$ Divide out common factors.

$= -\frac{1}{6}$ Multiply the fractions.

Skill Practice Divide.

15. $12 \div (-18)$ **16.** $\frac{3}{4} \div \left(-\frac{9}{16}\right)$

Classroom Examples: pp. 71–72, Exercises 30 and 78

TIP: If the numerator and denominator of a fraction have opposite signs, then the quotient will be negative. Therefore, a fraction has the same value whether the negative sign is written in the numerator, in the denominator, or in front of the fraction.

$$\frac{-3}{5} = \frac{3}{-5} = -\frac{3}{5}$$

Multiplication can be used to check any division problem. If $\frac{a}{b} = c$, then $bc = a$ (provided that $b \neq 0$). For example:

$$\frac{8}{-4} = -2 \rightarrow \underline{\text{Check}}: (-4)(-2) = 8 \checkmark$$

This relationship between multiplication and division can be used to investigate division problems involving the number zero.

1. The quotient of 0 and any nonzero number is 0. For example:

$$\frac{0}{6} = 0 \qquad \text{because } 6 \cdot 0 = 0 \checkmark$$

2. The quotient of any nonzero number and 0 is undefined. For example:

$$\frac{6}{0} = ?$$

   Finding the quotient $\frac{6}{0}$ is equivalent to asking, "What number times zero will equal 6?" That is, $(0)(?) = 6$. No real number satisfies this condition. Therefore, we say that division by zero is undefined.

3. The quotient of 0 and 0 cannot be determined. Evaluating an expression of the form $\frac{0}{0} = ?$ is equivalent to asking, "What number times zero will equal 0?" That is, $(0)(?) = 0$. Any real number will satisfy this requirement; however, expressions involving $\frac{0}{0}$ are usually discussed in advanced mathematics courses.

Instructor Note: Memory Device: Zero under the line, division undefined.

Answers

15. $-\frac{2}{3}$ **16.** $-\frac{4}{3}$

Division Involving Zero

Let a represent a nonzero real number. Then,

1. $\dfrac{0}{a} = 0$ **2.** $\dfrac{a}{0}$ is undefined

4. Order of Operations

Classroom Example: p. 72, Exercise 96

Example 5 Applying the Order of Operations

Simplify. $-8 + 8 \div (-2) \div (-6)$

Solution:

Animation

$-8 + 8 \div (-2) \div (-6)$	
$= -8 + (-4) \div (-6)$	Perform division before addition.
$= -8 + \dfrac{4}{6}$	The quotient of -4 and -6 is positive $\frac{4}{6}$ or $\frac{2}{3}$.
$= -\dfrac{8}{1} + \dfrac{2}{3}$	Write -8 as a fraction.
$= -\dfrac{24}{3} + \dfrac{2}{3}$	Get a common denominator.
$= -\dfrac{22}{3}$	Add.

Skill Practice Simplify.

17. $-36 + 36 \div (-4) \div (-3)$

Classroom Example: p. 72, Exercise 110

Example 6 Applying the Order of Operations

Simplify. $\dfrac{24 - 2[-3 + (5 - 8)]^2}{2|-12 + 3|}$

Solution:

$\dfrac{24 - 2[-3 + (5 - 8)]^2}{2\|-12 + 3\|}$	Simplify numerator and denominator separately.
$= \dfrac{24 - 2[-3 + (-3)]^2}{2\|-9\|}$	Simplify within the inner parentheses and absolute value.
$= \dfrac{24 - 2[-6]^2}{2(9)}$	Simplify within brackets, [ ]. Simplify the absolute value.
$= \dfrac{24 - 2(36)}{2(9)}$	Simplify exponents.
$= \dfrac{24 - 72}{18}$	Perform multiplication before subtraction.
$= \dfrac{-48}{18}$ or $-\dfrac{8}{3}$	Simplify to lowest terms.

Answer

17. -33

Skill Practice Simplify.

18. $\dfrac{100 - 3[-1 + (2 - 6)^2]}{|20 - 25|}$

Example 7 **Evaluating Algebraic Expressions**

Classroom Example: p. 73, Exercise 112

Given $y = -6$, evaluate the expressions.

a. y^2 **b.** $-y^2$

Solution:

a. y^2

$= (\quad)^2$	When substituting a number for a variable, use parentheses.
$= (-6)^2$	Substitute $y = -6$.
$= 36$	Square -6, that is, $(-6)(-6) = 36$.

b. $-y^2$

$= -(\quad)^2$	When substituting a number for a variable, use parentheses.
$= -(-6)^2$	Substitute $y = -6$.
$= -(36)$	Square -6 within parentheses to get 36.
$= -36$	Multiply by -1.

Skill Practice Given $a = -7$, evaluate the expressions.

19. a^2 **20.** $-a^2$

Answers

18. 11 **19.** 49 **20.** -49

Calculator Connections

Topic: Evaluating Exponential Expressions with Positive and Negative Bases

Be particularly careful when raising a negative number to an even power on a calculator. For example, the expressions $(-4)^2$ and -4^2 have different values. That is, $(-4)^2 = 16$ and $-4^2 = -16$. Verify these expressions on a calculator.

Scientific Calculator:

To evaluate $(-4)^2$

Enter: (4 +/-) x^2 **Result:** 16

To evaluate -4^2 on a scientific calculator, it is important to square 4 first and then take its opposite.

Enter: 4 x^2 +/- **Result:** -16

Graphing Calculator:

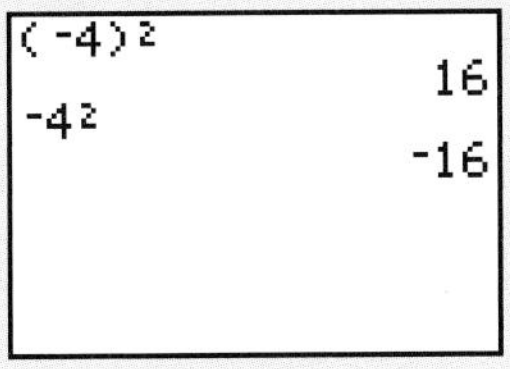

The graphing calculator allows for several methods of denoting the multiplication of two real numbers. For example, consider the product of −8 and 4.

```
-8*4
                -32
-8(4)
                -32
(-8)(4)
                -32
```

Calculator Exercises

Simplify the expression without the use of a calculator. Then use the calculator to verify your answer.

1. $-6(5)$ −30 **2.** $\dfrac{-5.2}{2.6}$ −2 **3.** $(-5)(-5)(-5)(-5)$ 625 **4.** $(-5)^4$ 625 **5.** -5^4 −625

6. -2.4^2 −5.76 **7.** $(-2.4)^2$ 5.76 **8.** $(-1)(-1)(-1)$ −1 **9.** $\dfrac{-8.4}{-2.1}$ 4 **10.** $90 \div (-5)(2)$ −36

Section 1.6 Practice Exercises

Study Skills Exercise

For additional exercises, see Classroom Activities 1.6A–1.6D in the *Student's Resource Manual* at www.mhhe.com/moh.

To familiarize yourself with some of the helpful features of the text, look through this section and write down a page number that contains:

a. An Avoiding Mistakes box ______________

b. A Tip box ______________

c. A key term (shown in bold) ______________

Vocabulary and Key Concepts

1. a. If a is a nonzero real number, then the reciprocal of a is $\underline{\frac{1}{a}}$.

b. If either a or b is zero then the product $ab = \underline{0}$.

c. If $a = 0$, and $b \neq 0$, then $\frac{a}{b} = \underline{0}$.

d. If $a \neq 0$ and $b = 0$, then $\frac{a}{b}$ is undefined.

e. If a and b have the same sign, then the product ab is (choose one: positive or negative). positive

f. If a and b have different signs, then the quotient $\frac{a}{b}$ is (choose one: positive or negative). negative

g. The product of a number and its reciprocal is $\underline{1}$. For example $-\frac{2}{3} \cdot \left(-\frac{3}{2}\right) = 1$

h. Which of the following expressions represents the product of 2 and x? All of these

a. $2x$ **b.** $2 \cdot x$ **c.** $2(x)$ **d.** $(2)x$ **e.** $(2)(x)$

Review Exercises

For Exercises 2–6, determine if the expression is true or false.

2. $6 + (-2) > -5 + 6$ True

3. $|-6| + |-14| \le |-3| + |-17|$ True

4. $\sqrt{36} - |-6| > 0$ False

5. $\sqrt{9} + |-3| \le 0$ False

6. $14 - |-3| \ge 12 + \sqrt{25}$ False

Concept 1: Multiplication of Real Numbers

For Exercises 7–14, multiply the real numbers. **(See Example 1.)**

7. $8(-7)$ -56

8. $(-3) \cdot 4$ -12

9. $(-11)(-13)$ 143

10. $(-5)(-26)$ 130

11. $(-2.2)(5.8)$ -12.76

12. $(9.1)(-4.5)$ -40.95

13. $\left(-\frac{2}{3}\right)\left(-\frac{9}{8}\right)$ $\frac{3}{4}$

14. $\left(-\frac{5}{4}\right)\left(-\frac{12}{25}\right)$ $\frac{3}{5}$

Concept 2: Exponential Expressions

For Exercises 15–22, simplify the exponential expressions. **(See Example 2.)**

15. $(-6)^2$ 36

16. $(-10)^2$ 100

17. -6^2 -36

18. -10^2 -100

19. $\left(-\frac{3}{5}\right)^3$ $-\frac{27}{125}$

20. $\left(-\frac{5}{2}\right)^3$ $-\frac{125}{8}$

21. $(-0.2)^4$ 0.0016

22. $(-0.1)^4$ 0.0001

Concept 3: Division of Real Numbers

For Exercises 23–30, divide the real numbers. **(See Examples 3–4.)**

23. $\frac{54}{-9}$ -6

24. $\frac{-27}{3}$ -9

25. $\frac{-15}{-17}$ $\frac{15}{17}$

26. $\frac{-21}{-16}$ $\frac{21}{16}$

27. $\frac{-14}{-14}$ 1

28. $\frac{-21}{-21}$ 1

29. $\frac{13}{-65}$ $-\frac{1}{5}$

30. $\frac{7}{-77}$ $-\frac{1}{11}$

For Exercises 31–38, show how multiplication can be used to check the division problems.

31. $\frac{14}{-2} = -7$
$(-2)(-7) = 14$

32. $\frac{-18}{-6} = 3$
$(-6)(3) = -18$

33. $\frac{0}{-5} = 0$
$-5 \cdot 0 = 0$

34. $\frac{0}{-4} = 0$
$-4 \cdot 0 = 0$

35. $\frac{6}{0}$ is undefined
No number multiplied by zero equals 6.

36. $\frac{-4}{0}$ is undefined
No number multiplied by zero equals -4.

37. $-24 \div (-6) = 4$
$(-6)(4) = -24$

38. $-18 \div 2 = -9$
$(2)(-9) = -18$

Mixed Exercises

For Exercises 39–78, multiply or divide as indicated.

39. $2 \cdot 3$ 6

40. $8 \cdot 6$ 48

41. $2(-3)$ -6

42. $8(-6)$ -48

43. $(-24) \div 3$ -8

44. $(-52) \div 2$ -26

45. $(-24) \div (-3)$ 8

46. $(-52) \div (-2)$ 26

47. $-6 \cdot 0$ 0

48. $-8 \cdot 0$ 0

49. $-18 \div 0$ Undefined

50. $-42 \div 0$ Undefined

51. $0\left(-\frac{2}{5}\right)$ 0

52. $0\left(-\frac{1}{8}\right)$ 0

53. $0 \div \left(-\frac{1}{10}\right)$ 0

54. $0 \div \left(\frac{4}{9}\right)$ 0

55. $\frac{-9}{6}$ $-\frac{3}{2}$

56. $\frac{-15}{10}$ $-\frac{3}{2}$

57. $\frac{-30}{-100}$ $\frac{3}{10}$

58. $\frac{-250}{-1000}$ $\frac{1}{4}$

59. $\frac{26}{-13}$ -2

60. $\frac{52}{-4}$ -13

61. $1.72(-4.6)$ -7.912

62. $361.3(-14.9)$ -5383.37

63. $-0.02(-4.6)$ 0.092

64. $-0.06(-2.15)$ 0.129

65. $\frac{14.4}{-2.4}$ -6

66. $\frac{50.4}{-6.3}$ -8

67. $\frac{-5.25}{-2.5}$ 2.1

68. $\frac{-8.5}{-27.2}$ 0.3125

69. $(-3)^2$ 9

70. $(-7)^2$ 49

71. -3^2 -9

72. -7^2 -49

73. $\left(-\frac{4}{3}\right)^3$ $-\frac{64}{27}$

74. $\left(-\frac{1}{5}\right)^3$ $-\frac{1}{125}$

75. $(-6.8) \div (-0.02)$ 340

76. $(-12.3) \div (-0.03)$ 410

77. $\left(-\frac{7}{8}\right) \div \left(-\frac{9}{16}\right)$ $\frac{14}{9}$

78. $\left(-\frac{22}{23}\right) \div \left(-\frac{11}{3}\right)$ $\frac{6}{23}$

Concept 4: Order of Operations

For Exercises 79–110, perform the indicated operations. **(See Examples 5–6.)**

79. $(-2)(-5)(-3)$ -30

80. $(-6)(-1)(-10)$ -60

81. $(-8)(-4)(-1)(-3)$ 96

82. $(-6)(-3)(-1)(-5)$ 90

83. $100 \div (-10) \div (-5)$ 2

84. $150 \div (-15) \div (-2)$ 5

85. $-12 \div (-6) \div (-2)$ -1

86. $-36 \div (-2) \div 6$ 3

87. $\frac{2}{5} \cdot \frac{1}{3} \cdot \left(-\frac{10}{11}\right)$ $-\frac{4}{33}$

88. $\left(-\frac{9}{8}\right) \cdot \left(-\frac{2}{3}\right) \cdot \left(1\frac{5}{12}\right)$ $\frac{17}{16}$

89. $\left(1\frac{1}{3}\right) \div 3 \div \left(-\frac{7}{9}\right)$ $-\frac{4}{7}$

90. $-\frac{7}{8} \div \left(3\frac{1}{4}\right) \div (-2)$ $\frac{7}{52}$

91. $12 \div (-2)(4)$ -24

92. $(-6) \cdot 7 \div (-2)$ 21

93. $\left(-\frac{12}{5}\right) \div (-6) \cdot \left(-\frac{1}{8}\right)$ $-\frac{1}{20}$

94. $10 \cdot \frac{1}{3} \div \frac{25}{6}$ $\frac{4}{5}$

95. $8 - 2^3 \cdot 5 + 3 - (-6)$ -23

96. $-14 \div (-7) - 8 \cdot 2 + 3^3$ 13

97. $-(2-8)^2 \div (-6) \cdot 2$ 12

98. $-(3-5)^2 \cdot 6 \div (-4)$ 6

99. $\frac{6(-4) - 2(5-8)}{-6-3-5}$ $\frac{9}{7}$

100. $\frac{3(-4) - 5(9-11)}{-9-2-3}$ $\frac{1}{7}$

101. $\frac{-4+5}{(-2) \cdot 5 + 10}$ Undefined

102. $\frac{-3+10}{2(-4)+8}$ Undefined

103. $-4 - 3[2 - (-5+3)] - 8 \cdot 2^2$ -48

104. $-6 - 5[-4 - (6-12)] + (-5)^2$ 9

105. $-|-1| - |5|$ -6

106. $-|-10| - |6|$ -16

107. $\frac{|2-9| - |5-7|}{10-15}$ -1

108. $\frac{|-2+6| - |3-5|}{13-11}$ 1

109. $\frac{6 - 3[2-(6-8)]^2}{-2|2-5|}$ 7

110. $\frac{12 - 4[-6-(5-8)]^2}{4|6-10|}$ $-\frac{3}{2}$

For Exercises 111–116, evaluate the expression for $x = -2$, $y = -4$, and $z = 6$. **(See Example 7.)**

111. $-x^2$ -4

112. x^2 4

113. $4(2x - z)$ -40

114. $6(3x + y)$ -60

115. $\dfrac{3x + 2y}{y}$ $\dfrac{7}{2}$

116. $\dfrac{2z - y}{x}$ -8

117. Is the expression $\dfrac{10}{5x}$ equal to $10/5x$? Explain.
No. The first expression is equivalent to $10 \div (5x)$. The second is $10 \div 5 \cdot x$.

118. Is the expression $10/(5x)$ equal to $\dfrac{10}{5x}$? Explain.
Yes, the parentheses indicate that the divisor is the quantity $5x$.

For Exercises 119–126, write each English phrase as an algebraic expression. Then evaluate the expression.

119. The product of -3.75 and 0.3
$-3.75(0.3)$; -1.125

120. The product of -0.4 and -1.258
$(-0.4)(-1.258)$; 0.5032

121. The quotient of $\frac{16}{5}$ and $\left(-\frac{8}{9}\right)$ $\quad \dfrac{16}{5} \div \left(-\dfrac{8}{9}\right)$; $-\dfrac{18}{5}$

122. The quotient of $\left(-\frac{3}{14}\right)$ and $\frac{1}{7}$ $\quad -\dfrac{3}{14} \div \dfrac{1}{7}$; $-\dfrac{3}{2}$

123. The number -0.4 plus the quantity 6 times -0.42
$-0.4 + 6(-0.42)$; -2.92

124. The number 0.5 plus the quantity -2 times 0.125
$0.5 + (-2)(0.125)$; 0.25

125. The number $-\frac{1}{4}$ minus the quantity 6 times $-\frac{1}{3}$
$-\dfrac{1}{4} - 6\left(-\dfrac{1}{3}\right)$; $\dfrac{7}{4}$

126. Negative five minus the quantity $\left(-\frac{5}{6}\right)$ times $\frac{3}{8}$
$-5 - \left(-\dfrac{5}{6}\right)\dfrac{3}{8}$; $-\dfrac{75}{16}$

127. For 3 weeks, Jim pays \$2 a week for lottery tickets. Jim has one winning ticket for \$3. Write an expression that describes his net gain or loss. How much money has Jim won or lost? $3(-2) + 3 = -3$; loss of \$3

128. Stephanie pays \$2 a week for 6 weeks for lottery tickets. Stephanie has one winning ticket for \$5. Write an expression that describes her net gain or loss. How much money has Stephanie won or lost? $-2(6) + 5 = -7$; loss of \$7

© Buena Vista Images/Getty Images RF

129. Lorne sells ads for the local newspaper and has a quota for the number of ads he must sell each week. For the first two days of the week, Lorne was 5 above his daily quota. For the last three days of the week, Lorne was 3 below his daily quota. Write an expression that describes the net amount he was above or below his quota. Interpret the result. $2(5) + 3(-3) = 1$; Lorne was 1 sale above quota for the week.

130. Valerie trades stocks each day and analyzes her results at the end of the week. The first day of the week she had a profit of \$650. The next two days she had a loss of \$400 each day and the last two days she had a loss of \$150 each day. Write an expression that describes Valerie's profit or loss for the week. Interpret the result.
$650 + 2(-400) + 2(-150) = -450$; Valerie lost \$450 for the week.

131. A pediatrician analyzed the effect of a special baby food on five toddlers. He recorded the amount of weight lost or gained (in ounces) by each child for one month as shown in the table.

Baby	A	B	C	D	E
Gain/Loss (oz)	12	−15	4	−9	3

$\dfrac{12 + (-15) + 4 + (-9) + 3}{5} = -1$; The average loss was 1 oz.

Write an expression to calculate the average gain or loss in weight of the children and then simplify. Interpret your answer. (*Hint*: To find the *average* (mean) of a set of values, add the values and divide by the number of values.)

132. At the end of a 2-month class, a personal trainer analyzed the effect of her new exercise routine by recording the gain or loss (in inches) in waist measurements of her clients. The results are shown in the table.

Client	A	B	C	D	E	F
Gain/Loss (in.)	−1.5	−2	1.5	2.5	−3	−0.5

Write an expression to calculate the average gain or loss in waist measurement and then simplify. Interpret your answer.
$\dfrac{-1.5 + (-2) + 1.5 + 2.5 + (-3) + (-0.5)}{6} = -0.5$; The average loss was 0.5 in.

133. Evaluate the expressions in parts (a) and (b).

a. $-4 - 3 - 2 - 1$ -10

b. $-4(-3)(-2)(-1)$ 24

c. Explain the difference between the operations in parts (a) and (b). In part (a), we subtract; in part (b), we multiply.

134. Evaluate the expressions in parts (a) and (b).

a. $-10 - 9 - 8 - 7$ -34

b. $-10(-9)(-8)(-7)$ 5040

c. Explain the difference between the operations in parts (a) and (b). In part (a), we subtract; in part (b), we multiply.

Problem Recognition Exercises

Adding, Subtracting, Multiplying, and Dividing Real Numbers

Perform the indicated operations.

1. a. $-8 - (-4)$ -4 **b.** $-8(-4)$ 32 **c.** $-8 + (-4)$ -12 **d.** $-8 \div (-4)$ 2

2. a. $12 + (-2)$ 10 **b.** $12 - (-2)$ 14 **c.** $12(-2)$ -24 **d.** $12 \div (-2)$ -6

3. a. $-36 + 9$ -27 **b.** $-36(9)$ -324 **c.** $-36 \div 9$ -4 **d.** $-36 - 9$ -45

4. a. $27 - (-3)$ 30 **b.** $27 + (-3)$ 24 **c.** $27(-3)$ -81 **d.** $27 \div (-3)$ -9

5. a. $-5(-10)$ 50 **b.** $-5 + (-10)$ -15 **c.** $-5 \div (-10)$ $\frac{1}{2}$ **d.** $-5 - (-10)$ 5

6. a. $-20 \div 4$ -5 **b.** $-20 - 4$ -24 **c.** $-20 + 4$ -16 **d.** $-20(4)$ -80

7. a. $-4(-16)$ 64 **b.** $-4 - (-16)$ 12 **c.** $-4 \div (-16)$ $\frac{1}{4}$ **d.** $-4 + (-16)$ -20

8. a. $-21 \div 3$ -7 **b.** $-21 - 3$ -24 **c.** $-21(3)$ -63 **d.** $-21 + 3$ -18

9. a. $80(-5)$ -400 **b.** $80 - (-5)$ 85 **c.** $80 \div (-5)$ -16 **d.** $80 + (-5)$ 75

10. a. $-14 - (-21)$ 7 **b.** $-14(-21)$ 294 **c.** $-14 \div (-21)$ $\frac{2}{3}$ **d.** $-14 + (-21)$ -35

11. a. $|-6| + |2|$ 8 **b.** $|-6 + 2|$ 4 **c.** $|-6| - |-2|$ 4 **d.** $|-6 - 2|$ 8

12. a. $-|9| - |-7|$ -16 **b.** $|-9| - |-7|$ 2 **c.** $-|9 - 7|$ -2 **d.** $|-9 - 7|$ 16

Properties of Real Numbers and Simplifying Expressions

Section 1.7

Concepts

1. Commutative Properties of Real Numbers
2. Associative Properties of Real Numbers
3. Identity and Inverse Properties of Real Numbers
4. Distributive Property of Multiplication over Addition
5. Algebraic Expressions

1. Commutative Properties of Real Numbers

When getting dressed, it makes no difference whether you put on your left shoe first and then your right shoe, or vice versa. This example illustrates a process in which the order does not affect the outcome. Such a process or operation is said to be *commutative*.

In algebra, the operations of addition and multiplication are commutative because the order in which we add or multiply two real numbers does not affect the result. For example:

$$10+5=5+10 \quad \text{and} \quad 10\cdot 5=5\cdot 10$$

Commutative Properties of Real Numbers

If a and b are real numbers, then

1. $a+b=b+a$ — **commutative property of addition**
2. $ab=ba$ — **commutative property of multiplication**

It is important to note that although the operations of addition and multiplication are commutative, subtraction and division are *not* commutative. For example:

$$\underbrace{10-5}_{5} \neq \underbrace{5-10}_{-5} \quad \text{and} \quad \underbrace{10\div 5}_{2} \neq \underbrace{5\div 10}_{\frac{1}{2}}$$

Example 1 Applying the Commutative Property of Addition

Classroom Example: p. 85, Exercise 16

Use the commutative property of addition to rewrite each expression.

a. $-3+(-7)$ **b.** $3x^3+5x^4$

Solution:

a. $-3+(-7)=-7+(-3)$

b. $3x^3+5x^4=5x^4+3x^3$

Skill Practice Use the commutative property of addition to rewrite each expression.

1. $-5+9$ **2.** $7y+x$

Recall that subtraction is not a commutative operation. However, if we rewrite $a-b$, as $a+(-b)$, we can apply the commutative property of addition. This is demonstrated in Example 2.

Answers

1. $9+(-5)$ **2.** $x+7y$

Classroom Example: p. 85, Exercise 24

Example 2 **Applying the Commutative Property of Addition**

Rewrite the expression in terms of addition. Then apply the commutative property of addition.

a. $5a - 3b$ **b.** $z^2 - \frac{1}{4}$

Solution:

a. $5a - 3b$

$= 5a + (-3b)$ Rewrite subtraction as addition of $-3b$.

$= -3b + 5a$ Apply the commutative property of addition.

b. $z^2 - \frac{1}{4}$

$= z^2 + \left(-\frac{1}{4}\right)$ Rewrite subtraction as addition of $-\frac{1}{4}$.

$= -\frac{1}{4} + z^2$ Apply the commutative property of addition.

Skill Practice Rewrite each expression in terms of addition. Then apply the commutative property of addition.

3. $8m - 2n$ **4.** $\frac{1}{3}x - \frac{3}{4}$

Classroom Example: p. 85, Exercise 22

Example 3 **Applying the Commutative Property of Multiplication**

Use the commutative property of multiplication to rewrite each expression.

a. $12(-6)$ **b.** $x \cdot 4$

Solution:

a. $12(-6) = -6(12)$

b. $x \cdot 4 = 4 \cdot x$ (or simply $4x$)

Skill Practice Use the commutative property of multiplication to rewrite each expression.

5. $-2(5)$ **6.** $y \cdot 6$

2. Associative Properties of Real Numbers

The associative property of real numbers states that the manner in which three or more real numbers are grouped under addition or multiplication will not affect the outcome. For example:

$$(5 + 10) + 2 = 5 + (10 + 2) \quad \text{and} \quad (5 \cdot 10)2 = 5(10 \cdot 2)$$
$$15 + 2 = 5 + 12 \qquad (50)2 = 5(20)$$
$$17 = 17 \qquad 100 = 100$$

Answers

3. $8m + (-2n); -2n + 8m$

4. $\frac{1}{3}x + \left(-\frac{3}{4}\right); -\frac{3}{4} + \frac{1}{3}x$

5. $5(-2)$ **6.** $6y$

Associative Properties of Real Numbers

If a, b, and c represent real numbers, then

1. $(a + b) + c = a + (b + c)$ **associative property of addition**
2. $(ab)c = a(bc)$ **associative property of multiplication**

Example 4 Applying the Associative Property

Classroom Examples: p. 85, Exercises 28 and 30

Use the associative property of addition or multiplication to rewrite each expression. Then simplify the expression if possible.

a. $(y + 5) + 6$ **b.** $4(5z)$ **c.** $-\frac{3}{2}\left(-\frac{2}{3}w\right)$

Solution:

a. $(y + 5) + 6$

$= y + (5 + 6)$ Apply the associative property of addition.

$= y + 11$ Simplify.

b. $4(5z)$

$= (4 \cdot 5)z$ Apply the associative property of multiplication.

$= 20z$ Simplify.

c. $-\frac{3}{2}\left(-\frac{2}{3}w\right)$

$= \left[-\frac{3}{2}\left(-\frac{2}{3}\right)\right]w$ Apply the associative property of multiplication.

$= 1w$ Simplify.

$= w$

Note: In most cases, a detailed application of the associative property will not be shown. Instead, the process will be written in one step, such as

$$(y + 5) + 6 = y + 11, \quad 4(5z) = 20z, \quad \text{and} \quad -\frac{3}{2}\left(-\frac{2}{3}w\right) = w$$

Skill Practice Use the associative property of addition or multiplication to rewrite each expression. Simplify if possible.

7. $(x + 4) + 3$ **8.** $-2(4x)$ **9.** $\frac{5}{4}\left(\frac{4}{5}t\right)$

3. Identity and Inverse Properties of Real Numbers

The number 0 has a special role under the operation of addition. Zero added to any real number does not change the number. Therefore, the number 0 is said to be the *additive identity* (also called the *identity element of addition*). For example:

$$-4 + 0 = -4 \quad 0 + 5.7 = 5.7 \quad 0 + \frac{3}{4} = \frac{3}{4}$$

Answers

7. $x + (4 + 3); x + 7$
8. $(-2 \cdot 4)x; -8x$
9. $\left(\frac{5}{4} \cdot \frac{4}{5}\right)t; t$

The number 1 has a special role under the operation of multiplication. Any real number multiplied by 1 does not change the number. Therefore, the number 1 is said to be the *multiplicative identity* (also called the *identity element of multiplication*). For example:

$$(-8)1 = -8 \quad 1(-2.85) = -2.85 \quad 1\left(\frac{1}{5}\right) = \frac{1}{5}$$

Identity Properties of Real Numbers

If a is a real number, then

1. $a + 0 = 0 + a = a$ **identity property of addition**
2. $a \cdot 1 = 1 \cdot a = a$ **identity property of multiplication**

The sum of a number and its opposite equals 0. For example, $-12 + 12 = 0$. For any real number, a, the opposite of a (also called the *additive inverse* of a) is $-a$ and $a + (-a) = -a + a = 0$. The inverse property of addition states that the sum of any number and its additive inverse is the identity element of addition, 0. For example:

Number	Additive Inverse (Opposite)	Sum
9	−9	$9 + (-9) = 0$
−21.6	21.6	$-21.6 + 21.6 = 0$
$\frac{2}{7}$	$-\frac{2}{7}$	$\frac{2}{7} + \left(-\frac{2}{7}\right) = 0$

If b is a nonzero real number, then the reciprocal of b (also called the *multiplicative inverse* of b) is $\frac{1}{b}$. The inverse property of multiplication states that the product of b and its multiplicative inverse is the identity element of multiplication, 1. Symbolically, we have $b \cdot \frac{1}{b} = \frac{1}{b} \cdot b = 1$. For example:

Number	Multiplicative Inverse (Reciprocal)	Product
7	$\frac{1}{7}$	$7 \cdot \frac{1}{7} = 1$
3.14	$\frac{1}{3.14}$	$3.14\left(\frac{1}{3.14}\right) = 1$
$-\frac{3}{5}$	$-\frac{5}{3}$	$-\frac{3}{5}\left(-\frac{5}{3}\right) = 1$

Inverse Properties of Real Numbers

If a is a real number and b is a nonzero real number, then

1. $a + (-a) = -a + a = 0$ **inverse property of addition**
2. $b \cdot \frac{1}{b} = \frac{1}{b} \cdot b = 1$ **inverse property of multiplication**

4. Distributive Property of Multiplication over Addition

The operations of addition and multiplication are related by an important property called the **distributive property of multiplication over addition**. Consider the expression $6(2 + 3)$. The order of operations indicates that the sum $2 + 3$ is evaluated first, and then the result is multiplied by 6:

$$6(2 + 3)$$
$$= 6(5)$$
$$= 30$$

Notice that the same result is obtained if the factor of 6 is multiplied by each of the numbers 2 and 3, and then their products are added:

$6(2 + 3)$ The factor of 6 is *distributed* to the numbers 2 and 3.

$= 6(2) + 6(3)$

$= 12 + 18$

$= 30$

The distributive property of multiplication over addition states that this is true in general.

TIP: The mathematical definition of the distributive property is consistent with the everyday meaning of the word *distribute*. To distribute means to "spread out from one to many." In the mathematical context, the factor *a* is distributed to both *b* and *c* in the parentheses.

Distributive Property of Multiplication over Addition

If *a, b,* and *c* are real numbers, then

$$a(b + c) = ab + ac \quad \text{and} \quad (b + c)a = ab + ac$$

Example 5 Applying the Distributive Property

Classroom Example: p. 85, Exercise 48

Apply the distributive property. $2(a + 6b + 7)$

Solution:

$2(a + 6b + 7)$

$= 2(a + 6b + 7)$

$= 2(a) + 2(6b) + 2(7)$ Apply the distributive property.

$= 2a + 12b + 14$ Simplify.

Skill Practice Apply the distributive property.

10. $7(x + 4y + z)$

Answer

10. $7x + 28y + 7z$

Because the difference of two expressions $a - b$ can be written in terms of addition as $a + (-b)$, the distributive property can be applied when the operation of subtraction is present within the parentheses. For example:

$5(y - 7)$	
$= 5[y + (-7)]$	Rewrite subtraction as addition of -7.
$= 5[y + (-7)]$	Apply the distributive property.
$= 5(y) + 5(-7)$	
$= 5y + (-35)$, or $5y - 35$	Simplify.

Classroom Example: p. 85, Exercise 60

Example 6 Applying the Distributive Property

Use the distributive property to rewrite each expression.

a. $-(-3a + 2b + 5c)$ **b.** $-6(2 - 4x)$

Solution:

a. $-(-3a + 2b + 5c)$

$= -1(-3a + 2b + 5c)$	The negative sign preceding the parentheses can be interpreted as taking the opposite of the quantity that follows or as $-1(-3a + 2b + 5c)$
$= -1(-3a + 2b + 5c)$	
$= -1(-3a) + (-1)(2b) + (-1)(5c)$	Apply the distributive property.
$= 3a + (-2b) + (-5c)$	Simplify.
$= 3a - 2b - 5c$	

TIP: Notice that a negative factor preceding the parentheses changes the signs of all the terms to which it is multiplied.

$$-1(-3a + 2b + 5c)$$
$$= +3a - 2b - 5c$$

b. $-6(2 - 4x)$

$= -6[2 + (-4x)]$	Change subtraction to addition of $-4x$.
$= -6[2 + (-4x)]$	Apply the distributive property. Notice that multiplying by -6 changes the signs of all terms to which it is applied.
$= -6(2) + (-6)(-4x)$	
$= -12 + 24x$	Simplify.

Skill Practice Use the distributive property to rewrite each expression.

11. $-(12x + 8y - 3z)$ **12.** $-6(-3a + 7b)$

Note: In most cases, the distributive property will be applied without as much detail as shown in Examples 5 and 6. Instead, the distributive property will be applied in one step.

$2(a + 6b + 7)$	$-(3a + 2b + 5c)$	$-6(2 - 4x)$
1 step $= 2a + 12b + 14$	1 step $= -3a - 2b - 5c$	1 step $= -12 + 24x$

Answers

11. $-12x - 8y + 3z$
12. $18a - 42b$

5. Algebraic Expressions

A **term** is a constant or the product or quotient of constants and variables. An algebraic expression is the sum of one or more terms. For example, the expression

$$-7x^2 + xy - 100 \quad \text{or} \quad -7x^2 + xy + (-100)$$

consists of the terms $-7x^2$, xy, and -100.

The terms $-7x^2$ and xy are **variable terms** and the term -100 is called a **constant term**. It is important to distinguish between a term and the factors within a term. For example, the quantity xy is one term, and the values x and y are factors within the term. The constant factor in a term is called the *numerical coefficient* (or simply **coefficient**) of the term. In the terms $-7x^2$, xy, and -100, the coefficients are -7, 1, and -100, respectively.

Terms are ***like* terms** if they each have the same variables, and the corresponding variables are raised to the same powers. For example:

***Like* Terms**	**Unlike Terms**	
$-3b$ and $5b$	$-5c$ and $7d$	(different variables)
$9p^2q^3$ and p^2q^3	$4p^2q^3$ and $8p^3q^2$	(different powers)
$5w$ and $2w$	$5w$ and 2	(different variables)

Example 7 Identifying Terms, Factors, Coefficients, and *Like* Terms

Classroom Examples: p. 86, Exercises 82 and 84

a. List the terms of the expression $5x^2 - 3x + 2$.

b. Identify the coefficient of the term $6yz^3$.

c. Which of the pairs are *like* terms: $8b, 3b^2$ *or* $4c^2d, -6c^2d$?

Solution:

a. The terms of the expression $5x^2 - 3x + 2$ are $5x^2$, $-3x$, and 2.

b. The coefficient of $6yz^3$ is 6.

c. $4c^2d$ and $-6c^2d$ are *like* terms.

Skill Practice

13. List the terms in the expression. $4xy - 9x^2 + 15$

14. Identify the coefficients of each term in the expression. $2a - b + c - 80$

15. Which of the pairs are *like* terms? $5x^3, 5x$ or $-7x^2, 11x^2$

Two terms can be added or subtracted only if they are *like* terms. To add or subtract *like* terms, we use the distributive property as shown in Example 8.

Answers

13. $4xy, -9x^2, 15$

14. 2, −1, 1, −80

15. $-7x^2$ and $11x^2$ are *like* terms.

Classroom Example: p. 87, Exercise 90

Example 8 Using the Distributive Property to Add and Subtract *Like* Terms

Add or subtract as indicated.

a. $7x + 2x$ **b.** $-2p + 3p - p$

Solution:

a. $7x + 2x$

$= (7 + 2)x$ Apply the distributive property.

$= 9x$ Simplify.

b. $-2p + 3p - p$

$= -2p + 3p - 1p$ Note that $-p$ equals $-1p$.

$= (-2 + 3 - 1)p$ Apply the distributive property.

$= (0)p$ Simplify.

$= 0$

Skill Practice Simplify by adding *like* terms.

16. $8x + 3x$ **17.** $-6a + 4a + a$

Although the distributive property is used to add and subtract *like* terms, it is tedious to write each step. Observe that adding or subtracting *like* terms is a matter of adding or subtracting the coefficients and leaving the variable factors unchanged. This can be shown in one step, a shortcut that we will use throughout the text. For example:

$$7x + 2x = 9x \qquad -2p + 3p - 1p = 0p = 0 \qquad -3a - 6a = -9a$$

Classroom Examples: p. 87, Exercises 92 and 94

Instructor Note: Ask students why $2x^2 + 3x^2$ is not $5x^4$.

Example 9 Combining *Like* Terms

Simplify by combining *like* terms.

a. $3yz + 5 - 2yz + 9$ **b.** $1.2w^3 + 5.7w^3$

Solution:

a. $3yz + 5 - 2yz + 9$

$= 3yz - 2yz + 5 + 9$ Arrange *like* terms together. Notice that constants such as 5 and 9 are *like* terms.

$= 1yz + 14$ Combine *like* terms.

$= yz + 14$

b. $1.2w^3 + 5.7w^3$

$= 6.9w^3$ Combine *like* terms.

Skill Practice Simplify by combining *like* terms.

18. $4pq - 7 + 5pq - 8$ **19.** $8.3x^2 + 5.1x^2$

Answers

16. $11x$ **17.** $-a$

18. $9pq - 15$ **19.** $13.4x^2$

When we apply the distributive property, the parentheses are removed. Sometimes this is referred to as *clearing parentheses.* In Examples 10 and 11, we clear parentheses and combine *like* terms.

Example 10 **Clearing Parentheses and Combining *Like* Terms**

Classroom Example: p. 87, Exercises 104

Simplify by *clearing parentheses* and combining *like* terms. $5 - 2(3x + 7)$

Solution:

$5 - 2(3x + 7)$ The order of operations indicates that we must perform multiplication before subtraction.

It is important to understand that a factor of -2 (not 2) will be multiplied to all terms within the parentheses. To see why this is so, we rewrite the subtraction in terms of addition.

$= 5 + (-2)(3x + 7)$	Change subtraction to addition.
$= 5 + (-2)(3x + 7)$	A factor of -2 is to be distributed to terms in the parentheses.
$= 5 + (-2)(3x) + (-2)(7)$	Apply the distributive property.
$= 5 + (-6x) + (-14)$	Simplify.
$= 5 + (-14) + (-6x)$	Arrange *like* terms together.
$= -9 + (-6x)$	Combine *like* terms.
$= -9 - 6x$	Simplify by changing addition of the opposite to subtraction.

Skill Practice Clear the parentheses and combine *like* terms.

20. $9 - 5(2x - 7)$

Example 11 **Clearing Parentheses and Combining *Like* Terms**

Classroom Examples: p. 87, Exercises 108 and 116

Simplify by clearing parentheses and combining *like* terms.

a. $\frac{1}{4}(4k + 2) - \frac{1}{2}(6k + 1)$ **b.** $-(4s - 6t) - (3t + 5s) - 2s$

Solution:

a. $\frac{1}{4}(4k + 2) - \frac{1}{2}(6k + 1)$

$= \frac{4}{4}k + \frac{2}{4} - \frac{6}{2}k - \frac{1}{2}$	Apply the distributive property. Notice that a factor of $-\frac{1}{2}$ is distributed through the second parentheses and changes the signs.
$= k + \frac{1}{2} - 3k - \frac{1}{2}$	Simplify fractions.
$= k - 3k + \frac{1}{2} - \frac{1}{2}$	Arrange *like* terms together.
$= -2k + 0$	Combine *like* terms.
$= -2k$	

Answer

20. $-10x + 44$

b. $-(4s - 6t) - (3t + 5s) - 2s$

$= -1(4s - 6t) - 1(3t + 5s) - 2s$	Notice that a factor of -1 is distributed through each parentheses.
$= -4s + 6t - 3t - 5s - 2s$	Apply the distributive property.
$= -4s - 5s - 2s + 6t - 3t$	Arrange *like* terms together.
$= -11s + 3t$	Combine *like* terms.

Skill Practice Clear the parentheses and combine *like* terms.

21. $\frac{1}{2}(8x + 4) + \frac{1}{3}(3x - 9)$ **22.** $-4(x + 2y) - (2x - y) - 5x$

Classroom Example: p. 87, Exercise 124

Example 12 Clearing Parentheses and Combining *Like* Terms

Simplify by clearing parentheses and combining *like* terms.

$$-7a - 4[3a - 2(a + 6)] - 4$$

Solution:

$-7a - 4[3a - 2(a + 6)] - 4$

$= -7a - 4[3a - 2a - 12] - 4$	Apply the distributive property to clear the innermost parentheses.
$= -7a - 4[a - 12] - 4$	Simplify within brackets by combining *like* terms.
$= -7a - 4a + 48 - 4$	Apply the distributive property to clear the brackets.
$= -11a + 44$	Combine *like* terms.

Avoiding Mistakes

First clear the innermost parentheses and combine *like* terms within the brackets. Then use the distributive property to clear the brackets.

Skill Practice Clear the parentheses and combine *like* terms.

23. $6 - 5[-2y - 4(2y - 5)]$

Answers

21. $5x - 1$ **22.** $-11x - 7y$
23. $50y - 94$

Section 1.7 Practice Exercises

For additional exercises, see Classroom Activities 1.7A–1.7D in the *Student's Resource Manual* at www.mhhe.com/moh.

Study Skills Exercise

Write down the page number(s) for the Chapter Summary for this chapter. Describe one way in which you can use the Summary found at the end of each chapter.

Vocabulary and Key Concepts

1. a. Given the expression $12y + ab - 2x + 18$, the terms $12y$, ab, and $-2x$ are variable terms, whereas 18 is a __constant__ term.

b. The constant factor in a term is called the __coefficient__ of the term.

c. Given the expression x, the value of the coefficient is __1__, and the exponent is __1__.

d. Terms that have the same variables, with corresponding variables raised to the same powers, are called __like__ terms.

Review Exercises

For Exercises 2–14, perform the indicated operations.

2. $(-6) + 14$ 8
3. $(-2) + 9$ 7
4. $-13 - (-5)$ -8
5. $-1 - (-19)$ 18

6. $18 \div (-4)$ $-\frac{9}{2}$ or -4.5
7. $-27 \div 5$ $-\frac{27}{5}$ or -5.4
8. $-3 \cdot 0$ 0
9. $0(-15)$ 0

10. $\frac{1}{2} + \frac{3}{8}$ $\frac{7}{8}$
11. $\frac{25}{21} - \frac{6}{7}$ $\frac{1}{3}$
12. $\left(-\frac{3}{5}\right)\left(\frac{4}{27}\right)$ $-\frac{4}{45}$
13. $\left(-\frac{11}{12}\right) \div \left(-\frac{5}{4}\right)$ $\frac{11}{15}$

14. $25 \cdot \left(-\frac{4}{5}\right)$ -20

Concept 1: Commutative Properties of Real Numbers

For Exercises 15–22, rewrite each expression using the commutative property of addition or the commutative property of multiplication. **(See Examples 1 and 3.)**

15. $5 + (-8)$ $-8 + 5$
16. $7 + (-2)$ $-2 + 7$
17. $8 + x$ $x + 8$
18. $p + 11$ $11 + p$

19. $5(4)$ $4(5)$
20. $10(8)$ $8(10)$
21. $x(-12)$ $-12x$
22. $y(-23)$ $-23y$

For Exercises 23–26, rewrite each expression using addition. Then apply the commutative property of addition. **(See Example 2.)**

23. $x - 3$
$x + (-3); -3 + x$
24. $y - 7$
$y + (-7); -7 + y$
25. $4p - 9$
$4p + (-9); -9 + 4p$
26. $3m - 12$
$3m + (-12); -12 + 3m$

Concept 2: Associative Properties of Real Numbers

For Exercises 27–38, use the associative property of addition or multiplication to rewrite each expression. Then simplify the expression if possible. **(See Example 4.)**

27. $(x + 4) + 9$
$x + (4 + 9); x + 13$
28. $-3 + (5 + z)$
$(-3 + 5) + z; 2 + z$
29. $-5(3x)$
$(-5 \cdot 3)x; -15x$
30. $-12(4z)$
$(-12 \cdot 4)z; -48z$

31. $\frac{6}{11}\left(\frac{11}{6}x\right)$ $\left(\frac{6}{11} \cdot \frac{11}{6}\right)x; x$
32. $\frac{3}{5}\left(\frac{5}{3}x\right)$ $\left(\frac{3}{5} \cdot \frac{5}{3}\right)x; x$
33. $-4\left(-\frac{1}{4}t\right)$ $\left(-4 \cdot -\frac{1}{4}\right)t; t$
34. $-5\left(-\frac{1}{5}w\right)$ $\left(-5 \cdot -\frac{1}{5}\right)w; w$

35. $-8 + (2 + y)$
$(-8 + 2) + y; -6 + y$
36. $[x + (-5)] + 7$
$x + (-5 + 7); x + 2$
37. $-5(2x)$
$(-5 \cdot 2)x; -10x$
38. $-10(6t)$
$(-10 \cdot 6)t; -60t$

Concept 3: Identity and Inverse Properties of Real Numbers

39. What is another name for multiplicative inverse?
Reciprocal
40. What is another name for additive inverse?
Opposite
41. What is the additive identity? 0
42. What is the multiplicative identity? 1

Concept 4: Distributive Property of Multiplication over Addition

For Exercises 43–62, use the distributive property to clear parentheses. **(See Examples 5–6.)**

43. $6(5x + 1)$
$30x + 6$
44. $2(x + 7)$
$2x + 14$
45. $-2(a + 8)$
$-2a - 16$
46. $-3(2z + 9)$
$-6z - 27$

47. $3(5c - d)$
$15c - 3d$
48. $4(w - 13z)$
$4w - 52z$
49. $-7(y - 2)$
$-7y + 14$
50. $-2(4x - 1)$
$-8x + 2$

51. $-\frac{2}{3}(x - 6)$ $-\frac{2}{3}x + 4$
52. $-\frac{1}{4}(2b - 8)$ $-\frac{1}{2}b + 2$
53. $\frac{1}{3}(m - 3)$ $\frac{1}{3}m - 1$
54. $\frac{2}{5}(n - 5)$ $\frac{2}{5}n - 2$

55. $-(2p + 10)$
$-2p - 10$
56. $-(7q + 1)$
$-7q - 1$
57. $-2(-3w - 5z + 8)$
$6w + 10z - 16$
58. $-4(-7a - b - 3)$
$28a + 4b + 12$

59. $4(x + 2y - z)$
$4x + 8y - 4z$
60. $-6(2a - b + c)$
$-12a + 6b - 6c$
61. $-(-6w + x - 3y)$
$6w - x + 3y$
62. $-(-p - 5q - 10r)$
$p + 5q + 10r$

Mixed Exercises

For Exercises 63–70, use the associative property or distributive property to clear parentheses.

63. $2(3 + x)$ $6 + 2x$ **64.** $5(4 + y)$ $20 + 5y$ **65.** $4(6z)$ $24z$ **66.** $8(2p)$ $16p$

67. $-2(7x)$ $-14x$ **68.** $3(-11t)$ $-33t$ **69.** $-4(1 + x)$ $-4 - 4x$ **70.** $-9(2 + y)$ $-18 - 9y$

For Exercises 71–79, match each statement with the property that describes it.

71. $6 \cdot \frac{1}{6} = 1$ b

72. $7(4 \cdot 9) = (7 \cdot 4)9$ f

73. $2(3 + k) = 6 + 2k$ i

74. $3 \cdot 7 = 7 \cdot 3$ c

75. $5 + (-5) = 0$ g

76. $18 \cdot 1 = 18$ e

77. $(3 + 7) + 19 = 3 + (7 + 19)$ d

78. $23 + 6 = 6 + 23$ a

79. $3 + 0 = 3$ h

a. Commutative property of addition

b. Inverse property of multiplication

Animation

c. Commutative property of multiplication

d. Associative property of addition

e. Identity property of multiplication

f. Associative property of multiplication

g. Inverse property of addition

h. Identity property of addition

i. Distributive property of multiplication over addition

Concept 5: Algebraic Expressions

For Exercises 80–83, for each expression list the terms and their coefficients. **(See Example 7.)**

80. $3xy - 6x^2 + y - 17$

Term	Coefficient
$3xy$	3
$-6x^2$	−6
y	1
−17	−17

81. $2x - y + 18xy + 5$

Term	Coefficient
$2x$	2
$-y$	−1
$18xy$	18
5	5

82. $x^4 - 10xy + 12 - y$

Term	Coefficient
x^4	1
$-10xy$	−10
12	12
$-y$	−1

83. $-x + 8y - 9x^2y - 3$

Term	Coefficient
$-x$	−1
$8y$	8
$-9x^2y$	−9
−3	−3

84. Explain why $12x$ and $12x^2$ are not *like* terms.
The exponents on x are different.

85. Explain why $3x$ and $3xy$ are not *like* terms.
The variable factors are different.

86. Explain why $7z$ and $\sqrt{13}z$ are *like* terms.
The variables are the same and raised to the same power.

87. Explain why πx and $8x$ are *like* terms.
The variables are the same and raised to the same power.

88. Write three different *like* terms.
For example: $5y$, $-2y$, y

89. Write three terms that are not *like*.
For example: $5y$, $-2x$, 6

For Exercises 90–98, simplify by combining *like* terms. **(See Examples 8–9.)**

90. $5k - 10k$ $-5k$

91. $-4p - 2p$ $-6p$

92. $-7x^2 + 14x^2$ $7x^2$

93. $2y^2 - 5y^2 - 3y^2$ $-6y^2$

94. $2ab + 5 + 3ab - 2$ $5ab + 3$

95. $8x^3y + 3 - 7 - x^3y$ $7x^3y - 4$

96. $\frac{1}{4}a + b - \frac{3}{4}a - 5b$ $-\frac{1}{2}a - 4b$

97. $\frac{2}{5} + 2t - \frac{3}{5} + t - \frac{6}{5}$ $3t - \frac{7}{5}$

98. $2.8z - 8.1z + 6 - 15.2$ $-5.3z - 9.2$

For Exercises 99–126, simplify by clearing parentheses and combining *like* terms. **(See Examples 10–12.)**

99. $-3(2x - 4) + 10$ $-6x + 22$

100. $-2(4a + 3) - 14$ $-8a - 20$

101. $4(w + 3) - 12$ $4w$

102. $5(2r + 6) - 30$ $10r$

103. $5 - 3(x - 4)$ $-3x + 17$

104. $4 - 2(3x + 8)$ $-6x - 12$

105. $-3(2t + 4w) + 8(2t - 4w)$ $10t - 44w$

106. $-5(5y + 9z) + 3(3y + 6z)$ $-16y - 27z$

107. $2(q - 5u) - (2q + 8u)$ $-18u$

108. $6(x + 3y) - (6x - 5y)$ $23y$

109. $-\frac{1}{3}(6t + 9) + 10$ $-2t + 7$

110. $-\frac{3}{4}(8 + 4q) + 7$ $-3q + 1$

111. $10(5.1a - 3.1) + 4$ $51a - 27$

112. $100(-3.14p - 1.05) + 212$ $-314p + 107$

113. $-4m + 2(m - 3) + 2m$ -6

114. $-3b + 4(b + 2) - 8b$ $-7b + 8$

115. $\frac{1}{2}(10q - 2) + \frac{1}{3}(2 - 3q)$ $4q - \frac{1}{3}$

116. $\frac{1}{5}(15 - 4p) - \frac{1}{10}(10p + 5)$ $-\frac{9}{5}p + \frac{5}{2}$

117. $7n - 2(n - 3) - 6 + n$ $6n$

118. $8k - 4(k - 1) + 7 - k$ $3k + 11$

119. $6(x + 3) - 12 - 4(x - 3)$ $2x + 18$

120. $5(y - 4) + 3 - 6(y - 7)$ $-y + 25$

121. $0.2(6c - 1.6) + c$ $2.2c - 0.32$

122. $-1.1(5 + 8x) - 3.1$ $-8.8x - 8.6$

123. $6 + 2[-8 - 3(2x + 4)] + 10x$ $-2x - 34$

124. $-3 + 5[-3 - 4(y + 2)] - 8y$ $-28y - 58$

125. $1 - 3[2(z + 1) - 5(z - 2)]$ $9z - 35$

126. $1 - 6[3(2t + 2) - 8(t + 2)]$ $12t + 61$

Expanding Your Skills

For Exercises 127–134, determine if the expressions are equivalent. If two expressions are not equivalent, state why.

127. $3a + b, b + 3a$ Equivalent

128. $4y + 1, 1 + 4y$ Equivalent

129. $2c + 7, 9c$ Not equivalent. The terms are not *like* terms and cannot be combined.

130. $5z + 4, 9z$ Not equivalent. The terms are not *like* terms and cannot be combined.

131. $5x - 3, 3 - 5x$ Not equivalent; subtraction is not commutative.

132. $6d - 7, 7 - 6d$ Not equivalent; subtraction is not commutative.

133. $5x - 3, -3 + 5x$ Equivalent

134. $8 - 2x, -2x + 8$ Equivalent

135. As a small child in school, the great mathematician Karl Friedrich Gauss (1777–1855) was said to have found the sum of the integers from 1 to 100 mentally:

$$1 + 2 + 3 + 4 + \cdots + 99 + 100$$

Rather than adding the numbers sequentially, he added the numbers in pairs:

$$(1 + 99) + (2 + 98) + (3 + 97) + \cdots + 100$$

a. Use this technique to add the integers from 1 to 10. 55

$$1 + 2 + 3 + 4 + 5 + 6 + 7 + 8 + 9 + 10$$

b. Use this technique to add the integers from 1 to 20. 210

Group Activity

Evaluating Formulas Using a Calculator

Materials: A calculator

Estimated Time: 20 minutes

Group Size: 2

In this chapter, we learned one of the most important concepts in mathematics—the order of operations. The proper order of operations is required whenever we evaluate any mathematical expression. The following formulas are taken from applications from science, mathematics, statistics, and business. These are just some samples of what you may encounter as you work your way through college.

For Exercises 1–8, substitute the given values into the formula. Then use a calculator and the proper order of operations to simplify the result. Round to three decimal places if necessary.

1. $F = \frac{9}{5}C + 32$ (biology) $C = 35$ $F = 95$

2. $V = \frac{nRT}{P}$ (chemistry) $n = 1.00, R = 0.0821, T = 273.15, P = 1.0$ $V = 22.426$

3. $R = k\left(\frac{L}{r^2}\right)$ (electronics) $k = 0.05, L = 200, r = 0.5$ $R = 40$

4. $m = \frac{y_2 - y_1}{x_2 - x_1}$ (mathematics) $x_1 = -8.3,\ x_2 = 3.3,\ y_1 = 4.6,\ y_2 = -9.2$ $m = -1.190$

5. $z = \frac{\bar{x} - \mu}{\frac{\sigma}{\sqrt{n}}}$ (statistics) $\bar{x} = 69, \mu = 55, \sigma = 20, n = 25$ $z = 3.5$

6. $S = R\left[\frac{(1+i)^n - 1}{i}\right]$ (finance) $R = 200, i = 0.08, n = 30$ $S = 22{,}656.642$

7. $x = \frac{-b + \sqrt{b^2 - 4ac}}{2a}$ (mathematics) $a = 2, b = -7, c = -15$ $x = 5$

8. $h = \frac{1}{2}gt^2 + v_0t + h_0$ (physics) $g = -32, t = 2.4,\ v_0 = 192,\ h_0 = 288$ $h = 656.64$

Chapter 1 Summary

Section 1.1 Fractions

Key Concepts

Simplifying Fractions

Divide the numerator and denominator by their greatest common factor.

Multiplication of Fractions

$$\frac{a}{b} \times \frac{c}{d} = \frac{a \times c}{b \times d}$$

Division of Fractions

$$\frac{a}{b} \div \frac{c}{d} = \frac{a}{b} \times \frac{d}{c}$$

Addition and Subtraction of Fractions

$$\frac{a}{b} + \frac{c}{b} = \frac{a+c}{b} \quad \text{and} \quad \frac{a}{b} - \frac{c}{b} = \frac{a-c}{b}$$

To perform operations on mixed numbers, convert to improper fractions.

Examples

Example 1

$$\frac{60}{84} = \frac{5 \times \overset{1}{\cancel{12}}}{7 \times \underset{1}{\cancel{12}}} = \frac{5}{7}$$

Example 2

$$\frac{25}{108} \times \frac{27}{40} = \frac{\overset{5}{\cancel{25}}}{\underset{4}{\cancel{108}}} \times \frac{\overset{1}{\cancel{27}}}{\underset{8}{\cancel{40}}}$$

$$= \frac{5 \times 1}{4 \times 8} = \frac{5}{32}$$

Example 3

$$\frac{95}{49} \div \frac{65}{42} = \frac{\overset{19}{\cancel{95}}}{\underset{7}{\cancel{49}}} \times \frac{\overset{6}{\cancel{42}}}{\underset{13}{\cancel{65}}}$$

$$= \frac{19 \times 6}{7 \times 13} = \frac{114}{91}$$

Example 4

$$\frac{8}{9} + \frac{2}{15} = \frac{8 \times 5}{9 \times 5} + \frac{2 \times 3}{15 \times 3}$$

$$= \frac{40}{45} + \frac{6}{45} = \frac{46}{45}$$

The least common denominator (LCD) of 9 and 15 is 45.

Example 5

$$2\frac{5}{6} - 1\frac{1}{3} = \frac{17}{6} - \frac{4}{3}$$

$$= \frac{17}{6} - \frac{4 \times 2}{3 \times 2} = \frac{17}{6} - \frac{8}{6}$$

$$= \frac{9}{6}$$

$$= \frac{3}{2} \text{ or } 1\frac{1}{2}$$

The LCD is 6.

Section 1.2 Introduction to Algebra and the Set of Real Numbers

Key Concepts

A **variable** is a symbol or letter used to represent an unknown number.

A **constant** is a value that is not variable.

An algebraic **expression** is a collection of variables and constants under algebraic operations.

Natural numbers: $\{1, 2, 3, \ldots\}$

Whole numbers: $\{0, 1, 2, 3, \ldots\}$

Integers: $\{\ldots -3, -2, -1, 0, 1, 2, 3, \ldots\}$

Rational numbers: The set of numbers that can be expressed in the form $\frac{p}{q}$, where p and q are integers and q does not equal 0. In decimal form, rational numbers are terminating or repeating decimals.

Irrational numbers: A subset of the real numbers whose elements cannot be written as a ratio of two integers. In decimal form, irrational numbers are nonterminating, nonrepeating decimals.

Real numbers: The set of both the rational numbers and the irrational numbers.

$a < b$ "a is less than b."

$a > b$ "a is greater than b."

$a \leq b$ "a is less than or equal to b."

$a \geq b$ "a is greater than or equal to b."

Two numbers that are the same distance from zero but on opposite sides of zero on the number line are called **opposites**. The opposite of a is denoted $-a$.

The **absolute value** of a real number, a, denoted $|a|$, is the distance between a and 0 on the number line.

If $a \geq 0$, $|a| = a$

If $a < 0$, $|a| = -a$

Examples

Example 1

Variables: x, y, z, a, b

Constants: $2, -3, \pi$

Expressions: $2x + 5, 3a + b^2$

Example 2

-5, 0, and 4 are integers.

$-\frac{5}{2}$, -0.5, and $0.\overline{3}$ are rational numbers.

$\sqrt{7}, -\sqrt{2}$, and π are irrational numbers.

Example 3

All real numbers can be located on the real number line.

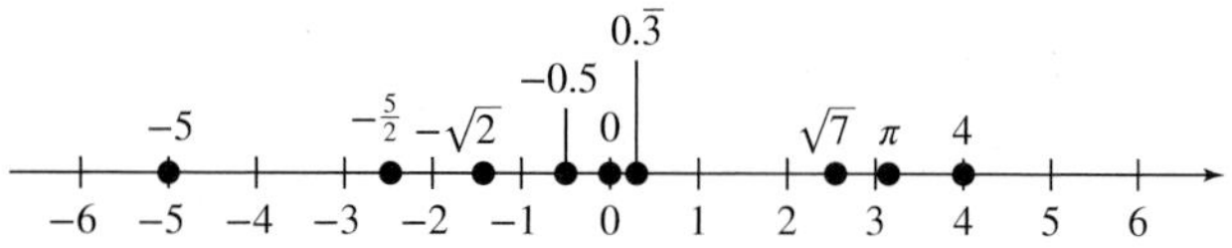

Example 4

$5 < 7$ "5 is less than 7."

$-2 > -10$ "-2 is greater than -10."

$y \leq 3.4$ "y is less than or equal to 3.4."

$x \geq \frac{1}{2}$ "x is greater than or equal to $\frac{1}{2}$."

Example 5

5 and -5 are opposites.

Example 6

$|7| = 7$

$|-7| = 7$

Section 1.3 Exponents, Square Roots, and the Order of Operations

Key Concepts

$b^n = \underbrace{b \cdot b \cdot b \cdot b \cdot \ldots b}_{n \text{ factors of } b}$ b is the **base**, n is the **exponent**

$\sqrt{x}$ is the positive **square root** of x.

The Order of Operations

1. Simplify expressions within parentheses and other grouping symbols first.
2. Evaluate expressions involving exponents, radicals, and absolute values.
3. Perform multiplication or division in the order that they occur from left to right.
4. Perform addition or subtraction in the order that they occur from left to right.

Examples

Example 1

$5^3 = 5 \cdot 5 \cdot 5 = 125$

Example 2

$\sqrt{49} = 7$

Example 3

$10 + 5(3 - 1)^2 - \sqrt{5 - 1}$

$= 10 + 5(2)^2 - \sqrt{4}$ Work within grouping symbols.

$= 10 + 5(4) - 2$ Simplify exponents and radicals.

$= 10 + 20 - 2$ Perform multiplication.

$= 30 - 2$ Add and subtract, left to right.

$= 28$

Section 1.4 Addition of Real Numbers

Key Concepts

Addition of Two Real Numbers

Same Signs. Add the absolute values of the numbers and apply the common sign to the sum.

Different Signs. Subtract the smaller absolute value from the larger absolute value. Then apply the sign of the number having the larger absolute value.

Examples

Example 1

$-3 + (-4) = -7$

$-1.3 + (-9.1) = -10.4$

Example 2

$-5 + 7 = 2$

$\frac{2}{3} + \left(-\frac{7}{3}\right) = -\frac{5}{3}$

Section 1.5 Subtraction of Real Numbers

Key Concepts

Subtraction of Two Real Numbers

Add the opposite of the second number to the first number. That is,

$a - b = a + (-b)$

Examples

Example 1

$7 - (-5) = 7 + (5) = 12$

$-3 - 5 = -3 + (-5) = -8$

$-11 - (-2) = -11 + (2) = -9$

Section 1.6 Multiplication and Division of Real Numbers

Key Concepts

Multiplication and Division of Two Real Numbers

Same Signs

Product is positive.

Quotient is positive.

Different Signs

Product is negative.

Quotient is negative.

The **reciprocal** of a nonzero number a is $\frac{1}{a}$.

Multiplication and Division Involving Zero

The product of any real number and 0 is 0.

The quotient of 0 and any nonzero real number is 0.

The quotient of any nonzero real number and 0 is undefined.

Examples

Example 1

$(-5)(-2) = 10 \qquad \frac{-20}{-4} = 5$

Example 2

$(-3)(7) = -21 \qquad \frac{-4}{8} = -\frac{1}{2}$

Example 3

$-3^4 = -1(3 \cdot 3 \cdot 3 \cdot 3) = -81$

$(-3)^4 = (-3)(-3)(-3)(-3) = 81$

Example 4

The reciprocal of -6 is $-\frac{1}{6}$.

Example 5

$4 \cdot 0 = 0$

$0 \div 4 = 0$

$4 \div 0$ is undefined.

Section 1.7 Properties of Real Numbers and Simplifying Expressions

Key Concepts

Properties of Real Numbers

Commutative Properties

$a + b = b + a$

$ab = ba$

Associative Properties

$(a + b) + c = a + (b + c)$

$(ab)c = a(bc)$

Identity Properties

$0 + a = a$

$1 \cdot a = a$

Inverse Properties

$a + (-a) = 0$

$b \cdot \frac{1}{b} = 1$ for $b \neq 0$

Distributive Property of Multiplication over Addition

$a(b + c) = ab + ac$

A **term** is a constant or the product or quotient of constants and variables. The **coefficient** of a term is the numerical factor of the term.

***Like* terms** have the same variables, and the corresponding variables have the same powers.

Terms can be added or subtracted if they are *like* terms. Sometimes it is necessary to clear parentheses before adding or subtracting *like* terms.

Examples

Example 1

$(-5) + (-7) = (-7) + (-5)$

$3 \cdot 8 = 8 \cdot 3$

Example 2

$(2 + 3) + 10 = 2 + (3 + 10)$

$(2 \cdot 4) \cdot 5 = 2 \cdot (4 \cdot 5)$

Example 3

$0 + (-5) = -5$

$1(-8) = -8$

Example 4

$1.5 + (-1.5) = 0$

$6 \cdot \frac{1}{6} = 1$

Example 5

$$\begin{aligned} -2(x - 3y) &= (-2)x + (-2)(-3y) \\ &= -2x + 6y \end{aligned}$$

Example 6

$-2x$ is a term with coefficient -2.
yz^2 is a term with coefficient 1.

$3x$ and $-5x$ are *like* terms.
$4a^2b$ and $4ab$ are not *like* terms.

Example 7

$-2w - 4(w - 2) + 3$

$= -2w - 4w + 8 + 3$ Clear parentheses.

$= -6w + 11$ Combine *like* terms.

Chapter 1 Review Exercises

Section 1.1

For Exercises 1–4, identify as a proper or improper fraction.

1. $\frac{14}{5}$ Improper **2.** $\frac{1}{6}$ Proper **3.** $\frac{3}{3}$ Improper **4.** $\frac{7}{1}$ Improper

5. Write 112 as a product of primes. $2 \times 2 \times 2 \times 2 \times 7$

6. Simplify. $\frac{84}{70}$ $\frac{6}{5}$

For Exercises 7–12, perform the indicated operations.

7. $\frac{2}{9} + \frac{3}{4}$ $\frac{35}{36}$ **8.** $\frac{7}{8} - \frac{1}{16}$ $\frac{13}{16}$ **9.** $\frac{21}{24} \times \frac{16}{49}$ $\frac{2}{7}$

10. $\frac{68}{34} \div \frac{20}{12}$ $\frac{6}{5}$ or $1\frac{1}{5}$ **11.** $5\frac{1}{3} \div 1\frac{7}{9}$ 3 **12.** $3\frac{4}{5} - 2\frac{1}{10}$ $\frac{17}{10}$ or $1\frac{7}{10}$

13. The surface area of the Earth is approximately 510 million km^2. If water covers about $\frac{7}{10}$ of the surface, how many square kilometers of the Earth is covered by water? 357 million km^2

Section 1.2

14. Given the set $\{7, \frac{1}{3}, -4, 0, -\sqrt{3}, -0.\overline{2}, \pi, 1\}$,

a. List the natural numbers. 7, 1

b. List the integers. 7, −4, 0, 1

c. List the whole numbers. 7, 0, 1

d. List the rational numbers. $7, \frac{1}{3}, -4, 0, -0.\overline{2}, 1$

e. List the irrational numbers. $-\sqrt{3}, \pi$

f. List the real numbers. $7, \frac{1}{3}, -4, 0, -\sqrt{3}, -0.\overline{2}, \pi, 1$

For Exercises 15–18, determine the absolute value.

15. $\left|\frac{1}{2}\right|$ $\frac{1}{2}$ **16.** $|-6|$ 6 **17.** $|-\sqrt{7}|$ $\sqrt{7}$ **18.** $|0|$ 0

For Exercises 19–27, identify whether the inequality is true or false.

19. $-6 > -1$ False **20.** $0 < -5$ False **21.** $-10 \le 0$ True

22. $5 \ne -5$ True **23.** $7 \ge 7$ True **24.** $7 \ge -7$ True

25. $0 \le -3$ False **26.** $-\frac{2}{3} \le -\frac{2}{3}$ True **27.** $|-3| > -|3|$ True

For Exercises 28–31, evaluate each expression for $x = 8, y = 4$, and $z = 1$.

28. $x - 2y$ 0 **29.** $x^2 - y$ 60

30. $\sqrt{x + z}$ 3 **31.** $\sqrt{x + 2y}$ 4

Section 1.3

For Exercises 32–37, write each English phrase as an algebraic expression.

32. The product of x and $\frac{2}{3}$ $x \cdot \frac{2}{3}$ or $\frac{2}{3}x$

33. The quotient of 7 and y $\frac{7}{y}$ or $7 \div y$

34. The sum of 2 and $3b$ $2 + 3b$

35. The difference of a and 5 $a - 5$

36. Two more than $5k$ $5k + 2$

37. Seven less than $13z$ $13z - 7$

For Exercises 38–43, simplify the expressions.

38. 6^3 216 **39.** 15^2 225 **40.** $\sqrt{36}$ 6

41. $\frac{1}{\sqrt{100}}$ $\frac{1}{10}$ **42.** $\left(\frac{1}{4}\right)^2$ $\frac{1}{16}$ **43.** $\left(\frac{3}{2}\right)^3$ $\frac{27}{8}$

For Exercises 44–47, perform the indicated operations.

44. $15 - 7 \cdot 2 + 12$ 13 **45.** $|-11| + |5| - (7 - 2)$ 11

46. $4^2 - (5 - 2)^2$ 7 **47.** $22 - 3(8 \div 4)^2$ 10

Section 1.4

For Exercises 48–60, add.

48. $-6 + 8$ 2 **49.** $14 + (-10)$ 4

50. $21 + (-6)$ 15 **51.** $-12 + (-5)$ −17

52. $\frac{2}{7} + \left(-\frac{1}{9}\right)$ $\frac{11}{63}$ **53.** $\left(-\frac{8}{11}\right) + \left(\frac{1}{2}\right)$ $-\frac{5}{22}$

54. $\left(-\frac{1}{10}\right) + \left(-\frac{5}{6}\right)$ $-\frac{14}{15}$ **55.** $\left(-\frac{5}{2}\right) + \left(-\frac{1}{5}\right)$ $-\frac{27}{10}$

56. $-8.17 + 6.02$ −2.15 **57.** $2.9 + (-7.18)$ −4.28

58. $13 + (-2) + (-8)$ 3

59. $-5 + (-7) + 20$ 8

60. $2 + 5 + (-8) + (-7) + 0 + 13 + (-1)$ 4

61. Under what conditions will the expression $a + b$ be negative? When a and b are both negative or when a and b have different signs and the number with the larger absolute value is negative.

62. Richard's checkbook was overdrawn by \$45 (that is, his balance was -45). He deposited \$117 but then wrote a check for \$80. Was the deposit enough to cover the check? Explain.
No. He is still overdrawn by \$8.

Section 1.5

For Exercises 63–75, subtract.

63. $13 - 25$ -12

64. $31 - (-2)$ 33

65. $-8 - (-7)$ -1

66. $-2 - 15$ -17

67. $\left(-\frac{7}{9}\right) - \frac{5}{6}$ $-\frac{29}{18}$

68. $\frac{1}{3} - \frac{9}{8}$ $-\frac{19}{24}$

69. $7 - 8.2$ -1.2

70. $-1.05 - 3.2$ -4.25

71. $-16.1 - (-5.9)$ -10.2

72. $7.09 - (-5)$ 12.09

73. $\frac{11}{2} - \left(-\frac{1}{6}\right) - \frac{7}{3}$ $\frac{10}{3}$

74. $-\frac{4}{5} - \frac{7}{10} - \left(-\frac{13}{20}\right)$ $-\frac{17}{20}$

75. $6 - 14 - (-1) - 10 - (-21) - 5$ -1

76. Under what conditions will the expression $a - b$ be negative? If $a < b$

For Exercises 77–81, write an algebraic expression and simplify.

77. -18 subtracted from -7
$-7 - (-18)$; 11

78. The difference of -6 and 41
$-6 - 41$; -47

79. Seven decreased by 13
$7 - 13$; -6

80. Five subtracted from the difference of 20 and -7
$[20 - (-7)] - 5$; 22

81. The sum of 6 and -12, decreased by 21
$[6 + (-12)] - 21$; -27

82. In Nevada, the highest temperature ever recorded was 125°F and the lowest was -50°F. Find the difference between the highest and lowest temperatures. (*Source: Information Please Almanac*)
175°F

Section 1.6

For Exercises 83–100, multiply or divide as indicated.

83. $10(-17)$ -170

84. $(-7)13$ -91

85. $(-52) \div 26$ -2

86. $(-48) \div (-16)$ 3

87. $\frac{7}{4} \div \left(-\frac{21}{2}\right)$ $-\frac{1}{6}$

88. $\frac{2}{3}\left(-\frac{12}{11}\right)$ $-\frac{8}{11}$

89. $-\frac{21}{5} \cdot 0$ 0

90. $\frac{3}{4} \div 0$ Undefined

91. $0 \div (-14)$ 0

92. $(-0.45)(-5)$ 2.25

93. $\frac{-21}{14}$ $-\frac{3}{2}$

94. $\frac{-13}{-52}$ $\frac{1}{4}$

95. $(5)(-2)(3)$ -30

96. $(-6)(-5)(15)$ 450

97. $\left(-\frac{1}{2}\right)\left(\frac{7}{8}\right)\left(-\frac{4}{7}\right)$ $\frac{1}{4}$

98. $\left(\frac{12}{13}\right)\left(-\frac{1}{6}\right)\left(\frac{13}{14}\right)$ $-\frac{1}{7}$

99. $40 \div 4 \div (-5)$ -2

100. $\frac{10}{11} \div \frac{7}{11} \div \frac{5}{9}$ $\frac{18}{7}$

For Exercises 101–106, perform the indicated operations.

101. $9 - 4[-2(4 - 8) - 5(3 - 1)]$ 17

102. $\frac{8(-3) - 6}{-7 - (-2)}$ 6

103. $\frac{2}{3} - \left(\frac{3}{8} + \frac{5}{6}\right) \div \frac{5}{3}$ $-\frac{7}{120}$

104. $5.4 - (0.3)^2 \div 0.09$ 4.4

105. $\frac{5 - [3 - (-4)^2]}{36 \div (-2)(3)}$ $-\frac{1}{3}$

106. $|-8 + 5| - \sqrt{5^2 - 3^2}$ -1

For Exercises 107–110, evaluate each expression given the values $x = 4$ and $y = -9$.

107. $3(x + 2) \div y$ -2

108. $\sqrt{x} - y$ 11

109. $-xy$ 36

110. $3x + 2y$ -6

111. In statistics the formula $x = \mu + z\sigma$ is used to find cutoff values for data that follow a bellshaped curve Find x if $\mu = 100$, $z = -1.96$, and $\sigma = 15$. 70.6

For Exercises 112–118, answer true or false. If a statement is false, explain why.

112. If n is positive, then $-n$ is negative True

113. If m is negative, then m^4 is negative. False, any nonzero real number raised to an even power is positive.

114. If m is negative, then m^3 is negative. True

115. If $m > 0$ and $n > 0$, then $mn > 0$. True

116. If $p < 0$ and $q < 0$, then $pq < 0$. False, the product of two negative numbers is positive.

117. A number and its reciprocal have the same signs. True

118. A nonzero number and its opposite have different signs. True

Section 1.7

For Exercises 119–126, answers may vary.

119. Give an example of the commutative property of addition.
For example: $2 + 3 = 3 + 2$

120. Give an example of the associative property of addition.
For example: $(2 + 3) + 4 = 2 + (3 + 4)$

121. Give an example of the inverse property of addition.
For example: $5 + (-5) = 0$

122. Give an example of the identity property of addition.
For example: $7 + 0 = 7$

123. Give an example of the commutative property of multiplication.
For example: $5 \cdot 2 = 2 \cdot 5$

124. Give an example of the associative property of multiplication.
For example: $(8 \cdot 2)10 = 8(2 \cdot 10)$

125. Give an example of the inverse property of multiplication.
For example: $3 \cdot \frac{1}{3} = 1$

126. Give an example of the identity property of multiplication. For example: $8 \cdot 1 = 8$

127. Explain why $5x - 2y$ is the same as $-2y + 5x$.
$5x - 2y = 5x + (-2y)$, then use the commutative property of addition.

128. Explain why $3a - 9y$ is the same as $-9y + 3a$.
$3a - 9y = 3a + (-9y)$, then use the commutative property of addition.

129. List the terms of the expression:
$3y + 10x - 12 + xy$
$3y, 10x, -12, xy$

130. Identify the coefficients for the terms listed in Exercise 129.
3, 10, −12, 1

For Exercises 131–132, simplify by combining *like* terms.

131. $3a + 3b - 4b + 5a - 10$
$8a - b - 10$

132. $-6p + 2q + 9 - 13q - p + 7$
$-7p - 11q + 16$

For Exercises 133–134, use the distributive property to clear the parentheses.

133. $-2(4z + 9)$
$-8z - 18$

134. $5(4w - 8y + 1)$
$20w - 40y + 5$

For Exercises 135–140, simplify each expression.

135. $2p - (p + 5w) + 3w$ $p - 2w$

136. $6(h + 3m) - 7h - 4m$ $-h + 14m$

137. $\frac{1}{2}(-6q) + q - 4\left(3q + \frac{1}{4}\right)$ $-14q - 1$

138. $0.3b + 12(0.2 - 0.5b)$ $-5.7b + 2.4$

139. $-4[2(x + 1) - (3x + 8)]$ $4x + 24$

140. $5[(7y - 3) + 3(y + 8)]$ $50y + 105$

Chapter 1 Test

1. Simplify. $\frac{135}{36}$ $\frac{15}{4}$

2. Add and subtract. $\frac{5}{4} - \frac{5}{12} + \frac{2}{3}$ $\frac{3}{2}$

3. Divide. $4\frac{1}{12} \div 1\frac{1}{3}$ $3\frac{1}{16}$

4. Subtract. $4\frac{1}{4} - 1\frac{7}{8}$ $2\frac{3}{8}$

5. Is $0.\overline{315}$ a rational number or an irrational number? Explain your reasoning.
Rational, all repeating decimals are rational numbers.

6. Use the definition of exponents to expand the expressions:

 a. $(4x)^3$ $(4x)(4x)(4x)$ b. $4x^3$ $4 \cdot x \cdot x \cdot x$

7. Plot the points on a number line: $|3|, 0, -2, 0.5, \left|-\frac{3}{2}\right|, \sqrt{16}$.

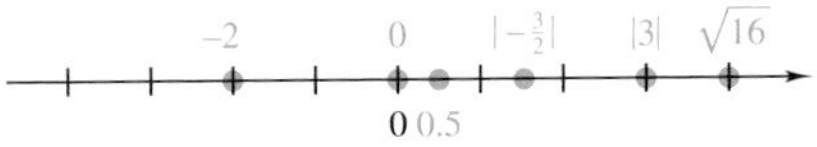

8. Use the number line in Exercise 7 to identify whether the statements are true or false.

 a. $|3| < -2$ False b. $0 \le \left|-\frac{3}{2}\right|$ True

 c. $-2 < 0.5$ True d. $|3| \ge \left|-\frac{3}{2}\right|$ True

9. Identify the property that justifies each statement.

 a. $6(-8) = (-8)6$ Commutative property of multiplication b. $5 + 0 = 5$ Identity property of addition

 c. $(2 + 3) + 4 = 2 + (3 + 4)$ Associative property of addition

 d. $\frac{1}{7} \cdot 7 = 1$ Inverse property of multiplication e. $8[7(-3)] = (8 \cdot 7)(-3)$ Associative property of multiplication

10. Write each expression as an English phrase.

 a. $2(a - b)$. Twice the difference of a and b

 b. $2a - b$. (Answers may vary.) b subtracted from twice a

11. Write the phrase as an algebraic expression: "The quotient of the square root of c and the square of d." $\frac{\sqrt{c}}{d^2}$ or $\sqrt{c} \div d^2$

For Exercises 12–14, write each English statement as an algebraic expression. Then simplify the expression.

12. Subtract −4 from 12 $12 - (-4)$; 16

13. Find the difference of 6 and 8 $6 - 8$; −2

14. The quotient of 10 and −12 $\frac{10}{-12}$; $-\frac{5}{6}$

For Exercises 15–29, perform the indicated operations.

15. $-\frac{1}{8} + \left(-\frac{3}{4}\right)$ $-\frac{7}{8}$

16. $-84 \div 7$ −12

17. $21 - (-7)$ 28

18. $-15 - (-3)$ −12

19. $-14 + (-2) - 16$ −32

20. $(-16)(-2)(-1)(-3)$ 96

21. $-22 \cdot 0$ 0

22. $38 \div 0$ Undefined

23. $18 + (-12)$ 6

24. $-10.06 - (-14.72)$ 4.66

25. $7(-4)$ −28

26. $\frac{2}{5} \div \left(-\frac{7}{10}\right) \cdot \left(-\frac{7}{6}\right)$ $\frac{2}{3}$

27. $\frac{\sqrt{5^2 - 4^2}}{|-12 + 3|}$ $\frac{1}{3}$

28. $8 - [(2 - 4) - (8 - 9)]$ 9

29. $(8 - 10) \cdot \frac{3}{2} + (-5)$ −8

30. The average high temperature in January for Nova Scotia, Canada, is −1.2°C. The average low is −10.7°C. Find the difference between the average high and the average low. The difference is 9.5°C.

31. In the third quarter of a football game, a quarterback made a 5-yd gain, a 2-yd gain, a 10-yd loss, and then a 4-yd gain.

 a. Write an expression using addition to describe the quarterback's movement. $5 + 2 + (-10) + 4$

 b. Evaluate the expression from part (a) to determine the quarterback's net gain or loss in yards. He gained 1 yd.

For Exercises 32–36, simplify each expression.

32. $3k - 20 + (-9k) + 12$ $-6k - 8$

33. $-5x - 4y + 3 - 7x + 6y - 7$ $-12x + 2y - 4$

34. $4(p - 5) - (8p + 3)$ $-4p - 23$

35. $-3(4m + 8p - 7)$ $-12m - 24p + 21$

36. $\frac{1}{2}(12p - 4) + \frac{1}{3}(2 - 6p)$ $4p - \frac{4}{3}$

For Exercises 37–40, evaluate each expression given the values $x = 4$ and $y = -3$ and $z = -7$.

37. $y^2 - x$ 5

38. $3x - 2y$ 18

39. $y(x - 2)$ −6

40. $-y^2 - 4x + z$ −32

Linear Equations and Inequalities

2

CHAPTER OUTLINE

Mathematics as a Language

Languages make use of symbols to represent sounds and other conventions used in speech and writing. The letters of the alphabet and punctuation marks are all examples of these symbols. Mathematicians cleverly adopted the use of symbols as a way to give a temporary nickname to *unknowns* in order to simplify the problem-solving process.

Suppose that the maximum recommended heart rate for an adult is given by 220 minus the age (in years) of the adult. If we let a be the age of an adult in years, then the expression $220 - a$ represents the adult's maximum recommended heart rate.

If Alan is 60 years old, his maximum heart rate is found by substituting 60 for a. Thus, Alan's maximum recommended heart rate is $220 - 60$, which is 160 beats per minute.

If we know that Ben's recommended heart rate is 178, then we can solve an equation to determine his age, a.

$$220 - a = 178$$
$$-a = 178 - 220$$
$$-a = -42$$
$$a = 42 \quad \text{Ben is 42 years old.}$$

Section 2.1 Addition, Subtraction, Multiplication, and Division Properties of Equality

Concepts

1. Definition of a Linear Equation in One Variable
2. Addition and Subtraction Properties of Equality
3. Multiplication and Division Properties of Equality
4. Translations

1. Definition of a Linear Equation in One Variable

An **equation** is a statement that indicates that two expressions are equal. The following are equations.

$$x = 5 \qquad y + 2 = 12 \qquad -4z = 28$$

All equations have an equal sign. Furthermore, notice that the equal sign separates the equation into two parts, the left-hand side and the right-hand side. A **solution to an equation** is a value of the variable that makes the equation a true statement. Substituting a solution into an equation for the variable makes the right-hand side equal to the left-hand side.

Equation	Solution	Check	
$x = 5$	5	$x = 5$ ↓ $5 = 5$ ✓	Substitute 5 for x. Right-hand side equals left-hand side.
$y + 2 = 12$	10	$y + 2 = 12$ ↓ $10 + 2 = 12$ ✓	Substitute 10 for y. Right-hand side equals left-hand side.
$-4z = 28$	-7	$-4z = 28$ ↓ $-4(-7) = 28$ ✓	Substitute -7 for z. Right-hand side equals left-hand side.

Avoiding Mistakes

Be sure to notice the difference between solving an equation versus simplifying an expression. For example, $2x + 1 = 7$ is an equation, whose solution is 3, while $2x + 1 + 7$ is an expression that simplifies to $2x + 8$.

Classroom Examples: p. 110, Exercises 10 and 14

Example 1 Determining Whether a Number Is a Solution to an Equation

Determine whether the given number is a solution to the equation.

a. $4x + 7 = 5;\ -\frac{1}{2}$ **b.** $-4 = 6w - 14;\ 3$

Solution:

a.

$4x + 7 = 5$

$4(-\frac{1}{2}) + 7 \stackrel{?}{=} 5$ Substitute $-\frac{1}{2}$ for x.

$-2 + 7 \stackrel{?}{=} 5$ Simplify.

$5 \stackrel{?}{=} 5$ ✓ Right-hand side equals the left-hand side. Thus, $-\frac{1}{2}$ *is a solution* to the equation $4x + 7 = 5$.

b. $-4 = 6w - 14$

$-4 \stackrel{?}{=} 6(3) - 14$ Substitute 3 for w.

$-4 \stackrel{?}{=} 18 - 14$ Simplify.

$-4 \neq 4$ Right-hand side does not equal left-hand side. Thus, 3 *is not a solution* to the equation $-4 = 6w - 14$.

Skill Practice Determine whether the given number is a solution to the equation.

1. $4x - 1 = 7;\ 3$ **2.** $9 = -2y + 5;\ -2$

Answers

1. No 2. Yes

The set of all solutions to an equation is called the **solution set** and is written with set braces. For example, the solution set for Example 1(a) is $\{-\frac{1}{2}\}$.

In the study of algebra, you will encounter a variety of equations. In this chapter, we will focus on a specific type of equation called a linear equation in one variable.

Definition of a Linear Equation in One Variable

Let a, b, and c be real numbers such that $a \neq 0$. A **linear equation in one variable** is an equation that can be written in the form

$$ax + b = c$$

Note: A linear equation in one variable is often called a first-degree equation because the variable x has an implied exponent of 1.

Examples	**Notes**
$2x + 4 = 20$	$a = 2, b = 4, c = 20$
$-3x - 5 = 16$ can be written as $-3x + (-5) = 16$	$a = -3, b = -5, c = 16$
$5x + 9 - 4x = 1$ can be written as $x + 9 = 1$	$a = 1, b = 9, c = 1$

2. Addition and Subtraction Properties of Equality

If two equations have the same solution set, then the equations are equivalent. For example, the following equations are equivalent because the solution set for each equation is $\{6\}$.

Equivalent Equations		**Check the Solution 6**
$2x - 5 = 7$	$\longrightarrow$	$2(6) - 5 \stackrel{?}{=} 7 \Rightarrow 12 - 5 \stackrel{?}{=} 7$ ✓
$2x = 12$	$\longrightarrow$	$2(6) \stackrel{?}{=} 12 \Rightarrow 12 \stackrel{?}{=} 12$ ✓
$x = 6$	$\longrightarrow$	$6 \stackrel{?}{=} 6 \Rightarrow 6 \stackrel{?}{=} 6$ ✓

To solve a linear equation, $ax + b = c$, the goal is to find *all* values of x that make the equation true. One general strategy for solving an equation is to rewrite it as an equivalent but simpler equation. This process is repeated until the equation can be written in the form $x =$ number. We call this "isolating the variable." The addition and subtraction properties of equality help us isolate the variable.

Addition and Subtraction Properties of Equality

Let a, b, and c represent algebraic expressions.

1. **Addition property of equality:** If $a = b$, then $a + c = b + c$

2. ***Subtraction property of equality:** If $a = b$, then $a - c = b - c$

*The subtraction property of equality follows directly from the addition property, because subtraction is defined in terms of addition.

If $a + (-c) = b + (-c)$

then, $a - c = b - c$

The addition and subtraction properties of equality indicate that adding or subtracting the same quantity on each side of an equation results in an equivalent equation. This means that if two equal quantities are increased or decreased by the same amount, then the resulting quantities will also be equal (Figure 2-1).

$$50 = 50$$
$$50 + 20 = 50 + 20$$
$$70 = 70$$

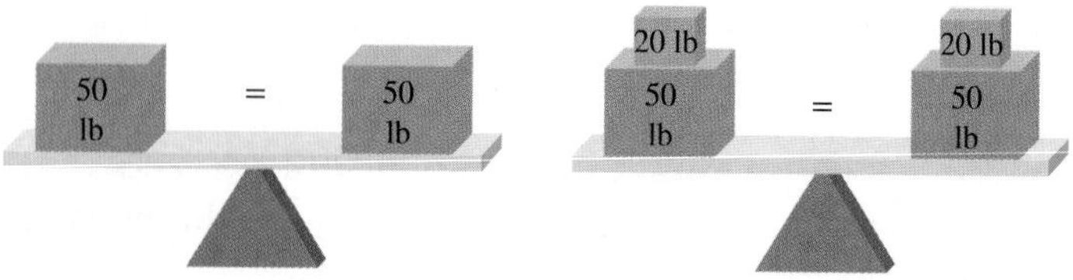

Figure 2-1

Classroom Examples: p. 110, Exercises 16 and 18

Example 2 Applying the Addition and Subtraction Properties of Equality

Solve the equations.

a. $p - 4 = 11$ **b.** $w + 5 = -2$

Solution:

In each equation, the goal is to isolate the variable on one side of the equation. To accomplish this, we use the fact that the sum of a number and its opposite is zero and the difference of a number and itself is zero.

a.

$p - 4 = 11$	
$p - 4 + 4 = 11 + 4$	To isolate p, add 4 to both sides $(-4 + 4 = 0)$.
$p + 0 = 15$	Simplify.
$p = 15$	Check by substituting $p = 15$ into the original equation.

Check: $p - 4 = 11$
$15 - 4 \stackrel{?}{=} 11$
$11 \stackrel{?}{=} 11$ ✓ True

The solution set is $\{15\}$.

b.

$w + 5 = -2$	
$w + 5 - 5 = -2 - 5$	To isolate w, subtract 5 from both sides. $(5 - 5 = 0)$.
$w + 0 = -7$	Simplify.
$w = -7$	Check by substituting $w = -7$ into the original equation.

Check: $w + 5 = -2$
$-7 + 5 \stackrel{?}{=} -2$
$-2 \stackrel{?}{=} -2$ ✓ True

The solution set is $\{-7\}$.

Skill Practice Solve the equations.

3. $v - 7 = 2$ **4.** $x + 4 = 4$

Answers

3. $\{9\}$ **4.** $\{0\}$

Example 3 **Applying the Addition and Subtraction Properties of Equality**

Classroom Examples: p. 110, Exercises 30 and 32

Solve the equations.

a. $\frac{9}{4} = q - \frac{3}{4}$ **b.** $-1.2 + z = 4.6$

Solution:

a.

$$\frac{9}{4} = q - \frac{3}{4}$$

$$\frac{9}{4} + \frac{3}{4} = q - \frac{3}{4} + \frac{3}{4}$$ To isolate q, add $\frac{3}{4}$ to both sides $(-\frac{3}{4} + \frac{3}{4} = 0)$.

$$\frac{12}{4} = q + 0$$ Simplify.

$3 = q$ or equivalently, $q = 3$

TIP: The variable may be isolated on either side of the equation.

Check: $\frac{9}{4} = q - \frac{3}{4}$

$\frac{9}{4} \stackrel{?}{=} 3 - \frac{3}{4}$ Substitute $q = 3$.

$\frac{9}{4} \stackrel{?}{=} \frac{12}{4} - \frac{3}{4}$ Common denominator

$\frac{9}{4} \stackrel{?}{=} \frac{9}{4}$ ✓ True

The solution set is $\{3\}$.

b.

$$-1.2 + z = 4.6$$

$$-1.2 + 1.2 + z = 4.6 + 1.2$$ To isolate z, add 1.2 to both sides.

$$0 + z = 5.8$$

$$z = 5.8$$

Check: $-1.2 + z = 4.6$

$-1.2 + 5.8 \stackrel{?}{=} 4.6$ Substitute $z = 5.8$.

$4.6 \stackrel{?}{=} 4.6$ ✓ True

The solution set is $\{5.8\}$.

Skill Practice Solve the equations.

5. $\frac{1}{4} = a - \frac{2}{3}$ **6.** $-8.1 + w = 11.5$

3. Multiplication and Division Properties of Equality

Adding or subtracting the same quantity to both sides of an equation results in an equivalent equation. In a similar way, multiplying or dividing both sides of an equation by the same nonzero quantity also results in an equivalent equation. This is stated formally as the multiplication and division properties of equality.

Answers

5. $\left\{\frac{11}{12}\right\}$ **6.** $\{19.6\}$

Multiplication and Division Properties of Equality

Let a, b, and c represent algebraic expressions, $c \neq 0$.

1. **Multiplication property of equality:** If $a = b$, then $ac = bc$
2. ***Division property of equality:** If $a = b$ then $\dfrac{a}{c} = \dfrac{b}{c}$

*The division property of equality follows directly from the multiplication property because division is defined as multiplication by the reciprocal.

$$\text{If} \quad a \cdot \frac{1}{c} = b \cdot \frac{1}{c}$$

$$\text{then,} \quad \frac{a}{c} = \frac{b}{c}$$

To understand the multiplication property of equality, suppose we start with a true equation such as $10 = 10$. If both sides of the equation are multiplied by a constant such as 3, the result is also a true statement (Figure 2-2).

$$10 = 10$$
$$3 \cdot 10 = 3 \cdot 10$$
$$30 = 30$$

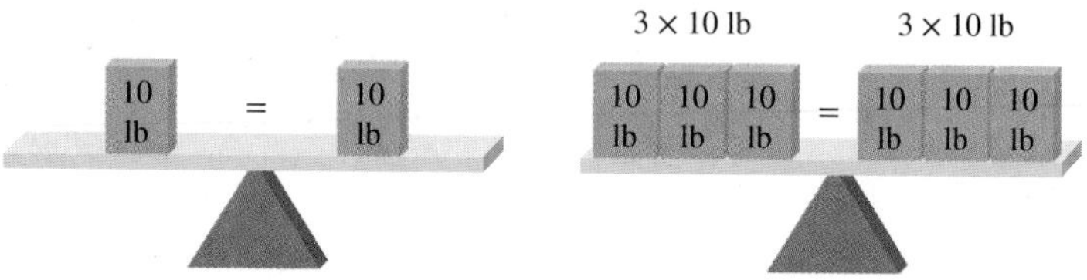

Figure 2-2

Similarly, if both sides of the equation are divided by a nonzero real number such as 2, the result is also a true statement (Figure 2-3).

$$10 = 10$$
$$\frac{10}{2} = \frac{10}{2}$$
$$5 = 5$$

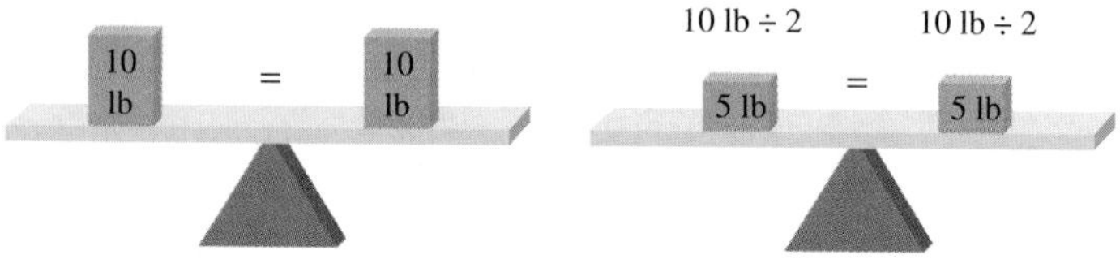

Figure 2-3

TIP: The product of a number and its reciprocal is always 1. For example:

$$\frac{1}{5}(5) = 1$$
$$-\frac{7}{2}\left(-\frac{2}{7}\right) = 1$$

To solve an equation in the variable x, the goal is to write the equation in the form $x =$ number. In particular, notice that we desire the coefficient of x to be 1. That is, we want to write the equation as $1x =$ number. Therefore, to solve an equation such as $5x = 15$, we can multiply both sides of the equation by the reciprocal of the x-term coefficient. In this case, multiply both sides by the reciprocal of 5, which is $\frac{1}{5}$.

$$5x = 15$$

$$\frac{1}{5}(5x) = \frac{1}{5}(15) \qquad \text{Multiply by } \frac{1}{5}.$$

$$1x = 3 \qquad \text{The coefficient of the } x\text{-term is now 1.}$$

$$x = 3$$

The division property of equality can also be used to solve the equation $5x = 15$ by dividing both sides by the coefficient of the x-term. In this case, divide both sides by 5 to make the coefficient of x equal to 1.

$5x = 15$

$\frac{5x}{5} = \frac{15}{5}$ Divide by 5.

$1x = 3$ The coefficient of the x-term is now 1.

$x = 3$

TIP: The quotient of a nonzero real number and itself is always 1. For example:

$$\frac{5}{5} = 1$$

$$\frac{-3.5}{-3.5} = 1$$

Example 4 Applying the Division Property of Equality

Classroom Examples: p. 110, Exercises 38 and 50

Solve the equations using the division property of equality.

a. $12x = 60$ **b.** $48 = -8w$ **c.** $-x = 8$

Solution:

a. $12x = 60$

$\frac{12x}{12} = \frac{60}{12}$ To obtain a coefficient of 1 for the x-term, divide both sides by 12.

$1x = 5$ Simplify.

$x = 5$ Check: $12x = 60$

$12(5) \stackrel{?}{=} 60$

The solution set is $\{5\}$. $60 \stackrel{?}{=} 60$ ✓ True

b. $48 = -8w$

$\frac{48}{-8} = \frac{-8w}{-8}$ To obtain a coefficient of 1 for the w-term, divide both sides by -8.

$-6 = 1w$ Simplify.

$-6 = w$ Check: $48 = -8w$

$48 \stackrel{?}{=} -8(-6)$

The solution set is $\{-6\}$. $48 \stackrel{?}{=} 48$ ✓ True

c. $-x = 8$ Note that $-x$ is equivalent to $-1 \cdot x$.

$-1x = 8$

$\frac{-1x}{-1} = \frac{8}{-1}$ To obtain a coefficient of 1 for the x-term, divide by -1.

$x = -8$ Check: $-x = 8$

$-(-8) \stackrel{?}{=} 8$

The solution set is $\{-8\}$. $8 \stackrel{?}{=} 8$ ✓ True

TIP: In Example 4(c), we could also have *multiplied* both sides by -1 to create a coefficient of 1 on the x-term.

$$-x = 8$$
$$(-1)(-x) = (-1)8$$
$$x = -8$$

Skill Practice Solve the equations.

7. $4x = -20$ **8.** $100 = -4p$ **9.** $-y = -11$

Answers

7. $\{-5\}$ **8.** $\{-25\}$ **9.** $\{11\}$

Classroom Example: p. 110, Exercise 46

Example 5 **Applying the Multiplication Property of Equality**

Solve the equation by using the multiplication property of equality.

$$-\frac{2}{9}q = \frac{1}{3}$$

Solution:

$$-\frac{2}{9}q = \frac{1}{3}$$

$$\left(-\frac{9}{2}\right)\left(-\frac{2}{9}q\right) = \frac{1}{3}\left(-\frac{9}{2}\right)$$ To obtain a coefficient of 1 for the q-term, multiply by the reciprocal of $-\frac{2}{9}$, which is $-\frac{9}{2}$.

$$1q = -\frac{3}{2}$$ Simplify. The product of a number and its reciprocal is 1.

$$q = -\frac{3}{2}$$

Check: $-\frac{2}{9}q = \frac{1}{3}$

$$-\frac{2}{9}\left(-\frac{3}{2}\right) \stackrel{?}{=} \frac{1}{3}$$

$$\frac{1}{3} \stackrel{?}{=} \frac{1}{3} \checkmark \quad \text{True}$$

The solution set is $\left\{-\frac{3}{2}\right\}$.

Skill Practice Solve the equation.

10. $-\frac{2}{3}a = \frac{1}{4}$

TIP: When applying the multiplication or division property of equality to obtain a coefficient of 1 for the variable term, we will generally use the following convention:

- If the coefficient of the variable term is expressed as a fraction, we will usually multiply both sides by its reciprocal, as in Example 5.
- If the coefficient of the variable term is an integer or decimal, we will divide both sides by the coefficient itself, as in Example 6.

Classroom Example: p. 110, Exercise 52

Example 6 **Applying the Division Property of Equality**

Solve the equation by using the division property of equality.

$$-3.43 = -0.7z$$

Solution:

$$-3.43 = -0.7z$$

$$\frac{-3.43}{-0.7} = \frac{-0.7z}{-0.7}$$ To obtain a coefficient of 1 for the z-term, divide by -0.7.

$$4.9 = 1z$$ Simplify.

$$4.9 = z$$

$$z = 4.9$$

Check: $-3.43 = -0.7z$

$$-3.43 \stackrel{?}{=} -0.7(4.9)$$

$$-3.43 \stackrel{?}{=} -3.43 \checkmark \quad \text{True}$$

The solution set is $\{4.9\}$.

Answer

10. $\left\{-\frac{3}{8}\right\}$

Skill Practice Solve the equation.

11. $6.82 = 2.2w$

Example 7 **Applying the Multiplication Property of Equality**

Classroom Example: p. 110, Exercise 42

Solve the equation by using the multiplication property of equality.

$$\frac{d}{6} = -4$$

Solution:

$\frac{d}{6} = -4$

$\frac{1}{6}d = -4$ $\qquad$ $\frac{d}{6}$ is equivalent to $\frac{1}{6}d$.

$\frac{6}{1} \cdot \frac{1}{6}d = -4 \cdot \frac{6}{1}$ $\qquad$ To obtain a coefficient of 1 for the d-term, multiply by the reciprocal of $\frac{1}{6}$, which is $\frac{6}{1}$.

$1d = -24$ $\qquad$ Simplify.

$d = -24$ $\qquad$ Check: $\frac{d}{6} = -4$

$$\frac{-24}{6} \stackrel{?}{=} -4$$

The solution set is $\{-24\}$. $\qquad$ $-4 \stackrel{?}{=} -4$ ✓ True

Instructor Note: Remind students that dividing by a number is the same as multiplying by its reciprocal. Thus, $\frac{d}{6} = \frac{1}{6}d$

Skill Practice Solve the equation.

12. $\frac{x}{5} = -8$

It is important to distinguish between cases where the addition or subtraction properties of equality should be used to isolate a variable versus those in which the multiplication or division property of equality should be used. Remember the goal is to isolate the variable term and obtain a coefficient of 1. Compare the equations:

$$5 + x = 20 \qquad \text{and} \qquad 5x = 20$$

In the first equation, the relationship between 5 and x is addition. Therefore, we want to reverse the process by subtracting 5 from both sides. In the second equation, the relationship between 5 and x is multiplication. To isolate x, we reverse the process by dividing by 5 or equivalently, multiplying by the reciprocal, $\frac{1}{5}$.

$$5 + x = 20 \qquad \text{and} \qquad 5x = 20$$

$$5 - 5 + x = 20 - 5 \qquad\qquad \frac{5x}{5} = \frac{20}{5}$$

$$x = 15 \qquad\qquad x = 4$$

Answers

11. {3.1} **12.** {−40}

4. Translations

We have already practiced writing an English sentence as a mathematical equation. Recall that several key words translate to the algebraic operations of addition, subtraction, multiplication, and division.

Classroom Examples: p. 110, Exercises 60 and 62

Example 8 Translating to a Linear Equation

Write an algebraic equation to represent each English sentence. Then solve the equation.

a. The quotient of a number and 4 is 6.

b. The product of a number and 4 is 6.

c. Negative twelve is equal to the sum of −5 and a number.

d. The value 1.4 subtracted from a number is 5.7.

Solution:

For each case we will let x represent the unknown number.

a. The quotient of a number and 4 is 6.

$$\frac{x}{4} = 6$$

$$4 \cdot \frac{x}{4} = 4 \cdot 6 \qquad \text{Multiply both sides by 4.}$$

$$\frac{4}{1} \cdot \frac{x}{4} = 4 \cdot 6$$

$$x = 24 \qquad \underline{\text{Check}}: \frac{24}{4} \stackrel{?}{=} 6 \checkmark \quad \text{True}$$

The number is 24.

b. The product of a number and 4 is 6.

$$4x = 6$$

$$\frac{4x}{4} = \frac{6}{4} \qquad \text{Divide both sides by 4.}$$

$$x = \frac{3}{2} \qquad \underline{\text{Check}}: 4\left(\frac{3}{2}\right) \stackrel{?}{=} 6 \checkmark \quad \text{True}$$

The number is $\frac{3}{2}$.

c. Negative twelve is equal to the sum of −5 and a number.

$$-12 = -5 + x$$

$$-12 + 5 = -5 + 5 + x \qquad \text{Add 5 to both sides.}$$

$$-7 = x \qquad \underline{\text{Check}}: -12 \stackrel{?}{=} -5 + (-7) \checkmark \quad \text{True}$$

The number is −7.

d. The value 1.4 subtracted from a number is 5.7.

$$x - 1.4 = 5.7$$

$$x - 1.4 + 1.4 = 5.7 + 1.4 \qquad \text{Add 1.4 to both sides.}$$

$$x = 7.1 \qquad \underline{\text{Check}}: \; 7.1 - 1.4 \stackrel{?}{=} 5.7 \checkmark \quad \text{True}$$

The number is 7.1.

Skill Practice Write an algebraic equation to represent each English sentence. Then solve the equation.

13. The quotient of a number and −2 is 8.

14. The product of a number and −3 is −24.

15. The sum of a number and 6 is −20.

16. 13 is equal to 5 subtracted from a number.

Answers

13. $\frac{x}{-2} = 8$; The number is −16.

14. $-3x = -24$; The number is 8.

15. $y + 6 = -20$; The number is −26.

16. $13 = x - 5$; The number is 18.

Section 2.1 Practice Exercises

For additional exercises, see Classroom Activities 2.1A–2.1D in the *Student's Resource Manual* at www.mhhe.com/moh.

Study Skills Exercise

After getting a test back, it is a good idea to correct the test so that you do not make the same errors again. One recommended approach is to use a clean sheet of paper, and divide the paper down the middle vertically as shown. For each problem that you missed on the test, rework the problem correctly on the left-hand side of the paper. Then give a written explanation on the right-hand side of the paper. To reinforce the correct procedure, do four more problems of that type.

Take the time this week to make corrections from your last test.

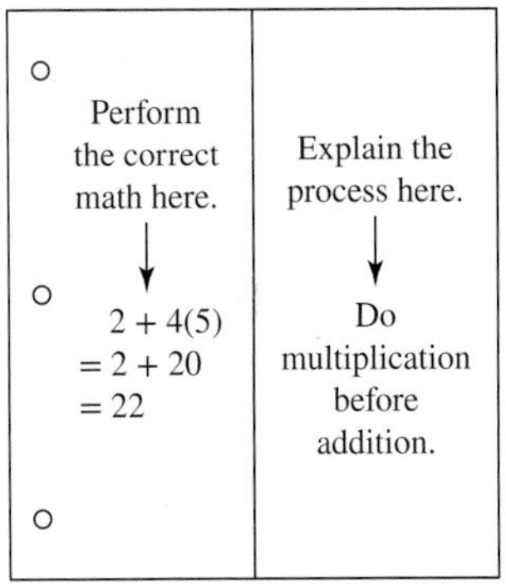

Vocabulary and Key Concepts

1. a. An ___equation___ is a statement that indicates that two expressions are equal.

b. A ___solution___ to an equation is a value of the variable that makes the equation a true statement.

c. An equation that can be written in the form $ax + b = c$ $(a \neq 0)$ is called a ___linear___ equation in one variable.

d. The set of all solutions to an equation is called the ___solution set___.

Concept 1: Definition of a Linear Equation in One Variable

For Exercises 2–6, identify the following as either an expression or an equation.

2. $2 - 8x + 10$
Expression

3. $x - 4 + 5x$
Expression

4. $8x + 2 = 7$
Equation

5. $9 = 2x - 4$
Equation

6. $3x^2 + x = -3$
Equation

7. Explain how to determine if a number is a solution to an equation.
Substitute the value into the equation and determine if the right-hand side is equal to the left-hand side.

8. Explain why the equations $6x = 12$ and $x = 2$ are *equivalent equations*.
They are equivalent equations because their solution sets are the same. The solution set is {2} in both cases.

For Exercises 9–14, determine whether the given number is a solution to the equation. **(See Example 1.)**

9. $x - 1 = 5;\ 4$ No

10. $x - 2 = 1;\ -1$ No

11. $5x = -10;\ -2$ Yes

12. $3x = 21;\ 7$ Yes

13. $3x + 9 = 3;\ -2$ Yes

14. $2x - 1 = -3;\ -1$ Yes

Concept 2: Addition and Subtraction Properties of Equality

For Exercises 15–34, solve each equation using the addition or subtraction property of equality. Be sure to check your answers. **(See Examples 2–3.)**

15. $x + 6 = 5$ $\{-1\}$

16. $x - 2 = 10$ $\{12\}$

17. $q - 14 = 6$ $\{20\}$

18. $w + 3 = -5$ $\{-8\}$

19. $2 + m = -15$ $\{-17\}$

20. $-6 + n = 10$ $\{16\}$

21. $-23 = y - 7$ $\{-16\}$

22. $-9 = -21 + b$ $\{12\}$

23. $4 + c = 4$ $\{0\}$

24. $-13 + b = -13$ $\{0\}$

25. $4.1 = 2.8 + a$ $\{1.3\}$

26. $5.1 = -2.5 + y$ $\{7.6\}$

27. $5 = z - \frac{1}{2}$ $\left\{\frac{11}{2}\right\}$ or $\left\{5\frac{1}{2}\right\}$

28. $-7 = p + \frac{2}{3}$ $\left\{-\frac{23}{3}\right\}$ or $\left\{-7\frac{2}{3}\right\}$

29. $x + \frac{5}{2} = \frac{1}{2}$ $\{-2\}$

30. $\frac{7}{3} = x - \frac{2}{3}$ $\{3\}$

31. $-6.02 + c = -8.15$ $\{-2.13\}$

32. $p + 0.035 = -1.12$ $\{-1.155\}$

33. $3.245 + t = -0.0225$ $\{-3.2675\}$

34. $-1.004 + k = 3.0589$ $\{4.0629\}$

Concept 3: Multiplication and Division Properties of Equality

For Exercises 35–54, solve each equation using the multiplication or division property of equality. Be sure to check your answers. **(See Examples 4–7.)**

35. $6x = 54$ $\{9\}$

36. $2w = 8$ $\{4\}$

37. $12 = -3p$ $\{-4\}$

38. $6 = -2q$ $\{-3\}$

39. $-5y = 0$ $\{0\}$

40. $-3k = 0$ $\{0\}$

41. $-\frac{y}{5} = 3$ $\{-15\}$

42. $-\frac{z}{7} = 1$ $\{-7\}$

43. $\frac{4}{5} = -t$ $\left\{-\frac{4}{5}\right\}$

44. $-\frac{3}{7} = -h$ $\left\{\frac{3}{7}\right\}$

45. $\frac{2}{5}a = -4$ $\{-10\}$

46. $\frac{3}{8}b = -9$ $\{-24\}$

47. $-\frac{1}{5}b = -\frac{4}{5}$ $\{4\}$

48. $-\frac{3}{10}w = \frac{2}{5}$ $\left\{-\frac{4}{3}\right\}$

49. $-41 = -x$ $\{41\}$

50. $32 = -y$ $\{-32\}$

51. $3.81 = -0.03p$ $\{-127\}$

52. $2.75 = -0.5q$ $\{-5.5\}$

53. $5.82y = -15.132$ $\{-2.6\}$

54. $-32.3x = -0.4522$ $\{0.014\}$

Concept 4: Translations

For Exercises 55–66, write an algebraic equation to represent each English sentence. (Let x represent the unknown number.) Then solve the equation. **(See Example 8.)**

55. The sum of negative eight and a number is forty-two. $-8 + x = 42$; The number is 50.

56. The sum of thirty-one and a number is thirteen. $31 + x = 13$; The number is -18.

57. The difference of a number and negative six is eighteen. $x - (-6) = 18$; The number is 12.

58. The sum of negative twelve and a number is negative fifteen. $-12 + x = -15$; The number is -3.

59. The product of a number and seven is the same as negative sixty-three. $x \cdot 7 = -63$ or $7x = -63$; The number is -9.

60. The product of negative three and a number is the same as twenty-four. $-3x = 24$; The number is -8.

61. The value 3.2 subtracted from a number is 2.1. $x - 3.2 = 2.1$; The number is 5.3.

62. The value -3 subtracted from a number is 4. $x - (-3) = 4$; The number is 1.

63. The quotient of a number and twelve is one-third. $\frac{x}{12} = \frac{1}{3}$; The number is 4.

64. Eighteen is equal to the quotient of a number and two. $18 = \frac{x}{2}$; The number is 36.

65. The sum of a number and $\frac{5}{8}$ is $\frac{13}{8}$. $x + \frac{5}{8} = \frac{13}{8}$; The number is 1.

66. The difference of a number and $\frac{2}{3}$ is $\frac{1}{3}$. $x - \frac{2}{3} = \frac{1}{3}$; The number is 1.

Mixed Exercises

For Exercises 67–90, solve each equation using the appropriate property of equality.

67. a. $x - 9 = 1$ $\{10\}$
b. $-9x = 1$ $\left\{-\frac{1}{9}\right\}$

68. a. $k - 2 = -4$ $\{-2\}$
b. $-2k = -4$ $\{2\}$

69. a. $-\frac{2}{3}h = 8$ $\{-12\}$
b. $\frac{2}{3} + h = 8$ $\left\{\frac{22}{3}\right\}$

70. a. $\frac{3}{4}p = 15$ $\{20\}$
b. $\frac{3}{4} + p = 15$ $\left\{\frac{57}{4}\right\}$

71. $\frac{r}{3} = -12$ $\{-36\}$

72. $\frac{d}{-4} = 5$ $\{-20\}$

73. $k + 16 = 32$ $\{16\}$

74. $-18 = -9 + t$ $\{-9\}$

75. $16k = 32$ $\{2\}$

76. $-18 = -9t$ $\{2\}$

77. $7 = -4q$ $\left\{-\frac{7}{4}\right\}$

78. $-3s = 10$ $\left\{-\frac{10}{3}\right\}$

79. $-4 + q = 7$ $\{11\}$

80. $s - 3 = 10$ $\{13\}$

81. $-\frac{1}{3}d = 12$ $\{-36\}$

82. $-\frac{2}{5}m = 10$ $\{-25\}$

83. $4 = \frac{1}{2} + z$ $\left\{\frac{7}{2}\right\}$

84. $3 = \frac{1}{4} + p$ $\left\{\frac{11}{4}\right\}$

85. $1.2y = 4.8$ $\{4\}$

86. $4.3w = 8.6$ $\{2\}$

87. $4.8 = 1.2 + y$ $\{3.6\}$

88. $8.6 = w - 4.3$ $\{12.9\}$

89. $0.0034 = y - 0.405$ $\{0.4084\}$

90. $-0.98 = m + 1.0034$ $\{-1.9834\}$

For Exercises 91–98, determine if the equation is a linear equation in one variable. Answer yes or no.

91. $4p + 5 = 0$ Yes

92. $3x - 5y = 0$ No

93. $4 + 2a^2 = 5$ No

94. $-8t = 7$ Yes

95. $x - 4 = 9$ Yes

96. $2x^3 + y = 0$ No

97. $19b = -3$ Yes

98. $13 + x = 19$ Yes

Expanding Your Skills

For Exercises 99–104, construct an equation with the given solution set. Answers will vary.

99. $\{6\}$ For example: $y + 9 = 15$

100. $\{2\}$ For example: $1 + x = 3$

101. $\{-4\}$ For example: $2p = -8$

102. $\{-10\}$ For example: $-4t = 40$

103. $\{0\}$ For example: $5a + 5 = 5$

104. $\{1\}$ For example: $6k + 1 = 7$

For Exercises 105–108, simplify by collecting the *like* terms. Then solve the equation.

105. $5x - 4x + 7 = 8 - 2$ $\{-1\}$

106. $2 + 3 = 2y + 1 - y$ $\{4\}$

107. $6p - 3p = 15 + 6$ $\{7\}$

108. $12 - 20 = 2t + 2t$ $\{-2\}$

Section 2.2 Solving Linear Equations

Concepts

1. Linear Equations Involving Multiple Steps
2. Procedure for Solving a Linear Equation in One Variable
3. Conditional Equations, Identities, and Contradictions

1. Linear Equations Involving Multiple Steps

Previously we studied a one-step process to solve linear equations by using the addition, subtraction, multiplication, and division properties of equality. In Example 1, we solve the equation $-2w - 7 = 11$. Solving this equation will require multiple steps. To understand the proper steps, always remember that the ultimate goal is to isolate the variable. Therefore, we will first isolate the *term* containing the variable before dividing both sides by -2.

Classroom Example: p. 119, Exercise 14

Example 1 Solving a Linear Equation

Solve the equation. $-2w - 7 = 11$

Solution:

$$-2w - 7 = 11$$

$$-2w - 7 + 7 = 11 + 7$$ Add 7 to both sides of the equation. This isolates the w-term.

$$-2w = 18$$

$$\frac{-2w}{-2} = \frac{18}{-2}$$ Next, apply the division property of equality to obtain a coefficient of 1 for w. Divide by -2 on both sides.

$$w = -9$$

Check:

$$-2w - 7 = 11$$

$$-2(-9) - 7 \stackrel{?}{=} 11$$ Substitute $w = -9$ in the original equation.

$$18 - 7 \stackrel{?}{=} 11$$

$$11 \stackrel{?}{=} 11 \checkmark$$ True

The solution set is $\{-9\}$.

Skill Practice Solve the equation.

1. $-5y - 5 = 10$

Classroom Example: p. 119, Exercise 22

Example 2 Solving a Linear Equation

Solve the equation. $2 = \frac{1}{5}x + 3$

Solution:

$$2 = \frac{1}{5}x + 3$$

$$2 - 3 = \frac{1}{5}x + 3 - 3$$ Subtract 3 from both sides. This isolates the x-term.

$$-1 = \frac{1}{5}x$$ Simplify.

Answer

1. $\{-3\}$

$5(-1) = 5 \cdot \left(\frac{1}{5}x\right)$	Next, apply the multiplication property of equality to obtain a coefficient of 1 for *x*.
$-5 = 1x$	
$-5 = x$	Simplify. The answer checks in the original equation.

The solution set is $\{-5\}$.

Skill Practice Solve the equation.

2. $2 = \frac{1}{2}a - 7$

In Example 3, the variable *x* appears on both sides of the equation. In this case, apply the addition or subtraction property of equality to collect the variable terms on one side of the equation and the constant terms on the other side. Then use the multiplication or division property of equality to get a coefficient equal to 1 on the variable term.

Example 3 Solving a Linear Equation

Classroom Example: p. 119, Exercise 30

Solve the equation. $6x - 4 = 2x - 8$

Solution:

$6x - 4 = 2x - 8$	
$6x - 2x - 4 = 2x - 2x - 8$	Subtract $2x$ from both sides leaving $0x$ on the right-hand side.
$4x - 4 = 0x - 8$	Simplify.
$4x - 4 = -8$	The *x*-terms have now been combined on one side of the equation.
$4x - 4 + 4 = -8 + 4$	Add 4 to both sides of the equation. This combines the constant terms on the *other* side of the equation.
$4x = -4$	
$\frac{4x}{4} = \frac{-4}{4}$	To obtain a coefficient of 1 for *x*, divide both sides of the equation by 4.
$x = -1$	The answer checks in the original equation.

The solution set is $\{-1\}$.

Skill Practice Solve the equation.

3. $10x - 3 = 4x - 2$

Answers

2. $\{18\}$ **3.** $\left\{\frac{1}{6}\right\}$

TIP: It is important to note that the variable may be isolated on either side of the equation. We will solve the equation from Example 3 again, this time isolating the variable on the right-hand side.

$$6x - 4 = 2x - 8$$

$$6x - 6x - 4 = 2x - 6x - 8 \quad \text{Subtract } 6x \text{ on both sides.}$$

$$0x - 4 = -4x - 8$$

$$-4 = -4x - 8$$

$$-4 + 8 = -4x - 8 + 8 \quad \text{Add 8 to both sides.}$$

$$4 = -4x$$

$$\frac{4}{-4} = \frac{-4x}{-4} \quad \text{Divide both sides by } -4.$$

$$-1 = x \quad \text{or equivalently } x = -1$$

2. Procedure for Solving a Linear Equation in One Variable

In some cases, it is necessary to simplify both sides of a linear equation before applying the properties of equality. Therefore, we offer the following steps to solve a linear equation in one variable.

Solving a Linear Equation in One Variable

Step 1 Simplify both sides of the equation.
- Clear parentheses
- Combine *like* terms

Step 2 Use the addition or subtraction property of equality to collect the variable terms on one side of the equation.

Step 3 Use the addition or subtraction property of equality to collect the constant terms on the other side of the equation.

Step 4 Use the multiplication or division property of equality to make the coefficient of the variable term equal to 1.

Step 5 Check your answer.

Classroom Example: p. 119, Exercise 44

Example 4 Solving a Linear Equation

Solve the equation. $7 + 3 = 2(p - 3)$

Solution:

$7 + 3 = 2(p - 3)$

$10 = 2p - 6$ **Step 1:** Simplify both sides of the equation by clearing parentheses and combining *like* terms.

Step 2: The variable terms are already on one side.

$10 + 6 = 2p - 6 + 6$ **Step 3:** Add 6 to both sides to collect the constant terms on the other side.

$16 = 2p$

$\dfrac{16}{2} = \dfrac{2p}{2}$	**Step 4:**	Divide both sides by 2 to obtain a coefficient of 1 for p.
$8 = p$	**Step 5:**	Check:
		$7 + 3 = 2(p - 3)$
		$10 \stackrel{?}{=} 2(8 - 3)$
		$10 \stackrel{?}{=} 2(5)$
The solution set is $\{8\}$.		$10 \stackrel{?}{=} 10$ ✓ True

Skill Practice Solve the equation.

4. $12 + 2 = 7(3 - y)$

Example 5 Solving a Linear Equation

Solve the equation. $2.2y - 8.3 = 6.2y + 12.1$

Solution:

$2.2y - 8.3 = 6.2y + 12.1$	**Step 1:**	The right- and left-hand sides are already simplified.
$2.2y - 2.2y - 8.3 = 6.2y - 2.2y + 12.1$ $-8.3 = 4y + 12.1$	**Step 2:**	Subtract 2.2y from both sides to collect the variable terms on one side of the equation.
$-8.3 - 12.1 = 4y + 12.1 - 12.1$ $-20.4 = 4y$	**Step 3:**	Subtract 12.1 from both sides to collect the constant terms on the other side.
$\dfrac{-20.4}{4} = \dfrac{4y}{4}$ $-5.1 = y$	**Step 4:**	To obtain a coefficient of 1 for the y-term, divide both sides of the equation by 4.
$y = -5.1$	**Step 5:**	Check:
		$2.2y - 8.3 = 6.2y + 12.1$
		$2.2(-5.1) - 8.3 \stackrel{?}{=} 6.2(-5.1) + 12.1$
		$-11.22 - 8.3 \stackrel{?}{=} -31.62 + 12.1$
The solution set is $\{-5.1\}$.		$-19.52 \stackrel{?}{=} -19.52$ ✓ True

Skill Practice Solve the equation.

5. $1.5t + 2.3 = 3.5t - 1.9$

Classroom Example: p. 119, Exercise 46

TIP: In Examples 5 and 6 we collected the variable terms on the right side to avoid negative coefficients on the variable term.

Answers

4. {1} **5.** {2.1}

Classroom Example: p. 119, Exercise 50

Example 6 Solving a Linear Equation

Solve the equation. $2 + 7x - 5 = 6(x + 3) + 2x$

Solution:

$2 + 7x - 5 = 6(x + 3) + 2x$

$-3 + 7x = 6x + 18 + 2x$ **Step 1:** Add *like* terms on the left. Clear parentheses on the right.

$-3 + 7x = 8x + 18$ Combine *like* terms.

$-3 + 7x - 7x = 8x - 7x + 18$ **Step 2:** Subtract $7x$ from both sides.

$-3 = x + 18$ Simplify.

$-3 - 18 = x + 18 - 8$ **Step 3:** Subtract 18 from both sides.

$-21 = x$ **Step 4:** Because the coefficient of the x term is already 1, there is no need to apply the multiplication or division property of equality.

$x = -21$

The solution set is $\{-21\}$. **Step 5:** The check is left to the reader.

Skill Practice Solve the equation.

6. $4(2y - 1) + y = 6y + 3 - y$

Classroom Example: p. 119, Exercise 54

Example 7 Solving a Linear Equation

Solve the equation. $9 - (z - 3) + 4z = 4z - 5(z + 2) - 6$

Solution:

$9 - (z - 3) + 4z = 4z - 5(z + 2) - 6$

$9 - z + 3 + 4z = 4z - 5z - 10 - 6$ **Step 1:** Clear parentheses.

$12 + 3z = -z - 16$ Combine *like* terms.

$12 + 3z + z = -z + z - 16$ **Step 2:** Add z to both sides.

$12 + 4z = -16$

$12 - 12 + 4z = -16 - 12$ **Step 3:** Subtract 12 from both sides.

$4z = -28$

$\frac{4z}{4} = \frac{-28}{4}$ **Step 4:** Divide both sides by 4.

$z = -7$ **Step 5:** The check is left for the reader.

The solution set is $\{-7\}$.

Avoiding Mistakes

When distributing a negative number through a set of parentheses, be sure to change the signs of every term within the parentheses.

Skill Practice Solve the equation.

7. $10 - (x + 5) + 3x = 6x - 5(x - 1) - 3$

Answers

6. $\left\{\frac{7}{4}\right\}$ **7.** $\{-3\}$

3. Conditional Equations, Identities, and Contradictions

The solutions to an equation are the values of x that make the equation a true statement. A linear equation in one variable has one unique solution. Some types of equations, however, have no solution while others have infinitely many solutions.

I. Conditional Equations

An equation that is true for some values of the variable but false for other values is called a **conditional equation**. The equation $x + 4 = 6$, for example, is true on the condition that $x = 2$. For other values of x, the statement $x + 4 = 6$ is false.

$$x + 4 = 6$$
$$x + 4 - 4 = 6 - 4$$
$$x = 2 \quad \text{(Conditional equation)} \quad \text{Solution set: } \{2\}$$

II. Contradictions

Some equations have no solution, such as $x + 1 = x + 2$. There is no value of x, that when increased by 1 will equal the same value increased by 2. If we try to solve the equation by subtracting x from both sides, we get the contradiction $1 = 2$. This indicates that the equation has no solution. An equation that has no solution is called a **contradiction**. The solution set is the empty set. The **empty set** is the set with no elements and is denoted by { }.

TIP: The empty set is also called the null set and can be expressed by the symbol $\varnothing$.

$$x + 1 = x + 2$$
$$x - x + 1 = x - x + 2$$
$$1 = 2 \quad \text{(Contradiction)} \quad \text{Solution set: } \{\ \}$$

Avoiding Mistakes

There are two ways to express the empty set: { } or $\varnothing$. Be sure that you do not use them together. It would be incorrect to write $\{\varnothing\}$.

III. Identities

An equation that has all real numbers as its solution set is called an **identity**. For example, consider the equation, $x + 4 = x + 4$. Because the left- and right-hand sides are *identical*, any real number substituted for x will result in equal quantities on both sides. If we subtract x from both sides of the equation, we get the identity $4 = 4$. In such a case, the solution is the set of all real numbers.

$$x + 4 = x + 4$$
$$x - x + 4 = x - x + 4$$
$$4 = 4 \quad \text{(Identity)} \quad \text{Solution set: The set of real numbers.}$$

Example 8 Identifying Conditional Equations, Contradictions, and Identities

Classroom Examples: p. 120, Exercises 60, 62, and 64

Solve the equation. Identify each equation as a conditional equation, a contradiction, or an identity.

a. $4k - 5 = 2(2k - 3) + 1$ **b.** $2(b - 4) = 2b - 7$ **c.** $3x + 7 = 2x - 5$

Solution:

a.

$4k - 5 = 2(2k - 3) + 1$	
$4k - 5 = 4k - 6 + 1$	Clear parentheses.
$4k - 5 = 4k - 5$	Combine *like* terms.
$4k - 4k - 5 = 4k - 4k - 5$	Subtract $4k$ from both sides.
$-5 = -5$ (Identity)	

This is an identity. Solution set: The set of real numbers.

b.
$$2(b-4) = 2b-7$$
$$2b-8 = 2b-7 \quad \text{Clear parentheses.}$$
$$2b-2b-8 = 2b-2b-7 \quad \text{Subtract } 2b \text{ from both sides.}$$
$$-8 = -7 \quad \text{(Contradiction)}$$
This is a contradiction. Solution set: { }

c.
$$3x+7 = 2x-5$$
$$3x-2x+7 = 2x-2x-5 \quad \text{Subtract } 2x \text{ from both sides.}$$
$$x+7 = -5 \quad \text{Simplify.}$$
$$x+7-7 = -5-7 \quad \text{Subtract 7 from both sides.}$$
$$x = -12 \quad \text{(Conditional equation)}$$
This is a conditional equation. The solution set is $\{-12\}$. (The equation is true only on the condition that $x = -12$.)

Skill Practice Solve the equation. Identify the equation as a conditional equation, a contradiction, or an identity.

8. $4(2t+1) - 1 = 8t+3$ **9.** $3x - 5 = 4x + 1 - x$ **10.** $6(v-2) = 2v - 4$

Answers

8. The set of real numbers; identity
9. { }; contradiction
10. {2}; conditional equation

Section 2.2 Practice Exercises

Study Skills Exercise

For additional exercises, see Classroom Activities 2.2A–2.2C in the *Student's Resource Manual* at www.mhhe.com/moh.

Several strategies are given here about taking notes. Check the activities that you routinely do and discuss how the other suggestions may improve your learning.

_______ Read your notes after class and fill in details.
_______ Highlight important terms and definitions.
_______ Review your notes from the previous class.
_______ Bring pencils (more than one) and paper to class.
_______ Sit in class where you can clearly read the board and hear your instructor.
_______ Turn off your cell phone and keep it off your desk to avoid distraction.

Vocabulary and Key Concepts

1. a. A ___conditional___ equation is true for some values of the variable, but false for other values.

b. An equation that has no solution is called a ___contradiction___.

c. The set containing no elements is called the ___empty or null___ set.

d. An equation that has all real numbers as its solution set is called an ___identity___.

Review Exercises

For Exercises 2–5, simplify each expression by clearing parentheses and combining *like* terms.

2. $5z + 2 - 7z - 3z$ $-5z+2$

3. $10 - 4w + 7w - 2 + w$ $4w+8$

4. $-(-7p+9) + (3p-1)$ $10p-10$

5. $8y - (2y+3) - 19$ $6y-22$

6. Explain the difference between simplifying an expression and solving an equation.
To simplify an expression, clear parentheses and combine *like* terms. To solve an equation, use the addition, subtraction, multiplication, and division properties of equality to isolate the variable.

For Exercises 7–12, solve each equation using the addition, subtraction, multiplication, or division property of equality.

7. $7 = p - 12$ $\{19\}$

8. $5w = -30$ $\{-6\}$

9. $-7y = 21$ $\{-3\}$

10. $x + 8 = -15$ $\{-23\}$

11. $z - 23 = -28$ $\{-5\}$

12. $-\frac{9}{8} = -\frac{3}{4}k$ $\left\{\frac{3}{2}\right\}$

Concept 1: Linear Equations Involving Multiple Steps

For Exercises 13–36, solve each equation using the steps outlined in the text. **(See Examples 1–3.)**

13. $6z + 1 = 13$ $\{2\}$

14. $5x + 2 = -13$ $\{-3\}$

15. $3y - 4 = 14$ $\{6\}$

16. $-7w - 5 = -19$ $\{2\}$

17. $-2p + 8 = 3$ $\left\{\frac{5}{2}\right\}$

18. $2b - \frac{1}{4} = 5$ $\left\{\frac{21}{8}\right\}$

19. $0.2x + 3.1 = -5.3$ $\{-42\}$

20. $-1.8 + 2.4a = -6.6$ $\{-2\}$

21. $\frac{5}{8} = \frac{1}{4} - \frac{1}{2}p$ $\left\{-\frac{3}{4}\right\}$

22. $\frac{6}{7} = \frac{1}{7} + \frac{5}{3}r$ $\left\{\frac{3}{7}\right\}$

23. $7w - 6w + 1 = 10 - 4$ $\{5\}$

24. $5v - 3 - 4v = 13$ $\{16\}$

25. $11h - 8 - 9h = -16$ $\{-4\}$

26. $6u - 5 - 8u = -7$ $\{1\}$

27. $3a + 7 = 2a - 19$ $\{-26\}$

28. $6b - 20 = 14 + 5b$ $\{34\}$

29. $-4r - 28 = -58 - r$ $\{10\}$

30. $-6x - 7 = -3 - 8x$ $\{2\}$

31. $-2z - 8 = -z$ $\{-8\}$

32. $-7t + 4 = -6t$ $\{4\}$

33. $\frac{5}{6}x + \frac{2}{3} = -\frac{1}{6}x - \frac{5}{3}$ $\left\{-\frac{7}{3}\right\}$

34. $\frac{3}{7}x - \frac{1}{4} = -\frac{4}{7}x - \frac{5}{4}$ $\{-1\}$

35. $3y - 2 = 5y - 2$ $\{0\}$

36. $4 + 10t = -8t + 4$ $\{0\}$

Concept 2: Procedure for Solving a Linear Equation in One Variable

For Exercises 37–58, solve each equation using the steps outlined in the text. **(See Examples 4–7.)**

37. $4q + 14 = 2$ $\{-3\}$

38. $6 = 7m - 1$ $\{1\}$

39. $-9 = 4n - 1$ $\{-2\}$

40. $-\frac{1}{2} - 4x = 8$ $\left\{-\frac{17}{8}\right\}$

41. $3(2p - 4) = 15$ $\left\{\frac{9}{2}\right\}$

42. $4(t + 15) = 20$ $\{-10\}$

43. $6(3x + 2) - 10 = -4$ $\left\{-\frac{1}{3}\right\}$

44. $4(2k + 1) - 1 = 5$ $\left\{\frac{1}{4}\right\}$

45. $3.4x - 2.5 = 2.8x + 3.5$ $\{10\}$

46. $5.8w + 1.1 = 6.3w + 5.6$ $\{-9\}$

47. $17(s + 3) = 4(s - 10) + 13$ $\{-6\}$

48. $5(4 + p) = 3(3p - 1) - 9$ $\{8\}$

49. $6(3t - 4) + 10 = 5(t - 2) - (3t + 4)$ $\{0\}$

50. $-5y + 2(2y + 1) = 2(5y - 1) - 7$ $\{1\}$

51. $5 - 3(x + 2) = 5$ $\{-2\}$

52. $1 - 6(2 - h) = 7$ $\{3\}$

53. $3(2z - 6) - 4(3z + 1) = 5 - 2(z + 1)$ $\left\{-\frac{25}{4}\right\}$

54. $-2(4a + 3) - 5(2 - a) = 3(2a + 3) - 7$ $\{-2\}$

55. $-2[(4p+1)-(3p-1)]=5(3-p)-9$ $\left\{\frac{10}{3}\right\}$

56. $5-(6k+1)=2[(5k-3)-(k-2)]$ $\left\{\frac{3}{7}\right\}$

57. $3(-0.9n+0.5)=-3.5n+1.3$ $\{-0.25\}$

58. $7(0.4m-0.1)=5.2m+0.86$ $\{-0.65\}$

Concept 3: Conditional Equations, Identities, and Contradictions

For Exercises 59–64, solve each equation. Identify as a conditional equation, an identity, or a contradiction. **(See Example 8.)**

59. $2(k-7)=2k-13$ $\{\ \}$; contradiction

60. $5h+4=5(h+1)-1$ The set of real numbers; identity

61. $7x+3=6(x-2)$ $\{-15\}$; conditional equation

62. $3y-1=1+3y$ $\{\ \}$; contradiction

63. $3-5.2p=-5.2p+3$ The set of real numbers; identity

64. $2(q+3)=4q+q-9$ $\{5\}$; conditional equation

65. A conditional linear equation has (choose one): one solution, no solution, or infinitely many solutions. One solution

66. An equation that is a contradiction has (choose one): one solution, no solution, or infinitely many solutions. No solution

67. An equation that is an identity has (choose one): one solution, no solution, or infinitely many solutions. Infinitely many solutions

68. If the only solution to a linear equation is 5, then is the equation a conditional equation, an identity, or a contradiction? Conditional equation

Mixed Exercises

For Exercises 69–92, solve each equation.

69. $4p-6=8+2p$ $\{7\}$

70. $\frac{1}{2}t-2=3$ $\{10\}$

71. $2k-9=-8$ $\left\{\frac{1}{2}\right\}$

72. $3(y-2)+5=5$ $\{2\}$

73. $7(w-2)=-14-3w$ $\{0\}$

74. $0.24=0.4m$ $\{0.6\}$

75. $2(x+2)-3=2x+1$ The set of real numbers

76. $n+\frac{1}{4}=-\frac{1}{2}$ $\left\{-\frac{3}{4}\right\}$

77. $0.5b=-23$ $\{-46\}$

78. $3(2r+1)=6(r+2)-6$ $\{\ \}$

79. $8-2q=4$ $\{2\}$

80. $\frac{x}{7}-3=1$ $\{28\}$

81. $2-4(y-5)=-4$ $\left\{\frac{13}{2}\right\}$

82. $4-3(4p-1)=-8$ $\left\{\frac{5}{4}\right\}$

83. $0.4(a+20)=6$ $\{-5\}$

84. $2.2r-12=3.4$ $\{7\}$

85. $10(2n+1)-6=20(n-1)+12$ $\{\ \}$

86. $\frac{2}{5}y+5=-3$ $\{-20\}$

87. $c+0.123=2.328$ $\{2.205\}$

88. $4(2z+3)=8(z-3)+36$ The set of real numbers

89. $\frac{4}{5}t-1=\frac{1}{5}t+5$ $\{10\}$

90. $6g-8=4-3g$ $\left\{\frac{4}{3}\right\}$

91. $8-(3q+4)=6-q$ $\{-1\}$

92. $6w-(8+2w)=2(w-4)$ $\{0\}$

Expanding Your Skills

93. Suppose the solution set for x in the equation $x+a=10$ is $\{-5\}$. Find the value of a. $a=15$

94. Suppose the solution set for x in the equation $x+a=-12$ is $\{6\}$. Find the value of a. $a=-18$

95. Suppose the solution set for x in the equation $ax=12$ is $\{3\}$. Find the value of a. $a=4$

96. Suppose the solution set for x in the equation $ax=49.5$ is $\{11\}$. Find the value of a. $a=4.5$

97. Write an equation that is an identity. Answers may vary. For example: $5x+2=2+5x$

98. Write an equation that is a contradiction. Answers may vary. For example: $4x-3=4x+1$

Linear Equations: Clearing Fractions and Decimals

Section 2.3

Concepts

1. Linear Equations Containing Fractions
2. Linear Equations Containing Decimals

1. Linear Equations Containing Fractions

Linear equations that contain fractions can be solved in different ways. The first procedure, illustrated here, uses the method previously outlined.

$$\frac{5}{6}x - \frac{3}{4} = \frac{1}{3}$$

$$\frac{5}{6}x - \frac{3}{4} + \frac{3}{4} = \frac{1}{3} + \frac{3}{4}$$ To isolate the variable term, add $\frac{3}{4}$ to both sides.

$$\frac{5}{6}x = \frac{4}{12} + \frac{9}{12}$$ Find the common denominator on the right-hand side.

$$\frac{5}{6}x = \frac{13}{12}$$ Simplify.

$$\frac{6}{5}\left(\frac{5}{6}x\right) = \frac{\overset{1}{\cancel{6}}}{5}\left(\frac{13}{\underset{2}{\cancel{12}}}\right)$$ Multiply by the reciprocal of $\frac{5}{6}$, which is $\frac{6}{5}$.

$$x = \frac{13}{10}$$ The solution set is $\left\{\frac{13}{10}\right\}$.

Sometimes it is simpler to solve an equation with fractions by eliminating the fractions first by using a process called **clearing fractions**. To clear fractions in the equation $\frac{5}{6}x - \frac{3}{4} = \frac{1}{3}$, we can apply the multiplication property of equality to multiply both sides of the equation by the least common denominator (LCD). In this case, the LCD of $\frac{5}{6}x$, $-\frac{3}{4}$, and $\frac{1}{3}$ is 12. Because each denominator in the equation is a factor of 12, we can simplify common factors to leave integer coefficients for each term.

Example 1 Solving a Linear Equation by Clearing Fractions

Classroom Example: p. 126, Exercise 18

Solve the equation by clearing fractions first. $\frac{5}{6}x - \frac{3}{4} = \frac{1}{3}$

Solution:

$$\frac{5}{6}x - \frac{3}{4} = \frac{1}{3}$$ The LCD of $\frac{5}{6}x$, $-\frac{3}{4}$, and $\frac{1}{3}$ is 12.

$$12\left(\frac{5}{6}x - \frac{3}{4}\right) = 12\left(\frac{1}{3}\right)$$ Multiply both sides of the equation by the LCD, 12.

$$\frac{\overset{2}{\cancel{12}}}{1}\left(\frac{5}{\cancel{6}}x\right) - \frac{\overset{3}{\cancel{12}}}{1}\left(\frac{3}{\cancel{4}}\right) = \frac{\overset{4}{\cancel{12}}}{1}\left(\frac{1}{\cancel{3}}\right)$$ Apply the distributive property (recall that $12 = \frac{12}{1}$).

$$2(5x) - 3(3) = 4(1)$$ Simplify common factors to clear the fractions.

$$10x - 9 = 4$$

$$10x - 9 + 9 = 4 + 9$$ Add 9 to both sides.

$$10x = 13$$

$$\frac{10x}{10} = \frac{13}{10}$$ Divide both sides by 10.

$$x = \frac{13}{10}$$ The solution set is $\left\{\frac{13}{10}\right\}$.

TIP: Recall that the multiplication property of equality indicates that multiplying both sides of an equation by a nonzero constant results in an equivalent equation.

TIP: The fractions in this equation can be eliminated by multiplying both sides of the equation by *any* common multiple of the denominators. These include 12, 24, 36, 48, and so on. We chose 12 because it is the *least* common multiple.

Skill Practice Solve the equation by clearing fractions.

1. $\frac{2}{5}y + \frac{1}{2} = -\frac{7}{10}$

In this section, we combine the process for clearing fractions and decimals with the general strategies for solving linear equations. To solve a linear equation, it is important to follow these steps.

Solving a Linear Equation in One Variable

Step 1 Simplify both sides of the equation.
- Clear parentheses
- Consider clearing fractions and decimals (if any are present) by multiplying both sides of the equation by a common denominator of all terms
- Combine *like* terms

Step 2 Use the addition or subtraction property of equality to collect the variable terms on one side of the equation.

Step 3 Use the addition or subtraction property of equality to collect the constant terms on the other side of the equation.

Step 4 Use the multiplication or division property of equality to make the coefficient of the variable term equal to 1.

Step 5 Check your answer.

Classroom Example: p. 126, Exercise 22

Example 2 Solving a Linear Equation Containing Fractions

Solve the equation. $\frac{1}{6}x - \frac{2}{3} = \frac{1}{5}x - 1$

Solution:

$$\frac{1}{6}x - \frac{2}{3} = \frac{1}{5}x - 1$$ The LCD of $\frac{1}{6}x$, $-\frac{2}{3}$, $\frac{1}{5}x$, and $\frac{-1}{1}$ is 30.

$$30\left(\frac{1}{6}x - \frac{2}{3}\right) = 30\left(\frac{1}{5}x - 1\right)$$ Multiply by the LCD, 30.

$$\frac{\overset{5}{\cancel{30}}}{1} \cdot \frac{1}{\cancel{6}}x - \frac{\overset{10}{\cancel{30}}}{1} \cdot \frac{2}{\cancel{3}} = \frac{\overset{6}{\cancel{30}}}{1} \cdot \frac{1}{\cancel{5}}x - 30(1)$$ Apply the distributive property (recall $30 = \frac{30}{1}$).

$$5x - 20 = 6x - 30$$ Clear fractions.

$$5x - 6x - 20 = 6x - 6x - 30$$ Subtract $6x$ from both sides.

$$-x - 20 = -30$$

Answers

1. $\{-3\}$

$$-x - 20 + 20 = -30 + 20$$ Add 20 to both sides.

$$-x = -10$$

$$\frac{-x}{-1} = \frac{-10}{-1}$$ Divide both sides by -1.

$$x = 10$$ The check is left to the reader.

The solution set is $\{10\}$.

Skill Practice Solve the equation.

2. $\frac{2}{5}x - \frac{1}{2} = \frac{7}{4} + \frac{3}{10}x$

Example 3 **Solving a Linear Equation Containing Fractions**

Classroom Example: p. 126, Exercise 26

Solve the equation. $\frac{1}{3}(x + 7) - \frac{1}{2}(x + 1) = 4$

Solution:

$$\frac{1}{3}(x + 7) - \frac{1}{2}(x + 1) = 4$$

$$\frac{1}{3}x + \frac{7}{3} - \frac{1}{2}x - \frac{1}{2} = 4$$ Clear parentheses.

$$6\left(\frac{1}{3}x + \frac{7}{3} - \frac{1}{2}x - \frac{1}{2}\right) = 6(4)$$ The LCD of $\frac{1}{3}x$, $\frac{7}{3}$, $-\frac{1}{2}x$, $-\frac{1}{2}$, and $\frac{4}{1}$ is 6.

$$\frac{\overset{2}{\cancel{6}}}{1} \cdot \frac{1}{\cancel{3}}x + \frac{\overset{2}{\cancel{6}}}{1} \cdot \frac{7}{\cancel{3}} + \frac{\overset{3}{\cancel{6}}}{1}\left(-\frac{1}{\cancel{2}}x\right) + \frac{\overset{3}{\cancel{6}}}{1}\left(-\frac{1}{\cancel{2}}\right) = 6(4)$$ Apply the distributive property.

$$2x + 14 - 3x - 3 = 24$$

$$-x + 11 = 24$$ Combine *like* terms.

$$-x + 11 - 11 = 24 - 11$$ Subtract 11.

$$-x = 13$$

$$\frac{-x}{-1} = \frac{13}{-1}$$ Divide by -1.

$$x = -13$$ The check is left to the reader.

The solution set is $\{-13\}$.

TIP: In Example 3 both parentheses and fractions are present within the equation. In such a case, we recommend that you clear parentheses first. Then clear the fractions.

Avoiding Mistakes

When multiplying an equation by the LCD, be sure to multiply all terms on both sides of the equation, including terms that are not fractions.

Skill Practice Solve the equation.

3. $\frac{1}{5}(z + 1) + \frac{1}{4}(z + 3) = 2$

Answers

2. $\left\{\frac{45}{2}\right\}$ **3.** $\left\{\frac{7}{3}\right\}$

Classroom Example: p. 127, Exercise 32

Example 4 **Solving a Linear Equation Containing Fractions**

Solve the equation. $\frac{x-2}{5} - \frac{x-4}{2} = 2$

Solution:

$$\frac{x-2}{5} - \frac{x-4}{2} = \frac{2}{1}$$ The LCD of $\frac{x-2}{5}$, $\frac{x-4}{2}$, and $\frac{2}{1}$ is 10.

$$10\left(\frac{x-2}{5} - \frac{x-4}{2}\right) = 10\left(\frac{2}{1}\right)$$ Multiply both sides by 10.

$$\frac{\overset{2}{\cancel{10}}}{1} \cdot \left(\frac{x-2}{\cancel{5}}\right) - \frac{\overset{5}{\cancel{10}}}{1} \cdot \left(\frac{x-4}{\cancel{2}}\right) = \frac{10}{1} \cdot \left(\frac{2}{1}\right)$$ Apply the distributive property.

$$2(x-2) - 5(x-4) = 20$$ Clear fractions.

$$2x - 4 - 5x + 20 = 20$$ Apply the distributive property.

$$-3x + 16 = 20$$ Simplify both sides of the equation.

$$-3x + 16 - 16 = 20 - 16$$ Subtract 16 from both sides.

$$-3x = 4$$

$$\frac{-3x}{-3} = \frac{4}{-3}$$ Divide both sides by −3.

$$x = -\frac{4}{3}$$ The check is left to the reader.

The solution set is $\left\{-\frac{4}{3}\right\}$.

Skill Practice Solve the equation.

4. $\frac{x+1}{4} + \frac{x+2}{6} = 1$

Avoiding Mistakes

In Example 4, several of the fractions in the equation have two terms in the numerator. It is important to enclose these fractions in parentheses when clearing fractions. In this way, we will remember to use the distributive property to multiply the factors shown in blue with both terms from the numerator of the fractions.

2. Linear Equations Containing Decimals

The same procedure used to clear fractions in an equation can be used to **clear decimals**. For example, consider the equation

$$2.5x + 3 = 1.7x - 6.6$$

Recall that any terminating decimal can be written as a fraction. Therefore, the equation can be interpreted as

$$\frac{25}{10}x + 3 = \frac{17}{10}x - \frac{66}{10}$$

A convenient common denominator of all terms is 10. Therefore, we can multiply the original equation by 10 to clear decimals.

$$10(2.5x + 3) = 10(1.7x - 6.6)$$
$$25x + 30 = 17x - 66$$

Multiplying by the appropriate power of 10 moves the decimal points so that all coefficients become integers.

Answer

4. {1}

Example 5 **Solving a Linear Equation Containing Decimals**

Solve the equation by clearing decimals. $2.5x + 3 = 1.7x - 6.6$

Solution:

$2.5x + 3 = 1.7x - 6.6$	
$10(2.5x + 3) = 10(1.7x - 6.6)$	Multiply both sides of the equation by 10.
$25x + 30 = 17x - 66$	Apply the distributive property.
$25x - 17x + 30 = 17x - 17x - 66$	Subtract $17x$ from both sides.
$8x + 30 = -66$	
$8x + 30 - 30 = -66 - 30$	Subtract 30 from both sides.
$8x = -96$	
$\frac{8x}{8} = \frac{-96}{8}$	Divide both sides by 8.
$x = -12$	The check is left to the reader.

The solution set is $\{-12\}$.

Classroom Example: p. 127, Exercise 40

TIP: Notice that multiplying a decimal number by 10 has the effect of moving the decimal point one place to the right. Similarly, multiplying by 100 moves the decimal point two places to the right, and so on.

Skill Practice Solve the equation.

5. $1.2w + 3.5 = 2.1 + w$

Example 6 **Solving a Linear Equation Containing Decimals**

Solve the equation by clearing decimals. $0.2(x + 4) - 0.45(x + 9) = 12$

Solution:

$0.2(x + 4) - 0.45(x + 9) = 12$	
$0.2x + 0.8 - 0.45x - 4.05 = 12$	Clear parentheses first.
$100(0.2x + 0.8 - 0.45x - 4.05) = 100(12)$	Multiply both sides by 100.
$20x + 80 - 45x - 405 = 1200$	Apply the distributive property.
$-25x - 325 = 1200$	Simplify both sides.
$-25x - 325 + 325 = 1200 + 325$	Add 325 to both sides.
$-25x = 1525$	
$\frac{-25x}{-25} = \frac{1525}{-25}$	Divide both sides by -25.
$x = -61$	The check is left to the reader.

The solution set is $\{-61\}$.

Classroom Example: p. 127, Exercise 46

TIP: The terms with the most digits following the decimal point are $-0.45x$ and -4.05. Each of these is written to the hundredths place. Therefore, we multiply both sides by 100.

Skill Practice Solve the equation.

6. $0.25(x + 2) - 0.15(x + 3) = 4$

Answers

5. $\{-7\}$ **6.** $\{39.5\}$

Section 2.3 Practice Exercises

For additional exercises, see Classroom Activities 2.3A–2.3B in the *Student's Resource Manual* at www.mhhe.com/moh.

Study Skills Exercise

Instructors vary in what they emphasize on tests. For example, test material may come from the textbook, notes, handouts, or homework. What does your instructor emphasize?

Vocabulary and Key Concepts

1. a. The process of eliminating fractions in an equation by multiplying both sides of the equation by the LCD is called clearing fractions.

   b. The process of eliminating decimals in an equation by multiplying both sides of the equation by a power of 10 is called clearing decimals.

Review Exercises

For Exercises 2–8, solve each equation.

2. $-5t - 17 = -2t + 49$ {−22}
3. $5(x + 2) - 3 = 4x + 5$ {−2}
4. $-2(2x - 4x) = 6 + 18$ {6}
5. $3(2y + 3) - 4(-y + 1) = 7y - 10$ {−5}
6. $-(3w + 4) + 5(w - 2) - 3(6w - 8) = 10$ {0}
7. $7x + 2 = 7(x - 12)$ { }
8. $2(3x - 6) = 3(2x - 4)$ The set of real numbers

Concept 1: Linear Equations Containing Fractions

For Exercises 9–14, determine which of the values could be used to clear fractions or decimals in the given equation.

9. $\frac{2}{3}x - \frac{1}{6} = \frac{x}{9}$

   Values: 6, 9, 12, 18, 24, 36 18, 36

10. $\frac{1}{4}x - \frac{2}{7} = \frac{1}{2}x + 2$

    Values: 4, 7, 14, 21, 28, 42 28

11. $0.02x + 0.5 = 0.35x + 1.2$

    Values: 10; 100; 1000; 10,000
    100; 1000; 10,000

12. $0.003 - 0.002x = 0.1x$

    Values: 10; 100; 1000; 10,000
    1000; 10,000

13. $\frac{1}{6}x + \frac{7}{10} = x$

    Values: 3, 6, 10, 30, 60
    30, 60

14. $2x - \frac{5}{2} = \frac{x}{3} - \frac{1}{4}$

    Values: 2, 3, 4, 6, 12, 24
    12, 24

For Exercises 15–36, solve each equation. **(See Examples 1–4.)**

15. $\frac{1}{2}x + 3 = 5$ {4}
16. $\frac{1}{3}y - 4 = 9$ {39}
17. $\frac{2}{15}z + 3 = \frac{7}{5}$ {−12}
18. $\frac{1}{6}y + 2 = \frac{5}{12}$ $\left\{-\frac{19}{2}\right\}$
19. $\frac{1}{3}q + \frac{3}{5} = \frac{1}{15}q - \frac{2}{5}$ $\left\{-\frac{15}{4}\right\}$
20. $\frac{3}{7}x - 5 = \frac{24}{7}x + 7$ {−4}
21. $\frac{12}{5}w + 7 = 31 - \frac{3}{5}w$ {8}
22. $-\frac{1}{9}p - \frac{5}{18} = -\frac{1}{6}p + \frac{1}{3}$ {11}
23. $\frac{1}{4}(3m - 4) - \frac{1}{5} = \frac{1}{4}m + \frac{3}{10}$ {3}
24. $\frac{1}{25}(20 - t) = \frac{4}{25}t - \frac{3}{5}$ {7}
25. $\frac{1}{6}(5s + 3) = \frac{1}{2}(s + 11)$ {15}
26. $\frac{1}{12}(4n - 3) = \frac{1}{4}(2n + 1)$ {−3}
27. $\frac{2}{3}x + 4 = \frac{2}{3}x - 6$ { }

28. $-\frac{1}{9}a + \frac{2}{9} = \frac{1}{3} - \frac{1}{9}a$ { }

29. $\frac{1}{6}(2c - 1) = \frac{1}{3}c - \frac{1}{6}$ The set of real numbers

30. $\frac{3}{2}b - 1 = \frac{1}{8}(12b - 8)$ The set of real numbers

31. $\frac{2x + 1}{3} + \frac{x - 1}{3} = 5$ {5}

32. $\frac{4y - 2}{5} - \frac{y + 4}{5} = -3$ {−3}

33. $\frac{3w - 2}{6} = 1 - \frac{w - 1}{3}$ {2}

34. $\frac{z - 7}{4} = \frac{6z - 1}{8} - 2$ $\left\{\frac{3}{4}\right\}$

35. $\frac{x + 3}{3} - \frac{x - 1}{2} = 4$ {−15}

36. $\frac{5y - 1}{2} - \frac{y + 4}{5} = 1$ {1}

Concept 2: Linear Equations Containing Decimals

For Exercises 37–54, solve each equation. **(See Examples 5–6.)**

37. $9.2y - 4.3 = 50.9$ {6}

38. $-6.3x + 1.5 = -4.8$ {1}

39. $0.05z + 0.2 = 0.15z - 10.5$ {107}

40. $21.1w + 4.6 = 10.9w + 35.2$ {3}

41. $0.2p - 1.4 = 0.2(p - 7)$ The set of real numbers

42. $0.5(3q + 87) = 1.5q + 43.5$ The set of real numbers

43. $0.20x + 53.60 = x$ {67}

44. $z + 0.06z = 3816$ {3600}

45. $0.15(90) + 0.05p = 0.1(90 + p)$ {90}

46. $0.25(60) + 0.10x = 0.15(60 + x)$ {120}

47. $0.40(y + 10) - 0.60(y + 2) = 2$ {4}

48. $0.75(x - 2) + 0.25(x + 4) = 0.5$ {1}

49. $0.12x + 3 - 0.8x = 0.22x - 0.6$ {4}

50. $0.4x + 0.2 = -3.6 - 0.6x$ {−3.8}

51. $0.06(x - 0.5) = 0.06x + 0.01$ { }

52. $0.125x = 0.025(5x + 1)$ { }

53. $-3.5x + 1.3 = -0.3(9x - 5)$ {−0.25}

54. $x + 4 = 2(0.4x + 1.3)$ {−7}

Mixed Exercises

For Exercises 55–64, solve each equation.

55. $0.2x - 1.8 = -3$ {−6}

56. $9.8h + 2 = 3.8h + 20$ {3}

57. $\frac{1}{4}(x + 4) = \frac{1}{5}(2x + 3)$ $\left\{\frac{8}{3}\right\}$ or $\left\{2\frac{2}{3}\right\}$

58. $\frac{2}{3}(y - 1) = \frac{3}{4}(3y - 2)$ $\left\{\frac{10}{19}\right\}$

59. $0.05(2t - 1) - 0.03(4t - 1) = 0.2$ {−11}

60. $0.3(x + 6) - 0.7(x + 2) = 4$ {−9}

61. $\frac{2k + 5}{4} = 2 - \frac{k + 2}{3}$ $\left\{\frac{1}{10}\right\}$

62. $\frac{3d - 4}{6} + 1 = \frac{d + 1}{8}$ $\left\{-\frac{5}{9}\right\}$

63. $\frac{1}{8}v + \frac{2}{3} = \frac{1}{6}v + \frac{3}{4}$ {−2}

64. $\frac{2}{5}z - \frac{1}{4} = \frac{3}{10}z + \frac{1}{2}$ $\left\{\frac{15}{2}\right\}$

Expanding Your Skills

For Exercises 65–68, solve each equation.

65. $\frac{1}{2}a + 0.4 = -0.7 - \frac{3}{5}a$ {−1}

66. $\frac{3}{4}c - 0.11 = 0.23(c - 5)$ {−2}

67. $0.8 + \frac{7}{10}b = \frac{3}{2}b - 0.8$ {2}

68. $0.78 - \frac{1}{25}h = \frac{3}{5}h - 0.5$ {2}

Problem Recognition Exercises

Equations vs. Expressions

For Exercises 1–32, identify each exercise as an expression or an equation. Then simplify the expression or solve the equation.

1. $2b + 23 - 6b - 5$
Expression; $-4b + 18$

2. $10p - 9 + 2p - 3 + 8p - 18$
Expression; $20p - 30$

3. $\frac{y}{4} = -2$ Equation; $\{-8\}$

4. $-\frac{x}{2} = 7$ Equation; $\{-14\}$

5. $3(4h - 2) - (5h - 8) = 8 - (2h + 3)$ Equation; $\left\{\frac{1}{3}\right\}$

6. $7y - 3(2y + 5) = 7 - (10 - 10y)$
Equation; $\left\{-\frac{4}{3}\right\}$

7. $3(8z - 1) + 10 - 6(5 + 3z)$
Expression; $6z - 23$

8. $-5(1 - x) - 3(2x + 3) + 5$
Expression; $-x - 9$

9. $6c + 3(c + 1) = 10$
Equation; $\left\{\frac{7}{9}\right\}$

10. $-9 + 5(2y + 3) = -7$
Equation; $\left\{-\frac{13}{10}\right\}$

11. $0.5(2a - 3) - 0.1 = 0.4(6 + 2a)$
Equation; $\{20\}$

12. $0.07(2v - 4) = 0.1(v - 4)$
Equation; $\{-3\}$

13. $-\frac{5}{9}w + \frac{11}{12} = \frac{23}{36}$ Equation; $\left\{\frac{1}{2}\right\}$

14. $\frac{3}{8}t - \frac{5}{8} = \frac{1}{2}t + \frac{1}{8}$
Equation; $\{-6\}$

15. $\frac{3}{4}x + \frac{1}{2} - \frac{1}{8}x + \frac{5}{4}$
Expression; $\frac{5}{8}x + \frac{7}{4}$

16. $\frac{7}{3}(6 - 12t) + \frac{1}{2}(4t + 8)$
Expression; $-26t + 18$

17. $2z - 7 = 2(z - 13)$
Equation; $\{\ \}$

18. $-6x + 2(x + 1) = -2(2x + 3)$
Equation; $\{\ \}$

19. $\frac{2x - 1}{4} + \frac{3x + 2}{6} = 2$
Equation; $\left\{\frac{23}{12}\right\}$

20. $\frac{w - 4}{6} - \frac{3w - 1}{2} = -1$
Equation; $\left\{\frac{5}{8}\right\}$

21. $4b - 8 - b = -3b + 2(3b - 4)$
Equation; The set of real numbers

22. $-k - 41 - 2 - k = -2(20 + k) - 3$
Equation; The set of real numbers

23. $\frac{4}{3}(6y - 3) = 0$
Equation; $\left\{\frac{1}{2}\right\}$

24. $\frac{1}{2}(2c - 4) + 3 = \frac{1}{3}(6c + 3)$
Equation; $\{0\}$

25. $3(x + 6) - 7(x + 2) - 4(1 - x)$
Expression; 0

26. $-10(2k + 1) - 4(4 - 5k) + 25$
Expression; -1

27. $3 - 2[4a - 5(a + 1)]$
Expression; $2a + 13$

28. $-9 - 4[3 - 2(q + 3)]$
Expression; $8q + 3$

29. $4 + 2[8 - (6 + x)] = -2(x - 1) - 4 + x$
Equation; $\{10\}$

30. $-1 - 5[2 + 3(w - 2)] = 5(w + 4)$ Equation; $\left\{-\frac{1}{20}\right\}$

31. $\frac{1}{6}y + y - \frac{1}{3}(4y - 1)$
Expression; $-\frac{1}{6}y + \frac{1}{3}$

32. $\frac{1}{2} - \frac{1}{5}\left(x + \frac{1}{2}\right) + \frac{9}{10}x$ Expression; $\frac{7}{10}x + \frac{2}{5}$

Section 2.4 Applications of Linear Equations: Introduction to Problem Solving

Concepts

1. Problem-Solving Strategies
2. Translations Involving Linear Equations
3. Consecutive Integer Problems
4. Applications of Linear Equations

1. Problem-Solving Strategies

Linear equations can be used to solve many real-world applications. However, with "word problems," students often do not know where to start. To help organize the problem-solving process, we offer the following guidelines:

Problem-Solving Flowchart for Word Problems

Step 1	Read the problem carefully.	• Familiarize yourself with the problem. Identify the unknown, and if possible, estimate the answer.
Step 2	Assign labels to unknown quantities.	• Identify the unknown quantity or quantities. Let x or another variable represent one of the unknowns. Draw a picture and write down relevant formulas.
Step 3	Write a verbal model.	• Write an equation in *words*.
Step 4	Write a mathematical equation.	• Replace the verbal model with a mathematical equation using x or another variable.
Step 5	Solve the equation.	• Solve for the variable using the steps for solving linear equations.
Step 6	Interpret the results and write the final answer in words.	• Once you have obtained a numerical value for the variable, recall what it represents in the context of the problem. Can this value be used to determine other unknowns in the problem? Write an answer to the word problem in *words*.

Instructor Note: Remind students that x is a convenient variable, but any letter can be used. For example, for an unknown width use w.

Avoiding Mistakes

Once you have reached a solution to a word problem, verify that it is reasonable in the context of the problem.

2. Translations Involving Linear Equations

We have already practiced translating an English sentence to a mathematical equation. Recall that several key words translate to the algebraic operations of addition, subtraction, multiplication, and division.

Example 1 Translating to a Linear Equation

The sum of a number and negative eleven is negative fifteen. Find the number.

Solution:

	Step 1: Read the problem.
Let x represent the unknown number.	**Step 2:** Label the unknown.
(a number) + (−11) = (−15) [the sum of → +, is → =]	**Step 3:** Write a verbal model.
$x + (-11) = -15$	**Step 4:** Write an equation.
$x + (-11) + 11 = -15 + 11$	**Step 5:** Solve the equation.
$x = -4$	
The number is −4.	**Step 6:** Write the final answer in words.

Classroom Example: p. 136, Exercise 10

Skill Practice

1. The sum of a number and negative seven is 12. Find the number.

Answer

1. The number is 19.

Classroom Example: p. 136, Exercise 14

Example 2 **Translating to a Linear Equation**

Forty less than five times a number is fifty-two less than the number. Find the number.

Solution:

Step 1: Read the problem.

Let x represent the unknown number. **Step 2:** Label the unknown.

Step 3: Write a verbal model.

$$\begin{pmatrix}\text{5 times}\\ \text{a number}\end{pmatrix} \overset{\text{less}}{-} (40) \overset{\text{is}}{=} \begin{pmatrix}\text{the}\\ \text{number}\end{pmatrix} \overset{\text{less}}{-} (52)$$

Step 4: Write an equation.

$$5x \quad - \quad 40 \quad = \quad x \quad - \quad 52$$

Step 5: Solve the equation.

$$5x - 40 = x - 52$$

$$5x - x - 40 = x - x - 52$$

$$4x - 40 = -52$$

$$4x - 40 + 40 = -52 + 40$$

$$4x = -12$$

$$\frac{4x}{4} = \frac{-12}{4}$$

$$x = -3$$

The number is -3. **Step 6:** Write the final answer in words.

Avoiding Mistakes

It is important to remember that subtraction is not a commutative operation. Therefore, the order in which two real numbers are subtracted affects the outcome. The expression "forty less than five times a number" must be translated as: $5x - 40$ (not $40 - 5x$). Similarly, "fifty-two less than the number" must be translated as: $x - 52$ (not $52 - x$).

Skill Practice

2. Thirteen more than twice a number is 5 more than the number. Find the number.

Classroom Example: p. 136, Exercise 18

Example 3 **Translating to a Linear Equation**

Twice the sum of a number and six is two more than three times the number. Find the number.

Solution:

Step 1: Read the problem.

Let x represent the unknown number. **Step 2:** Label the unknown.

Step 3: Write a verbal model.

Step 4: Write an equation.

$$\overset{\text{twice}}{2} \cdot \overset{\text{the sum}}{(x + 6)} \overset{\text{is}}{=} \underset{\text{three times a number}}{3x} \overset{\text{2 more than}}{+ 2}$$

Answer

2. The number is -8.

$$2(x + 6) = 3x + 2$$ **Step 5:** Solve the equation.

$$2x + 12 = 3x + 2$$

$$2x - 2x + 12 = 3x - 2x + 2$$

$$12 = x + 2$$

$$12 - 2 = x + 2 - 2$$

$$10 = x$$

The number is 10. **Step 6:** Write the final answer in words.

Avoiding Mistakes

It is important to enclose "the sum of a number and six" within parentheses so that the entire quantity is multiplied by 2. Forgetting the parentheses would imply that only the x-term is multiplied by 2.

Correct: $2(x + 6)$

Incorrect: $2x + 6$

Skill Practice

3. Three times the sum of a number and eight is 4 more than the number. Find the number.

3. Consecutive Integer Problems

The word *consecutive* means "following one after the other in order without gaps." The numbers 6, 7, and 8 are examples of three **consecutive integers**. The numbers −4, −2, 0, and 2 are examples of **consecutive even integers**. The numbers 23, 25, and 27 are examples of **consecutive odd integers**.

Notice that any two consecutive integers differ by 1. Therefore, if x represents an integer, then $(x + 1)$ represents the next larger consecutive integer (Figure 2-4).

Instructor Note: Explain to students that we could let x be the larger of two consecutive integers. Then $x - 1$ is the next smaller integer. However, using x and $x + 1$ generally causes less confusion for students.

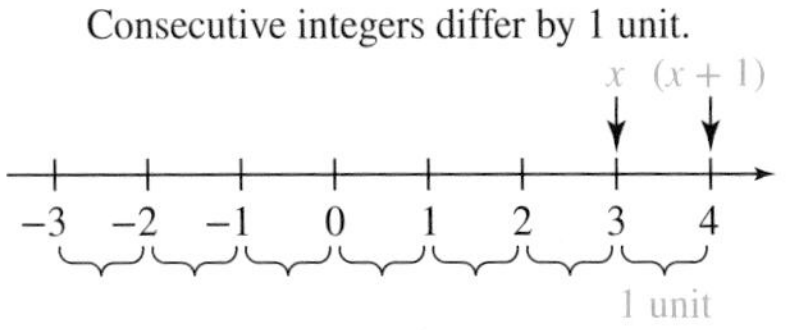

Figure 2-4

Any two consecutive even integers differ by 2. Therefore, if x represents an even integer, then $(x + 2)$ represents the next consecutive larger even integer (Figure 2-5).

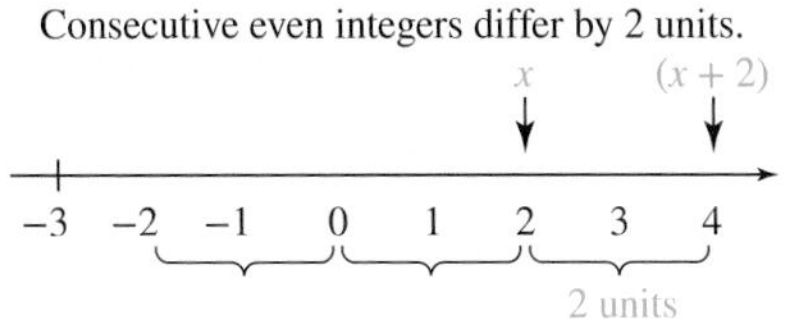

Figure 2-5

Likewise, any two consecutive odd integers differ by 2. If x represents an odd integer, then $(x + 2)$ is the next larger odd integer (Figure 2-6).

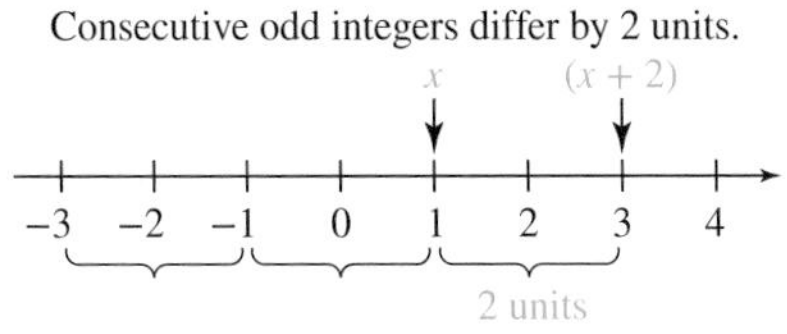

Figure 2-6

Answer

3. The number is −10.

Classroom Example: p. 136, Exercise 22

Example 4 Solving an Application Involving Consecutive Integers

The sum of two consecutive odd integers is -188. Find the integers.

Solution:

In this example we have two unknown integers. We can let x represent either of the unknowns.

Step 1: Read the problem.

Suppose x represents the first odd integer. **Step 2:** Label the unknowns.

Then $(x + 2)$ represents the second odd integer.

$$\begin{pmatrix}\text{First}\\ \text{integer}\end{pmatrix} + \begin{pmatrix}\text{second}\\ \text{integer}\end{pmatrix} = (\text{total})$$

Step 3: Write a verbal model.

$$x \quad + \quad (x+2) \quad = -188$$

Step 4: Write a mathematical equation.

$$x + (x+2) = -188$$

$$2x + 2 = -188$$

Step 5: Solve for x.

$$2x + 2 - 2 = -188 - 2$$

$$2x = -190$$

$$\frac{2x}{2} = \frac{-190}{2}$$

$$x = -95$$

The first integer is $x = -95$. **Step 6:** Interpret the results and write the answer in words.

The second integer is $x + 2 = -95 + 2 = -93$.

The two integers are -95 and -93.

TIP: With word problems, it is advisable to check that the answer is reasonable.

The numbers -95 and -93 are consecutive odd integers. Furthermore, their sum is -188 as desired.

Skill Practice

4. The sum of two consecutive even integers is 66. Find the integers.

Classroom Example: p. 136, Exercise 30

Example 5 Solving an Application Involving Consecutive Integers

Ten times the smallest of three consecutive integers is twenty-two more than three times the sum of the integers. Find the integers.

Solution:

Step 1: Read the problem.

Let x represent the first integer. **Step 2:** Label the unknowns.

$x + 1$ represents the second consecutive integer.

$x + 2$ represents the third consecutive integer.

Answer

4. The integers are 32 and 34.

$$\begin{pmatrix}\text{10 times}\\ \text{the first}\\ \text{integer}\end{pmatrix} = \begin{pmatrix}\text{3 times}\\ \text{the sum of}\\ \text{the integers}\end{pmatrix} + 22$$

Step 3: Write a verbal model.

10 times the first integer → is → 3 times → 22 more than

$$10x = \underbrace{3[(x) + (x + 1) + (x + 2)]}_{\text{the sum of the integers}} + 22$$

Step 4: Write a mathematical equation.

$$10x = 3(x + x + 1 + x + 2) + 22$$

Step 5: Solve the equation.

$$10x = 3(3x + 3) + 22$$

Clear parentheses.

$$10x = 9x + 9 + 22$$

Combine *like* terms.

$$10x = 9x + 31$$

$$10x - 9x = 9x - 9x + 31$$

Isolate the x-terms on one side.

$$x = 31$$

The first integer is $x = 31$.

The second integer is $x + 1 = 31 + 1 = 32$.

The third integer is $x + 2 = 31 + 2 = 33$.

The three integers are 31, 32, and 33.

Step 6: Interpret the results and write the answer in words.

Skill Practice

5. Five times the smallest of three consecutive integers is 17 less than twice the sum of the integers. Find the integers.

4. Applications of Linear Equations

Example 6 Using a Linear Equation in an Application

Classroom Example: p. 137, Exercise 32

A carpenter cuts a 6-ft board in two pieces. One piece must be three times as long as the other. Find the length of each piece.

Solution:

In this problem, one piece must be three times as long as the other. Thus, if x represents the length of one piece, then $3x$ can represent the length of the other.

Step 1: Read the problem completely.

x represents the length of the smaller piece.
$3x$ represents the length of the longer piece.

Step 2: Label the unknowns. Draw a figure.

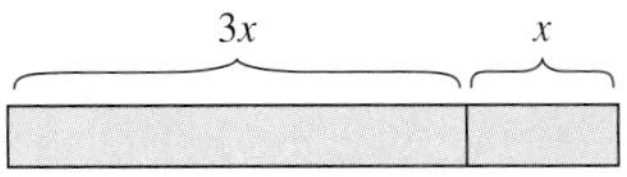

Answer

5. The integers are 11, 12, and 13.

$$\begin{pmatrix}\text{Length of}\\ \text{one piece}\end{pmatrix} + \begin{pmatrix}\text{length of}\\ \text{other piece}\end{pmatrix} = \begin{pmatrix}\text{total length}\\ \text{of the board}\end{pmatrix}$$

Step 3: Write a verbal model.

$$x \quad + \quad 3x \quad = \quad 6$$

Step 4: Write an equation.

$$4x = 6$$

$$\frac{4x}{4} = \frac{6}{4}$$

$$x = 1.5$$

Step 5: Solve the equation.

The smaller piece is $x = 1.5$ ft.

The longer piece is $3x$ or $3(1.5 \text{ ft}) = 4.5$ ft.

Step 6: Interpret the results.

TIP: The variable can represent either unknown. In Example 6, if we let x represent the length of the longer piece of board, then $\frac{1}{3}x$ would represent the length of the smaller piece. The equation would become $x + \frac{1}{3}x = 6$. Try solving this equation and interpreting the result.

Skill Practice

6. A plumber cuts a 96-in. piece of pipe into two pieces. One piece is five times longer than the other piece. How long is each piece?

Classroom Example: p. 137, Exercise 38

Example 7 Using a Linear Equation in an Application

In a recent Olympics, the United States won the greatest number of overall medals, followed by China. The United States won 16 more medals than China, and together they brought home a total of 192 medals. How many medals did each country win?

Source: U.S. Department of Defense

Solution:

In this example, we have two unknowns. The variable x can represent either quantity. However, the number of medals won by the United States is given in terms of the number won by China.

Step 1: Read the problem.

Let x represent the number of medals won by China.

Then let $x + 16$ represent the number of medals won by the United States.

Step 2: Label the variables.

$$\begin{pmatrix}\text{Number of}\\ \text{medals won}\\ \text{by China}\end{pmatrix} + \begin{pmatrix}\text{Number of medals}\\ \text{won by the}\\ \text{United States}\end{pmatrix} = \begin{pmatrix}\text{Total}\\ \text{number}\\ \text{of medals}\end{pmatrix}$$

Step 3: Write a verbal model.

$$x \quad + \quad (x + 16) \quad = \quad 192$$

Step 4: Write an equation.

$$2x + 16 = 192$$

$$2x = 176$$

$$x = 88$$

Step 5: Solve the equation.

- Medals won by China, $x = 88$
- Medals won by the United States, $x + 16 = (88) + 16 = 104$

China won 88 medals and the United States won 104 medals.

Answer

6. One piece is 80 in. and the other is 16 in.

Skill Practice

7. There are 40 students in an algebra class. There are 4 more women than men. How many women and how many men are in the class?

Answer

7. There are 22 women and 18 men.

Section 2.4 Practice Exercises

For additional exercises, see Classroom Activities 2.4A–2.4C in the *Student's Resource Manual* at www.mhhe.com/moh.

Study Skills Exercise

After doing a section of homework, check the answers to the odd-numbered exercises in the back of the text. Choose a method to identify the exercises that gave you trouble (i.e., circle the number or put a star by the number). List some reasons why it is important to label these problems.

Vocabulary and Key Concepts

1. **a.** Integers that follow one after the other without "gaps" are called consecutive integers.
   b. The integers −2, 0, 2, and 4 are examples of consecutive even integers.
   c. The integers −3, −1, 1, and 3 are examples of consecutive odd integers.
   d. Two consecutive integers differ by 1.
   e. Two consecutive odd integers differ by 2.
   f. Two consecutive even integers differ by 2.

Concept 2: Translations Involving Linear Equations

For Exercises 2–8, write an expression representing the unknown quantity.

2. In a math class, the number of students who received an "A" in the class was 5 more than the number of students who received a "B." If x represents the number of "B" students, write an expression for the number of "A" students. $x + 5$

3. There are 5,682,080 fewer men than women on a particular social media site. If x represents the number of women using that site, write an expression for the number of men using that site. $x - 5{,}682{,}080$

4. At a recent motorcycle rally, the number of men exceeded the number of women by 216. If x represents the number of women, write an expression for the number of men. $x + 216$

5. There are 10 times as many users of a social media site than there are of a social news site. If x represents the number of users of the news site, write an expression for the number of users of the social media site. $10x$

6. Rebecca downloaded twice as many songs as Nigel. If x represents the number of songs downloaded by Nigel, write an expression for the number downloaded by Rebecca. $2x$

© McGraw-Hill Education/ Mark Dierker

7. Sidney made \$20 less than three times Casey's weekly salary. If x represents Casey's weekly salary, write an expression for Sidney's weekly salary. $3x - 20$

8. David scored 26 points less than twice the number of points Rich scored in a video game. If x represents the number of points scored by Rich, write an expression representing the number of points scored by David. $2x - 26$

For Exercises 9–18, use the Problem-Solving Flowchart for Word Problems. **(See Examples 1–3.)**

9. Six less than a number is -10. Find the number. The number is -4.

10. Fifteen less than a number is 41. Find the number. The number is 56.

11. Twice the sum of a number and seven is eight. Find the number. The number is -3.

12. Twice the sum of a number and negative two is sixteen. Find the number. The number is 10.

13. A number added to five is the same as twice the number. Find the number. The number is 5.

14. Three times a number is the same as the difference of twice the number and seven. Find the number. The number is -7.

15. The sum of six times a number and ten is equal to the difference of the number and fifteen. Find the number. The number is -5.

16. The difference of fourteen and three times a number is the same as the sum of the number and negative ten. Find the number. The number is 6.

17. If the difference of a number and four is tripled, the result is six less than the number. Find the number. The number is 3.

18. Twice the sum of a number and eleven is twenty-two less than three times the number. Find the number. The number is 44.

Concept 3: Consecutive Integer Problems

19. a. If x represents the smallest of three consecutive integers, write an expression to represent each of the next two consecutive integers. $x + 1, x + 2$

b. If x represents the largest of three consecutive integers, write an expression to represent each of the previous two consecutive integers. $x - 1, x - 2$

20. a. If x represents the smallest of three consecutive odd integers, write an expression to represent each of the next two consecutive odd integers. $x + 2, x + 4$

b. If x represents the largest of three consecutive odd integers, write an expression to represent each of the previous two consecutive odd integers. $x - 2, x - 4$

For Exercises 21–30, use the Problem-Solving Flowchart for Word Problems. **(See Examples 4–5.)**

21. The sum of two consecutive integers is -67. Find the integers. The integers are -34 and -33.

22. The sum of two consecutive odd integers is 52. Find the integers. The integers are 25 and 27.

23. The sum of two consecutive odd integers is 28. Find the integers. The integers are 13 and 15.

24. The sum of three consecutive even integers is 66. Find the integers. The integers are 20, 22, and 24.

25. The perimeter of a pentagon (a five-sided polygon) is 80 in. The five sides are represented by consecutive integers. Find the lengths of the sides. The sides are 14 in., 15 in., 16 in., 17 in., and 18 in.

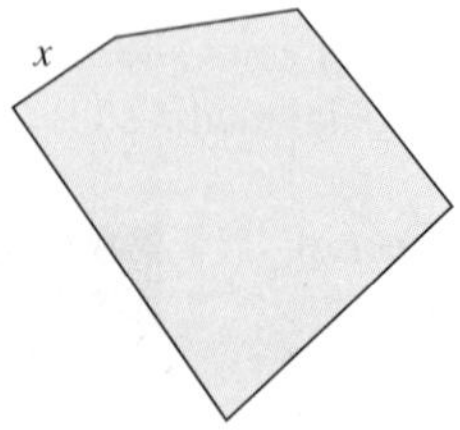

26. The perimeter of a triangle is 96 in. The lengths of the sides are represented by consecutive integers. Find the lengths of the sides. The sides are 31 in., 32 in., and 33 in.

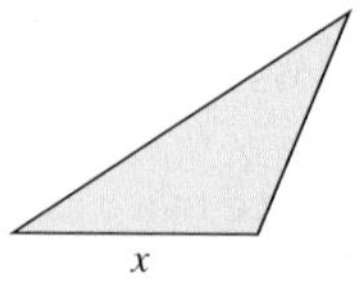

27. The sum of three consecutive even integers is 48 less than twice the smallest of the three integers. Find the integers. The integers are -54, -52, and -50.

28. The sum of three consecutive odd integers is 89 less than twice the largest integer. Find the integers. The integers are -87, -85, and -83.

29. Eight times the sum of three consecutive odd integers is 210 more than ten times the middle integer. Find the integers. The integers are 13, 15, and 17.

30. Five times the sum of three consecutive even integers is 140 more than ten times the smallest of the integers. Find the integers. The integers are 22, 24, and 26.

Concept 4: Applications of Linear Equations

For Exercises 31–42, use the Problem-Solving Flowchart for Word Problems to solve the problems.

31. A board is 86 cm in length and must be cut so that one piece is 20 cm longer than the other piece. Find the length of each piece. **(See Example 6.)** The lengths of the pieces are 33 cm and 53 cm.

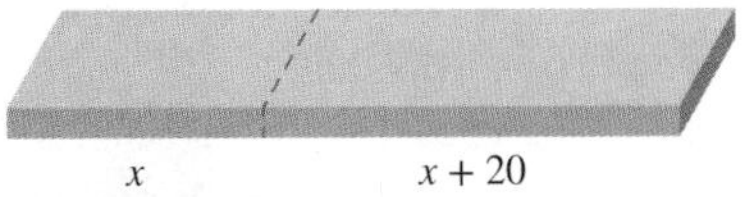

Animation

32. A rope is 54 in. in length and must be cut into two pieces. If one piece must be twice as long as the other, find the length of each piece. The lengths of the pieces are 18 in. and 36 in.

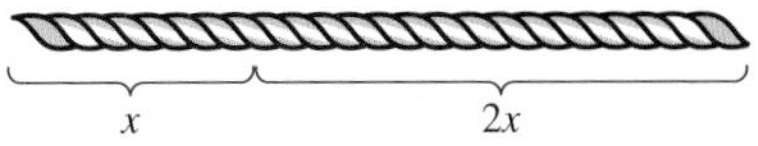

33. Karen's music library contains 12 fewer playlists than Clarann's music library. The total number of playlists for both music libraries is 58. Find the number of playlists in each person's music library. Karen's music library has 23 playlists and Claran's library has 35 playlists.

34. Maria has 15 fewer apps on her phone than Orlando. If the total number of apps on both phones is 29, how many apps are on each phone? Maria has 7 apps and Orlando has 22 apps.

35. For a recent year, 31 more Democrats than Republicans were in the U.S. House of Representatives. If the total number of representatives in the House from these two parties was 433, find the number of representatives from each party. There were 201 Republicans and 232 Democrats.

36. For a recent year, the number of men in the U.S. Senate totaled 4 more than five times the number of women. Find the number of men and the number of women in the Senate given that the Senate has 100 members. There were 84 men and 16 women.

37. A car dealership sells SUVs and passenger cars. For a recent year, 40 more SUVs were sold than passenger cars. If a total of 420 vehicles were sold, determine the number of each type of vehicle sold. **(See Example 7.)** There were 190 passenger cars and 230 SUVs sold.

38. Two of the largest Internet retailers are eBay and Amazon. Recently, the estimated U.S. sales of eBay were \$0.1 billion less than twice the sales of Amazon. Given the total sales of \$5.6 billion, determine the sales of eBay and Amazon. eBay's sales were \$3.7 billion and Amazon's sales were \$1.9 billion.

39. The longest river in Africa is the Nile. It is 2455 km longer than the Congo River, also in Africa. The sum of the lengths of these rivers is 11,195 km. What is the length of each river? The Congo River is 4370 km long, and the Nile River is 6825 km.

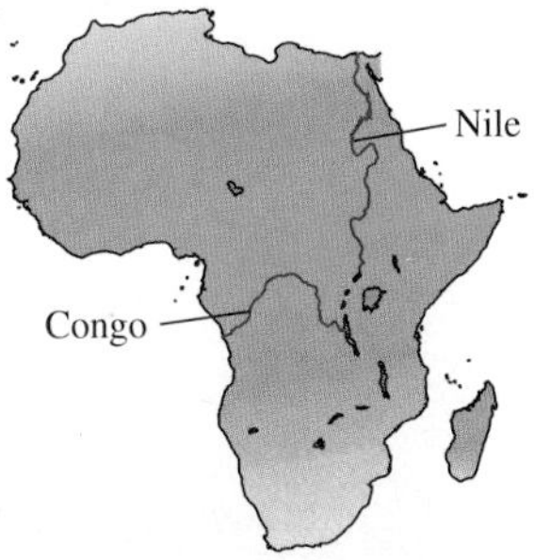

40. The average depth of the Gulf of Mexico is three times the depth of the Red Sea. The difference between the average depths is 1078 m. What is the average depth of the Gulf of Mexico and the average depth of the Red Sea? The average depth of the Red Sea is 539 m and that of the Gulf of Mexico is 1617 m.

41. Asia and Africa are the two largest continents in the world. The land area of Asia is approximately 14,514,000 km^2 larger than the land area of Africa. Together their total area is 74,644,000 km^2. Find the land area of Asia and the land area of Africa. The area of Africa is 30,065,000 km^2. The area of Asia is 44,579,000 km^2.

42. Mt. Everest, the highest mountain in the world, is 2654 m higher than Mt. McKinley, the highest mountain in the United States. If the sum of their heights is 15,042 m, find the height of each mountain. Mt. McKinley is 6194 m high. Mt. Everest is 8848 m high.

© J. Luke/PhotoLink/Getty Images RF

Mixed Exercises

43. A group of hikers walked from Hawk Mt. Shelter to Blood Mt. Shelter along the Appalachian Trail, a total distance of 20.5 mi. It took 2 days for the walk. The second day the hikers walked 4.1 mi less than they did on the first day. How far did they walk each day? They walked 12.3 mi on the first day and 8.2 mi on the second.

© Corbis/age fotostock RF

44. \$120 is to be divided among three restaurant servers. Angie made \$10 more than Marie. Gwen, who went home sick, made \$25 less than Marie. How much money should each server get? Marie made \$45, Angie made \$55, and Gwen made \$20.

45. A 4-ft piece of PVC pipe is cut into three pieces. The longest piece is 5 in. shorter than three times the shortest piece. The middle piece is 8 in. longer than the shortest piece. How long is each piece? The pieces are 9 in., 17 in., and 22 in.

46. A 6-ft piece of copper wire must be cut into three pieces. The shortest piece is 16 in. less than the middle piece. The longest piece is twice as long as the middle piece. How long is each piece? The pieces are 6 in., 22 in., and 44 in.

47. Three consecutive integers are such that three times the largest exceeds the sum of the two smaller integers by 47. Find the integers. The integers are 42, 43, and 44.

48. Four times the smallest of three consecutive odd integers is 236 more than the sum of the other two integers. Find the integers. The integers are 121, 123, and 125.

49. The winner and runner-up of a TV music contest had lucrative earnings immediately after the show's finale. The runner-up earned \$2 million less than half of the winner's earnings. If their combined earnings totaled \$19 million, how much did each person make? The winner earned \$14 million and the runner-up earned \$5 million.

50. One TV series ran 97 fewer episodes than twice the number of a second TV series. If the total number of episodes is 998, determine the number of each show produced. There were 633 episodes of the first series and 365 episodes of the second series.

51. Five times the difference of a number and three is four less than four times the number. Find the number. The number is 11.

52. Three times the difference of a number and seven is one less than twice the number. Find the number. The number is 20.

53. The sum of the page numbers on two facing pages in a book is 941. What are the page numbers? The page numbers are 470 and 471.

54. Three raffle tickets are represented by three consecutive integers. If the sum of the three integers is 2,666,031, find the numbers. The ticket numbers are 888,676; 888,677; and 888,678.

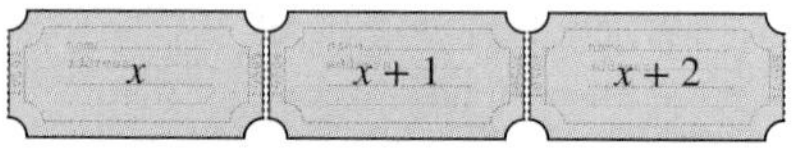

55. If three is added to five times a number, the result is forty-three more than the number. Find the number. The number is 10.

56. If seven is added to three times a number, the result is thirty-one more than the number. Find the number. The number is 12.

57. The deepest point in the Pacific Ocean is 676 m more than twice the deepest point in the Arctic Ocean. If the deepest point in the Pacific is 10,920 m, how many meters is the deepest point in the Arctic Ocean? The deepest point in the Arctic Ocean is 5122 m.

58. The area of Greenland is 201,900 km^2 less than three times the area of New Guinea. What is the area of New Guinea if the area of Greenland is 2,175,600 km^2? The area of New Guinea is 792,500 km^2.

59. The sum of twice a number and $\frac{3}{4}$ is the same as the difference of four times the number and $\frac{1}{8}$. Find the number. The number is $\frac{7}{16}$.

60. The difference of a number and $-\frac{11}{12}$ is the same as the difference of three times the number and $\frac{1}{6}$. Find the number. The number is $\frac{13}{24}$.

61. The product of a number and 3.86 is equal to 7.15 more than the number. Find the number. The number is 2.5.

62. The product of a number and 4.6 is 33.12 less than the number. Find the number. The number is −9.2.

Applications Involving Percents

Section 2.5

1. Basic Percent Equations

Concepts

1. Basic Percent Equations
2. Applications Involving Simple Interest
3. Applications Involving Discount and Markup

Recall that the word *percent* as meaning "per hundred."

Percent	Interpretation
63% of homes have a computer	63 out of 100 homes have a computer.
5% sales tax	5¢ in tax is charged for every 100¢ in merchandise.
15% commission	\$15 is earned in commission for every \$100 sold.

Percents come up in a variety of applications in day-to-day life. Many such applications follow the basic percent equation:

Amount = (percent)(base)   Basic percent equation

In Example 1, we apply the basic percent equation to compute sales tax.

Example 1 **Computing Sales Tax**

Classroom Example: p. 144, Exercise 18

© BrandX/Punchstock RF

A new digital camera costs \$429.95.

a. Compute the sales tax if the tax rate is 4%.

b. Determine the total cost, including tax.

Solution:

Step 1: Read the problem.

a. Let x represent the amount of tax. — **Step 2:** Label the variable.

Amount = (percent) · (base)
↓ ↓ ↓
Sales tax = (tax rate)(price of merchandise)

Step 3: Write a verbal model. Apply the percent equation to compute sales tax.

$x = (0.04)(\$429.95)$ — **Step 4:** Write a mathematical equation.

Avoiding Mistakes

Be sure to use the decimal form of a percent within an equation.

4% = 0.04

$x = \$17.198$ — **Step 5:** Solve the equation.

$x = \$17.20$ — Round to the nearest cent.

The tax on the merchandise is \$17.20. — **Step 6:** Interpret the results.

b. The total cost is found by:

total cost = cost of merchandise + amount of tax

Therefore, the total cost is \$429.95 + \$17.20 = \$447.15.

Skill Practice

1. Find the amount of tax on a portable CD player that sells for \$89. Assume the tax rate is 6%.
2. Find the total cost including tax.

In Example 2, we solve a problem in which the percent is unknown.

Classroom Example: p. 144, Exercise 22

Example 2 Finding an Unknown Percent

A group of 240 college men were asked what intramural sport they most enjoyed playing. The results are in the graph. What percent of the men surveyed preferred tennis?

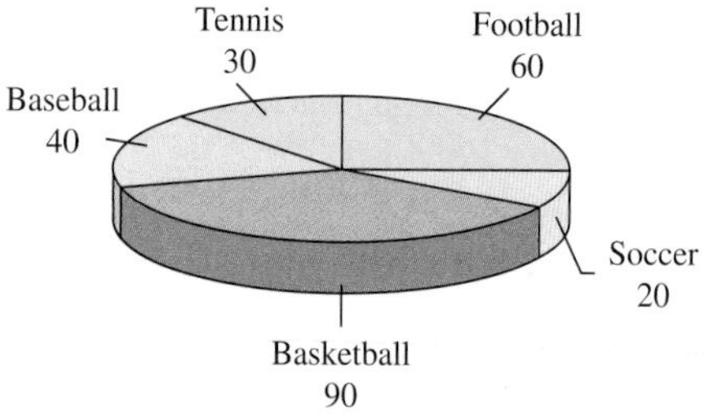

Solution:

	Step 1: Read the problem.
Let x represent the unknown percent (in decimal form).	**Step 2:** Label the variable.
The problem can be rephrased as:	
30 is what percent of 240? $30 = x \cdot 240$	**Step 3:** Write a verbal model. **Step 4:** Write a mathematical equation.
$30 = 240x$	**Step 5:** Solve the equation.
$\dfrac{30}{240} = \dfrac{240x}{240}$	Divide both sides by 240.
$0.125 = x$	
$0.125 \times 100\% = 12.5\%$	**Step 6:** Interpret the results. Change the value of x to a percent form by multiplying by 100%.
In this survey, 12.5% of men prefer tennis.	

Skill Practice Refer to the graph in Example 2.

3. What percent of the men surveyed prefer basketball as their favorite intramural sport?

Answers

1. The amount of tax is \$5.34.
2. The total cost is \$94.34.
3. 37.5% of the men surveyed prefer basketball.

Classroom Example: p. 144, Exercise 24

© Stockbyte/Getty Images RF

Example 3 Solving a Percent Equation with an Unknown Base

Andrea spends 20% of her monthly paycheck on rent each month. If her rent payment is \$950, what is her monthly paycheck?

Solution:

Step 1: Read the problem.

Let x represent the amount of Andrea's monthly paycheck.

Step 2: Label the variables.

The problem can be rephrased as:

\$950 is 20% of what number?

Step 3: Write a verbal model.

$$950 = 0.20 \cdot x$$

Step 4: Write a mathematical equation.

$$950 = 0.20x$$

Step 5: Solve the equation.

$$\frac{950}{0.20} = \frac{0.20x}{0.20}$$

Divide both sides by 0.20.

$$4750 = x$$

Andrea's monthly paycheck is \$4750.

Step 6: Interpret the results.

Skill Practice

4. In order to pass an exam, a student must answer 70% of the questions correctly. If answering 42 questions correctly results in a 70% score, how many questions are on the test?

2. Applications Involving Simple Interest

One important application of percents is in computing simple interest on a loan or on an investment.

Simple interest is interest that is earned or owed on principal (the original amount of money invested or borrowed). The following formula is used to compute simple interest.

$$\begin{pmatrix}\text{Simple}\\ \text{interest}\end{pmatrix} = (\text{principal})\begin{pmatrix}\text{annual}\\ \text{interest rate}\end{pmatrix}\begin{pmatrix}\text{time}\\ \text{in years}\end{pmatrix}$$

This formula is often written symbolically as $I = Prt$. In this formula, I represents the simple interest, P represents the principal, r represents the annual interest rate, and t is the time of the investment in years.

For example, to find the simple interest earned on \$2000 invested at 7.5% interest for 3 years, we have $P = \$2000$, $r = 0.075$, and $t = 3$. Thus,

$$I = Prt$$
$$\text{Interest} = (\$2000)(0.075)(3)$$
$$= \$450$$

Answer

4. There are 60 questions on the test.

Classroom Example: p. 144, Exercise 28

© Ingram Publishing RF

Avoiding Mistakes

The interest is computed on the original principal, P, not on the total amount \$20,250. That is, the interest is $P(0.025)(5)$, not $(\$20{,}250)(0.025)(5)$.

Example 4 Applying Simple Interest

Jorge wants to save money to buy a car in 5 years. If Jorge needs to have \$20,250 at the end of 5 years, how much money would he need to invest in a certificate of deposit (CD) at a 2.5% interest rate?

Solution:

Step 1: Read the problem.

Let P represent the original amount invested. **Step 2:** Label the variables.

$\begin{pmatrix}\text{Original}\\ \text{principal}\end{pmatrix} + (\text{interest}) = (\text{total})$ **Step 3:** Write a verbal model.

$P + Prt = \text{total}$ **Step 4:** Write a mathematical equation.

$P + P(0.025)(5) = 20{,}250$

$P + 0.125P = 20{,}250$ **Step 5:** Solve the equation.

$1.125P = 20{,}250$

$\dfrac{1.125P}{1.125} = \dfrac{20{,}250}{1.125}$

$P = 18{,}000$

The original investment should be \$18,000. **Step 6:** Interpret the results and write the answer in words.

Skill Practice

5. Cassandra invested some money in her bank account, and after 10 years at 4% simple interest, it has grown to \$7700. What was the initial amount invested?

3. Applications Involving Discount and Markup

Applications involving percent increase and percent decrease are abundant in many real-world settings. Sales tax, for example, is essentially a markup by a state or local government. It is important to understand that percent increase or decrease is always computed on the original amount given.

In Example 5, we illustrate an example of percent decrease in an application where merchandise is discounted.

Classroom Example: p. 145, Exercise 36

Example 5 Applying Percents to a Discount Problem

After a 38% discount, a used treadmill costs \$868 on eBay. What was the original cost of the treadmill?

Solution:

Step 1: Read the problem.

Let x be the original cost of the treadmill. **Step 2:** Label the variables.

Answer

5. The initial investment was \$5500.

$$\begin{pmatrix}\text{Original}\\ \text{cost}\end{pmatrix} - (\text{discount}) = \begin{pmatrix}\text{sale}\\ \text{price}\end{pmatrix}$$

Step 3: Write a verbal model.

$$x \quad - \quad 0.38(x) \quad = \quad 868$$

Step 4: Write a mathematical equation. The discount is a percent of the *original* amount.

$$x - 0.38x = 868$$

Step 5: Solve the equation.

$$0.62x = 868$$

Combine *like* terms.

$$\frac{0.62x}{0.62} = \frac{868}{0.62}$$

Divide by 0.62.

$$x = 1400$$

The original cost of the treadmill was $1400.

Step 6: Interpret the result.

© Comstock Images/Alamy RF

Skill Practice

6. A camera is on sale for $151.20. This is after a 20% discount. What was the original cost?

Answer

6. The camera originally cost $189.

Section 2.5 Practice Exercises

For additional exercises, see Classroom Activities 2.5A–2.5D in the *Student's Resource Manual* at www.mhhe.com/moh.

Study Skills Exercise

It is always helpful to read the material in a section and make notes before it is presented in class. Writing notes ahead of time will free you to listen more in class and to pay special attention to the concepts that need clarification. Refer to your class syllabus and identify the next two sections that will be covered in class. Then determine a time when you can read these sections before class.

Vocabulary and Key Concepts

1. a. Interest that is earned on principal is called simple interest.

b. 82% means 82 out of 100.

Review Exercises

For Exercises 2–4, use the steps for problem solving to find the unknown quantities.

2. The difference of four times a number and 17 is 5 less than the number. Find the number.

The number is 4.

3. Find two consecutive integers such that three times the larger is the same as 45 more than the smaller.

The numbers are 21 and 22.

4. The height of the Great Pyramid of Giza is 17 m more than twice the height of the pyramid found in Saqqara. If the difference in their heights is 77 m, find the height of each pyramid.

The pyramid at Saqqara is 60 m high, and the Great Pyramid is 137 m high.

Concept 1: Basic Percent Equations

For Exercises 5–16, find the missing values.

5. 45 is what percent of 360? 12.5%

6. 338 is what percent of 520? 65%

7. 544 is what percent of 640? 85%

8. 576 is what percent of 800? 72%

9. What is 0.5% of 150? 0.75

10. What is 9.5% of 616? 58.52

11. What is 142% of 740? 1050.8

12. What is 156% of 280? 436.8

13. 177 is 20% of what number? 885

14. 126 is 15% of what number? 840

15. 275 is 12.5% of what number? 2200

16. 594 is 45% of what number? 1320

17. A drill is on sale for $99.99. If the sales tax rate is 7%, how much will Molly have to pay for the drill? **(See Example 1.)** Molly will have to pay $106.99.

18. Patrick purchased four new tires that were regularly priced at $94.99 each, but are on sale for $20 off per tire. If the sales tax rate is 6%, how much will be charged to Patrick's VISA card? Patrick will have to pay $317.96.

For Exercises 19–22, use the graph showing the distribution for leading forms of cancer in men. (*Source:* Centers for Disease Control)

Percent of Cancer Cases by Type (Men)

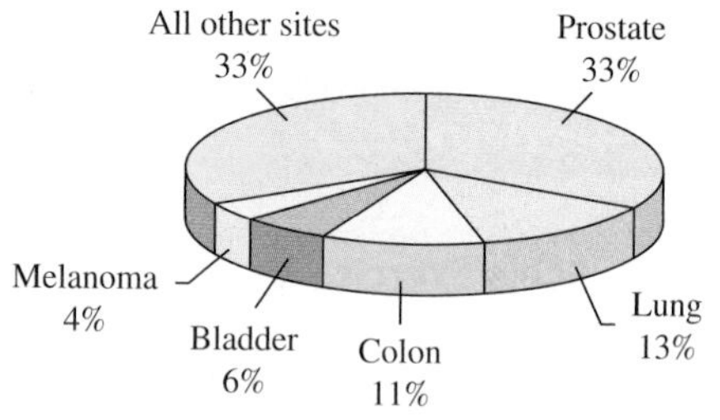

19. If there are 700,000 cases of cancer in men in the United States, approximately how many are prostate cancer? Approximately 231,000 cases

20. Approximately how many cases of lung cancer would be expected in 700,000 cancer cases among men in the United States? Approximately 91,000 cases

21. There were 14,000 cases of cancer of the pancreas diagnosed out of 700,000 cancer cases. What percent is this? **(See Example 2.)** 2%

22. There were 21,000 cases of leukemia diagnosed out of 700,000 cancer cases. What percent is this? 3%

23. Javon is in a 28% tax bracket for his federal income tax. If the amount of money that he paid for federal income tax was $23,520, what was his taxable income? **(See Example 3.)** Javon's taxable income was $84,000.

24. In a recent survey of college-educated adults, 155 indicated that they regularly work more than 50 hr a week. If this represents 31% of those surveyed, how many people were in the survey? There were 500 people in the survey.

Concept 2: Applications Involving Simple Interest

25. Aidan is trying to save money and has $1800 to set aside in some type of savings account. He checked his bank one day, and found that the rate for a 12-month CD had an annual percentage yield (APY) of 1.25%. The interest rate on his savings account was 0.75% APY. How much more simple interest would Aidan earn if he invested in a CD for 12 months rather than leaving the $1800 in a regular savings account? Aidan would earn $9 more in the CD.

26. How much interest will Roxanne have to pay if she borrows $2000 for 2 years at a simple interest rate of 4%? Roxanne will have to pay $160.

27. Bob borrowed money for 1 year at 5% simple interest. If he had to pay back a total of $1260, how much did he originally borrow? **(See Example 4.)** Bob borrowed $1200.

28. Andrea borrowed some money for 2 years at 6% simple interest. If she had to pay back a total of $3640, how much did she originally borrow? Andrea borrowed $3250.

29. If \$1500 grows to \$1950 after 5 years, find the simple interest rate. The rate is 6%.

30. If \$9000 grows to \$10,440 in 2 years, find the simple interest rate. The rate is 8%.

31. Perry is planning a vacation to Europe in 2 years. How much should he invest in an account that pays 3% simple interest to get the \$3500 that he needs for the trip? Round to the nearest dollar. Perry needs to invest \$3302.

32. Sherica invested in a mutual fund and at the end of 20 years she has \$14,300 in her account. If the mutual fund returned an average yield of 8%, how much did she originally invest? Sherica invested \$5500.

Concept 3: Applications Involving Discount and Markup

33. A hands-free kit for a car costs \$62. An electronics store has it on sale for 12% off with free installation.

a. What is the discount on the hands-free kit? \$7.44

b. What is the sale price? \$54.56

34. A tablet originally selling for \$550 is on sale for 10% off.

a. What is the discount on the tablet? \$55

b. What is the sale price? \$495

35. A digital camera is on sale for \$400. This price is 15% off the original price. What was the original price? Round to the nearest cent. **(See Example 5.)** The original price was \$470.59.

36. A Blu-ray disc is on sale for \$18. If this represents an 18% discount rate, what was the original price? The original price was \$21.95.

37. The original price of an Audio Jukebox was \$250. It is on sale for \$220. What percent discount does this represent? The discount rate is 12%.

38. During its first year, a gaming console sold for \$425 in stores. This product was in such demand that it sold for \$800 online. What percent markup does this represent? (Round to the nearest whole percent.) The markup rate is 88%.

39. A doctor ordered a dosage of medicine for a patient. After 2 days, she increased the dosage by 20% and the new dosage came to 18 cc. What was the original dosage? The original dosage was 15 cc.

40. In one area, the cable company marked up the monthly cost by 6%. The new cost is \$63.60 per month. What was the cost before the increase? The original cost was \$60.

Mixed Exercises

41. Sun Lei bought a laptop computer for \$1800. The total cost, including tax, came to \$1890. What is the tax rate? The tax rate is 5%.

© Creatas/PictureQuest RF

42. Jamie purchased a beach umbrella and paid \$32.04, including tax. If the price before tax is \$29.80, what is the sales tax rate (round to the nearest tenth of a percent)? The tax rate is 7.5%.

© Tero Hakala/123RF

43. To discourage tobacco use and to increase state revenue, several states tax tobacco products. One year, the state of New York increased taxes on tobacco, resulting in a 11% increase in the retail price of a pack of cigarettes. If the new price of a pack of cigarettes is \$12.85, what was the cost before the increase in tax? The original cost was \$11.58 per pack.

44. A hotel room rented for 5 nights costs \$706.25 including 13% in taxes. Find the original price of the room (before tax) for the 5 nights. Then find the price per night. The 5 nights (without tax) costs \$625. The price per night is \$125.

45. Deon purchased a house and sold it for a 24% profit. If he sold the house for $260,400, what was the original purchase price? The original price was $210,000.

© Comstock/PunchStock RF

46. To meet the rising cost of energy, the yearly membership at a YMCA had to be increased by 12.5% from the past year. The yearly membership fee is currently $450. What was the cost of membership last year? The cost was $400.

© Image100/Corbis RF

47. Alina earns $1600 per month plus a 12% commission on pharmaceutical sales. If she sold $25,000 in pharmaceuticals one month, what was her salary that month? Alina made $4600 that month.

48. Dan sold a beachfront home for $650,000. If his commission rate is 4%, what did he earn in commission? Dan earned $26,000.

49. Diane sells women's sportswear at a department store. She earns a regular salary and, as a bonus, she receives a commission of 4% on all sales over $200. If Diane earned an extra $25.80 last week in commission, how much merchandise did she sell over $200? Diane sold $645 over $200 worth of merchandise.

50. For selling software, Tom received a bonus commission based on sales over $500. If he received $180 in commission for selling a total of $2300 worth of software, what is his commission rate? Tom's commission rate is 10%.

Section 2.6 Formulas and Applications of Geometry

Concepts

1. Literal Equations and Formulas
2. Geometry Applications

1. Literal Equations and Formulas

A *literal equation* is an equation that has more than one variable. A formula is a literal equation with a specific application. For example, the perimeter of a triangle (distance around the triangle) can be found by the formula $P = a + b + c$, where a, b, and c are the lengths of the sides (Figure 2-7).

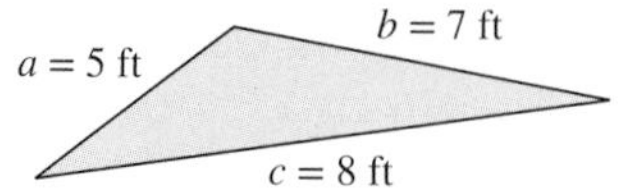

$$P = a + b + c$$
$$= 5 \text{ ft} + 7 \text{ ft} + 8 \text{ ft}$$
$$= 20 \text{ ft}$$

Figure 2-7

In this section, we will learn how to rewrite formulas to solve for a different variable within the formula. Suppose, for example, that the perimeter of a triangle is known and two of the sides are known (say, sides a and b). Then the third side, c, can be found by subtracting the lengths of the known sides from the perimeter (Figure 2-8).

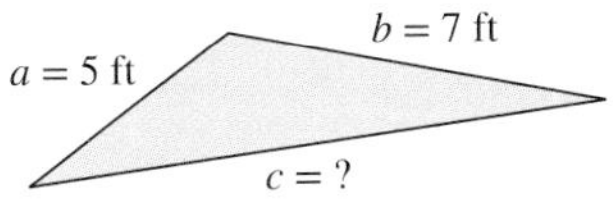

If the perimeter is 20 ft, then
$c = P - a - b$
$= 20 \text{ ft} - 5 \text{ ft} - 7 \text{ ft}$
$= 8$ ft

Figure 2-8

To solve a formula for a different variable, we use the same properties of equality outlined in the earlier sections of this chapter. For example, consider the two equations $2x + 3 = 11$ and $wx + y = z$. Suppose we want to solve for x in each case:

$2x + 3 = 11$		$wx + y = z$	
$2x + 3 - 3 = 11 - 3$	Subtract 3.	$wx + y - y = z - y$	Subtract y.
$2x = 8$		$wx = z - y$	
$\frac{2x}{2} = \frac{8}{2}$	Divide by 2.	$\frac{wx}{w} = \frac{z - y}{w}$	Divide by w.
$x = 4$		$x = \frac{z - y}{w}$	

The equation on the left has only one variable and we are able to simplify the equation to find a numerical value for x. The equation on the right has multiple variables. Because we do not know the values of w, y, and z, we are not able to simplify further. The value of x is left as a formula in terms of w, y, and z.

Example 1 Solving for an Indicated Variable

Classroom Examples: p. 153, Exercises 16 and 24

Solve for the indicated variable.

a. $d = rt$ for t **b.** $5x + 2y = 12$ for y

Solution:

a. $d = rt$ for t The goal is to isolate the variable t.

$\frac{d}{r} = \frac{rt}{r}$ Because the relationship between r and t is multiplication, we reverse the process by dividing both sides by r.

$\frac{d}{r} = t$, or equivalently $t = \frac{d}{r}$

b.

$5x + 2y = 12$ for y	The goal is to solve for y.
$5x - 5x + 2y = 12 - 5x$	Subtract $5x$ from both sides to isolate the y term.
$2y = -5x + 12$	$-5x + 12$ is the same as $12 - 5x$.
$\frac{2y}{2} = \frac{-5x + 12}{2}$	Divide both sides by 2 to isolate y.
$y = \frac{-5x + 12}{2}$	

Avoiding Mistakes

In the expression $\frac{-5x+12}{2}$ do not try to divide the 2 into the 12. The divisor of 2 is dividing the entire quantity, $-5x+12$ (not just the 12).

We may, however, apply the divisor to each term individually in the numerator. That is, $y = \frac{-5x+12}{2}$ can be written in several different forms. Each is correct.

$$y = \frac{-5x+12}{2} \quad \text{or} \quad y = \frac{-5x}{2} + \frac{12}{2} \Rightarrow y = -\frac{5}{2}x + 6$$

Skill Practice Solve for the indicated variable.

1. $A = lw$ for l **2.** $-2a + 4b = 7$ for a

Classroom Example: p. 153, Exercise 36

Example 2 Solving for an Indicated Variable

The formula $C = \frac{5}{9}(F - 32)$ is used to find the temperature, C, in degrees Celsius for a given temperature expressed in degrees Fahrenheit, F. Solve the formula $C = \frac{5}{9}(F - 32)$ for F.

Solution:

$$C = \frac{5}{9}(F - 32)$$

$$C = \frac{5}{9}F - \frac{5}{9} \cdot 32 \qquad \text{Clear parentheses.}$$

$$C = \frac{5}{9}F - \frac{160}{9} \qquad \text{Multiply: } \frac{5}{9} \cdot \frac{32}{1} = \frac{160}{9}$$

$$9(C) = 9\left(\frac{5}{9}F - \frac{160}{9}\right) \qquad \text{Multiply by the LCD to clear fractions.}$$

$$9C = \frac{9}{1} \cdot \frac{5}{9}F - \frac{9}{1} \cdot \frac{160}{9} \qquad \text{Apply the distributive property.}$$

$$9C = 5F - 160 \qquad \text{Simplify.}$$

$$9C + 160 = 5F - 160 + 160 \qquad \text{Add 160 to both sides.}$$

$$9C + 160 = 5F$$

$$\frac{9C + 160}{5} = \frac{5F}{5} \qquad \text{Divide both sides by 5.}$$

$$\frac{9C + 160}{5} = F$$

The answer may be written in several forms:

$$F = \frac{9C + 160}{5} \quad \text{or} \quad F = \frac{9C}{5} + \frac{160}{5} \Rightarrow F = \frac{9}{5}C + 32$$

Skill Practice Solve for the indicated variable.

3. $y = \frac{1}{3}(x - 7)$ for x.

Answers

1. $l = \frac{A}{w}$
2. $a = \frac{7 - 4b}{-2}$ or $a = \frac{4b - 7}{2}$ or $a = 2b - \frac{7}{2}$
3. $x = 3y + 7$

2. Geometry Applications

In Examples 3 through 6 and the related exercises, we use facts and formulas from geometry.

Example 3 **Solving a Geometry Application Involving Perimeter**

Classroom Example: p. 153, Exercise 46

The length of a rectangular lot is 1 m less than twice the width. If the perimeter is 190 m, find the length and width.

Solution:

Step 1: Read the problem.

Let x represent the width of the rectangle. **Step 2:** Label the variables.

Then $2x - 1$ represents the length.

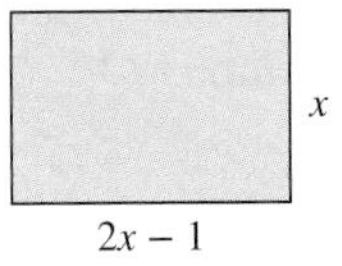

$$P = 2l + 2w$$ **Step 3:** Write the formula for perimeter.

$$190 = 2(2x - 1) + 2(x)$$ **Step 4:** Write an equation in terms of x.

$$190 = 4x - 2 + 2x$$ **Step 5:** Solve for x.

$$190 = 6x - 2$$

$$192 = 6x$$

$$\frac{192}{6} = \frac{6x}{6}$$

$$32 = x$$

The width is $x = 32$. **Step 6:** Interpret the results and write the answer in words.

The length is $2x - 1 = 2(32) - 1 = 63$.

The width of the rectangular lot is 32 m and the length is 63 m.

Skill Practice

4. The length of a rectangle is 10 ft less than twice the width. If the perimeter is 178 ft, find the length and width.

Recall some facts about angles.

- Two angles are complementary if the sum of their measures is 90°.
- Two angles are supplementary if the sum of their measures is 180°.
- The sum of the measures of the angles within a triangle is 180°.
- The measures of vertical angles are equal.

Answer

4. The length is 56 ft, and the width is 33 ft.

Classroom Example: p. 154, Exercise 50

Example 4 Solving a Geometry Application Involving Complementary Angles

Two complementary angles are drawn such that one angle is 4° more than seven times the other angle. Find the measure of each angle.

Solution:

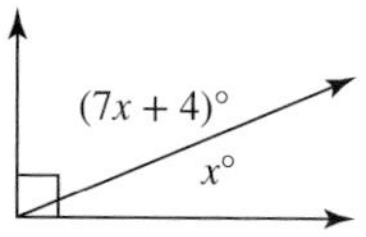

	Step 1: Read the problem.
Let x represent the measure of one angle.	**Step 2:** Label the variables.
Then $7x + 4$ represents the measure of the other angle.	
The angles are complementary, so their sum must be 90°.	
$\begin{pmatrix}\text{Measure of}\\ \text{first angle}\end{pmatrix} + \begin{pmatrix}\text{measure of}\\ \text{second angle}\end{pmatrix} = 90^\circ$	**Step 3:** Write a verbal model.
$x + 7x + 4 = 90$	**Step 4:** Write a mathematical equation.
$8x + 4 = 90$ $8x = 86$ $\frac{8x}{8} = \frac{86}{8}$ $x = 10.75$	**Step 5:** Solve for x.
One angle is $x = 10.75$.	**Step 6:** Interpret the results and write the answer in words.

The other angle is $7x + 4 = 7(10.75) + 4 = 79.25$.

The angles are 10.75° and 79.25°.

Skill Practice

5. Two complementary angles are constructed so that one measures 1° less than six times the other. Find the measures of the angles.

Classroom Example: p. 154, Exercise 58

Example 5 Solving a Geometry Application Involving Angles in a Triangle

One angle in a triangle is twice as large as the smallest angle. The third angle is 10° more than seven times the smallest angle. Find the measure of each angle.

Solution:

	Step 1: Read the problem.
Let x represent the measure of the smallest angle.	**Step 2:** Label the variables.
Then $2x$ and $7x + 10$ represent the measures of the other two angles.	

The sum of the angles must be 180°.

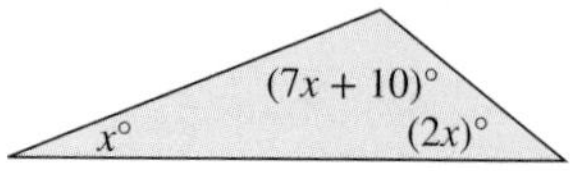

Answer

5. The angles are 13° and 77°.

$$\begin{pmatrix}\text{Measure of}\\\text{first angle}\end{pmatrix} + \begin{pmatrix}\text{measure of}\\\text{second angle}\end{pmatrix} + \begin{pmatrix}\text{measure of}\\\text{third angle}\end{pmatrix} = 180°$$ **Step 3:** Write a verbal model.

$$x + 2x + (7x + 10) = 180$$ **Step 4:** Write a mathematical equation.

$$x + 2x + 7x + 10 = 180$$ **Step 5:** Solve for x.

$$10x + 10 = 180$$

$$10x = 170$$

$$x = 17$$ **Step 6:** Interpret the results and write the answer in words.

The smallest angle is $x = 17$.

The other angles are $2x = 2(17) = 34$

$$7x + 10 = 7(17) + 10 = 129$$

The angles are 17°, 34°, and 129°.

Skill Practice

6. In a triangle, the measure of the first angle is 80° greater than the measure of the second angle. The measure of the third angle is twice that of the second. Find the measures of the angles.

Example 6 **Solving a Geometry Application Involving Circumference**

Classroom Example: p. 155, Exercise 66

The distance around a circular garden is 188.4 ft. Find the radius to the nearest tenth of a foot. Use 3.14 for π.

Solution:

$C = 2\pi r$ Use the formula for the circumference of a circle.

$188.4 = 2\pi r$ Substitute 188.4 for C.

$\dfrac{188.4}{2\pi} = \dfrac{2\pi r}{2\pi}$ Divide both sides by 2π.

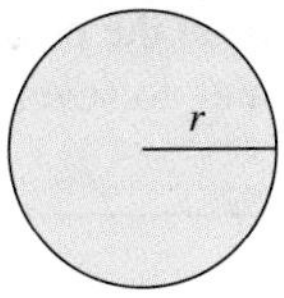

$C = 188.4$ ft

$$\frac{188.4}{2\pi} = r$$

$$r \approx \frac{188.4}{2(3.14)}$$

$$= 30.0$$

The radius is approximately 30.0 ft.

Skill Practice

7. The circumference of a drain pipe is 12.5 cm. Find the radius. Round to the nearest tenth of a centimeter.

Answers

6. The angles are 25°, 50°, and 105°.
7. The radius is 2.0 cm.

Calculator Connections

Topic: Using the π Key on a Calculator

In Example 6 we could have obtained a more accurate result if we had used the π key on a calculator.

Note that parentheses are required to divide 188.4 by the quantity 2π. This guarantees that the calculator follows the implied order of operations. Without parentheses, the calculator would divide 188.4 by 2 and then multiply the result by π.

Scientific Calculator

Enter: 188.4 [÷] [(] 2 [×] [π] [)] [=] **Result:** 29.98479128 correct

Enter: 188.4 [÷] 2 [×] [π] [=] **Result:** 295.938028 incorrect

Graphing Calculator

```
188.4/(2π)
       29.98479128   ← Correct
188.4/2π
        295.938028   ← Incorrect
```

Calculator Exercises

Approximate the expressions with a calculator. Round to three decimal places if necessary.

1. $\dfrac{880}{2\pi}$ 140.056
2. $\dfrac{1600}{\pi(4)^2}$ 31.831
3. $\dfrac{20}{5\pi}$ 1.273
4. $\dfrac{10}{7\pi}$ 0.455

Section 2.6 Practice Exercises

For additional exercises, see Classroom Activities 2.6A–2.6C in the *Student's Resource Manual* at www.mhhe.com/moh.

Study Skills Exercise

A good technique for studying for a test is to choose four problems from each section of the chapter and write the problems along with the directions on 3 × 5 cards. On the back of each card, put the page number where you found that problem. Then shuffle the cards and test yourself on the procedure to solve each problem. If you find one that you do not know how to solve, look at the page number and do several of that type. Write four problems you would choose for this section.

Review Exercises

For Exercises 1–8, solve the equation.

1. $3(2y + 3) - 4(-y + 1) = 7y - 10$ {−5}
2. $-(3w + 4) + 5(w - 2) - 3(6w - 8) = 10$ {0}
3. $\frac{1}{2}(x - 3) + \frac{3}{4} = 3x - \frac{3}{4}$ {0}
4. $\frac{5}{6}x + \frac{1}{2} = \frac{1}{4}(x - 4)$ $\left\{-\frac{18}{7}\right\}$
5. $0.5(y + 2) - 0.3 = 0.4y + 0.5$ {−2}
6. $0.25(500 - x) + 0.15x = 75$ {500}
7. $8b + 6(7 - 2b) = -4(b + 1)$ { }
8. $2 - 5(t - 3) + t = 7t - (6t + 8)$ {5}

Concept 1: Literal Equations and Formulas

For Exercises 9–40, solve for the indicated variable. **(See Examples 1–2.)**

9. $P = a + b + c$ for a
$a = P - b - c$

10. $P = a + b + c$ for b
$b = P - a - c$

11. $x = y - z$ for y
$y = x + z$

12. $c + d = e$ for d
$d = e - c$

13. $p = 250 + q$ for q
$q = p - 250$

14. $y = 35 + x$ for x
$x = y - 35$

15. $A = bh$ for b $b = \frac{A}{h}$

16. $d = rt$ for r $r = \frac{d}{t}$

17. $PV = nrt$ for t $t = \frac{PV}{nr}$

18. $P_1V_1 = P_2V_2$ for V_1 $V_1 = \frac{P_2V_2}{P_1}$

19. $x - y = 5$ for x $x = 5 + y$

20. $x + y = -2$ for y $y = -2 - x$

21. $3x + y = -19$ for y
$y = -3x - 19$

22. $x - 6y = -10$ for x
$x = 6y - 10$

23. $2x + 3y = 6$ for y
$y = \frac{-2x + 6}{3}$ or $y = -\frac{2}{3}x + 2$

24. $7x + 3y = 1$ for y
$y = \frac{-7x + 1}{3}$ or $y = -\frac{7}{3}x + \frac{1}{3}$

25. $-2x - y = 9$ for x
$x = \frac{y + 9}{-2}$ or $x = -\frac{1}{2}y - \frac{9}{2}$

26. $3x - y = -13$ for x
$x = \frac{y - 13}{3}$ or $x = \frac{1}{3}y - \frac{13}{3}$

27. $4x - 3y = 12$ for y
$y = \frac{-4x + 12}{-3}$ or $y = \frac{4}{3}x - 4$

28. $6x - 3y = 4$ for y
$y = \frac{-6x + 4}{-3}$ or $y = 2x - \frac{4}{3}$

29. $ax + by = c$ for y
$y = \frac{-ax + c}{b}$ or $y = -\frac{a}{b}x + \frac{c}{b}$

30. $ax + by = c$ for x
$x = \frac{-by + c}{a}$ or $x = -\frac{b}{a}y + \frac{c}{a}$

31. $A = P(1 + rt)$ for t
$t = \frac{A - P}{Pr}$ or $t = \frac{A}{Pr} - \frac{1}{r}$

32. $P = 2(L + w)$ for L
$L = \frac{P - 2w}{2}$ or $L = \frac{P}{2} - w$

33. $a = 2(b + c)$ for c
$c = \frac{a - 2b}{2}$ or $c = \frac{a}{2} - b$

34. $3(x + y) = z$ for x
$x = \frac{z - 3y}{3}$ or $x = \frac{z}{3} - y$

35. $Q = \frac{x + y}{2}$ for y
$y = 2Q - x$

36. $Q = \frac{a - b}{2}$ for a
$a = 2Q + b$

37. $M = \frac{a}{S}$ for a
$a = MS$

38. $A = \frac{1}{3}(a + b + c)$ for c
$c = 3A - a - b$

39. $P = I^2R$ for R $R = \frac{P}{I^2}$

40. $F = \frac{GMm}{d^2}$ for m $m = \frac{Fd^2}{GM}$

Concept 2: Geometry Applications

For Exercises 41–62, use the Problem-Solving Flowchart for Word Problems.

41. The perimeter of a rectangular garden is 24 ft. The length is 2 ft more than the width. Find the length and the width of the garden. **(See Example 3.)**
The length is 7 ft and the width is 5 ft.

42. In a small rectangular wallet photo, the width is 7 cm less than the length. If the perimeter of the photo is 34 cm, find the length and width.
The length is 12 cm and the width is 5 cm.

43. The length of a rectangular parking area is four times the width. The perimeter is 300 yd. Find the length and width of the parking area. The length is 120 yd and the width is 30 yd.

44. The width of Jason's workbench is $\frac{1}{2}$ the length. The perimeter is 240 in. Find the length and the width of the workbench. The length is 80 in. and the width is 40 in.

45. A builder buys a rectangular lot of land such that the length is 5 m less than two times the width. If the perimeter is 590 m, find the length and the width. The length is 195 m and the width is 100 m.

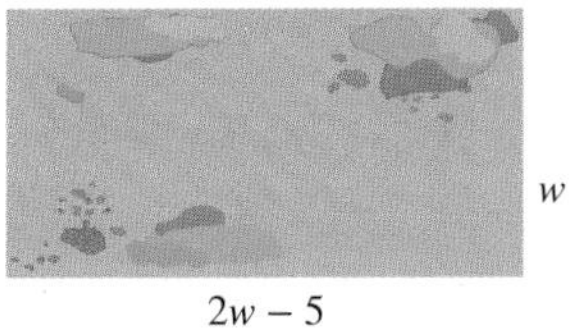

46. The perimeter of a rectangular pool is 140 yd. If the length is 20 yd less than twice the width, find the length and the width.
The length is 40 yd and the width is 30 yd.

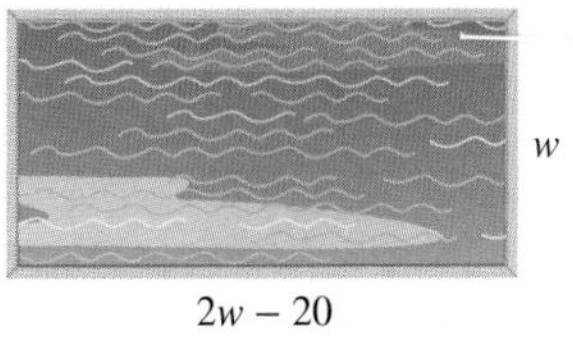

47. A triangular parking lot has two sides that are the same length, and the third side is 5 m longer. If the perimeter is 71 m, find the lengths of the sides. The sides are 22 m, 22 m, and 27 m.

48. The perimeter of a triangle is 16 ft. One side is 3 ft longer than the shortest side. The third side is 1 ft longer than the shortest side. Find the lengths of the sides. The sides are 4 ft, 5 ft, and 7 ft.

49. Sometimes memory devices are helpful for remembering mathematical facts. Recall that the sum of two complementary angles is 90°. That is, two complementary angles when added together form a right angle or “corner.” The words ***Complementary*** and ***Corner*** both start with the letter “***C***.” Derive your own memory device for remembering that the sum of two supplementary angles is 180°. “Adjacent supplementary angles form a straight angle.” The words *Supplementary* and *Straight* both begin with the same letter.

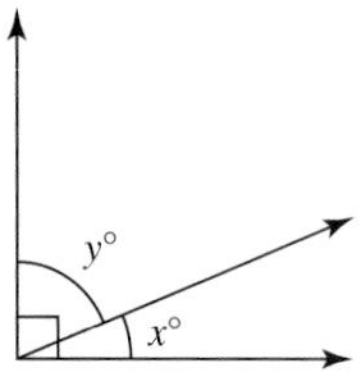

$x° + y° = 90°$

Complementary angles form a “Corner”

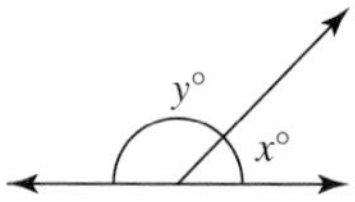

$x° + y° = 180°$

Supplementary angles . . .

50. Two angles are complementary. One angle is 20° less than the other angle. Find the measures of the angles.
The angles are 55° and 35°.

51. Two angles are complementary. One angle is 4° less than three times the other angle. Find the measures of the angles. **(See Example 4.)**
The angles are 23.5° and 66.5°.

52. Two angles are supplementary. One angle is three times as large as the other angle. Find the measures of the angles. The angles are 45° and 135°.

53. Two angles are supplementary. One angle is 6° more than four times the other. Find the measures of the angles. The angles are 34.8° and 145.2°.

54. Refer to the figure. The angles, $\angle a$ and $\angle b$, are vertical angles.

a. If the measure of $\angle a$ is 32°, what is the measure of $\angle b$?

b. What is the measure of the supplement of $\angle a$?

a. The measure of $\angle b$ is 32°.
b. The supplement is 148°.

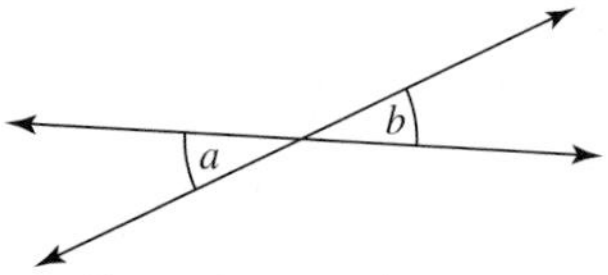

Figure for Exercise 54

55. Find the measures of the vertical angles labeled in the figure by first solving for x.
$x = 20$; the vertical angles measure 37°.

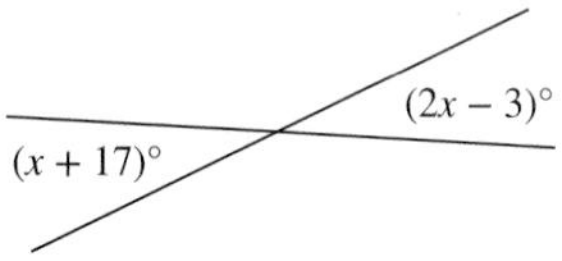

56. Find the measures of the vertical angles labeled in the figure by first solving for y.
$y = 40$; the vertical angles measure 146°.

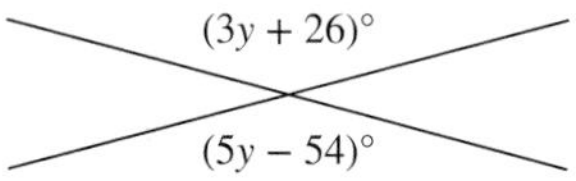

57. The largest angle in a triangle is three times the smallest angle. The middle angle is two times the smallest angle. Given that the sum of the angles in a triangle is 180°, find the measure of each angle. **(See Example 5.)**
The measures of the angles are 30°, 60°, and 90°.

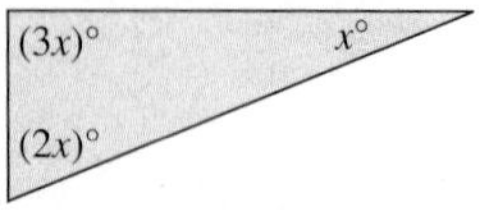

Animation

58. The smallest angle in a triangle measures 90° less than the largest angle. The middle angle measures 60° less than the largest angle. Find the measure of each angle.
The measures of the angles are 20°, 50°, and 110°.

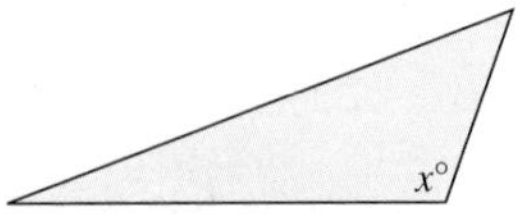

59. The smallest angle in a triangle is half the largest angle. The middle angle measures 30° less than the largest angle. Find the measure of each angle.
The measures of the angles are 42°, 54°, and 84°.

60. The largest angle of a triangle is three times the middle angle. The smallest angle measures 10° less than the middle angle. Find the measure of each angle.
The measures of the angles are 38°, 28°, and 114°.

61. Find the value of x and the measure of each angle labeled in the figure.
$x = 17$; the measures of the angles are 34° and 56°.

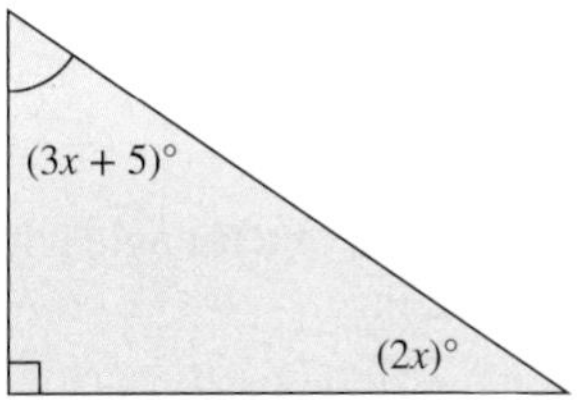

62. Find the value of y and the measure of each angle labeled in the figure.
$y = 26.5$; the measures of the angles are 28.5° and 61.5°.

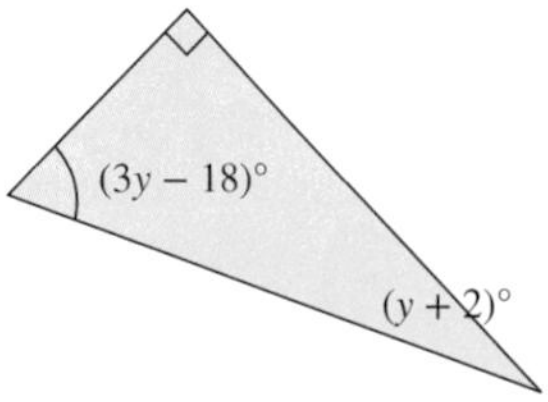

63. **a.** A rectangle has length l and width w. Write a formula for the area.
$A = lw$

b. Solve the formula for the width, w. $w = \frac{A}{l}$

c. The area of a rectangular volleyball court is 1740.5 ft² and the length is 59 ft. Find the width.
The width is 29.5 ft.

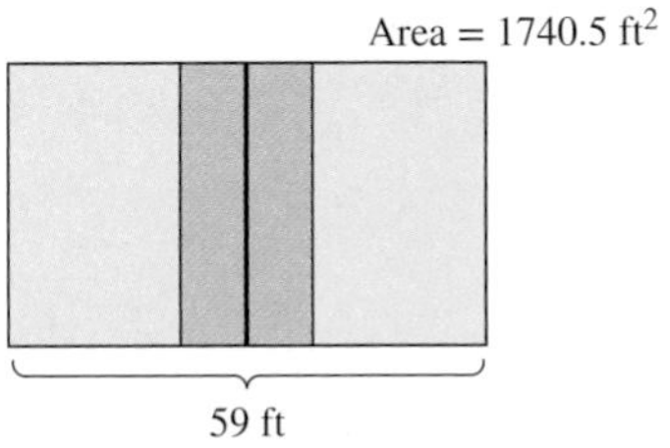

64. **a.** A parallelogram has height h and base b. Write a formula for the area.
$A = bh$

b. Solve the formula for the base, b. $b = \frac{A}{h}$

c. Find the base of the parallelogram pictured if the area is 40 m².
The base is 8 m.

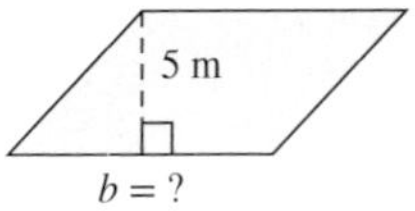

65. **a.** A rectangle has length l and width w. Write a formula for the perimeter. $P = 2l + 2w$

b. Solve the formula for the length, l. $l = \frac{P - 2w}{2}$

c. The perimeter of the soccer field at Giants Stadium is 338 m. If the width is 66 m, find the length. The length is 103 m.

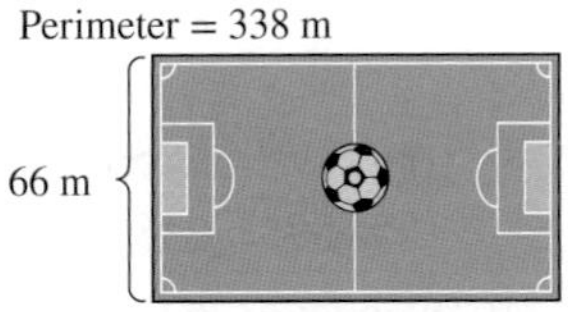

66. **a.** A triangle has height h and base b. Write a formula for the area. $A = \frac{1}{2}bh$

b. Solve the formula for the height, h. $h = \frac{2A}{b}$

c. Find the height of the triangle pictured if the area is 12 km².
The height is 4 km.

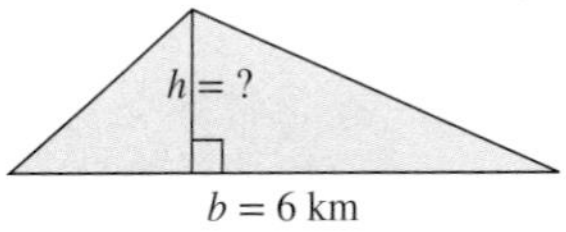

67. **a.** A circle has a radius of r. Write a formula for the circumference. **(See Example 6.)** $C = 2\pi r$

b. Solve the formula for the radius, r. $r = \frac{C}{2\pi}$

c. The circumference of the circular Buckingham Fountain in Chicago is approximately 880 ft. Find the radius. Round to the nearest foot.
The radius is approximately 140 ft.

© Brand X Pictures/Getty Images RF

68. **a.** The length of each side of a square is s. Write a formula for the perimeter of the square. $P = 4s$

b. Solve the formula for the length of a side, s. $s = \frac{P}{4}$

c. The Pyramid of Khufu (known as the Great Pyramid) at Giza has a square base. If the distance around the bottom is 921.6 m, find the length of the sides at the bottom of the pyramid.
The length of each side at the bottom of the pyramid is 230.4 m.

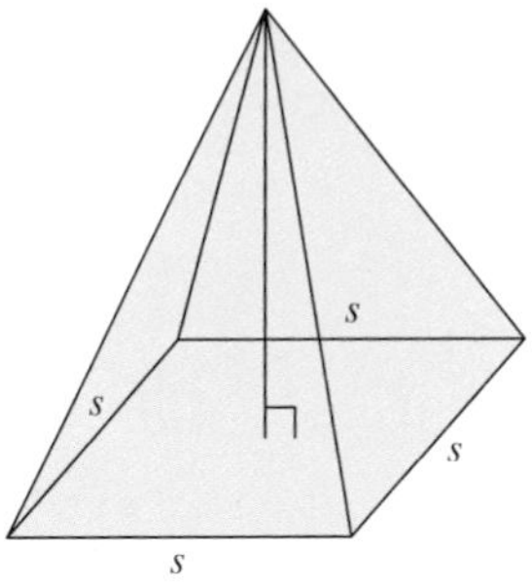

Writing   Translating Expression   Geometry   Scientific Calculator   Video

Expanding Your Skills

For Exercises 69–70, find the indicated area or volume. Be sure to include the proper units and round each answer to two decimal places if necessary.

69. **a.** Find the area of a circle with radius 11.5 m. Use the π key on the calculator. 415.48 m^2

b. Find the volume of a right circular cylinder with radius 11.5 m and height 25 m. 10,386.89 m^3

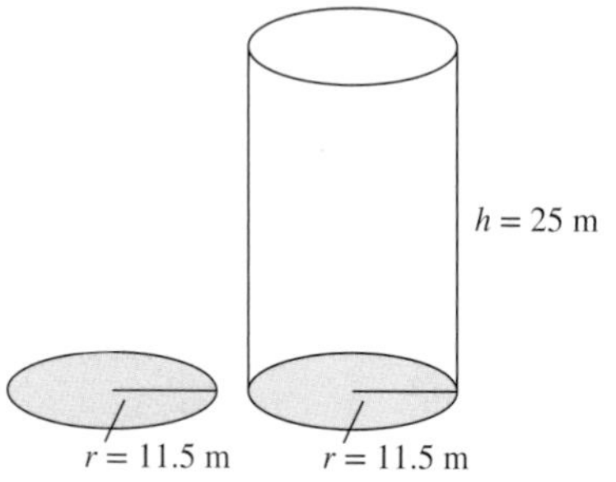

70. **a.** Find the area of a parallelogram with base 30 in. and height 12 in.
360 in.^{2}

b. Find the area of a triangle with base 30 in. and height 12 in.
180 in.^{2}

c. Compare the areas found in parts (a) and (b).
The area of the triangle is one-half the area of the parallelogram.

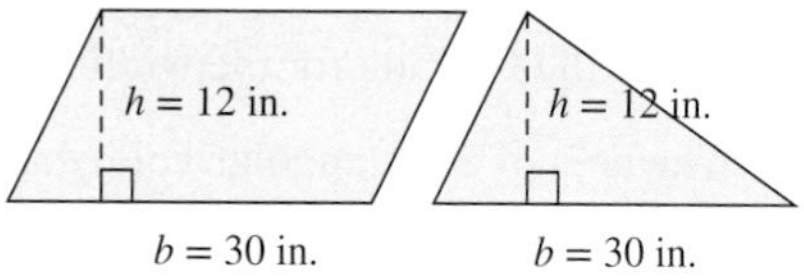

Section 2.7 Mixture Applications and Uniform Motion

Concepts

1. Applications Involving Cost
2. Applications Involving Mixtures
3. Applications Involving Uniform Motion

1. Applications Involving Cost

In Examples 1 and 2, we will look at different kinds of mixture problems. The first example "mixes" two types of theater tickets, adult tickets that sell for \$12 and children's tickets that sell for \$9. Furthermore, there were 300 tickets sold for a total revenue of \$3060. Before attempting the problem, we should try to gain some familiarity. Let's try a few combinations to see how many of each type of ticket might have been sold.

Suppose 100 adult tickets were sold and 200 children's tickets were sold (a total of 300 tickets).

- 100 adult tickets at \$12 each gives 100(\$12) = \$1200
- 200 children's tickets at \$9 each gives 200(\$9) = \$1800

Total revenue: \$3000 (not enough)

Suppose 150 adult tickets were sold and 150 children's tickets were sold (a total of 300 tickets).

- 150 adult tickets at \$12 each gives 150(\$12) = \$1800
- 150 children's tickets at \$9 each gives 150(\$9) = \$1350

Total revenue: \$3150 (too much)

As you can see, the trial-and-error process can be tedious and time consuming. Therefore, we will use algebra to determine the correct combination of each type of ticket.

Suppose we let x represent the number of adult tickets. Then the number of children's tickets is the *total minus x*. That is,

$$\begin{pmatrix}\text{Number of}\\ \text{children's tickets}\end{pmatrix} = \begin{pmatrix}\text{total number}\\ \text{of tickets}\end{pmatrix} - \begin{pmatrix}\text{number of}\\ \text{adult tickets, } x\end{pmatrix}$$

$$\text{Number of children's tickets} = 300 - x.$$

Notice that the number of tickets sold times the price per ticket gives the revenue:

- x adult tickets at \$12 each gives a revenue of: $x(\$12)$ or simply $12x$.
- $300 - x$ children's tickets at \$9 each gives: $(300 - x)(\$9)$ or $9(300 - x)$.

This will help us set up an equation in Example 1.

Example 1 **Solving a Mixture Problem Involving Ticket Sales**

Classroom Example: p. 162, Exercise 14

At a community theater, 300 tickets were sold. Adult tickets cost \$12 and tickets for children cost \$9. If the total revenue from ticket sales was \$3060, determine the number of each type of ticket sold.

© Uppercut/Getty Images RF

Solution:

Step 1: Read the problem.

Let x represent the number of adult tickets sold.
$300 - x$ is the number of children's tickets.

Step 2: Label the variables.

	\$12 Tickets	\$9 Tickets	Total
Number of tickets	x	$300 - x$	300
Revenue	$12x$	$9(300 - x)$	3060

$$\begin{pmatrix}\text{Revenue from}\\ \text{adult tickets}\end{pmatrix} + \begin{pmatrix}\text{revenue from}\\ \text{children's tickets}\end{pmatrix} = \begin{pmatrix}\text{total}\\ \text{revenue}\end{pmatrix}$$

Step 3: Write a verbal model.

$$12x \quad + \quad 9(300 - x) \quad = \quad 3060$$

Step 4: Write a mathematical equation.

$$12x + 9(300 - x) = 3060$$

Step 5: Solve the equation.

$$12x + 2700 - 9x = 3060$$
$$3x + 2700 = 3060$$
$$3x = 360$$
$$x = 120$$

Step 6: Interpret the results.

There were 120 adult tickets sold.
The number of children's tickets is $300 - x$ which is 180.

Avoiding Mistakes

Check that the answer is reasonable. 120 adult tickets and 180 children's tickets makes 300 total tickets.

Furthermore, 120 adult tickets at \$12 each amounts to \$1440, and 180 children's tickets at \$9 each amounts to \$1620. The total revenue is \$3060 as expected.

Skill Practice

1. At a Performing Arts Center, seats in the orchestra section cost \$18 and seats in the balcony cost \$12. If there were 120 seats sold for one performance, for a total revenue of \$1920, how many of each type of seat were sold?

Answer

1. There were 80 seats in the orchestra section, and there were 40 in the balcony.

2. Applications Involving Mixtures

Classroom Example: p. 163, Exercise 24

Example 2 Solving a Mixture Application

How many liters (L) of a 60% antifreeze solution must be added to 8 L of a 10% antifreeze solution to produce a 20% antifreeze solution?

Solution:

The information can be organized in a table. Notice that an algebraic equation is derived from the second row of the table. This relates the number of liters of pure antifreeze in each container.

Step 1: Read the problem.

	60% Antifreeze	10% Antifreeze	Final Mixture: 20% Antifreeze
Number of liters of solution	x	8	$(8 + x)$
Number of liters of pure antifreeze	$0.60x$	$0.10(8)$	$0.20(8 + x)$

Step 2: Label the variables.

TIP: To determine the amount of pure antifreeze in a given solution, multiply the concentration rate by the amount of solution. For example, 8 L of a 10% solutions means that

$$(0.10)(8 \text{ L}) = 0.8 \text{ L}$$

of the solution is pure antifreeze. The rest is something else such as water.

The amount of pure antifreeze in the final solution equals the sum of the amounts of antifreeze in the first two solutions.

$$\begin{pmatrix}\text{Pure antifreeze}\\ \text{from solution 1}\end{pmatrix} + \begin{pmatrix}\text{pure antifreeze}\\ \text{from solution 2}\end{pmatrix} = \begin{pmatrix}\text{pure antifreeze}\\ \text{in the final solution}\end{pmatrix}$$

Step 3: Write a verbal model.

$$0.60x \quad + \quad 0.10(8) \quad = \quad 0.20(8 + x)$$

$$0.60x + 0.10(8) = 0.20(8 + x)$$

Step 4: Write a mathematical equation.

$$0.6x + 0.8 = 1.6 + 0.2x$$

Step 5: Solve the equation.

$$0.6x - 0.2x + 0.8 = 1.6 + 0.2x - 0.2x \qquad \text{Subtract } 0.2x.$$

$$0.4x + 0.8 = 1.6$$

$$0.4x + 0.8 - 0.8 = 1.6 - 0.8 \qquad \text{Subtract } 0.8.$$

$$0.4x = 0.8$$

$$\frac{0.4x}{0.4} = \frac{0.8}{0.4} \qquad \text{Divide by } 0.4.$$

$$x = 2$$

Step 6: Interpret the result.

Therefore, 2 L of 60% antifreeze solution is necessary to make a final solution that is 20% antifreeze.

Skill Practice

2. How many gallons of a 5% bleach solution must be added to 10 gallons (gal) of a 20% bleach solution to produce a solution that is 15% bleach?

Answer

2. 5 gal is needed.

3. Applications Involving Uniform Motion

The formula (distance) = (rate)(time) or simply, $d = rt$, relates the distance traveled to the rate of travel and the time of travel.

For example, if a car travels at 60 mph for 3 hours, then

$$d = (60 \text{ mph})(3 \text{ hours})$$
$$= 180 \text{ miles}$$

If a car travels at 60 mph for x hours, then

$$d = (60 \text{ mph})(x \text{ hours})$$
$$= 60x \text{ miles}$$

Example 3 **Solving an Application Involving Distance, Rate, and Time**

Classroom Example: p. 163, Exercise 32

One bicyclist rides 4 mph faster than another bicyclist. The faster rider takes 3 hr to complete a race, while the slower rider takes 4 hr. Find the speed for each rider.

Solution:

Step 1: Read the problem.

The problem is asking us to find the speed of each rider.

Let x represent the speed of the slower rider. Then $(x + 4)$ is the speed of the faster rider.

Step 2: Label the variables and organize the information given in the problem. A distance-rate-time chart may be helpful.

	Distance	Rate	Time
Faster rider	$3(x + 4)$	$x + 4$	3
Slower rider	$4(x)$	x	4

↑

To complete the first column, we can use the relationship, $d = rt$.

Because the riders are riding in the same race, their distances are equal.

$$\begin{pmatrix}\text{Distance}\\ \text{by faster rider}\end{pmatrix} = \begin{pmatrix}\text{distance}\\ \text{by slower rider}\end{pmatrix}$$

Step 3: Write a verbal model.

$$3(x + 4) = 4(x)$$

Step 4: Write a mathematical equation.

$$3x + 12 = 4x$$

Step 5: Solve the equation.

$$12 = x$$

Subtract $3x$ from both sides.

The variable x represents the slower rider's rate. The quantity $x + 4$ is the faster rider's rate. Thus, if $x = 12$, then $x + 4 = 16$.

Avoiding Mistakes

Check that the answer is reasonable. If the slower rider rides at 12 mph for 4 hr, he travels 48 mi. If the faster rider rides at 16 mph for 3 hr, he also travels 48 mi as expected.

The slower rider travels 12 mph and the faster rider travels 16 mph.

Skill Practice

3. An express train travels 25 mph faster than a cargo train. It takes the express train 6 hr to travel a route, and it takes 9 hr for the cargo train to travel the same route. Find the speed of each train.

Answer

3. The express train travels 75 mph, and the cargo train travels 50 mph.

Classroom Example: p. 164, Exercise 38

Example 4 Solving an Application Involving Distance, Rate, and Time

Two families that live 270 mi apart plan to meet for an afternoon picnic at a park that is located between their two homes. Both families leave at 9.00 A.M., but one family averages 12 mph faster than the other family. If the families meet at the designated spot $2\frac{1}{2}$ hr later, determine

a. The average rate of speed for each family.

b. The distance each family traveled to the picnic.

Solution:

For simplicity, we will call the two families, Family A and Family B. Let Family A be the family that travels at the slower rate (Figure 2-9).

Step 1: Read the problem and draw a sketch.

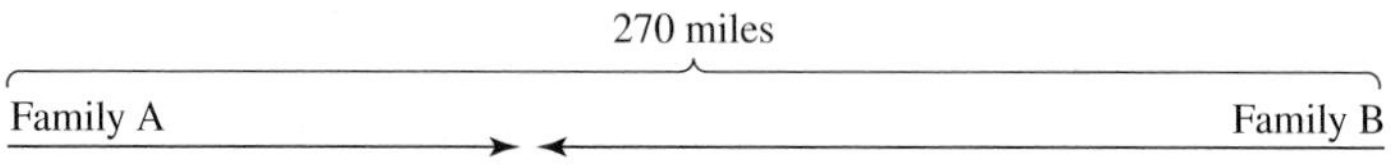

Figure 2-9

Let x represent the rate of Family A.

Then $(x + 12)$ is the rate of Family B.

Step 2: Label the variables.

	Distance	Rate	Time
Family A	$2.5x$	x	2.5
Family B	$2.5(x + 12)$	$x + 12$	2.5

To complete the first column, we can multiply rate and time: $d = rt$.

To set up an equation, recall that the total distance between the two families is given as 270 mi.

$$\begin{pmatrix}\text{Distance}\\ \text{traveled by}\\ \text{Family A}\end{pmatrix} + \begin{pmatrix}\text{distance}\\ \text{traveled by}\\ \text{Family B}\end{pmatrix} = \begin{pmatrix}\text{total}\\ \text{distance}\end{pmatrix}$$

Step 3: Write a verbal model.

$$2.5x \quad + \quad 2.5(x + 12) \quad = \quad 270$$

Step 4: Write a mathematical equation.

$$2.5x + 2.5(x + 12) = 270$$
$$2.5x + 2.5x + 30 = 270$$
$$5.0x + 30 = 270$$
$$5x = 240$$
$$x = 48$$

Step 5: Solve for x.

a. Family A traveled 48 mph.

Family B traveled $x + 12 = 48 + 12 = 60$ mph.

Step 6: Interpret the results and write the answer in words.

b. To compute the distance each family traveled, use $d = rt$.

Family A traveled (48 mph)(2.5 hr) = 120 mi.

Family B traveled (60 mph)(2.5 hr) = 150 mi.

Skill Practice

4. A Piper airplane has an average air speed that is 10 mph faster than a Cessna 150 airplane. If the combined distance traveled by these two small planes is 690 mi after 3 hr, what is the average speed of each plane?

Answer

4. The Cessna's speed is 110 mph, and the Piper's speed is 120 mph.

Section 2.7 Practice Exercises

For additional exercises, see Classroom Activities 2.7A–2.7C in the *Student's Resource Manual* at www.mhhe.com/moh.

Study Skills Exercise

The following is a list of steps to help you solve word problems. Check those that you follow on a regular basis when solving a word problem. Place an asterisk next to the steps that you need to improve.

_____ Read through the entire problem before writing anything down.

_____ Write down exactly what you are being asked to find.

_____ Write down what is known and assign variables to what is unknown.

_____ Draw a figure or diagram if it will help you understand the problem.

_____ Highlight key words like total, sum, difference, etc.

_____ Translate the word problem to a mathematical problem.

_____ After solving, check that your answer makes sense.

Review Exercises

For Exercises 1–3, solve for the indicated variable.

1. $ax - by = c$ for x $x = \frac{c + by}{a}$

2. $cd = r$ for c $c = \frac{r}{d}$

3. $7x + xy = 18$ for y $y = \frac{18 - 7x}{x}$

For Exercises 4–6, solve each equation.

4. $-2d + 11 = 4 - d$ $\{7\}$

5. $3(2y + 5) - 8(y - 1) = 3y + 3$ $\{4\}$

6. $0.02x + 0.04(10 - x) = 1.26$ $\{-43\}$

Concept 1: Applications Involving Cost

For Exercises 7–12, write an algebraic expression as indicated.

7. Two numbers total 200. Let t represent one of the numbers. Write an algebraic expression for the other number. $200 - t$

8. The total of two numbers is 43. Let s represent one of the numbers. Write an algebraic expression for the other number. $43 - s$

9. Olivia needs to bring 100 cookies to her friend's party. She has already baked x cookies. Write an algebraic expression for the number of cookies Olivia still needs to bake. $100 - x$

© Comstock Images/Jupiter Images RF

10. Rachel needs a mixture of 55 pounds (lb) of nuts consisting of peanuts and cashews. Let p represent the number of pounds of peanuts in the mixture. Write an algebraic expression for the number of pounds of cashews that she needs to add. $55 - p$

© McGraw-Hill Education/Jill Braaten, photographer

11. Max has a total of $3000 in two bank accounts. Let y represent the amount in one account. Write an algebraic expression for the amount in the other account. $3000 - y$

12. Roberto has a total of $7500 in two savings accounts. Let z represent the amount in one account. Write an algebraic expression for the amount in the other account. $7500 - z$

13. A church had an ice cream social and sold tickets for $3 and $2. When the social was over, 81 tickets had been sold totaling $215. How many of each type of ticket did the church sell? **(See Example 1.)**
53 tickets were sold at $3 and 28 tickets were sold at $2.

	$3 Tickets	$2 Tickets	Total
Number of tickets			
Cost of tickets			

14. Anna is a teacher at an elementary school. She purchased 72 tickets to take the first-grade children and some parents on a field trip to the zoo. She purchased children's tickets for $10 each and adult tickets for $18 each. She spent a total of $856. How many of each type of ticket did she buy?
Anna purchased 17 adult tickets and 55 children's tickets.

	Adults	Children	Total
Number of tickets			
Cost of tickets			

15. Josh downloaded 25 songs from an online site. Some songs cost $1.29 and some cost $1.49. He spent a total of $33.85. How many songs at each price were purchased? There were 17 songs purchased at $1.29 and 8 songs purchased at $1.49.

16. During the past year, Kris purchased 30 books at a wholesale club store. She purchased softcover books for $4.50 each and hardcover books for $13.50 each. The total cost of the books was $216. How many of each type of book did she purchase? Kris purchased 21 softcover books and 9 hardcover books.

© Royalty Free/Corbis RF

17. During the past year, Amber purchased 32 books for her e-reader. She purchased some books for $6.99 and others for $9.99. If she spent a total of $256.68, how many books from each price category did she buy?
Amber bought 21 books at $6.99 and 11 books at $9.99.

18. Steven wants to buy some candy with his birthday money. He can choose from jelly beans that sell for $6.99 per pound and a variety mix that sells for $3.99. He likes to have twice the amount of jelly beans as the variety mix. If he spent a total of $53.91, how many pounds of each type of candy did he buy?
Steven bought 6 lb of jelly beans and 3 lb of the variety mix.

Concept 2: Applications Involving Mixtures

For Exercises 19–22, write an algebraic expression as indicated.

19. A container holds 7 ounces (oz) of liquid. Let x represent the number of ounces of liquid in another container. Write an expression for the total amount of liquid. $x + 7$

20. A bucket contains 2.5 L of a bleach solution. Let n represent the number of liters of bleach solution in a second bucket. Write an expression for the total amount of bleach solution. $n + 2.5$

21. If Charlene invests \$2000 in a certificate of deposit and d dollars in a stock, write an expression for the total amount she invested. $d + 2000$

22. James has \$5000 in one savings account. Let y represent the amount he has in another savings account. Write an expression for the total amount of money in both accounts. $y + 5000$

23. How much of a 5% ethanol fuel mixture should be mixed with 2000 gal of 10% ethanol fuel mixture to get a mixture that is 9% ethanol. **(See Example 2.)** Mix 500 gal of 5% ethanol fuel mixture.

Animation

	5% Ethanol	10% Ethanol	Final Mixture: 9% Ethanol
Number of gallons of fuel mixture			
Number of gallons of pure ethanol			

24. How many ounces of a 50% antifreeze solution must be mixed with 10 oz of an 80% antifreeze solution to produce a 60% antifreeze solution? Mix 20 oz of 50% antifreeze solution.

	50% Antifreeze	80% Antifreeze	Final Mixture: 60% Antifreeze
Number of ounces of solution			
Number of ounces of pure antifreeze			

25. A pharmacist needs to mix a 1% saline (salt) solution with 24 milliliters (mL) of a 16% saline solution to obtain a 9% saline solution. How many milliliters of the 1% solution must she use? The pharmacist needs to use 21 mL of the 1% saline solution.

26. A landscaper needs to mix a 75% pesticide solution with 30 gal of a 25% pesticide solution to obtain a 60% pesticide solution. How many gallons of the 75% solution must he use? The landscaper needs to use 70 gal of the 75% pesticide solution.

27. To clean a concrete driveway, a contractor needs a solution that is 30% acid. How many ounces of a 50% acid solution must be mixed with 15 oz of a 21% solution to obtain a 30% acid solution? The contractor needs to mix 6.75 oz of 50% acid solution.

28. A veterinarian needs a mixture that contains 12% of a certain medication to treat an injured bird. How many milliliters of a 16% solution should be mixed with 6 mL of a 7% solution to obtain a solution that is 12% medication? The veterinarian needs to use 7.5 mL of the 16% solution.

Concept 3: Applications Involving Uniform Motion

29. **a.** If a car travels 60 mph for 5 hr, find the distance traveled. 300 mi

b. If a car travels at x miles per hour for 5 hr, write an expression that represents the distance traveled. $5x$

c. If a car travels at $x + 12$ mph for 5 hr, write an expression that represents the distance traveled. $5(x + 12)$ or $5x + 60$

30. **a.** If a plane travels 550 mph for 2.5 hr, find the distance traveled. 1375 mi

b. If a plane travels at x miles per hour for 2.5 hr, write an expression that represents the distance traveled. $2.5x$

c. If a plane travels at $x - 100$ mph for 2.5 hr, write an expression that represents the distance traveled. $2.5(x - 100)$ or $2.5x - 250$

31. A woman can walk 2 mph faster down a trail to Cochita Lake than she can on the return trip uphill. It takes her 2 hr to get to the lake and 4 hr to return. What is her speed walking down to the lake? **(See Example 3.)** She walks 4 mph to the lake.

	Distance	Rate	Time
Downhill to the lake			
Uphill from the lake			

32. A car travels 20 mph slower in a bad rain storm than in sunny weather. The car travels the same distance in 2 hr in sunny weather as it does in 3 hr in rainy weather. Find the speed of the car in sunny weather. The car travels 60 mph in sunny weather.

	Distance	Rate	Time
Rain storm			
Sunny weather			

33. Bryan hiked up to the top of City Creek in 3 hr and then returned down the canyon to the trailhead in another 2 hr. His speed downhill was 1 mph faster than his speed uphill. How far up the canyon did he hike? Bryan hiked 6 mi up the canyon.

34. Laura hiked up Lamb's Canyon in 2 hr and then ran back down in 1 hr. Her speed running downhill was 2.5 mph faster than her speed hiking uphill. How far up the canyon did she hike? Laura hiked 5 mi up the canyon.

35. Hazel and Emilie fly from Atlanta to San Diego. The flight from Atlanta to San Diego is against the wind and takes 4 hr. The return flight with the wind takes 3.5 hr. If the wind speed is 40 mph, find the speed of the plane in still air. The plane travels 600 mph in still air.

36. A boat on the Potomac River travels the same distance downstream with the current in $\frac{2}{3}$ hr as it does going upstream against the current in 1 hr. If the speed of the current is 3 mph, find the speed of the boat in still water. The speed of the boat is 15 mph in still water.

37. Two cars are 200 mi apart and travel toward each other on the same road. They meet in 2 hr. One car travels 4 mph faster than the other. What is the speed of each car? **(See Example 4.)** The slower car travels 48 mph and the faster car travels 52 mph.

38. Two cars are 238 mi apart and travel toward each other along the same road. They meet in 2 hr. One car travels 5 mph slower than the other. What is the speed of each car? The cars are traveling 62 mph and 57 mph.

39. After Hurricane Katrina, a rescue vehicle leaves a station at noon and heads for New Orleans. An hour later a second vehicle traveling 10 mph faster leaves the same station. By 4:00 P.M., the first vehicle reaches its destination, and the second is still 10 mi away. How fast is each vehicle? The speeds of the vehicles are 40 mph and 50 mph.

40. A truck leaves a truck stop at 9:00 A.M. and travels toward Sturgis, Wyoming. At 10:00 A.M., a motorcycle leaves the same truck stop and travels the same route. The motorcycle travels 15 mph faster than the truck. By noon, the truck has traveled 20 mi farther than the motorcycle. How fast is each vehicle? The speed of the motorcycle is 65 mph and the speed of the truck is 50 mph.

41. In the Disney Marathon, Jeanette's speed running is twice Sarah's speed walking. After 2 hr, Jeanette is 7 mi ahead of Sarah. Find Jeanette's speed and Sarah's speed. Sarah walks 3.5 mph and Jeanette runs 7 mph.

42. Two canoes travel down a river, starting at 9:00 A.M. One canoe travels twice as fast as the other. After 3.5 hr, the canoes are 5.25 mi apart. Find the speed of each canoe. The canoes travel 1.5 mph and 3 mph.

Mixed Exercises

43. A certain granola mixture is 10% peanuts.

a. If a container has 20 lb of granola, how many pounds of peanuts are there? 2 lb

b. If a container has x pounds of granola, write an expression that represents the number of pounds of peanuts in the granola. $0.10x$

c. If a container has $x + 3$ lb of granola, write an expression that represents the number of pounds of peanuts. $0.10(x + 3) = 0.10x + 0.30$

44. A certain blend of coffee sells for $9.00 per pound.

a. If a container has 20 lb of coffee, how much will it cost? $180

b. If a container has x pounds of coffee, write an expression that represents the cost. $9x$

c. If a container has $40 - x$ pounds of this coffee, write an expression that represents the cost. $9(40 - x) = 360 - 9x$

45. The Coffee Company mixes coffee worth $12 per pound with coffee worth $8 per pound to produce 50 lb of coffee worth $8.80 per pound. How many pounds of the $12 coffee and how many pounds of the $8 coffee must be used? Mix 10 lb of coffee sold at $12 per pound and 40 lb of coffee sold at $8 per pound.

	$12 Coffee	$8 Coffee	Total
Number of pounds			
Value of coffee			

46. The Nut House sells pecans worth $4 per pound and cashews worth $6 per pound. How many pounds of pecans and how many pounds of cashews must be mixed to form 16 lb of a nut mixture worth $4.50 per pound? Mix 12 lb of pecans and 4 lb of cashews.

	$4 Pecans	$6 Cashews	Total
Number of pounds			
Value of nuts			

47. A boat in distress, 21 nautical miles from a marina, travels toward the marina at 3 knots (nautical miles per hour). A coast guard cruiser leaves the marina and travels toward the boat at 25 knots. How long will it take for the boats to reach each other? The boats will meet in $\frac{3}{4}$ hr (45 min).

© Dennis MacDonald/Alamy RF

48. An air traffic controller observes a plane heading from New York to San Francisco traveling at 450 mph. At the same time, another plane leaves San Francisco and travels 500 mph to New York. If the distance between the airports is 2850 mi, how long will it take for the planes to pass each other? The planes will pass in 3 hr.

49. Surfer Sam purchased a total of 21 items at the surf shop. He bought wax for \$3.00 per package and sunscreen for \$8.00 per bottle. He spent a total of \$88.00. How many of each item did he purchase? Sam purchased 16 packages of wax and 5 bottles of sunscreen.

50. Tonya Toast loves jam. She purchased 30 jars of gourmet jam for \$178.50. She bought raspberry jam for \$6.25 per jar and strawberry jam for \$5.50 per jar. How many jars of each did she purchase? Tonya purchased 18 jars of raspberry and 12 jars of strawberry.

51. How many quarts of 85% chlorine solution must be mixed with 5 quarts of 25% chlorine solution to obtain a 45% chlorine solution? 2.5 quarts of 85% chlorine solution

52. How many liters of a 58% sugar solution must be added to 14 L of a 40% sugar solution to obtain a 50% sugar solution? 17.5 L of 58% sugar solution.

Expanding Your Skills

53. How much pure water must be mixed with 12 L of a 40% alcohol solution to obtain a 15% alcohol solution? (*Hint:* Pure water is 0% alcohol.) 20 L of water must be added.

54. How much pure water must be mixed with 10 oz of a 60% alcohol solution to obtain a 25% alcohol solution? 14 oz of water must be added.

55. Amtrak Acela Express is a high-speed train that runs in the United States between Washington, D.C. and Boston. In Japan, a bullet train along the Sanyo line operates at an average speed of 60 km/hr faster than the Amtrak Acela Express. It takes the Japanese bullet train 2.7 hr to travel the same distance as the Acela Express can travel in 3.375 hr. Find the speed of each train. The Japanese bullet train travels 300 km/hr and the Acela Express travels 240 km/hr.

56. Amtrak Acela Express is a high-speed train along the northeast corridor between Washington, D.C. and Boston. Since its debut, it cuts the travel time from 4 hr 10 min to 3 hr 20 min. On average, if the Acela Express is 30 mph faster than the old train, find the speed of the Acela Express. (*Hint:* 4 hr 10 min = $4\frac{1}{6}$ hr.) The speed of the Acela Express in 150 mph.

Linear Inequalities

Section 2.8

Concepts

1. Graphing Linear Inequalities
2. Set-Builder Notation and Interval Notation
3. Addition and Subtraction Properties of Inequality
4. Multiplication and Division Properties of Inequality
5. Inequalities of the Form $a < x < b$
6. Applications of Linear Inequalities

1. Graphing Linear Inequalities

Consider the following two statements.

$$2x + 7 = 11 \quad \text{and} \quad 2x + 7 < 11$$

The first statement is an equation (it has an = sign). The second statement is an inequality (it has an inequality symbol, <). In this section, we will learn how to solve linear *inequalities*, such as $2x + 7 < 11$.

A Linear Inequality in One Variable

A **linear inequality in one variable**, x, is any inequality that can be written in the form:

$$ax + b < c, \quad ax + b \leq c, \quad ax + b > c, \quad \text{or} \quad ax + b \geq c, \text{ where } a \neq 0.$$

The following inequalities are linear equalities in one variable.

$$2x - 3 < 11 \qquad -4z - 3 > 0 \qquad a \leq 4 \qquad 5.2y \geq 10.4$$

The number line is a useful tool to visualize the solution set of an equation or inequality. For example, the solution set to the equation $x = 2$ is $\{2\}$ and may be graphed as a single point on the number line.

$x = 2$

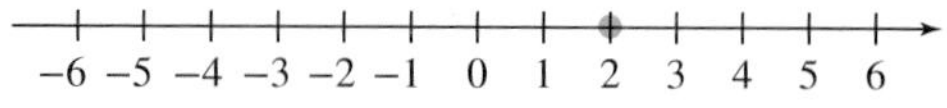

The solution set to an inequality is the set of real numbers that make the inequality a true statement. For example, the solution set to the inequality $x \geq 2$ is all real numbers 2 or greater. Because the solution set has an infinite number of values, we cannot list all of the individual solutions. However, we can graph the solution set on the number line.

$x \geq 2$

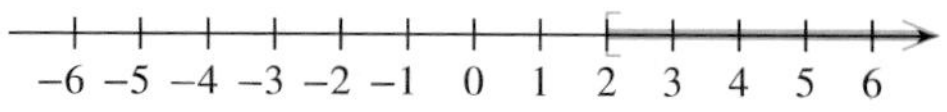

The square bracket symbol, [, is used on the graph to indicate that the point $x = 2$ is included in the solution set. By convention, square brackets, either [or], are used to *include* a point on a number line. Parentheses, (or), are used to *exclude* a point on a number line.

The solution set of the inequality $x > 2$ includes the real numbers greater than 2 but not equal to 2. Therefore, a "(" symbol is used on the graph to indicate that $x = 2$ is not included.

$x > 2$

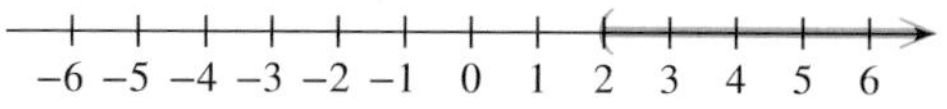

In Example 1, we demonstrate how to graph linear inequalities. To graph an inequality means that we graph its solution set. That is, we graph all of the values on the number line that make the inequality true.

Classroom Examples: p. 176, Exercises 6 and 10

Example 1 Graphing Linear Inequalities

Graph the solution sets.

a. $x > -1$ **b.** $c \leq \dfrac{7}{3}$ **c.** $3 > y$

Solution:

a. $x > -1$

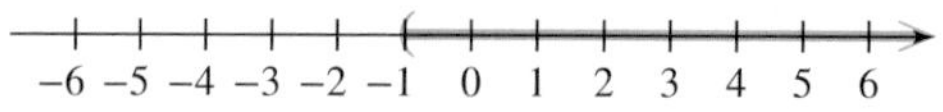

The solution set is the set of all real numbers strictly greater than -1. Therefore, we graph the region on the number line to the right of -1. Because $x = -1$ is not included in the solution set, we use the "(" symbol at $x = -1$.

Instructor Note: Students sometimes confuse the meaning of $x > 1$ to think it means the set $\{2, 3, 4 \ldots\}$. They don't think about the real number line. They don't see that 1.00000001 is a solution.

b. $c \leq \frac{7}{3}$ is equivalent to $c \leq 2\frac{1}{3}$.

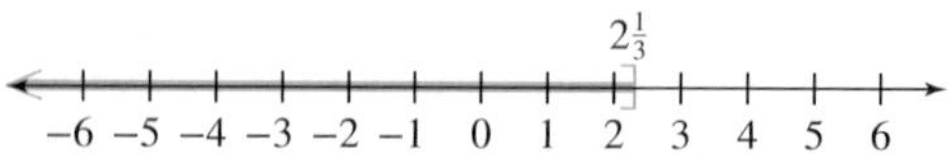

The solution set is the set of all real numbers less than or equal to $2\frac{1}{3}$. Therefore, graph the region on the number line to the left of and including $2\frac{1}{3}$. Use the symbol] to indicate that $c = 2\frac{1}{3}$ is included in the solution set.

c. $3 > y$ This inequality reads "3 is greater than y." This is equivalent to saying, "y is less than 3." The inequality $3 > y$ can also be written as $y < 3$.

$y < 3$

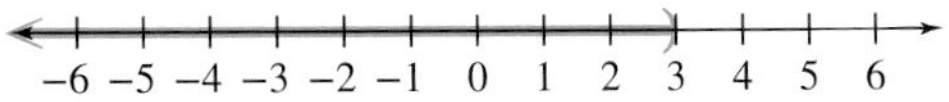

The solution set is the set of real numbers less than 3. Therefore, graph the region on the number line to the left of 3. Use the symbol ")" to denote that the endpoint, 3, is not included in the solution.

Skill Practice Graph the solution sets.

1. $y < 0$ **2.** $x \geq -\dfrac{5}{4}$ **3.** $5 \geq a$

TIP: Some textbooks use a closed circle or an open circle (● or ○) rather than a bracket or parenthesis to denote inclusion or exclusion of a value on the real number line. For example, the solution sets for the inequalities $x > -1$ and $c \leq \frac{7}{3}$ are graphed here.

$x > -1$

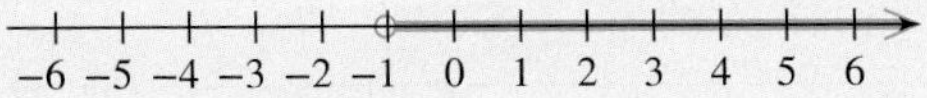

$c \leq \frac{7}{3}$

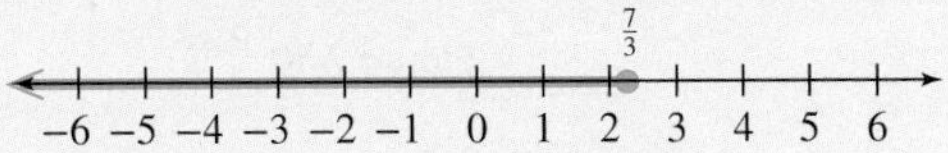

A statement that involves more than one inequality is called a **compound inequality**. One type of compound inequality is used to indicate that one number is between two others. For example, the inequality $-2 < x < 5$ means that $-2 < x$ and $x < 5$. In words, this is easiest to understand if we read the variable first: x is greater than -2 and x is less than 5. The numbers satisfied by these two conditions are those between -2 and 5.

Example 2 Graphing a Compound Inequality

Classroom Example: p. 176, Exercise 12

Graph the solution set of the inequality: $-4.1 < y \leq -1.7$

Solution:

$-4.1 < y \leq -1.7$ means that

$-4.1 < y$ and $y \leq -1.7$

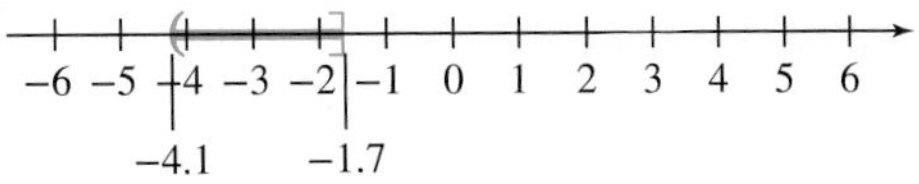

Shade the region of the number line greater than -4.1 and less than or equal to -1.7.

Skill Practice Graph the solution set.

4. $0 \leq y \leq 8.5$

Answers

1.

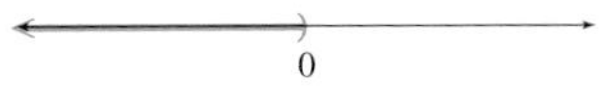

2.

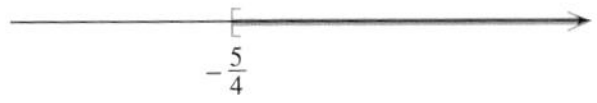

3.

4.

2. Set-Builder Notation and Interval Notation

Graphing the solution set to an inequality is one way to define the set. Two other methods are to use **set-builder notation** or **interval notation**.

Set-Builder Notation

The solution to the inequality $x \geq 2$ can be expressed in set-builder notation as follows:

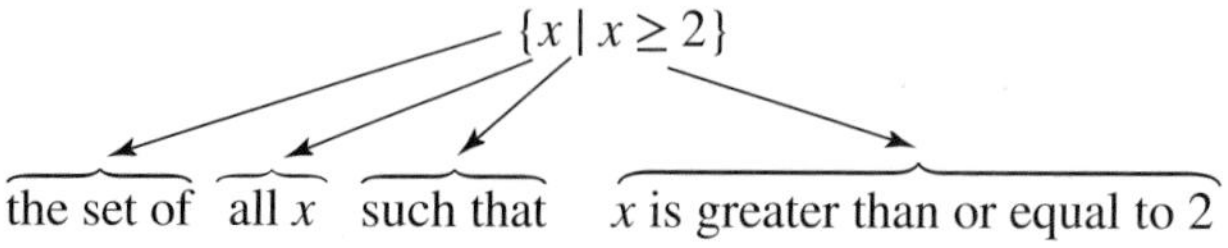

Interval Notation

To understand interval notation, first think of a number line extending infinitely far to the right and infinitely far to the left. Sometimes we use the infinity symbol, ∞, or negative infinity symbol, $-\infty$, to label the far right and far left ends of the number line (Figure 2-10).

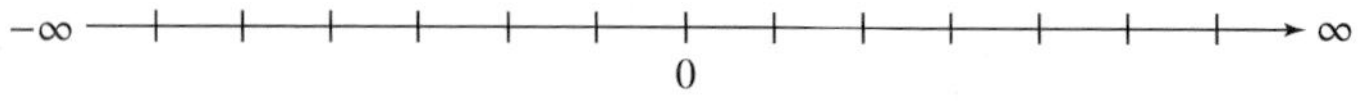

Figure 2-10

To express the solution set of an inequality in interval notation, sketch the graph first. Then use the endpoints to define the interval.

Inequality	Graph	Interval Notation
$x \geq 2$	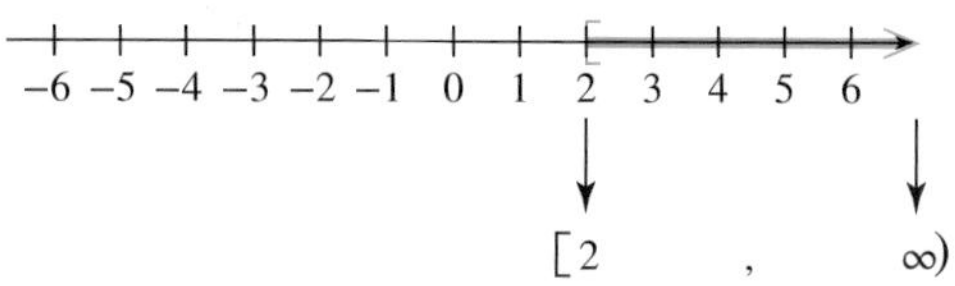	$[2, \infty)$

The graph of the solution set $x \geq 2$ begins at 2 and extends infinitely far to the right. The corresponding interval notation begins at 2 and extends to ∞. Notice that a square bracket [is used at 2 for both the graph and the interval notation. A parenthesis is always used at ∞ and for $-\infty$, because there is no endpoint.

Using Interval Notation

- The endpoints used in interval notation are always written from left to right. That is, the smaller number is written first, followed by a comma, followed by the larger number.
- A parenthesis, (or), indicates that an endpoint is *excluded* from the set.
- A square bracket, [or], indicates that an endpoint is *included* in the set.
- A parenthesis, (or), is always used with $-\infty$ or ∞, respectively.

In Table 2-1, we present examples of eight different scenarios for interval notation and the corresponding graph.

Table 2-1

Interval Notation	Graph	Interval Notation	Graph
(a, ∞)	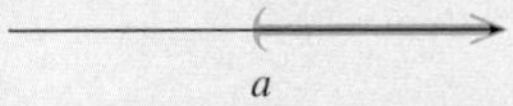	$[a, \infty)$	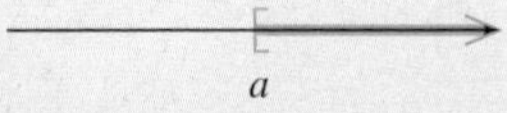
$(-\infty, a)$	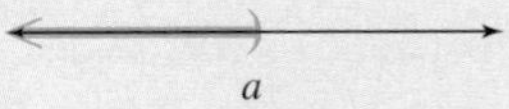	$(-\infty, a]$	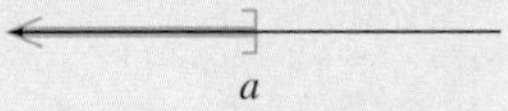
(a, b)		$[a, b]$	
$(a, b]$		$[a, b)$	

Example 3 **Using Set-Builder Notation and Interval Notation**

Complete the chart.

Set-Builder Notation	Graph	Interval Notation
	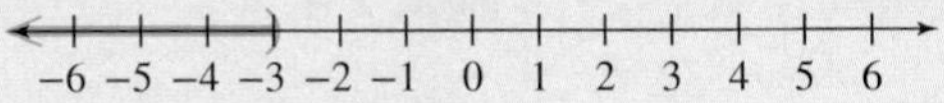	
		$[-\frac{1}{2}, \infty)$
$\{y \mid -2 \le y < 4\}$		

Solution:

Set-Builder Notation	Graph	Interval Notation
$\{x \mid x < -3\}$	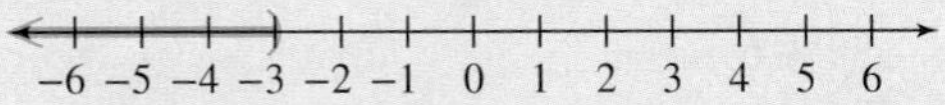	$(-\infty, -3)$
$\{x \mid x \ge -\frac{1}{2}\}$	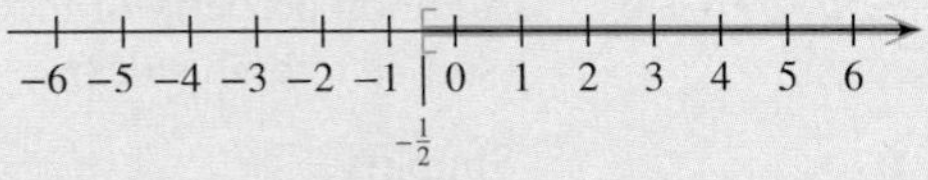	$[-\frac{1}{2}, \infty)$
$\{y \mid -2 \le y < 4\}$	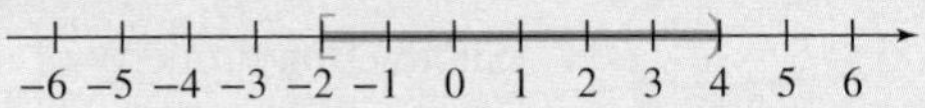	$[-2, 4)$

Classroom Examples: pp. 176–177, Exercises 20, 24, and 30

Skill Practice Express each of the following in set-builder notation and interval notation.

5. 

6. $x < \frac{3}{2}$

7. 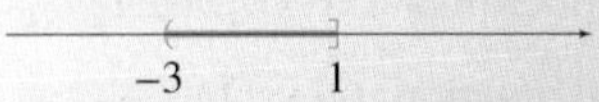

3. Addition and Subtraction Properties of Inequality

The process to solve a linear inequality is very similar to the method used to solve linear equations. Recall that adding or subtracting the same quantity to both sides of an equation results in an equivalent equation. The addition and subtraction properties of inequality state that the same is true for an inequality.

Answers

5. $\{x \mid x \ge -2\}$; $[-2, \infty)$
6. $\left\{x \middle| x < \frac{3}{2}\right\}$; $\left(-\infty, \frac{3}{2}\right)$
7. $\{x \mid -3 < x \le 1\}$; $(-3, 1]$

Addition and Subtraction Properties of Inequality

Let a, b, and c represent real numbers.

1. *Addition Property of Inequality: If $a < b$, then $a + c < b + c$
2. *Subtraction Property of Inequality: If $a < b$, then $a - c < b - c$

*These properties may also be stated for $a \le b$, $a > b$, and $a \ge b$.

To illustrate the addition and subtraction properties of inequality, consider the inequality $5 > 3$. If we add or subtract a real number such as 4 to both sides, the left-hand side will still be greater than the right-hand side. (See Figure 2-11.)

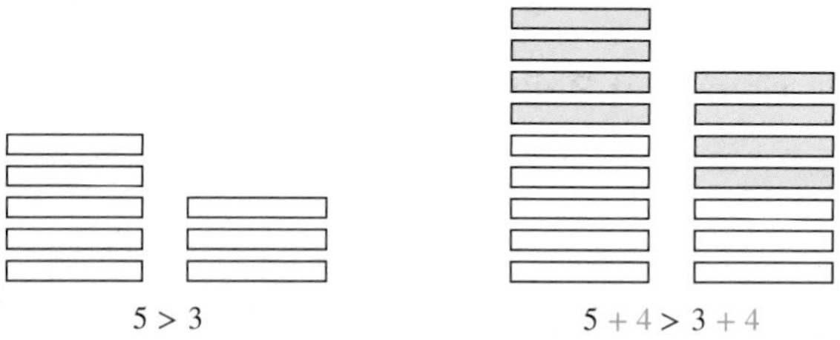

Figure 2-11

Classroom Example: p. 178, Exercise 52

Example 4 Solving a Linear Inequality

Solve the inequality and graph the solution set. Express the solution set in set-builder notation and in interval notation.

$$-2p + 5 < -3p + 6$$

Solution:

$-2p + 5 < -3p + 6$

$-2p + 3p + 5 < -3p + 3p + 6$ Addition property of inequality (add $3p$ to both sides).

$p + 5 < 6$ Simplify.

$p + 5 - 5 < 6 - 5$ Subtraction property of inequality.

$p < 1$

Instructor Note: Ask students whether 1 is a solution to the inequality.

Graph: 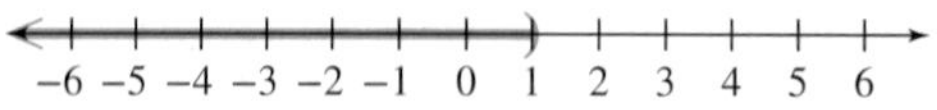

Set-builder notation: $\{p \mid p < 1\}$

Interval notation: $(-\infty, 1)$

Skill Practice Solve the inequality and graph the solution set. Express the solution set in set-builder notation and interval notation.

8. $2y - 5 < y - 11$

Answer

8. 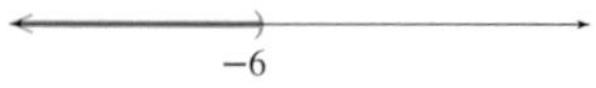

$\{y \mid y < -6\}$; $(-\infty, -6)$

TIP: The solution to an inequality gives a set of values that make the original inequality true. Therefore, you can test your final answer by using *test points.* That is, pick a value in the proposed solution set and verify that it makes the original inequality true. Furthermore, any test point picked outside the solution set should make the original inequality false. For example,

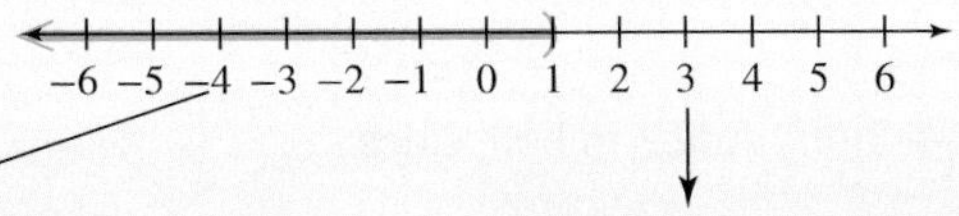

Pick $p = -4$ as an arbitrary test point within the proposed solution set.

$$-2p + 5 < -3p + 6$$
$$-2(-4) + 5 \overset{?}{<} -3(-4) + 6$$
$$8 + 5 \overset{?}{<} 12 + 6$$
$$13 < 18 \checkmark \quad \text{True}$$

Pick $p = 3$ as an arbitrary test point outside the proposed solution set.

$$-2p + 5 < -3p + 6$$
$$-2(3) + 5 \overset{?}{<} -3(3) + 6$$
$$-6 + 5 \overset{?}{<} -9 + 6$$
$$-1 \overset{?}{<} -3 \quad \text{False}$$

4. Multiplication and Division Properties of Inequality

Multiplying both sides of an equation by the same quantity results in an equivalent equation. However, the same is not always true for an inequality. If you multiply or divide an inequality by a negative quantity, the direction of the inequality symbol must be reversed.

For example, consider multiplying or dividing the inequality, $4 < 5$ by -1.

Multiply/Divide by -1: $4 < 5$ → $-4 > -5$

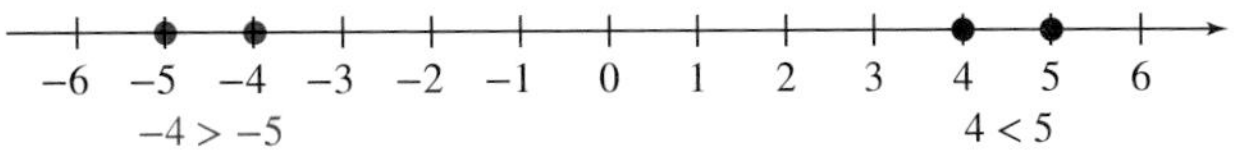

Figure 2-12

Instructor Note: Show that this works for other situations. Start with two negative numbers or one positive and one negative. Show that multiplying or dividing by −1 changes the direction of the inequality sign.

The number 4 lies to the left of 5 on the number line. However, −4 lies to the right of −5 (Figure 2-12). Changing the sign of two numbers changes their relative position on the number line. This is stated formally in the multiplication and division properties of inequality.

Multiplication and Division Properties of Inequality

Let a, b, and c represent real numbers, $c \neq 0$.

*If c is positive and $a < b$, then $ac < bc$ and $\frac{a}{c} < \frac{b}{c}$

*If c is negative and $a < b$, then $ac > bc$ and $\frac{a}{c} > \frac{b}{c}$

The second statement indicates that if both sides of an inequality are multiplied or divided by a negative quantity, the inequality sign must be reversed.

*These properties may also be stated for $a \leq b$, $a > b$, and $a \geq b$.

Classroom Example: p. 178, Exercise 74

Example 5 Solving a Linear Inequality

Solve the inequality and graph the solution set. Express the solution set in set-builder notation and in interval notation.

$$-5x - 3 \le 12$$

Solution:

$-5x - 3 \le 12$

$-5x - 3 + 3 \le 12 + 3$ Add 3 to both sides.

$-5x \le 15$

$\dfrac{-5x}{-5} \ge \dfrac{15}{-5}$ Divide by -5. Reverse the direction of the inequality sign.

$x \ge -3$

Set-builder notation: $\{x \mid x \ge -3\}$

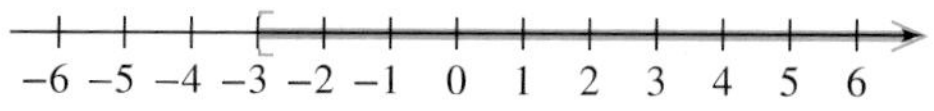

Interval notation: $[-3, \infty)$

TIP: The inequality $-5x - 3 \le 12$, could have been solved by isolating x on the right-hand side of the inequality. This would create a positive coefficient on the variable term and eliminate the need to divide by a negative number.

$-5x - 3 \le 12$

$-3 \le 5x + 12$

$-15 \le 5x$ Notice that the coefficient of x is positive.

$\dfrac{-15}{5} \le \dfrac{5x}{5}$ Do not reverse the inequality sign because we are dividing by a positive number.

$-3 \le x$, or equivalently, $x \ge -3$

Skill Practice Solve the inequality and graph the solution set. Express the solution set in set-builder notation and in interval notation.

9. $-5p + 2 > 22$

Classroom Example: p. 178, Exercise 86

Example 6 Solving a Linear Inequality

Solve the inequality and graph the solution set. Express the solution set in set-builder notation and in interval notation.

$$12 - 2(y + 3) < -3(2y - 1) + 2y$$

Solution:

$12 - 2(y + 3) < -3(2y - 1) + 2y$

$12 - 2y - 6 < -6y + 3 + 2y$ Clear parentheses.

$-2y + 6 < -4y + 3$ Combine *like* terms.

$-2y + 4y + 6 < -4y + 4y + 3$ Add $4y$ to both sides.

$2y + 6 < 3$ Simplify.

$2y + 6 + (-6) < 3 + (-6)$ Add -6 to both sides.

$2y < -3$ Simplify.

$\dfrac{2y}{2} < \dfrac{-3}{2}$ Divide by 2. The direction of the inequality sign is *not* reversed because we divided by a positive number.

$y < -\dfrac{3}{2}$

Answer

9. 

$\{p \mid p < -4\}$; $(-\infty, -4)$

Set-builder notation: $\left\{y \middle| y < -\frac{3}{2}\right\}$

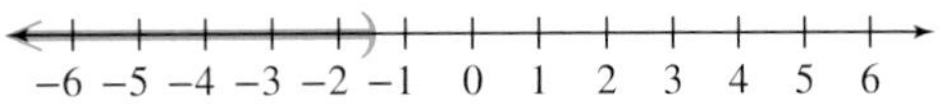

Interval notation: $\left(-\infty, -\frac{3}{2}\right)$

Skill Practice Solve the inequality and graph the solution set. Express the solution set in set-builder notation and in interval notation.

10. $-8 - 8(2x - 4) > -5(4x - 5) - 21$

Example 7 Solving a Linear Inequality

Solve the inequality and graph the solution set. Express the solution set in set-builder notation and in interval notation.

$$-\frac{1}{4}k + \frac{1}{6} \le 2 + \frac{2}{3}k$$

Classroom Example: p. 178, Exercise 90

Solution:

$$-\frac{1}{4}k + \frac{1}{6} \le 2 + \frac{2}{3}k$$

$$12\left(-\frac{1}{4}k + \frac{1}{6}\right) \le 12\left(2 + \frac{2}{3}k\right)$$ Multiply both sides by 12 to clear fractions. (Because we multiplied by a positive number, the inequality sign is not reversed.)

$$\frac{12}{1}\left(-\frac{1}{4}k\right) + \frac{12}{1}\left(\frac{1}{6}\right) \le 12(2) + \frac{12}{1}\left(\frac{2}{3}k\right)$$ Apply the distributive property.

$$-3k + 2 \le 24 + 8k$$ Simplify.

$$-3k - 8k + 2 \le 24 + 8k - 8k$$ Subtract $8k$ from both sides.

$$-11k + 2 \le 24$$

$$-11k + 2 - 2 \le 24 - 2$$ Subtract 2 from both sides.

$$-11k \le 22$$

$$\frac{-11k}{-11} \ge \frac{22}{-11}$$ Divide both sides by -11. Reverse the inequality sign.

$$k \ge -2$$

Set-builder notation: $\{k \mid k \ge -2\}$

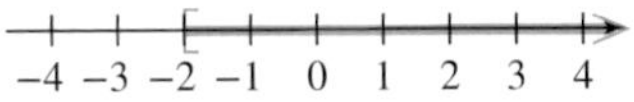

Interval notation: $[-2, \infty)$

Skill Practice Solve the inequality and graph the solution set. Express the solution set in set-builder notation and in interval notation.

11. $\frac{1}{5}t + 7 \le \frac{1}{2}t - 2$

Answers

10.
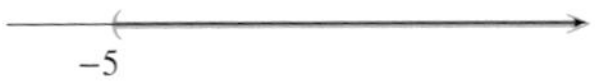

$\{x \mid x > -5\}$; $(-5, \infty)$

11.
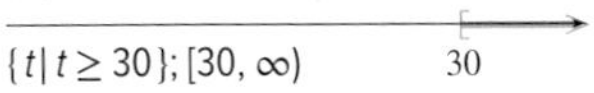

$\{t \mid t \ge 30\}$; $[30, \infty)$

5. Inequalities of the Form $a < x < b$

To solve a compound inequality of the form $a < x < b$ we can work with the inequality as a three-part inequality and isolate the variable, x, as demonstrated in Example 8.

Classroom Example: p. 178, Exercise 70

Example 8 Solving a Compound Inequality of the Form $a < x < b$

Solve the inequality and graph the solution set. Express the solution set in set-builder notation and in interval notation.

$$-3 \leq 2x + 1 < 7$$

Solution:

To solve the compound inequality $-3 \leq 2x + 1 < 7$ isolate the variable x in the middle. The operations performed on the middle portion of the inequality must also be performed on the left-hand side and right-hand side.

$-3 \leq 2x + 1 < 7$

$-3 - 1 \leq 2x + 1 - 1 < 7 - 1$ Subtract 1 from all three parts of the inequality.

$-4 \leq 2x < 6$ Simplify.

$\dfrac{-4}{2} \leq \dfrac{2x}{2} < \dfrac{6}{2}$ Divide by 2 in all three parts of the inequality.

$-2 \leq x < 3$

Set-builder notation: $\{x \mid -2 \leq x < 3\}$

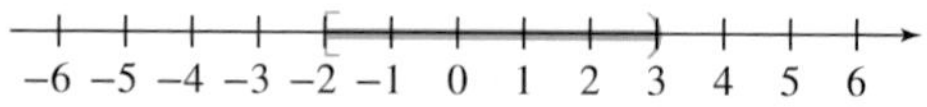

Interval notation: $[-2, 3)$

Skill Practice Solve the inequality and graph the solution set. Express the solution set in set-builder notation and in interval notation.

12. $-3 \leq -5 + 2y < 11$

6. Applications of Linear Inequalities

Table 2-2 provides several commonly used translations to express inequalities.

Table 2-2

English Phrase	Mathematical Inequality
a is less than b	$a < b$
a is greater than b a exceeds b	$a > b$
a is less than or equal to b a is at most b a is no more than b	$a \leq b$
a is greater than or equal to b a is at least b a is no less than b	$a \geq b$

Answer

12. 

$\{y \mid 1 \leq y < 8\}$; $[1, 8)$

Example 9 **Translating Expressions Involving Inequalities**

Classroom Examples: p. 179, Exercises 106 and 108

Write the English phrases as mathematical inequalities.

a. Claude's annual salary, s, is no more than \$40,000.

b. A citizen must be at least 18 years old to vote. (Let a represent a citizen's age.)

c. An amusement park ride has a height requirement between 48 in. and 70 in. (Let h represent height in inches.)

Solution:

a. $s \le 40{,}000$	Claude's annual salary, s, is no more than \$40,000.
b. $a \ge 18$	A citizen must be at least 18 years old to vote.
c. $48 < h < 70$	An amusement park ride has a height requirement between 48 in. and 70 in.

Skill Practice Write the English phrase as a mathematical inequality.

13. Bill needs a score of at least 92 on the final exam. Let x represent Bill's score.

14. Fewer than 19 cars are in the parking lot. Let c represent the number of cars.

15. The heights, h, of women who wear petite size clothing are typically between 58 in. and 63 in., inclusive.

Linear inequalities are found in a variety of applications. Example 10 can help you determine the minimum grade you need on an exam to get an A in your math course.

Example 10 **Solving an Application with Linear Inequalities**

Classroom Example: p. 179, Exercise 112

To earn an A in a math class, Alsha must average at least 90 on all of her tests. Suppose Alsha has scored 79, 86, 93, 90, and 95 on her first five math tests. Determine the minimum score she needs on her sixth test to get an A in the class.

Solution:

Let x represent the score on the sixth exam.	Label the variable.
$\begin{pmatrix}\text{Average of}\\ \text{all tests}\end{pmatrix} \ge 90$	Create a verbal model.
$\dfrac{79 + 86 + 93 + 90 + 95 + x}{6} \ge 90$	The average score is found by taking the sum of the test scores and dividing by the number of scores.
$\dfrac{443 + x}{6} \ge 90$	Simplify.
$6\left(\dfrac{443 + x}{6}\right) \ge (90)6$	Multiply both sides by 6 to clear fractions.
$443 + x \ge 540$	Solve the inequality.
$x \ge 540 - 443$	Subtract 443 from both sides.
$x \ge 97$	Interpret the results.

Alsha must score at least 97 on her sixth exam to receive an A in the course.

Skill Practice

16. To get at least a B in math, Simon must average at least 80 on all tests. Suppose Simon has scored 60, 72, 98, and 85 on the first four tests. Determine the minimum score he needs on the fifth test to receive a B.

Answers

13. $x \ge 92$
14. $c < 19$
15. $58 \le h \le 63$
16. Simon needs at least 85.

Section 2.8 Practice Exercises

For additional exercises, see Classroom Activities 2.8A–2.8D in the *Student's Resource Manual* at www.mhhe.com/moh.

Study Skills Exercise

Find the page numbers for the Chapter Review Exercises, the Chapter Test, and the Cumulative Review Exercises for this chapter.

Chapter Review Exercises __________________ Chapter Test __________________

Cumulative Review Exercises __________________

Compare these features and state the advantages of each.

Vocabulary and Key Concepts

1. a. A relationship of the form $ax + b > c$ or $ax + b < c$ $(a \neq 0)$ is called a linear inequality in one variable.

b. A statement that involves more than one inequality is called a compound inequality.

c. The notation $\{x \mid x > -9\}$ is an example of set-builder notation, whereas $(-9, \infty)$ is an example of interval notation.

Review Problems

For Exercises 2–4, solve the equation.

2. $10y - 7(y + 8) + 13 = 13 - 6(2y + 1)$ $\left\{\frac{10}{3}\right\}$

3. $3(x + 2) - (2x - 7) = -(5x - 1) - 2(x + 6)$ $\{-3\}$

4. $6 - 8(x + 3) + 5x = 5x - (2x - 5) + 13$ $\{-6\}$

Concept 1: Graphing Linear Inequalities

For Exercises 5–16, graph the solution set of each inequality. **(See Examples 1–2.)**

5. $x > 5$

6. $x \geq -7.2$

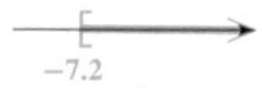

7. $x \leq \frac{5}{2}$

8. $x < -1$

9. $13 > p$

10. $-12 \geq t$

11. $2 \leq y \leq 6.5$

12. $-3 \leq m \leq \frac{8}{9}$

13. $0 < x < 4$

14. $-4 < y < 1$

15. $1 < p \leq 8$

16. $-3 \leq t < 3$

Concept 2: Set-Builder Notation and Interval Notation

For Exercises 17–22, graph each inequality and write the solution set in interval notation. **(See Example 3.)**

Set-Builder Notation	Graph	Interval Notation
17. $\{x \mid x \geq 6\}$		$[6, \infty)$
18. $\left\{x \,\middle|\, \frac{1}{2} < x \leq 4\right\}$		$\left(\frac{1}{2}, 4\right]$
19. $\{x \mid x \leq 2.1\}$	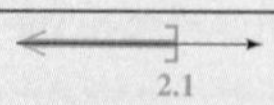	$(-\infty, 2.1]$
20. $\left\{x \,\middle|\, x > \frac{7}{3}\right\}$		$\left(\frac{7}{3}, \infty\right)$
21. $\{x \mid -2 < x \leq 7\}$		$(-2, 7]$
22. $\{x \mid x < -5\}$		$(-\infty, -5)$

Animation

Writing Translating Expression Geometry Scientific Calculator Video

For Exercises 23–28, write each set in set-builder notation and in interval notation. **(See Example 3.)**

Set-Builder Notation	Graph	Interval Notation
23. $\left\{x \mid x > \frac{3}{4}\right\}$	$\frac{3}{4}$	$\left(\frac{3}{4}, \infty\right)$
24. $\{x \mid x \leq -0.3\}$	-0.3	$(-\infty, -0.3]$
25. $\{x \mid -1 < x < 8\}$	-1 8	$(-1, 8)$
26. $\{x \mid x \geq 0\}$	0	$[0, \infty)$
27. $\{x \mid x \leq -14\}$	-14	$(-\infty, -14]$
28. $\{x \mid 0 < x \leq 9\}$	0 9	$(0, 9]$

For Exercises 29–34, graph each set and write the set in set-builder notation. **(See Example 3.)**

Set-Builder Notation	Graph	Interval Notation
29. $\{x \mid x \geq 18\}$	18	$[18, \infty)$
30. $\{x \mid -10 \leq x \leq -2\}$	-10 -2	$[-10, -2]$
31. $\{x \mid x < -0.6\}$	-0.6	$(-\infty, -0.6)$
32. $\left\{x \mid x < \frac{5}{3}\right\}$	$\frac{5}{3}$	$\left(-\infty, \frac{5}{3}\right)$
33. $\{x \mid -3.5 \leq x < 7.1\}$	-3.5 7.1	$[-3.5, 7.1)$
34. $\{x \mid x \geq -10\}$	-10	$[-10, \infty)$

Concepts 3–4: Properties of Inequality

For Exercises 35–42, solve the equation in part (a). For part (b), solve the inequality and graph the solution set. Write the answer in set-builder notation and interval notation. **(See Examples 4–7.)**

35. a. $x + 3 = 6$ $\{3\}$

b. $x + 3 > 6$

3

$\{x \mid x > 3\}$; $(3, \infty)$

36. a. $y - 6 = 12$ $\{18\}$

b. $y - 6 \geq 12$

18

$\{y \mid y \geq 18\}$; $[18, \infty)$

37. a. $p - 4 = 9$ $\{13\}$

b. $p - 4 \leq 9$

$\{p \mid p \leq 13\}$; $(-\infty, 13]$ 13

38. a. $k + 8 = 10$ $\{2\}$

b. $k + 8 < 10$

2

$\{k \mid k < 2\}$; $(-\infty, 2)$

39. a. $4c = -12$ $\{-3\}$

b. $4c < -12$

-3

$\{c \mid c < -3\}$; $(-\infty, -3)$

40. a. $5d = -35$ $\{-7\}$

b. $5d > -35$

-7

$\{d \mid d > -7\}$; $(-7, \infty)$

41. a. $-10z = 15$ $\left\{-\frac{3}{2}\right\}$

b. $-10z \leq 15$

$-\frac{3}{2}$

$\left\{z \mid z \geq -\frac{3}{2}\right\}$; $\left[-\frac{3}{2}, \infty\right)$

42. a. $-2w = 14$ $\{-7\}$

b. $-2w < 14$

-7

$\{w \mid w > -7\}$; $(-7, \infty)$

Concept 5: Inequalities of the Form $a < x < b$

For Exercises 43–48, graph the solution and write the set in interval notation. **(See Example 8.)**

43. $-1 < y \leq 4$ $(-1, 4]$

-1 4

44. $2.5 \leq t < 5.7$ $[2.5, 5.7)$

2.5 5.7

45. $0 < x + 3 < 8$ $(-3, 5)$

-3 5

46. $-2 \leq x - 4 \leq 3$ $[2, 7]$

2 7

47. $8 \leq 4x \leq 24$ $[2, 6]$

2 6

48. $-9 < 3x < 12$ $(-3, 4)$

-3 4

Mixed Exercises

For Exercises 49–96, solve the inequality and graph the solution set. Write the solution set in (a) set-builder notation and (b) interval notation. **(See Exercises 4–8.)**

49. $x + 5 \le 6$

1 a. $\{x \mid x \le 1\}$ b. $(-\infty, 1]$

50. $y - 7 < 6$

a. $\{y \mid y < 13\}$ b. $(-\infty, 13)$ 13

51. $3q - 7 > 2q + 3$

10 a. $\{q \mid q > 10\}$ b. $(10, \infty)$

52. $5r + 4 \ge 4r - 1$

−5 a. $\{r \mid r \ge -5\}$ b. $[-5, \infty)$

53. $4 < 1 + x$

3 a. $\{x \mid x > 3\}$ b. $(3, \infty)$

54. $3 > z - 6$

a. $\{z \mid z < 9\}$ 9 b. $(-\infty, 9)$

55. $3c > 6$

2 a. $\{c \mid c > 2\}$ b. $(2, \infty)$

56. $4d \le 12$

3 a. $\{d \mid d \le 3\}$ b. $(-\infty, 3]$

57. $-3c > 6$

−2 a. $\{c \mid c < -2\}$ b. $(-\infty, -2)$

58. $-4d \le 12$

−3 a. $\{d \mid d \ge -3\}$ b. $[-3, \infty)$

59. $-h \le -14$

14 a. $\{h \mid h \ge 14\}$ b. $[14, \infty)$

60. $-q > -7$

a. $\{q \mid q < 7\}$ 7 b. $(-\infty, 7)$

61. $12 \ge -\dfrac{x}{2}$

−24
a. $\{x \mid x \ge -24\}$ b. $[-24, \infty)$

62. $6 < -\dfrac{m}{3}$

−18
a. $\{m \mid m < -18\}$ b. $(-\infty, -18)$

63. $-2 \le p + 1 < 4$

−3 3
a. $\{p \mid -3 \le p < 3\}$ b. $[-3, 3)$

64. $0 < k + 7 < 6$

a. $\{k \mid -7 < k < -1\}$ b. $(-7, -1)$

−7 −1

65. $-3 < 6h - 3 < 12$

a. $\left\{h \,\middle|\, 0 < h < \dfrac{5}{2}\right\}$ b. $\left(0, \dfrac{5}{2}\right)$

0 $\frac{5}{2}$

66. $-6 \le 4a - 2 \le 12$

a. $\left\{a \,\middle|\, -1 \le a \le \dfrac{7}{2}\right\}$ b. $\left[-1, \dfrac{7}{2}\right]$

−1 $\frac{7}{2}$

67. $-24 < -2x < -20$

a. $\{x \mid 10 < x < 12\}$ b. $(10, 12)$

10 12

68. $-12 \le -3x \le 6$

a. $\{x \mid -2 \le x \le 4\}$ b. $[-2, 4]$

−2 4

69. $-3 \le \dfrac{1}{4}x - 1 < 5$

−8 24
a. $\{x \mid -8 \le x < 24\}$ b. $[-8, 24)$

70. $-2 < \dfrac{1}{3}x - 2 \le 2$

0 12
a. $\{x \mid 0 < x \le 12\}$ b. $(0, 12]$

71. $-\dfrac{2}{3}y < 6$

−9
a. $\{y \mid y > -9\}$ b. $(-9, \infty)$

72. $\dfrac{3}{4}x \le -12$

−16
a. $\{x \mid x \le -16\}$ b. $(-\infty, -16]$

73. $-2x - 4 \le 11$

$-\frac{15}{2}$ a. $\left\{x \,\middle|\, x \ge -\dfrac{15}{2}\right\}$ b. $\left[-\dfrac{15}{2}, \infty\right)$

74. $-3x + 1 > 0$

$\frac{1}{3}$ a. $\left\{x \,\middle|\, x < \dfrac{1}{3}\right\}$ b. $\left(-\infty, \dfrac{1}{3}\right)$

75. $-12 > 7x + 9$

−3 a. $\{x \mid x < -3\}$ b. $(-\infty, -3)$

76. $8 < 2x - 10$

a. $\{x \mid x > 9\}$ 9 b. $(9, \infty)$

77. $-7b - 3 \le 2b$

$-\frac{1}{3}$ a. $\left\{b \,\middle|\, b \ge -\dfrac{1}{3}\right\}$ b. $\left[-\dfrac{1}{3}, \infty\right)$

78. $3t \ge 7t - 35$

$\frac{35}{4}$ a. $\left\{t \,\middle|\, t \le \dfrac{35}{4}\right\}$ b. $\left(-\infty, \dfrac{35}{4}\right]$

79. $4n + 2 < 6n + 8$

−3
a. $\{n \mid n > -3\}$ b. $(-3, \infty)$

80. $2w - 1 \le 5w + 8$

−3
a. $\{w \mid w \ge -3\}$ b. $[-3, \infty)$

81. $8 - 6(x - 3) > -4x + 12$

7
a. $\{x \mid x < 7\}$ b. $(-\infty, 7)$

82. $3 - 4(h - 2) > -5h + 6$

a. $\{h \mid h > -5\}$ b. $(-5, \infty)$

−5

83. $3(x + 1) - 2 \le \dfrac{1}{2}(4x - 8)$

a. $\{x \mid x \le -5\}$ b. $(-\infty, -5]$

−5

84. $8 - (2x - 5) \ge \dfrac{1}{3}(9x - 6)$

a. $\{x \mid x \le 3\}$ b. $(-\infty, 3]$

3

85. $4(z - 1) - 6 \ge 6(2z + 3) - 12$

a. $\{z \mid z \le -2\}$ b. $(-\infty, -2]$

−2

86. $3(2x + 5) + 2 < 5(2x + 2) + 3$

a. $\{x \mid x > 1\}$ b. $(1, \infty)$

1

87. $2a + 3(a + 5) > -4a - (3a - 1) + 6$

a. $\left\{a \,\middle|\, a > -\dfrac{2}{3}\right\}$ b. $\left(-\dfrac{2}{3}, \infty\right)$

$-\frac{2}{3}$

88. $13 + 7(2y - 3) \le 12 + 3(3y - 1)$

$\frac{17}{5}$

a. $\left\{y \,\middle|\, y \le \dfrac{17}{5}\right\}$ b. $\left(-\infty, \dfrac{17}{5}\right]$

89. $\dfrac{7}{6}p + \dfrac{4}{3} \ge \dfrac{11}{6}p - \dfrac{7}{6}$

$\frac{15}{4}$

a. $\left\{p \,\middle|\, p \le \dfrac{15}{4}\right\}$ b. $\left(-\infty, \dfrac{15}{4}\right]$

90. $\dfrac{1}{3}w - \dfrac{1}{2} \le \dfrac{5}{6}w + \dfrac{1}{2}$

−2
a. $\{w \mid w \ge -2\}$ b. $[-2, \infty)$

91. $\frac{y-6}{3} > y + 4$ −9 a. $\{y \mid y < -9\}$ b. $(-\infty, -9)$

92. $\frac{5t+7}{2} < t - 4$ −5 a. $\{t \mid t < -5\}$ b. $(-\infty, -5)$

93. $-1.2a - 0.4 < -0.4a + 2$ −3 a. $\{a \mid a > -3\}$ b. $(-3, \infty)$

94. $-0.4c + 1.2 > -2c - 0.4$ −1 a. $\{c \mid c > -1\}$ b. $(-1, \infty)$

95. $-2x + 5 \geq -x + 5$ 0 a. $\{x \mid x \leq 0\}$ b. $(-\infty, 0]$

96. $4x - 6 < 5x - 6$ 0 a. $\{x \mid x > 0\}$ b. $(0, \infty)$

For Exercises 97–100, determine whether the given number is a solution to the inequality.

97. $-2x + 5 < 4;\quad x = -2$ No

98. $-3y - 7 > 5;\quad y = 6$ No

99. $4(p + 7) - 1 > 2 + p;\quad p = 1$ Yes

100. $3 - k < 2(-1 + k);\quad k = 4$ Yes

Concept 6: Applications of Linear Inequalities

For Exercises 101–110, write each English phrase as a mathematical inequality. **(See Example 9.)**

101. The length of a fish, L, was at least 10 in. $L \geq 10$

102. Tasha's average test score, t, exceeded 90. $t > 90$

103. The wind speed, w, exceeded 75 mph. $w > 75$

104. The height of a cave, h, was no more than 2 ft. $h \leq 2$

105. The temperature of the water in Blue Spring, t, is no more than 72°F. $t \leq 72$

106. The temperature on the tennis court, t, was no less than 100°F. $t \geq 100$

107. The length of the hike, L, was no less than 8 km. $L \geq 8$

108. The depth, d, of a certain pool was at most 10 ft. $d \leq 10$

109. The snowfall, h, in Monroe County is between 2 in. and 5 in. $2 < h < 5$

110. The cost, c, of carpeting a room is between \$300 and \$400. $300 < c < 400$

111. The average summer rainfall for Miami, Florida, for June, July, and August is 7.4 in. per month. If Miami receives 5.9 in. of rain in June and 6.1 in. in July, how much rain is required in August to exceed the 3-month summer average? **(See Example 10.)**
More than 10.2 in. of rain is needed.

112. The average winter snowfall for Burlington, Vermont, for December, January, and February is 18.7 in. per month. If Burlington receives 22 in. of snow in December and 24 in. in January, how much snow is required in February to exceed the 3-month winter average? More than 10.1 in. of snow is needed.

113. To earn a B in chemistry, Trevor's average on his five tests must be at least 80. Suppose that Trevor has scored 85, 75, 72, and 82 on his first four chemistry tests. Determine the minimum score needed on his fifth test to get a B in the class.
Trevor needs at least 86 to get a B in the course.

114. In speech class, Carolyn needs at least a B+ to keep her financial aid. To earn a B+, the average of her four speeches must be at least an 85. On the first three speeches she scored 87, 75, and 82. Determine the minimum score on her fourth speech to get a B+. Carolyn needs at least 96 on her last speech.

115. An artist paints wooden birdhouses. She buys the birdhouses for \$9 each. However, for large orders, the price per birdhouse is discounted by a percentage off the original price. Let x represent the number of birdhouses ordered. The corresponding discount is given in the table.

Size of Order	Discount
$x \leq 49$	0%
$50 \leq x \leq 99$	5%
$100 \leq x \leq 199$	10%
$x \geq 200$	20%

a. If the artist places an order for 190 birdhouses, compute the total cost. \$1539

b. Which costs more: 190 birdhouses or 200 birdhouses? Explain your answer.
200 birdhouses cost \$1440. It is cheaper to purchase 200 birdhouses because the discount is greater.

116. A wholesaler sells T-shirts to a surf shop at \$8 per shirt. However, for large orders, the price per shirt is discounted by a percentage off the original price. Let x represent the number of shirts ordered. The corresponding discount is given in the table.

Number of Shirts Ordered	Discount
$x \le 24$	0%
$25 \le x \le 49$	2%
$50 \le x \le 99$	4%
$100 \le x \le 149$	6%
$x \ge 150$	8%

a. If the surf shop orders 50 shirts, compute the total cost. \$384

b. Which costs more: 148 shirts or 150 shirts? Explain your answer.
It costs \$1112.96 for 148 shirts and \$1104.00 for 150 shirts. 150 shirts cost less than 148 shirts because the discount is greater.

117. To print a flyer for a new business, Company A charges \$39.99 for the design plus \$0.50 per flyer. Company B charges \$0.60 per flyer but has no design fee. For how many flyers would Company A be a better deal?
Company A is better if more than 400 flyers are printed.

118. Melissa runs a landscaping business. She has equipment and fuel expenses of \$313 per month. If she charges \$45 for each lawn, how many lawns must she service to make a profit of at least \$600 a month?
Melissa must service at least 21 lawns.

119. Madison is planning a 5-night trip to Cancun, Mexico, with her friends. The airfare is \$475, her share of the hotel room is \$54 per night, and her budget for food and entertainment is \$350. She has \$700 in savings and has a job earning \$10 per hour babysitting. What is the minimum number of hours of babysitting that Madison needs so that she will have enough money to take the trip? Madison needs to babysit a minimum of 39.5 hr.

120. Luke and Landon are both tutors. Luke charges \$50 for an initial assessment and \$25 per hour for each hour he tutors. Landon charges \$100 for an initial assessment and \$20 per hour for tutoring. After how many hours of tutoring will Luke surpass Landon in earnings? After 10 hr of tutoring, Luke's earnings will surpass Landon's earnings.

Group Activity

Computing Body Mass Index (BMI)

Materials: Calculator

Estimated Time: 10 minutes

Group Size: 2

Body mass index is a statistical measure of an individual's weight in relation to the person's height. It is computed by

$$\text{BMI} = \frac{703W}{h^2}$$

where W is a person's weight in *pounds*.
h is the person's height in *inches*.

The National Institutes of Health (NIH) categorizes body mass indices as shown in the table.

Body Mass Index (BMI)	Weight Status
$18.5 \le \text{BMI} \le 24.9$	considered ideal
$25.0 \le \text{BMI} \le 29.9$	considered overweight
$\text{BMI} \ge 30.0$	considered obese

1. Compute the body mass index for a person 5′4″ tall weighing 160 lb. Is this person's weight considered ideal?
27.5; No, the person is considered overweight.

2. At the time that basketball legend Michael Jordan played for the Chicago Bulls, he was 210 lb and stood 6′6″ tall. What was Michael Jordan's body mass index? 24.3

3. For a fixed height, body mass index is a function of a person's weight only. For example, for a person 72 in. tall (6 ft), solve the following inequality to determine the person's ideal weight range. 136.4 lb $\le W \le$ 183.6 lb

$$18.5 \le \frac{703W}{(72)^2} \le 24.9$$

4. At the time that professional bodybuilder, Jay Cutler, won the Mr. Olympia contest he was 260 lb and stood 5′10″ tall.

a. What was Jay Cutler's body mass index? 37.3

b. As a bodybuilder, Jay Cutler has an extraordinarily small percentage of body fat. Yet, according to the chart, would he be considered overweight or obese? Why do you think that the formula is not an accurate measurement of Mr. Cutler's weight status? Jay Cutler's BMI was 37.3 which placed him in the "obese" category. However, BMI is meant to be used as a simple means of classifying physically inactive individuals with an average body composition. The BMI formula does not account for other factors affecting a person's weight such as fitness level, muscle mass, bone structure, and gender.

Chapter 2 Summary

Section 2.1 Addition, Subtraction, Multiplication, and Division Properties of Equality

Key Concepts

An equation is an algebraic statement that indicates two expressions are equal. A **solution to an equation** is a value of the variable that makes the equation a true statement. The set of all solutions to an equation is the solution set of the equation.

A **linear equation in one variable** can be written in the form $ax + b = c$, where $a \neq 0$.

Addition Property of Equality:

If $a = b$, then $a + c = b + c$

Subtraction Property of Equality:

If $a = b$, then $a - c = b - c$

Multiplication Property of Equality:

If $a = b$, then $ac = bc \quad (c \neq 0)$

Division Property of Equality:

If $a = b$, then $\frac{a}{c} = \frac{b}{c} \quad (c \neq 0)$

Examples

Example 1

$2x + 1 = 9$ is an equation with solution set $\{4\}$.

Check: $2(4) + 1 \stackrel{?}{=} 9$

$8 + 1 \stackrel{?}{=} 9$

$9 \stackrel{?}{=} 9$ ✓ True

Example 2

$$x - 5 = 12$$
$$x - 5 + 5 = 12 + 5$$
$$x = 17$$ The solution set is $\{17\}$.

Example 3

$$z + 1.44 = 2.33$$
$$z + 1.44 - 1.44 = 2.33 - 1.44$$
$$z = 0.89$$ The solution set is $\{0.89\}$.

Example 4

$$\frac{3}{4}x = 12$$
$$\frac{4}{3} \cdot \frac{3}{4}x = 12 \cdot \frac{4}{3}$$
$$x = 16$$ The solution set is $\{16\}$.

Example 5

$$16 = 8y$$
$$\frac{16}{8} = \frac{8y}{8}$$
$$2 = y$$ The solution set is $\{2\}$.

Section 2.2 Solving Linear Equations

Key Concepts

Steps for Solving a Linear Equation in One Variable:

1. Simplify both sides of the equation.
   - Clear parentheses
   - Combine *like* terms
2. Use the addition or subtraction property of equality to collect the variable terms on one side of the equation.
3. Use the addition or subtraction property of equality to collect the constant terms on the other side of the equation.
4. Use the multiplication or division property of equality to make the coefficient of the variable term equal to 1.
5. Check your answer.

Examples

Example 1

$5y + 7 = 3(y - 1) + 2$

$5y + 7 = 3y - 3 + 2$ Clear parentheses.

$5y + 7 = 3y - 1$ Combine *like* terms.

$2y + 7 = -1$ Collect the variable terms.

$2y = -8$ Collect the constant terms.

$y = -4$ Divide both sides by 2.

Check:

$5(-4) + 7 \stackrel{?}{=} 3[(-4) - 1] + 2$

$-20 + 7 \stackrel{?}{=} 3(-5) + 2$

$-13 \stackrel{?}{=} -15 + 2$

$-13 \stackrel{?}{=} -13$ ✓ True

The solution set is $\{-4\}$.

A **conditional equation** is true for some values of the variable but is false for other values.

Example 2

$x + 5 = 7$ is a conditional equation because it is true only on the condition that $x = 2$.

Solution set: $\{2\}$

An equation that has all real numbers as its solution set is an **identity**.

Example 3

$x + 4 = 2(x + 2) - x$

$x + 4 = 2x + 4 - x$

$x + 4 = x + 4$

$4 = 4$ is an identity.

Solution set: The set of real numbers.

An equation that has no solution is a **contradiction**.

Example 4

$y - 5 = 2(y + 3) - y$

$y - 5 = 2y + 6 - y$

$y - 5 = y + 6$

$-5 = 6$ is a contradiction.

Solution set: $\{\ \}$

Section 2.3 Linear Equations: Clearing Fractions and Decimals

Key Concepts

Steps for Solving a Linear Equation in One Variable:

1. Simplify both sides of the equation.
   - Clear parentheses
   - Consider clearing fractions or decimals (if any are present) by multiplying both sides of the equation by a common denominator of all terms
   - Combine *like* terms
2. Use the addition or subtraction property of equality to collect the variable terms on one side of the equation.
3. Use the addition or subtraction property of equality to collect the constant terms on the other side of the equation.
4. Use the multiplication or division property of equality to make the coefficient of the variable term equal to 1.
5. Check your answer.

Examples

Example 1

$$\frac{1}{2}x - 2 - \frac{3}{4}x = \frac{7}{4}$$

$$\frac{4}{1}\left(\frac{1}{2}x - 2 - \frac{3}{4}x\right) = \frac{4}{1}\left(\frac{7}{4}\right) \quad \text{Multiply by the LCD.}$$

$$\frac{4}{1}\left(\frac{1}{2}x\right) - \frac{4}{1}\left(\frac{2}{1}\right) - \frac{4}{1}\left(\frac{3}{4}x\right) = \frac{4}{1}\left(\frac{7}{4}\right)$$

$$2x - 8 - 3x = 7 \quad \text{Apply distributive property.}$$

$$-x - 8 = 7 \quad \text{Combine } like \text{ terms.}$$

$$-x = 15 \quad \text{Add 8 to both sides.}$$

$$x = -15 \quad \text{Divide by } -1.$$

The solution set is $\{-15\}$.

Example 2

$$-1.2x - 5.1 = 16.5$$

$$10(-1.2x - 5.1) = 10(16.5) \quad \text{Multiply both sides by 10.}$$

$$-12x - 51 = 165$$

$$-12x = 216$$

$$\frac{-12x}{-12} = \frac{216}{-12}$$

$$x = -18$$

The solution set is $\{-18\}$.

Section 2.4 Applications of Linear Equations: Introduction to Problem Solving

Key Concepts

Problem-Solving Steps for Word Problems:

1. Read the problem carefully.
2. Assign labels to unknown quantities.
3. Write a verbal model.
4. Write a mathematical equation.
5. Solve the equation.
6. Interpret the results and write the answer in words.

Examples

Example 1

The perimeter of a triangle is 54 m. The lengths of the sides are represented by three consecutive even integers. Find the lengths of the three sides.

1. Read the problem.

2. Let x represent one side, $x + 2$ represent the second side, and $x + 4$ represent the third side.

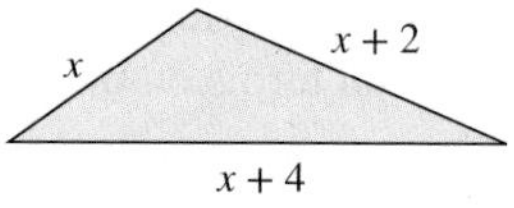

3. $\begin{pmatrix}\text{Length of} \\ \text{first side}\end{pmatrix} + \begin{pmatrix}\text{length of} \\ \text{second side}\end{pmatrix} + \begin{pmatrix}\text{length of} \\ \text{third side}\end{pmatrix}$

   $= \text{perimeter}$

4. $x + (x + 2) + (x + 4) = 54$

5. $3x + 6 = 54$
   $3x = 48$
   $x = 16$

6. $x = 16$ represents the length of the shortest side. The lengths of the other sides are given by $x + 2 = 18$ and $x + 4 = 20$.

   The lengths of the three sides are 16 m, 18 m, and 20 m.

Section 2.5 Applications Involving Percents

Key Concepts

The following formula will help you solve basic percent problems.

Amount = (percent)(base)

One common use of percents is in computing **sales tax**.

Another use of percents is in computing **simple interest** using the formula:

$$\begin{pmatrix}\text{Simple}\\ \text{interest}\end{pmatrix} = (\text{principal})\begin{pmatrix}\text{annual}\\ \text{interest}\\ \text{rate}\end{pmatrix}\begin{pmatrix}\text{time in}\\ \text{years}\end{pmatrix}$$

or $I = Prt$.

Examples

Example 1

A flat screen television costs \$1260.00 after a 5% sales tax is included. What was the price before tax?

$$\begin{pmatrix}\text{Price}\\ \text{before tax}\end{pmatrix} + (\text{tax}) = \begin{pmatrix}\text{total}\\ \text{price}\end{pmatrix}$$

$$x + 0.05x = 1260$$
$$1.05x = 1260$$
$$x = 1200$$

The television costs \$1200 before tax.

Example 2

John Li invests \$5400 at 2.5% simple interest. How much interest does he earn after 5 years?

$I = Prt$

$I = (\$5400)(0.025)(5)$

$I = \$675$

Section 2.6 Formulas and Applications of Geometry

Key Concepts

A **literal equation** is an equation that has more than one variable. Often such an equation can be manipulated to solve for different variables.

Examples

Example 1

$P = 2a + b$, solve for a.

$P - b = 2a + b - b$

$P - b = 2a$

$\frac{P-b}{2} = \frac{2a}{2}$

$\frac{P-b}{2} = a$ or $a = \frac{P-b}{2}$

Example 2

Find the length of a side of a square whose perimeter is 28 ft.

Use the formula $P = 4s$. Substitute 28 for P and solve:

$P = 4s$

$28 = 4s$

$7 = s$

The length of a side of the square is 7 ft.

Section 2.7 Mixture Applications and Uniform Motion

Examples

Example 1 illustrates a mixture problem.

Example 1

How much 80% disinfectant solution should be mixed with 8 L of a 30% disinfectant solution to make a 40% solution?

	80% Solution	30% Solution	40% Solution
Amount of Solution	x	8	$x + 8$
Amount of Pure Disinfectant	$0.80x$	$0.30(8)$	$0.40(x + 8)$

$0.80x + 0.30(8) = 0.40(x + 8)$

$0.80x + 2.4 = 0.40x + 3.2$

$0.40x + 2.4 = 3.2$ Subtract $0.40x$.

$0.40x = 0.80$ Subtract 2.4.

$x = 2$ Divide by 0.40.

2 L of 80% solution is needed.

Examples

Example 2 illustrates a uniform motion problem.

Example 2

Jack and Diane participate in a bicycle race. Jack rides the first half of the race in 1.5 hr. Diane rides the second half at a rate 5 mph slower than Jack and completes her portion in 2 hr. How fast does each person ride?

	Distance	Rate	Time
Jack	$1.5x$	x	1.5
Diane	$2(x - 5)$	$x - 5$	2

$$\begin{pmatrix}\text{Distance}\\ \text{Jack rides}\end{pmatrix} = \begin{pmatrix}\text{distance}\\ \text{Diane rides}\end{pmatrix}$$

$1.5x = 2(x - 5)$

$1.5x = 2x - 10$

$-0.5x = -10$ Subtract $2x$.

$x = 20$ Divide by -0.5.

Jack's speed is x. Jack rides 20 mph. Diane's speed is $x - 5$, which is 15 mph.

Section 2.8 Linear Inequalities

Key Concepts

A **linear inequality in one variable**, x, is any relationship in the form: $ax + b < c$, $ax + b > c$, $ax + b \leq c$, or $ax + b \geq c$, where $a \neq 0$.

The solution set to an inequality can be expressed as a graph or in **set-builder notation** or in **interval notation**.

When graphing an inequality or when writing interval notation, a parenthesis, (or), is used to denote that an endpoint is *not included* in a solution set. A square bracket, [or], is used to show that an endpoint *is included* in a solution set. A parenthesis (or) is always used with $-\infty$ and ∞, respectively.

The inequality $a < x < b$ is used to show that x is greater than a and less than b. That is, x is *between* a and b.

Multiplying or dividing an inequality by a negative quantity requires the direction of the inequality sign to be reversed.

Example

Example 1

$-2x + 6 \geq 14$

$-2x + 6 - 6 \geq 14 - 6$ Subtract 6.

$-2x \geq 8$ Simplify.

$\dfrac{-2x}{-2} \leq \dfrac{8}{-2}$ Divide by -2. Reverse the inequality sign.

$x \leq -4$

Graph: 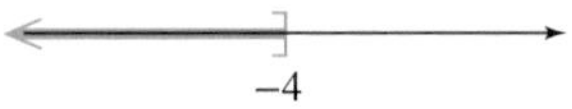

Set-builder notation: $\{x \mid x \leq -4\}$

Interval notation: $(-\infty, -4]$

Chapter 2 Review Exercises

Section 2.1

1. Label the following as either an expression or an equation:

   a. $3x + y = 10$ Equation
   b. $9x + 10x - 2xy$ Expression
   c. $4(x + 3) = 12$ Equation
   d. $-5x = 7$ Equation

2. Explain how to determine whether an equation is linear in one variable. A linear equation can be written in the form $ax + b = c$, $a \neq 0$.

3. Determine if the given equation is a linear equation in one variable. Answer yes or no.

   a. $4x^2 + 8 = -10$ No
   b. $x + 18 = 72$ Yes
   c. $-3 + 2y^2 = 0$ No
   d. $-4p - 5 = 6p$ Yes

4. For the equation, $4y + 9 = -3$, determine if the given numbers are solutions.

   a. $y = 3$ No
   b. $y = -3$ Yes

For Exercises 5–12, solve each equation using the addition property, subtraction property, multiplication property, or division property of equality.

5. $a + 6 = -2$ $\{-8\}$
6. $6 = z - 9$ $\{15\}$
7. $-\frac{3}{4} + k = \frac{9}{2}$ $\left\{\frac{21}{4}\right\}$
8. $0.1r = 7$ $\{70\}$
9. $-5x = 21$ $\left\{-\frac{21}{5}\right\}$
10. $\frac{t}{3} = -20$ $\{-60\}$
11. $-\frac{2}{5}k = \frac{4}{7}$ $\left\{-\frac{10}{7}\right\}$
12. $-m = -27$ $\{27\}$

13. The quotient of a number and negative six is equal to negative ten. Find the number. The number is 60.

14. The difference of a number and $-\frac{1}{8}$ is $\frac{5}{12}$. Find the number. The number is $\frac{7}{24}$.

15. Four subtracted from a number is negative twelve. Find the number. The number is -8.

16. The product of a number and $\frac{1}{4}$ is $-\frac{1}{2}$. Find the number. The number is -2.

Section 2.2

For Exercises 17–28, solve each equation.

17. $4d + 2 = 6$ $\{1\}$
18. $5c - 6 = -9$ $\left\{-\frac{3}{5}\right\}$
19. $-7c = -3c - 8$ $\{2\}$
20. $-28 = 5w + 2$ $\{-6\}$
21. $\frac{b}{3} + 1 = 0$ $\{-3\}$
22. $\frac{2}{3}h - 5 = 7$ $\{18\}$
23. $-3p + 7 = 5p + 1$ $\left\{\frac{3}{4}\right\}$
24. $4t - 6 = 12t + 18$ $\{-3\}$
25. $4a - 9 = 3(a - 3)$ $\{0\}$
26. $3(2c + 5) = -2(c - 8)$ $\left\{\frac{1}{8}\right\}$
27. $7b + 3(b - 1) + 3 = 2(b + 8)$ $\{2\}$
28. $2 + (18 - x) + 2(x - 1) = 4(x + 2) - 8$ $\{6\}$

29. Explain the difference between an equation that is a contradiction and an equation that is an identity. A contradiction has no solution and an identity is true for all real numbers.

For Exercises 30–35, label each equation as a conditional equation, a contradiction, or an identity.

30. $x + 3 = 3 + x$ Identity
31. $3x - 19 = 2x + 1$ Conditional equation
32. $5x + 6 = 5x - 28$ Contradiction
33. $2x - 8 = 2(x - 4)$ Identity
34. $-8x - 9 = -8(x - 9)$ Contradiction
35. $4x - 4 = 3x - 2$ Conditional equation

Section 2.3

For Exercises 36–53, solve each equation.

36. $\frac{x}{8} - \frac{1}{4} = \frac{1}{2}$ $\{6\}$
37. $\frac{y}{15} - \frac{2}{3} = \frac{4}{5}$ $\{22\}$
38. $\frac{x + 5}{2} - \frac{2x + 10}{9} = 5$ $\{13\}$
39. $\frac{x - 6}{3} - \frac{2x + 8}{2} = 12$ $\{-27\}$
40. $\frac{1}{10}p - 3 = \frac{2}{5}p$ $\{-10\}$
41. $\frac{1}{4}y - \frac{3}{4} = \frac{1}{2}y + 1$ $\{-7\}$
42. $-\frac{1}{4}(2 - 3t) = \frac{3}{4}$ $\left\{\frac{5}{3}\right\}$
43. $\frac{2}{7}(w + 4) = \frac{1}{2}$ $\left\{-\frac{9}{4}\right\}$
44. $17.3 - 2.7q = 10.55$ $\{2.5\}$
45. $4.9z + 4.6 = 3.2z - 2.2$ $\{-4\}$
46. $5.74a + 9.28 = 2.24a - 5.42$ $\{-4.2\}$
47. $62.84t - 123.66 = 4(2.36 + 2.4t)$ $\{2.5\}$

48. $0.05x + 0.10(24 - x) = 0.75(24)$ $\{-312\}$

49. $0.20(x + 4) + 0.65x = 0.20(854)$ $\{200\}$

50. $100 - (t - 6) = -(t - 1)$ $\{\ \}$

51. $3 - (x + 4) + 5 = 3x + 10 - 4x$ $\{\ \}$

52. $5t - (2t + 14) = 3t - 14$ The set of real numbers

53. $9 - 6(2x + 1) = -3(4z - 1)$
The set of real numbers

Section 2.4

54. Twelve added to the sum of a number and two is forty-four. Find the number. The number is 30.

55. Twenty added to the sum of a number and six is thirty-seven. Find the number. The number is 11.

56. Three times a number is the same as the difference of twice the number and seven. Find the number. The number is −7.

57. Eight less than five times a number is forty-eight less than the number. Find the number.
The number is −10.

58. Three times the largest of three consecutive even integers is 76 more than the sum of the other two integers. Find the integers.
The integers are 66, 68, and 70.

59. Ten times the smallest of three consecutive integers is 213 more than the sum of the other two integers. Find the integers.
The integers are 27, 28, and 29.

60. The perimeter of a triangle is 78 in. The lengths of the sides are represented by three consecutive integers. Find the lengths of the sides of the triangle. The sides are 25 in., 26 in., and 27 in.

61. The perimeter of a pentagon (a five-sided polygon) is 190 cm. The lengths of the sides are represented by consecutive integers. Find the lengths of the sides. The sides are 36 cm, 37 cm, 38 cm, 39 cm, and 40 cm.

62. Minimum salaries of major league baseball players soared after a new ruling in 1975. In 2010, the minimum salary for a major league player was $400,000. This is 25 times the minimum salary in 1975. Find the minimum salary in 1975.
In 1975 the minimum salary was $16,000.

63. The state of Indiana has approximately 2.1 million more people than Kentucky. Together their populations total 10.3 million. Approximately how many people are in each state? Indiana has 6.2 million people and Kentucky has 4.1 million.

Section 2.5

For Exercises 64–69, solve each problem involving percents.

64. What is 35% of 68?
23.8

65. What is 4% of 720?
28.8

66. 53.5 is what percent of 428? 12.5%

67. 68.4 is what percent of 72? 95%

68. 24 is 15% of what number? 160

69. 8.75 is 0.5% of what number? 1750

70. A couple spent a total of $50.40 for dinner. This included a 20% tip and 6% sales tax on the price of the meal. What was the price of the dinner before tax and tip? The dinner was $40 before tax and tip.

71. Anna Tsao invested $3000 in an account paying 8% simple interest.

a. How much interest will she earn in $3\frac{1}{2}$ years?
$840

b. What will her balance be at that time?
$3840

72. Eduardo invested money in an account earning 4% simple interest. At the end of 5 years, he had a total of $14,400. How much money did he originally invest? He invested $12,000.

73. A novel is discounted 30%. The sale price is $20.65. What was the original price? The novel originally cost $29.50.

Section 2.6

For Exercises 74–81, solve for the indicated variable.

74. $C = K - 273$ for K $K = C + 273$

75. $K = C + 273$ for C $C = K - 273$

76. $P = 4s$ for s $s = \frac{P}{4}$

77. $P = 3s$ for s $s = \frac{P}{3}$

78. $y = mx + b$ for x $x = \frac{y - b}{m}$

79. $a + bx = c$ for x $x = \frac{c - a}{b}$

80. $2x + 5y = -2$ for y $y = \frac{-2x - 2}{5}$

81. $4(a + b) = Q$ for b $b = \frac{Q - 4a}{4}$ or $b = \frac{Q}{4} - a$

For Exercises 82–88, use an appropriate geometry formula to solve the problem.

82. Find the height of a parallelogram whose area is 42 m^2 and whose base is 6 m. The height is 7 m.

83. The volume of a cone is given by the formula $V = \frac{1}{3}\pi r^2 h$.

a. Solve the formula for h. $h = \frac{3V}{\pi r^2}$

b. Find the height of a right circular cone whose volume is 47.8 in.^3 and whose radius is 3 in. Round to the nearest tenth of an inch.
The height is 5.1 in.

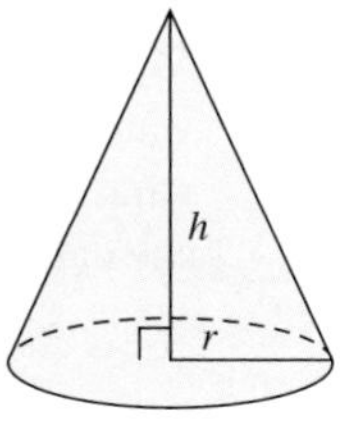

84. The smallest angle of a triangle is 2° more than $\frac{1}{4}$ of the largest angle. The middle angle is 2° less than the largest angle. Find the measure of each angle. The angles are 22°, 78°, and 80°.

85. A carpenter uses a special saw to cut an angle on a piece of framing. If the angles are complementary and one angle is 10° more than the other, find the measure of each angle. The angles are 50° and 40°.

86. A rectangular window has width 1 ft less than its length. The perimeter is 18 ft. Find the length and the width of the window.
The length is 5 ft and the width is 4 ft.

87. Find the measure of the vertical angles by first solving for x. $x = 20$. The angle measure is 65°.

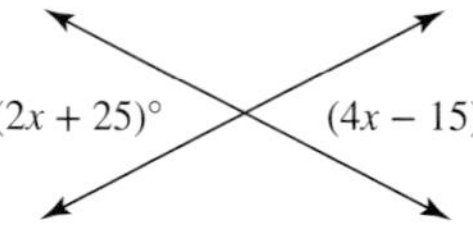

88. Find the measure of angle y.
The measure of angle y is 53°.

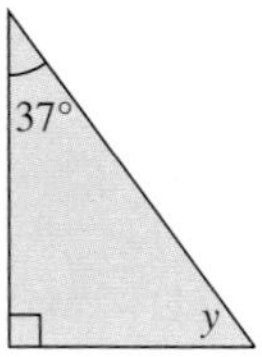

Section 2.7

89. In stormy conditions, a delivery truck can travel a route in 14 hr. In good weather, the same trip can be made in 10.5 hr because the truck travels 15 km/hr faster. Find the speed of the truck in stormy weather and the speed in good weather.
The truck travels 45 km/hr in bad weather and 60 km/hr in good weather.

90. Winston and Gus ride their bicycles in a relay. Each person rides the same distance. Winston rides 3 mph faster than Gus and finishes the course in 2.5 hr. Gus finishes in 3 hr. How fast does each person ride? Gus rides 15 mph and Winston rides 18 mph.

91. Two cars leave a rest stop on Interstate I-10 at the same time. One heads east and the other heads west. One car travels 55 mph and the other 62 mph. How long will it take for them to be 327.6 mi apart? The cars will be 327.6 mi apart after 2.8 hr (2 hr and 48 min).

92. Two hikers begin at the same time at opposite ends of a 9-mi trail and walk toward each other. One hiker walks 2.5 mph and the other walks 1.5 mph. How long will it be before they meet?
They meet in 2.25 hr (2 hr and 15 min).

93. How much ground beef with 24% fat should be mixed with 8 lb of ground sirloin that is 6% fat to make a mixture that is 9.6% fat? 2 lb of 24% fat content beef is needed.

94. A soldering compound with 40% lead (the rest is tin) must be combined with 80 lb of solder that is 75% lead to make a compound that is 68% lead. How much solder with 40% lead should be used? 20 lb of the 40% solder should be used.

Section 2.8

For Exercises 95–97, graph each inequality and write the set in interval notation.

95. $\{x \mid x > -2\}$ $(-2, \infty)$

96. $\left\{x \mid x \leq \frac{1}{2}\right\}$ $\left(-\infty, \frac{1}{2}\right]$

97. $\{x \mid -1 < x \leq 4\}$ $(-1, 4]$

98. A landscaper buys potted geraniums from a nursery at a price of $5 per plant. However, for large orders, the price per plant is discounted by a percentage off the original price. Let x represent the number of potted plants ordered. The corresponding discount is given in the table.

Number of Plants	Discount
$x \leq 99$	0%
$100 \leq x \leq 199$	2%
$200 \leq x \leq 299$	4%
$x \geq 300$	6%

a. Find the cost to purchase 130 plants. $637

b. Which costs more, 300 plants or 295 plants? Explain your answer. 300 plants cost $1410, and 295 plants cost $1416. 295 plants costs more.

For Exercises 99–109, solve the inequality. Graph the solution set and write the answer in set-builder notation and interval notation.

99. $c + 6 < 23$

$\{c|c < 17\}$; $(-\infty, 17)$

100. $3w - 4 > -5$
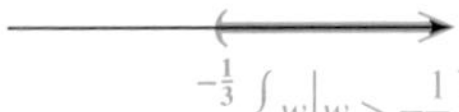

$\left\{w \middle| w > -\frac{1}{3}\right\}$; $\left(-\frac{1}{3}, \infty\right)$

101. $-2x - 7 \geq 5$

$\{x|x \leq -6\}$; $(-\infty, -6]$

102. $5(y + 2) \leq -4$
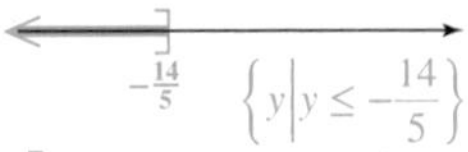

$\left\{y \middle| y \leq -\frac{14}{5}\right\}$; $\left(-\infty, -\frac{14}{5}\right]$

103. $-\frac{3}{7}a \leq -21$

$\{a|a \geq 49\}$; $[49, \infty)$

104. $1.3 > 0.4t - 12.5$

$\{t|t < 34.5\}$; $(-\infty, 34.5)$

105. $4k + 23 < 7k - 31$

$\{k|k > 18\}$; $(18, \infty)$

106. $\frac{6}{5}h - \frac{1}{5} \leq \frac{3}{10} + h$
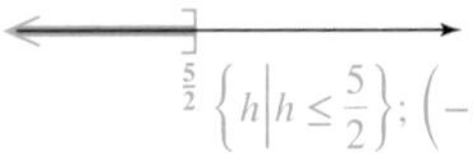

$\left\{h \middle| h \leq \frac{5}{2}\right\}$; $\left(-\infty, \frac{5}{2}\right]$

107. $-5x - 2(4x - 3) + 6 > 17 - 4(x - 1)$
$\{x|x < -1\}$; $(-\infty, -1)$

108. $-6 < 2b \leq 14$

$\{b|-3 < b \leq 7\}$; $(-3, 7]$

109. $-2 \leq z + 4 \leq 9$

$\{z|-6 \leq z \leq 5\}$; $[-6, 5]$

110. The summer average rainfall for Bermuda for June, July, and August is 5.3 in. per month. If Bermuda receives 6.3 in. of rain in June and 7.1 in. in July, how much rain is required in August to exceed the 3-month summer average? More than 2.5 in. is required.

111. Collette has \$15.00 to spend on dinner. Of this, 25% will cover the tax and tip, resulting in \$11.25 for her to spend on food. If Collette wants veggies and blue cheese, fries, and a drink, what is the maximum number of chicken wings she can get? Collette can have at most 18 wings.

Chapter 2 Test

1. Which of the equations have $x = -3$ as a solution?

a. $4x + 1 = 10$ **b.** $6(x - 1) = x - 21$

c. $5x - 2 = 2x + 1$ **d.** $\frac{1}{3}x + 1 = 0$ b, d

2. a. Simplify: $3x - 1 + 2x + 8$ $5x + 7$

b. Solve: $3x - 1 = 2x + 8$ $\{9\}$

For Exercises 3–13, solve each equation.

3. $-3x + 5 = -2$ $\left\{\frac{7}{3}\right\}$

4. $3h + 1 = 3(h + 1)$ { }

5. $t + 3 = -13$ $\{-16\}$

6. $2 + d = 2 - 3(d - 5) - 2$ $\left\{\frac{13}{4}\right\}$

7. $8 = p - 4$ $\{12\}$

8. $\frac{3}{7} + \frac{2}{5}x = -\frac{1}{5}x + 1$ $\left\{\frac{20}{21}\right\}$

9. $\frac{t}{8} = -\frac{2}{9}$ $\left\{-\frac{16}{9}\right\}$

10. $2(p - 4) = p + 7$ $\{15\}$

11. $-5(x + 2) + 8x = -2 + 3x - 8$
The set of real numbers

12. $\frac{3x + 1}{2} - \frac{4x - 3}{3} = 1$ $\{-3\}$

13. $0.5c - 1.9 = 2.8 + 0.6c$ $\{-47\}$

14. Solve the equation for y: $3x + y = -4$
$y = -3x - 4$

15. Solve $C = 2\pi r$ for r. $r = \frac{C}{2\pi}$

16. 13% of what is 11.7? 90

17. Graph the inequalities and write the sets in interval notation.

a. $\{x \mid x < 0\}$ $(-\infty, 0)$ 

b. $\{x \mid -2 \le x < 5\}$ 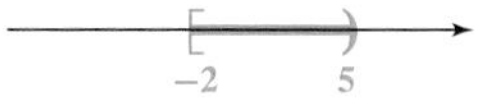
$[-2, 5)$

For Exercises 18–21, solve the inequality. Graph the solution and write the solution set in set-builder notation and interval notation.

18. $5x + 14 > -2x$ 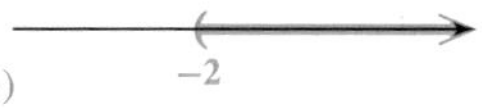
$\{x \mid x > -2\}$; $(-2, \infty)$

19. $2(3 - x) \ge 14$ 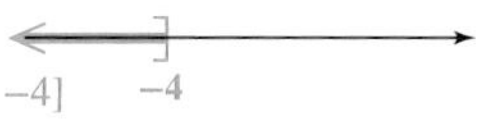
$\{x \mid x \le -4\}$; $(-\infty, -4]$

20. $3(2y - 4) + 1 > 2(2y - 3) - 8$ 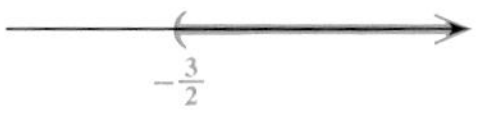
$\left\{y \middle| y > -\frac{3}{2}\right\}$; $\left(-\frac{3}{2}, \infty\right)$

21. $-13 \le 3p + 2 \le 5$ 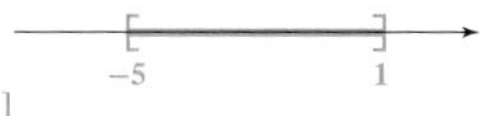
$\{p \mid -5 \le p \le 1\}$; $[-5, 1]$

22. The total bill for a pair of basketball shoes (including sales tax) is \$87.74. If the tax rate is 7%, find the cost of the shoes before tax.
The cost was \$82.00.

23. Clarita borrowed money at a 6% simple interest rate. If she paid back a total of \$8000 at the end of 10 yr, how much did she originally borrow?
Clarita originally borrowed \$5000.

24. One number is four plus one-half of another. The sum of the numbers is 31. Find the numbers.
The numbers are 18 and 13.

25. Two families leave their homes at the same time to meet for lunch. The families live 210 mi apart, and one family drives 5 mph slower than the other. If it takes them 2 hr to meet at a point between their homes, how fast does each family travel?
One family travels 55 mph and the other travels 50 mph.

26. The average winter snowfall for Syracuse, New York, for December, January, and February is 27.5 in. per month. If Syracuse receives 24 in. of snow in December and 32 in. in January, how much snow is required in February to exceed the 3-month average? More than 26.5 in. is required.

27. The perimeter of a pentagon (a five-sided polygon) is 315 in. The lengths of the sides are represented by consecutive integers. Find the measures of the sides.
The sides are 61 in., 62 in., 63 in., 64 in., and 65 in.

28. Matthew mixes macadamia nuts that cost \$9.00 per pound with 50 lb of peanuts that cost \$5.00 per pound. How many pounds of macadamia nuts should he mix to make a nut mixture that costs \$6.50 per pound?
Matthew needs 30 lb of macadamia nuts.

29. A couple purchased two hockey tickets and two basketball tickets for \$153.92. A hockey ticket cost \$4.32 more than a basketball ticket. What were the prices of the individual tickets? Each basketball ticket was \$36.32, and each hockey ticket was \$40.64.

30. Two angles are complementary. One angle is 26° more than the other angle. What are the measures of the angles? The measures of the angles are 32° and 58°.

31. The length of a soccer field for international matches is 40 m less than twice its width. If the perimeter is 370 m, what are the dimensions of the field? The field is 110 m long and 75 m wide.

32. Given the triangle, find the measure of each angle by first solving for y. $y = 30$; The measures of the angles are 30°, 39°, and 111°.

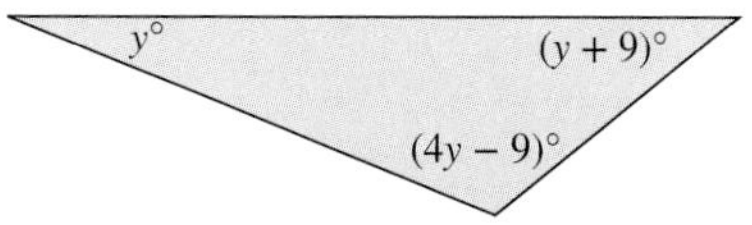

Chapters 1-2 Cumulative Review Exercises

For Exercises 1–5, perform the indicated operations.

1. $\left|-\frac{1}{5} + \frac{7}{10}\right|$ $\frac{1}{2}$

2. $5 - 2[3 - (4 - 7)]$ -7

3. $-\frac{2}{3} + \left(\frac{1}{2}\right)^2$ $-\frac{5}{12}$

4. $-3^2 + (-5)^2$ 16

5. $\sqrt{5 - (-20) - 3^2}$ 4

For Exercises 6–7, translate the mathematical expressions and simplify the results.

6. The square root of the difference of five squared and nine $\sqrt{5^2 - 9}$; 4

7. The sum of −14 and 12 $-14 + 12$; -2

8. List the terms of the expression: $-7x^2y + 4xy - 6$ $-7x^2y, 4xy, -6$

9. Simplify: $-4[2x - 3(x + 4)] + 5(x - 7)$
$9x + 13$

For Exercises 10–15, solve each equation.

10. $8t - 8 = 24$ $\{4\}$

11. $-2.5x - 5.2 = 12.8$ $\{-7.2\}$

12. $-5(p-3)+2p=3(5-p)$ The set of real numbers

13. $\frac{x+3}{5}-\frac{x+2}{2}=2$ $\{-8\}$

14. $\frac{2}{9}x-\frac{1}{3}=x+\frac{1}{9}$ $\left\{-\frac{4}{7}\right\}$

15. $-0.6w=48$ $\{-80\}$

16. The sum of two consecutive odd integers is 156. Find the integers. The numbers are 77 and 79.

17. The cost of a smartphone speaker dock (including sales tax) is $374.50. If the tax rate is 7%, find the cost of the speaker dock before tax.
The cost before tax was $350.00.

18. The area of a triangle is 41 cm^2. Find the height of the triangle if the base is 12 cm.

The height is $\frac{41}{6}$ cm or $6\frac{5}{6}$ cm.

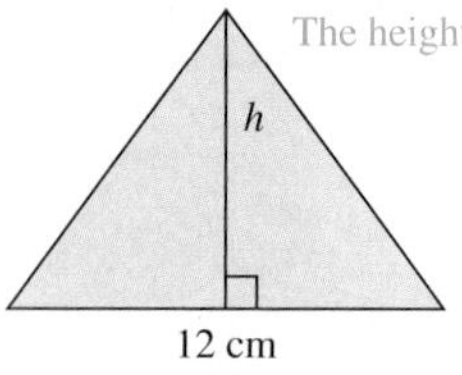

For Exercises 19–20, solve the inequality. Graph the solution set on a number line and express the solution in set-builder notation and interval notation.

19. $-3x-3(x+1)<9$
$\{x \mid x>-2\}$; $(-2, \infty)$

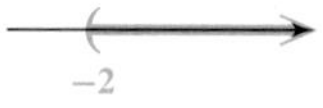

20. $-6\le 2x-4\le 14$
$\{x \mid -1\le x\le 9\}$; $[-1, 9]$

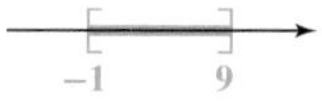

Graphing Linear Equations in Two Variables

3

CHAPTER OUTLINE

Mathematics in Gaming

Imagine that you are playing a game of *Battleship*. You say "E-5" to your opponent and his face saddens as he realizes you have sunk his ship. In this game, the "E" and the "5" represent a row or column in a grid, thus defining a *location* on a map. In mathematics we use **ordered pairs**, two numbers of the form (x, y), to determine the location of a point. Furthermore, an equation involving x and y defines a line or curve in a plane that might be the path of a battleship or other object in a computer game.

For example, suppose that a battleship follows the path defined by $y = 2x + 1$. The value of y depends on the value of x, where y is 1 more than double the value of x. We can determine the value of y for any given value of x by using substitution.

© ERproductions Ltd/Getty Images RF

If $x = 1$, then $y = 2(1) + 1 = 3$. Thus, the ordered pair (1, 3) represents a point on the path of the ship.

If $x = 2$, then $y = 2(2) + 1 = 5$. Thus, the ordered pair (2, 5) represents a point on the path of the ship.

In this chapter, we will study equations in x and y and their related graphs. This is important content for a variety of applications, including computer gaming.

Section 3.1 Rectangular Coordinate System

Concepts

1. Interpreting Graphs
2. Plotting Points in a Rectangular Coordinate System
3. Applications of Plotting and Identifying Points

1. Interpreting Graphs

Mathematics is a powerful tool used by scientists and has directly contributed to the highly technical world in which we live. Applications of mathematics have led to advances in the sciences, business, computer technology, and medicine.

One fundamental application of mathematics is the graphical representation of numerical information (or data). For example, Table 3-1 represents the number of clients admitted to a drug and alcohol rehabilitation program over a 12-month period.

Table 3-1

	Month	Number of Clients
Jan.	1	55
Feb.	2	62
March	3	64
April	4	60
May	5	70
June	6	73
July	7	77
Aug.	8	80
Sept.	9	80
Oct.	10	74
Nov.	11	85
Dec.	12	90

In table form, the information is difficult to picture and interpret. It appears that on a monthly basis, the number of clients fluctuates. However, when the data are represented in a graph, an upward trend is clear (Figure 3-1).

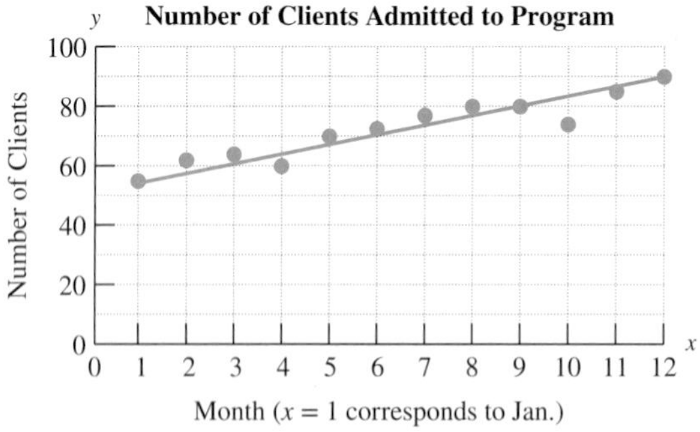

Figure 3-1

From the increase in clients shown in this graph, management for the rehabilitation center might make plans for the future. If the trend continues, management might consider expanding its facilities and increasing its staff to accommodate the expected increase in clients.

Example 1 Interpreting a Graph

Classroom Example: p. 199, Exercise 4

Refer to Figure 3-1 and Table 3-1.

a. For which month was the number of clients the greatest?

b. How many clients were served in the first month (January)?

c. Which month corresponds to 60 clients served?

d. Between which two consecutive months did the number of clients decrease?

e. Between which two consecutive months did the number of clients remain the same?

Solution:

a. Month 12 (December) corresponds to the highest point on the graph. This represents the greatest number of clients, 90.

b. In month 1 (January), there were 55 clients served.

c. Month 4 (April).

d. The number of clients decreased between months 3 and 4 and between months 9 and 10.

e. The number of clients remained the same between months 8 and 9.

Skill Practice Refer to Figure 3-1 and Table 3-1.

1. How many clients were served in October?
2. Which month corresponds to 70 clients?
3. What is the difference between the number of clients in month 12 and month 1?
4. For which month was the number of clients the least?

2. Plotting Points in a Rectangular Coordinate System

The data in Table 3-1 represent a relationship between two variables—the month number and the number of clients. The graph in Figure 3-1 enables us to visualize this relationship. In picturing the relationship between two quantities, we often use a graph with two number lines drawn at right angles to each other (Figure 3-2). This forms a **rectangular coordinate system**. The horizontal line is called the ***x*-axis**, and the vertical line is called the ***y*-axis**. The point where the lines intersect is called the **origin**. On the x-axis, the numbers to the right of the origin are positive and the numbers to the left are negative. On the y-axis, the numbers above the origin are positive and the numbers below are negative. The x- and y-axes divide the graphing area into four regions called **quadrants**.

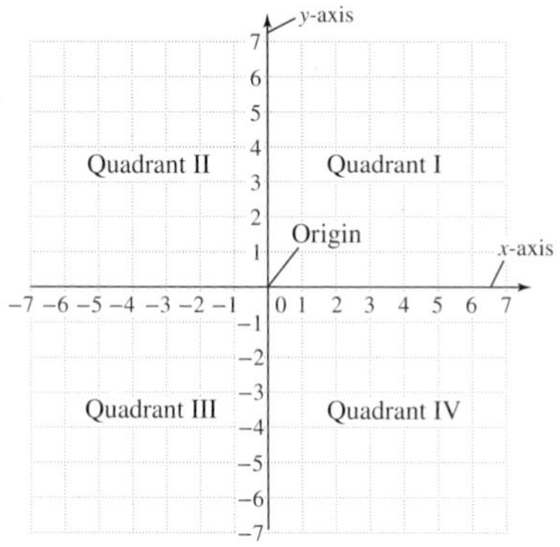

Figure 3-2

Animation

Answers

1. 74 clients
2. Month 5 (May)
3. 35 clients
4. Month 1 (January)

Points graphed in a rectangular coordinate system are defined by two numbers as an **ordered pair**, (x, y). The first number (called the ***x*-coordinate**, or the abscissa) is the horizontal position from the origin. The second number (called the ***y*-coordinate**, or the ordinate) is the vertical position from the origin. Example 2 shows how points are plotted in a rectangular coordinate system.

Classroom Example: p. 200, Exercise 10

Example 2 Plotting Points in a Rectangular Coordinate System

Plot the points.

a. $(4, 5)$ **b.** $(-4, -5)$ **c.** $(-1, 3)$ **d.** $(3, -1)$

e. $\left(\frac{1}{2}, -\frac{7}{3}\right)$ **f.** $(-2, 0)$ **g.** $(0, 0)$ **h.** $(\pi, 1.1)$

Solution:

See Figure 3-3.

a. The ordered pair $(4, 5)$ indicates that $x = 4$ and $y = 5$. Beginning at the origin, move 4 units in the positive x-direction (4 units to the right), and from there move 5 units in the positive y-direction (5 units up). Then plot the point. The point is in Quadrant I.

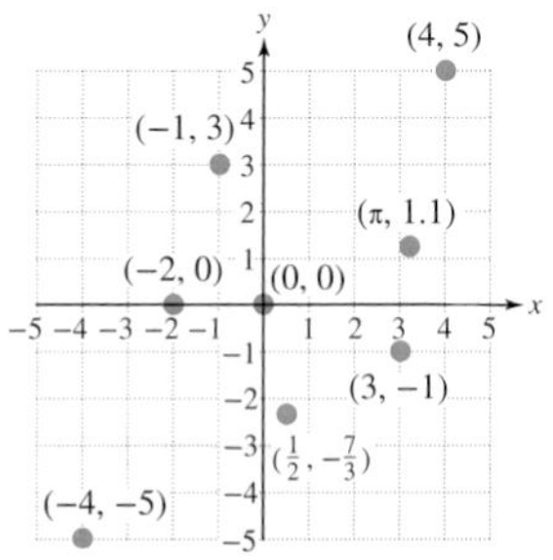

Figure 3-3

b. The ordered pair $(-4, -5)$ indicates that $x = -4$ and $y = -5$. Move 4 units in the negative x-direction (4 units to the left), and from there move 5 units in the negative y-direction (5 units down). Then plot the point. The point is in Quadrant III.

TIP: Notice that changing the order of the x- and y-coordinates changes the location of the point. For example, the point $(-1, 3)$ is in Quadrant II, whereas $(3, -1)$ is in Quadrant IV (Figure 3-3). This is why points are represented by *ordered* pairs. The order of the coordinates is important.

c. The ordered pair $(-1, 3)$ indicates that $x = -1$ and $y = 3$. Move 1 unit to the left and 3 units up. The point is in Quadrant II.

d. The ordered pair $(3, -1)$ indicates that $x = 3$ and $y = -1$. Move 3 units to the right and 1 unit down. The point is in Quadrant IV.

e. The improper fraction $-\frac{7}{3}$ can be written as the mixed number $-2\frac{1}{3}$. Therefore, to plot the point $\left(\frac{1}{2}, -\frac{7}{3}\right)$ move to the right $\frac{1}{2}$ unit, and down $2\frac{1}{3}$ units. The point is in Quadrant IV.

f. The point $(-2, 0)$ indicates $y = 0$. Therefore, the point is on the x-axis.

Avoiding Mistakes

Points that lie on either of the axes do not lie in any quadrant.

g. The point $(0, 0)$ is at the origin.

h. The irrational number, π, can be approximated as 3.14. Thus, the point $(\pi, 1.1)$ is located approximately 3.14 units to the right and 1.1 units up. The point is in Quadrant I.

Skill Practice

5. Plot the points.

$A(3, 4)$ $B(-2, 2)$ $C(4, 0)$ $D\left(\frac{5}{2}, -\frac{1}{2}\right)$ $E(-5, -2)$

Answer

5.

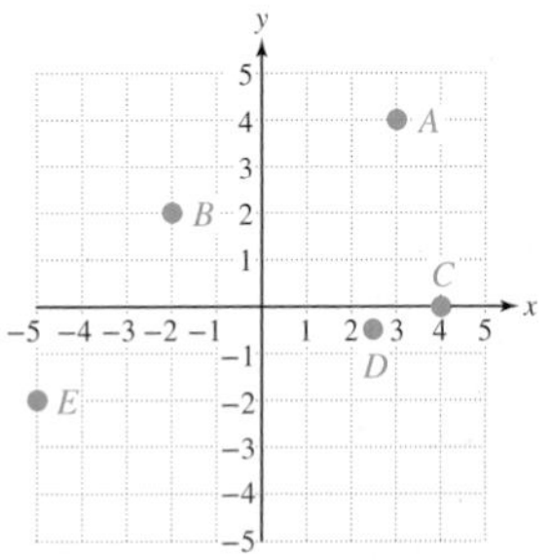

3. Applications of Plotting and Identifying Points

The effective use of graphs for mathematical models requires skill in identifying points and interpreting graphs.

Example 3 **Determining Points from a Graph**

Classroom Example: p. 201, Exercise 26

A map of a national park is drawn so that the origin is placed at the ranger station (Figure 3-4). Four fire observation towers are located at points A, B, C, and D. Estimate the coordinates of the fire towers relative to the ranger station (all distances are in miles).

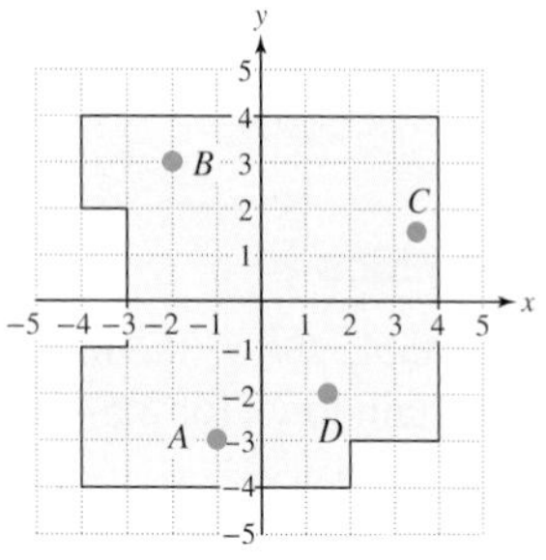

Figure 3-4

Solution:

Point A: $(-1, -3)$

Point B: $(-2, 3)$

Point C: $(3\frac{1}{2}, 1\frac{1}{2})$ or $(\frac{7}{2}, \frac{3}{2})$ or $(3.5, 1.5)$

Point D: $(1\frac{1}{2}, -2)$ or $(\frac{3}{2}, -2)$ or $(1.5, -2)$

Skill Practice

6. Towers are located at points A, B, C, and D. Estimate the coordinates of the towers.

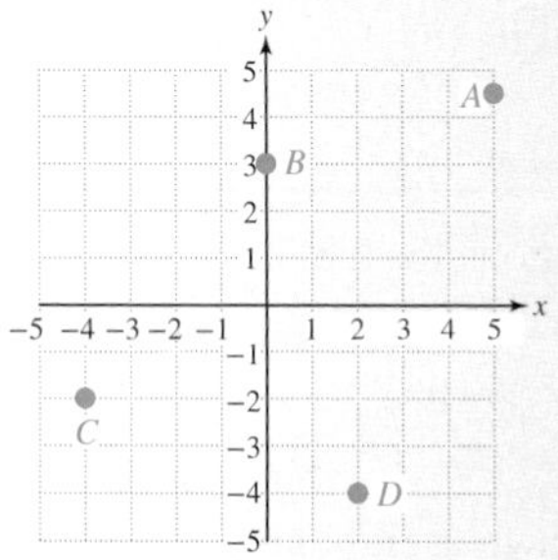

Example 4 **Plotting Points in an Application**

Classroom Example: p. 202, Exercise 28

The daily low temperaures (in degrees Fahrenheit) for one week in January for Sudbury, Ontario, Canada, are given in Table 3-2.

a. Write an ordered pair for each row in the table using the day number as the x-coordinate and the temperature as the y-coordinate.

b. Plot the ordered pairs from part (a) on a rectangular coordinate system.

Table 3-2

Day Number, x	Temperature (°F), y
1	−3
2	−5
3	1
4	6
5	5
6	0
7	−4

Solution:

a. Each ordered pair represents the day number and the corresponding low temperature for that day.

$(1, -3)$ $(2, -5)$ $(3, 1)$ $(4, 6)$ $(5, 5)$ $(6, 0)$ $(7, -4)$

Answer

6. $A(5, 4\frac{1}{2})$
$B(0, 3)$
$C(-4, -2)$
$D(2, -4)$

b. **Daily Low Temperatures (Fahrenheit) for Sudbury, Canada**

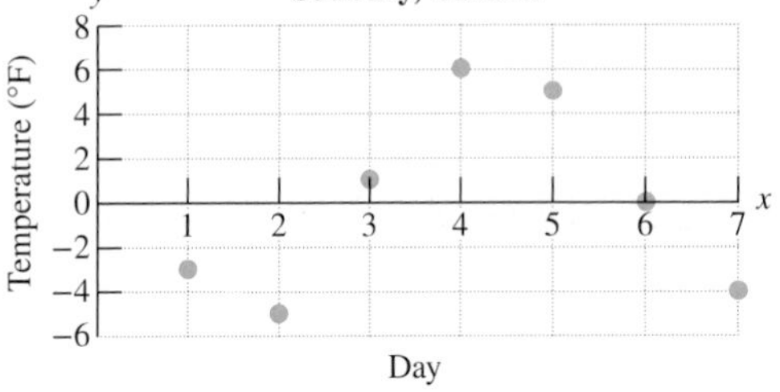

TIP: The graph in Example 4(b) shows only Quadrants I and IV because all *x*-coordinates are positive.

Answer

7.

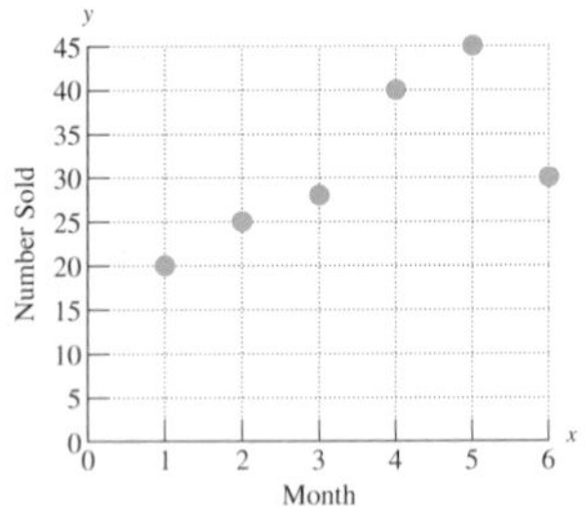

Skill Practice

7. The table shows the number of homes sold in a certain town for a 6-month period. Plot the ordered pairs.

Month, x	Number Sold, y
1	20
2	25
3	28
4	40
5	45
6	30

Section 3.1 Practice Exercisess

For additional exercises, see Classroom Activities 3.1A–3.1B in the *Student's Resource Manual* at www.mhhe.com/moh.

Study Skills Exercise

Before you begin the exercises in this section, make your test corrections for the previous test.

Vocabulary and Key Concepts

1. **a.** In a rectangular coordinate system, two number lines are drawn at right angles to each other. The horizontal line is called the ___x___-axis, and the vertical line is called the ___y-axis___.

b. A point in a rectangular coordinate system is defined by an ___ordered___ pair, (x, y).

c. In a rectangular coordinate system, the point where the x- and y-axes intersect is called the ___origin___ and is represented by the ordered pair ___(0, 0)___.

d. The x- and y-axes divide the coordinate plane into four regions called ___quadrants___.

e. A point with a positive x-coordinate and a ___negative___ y-coordinate is in Quadrant IV.

f. In Quadrant ___III___, both the x- and y-coordinates are negative.

Concept 1: Interpreting Graphs

For Exercises 2–6, refer to the graphs to answer the questions.
(See Example 1.)

2. The number of Botox® injection procedures (in millions) in the United States over a 6-yr period is shown in the graph.

a. For which year was the number of procedures the greatest? Year 3

b. Approximately how many procedures were performed in year 5? Approximately 2.9 million

c. Which year corresponds to 2.3 million procedures? Year 1

Number of Botox Procedures in the United States (in millions)

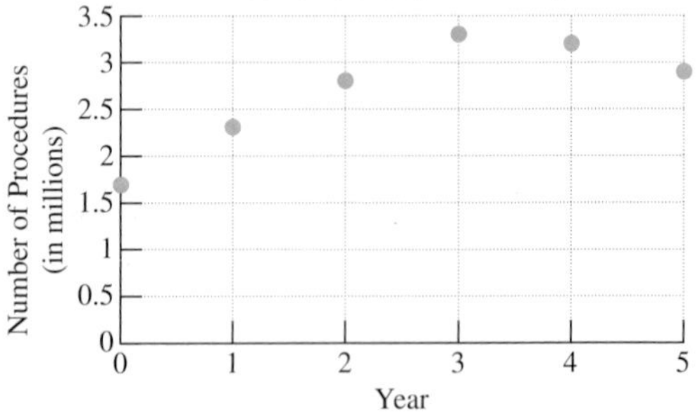

3. The number of patients served by a certain hospice care center for the first 12 months after it opened is shown in the graph.

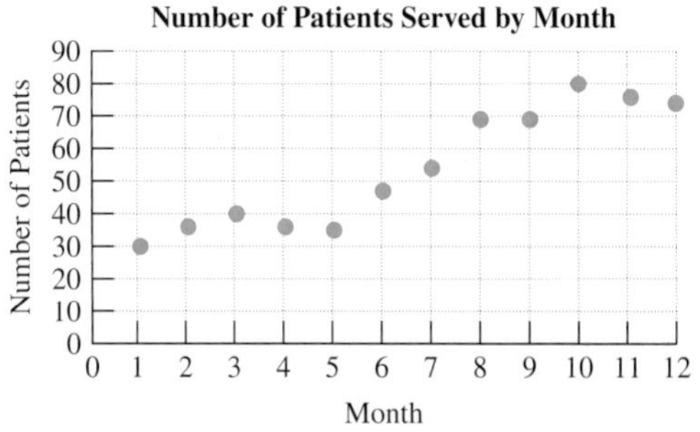

a. For which month was the number of patients greatest? Month 10

b. How many patients did the center serve in the first month? 30

c. Between which months did the number of patients decrease? Between months 3 and 5 and between months 10 and 12

d. Between which two months did the number of patients remain the same? Months 8 and 9

e. Which month corresponds to 40 patients served? Month 3

f. Approximately how many patients were served during the 10th month? 80

4. Recently the number of housing permits (in thousands) issued by a county in Texas between year 0 and year 6 is shown in the graph.

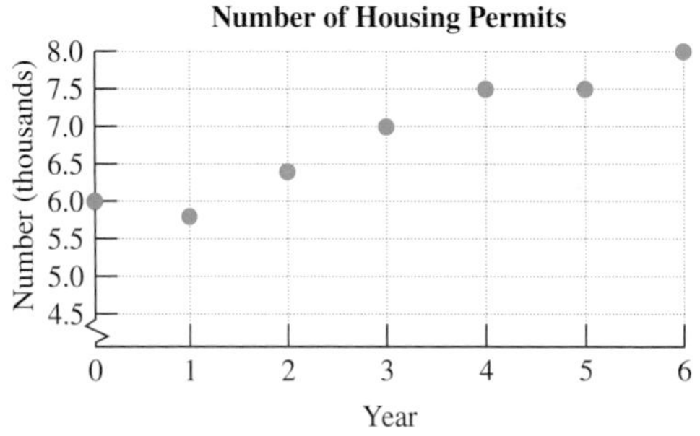

a. For which year was the number of permits greatest? Year 6

b. How many permits did the county issue in year 0? 6 thousand or 6000

c. Between which years did the number of permits decrease? Between year 0 and year 1

d. Between which two years did the number of permits remain the same? Between year 4 and year 5

e. Which year corresponds to 7000 permits issued? Year 3

5. The price per share of a stock (in dollars) over a period of 5 days is shown in the graph.

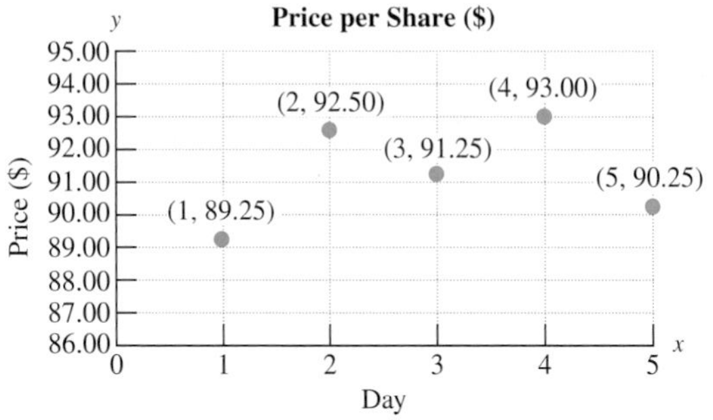

a. Interpret the meaning of the ordered pair (1, 89.25). On day 1 the price per share was $89.25.

b. What was the change in price between day 3 and day 4? $1.75

c. What was the change in price between day 4 and day 5? −$2.75

6. The price per share of a stock (in dollars) over a period of 5 days is shown in the graph.

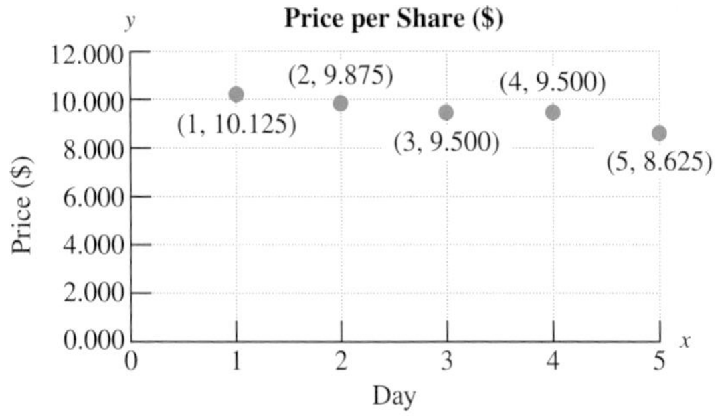

a. Interpret the meaning of the ordered pair (1, 10.125). On day 1 the price per share was $10.125.

b. What was the change between day 4 and day 5? −$0.875

c. What is the change between day 1 and day 5? −$1.50

Concept 2: Plotting Points in a Rectangular Coordinate System

7. Plot the points on a rectangular coordinate system. **(See Example 2.)**

a. (2, 6) **b.** (6, 2) **c.** (−7, 3)
d. (−7, −3) **e.** (0, −3) **f.** (−3, 0)
g. (6, −4) **h.** (0, 5)

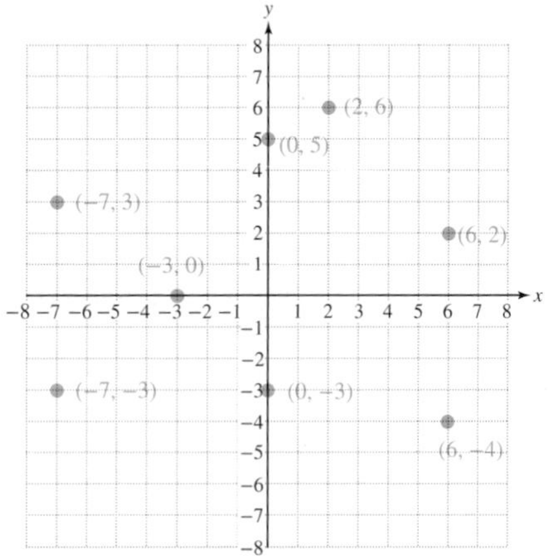

8. Plot the points on a rectangular coordinate system.

a. (4, 5) **b.** (−4, 5) **c.** (−6, 0)
d. (6, 0) **e.** (4, −5) **f.** (−4, −5)
g. (0, −2) **h.** (0, 0)

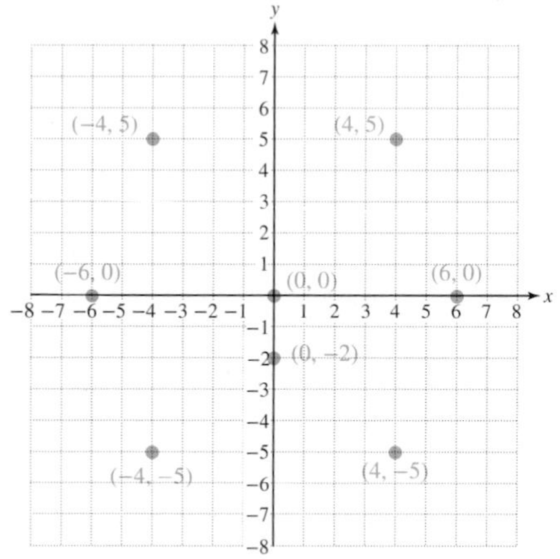

9. Plot the points on a rectangular coordinate system.

a. (−1, 5) **b.** (0, 4) **c.** $\left(-2, -\frac{3}{2}\right)$
d. (2, −1.75) **e.** (4, 2) **f.** (−6, 0)

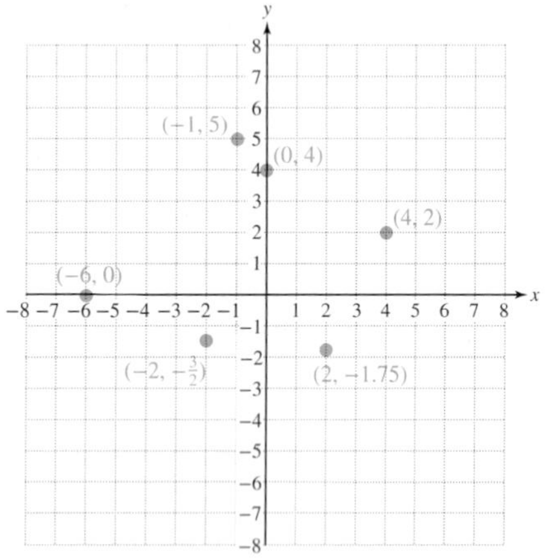

10. Plot the points on a rectangular coordinate system.

a. (7, 0) **b.** (−3, −2) **c.** $(6\frac{3}{5}, 1)$
d. (0, 1.5) **e.** $\left(\frac{7}{2}, -4\right)$ **f.** $\left(-\frac{7}{2}, 4\right)$

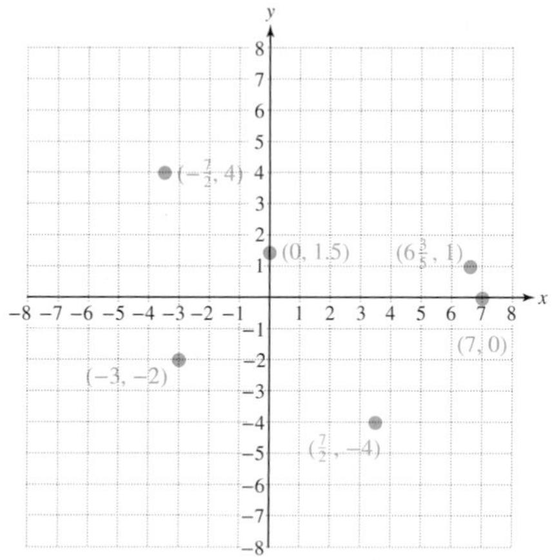

For Exercises 11–18, identify the quadrant in which the given point is located.

11. (13, −2) IV
12. (25, 16) I
13. (−8, 14) II
14. (−82, −71) III
15. (−5, −19) III
16. (−31, 6) II
17. $\left(\frac{5}{2}, \frac{7}{4}\right)$ I
18. (9, −40) IV

19. Explain why the point (0, −5) is *not* located in Quadrant IV.
(0, −5) lies on the *y*-axis.

20. Explain why the point (−1, 0) is *not* located in Quadrant II.
(−1, 0) lies on the *x*-axis.

21. Where is the point $(\frac{7}{8}, 0)$ located?
$(\frac{7}{8}, 0)$ is located on the *x*-axis.

22. Where is the point $(0, \frac{6}{5})$ located?
$(0, \frac{6}{5})$ is located on the *y*-axis.

Concept 3: Applications of Plotting and Identifying Points

For Exercises 23–24, refer to the graph. **(See Example 3.)**

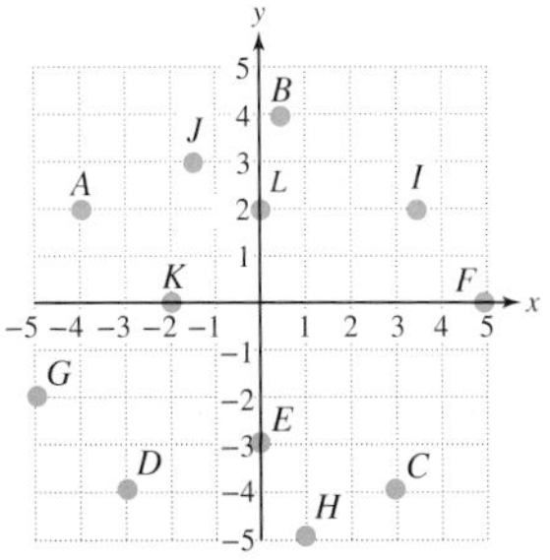

23. Estimate the coordinates of the points *A*, *B*, *C*, *D*, *E*, and *F*.
$A(-4, 2)$, $B(\frac{1}{2}, 4)$, $C(3, -4)$, $D(-3, -4)$, $E(0, -3)$, $F(5, 0)$

24. Estimate the coordinates of the points *G*, *H*, *I*, *J*, *K*, and *L*.
$G(-5, -2)$, $H(1, -5)$, $I(3\frac{1}{2}, 2)$, $J(-1\frac{1}{2}, 3)$, $K(-2, 0)$, $L(0, 2)$

25. A map of a park is laid out with the visitor center located at the origin. Five visitors are in the park located at points *A*, *B*, *C*, *D*, and *E*. All distances are in meters.

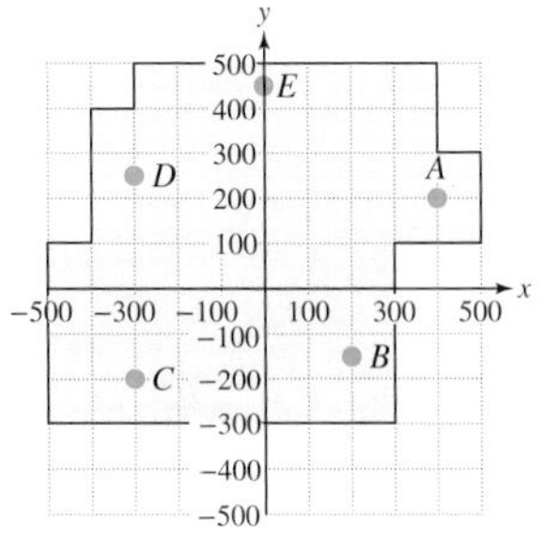

a. Estimate the coordinates of each visitor. **(See Example 3.)**
$A(400, 200)$, $B(200, -150)$, $C(-300, -200)$, $D(-300, 250)$, $E(0, 450)$

b. How far apart are visitors *C* and *D*? 450 m

26. A townhouse has a sprinkler system in the backyard. With the water source at the origin, the sprinkler heads are located at points *A*, *B*, *C*, *D*, and *E*. All distances are in feet.

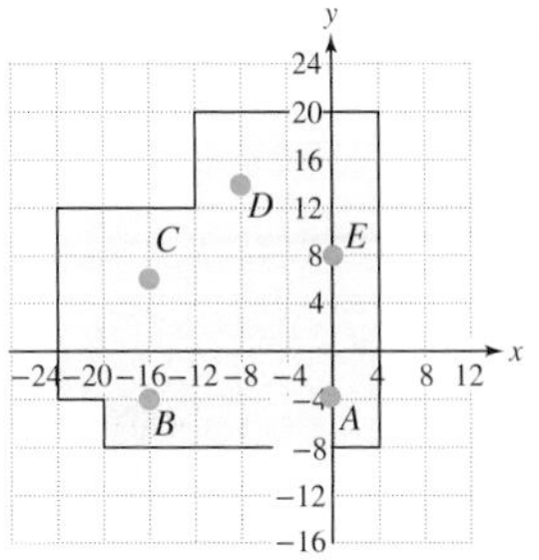

a. Estimate the coordinates of each sprinkler head.
$A(0, -4)$, $B(-16, -4)$, $C(-16, 6)$, $D(-8, 14)$, $E(0, 8)$

b. How far is the distance from sprinkler head *B* to *C*? 10 ft

27. A movie theater has kept records of popcorn sales versus movie attendance.

a. Use the table to write the corresponding ordered pairs using the movie attendance as the *x*-variable and sales of popcorn as the *y*-variable. Interpret the meaning of the first ordered pair. **(See Example 4.)**
(250, 225), (175, 193), (315, 330), (220, 209), (450, 570), (400, 480), (190, 185); the ordered pair (250, 225) means that 250 people produce $225 in popcorn sales.

© Ryan McVay/Getty Images RF

b. Plot the data points on a rectangular coordinate system.

Movie Attendance (Number of People)	Sales of Popcorn ($)
250	225
175	193
315	330
220	209
450	570
400	480
190	185

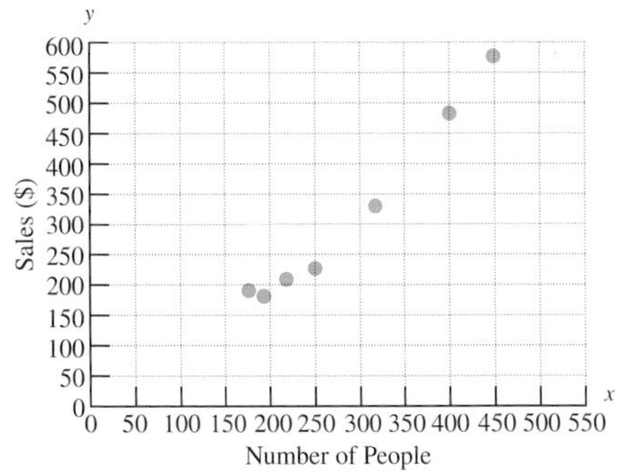

28. The age and systolic blood pressure (in millimeters of mercury, mm Hg) for eight different women are given in the table.

a. Write the corresponding ordered pairs using the woman's age as the x-variable and the systolic blood pressure as the y-variable. Interpret the meaning of the first ordered pair. (57, 149), (41, 120), (71, 158), (36, 115), (64, 151), (25, 110), (40, 118), (77, 165); the ordered pair (57, 149) means that a 57-year-old woman has a systolic blood pressure of 149 mm Hg.

b. Plot the data points on a rectangular coordinate system.

Age (Years)	Systolic Blood Pressure (mm Hg)
57	149
41	120
71	158
36	115
64	151
25	110
40	118
77	165

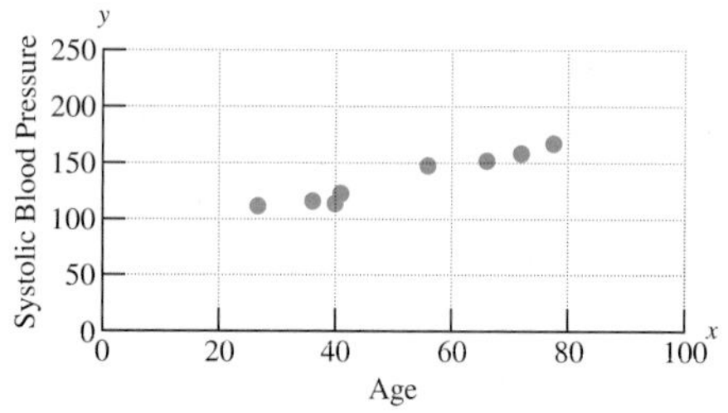

29. The following table shows the average temperature in degrees Celsius for Montreal, Quebec, Canada, by month.

a. Write the corresponding ordered pairs, letting $x = 1$ correspond to the month of January. (1, −10.2), (2, −9.0), (3, −2.5), (4, 5.7), (5, 13.0), (6, 18.3), (7, 20.9), (8, 19.6), (9, 14.8), (10, 8.7), (11, 2.0), (12, −6.9)

b. Plot the ordered pairs on a rectangular coordinate system.

Month, x		Temperature (°C), y
Jan.	1	−10.2
Feb.	2	−9.0
March	3	−2.5
April	4	5.7
May	5	13.0
June	6	18.3
July	7	20.9
Aug.	8	19.6
Sept.	9	14.8
Oct.	10	8.7
Nov.	11	2.0
Dec.	12	−6.9

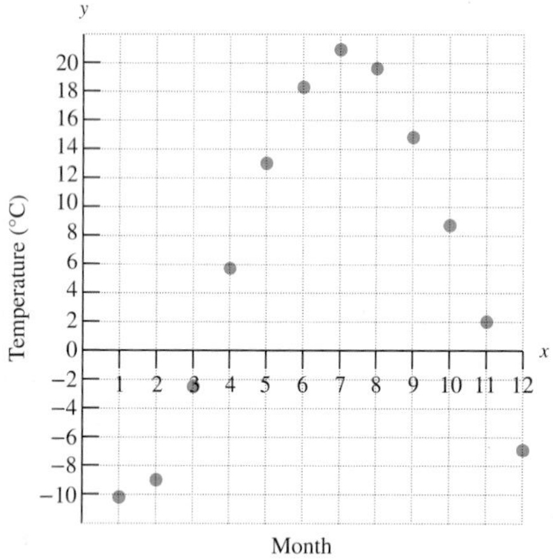

30. The table shows the average temperature in degrees Fahrenheit for Fairbanks, Alaska, by month.

a. Write the corresponding ordered pairs, letting $x = 1$ correspond to the month of January. (1, −12.8), (2, −4.0), (3, 8.4), (4, 30.2), (5, 48.2), (6, 59.4), (7, 61.5), (8, 56.7), (9, 45.0), (10, 25.0), (11, 6.1), (12, −10.1).

b. Plot the ordered pairs on a rectangular coordinate system.

Month, x		Temperature (°F), y
Jan.	1	−12.8
Feb.	2	−4.0
March	3	8.4
April	4	30.2
May	5	48.2
June	6	59.4
July	7	61.5
Aug.	8	56.7
Sept.	9	45.0
Oct.	10	25.0
Nov.	11	6.1
Dec.	12	−10.1

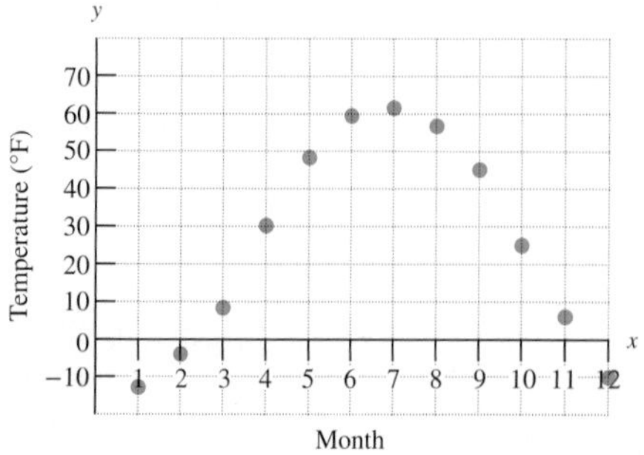

Expanding Your Skills

31. The data in the table give the percent of males and females who have completed 4 or more years of college education for selected years. Let x represent the number of years since 1960. Let y represent the percent of men and the percent of women that completed 4 or more years of college.

Year	x	Percent, y Men	Percent, y Women
1960	0	9.7	5.8
1970	10	13.5	8.1
1980	20	20.1	12.8
1990	30	24.4	18.4
2000	40	27.8	23.6
2005	45	28.9	26.5
2010	50	29.9	28.8

a. Plot the data points for men and for women on the same graph.

b. Is the percentage of men with 4 or more years of college increasing or decreasing? Increasing

c. Is the percentage of women with 4 or more years of college increasing or decreasing? Increasing

Percent of Males/Females with 4 or More Years of College, United States

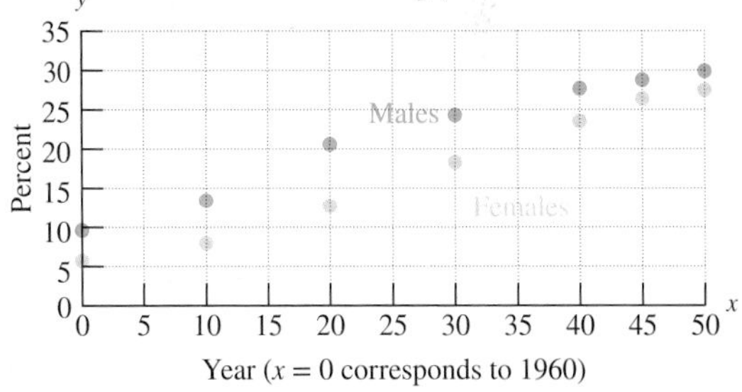

32. Use the data and graph from Exercise 31 to answer the questions.

a. In which year was the difference in percentages between men and women with 4 or more years of college the greatest? 1980

b. In which year was the difference in percentages between men and women the least? 2010

c. If the trend continues beyond the data in the graph, does it seem possible that in the future, the percentage of women with 4 or more years of college will be greater than or equal to the percentage of men? Yes

Linear Equations in Two Variables

Section 3.2

Concepts

1. Definition of a Linear Equation in Two Variables
2. Graphing Linear Equations in Two Variables by Plotting Points
3. x- and y-Intercepts
4. Horizontal and Vertical Lines

1. Definition of a Linear Equation in Two Variables

Recall that an equation in the form $ax + b = c$, where $a \neq 0$, is called a linear equation in one variable. A solution to such an equation is a value of x that makes the equation a true statement. For example, $3x + 5 = -1$ has a solution of -2.

In this section, we will look at linear equations in *two* variables.

Linear Equation in Two Variables

Let A, B, and C be real numbers such that A and B are not both zero. Then, an equation that can be written in the form:

$$Ax + By = C$$

is called a **linear equation in two variables**.

The equation $x + y = 4$ is a linear equation in two variables. A solution to such an equation is an ordered pair (x, y) that makes the equation a true statement. Several solutions to the equation $x + y = 4$ are listed here:

Solution:	**Check:**
(x, y)	$x + y = 4$
$(2, 2)$	$(2) + (2) = 4$ ✓
$(1, 3)$	$(1) + (3) = 4$ ✓
$(4, 0)$	$(4) + (0) = 4$ ✓
$(-1, 5)$	$(-1) + (5) = 4$ ✓

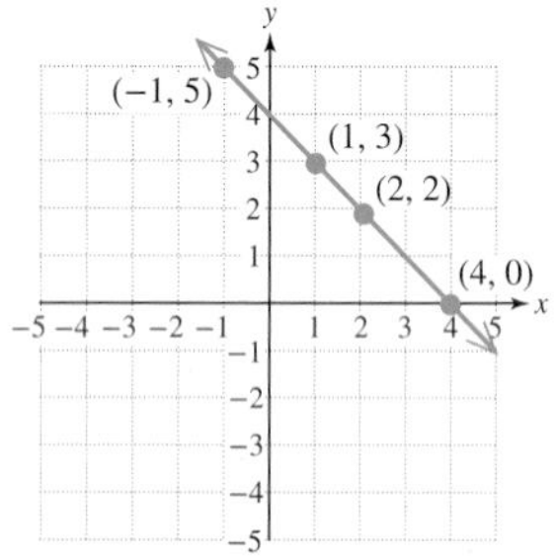

Figure 3-5

By graphing these ordered pairs, we see that the solution points line up (Figure 3-5).

Notice that there are infinitely many solutions to the equation $x + y = 4$ so they cannot all be listed. Therefore, to visualize all solutions to the equation $x + y = 4$, we draw the line through the points in the graph. Every point on the line represents an ordered pair solution to the equation $x + y = 4$, and the line represents the set of *all* solutions to the equation.

Classroom Examples: p. 213, Exercises 10 and 12

Example 1 Determining Solutions to a Linear Equation

For the linear equation, $6x - 5y = 12$, determine whether the given ordered pair is a solution.

a. $(2, 0)$ **b.** $(3, 1)$ **c.** $\left(1, -\frac{6}{5}\right)$

Solution:

a. $6x - 5y = 12$

$6(2) - 5(0) \stackrel{?}{=} 12$ Substitute $x = 2$ and $y = 0$.

$12 - 0 \stackrel{?}{=} 12$ ✓ True The ordered pair $(2, 0)$ is a solution.

b. $6x - 5y = 12$

$6(3) - 5(1) \stackrel{?}{=} 12$ Substitute $x = 3$ and $y = 1$.

$18 - 5 \neq 12$ The ordered pair $(3, 1)$ is *not* a solution.

c. $6x - 5y = 12$

$6(1) - 5\left(-\frac{6}{5}\right) \stackrel{?}{=} 12$ Substitute $x = 1$ and $y = -\frac{6}{5}$.

$6 + 6 \stackrel{?}{=} 12$ ✓ True The ordered pair $\left(1, -\frac{6}{5}\right)$ is a solution.

Skill Practice Given the equation $3x - 2y = -12$, determine whether the given ordered pair is a solution.

1. $(4, 0)$ **2.** $(-2, 3)$ **3.** $\left(1, \frac{15}{2}\right)$

2. Graphing Linear Equations in Two Variables by Plotting Points

In this section, we will graph linear equations in two variables.

Answers

1. No **2.** Yes **3.** Yes

The Graph of an Equation in Two Variables

The graph of an equation in two variables is the graph of all ordered pair solutions to the equation.

The word *linear* means "relating to or resembling a line." It is not surprising then that the solution set for any linear equation in two variables forms a line in a rectangular coordinate system. Because two points determine a line, to graph a linear equation it is sufficient to find two solution points and draw the line between them. We will find three solution points and use the third point as a check point. This process is demonstrated in Example 2.

Example 2 Graphing a Linear Equation

Classroom Example: p. 213, Exercise 18

Graph the equation $x - 2y = 8$.

Solution:

We will find three ordered pairs that are solutions to $x - 2y = 8$. To find the ordered pairs, choose an arbitrary value of x or y. Three choices are recorded in the table. To complete the table, individually substitute each choice into the equation and solve for the missing variable. The substituted value and the solution to the equation form an ordered pair.

x	y	
2		→ (2,)
	−1	→ (, −1)
0		→ (0,)

TIP: Usually we try to choose arbitrary values that will be convenient to graph.

From the first row, substitute $x = 2$:

$$x - 2y = 8$$
$$(2) - 2y = 8$$
$$-2y = 6$$
$$y = -3$$

From the second row, substitute $y = -1$:

$$x - 2y = 8$$
$$x - 2(-1) = 8$$
$$x + 2 = 8$$
$$x = 6$$

From the third row, substitute $x = 0$:

$$x - 2y = 8$$
$$(0) - 2y = 8$$
$$-2y = 8$$
$$y = -4$$

The completed table is shown with the corresponding ordered pairs.

x	y	
2	−3	→ (2, −3)
6	−1	→ (6, −1)
0	−4	→ (0, −4)

To graph the equation, plot the three solutions and draw the line through the points (Figure 3-6).

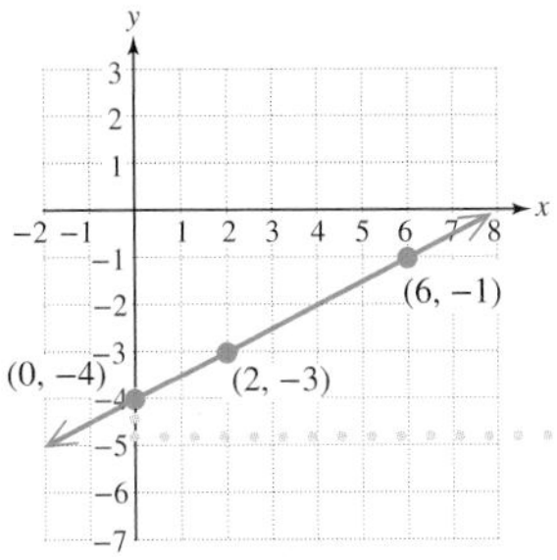

Figure 3-6

Avoiding Mistakes

Only two points are needed to graph a line. However, in Example 2, we found a third ordered pair, (0, −4). Notice that this point "lines up" with the other two points. If the three points do not line up, then we know that a mistake was made in solving for at least one of the ordered pairs.

Skill Practice

4. Graph the equation $2x + y = 6$.

Answer

4.

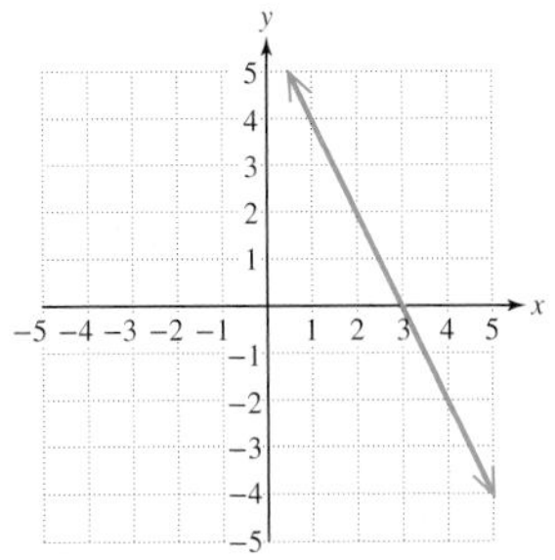

In Example 2, the original values for x and y given in the table were chosen arbitrarily by the authors. It is important to note, however, that once you choose an arbitrary value for x, the corresponding y-value is determined by the equation. Similarly, once you choose an arbitrary value for y, the x-value is determined by the equation.

Classroom Example: p. 213, Exercise 22

Example 3 Graphing a Linear Equation

Graph the equation $4x + 3y = 15$.

Solution:

We will find three ordered pairs that are solutions to the equation $4x + 3y = 15$. In the table, we have selected arbitrary values for x and y and must complete the ordered pairs. Notice that in this case, we are choosing zero for x and zero for y to illustrate that the resulting equation is often easy to solve.

x	y	
0		→ (0,)
	0	→ (, 0)
3		→ (3,)

From the first row, substitute $x = 0$:

$$4x + 3y = 15$$
$$4(0) + 3y = 15$$
$$3y = 15$$
$$y = 5$$

From the second row, substitute $y = 0$:

$$4x + 3y = 15$$
$$4x + 3(0) = 15$$
$$4x = 15$$
$$x = \frac{15}{4} \text{ or } 3\frac{3}{4}$$

From the third row, substitute $x = 3$:

$$4x + 3y = 15$$
$$4(3) + 3y = 15$$
$$12 + 3y = 15$$
$$3y = 3$$
$$y = 1$$

The completed table is shown with the corresponding ordered pairs.

x	y	
0	5	→ (0, 5)
$3\frac{3}{4}$	0	→ $(3\frac{3}{4}, 0)$
3	1	→ (3, 1)

To graph the equation, plot the three solutions and draw the line through the points (Figure 3-7).

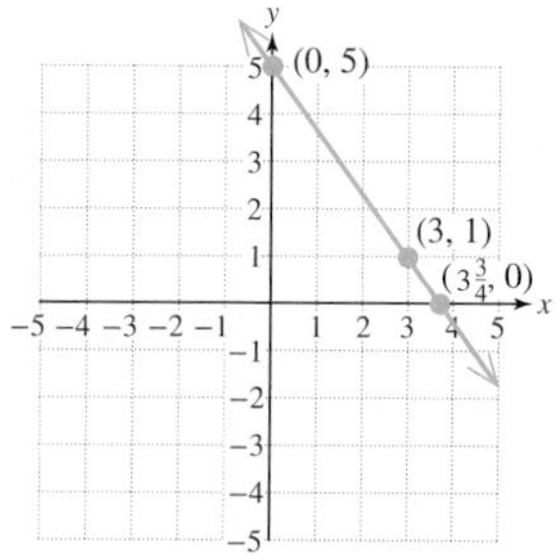

Figure 3-7

Skill Practice

5. Graph the equation $2x + 3y = 12$.

Answer

5.
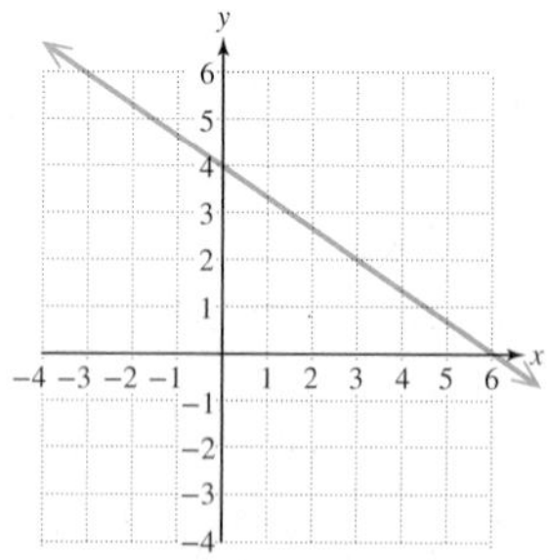

Example 4 Graphing a Linear Equation

Graph the equation $y = -\frac{1}{3}x + 1$.

Solution:

Because the y-variable is isolated in the equation, it is easy to substitute a value for x and simplify the right-hand side to find y. Since any number for x can be chosen, select numbers that are multiples of 3. These will simplify easily when multiplied by $-\frac{1}{3}$.

Classroom Example: p. 215, Exercise 38

x	y
3	
0	
−3	

$$y = -\frac{1}{3}x + 1$$

Let $x = 3$:

$$y = -\frac{1}{3}(3) + 1$$
$$y = -1 + 1$$
$$y = 0$$

Let $x = 0$:

$$y = -\frac{1}{3}(0) + 1$$
$$y = 0 + 1$$
$$y = 1$$

Let $x = -3$:

$$y = -\frac{1}{3}(-3) + 1$$
$$y = 1 + 1$$
$$y = 2$$

x	y	
3	0	→ (3, 0)
0	1	→ (0, 1)
−3	2	→ (−3, 2)

The line through the three ordered pairs (3, 0), (0, 1), and (−3, 2) is shown in Figure 3-8. The line represents the set of all solutions to the equation $y = -\frac{1}{3}x + 1$.

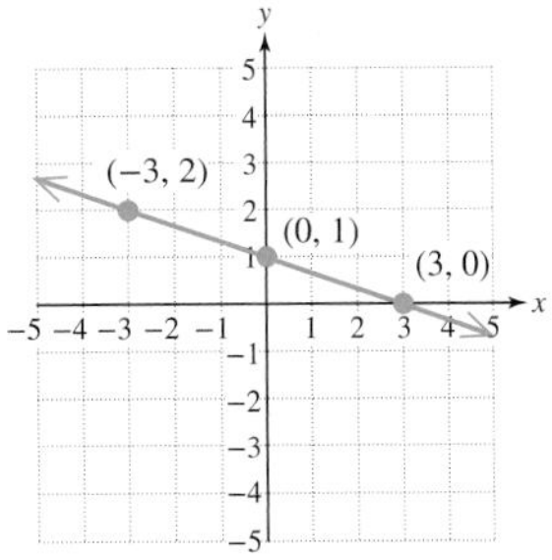

Figure 3-8

Skill Practice

6. Graph the equation $y = \frac{1}{2}x + 3$.

3. *x*- and *y*-Intercepts

The x- and y-intercepts are the points where the graph intersects the x- and y-axes, respectively. From Example 4, we see that the x-intercept is at the point (3, 0) and the y-intercept is at the point (0, 1). See Figure 3-8. Notice that a y-intercept is a point on the y-axis and must have an x-coordinate of 0. Likewise, an x-intercept is a point on the x-axis and must have a y-coordinate of 0.

Definitions of *x*- and *y*-Intercepts

An ***x*-intercept** of a graph is a point $(a, 0)$ where the graph intersects the x-axis.

A ***y*-intercept** of a graph is a point $(0, b)$ where the graph intersects the y-axis.

In some applications, an x-intercept is defined as the x-coordinate of a point of intersection that a graph makes with the x-axis. For example, if an x-intercept is at the point (3, 0), it is sometimes stated simply as 3 (the y-coordinate is assumed to be 0). Similarly, a y-intercept is sometimes defined as the y-coordinate of a point of intersection that a graph makes with the y-axis. For example, if a y-intercept is at the point (0, 7), it may be stated simply as 7 (the x-coordinate is assumed to be 0).

Although any two points may be used to graph a line, in some cases it is convenient to use the x- and y-intercepts of the line. To find the x- and y-intercepts of any two-variable equation in x and y, follow these steps:

Finding *x*- and *y*-Intercepts

- Find the x-intercept(s) by substituting $y = 0$ into the equation and solving for x.
- Find the y-intercept(s) by substituting $x = 0$ into the equation and solving for y.

Answer

6.

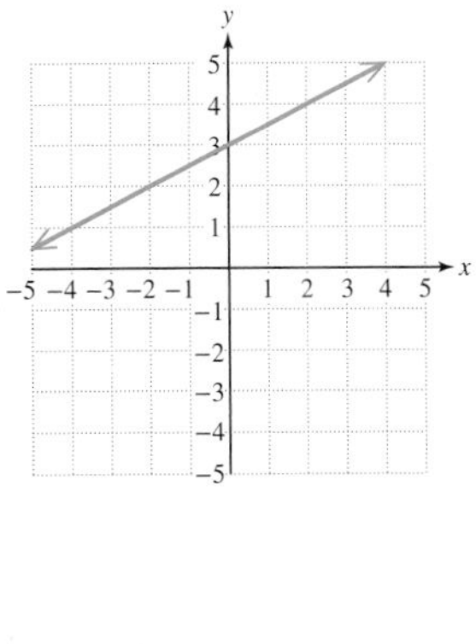

Classroom Example: p. 216, Exercise 50

Example 5 Finding the *x*- and *y*-Intercepts of a Line

Given the equation $-3x + 2y = 8$,

a. Find the x-intercept.

b. Find the y-intercept.

c. Graph the equation.

Solution:

a. To find the x-intercept, substitute $y = 0$.

$$-3x + 2y = 8$$
$$-3x + 2(0) = 8$$
$$-3x = 8$$
$$\frac{-3x}{-3} = \frac{8}{-3}$$
$$x = -\frac{8}{3}$$

The x-intercept is $(-\frac{8}{3}, 0)$.

b. To find the y-intercept, substitute $x = 0$.

$$-3x + 2y = 8$$
$$-3(0) + 2y = 8$$
$$2y = 8$$
$$y = 4$$

The y-intercept is $(0, 4)$.

Avoiding Mistakes

Be sure to write the x- and y-intercepts as two separate ordered pairs: $(-\frac{8}{3}, 0)$ and $(0, 4)$.

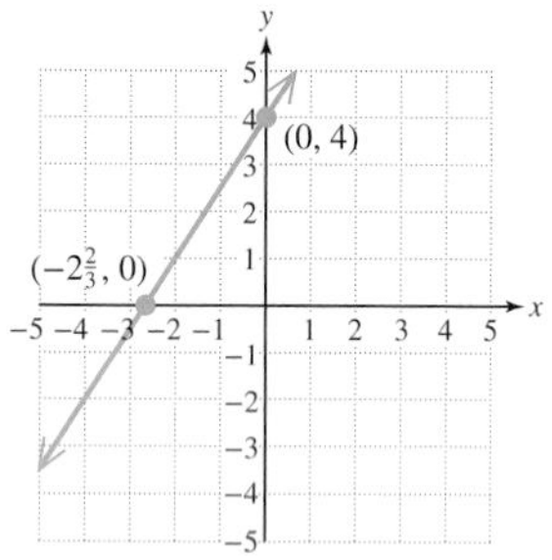

Figure 3-9

c. The line through the ordered pairs $(-\frac{8}{3}, 0)$ and $(0, 4)$ is shown in Figure 3-9. Note that the point $(-\frac{8}{3}, 0)$ can be written as $(-2\frac{2}{3}, 0)$.

The line represents the set of all solutions to the equation $-3x + 2y = 8$.

Skill Practice Given the equation $x - 3y = -4$,

7. Find the x-intercept. **8.** Find the y-intercept. **9.** Graph the equation.

Classroom Example: p. 216, Exercise 56

Example 6 Finding the *x*- and *y*-Intercepts of a Line

Given the equation $4x + 5y = 0$,

a. Find the x-intercept.

b. Find the y-intercept.

c. Graph the equation.

Solution:

a. To find the x-intercept, substitute $y = 0$.

$$4x + 5y = 0$$
$$4x + 5(0) = 0$$
$$4x = 0$$
$$x = 0$$

The x-intercept is $(0, 0)$.

b. To find the y-intercept, substitute $x = 0$.

$$4x + 5y = 0$$
$$4(0) + 5y = 0$$
$$5y = 0$$
$$y = 0$$

The y-intercept is $(0, 0)$.

Answers

7. $(-4, 0)$ **8.** $\left(0, \frac{4}{3}\right)$

9.

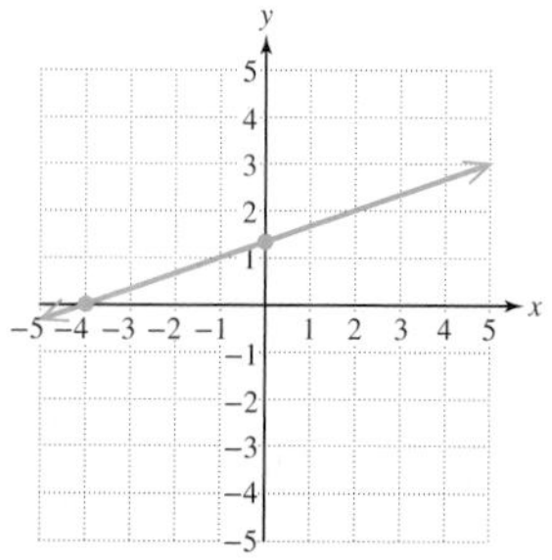

c. Because the x-intercept and the y-intercept are the same point (the origin), one or more additional points are needed to graph the line. In the table, we have arbitrarily selected additional values for x and y to find two more points on the line.

x	y
-5	
	2

<u>Let $x = -5$:</u>

$$4x + 5y = 0$$
$$4(-5) + 5y = 0$$
$$-20 + 5y = 0$$
$$5y = 20$$
$$y = 4$$

$(-5, 4)$ is a solution.

<u>Let $y = 2$:</u>

$$4x + 5y = 0$$
$$4x + 5(2) = 0$$
$$4x + 10 = 0$$
$$4x = -10$$
$$x = -\frac{10}{4}$$
$$x = -\frac{5}{2}$$

$(-\frac{5}{2}, 2)$ is a solution.

The line through the ordered pairs $(0, 0)$, $(-5, 4)$, and $(-\frac{5}{2}, 2)$ is shown in Figure 3-10. Note that the point $(-\frac{5}{2}, 2)$ can be written as $(-2\frac{1}{2}, 2)$.

The line represents the set of all solutions to the equation $4x + 5y = 0$.

x	y
-5	4
$-\frac{5}{2}$	2
0	0

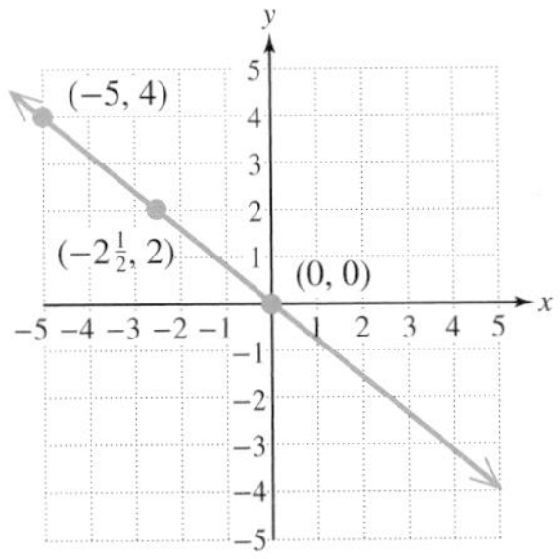

Figure 3-10

Avoiding Mistakes

Do not try to graph a line given only one point. There are infinitely many lines that pass through a single point.

Skill Practice Given the equation $2x - 3y = 0$,

10. Find the x-intercept. **11.** Find the y-intercept.

12. Graph the equation. (*Hint:* You may need to find an additional point.)

Instructor Note: Have students go back to the definition of a linear equation in two variables. Ask how equations like $x = 3$ and $y = -2$ fit the requirements of a linear equation in two variables.

4. Horizontal and Vertical Lines

Recall that a linear equation can be written in the form $Ax + By = C$, where A and B are not both zero. However, if A or B is 0, then the line is either horizontal or vertical. A horizontal line either lies on the x-axis or is parallel to the x-axis. A vertical line either lies on the y-axis or is parallel to the y-axis.

Equations of Vertical and Horizontal Lines

1. A **vertical line** can be represented by an equation of the form $x = k$, where k is a constant.
2. A **horizontal line** can be represented by an equation of the form $y = k$, where k is a constant.

Answers

10. (0, 0) **11.** (0, 0)

12.

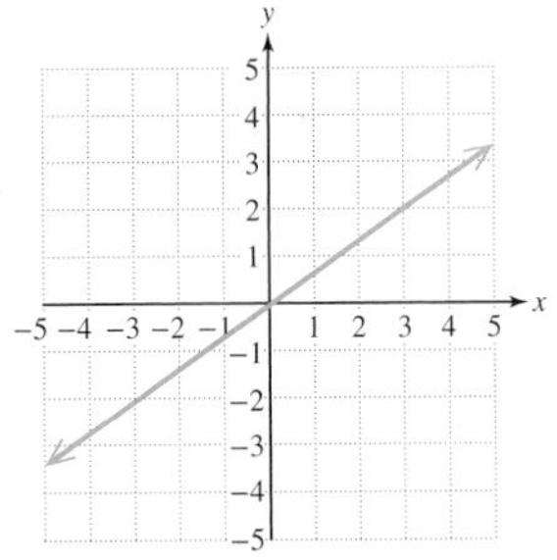

Classroom Example: p. 217, Exercise 68

Example 7 Graphing a Horizontal Line

Graph the equation $y = 3$.

Solution:

Because this equation is in the form $y = k$, the line is horizontal and must cross the y-axis at $y = 3$ (Figure 3-11).

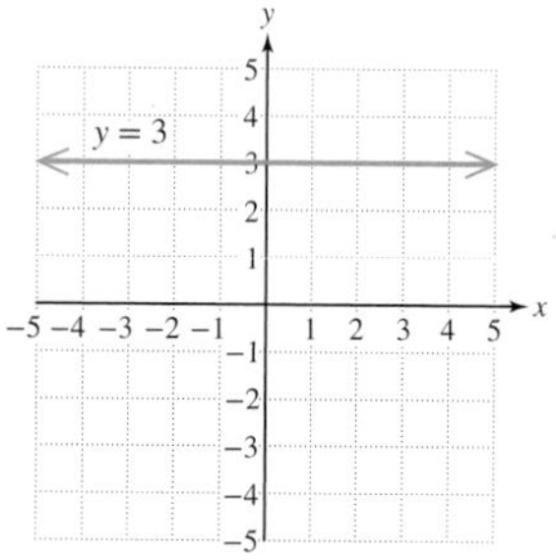

Figure 3-11

TIP: Notice that a horizontal line has a y-intercept, but does not have an x-intercept (unless the horizontal line is the x-axis itself).

Alternative Solution:

Create a table of values for the equation $y = 3$. The choice for the y-coordinate must be 3, but x can be any real number.

x	y
0	3
1	3
2	3

x can be any number. y must be 3.

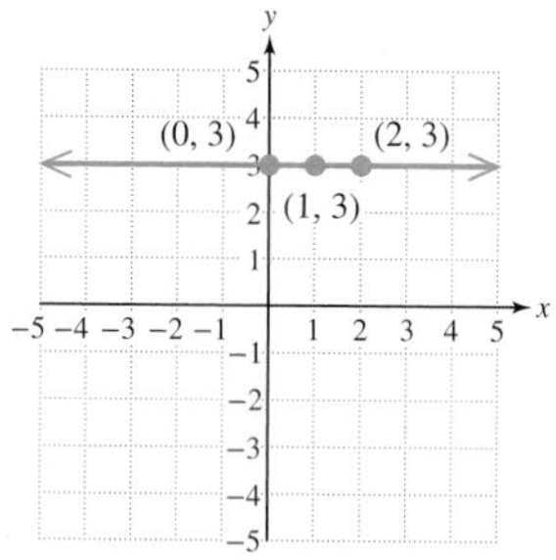

Skill Practice

13. Graph the equation. $y = -2$

Classroom Example: p. 217, Exercise 70

Example 8 Graphing a Vertical Line

Graph the equation $7x = -14$.

Solution:

Because the equation does not have a y-variable, we can solve the equation for x.

$$7x = -14 \qquad \text{is equivalent to} \qquad x = -2$$

This equation is in the form $x = k$, indicating that the line is vertical and must cross the x-axis at $x = -2$ (Figure 3-12).

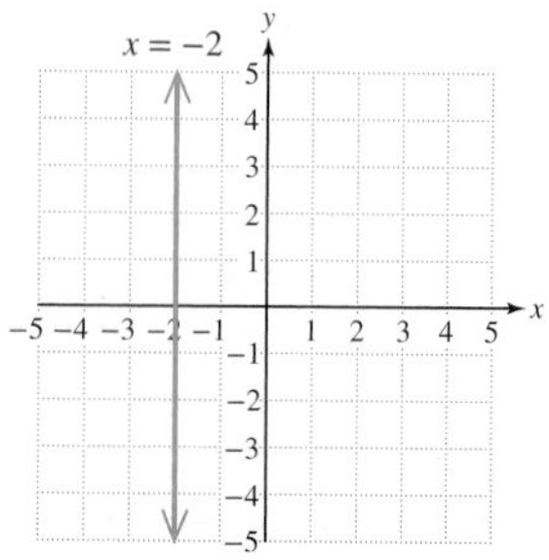

Figure 3-12

Answer

13.

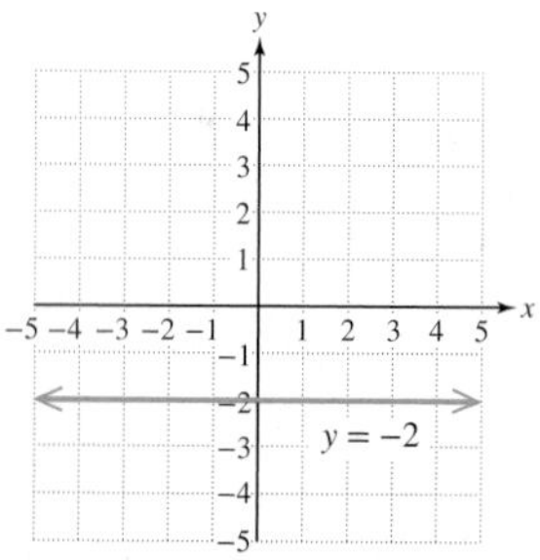

Alternative Solution:

Create a table of values for the equation $x = -2$. The choice for the x-coordinate must be -2, but y can be any real number.

x	y
−2	0
−2	3
−2	−4

x must be −2. y can be any number.

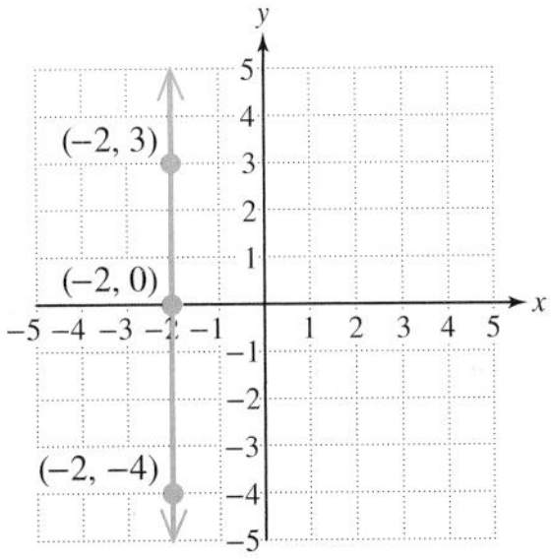

TIP: Notice that a vertical line has an x-intercept but does not have a y-intercept (unless the vertical line is the y-axis itself).

Skill Practice

14. Graph the equation. $3x = 12$

Answer

14.

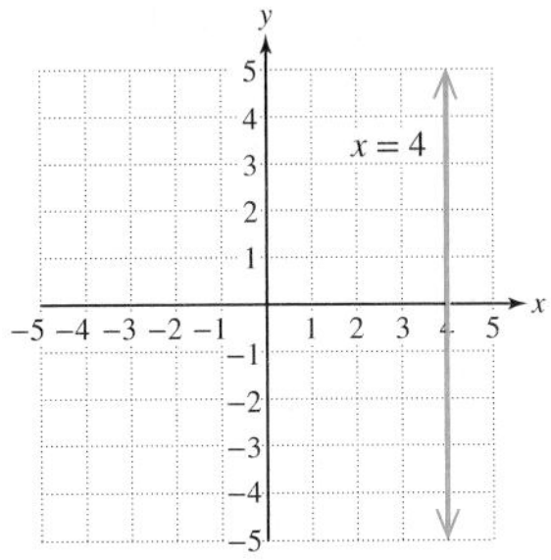

Calculator Connections

Topic: Graphing Linear Equations on an Appropriate Viewing Window

A viewing window of a graphing calculator shows a portion of a rectangular coordinate system. The standard viewing window for many calculators shows the x-axis between -10 and 10 and the y-axis between -10 and 10 (Figure 3-13). Furthermore, the scale defined by the "tick" marks on both the x- and y-axes is usually set to 1.

The "Standard Viewing Window"

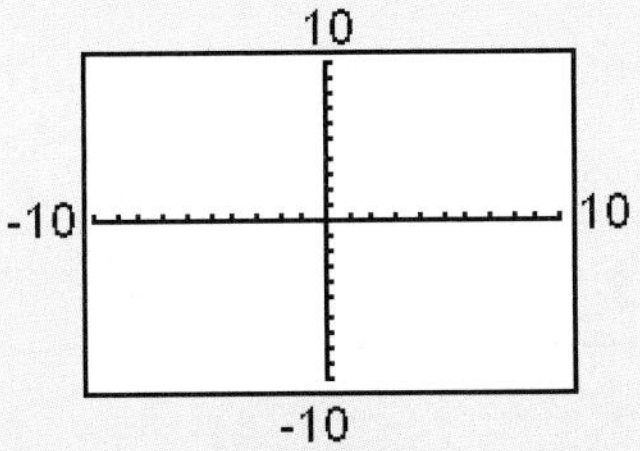

Figure 3-13

To graph an equation in x and y on a graphing calculator, the equation must be written with the y-variable isolated. For example, to graph the equation $x + 3y = 3$, we solve for y by applying the steps for solving a literal equation. The result, $y = -\frac{1}{3}x + 1$, can now be entered into a graphing calculator. To enter the equation $y = -\frac{1}{3}x + 1$, use parentheses around the fraction $\frac{1}{3}$. The *Graph* option displays the graph of the line.

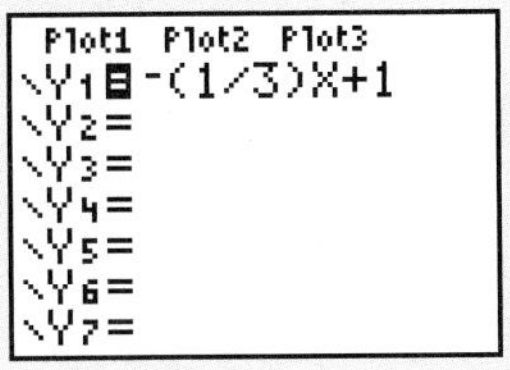

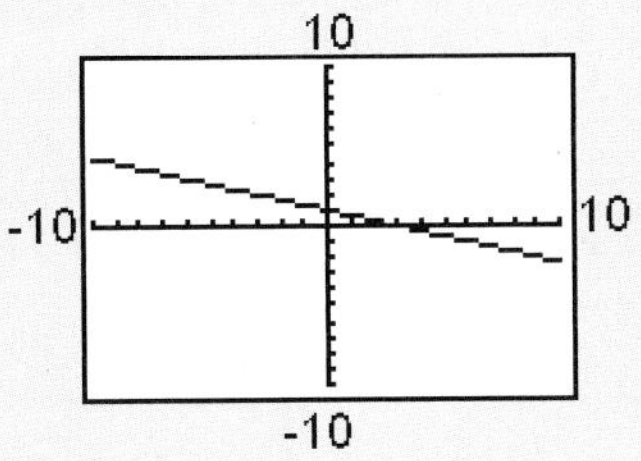

Sometimes the standard viewing window does not provide an adequate display for the graph of an equation. For example, the graph of $y = -x + 15$ is visible only in a small portion of the upper right corner of the standard viewing window.

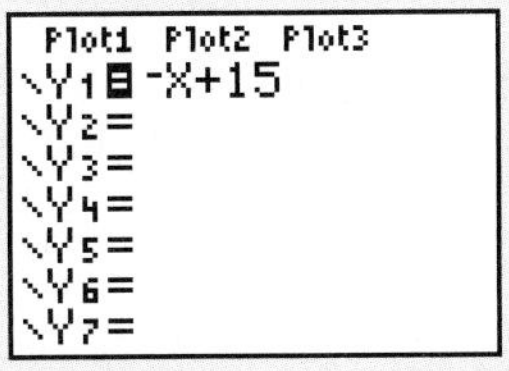

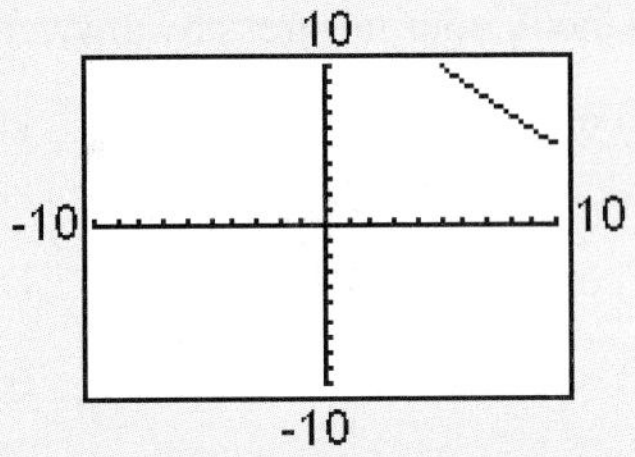

To see where this line crosses the x- and y-axes, we can change the viewing window to accommodate larger values of x and y. Most calculators have a *Range* feature or *Window* feature that allows the user to change the minimum and maximum x- and y-values.

To get a better picture of the equation $y = -x + 15$, change the minimum x-value to -10 and the maximum x-value to 20. Similarly, use a minimum y-value of -10 and a maximum y-value of 20.

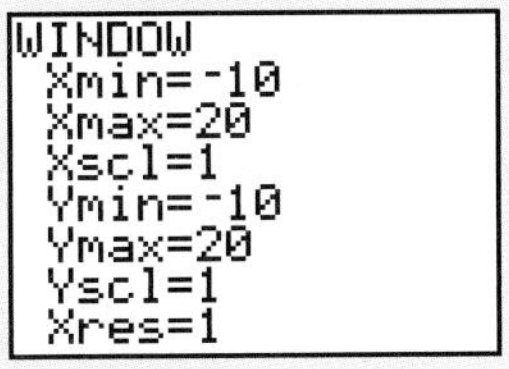

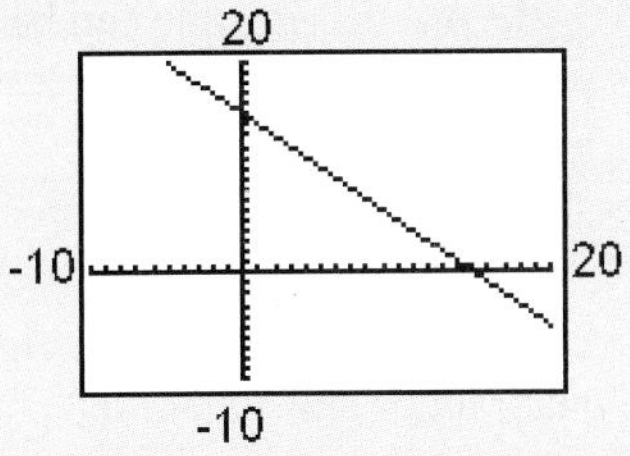

Calculator Exercises

For Exercises 1–8, graph the equations on the standard viewing window.

1. $y = -2x + 5$

2. $y = 3x - 1$

3. $y = \frac{1}{2}x - \frac{7}{2}$

4. $y = -\frac{3}{4}x + \frac{5}{3}$

5. $4x - 7y = 21$

6. $2x + 3y = 12$

7. $-3x - 4y = 6$

8. $-5x + 4y = 10$

For Exercises 9–12, graph the equations on the given viewing window.

9. $y = 3x + 15$ Window: $-10 \le x \le 10$
$-5 \le y \le 20$

10. $y = -2x - 25$ Window: $-30 \le x \le 30$
$-30 \le y \le 30$

Xscl = 3 (sets the x-axis tick marks to increments of 3)

Yscl = 3 (sets the y-axis tick marks to increments of 3)

11. $y = -0.2x + 0.04$

Window: $-0.1 \le x \le 0.3$
$-0.1 \le y \le 0.1$

Xscl = 0.01 (sets the x-axis tick marks to increments of 0.01)

Yscl = 0.01(sets the y-axis tick marks to increments of 0.01)

12. $y = 0.3x - 0.5$

Window: $-1 \le x \le 3$
$-1 \le y \le 1$

Xscl = 0.1 (sets the x-axis tick marks to increments of 0.1)

Yscl = 0.1 (sets the y-axis tick marks to increments of 0.1)

Section 3.2 Practice Exercises

For additional exercises, see Classroom Activities 3.2A–3.2C in the *Student's Resource Manual* at www.mhhe.com/moh.

Study Skills Exercise

Check your progress by answering these questions.

Yes ________ No ________ Did you have sufficient time to study for the test in the previous chapter? If not, what could you have done to create more time for studying?

Yes ________ No ________ Did you work all of the assigned homework problems in the previous chapter?

Yes ________ No ________ If you encountered difficulty, did you see your instructor or tutor for help?

Yes ________ No ________ Have you taken advantage of the textbook supplements such as the *Student Solutions Manual?*

Vocabulary and Key Concepts

1. a. A linear equation in two variables is an equation that can be written in the form $Ax + By = C$ where A and B are not both zero.

b. A point where a graph intersects the x-axis is called a(n) x-intercept.

c. A point where a graph intersects the y-axis is called a(n) y-intercept.

d. A vertical line can be represented by an equation of the form $x = k$, where k is a constant.

e. A horizontal line can be represented by an equation of the form $y = k$, where k is a constant.

Review Exercises

For Exercises 2–8, refer to the figure to give the coordinates of the labeled points, and state the quadrant or axis where the point is located.

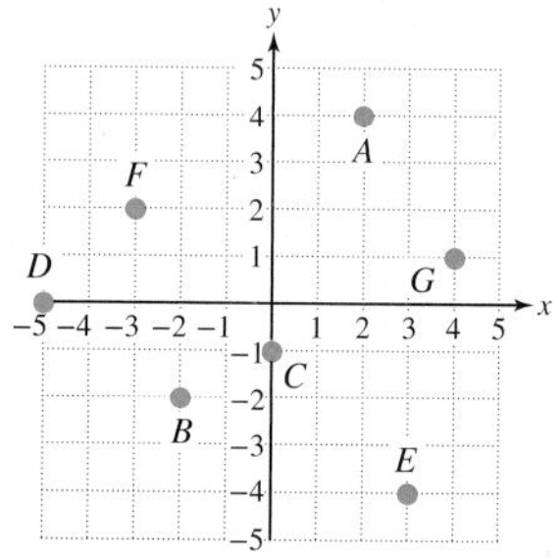

2. A (2, 4); quadrant I

3. B (−2, −2); quadrant III

4. C (0, −1); y-axis

5. D (−5, 0); x-axis

6. E (3, −4); quadrant IV

7. F (−3, 2); quadrant II

8. G (4, 1); quadrant I

Concept 1: Definition of a Linear Equation in Two Variables

For Exercises 9–17, determine whether the given ordered pair is a solution to the equation. **(See Example 1.)**

9. $x - y = 6$; $(8, 2)$ Yes

10. $y = 3x - 2$; $(1, 1)$ Yes

11. $y = -\frac{1}{3}x + 3$; $(-3, 4)$ Yes

12. $y = -\frac{5}{2}x + 5$; $\left(\frac{4}{5}, -3\right)$ No

13. $4x + 5y = 1$; $\left(\frac{1}{4}, -\frac{2}{5}\right)$ No

14. $y = 7$; $(0, 7)$ Yes

15. $y = -2$; $(-2, 6)$ No

16. $x = 1$; $(0, 1)$ No

17. $x = -5$; $(-5, 6)$ Yes

Concept 2: Graphing Linear Equations in Two Variables by Plotting Points

For Exercises 18–31, complete each table, and graph the corresponding ordered pairs. Draw the line defined by the points to represent all solutions to the equation. **(See Examples 2–4.)**

18. $x + y = 3$

x	y
2	1
0	3
−1	4
3	0

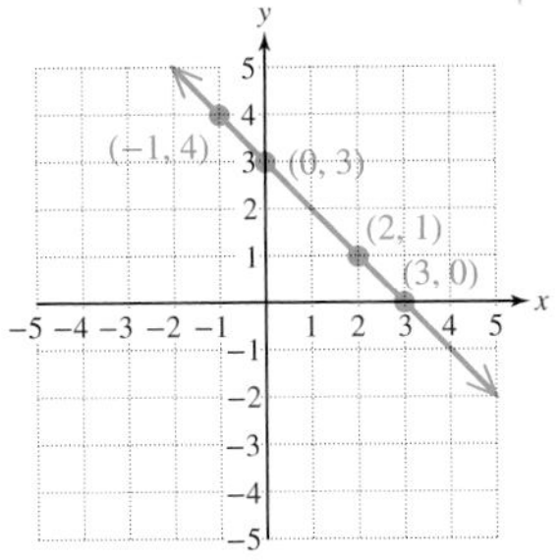

19. $x + y = -2$

x	y
1	−3
−2	0
−3	1
−4	2

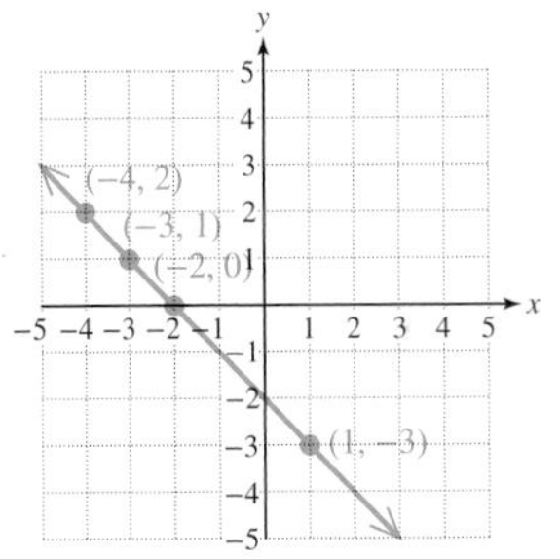

20. $y = 5x + 1$

x	y
1	6
0	1
−1	−4

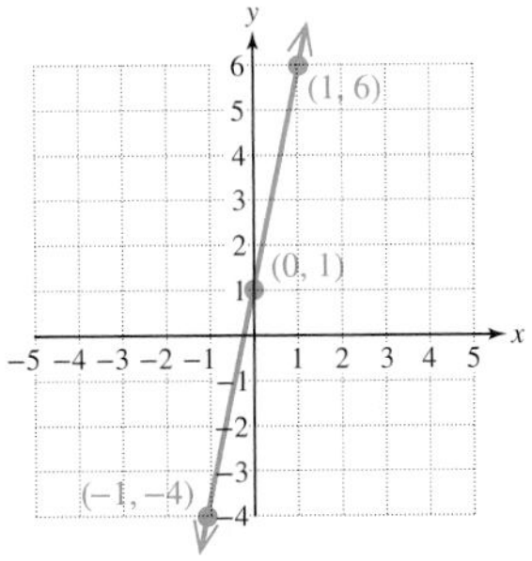

21. $y = -3x - 3$

x	y
−2	3
−1	0
−4	9

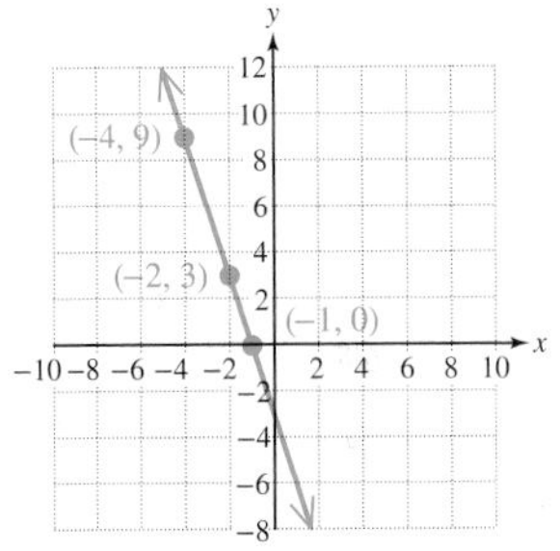

22. $2x - 3y = 6$

x	y
0	−2
3	0
2	−2/3

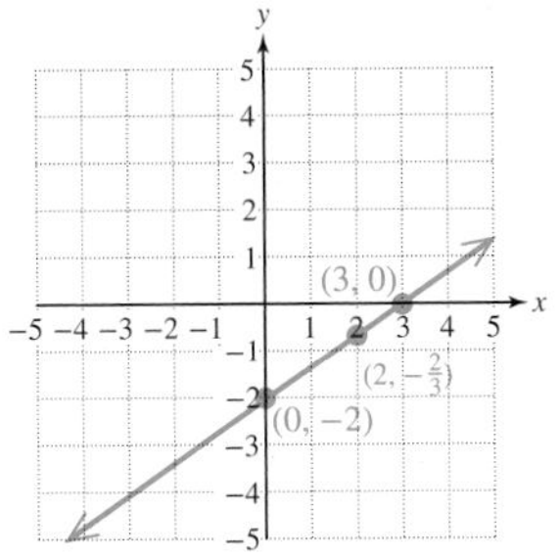

23. $4x + 2y = 8$

x	y
0	4
2	0
3	−2

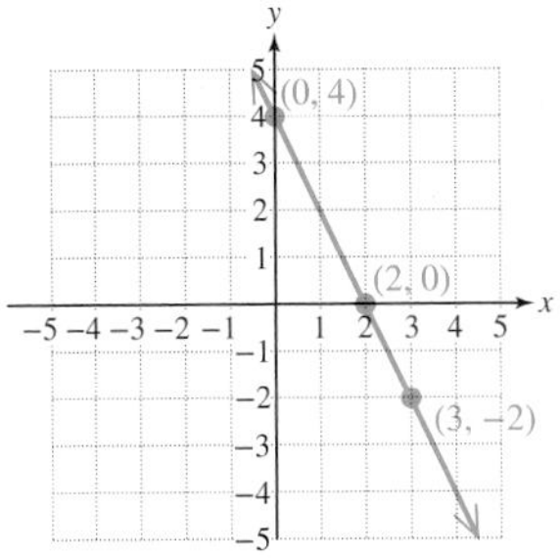

24. $y = \frac{2}{7}x - 5$

x	y
7	−3
−7	−7
0	−5

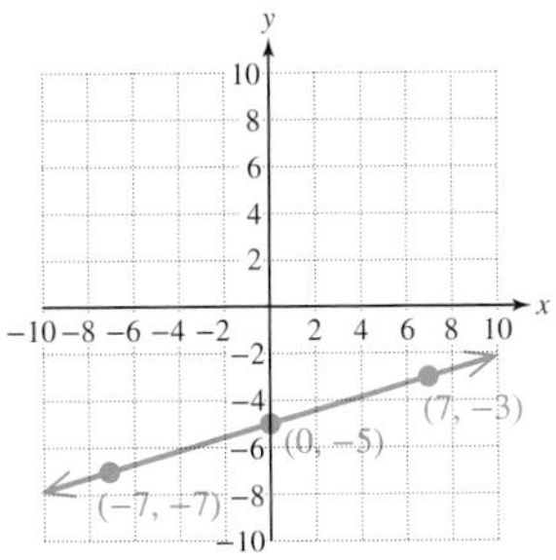

25. $y = -\frac{3}{5}x - 2$

x	y
0	−2
5	−5
10	−8

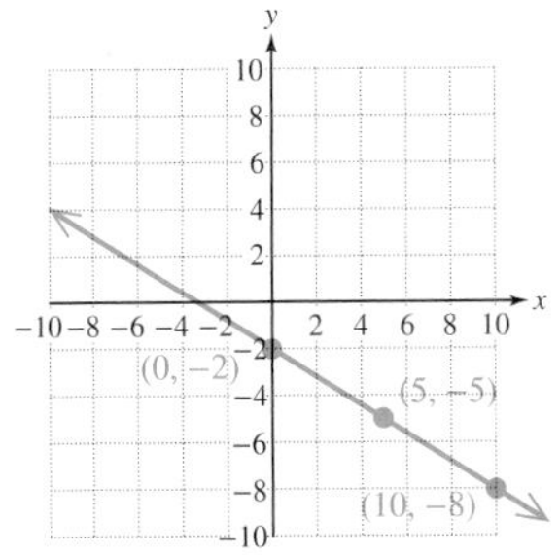

26. $y = 3$

x	y
2	3
0	3
−1	3

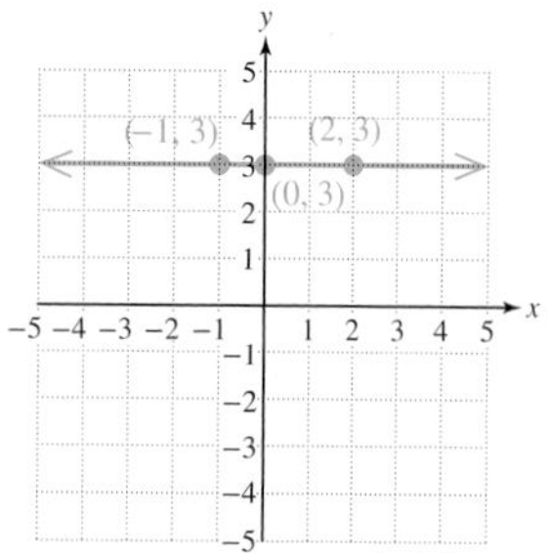

27. $y = -2$

x	y
0	−2
−3	−2
5	−2

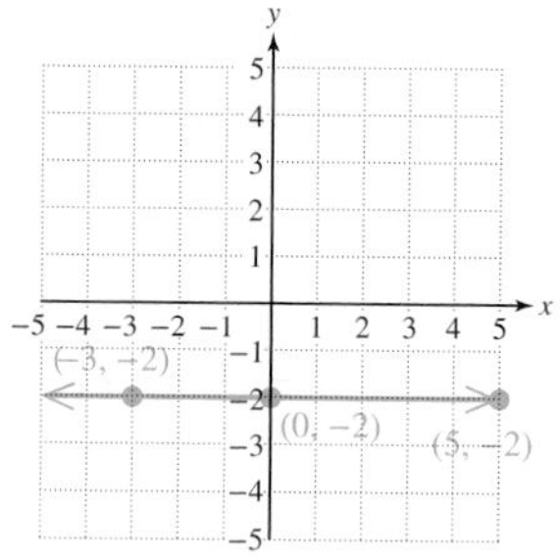

28. $x = -4$

x	y
−4	1
−4	−2
−4	4

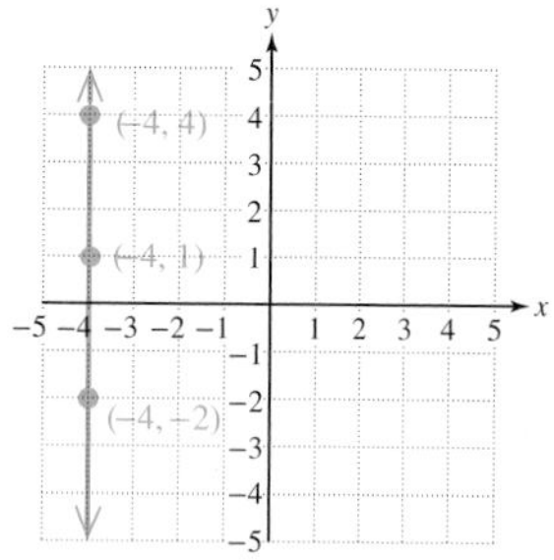

29. $x = \frac{3}{2}$

x	y
3/2	−1
3/2	2
3/2	−3

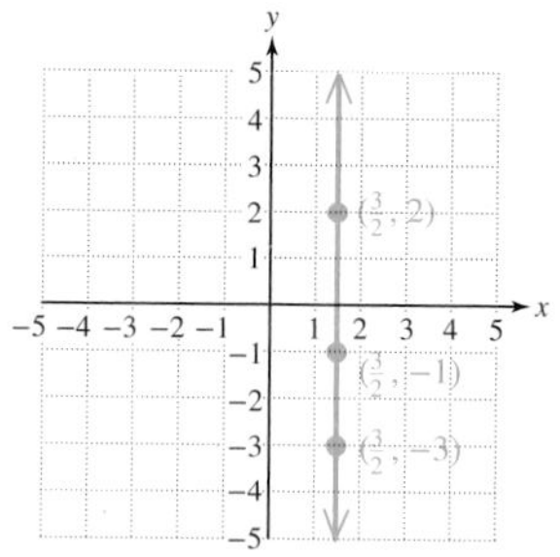

30. $y = -3.4x + 5.8$

x	y
0	5.8
1	2.4
2	−1

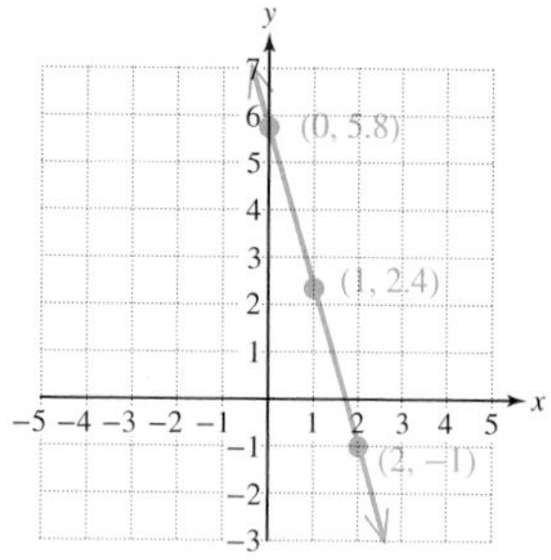

31. $y = -1.2x + 4.6$

x	y
0	4.6
1	3.4
2	2.2

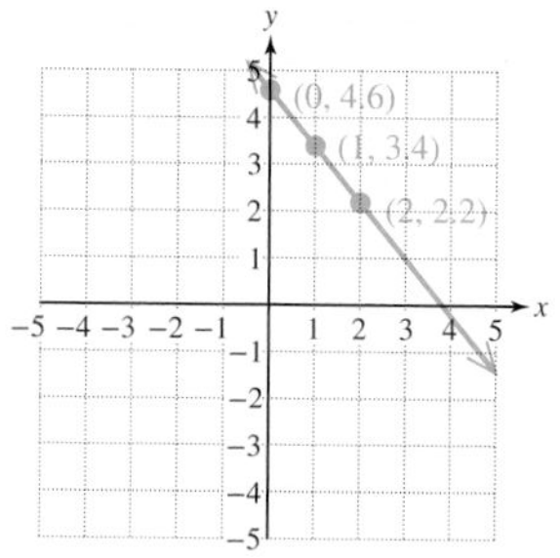

For Exercises 32–43, graph each line by making a table of at least three ordered pairs and plotting the points. **(See Example 4.)**

32. $x - y = 2$

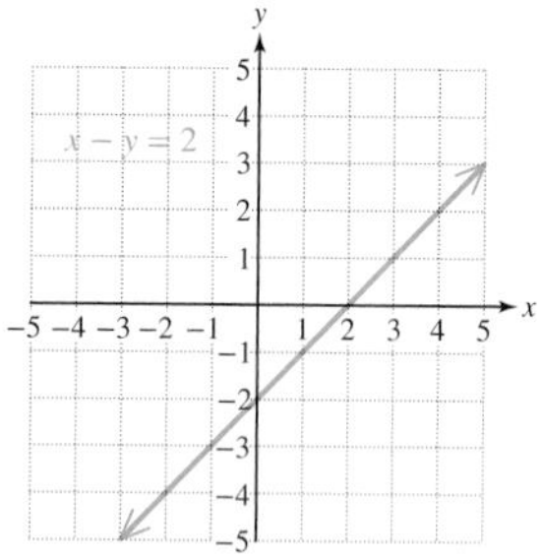

33. $x - y = 4$

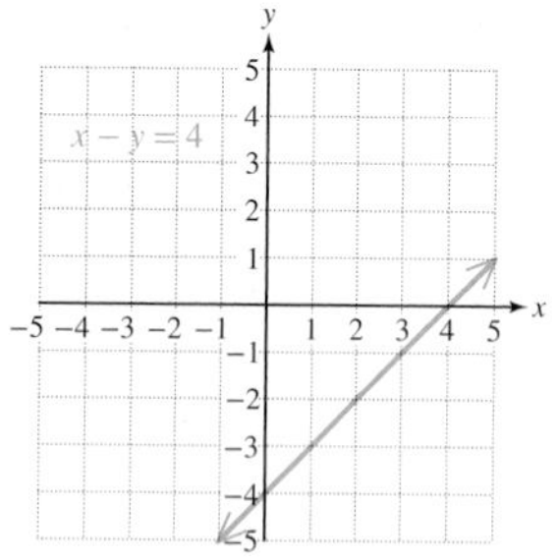

34. $-3x + y = -6$

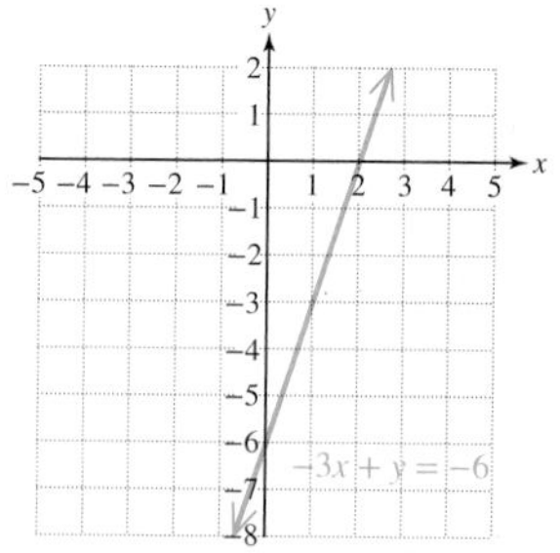

35. $2x - 5y = 10$

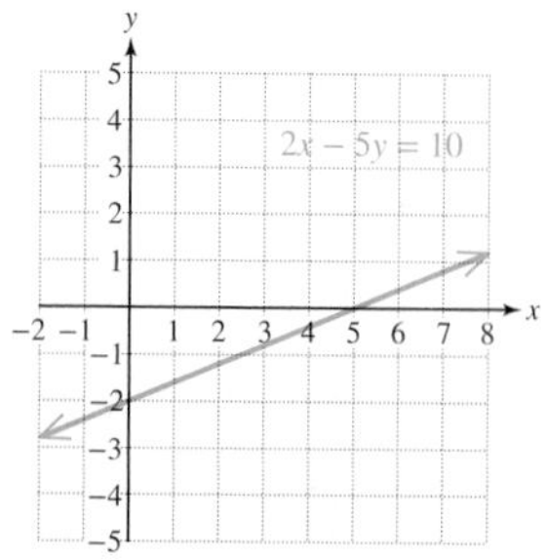

36. $y = 4x$

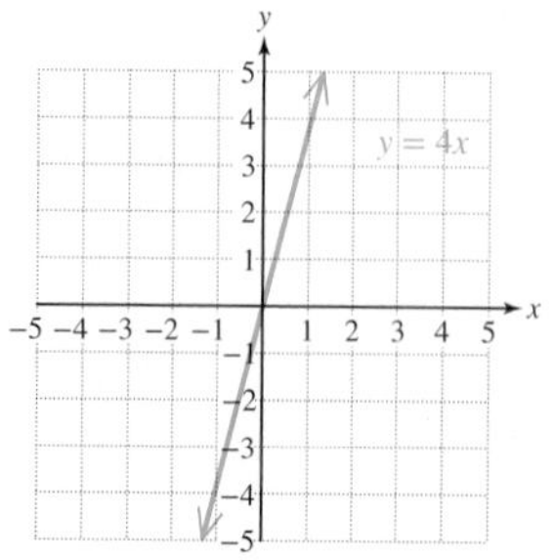

37. $y = -2x$

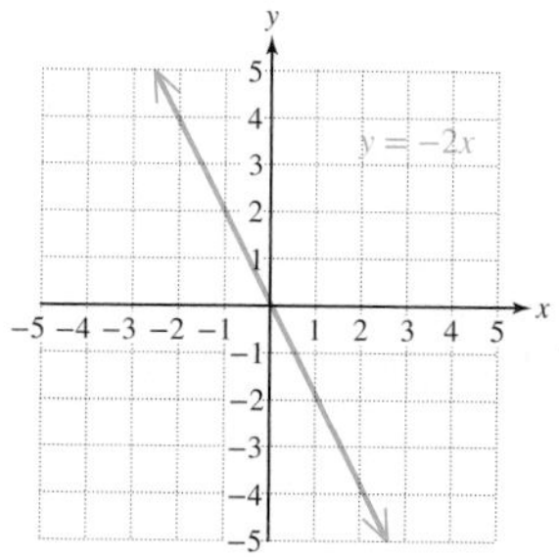

38. $y = -\frac{1}{2}x + 3$

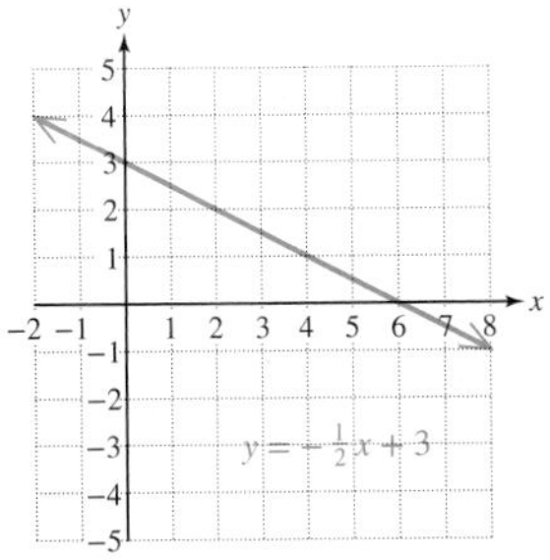

39. $y = \frac{1}{4}x - 2$

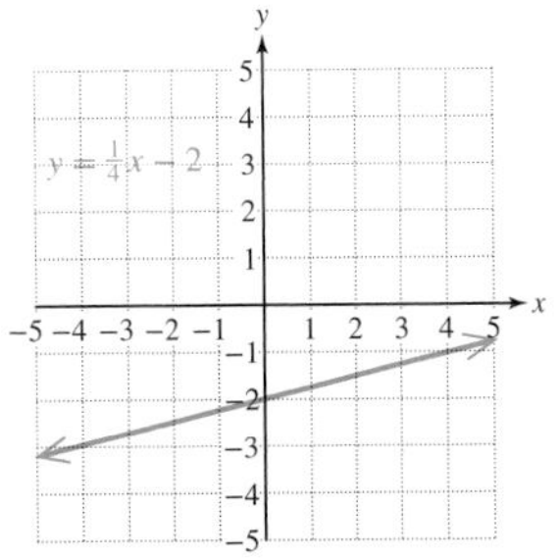

40. $x + y = 0$

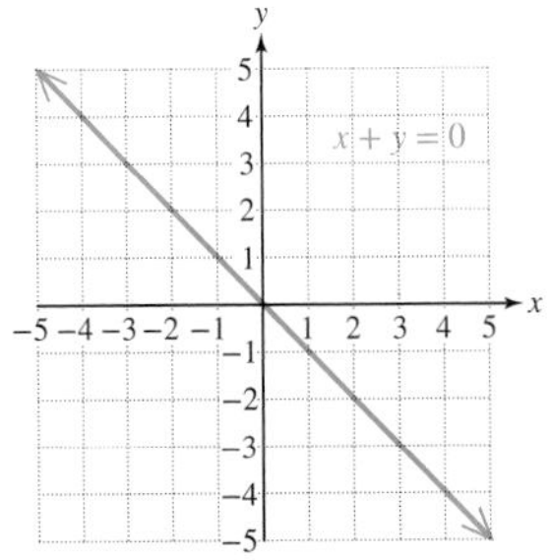

41. $-x + y = 0$

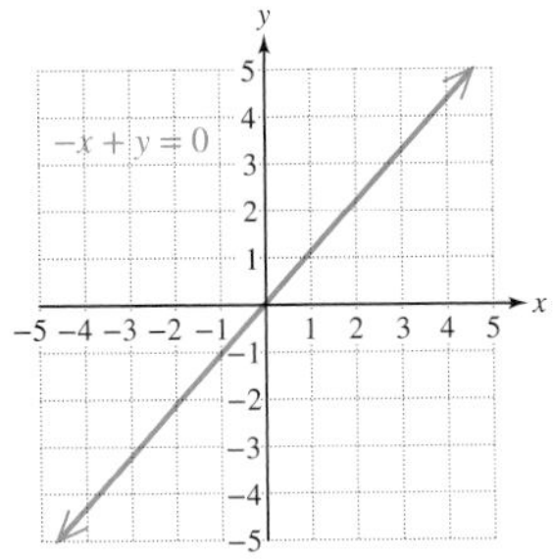

42. $50x - 40y = 200$

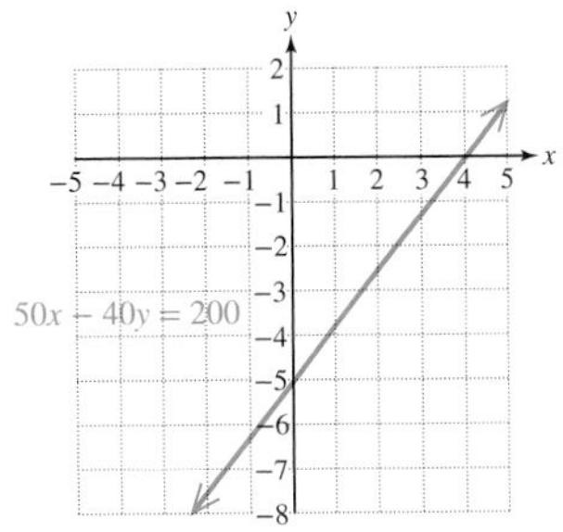

43. $-30x - 20y = 60$

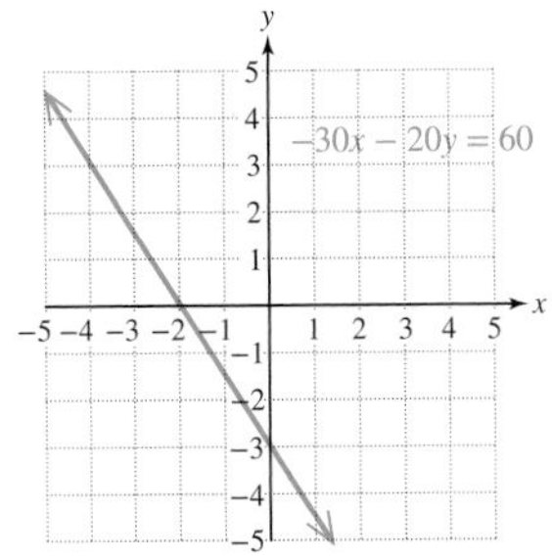

Concept 3: *x*- and *y*-Intercepts

44. The x-intercept is on which axis? x-axis

45. The y-intercept is on which axis? y-axis

For Exercises 46–49, estimate the coordinates of the x- and y-intercepts.

46.

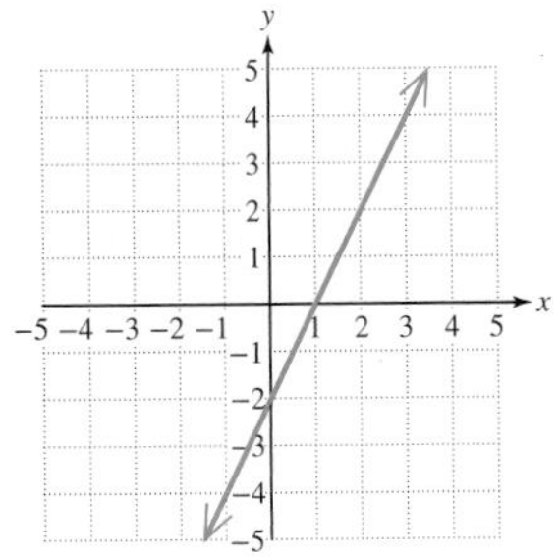

x-intercept: $(1, 0)$; y-intercept: $(0, -2)$

47.

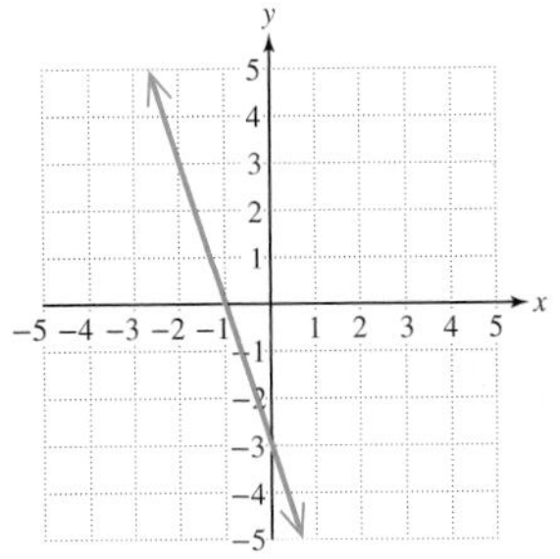

x-intercept: $(-1, 0)$; y-intercept: $(0, -3)$

48.

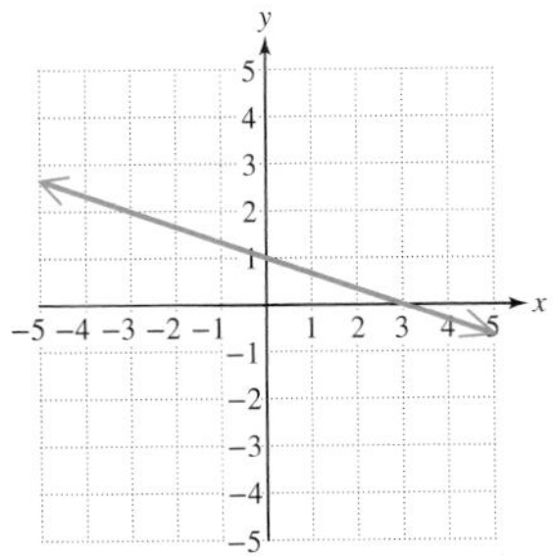

x-intercept: $(3, 0)$; y-intercept: $(0, 1)$

49.

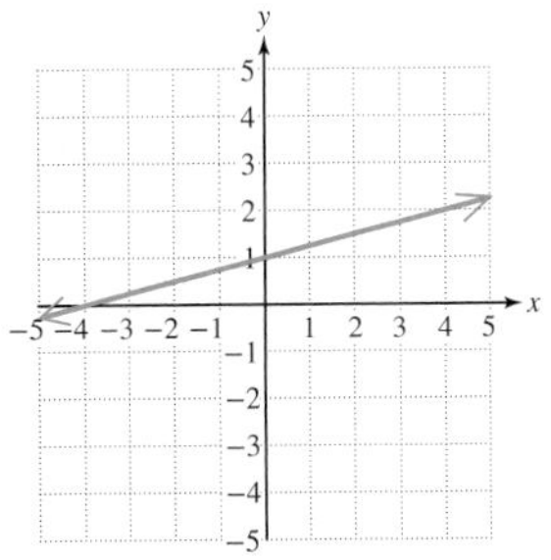

x-intercept: $(-4, 0)$; y-intercept: $(0, 1)$

For Exercises 50–61, find the x- and y-intercepts (if they exist), and graph the line. **(See Examples 5–6.)**

50. $5x + 2y = 5$ x-intercept: $(1, 0)$; y-intercept: $\left(0, \frac{5}{2}\right)$

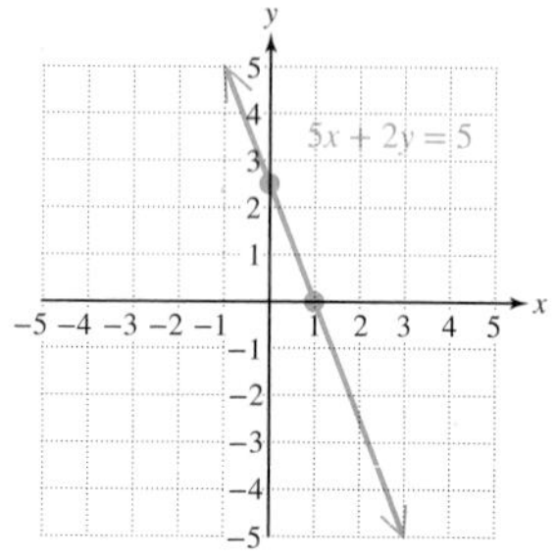

51. $4x - 3y = -9$ x-intercept: $\left(-\frac{9}{4}, 0\right)$; y-intercept: $(0, 3)$

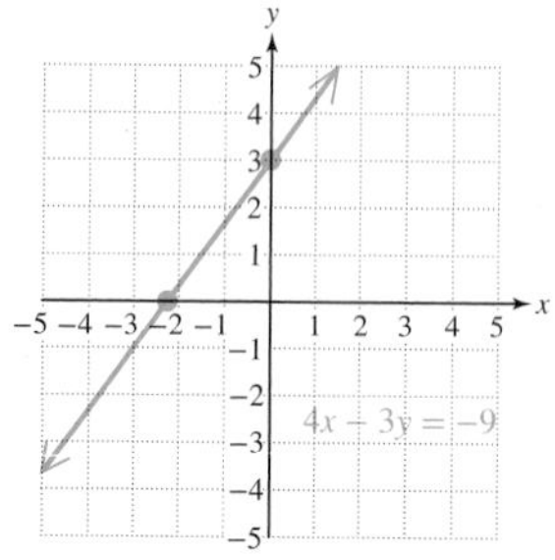

52. $y = \frac{2}{3}x - 1$ x-intercept: $\left(\frac{3}{2}, 0\right)$; y-intercept: $(0, -1)$

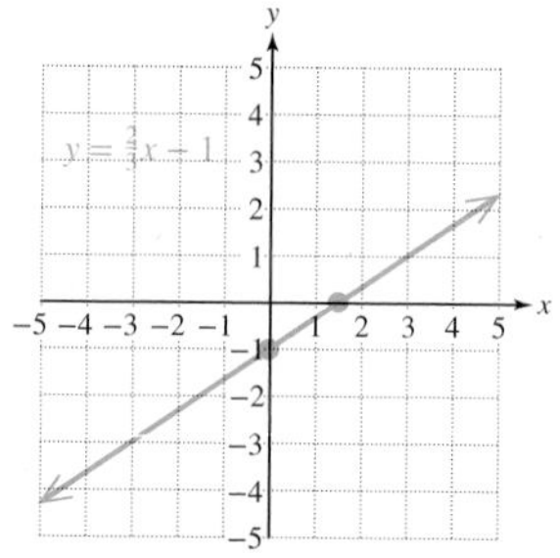

53. $y = -\frac{3}{4}x + 2$ x-intercept: $\left(\frac{8}{3}, 0\right)$; y-intercept: $(0, 2)$

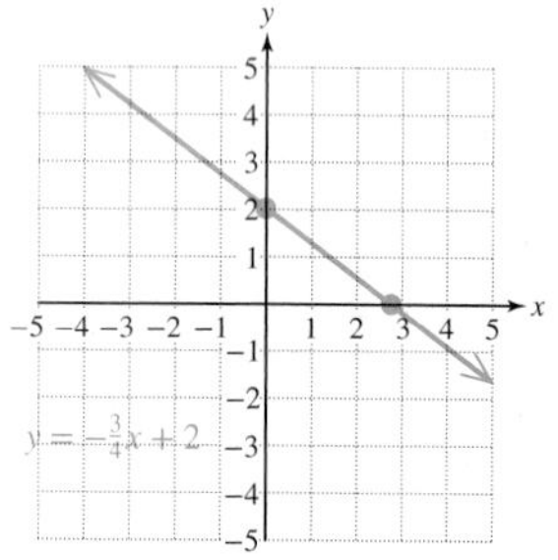

54. $x - 3 = y$ x-intercept: $(3, 0)$; y-intercept: $(0, -3)$

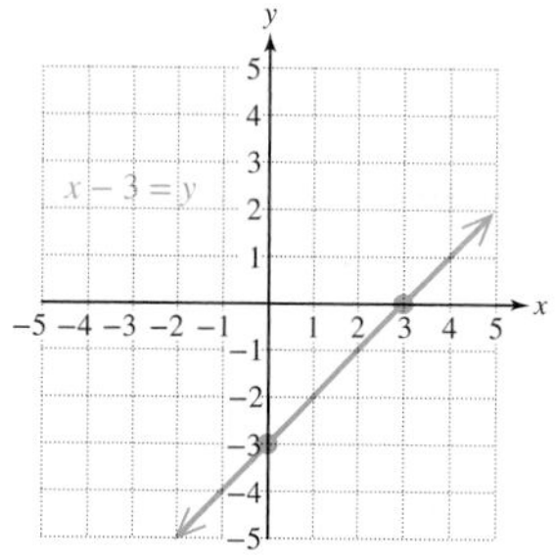

55. $2x + 8 = y$ x-intercept: $(-4, 0)$; y-intercept: $(0, 8)$

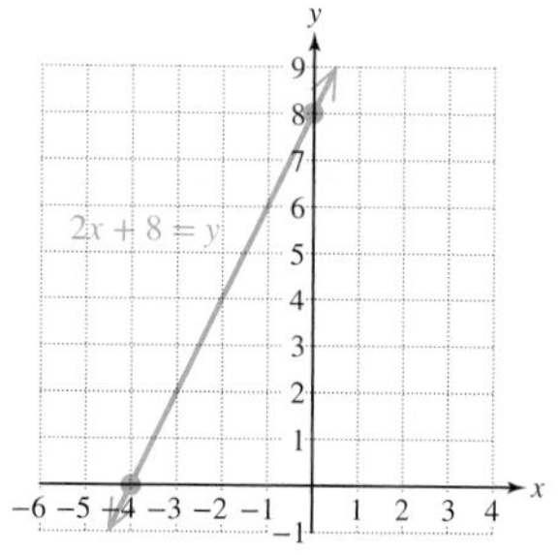

56. $-3x + y = 0$ x-intercept: $(0, 0)$; y-intercept: $(0, 0)$

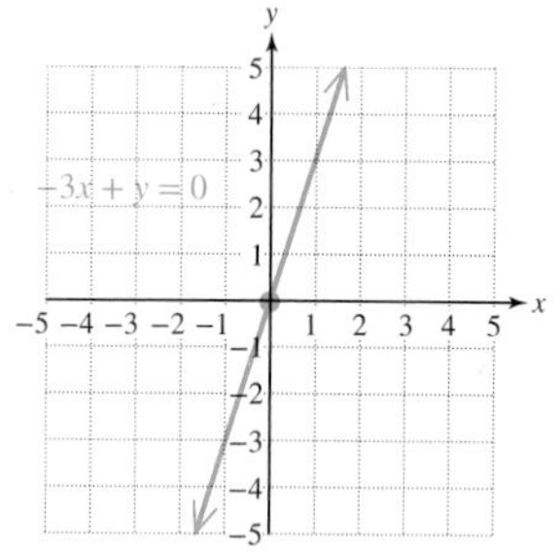

57. $2x - 2y = 0$ x-intercept: $(0, 0)$; y-intercept: $(0, 0)$

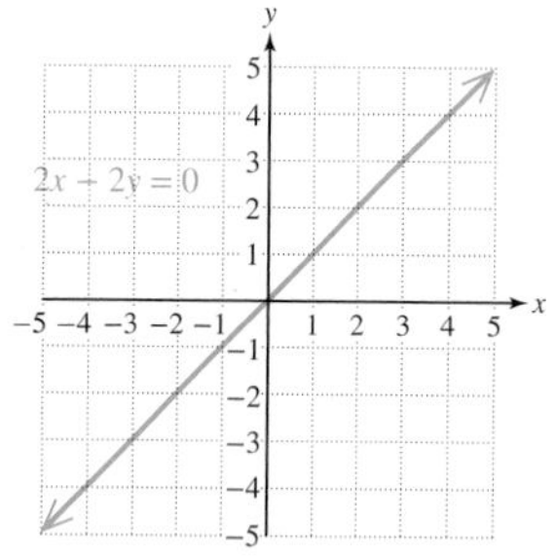

58. $25y = 10x + 100$ x-intercept: $(-10, 0)$; y-intercept: $(0, 4)$

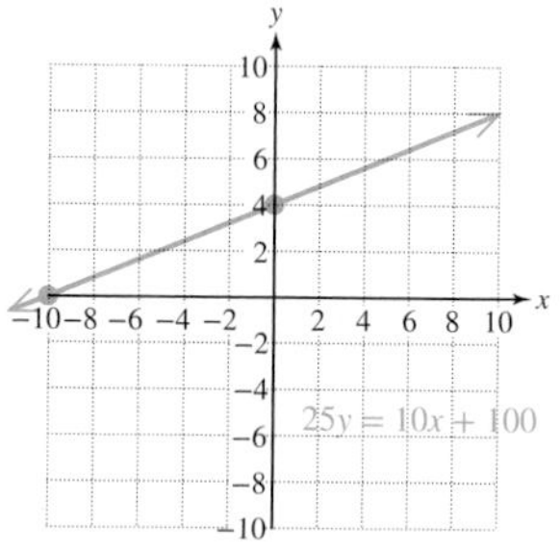

59. $20x = -40y + 200$
x-intercept: $(10, 0)$; y-intercept: $(0, 5)$

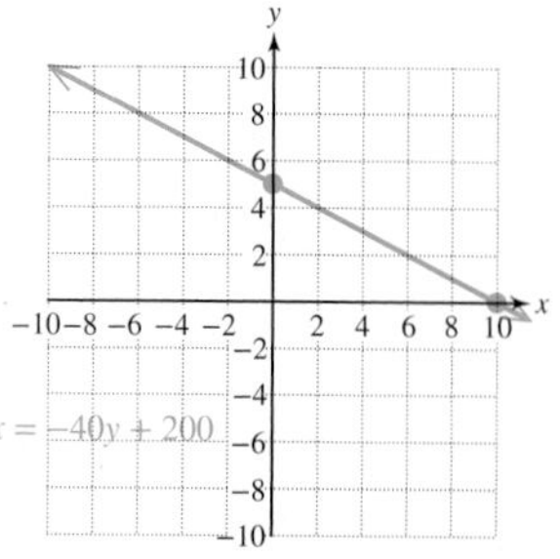

60. $x = 2y$
x-intercept: $(0, 0)$; y-intercept: $(0, 0)$

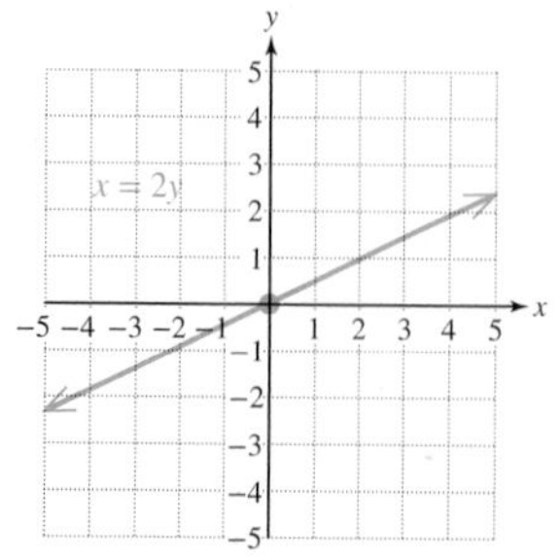

61. $x = -5y$
x-intercept: $(0, 0)$; y-intercept: $(0, 0)$

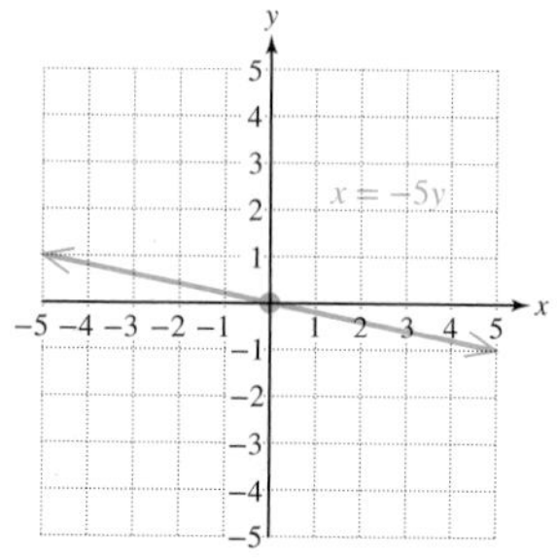

Concept 4: Horizontal and Vertical Lines

For Exercises 62–65, answer true or false. If the statement is false, rewrite it to be true.

62. The line defined by $x = 3$ is horizontal. False, $x = 3$ is vertical.

63. The line defined by $y = -4$ is horizontal. True

64. A line parallel to the y-axis is vertical. True

65. A line parallel to the x-axis is horizontal. True

For Exercises 66–74,

a. Identify the equation as representing a horizontal or vertical line.

b. Graph the line.

c. Identify the x- and y-intercepts if they exist. **(See Examples 7–8.)**

66. $x = 3$ a. Vertical line c. x-intercept: (3, 0); no y-intercept

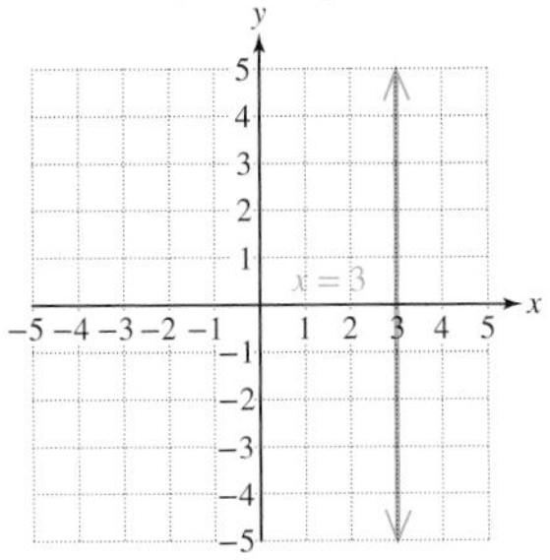

67. $y = -1$ a. Horizontal line c. no x-intercept; y-intercept: (0, −1)

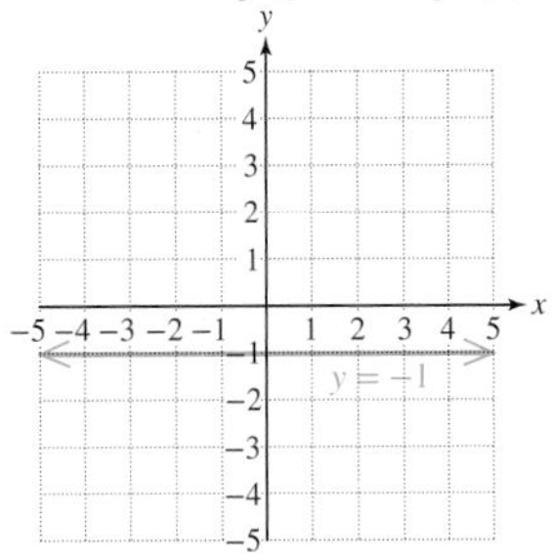

68. $-2y = 8$ a. Horizontal line c. no x-intercept; y-intercept: (0, −4)

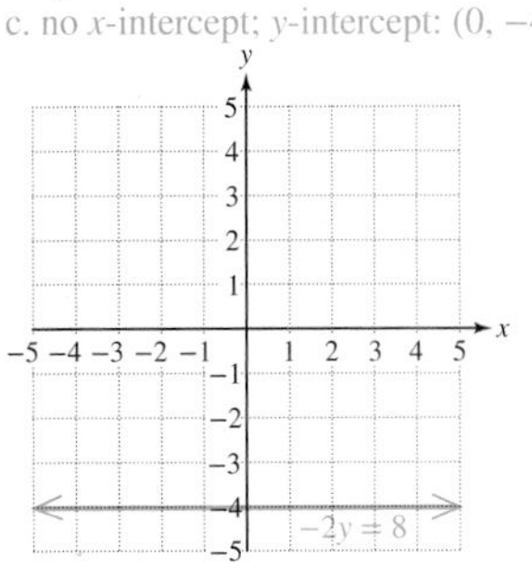

69. $5x = 20$ a. Vertical line c. x-intercept: (4, 0); no y-intercept

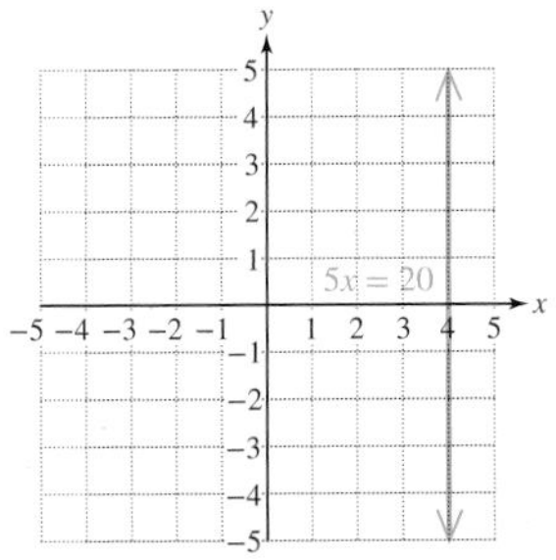

70. $x - 3 = -7$ a. Vertical line c. x-intercept: (−4, 0); no y-intercept

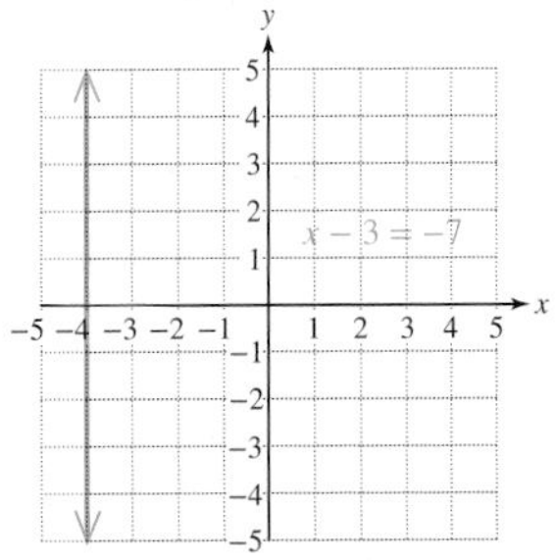

71. $y + 8 = 11$ a. Horizontal line c. no x-intercept; y-intercept: (0, 3)

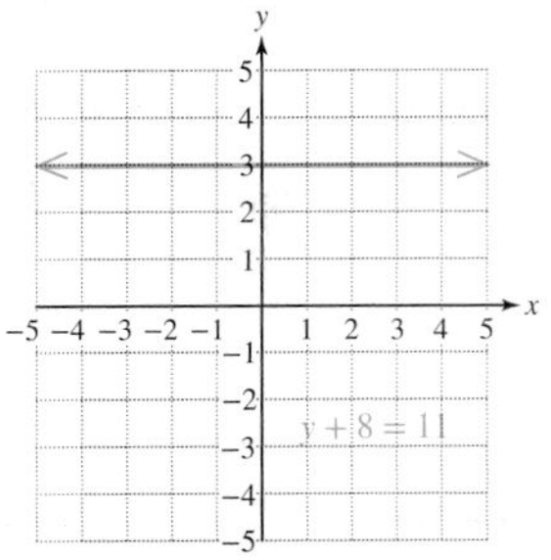

72. $3y = 0$ a. Horizontal line c. All points on the x-axis are x-intercepts; y-intercept: (0, 0)

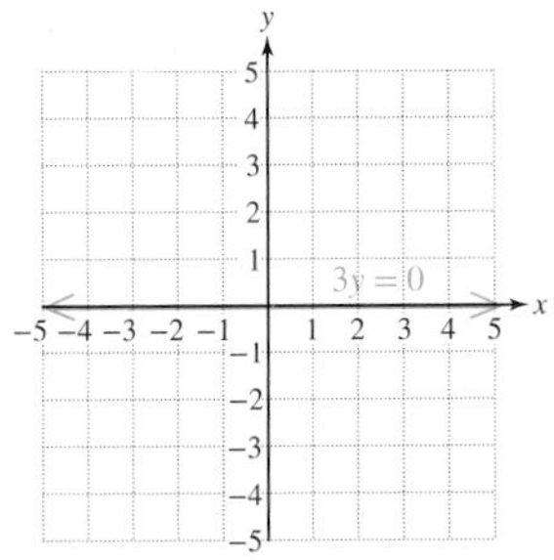

73. $5x = 0$ a. Vertical line c. All points on the y-axis are y-intercepts; x-intercept: (0, 0)

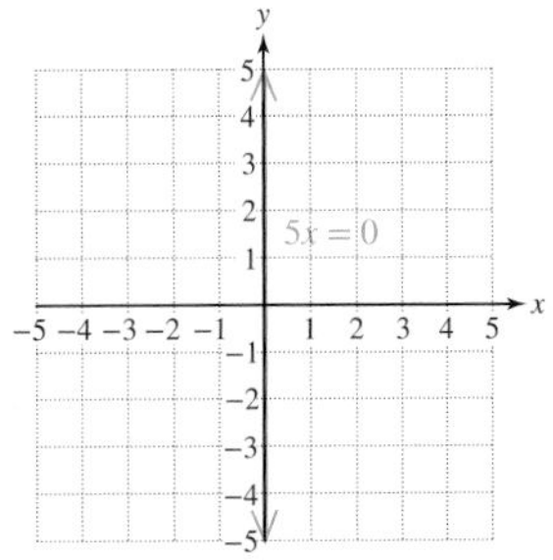

74. $2x + 7 = 10$ a. Vertical line c. x-intercept: $(\frac{3}{2}, 0)$; no y-intercept

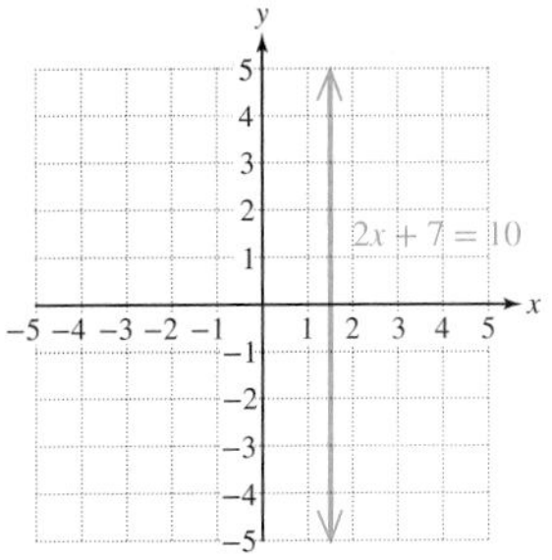

75. Explain why not every line has both an x- and a y-intercept. A horizontal line may not have an x-intercept. A vertical line may not have a y-intercept.

76. Which of the lines has an x-intercept?

a. $2x - 3y = 6$ **b.** $x = 5$ **c.** $2y = 8$ **d.** $-x + y = 0$ a, b, d

77. Which of the lines has a y-intercept?

a. $y = 2$ **b.** $x + y = 0$ **c.** $2x - 10 = 2$ **d.** $x + 4y = 8$ a, b, d

Expanding Your Skills

78. The store "CDs R US" sells all compact discs for \$13.99. The following equation represents the revenue, y, (in dollars) generated by selling x CDs.

$$y = 13.99x \quad (x \geq 0)$$

a. Find y when $x = 13$. $y = 181.87$

b. Find x when $y = 279.80$. $x = 20$

c. Write the ordered pairs from parts (a) and (b), and interpret their meaning in the context of the problem. (13, 181.87) Selling 13 compact discs yields \$181.87 in revenue. (20, 279.80) Selling 20 compact discs yields \$279.80 in revenue.

d. Graph the ordered pairs and the line defined by the points.

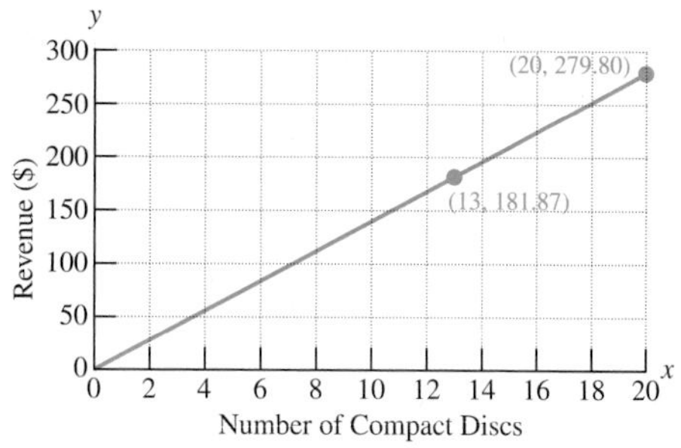

79. The value of a car depreciates once it is driven off of the dealer's lot. For a certain sub-compact car, the value of the car is given by the equation $y = -1025x + 12{,}215$ $(x \geq 0)$ where y is the value of the car in dollars x years after its purchase.

a. Find y when $x = 1$. $y = 11{,}190$

b. Find x when $y = 9140$. $x = 3$

c. Write the ordered pairs from parts (a) and (b), and interpret their meaning in the context of the problem. (1, 11,190) One year after purchase the value of the car is \$11,190. (3, 9140) Three years after purchase the value of the car is \$9140.

Section 3.3 Slope of a Line and Rate of Change

Concepts

1. Introduction to Slope
2. Slope Formula
3. Parallel and Perpendicular Lines
4. Applications of Slope: Rate of Change

1. Introduction to Slope

The x- and y-intercepts represent the points where a line crosses the x- and y-axes. Another important feature of a line is its slope. Geometrically, the slope of a line measures the "steepness" of the line. For example, two hiking trails are depicted by the lines in Figure 3-14.

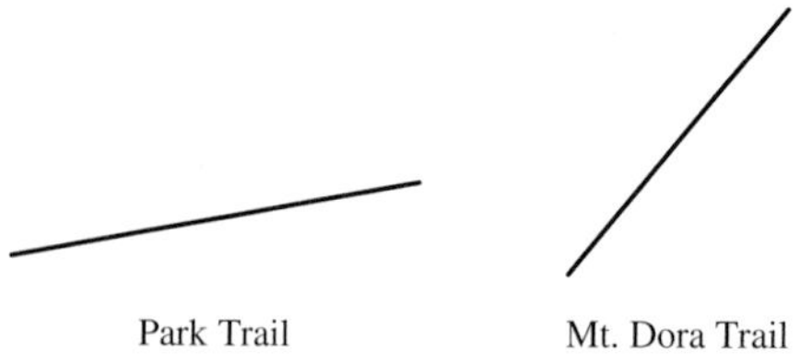

Figure 3-14

By visual inspection, Mt. Dora Trail is "steeper" than Park Trail. To measure the slope of a line quantitatively, consider two points on the line. The **slope** of the line is the ratio of the vertical change (change in y) between the two points and the horizontal change (change in x). As a memory device, we might think of the slope of a line as "rise over run." See Figure 3-15.

Animation

$$\text{Slope} = \frac{\text{change in } y}{\text{change in } x} = \frac{\text{rise}}{\text{run}}$$

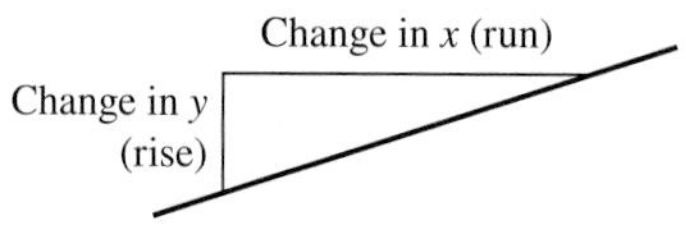

Figure 3-15

To move from point A to point B on Park Trail, rise 2 ft and move to the right 6 ft (Figure 3-16).

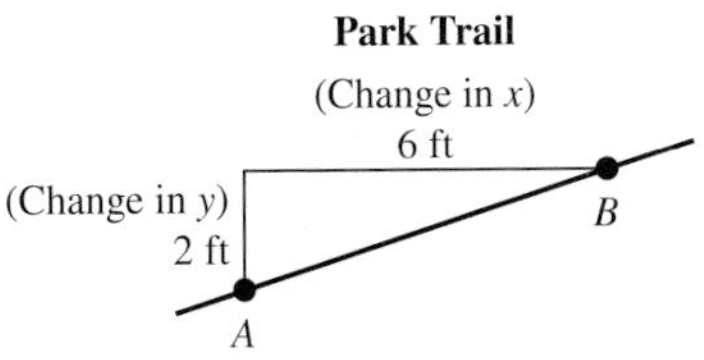

Figure 3-16

$$\text{Slope} = \frac{\text{change in } y}{\text{change in } x} = \frac{2 \text{ ft}}{6 \text{ ft}} = \frac{1}{3}$$

To move from point A to point B on Mt. Dora Trail, rise 5 ft and move to the right 4 ft (Figure 3-17).

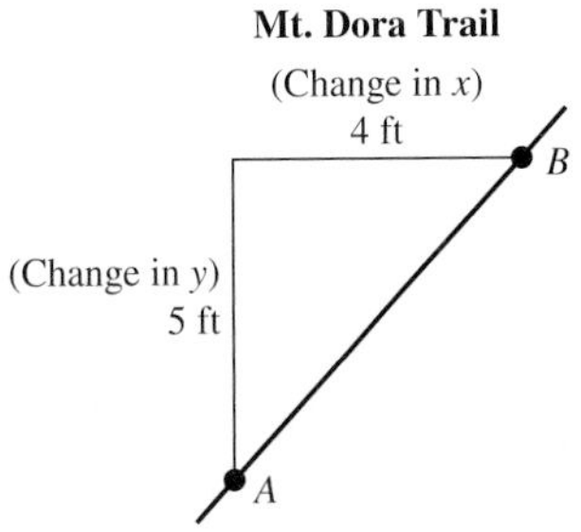

Figure 3-17

$$\text{Slope} = \frac{\text{change in } y}{\text{change in } x} = \frac{5 \text{ ft}}{4 \text{ ft}} = \frac{5}{4}$$

TIP: To find the slope, you can use any two points on the line. The ratio of rise to run will be the same.

The slope of Mt. Dora Trail is greater than the slope of Park Trail, confirming the observation that Mt. Dora Trail is steeper. On Mt. Dora Trail there is a 5-ft change in elevation for every 4 ft of horizontal distance (a 5:4 ratio). On Park Trail there is only a 2-ft change in elevation for every 6 ft of horizontal distance (a 1:3 ratio).

Example 1 Finding Slope in an Application

Classroom Example: p. 226, Exercise 10

Determine the slope of the ramp up the stairs.

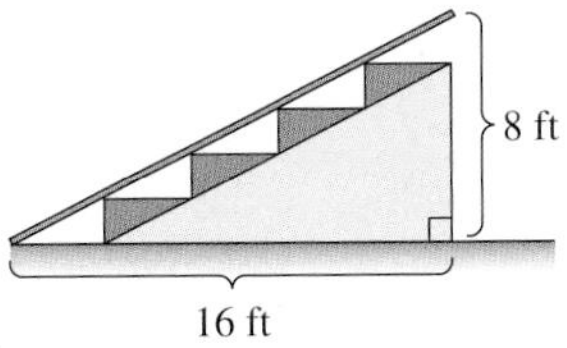

Solution:

$$\text{Slope} = \frac{\text{change in } y}{\text{change in } x} = \frac{8 \text{ ft}}{16 \text{ ft}}$$

$\frac{8}{16} = \frac{1}{2}$ Write the ratio for the slope and simplify.

The slope is $\frac{1}{2}$.

Skill Practice

1. Determine the slope of the aircraft's takeoff path. (Figure is not drawn to scale.)

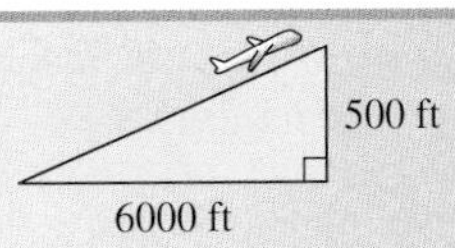

2. Slope Formula

The slope of a line may be found using any two points on the line—call these points (x_1, y_1) and (x_2, y_2). The numbers to the right and below the variables are called *subscripts*. In this instance, the subscript 1 indicates the coordinates of the first point, and the subscript 2 indicates the coordinates of the second point. The change in y between the points can be found by taking the difference of the y values: $y_2 - y_1$. The change in x can be found by taking the difference of the x values in the same order: $x_2 - x_1$ (Figure 3-18).

The slope of a line is often symbolized by the letter m and is given by the following formula.

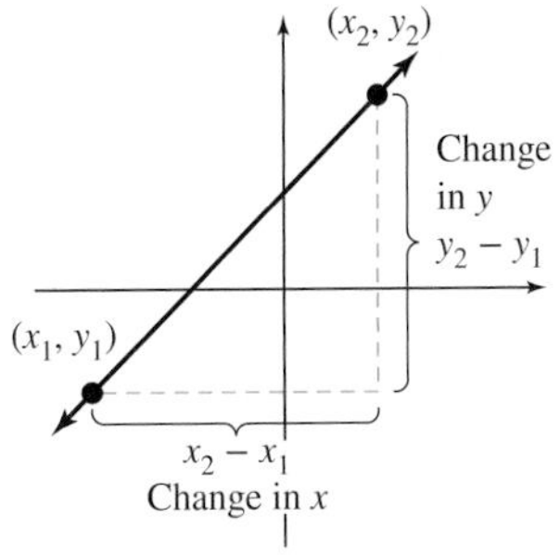

Figure 3-18

Answer

1. $\frac{500}{6000} = \frac{1}{12}$

Slope Formula

The slope of a line passing through the distinct points (x_1, y_1) and (x_2, y_2) is

$$m = \frac{y_2 - y_1}{x_2 - x_1} \quad \text{provided } x_2 - x_1 \neq 0.$$

Note: If $x_2 - x_1 = 0$, the slope is undefined.

Classroom Example: p. 228, Exercise 36

Example 2 Finding the Slope of a Line Given Two Points

Find the slope of the line through the points (−1, 3) and (−4, −2).

Solution:

To use the slope formula, first label the coordinates of each point and then substitute the coordinates into the slope formula.

$(-1, 3)$ and $(-4, -2)$
(x_1, y_1) $\quad$ (x_2, y_2) $\quad$ Label the points.

$$m = \frac{y_2 - y_1}{x_2 - x_1} = \frac{(-2) - (3)}{(-4) - (-1)} \quad \text{Apply the slope formula.}$$

$$= \frac{-5}{-3}$$

$$= \frac{5}{3} \quad \text{Simplify to lowest terms.}$$

Avoiding Mistakes

When calculating slope, always write the change in *y* in the numerator.

The slope of the line can be verified from the graph (Figure 3-19).

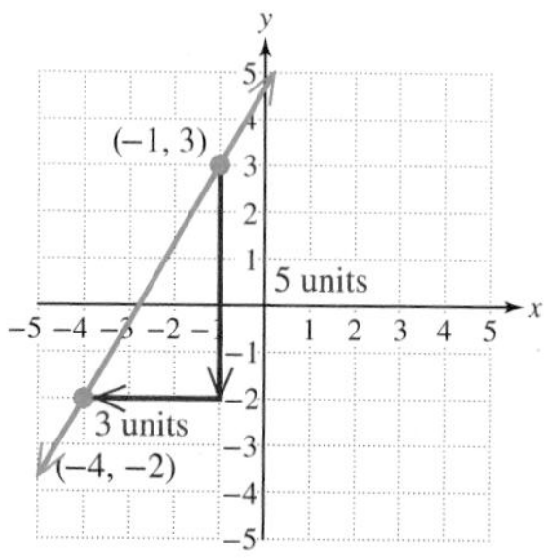

Figure 3-19

Skill Practice Find the slope of the line through the given points.

2. (−5, 2) and (1, 3)

TIP: The slope formula is not dependent on which point is labeled (x_1, y_1) and which point is labeled (x_2, y_2). In Example 2, reversing the order in which the points are labeled results in the same slope.

$(-1, 3)$ and $(-4, -2)$
(x_2, y_2) $\quad$ (x_1, y_1) $\quad$ Label the points.

$$m = \frac{(3) - (-2)}{(-1) - (-4)} = \frac{5}{3} \quad \text{Apply the slope formula.}$$

Answer

2. $\frac{1}{6}$

When you apply the slope formula, you will see that the slope of a line may be positive, negative, zero, or undefined.

- Lines that increase, or rise, from left to right have a positive slope.
- Lines that decrease, or fall, from left to right have a negative slope.
- Horizontal lines have a slope of zero.
- Vertical lines have an undefined slope.

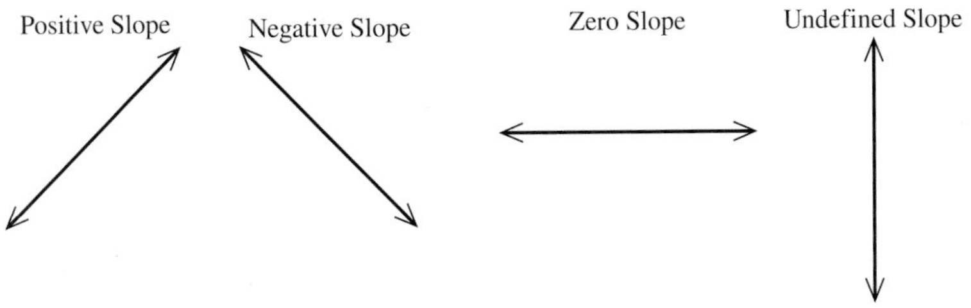

Example 3 **Finding the Slope of a Line Given Two Points**

Classroom Example: p. 228, Exercise 44

Find the slope of the line passing through the points $(-5, \frac{1}{2})$ and $(2, -\frac{3}{2})$.

Solution:

$\left(-5, \frac{1}{2}\right)$ and $\left(2, -\frac{3}{2}\right)$

(x_1, y_1) (x_2, y_2) Label the points.

$$m = \frac{y_2 - y_1}{x_2 - x_1} = \frac{\left(-\frac{3}{2}\right) - \left(\frac{1}{2}\right)}{(2) - (-5)}$$ Apply the slope formula.

$$= \frac{-\frac{4}{2}}{2 + 5}$$ Simplify.

$$= \frac{-2}{7} \quad \text{or} \quad -\frac{2}{7}$$

Avoiding Mistakes

When applying the slope formula, y_2 and x_2 are taken from the same ordered pair. Likewise y_1 and x_1 are taken from the same ordered pair.

By graphing the points $(-5, \frac{1}{2})$ and $(2, -\frac{3}{2})$, we can verify that the slope is $-\frac{2}{7}$ (Figure 3-20). Notice that the line slopes downward from left to right.

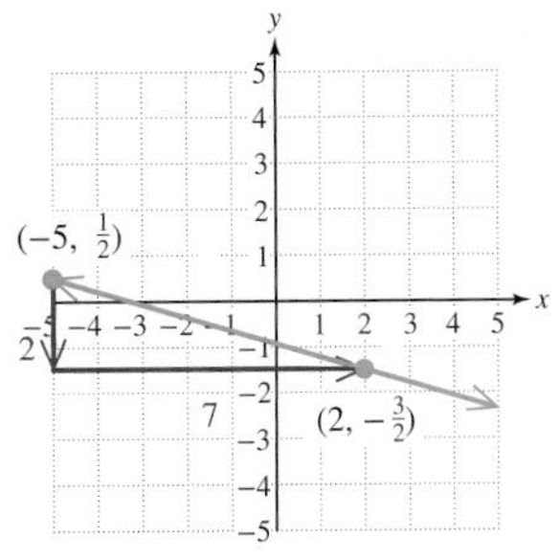

Figure 3-20

Skill Practice Find the slope of the line through the given points.

3. $\left(\frac{2}{3}, 0\right)$ and $\left(-\frac{1}{6}, 5\right)$

Answer

3. −6

Classroom Example: p. 228, Exercise 42

Example 4 Determining the Slope of a Vertical Line

Find the slope of the line passing through the points (2, −1) and (2, 4).

Solution:

(2, −1) and (2, 4)
(x_1, y_1) (x_2, y_2) Label the points.

$$m = \frac{y_2 - y_1}{x_2 - x_1} = \frac{(4) - (-1)}{(2) - (2)}$$ Apply the slope formula.

$$m = \frac{5}{0}$$ Undefined

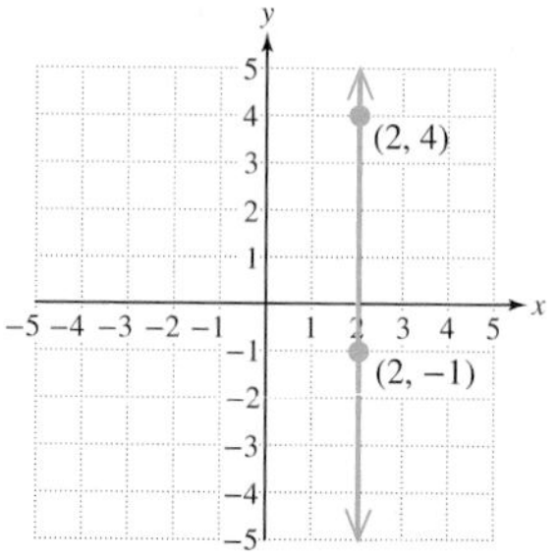

Figure 3-21

Because the slope, m, is undefined, we expect the points to form a vertical line as shown in Figure 3-21.

Skill Practice Find the slope of the line through the given points.

4. (5, 6) and (5, −2)

Classroom Example: p. 228, Exercise 40

Example 5 Determining the Slope of a Horizontal Line

Find the slope of the line passing through the points (3.4, −2) and (−3.5, −2).

Solution:

(3.4, −2) and (−3.5, −2)
(x_1, y_1) (x_2, y_2) Label the points.

$$m = \frac{y_2 - y_1}{x_2 - x_1} = \frac{(-2) - (-2)}{(-3.5) - (3.4)}$$ Apply the slope formula.

$$= \frac{-2 + 2}{-3.5 - 3.4} = \frac{0}{-6.9} = 0$$ Simplify.

Because the slope is 0, we expect the points to form a horizontal line, as shown in Figure 3-22.

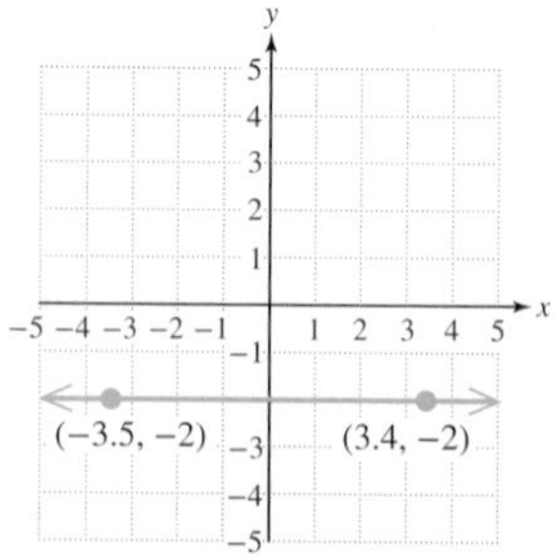

Figure 3-22

Skill Practice Find the slope of the line through the given points.

5. (3, 8) and (−5, 8)

Answers

4. Undefined 5. 0

3. Parallel and Perpendicular Lines

Lines in the same plane that do not intersect are called **parallel lines**. Parallel lines have the same slope and different y-intercepts (Figure 3-23).

Lines that intersect at a right angle are **perpendicular lines**. If two lines are perpendicular then the slope of one line is the opposite of the reciprocal of the slope of the other line (provided neither line is vertical) (Figure 3-24).

Instructor Note: If you use calculators for graphing lines, try graphing two lines with slopes that are similar ($y = x$ and $y = \frac{19}{20}x + 1$). They will appear parallel, but clearly we can show they are not by inspecting the equations. Sometimes students don't value what we do by hand until they see it does not always appear correctly on the calculator.

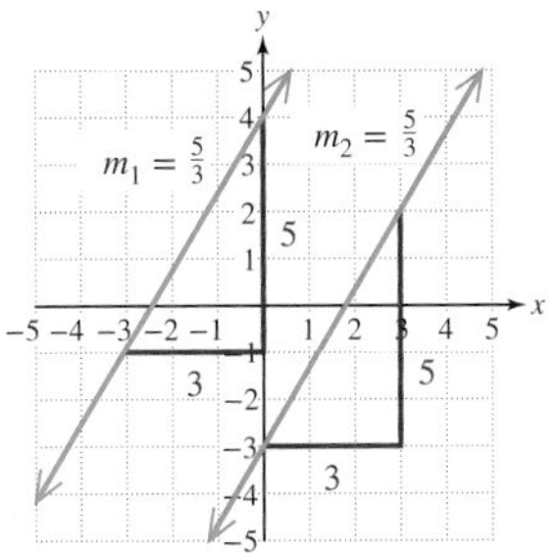

Figure 3-23

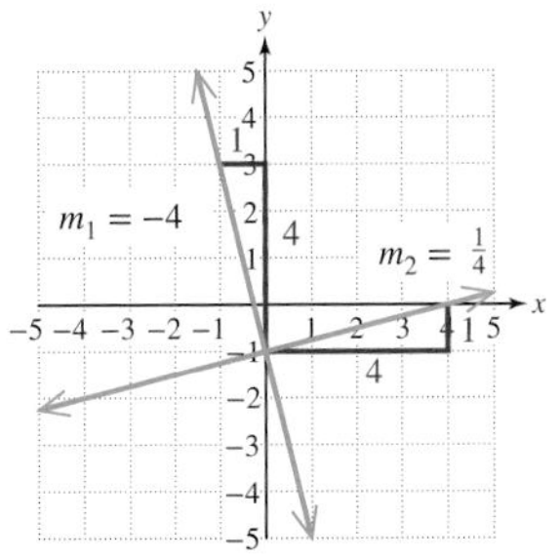

Figure 3-24

Slopes of Parallel Lines

If m_1 and m_2 represent the slopes of two parallel (nonvertical) lines, then

$$m_1 = m_2.$$

See Figure 3-23.

Slopes of Perpendicular Lines

If $m_1 \neq 0$ and $m_2 \neq 0$ represent the slopes of two perpendicular lines, then

$$m_1 = -\frac{1}{m_2} \quad \text{or equivalently, } m_1 m_2 = -1. \text{ See Figure 3-24.}$$

Instructor Note: Ask students how we know that all vertical lines are parallel and all horizontal lines are parallel.

Example 6 Determining the Slope of Parallel and Perpendicular Lines

Classroom Example: p. 228, Exercise 52

Suppose a given line has a slope of -6.

a. Find the slope of a line parallel to the line with the given slope.

b. Find the slope of a line perpendicular to the line with the given slope.

Solution:

a. Parallel lines must have the same slope. The slope of a line parallel to the given line is $m = -6$.

b. For perpendicular lines, the slope of one line must be the opposite of the reciprocal of the other. The slope of a line perpendicular to the given line is $m = -\left(\frac{1}{-6}\right) = \frac{1}{6}$.

Skill Practice A given line has a slope of $\frac{5}{3}$.

6. Find the slope of a line parallel to the given line.

7. Find the slope of a line perpendicular to the given line.

Answers

6. $\frac{5}{3}$ **7.** $-\frac{3}{5}$

If the slopes of two lines are known, then we can compare the slopes to determine if the lines are parallel, perpendicular, or neither.

Classroom Example: p. 228, Exercise 64

Example 7 Determining If Lines Are Parallel, Perpendicular, or Neither

Lines l_1 and l_2 pass through the given points. Determine if l_1 and l_2 are parallel, perpendicular, or neither.

l_1: (2, −7) and (4, 1) l_2: (−3, 1) and (1, 0)

Solution:

Find the slope of each line.

l_1: $\underset{(x_1, y_1)}{(2, -7)}$ and $\underset{(x_2, y_2)}{(4, 1)}$ l_2: $\underset{(x_1, y_1)}{(-3, 1)}$ and $\underset{(x_2, y_2)}{(1, 0)}$

$$m_1 = \frac{1-(-7)}{4-2} \qquad m_2 = \frac{0-1}{1-(-3)}$$

$$m_1 = \frac{8}{2} \qquad m_2 = \frac{-1}{4}$$

$$m_1 = 4 \qquad m_2 = -\frac{1}{4}$$

TIP: You can check that two lines are perpendicular by checking that the product of their slopes is −1.

$$4\left(-\frac{1}{4}\right) = -1$$

One slope is the opposite of the reciprocal of the other slope. Therefore, the lines are perpendicular.

Skill Practice Determine if lines l_1 and l_2 are parallel, perpendicular, or neither.

8. l_1: (−2, −3) and (4, −1)
l_2: (0, 2) and (−3, 1)

4. Applications of Slope: Rate of Change

In many applications, the interpretation of slope refers to the *rate of change* of the y-variable to the x-variable.

Classroom Example: p. 229, Exercise 72

Example 8 Interpreting Slope in an Application

The annual median income for males in the United States for selected years is shown in Figure 3-25. The trend is approximately linear. Find the slope of the line and interpret the meaning of the slope in the context of the problem.

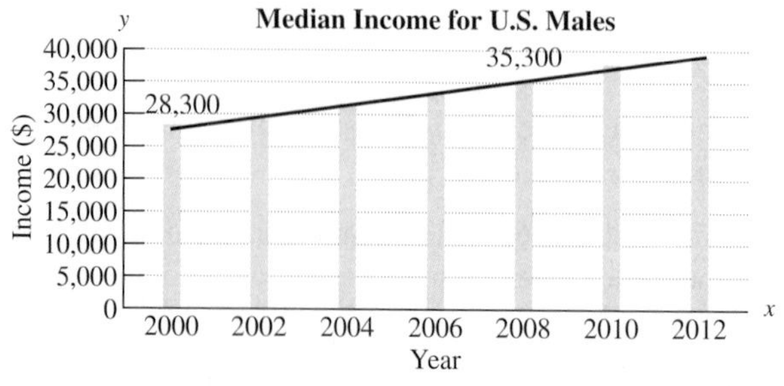

Figure 3-25

Source: U.S. Department of the Census

Answer

8. Parallel

Solution:

To determine the slope we need to know two points on the line. From the graph, the median income for males in the year 2000 was approximately \$28,300. This gives us the ordered pair (2000, 28,300). In the year 2008, the income was \$35,300. This gives the ordered pair (2008, 35,300).

$$\underset{(x_1,\, y_1)}{(2000, 28{,}300)} \quad \text{and} \quad \underset{(x_2,\, y_2)}{(2008, 35{,}300)}$$ Label the points.

$$m = \frac{y_2 - y_1}{x_2 - x_1} = \frac{35{,}300 - 28{,}300}{2008 - 2000}$$ Apply the slope formula.

$$= \frac{7000}{8}$$

$$= 875$$ Simplify.

The slope is 875. This tells us the rate of change of the y-variable (income) to the x-variable (years). This means that men's median income in the United States increased at a rate of \$875 per year during this time period.

Skill Practice

9. In the year 2000, the population of Alaska was approximately 630,000. By 2010, it had grown to 700,000. Use the ordered pairs (2000, 630,000) and (2010, 700,000) to determine the slope of the line through the points. Then interpret the meaning in the context of this problem.

Answer

9. $m = 7000$; The population of Alaska increased at a rate of 7000 people per year.

Section 3.3 Practice Exercises

For additional exercises, see Classroom Activities 3.3A–3.3C in the *Student's Resource Manual* at www.mhhe.com/moh.

Study Skills Exercise

Each day after finishing your homework, choose two or three odd-numbered problems or examples from that section. Write the problem with the directions on one side of a 3 × 5 card. On the back write the section, page, and problem number along with the answer. Each week, shuffle your cards and pull out a few at random, to give yourself a review of $\frac{1}{2}$-hr or more.

Vocabulary and Key Concepts

1. a. The ratio of the vertical change and the horizontal change between two distinct points (x_1, y_1) and (x_2, y_2) on a line is called the __slope__ of the line. The slope can be computed from the formula $m =$ __$\frac{y_2 - y_1}{x_2 - x_1}$__.

b. Lines in the same plane that do not intersect are called __parallel__ lines.

c. Two lines are perpendicular if they intersect at a __right__ angle.

d. If m_1 and m_2 represent the slopes of two nonvertical perpendicular lines then $m_1 \cdot m_2 =$ __-1__.

e. The slope of a vertical line is __undefined__. The slope of a __horizontal__ line is 0.

Review Exercises

For Exercises 2–6, find the x- and y-intercepts (if they exist). Then graph the line.

2. $x - 5 = 2$ x-intercept: (7, 0); y-intercept: none

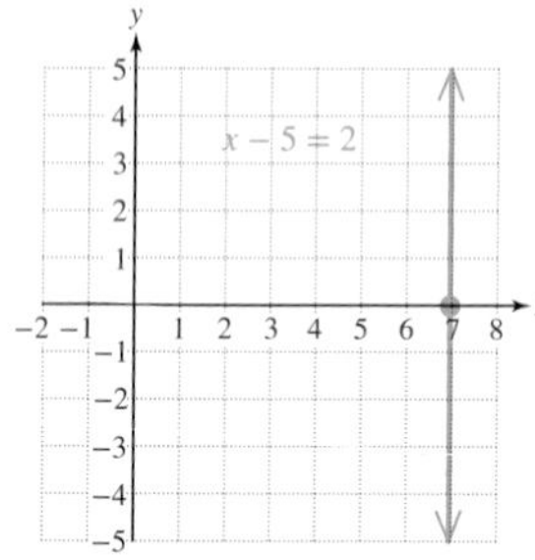

3. $x - 3y = 6$ x-intercept: (6, 0); y-intercept: (0, −2)

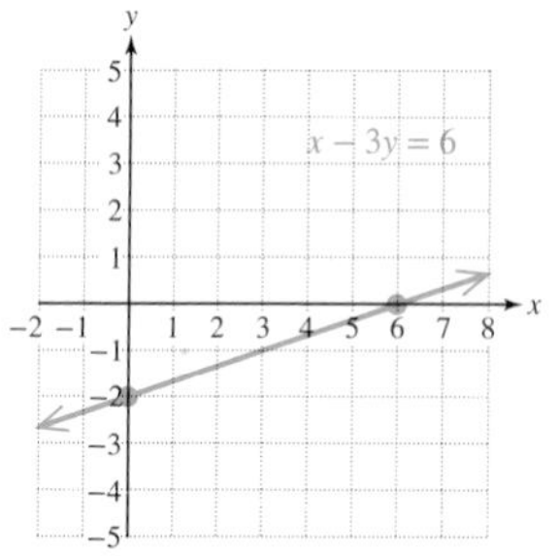

4. $y = \frac{2}{3}x$ x-intercept: (0, 0); y-intercept: (0, 0)

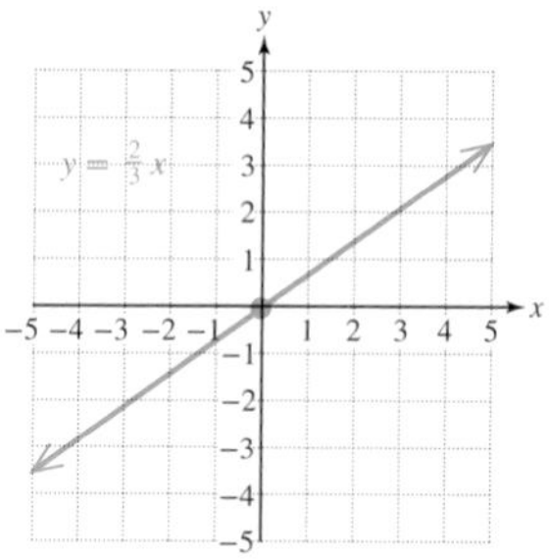

5. $2y - 3 = 0$ x-intercept: none; y-intercept: $(0, \frac{3}{2})$

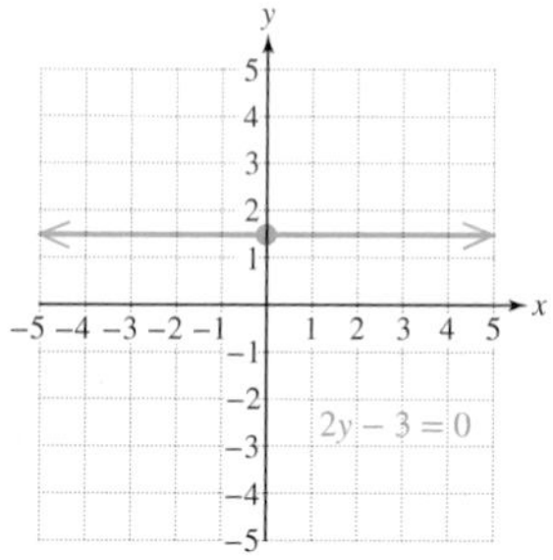

6. $2x = 4y$ x-intercept: (0, 0); y-intercept: (0, 0)

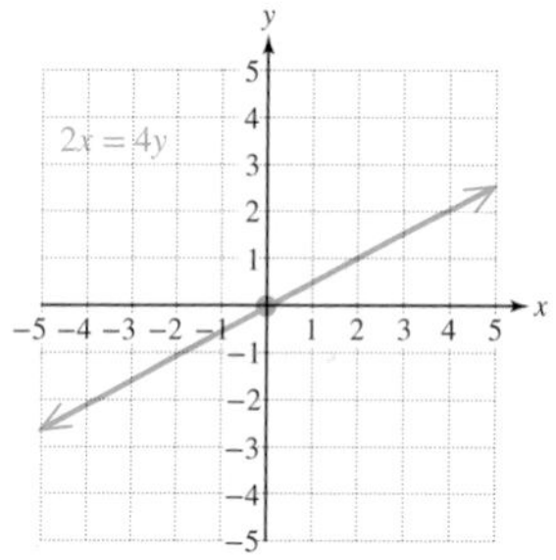

Concept 1: Introduction to Slope

7. Determine the slope of the roof.
(See Example 1.)

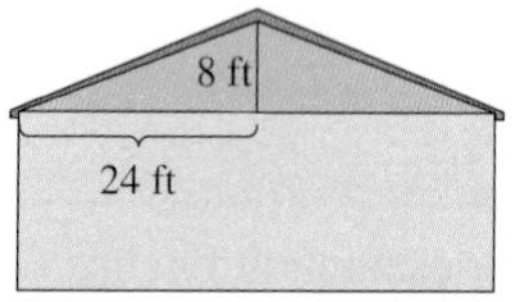

$m = \frac{1}{3}$

8. Determine the slope of the stairs.

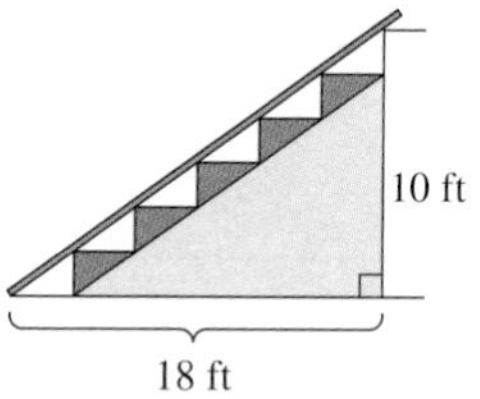

$m = \frac{5}{9}$

9. Calculate the slope of the handrail.

© Ryan McVay/Getty Images RF

$m = \frac{6}{11}$

10. Determine the slope of the treadmill

Animation

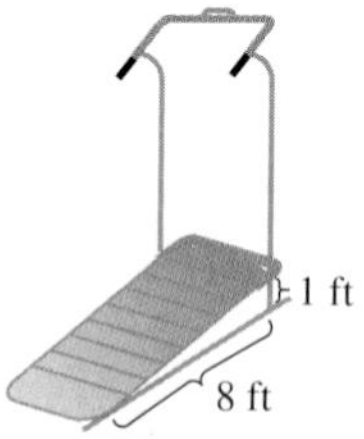

$m = \frac{1}{8}$

Concept 2: Slope Formula

For Exercises 11–14, fill in the blank with the appropriate term: *zero*, *negative*, *positive*, or *undefined*.

11. The slope of a line parallel to the y-axis is <u>undefined</u>.

12. The slope of a horizontal line is <u>zero</u>.

13. The slope of a line that rises from left to right is <u>positive</u>.

14. The slope of a line that falls from left to right is <u>negative</u>.

For Exercises 15–23, determine if the slope is positive, negative, zero, or undefined.

15. Negative

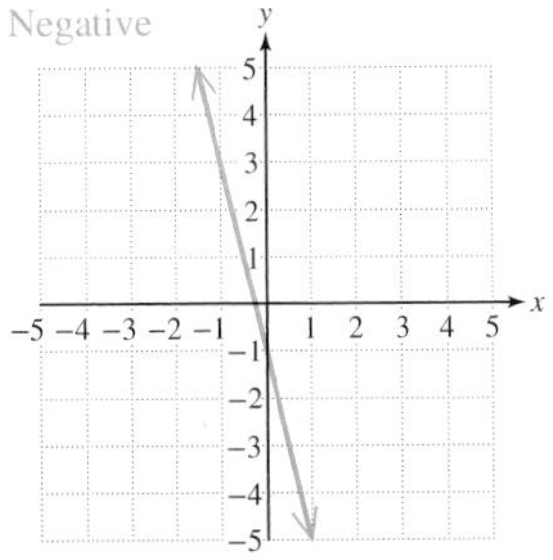

16. Undefined

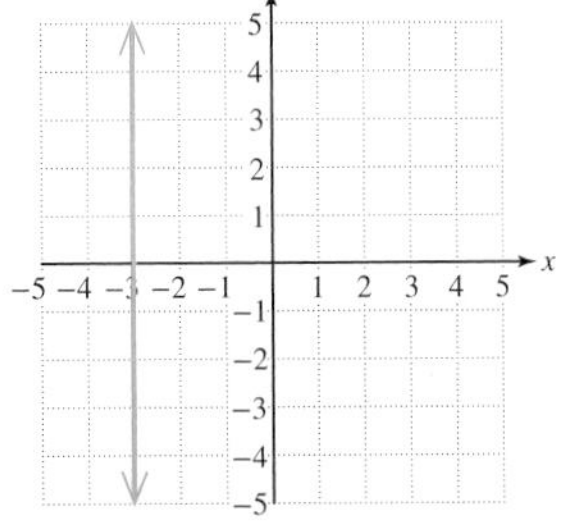

17. Zero

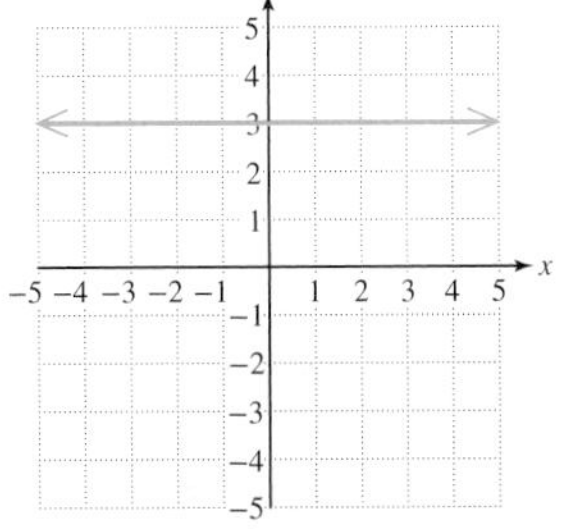

18. Negative

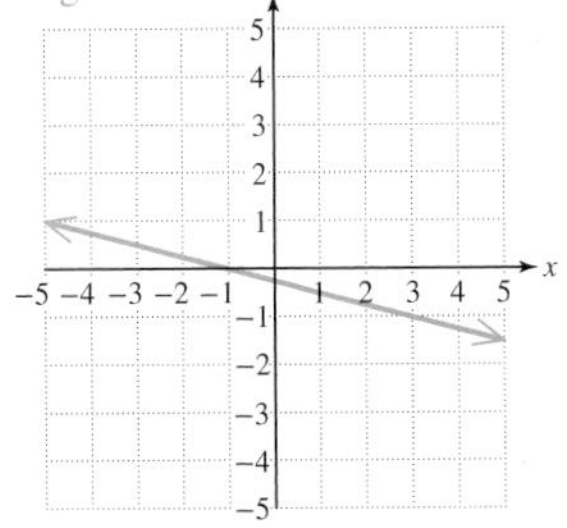

19. Undefined

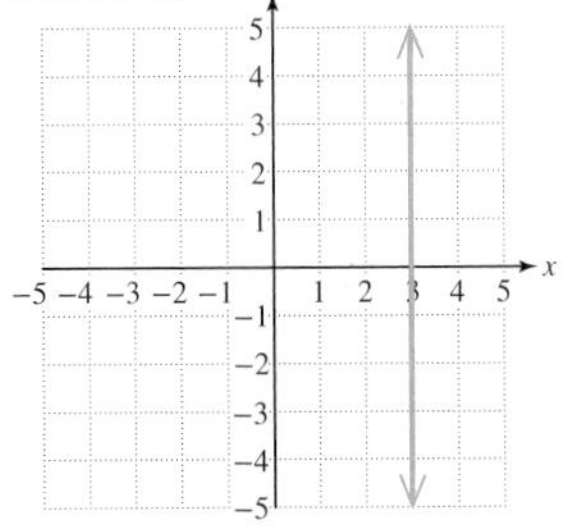

20. Zero

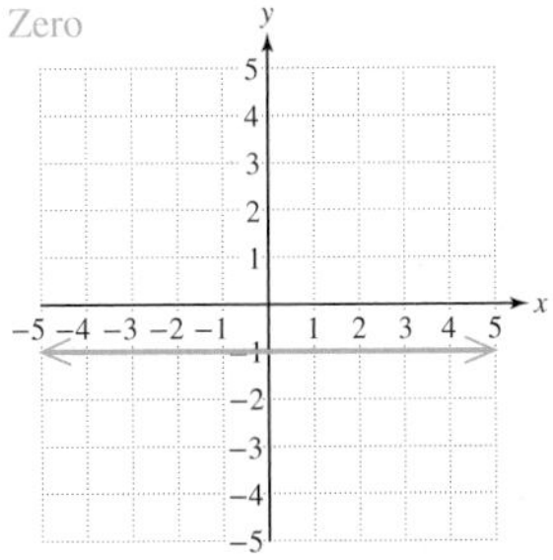

21. Positive

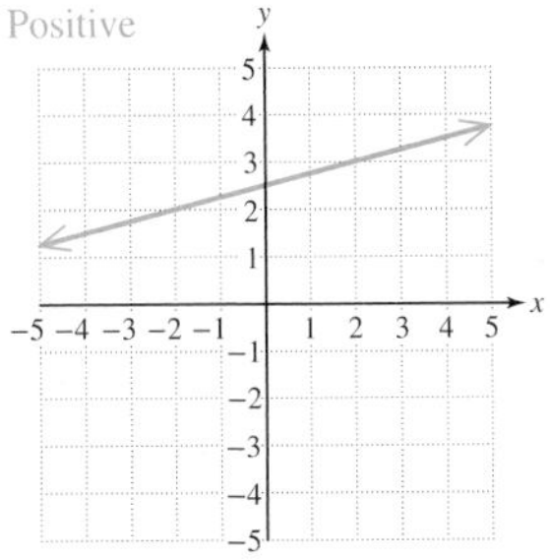

22. Positive

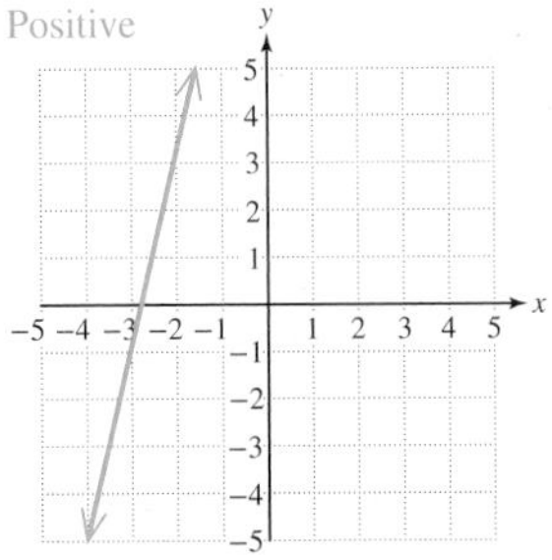

23. Negative

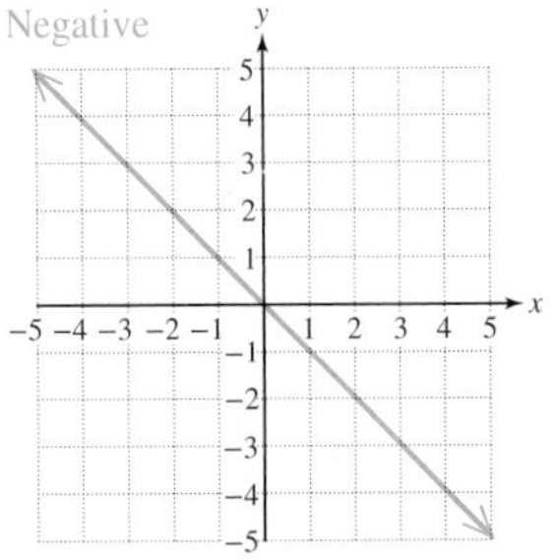

For Exercises 24–32, determine the slope by using the slope formula and any two points on the line. Check your answer by drawing a right triangle, where appropriate, and labeling the "rise" and "run."

24. $m = 2$

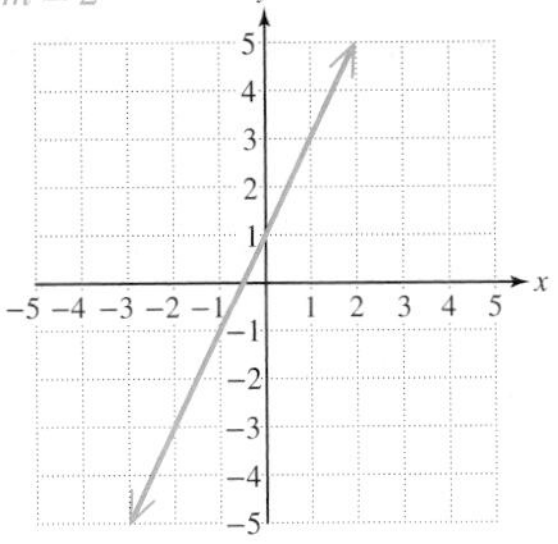

25. $m = \frac{1}{2}$

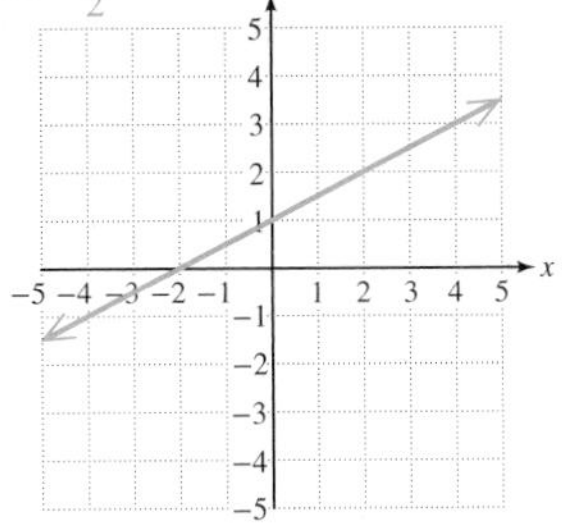

26. $m = -\frac{1}{3}$

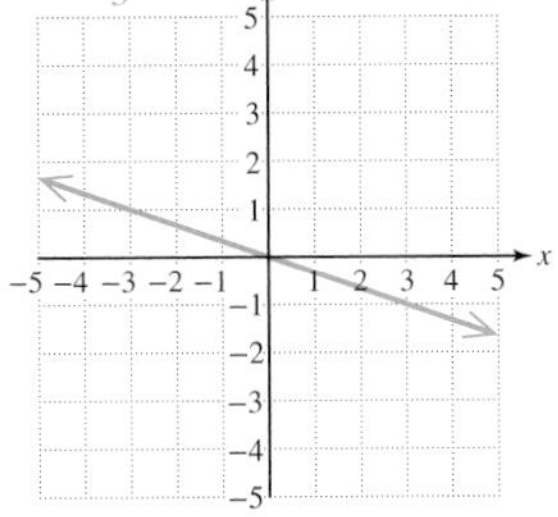

27. $m = -3$

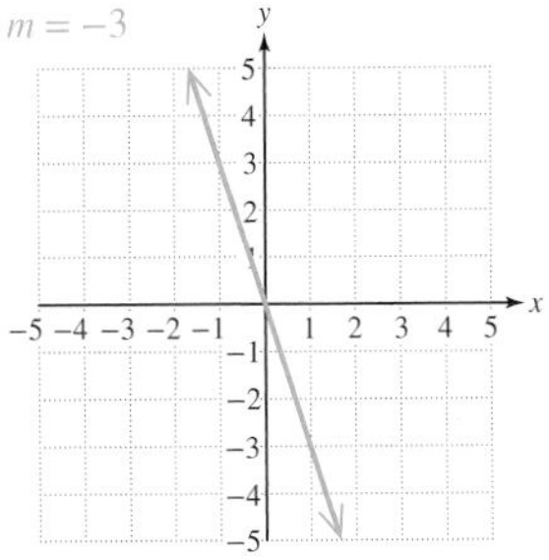

28. $m = 0$

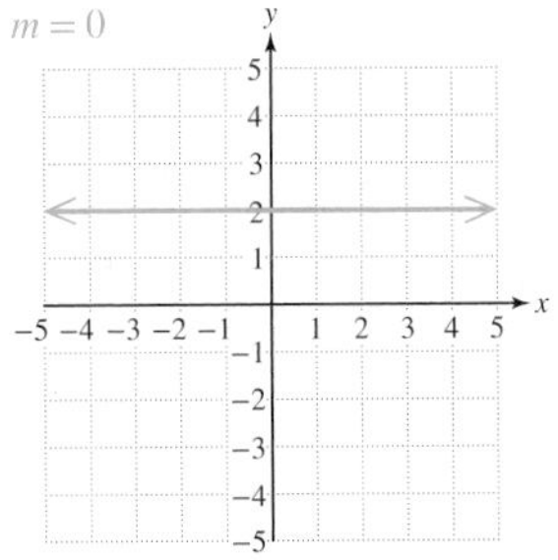

29. $m = 0$

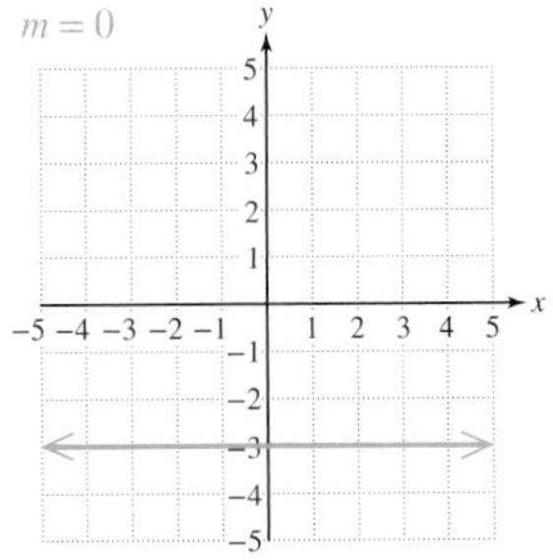

30. The slope is undefined.

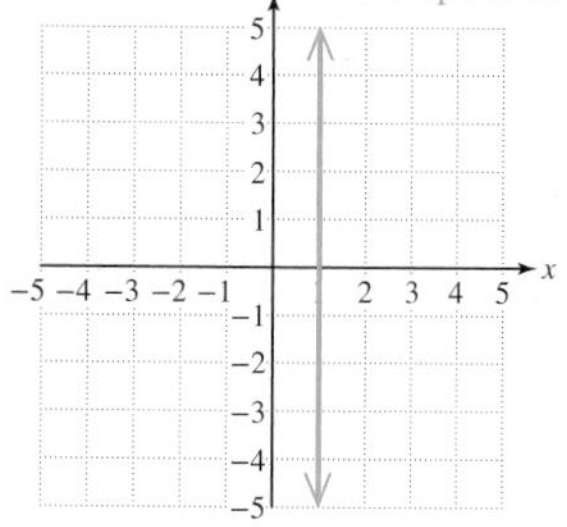

31. The slope is undefined.

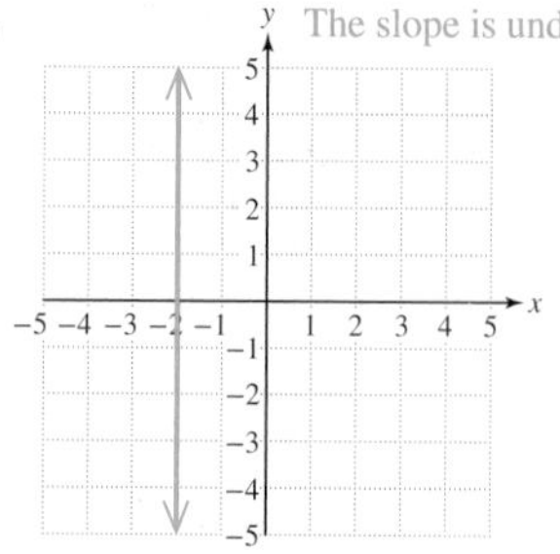

32. $m = -1$

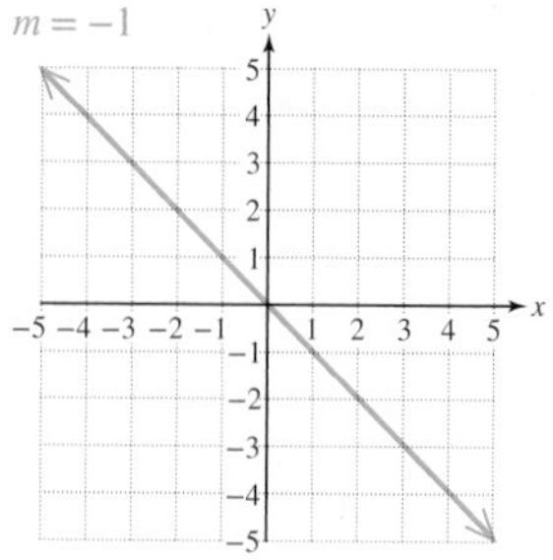

For Exercises 33–50, find the slope of the line that passes through the two points. **(See Example 2–5.)**

33. $(2, 4)$ and $(-4, 2)$ $\frac{1}{3}$

34. $(-5, 4)$ and $(-11, 12)$ $-\frac{4}{3}$

35. $(-2, 3)$ and $(1, -6)$ -3

36. $(-3, -4)$ and $(1, -5)$ $-\frac{1}{4}$

37. $(1, 5)$ and $(-4, 2)$ $\frac{3}{5}$

38. $(-6, -1)$ and $(-2, -3)$ $-\frac{1}{2}$

39. $(5, 3)$ and $(-2, 3)$ Zero

40. $(0, -1)$ and $(-4, -1)$ Zero

41. $(2, -7)$ and $(2, 5)$ Undefined

42. $(-4, 3)$ and $(-4, -4)$ Undefined

43. $\left(\frac{1}{2}, \frac{3}{5}\right)$ and $\left(\frac{1}{4}, -\frac{4}{5}\right)$ $\frac{28}{5}$

44. $\left(-\frac{2}{7}, \frac{1}{3}\right)$ and $\left(\frac{8}{7}, -\frac{5}{6}\right)$ $-\frac{49}{60}$

45. $(3, -1)$ and $(-5, 6)$ $-\frac{7}{8}$

46. $(-6, 5)$ and $(-10, 4)$ $\frac{1}{4}$

47. $(6.8, -3.4)$ and $(-3.2, 1.1)$ -0.45 or $-\frac{9}{20}$

48. $(-3.15, 8.25)$ and $(6.85, -4.25)$ -1.25 or $-\frac{5}{4}$

49. $(1994, 3.5)$ and $(2000, 2.6)$ -0.15 or $-\frac{3}{20}$

50. $(1988, 4.65)$ and $(1998, 9.25)$ 0.46 or $\frac{23}{50}$

Concept 3: Parallel and Perpendicular Lines

For Exercises 51–56, the slope of a line is given. **(See Example 6.)**

a. Determine the slope of a line parallel to the line with the given slope.

b. Determine the slope of a line perpendicular to the line with the given slope.

51. $m = -2$ a. -2 b. $\frac{1}{2}$

52. $m = \frac{2}{3}$ a. $\frac{2}{3}$ b. $-\frac{3}{2}$

53. $m = 0$ a. 0 b. undefined

54. The slope is undefined. a. undefined b. 0

55. $m = \frac{4}{5}$ a. $\frac{4}{5}$ b. $-\frac{5}{4}$

56. $m = -4$ a. -4 b. $\frac{1}{4}$

For Exercises 57–62, let m_1 and m_2 represent the slopes of two lines. Determine if the lines are parallel, perpendicular, or neither. **(See Example 6.)**

57. $m_1 = -2$, $m_2 = \frac{1}{2}$ Perpendicular

58. $m_1 = \frac{2}{3}$, $m_2 = \frac{3}{2}$ Neither

59. $m_1 = 1$, $m_2 = \frac{4}{4}$ Parallel

60. $m_1 = \frac{3}{4}$, $m_2 = -\frac{8}{6}$ Perpendicular

61. $m_1 = \frac{2}{7}$, $m_2 = -\frac{2}{7}$ Neither

62. $m_1 = 5$, $m_2 = 5$ Parallel

For Exercises 63–68, find the slopes of the lines l_1 and l_2 defined by the two given points. Then determine whether l_1 and l_2 are parallel, perpendicular, or neither. **(See Example 7.)**

63. l_1: $(2, 4)$ and $(-1, -2)$
l_2: $(1, 7)$ and $(0, 5)$
l_1: $m = 2$, l_2: $m = 2$; parallel

64. l_1: $(0, 0)$ and $(-2, 4)$
l_2: $(1, -5)$ and $(-1, -1)$
l_1: $m = -2$, l_2: $m = -2$; parallel

65. l_1: $(1, 9)$ and $(0, 4)$
l_2: $(5, 2)$ and $(10, 1)$
l_1: $m = 5$, l_2: $m = -\frac{1}{5}$; perpendicular

66. l_1: $(3, -4)$ and $(-1, -8)$
l_2: $(5, -5)$ and $(-2, 2)$
l_1: $m = 1$, l_2: $m = -1$; perpendicular

67. l_1: $(4, 4)$ and $(0, 3)$
l_2: $(1, 7)$ and $(-1, -1)$
l_1: $m = \frac{1}{4}$, l_2: $m = 4$; neither

68. l_1: $(3, 5)$ and $(-2, -5)$
l_2: $(2, 0)$ and $(-4, -3)$
l_1: $m = 2$, l_2: $m = \frac{1}{2}$; neither

Concept 4: Applications of Slope: Rate of Change

69. For a recent year, the average earnings for male workers between the ages of 25 and 34 with a high school diploma was \$32,000. Comparing this value in constant dollars to the average earnings 15 yr later showed that the average earnings have decreased to \$29,600. Find the average rate of change in dollars per year for this time period. [*Hint:* Use the ordered pairs (0, 32,000) and (15, 29,600).] The average rate of change is −\$160 per year.

70. In 1985, the U.S. Postal Service charged \$0.22 for first class letters and cards up to 1 oz. By 2015, the price had increased to \$0.49. Let x represent the year, and y represent the cost for 1 oz of first class postage. Find the average rate of change of the cost per year.
The cost increased at a rate of \$0.009 per year.

71. In 1985, there were 539 thousand male inmates in federal and state prisons. By 2010, the number increased to 1714 thousand. Let x represent the year, and let y represent the number of prisoners (in thousands).
(See Example 8.)

a. Using the ordered pairs (1985, 539) and (2010, 1714), find the slope of the line. $m = 47$

b. Interpret the slope in the context of this problem.
The number of male prisoners increased at a rate of 47 thousand per year during this time period.

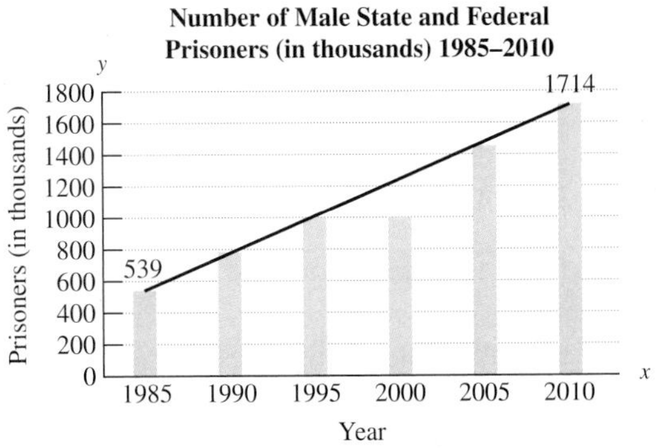

(*Source:* U.S. Bureau of Justice Statistics)

72. In the year 1985, there were 30 thousand female inmates in federal and state prisons. By 2010, the number increased to 120 thousand. Let x represent the year, and let y represent the number of prisoners (in thousands).

a. Using the ordered pairs (1985, 30) and (2010, 120), find the slope of the line. $m = 3.6$

b. Interpret the slope in the context of this problem.
The number of female prisoners increased at a rate of 3.6 thousand per year during this time period.

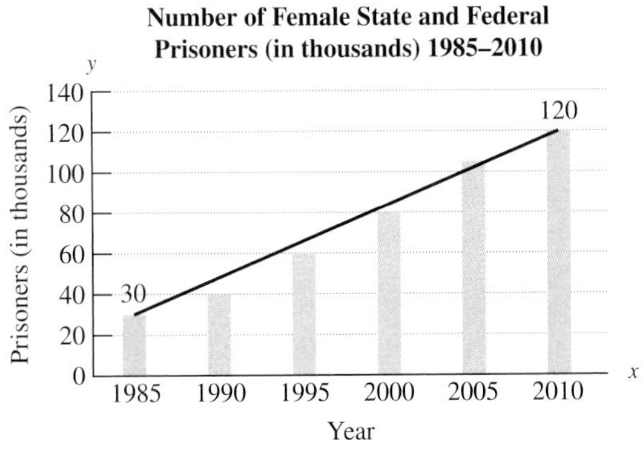

(*Source:* U.S. Bureau of Justice Statistics)

73. The distance, d (in miles), between a lightning strike and an observer is given by the equation $d = 0.2t$, where t is the time (in seconds) between seeing lightning and hearing thunder.

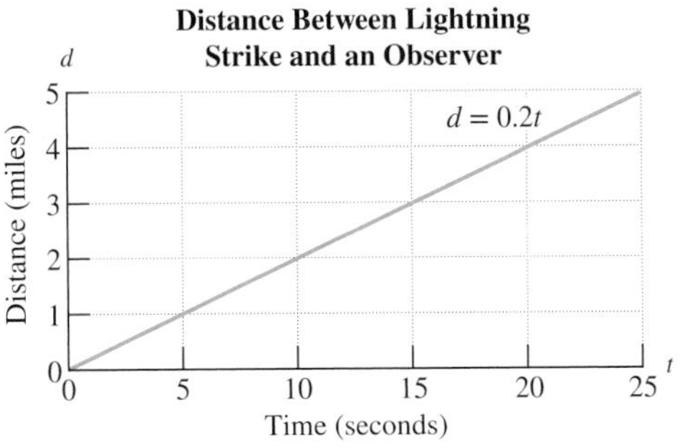

© Royalty Free/Corbis RF

a. If an observer counts 5 sec between seeing lightning and hearing thunder, how far away was the lightning strike? 1 mi

b. If an observer counts 10 sec between seeing lightning and hearing thunder, how far away was the lightning strike? 2 mi

c. If an observer counts 15 sec between seeing lightning and hearing thunder, how far away was the lightning strike? 3 mi

d. What is the slope of the line? Interpret the meaning of the slope in the context of this problem.
$m = 0.2$; The distance between a lightning strike and an observer increases by 0.2 mi for every additional second between seeing lightning and hearing thunder.

Writing Translating Expression Geometry Scientific Calculator Video

74. Michael wants to buy an efficient Smart car that according to the latest EPA standards gets 33 mpg in the city and 40 mpg on the highway. The car that Michael picked out costs \$12,600. His dad agreed to purchase the car if Michael would pay it off in equal monthly payments for the next 60 months. The equation $y = -210x + 12{,}600$ represents the amount, y (in dollars), that Michael owes his father after x months.

© Erica Simone Leeds

a. How much does Michael owe his dad after 5 months?
Michael owes \$11,550 after 5 months.

b. Determine the slope of the line and interpret its meaning in the context of this problem.
$m = -210$; The amount Michael owes his father decreases by \$210 per month.

Mixed Exercises

For Exercises 75–78, determine the slope of the line passing through points A and B.

75. Point A is located 3 units up and 4 units to the right of point B. $m = \frac{3}{4}$

76. Point A is located 2 units up and 5 units to the left of point B. $m = -\frac{2}{5}$

77. Point A is located 5 units to the right of point B. $m = 0$

78. Point A is located 3 units down from point B.
The slope is undefined.

79. Graph the line through the point $(1, -2)$ having slope $-\frac{2}{3}$. Then give two other points on the line.

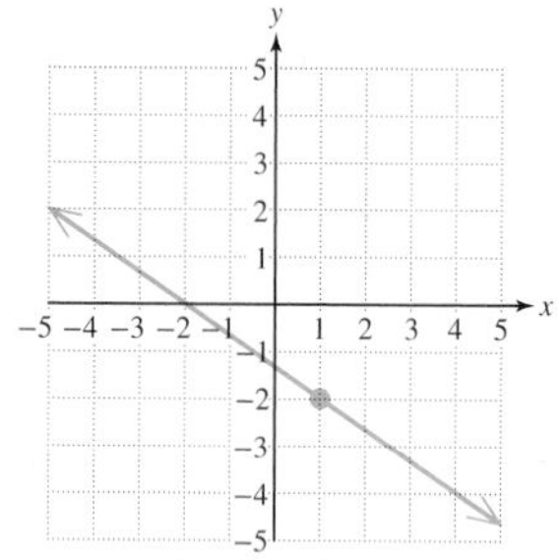
For example: $(4, -4)$ and $(-2, 0)$

80. Graph the line through the point $(1, 2)$ having slope $-\frac{3}{4}$. Then give two other points on the line.

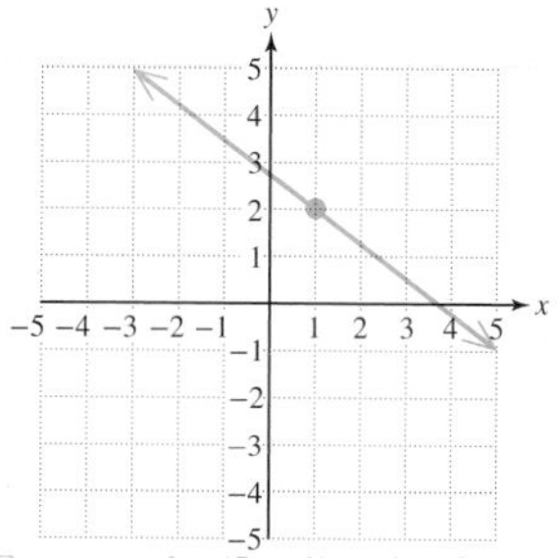
For example: $(5, -1)$ and $(-3, 5)$

81. Graph the line through the point $(2, 2)$ having slope 3. Then give two other points on the line.

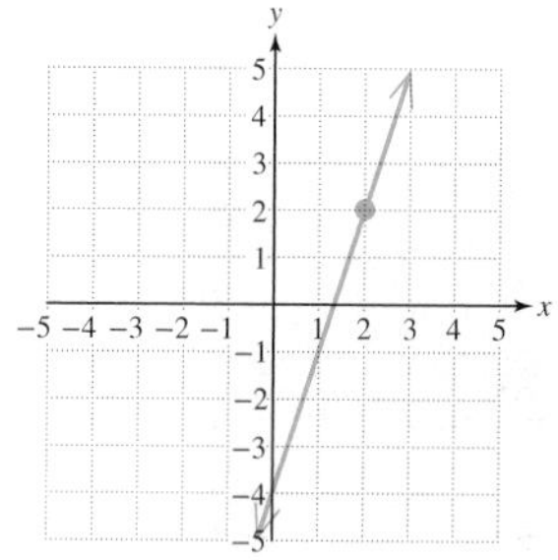
For example: $(3, 5)$ and $(1, -1)$

82. Graph the line through the point $(-1, 3)$ having slope 2. Then give two other points on the line.

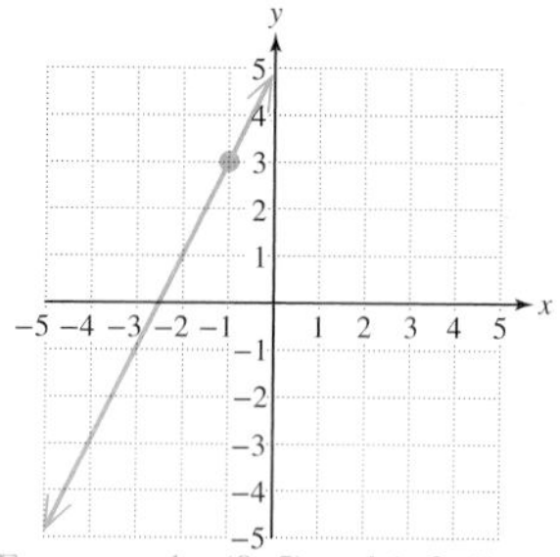
For example: $(0, 5)$ and $(-2, 1)$

83. Graph the line through $(-3, -2)$ with an undefined slope. Then give two other points on the line.

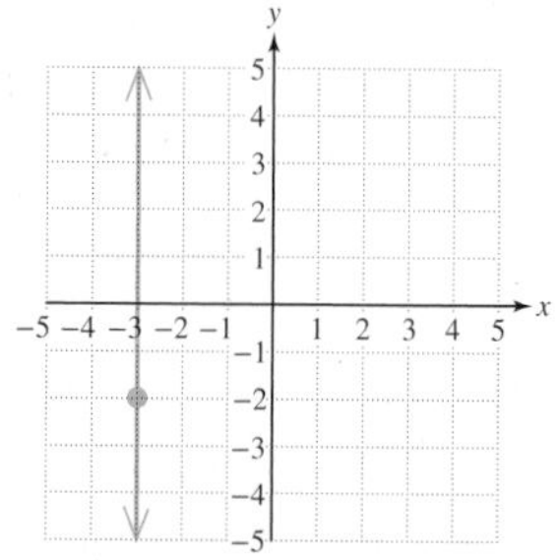
For example: $(-3, 1)$ and $(-3, 4)$

84. Graph the line through $(3, 3)$ with a slope of 0. Then give two other points on the line.

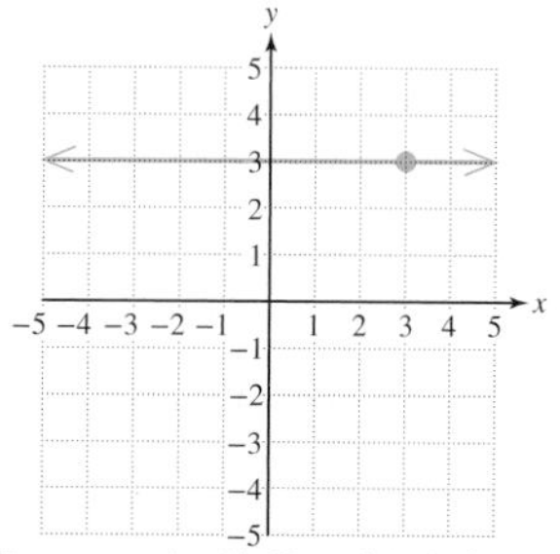
For example: $(4, 3)$ and $(-2, 3)$

For Exercises 85–90, draw a line as indicated. Answers may vary.

85. Draw a line with a positive slope and a positive y-intercept.

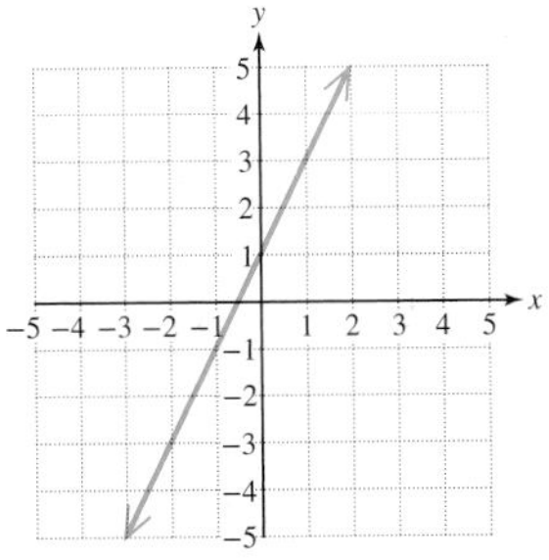

86. Draw a line with a positive slope and a negative y-intercept.

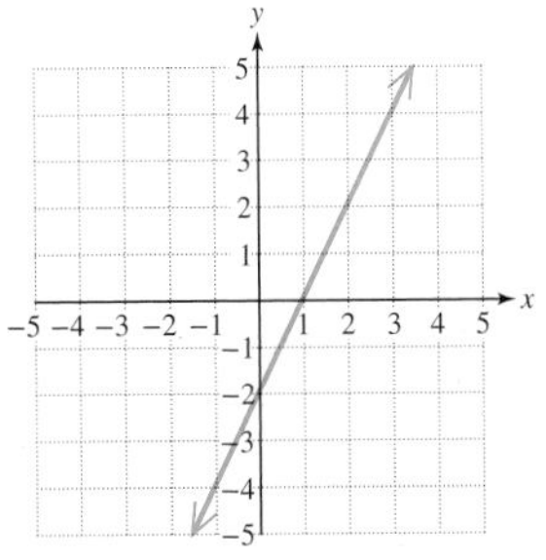

87. Draw a line with a negative slope and a negative y-intercept.

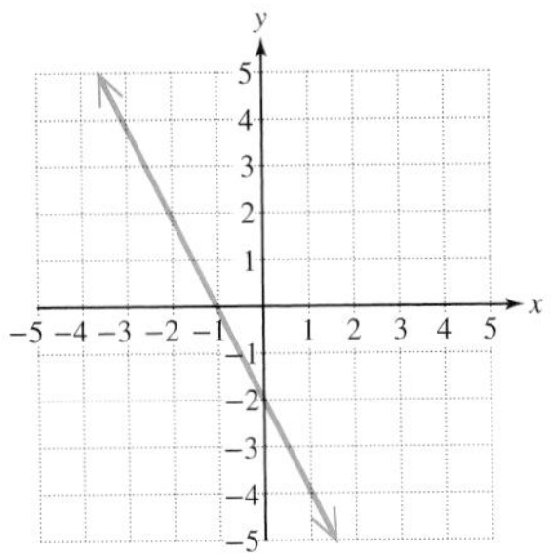

88. Draw a line with a negative slope and positive y-intercept.

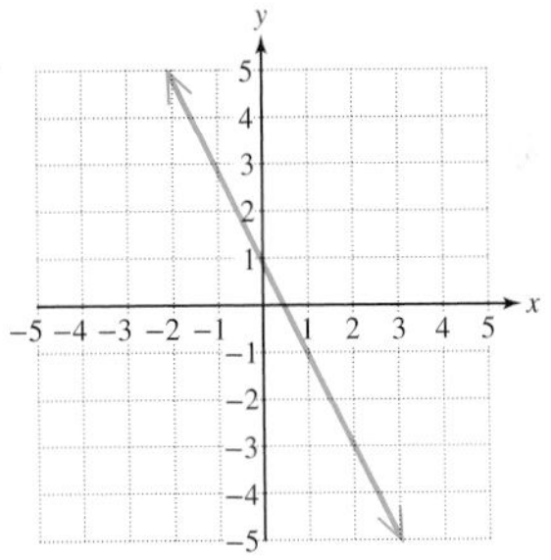

89. Draw a line with a zero slope and a positive y-intercept.

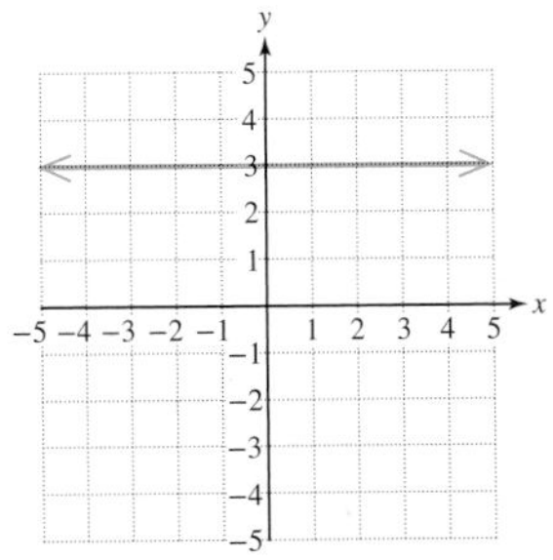

90. Draw a line with undefined slope and a negative x-intercept.

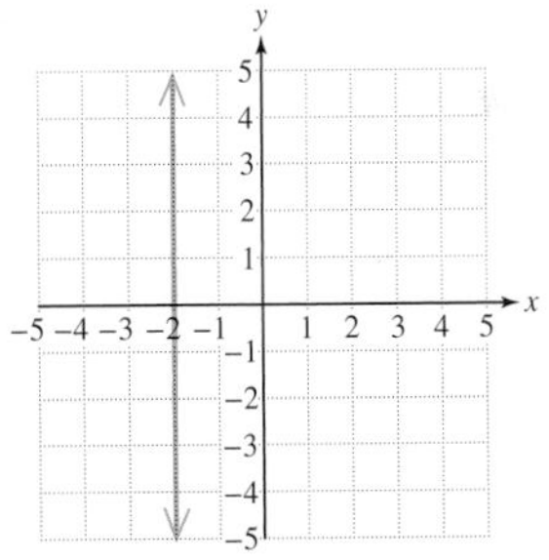

Expanding Your Skills

91. Determine the slope between the points $(a + b, 4m - n)$ and $(a - b, m + 2n)$. $\frac{3m - 3n}{2b}$ or $\frac{-3m + 3n}{-2b}$

92. Determine the slope between the points $(3c - d, s + t)$ and $(c - 2d, s - t)$. $\frac{2t}{2c + d}$ or $\frac{-2t}{-2c - d}$

93. Determine the x-intercept of the line $ax + by = c$. $\left(\frac{c}{a}, 0\right)$

94. Determine the y-intercept of the line $ax + by = c$. $\left(0, \frac{c}{b}\right)$

95. Find another point on the line that contains the point $(2, -1)$ and has a slope of $\frac{2}{5}$. For example: $(7, 1)$

96. Find another point on the line that contains the point $(-3, 4)$ and has a slope of $\frac{1}{4}$. For example: $(1, 5)$

Section 3.4 Slope-Intercept Form of a Linear Equation

Concepts

1. Slope-Intercept Form of a Linear Equation
2. Graphing a Line from Its Slope and y-Intercept
3. Determining Whether Two Lines Are Parallel, Perpendicular, or Neither
4. Writing an Equation of a Line Using Slope-Intercept Form

1. Slope-Intercept Form of a Linear Equation

We learned that the solutions to an equation of the form $Ax + By = C$ (where A and B are not both zero) represent a line in a rectangular coordinate system. An equation of a line written in this way is said to be in **standard form**. In this section, we will learn a new form, called **slope-intercept form**, that can be used to determine the slope and y-intercept of a line.

Let $(0, b)$ represent the y-intercept of a line. Let (x, y) represent any other point on the line. See Figure 3-26. Then the slope, m, of the line can be found as follows:

Let $(0, b)$ represent (x_1, y_1), and let (x, y) represent (x_2, y_2). Apply the slope formula.

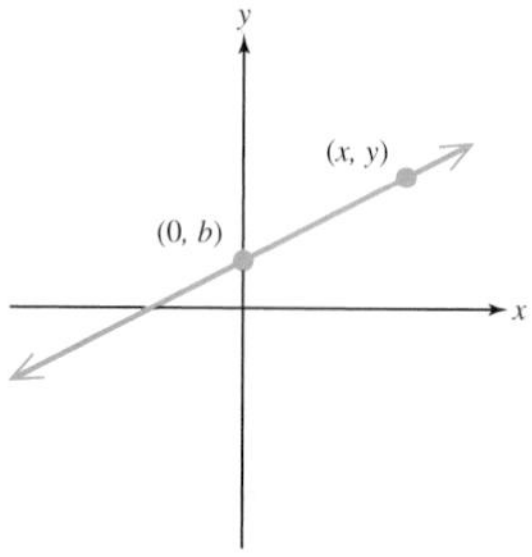

Figure 3-26

$$m = \frac{y_2 - y_1}{x_2 - x_1} \rightarrow m = \frac{y - b}{x - 0}$$ Apply the slope formula.

$$m = \frac{y - b}{x}$$ Simplify.

$$mx = \left(\frac{y - b}{x}\right)x$$ Multiply by x to clear fractions.

$$mx = y - b$$

$$mx + b = y - b + b$$ To isolate y, add b to both sides.

$$mx + b = y \quad \text{or} \quad y = mx + b$$ The equation is in slope-intercept form.

Slope-Intercept Form of a Linear Equation

$y = mx + b$ is the slope-intercept form of a linear equation.
m is the slope and the point $(0, b)$ is the y-intercept.

Classroom Examples: p. 238, Exercises 12 and 16

Example 1 Identifying the Slope and y-Intercept From a Linear Equation

For each equation, identify the slope and y-intercept.

a. $y = 3x - 1$ **b.** $y = -2.7x + 5$ **c.** $y = 4x$

Solution:

Each equation is written in slope-intercept form, $y = mx + b$. The slope is the coefficient of x, and the y-intercept is determined by the constant term.

a. $y = 3x - 1$ The slope is 3. The y-intercept is $(0, -1)$.

b. $y = -2.7x + 5$ The slope is -2.7. The y-intercept is $(0, 5)$.

c. $y = 4x$ can be written as $y = 4x + 0$. The slope is 4. The y-intercept is $(0, 0)$.

Skill Practice Identify the slope and the y-intercept.

1. $y = 4x + 6$ **2.** $y = 3.5x - 4.2$ **3.** $y = -7$

Answers

1. slope: 4; y-intercept: $(0, 6)$
2. slope: 3.5; y-intercept: $(0, -4.2)$
3. slope: 0; y-intercept: $(0, -7)$

Given an equation of a line, we can write the equation in slope-intercept form by solving the equation for the y-variable. This is demonstrated in Example 2.

Example 2 **Identifying the Slope and y-Intercept From a Linear Equation**

Classroom Example: p. 238, Exercise 22

Given the equation $-5x - 2y = 6$,

a. Write the equation in slope-intercept form.

b. Identify the slope and y-intercept.

Solution:

a. Write the equation in slope-intercept form, $y = mx + b$, by solving for y.

$$-5x - 2y = 6$$

$$-2y = 5x + 6 \qquad \text{Add } 5x \text{ to both sides.}$$

$$\frac{-2y}{-2} = \frac{5x + 6}{-2} \qquad \text{Divide both sides by } -2.$$

$$y = \frac{5x}{-2} + \frac{6}{-2} \qquad \text{Divide each term by } -2 \text{ and simplify.}$$

$$y = -\frac{5}{2}x - 3 \qquad \text{Slope-intercept form}$$

b. The slope is $-\frac{5}{2}$, and the y-intercept is $(0, -3)$.

Skill Practice Given the equation $2x - 6y = -3$.

4. Write the equation in slope-intercept form.

5. Identify the slope and the y-intercept.

2. Graphing a Line from Its Slope and y-Intercept

Slope-intercept form is a useful tool to graph a line. The y-intercept is a known point on the line. The slope indicates the direction of the line and can be used to find a second point. Using slope-intercept form to graph a line is demonstrated in Examples 3 and 4.

Example 3 **Graphing a Line Using the Slope and y-Intercept**

Classroom Example: p. 240, Exercise 44

Graph the equation $y = -\frac{5}{2}x - 3$ by using the slope and y-intercept.

Solution:

First plot the y-intercept, $(0, -3)$.

The slope $m = -\frac{5}{2}$ can be written as

$$m = \frac{-5}{2} \quad \begin{array}{l} \leftarrow \text{The change in } y \text{ is } -5. \\ \leftarrow \text{The change in } x \text{ is } 2. \end{array}$$

To find a second point on the line, start at the y-intercept and move down 5 units and to the right 2 units. Then draw the line through the two points (Figure 3-27).

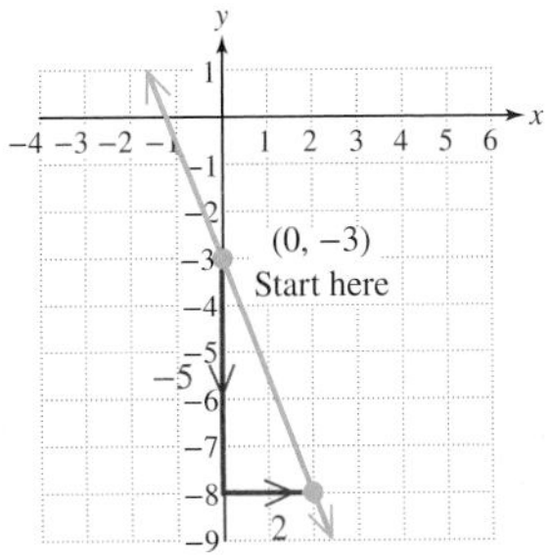

Figure 3-27

Answers

4. $y = \frac{1}{3}x + \frac{1}{2}$

5. slope is $\frac{1}{3}$; y-intercept is $\left(0, \frac{1}{2}\right)$

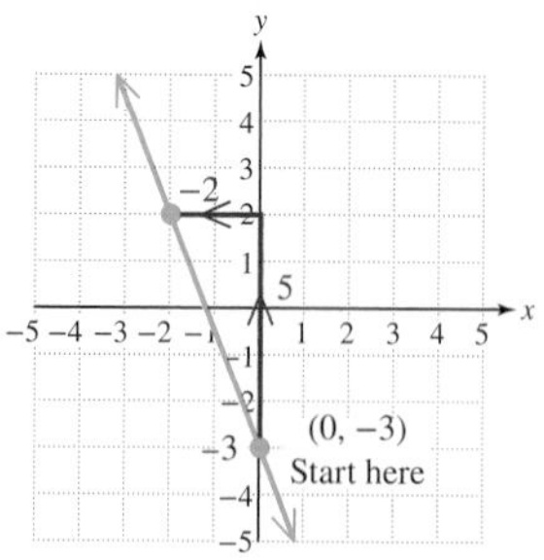

Figure 3-28

Similarly, the slope can be written as

$$m = \frac{5}{-2} \quad \begin{array}{l}\leftarrow \text{The change in } y \text{ is 5.} \\ \leftarrow \text{The change in } x \text{ is } -2.\end{array}$$

To find a second point, start at the y-intercept and move up 5 units and to the left 2 units. Then draw the line through the two points (Figure 3-28).

Skill Practice

6. Graph the equation by using the slope and y-intercept. $y = 2x - 3$

Classroom Example: p. 240, Exercise 50

Example 4 Graphing a Line Using the Slope and *y*-Intercept

Graph the equation $y = 4x$ by using the slope and y-intercept.

Solution:

The equation can be written as $y = 4x + 0$. Therefore, we can plot the y-intercept at (0, 0). The slope $m = 4$ can be written as

$$m = \frac{4}{1} \quad \begin{array}{l}\leftarrow \text{The change in } y \text{ is 4.} \\ \leftarrow \text{The change in } x \text{ is 1.}\end{array}$$

Animation

To find a second point on the line, start at the y-intercept and move up 4 units and to the right 1 unit. Then draw the line through the two points (Figure 3-29).

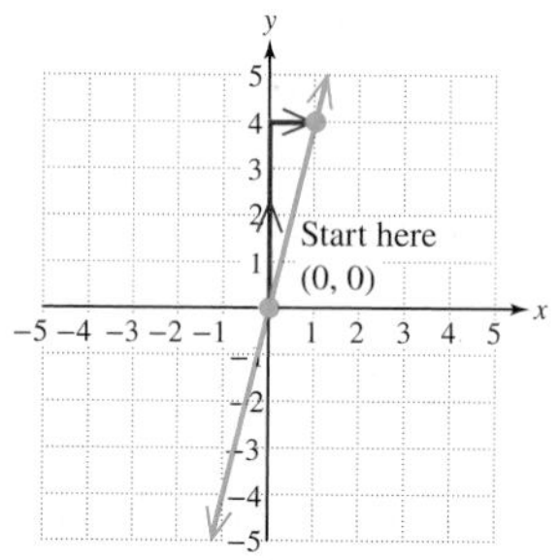

Figure 3-29

Skill Practice

7. Graph the equation by using the slope and y-intercept. $y = -\frac{1}{4}x$

Answers

6–7.

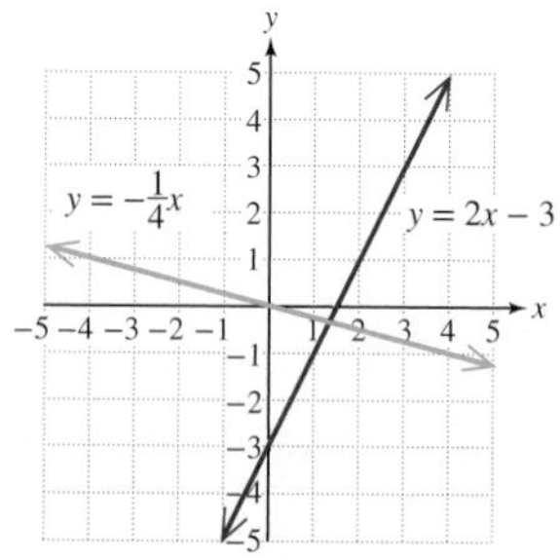

3. Determining Whether Two Lines Are Parallel, Perpendicular, or Neither

The slope-intercept form provides a means to find the slope of a line by inspection. Recall that if the slopes of two lines are known, then we can compare the slopes to determine if the lines are parallel, perpendicular, or neither parallel nor perpendicular. (Two distinct nonvertical lines are parallel if their slopes are equal. Two lines are perpendicular if the slope of one line is the opposite of the reciprocal of the slope of the other line.)

Example 5 **Determining If Two Lines Are Parallel, Perpendicular, or Neither**

Classroom Examples: p. 240, Exercises 54 and 56

For each pair of lines, determine if they are parallel, perpendicular, or neither.

a. l_1: $y = 3x - 5$ **b.** l_1: $y = \frac{3}{2}x + 2$

l_2: $y = 3x + 1$ l_2: $y = \frac{2}{3}x + 1$

Solution:

a. l_1: $y = 3x - 5$ The slope of l_1 is 3.

l_2: $y = 3x + 1$ The slope of l_2 is 3.

Because the slopes are the same, the lines are parallel.

b. l_1: $y = \frac{3}{2}x + 2$ The slope of l_1 is $\frac{3}{2}$.

l_2: $y = \frac{2}{3}x + 1$ The slope of l_2 is $\frac{2}{3}$.

The slopes are not the same. Therefore, the lines are not parallel. The values of the slopes are reciprocals, but they are not opposite in sign. Therefore, the lines are not perpendicular. The lines are neither parallel nor perpendicular.

Skill Practice For each pair of lines determine if they are parallel, perpendicular, or neither.

8. $y = 3x - 5$
$y = -3x - 15$

9. $y = \frac{5}{6}x - \frac{1}{2}$
$y = \frac{5}{6}x + \frac{1}{2}$

Example 6 **Determining If Two Lines Are Parallel, Perpendicular, or Neither**

Classroom Examples: p. 240, Exercises 62 and 64

For each pair of lines, determine if they are parallel, perpendicular, or neither.

a. l_1: $x - 3y = -9$ **b.** l_1: $x = 2$

l_2: $3x = -y + 4$ l_2: $2y = 8$

Solution:

a. First write the equation of each line in slope-intercept form.

l_1:
$$x - 3y = -9$$
$$-3y = -x - 9$$
$$\frac{-3y}{-3} = \frac{-x}{-3} - \frac{9}{-3}$$
$$y = \frac{1}{3}x + 3$$

l_2:
$$3x = -y + 4$$
$$3x + y = 4$$
$$y = -3x + 4$$

l_1: $y = \frac{1}{3}x + 3$ The slope of l_1 is $\frac{1}{3}$.

l_2: $y = -3x + 4$ The slope of l_2 is -3.

The slope of $\frac{1}{3}$ is the opposite of the reciprocal of -3. Therefore, the lines are perpendicular.

Answers

8. Neither **9.** Parallel

b. The equation $x = 2$ represents a vertical line because the equation is in the form $x = k$.

The equation $2y = 8$ can be simplified to $y = 4$, which represents a horizontal line.

In this example, we do not need to analyze the slopes because vertical lines and horizontal lines are perpendicular.

Skill Practice For each pair of lines, determine if they are parallel, perpendicular, or neither.

10. $x - 5y = 10$
$5x - 1 = -y$

11. $y = -5$
$x = 6$

4. Writing an Equation of a Line Using Slope-Intercept Form

The slope-intercept form of a linear equation can be used to write an equation of a line when the slope is known and the y-intercept is known.

Classroom Example: p. 241, Exercise 70

Example 7 Writing an Equation of a Line Using Slope-Intercept Form

Write an equation of the line whose slope is $\frac{2}{3}$ and whose y-intercept is $(0, 8)$.

Solution:

The slope is given as $m = \frac{2}{3}$, and the y-intercept $(0, b)$ is given as $(0, 8)$. Substitute the values $m = \frac{2}{3}$ and $b = 8$ into the slope-intercept form of a line.

$$y = mx + b$$
$$\downarrow \quad \downarrow$$
$$y = \frac{2}{3}x + 8$$

Skill Practice

12. Write an equation of the line whose slope is -4 and y-intercept is $(0, -10)$.

Classroom Example: p. 241, Exercise 74

Example 8 Writing an Equation of a Line Using Slope-Intercept Form

Write an equation of the line having a slope of 2 and passing through the point $(-3, 1)$.

Solution:

To find an equation of a line using slope-intercept form, it is necessary to find the value of m and b. The slope is given in the problem as $m = 2$. Therefore, the slope-intercept form becomes

$$y = mx + b$$
$$\downarrow$$
$$y = 2x + b$$

Answers

10. Perpendicular **11.** Perpendicular
12. $y = -4x - 10$

Because the point $(-3, 1)$ is on the line, it is a solution to the equation. Therefore, to find b, substitute the values of x and y from the ordered pair $(-3, 1)$ and solve the resulting equation for b.

$$y = 2x + b$$

$$1 = 2(-3) + b \qquad \text{Substitute } y = 1 \text{ and } x = -3.$$

$$1 = -6 + b \qquad \text{Simplify and solve for } b.$$

$$7 = b$$

Now with m and b known, the slope-intercept form is $y = 2x + 7$.

TIP: The equation from Example 8 can be checked by graphing the line $y = 2x + 7$. The slope $m = 2$ can be written as $m = \frac{2}{1}$. Therefore, to graph the line, start at the y-intercept $(0, 7)$ and move up 2 units and to the right 1 unit.

The graph verifies that the line passes through the point $(-3, 1)$ as it should.

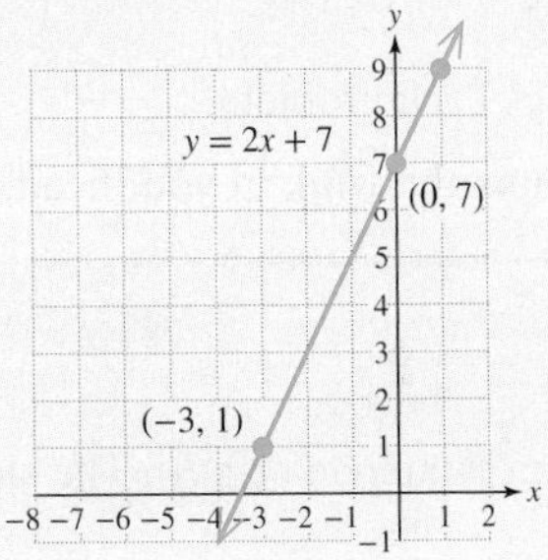

Skill Practice

13. Write an equation of the line having a slope of -3 and passing through the point $(-2, -5)$.

Answer

13. $y = -3x - 11$

Calculator Connections

Topic: Using the *ZSquare* Option in Zoom

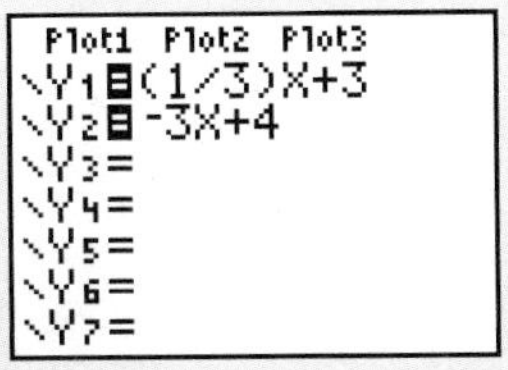

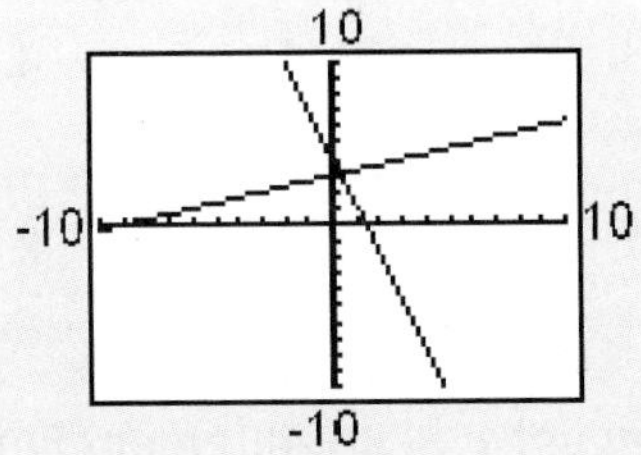

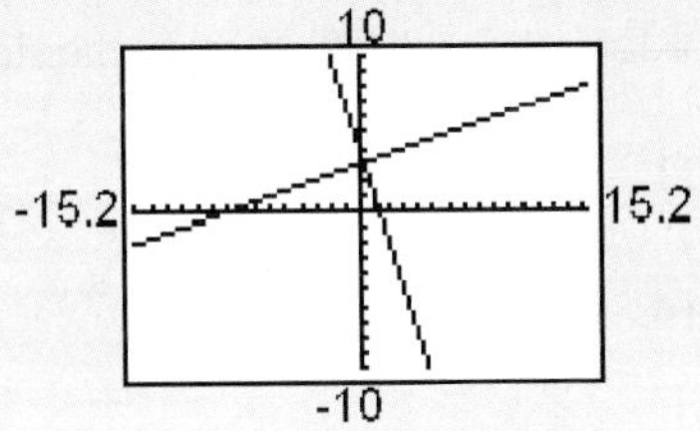

In Example 6(a) we found that the equations $y = \frac{1}{3}x + 3$ and $y = -3x + 4$ represent perpendicular lines. We can verify our results by graphing the lines on a graphing calculator.

Notice that the lines do not appear perpendicular in the calculator display on the standard viewing window. That is, they do not appear to form a right angle at the point of intersection. Because many calculators have a rectangular screen, the standard viewing window is elongated in the horizontal direction. To eliminate this distortion, try using a *ZSquare* option, which is located under the Zoom menu. This feature will set the viewing window so that equal distances on the display denote an equal number of units on the graph.

Calculator Exercises

For each pair of lines, determine if the lines are parallel, perpendicular, or neither. Then use a square viewing window to graph the lines on a graphing calculator to verify your results.

1. $x + y = 1$
$x - y = -3$ Perpendicular

2. $3x + y = -2$
$6x + 2y = 6$ Parallel

3. $2x - y = 4$
$3x + 2y = 4$ Neither

4. Graph the lines defined by $y = x + 1$ and $y = 0.99x + 3$. Are these lines parallel? Explain.
The lines may appear parallel; however, they are not parallel because the slopes are different.

5. Graph the lines defined by $y = -2x - 1$ and $y = -2x - 0.99$. Are these lines the same? Explain.
The lines may appear to coincide on a graph; however, they are not the same line because the y-intercepts are different.

6. Graph the line defined by $y = 0.001x + 3$. Is this line horizontal? Explain.
The line may appear to be horizontal, but it is not. The slope is 0.001 rather than 0.

Section 3.4 Practice Exercises

Study Skills Exercise

For additional exercises, see Classroom Activities 3.4A–3.4C in the *Student's Resource Manual* at www.mhhe.com/moh.

When taking a test, go through the test and do all the problems that you know first. Then go back and work on the problems that were more difficult. Give yourself a time limit for how much time you spend on each problem (maybe 3 to 5 min the first time through). Circle the importance of each statement.

	not important	somewhat important	very important
a. Read through the entire test first.	1	2	3
b. If time allows, go back and check each problem.	1	2	3
c. Write out all steps instead of doing the work in your head.	1	2	3

Vocabulary and Key Terms

1. a. Consider a line with slope m and y-intercept $(0, b)$. The slope-intercept form of an equation of the line is $y = mx + b$.

b. An equation of a line written in the form $Ax + By = C$ where A and B are not both zero is said to be in standard form.

Review Exercises

2. For each equation given, determine if the line is horizontal, vertical, or slanted.

a. $3x = 6$ vertical

b. $y + 3 = 6$ horizontal

c. $x + y = 6$ slanted

For Exercises 3–10, determine the x- and y-intercepts, if they exist.

3. $x - 5y = 10$ x-intercept: $(10, 0)$; y-intercept: $(0, -2)$

4. $3x + y = -12$ x-intercept: $(-4, 0)$; y-intercept: $(0, -12)$

5. $3y = -9$ x-intercept: none; y-intercept: $(0, -3)$

6. $2 + y = 5$ x-intercept: none; y-intercept: $(0, 3)$

7. $-4x = 6y$ x-intercept: $(0, 0)$; y-intercept: $(0, 0)$

8. $-x + 3 = 8$ x-intercept: $(-5, 0)$; y-intercept: none

9. $5x = 20$ x-intercept: $(4, 0)$; y-intercept: none

10. $y = \frac{1}{2}x$ x-intercept: $(0, 0)$; y-intercept: $(0, 0)$

Concept 1: Slope-Intercept Form of a Linear Equation

For Exercises 11–30, identify the slope and y-intercept, if they exist. **(See Examples 1–2.)**

11. $y = -2x + 3$ $m = -2$; y-intercept: $(0, 3)$

12. $y = \frac{2}{3}x + 5$ $m = \frac{2}{3}$; y-intercept: $(0, 5)$

13. $y = x - 2$ $m = 1$; y-intercept: $(0, -2)$

14. $y = -x + 6$ $m = -1$; y-intercept: $(0, 6)$

15. $y = -x$ $m = -1$; y-intercept: $(0; 0)$

16. $y = -5x$ $m = -5$; y-intercept: $(0, 0)$

17. $y = \frac{3}{4}x - 1$ $m = \frac{3}{4}$; y-interncept: $(0, -1)$

18. $y = x - \frac{5}{3}$ $m = 1$; y-intercept: $\left(0, -\frac{5}{3}\right)$

19. $2x - 5y = 4$ $m = \frac{2}{5}$; y-intercept: $\left(0, -\frac{4}{5}\right)$

20. $3x + 2y = 9$ $m = -\frac{3}{2}$; y-intercept: $\left(0, \frac{9}{2}\right)$

21. $3x - y = 5$ $m = 3$; y-intercept: $(0, -5)$

22. $7x - 3y = -6$ $m = \frac{7}{3}$; y-intercept: $(0, 2)$

23. $x + y = 6$ $m = -1$; y-intercept: $(0, 6)$

24. $x - y = 1$ $m = 1$; y-intercept: $(0, -1)$

25. $x + 6 = 8$ Undefined slope; no y-intercept

26. $-4 + x = 1$ Undefined slope; no y-intercept

27. $-8y = 2$ $m = 0$; y-intercept: $\left(0, -\frac{1}{4}\right)$

28. $1 - y = 9$ $m = 0$; y-intercept: $(0, -8)$

29. $3y - 2x = 0$ $m = \frac{2}{3}$; y-intercept: $(0, 0)$

30. $5x = 6y$ $m = \frac{5}{6}$; y-intercept: $(0, 0)$

Concept 2: Graphing a Line from Its Slope and *y*-Intercept

For Exercises 31–34, graph the line using the slope and *y*-intercept. **(See Examples 3–4.)**

31. Graph the line through the point (0, 2), having a slope of −4.

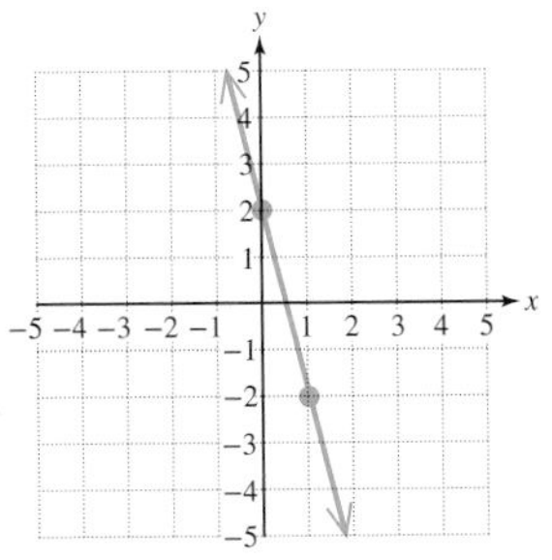

32. Graph the line through the point (0, −1), having a slope of −3.

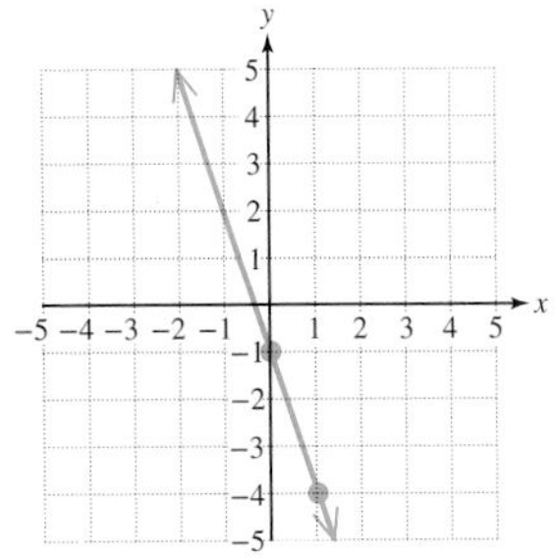

33. Graph the line through the point (0, −5), having a slope of $\frac{3}{2}$.

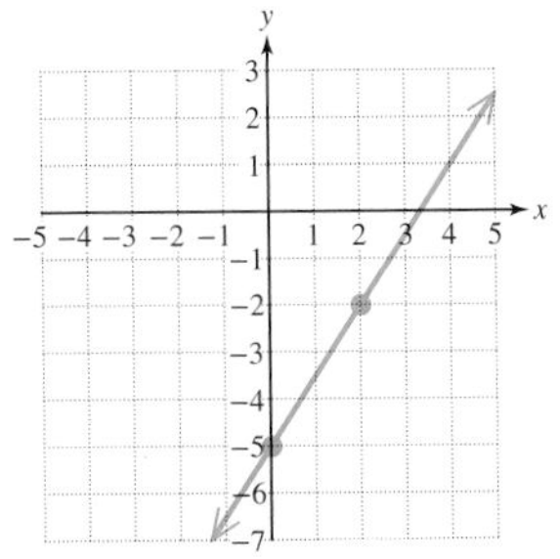

34. Graph the line through the point (0, 3), having a slope of $-\frac{1}{4}$.

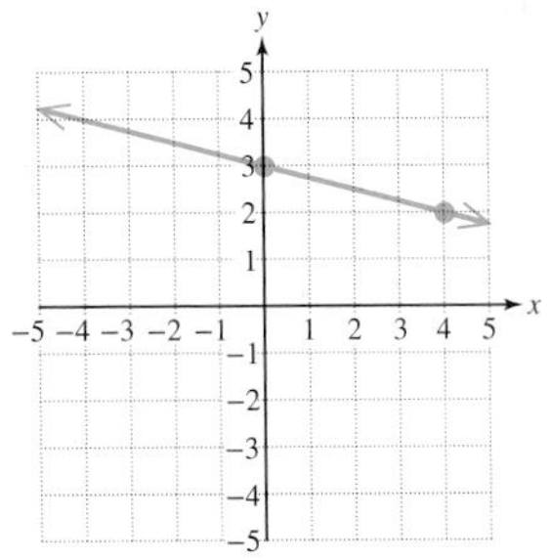

For Exercises 35–40, match the equation with the graph (a–f) by identifying if the slope is positive or negative and if the *y*-intercept is positive, negative, or zero.

35. $y = 2x + 3$ b

36. $y = -3x - 2$ d

37. $y = -\frac{1}{3}x + 3$ e

38. $y = \frac{1}{2}x - 2$ a

39. $y = x$ c

40. $y = -2x$ f

a.

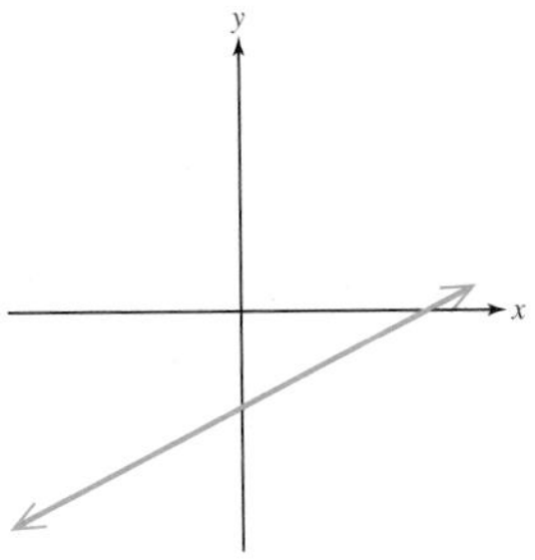

b.

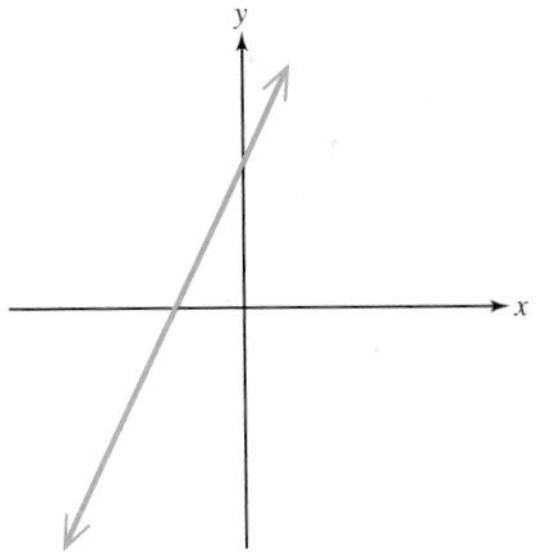

c.

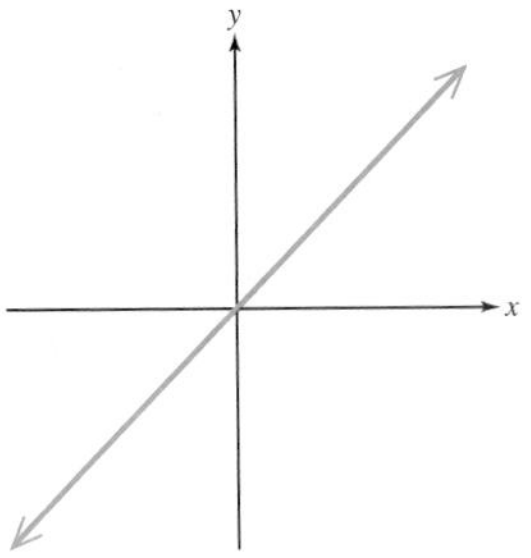

d.

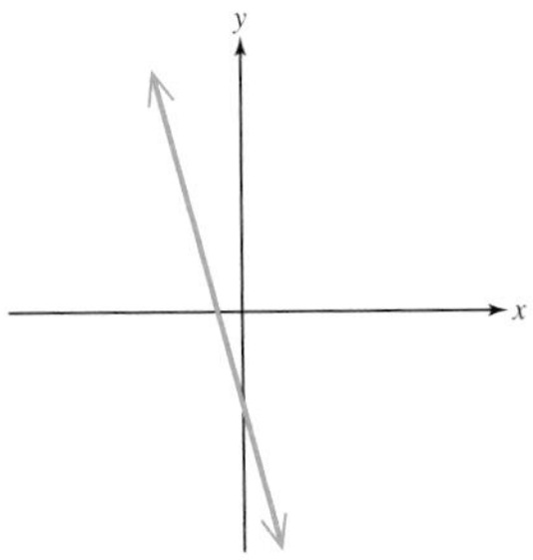

e.

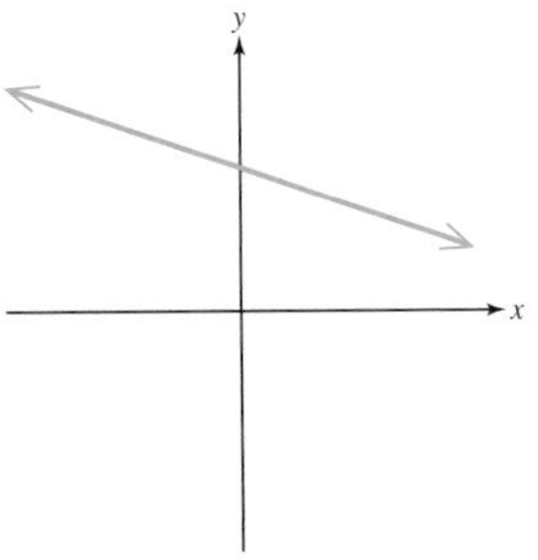

f.

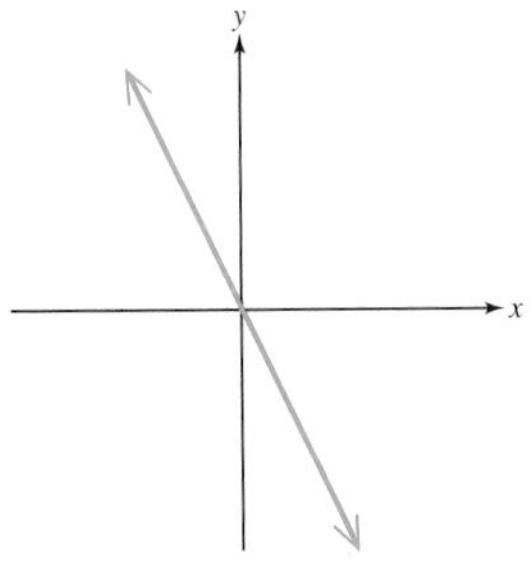

For Exercises 41–52, write each equation in slope-intercept form (if possible) and graph the line. **(See Examples 3–4.)**

41. $2x + y = 9$
$y = -2x + 9$

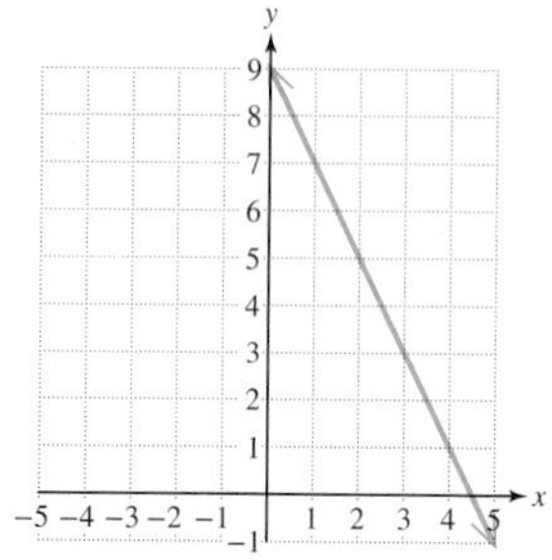

42. $-6x + y = 8$
$y = 6x + 8$

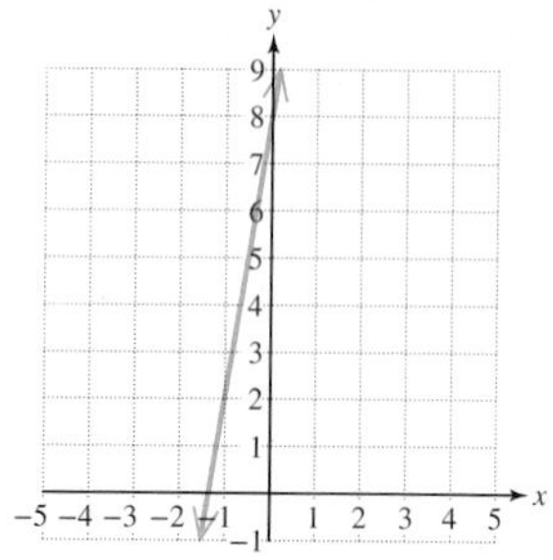

43. $x - 2y = 6$
$y = \frac{1}{2}x - 3$

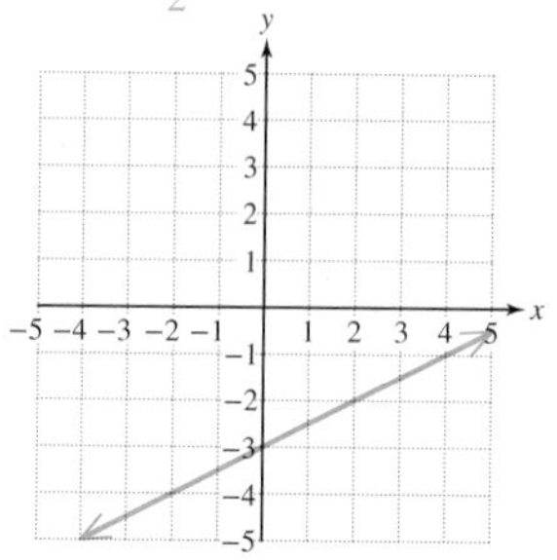

44. $5x - 2y = 2$
$y = \frac{5}{2}x - 1$

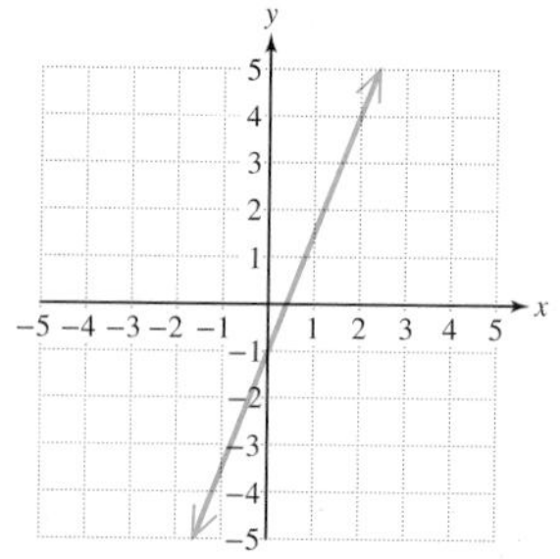

45. $2x = -4y + 6$
$y = -\frac{1}{2}x + \frac{3}{2}$

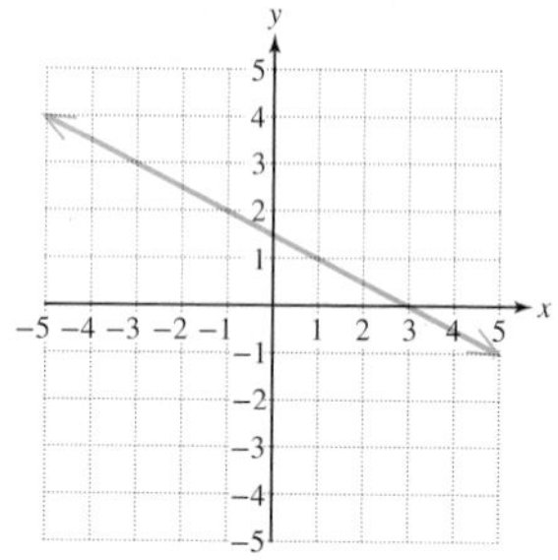

46. $6x = 2y - 14$
$y = 3x + 7$

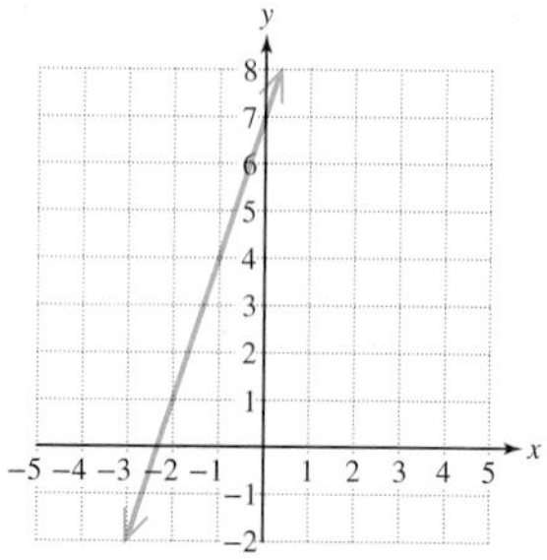

47. $x + y = 0$
$y = -x$

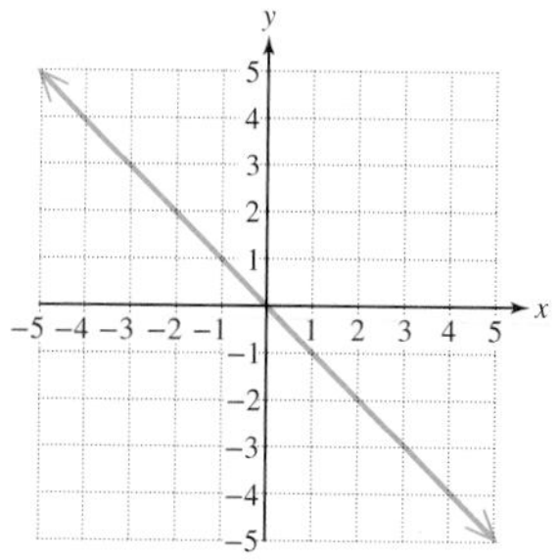

48. $x - y = 0$
$y = x$

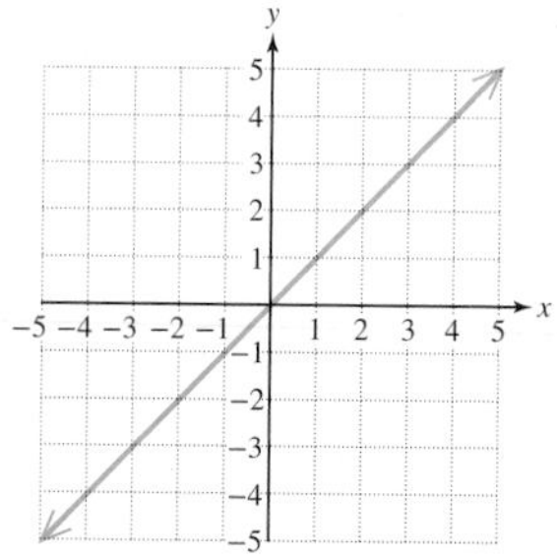

49. $5y = 4x$
$y = \frac{4}{5}x$

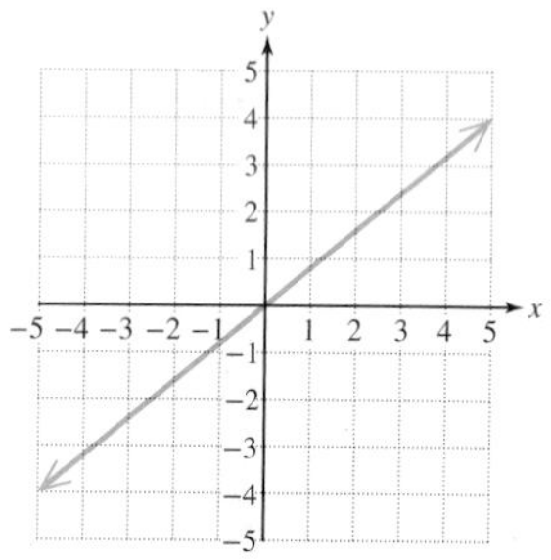

50. $-2x = 5y$
$y = -\frac{2}{5}x$

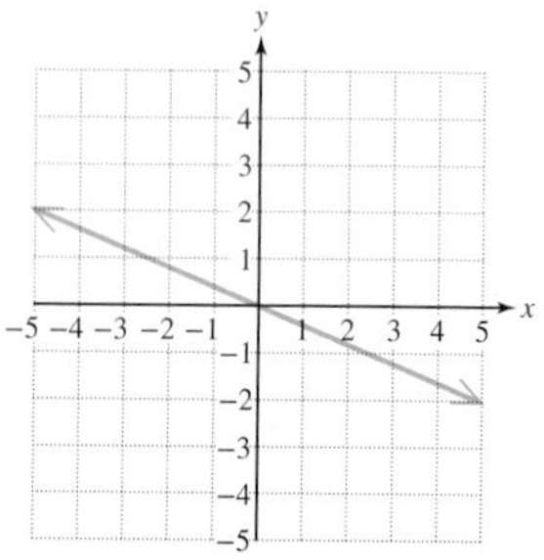

51. $3y + 2 = 0$
$y = -\frac{2}{3}$

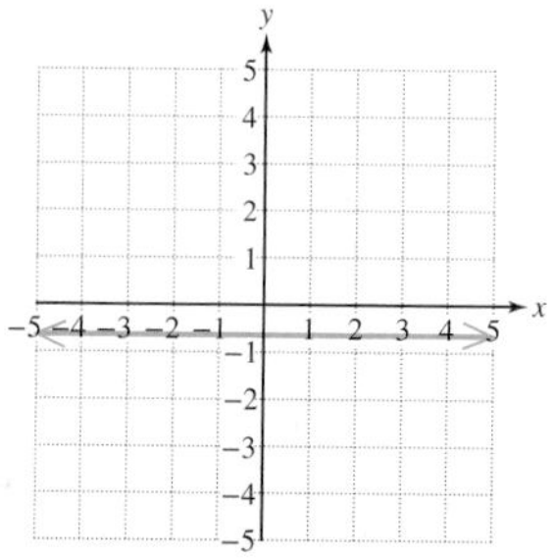

52. $1 + 5y = 6$
$y = 1$

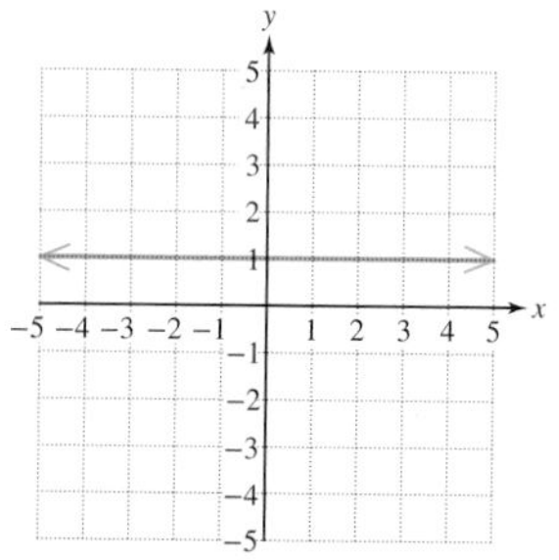

Concept 3: Determining Whether Two Lines Are Parallel, Perpendicular, or Neither

For Exercises 53–68, determine if the equations represent parallel lines, perpendicular lines, or neither. **(See Examples 5–6.)**

53. l_1: $y = -2x - 3$
l_2: $y = \frac{1}{2}x + 4$
Perpendicular

54. l_1: $y = \frac{4}{3}x - 2$
l_2: $y = -\frac{3}{4}x + 6$
Perpendicular

55. l_1: $y = \frac{4}{5}x - \frac{1}{2}$
l_2: $y = \frac{5}{4}x - \frac{2}{3}$
Neither

56. l_1: $y = \frac{1}{5}x + 1$
l_2: $y = 5x - 3$
Neither

57. l_1: $y = -9x + 6$
l_2: $y = -9x - 1$
Parallel

58. l_1: $y = 4x - 1$
l_2: $y = 4x + \frac{1}{2}$
Parallel

59. l_1: $x = 3$
l_2: $y = \frac{7}{4}$
Perpendicular

60. l_1: $y = \frac{2}{3}$
l_2: $x = 6$
Perpendicular

61. l_1: $2x = 4$
l_2: $6 = x$
Parallel

62. l_1: $2y = 7$
l_2: $y = 4$
Parallel

63. l_1: $2x + 3y = 6$
l_2: $3x - 2y = 12$
Perpendicular

64. l_1: $4x + 5y = 20$
l_2: $5x - 4y = 60$
Perpendicular

65. l_1: $4x + 2y = 6$
l_2: $4x + 8y = 16$
Neither

66. l_1: $3x + y = 5$
l_2: $x + 3y = 18$
Neither

67. l_1: $y = \frac{1}{5}x - 3$
l_2: $2x - 10y = 20$
Parallel

68. l_1: $y = \frac{1}{3}x + 2$
l_2: $-x + 3y = 12$
Parallel

Concept 4: Writing an Equation of a Line Using Slope-Intercept Form

For Exercises 69–80, write an equation of the line given the following information. Write the answer in slope-intercept form if possible. **(See Examples 7–8.)**

69. The slope is $-\frac{1}{3}$, and the y-intercept is (0, 2). $y = -\frac{1}{3}x + 2$

70. The slope is $\frac{2}{3}$, and the y-intercept is (0, −1). $y = \frac{2}{3}x - 1$

71. The slope is 10, and the y-intercept is (0, −19). $y = 10x - 19$

72. The slope is −14, and the y-intercept is (0, 2). $y = -14x + 2$

73. The slope is 6, and the line passes through the point (1, −2). $y = 6x - 8$

74. The slope is −4, and the line passes through the point (4, −3). $y = -4x + 13$

75. The slope is $\frac{1}{2}$, and the line passes through the point (−4, −5). $y = \frac{1}{2}x - 3$

76. The slope is $-\frac{2}{3}$, and the line passes through the point (3, −1). $y = -\frac{2}{3}x + 1$

77. The slope is 0, and the y-intercept is −11. $y = -11$

78. The slope is 0, and the y-intercept is $\frac{6}{7}$. $y = \frac{6}{7}$

79. The slope is 5, and the line passes through the origin. $y = 5x$

80. The slope is −3, and the line passes through the origin. $y = -3x$

Expanding Your Skills

For Exercises 81–86, write an equation of the line that passes through two points by following these steps:

Step 1: Find the slope of the line using the slope formula, $m = \frac{y_2 - y_1}{x_2 - x_1}$.

Step 2: Using the slope from Step 1 and either given point, follow the procedure given in Example 8 to find an equation of the line in slope-intercept form.

81. (2, −1) and (0, 3) $y = -2x + 3$

82. (4, −8) and (0, −4) $y = -x - 4$

83. (3, 1) and (−3, 3) $y = -\frac{1}{3}x + 2$

84. (2, −3) and (4, −2) $y = \frac{1}{2}x - 4$

85. (1, 3) and (−2, −9) $y = 4x - 1$

86. (1, 7) and (−2, 4) $y = x + 6$

87. The number of reported cases of Lyme disease in the United States can be modeled by the equation $y = 1203x + 10{,}006$. In this equation, x represents the number of years since 1993, and y represents the number of cases of Lyme disease.

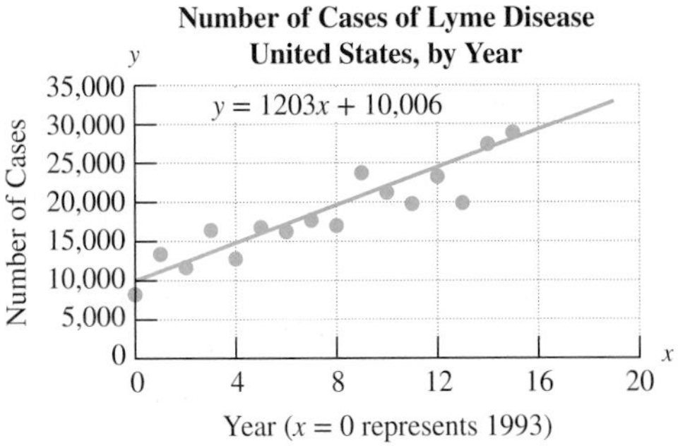

a. What is the slope of this line and what does it mean in the context of this problem? $m = 1203$; The slope represents the rate of increase in the number of cases of Lyme disease per year.

b. What is the y-intercept, and what does it mean in the context of this problem? (0, 10006); In the year 1993 there were 10,006 cases reported.

c. Use the model to estimate the number of cases of Lyme disease in the year 2010. 30,457 cases

d. During what year would the predicted number of cases be 42,487? $x = 27$; the year 2020

88. A phone bill is determined each month by a \$16.95 flat fee plus \$0.10/min of long distance. The equation, $C = 0.10x + 16.95$ represents the total monthly cost, C, for x minutes of long distance.

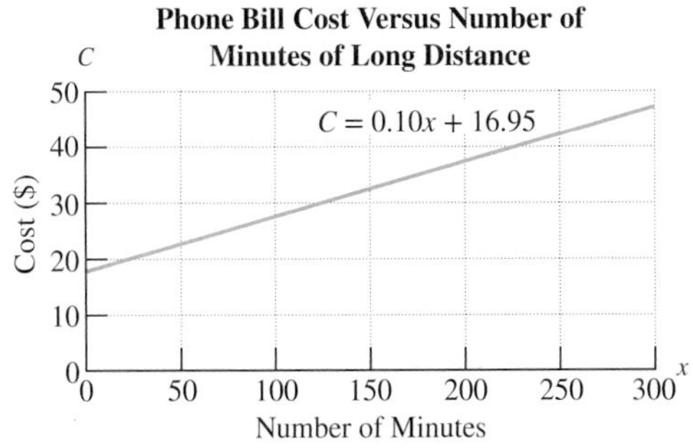

a. Identify the slope. Interpret the meaning of the slope in the context of this problem. $m = 0.10$. The cost increases by \$0.10/min of long distance.

b. Identify the C-intercept. Interpret the meaning of the C-intercept in the context of this problem. (0, 16.95). The monthly bill for 0 min is \$16.95.

c. Use the equation to determine the total cost of 234 min of long distance. The cost is \$40.35.

89. A linear equation is written in standard form if it can be written as $Ax + By = C$, where A and B are not both zero. Write the equation $Ax + By = C$ in slope-intercept form to show that the slope is given by the ratio, $-\frac{A}{B}$. $(B \neq 0.)$ $y = -\frac{A}{B}x + \frac{C}{B}$; the slope is $-\frac{A}{B}$.

For Exercises 90–93, use the result of Exercise 89 to find the slope of the line.

90. $2x + 5y = 8$ $m = -\frac{2}{5}$ **91.** $6x + 7y = -9$ $m = -\frac{6}{7}$ **92.** $4x - 3y = -5$ $m = \frac{4}{3}$ **93.** $11x - 8y = 4$ $m = \frac{11}{8}$

Problem Recognition Exercises

Linear Equations in Two Variables

For Exercises 1–20, choose the equation(s) from the column on the right whose graph satisfies the condition described. Give all possible answers.

a. $y = 5x$

b. $2x + 3y = 12$

c. $y = \frac{1}{2}x - 5$

d. $3x - 6y = 10$

e. $2y = -8$

f. $y = -2x + 4$

g. $3x = 1$

h. $x + 2y = 6$

1. Line whose slope is positive. a, c, d

2. Line whose slope is negative. b, f, h

3. Line that passes through the origin. a

4. Line that contains the point (3, –2). f

5. Line whose y-intercept is (0, 4). b, f

6. Line whose y-intercept is (0, –5). c

7. Line whose slope is $\frac{1}{2}$. c, d

8. Line whose slope is -2. f

9. Line whose slope is 0. e

10. Line whose slope is undefined. g

11. Line that is parallel to the line with equation $y = -\frac{2}{3}x + 4$. b

12. Line perpendicular to the line with equation $y = 2x + 9$. h

13. Line that is vertical. g

14. Line that is horizontal. e

15. Line whose x-intercept is (10, 0). c

16. Line whose x-intercept is (6, 0). b, h

17. Line that is parallel to the x-axis. e

18. Line that is perpendicular to the y-axis. e

19. Line with a negative slope and positive y-intercept. b, f, h

20. Line with a positive slope and negative y-intercept. c, d

Point-Slope Formula

Section 3.5

Concepts

1. Writing an Equation of a Line Using the Point-Slope Formula

The slope-intercept form of a line can be used as a tool to construct an equation of a line. Another useful tool to determine an equation of a line is the point-slope formula. The point-slope formula can be derived from the slope formula as follows.

Suppose a line passes through a given point (x_1, y_1) and has slope m. If (x, y) is any other point on the line, then the slope is given by

$m = \dfrac{y - y_1}{x - x_1}$	Slope formula
$m(x - x_1) = \dfrac{y - y_1}{\cancel{x - x_1}}\cancel{(x - x_1)}$	Clear fractions.
$m(x - x_1) = y - y_1$	
$y - y_1 = m(x - x_1)$	Point-slope formula

Point-Slope Formula

The **point-slope formula** is given by

$$y - y_1 = m(x - x_1)$$

where m is the slope of the line and (x_1, y_1) is any known point on the line.

Example 1 demonstrates how to use the point-slope formula to find an equation of a line when a point on the line and slope are given.

Example 1 Writing an Equation of a Line Using the Point-Slope Formula

Classroom Example: p. 248, Exercise 12

Use the point-slope formula to write an equation of the line having a slope of 3 and passing through the point (−2, −4). Write the answer in slope-intercept form.

Solution:

The slope of the line is given: $m = 3$

A point on the line is given: $(x_1, y_1) = (-2, -4)$

The point-slope formula:

$y - y_1 = m(x - x_1)$	
$y - (-4) = 3[x - (-2)]$	Substitute $m = 3$, $x_1 = -2$, and $y_1 = -4$.
$y + 4 = 3(x + 2)$	Simplify. Because the final answer is required in slope-intercept form, simplify the equation and solve for y.
$y + 4 = 3x + 6$	Apply the distributive property.
$y = 3x + 2$	Slope-intercept form

Instructor Note: Show students an alternative method using slope-intercept form.

$y = mx + b$ replace m, x, y
$-4 = 3(-2) + b$
$-4 = -6 + b$
$2 = b$

$y = mx + b$ replace m, b
$y = 3x + 2$

Skill Practice

1. Use the point-slope formula to write an equation of the line having a slope of −4 and passing through (−1, 5). Write the answer in slope-intercept form.

The equation $y = 3x + 2$ from Example 1 is graphed in Figure 3-30. Notice that the line does indeed pass through the point (−2, −4).

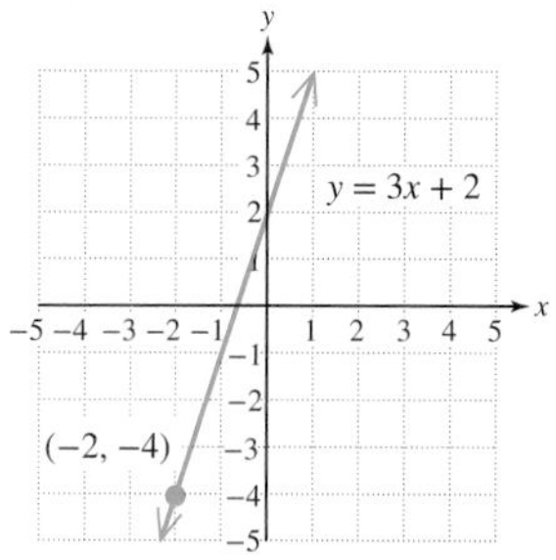

Figure 3-30

2. Writing an Equation of a Line Given Two Points

Example 2 is similar to Example 1; however, the slope must first be found from two given points.

Classroom Example: p. 249, Exercise 20

Example 2 **Writing an Equation of a Line Given Two Points**

Use the point-slope formula to find an equation of the line passing through the points (−2, 5) and (4, −1). Write the final answer in slope-intercept form.

Solution:

Given two points on a line, the slope can be found with the slope formula.

$(-2, 5)$ and $(4, -1)$
(x_1, y_1) (x_2, y_2) Label the points.

$$m = \frac{y_2 - y_1}{x_2 - x_1} = \frac{(-1) - (5)}{(4) - (-2)} = \frac{-6}{6} = -1$$

To apply the point-slope formula, use the slope, $m = -1$ and either given point. We will choose the point (−2, 5) as (x_1, y_1).

$y - y_1 = m(x - x_1)$

$y - 5 = -1[x - (-2)]$ Substitute $m = -1$, $x_1 = -2$, and $y_1 = 5$.

$y - 5 = -1(x + 2)$ Simplify.

$y - 5 = -x - 2$

$y = -x + 3$

TIP: The point-slope formula can be applied using either given point for (x_1, y_1). In Example 2, using the point (4, −1) for (x_1, y_1) produces the same result.

$y - y_1 = m(x - x_1)$

$y - (-1) = -1(x - 4)$

$y + 1 = -x + 4$

$y = -x + 3$

Skill Practice

2. Use the point-slope formula to write an equation of the line passing through the points (1, −1) and (−1, −5).

Answers

1. $y = -4x + 1$ 2. $y = 2x - 3$

The solution to Example 2 can be checked by graphing the line $y = -x + 3$ using the slope and y-intercept. Notice that the line passes through the points $(-2, 5)$ and $(4, -1)$ as expected. See Figure 3-31.

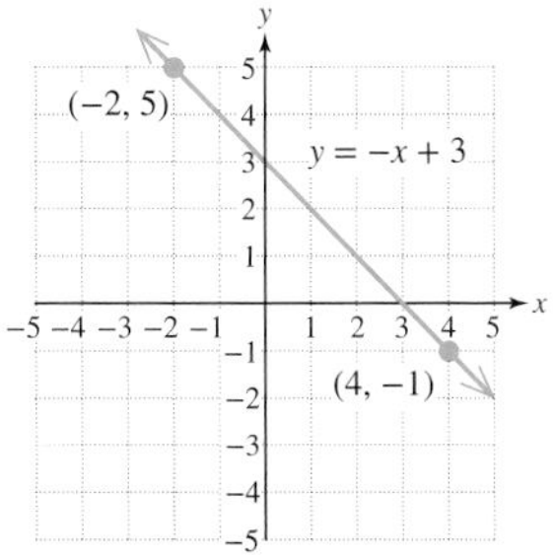

Figure 3-31

3. Writing an Equation of a Line Parallel or Perpendicular to Another Line

To write an equation of a line using the point-slope formula, the slope must be known. If the slope is not explicitly given, then other information must be used to determine the slope. In Example 2, the slope was found using the slope formula. Examples 3 and 4 show other situations in which we might find the slope.

Example 3 Writing an Equation of a Line Parallel to Another Line

Classroom Example: p. 249, Exercise 30

Use the point-slope formula to find an equation of the line passing through the point $(-1, 0)$ and parallel to the line $y = -4x + 3$. Write the final answer in slope-intercept form.

Solution:

Figure 3-32 shows the line $y = -4x + 3$ (pictured in black) and a line parallel to it (pictured in blue) that passes through the point $(-1, 0)$. The equation of the given line, $y = -4x + 3$, is written in slope-intercept form, and its slope is easily identified as -4. The line parallel to the given line must also have a slope of -4.

Apply the point-slope formula using $m = -4$ and the point $(x_1, y_1) = (-1, 0)$.

$$y - y_1 = m(x - x_1)$$
$$y - 0 = -4[x - (-1)]$$
$$y = -4(x + 1)$$
$$y = -4x - 4$$

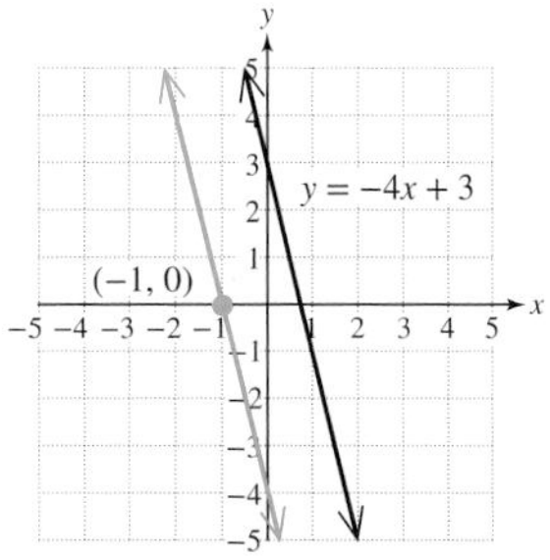

Figure 3-32

TIP: When writing an equation of a line, slope-intercept form or standard form is usually preferred. For instance, the solution to Example 3 can be written as follows.

Slope-intercept form:
$y = -4x - 4$

Standard form:
$4x + y = -4$

Skill Practice

3. Use the point-slope formula to write an equation of the line passing through $(8, 2)$ and parallel to the line $y = \frac{3}{4}x - \frac{1}{2}$.

Answer

3. $y = \frac{3}{4}x - 4$

Classroom Example: p. 249, Exercise 34

Example 4 Writing an Equation of a Line Perpendicular to Another Line

Use the point-slope formula to find an equation of the line passing through the point $(-3, 1)$ and perpendicular to the line $3x + y = -2$. Write the final answer in slope-intercept form.

Solution:

The given line can be written in slope-intercept form as $y = -3x - 2$. The slope of this line is -3. Therefore, the slope of a line perpendicular to the given line is $\frac{1}{3}$.

Apply the point-slope formula with $m = \frac{1}{3}$, and $(x_1, y_1) = (-3, 1)$.

$y - y_1 = m(x - x_1)$ Point-slope formula

$y - (1) = \frac{1}{3}[x - (-3)]$ Substitute $m = \frac{1}{3}$, $x_1 = -3$, and $y_1 = 1$.

$y - 1 = \frac{1}{3}(x + 3)$ To write the final answer in slope-intercept form, simplify the equation and solve for y.

$y - 1 = \frac{1}{3}x + 1$ Apply the distributive property.

$y = \frac{1}{3}x + 2$ Add 1 to both sides.

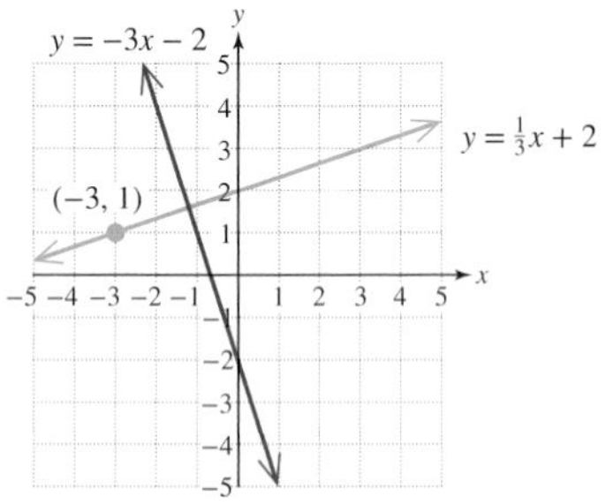

Figure 3-33

A sketch of the perpendicular lines $y = \frac{1}{3}x + 2$ and $y = -3x - 2$ is shown in Figure 3-33. Notice that the line $y = \frac{1}{3}x + 2$ passes through the point $(-3, 1)$ as expected.

Skill Practice

4. Write an equation of the line passing through the point $(10, 4)$ and perpendicular to the line $x + 2y = 1$.

4. Different Forms of Linear Equations: A Summary

A linear equation can be written in several different forms, as summarized in Table 3-3.

Table 3-3

Form	Example	Comments
Standard Form $Ax + By = C$	$4x + 2y = 8$	A and B must not both be zero.
Horizontal Line $y = k$ (k is constant)	$y = 4$	The slope is zero, and the y-intercept is $(0, k)$.
Vertical Line $x = k$ (k is constant)	$x = -1$	The slope is undefined, and the x-intercept is $(k, 0)$.
Slope-Intercept Form $y = mx + b$ the slope is m y-intercept is $(0, b)$	$y = -3x + 7$ Slope $= -3$ y-intercept is $(0, 7)$	Solving a linear equation for y results in slope-intercept form. The coefficient of the x-term is the slope, and the constant defines the location of the y-intercept.
Point-Slope Formula $y - y_1 = m(x - x_1)$	$m = -3$ $(x_1, y_1) = (4, 2)$ $y - 2 = -3(x - 4)$	This formula is typically used to build an equation of a line when a point on the line is known and the slope of the line is known.

Answer

4. $y = 2x - 16$

Although standard form and slope-intercept form can be used to express an equation of a line, often the slope-intercept form is used to give a *unique* representation of the line. For example, the following linear equations are all written in standard form, yet they each define the same line.

$$2x + 5y = 10$$
$$-4x - 10y = -20$$
$$6x + 15y = 30$$
$$\frac{2}{5}x + y = 2$$

The line can be written uniquely in slope-intercept form as: $y = -\frac{2}{5}x + 2$.

Although it is important to understand and apply slope-intercept form and the point-slope formula, they are not necessarily applicable to all problems, particularly when dealing with a horizontal or vertical line.

Example 5 **Writing an Equation of a Line**

Classroom Example: p. 250, Exercise 48

Find an equation of the line passing through the point (2, −4) and parallel to the *x*-axis.

Solution:

Because the line is parallel to the *x*-axis, the line must be horizontal. Recall that all horizontal lines can be written in the form $y = k$, where k is a constant. A quick sketch can help find the value of the constant. See Figure 3-34.

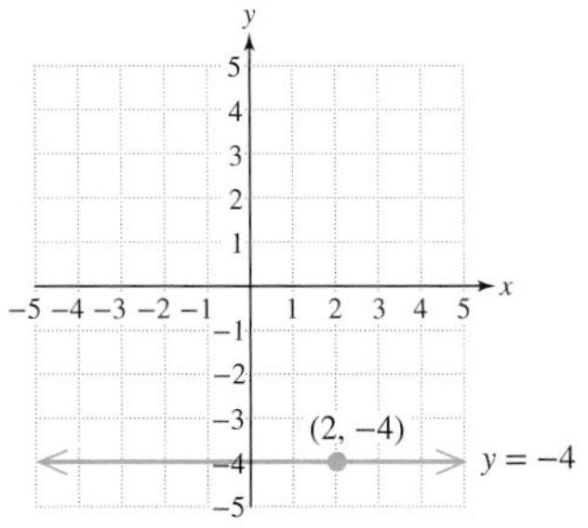

Figure 3-34

Because the line must pass through a point whose *y*-coordinate is −4, then the equation of the line must be $y = -4$.

Skill Practice

5. Write an equation for the vertical line that passes through the point (−7, 2).

Answer

5. $x = -7$

Section 3.5 Practice Exercises

Study Skills Exercise

For additional exercises, see Classroom Activity 3.5A in the *Student's Resource Manual* at www.mhhe.com/moh.

Prepare a one-page summary sheet with the most important information that you need for the test. On the day of the test, look at this sheet several times to refresh your memory instead of trying to memorize new information.

Vocabulary and Key Concepts

1. **a.** The standard form of an equation of a line is $Ax + By = C$, where A and B are not both zero and C is a constant.

b. A line defined by an equation $y = k$, where k is a constant is a (horizontal/vertical) line. horizontal

c. A line defined by an equation $x = k$, where k is a constant is a (horizontal/vertical) line. vertical

d. Given the slope-intercept form of an equation of a line, $y = mx + b$, the value of m is the slope and b is the y-intercept.

e. Given a point (x_1, y_1) on a line with slope m, the point-slope formula is given by $y - y_1 = m(x - x_1)$.

Review Exercises

For Exercises 2–6, graph each equation.

2. $-5x - 15 = 0$

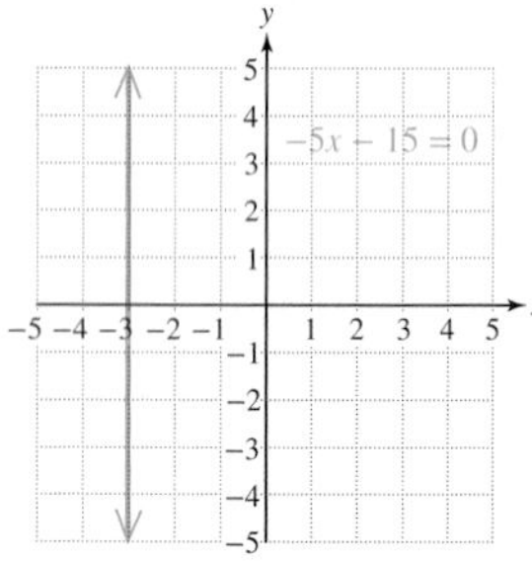

3. $2x - 3y = -3$

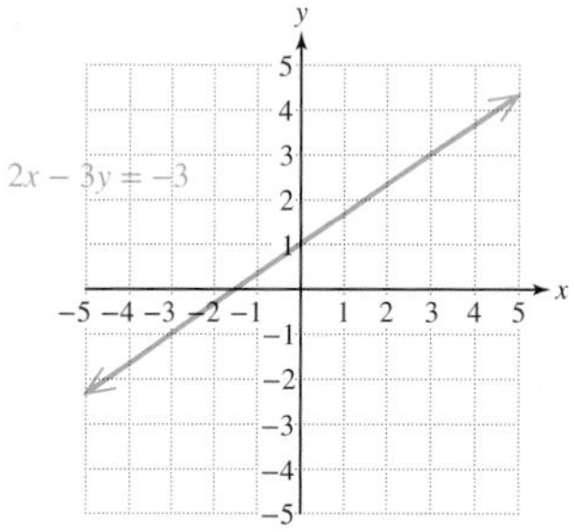

4. $y = -2x$

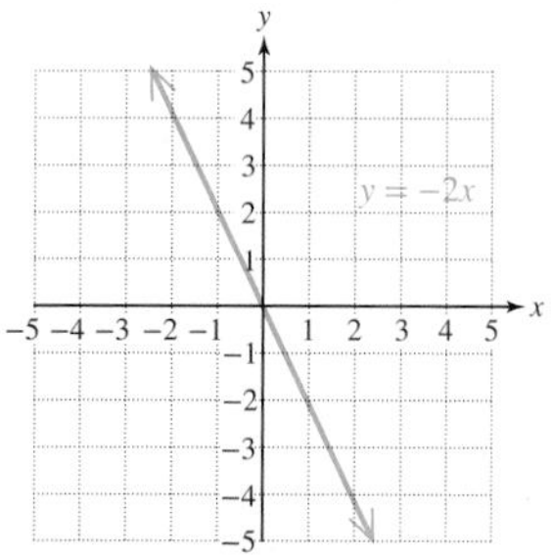

5. $3 - y = 9$

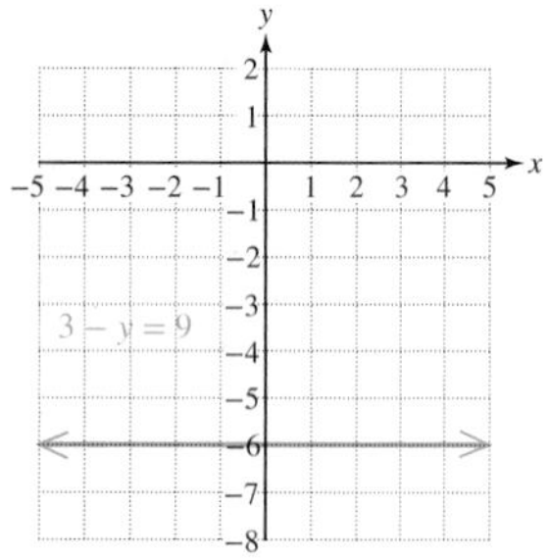

6. $y = \frac{4}{5}x$

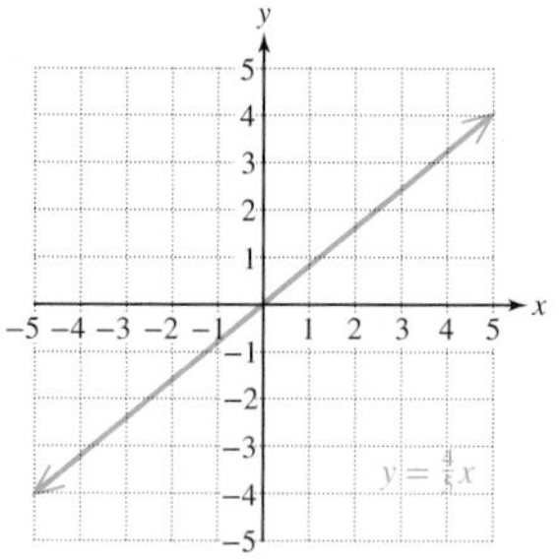

For Exercises 7–10, find the slope of the line that passes through the given points.

7. $(1, -3)$ and $(2, 6)$ 9

8. $(2, -4)$ and $(-2, 4)$ −2

9. $(-2, 5)$ and $(5, 5)$ 0

10. $(6.1, 2.5)$ and $(6.1, -1.5)$ Undefined

Concept 1: Writing an Equation of a Line Using the Point-Slope Formula

For Exercises 11–16, use the point-slope formula (if possible) to write an equation of the line given the following information. **(See Example 1.)**

11. The slope is 3, and the line passes through the point $(-2, 1)$.
$y = 3x + 7$ or $3x - y = -7$

12. The slope is -2, and the line passes through the point $(1, -5)$.
$y = -2x - 3$ or $2x + y = -3$

13. The slope is -4, and the line passes through the point $(-3, -2)$.
$y = -4x - 14$ or $4x + y = -14$

14. The slope is 5, and the line passes through the point $(-1, -3)$.
$y = 5x + 2$ or $5x - y = -2$

15. The slope is $-\frac{1}{2}$, and the line passes through $(-1, 0)$.
$y = -\frac{1}{2}x - \frac{1}{2}$ or $x + 2y = -1$

16. The slope is $-\frac{3}{4}$, and the line passes through $(2, 0)$.
$y = -\frac{3}{4}x + \frac{3}{2}$ or $3x + 4y = 6$

Concept 2: Writing an Equation of a Line Given Two Points

For Exercises 17–22, use the point-slope formula to write an equation of the line given the following information. **(See Example 2.)**

17. The line passes through the points $(-2, -6)$ and $(1, 0)$. $y = 2x - 2$ or $2x - y = 2$

18. The line passes through the points $(-2, 5)$ and $(0, 1)$. $y = -2x + 1$ or $2x + y = 1$

19. The line passes through the points $(0, -4)$ and $(-1, -3)$. $y = -x - 4$ or $x + y = -4$

20. The line passes through the points $(1, -3)$ and $(-7, 2)$. $y = -\frac{5}{8}x - \frac{19}{8}$ or $5x + 8y = -19$

21. The line passes through the points $(2.2, -3.3)$ and $(12.2, -5.3)$.
$y = -0.2x - 2.86$ or $20x + 100y = -286$

22. The line passes through the points $(4.7, -2.2)$ and $(-0.3, 6.8)$.
$y = -1.8x + 6.26$ or $180x + 100y = 626$

For Exercises 23–28, find an equation of the line through the given points. Write the final answer in slope-intercept form.

23.

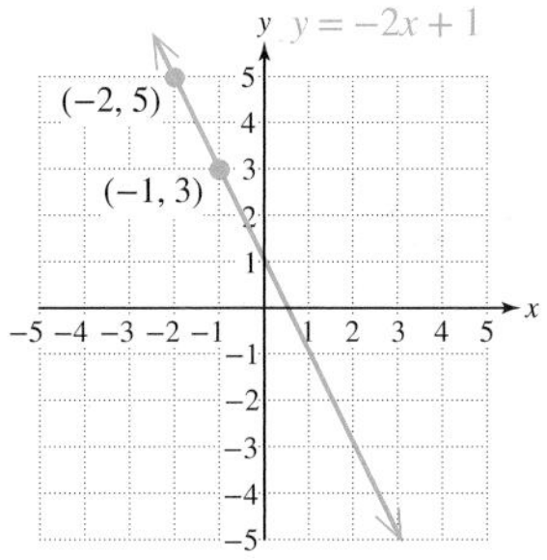

24.

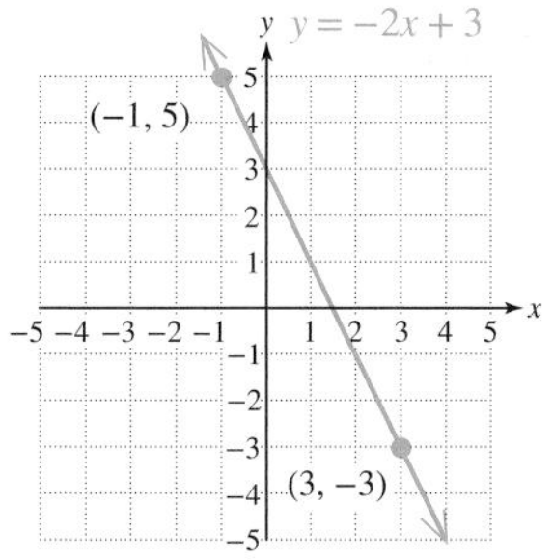

25.

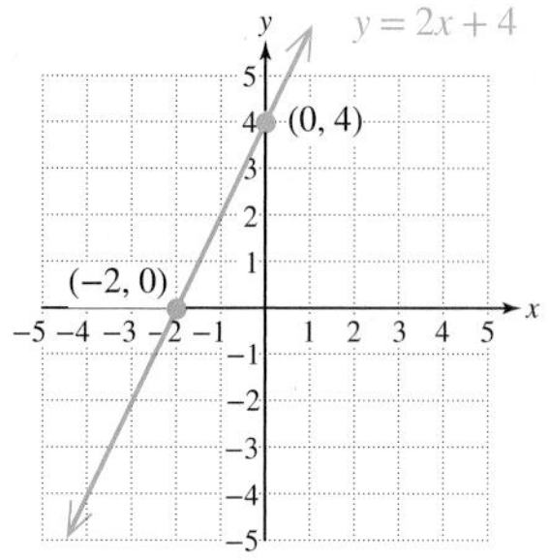

26.

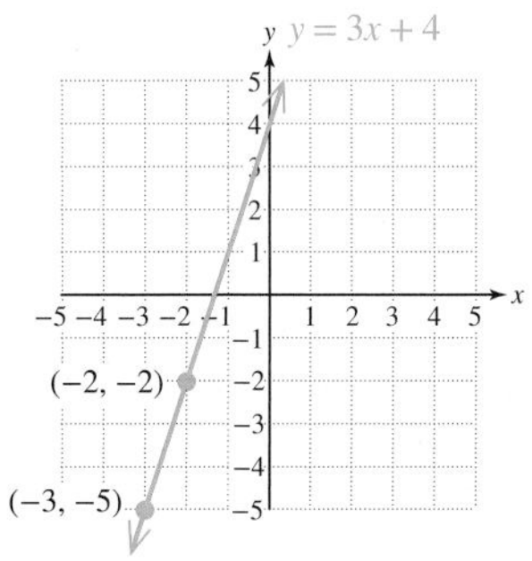

27.

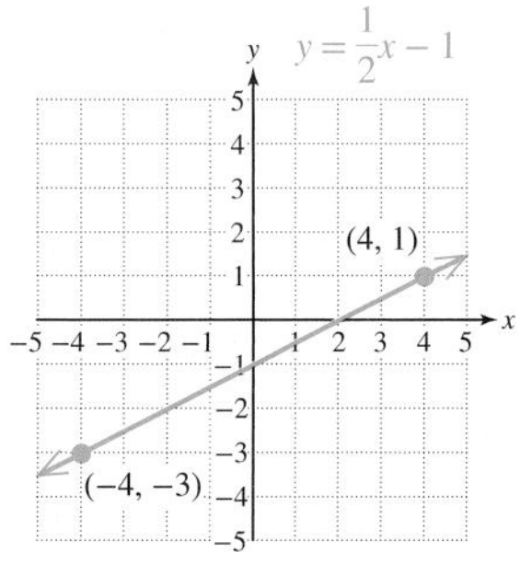

28.

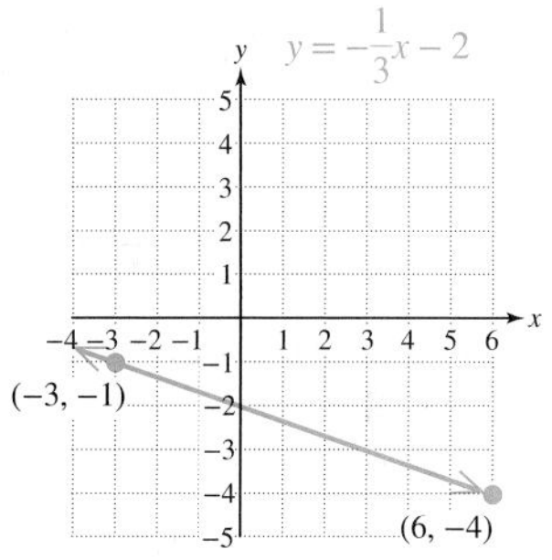

Concept 3: Writing an Equation of a Line Parallel or Perpendicular to Another Line

For Exercises 29–36, use the point-slope formula to write an equation of the line given the following information. **(See Examples 3–4.)**

29. The line passes through the point $(-3, 1)$ and is parallel to the line $y = 4x + 3$.
$y = 4x + 13$ or $4x - y = -13$

30. The line passes through the point $(4, -1)$ and is parallel to the line $y = 3x + 1$.
$y = 3x - 13$ or $3x - y = 13$

31. The line passes through the point $(4, 0)$ and is parallel to the line $3x + 2y = 8$. $y = -\frac{3}{2}x + 6$ or $3x + 2y = 12$

32. The line passes through the point $(2, 0)$ and is parallel to the line $5x + 3y = 6$. $y = -\frac{5}{3}x + \frac{10}{3}$ or $5x + 3y = 10$

33. The line passes through the point $(-5, 2)$ and is perpendicular to the line $y = \frac{1}{2}x + 3$.
$y = -2x - 8$ or $2x + y = -8$

34. The line passes through the point $(-2, -2)$ and is perpendicular to the line $y = \frac{1}{3}x - 5$.
$y = -3x - 8$ or $3x + y = -8$

35. The line passes through the point $(0, -6)$ and is perpendicular to the line $-5x + y = 4$.
$y = -\frac{1}{5}x - 6$ or $x + 5y = -30$

36. The line passes through the point $(0, -8)$ and is perpendicular to the line $2x - y = 5$.
$y = -\frac{1}{2}x - 8$ or $x + 2y = -16$

Concept 4: Different Forms of Linear Equations: A Summary

For Exercises 37–42, match the form or formula on the left with its name on the right.

37. $x = k$ iv — i. Standard form

38. $y = mx + b$ v — ii. Point-slope formula

39. $m = \dfrac{y_2 - y_1}{x_2 - x_1}$ vi — iii. Horizontal line

40. $y - y_1 = m(x - x_1)$ ii — iv. Vertical line

41. $y = k$ iii — v. Slope-intercept form

42. $Ax + By = C$ i — vi. Slope formula

For Exercises 43–48, find an equation for the line given the following information. **(See Example 5.)**

43. The line passes through the point (3, 1) and is parallel to the line $y = -4$. See the figure. $y = 1$

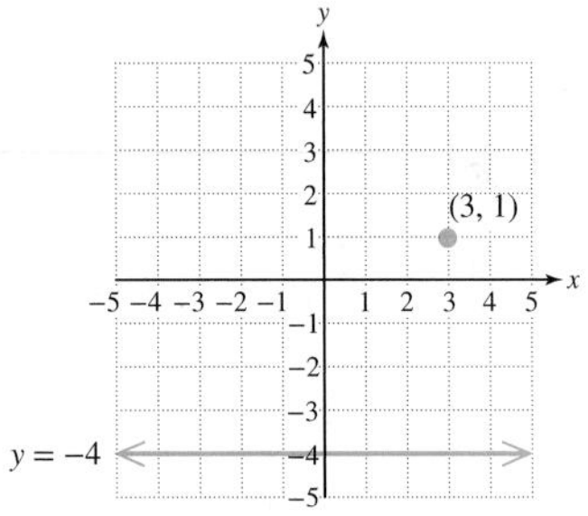

44. The line passes through the point (−1, 1) and is parallel to the line $y = 2$. See the figure. $y = 1$

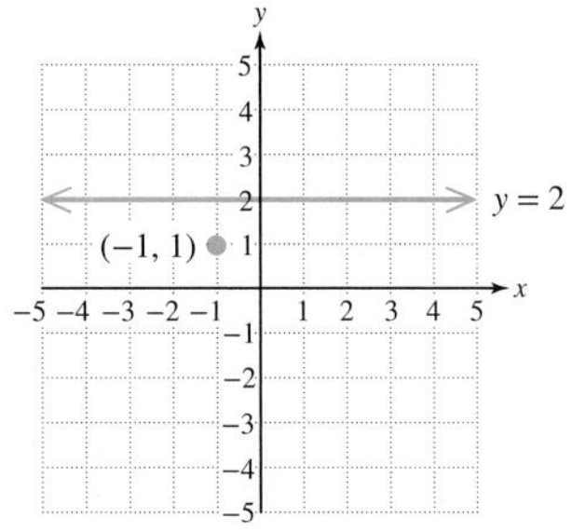

45. The line passes through the point (2, 6) and is perpendicular to the line $y = 1$. (*Hint:* Sketch the line first.) $x = 2$

46. The line passes through the point (0, 3) and is perpendicular to the line $y = -5$. (*Hint:* Sketch the line first.) $x = 0$

47. The line passes through the point (2, 2) and is perpendicular to the line $x = 0$. $y = 2$

48. The line passes through the point (5, −2) and is perpendicular to the line $x = 0$. $y = -2$

Mixed Exercises

For Exercises 49–60, write an equation of the line given the following information.

49. The slope is $\frac{1}{4}$, and the line passes through the point (−8, 6). $y = \frac{1}{4}x + 8$ or $x - 4y = -32$

50. The slope is $\frac{2}{5}$, and the line passes through the point (−5, 4). $y = \frac{2}{5}x + 6$ or $2x - 5y = -30$

51. The line passes through the point (4, 4) and is parallel to the line $3x - y = 6$. $y = 3x - 8$ or $3x - y = 8$

52. The line passes through the point (−1, −7) and is parallel to the line $5x + y = -5$. $y = -5x - 12$ or $5x + y = -12$

53. The slope is 4.5, and the line passes through the point (5.2, −2.2). $y = 4.5x - 25.6$ or $45x - 10y = 256$

54. The slope is −3.6, and the line passes through the point (10.0, 8.2). $y = -3.6x + 44.2$ or $36x + 10y = 442$

55. The slope is undefined, and the line passes through the point (−6, −3). $x = -6$

56. The slope is undefined, and the line passes through the point (2, −1). $x = 2$

57. The slope is 0, and the line passes through the point (3, −2). $y = -2$

58. The slope is 0, and the line passes through the point (0, 5). $y = 5$

59. The line passes through the points (−4, 0) and (−4, 3). $x = -4$

60. The line passes through the points (1, 3) and (1, −4). $x = 1$

Expanding Your Skills

For Exercises 61–64, write an equation in slope-intercept form for the line shown.

61.

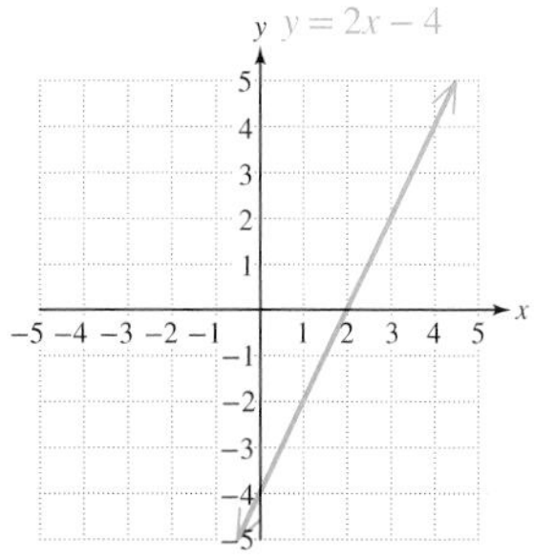

62.

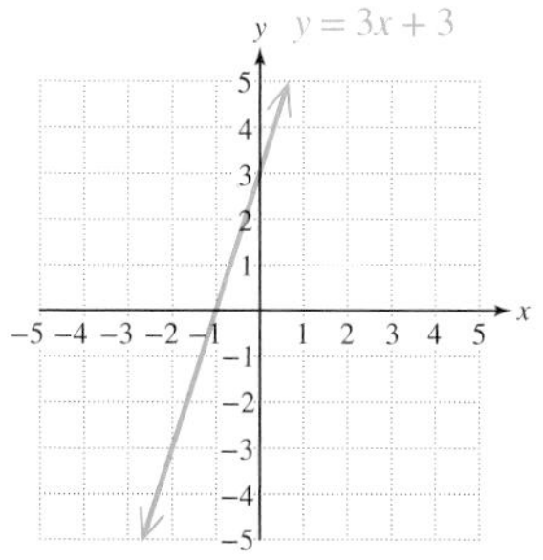

63.

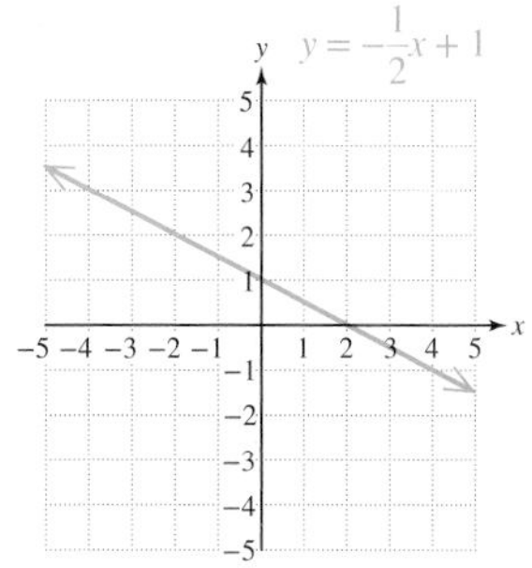

64.

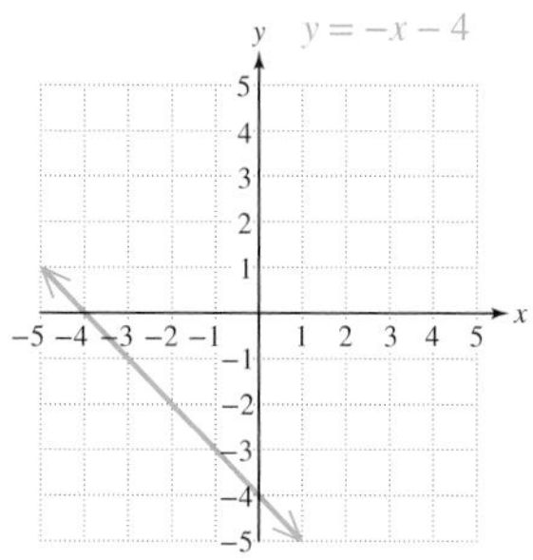

Applications of Linear Equations and Modeling

Section 3.6

Concepts

1. Interpreting a Linear Equation in Two Variables
2. Writing a Linear Model Using Observed Data Points
3. Writing a Linear Model Given a Fixed Value and a Rate of Change

1. Interpreting a Linear Equation in Two Variables

Linear equations can often be used to describe (or model) the relationship between two variables in a real-world event.

Example 1 Interpreting a Linear Equation

Since the year 1900, the tiger population in India has decreased linearly. A recent study showed this decrease can be approximated by the equation $y = -350x + 42{,}000$. The variable y represents the number of tigers left in India, and x represents the number of years since 1900.

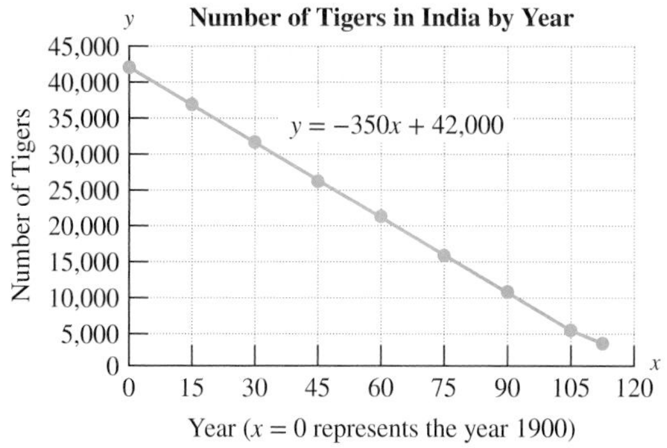

Classroom Example: p. 256, Exercise 10

a. Use the equation to estimate the number of tigers in 1960.

b. Use the equation to estimate the number of tigers in 2015.

c. Determine the slope of the line. Interpret the meaning of the slope in terms of the number of tigers and the year.

d. Determine the x-intercept. Interpret the meaning of the x-intercept in terms of the number of tigers.

Solution:

a. The year 1960 is 60 yr since 1900. Substitute $x = 60$ into the equation.

$y = -350x + 42{,}000$

$y = -350(60) + 42{,}000$

$= 21{,}000$ — There were approximately 21,000 tigers in India in 1960.

b. The year 2015 is 115 yr since 1900. Substitute $x = 115$.

$y = -350(115) + 42{,}000$

$= 1750$ — There were approximately 1750 tigers in India in 2015.

c. The slope is -350. — The slope means that the tiger population is decreasing by 350 tigers per year.

d. To find the x-intercept, substitute $y = 0$.

$y = -350x + 42{,}000$

$0 = -350x + 42{,}000$ — Substitute 0 for y.

$-42{,}000 = -350x$

$120 = x$

The x-intercept is (120, 0). This means that 120 yr after the year 1900, the tiger population would be expected to reach zero. That is, in the year 2020, there will be no tigers left in India if this linear trend continues.

Skill Practice

1. The cost y (in dollars) for a local move by a small moving company is given by $y = 60x + 100$, where x is the number of hours required for the move.

a. How much would be charged for a move that requires 3 hr?

b. How much would be charged for a move that requires 8 hr?

c. What is the slope of the line and what does it mean in the context of this problem?

d. Determine the y-intercept and interpret its meaning in the context of this problem.

Answers

1. a. \$280 **b.** \$580

c. 60; This means that for each additional hour of service, the cost of the move goes up by \$60.

d. (0, 100); The \$100 charge is a fixed fee in addition to the hourly rate.

2. Writing a Linear Model Using Observed Data Points

Example 2 Writing a Linear Model from Observed Data Points

Classroom Example: p. 258, Exercise 18

The monthly sales of hybrid cars sold in the United States are given for a recent year. The sales for the first 8 months of the year are shown in Figure 3-35. The value $x = 0$ represents January, $x = 1$ represents February, and so on.

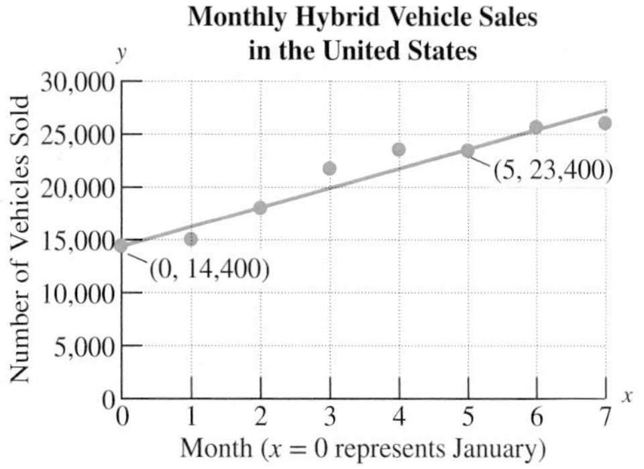

Figure 3-35

a. Use the data points from Figure 3-35 to find a linear equation that represents the monthly sales of hybrid cars in the United States. Let x represent the month number and let y represent the number of vehicles sold.

b. Use the linear equation in part (a) to estimate the number of hybrid vehicles sold in month 7 (August).

Solution:

a. The ordered pairs (0, 14,400) and (5, 23,400) are given in the graph. Use these points to find the slope.

(0, 14,400) and (5, 23,400) Label the points.

(x_1, y_1) (x_2, y_2)

$$m = \frac{y_2 - y_1}{x_2 - x_1} = \frac{23{,}400 - 14{,}400}{5 - 0}$$

$$= \frac{9000}{5}$$

$$= 1800$$

The slope is 1800. This indicates that sales increased by approximately 1800 per month during this time period.

With $m = 1800$, and the y-intercept given as (0, 14,400), we have the following linear equation in slope-intercept form.

$$y = 1800x + 14{,}400$$

b. To approximate the sales in month number 7, substitute $x = 7$ into the equation from part (a).

$y = 1800(7) + 14{,}400$ Substitute $x = 7$.

$= 27{,}000$

The monthly sales for August (month 7) would be 27,000 vehicles.

Skill Practice

2. Soft drink sales at a concession stand at a softball stadium have increased linearly over the course of the summer softball season.
   a. Use the given data points to find a linear equation that relates the sales, y, to week number, x.
   b. Use the equation to predict the number of soft drinks sold in week 10.

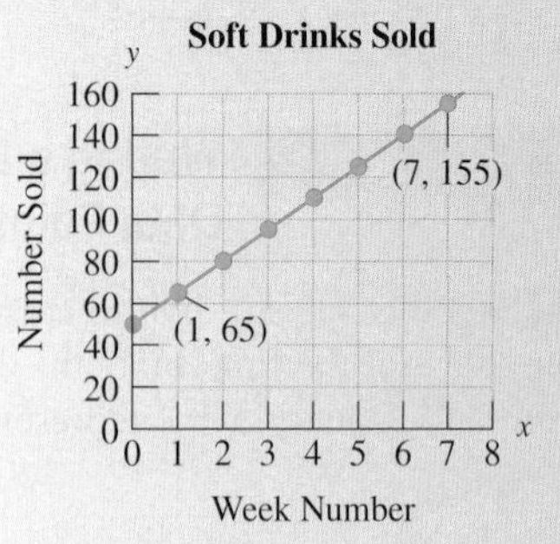

3. Writing a Linear Model Given a Fixed Value and a Rate of Change

Another way to look at the equation $y = mx + b$ is to identify the term mx as the variable term and the term b as the constant term. The value of the term mx will change with the value of x (this is why the slope, m, is called a *rate of change*). However, the term b will remain constant regardless of the value of x. With these ideas in mind, we can write a linear equation if the rate of change and the constant are known.

Classroom Example: p. 258, Exercise 20

Example 3 Writing a Linear Model

A stack of posters to advertise a production by the theater department costs \$19.95 plus \$1.50 per poster at the printer.

a. Write a linear equation to compute the cost, c, of buying x posters.

b. Use the equation to compute the cost of 125 posters.

Solution:

a. The constant cost is \$19.95. The variable cost is \$1.50 per poster. If m is replaced with 1.50 and b is replaced with 19.95, the equation is

$c = 1.50x + 19.95$ where c is the cost (in dollars) of buying x posters.

b. Because x represents the number of posters, substitute $x = 125$.

$$\begin{aligned} c &= 1.50(125) + 19.95 \\ &= 187.5 + 19.95 \\ &= 207.45 \end{aligned}$$

The total cost of buying 125 posters is \$207.45.

Skill Practice

3. The monthly cost for a "minimum use" cellular phone is \$19.95 plus \$0.10 per minute for all calls.
   a. Write a linear equation to compute the cost, c, of using t minutes.
   b. Use the equation to determine the cost of using 150 minutes.

Answers

2. a. $y = 15x + 50$ **b.** 200 soft drinks
3. a. $c = 0.10t + 19.95$ **b.** \$34.95

Calculator Connections

Topic: Using the Evaluate Feature on a Graphing Calculator

In Example 3, the equation $c = 1.50x + 19.95$ was used to represent the cost, c, to buy x posters. To graph this equation on a graphing calculator, first replace the variable c by y.

$$y = 1.50x + 19.95$$

We enter the equation into the calculator and set the viewing window.

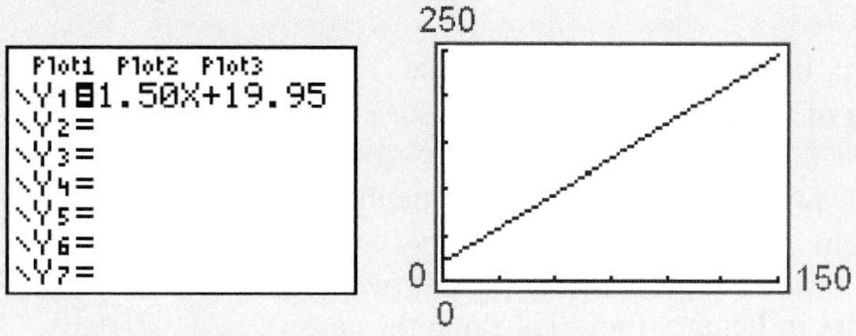

To evaluate the equation for a user-defined value of x, use the *Value* feature in the CALC menu. In this case, we entered $x = 125$, and the calculator returned $y = 207.45$.

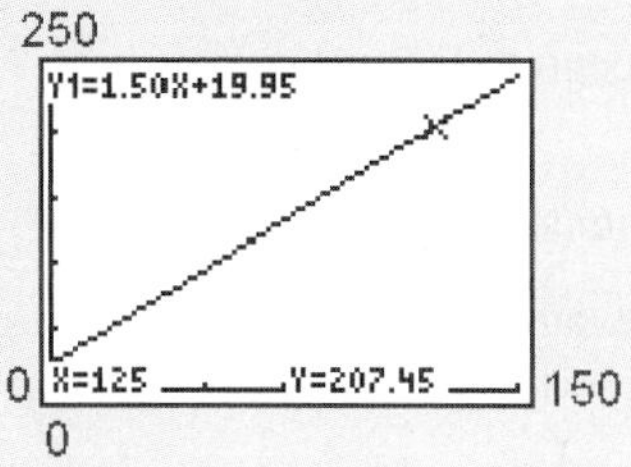

Calculator Exercises

Use a graphing calculator to graph the lines on an appropriate viewing window. Evaluate the equation at the given values of x.

1. $y = -4.6x + 27.1$ at $x = 3$ 13.3
2. $y = -3.6x - 42.3$ at $x = 0$ −42.3
3. $y = 40x + 105$ at $x = 6$ 345
4. $y = 20x - 65$ at $x = 8$ 95

Section 3.6 Practice Exercises

For additional exercises, see Classroom Activities 3.6A–3.6C in the *Student's Resource Manual* at www.mhhe.com/moh.

Study Skills Exercise

On test day, take a look at any formulas or important points that you had to memorize before you enter the classroom. Then when you sit down to take your test, write these formulas on the test or on scrap paper. This is called a memory dump. For practice write down the formulas involving slopes and equations of lines.

Review Exercises

1. Determine the slope of the line defined by $5x + 2y = -6$. $m = -\frac{5}{2}$
2. Determine the slope of the line defined by $2x - 8y = 15$. $m = \frac{1}{4}$

For Exercises 3–8, find the x- and y-intercepts of the lines, if possible.

3. $5x + 6y = 30$ x-intercept: $(6, 0)$; y-intercept: $(0, 5)$
4. $3x + 4y = 1$ x-intercept: $(\frac{1}{3}, 0)$; y-intercept: $(0, \frac{1}{4})$
5. $y = -2x - 4$ x-intercept: $(-2, 0)$; y-intercept: $(0, -4)$
6. $y = 5x$ x-intercept: $(0, 0)$; y-intercept: $(0, 0)$
7. $y = -9$ x-intercept: none; y-intercept: $(0, -9)$
8. $x = 2$ x-intercept: $(2, 0)$; y-intercept: none

Writing Translating Expression Geometry Scientific Calculator Video

Concept 1: Interpreting a Linear Equation in Two Variables

9. The minimum hourly wage, y (in dollars per hour), in the United States can be approximated by the equation $y = 0.14x + 1.60$. In this equation, x represents the number of years since 1970 ($x = 0$ represents 1970, $x = 5$ represents 1975, and so on). **(See Example 1.)**

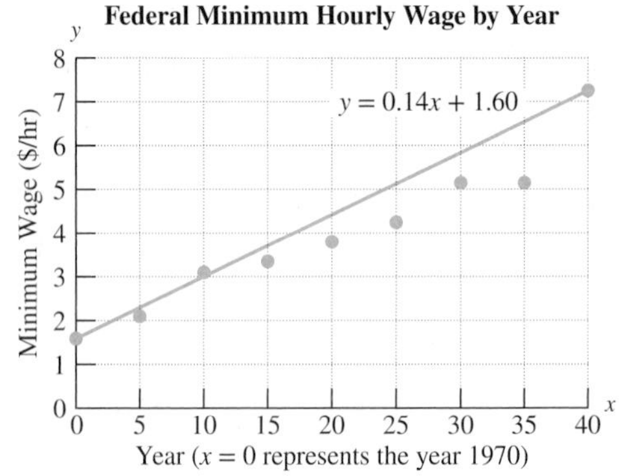

a. Use the equation to approximate the minimum wage in the year 1980. $3.00

b. Use the equation to estimate the minimum wage in 2015. $7.90

c. Determine the y-intercept. Interpret the meaning of the y-intercept in the context of this problem. The y-intercept is (0, 1.6). This indicates that the minimum wage was $1.60 per hour in the year 1970.

d. Determine the slope. Interpret the meaning of the slope in the context of this problem. The slope is 0.14. This indicates that the minimum wage has risen approximately $0.14 per year during this period.

10. The average daily temperature in January for cities along the eastern seaboard of the United States and Canada generally decreases for cities farther north. A city's latitude in the northern hemisphere is a measure of how far north it is on the globe.

The average temperature, y (measured in degrees Fahrenheit), can be described by the equation

$y = -2.333x + 124.0$ where x is the latitude of the city.

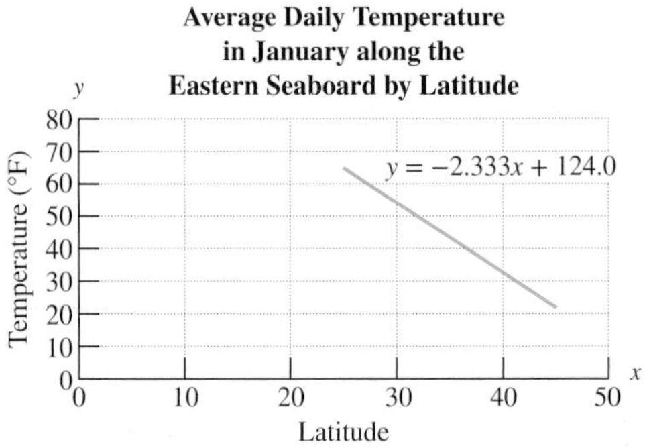

(*Source:* U.S.National Oceanic and Atmospheric Administration)

a. Use the equation to predict the average daily temperature in January for Philadelphia, Pennsylvania, whose latitude is 40.0°N. Round to one decimal place. 30.7°

b. Use the equation to predict the average daily temperature in January for Edmundston, New Brunswick, Canada, whose latitude is 47.4°N. Round to one decimal place. 13.4°

c. What is the slope of the line? Interpret the meaning of the slope in terms of latitude and temperature. $m = -2.333$. The average temperature in January decreases at a rate of 2.333° per 1° of latitude.

d. From the equation, determine the value of the x-intercept. Round to one decimal place. Interpret the meaning of the x-intercept in terms of latitude and temperature. (53.2, 0). At 53.2° latitude, the average temperature in January is 0°.

11. Veterinarians keep records of the weights of animals that are brought in for examination. Grindel, the cat, weighed 42 oz when she was 70 days old. She weighed 46 oz when she was 84 days old. Her sister, Frisco, weighed 40 oz when she was 70 days old and 48 oz at 84 days old.

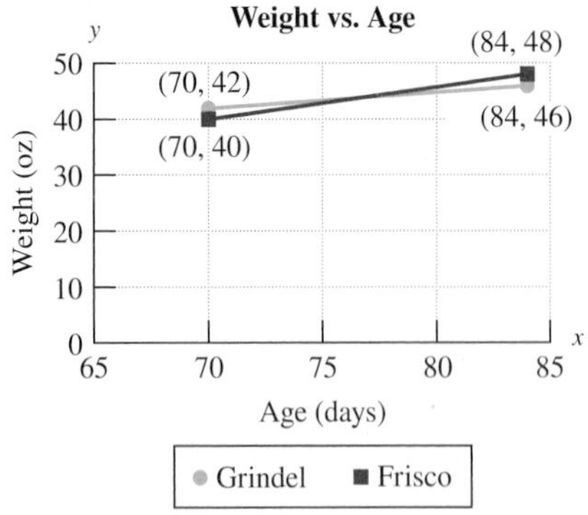

Courtesy Rick Iossi

a. Compute the slope of the line representing Grindel's weight. $m = \frac{2}{7}$

b. Compute the slope of the line representing Frisco's weight. $m = \frac{4}{7}$

c. Interpret the meaning of each slope in the context of this problem. $m = \frac{2}{7}$ means that Grindel's weight increased at a rate of 2 oz in 7 days. $m = \frac{4}{7}$ means that Frisco's weight increased at a rate of 4 oz in 7 days.

d. Which cat gained weight more rapidly during this time period? Frisco gained weight more rapidly.

12. The graph depicts the rise in the number of jail inmates in the United States since 2000. Two linear equations are given: one to describe the number of female inmates and one to describe the number of male inmates by year.

Let y represent the number of inmates (in thousands). Let x represent the number of years since 2000.

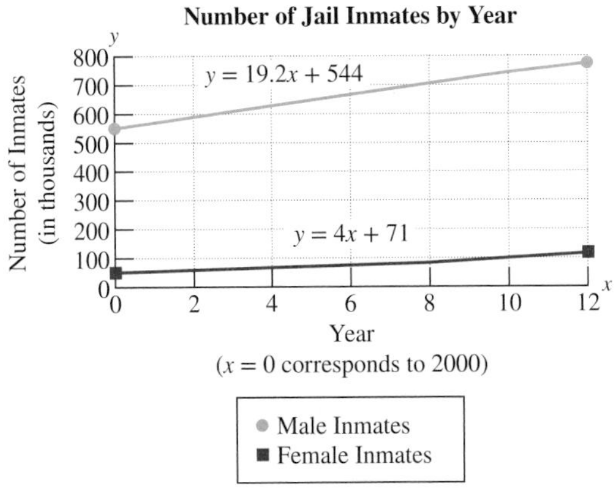

(*Source:* U.S. Bureau of Justice Statistics)

a. What is the slope of the line representing the number of female inmates? Interpret the meaning of the slope in the context of this problem. $m = 4$. The number of female inmates has increased by 4 thousand per year since 2000.

b. What is the slope of the line representing the number of male inmates? Interpret the meaning of the slope in the context of this problem. $m = 19.2$. The number of male inmates has increased by 19.2 thousand per year since 2000.

c. Which group, males or females, has the larger slope? What does this imply about the rise in the number of male and female prisoners? Males. The number of male inmates is increasing at a faster rate than the number of female inmates.

d. Assuming this trend continues, use the equation to predict the number of female inmates in 2020. 151 thousand or 151,000

13. The electric bill charge for a certain utility company is \$0.095 per kilowatt-hour plus a fixed monthly tax of \$11.95. The total cost, y, depends on the number of kilowatt-hours, x, according to the equation $y = 0.095x + 11.95$, $x \geq 0$.

a. Determine the cost of using 1000 kilowatt-hours. \$106.95

b. Determine the cost of using 2000 kilowatt-hours. \$201.95

c. Determine the y-intercept. Interpret the meaning of the y-intercept in the context of this problem. (0, 11.95). For 0 kilowatt-hours used, the cost consists of only the fixed monthly tax of \$11.95.

d. Determine the slope. Interpret the meaning of the slope in the context of this problem. $m = 0.095$. The cost increases at a rate of \$0.095 for each kilowatt-hour used.

14. For a recent year, children's admission to a State Fair was \$8. Ride tickets were \$0.75 each. The equation $y = 0.75x + 8$ represented the cost, y, in dollars to be admitted to the fair and to purchase x ride tickets.

a. Determine the slope of the line represented by $y = 0.75x + 8$. Interpret the meaning of the slope in the context of this problem. $m = 0.75$; The slope means that the cost increases at a rate of 75¢ per ride.

b. Determine the y-intercept. Interpret its meaning in the context of this problem. (0, 8); The cost was \$8 if 0 rides were purchased.

c. Use the equation to determine how much money a child need for admission and to ride 10 rides. \$15.50

Concept 2: Writing a Linear Model Using Observed Data Points

15. Meteorologists often measure the intensity of a tropical storm or hurricane by the maximum sustained wind speed and the minimum pressure. The relationship between these two quantities is approximately linear. Hurricane Katrina had a maximum sustained wind speed of 150 knots and a minimum pressure of 902 mb (millibars). Hurricane Ophelia had maximum sustained winds of 75 knots and a pressure of 976 mb. **(See Example 2.)**

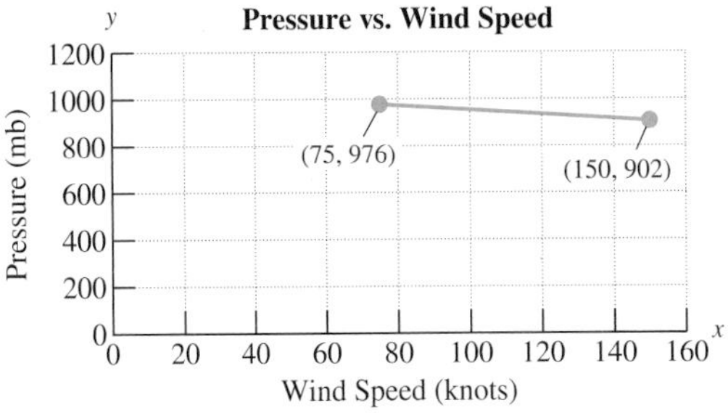

a. Find the slope of the line between these two points. Round to one decimal place. $m = -1.0$

b. Using the slope found in part (a) and the point (75, 976), find a linear model that represents the minimum pressure of a hurricane, y, versus its maximum sustained wind speed, x. $y = -1.0x + 1051$

c. Hurricane Dennis had a maximum wind speed of 130 knots. Using the equation found in part (b), predict the minimum pressure. The minimum pressure was approximately 921 mb.

16. The figure depicts a relationship between a person's height, y (in inches), and the length of the person's arm, x (measured in inches from shoulder to wrist).

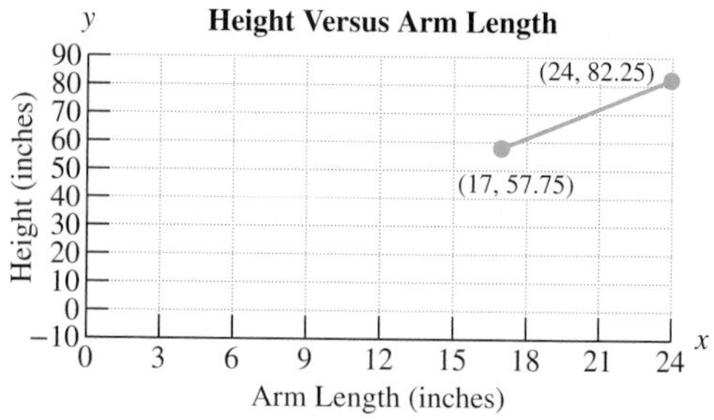

a. Use the points (17, 57.75) and (24, 82.25) to find a linear equation relating height to arm length. $y = 3.5x - 1.75$

b. What is the slope of the line? Interpret the slope in the context of this problem. $m = 3.5$. For each additional inch in length of a person's arm, the person's height increases by 3.5 in.

c. Use the equation from part (a) to estimate the height of a person whose arm length is 21.5 in. 73.5 in. or 6 ft $1\frac{1}{2}$ in.

17. Wind energy is one type of renewable energy that does not produce dangerous greenhouse gases as a by-product. The graph shows the consumption of wind energy in the United States for selected years. The variable y represents the amount of wind energy in trillions of Btu, and the variable x represents the number of years since 2000.

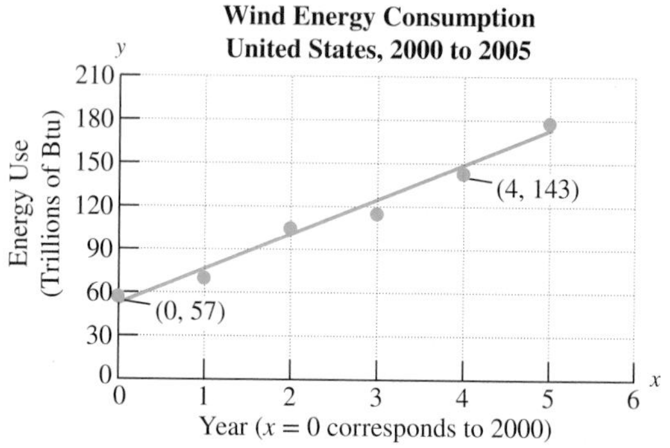

(*Source*: United States Department of Energy)

a. Use the points (0, 57) and (4, 143) to determine the slope of the line. $m = 21.5$

b. Interpret the slope in the context of this problem? The slope means that the consumption of wind energy in the United States increased by 21.5 trillion Btu per year.

c. Use the points (0, 57) and (4, 143) to find a linear equation relating the consumption of wind energy, y, to the number of years, x, since 2000. $y = 21.5x + 57$

d. If this linear trend continues beyond the observed data values, use the equation in part (c) to estimate the consumption of wind energy in the year 2010. 272 trillion Btu

18. The graph shows the average height for boys based on age. Let x represent a boy's age, and let y represent his height (in inches).

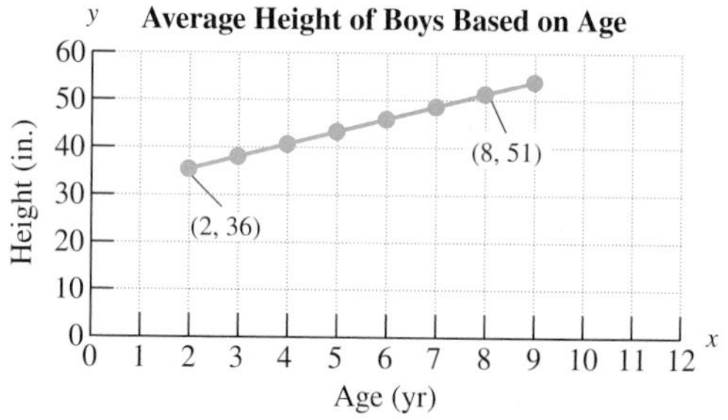

(*Source:* National Parenting Council)

a. Find a linear equation that represents the height of a boy versus his age. $y = 2.5x + 31$

b. Use the linear equation found in part (a) to predict the average height of a 5-year-old boy. 43.5 in.

Concept 3: Writing a Linear Model Given a Fixed Value and a Rate of Change

19. The owner of a restaurant franchise pays the parent company a monthly fee of \$5000 plus 10% of sales. **(See Example 3.)**

a. Write a linear model to compute the monthly payment, y, that the restaurant owner must pay the parent company for x dollars in sales. $y = 0.10x + 5000$

b. Use the equation to compute the amount that the owner has to pay if monthly sales are \$11,300. \$6130

20. Anabel lives in New York and likes to keep in touch with her family in Texas. She uses 10-10-987 to call them. The cost of a long distance call is \$0.83 plus \$0.06 per minute.

a. Write an equation that represents the cost, C, of a long distance call that is x minutes long. $C = 0.06x + 0.83$

b. Use the equation from part (a) to compute the cost of a long distance phone call that lasted 32 minutes. \$2.75

21. The cost to rent a 10 ft by 10 ft storage space is \$90 per month plus a nonrefundable deposit of \$105.

   a. Write a linear equation to compute the cost, y, of renting a 10 ft by 10 ft space for x months. $y = 90x + 105$

   b. What is the cost of renting such a storage space for 1 year (12 months)? \$1185.00

22. An air-conditioning and heating company has a fixed monthly cost of \$5000. Furthermore, each service call costs the company \$25.

   a. Write a linear equation to compute the total cost, y, for 1 month if x service calls are made. $y = 25x + 5000$

   b. Use the equation to compute the cost for 1 month if 150 service calls are made. \$8750.00

23. A bakery that specializes in bread rents a booth at a flea market. The daily cost to rent the booth is \$100. Each loaf of bread costs the bakery \$0.80 to produce.

   a. Write a linear equation to compute the total cost, y, for 1 day if x loaves of bread are produced. $y = 0.8x + 100$

   b. Use the equation to compute the cost for 1 day if 200 loaves of bread are produced. \$260.00

24. A beverage company rents a booth at an art show to sell lemonade. The daily cost to rent a booth is \$35. Each lemonade costs \$0.50 to produce.

   a. Write a linear equation to compute the total cost, y, for 1 day if x lemonades are produced. $y = 0.5x + 35$

   b. Use the equation to compute the cost for 1 day if 350 lemonades are produced. \$210.00

Group Activity

Modeling a Linear Equation

Materials: Yardstick or other device for making linear measurements

Estimated Time: 15–20 minutes

Group Size: 3

1. The members of each group should measure the length of their arms (in inches) from elbow to wrist. Record this measurement as x and the person's height (in inches) as y. Write these values as ordered pairs for each member of the group. Then write the ordered pairs on the board.

2. Next, copy the ordered pairs collected from all groups in the class and plot the ordered pairs. (This is called a "scatter diagram.") Answers will vary throughout this exercise.

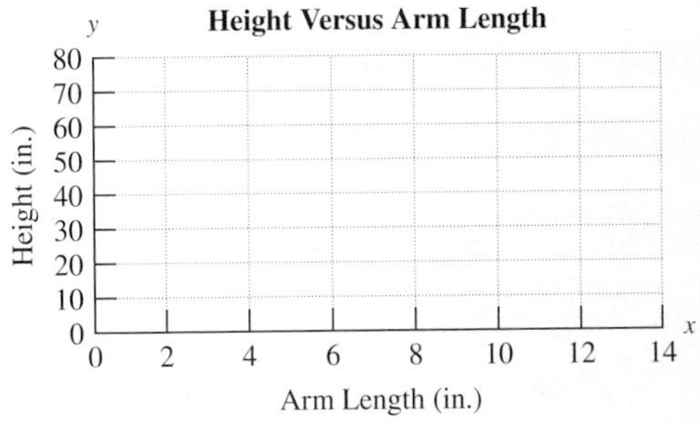

3. Select two ordered pairs that seem to follow the upward trend of the data. Using these data points, determine the slope of the line.

Slope: ______________________

4. Using the data points and slope from question 3, find an equation of the line through the two points. Write the equation in slope-intercept form, $y = mx + b$.

Equation: ______________________

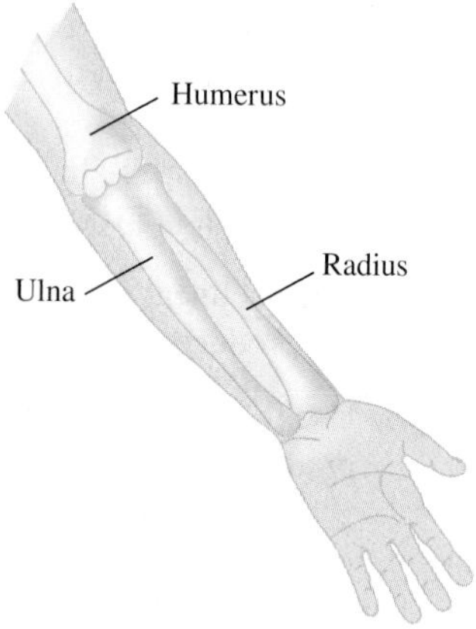

5. Using the equation from question 4, estimate the height of a person whose arm length from elbow to wrist is 8.5 in.

6. Suppose a crime scene investigator uncovers a partial skeleton and identifies a bone as a human ulna (the ulna is one of two bones in the forearm and extends from elbow to wrist). If the length of the bone is 12 in., estimate the height of the person before death. Would you expect this person to be male or female?

Chapter 3 Summary

Section 3.1 Rectangular Coordinate System

Key Concepts

Graphical representation of numerical data is often helpful to study problems in real-world applications.

A **rectangular coordinate system** is made up of a horizontal line called the ***x*-axis** and a vertical line called the ***y*-axis**. The point where the lines meet is the **origin**. The four regions of the plane are called **quadrants**.

The point (x, y) is an **ordered pair**. The first element in the ordered pair is the point's horizontal position from the origin. The second element in the ordered pair is the point's vertical position from the origin.

Example

Example 1

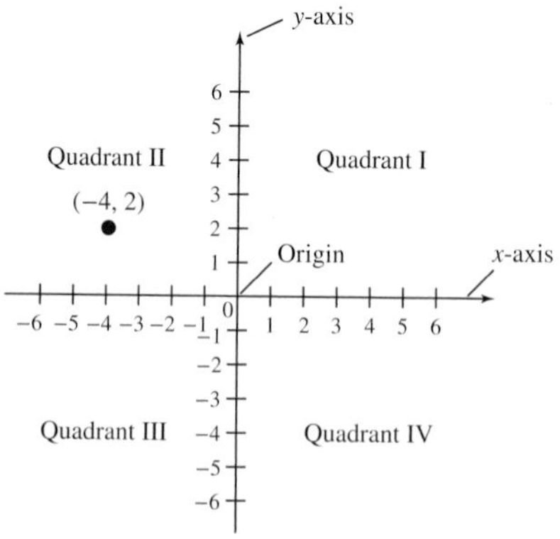

Section 3.2 Linear Equations in Two Variables

Key Concepts

An equation written in the form $Ax + By = C$ (where A and B are not both zero) is a **linear equation in two variables**.

A solution to a linear equation in x and y is an ordered pair (x, y) that makes the equation a true statement. The graph of the set of all solutions of a linear equation in two variables is a line in a rectangular coordinate system.

A linear equation can be graphed by finding at least two solutions and graphing the line through the points.

Examples

Example 1

Graph the equation $2x + y = 2$.

Select arbitrary values of x or y such as those shown in the table. Then complete the table to find the corresponding ordered pairs.

x	y	
0	2	→ $(0, 2)$
−1	4	→ $(-1, 4)$
1	0	→ $(1, 0)$

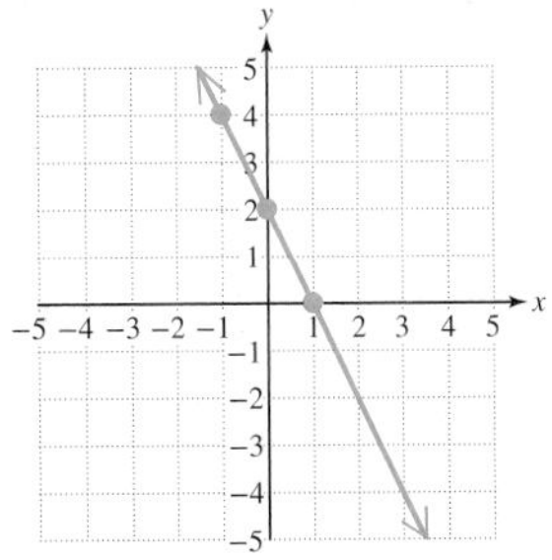

An ***x*-intercept** of a graph is a point $(a, 0)$ where the graph intersects the x-axis.

To find the x-intercept, let $y = 0$ and solve for x.

A ***y*-intercept** of a graph is a point $(0, b)$ where the graph intersects the y-axis.

To find the y-intercept, let $x = 0$ and solve for y.

Example 2

For the line $2x + y = 2$, find the x- and y-intercepts.

x-intercept	y-intercept
$2x + (0) = 2$	$2(0) + y = 2$
$2x = 2$	$0 + y = 2$
$x = 1$	$y = 2$
$(1, 0)$	$(0, 2)$

A **vertical line** can be represented by an equation of the form $x = k$.

A **horizontal line** can be represented by an equation of the form $y = k$.

Example 3

$x = 3$ represents a vertical line

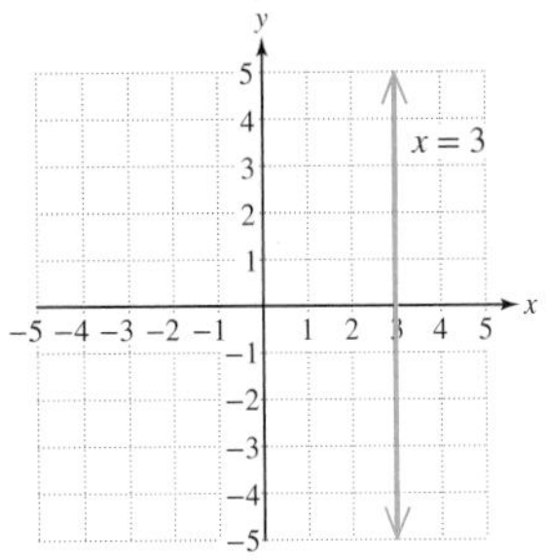

$y = 3$ represents a horizontal line

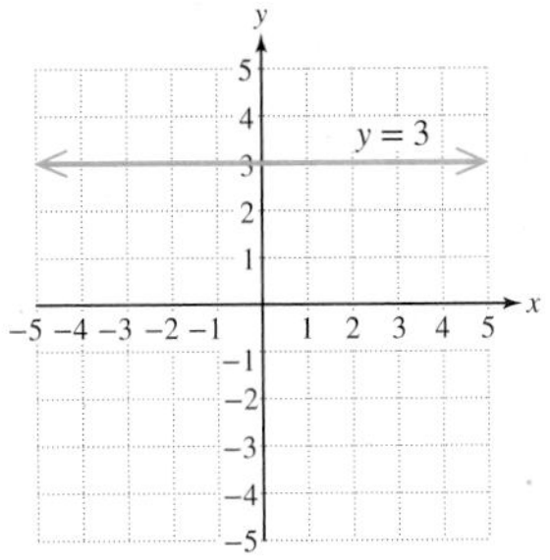

Section 3.3 Slope of a Line and Rate of Change

Key Concepts

The **slope**, m, of a line between two points (x_1, y_1) and (x_2, y_2) is given by

$$m = \frac{y_2 - y_1}{x_2 - x_1} \quad \text{or} \quad \frac{\text{change in } y}{\text{change in } x}$$

The slope of a line may be positive, negative, zero, or undefined.

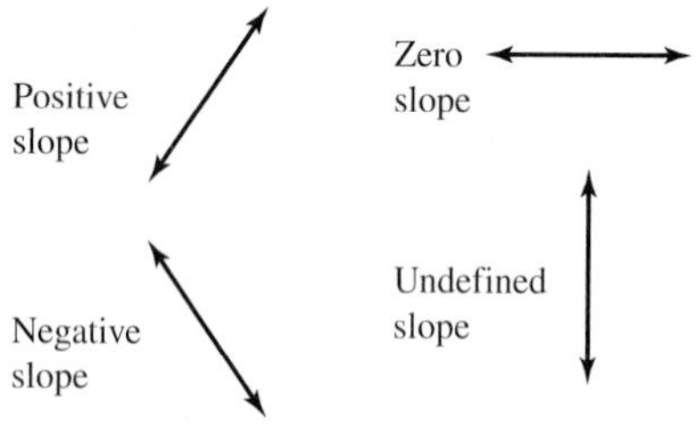

If m_1 and m_2 represent the slopes of two **parallel lines** (nonvertical), then $m_1 = m_2$.

If $m_1 \neq 0$ and $m_2 \neq 0$ represent the slopes of two nonvertical **perpendicular lines**, then

$$m_1 = -\frac{1}{m_2} \text{ or equivalently, } m_1 m_2 = -1.$$

Examples

Example 1

Find the slope of the line between $(1, -5)$ and $(-3, 7)$.

$$m = \frac{7-(-5)}{-3-1} = \frac{12}{-4} = -3$$

Example 2

The slope of the line $y = -2$ is 0 because the line is horizontal.

Example 3

The slope of the line $x = 4$ is undefined because the line is vertical.

Example 4

The slopes of two distinct lines are given. Determine whether the lines are parallel, perpendicular, or neither.

a. $m_1 = -7$ and $m_2 = -7$ Parallel

b. $m_1 = -\frac{1}{5}$ and $m_2 = 5$ Perpendicular

c. $m_1 = -\frac{3}{2}$ and $m_2 = -\frac{2}{3}$ Neither

Section 3.4 Slope-Intercept Form of a Linear Equation

Key Concepts

The **slope-intercept form** of a linear equation is

$$y = mx + b$$

where m is the slope of the line and $(0, b)$ is the y-intercept.

Slope-intercept form is used to identify the slope and y-intercept of a line when the equation is given.

Slope-intercept form can also be used to graph a line.

Examples

Example 1

Find the slope and y-intercept.

$7x - 2y = 4$

$-2y = -7x + 4$ Solve for y.

$$\frac{-2y}{-2} = \frac{-7x}{-2} + \frac{4}{-2}$$

$$y = \frac{7}{2}x - 2$$

The slope is $\frac{7}{2}$. The y-intercept is $(0, -2)$.

Example 2

Graph the line.

$$y = \frac{7}{2}x - 2$$

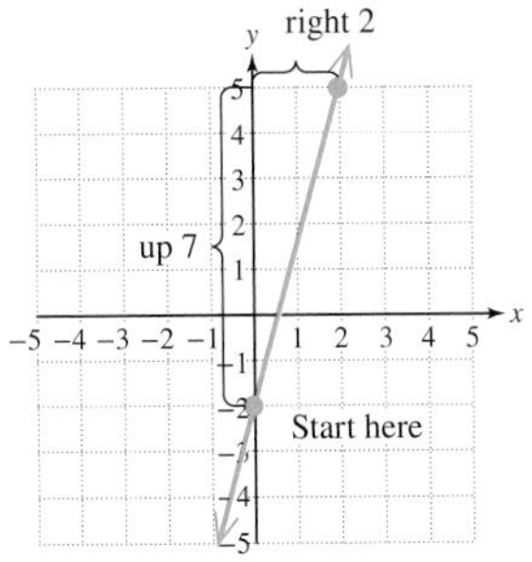

Section 3.5 Point-Slope Formula

Key Concepts

The **point-slope formula** is used primarily to construct an equation of a line given a point and the slope.

Equations of Lines—A Summary:

Standard form: $Ax + By = C$
Horizontal line: $y = k$
Vertical line: $x = k$
Slope-intercept form: $y = mx + b$
Point-slope formula: $y - y_1 = m(x - x_1)$

Example

Example 1

Find an equation of the line passing through the point $(6, -4)$ and having a slope of $-\frac{1}{2}$.

Label the given information:
$m = -\frac{1}{2}$ and $(x_1, y_1) = (6, -4)$

$$y - y_1 = m(x - x_1)$$

$$y - (-4) = -\tfrac{1}{2}(x - 6)$$

$$y + 4 = -\tfrac{1}{2}x + 3$$

$$y = -\tfrac{1}{2}x - 1$$

Section 3.6 Applications of Linear Equations and Modeling

Key Concepts

Linear equations can often be used to describe or model the relationship between variables in a real-world event. In such applications, the slope may be interpreted as a rate of change.

Example

Example 1

The number of drug-related arrests for a small city has been growing approximately linearly since 1985.

Let y represent the number of drug arrests, and let x represent the number of years after 1985.

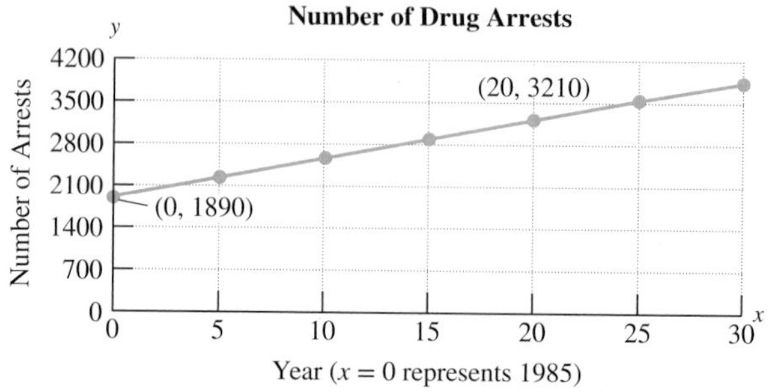

a. Use the ordered pairs (0, 1890) and (20, 3210) to find an equation of the line shown in the graph.

$$m = \frac{y_2 - y_1}{x_2 - x_1} = \frac{3210 - 1890}{20 - 0}$$

$$= \frac{1320}{20} = 66$$

The slope is 66, indicating that the number of drug arrests is increasing at a rate of 66 per year.
$m = 66$, and the y-intercept is (0, 1890). Thus,

$$y = mx + b \quad \Rightarrow \quad y = 66x + 1890$$

b. Use the equation in part (a) to estimate the number of drug-related arrests in the year 2015. (The year 2015 is 30 years after 1985. Hence, $x = 30$.)

$y = 66(30) + 1890$

$y = 3870$

For the year 2015, the number of drug arrests was approximately 3870.

Chapter 3 Review Exercises

Section 3.1

1. Graph the points on a rectangular coordinate system.

a. $\left(\frac{1}{2}, 5\right)$ **b.** $(-1, 4)$ **c.** $(2, -1)$

d. $(0, 3)$ **e.** $(0, 0)$ **f.** $\left(-\frac{8}{5}, 0\right)$

g. $(-2, -5)$ **h.** $(3, 1)$

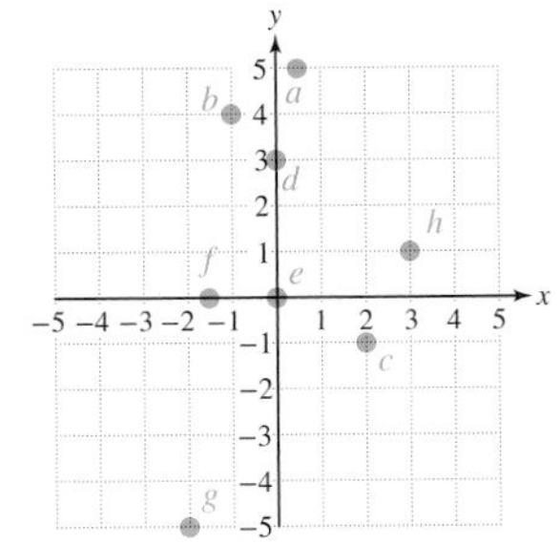

2. Estimate the coordinates of the points *A*, *B*, *C*, *D*, *E*, and *F*.
$A(4, -3)$; $B(-3, -2)$; $C(\frac{5}{2}, 5)$; $D(-4, 1)$; $E(-\frac{1}{2}, 0)$; $F(0, -5)$

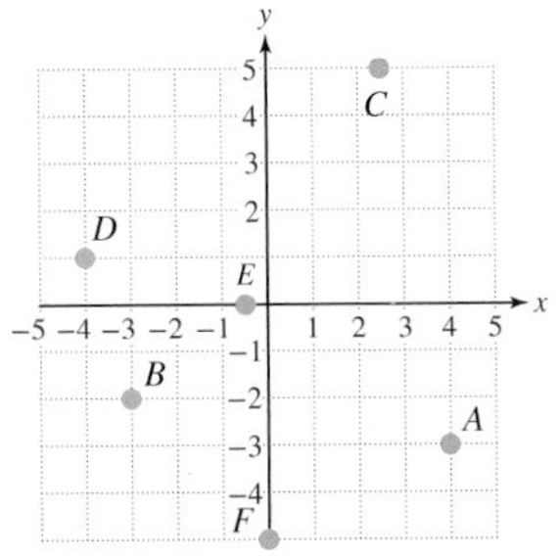

For Exercises 3–8, determine the quadrant in which the given point is located.

3. $(-2, -10)$ III **4.** $(-4, 6)$ II

5. $(3, -5)$ IV **6.** $\left(\frac{1}{2}, \frac{7}{5}\right)$ I

7. $(\pi, -2.7)$ IV **8.** $(-1.2, -6.8)$ III

9. On which axis is the point (2, 0) located? *x*-axis

10. On which axis is the point (0, −3) located? *y*-axis

11. The price per share of a stock (in dollars) over a period of 5 days is shown in the graph.

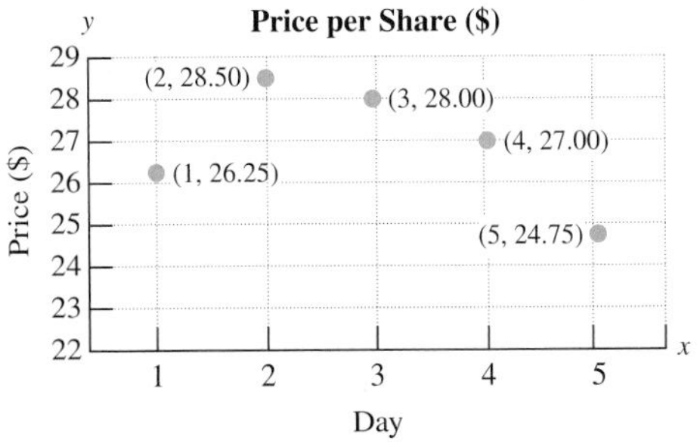

a. Interpret the meaning of the ordered pair (1, 26.25). On day 1, the price was $26.25.

b. On which day was the price the highest? Day 2

c. What was the increase in price between day 1 and day 2? $2.25

12. The number of space shuttle launches for selected years is given by the ordered pairs. Let *x* represent the number of years since 1995. Let *y* represent the number of launches.

(1, 7) (2, 8) (3, 5) (4, 3)

(5, 5) (6, 6) (7, 5) (8, 1)

a. Interpret the meaning of the ordered pair (8, 1). In 2003 (8 years after 1995), there was only one space shuttle launch. (This was the year that the Columbia and its crew were lost.)

b. Plot the points on a rectangular coordinate system.

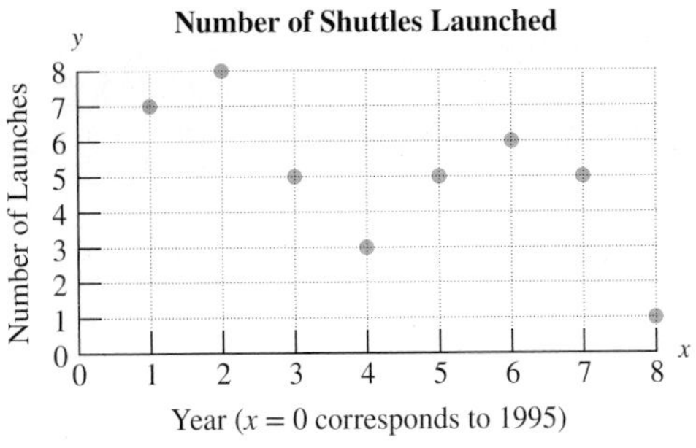

Section 3.2

For Exercises 13–16, determine if the given ordered pair is a solution to the equation.

13. $5x - 3y = 12$; $(0, 4)$ No

14. $2x - 4y = -6$; $(3, 0)$ No

15. $y = \frac{1}{3}x - 2$; $(9, 1)$ Yes

16. $y = -\frac{2}{5}x + 1$; $(-10, 5)$ Yes

For Exercises 17–20, complete the table and graph the corresponding ordered pairs. Graph the line through the points to represent all solutions to the equation.

17. $3x - y = 5$

x	y
2	1
3	4
1	−2

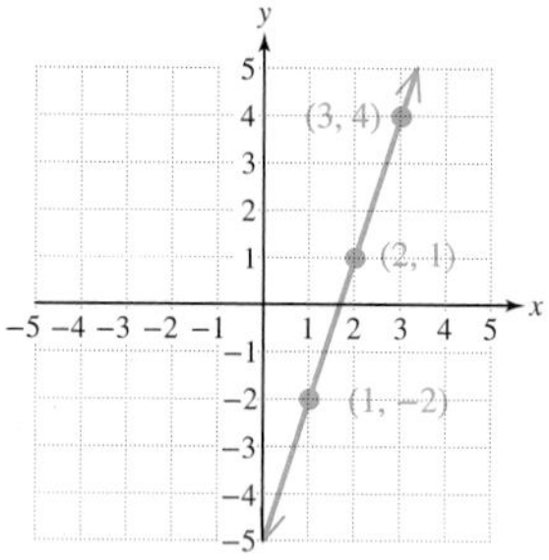

18. $\frac{1}{2}x + 3y = 6$

x	y
0	2
−2	7/3
−6	3

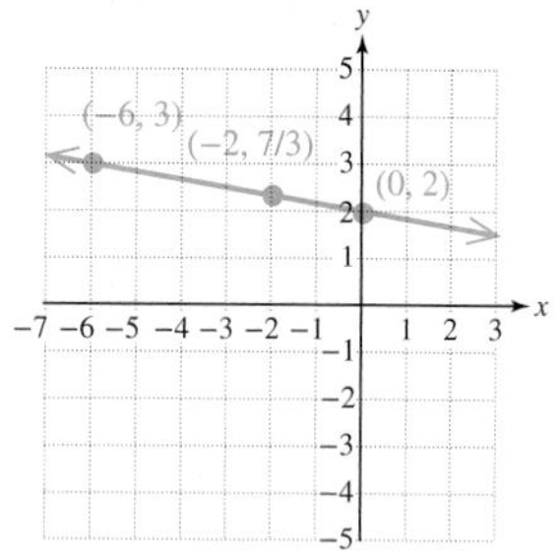

19. $y = \frac{2}{3}x - 1$

x	y
0	−1
3	1
−6	−5

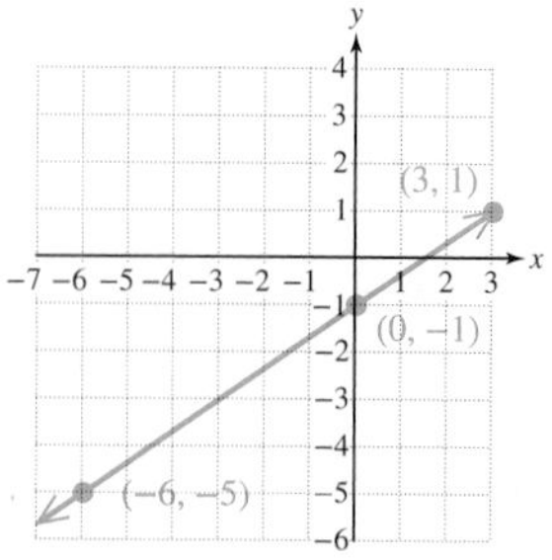

20. $y = -2x - 3$

x	y
0	−3
−3	3
1	−5

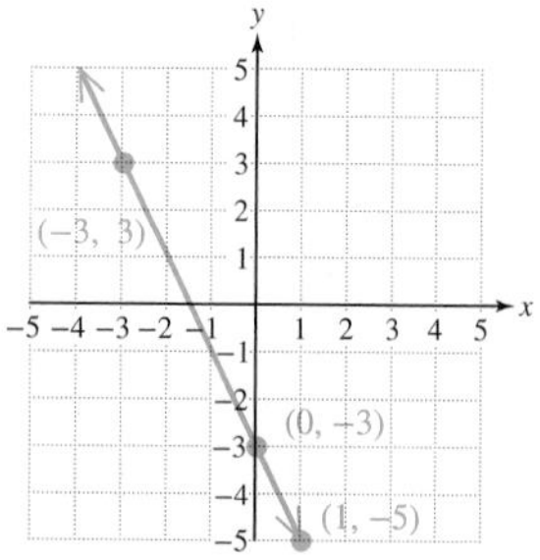

For Exercises 21–24, graph the equation.

21. $x + 2y = 4$

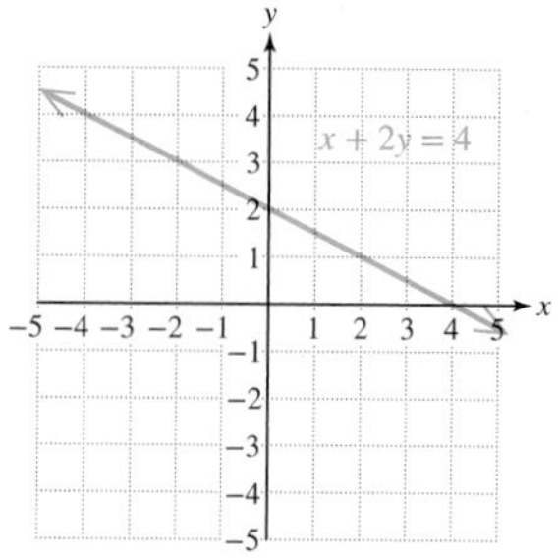

22. $x - y = 5$

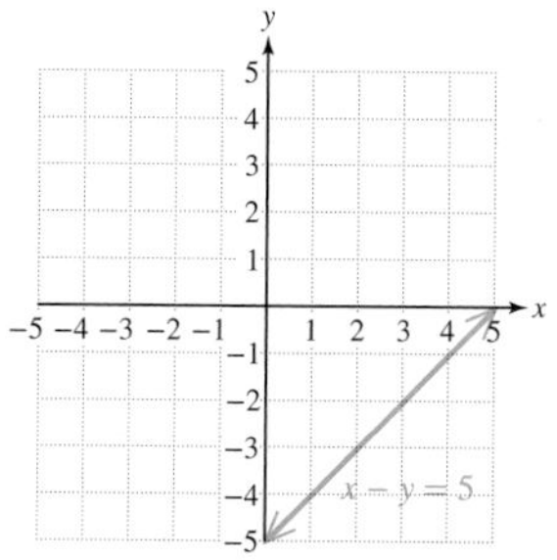

23. $y = 3x$

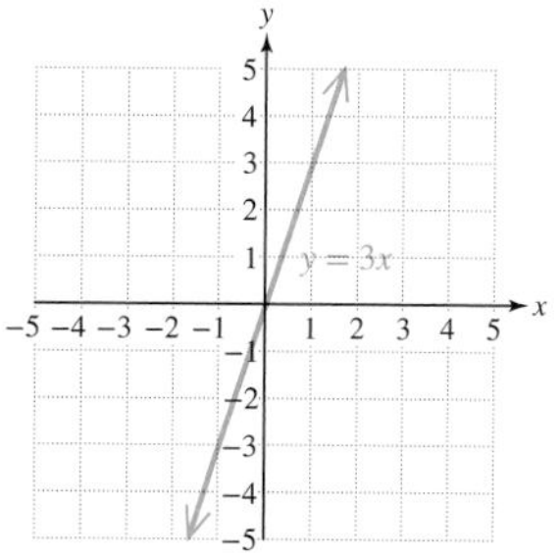

24. $y = \frac{1}{4}x$

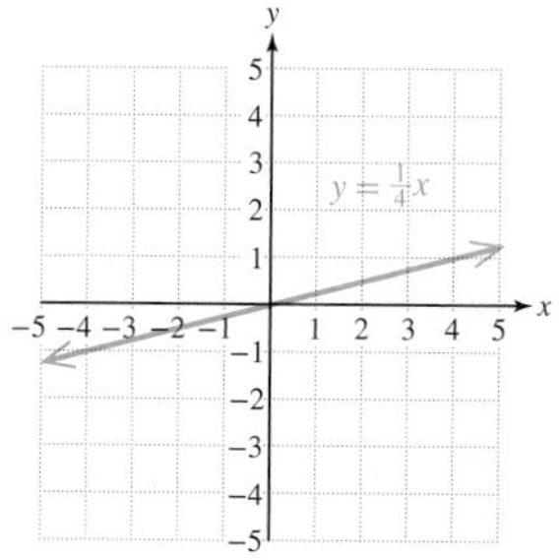

For Exercises 25–28, identify the line as horizontal or vertical. Then graph the equation.

25. $3x - 2 = 10$ Vertical

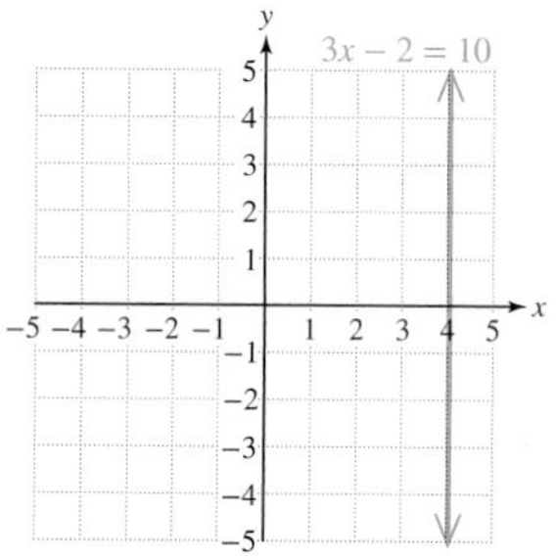

26. $2x + 1 = -2$ Vertical

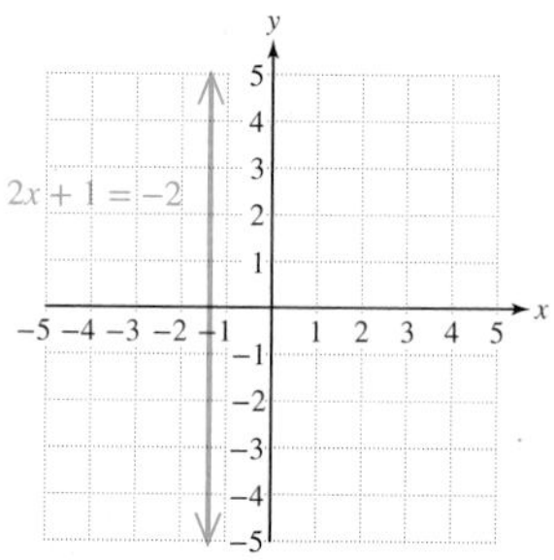

27. $6y + 1 = 13$
Horizontal

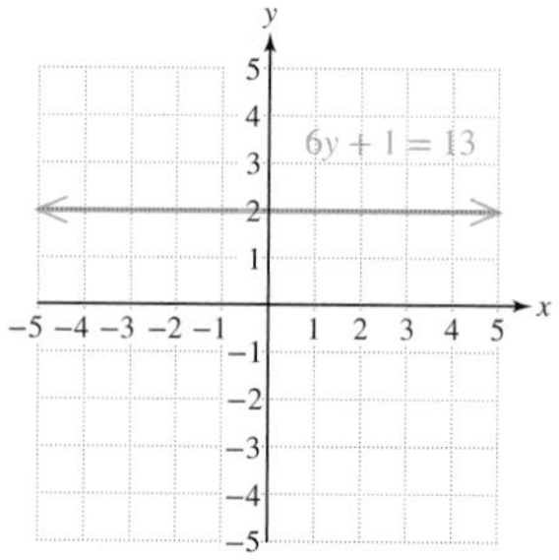

28. $5y - 1 = 14$
Horizontal

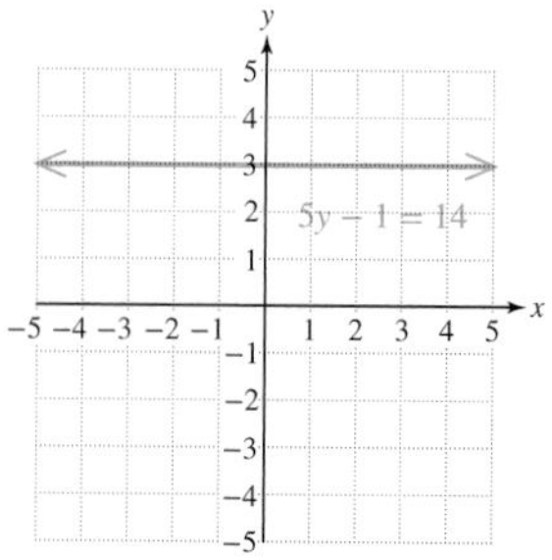

For Exercises 29–36, find the x- and y-intercepts if they exist.

29. $-4x + 8y = 12$ x-intercept: $(-3, 0)$; y-intercept: $\left(0, \frac{3}{2}\right)$

30. $2x + y = 6$ x-intercept: $(3, 0)$; y-intercept: $(0, 6)$

31. $y = 8x$ x-intercept: $(0, 0)$; y-intercept: $(0, 0)$

32. $5x - y = 0$ x-intercept: $(0, 0)$; y-intercept: $(0, 0)$

33. $6y = -24$ x-intercept: none; y-intercept: $(0, -4)$

34. $2y - 3 = 1$ x-intercept: none; y-intercept: $(0, 2)$

35. $2x + 5 = 0$ x-intercept: $\left(-\frac{5}{2}, 0\right)$; y-intercept: none

36. $-3x + 1 = 0$ x-intercept: $\left(\frac{1}{3}, 0\right)$; y-intercept: none

Section 3.3

37. What is the slope of the ladder leaning up against the wall? $m = \frac{12}{5}$

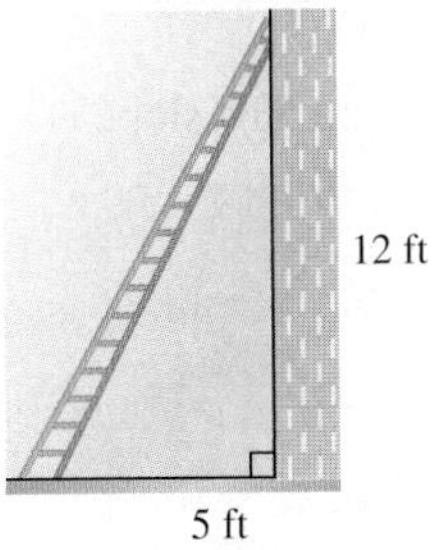

38. Point A is located 4 units down and 2 units to the right of point B. What is the slope of the line through points A and B? -2

39. Determine the slope of the line that passes through the points $(7, -9)$ and $(-5, -1)$. $-\frac{2}{3}$

40. Determine the slope of the line that has x- and y-intercepts of $(-1, 0)$ and $(0, 8)$. 8

41. Determine the slope of the line that passes through the points $(3, 0)$ and $(3, -7)$. Undefined

42. Determine the slope of the line given by $y = -1$. 0

43. A given line has a slope of -5.

a. What is the slope of a line parallel to the given line? -5

b. What is the slope of a line perpendicular to the given line? $\frac{1}{5}$

44. A given line has a slope of 0.

a. What is the slope of a line parallel to the given line? 0

b. What is the slope of a line perpendicular to the given line? Undefined

For Exercises 45–48, find the slopes of the lines l_1 and l_2 from the two given points. Then determine whether l_1 and l_2 are parallel, perpendicular, or neither.

45. l_1: $(3, 7)$ and $(0, 5)$ $m_1 = \frac{2}{3}$

l_2: $(6, 3)$ and $(-3, -3)$ $m_2 = \frac{2}{3}$; parallel

46. l_1: $(-2, 1)$ and $(-1, 9)$ $m_1 = 8$

l_2: $(0, -6)$ and $(2, 10)$ $m_2 = 8$; parallel

47. l_1: $(0, \frac{5}{6})$ and $(2, 0)$ $m_1 = -\frac{5}{12}$

l_2: $(0, \frac{6}{5})$ and $(-\frac{1}{2}, 0)$ $m_2 = \frac{12}{5}$; perpendicular

48. l_1: $(1, 1)$ and $(1, -8)$ m_1 is undefined

l_2: $(4, -5)$ and $(7, -5)$ $m_2 = 0$; perpendicular

49. Carol's electric bill had an initial reading of 35,955 kilowatt-hours at the beginning of the month. At the end of the month the reading was 37,005 kilowatt-hours. Let x represent the day of the month and y represent the reading on the meter in kilowatt-hours.

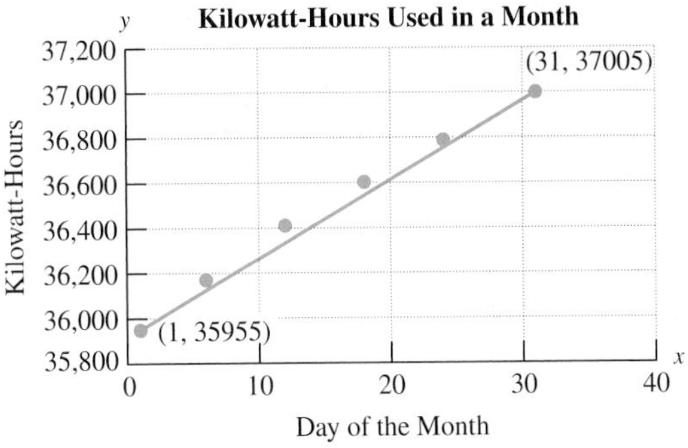

a. Using the ordered pairs $(1, 35955)$ and $(31, 37005)$, find the slope of the line. $m = 35$

b. Interpret the slope in the context of this problem. The number of kilowatt-hours increased at a rate of 35 kilowatt-hours per day.

50. New car sales were recorded over a 5-yr period in Maryland. Let x represent the year and y represent the number of new cars sold.

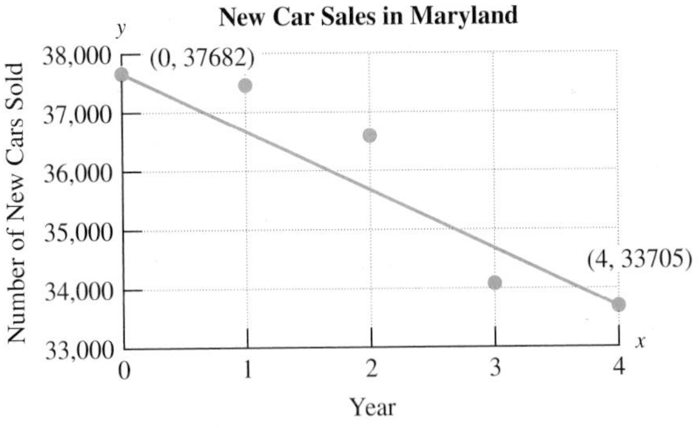

a. Using the ordered pairs $(0, 37682)$ and $(4, 33705)$, find the slope of the line. Round to the nearest whole unit. $m = -994$

b. Interpret the slope in the context of this problem. The number of new cars sold in Maryland decreased at a rate of 994 cars per year.

Section 3.4

For Exercises 51–56, write each equation in slope-intercept form. Identify the slope and the y-intercept.

51. $5x - 2y = 10$ $y = \frac{5}{2}x - 5$; $m = \frac{5}{2}$; y-intercept: $(0, -5)$

52. $3x + 4y = 12$ $y = -\frac{3}{4}x + 3$; $m = -\frac{3}{4}$; y-intercept: $(0, 3)$

53. $x - 3y = 0$ $y = \frac{1}{3}x$; $m = \frac{1}{3}$; y-intercept: $(0, 0)$

54. $5y - 8 = 4$ $y = \frac{12}{5}$; $m = 0$; y-intercept: $\left(0, \frac{12}{5}\right)$

55. $2y = -5$ $y = -\frac{5}{2}$; $m = 0$; y-intercept: $\left(0, -\frac{5}{2}\right)$

56. $y - x = 0$ $y = x$; $m = 1$; y-intercept: $(0, 0)$

For Exercises 57–62, determine whether the equations represent parallel lines, perpendicular lines, or neither.

57. l_1: $y = \frac{3}{5}x + 3$

l_2: $y = \frac{5}{3}x + 1$

Neither

58. l_1: $2x - 5y = 10$

l_2: $5x + 2y = 20$

Perpendicular

59. l_1: $3x + 2y = 6$

l_2: $-6x - 4y = 4$

Parallel

60. l_1: $y = \frac{1}{4}x - 3$

l_2: $-x + 4y = 8$

Parallel

61. l_1: $2x = 4$

l_2: $y = 6$ Perpendicular

62. l_1: $y = \frac{2}{9}x + 4$

l_2: $y = \frac{9}{2}x - 3$

Neither

63. Write an equation of the line whose slope is $-\frac{4}{3}$ and whose y-intercept is $(0, -1)$.
$y = -\frac{4}{3}x - 1$ or $4x + 3y = -3$

64. Write an equation of the line that passes through the origin and has a slope of 5.
$y = 5x$ or $5x - y = 0$

65. Write an equation of the line with slope $-\frac{4}{3}$ that passes through the point $(-6, 2)$.
$y = -\frac{4}{3}x - 6$ or $4x + 3y = -18$

66. Write an equation of the line with slope 5 that passes through the point $(-1, -8)$.
$y = 5x - 3$ or $5x - y = 3$

Section 3.5

67. Write a linear equation in two variables in slope-intercept form. (Answers may vary.)
For example: $y = 3x + 2$

68. Write a linear equation in two variables in standard form. (Answers may vary.)
For example: $5x + 2y = -4$

69. Write the slope formula to find the slope of the line between the points (x_1, y_1) and (x_2, y_2).
$m = \frac{y_2 - y_1}{x_2 - x_1}$

70. Write the point-slope formula. $y - y_1 = m(x - x_1)$

71. Write an equation of a vertical line (answers may vary). For example: $x = 6$

72. Write an equation of a horizontal line (answers may vary). For example: $y = -5$

For Exercises 73–78, write an equation of a line given the following information.

73. The slope is -6, and the line passes through the point $(-1, 8)$. $y = -6x + 2$ or $6x + y = 2$

74. The slope is $\frac{2}{3}$, and the line passes through the point $(5, 5)$. $y = \frac{2}{3}x + \frac{5}{3}$ or $2x - 3y = -5$

75. The line passes through the points $(0, -4)$ and $(8, -2)$. $y = \frac{1}{4}x - 4$ or $x - 4y = 16$

76. The line passes through the points $(2, -5)$ and $(8, -5)$. $y = -5$

77. The line passes through the point $(5, 12)$ and is perpendicular to the line $y = -\frac{5}{6}x - 3$.
$y = \frac{6}{5}x + 6$ or $6x - 5y = -30$

78. The line passes through the point $(-6, 7)$ and is parallel to the line $4x - y = 0$. $y = 4x + 31$ or $4x - y = -31$

Section 3.6

79. The graph shows the average height for girls based on age (*Source:* National Parenting Council). Let x represent a girl's age, and let y represent her height (in inches).

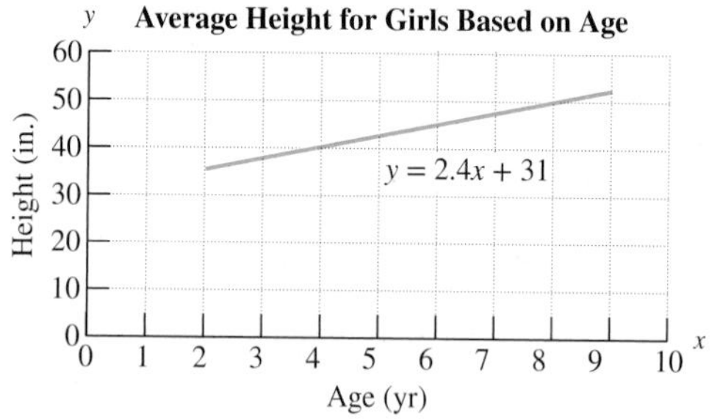

a. Use the equation to estimate the average height of a 7-year-old girl. 47.8 in.

b. What is the slope of the line? Interpret the meaning of the slope in the context of the problem.
The slope is 2.4 and indicates that the average height for girls increases at a rate of 2.4 in. per year.

80. The number of drug prescriptions increased between 2000 and 2010 (see graph). Let x represent the number of years since 2000. Let y represent the number of prescriptions (in millions).

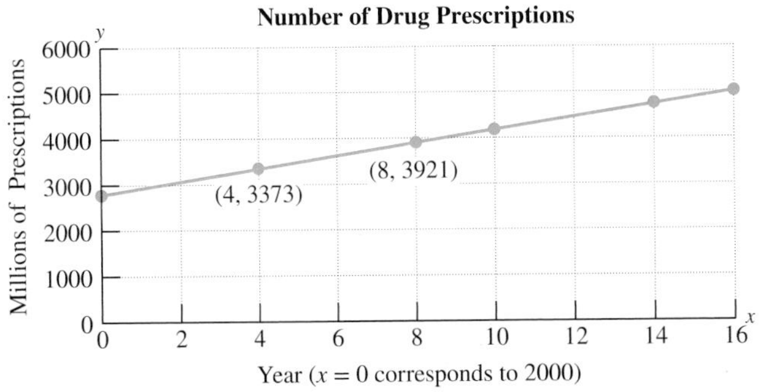

a. Using the ordered pairs (4, 3373) and (8, 3921) find the slope of the line. $m = 137$

b. Interpret the meaning of the slope in the context of this problem. The number of prescriptions increased by 137 million per year during this time period.

c. Find a linear equation that represents the number of prescriptions, y, versus the number of years, x, since 2000. $y = 137x + 2825$

d. Use the equation from part (c) to estimate the number of prescriptions for the year 2015. 4880 million

81. A water purification company charges \$20 per month and a \$55 installation fee.

a. Write a linear equation to compute the total cost, y, of renting this system for x months. $y = 20x + 55$

b. Use the equation from part (a) to determine the total cost to rent the system for 9 months. \$235

82. A small cleaning company has a fixed monthly cost of \$700 and a variable cost of \$8 per service call.

a. Write a linear equation to compute the total cost, y, of making x service calls in one month. $y = 8x + 700$

b. Use the equation from part (a) to determine the total cost of making 80 service calls. \$1340

Chapter 3 Test

1. In which quadrant is the given point located?

a. $\left(-\frac{7}{2}, 4\right)$ II **b.** $(4.6, -2)$ IV **c.** $(-37, -45)$ III

2. What is the y-coordinate for a point on the x-axis? 0

3. What is the x-coordinate for a point on the y-axis? 0

4. Bamboo is the fastest growing woody plant on earth. At a bamboo farm, the height of a black bamboo plant (phyllostachys nigra) is measured for selected days. Let x represent the day number and y represent the height of the plant.

Day, x	Height (inches), y
4	14
8	28
12	42
16	56
20	70

a. Write the data as ordered pairs and interpret the meaning of the first ordered pair.
(4, 14) After 4 days the bamboo plant is 14 in. tall. (8, 28), (12, 42), (16, 56), (20, 70)

b. Graph the ordered pairs on a rectangular coordinate system.

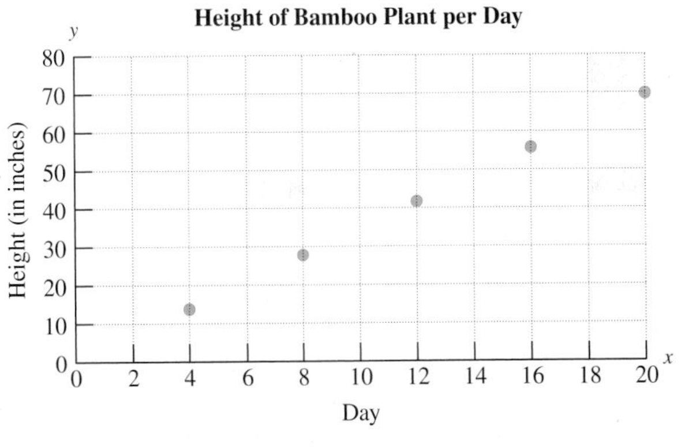

c. From the graph, estimate the height of the bamboo plant after 10 days. Approximately 35 in.

5. Determine whether the ordered pair is a solution to the equation $2x - y = 6$.

a. $(0, 6)$ No **b.** $(4, 2)$ Yes

c. $(3, 0)$ Yes **d.** $\left(\frac{9}{2}, 3\right)$ Yes

6. Given the equation $y = \frac{1}{4}x - 2$, complete the table. Plot the ordered pairs and graph the line through the points to represent the set of all solutions to the equation.

x	y
0	-2
4	-1
6	$-\frac{1}{2}$

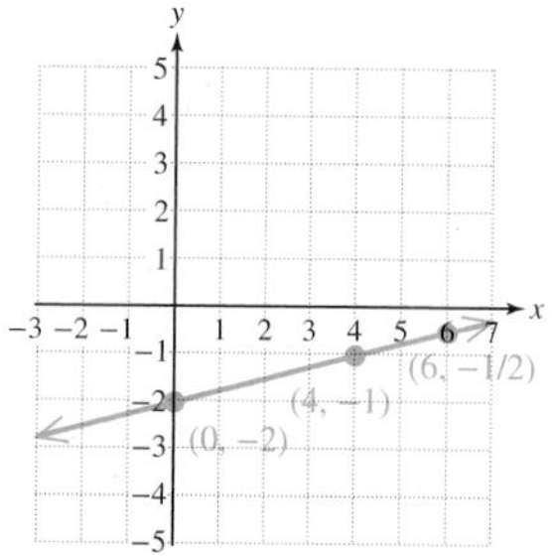

For Exercises 7–10, graph the equations.

7. $y = 3x + 2$

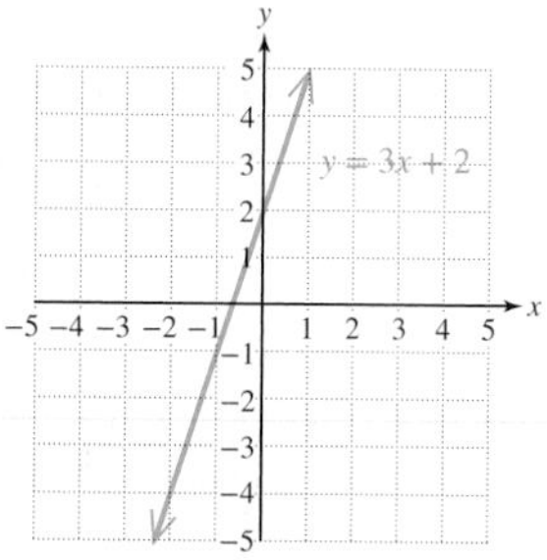

8. $2x + 5y = 0$

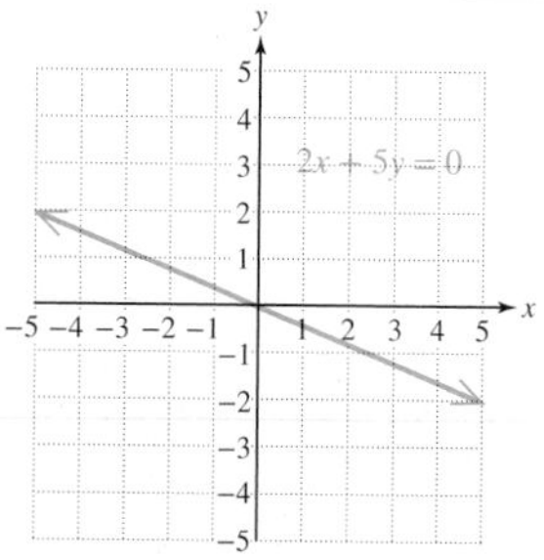

9. $3x + 2y = 8$

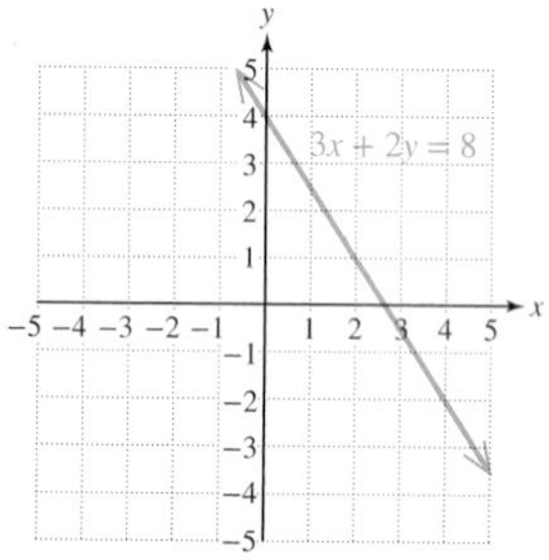

10. $y = \dfrac{3}{4}x - 2$

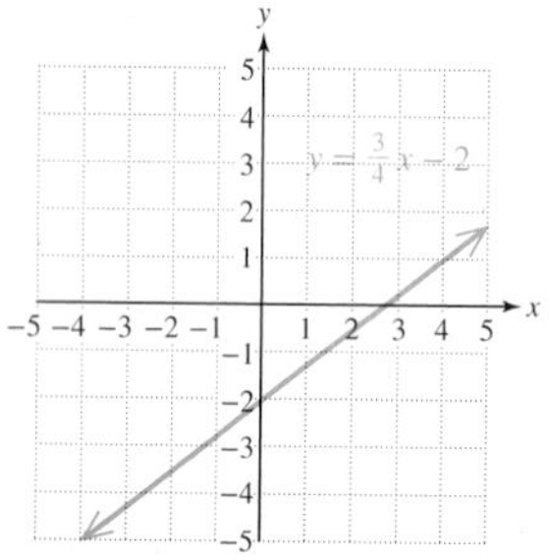

For Exercises 11–12, determine whether the equation represents a horizontal or vertical line. Then graph the line.

11. $-6y = 18$ Horizontal

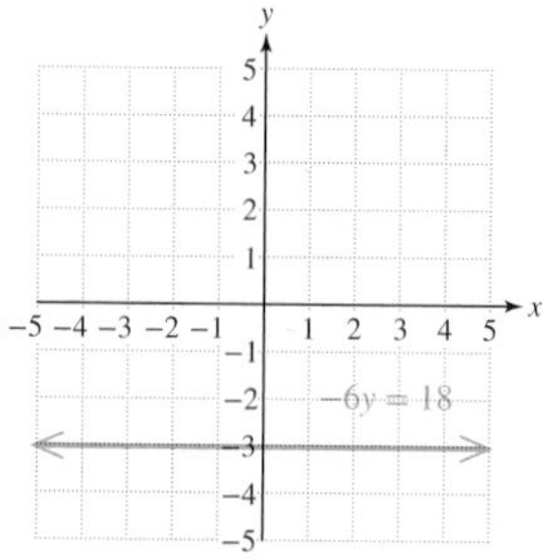

12. $5x + 1 = 8$ Vertical

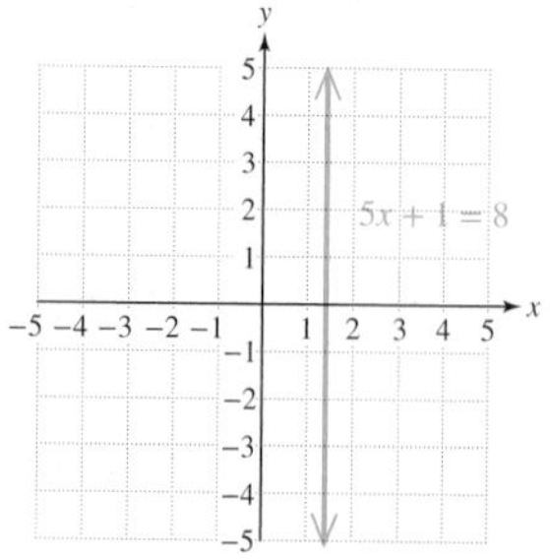

For Exercises 13–16, determine the x- and y-intercepts if they exist.

13. $-4x + 3y = 6$ x-intercept: $\left(-\frac{3}{2}, 0\right)$; y-intercept: $(0, 2)$

14. $2y = 6x$ x-intercept: $(0, 0)$; y-intercept: $(0, 0)$

15. $x = 4$ x-intercept: $(4, 0)$; y-intercept: none

16. $y - 3 = 0$ x-intercept: none; y-intercept: $(0, 3)$

17. What is the slope of the hill? $\frac{2}{5}$

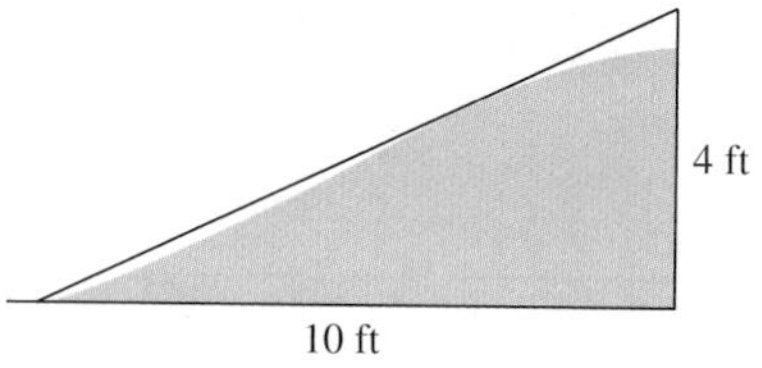

18. a. Find the slope of the line that passes through the points $(-2, 0)$ and $(-5, -1)$. $\frac{1}{3}$

b. Find the slope of the line $4x - 3y = 9$. $\frac{4}{3}$

19. a. What is the slope of a line parallel to the line $x + 4y = -16$? $-\frac{1}{4}$

b. What is the slope of a line perpendicular to the line $x + 4y = -16$? 4

20. a. What is the slope of the line $x = 5$? Undefined

b. What is the slope of the line $y = -3$? 0

21. Carlos called a local truck rental company and got quotes for renting a truck. He was told that it would cost \$41.95 to rent a truck for one day to travel 20 miles. It costs \$89.95 to rent the truck for one day to travel 100 miles. Let x represent the number of miles driven and y represent the cost of the rental.

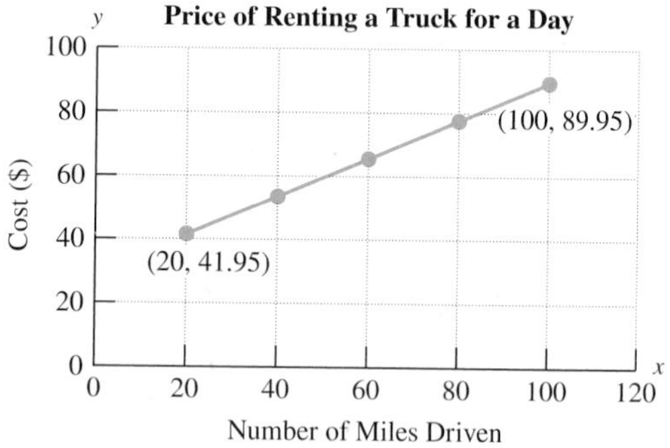

a. Using the ordered pairs (20, 41.95) and (100, 89.95), find the slope of the line. $m = 0.6$

b. Interpret the slope in the context of this problem. The cost of renting a truck increases at a rate of \$0.60 per mile.

22. Determine whether the lines through the given points are parallel, perpendicular, or neither.

l_1: (1, 4), (−1, −2) l_2: (0, −5), (−2, −11)
Parallel

23. Determine whether the equations represent parallel lines, perpendicular lines, or neither.

l_1: $2y = 3x - 3$ l_2: $4x = -6y + 1$
Perpendicular

24. Write an equation of the line that passes through the point (3, 0) and is parallel to the line $2x + 6y = -5$. $y = -\frac{1}{3}x + 1$ or $x + 3y = 3$

25. Write an equation of the line that passes through the points (2, 8) and (4, 1). $y = -\frac{7}{2}x + 15$ or $7x + 2y = 30$

26. Write an equation of the line that has y-intercept $(0, \frac{1}{2})$ and slope $\frac{1}{4}$. $y = \frac{1}{4}x + \frac{1}{2}$ or $x - 4y = -2$

27. Write an equation of the line that passes through the point (−3, −1) and is perpendicular to the line $x + 3y = 9$. $y = 3x + 8$ or $3x - y = -8$

28. Write an equation of the line that passes through the point (2, −6) and is parallel to the x-axis. $y = -6$

29. Write an equation of the line that has slope −1 and passes through the point (−5, 2).
$y = -x - 3$ or $x + y = -3$

30. To attend a state fair, the cost is \$10 per person to cover exhibits and musical entertainment. There is an additional cost of \$1.50 per ride.

  a. Write an equation that gives the total cost, y, of visiting the state fair and going on x rides.
  $y = 1.5x + 10$

  b. Use the equation from part (a) to determine the cost of going to the state fair and going on 10 rides. \$25

31. The number of medical doctors for selected years is shown in the graph. Let x represent the number of years since 1980, and let y represent the number of medical doctors (in thousands) in the United States.

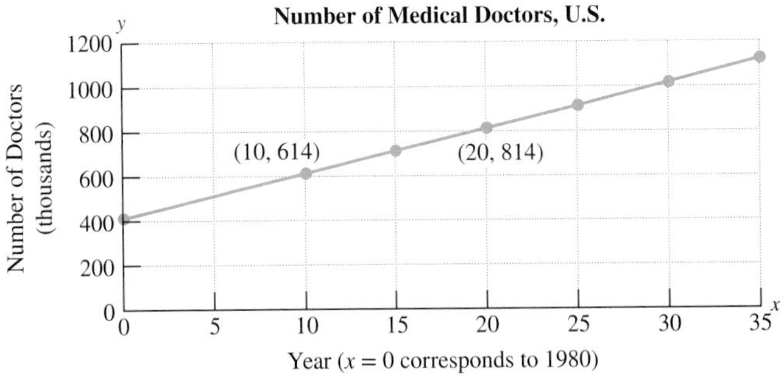

  a. Find the slope of the line shown in the graph. Interpret the meaning of the slope in the context of this problem. $m = 20$; The slope indicates that there is an increase of 20 thousand medical doctors per year.

  b. Find an equation of the line.
  $y = 20x + 414$

  c. Use the equation from part (b) to estimate the number of medical doctors in the United States for the year 2015.
  1114 thousand or, equivalently, 1,114,000

Chapters 1–3 Cumulative Review Exercises

1. Identify the number as rational or irrational.

  a. −3 Rational b. $\frac{5}{4}$ Rational c. $\sqrt{10}$ Irrational d. 0 Rational

2. Write the opposite and the absolute value for each number.

  a. $-\frac{2}{3}$ $\frac{2}{3}$; $\frac{2}{3}$ b. 5.3 −5.3; 5.3

3. Simplify the expression using the order of operations. $32 \div 2 \cdot 4 + 5$ 69

4. Add. $3 + (-8) + 2 + (-10)$ −13

5. Subtract. $16 - 5 - (-7)$ 18

For Exercises 6–7, translate the English phrase into an algebraic expression. Then evaluate the expression.

6. The quotient of $\frac{3}{4}$ and $-\frac{7}{8}$ $\frac{3}{4} \div \left(-\frac{7}{8}\right)$; $-\frac{6}{7}$

7. The product of −2.1 and −6 (−2.1)(−6); 12.6

8. Name the property that is illustrated by the following statement. $6 + (8 + 2) = (6 + 8) + 2$ The associative property of addition

For Exercises 9–12, solve each equation.

9. $6x - 10 = 14$
$\{4\}$

10. $3(m + 2) - 3 = 2m + 8$
$\{5\}$

11. $\frac{2}{3}y - \frac{1}{6} = y + \frac{4}{3}$
$\left\{-\frac{9}{2}\right\}$

12. $1.7z + 2 = -2(0.3z + 1.3)$
$\{-2\}$

13. The area of Texas is 267,277 mi^2. If this is 712 mi^2 less than 29 times the area of Maine, find the area of Maine. 9241 mi^2

14. For the formula $3a + b = c$, solve for a. $a = \frac{c - b}{3}$

15. Graph the equation $-6x + 2y = 0$.

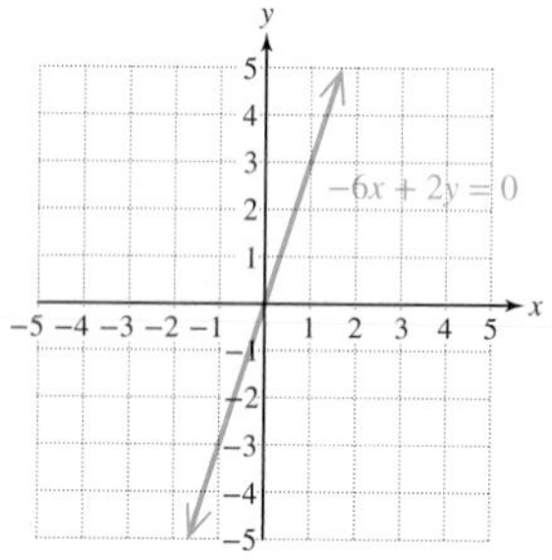

16. Find the x- and y-intercepts of $-2x + 4y = 4$.
x-intercept: $(-2, 0)$; y-intercept: $(0, 1)$

17. Write the equation in slope-intercept form. Then identify the slope and y-intercept. $3x + 2y = -12$
$y = -\frac{3}{2}x - 6$; slope: $-\frac{3}{2}$; y-intercept: $(0, -6)$

18. Explain why the line $2x + 3 = 5$ has only one intercept. $2x + 3 = 5$ can be written as $x = 1$, which represents a vertical line. A vertical line of the form $x = k$ $(k \neq 0)$ has an x-intercept of $(k, 0)$ and no y-intercept.

19. Find an equation of a line passing through $(2, -5)$ with slope -3. $y = -3x + 1$ or $3x + y = 1$

20. Find an equation of the line passing through $(0, 6)$ and $(-3, 4)$. $y = \frac{2}{3}x + 6$ or $2x - 3y = -18$

Systems of Linear Equations in Two Variables

4

CHAPTER OUTLINE

Mathematics in Business

Suppose that you have been invited to an end-of-semester party. You ask your friend for directions and she says, "It's on Earl Street and 10th Avenue." If we think of Earl Street and 10th Avenue as lines, then we know that the house is located where these lines intersect. In mathematics, we call these intersections **solutions** to **systems of linear equations**. Furthermore, the applications of systems of linear equations are numerous.

© Lissa Harrison

Imagine that the total price of buying a shirt and a tie is normally $42. If the items are on sale and priced at 60% and 90% of the original values, respectively, then the total cost is $30. To determine the original cost *s* of a single shirt and the original cost *t* of a single tie, we can set up a system of two equations.

Original Price: $s + t = 42$
Discounted Price: $0.60s + 0.90t = 30$

With techniques you will learn in this chapter, you can determine that the solution to this system is (26, 16). This means that the ordered pair (26, 16) satisfies both equations and that the point (26, 16) is a point of intersection of the lines defined by the equations in the system. The solution also tells us that the original cost of a shirt is $26 and the original cost of a tie is $16.

In this chapter, you will learn that some systems of linear equations have no solution, indicating that the related lines never intersect. This is similar to parallel streets that never meet. Other systems of linear equations may have infinitely many solutions. This occurs if the equations represent the same line.

Section 4.1 Solving Systems of Equations by the Graphing Method

Concepts

1. Solutions to a System of Linear Equations
2. Solving Systems of Linear Equations by Graphing

1. Solutions to a System of Linear Equations

Recall that a linear equation in two variables has an infinite number of solutions. The set of all solutions to a linear equation forms a line in a rectangular coordinate system. Two or more linear equations form a **system of linear equations**. For example, here are three systems of equations:

$$\begin{aligned} x - 3y &= -5 \\ 2x + 4y &= 10 \end{aligned} \qquad \begin{aligned} y &= \tfrac{1}{4}x - \tfrac{3}{4} \\ -2x + 8y &= -6 \end{aligned} \qquad \begin{aligned} 5a + b &= 4 \\ -10a - 2b &= 8 \end{aligned}$$

A **solution to a system of linear equations** is an ordered pair that is a solution to *both* individual linear equations.

Classroom Examples: p. 280, Exercises 4 and 6

Example 1 Determining Solutions to a System of Linear Equations

Determine whether the ordered pairs are solutions to the system.

$$\begin{aligned} x + y &= 4 \\ -2x + y &= -5 \end{aligned}$$

a. (3, 1) **b.** (0, 4)

Solution:

a. Substitute the ordered pair (3, 1) into both equations:

$$x + y = 4 \longrightarrow (3) + (1) \stackrel{?}{=} 4 ✓ \quad \text{True}$$
$$-2x + y = -5 \longrightarrow -2(3) + (1) \stackrel{?}{=} -5 ✓ \quad \text{True}$$

Because the ordered pair (3, 1) is a solution to both equations, it is a solution to the *system* of equations.

Avoiding Mistakes

It is important to test an ordered pair in *both* equations to determine if the ordered pair is a solution.

b. Substitute the ordered pair (0, 4) into both equations.

$$x + y = 4 \longrightarrow (0) + (4) \stackrel{?}{=} 4 ✓ \quad \text{True}$$
$$-2x + y = -5 \longrightarrow -2(0) + (4) \stackrel{?}{=} -5 \quad \text{False}$$

Because the ordered pair (0, 4) is not a solution to the second equation, it is *not* a solution to the system of equations.

Skill Practice Determine whether the ordered pair is a solution to the system.

$$\begin{aligned} 5x - 2y &= 24 \\ 2x + y &= 6 \end{aligned}$$

1. (6, 3) **2.** (4, −2)

A solution to a system of two linear equations can be interpreted graphically as a point of intersection of the two lines. Using slope-intercept form to graph the lines from Example 1, we have

$$l_1: \quad x + y = 4 \longrightarrow y = -x + 4$$
$$l_2: \quad -2x + y = -5 \longrightarrow y = 2x - 5$$

Answers

1. No
2. Yes

All points on l_1 are solutions to the equation $y = -x + 4$.
All points on l_2 are solutions to the equation $y = 2x - 5$.
The point of intersection (3, 1) is the only point that is a solution to both equations. (See Figure 4-1.)

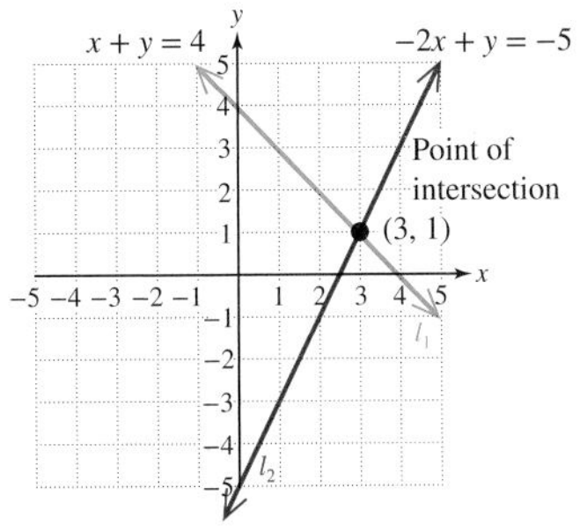

Figure 4-1

When two lines are drawn in a rectangular coordinate system, three geometric relationships are possible:

1. Two lines may intersect at *exactly one point*.

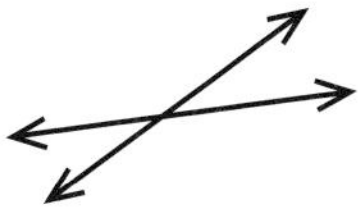

2. Two lines may intersect at *no point*. This occurs if the lines are parallel.

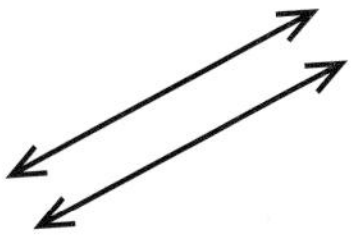

3. Two lines may intersect at *infinitely many points* along the line. This occurs if the equations represent the same line (the lines coincide).

If a system of linear equations has one or more solutions, the system is said to be **consistent**. If a system of linear equations has no solution, it is said to be **inconsistent**.

If two equations represent the same line, the equations are said to be **dependent equations**. In this case, all points on the line are solutions to the system. If two equations represent two different lines, the equations are said to be **independent equations**. In this case, the lines either intersect at one point or are parallel.

Solutions to Systems of Linear Equations in Two Variables

One Unique Solution	No Solution	Infinitely Many Solutions
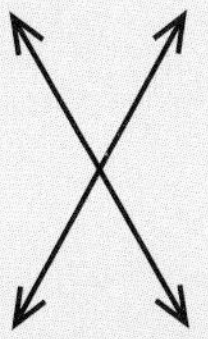	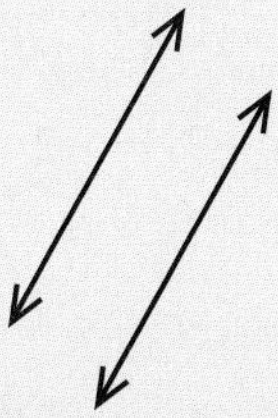	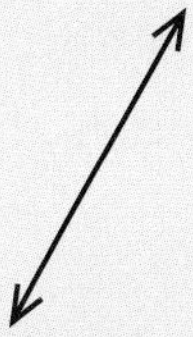
One point of intersection	Parallel lines	Coinciding lines
• System is consistent.	• System is inconsistent.	• System is consistent.
• Equations are independent.	• Equations are independent.	• Equations are dependent.

2. Solving Systems of Linear Equations by Graphing

One way to find a solution to a system of equations is to graph the equations and find the point (or points) of intersection. This is called the *graphing method* to solve a system of equations.

Classroom Example: p. 282, Exercise 32

Example 2 Solving a System of Linear Equations by Graphing

Solve the system by the graphing method.

$$y = 2x$$
$$y = 2$$

Solution:

The equation $y = 2x$ is written in slope-intercept form as $y = 2x + 0$. The line passes through the origin, with a slope of 2.

The line $y = 2$ is a horizontal line and has a slope of 0.

Because the lines have different slopes, the lines must be different and nonparallel. From this, we know that the lines must intersect at exactly one point. Graph the lines to find the point of intersection (Figure 4-2).

The point (1, 2) appears to be the point of intersection. This can be confirmed by substituting $x = 1$ and $y = 2$ into both original equations.

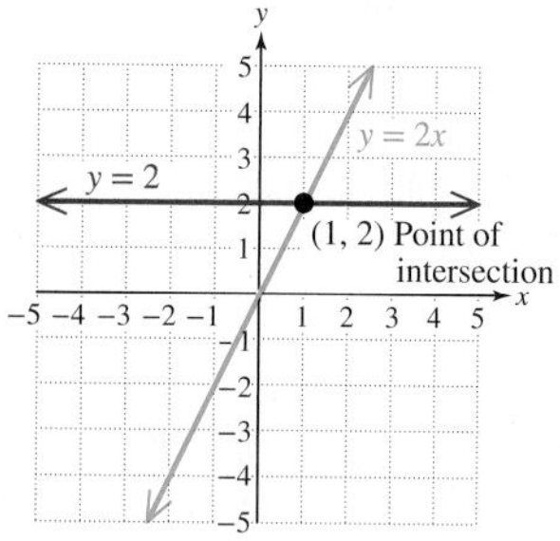

Figure 4-2

$$y = 2x \quad (2) \stackrel{?}{=} 2(1) \checkmark \quad \text{True}$$
$$y = 2 \quad (2) \stackrel{?}{=} 2 \checkmark \quad \text{True}$$

The solution set is {(1, 2)}.

Skill Practice Solve the system by the graphing method.

3. $y = -3x$
$x = -1$

Classroom Example: p. 282, Exercise 30

Example 3 Solving a System of Linear Equations by Graphing

Solve the system by the graphing method.

$$x - 2y = -2$$
$$-3x + 2y = 6$$

Solution:

One method to graph the lines is to write each equation in slope-intercept form, $y = mx + b$.

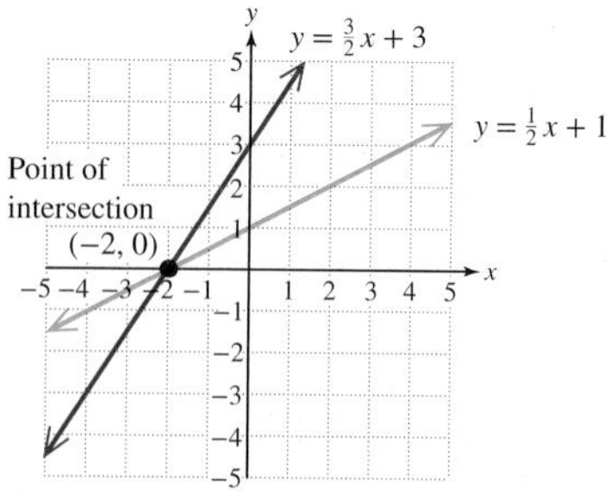

Figure 4-3

Equation 1

$$x - 2y = -2$$
$$-2y = -x - 2$$
$$\frac{-2y}{-2} = \frac{-x}{-2} - \frac{2}{-2}$$
$$y = \frac{1}{2}x + 1$$

Equation 2

$$-3x + 2y = 6$$
$$2y = 3x + 6$$
$$\frac{2y}{2} = \frac{3x}{2} + \frac{6}{2}$$
$$y = \frac{3}{2}x + 3$$

From their slope-intercept forms, we see that the lines have different slopes, indicating that the lines are different and nonparallel. Therefore, the lines must intersect at exactly one point. Graph the lines to find that point (Figure 4-3).

Answer

3. {(−1, 3)}

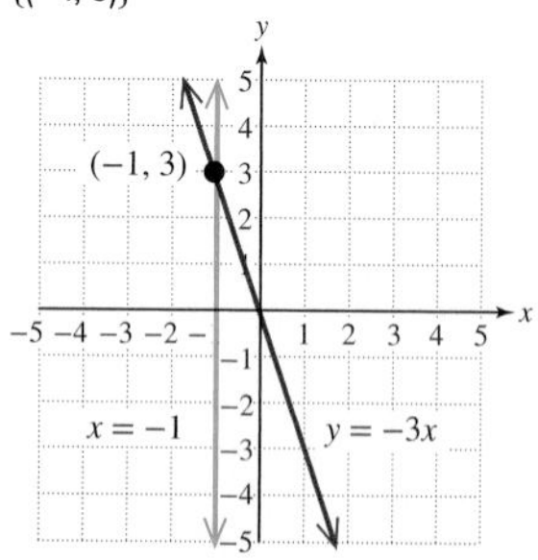

The point $(-2, 0)$ appears to be the point of intersection. This can be confirmed by substituting $x = -2$ and $y = 0$ into both equations.

$$x - 2y = -2 \longrightarrow (-2) - 2(0) \stackrel{?}{=} -2 \checkmark \quad \text{True}$$

$$-3x + 2y = 6 \longrightarrow -3(-2) + 2(0) \stackrel{?}{=} 6 \checkmark \quad \text{True}$$

The solution set is $\{(-2, 0)\}$.

Skill Practice **Solve the system by the graphing method.**

4. $y = 2x - 3$

$6x + 2y = 4$

TIP: In Examples 2 and 3, the lines could also have been graphed by using the *x*- and *y*-intercepts or by using a table of points. However, the advantage of writing the equations in slope-intercept form is that we can compare the slopes and *y*-intercepts of the two lines.

1. If the slopes differ, the lines are different and nonparallel and must intersect at exactly one point.
2. If the slopes are the same and the *y*-intercepts are different, the lines are parallel and will not intersect.
3. If the slopes are the same and the *y*-intercepts are the same, the two equations represent the same line.

Example 4 Graphing an Inconsistent System

Solve the system by graphing.

$$-x + 3y = -6$$

$$6y = 2x + 6$$

Solution:

To graph the lines, write each equation in slope-intercept form.

Equation 1	**Equation 2**
$-x + 3y = -6$	$6y = 2x + 6$
$3y = x - 6$	
$\frac{3y}{3} = \frac{x}{3} - \frac{6}{3}$	$\frac{6y}{6} = \frac{2x}{6} + \frac{6}{6}$
$y = \frac{1}{3}x - 2$	$y = \frac{1}{3}x + 1$

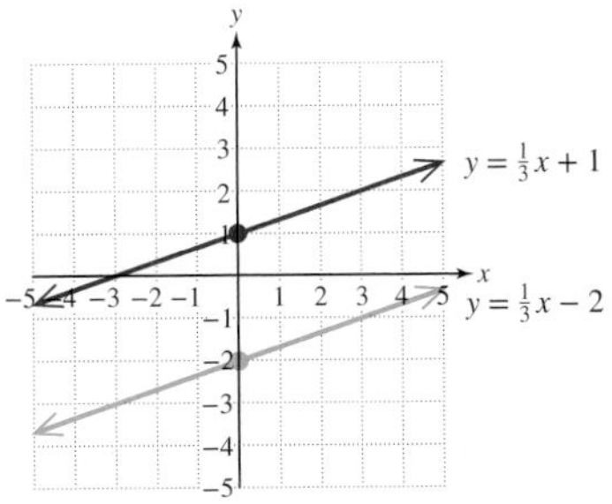

Figure 4-4

Because the lines have the same slope but different *y*-intercepts, they are parallel (Figure 4-4). Two parallel lines do not intersect, which implies that the system has no solution. Therefore, the solution set is the empty set, { }. The system is inconsistent.

Skill Practice Solve the system by graphing.

5. $4x + y = 8$

$y = -4x + 3$

Classroom Example: p. 282, Exercise 34

Answers

4. $\{(1, -1)\}$

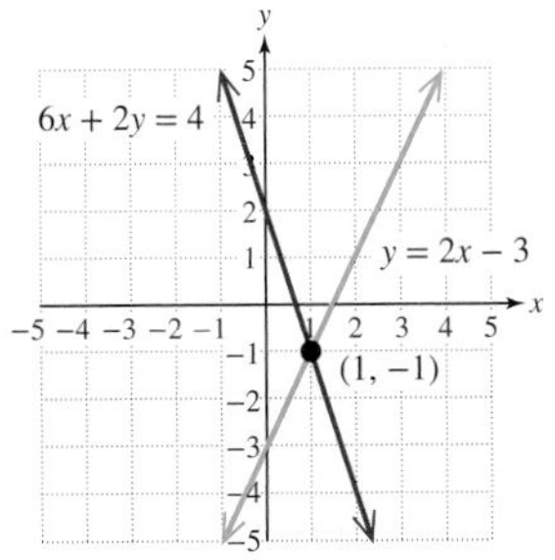

5.

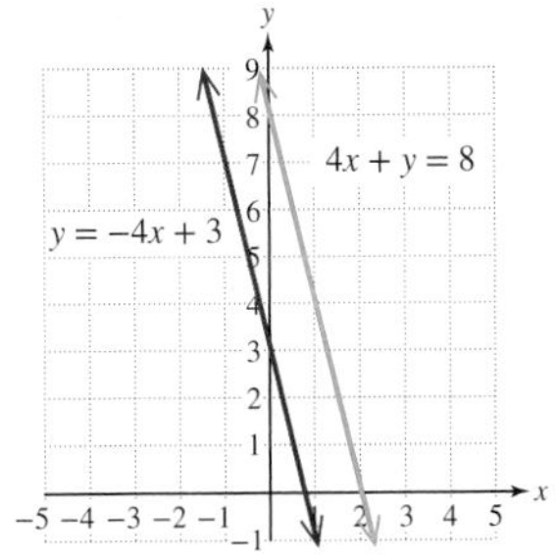

{ } The lines are parallel. The system is inconsistent.

Classroom Example: p. 282, Exercise 36

Example 5 Graphing a System of Dependent Equations

Solve the system by graphing.

$$x + 4y = 8$$
$$y = -\frac{1}{4}x + 2$$

TIP: The solution set to a system of dependent equations uses set-builder notation to describe the common line of intersection. Any form of the equation can be used. For example, in Example 5, we show the equation written in slope-intercept form and in standard form.

$$\left\{(x, y) \middle| y = -\frac{1}{4}x + 2\right\}$$
or
$$\{(x, y) \mid x + 4y = 8\}$$

Solution:

Write the first equation in slope-intercept form. The second equation is already in slope-intercept form.

Equation 1

$$x + 4y = 8$$
$$4y = -x + 8$$
$$\frac{4y}{4} = \frac{-x}{4} + \frac{8}{4}$$
$$y = -\frac{1}{4}x + 2$$

Equation 2

$$y = -\frac{1}{4}x + 2$$

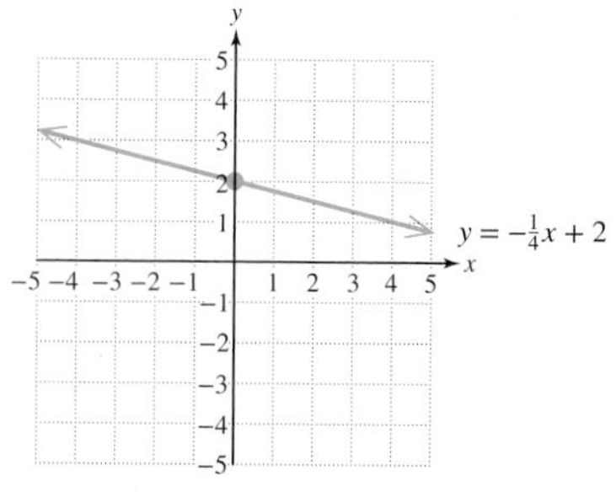

Figure 4-5

Notice that the slope-intercept forms of the two lines are identical. Therefore, the equations represent the same line (Figure 4-5). The equations are dependent, and the solution to the system of equations is the set of all points on the line.

Because there are infinitely many points on the line, the ordered pairs in the solution set cannot all be listed. Therefore, we can write the solution in set-builder notation: $\{(x, y) \mid y = -\frac{1}{4}x + 2\}$. This can be read as "the set of all ordered pairs (x, y) such that the ordered pairs satisfy the equation $y = -\frac{1}{4}x + 2$."

In summary:

- There are infinitely many solutions to the system of equations.
- The solution set is $\{(x, y) \mid y = -\frac{1}{4}x + 2\}$, or equivalently $\{(x, y) \mid x + 4y = 8\}$.
- The equations are dependent.

Skill Practice Solve the system by graphing.

6. $x - 3y = 6$

$$y = \frac{1}{3}x - 2$$

Answer

6.

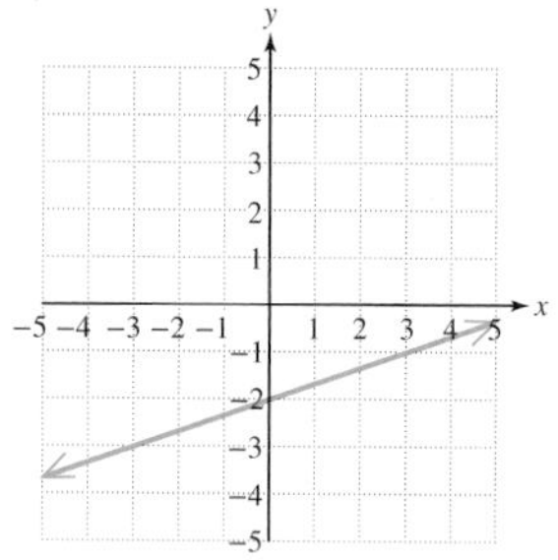

$$\left\{(x, y) \middle| y = \frac{1}{3}x - 2\right\}$$

The equations are dependent.

Calculator Connections

Topic: Graphing Systems of Linear Equations in Two Variables

The solution to a system of equations can be found by using either a *Trace* feature or an *Intersect* feature on a graphing calculator to find the point of intersection of two graphs.

For example, consider the system:

$$-2x + y = 6$$
$$5x + y = -1$$

First graph the equations together on the same viewing window. Recall that to enter the equations into the calculator, the equations must be written with the y variable isolated.

$$-2x + y = 6 \xrightarrow{\text{Isolate } y.} y = 2x + 6$$
$$5x + y = -1 \longrightarrow y = -5x - 1$$

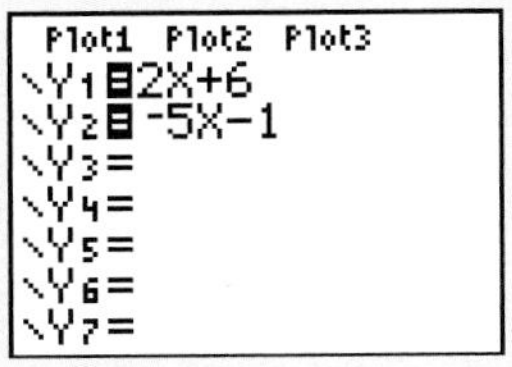

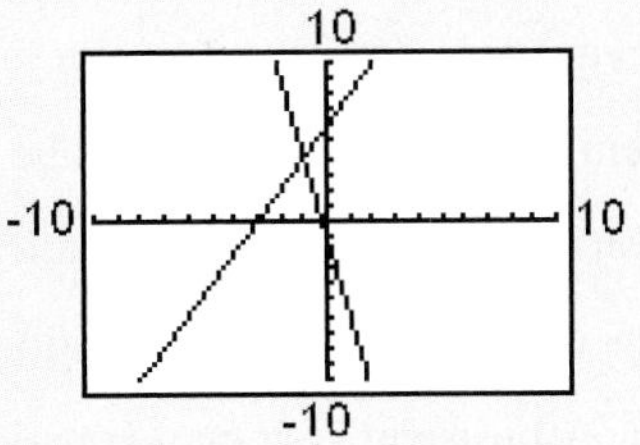

By inspection of the graph, it appears that the solution is $(-1, 4)$. The *Trace* option on the calculator may come close to $(-1, 4)$ but may not show the exact solution (Figure 4-6). However, an *Intersect* feature on a graphing calculator may provide the exact solution (Figure 4-7).

Using *Trace*

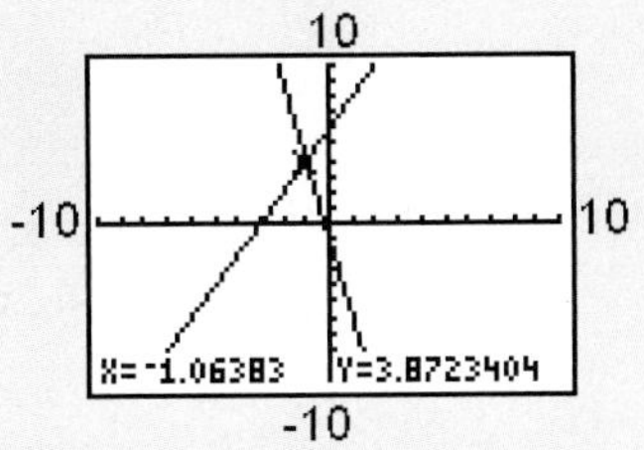

Figure 4-6

Using *Intersect*

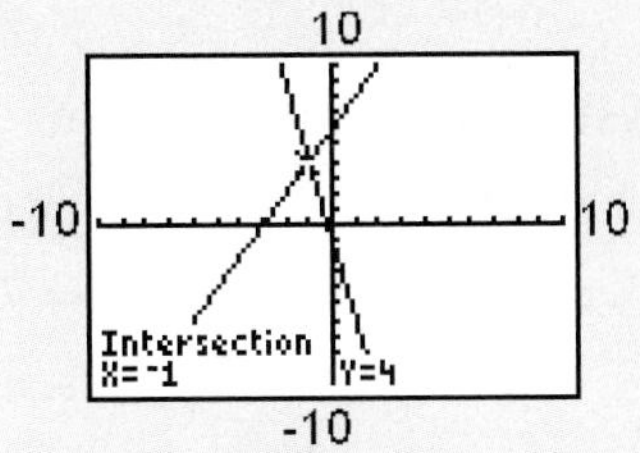

Figure 4-7

Calculator Exercises

Use a graphing calculator to graph each pair of linear equations on the same viewing window. Use a *Trace* or *Intersect* feature to find the point(s) of intersection. Then write the solution set.

1. $y = 2x - 3$ $\{(2, 1)\}$
$y = -4x + 9$

2. $y = -\frac{1}{2}x + 2$ $\{(6, -1)\}$
$y = \frac{1}{3}x - 3$

3. $x + y = 4$ (Example 1)
$-2x + y = -5$ $\{(3, 1)\}$

4. $x - 2y = -2$ (Example 3)
$-3x + 2y = 6$
$\{(-2, 0)\}$

5. $-x + 3y = -6$ (Example 4)
$6y = 2x + 6$
{ }

6. $x + 4y = 8$ (Example 5)
$y = -\frac{1}{4}x + 2$ $\left\{(x, y) \middle| y = -\frac{1}{4}x + 2\right\}$

Section 4.1 Practice Exercises

Study Skills Exercise

For additional exercises, see Classroom Activity 4.1A, in the *Student's Resource Manual* at www.mhhe.com/moh.

It is important to keep track of your grade throughout the semester. Take a minute to compute your grade at this point. Are you earning the grade that you want? If not, maybe organizing a study group would help.

In a study group, check the activities that you might try to help you learn and understand the material.

_____ Quiz each other by asking each other questions.

_____ Practice teaching each other.

_____ Share and compare class notes.

_____ Support and encourage each other.

_____ Work together on exercises and sample problems.

Vocabulary and Key Concepts

1. **a.** A system of linear equations consists of two or more linear equations.

   b. A solution to a system of linear equations must be a solution to both individual equations in the system.

   c. Graphically, a solution to a system of linear equations in two variables is a point where the lines intersect.

   d. A system of equations that has one or more solutions is said to be consistent.

   e. The solution set to an inconsistent system of equations is { }.

   f. Two equations in a system of linear equations in two variables are said to be dependent if they represent the same line.

   g. Two equations in a system of linear equations in two variables are said to be independent if they represent different lines.

Concept 1: Solutions to a System of Linear Equations

For Exercises 2–10, determine if the given point is a solution to the system. **(See Example 1.)**

2. $6x - y = -9$ $(-1, 3)$
$x + 2y = 5$ Yes

3. $3x - y = 7$ $(2, -1)$
$x - 2y = 4$ Yes

4. $x - y = 3$ $(4, 1)$
$x + y = 5$ Yes

5. $4y = -3x + 12$ $(0, 4)$
$y = \frac{2}{3}x - 4$ No

6. $y = -\frac{1}{3}x + 2$ $(9, -1)$
$x = 2y + 6$ No

7. $3x - 6y = 9$ $\left(4, \frac{1}{2}\right)$
$x - 2y = 3$ Yes

8. $x - y = 4$ $(6, 2)$
$3x - 3y = 12$ Yes

9. $\frac{1}{3}x = \frac{2}{5}y - \frac{4}{5}$ $(0, 2)$
$\frac{3}{4}x + \frac{1}{2}y = 2$ No

10. $\frac{1}{4}x + \frac{1}{2}y = \frac{3}{2}$ $(4, 1)$
$y = \frac{3}{2}x - 6$ No

For Exercises 11–14, match the graph of the system of equations with the appropriate description of the solution.

11. b

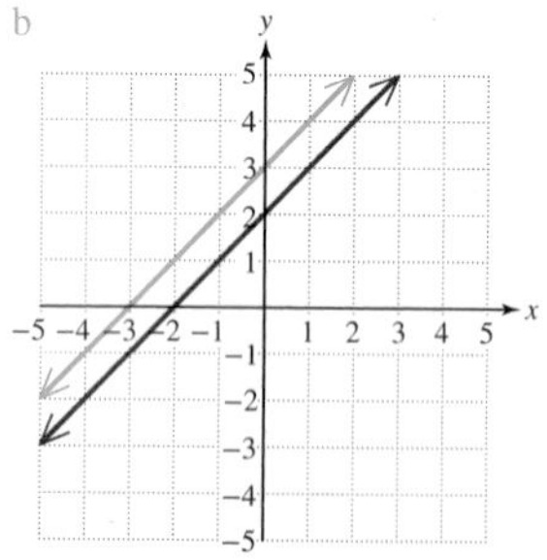

a. The solution set is {(1, 3)}.

b. { }

c. There are infinitely many solutions.

d. The solution set is {(0, 0)}.

12. c

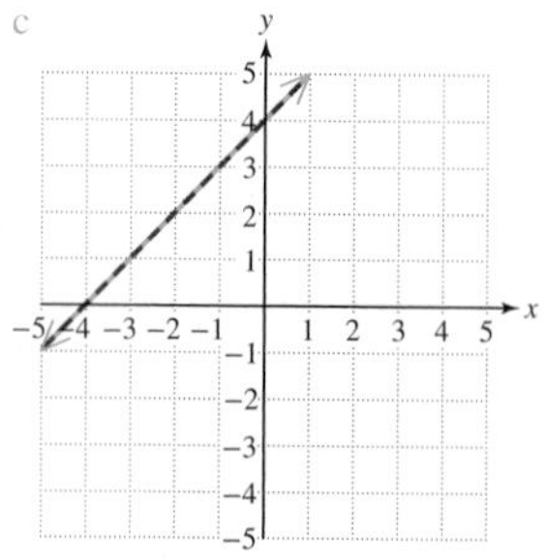

13. d

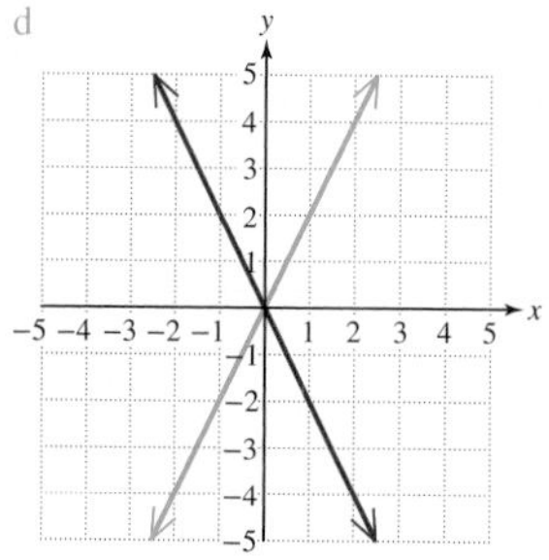

14. a

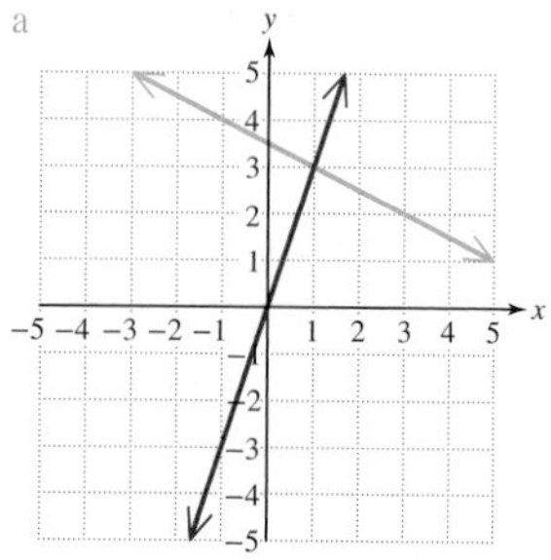

15. Graph each system of equations.

a. $y = 2x - 3$
$y = 2x + 5$

b. $y = 2x + 1$
$y = 4x - 1$

c. $y = 3x - 5$
$y = 3x - 5$

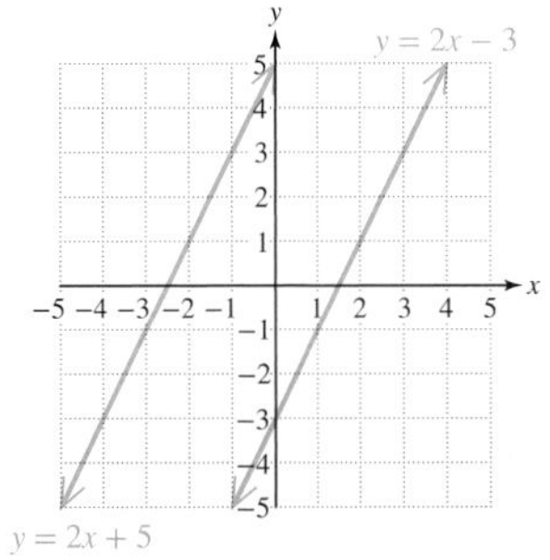

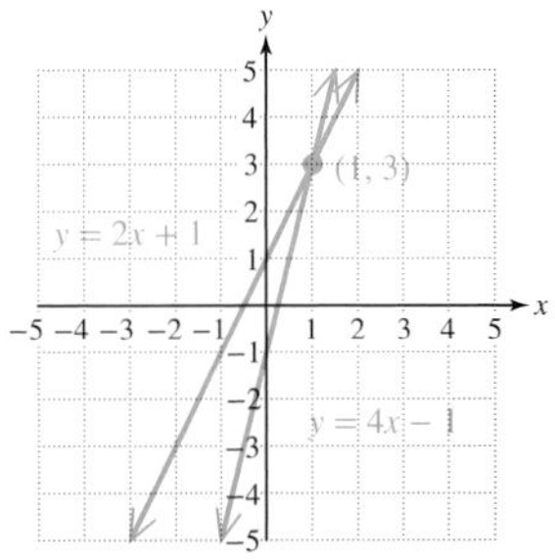

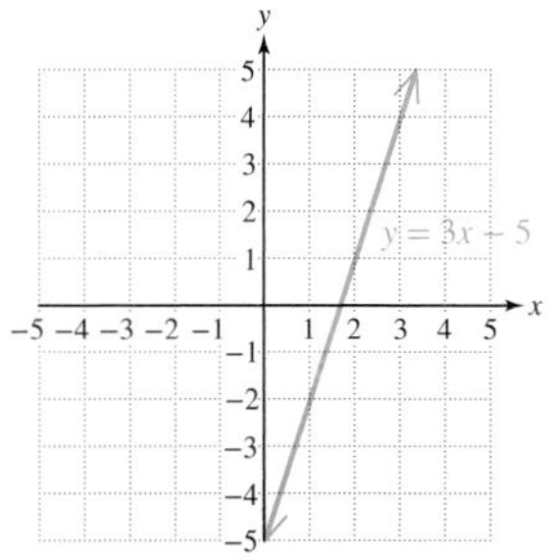

For Exercises 16–26, determine which system of equations (a, b, or c) makes the statement true. (*Hint:* Refer to the graphs from Exercise 15.)

a. $y = 2x - 3$
$y = 2x + 5$

b. $y = 2x + 1$
$y = 4x - 1$

c. $y = 3x - 5$
$y = 3x - 5$

16. The lines are parallel. a

17. The lines coincide. c

18. The lines intersect at exactly one point. b

19. The system is inconsistent. a

20. The equations are dependent. c

21. The lines have the same slope but different y-intercepts. a

22. The lines have the same slope and same y-intercept. c

23. The lines have different slopes. b

24. The system has exactly one solution. b

25. The system has infinitely many solutions. c

26. The system has no solution. a

Concept 2: Solving Systems of Linear Equations by Graphing

For Exercises 27–50, solve the system by graphing. For systems that do not have one unique solution, also state the number of solutions and whether the system is inconsistent or the equations are dependent. **(See Examples 2–5.)**

27. $y = -x + 4$
$y = x - 2$ {(3, 1)}

28. $y = 3x + 2$
$y = 2x$ {(−2, −4)}

29. $2x + y = 0$
$3x + y = 1$ {(1, −2)}

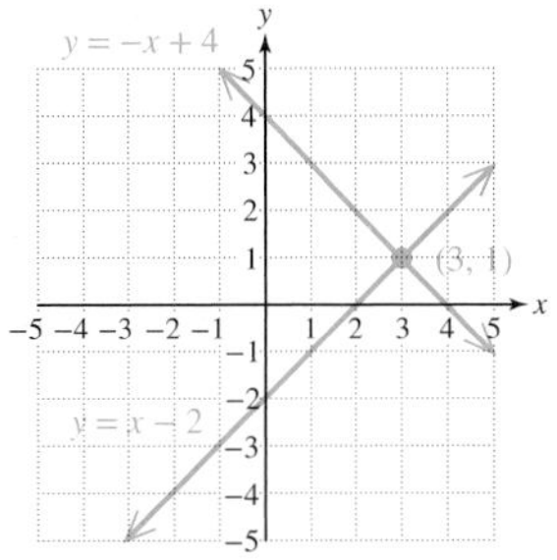

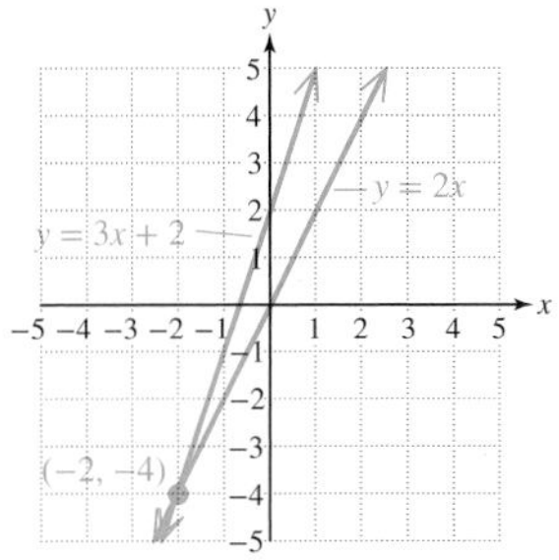

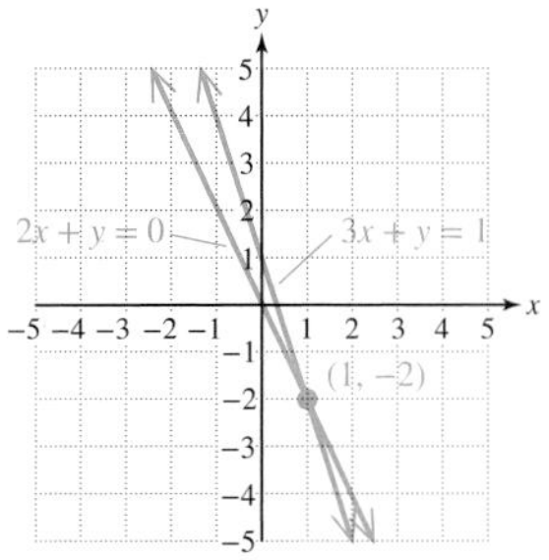

30. $x + y = -1$
$2x - y = -5$ $\{(-2, 1)\}$

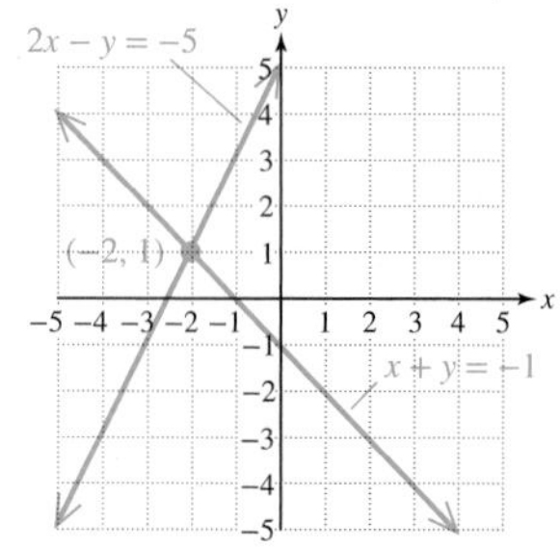

31. $2x + y = 6$
$x = 1$ $\{(1, 4)\}$

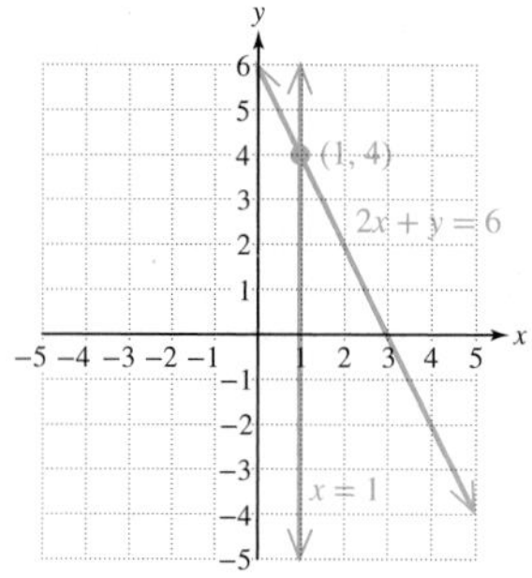

32. $4x + 3y = 9$
$x = 3$ $\{(3, -1)\}$

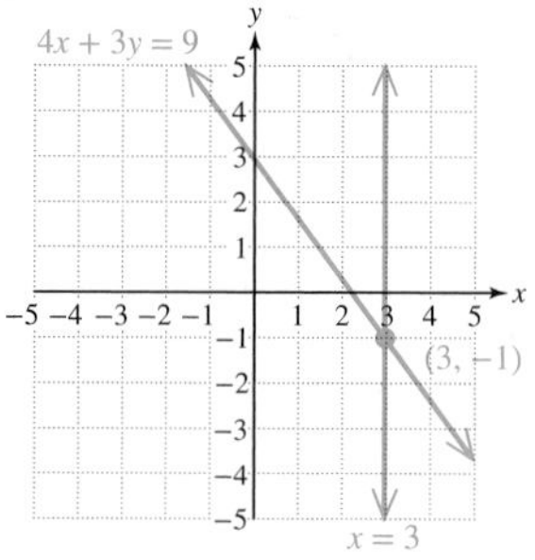

33. $-6x - 3y = 0$
$4x + 2y = 4$ No solution; { }; inconsistent system

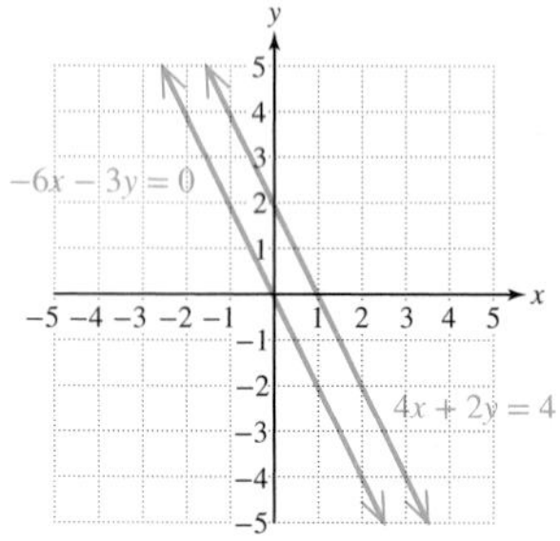

34. $2x - 6y = 12$
$-3x + 9y = 12$ No solution; { }; inconsistent system

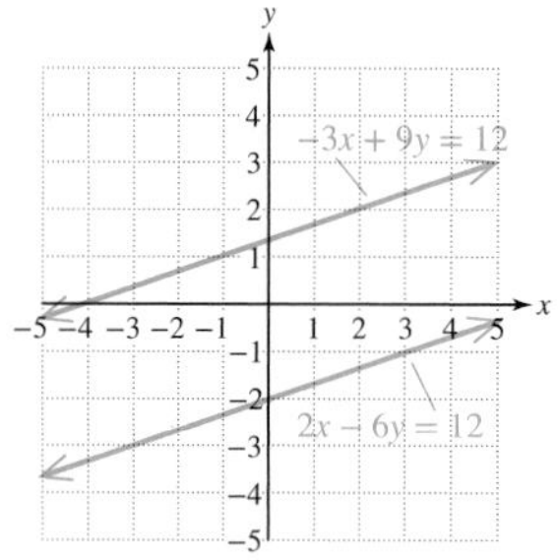

35. $-2x + y = 3$
$6x - 3y = -9$ Infinitely many solutions; $\{(x, y) \mid -2x + y = 3\}$; dependent equations

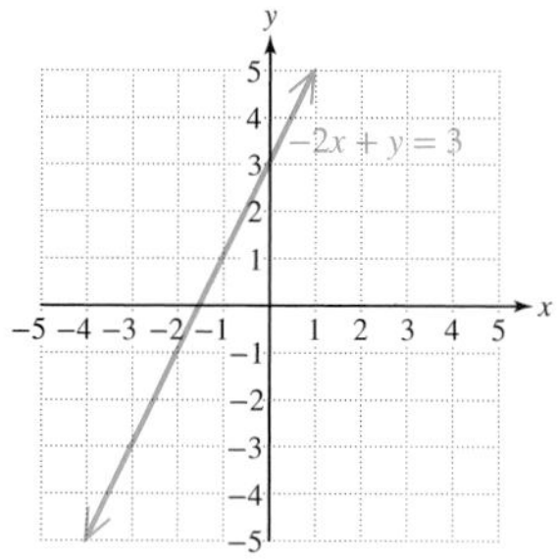

36. $x + 3y = 0$
$-2x - 6y = 0$ Infinitely many solutions; $\{(x, y) \mid x + 3y = 0\}$; dependent equations

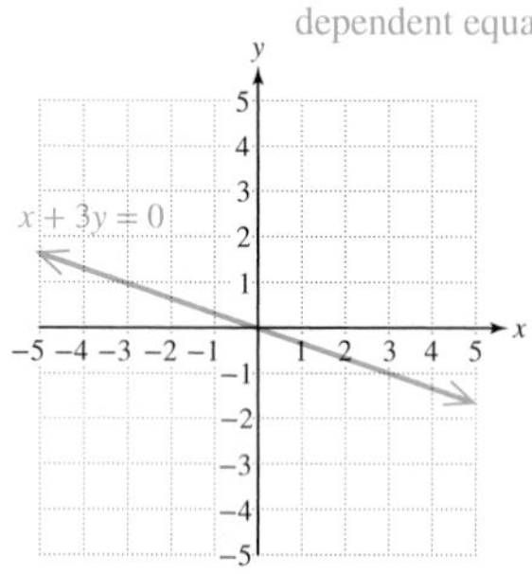

37. $y = 6$
$2x + 3y = 12$ $\{(-3, 6)\}$

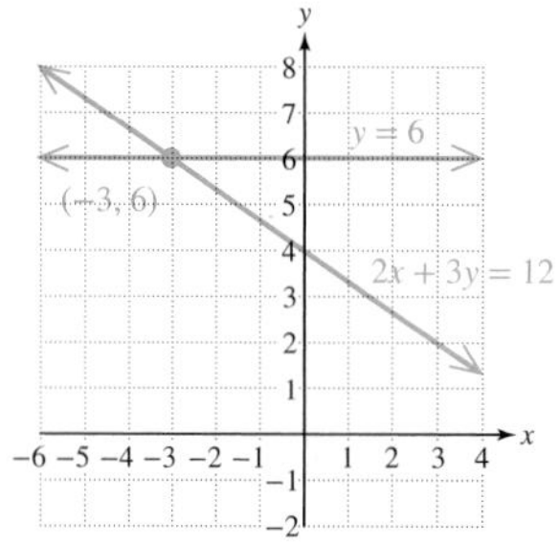

38. $y = -2$
$x - 2y = 10$ $\{(6, -2)\}$

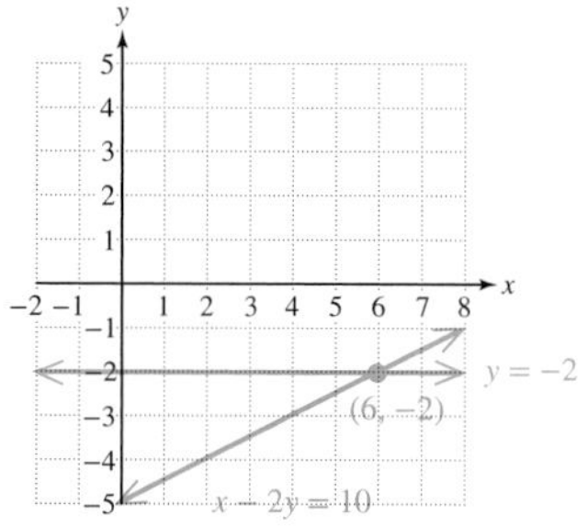

39. $x = 4 + y$
$3y = -3x$ $\{(2, -2)\}$

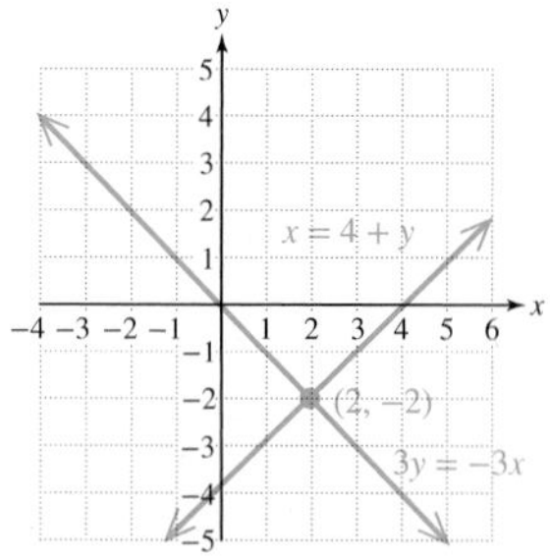

40. $3y = 4x$
$x - y = -1$ $\{(3, 4)\}$

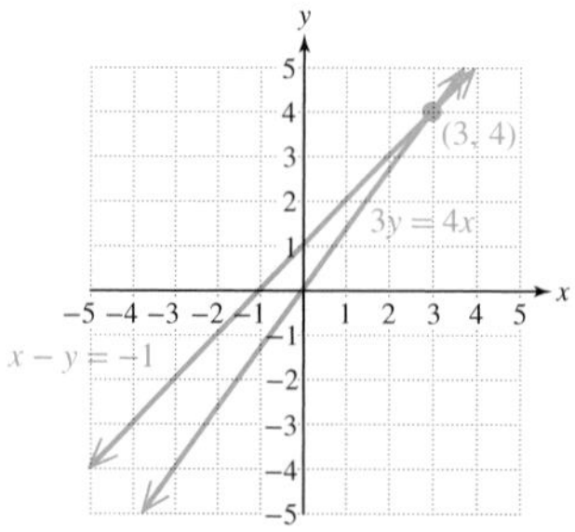

41. $-x + y = 3$
$4y = 4x + 6$ No solution; { }; inconsistent system

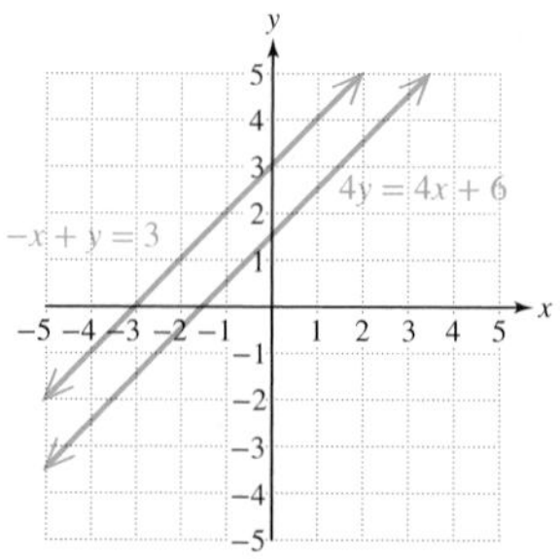

42. $x - y = 4$
$3y = 3x + 6$ No solution; { }; inconsistent system

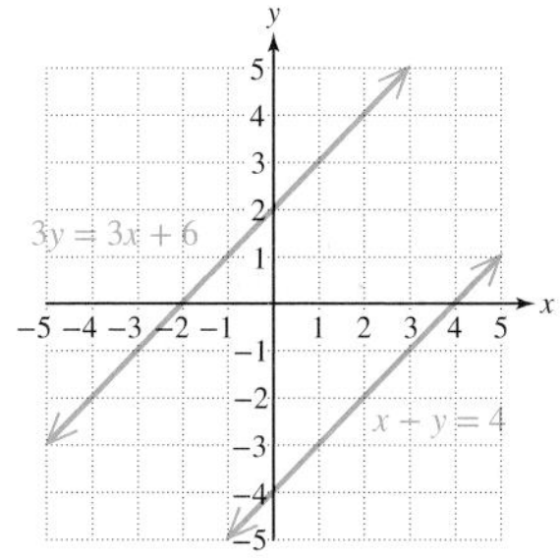

43. $x = 4$
$2y = 4$ {(4, 2)}

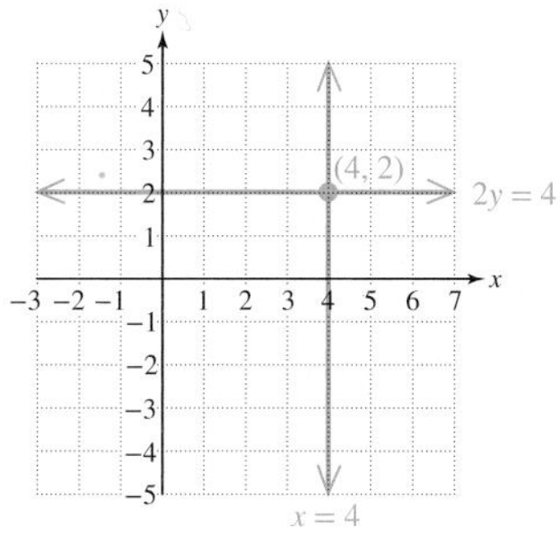

44. $-3x = 6$
$y = 2$ {(−2, 2)}

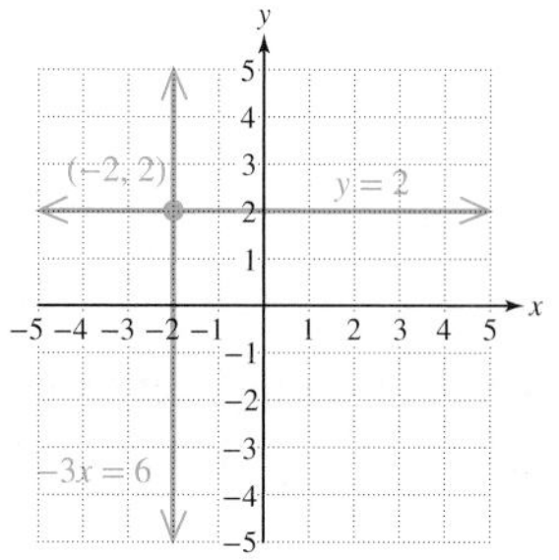

45. $2x + y = 4$
$4x - 2y = 0$ {(1, 2)}

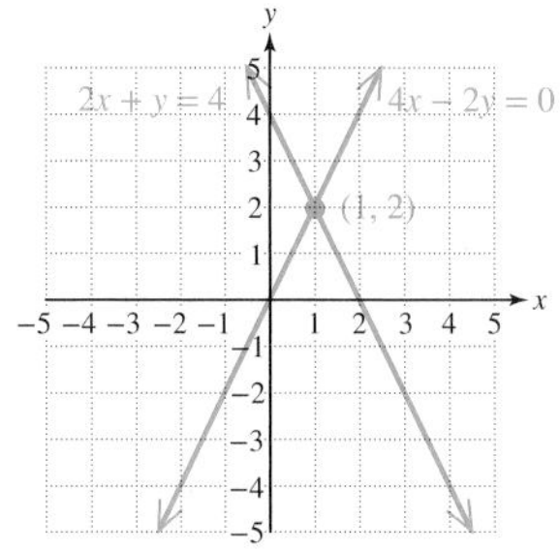

46. $3x + 3y = 3$
$2x - y = 5$ {(2, −1)}

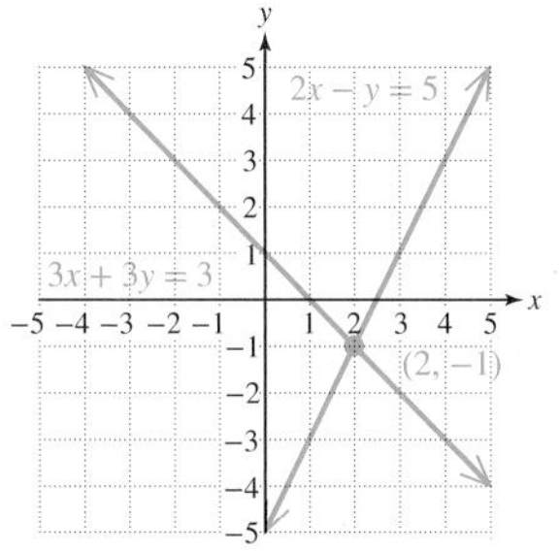

47. $y = 0.5x + 2$
$-x + 2y = 4$ Infinitely many solutions; $\{(x, y) \mid y = 0.5x + 2\}$; dependent equations

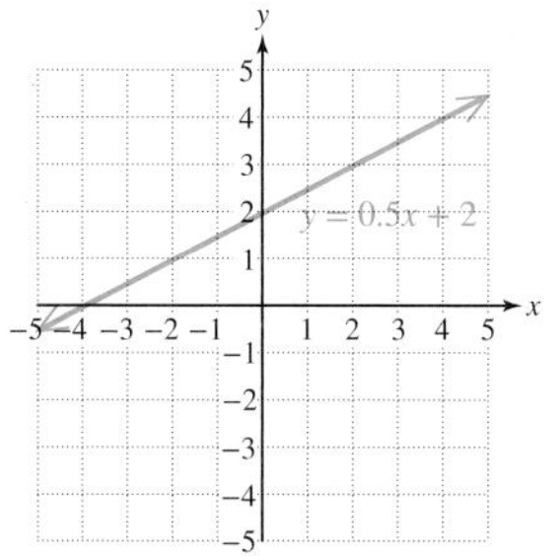

48. $3x - 4y = 6$
$-6x + 8y = -12$ Infinitely many solutions; $\{(x, y) \mid 3x - 4y = 6\}$; dependent equations

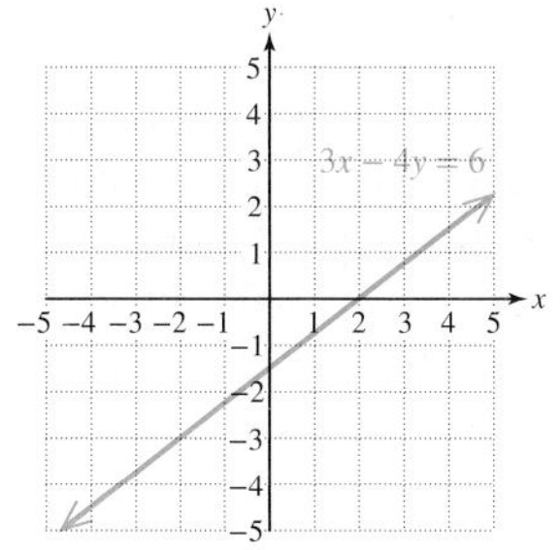

49. $x - 3y = 0$
$y = -x - 4$ {(−3, −1)}

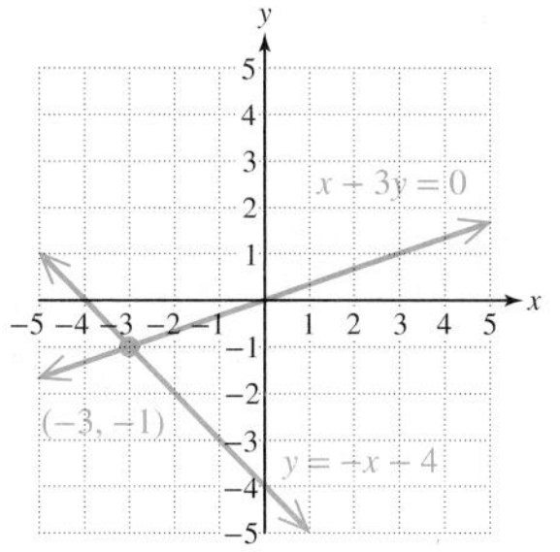

50. $-6x + 3y = -6$
$4x + y = -2$ {(0, −2)}

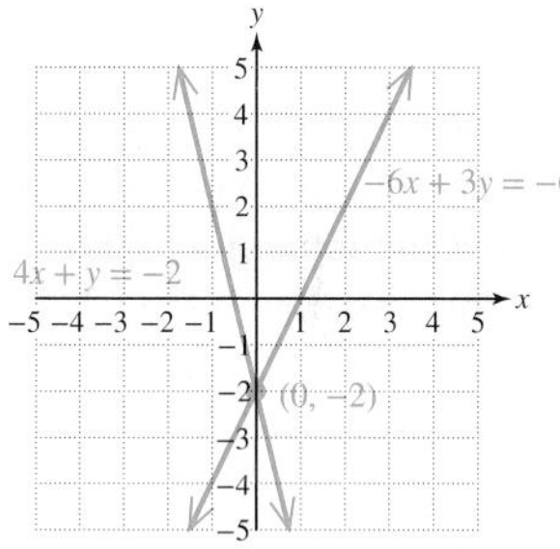

51. A wholesale club offers two types of memberships. The Executive Membership is \$100 per year, including an annual 2% reward. The Business Membership is \$50 per year without a reward. The total cost for membership, y, depends on the amount of money spent on merchandise, x, and can be represented by the following equations:

Executive Membership: $y = 100 - 0.02x$

Business Membership: $y = 50$

According to the graph, how much money spent on merchandise would result in the same cost for each membership?
The same cost occurs when \$2500 of merchandise is purchased.

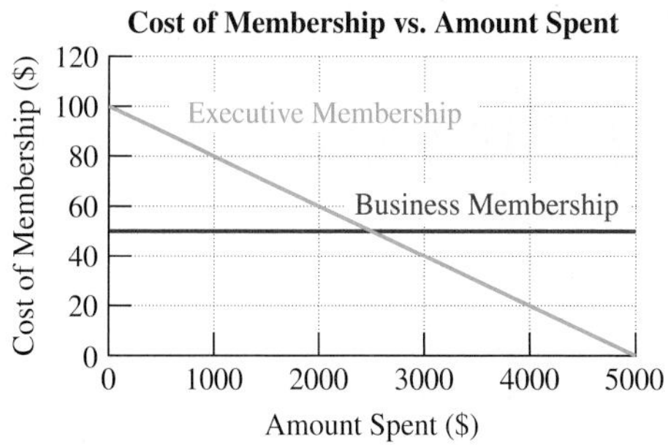

52. The cost to rent a 10 ft by 10 ft storage space is different for two different storage companies. The Storage Bin charges \$90 per month plus a nonrefundable deposit of \$120. AAA Storage charges \$110 per month with no deposit. The total cost, y, to rent a 10 ft by 10 ft space depends on the number of months, x, according to the equations

The Storage Bin: $y = 90x + 120$

AAA Storage: $y = 110x$

From the graph, determine the number of months required for which the cost to rent space is equal for both companies.
For 6 months, the cost is \$660 for each company.

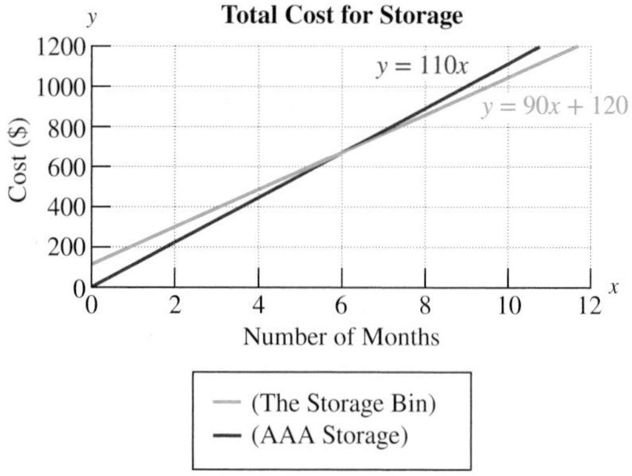

For the systems graphed in Exercises 53–54, explain why the ordered pair cannot be a solution to the system of equations.

53. $(-3, 1)$ The point of intersection is below the x-axis and cannot have a positive y-coordinate.

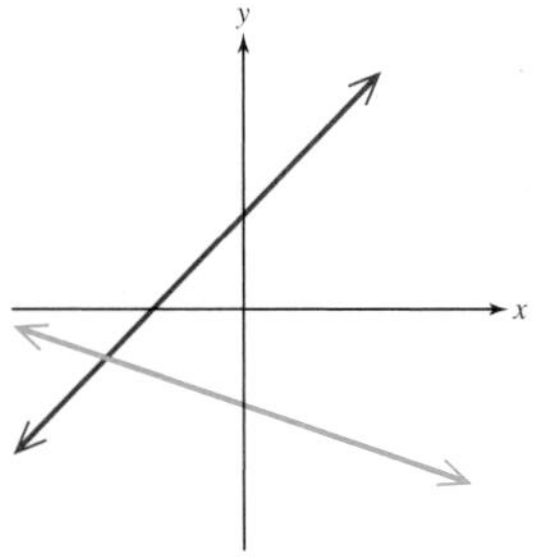

54. $(-1, -4)$ The point of intersection is above the x-axis and cannot have a negative y-coordinate.

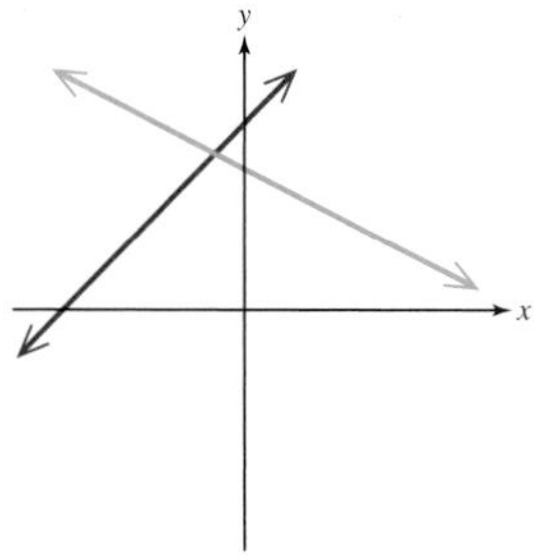

Expanding Your Skills

55. Write a system of linear equations whose solution set is $\{(2, 1)\}$. For example: $4x + y = 9$, $-2x - y = -5$

56. Write a system of linear equations whose solution set is $\{(1, 4)\}$. For example: $x - 3y = -11$, $3x + y = 7$

57. One equation in a system of linear equations is $x + y = 4$. Write a second equation such that the system will have no solution. (Answers may vary.) For example: $2x + 2y = 1$

58. One equation in a system of linear equations is $x - y = 3$. Write a second equation such that the system will have infinitely many solutions. (Answers may vary.) For example: $3x - 3y = 9$

Section 4.2 Solving Systems of Equations by the Substitution Method

Concepts

1. Solving Systems of Linear Equations by Using the Substitution Method
2. Applications of the Substitution Method

1. Solving Systems of Linear Equations by Using the Substitution Method

We have used the graphing method to find the solution set to a system of equations. However, sometimes it is difficult to determine the solution using this method because of limitations in the accuracy of the graph. This is particularly true when the coordinates of a solution are not integer values or when the solution is a point not sufficiently close to the origin. Identifying the coordinates of the point $(\frac{3}{17}, -\frac{23}{9})$ or $(-251, 8349)$, for example, might be difficult from a graph.

In this section, we will cover the *substitution method* to solve systems of equations. This is an algebraic method that does not require graphing the individual equations. We demonstrate the substitution method in Examples 1 through 5.

Example 1 Solving a System of Linear Equations by Using the Substitution Method

Classroom Example: p. 292, Exercise 14

Solve the system by using the substitution method.

$$x = 2y - 3$$
$$-4x + 3y = 2$$

Solution:

The variable x has been isolated in the first equation. The quantity $2y - 3$ is equal to x and therefore can be substituted for x in the second equation. This leaves the second equation in terms of y only.

First equation: $x = 2y - 3$

Second equation: $-4x + 3y = 2$

$-4(2y - 3) + 3y = 2$ This equation now contains only one variable.

$-8y + 12 + 3y = 2$ Solve the resulting equation.

$-5y + 12 = 2$

$-5y = -10$

$y = 2$

To find x, substitute $y = 2$ back into the first equation.

$$x = 2y - 3$$
$$x = 2(2) - 3$$
$$x = 1$$

Avoiding Mistakes

Remember to solve for *both* variables in the system.

Check the ordered pair (1, 2) in both original equations.

$x = 2y - 3 \longrightarrow 1 \stackrel{?}{=} 2(2) - 3$ ✓ True

$-4x + 3y = 2 \longrightarrow -4(1) + 3(2) \stackrel{?}{=} 2$ ✓ True

The solution set is $\{(1, 2)\}$.

Skill Practice Solve the system by using the substitution method.

1. $2x + 3y = -2$
   $y = x + 1$

Instructor Note: Remind students that they can also graph a system of equations to determine if an answer is reasonable.

In Example 1, we eliminated the x variable from the second equation by substituting an equivalent expression for x. The resulting equation was relatively simple to solve because it had only one variable. This is the premise of the substitution method.

Answer

1. $\{(-1, 0)\}$

The substitution method can be summarized as follows.

Solving a System of Equations by Using the Substitution Method

Step 1 Isolate one of the variables from one equation.

Step 2 Substitute the expression found in step 1 into the other equation.

Step 3 Solve the resulting equation.

Step 4 Substitute the value found in step 3 back into the equation in step 1 to find the value of the remaining variable.

Step 5 Check the ordered pair in both original equations.

Classroom Example: p. 292, Exercise 22

Example 2 **Solving a System of Linear Equations by Using the Substitution Method**

Solve the system by using the substitution method.

$$x + y = 4$$
$$-5x + 3y = -12$$

Solution:

The x or y variable in the first equation is easy to isolate because the coefficients are both 1. While either variable can be isolated, we arbitrarily choose to solve for the x variable.

$x + y = 4 \longrightarrow x = 4 - y$ — **Step 1:** Isolate x in the first equation.

$-5(4 - y) + 3y = -12$ — **Step 2:** Substitute $4 - y$ for x in the other equation.

Step 3: Solve for y.

$$-20 + 5y + 3y = -12$$
$$-20 + 8y = -12$$
$$8y = 8$$
$$y = 1$$

Step 4: Substitute $y = 1$ into the equation $x = 4 - y$.

$$x = 4 - y$$
$$x = 4 - 1$$
$$x = 3$$

Step 5: Check the ordered pair (3, 1) in both original equations.

$x + y = 4$	$(3) + (1) \stackrel{?}{=} 4$ ✓	True
$-5x + 3y = -12$	$-5(3) + 3(1) \stackrel{?}{=} -12$ ✓	True

The solution set is $\{(3, 1)\}$.

Avoiding Mistakes

Although we solved for y first, be sure to write the x-coordinate first in the ordered pair. Remember that (1, 3) is not the same as (3, 1).

TIP: The solution to a system of linear equations can be confirmed by graphing. The system from Example 2 is graphed here.

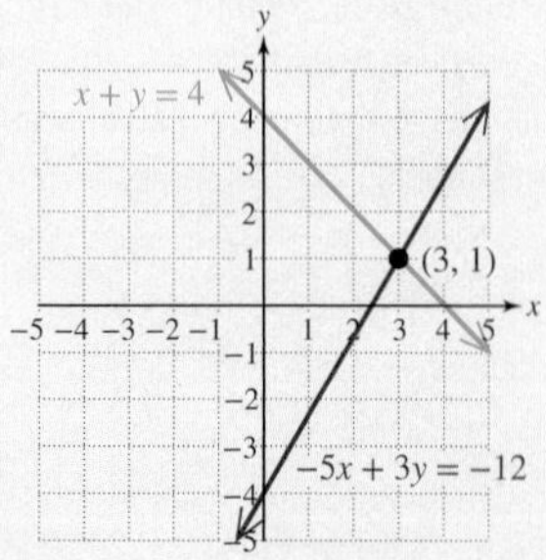

Skill Practice Solve the system by using the substitution method.

2. $x + y = 3$
$-2x + 3y = 9$

Answer

2. $\{(0, 3)\}$

Example 3 Solving a System of Linear Equations by Using the Substitution Method

Classroom Example: p. 292, Exercise 24

Solve the system by using the substitution method.

$$3x + 5y = 17$$
$$2x - y = -6$$

Solution:

The y variable in the second equation is the easiest variable to isolate because its coefficient is -1.

$3x + 5y = 17$

$2x - y = -6 \longrightarrow -y = -2x - 6$

$y = 2x + 6$ **Step 1:** Isolate y in the second equation.

$3x + 5(2x + 6) = 17$ **Step 2:** Substitute the quantity $2x + 6$ for y in the other equation.

$3x + 10x + 30 = 17$ **Step 3:** Solve for x.

$13x + 30 = 17$

$13x = 17 - 30$

$13x = -13$

$x = -1$

$y = 2x + 6$ **Step 4:** Substitute $x = -1$ into the equation $y = 2x + 6$.

$y = 2(-1) + 6$

$y = -2 + 6$

$y = 4$

Step 5: The ordered pair $(-1, 4)$ can be checked in the original equations to verify the answer.

$3x + 5y = 17 \longrightarrow 3(-1) + 5(4) \stackrel{?}{=} 17 \longrightarrow -3 + 20 \stackrel{?}{=} 17$ ✓ True

$2x - y = -6 \longrightarrow 2(-1) - (4) \stackrel{?}{=} -6 \longrightarrow -2 - 4 \stackrel{?}{=} -6$ ✓ True

The solution set is $\{(-1, 4)\}$.

Avoiding Mistakes

Do not substitute $y = 2x + 6$ into the same equation from which it came. This mistake will result in an identity:

$$2x - y = -6$$
$$2x - (2x + 6) = -6$$
$$2x - 2x - 6 = -6$$
$$-6 = -6$$

Skill Practice Solve the system by using the substitution method.

3. $x + 4y = 11$
$2x - 5y = -4$

Answer

3. $\{(3, 2)\}$

Recall that a system of linear equations may represent two parallel lines. In such a case, there is no solution to the system.

Classroom Example: p. 292, Exercise 26

Example 4 Solving an Inconsistent System Using Substitution

Solve the system by using the substitution method.

$$2x + 3y = 6$$
$$y = -\tfrac{2}{3}x + 4$$

Solution:

$$2x + 3y = 6$$
$$y = -\tfrac{2}{3}x + 4$$

Step 1: The variable y is already isolated in the second equation.

$$2x + 3(-\tfrac{2}{3}x + 4) = 6$$

Step 2: Substitute $y = -\frac{2}{3}x + 4$ from the second equation into the first equation.

$$2x - 2x + 12 = 6$$

Step 3: Solve the resulting equation.

$$12 = 6 \quad \text{(contradiction)}$$

The equation results in a contradiction. There are no values of x and y that will make 12 equal to 6. Therefore, the solution set is { }, and the system is inconsistent.

Skill Practice Solve the system by using the substitution method.

4. $y = -\dfrac{1}{2}x + 3$

$2x + 4y = 5$

TIP: The answer to Example 4 can be verified by writing each equation in slope-intercept form and graphing the lines.

Instructor Note: Remind students that when we solved equations in one variable, a contradiction had no solution. For example, the equation $x + 3 = x + 2$ has no solution.

Equation 1

$$2x + 3y = 6$$
$$3y = -2x + 6$$
$$\frac{3y}{3} = \frac{-2x}{3} + \frac{6}{3}$$
$$y = -\frac{2}{3}x + 2$$

Equation 2

$$y = -\frac{2}{3}x + 4$$

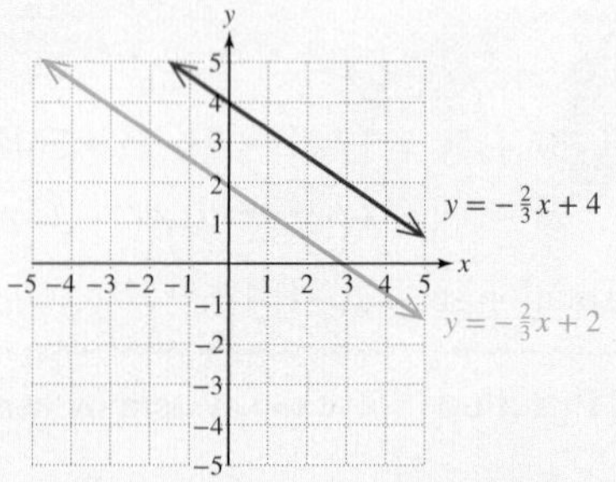

The equations indicate that the lines have the same slope but different y-intercepts. Therefore, the lines must be parallel. There is no point of intersection, indicating that the system has no solution, { }.

Answer

4. { }

Recall that a system of two linear equations may represent the same line. In such a case, the solution is the set of all points on the line.

Example 5 **Solving a System of Dependent Equations Using Substitution**

Classroom Example: p. 293, Exercise 40

Solve the system by using the substitution method.

$$\frac{1}{2}x - \frac{1}{4}y = 1$$
$$6x - 3y = 12$$

Solution:

$\frac{1}{2}x - \frac{1}{4}y = 1$ — To make the first equation easier to work with, we have the option of clearing fractions.

$6x - 3y = 12$

$$\frac{1}{2}x - \frac{1}{4}y = 1 \xrightarrow{\text{Multiply by 4.}} 4\left(\frac{1}{2}x\right) - 4\left(\frac{1}{4}y\right) = 4(1) \rightarrow 2x - y = 4$$

Now the system becomes:

$2x - y = 4$ — The y variable in the first equation is the easiest to isolate because its coefficient is -1.

$6x - 3y = 12$

$$2x - y = 4 \xrightarrow{\text{Solve for } y.} -y = -2x + 4 \rightarrow y = 2x - 4$$
$$6x - 3y = 12$$

Step 1: Isolate one of the variables.

$$6x - 3(2x - 4) = 12$$

Step 2: Substitute $y = 2x - 4$ from the first equation into the second equation.

$$6x - 6x + 12 = 12$$
$$12 = 12 \quad \text{(identity)}$$

Step 3: Solve the resulting equation.

Because the equation produces an identity, all values of x make this equation true. Thus, x can be any real number. Substituting any real number, x, into the equation $y = 2x - 4$ produces an ordered pair on the line $y = 2x - 4$. Hence, the solution set to the system of equations is the set of all ordered pairs on the line $y = 2x - 4$. This can be written as $\{(x, y) \mid y = 2x - 4\}$. The equations are dependent.

Skill Practice Solve the system by using the substitution method.

5. $2x + \frac{1}{3}y = -\frac{1}{3}$

$12x + 2y = -2$

Answer

5. Infinitely many solutions; $\{(x, y) \mid 12x + 2y = -2\}$; dependent equations

TIP: The solution to Example 5 can be verified by writing each equation in slope-intercept form and graphing the lines.

Equation 1	**Equation 2**
$\frac{1}{2}x - \frac{1}{4}y = 1$	$6x - 3y = 12$
Clear fractions $2x - y = 4$	$-3y = -6x + 12$
$-y = -2x + 4$	$\frac{-3y}{-3} = \frac{-6x}{-3} + \frac{12}{-3}$
$y = 2x - 4$	$y = 2x - 4$

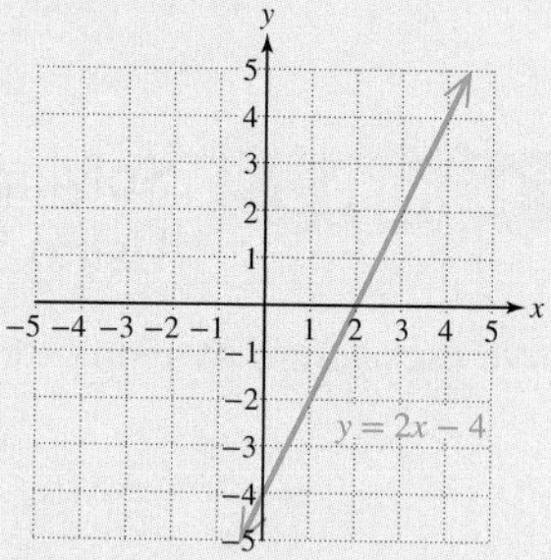

Notice that the slope-intercept forms for both equations are identical. The equations represent the same line, indicating that they are dependent. Each point on the line is a solution to the system of equations.

The following summary reviews the three different geometric relationships between two lines and the solutions to the corresponding systems of equations.

Interpreting Solutions to a System of Two Linear Equations

- The lines may intersect at one point (yielding one unique solution).
- The lines may be parallel and have no point of intersection (yielding no solution). This is detected algebraically when a contradiction (false statement) is obtained (for example, $0 = -3$ or $12 = 6$).
- The lines may be the same and intersect at all points on the line (yielding an infinite number of solutions). This is detected algebraically when an identity is obtained (for example, $0 = 0$ or $12 = 12$).

2. Applications of the Substitution Method

We have already encountered word problems using one linear equation and one variable. In this chapter, we investigate application problems with two unknowns. In such a case, we can use two variables to represent the unknown quantities. However, if two variables are used, we must write a system of *two* distinct equations.

Classroom Example: p. 293, Exercise 52

Example 6 Applying the Substitution Method

One number is 3 more than 4 times another. Their sum is 133. Find the numbers.

Solution:

We can use two variables to represent the two unknown numbers.

Let x represent one number.
Let y represent the other number. Label the variables.

We must now write two equations. Each of the first two sentences gives a relationship between x and y:

One number is 3 more than 4 times another. → $x = 4y + 3$ (first equation)

Their sum is 133. → $x + y = 133$ (second equation)

$(4y + 3) + y = 133$ — Substitute $x = 4y + 3$ into the second equation, $x + y = 133$.

$5y + 3 = 133$ — Solve the resulting equation.

$5y = 130$

$y = 26$

$x = 4y + 3$

$x = 4(26) + 3$ — To solve for x, substitute $y = 26$ into the equation $x = 4y + 3$.

$x = 104 + 3$

$x = 107$

One number is 26, and the other is 107.

Avoiding Mistakes

Notice that the answer for an application is not represented by an ordered pair.

TIP: Check that the numbers 26 and 107 meet the conditions of Example 6.

- 4 times 26 is 104. Three more than 104 is 107. ✓
- The sum of the numbers should be 133: $26 + 107 = 133$ ✓

Skill Practice

6. One number is 16 more than another. Their sum is 92. Use a system of equations to find the numbers.

Example 7 Using the Substitution Method in a Geometry Application

Classroom Example: p. 293, Exercise 56

Two angles are supplementary. The measure of one angle is 15° more than twice the measure of the other angle. Find the measures of the two angles.

Solution:

Let x represent the measure of one angle.
Let y represent the measure of the other angle.

The sum of the measures of supplementary angles is 180°. → $x + y = 180$

The measure of one angle is 15° more than twice the other angle. → $x = 2y + 15$

$x + y = 180$

$x = 2y + 15$ — The x variable in the second equation is already isolated.

$(2y + 15) + y = 180$ — Substitute $2y + 15$ into the first equation for x.

$2y + 15 + y = 180$ — Solve the resulting equation.

$3y + 15 = 180$

$3y = 165$

$y = 55$

$x = 2y + 15$ — Substitute $y = 55$ into the equation $x = 2y + 15$.

$x = 2(55) + 15$

$x = 110 + 15$

$x = 125$

One angle is 55°, and the other is 125°.

TIP: Check that the angles 55° and 125° meet the conditions of Example 7.

- Because $55° + 125° = 180°$, the angles are supplementary. ✓
- The angle 125° is 15° more than twice 55°: $125° = 2(55°) + 15°$ ✓

Answer

6. One number is 38, and the other number is 54.

Skill Practice

7. The measure of one angle is 2° less than 3 times the measure of another angle. The angles are complementary. Use a system of equations to find the measures of the two angles.

Answer

7. The measures of the angles are 23° and 67°.

Section 4.2 Practice Exercises

Review Exercises

For additional exercises, see Classroom Activities 4.2A–4.2C in the *Student's Resource Manual* at www.mhhe.com/moh.

For Exercises 1–6, write each pair of lines in slope-intercept form. Then identify whether the lines intersect in exactly one point or if the lines are parallel or coinciding.

1. $2x - y = 4$ $y = 2x - 4$
$-2y = -4x + 8$
$y = 2x - 4$; coinciding lines

2. $x - 2y = 5$ $y = \frac{1}{2}x - \frac{5}{2}$
$3x = 6y + 15$
$y = \frac{1}{2}x - \frac{5}{2}$; coinciding lines

3. $2x + 3y = 6$ $y = -\frac{2}{3}x + 2$
$x - y = 5$
$y = x - 5$; intersecting lines

4. $x - y = -1$ $y = x + 1$
$x + 2y = 4$ $y = -\frac{1}{2}x + 2$; intersecting lines

5. $2x = \frac{1}{2}y + 2$ $y = 4x - 4$
$4x - y = 13$ $y = 4x - 13$; parallel lines

6. $4y = 3x$ $y = \frac{3}{4}x$
$3x - 4y = 15$ $y = \frac{3}{4}x - \frac{15}{4}$; parallel lines

Concept 1: Solving Systems of Linear Equations by Using the Substitution Method

For Exercises 7–10, solve each system by using the substitution method. **(See Example 1.)**

7. $3x + 2y = -3$
$y = 2x - 12$
$\{(3, -6)\}$

8. $4x - 3y = -19$
$y = -2x + 13$
$\{(2, 9)\}$

9. $x = -4y + 16$
$3x + 5y = 20$
$\{(0, 4)\}$

10. $x = -y + 3$
$-2x + y = 6$
$\{(-1, 4)\}$

11. Given the system: $4x - 2y = -6$
$3x + y = 8$

a. Which variable from which equation is easiest to isolate and why? y in the second equation is easiest to isolate because its coefficient is 1.

b. Solve the system by using the substitution method. $\{(1, 5)\}$

12. Given the system: $x - 5y = 2$
$11x + 13y = 22$

a. Which variable from which equation is easiest to isolate and why? x in the first equation is easiest to isolate because its coefficient is 1.

b. Solve the system by using the substitution method. $\{(2, 0)\}$

For Exercises 13–48, solve the system by using the substitution method. For systems that do not have one unique solution, also state the number of solutions and whether the system is inconsistent or the equations are dependent. **(See Examples 1–5.)**

13. $x = 3y - 1$ $\{(5, 2)\}$
$2x - 4y = 2$

14. $2y = x + 9$ $\{(-1, 4)\}$
$y = -3x + 1$

15. $-2x + 5y = 5$ $\{(10, 5)\}$
$x = 4y - 10$

16. $y = -2x + 27$ $\{(11, 5)\}$
$3x - 7y = -2$

17. $4x - y = -1$ $\left\{\left(\frac{1}{2}, 3\right)\right\}$
$2x + 4y = 13$

18. $5x - 3y = -2$ $\left\{\left(\frac{1}{5}, 1\right)\right\}$
$10x - y = 1$

19. $4x - 3y = 11$ $\{(5, 3)\}$
$x = 5$

20. $y = -3x - 9$ $\{(-7, 12)\}$
$y = 12$

21. $4x = 8y + 4$ $\{(1, 0)\}$
$5x - 3y = 5$

22. $3y = 6x - 6$ $\{(2, 2)\}$
$-3x + y = -4$

23. $x - 3y = -11$ $\{(1, 4)\}$
$6x - y = 2$

24. $-2x - y = 9$ $\{(-6, 3)\}$
$x + 7y = 15$

25. $3x + 2y = -1$
$\frac{3}{2}x + y = 4$
No solution; { }; inconsistent system

26. $5x - 2y = 6$
$-\frac{5}{2}x + y = 5$
No solution; { }; inconsistent system

27. $10x - 30y = -10$
$2x - 6y = -2$
Infinitely many solutions; $\{(x, y) \mid 2x - 6y = -2\}$; dependent equations

28. $3x + 6y = 6$
$-6x - 12y = -12$
Infinitely many solutions; $\{(x, y) \mid 3x + 6y = 6\}$; dependent equations

Writing Translating Expression Geometry Scientific Calculator Video

29. $2x + y = 3$
$y = -7$
$\{(5, -7)\}$

30. $-3x = 2y + 23$
$x = -1$
$\{(-1, -10)\}$

31. $x + 2y = -2$
$4x = -2y - 17$
$\left\{\left(-5, \frac{3}{2}\right)\right\}$

32. $x + y = 1$
$2x - y = -2$
$\left\{\left(-\frac{1}{3}, \frac{4}{3}\right)\right\}$

33. $y = -\frac{1}{2}x - 4$
$y = 4x - 13$
$\{(2, -5)\}$

34. $y = \frac{2}{3}x - 3$
$y = 6x - 19$
$\{(3, -1)\}$

35. $y = 6$
$y - 4 = -2x - 6$
$\{(-4, 6)\}$

36. $x = 9$
$x - 3 = 6y + 12$
$\{(9, -1)\}$

37. $3x + 2y = 4$
$2x - 3y = -6$
$\{(0, 2)\}$

38. $4x + 3y = 4$
$-2x + 5y = -2$
$\{(1, 0)\}$

39. $y = 0.25x + 1$
$-x + 4y = 4$
Infinitely many solutions; $\{(x, y) \mid y = 0.25x + 1\}$; dependent equations

40. $y = 0.75x - 3$
$-3x + 4y = -12$
Infinitely many solutions; $\{(x, y) \mid -3x + 4y = -12\}$; dependent equations

41. $11x + 6y = 17$
$5x - 4y = 1$
$\{(1, 1)\}$

42. $3x - 8y = 7$
$10x - 5y = 45$
$\{(5, 1)\}$

43. $x + 2y = 4$
$4y = -2x - 8$
No solution; $\{\ \}$; inconsistent system

44. $-y = x - 6$
$2x + 2y = 4$
No solution; $\{\ \}$; inconsistent system

45. $2x = 3 - y$
$x + y = 4$
$\{(-1, 5)\}$

46. $2x = 4 + 2y$
$3x + y = 10$
$\{(3, 1)\}$

47. $\frac{x}{3} + \frac{y}{2} = -4$
$x - 3y = 6$
$\{(-6, -4)\}$

48. $x - 2y = -5$
$\frac{2x}{3} + \frac{y}{3} = 0$
$\{(-1, 2)\}$

Concept 2: Applications of the Substitution Method

For Exercises 49–58, set up a system of linear equations and solve for the indicated quantities. **(See Examples 6–7.)**

49. Two numbers have a sum of 106. One number is 10 less than the other. Find the numbers. The numbers are 48 and 58.

50. Two positive numbers have a difference of 8. The larger number is 2 less than 3 times the smaller number. Find the numbers. The numbers are 13 and 5.

51. The difference between two positive numbers is 26. The larger number is 3 times the smaller. Find the numbers. The numbers are 13 and 39.

52. The sum of two numbers is 956. One number is 94 less than 6 times the other. Find the numbers. The numbers are 150 and 806.

53. Two angles are supplementary. One angle is 15° more than 10 times the other angle. Find the measure of each angle. The angles are 165° and 15°.

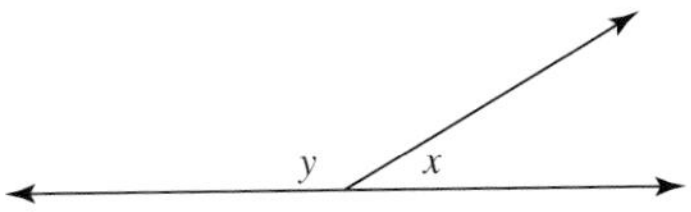

54. Two angles are complementary. One angle is 1° less than 6 times the other angle. Find the measure of each angle. The angles are 13° and 77°.

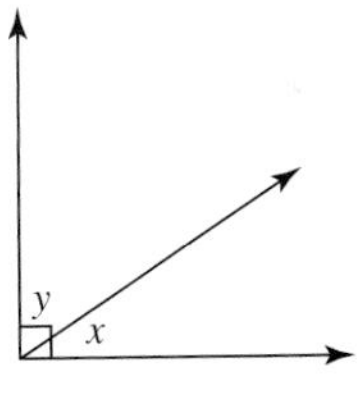

55. Two angles are complementary. One angle is 10° more than 3 times the other angle. Find the measure of each angle. The angles are 70° and 20°.

56. Two angles are supplementary. One angle is 5° less than twice the other angle. Find the measure of each angle. The angles are $118\frac{1}{3}°$ and $61\frac{2}{3}°$.

57. In a right triangle, one of the acute angles is 6° less than the other acute angle. Find the measure of each acute angle. The angles are 42° and 48°.

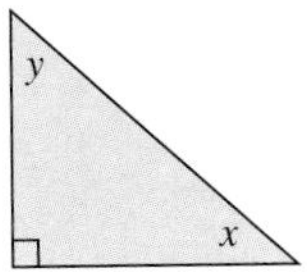

58. In a right triangle, one of the acute angles is 9° less than twice the other acute angle. Find the measure of each acute angle. The angles are 57° and 33°.

Expanding Your Skills

59. The following system consists of dependent equations and therefore has infinitely many solutions. Find three ordered pairs that are solutions to the system of equations.

$$y = 2x + 3$$
$$-4x + 2y = 6$$

For example: (0, 3), (1, 5), (−1, 1)

60. The following system consists of dependent equations and therefore has infinitely many solutions. Find three ordered pairs that are solutions to the system of equations.

$$y = -x + 1$$
$$2x + 2y = 2$$

For example: (0, 1), (1, 0), (−1, 2)

Section 4.3 Solving Systems of Equations by the Addition Method

Concepts

1. Solving Systems of Linear Equations by Using the Addition Method
2. Summary of Methods for Solving Systems of Linear Equations in Two Variables

1. Solving Systems of Linear Equations by Using the Addition Method

In this section, we present another algebraic method to solve a system of linear equations. This method is called the *addition method* and its underlying principle is to add multiples of the given equations to eliminate a variable from the system. For this reason, the addition method is sometimes called the *elimination method.*

Classroom Example: p. 301, Exercise 10

Example 1 Solving a System of Linear Equations by Using the Addition Method

Solve the system by using the addition method.

$$x + y = -2$$
$$x - y = -6$$

Solution:

Notice that the coefficients of the y variables are opposites:

$$x + 1y = -2 \quad \text{Coefficient is 1.}$$
$$x - 1y = -6 \quad \text{Coefficient is } -1.$$

Because the coefficients of the y variables are opposites, we can add the two equations to eliminate the y variable.

$$x + y = -2$$
$$\underline{x - y = -6}$$
$$2x \quad = -8$$

After adding the equations, we have one equation and one variable.

$$2x = -8$$

Solve the resulting equation.

$$x = -4$$

To find the value of y, substitute $x = -4$ into *either* of the original equations.

$$x + y = -2 \qquad \text{First equation}$$
$$(-4) + y = -2$$
$$y = -2 + 4$$
$$y = 2 \qquad \text{The ordered pair is } (-4, 2).$$

Check:

$x + y = -2 \longrightarrow (-4) + (2) \stackrel{?}{=} -2 \longrightarrow -2 \stackrel{?}{=} -2$ ✓ True

$x - y = -6 \longrightarrow (-4) - (2) \stackrel{?}{=} -6 \longrightarrow -6 \stackrel{?}{=} -6$ ✓ True

The solution set is $\{(-4, 2)\}$.

Skill Practice Solve the system by using the addition method.

1. $x + y = 13$
   $2x - y = 2$

TIP: In Example 1, notice that the value $x = -4$ could have been substituted into the second equation, to obtain the same value for y.

$$x - y = -6$$
$$(-4) - y = -6$$
$$-y = -6 + 4$$
$$-y = -2$$
$$y = 2$$

It is important to note that the addition method works on the premise that the two equations have *opposite* values for the coefficients of one of the variables. Sometimes it is necessary to manipulate the original equations to create two coefficients that are opposites. This is accomplished by multiplying one or both equations by an appropriate constant. The process is outlined as follows.

Solving a System of Equations by Using the Addition Method

Step 1 Write both equations in standard form: $Ax + By = C$

Step 2 Clear fractions or decimals (optional).

Step 3 Multiply one or both equations by nonzero constants to create opposite coefficients for one of the variables.

Step 4 Add the equations from step 3 to eliminate one variable.

Step 5 Solve for the remaining variable.

Step 6 Substitute the known value from step 5 into one of the original equations to solve for the other variable.

Step 7 Check the ordered pair in both equations.

Instructor Note: Point out that in step 3 it does not matter whether we create opposites for the x variables or the y variables.

Answer

1. $\{(5, 8)\}$

Classroom Example: p. 301, Exercise 14

Example 2 Solving a System of Linear Equations by Using the Addition Method

Solve the system by using the addition method.

$$3x + 5y = 17$$
$$2x - y = -6$$

Solution:

$3x + 5y = 17$ **Step 1:** Both equations are already written in standard form.

$2x - y = -6$ **Step 2:** There are no fractions or decimals.

Notice that neither the coefficients of x nor the coefficients of y are opposites. However, multiplying the second equation by 5 creates the term $-5y$ in the second equation. This is the opposite of the term $+5y$ in the first equation.

Avoiding Mistakes

Remember to multiply the chosen constant on *both* sides of the equation.

$3x + 5y = 17 \longrightarrow 3x + 5y = 17$ **Step 3:** Multiply the second equation by 5.

$2x - y = -6 \xrightarrow{\text{Multiply by 5.}} 10x - 5y = -30$

$13x = -13$ **Step 4:** Add the equations.

$13x = -13$ **Step 5:** Solve the equation.

$x = -1$

$3x + 5y = 17$ First equation **Step 6:** Substitute $x = -1$ into one of the original equations.

$3(-1) + 5y = 17$

$-3 + 5y = 17$

$5y = 20$

$y = 4$ **Step 7:** Check $(-1, 4)$ in both original equations.

TIP: In Example 2, we could have eliminated the x variable by multiplying the first equation by 2 and the second equation by -3.

Check:

$3x + 5y = 17 \longrightarrow 3(-1) + 5(4) \stackrel{?}{=} 17 \longrightarrow -3 + 20 \stackrel{?}{=} 17$ ✓ True

$2x - y = -6 \longrightarrow 2(-1) - (4) \stackrel{?}{=} -6 \longrightarrow -2 - 4 \stackrel{?}{=} -6$ ✓ True

The solution set is $\{(-1, 4)\}$.

Skill Practice Solve the system by using the addition method.

2. $4x + 3y = 3$
$x - 2y = 9$

In Example 3, the system of equations uses the variables a and b instead of x and y. In such a case, we will write the solution as an ordered pair with the variables written in alphabetical order, such as (a, b).

Answer

2. $\{(3, -3)\}$

Example 3 Solving a System of Linear Equations by Using the Addition Method

Classroom Example: p. 302, Exercise 18

Solve the system by using the addition method.

$$5b = 7a + 8$$
$$-4a - 2b = -10$$

Solution:

Step 1: Write the equations in standard form.

The first equation becomes: $5b = 7a + 8 \longrightarrow -7a + 5b = 8$

The system becomes:

$$-7a + 5b = 8$$
$$-4a - 2b = -10$$

Step 2: There are no fractions or decimals.

Step 3: We need to obtain opposite coefficients on either the a or b term.

Notice that neither the coefficients of a nor the coefficients of b are opposites. However, it is possible to change the coefficients of b to 10 and -10 (this is because the LCM of 5 and 2 is 10). This is accomplished by multiplying the first equation by 2 and the second equation by 5.

$$-7a + 5b = 8 \xrightarrow{\text{Multiply by 2.}} -14a + 10b = 16$$
$$-4a - 2b = -10 \xrightarrow[\text{Multiply by 5.}]{} \underline{-20a - 10b = -50}$$
$$-34a = -34$$

Step 4: Add the equations.

$$-34a = -34$$
$$\frac{-34a}{-34} = \frac{-34}{-34}$$
$$a = 1$$

Step 5: Solve the resulting equation.

$5b = 7a + 8$ First equation

Step 6: Substitute $a = 1$ into one of the original equations.

$$5b = 7(1) + 8$$
$$5b = 15$$
$$b = 3$$

Step 7: Check (1, 3) in the original equations.

Check:

$5b = 7a + 8 \longrightarrow 5(3) \stackrel{?}{=} 7(1) + 8 \longrightarrow 15 \stackrel{?}{=} 7 + 8$ ✓ True

$-4a - 2b = -10 \longrightarrow -4(1) - 2(3) \stackrel{?}{=} -10 \longrightarrow -4 - 6 \stackrel{?}{=} -10$ ✓ True

The solution set is $\{(1, 3)\}$.

Skill Practice Solve the system by using the addition method.

3. $8n = 4 - 5m$
   $7m + 6n = -10$

Answer

3. $\{(-4, 3)\}$

Classroom Example: p. 302, Exercise 22

Example 4 Solving a System of Linear Equations by Using the Addition Method

Solve the system by using the addition method.

$$34x - 22y = 4$$
$$17x - 88y = -19$$

Solution:

The equations are already in standard form. There are no fractions or decimals to clear.

$$34x - 22y = 4 \longrightarrow \quad 34x - 22y = 4$$
$$17x - 88y = -19 \xrightarrow{\text{Multiply by } -2.} \quad \underline{-34x + 176y = 38}$$
$$154y = 42$$

Solve for y. $154y = 42$

$$\frac{154y}{154} = \frac{42}{154}$$

Simplify. $y = \dfrac{3}{11}$

To find the value of x, we normally substitute y into one of the original equations and solve for x. In this example, we will show an alternative method for finding x. By repeating the addition method, this time eliminating y, we can solve for x. This approach enables us to avoid substitution of the fractional value for y.

$$34x - 22y = 4 \xrightarrow{\text{Multiply by } -4.} \quad -136x + 88y = -16$$
$$17x - 88y = -19 \longrightarrow \quad \underline{17x - 88y = -19}$$
$$-119x \quad = -35$$

Solve for x. $-119x = -35$

$$\frac{-119x}{-119} = \frac{-35}{-119}$$

Simplify. $x = \dfrac{5}{17}$

The ordered pair $\left(\frac{5}{17}, \frac{3}{11}\right)$ can be checked in the original equations.

$34x - 22y = 4$	$17x - 88y = -19$
$34\left(\frac{5}{17}\right) - 22\left(\frac{3}{11}\right) \stackrel{?}{=} 4$	$17\left(\frac{5}{17}\right) - 88\left(\frac{3}{11}\right) \stackrel{?}{=} -19$
$10 - 6 \stackrel{?}{=} 4$ ✓ True	$5 - 24 \stackrel{?}{=} -19$ ✓ True

The solution set is $\left\{\left(\frac{5}{17}, \frac{3}{11}\right)\right\}$.

Skill Practice Solve the system by using the addition method.

4. $15x - 16y = 1$

$45x + 4y = 16$

Answer

4. $\left\{\left(\frac{1}{3}, \frac{1}{4}\right)\right\}$

Example 5 **Solving an Inconsistent System by the Addition Method**

Classroom Example: p. 302, Exercise 32

Solve the system by using the addition method.

$$2x - 5y = 10$$
$$\frac{1}{2}x - \frac{5}{4}y = 1$$

Solution:

$2x - 5y = 10$

$\frac{1}{2}x - \frac{5}{4}y = 1$

Step 1: The equations are in standard form.

Step 2: Multiply both sides of the second equation by 4 to clear fractions.

$$\frac{1}{2}x - \frac{5}{4}y = 1 \longrightarrow 4\left(\frac{1}{2}x - \frac{5}{4}y\right) = 4(1) \longrightarrow 2x - 5y = 4$$

Now the system becomes $2x - 5y = 10$

$2x - 5y = 4$

To make either the x coefficients or y coefficients opposites, multiply either equation by -1.

$$2x - 5y = 10 \xrightarrow{\text{Multiply by } -1.} -2x + 5y = -10$$
$$2x - 5y = 4 \longrightarrow \underline{2x - 5y = 4}$$
$$0 = -6$$

Step 3: Create opposite coefficients.

Step 4: Add the equations.

Because the result is a contradiction, the solution set is { }, and the system of equations is inconsistent. Writing each equation in slope-intercept form verifies that the lines are parallel (Figure 4-8).

$$2x - 5y = 10 \xrightarrow{\text{slope-intercept form}} y = \frac{2}{5}x - 2$$

$$\frac{1}{2}x - \frac{5}{4}y = 1 \xrightarrow{\text{slope-intercept form}} y = \frac{2}{5}x - \frac{4}{5}$$

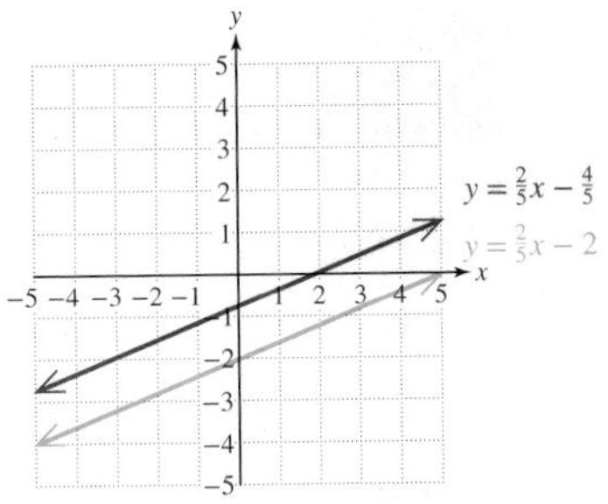

Figure 4-8

Skill Practice Solve the system by using the addition method.

5. $\frac{2}{3}x - \frac{3}{4}y = 2$

$8x - 9y = 6$

Answer

5. { }

Classroom Example: p. 302, Exercise 34

Example 6 Solving a System of Dependent Equations by the Addition Method

Solve the system by using the addition method.

$$3x - y = 4$$
$$2y = 6x - 8$$

Solution:

$3x - y = 4 \longrightarrow 3x - y = 4$ **Step 1:** Write the equations in standard form.

$2y = 6x - 8 \longrightarrow -6x + 2y = -8$ **Step 2:** There are no fractions or decimals.

Notice that the equations differ exactly by a factor of -2, which indicates that these two equations represent the same line. Multiply the first equation by 2 to create opposite coefficients for the variables.

$3x - y = 4 \xrightarrow{\text{Multiply by 2.}} 6x - 2y = 8$ **Step 3:** Create opposite coefficients.

$-6x + 2y = -8 \qquad\qquad -6x + 2y = -8$

$0 = 0$ **Step 4:** Add the equations.

Because the resulting equation is an identity, the original equations represent the same line. This can be confirmed by writing each equation in slope-intercept form.

$$3x - y = 4 \longrightarrow -y = -3x + 4 \longrightarrow y = 3x - 4$$
$$-6x + 2y = -8 \longrightarrow 2y = 6x - 8 \longrightarrow y = 3x - 4$$

The solution is the set of all points on the line, or equivalently, $\{(x, y) \mid y = 3x - 4\}$.

Skill Practice Solve the system by using the addition method.

6. $3x = 3y + 15$
   $2x - 2y = 10$

2. Summary of Methods for Solving Systems of Linear Equations in Two Variables

If no method of solving a system of linear equations is specified, you may use the method of your choice. However, we recommend the following guidelines:

1. If one of the equations is written with a variable isolated, the substitution method is a good choice. For example:

$$2x + 5y = 2 \qquad \text{or} \qquad y = \frac{1}{3}x - 2$$
$$x = y - 6 \qquad\qquad\qquad x - 6y = 9$$

2. If both equations are written in standard form, $Ax + By = C$, where none of the variables has coefficients of 1 or -1, then the addition method is a good choice.

$$4x + 5y = 12$$
$$5x + 3y = 15$$

3. If both equations are written in standard form, $Ax + By = C$, and at least one variable has a coefficient of 1 or -1, then either the substitution method or the addition method is a good choice.

Answer

6. $\{(x, y) \mid 2x - 2y = 10\}$

Section 4.3 Practice Exercises

For additional exercises, see Classroom Activities 4.3A–4.3B in the *Student's Resource Manual* at www.mhhe.com/moh.

Study Skills Exercise

Now that you have learned three methods of solving a system of linear equations with two variables, choose a system and solve it all three ways. There are two advantages to this. One is to check your answer (you should get the same answer using all three methods). The second advantage is to show you which method is the easiest for you to use.

Solve the system by using the graphing method, the substitution method, and the addition method.

$$2x + y = -7$$
$$x - 10 = 4y$$

Review Exercises

For Exercises 1–5, check whether the given ordered pair is a solution to the system.

1. $-\frac{3}{4}x + 2y = -10$ $\quad$ (8, −2) $\quad$ No
   $x - \frac{1}{2}y = 7$

2. $x + y = 8$ $\quad$ (5, 3) $\quad$ Yes
   $y = x - 2$

3. $x = y + 1$ $\quad$ (3, 2) $\quad$ No
   $-x + 2y = 0$

4. $3x + 2y = 14$ $\quad$ (5, −2) $\quad$ No
   $5x - 2y = 29$

5. $x = 2y - 11$ $\quad$ (−3, 4) $\quad$ Yes
   $-x + 5y = 23$

Concept 1: Solving Systems of Linear Equations by Using the Addition Method

For Exercises 6–7, answer as true or false.

6. Given the system $5x - 4y = 1$
   $7x - 2y = 5$
   a. To eliminate the y variable using the addition method, multiply the second equation by 2. False, multiply by −2.
   b. To eliminate the x variable using the addition method, multiply the first equation by 7 and the second equation by −5. True

7. Given the system $3x + 5y = -1$
   $9x - 8y = -26$
   a. To eliminate the x variable using the addition method, multiply the first equation by −3. True
   b. To eliminate the y variable using the addition method, multiply the first equation by 8 and the second equation by −5. False, multiply the second equation by 5.

8. Given the system $3x - 4y = 2$
   $17x + y = 35$
   a. Which variable, x or y, is easier to eliminate using the addition method? y would be easier.
   b. Solve the system using the addition method. {(2, 1)}

9. Given the system $-2x + 5y = -15$
   $6x - 7y = 21$
   a. Which variable, x or y, is easier to eliminate using the addition method? x would be easier.
   b. Solve the system using the addition method. {(0, −3)}

For Exercises 10–24, solve each system using the addition method. **(See Examples 1–4.)**

10. $x + 2y = 8$ $\quad$ {(2, 3)}
    $5x - 2y = 4$

11. $2x - 3y = 11$ $\quad$ {(4, −1)}
    $-4x + 3y = -19$

12. $a + b = 3$ $\quad$ {(5, −2)}
    $3a + b = 13$

13. $-2u + 6v = 10$ $\quad$ {(4, 3)}
    $-2u + v = -5$

14. $-3x + y = 1$ $\quad$ {(0, 1)}
    $-6x - 2y = -2$

15. $5m - 2n = 4$ $\quad$ {(2, 3)}
    $3m + n = 9$

16. $3x - 5y = 13$ $\{(1, -2)\}$
$x - 2y = 5$

17. $7a + 2b = -1$ $\{(1, -4)\}$
$3a - 4b = 19$

18. $6c - 2d = -2$ $\{(1, 4)\}$
$5c = -3d + 17$

19. $2s + 3t = -1$ $\{(1, -1)\}$
$5s = 2t + 7$

20. $6y - 4z = -2$ $\{(3, 5)\}$
$4y + 6z = 42$

21. $4k - 2r = -4$ $\{(-4, -6)\}$
$3k - 5r = 18$

22. $2x + 3y = 6$ $\left\{\left(\frac{21}{5}, -\frac{4}{5}\right)\right\}$
$x - y = 5$

23. $6x + 6y = 8$ $\left\{\left(\frac{7}{9}, \frac{5}{9}\right)\right\}$
$9x - 18y = -3$

24. $2x - 5y = 4$ $\left\{\left(\frac{8}{9}, -\frac{4}{9}\right)\right\}$
$3x - 3y = 4$

25. In solving a system of equations, suppose you get the statement $0 = 5$. How many solutions will the system have? What can you say about the graphs of these equations?
The system will have no solution. The lines are parallel.

26. In solving a system of equations, suppose you get the statement $0 = 0$. How many solutions will the system have? What can you say about the graphs of these equations?
There are infinitely many solutions. The lines coincide.

27. In solving a system of equations, suppose you get the statement $3 = 3$. How many solutions will the system have? What can you say about the graphs of these equations?
There are infinitely many solutions. The lines coincide.

28. In solving a system of equations, suppose you get the statement $2 = -5$. How many solutions will the system have? What can you say about the graphs of these equations?
The system will have no solution. The lines are parallel.

29. Suppose in solving a system of linear equations, you get the statement $x = 0$. How many solutions will the system have? What can you say about the graphs of these equations?
The system will have one solution. The lines intersect at a point whose x-coordinate is 0.

30. Suppose in solving a system of linear equations, you get the statement $y = 0$. How many solutions will the system have? What can you say about the graphs of these equations?
The system will have one solution. The lines intersect at a point whose y-coordinate is 0.

For Exercises 31–42, solve the system by using the addition method. For systems that do not have one unique solution, also state the number of solutions and whether the system is inconsistent or the equations are dependent. **(See Examples 5–6.)**

31. $-2x + y = -5$
$8x - 4y = 12$
No solution; { }; inconsistent system

32. $x - 3y = 2$
$-5x + 15y = 10$
No solution; { }; inconsistent system

33. $x + 2y = 2$
$-3x - 6y = -6$
Infinitely many solutions; $\{(x, y) \mid x + 2y = 2\}$; dependent equations

34. $4x - 3y = 6$
$-12x + 9y = -18$
Infinitely many solutions; $\{(x, y) \mid 4x - 3y = 6\}$; dependent equations

35. $3a + 2b = 11$ $\{(1, 4)\}$
$7a - 3b = -5$

36. $4y + 5z = -2$
$5y - 3z = 16$
$\{(2, -2)\}$

37. $3x - 5y = 7$
$5x - 2y = -1$
$\{(-1, -2)\}$

38. $4s + 3t = 9$ $\{(0, 3)\}$
$3s + 4t = 12$

39. $2x + 2 = -3y + 9$
$3x - 10 = -4y$
$\{(2, 1)\}$

40. $-3x + 6 + 7y = 5$ $\{(5, 2)\}$
$5y = 2x$

41. $4x - 5y = 0$
$8(x - 1) = 10y$
No solution; { }; inconsistent system

42. $y = 2x + 1$
$-3(2x - y) = 0$
No solution; { }; inconsistent system

Concept 2: Summary of Methods for Solving Systems of Linear Equations in Two Variables

For Exercises 43–63, solve each system of equations by either the addition method or the substitution method.

43. $5x - 2y = 4$ $\{(2, 3)\}$
$y = -3x + 9$

44. $-x = 8y + 5$ $\{(-5, 0)\}$
$4x - 3y = -20$

45. $0.1x + 0.1y = 0.6$ $\{(3.5, 2.5)\}$
$0.1x - 0.1y = 0.1$

46. $0.1x + 0.1y = 0.2$ $\{(2.5, -0.5)\}$
$0.1x - 0.1y = 0.3$

47. $3x = 5y - 9$ $\left\{\left(\frac{1}{3}, 2\right)\right\}$
$2y = 3x + 3$

48. $10x - 5 = 3y$ $\left\{\left(\frac{1}{2}, 0\right)\right\}$
$4x + 5y = 2$

49. $\frac{1}{10}y = -\frac{1}{2}x - \frac{1}{2}$ $\{(-2, 5)\}$

$\frac{3}{2}x - \frac{3}{4} = -\frac{3}{4}y$

50. $x + \frac{5}{4}y = -\frac{1}{2}$ $\{(-3, 2)\}$

$\frac{3}{4}x = -\frac{1}{2}y - \frac{5}{4}$

51. $x = -\frac{1}{2}$ $\left\{\left(-\frac{1}{2}, 1\right)\right\}$

$6x - 5y = -8$

52. $4x - 2y = 1$ $\left\{\left(\frac{7}{4}, 3\right)\right\}$

$y = 3$

53. $0.02x + 0.04y = 0.12$ $\{(0, 3)\}$

$0.03x - 0.05y = -0.15$

54. $-0.04x + 0.03y = 0.03$ $\{(0, 1)\}$

$-0.06x - 0.02y = -0.02$

55. $8x - 16y = 24$

$2x - 4y = 0$

$\{\ \}$

56. $y = -\frac{1}{2}x - 5$

$2x + 4y = -8$

$\{\ \}$

57. $\frac{m}{2} + \frac{n}{5} = \frac{13}{10}$

$3m - 3n = m - 10$

$\{(1, 4)\}$

58. $\frac{a}{4} - \frac{3b}{2} = \frac{15}{2}$ $\{(0, -5)\}$

$a + 2b = -10$

59. $2m - 6n = m + 4$ $\{(4, 0)\}$

$3m + 8 = 5m - n$

60. $m - 3n = 10$ $\{(4, -2)\}$

$3m + 12n = -12$

61. $9a - 2b = 8$

$18a + 6 = 4b + 22$

Infinitely many solutions; $\{(a, b) \mid 9a - 2b = 8\}$

62. $a = 5 + 2b$

$3a - 6b = 15$

Infinitely many solutions; $\{(a, b) \mid a = 5 + 2b\}$

63. $6x - 5y = 7$ $\left\{\left(\frac{7}{16}, -\frac{7}{8}\right)\right\}$

$4x - 6y = 7$

For Exercises 64–69, use a system of linear equations, and solve for the indicated quantities.

64. The sum of two positive numbers is 26. Their difference is 14. Find the numbers.
The numbers are 20 and 6.

65. The difference of two positive numbers is 2. The sum of the numbers is 36. Find the numbers.
The numbers are 17 and 19.

66. Eight times the smaller of two numbers plus 2 times the larger number is 44. Three times the smaller number minus 2 times the larger number is zero. Find the numbers.
The numbers are 4 and 6.

67. Six times the smaller of two numbers minus the larger number is −9. Ten times the smaller number plus five times the larger number is 5. Find the numbers.
The numbers are −1 and 3.

68. Twice the difference of two angles is 64°. If the angles are complementary, find the measures of the angles. The angles are 61° and 29°.

69. The difference of an angle and twice another angle is 42°. If the angles are supplementary, find the measures of the angles.
The angles are 46° and 134°.

For Exercises 70–72, solve the system by using each of the three methods: (a) the graphing method, (b) the substitution method, and (c) the addition method.

70. $2x + y = 1$

$-4x - 2y = -2$

Infinitely many solutions; $\{(x, y) \mid 2x + y = 1\}$

71. $3x + y = 6$

$-2x + 2y = 4$

$\{(1, 3)\}$

72. $2x - 2y = 6$

$5y = 5x + 5$

$\{\ \}$

Expanding Your Skills

73. Explain why a system of linear equations cannot have exactly two solutions. One line within the system of equations would have to "bend" for the system to have exactly two points of intersection. This is not possible.

74. The solution to the system of linear equations is $\{(1, 2)\}$. Find A and B.

$Ax + 3y = 8$ $A = 2, B = -4$

$x + By = -7$

75. The solution to the system of linear equations is $\{(-3, 4)\}$. Find A and B.

$4x + Ay = -32$ $A = -5, B = 2$

$Bx + 6y = 18$

Problem Recognition Exercises

Systems of Equations

For Exercises 1–6 determine the number of solutions to the system without solving the system. Explain your answers.

1. $y = -4x + 2$
$y = -4x + 2$
Infinitely many solutions. The equations represent the same line.

2. $y = -4x + 6$
$y = -4x + 1$
No solution. The equations represent parallel lines.

3. $y = 4x - 3$
$y = -4x + 5$
One solution. The equations represent intersecting lines.

4. $y = 7$
$2x + 3y = 1$
One solution. The equations represent intersecting lines.

5. $2x + 3y = 1$
$2x + 3y = 8$
No solution. The equations represent parallel lines.

6. $8x - 2y = 6$
$12x - 3y = 9$
Infinitely many solutions. The equations represent the same line.

For Exercises 7–10, a method of solving has been suggested for each system of equations. Explain why that method was suggested for the system and then solve the system using the method given.

7. $2x - 5y = -11$
$7x + 5y = -16$
Addition Method
The y variable will easily be eliminated by adding the equations. The solution set is $\{(-3, 1)\}$.

8. $4x + 11y = 56$
$-2x - 5y = -26$
Addition Method
The x variable will easily be eliminated by multiplying the second equation by 2 and then adding the equations. The solution set is $\{(3, 4)\}$.

9. $x = -3y + 4$
$5x + 4y = -2$
Substitution Method
Because the variable x is already isolated in the first equation, the expression $-3y + 4$ can be easily substituted for x in the second equation. The solution set is $\{(-2, 2)\}$.

10. $2x + 3y = 16$
$y = x - 8$
Substitution Method
Because the variable y is already isolated in the second equation, the expression $x - 8$ can be easily substituted for y in the first equation. The solution set is $\{(8, 0)\}$.

For Exercises 11–30, solve each system using the method of your choice. For systems that do not have one unique solution, also state the number of solutions and whether the system is inconsistent or the equations are dependent.

11. $x = -2y + 5$
$2x - 4y = 10$
$\{(5, 0)\}$

12. $y = -3x - 4$
$2x - y = 9$
$\{(1, -7)\}$

13. $3x - 2y = 22$
$5x + 2y = 10$
$\{(4, -5)\}$

14. $-4x + 2y = -2$
$4x - 5y = -7$
$\{(2, 3)\}$

15. $\frac{1}{3}x + \frac{1}{2}y = \frac{2}{3}$
$-\frac{2}{3}x + y = -\frac{4}{3}$
$\{(2, 0)\}$

16. $\frac{1}{4}x + \frac{2}{5}y = 6$
$\frac{1}{2}x - \frac{1}{10}y = 3$
$\{(8, 10)\}$

17. $2c + 7d = -1$
$c = 2$
$\left\{\left(2, -\frac{5}{7}\right)\right\}$

18. $-3w + 5z = -6$
$z = -4$
$\left\{\left(-\frac{14}{3}, -4\right)\right\}$

19. $y = 0.4x - 0.3$
$-4x + 10y = 20$
No solution; { }; inconsistent system

20. $x = -0.5y + 0.1$
$-10x - 5y = 2$
No solution; { }; inconsistent system

21. $3a + 7b = -3$
$-11a + 3b = 11$
$\{(-1, 0)\}$

22. $2v - 5w = 10$
$9v + 7w = 45$
$\{(5, 0)\}$

23. $y = 2x - 14$
$4x - 2y = 28$
Infinitely many solutions; $\{(x, y) \mid y = 2x - 14\}$; dependent equations

24. $x = 5y - 9$
$-2x + 10y = 18$
Infinitely many solutions; $\{(x, y) \mid x = 5y - 9\}$; dependent equations

25. $x + y = 3200$
$0.06x + 0.04y = 172$
$\{(2200, 1000)\}$

26. $x + y = 4500$
$0.07x + 0.05y = 291$
$\{(3300, 1200)\}$

27. $3x + y - 7 = x - 4$
$3x - 4y + 4 = -6y + 5$
$\{(5, -7)\}$

28. $7y - 8y - 3 = -3x + 4$
$10x - 5y - 12 = 13$
$\{(2, -1)\}$

29. $3x - 6y = -1$
$9x + 4y = 8$
$\left\{\left(\frac{2}{3}, \frac{1}{2}\right)\right\}$

30. $8x - 2y = 5$
$12x + 4y = -3$
$\left\{\left(\frac{1}{4}, -\frac{3}{2}\right)\right\}$

Applications of Linear Equations in Two Variables

Section 4.4

Concepts

1. Applications Involving Cost
2. Applications Involving Principal and Interest
3. Applications Involving Mixtures
4. Applications Involving Distance, Rate, and Time

1. Applications Involving Cost

We have solved several applied problems by setting up a linear equation in one variable. When solving an application that involves two unknowns, sometimes it is convenient to use a system of linear equations in two variables.

Example 1 Using a System of Linear Equations Involving Cost

Classroom Example: p. 311, Exercise 10

At a movie theater a couple buys one large popcorn and two small drinks for \$12.50. A group of teenagers buys two large popcorns and five small drinks for \$28.50. Find the cost of one large popcorn and the cost of one small drink.

© Burke/Triolo/Brand X Pictures RF

Solution:

In this application we have two unknowns, which we can represent by x and y.

Let x represent the cost of one large popcorn.
Let y represent the cost of one small drink.

We must now write two equations. Each of the first two sentences in the problem gives a relationship between x and y:

$$\begin{pmatrix}\text{Cost of 1}\\ \text{popcorn}\end{pmatrix} + \begin{pmatrix}\text{cost of 2}\\ \text{drinks}\end{pmatrix} = \begin{pmatrix}\text{total}\\ \text{cost}\end{pmatrix} \longrightarrow x + 2y = 12.50$$

$$\begin{pmatrix}\text{Cost of 2}\\ \text{popcorns}\end{pmatrix} + \begin{pmatrix}\text{cost of 5}\\ \text{drinks}\end{pmatrix} = \begin{pmatrix}\text{total}\\ \text{cost}\end{pmatrix} \longrightarrow 2x + 5y = 28.50$$

To solve this system, we may either use the substitution method or the addition method. We will use the substitution method by solving for x in the first equation.

$$x + 2y = 12.50 \longrightarrow x = -2y + 12.50$$ Isolate x in the first equation.

$$2x + 5y = 28.50$$

$$2(-2y + 12.50) + 5y = 28.50$$ Substitute $x = -2y + 12.50$ into the other equation.

$$-4y + 25.00 + 5y = 28.50$$ Solve for y.

$$y + 25.00 = 28.50$$

$$y = 3.50$$

$$x = -2y + 12.50$$

$$x = -2(3.50) + 12.50$$ Substitute $y = 3.50$ into the equation $x = -2y + 12.50$.

$$x = -7.00 + 12.50$$

$$x = 5.50$$

The cost of one large popcorn is \$5.50 and the cost of one small drink is \$3.50.

Check by verifying that the solution meets the specified conditions.

1 popcorn + 2 drinks = 1(\$5.50) + 2(\$3.50) = \$12.50 ✓ True

2 popcorns + 5 drinks = 2(\$5.50) + 5(\$3.50) = \$28.50 ✓ True

Skill Practice

1. Lynn went to a fast-food restaurant and spent \$20.00. She purchased 4 hamburgers and 5 orders of fries. The next day, Ricardo went to the same restaurant and purchased 10 hamburgers and 7 orders of fries. He spent \$41.20. Use a system of equations to determine the cost of a burger and the cost of an order of fries.

2. Applications Involving Principal and Interest

Simple interest is interest computed on the principal amount of money invested (or borrowed). Simple interest, I, is found by using the formula

$I = Prt$ where P is the principal,
r is the annual interest rate, and
t is the time in years.

In Example 2, we apply the concept of simple interest to two accounts to produce a desired amount of interest after 1 year.

Classroom Example: p. 311, Exercise 18

Example 2 Using a System of Linear Equations Involving Investments

Joanne has a total of \$6000 to deposit in two accounts. One account earns 3.5% simple interest and the other earns 2.5% simple interest. If the total amount of interest at the end of 1 year is \$195, find the amount she deposited in each account.

Solution:

Let x represent the principal deposited in the 2.5% account.
Let y represent the principal deposited in the 3.5% account.

	2.5% Account	3.5% Account	Total
Principal	x	y	6000
Interest ($I = Prt$)	$0.025x(1)$	$0.035y(1)$	195

Each row of the table yields an equation in x and y:

$$\begin{pmatrix}\text{Principal}\\ \text{invested}\\ \text{at } 2.5\%\end{pmatrix} + \begin{pmatrix}\text{principal}\\ \text{invested}\\ \text{at } 3.5\%\end{pmatrix} = \begin{pmatrix}\text{total}\\ \text{principal}\end{pmatrix} \longrightarrow x + y = 6000$$

$$\begin{pmatrix}\text{Interest}\\ \text{earned}\\ \text{at } 2.5\%\end{pmatrix} + \begin{pmatrix}\text{interest}\\ \text{earned}\\ \text{at } 3.5\%\end{pmatrix} = \begin{pmatrix}\text{total}\\ \text{interest}\end{pmatrix} \longrightarrow 0.025x + 0.035y = 195$$

We will choose the addition method to solve the system of equations. First multiply the second equation by 1000 to clear decimals.

Answer

1. The cost of a burger is \$3.00, and the cost of an order of fries is \$1.60.

$$\begin{array}{rlrl} x + y = 6000 \longrightarrow & x + y = 6000 & \xrightarrow{\text{Multiply by } -25.} & -25x - 25y = -150{,}000 \\ 0.025x + 0.035y = 195 \xrightarrow[\text{Multiply by 1000.}]{} & 25x + 35y = 195{,}000 & \longrightarrow & \underline{25x + 35y = 195{,}000} \\ & & & 10y = 45{,}000 \end{array}$$

$10y = 45{,}000$ After eliminating the x variable, solve for y.

$$\frac{10y}{10} = \frac{45{,}000}{10}$$

$y = 4500$ The amount invested in the 3.5% account is \$4500.

$x + y = 6000$ Substitute $y = 4500$ into the equation $x + y = 6000$.

$x + 4500 = 6000$

$x = 1500$ The amount invested in the 2.5% account is \$1500.

Joanne deposited \$1500 in the 2.5% account and \$4500 in the 3.5% account.

To check, verify that the conditions of the problem have been met.

1. The sum of \$1500 and \$4500 is \$6000 as desired. ✓ True
2. The interest earned on \$1500 at 2.5% is: $0.025(\$1500) = \$37.50$
   The interest earned on \$4500 at 3.5% is: $0.035(\$4500) = \$157.50$
   Total interest: \$195.00 ✓ True

Skill Practice

2. Addie has a total of \$8000 in two accounts. One pays 5% interest, and the other pays 6.5% interest. At the end of one year, she earned \$475 interest. Use a system of equations to determine the amount invested in each account.

3. Applications Involving Mixtures

Example 3 **Using a System of Linear Equations in a Mixture Application**

Classroom Example: p. 312, Exercise 22

According to new hospital standards, a certain disinfectant solution needs to be 20% alcohol instead of 10% alcohol. There is a 40% alcohol disinfectant available to adjust the mixture. Determine the amount of 10% solution and the amount of 40% solution to produce 30 L of a 20% solution.

Solution:

Each solution contains a percentage of alcohol plus some other mixing agent such as water. Before we set up a system of equations to model this situation, it is helpful to have background understanding of the problem. In Figure 4-9, the liquid depicted in blue is pure alcohol and the liquid shown in gray is the mixing agent (such as water). Together these liquids form a solution. (Realistically the mixture may not separate as shown, but this image may be helpful for your understanding.)

Let x represent the number of liters of 10% solution.
Let y represent the number of liters of 40% solution.

Answer

2. \$3000 is invested at 5%, and \$5000 is invested at 6.5%.

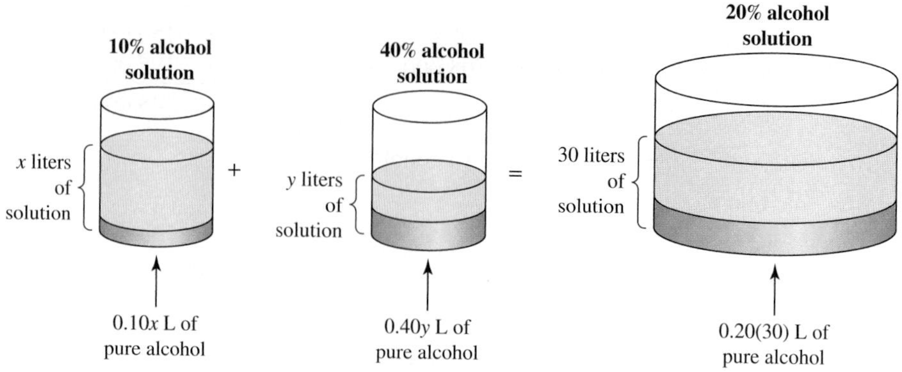

Figure 4-9

The information given in the statement of the problem can be organized in a chart.

	10% Alcohol	40% Alcohol	20% Alcohol
Number of liters of solution	x	y	30
Number of liters of pure alcohol	$0.10x$	$0.40y$	$0.20(30) = 6$

From the first row, we have

$$\begin{pmatrix}\text{Amount of}\\ \text{10\% solution}\end{pmatrix} + \begin{pmatrix}\text{amount of}\\ \text{40\% solution}\end{pmatrix} = \begin{pmatrix}\text{total amount}\\ \text{of 20\% solution}\end{pmatrix} \rightarrow x + y = 30$$

From the second row, we have

$$\begin{pmatrix}\text{Amount of}\\ \text{alcohol in}\\ \text{10\% solution}\end{pmatrix} + \begin{pmatrix}\text{amount of}\\ \text{alcohol in}\\ \text{40\% solution}\end{pmatrix} = \begin{pmatrix}\text{total amount of}\\ \text{alcohol in}\\ \text{20\% solution}\end{pmatrix} \rightarrow 0.10x + 0.40y = 6$$

We will solve the system with the addition method by first clearing decimals.

$$\begin{aligned} x + y &= 30 &\longrightarrow\quad x + y &= 30 \xrightarrow{\text{Multiply by } -1.} & -x - y &= -30 \\ 0.10x + 0.40y &= 6 &\xrightarrow[\text{Multiply by 10.}]{}\quad x + 4y &= 60 \longrightarrow & x + 4y &= 60 \\ & & & & 3y &= 30 \end{aligned}$$

$3y = 30$ After eliminating the x variable, solve for y.

$y = 10$ 10 L of 40% solution is needed.

$x + y = 30$ Substitute $y = 10$ into either of the original equations.

$x + (10) = 30$

$x = 20$ 20 L of 10% solution is needed.

10 L of 40% solution must be mixed with 20 L of 10% solution.

Skill Practice

3. How many ounces of 20% and 35% acid solution should be mixed together to obtain 15 oz of 30% acid solution?

Answer

3. 10 oz of the 35% solution, and 5 oz of the 20% solution.

4. Applications Involving Distance, Rate, and Time

The following formula relates the distance traveled to the rate and time of travel.

$$d = rt \qquad \text{distance} = \text{rate} \cdot \text{time}$$

For example, if a car travels 60 mph for 3 hr, then

$$d = (60 \text{ mph})(3 \text{ hr})$$
$$= 180 \text{ mi}$$

If a car travels 60 mph for x hr, then

$$d = (60 \text{ mph})(x \text{ hr})$$
$$= 60x \text{ mi}$$

The relationship $d = rt$ is used in Example 4.

Example 4 **Using a System of Linear Equations in a Distance, Rate, and Time Application**

Classroom Example: p. 312, Exercise 30

A plane travels with the wind from Kansas City, Missouri, to Denver, Colorado, a distance of 600 mi in 2 hr. The return trip against the same wind takes 3 hr. Find the speed of the plane in still air, and find the speed of the wind.

© Stockbyte/Punchstock Images RF

Solution:

Let p represent the speed of the plane in still air.
Let w represent the speed of the wind.

Notice that when the plane travels with the wind, the net speed is $p + w$. When the plane travels against the wind, the net speed is $p - w$.

The information given in the problem can be organized in a chart.

	Distance	Rate	Time
With the wind	600	$p + w$	2
Against the wind	600	$p - w$	3

To set up two equations in p and w, recall that $d = rt$.

From the first row, we have

$$\begin{pmatrix}\text{Distance}\\ \text{with the wind}\end{pmatrix} = \begin{pmatrix}\text{rate with}\\ \text{the wind}\end{pmatrix}\begin{pmatrix}\text{time traveled}\\ \text{with the wind}\end{pmatrix} \longrightarrow 600 = (p + w) \cdot 2$$

From the second row, we have

$$\begin{pmatrix}\text{Distance}\\ \text{against the wind}\end{pmatrix} = \begin{pmatrix}\text{rate against}\\ \text{the wind}\end{pmatrix}\begin{pmatrix}\text{time traveled}\\ \text{against the wind}\end{pmatrix} \longrightarrow 600 = (p - w) \cdot 3$$

Using the distributive property to clear parentheses produces the following system:

$$2p + 2w = 600$$
$$3p - 3w = 600$$

The coefficients of the w variable can be changed to 6 and -6 by multiplying the first equation by 3 and the second equation by 2.

$$\begin{array}{lcr} 2p + 2w = 600 & \xrightarrow{\text{Multiply by 3.}} & 6p + 6w = 1800 \\ 3p - 3w = 600 & \xrightarrow[\text{Multiply by 2.}]{} & 6p - 6w = 1200 \\ & & \overline{12p \qquad = 3000} \end{array}$$

$$12p = 3000$$

$$\frac{12p}{12} = \frac{3000}{12}$$

$$p = 250$$ The speed of the plane in still air is 250 mph.

TIP: To create opposite coefficients on the w variables, we could have divided the first equation by 2 and divided the second equation by 3:

$$\begin{array}{lcr} 2p + 2w = 600 & \xrightarrow{\text{Divide by 2.}} & p + w = 300 \\ 3p - 3w = 600 & \xrightarrow[\text{Divide by 3.}]{} & p - w = 200 \\ & & \overline{2p \qquad = 500} \\ & & p = 250 \end{array}$$

$2p + 2w = 600$ Substitute $p = 250$ into the first equation.

$2(250) + 2w = 600$

$500 + 2w = 600$

$2w = 100$

$w = 50$ The speed of the wind is 50 mph.

The speed of the plane in still air is 250 mph. The speed of the wind is 50 mph.

Skill Practice

4. Dan and Cheryl paddled their canoe 40 mi in 5 hr with the current and 16 mi in 8 hr against the current. Find the speed of the current and the speed of the canoe in still water.

Answer

4. The speed of the canoe in still water is 5 mph. The speed of the current is 3 mph.

Section 4.4 Practice Exercises

For additional exercises, see Classroom Activities 4.4A–4.4D in the *Student's Resource Manual* at www.mhhe.com/moh.

Review Exercises

For Exercises 1–4, solve each system of equations by three different methods:

a. Graphing method **b.** Substitution method **c.** Addition method

1. $-2x + y = 6$
$2x + y = 2$ $\{(-1, 4)\}$

2. $x - y = 2$
$x + y = 6$ $\{(4, 2)\}$

3. $y = -2x + 6$
$4x - 2y = 8$ $\left\{\left(\frac{5}{2}, 1\right)\right\}$

4. $2x = y + 4$
$4x = 2y + 8$ Infinitely many solutions; $\{(x, y) \mid 2x = y + 4\}$

Writing   Translating Expression   Geometry   Scientific Calculator   Video

For Exercises 5–8, set up a system of linear equations in two variables and solve for the unknown quantities.

5. One number is eight more than twice another. Their sum is 20. Find the numbers.
The numbers are 4 and 16.

6. The difference of two positive numbers is 264. The larger number is three times the smaller number. Find the numbers.
The numbers are 132 and 396.

7. Two angles are complementary. The measure of one angle is 10° less than nine times the measure of the other. Find the measure of each angle.
The angles are 80° and 10°.

8. Two angles are supplementary. The measure of one angle is 9° more than twice the measure of the other angle. Find the measure of each angle.
The angles are 123° and 57°.

Concept 1: Applications Involving Cost

9. An online store sells old video games and DVDs as a bundle. A bundle of two video games and three DVDs can be purchased for \$88. A bundle of one video game and two DVDs can be purchased for \$51.50. Find the cost of one video game and the cost of one DVD in the bundle. **(See Example 1.)**
A video game costs \$21.50 and a DVD costs \$15.

10. Tanya bought three adult tickets and one children's ticket to a movie for \$32.00. Li bought two adult tickets and five children's tickets for \$49.50. Find the cost of one adult ticket and the cost of one children's ticket. Adult tickets cost \$8.50 each, and children's tickets cost \$6.50 each.

11. Nora bought 100 shares of a technology stock and 200 shares of a mutual fund for \$3800. Her sister, Erin, bought 300 shares of the technology stock and 50 shares of the same mutual fund for \$5350. Find the cost per share of the technology stock, and the cost per share of the mutual fund.
Technology stock costs \$16 per share, and the mutual fund costs \$11 per share.

12. Eight students in Ms. Reese's class decided to purchase their textbooks from two different sources. Some students purchased the textbook from the college bookstore for \$95.50. The other students purchased the textbook from an online discount store for \$65 per book. If the total amount spent by the eight students is \$611.50, how many students purchased the book online? Five students purchased the book online.

13. Mylee is a stamp collector and buys commemorative stamps. Suppose she buys a combination of 47-cent stamps and 34-cent stamps at the post office. If she spends exactly \$21.55 on 50 stamps, how many of each type did she buy?
Mylee bought thirty-five 47-cent stamps and fifteen 34-cent stamps.

14. Zoey purchased some beef and some chicken for a family barbeque. The beef cost \$6.00 per pound and the chicken cost \$4.50 per pound. She bought a total of 18 lb of meat and spent \$96. How much of each type of meat did she purchase? She bought 10 lb of beef and 8 lb of chicken.

Concept 2: Applications Involving Principal and Interest

15. Shanelle invested \$10,000, and at the end of 1 year, she received \$805 in interest. She invested part of the money in an account earning 10% simple interest and the remaining money in an account earning 7% simple interest. How much did she invest in each account? **(See Example 2.)**
Shanelle invested \$3500 in the 10% account and \$6500 in the 7% account.

	10% Account	7% Account	Total
Principal invested			
Interest earned			

16. \$12,000 was borrowed from two sources, one that charges 12% simple interest and the other that charges 8% simple interest. If the total interest at the end of 1 year was \$1240, how much money was borrowed from each source?
\$7000 was borrowed from the 12% account and \$5000 was borrowed from the 8% account.

	12% Account	8% Account	Total
Principal borrowed			
Interest earned			

17. Troy borrowed a total of \$12,000 in two different loans to help pay for his new truck. One loan charges 9% simple interest, and the other charges 6% simple interest. If he is charged \$810 in interest after 1 year, find the amount borrowed at each rate.
\$9000 was borrowed at 6%, and \$3000 was borrowed at 9%.

18. Blake has a total of \$4000 to invest in two accounts. One account earns 2% simple interest, and the other earns 5% simple interest. How much should be invested in each account to earn exactly \$155 at the end of 1 year?
\$1500 must be invested in the 2% account and \$2500 invested in the 5% account.

19. Suppose a rich uncle dies and leaves you an inheritance of $30,000. You decide to invest part of the money in a relatively safe bond fund that returns 8%. You invest the rest of the money in a riskier stock fund that you hope will return 12% at the end of 1 year. If you need $3120 at the end of 1 year to make a down payment on a car, how much should you invest at each rate?
Invest $12,000 in the bond fund and $18,000 in the stock fund.

20. As part of his retirement strategy, John plans to invest $200,000 in two different funds. He projects that the moderately high risk investments should return, over time, about 9% per year, while the low risk investments should return about 4% per year. If he wants a supplemental income of $12,000 a year, how should he divide his investments?
He should invest $80,000 at 9% and $120,000 at 4%.

Concept 3: Applications Involving Mixtures

21. How much 50% disinfectant solution must be mixed with a 40% disinfectant solution to produce 25 gal of a 46% disinfectant solution? **(See Example 3.)** 15 gal of the 50% mixture should be mixed with 10 gal of the 40% mixture.

	50% Mixture	40% Mixture	46% Mixture
Amount of solution			
Amount of disinfectant			

22. How many gallons of 20% antifreeze solution and a 10% antifreeze solution must be mixed to obtain 40 gal of a 16% antifreeze solution?
24 gal of the 20% mixture should be mixed with 16 gal of the 10% mixture.

	20% Mixture	10% Mixture	16% Mixture
Amount of solution			
Amount of antifreeze			

23. How much 45% disinfectant solution must be mixed with a 30% disinfectant solution to produce 20 gal of a 39% disinfectant solution?
12 gal of the 45% disinfectant solution should be mixed with 8 gal of the 30% disinfectant solution.

25. A chemist needs 50 mL of a 16% salt solution for an experiment. She can only find a 13% salt solution and an 18% salt solution in the supply room. How many milliliters of the 13% solution should be mixed with the 18% solution to produce the desired amount of the 16% solution? She should mix 20 mL of the 13% solution with 30 mL of the 18% solution.

27. The cooling system in most cars requires a mixture that is 50% antifreeze. How many liters of pure antifreeze and how many liters of 40% antifreeze solution should Chad mix to obtain 6 L of 50% antifreeze solution? (*Hint:* Pure antifreeze is 100% antifreeze.) Chad needs 1 L of pure antifreeze and 5 L of the 40% solution.

24. How many gallons of a 25% antifreeze solution and a 15% antifreeze solution must be mixed to obtain 15 gal of a 23% antifreeze solution?
12 gal of the 25% antifreeze solution should be mixed with 3 gal of the 15% antifreeze solution.

26. Meadowsilver Dairy keeps two kinds of milk on hand, skim milk that has 0.3% butterfat and whole milk that contains 3.3% butterfat. How many gallons of each type of milk does the company need to produce 300 gal of 1% milk for the P&A grocery store?
It needs 230 gal of skim milk and 70 gal of whole milk.

28. Silvia wants to mix a 40% apple juice drink with pure apple juice to make 2 L of a juice drink that is 80% apple juice. How much pure apple juice should she use? Silvia should use $1\frac{1}{3}$ L of pure apple juice.

Concept 4: Applications Involving Distance, Rate, and Time

29. It takes a boat 2 hr to go 16 mi downstream with the current and 4 hr to return against the current. Find the speed of the boat in still water and the speed of the current. **(See Example 4.)** The speed of the boat in still water is 6 mph, and the speed of the current is 2 mph.

	Distance	Rate	Time
Downstream			
Upstream			

30. A boat takes 1.5 hr to go 12 mi upstream against the current. It can go 24 mi downstream with the current in the same amount of time. Find the speed of the current and the speed of the boat in still water. The speed of the boat is 12 mph, and the speed of the current is 4 mph.

	Distance	Rate	Time
Upstream			
Downstream			

31. A plane can fly 960 mi with the wind in 3 hr. It takes the same amount of time to fly 840 mi against the wind. What is the speed of the plane in still air and the speed of the wind? The speed of the plane in still air is 300 mph, and the wind is 20 mph.

32. A plane flies 720 mi with the wind in 3 hr. The return trip against the wind takes 4 hr. What is the speed of the wind and the speed of the plane in still air? The speed of the plane in still air is 210 mph, and the wind is 30 mph.

33. Tony Markins flew from JFK Airport to London. It took him 6 hr to fly with the wind, and 8 hr on the return flight against the wind. If the distance is approximately 3600 mi, determine the speed of the plane in still air and the speed of the wind. The speed of the plane in still air is 525 mph and the speed of the wind is 75 mph.

© Royalty Free/Corbis RF

34. A riverboat cruise upstream on the Mississippi River from New Orleans, Louisiana, to Natchez, Mississippi, takes 10 hr and covers 140 mi. The return trip downstream with the current takes only 7 hr. Find the speed of the riverboat in still water and the speed of the current. The speed of the boat in still water is 17 mph and the speed of the current is 3 mph.

© S. Solum/PhotoLink/Getty Images RF

Mixed Exercises

35. Debi has $2.80 in a collection of dimes and nickels. The number of nickels is five more than the number of dimes. Find the number of each type of coin. There are 17 dimes and 22 nickels.

36. A child collects state quarters and new $1 coins. If she has a total of 25 coins, and the number of quarters is nine more than the number of dollar coins, how many of each type of coin does she have? She has eight $1 coins and 17 quarters.

37. How many quarts of water should be mixed with a 30% vinegar solution to obtain 12 qt of a 25% vinegar solution? (*Hint:* Water is 0% vinegar.) 2 qt of water should be mixed.

38. How much water should be mixed with an 8% plant fertilizer solution to make a half gallon of a 6% plant fertilizer solution? $\frac{1}{8}$ (or 0.125) gal of water should be mixed.

39. In the 1961–1962 NBA basketball season, Wilt Chamberlain of the Philadelphia Warriors made 2432 baskets. Some of the baskets were free throws (worth 1 point each) and some were field goals (worth 2 points each). The number of field goals was 762 more than the number of free throws.

a. How many field goals did he make and how many free throws did he make? 835 free throws and 1597 field goals

b. What was the total number of points scored? 4029 points

c. If Wilt Chamberlain played 80 games during this season, what was the average number of points per game? Approximately 50 points per game

40. In the 1971–1972 NBA basketball season, Kareem Abdul-Jabbar of the Milwaukee Bucks made 1663 baskets. Some of the baskets were free throws (worth 1 point each) and some were field goals (worth 2 points each). The number of field goals he scored was 151 more than twice the number of free throws.

a. How many field goals did he make and how many free throws did he make? 504 free throws and 1159 field goals

b. What was the total number of points scored? 2822 points

c. If Kareem Abdul-Jabbar played 81 games during this season, what was the average number of points per game? Approximately 35 points per game

41. A small plane can fly 350 mi with the wind in $1\frac{3}{4}$ hr. In the same amount of time, the same plane can travel only 210 mi against the wind. What is the speed of the plane in still air and the speed of the wind? The speed of the plane in still air is 160 mph, and the wind is 40 mph.

42. A plane takes 2 hr to travel 1000 mi with the wind. It can travel only 880 mi against the wind in the same amount of time. Find the speed of the wind and the speed of the plane in still air. The speed of the plane in still air is 470 mph, and the wind is 30 mph.

43. A total of \$60,000 is invested in two accounts, one that earns 5.5% simple interest, and one that earns 6.5% simple interest. If the total interest at the end of 1 year is \$3750, find the amount invested in each account. \$15,000 was invested in the 5.5% account, and \$45,000 was invested in the 6.5% account.

44. Jacques borrows a total of \$15,000. Part of the money is borrowed from a bank that charges 12% simple interest per year. Jacques borrows the remaining part of the money from his sister and promises to pay her 7% simple interest per year. If Jacques' total interest for the year is \$1475, find the amount he borrowed from each source. Jacques borrowed \$8500 at 12%, and \$6500 at 7%.

45. At the holidays, Erica likes to sell a candy/nut mixture to her neighbors. She wants to combine candy that costs \$1.80 per pound with nuts that cost \$1.20 per pound. If Erica needs 20 lb of mixture that will sell for \$1.56 per pound, how many pounds of candy and how many pounds of nuts should she use? 12 lb of candy should be mixed with 8 lb of nuts.

© McGraw-Hill Education/
Jill Braaten

46. Mary Lee's natural food store sells a combination of teas. The most popular is a mixture of a tea that sells for \$3.00 per pound with one that sells for \$4.00 per pound. If she needs 40 lb of tea that will sell for \$3.65 per pound, how many pounds of each tea should she use? 14 lb of \$3 per pound tea should be mixed with 26 lb of \$4 per pound tea.

© Steve Mason/Getty Images RF

47. In the 1994 Super Bowl, the Dallas Cowboys scored four more points than twice the number of points scored by the Buffalo Bills. If the total number of points scored by both teams was 43, find the number of points scored by each team. Dallas scored 30 points, and Buffalo scored 13 points.

48. In the 1973 Super Bowl, the Miami Dolphins scored twice as many points as the Washington Redskins. If the total number of points scored by both teams was 21, find the number of points scored by each team. Miami scored 14 points, and Washington scored 7 points.

© herreid/Getty Images RF

Expanding Your Skills

49. In a survey conducted among 500 college students, 340 said that the campus lacked adequate lighting. If $\frac{4}{5}$ of the women and $\frac{1}{2}$ of the men said that they thought the campus lacked adequate lighting, how many men and how many women were in the survey? There were 300 women and 200 men in the survey.

50. During a 1-hr television program, there were 22 commercials. Some commercials were 15 sec and some were 30 sec long. Find the number of 15-sec commercials and the number of 30-sec commercials if the total playing time for commercials was 9.5 min. There are six 15-sec commercials and sixteen 30-sec commercials.

Section 4.5 Systems of Linear Equations in Three Variables

Concepts

1. Solutions to Systems of Linear Equations in Three Variables
2. Solving Systems of Linear Equations in Three Variables

1. Solutions to Systems of Linear Equations in Three Variables

In this section, we will expand the discussion of solving systems of linear equations in two variables to solving systems involving three variables.

A **linear equation in three variables** can be written in the form $Ax + By + Cz = D$, where A, B, and C are not all zero. For example, the equation $2x + 3y + z = 6$ is a linear equation in three variables. Solutions to this equation are **ordered triples** of the form (x, y, z) that satisfy the equation. Some solutions to the equation $2x + 3y + z = 6$ are

Solution:	Check:
$(1, 1, 1) \longrightarrow$	$2(1) + 3(1) + (1) = 6$ ✓ True
$(2, 0, 2) \longrightarrow$	$2(2) + 3(0) + (2) = 6$ ✓ True
$(0, 1, 3) \longrightarrow$	$2(0) + 3(1) + (3) = 6$ ✓ True

Infinitely many ordered triples serve as solutions to the equation $2x + 3y + z = 6$.

The set of all ordered triples that are solutions to a linear equation in three variables may be represented graphically by a plane in space. Figure 4-10 shows a portion of the plane $2x + 3y + z = 6$ in a 3-dimensional coordinate system.

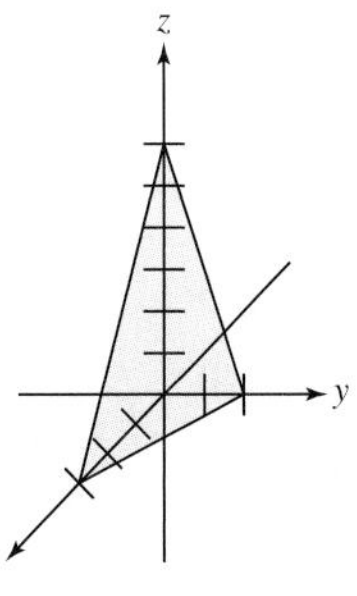

Figure 4-10

A solution to a system of linear equations in three variables is an ordered triple that satisfies *each* equation. Geometrically, a solution is a point of intersection of the planes represented by the equations in the system.

A system of linear equations in three variables may have *one unique solution, infinitely many solutions,* or *no solution*.

Instructor Note: 3D physical models work well here. It is hard to visualize on a flat page.

One unique solution (planes intersect at one point)
- The system is consistent.
- The equations are independent.

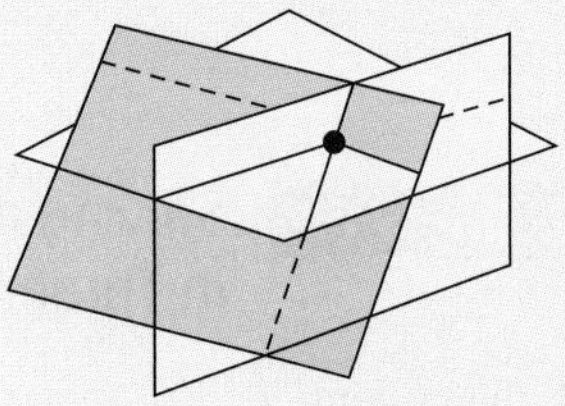

No solution (the three planes do not all intersect)
- The system is inconsistent.
- The equations are independent.

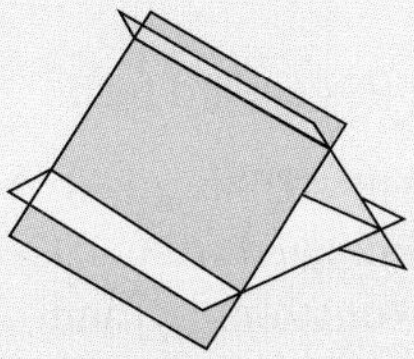
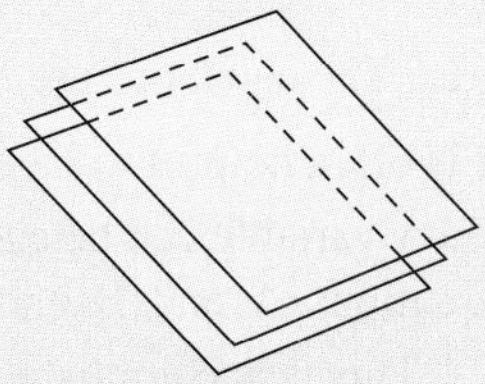
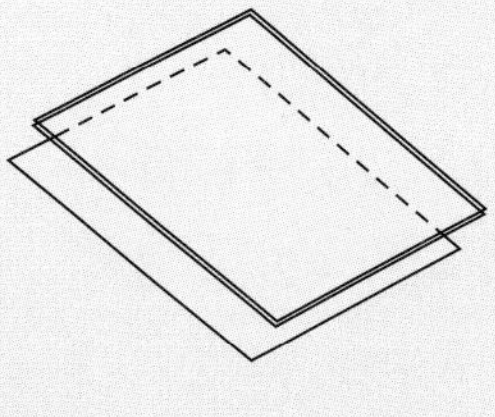

Infinitely many solutions (planes intersect at infinitely many points)
- The system is consistent.
- The equations are dependent.

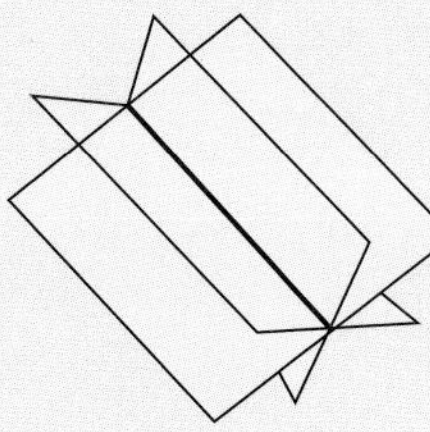
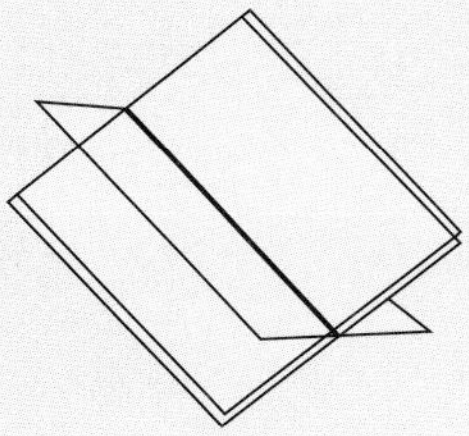
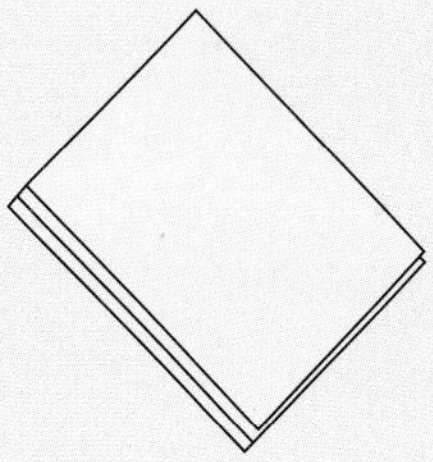

2. Solving Systems of Linear Equations in Three Variables

To solve a system involving three variables, the goal is to eliminate one variable. This reduces the system to two equations in two variables. One strategy for eliminating a variable is to pair up the original equations two at a time.

Solving a System of Three Linear Equations in Three Variables

Step 1 Write each equation in standard form $Ax + By + Cz = D$.

Step 2 Choose a pair of equations, and eliminate one of the variables by using the addition method.

Step 3 Choose a different pair of equations and eliminate the *same* variable.

Step 4 Once steps 2 and 3 are complete, you should have two equations in two variables. Solve this system by using the substitution or the addition method.

Step 5 Substitute the values of the variables found in step 4 into any of the three original equations that contain the third variable. Solve for the third variable.

Step 6 Check the ordered triple in each of the original equations.

Classroom Example: p. 321, Exercise 12

Example 1 Solving a System of Linear Equations in Three Variables

Solve the system.

$$\begin{aligned} 2x + y - 3z &= -7 \\ 3x - 2y + z &= 11 \\ -2x - 3y - 2z &= 3 \end{aligned}$$

Solution:

$\boxed{A}$ $2x + y - 3z = -7$

$\boxed{B}$ $3x - 2y + z = 11$

$\boxed{C}$ $-2x - 3y - 2z = 3$

Step 1: The equations are already in standard form.

- It is often helpful to label the equations.
- The y variable can be easily eliminated from equations $\boxed{A}$ and $\boxed{B}$ and from equations $\boxed{A}$ and $\boxed{C}$. This is accomplished by creating opposite coefficients for the y terms and then adding the equations.

Step 2: Eliminate the y-variable from equations $\boxed{A}$ and $\boxed{B}$.

$\boxed{A}$ $2x + y - 3z = -7 \xrightarrow{\text{Multiply by 2.}} 4x + 2y - 6z = -14$

$\boxed{B}$ $3x - 2y + z = 11 \longrightarrow \underline{3x - 2y + z = 11}$

$7x - 5z = -3$ $\boxed{D}$

Step 3: Eliminate the y-variable again, this time from equations $\boxed{A}$ and $\boxed{C}$.

$$\boxed{A}\quad 2x + y - 3z = -7 \xrightarrow{\text{Multiply by 3.}} 6x + 3y - 9z = -21$$

$$\boxed{C}\quad -2x - 3y - 2z = 3 \longrightarrow -2x - 3y - 2z = 3$$

$$4x \qquad - 11z = -18 \quad \boxed{E}$$

Step 4: Now equations $\boxed{D}$ and $\boxed{E}$ can be paired up to form a linear system in two variables. Solve this system.

$$\boxed{D}\quad 7x - 5z = -3 \xrightarrow{\text{Multiply by } -4.} -28x + 20z = 12$$

$$\boxed{E}\quad 4x - 11z = -18 \xrightarrow[\text{Multiply by 7.}]{} 28x - 77z = -126$$

$$-57z = -114$$

$$z = 2$$

Once one variable has been found, substitute this value into either equation in the two-variable system, that is, either equation $\boxed{D}$ or $\boxed{E}$.

$\boxed{D}\quad 7x - 5z = -3$

$7x - 5(2) = -3$ Substitute $z = 2$ into equation $\boxed{D}$.

$7x - 10 = -3$

$7x = 7$

$x = 1$

$\boxed{A}\quad 2x + y - 3z = -7$

$2(1) + y - 3(2) = -7$

$2 + y - 6 = -7$

$y - 4 = -7$

$y = -3$

Step 5: Now that two variables are known, substitute these values for x and z into any of the original three equations to find the remaining variable y. Substitute $x = 1$ and $z = 2$ into equation $\boxed{A}$.

Step 6: Check the ordered triple, $(1, -3, 2)$, in the three original equations.

<u>Check</u>: $2x + y - 3z = -7 \rightarrow 2(1) + (-3) - 3(2) = -7$ ✓ True

$3x - 2y + z = 11 \rightarrow 3(1) - 2(-3) + (2) = 11$ ✓ True

$-2x - 3y - 2z = 3 \rightarrow -2(1) - 3(-3) - 2(2) = 3$ ✓ True

The solution set is $\{(1, -3, 2)\}$.

TIP: It is important to note that in steps 2 and 3, the *same* variable is eliminated.

Instructor Note: Since any of the variables x, y, or z can be eliminated first, it is important to discuss a strategy for selecting the best variable to target.

Skill Practice Solve the system.

1. $x + 2y + z = 1$

$3x - y + 2z = 13$

$2x + 3y - z = -8$

Answer

1. $\{(1, -2, 4)\}$

Classroom Example: p. 321, Exercise 22

Example 2 Solving a System of Linear Equations in Three Variables

Solve the system.

$$\begin{aligned} 3x + y - 5 &= 0 \\ z &= 7 + 2y \\ x + 3z &= 17 \end{aligned}$$

Solution:

$$\boxed{A}\quad 3x + y = 5$$
$$\boxed{B}\quad -2y + z = 7$$
$$\boxed{C}\quad x + 3z = 17$$

Step 1: Write equations in standard form, $Ax + By + Cz = D$.

Steps 2 and 3: Note equation $\boxed{C}$ is missing the y-variable. Therefore, we can eliminate the y-variable by pairing up equations $\boxed{A}$ and $\boxed{B}$.

$$\boxed{A}\; 3x + y = 5 \xrightarrow{\text{Multiply by 2.}} 6x + 2y = 10$$
$$\boxed{B}\; -2y + z = 7 \longrightarrow -2y + z = 7$$
$$6x + z = 17 \quad \boxed{D}$$

Step 4: Now we pair up equations $\boxed{C}$ and $\boxed{D}$ to eliminate the z-variable.

$$\boxed{C}\; x + 3z = 17 \longrightarrow x + 3y = 17$$
$$\boxed{D}\; 6x + z = 17 \xrightarrow[\text{Multiply by } -3.]{} -18x - 3z = -51$$
$$-17x = -34$$
$$x = 2$$

Step 5: Now substitute $x = 2$ into equations $\boxed{A}$ and $\boxed{C}$ to find the remaining variables.

$$\boxed{A}\quad \begin{aligned} 3x + y &= 5 \\ 3(2) + y &= 5 \\ 6 + y &= 5 \\ y &= -1 \end{aligned} \qquad\qquad \boxed{C}\quad \begin{aligned} x + 3z &= 17 \\ (2) + 3z &= 17 \\ 3z &= 15 \\ z &= 5 \end{aligned}$$

Step 6: Check $(2, -1, 5)$ in the three original equations.

Check:
$$3x + y - 5 = 0 \longrightarrow 3(2) + (-1) - 5 = 0 \checkmark \text{ True}$$
$$z = 7 + 2y \longrightarrow 5 = 7 + 2(-1) \checkmark \text{ True}$$
$$x + 3z = 17 \longrightarrow (2) + 3(5) = 17 \checkmark \text{ True}$$

The solution set is $\{(2, -1, 5)\}$.

Skill Practice Solve the system.

2.
$$\begin{aligned} 4y &= x + 4 \\ 2x + z &= 5 \\ y - 14 &= 4z \end{aligned}$$

Answer

2. $\{(4, 2, -3)\}$

Example 3
Solving a System of Dependent Equations

Classroom Example: p. 322, Exercise 44

Solve the system. If there is not a unique solution, state the number of solutions and whether the system is inconsistent or the equations are dependent.

$$\boxed{A}\ 3x + y - z = 8$$
$$\boxed{B}\ 2x - y + 2z = 3$$
$$\boxed{C}\ x + 2y - 3z = 5$$

Solution:

First, make a decision regarding the variable to eliminate. The y-variable is particularly easy to eliminate because the coefficients of y in equations $\boxed{A}$ and $\boxed{B}$ are already opposites. The y-variable can be eliminated from equations $\boxed{B}$ and $\boxed{C}$ by multiplying equation $\boxed{B}$ by 2.

$$\begin{array}{ll} \boxed{A} & 3x + y - z = 8 \\ \boxed{B} & 2x - y + 2z = 3 \\ \hline & 5x \qquad + z = 11 \quad \boxed{D} \end{array}$$

Pair up equations $\boxed{A}$ and $\boxed{B}$ to eliminate y.

$$\begin{array}{llll} \boxed{B} & 2x - y + 2z = 3 & \xrightarrow{\text{Multiply by 2.}} & 4x - 2y + 4z = 6 \\ \boxed{C} & x + 2y - 3z = 5 & \longrightarrow & x + 2y - 3z = 5 \\ \hline & & & 5x \qquad + z = 11 \quad \boxed{E} \end{array}$$

Pair up equations $\boxed{B}$ and $\boxed{C}$ to eliminate y.

Because equations $\boxed{D}$ and $\boxed{E}$ are equivalent equations, this is a dependent system. By eliminating variables we obtain the identity $0 = 0$.

$$\begin{array}{llll} \boxed{D} & 5x + z = 11 & \xrightarrow{\text{Multiply by } -1.} & -5x - z = -11 \\ \boxed{E} & 5x + z = 11 & \longrightarrow & 5x + z = 11 \\ \hline & & & 0 = 0 \end{array}$$

The result $0 = 0$ indicates that there are infinitely many solutions and that the equations are dependent.

Skill Practice Solve the system. If the system does not have a unique solution, state the number of solutions and whether the system is inconsistent or the equations are dependent.

3.
$$\begin{aligned} x + y + z &= 8 \\ 2x - y + z &= 6 \\ -5x - 2y - 4z &= -30 \end{aligned}$$

Answer

3. Infinitely many solutions; dependent equations

Classroom Example: p. 322, Exercise 38

Example 4 Solving an Inconsistent System of Linear Equations

Solve the system. If there is not a unique solution, state the number of solutions and whether the system is inconsistent or the equations are dependent.

$$2x + 3y - 7z = 4$$
$$-4x - 6y + 14z = 1$$
$$5x + y - 3z = 6$$

Solution:

We will eliminate the x-variable.

$$\boxed{A}\quad 2x + 3y - 7z = 4 \xrightarrow{\text{Multiply by 2.}} 4x + 6y - 14z = 8$$
$$\boxed{B}\quad -4x - 6y + 14z = 1 \longrightarrow \underline{-4x - 6y + 14z = 1}$$
$$\boxed{C}\quad 5x + y - 3z = 6 \qquad\qquad 0 = 9 \quad \text{(contradiction)}$$

The result $0 = 9$ is a contradiction, indicating that the system has no solution. The system is inconsistent.

Skill Practice Solve the system. If the system does not have a unique solution, state the number of solutions and whether the system is inconsistent or the equations are dependent.

4. $x - 2y + z = 5$
$x - 3y + 2z = -7$
$-2x + 4y - 2z = 6$

Answer

4. No solution; inconsistent system

Section 4.5 Practice Exercises

For additional exercises, see Classroom Activities 4.5A–4.5B in the *Student's Resource Manual* at www.mhhe.com/moh.

Vocabulary and Key Concepts

1. **a.** An equation written in the form $Ax + By + Cz = D$, where A, B, and C are not all zero, is called a ___linear___ equation in three variables.

   b. Solutions to a linear equation in three variables are of the form (x, y, z) and are called ___ordered triples___.

Review Exercises

For Exercises 2–4, solve the systems by using two methods: (**a**) the substitution method and (**b**) the addition method.

2. $3x + y = 4$
$4x + y = 5$ $\{(1, 1)\}$

3. $2x - 5y = 3$ $\{\ \}$
$-4x + 10y = 3$

4. $4x - 6y = 5$
$x = \frac{3}{2}y + \frac{5}{4}$ Infinitely many solutions; $\{(x, y) \mid 4x - 6y = 5\}$

5. Two cars leave Kansas City at the same time. One travels east and one travels west. After 3 hr the cars are 369 mi apart. If one car travels 7 mph slower than the other, find the speed of each car.
The speeds are 65 mph and 58 mph.

Concept 1: Solutions to Systems of Linear Equations in Three Variables

6. How many solutions are possible when solving a system of three equations with three variables?
One solution, no solution, or infinitely many solutions

7. Which of the following points are solutions to the system? (4, 0, 2) is a solution.

$(2, 1, 7), (3, -10, -6), (4, 0, 2)$

$$\begin{aligned} 2x - y + z &= 10 \\ 4x + 2y - 3z &= 10 \\ x - 3y + 2z &= 8 \end{aligned}$$

8. Which of the following points are solutions to the system? (4, 2, 1) is a solution.

$(1, 1, 3), (0, 0, 4), (4, 2, 1)$

$$\begin{aligned} -3x - 3y - 6z &= -24 \\ -9x - 6y + 3z &= -45 \\ 9x + 3y - 9z &= 33 \end{aligned}$$

9. Which of the following points are solutions to the system? (1, 1, 1) is a solution.

$(12, 2, -2), (4, 2, 1), (1, 1, 1)$

$$\begin{aligned} -x - y - 4z &= -6 \\ x - 3y + z &= -1 \\ 4x + y - z &= 4 \end{aligned}$$

10. Which of the following points are solutions to the system? None

$(0, 4, 3), (3, 6, 10), (3, 3, 1)$

$$\begin{aligned} x + 2y - z &= 5 \\ x - 3y + z &= -5 \\ -2x + y - z &= -4 \end{aligned}$$

Concept 2: Solving Systems of Linear Equations in Three Variables

For Exercises 11–34, solve the system of equations. **(See Examples 1–2.)**

11.
$$\begin{aligned} 2x + y - 3z &= -12 \\ 3x - 2y - z &= 3 \\ -x + 5y + 2z &= -3 \end{aligned}$$
$\{(1, -2, 4)\}$

12.
$$\begin{aligned} -3x - 2y + 4z &= -15 \\ 2x + 5y - 3z &= 3 \\ 4x - y + 7z &= 15 \end{aligned}$$
$\{(5, -2, -1)\}$

13.
$$\begin{aligned} x - 3y - 4z &= -7 \\ 5x + 2y + 2z &= -1 \\ 4x - y - 5z &= -6 \end{aligned}$$
$\{(-1, 2, 0)\}$

14.
$$\begin{aligned} 6x - 5y + z &= 7 \\ 5x + 3y + 2z &= 0 \\ -2x + y - 3z &= 11 \end{aligned}$$
$\{(2, 0, -5)\}$

15.
$$\begin{aligned} -3x + y - z &= 8 \\ -4x + 2y + 3z &= -3 \\ 2x + 3y - 2z &= -1 \end{aligned}$$
$\{(-2, -1, -3)\}$

16.
$$\begin{aligned} 2x + 3y + 3z &= 15 \\ 3x - 6y - 6z &= -23 \\ -9x - 3y + 6z &= 8 \end{aligned}$$
$\left\{\left(1, 1, \frac{10}{3}\right)\right\}$

17.
$$\begin{aligned} 4x + 2z &= 12 + 3y \\ 2x &= 3x + 3z - 5 \\ y &= 2x + 7z + 8 \end{aligned}$$
$\{(1, -4, -2)\}$

18.
$$\begin{aligned} y &= 2x + z + 1 \\ -3x - 1 &= -2y + 2z \\ 5x + 3z &= 16 - 3y \end{aligned}$$
$\{(-1, 3, 4)\}$

19.
$$\begin{aligned} x + y + z &= 6 \\ -x + y - z &= -2 \\ 2x + 3y + z &= 11 \end{aligned}$$
$\{(1, 2, 3)\}$

20.
$$\begin{aligned} x - y - z &= -11 \\ x + y - z &= 15 \\ 2x - y + z &= -9 \end{aligned}$$
$\{(2, 13, 0)\}$

21.
$$\begin{aligned} 2x - 3y + 2z &= -1 \\ x + 2y &= -4 \\ x + z &= 1 \end{aligned}$$
$\{(-6, 1, 7)\}$

22.
$$\begin{aligned} x + y + z &= 2 \\ 2x - z &= 5 \\ 3y + z &= 2 \end{aligned}$$
$\{(2, 1, -1)\}$

23.
$$\begin{aligned} 4x + 9y &= 8 \\ 8x + 6z &= -1 \\ 6y + 6z &= -1 \end{aligned}$$
$\left\{\left(\frac{1}{2}, \frac{2}{3}, -\frac{5}{6}\right)\right\}$

24.
$$\begin{aligned} 3x + 2z &= 11 \\ y - 7z &= 4 \\ x - 6y &= 1 \end{aligned}$$
$\left\{\left(4, \frac{1}{2}, -\frac{1}{2}\right)\right\}$

25.
$$\begin{aligned} 2x + 3y - 2z &= 8 \\ x - 4y + z &= -8 \\ -4x + 3y + 2z &= 3 \end{aligned}$$
$\left\{\left(\frac{1}{2}, 2, -\frac{1}{2}\right)\right\}$

26.
$$\begin{aligned} 5x - 3y + z &= 4 \\ -x + 6y + 4z &= 1 \\ 2x + 3y - z &= 3 \end{aligned}$$
$\left\{\left(1, \frac{1}{3}, 0\right)\right\}$

27.
$$\begin{aligned} 5y &= -7 + 4z \\ x + 3y + 3 &= 0 \\ 2x &= 14 + z \end{aligned}$$
$\{(6, -3, -2)\}$

28.
$$\begin{aligned} 4(x - z) &= -1 \\ 3y + z &= 1 \\ 4x &= 3 + y \end{aligned}$$
$\left\{\left(\frac{3}{4}, 0, 1\right)\right\}$

29.
$$\begin{aligned} x + z &= -16 + 3y \\ 2(y + z) &= 12 - 5y \\ 3x + 8 &= y - z \end{aligned}$$
{(0, 4, −4)}

30.
$$\begin{aligned} 4(x - 2y) &= 8 - 3z \\ 4y + 13 &= 3x + z \\ x - 3y &= -2(z + 2) \end{aligned}$$
{(7, 1, −4)}

31.
$$\begin{aligned} \tfrac{1}{3}x + \tfrac{1}{2}y + \tfrac{1}{6}z &= \tfrac{1}{6} \\ \tfrac{1}{5}x + y - \tfrac{3}{5}z &= \tfrac{4}{5} \\ x - \tfrac{4}{9}y + \tfrac{2}{3}z &= \tfrac{1}{3} \end{aligned}$$
{(1, 0, −1)}

32.
$$\begin{aligned} \tfrac{1}{2}x + \tfrac{5}{2}z &= -1 \\ \tfrac{1}{4}x - \tfrac{1}{6}y - \tfrac{2}{3}z &= 3 \\ -\tfrac{1}{2}x + \tfrac{5}{8}y + \tfrac{1}{8}z &= -3 \end{aligned}$$
{(8, 2, −2)}

33.
$$\begin{aligned} 0.1x - 0.6y + z &= -6.8 \\ 0.7x - 0.3z &= -14 \\ y + 0.5z &= 8 \end{aligned}$$
{(−20, 8, 0)}

34.
$$\begin{aligned} 0.5x + y &= 10 \\ -0.2y + 0.5z &= 0.5 \\ -0.3x - z &= -6 \end{aligned}$$
{(10, 5, 3)}

Mixed Exercises

For Exercises 35–46, solve the system. If there is not a unique solution, state whether the system is inconsistent or the equations are dependent. **(See Examples 1–4.)**

35.
$$\begin{aligned} 2x + y + 3z &= 2 \\ x - y + 2z &= -4 \\ -2x + 2y - 4z &= 8 \end{aligned}$$
Dependent equations

36.
$$\begin{aligned} x + y &= z \\ 2x + 4y - 2z &= 6 \\ 3x + 6y - 3z &= 9 \end{aligned}$$
Dependent equations

37.
$$\begin{aligned} 6x - 2y + 2z &= 2 \\ 4x + 8y - 2z &= 5 \\ -2x - 4y + z &= -2 \end{aligned}$$
Inconsistent system

38.
$$\begin{aligned} 3x + 2y + z &= 3 \\ x - 3y + z &= 4 \\ -6x - 4y - 2z &= 1 \end{aligned}$$
Inconsistent system

39.
$$\begin{aligned} \tfrac{1}{2}x + \tfrac{2}{3}y &= \tfrac{5}{2} \\ \tfrac{1}{5}x - \tfrac{1}{2}z &= -\tfrac{3}{10} \\ \tfrac{1}{3}y - \tfrac{1}{4}z &= \tfrac{3}{4} \end{aligned}$$
{(1, 3, 1)}

40.
$$\begin{aligned} \tfrac{1}{2}x + \tfrac{1}{4}y + z &= 3 \\ \tfrac{1}{8}x + \tfrac{1}{4}y + \tfrac{1}{4}z &= \tfrac{9}{8} \\ x - y - \tfrac{2}{3}z &= \tfrac{1}{3} \end{aligned}$$
{(3, 2, 1)}

41.
$$\begin{aligned} 3(2x + y) &= 4(3z - 1) \\ y + 4z &= 2(3 + 5x) \\ 2(x + z) &= y - 1 \end{aligned}$$
$\left\{\left(-\frac{1}{2}, \frac{1}{3}, \frac{1}{6}\right)\right\}$

42.
$$\begin{aligned} 5(y - 2z) &= 9x - 11 \\ 2(3x + z) &= 5 + y \\ 3x &= z + 2(y + 1) \end{aligned}$$
$\left\{\left(\frac{2}{3}, -\frac{1}{5}, \frac{2}{5}\right)\right\}$

43.
$$\begin{aligned} 2x + y &= 3(z - 1) \\ 3x - 2(y - 2z) &= 1 \\ 2(2x - 3z) &= -6 - 2y \end{aligned}$$
Dependent equations

44.
$$\begin{aligned} 2x + y &= -3 \\ 2y + 16z &= -10 \\ -7x - 3y + 4z &= 8 \end{aligned}$$
Dependent equations

45.
$$\begin{aligned} -0.1y + 0.2z &= 0.2 \\ 0.1x + 0.1y + 0.1z &= 0.2 \\ -0.1x + 0.3z &= 0.2 \end{aligned}$$
{(1, 0, 1)}

46.
$$\begin{aligned} 0.1x - 0.2y &= 0 \\ 0.3y + 0.1z &= -0.1 \\ 0.4x - 0.1z &= 1.2 \end{aligned}$$
{(2, 1, −4)}

Expanding Your Skills

The systems in Exercises 47–50 are called homogeneous systems because each system has (0, 0, 0) as a solution. However, if the equations are dependent, there will be infinitely many more solutions. For each system determine whether (0, 0, 0) is the only solution or if the equations are dependent.

47.
$$\begin{aligned} 2x - 4y + 8z &= 0 \\ -x - 3y + z &= 0 \\ x - 2y + 5z &= 0 \end{aligned}$$
{(0, 0, 0)}

48.
$$\begin{aligned} 2x - 4y + z &= 0 \\ x - 3y - z &= 0 \\ 3x - y + 2z &= 0 \end{aligned}$$
{(0, 0, 0)}

49.
$$\begin{aligned} 4x - 2y - 3z &= 0 \\ -8x - y + z &= 0 \\ 2x - y - \frac{3}{2}z &= 0 \end{aligned}$$
Dependent equations

50.
$$\begin{aligned} 5x + y &= 0 \\ 4y - z &= 0 \\ 5x + 5y - z &= 0 \end{aligned}$$
Dependent equations

Applications of Systems of Linear Equations in Three Variables

Section 4.6

Objectives

1. Applications Involving Geometry
2. Applications Involving Mixtures

1. Applications Involving Geometry

In this section we solve several applications of linear equations in three variables.

Example 1 **Applying Systems of Linear Equations in Three Variables**

Classroom Example: p. 325, Exercise 6

In a triangle, the smallest angle measures 10° more than one-half of the largest angle. The middle angle measures 12° more than the smallest angle. Find the measure of each angle.

Solution:

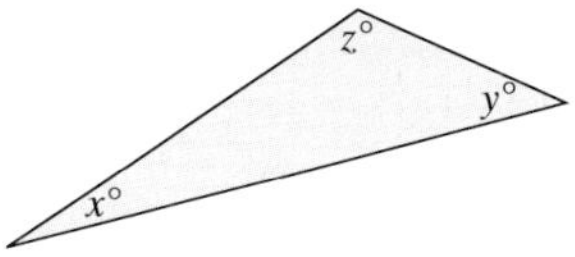

Let x represent the measure of the smallest angle.

Let y represent the measure of the middle angle.

Let z represent the measure of the largest angle.

To solve for three variables, we need to establish three independent relationships among x, y, and z.

A $x = \frac{1}{2}z + 10$	The smallest angle measures 10° more than one-half the measure of the largest angle.
B $y = x + 12$	The middle angle measures 12° more than the measure of the smallest angle.
C $x + y + z = 180$	The sum of the interior angles of a triangle measures 180°.

Clear fractions and write each equation in standard form.

Standard Form

A $x = \frac{1}{2}z + 10 \xrightarrow{\text{Multiply by 2.}} 2x = z + 20 \longrightarrow 2x - z = 20$

B $y = x + 12 \longrightarrow -x + y = 12$

C $x + y + z = 180 \longrightarrow x + y + z = 180$

Notice equation B is missing the z-variable. Therefore, we can eliminate z again by pairing up equations A and C.

A $2x - z = 20$

C $x + y + z = 180$

$3x + y = 200$ D

[B] $-x + y = 12$	Multiply by −1. →	$x - y = -12$	Pair up equations [B] and [D] to form a system of two variables.
[D] $3x + y = 200$	→	$3x + y = 200$	
		$4x \quad = 188$	
		$x = 47$	Solve for x.

From equation [B] we have $-x + y = 12 \longrightarrow -47 + y = 12 \rightarrow y = 59$

From equation [C] we have $x + y + z = 180 \rightarrow 47 + 59 + z = 180 \rightarrow z = 74$

The smallest angle measures 47°, the middle angle measures 59°, and the largest angle measures 74°.

Skill Practice

1. The perimeter of a triangle is 30 in. The shortest side is 4 in. shorter than the longest side. The longest side is 6 in. less than the sum of the other two sides. Find the length of each side.

2. Applications Involving Mixtures

Classroom Example: p. 326, Exercise 14

Example 2 Applying Systems of Linear Equations to Nutrition

Doctors have become increasingly concerned about the sodium intake in the U.S. diet. Recommendations by the American Medical Association indicate that most individuals should not exceed 2400 mg of sodium per day.

Liz ate 1 slice of pizza, 1 serving of ice cream, and 1 glass of soda for a total of 1030 mg of sodium. David ate 3 slices of pizza, no ice cream, and 2 glasses of soda for a total of 2420 mg of sodium. Melinda ate 2 slices of pizza, 1 serving of ice cream, and 2 glasses of soda for a total of 1910 mg of sodium. How much sodium is in one serving of each item?

Solution:

Let x represent the sodium content of 1 slice of pizza.

Let y represent the sodium content of 1 serving of ice cream.

Let z represent the sodium content of 1 glass of soda.

From Liz's meal we have: [A] $x + y + z = 1030$

From David's meal we have: [B] $3x + 2z = 2420$

From Melinda's meal we have: [C] $2x + y + 2z = 1910$

Equation [B] is missing the y-variable. Eliminating y from equations [A] and [C], we have

[A] $x + y + z = 1030$	Multiply by −1. →	$-x - y - z = -1030$
[C] $2x + y + 2z = 1910$	→	$2x + y + 2z = 1910$
		[D] $x + z = 880$

Solve the system formed by equations [B] and [D].

[B] $3x + 2z = 2420$	→	$3x + 2z = 2420$
[D] $x + z = 880$	Multiply by −2. →	$-2x - 2z = -1760$
		$x = 660$

Answer

1. The sides are 8 in., 10 in., and 12 in.

From equation D we have $x + z = 800 \longrightarrow 660 + z = 880 \longrightarrow z = 220$

From equation A we have $x + y + z = 1030 \rightarrow 660 + y + 220 = 1030 \rightarrow y = 150$

Therefore, 1 slice of pizza has 660 mg of sodium, 1 serving of ice cream has 150 mg of sodium, and 1 glass of soda has 220 mg of sodium.

Skill Practice

2. Annette, Barb, and Carlita work in a clothing shop. One day the three had combined sales of \$1480. Annette sold \$120 more than Barb. Barb and Carlita combined sold \$280 more than Annette. How much did each person sell?

Answer

2. Annette sold \$600, Barb sold \$480, and Carlita sold \$400.

Section 4.6 Practice Exercises

For additional exercises, see Classroom Activities 4.6A–4.6B in the *Student's Resource Manual* at www.mhhe.com/moh.

Review Exercises

For Exercises 1–4, solve the system. If there is not a unique solution, state whether the system is inconsistent or the equations are dependent.

1. $$\begin{aligned} -5y - z &= -8 \\ x + 10y + 2z &= 9 \\ -3x + y &= 21 \end{aligned}$$ $\{(-7, 0, 8)\}$

2. $$\begin{aligned} 8x - y + 2z &= 18 \\ x + y - 5z &= -21 \\ 4x - 0.5y + z &= 9 \end{aligned}$$ Dependent equations

3. $$\begin{aligned} \frac{1}{2}x - y + \frac{5}{6}z &= 4 \\ \frac{3}{2}x - 3y + \frac{5}{2}z &= 6 \\ -\frac{1}{4}x + y - \frac{1}{3}z &= -2 \end{aligned}$$ Inconsistent system

4. $$\begin{aligned} 12x - y + z &= -6 \\ -6x + 2y - 3z &= 5 \\ 6x + y - z &= 3 \end{aligned}$$ $\left\{\left(-\frac{1}{6}, 8, 4\right)\right\}$

Concept 1: Applications Involving Geometry

5. A triangle has one angle that measures 5° more than twice the smallest angle, and the largest angle measures 11° less than 3 times the measure of the smallest angle. Find the measures of the three angles. **(See Example 1.)** 67°, 82°, 31°

6. The largest angle of a triangle measures 4° less than 5 times the measure of the smallest angle. The middle angle measures twice that of the smallest angle. Find the measures of the three angles. 111°, 46°, 23°

7. One angle of a triangle measures 6° more than twice the measure of the smallest angle. The third angle measures 1° less than four times the smallest. Find the measures of the three angles. 25°, 56°, 99°

8. In a triangle the smallest angle measures 12° less than the middle angle. The measure of the largest angle is equal to the sum of the other two. Find the measures of the three angles. 39°, 51°, 90°

9. The perimeter of a triangle is 55 cm. The measure of the shortest side is 8 cm less than the middle side. The measure of the longest side is 1 cm less than the sum of the other two sides. Find the lengths of the sides. 10 cm, 18 cm, 27 cm

10. The perimeter of a triangle is 5 ft. The longest side of the triangle measures 20 in. more than the shortest side. The middle side is 3 times the measure of the shortest side. Find the lengths of the three sides in *inches*. 8 in., 24 in., 28 in.

11. The perimeter of a triangle is 4.5 ft. The shortest side measures 2 in. less than half the longest side. The longest side measures 2 in. less than the sum of the other two sides. Find the lengths of the sides in *inches*. 11 in., 17 in., 26 in.

12. The perimeter of a triangle is 7 m. The length of the longest side is twice the length of the shortest side. The sum of the lengths of the shortest side and the middle side is 1 m more than the length of the longest side. Find the lengths of the sides. $1\frac{1}{2}$ m, $2\frac{1}{2}$ m, 3 m

Concept 2: Applications Involving Mixtures

13. Sean kept track of his fiber intake from three sources for 3 weeks. The first week he had 3 servings of a fiber supplement, 1 serving of oatmeal, and 4 servings of cereal, which totaled 19 g of fiber. The second week he had 2 servings of the fiber supplement, 4 servings of oatmeal, and 2 servings of cereal totaling 25 g. The third week he had 5 servings of the fiber supplement, 3 servings of oatmeal, and 2 servings of cereal for a total of 30 g. Find the amount of fiber in one serving of each of the following: the fiber supplement, the oatmeal, and the cereal. **(See Example 2.)** The fiber supplement has 3 g; the oatmeal has 4 g; and the cereal has 1.5 g.

14. Natalie kept track of her calcium intake from three sources for 3 days. The first day she had 1 glass of milk, 1 serving of ice cream, and 1 calcium supplement in pill form which totaled 1180 mg of calcium. The second day she had 2 glasses of milk, 1 serving of ice cream, and 1 calcium supplement totaling 1680 mg. The third day she had 1 glass of milk, 2 servings of ice cream, and 1 calcium supplement for a total of 1260 mg. Find the amount of calcium in one glass of milk, in one serving of ice cream, and in one calcium supplement. The milk has 500 mg; the ice cream has 80 mg; and the calcium supplement has 600 mg.

15. Kyoki invested a total of $10,000 into bonds, mutual funds, and a Treasury note. He put the same amount of money in the money market account as he did in bonds. For 1 year, the bonds paid 5% interest, the mutual funds paid 8%, and the Treasury note paid 4%. At the end of the year, Kyoki earned $660 in interest. How much did he invest in each account? Kyoki invested $2000 in bonds, $6000 in mutual funds, and $2000 in the Treasury note.

16. Walter had $25,000 to invest. He split the money into three types of investment: small caps earning 6%, global market investments earning 10%, and a balanced fund earning 9%. He put twice as much money in the global account as he did in the balanced fund. If his earnings for the first year totaled $2160, how much did he invest in each account? Walter invested $7000 in small caps, $6000 in the balanced fund, and $12,000 in global markets.

17. Winston deposited $4500 into three accounts: one pays 5% interest, another pays 5.5% interest, and the third pays 4% interest. He deposits $1000 more in the 5.5% account than he does in the 4% account. After the first year, he earned a total of $225 interest. How much did he deposit into each account? $1500 at 5%, $2000 at 5.5%, $1000 at 4%

18. Raeann deposited $8000 into three accounts at her credit union: a checking account that pays 1.2% interest, a savings account that pays 2.5% interest, and a money market account that pays 3% interest. If she put 3 times more money in the 3% account than she did in the 1.2% account, and her total interest for 1 year was $202, how much did she deposit into each account? $1000 at 1.2%, $4000 at 2.5%, $3000 at 3%

19. A basketball player scored 29 points in one game. In basketball, some baskets are worth 3 points, some are worth 2 points, and free throws are worth 1 point. He scored four more 2-point baskets than he did 3-point baskets. The number of free throws is one less than the number of 2-point baskets. How many free throws, 2-point shots, and 3-point shots did he make? He made six free throws, seven 2-point shots, and three 3-point shots.

20. Goofie Golf has 18 holes that are par 3, par 4, or par 5. Most of the holes are par 4. In fact, there are 3 times as many par 4s as par 3s. There are 3 more par 5s than par 3s. How many of each type are there?
Three par 3s, nine par 4s, six par 5s

© Getty Images RF

21. Combining peanuts, pecans, and cashews makes a party mixture of nuts. If the amount of peanuts equals the amount of pecans and cashews combined, and if there are twice as many cashews as pecans, how many ounces of each nut is used to make 48 oz of party mixture?
24 oz peanuts, 8 oz pecans, 16 oz cashews

22. Souvenir hats, T-shirts, and jackets are sold at a rock concert. Three hats, two T-shirts, and one jacket cost \$140. Two hats, two T-shirts, and two jackets cost \$170. One hat, three T-shirts, and two jackets cost \$180. Find the prices of the individual items. Hats \$15, T-shirts \$25, jackets \$45

23. A theater charges \$70 per seat for seats in section A, \$65 per seat for seats in section B, and \$44 per seat for seats in section C. 2400 tickets are sold for a total of \$153,000 in revenue. If there are 600 more seats sold in section A than the other two sections combined, how many seats in each section were sold? 1500 seats in section A, 400 seats in section B, and 500 seats in section C were sold.

24. Annie and Maria traveled overseas for seven days and stayed in three different hotels in three different cities: Stockholm, Sweden; Oslo, Norway; and Paris, France.

The total bill for all seven nights (not including tax) was \$1040. The total tax was \$106. The nightly cost (excluding tax) to stay at the hotel in Paris was \$80 more than the nightly cost (excluding tax) to stay in Oslo. Find the cost per night for each hotel excluding tax. Paris hotel \$200/night; Stockholm hotel \$150/night; Oslo hotel \$120/night

City	Number of Nights	Cost/Night (\$)	Tax Rate
Paris, France	1	x	8%
Stockholm, Sweden	4	y	11%
Oslo, Norway	2	z	10%

Group Activity

Creating Linear Models from Data

Materials: Two pieces of rope for each group. The ropes should be of different thicknesses. The piece of thicker rope should be between 4 and 5 ft long. The thinner piece of rope should be 8 to 12 in. shorter than the thicker rope. You will also need a yardstick or other device for making linear measurements.

Estimated Time: 30–35 minutes

Group Size: 4 (2 pairs)

1. Each group of 4 should divide into two pairs, and each pair will be given a piece of rope. Each pair will measure the initial length of rope. Then students will tie a series of knots in the rope and measure the new length after each knot is tied. (*Hint:* Try to tie the knots with an equal amount of force each time. Also, as the ropes are straightened for measurement, try to use the same amount of tension in the rope.) The results should be recorded in the table.

Thick Rope

Number of Knots, x	Length (in.), y
0	
1	
2	
3	
4	

Thin Rope

Number of Knots, x	Length (in.), y
0	
1	
2	
3	
4	

Answers will vary throughout this exercise.

2. Graph each set of data points. Use a different color pen or pencil for each set of points. Does it appear that each set of data follows a linear trend? For each data set, draw a representative line.

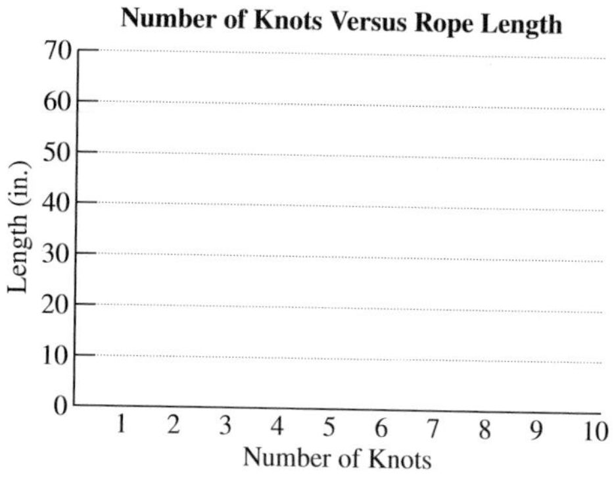

3. Each time a knot is tied, the rope decreases in length. Using the results from question 1, compute the average amount of length lost per knot tied.

For the thick rope, the length decreases by __________ inches per knot tied.

For the thin rope, the length decreases by __________ inches per knot tied.

4. For each set of data points, find an equation of the line through the points. Write the equation in slope-intercept form, $y = mx + b$.

Equation for the thick rope: ______________________________

Equation for the thin rope: ______________________________

What does the slope of each line represent? ______________________________

What does the y-intercept for each line represent? ______________________________

5. Next, you will try to predict the number of knots that you need to tie in each rope so that the ropes will be equal in length. To do this, solve the system of equations in question 4.

Solution to the system of equations: (____, ____)

↑ number of knots, x ↑ length, y

Interpret the meaning of the ordered pair in terms of the number of knots tied and the lengths of the ropes.

6. Check your answer from question 5 by actually tying the required number of knots in each rope. After doing this, are the ropes the same length? What is the length of each rope? Does this match the length predicted from question 5?

Chapter 4 Summary

Section 4.1 Solving Systems of Equations by the Graphing Method

Key Concepts

A **system of two linear equations** can be solved by graphing.

A **solution to a system of linear equations** is an ordered pair that satisfies both equations in the system. Graphically, this represents a point of intersection of the lines.

There may be one solution, infinitely many solutions, or no solution.

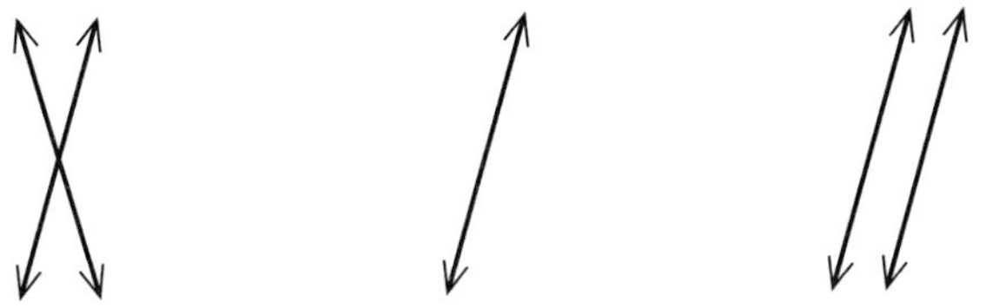

One solution, Consistent, Independent

Infinitely many solutions, Consistent, Dependent

No solution, Inconsistent, Independent

A system of equations is **consistent** if there is at least one solution. A system is **inconsistent** if there is no solution.

If two equations represent the same line, the equations are said to be **dependent equations**. In this case, all points on the line are solutions to the system. If two equations represent two different lines, the equations are said to be **independent equations**. In this case, the lines either intersect at one point or are parallel.

Examples

Example 1

Solve by using the graphing method.

$x + y = 3$

$2x - y = 0$

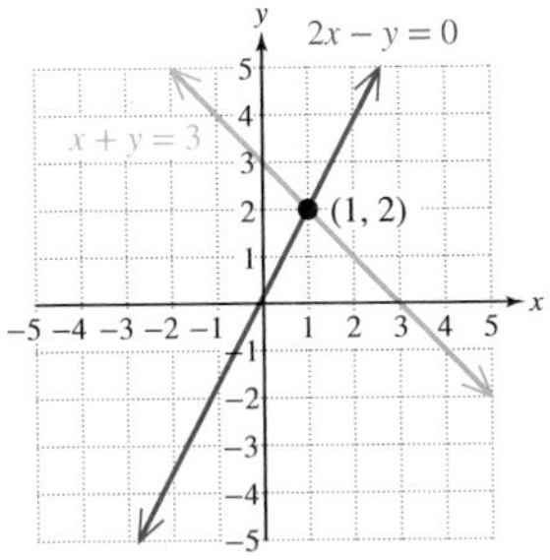

The solution set is $\{(1, 2)\}$.

Example 2

Solve by using the graphing method.

$3x - 2y = 2$

$-6x + 4y = 4$

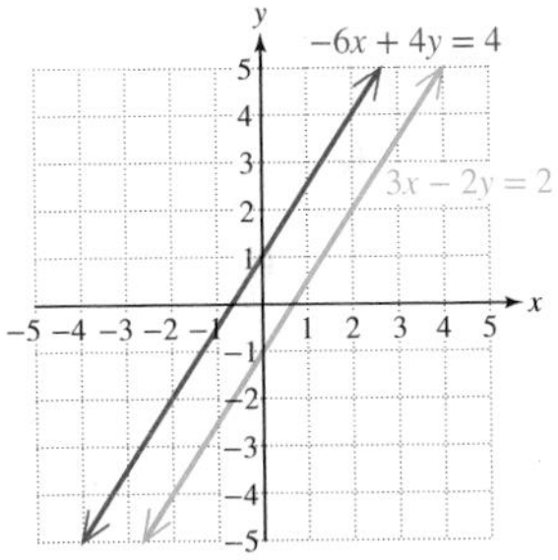

There is no solution, { }. The system is inconsistent.

Example 3

Solve by using the graphing method.

$x + 2y = 2$

$-3x - 6y = -6$

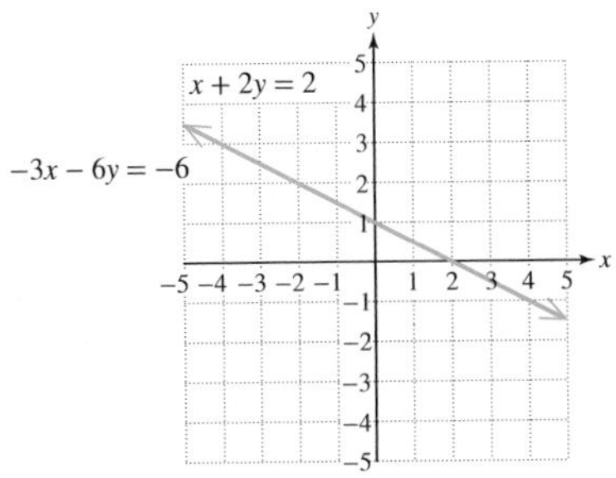

The equations are dependent, and the solution set consists of all points on the line, given by $\{(x, y)\,|\,x + 2y = 2\}$.

Section 4.2 Solving Systems of Equations by the Substitution Method

Key Concepts

Solving a System of Equations by Using the Substitution Method:

1. Isolate one of the variables from one equation.
2. Substitute the expression found in step 1 into the other equation.
3. Solve the resulting equation.
4. Substitute the value found in step 3 back into the equation in step 1 to find the remaining variable.
5. Check the ordered pair in both original equations.

An inconsistent system has no solution and is detected algebraically by a contradiction (such as $0 = 3$).

If two linear equations represent the same line, the equations are dependent. This is detected algebraically by an identity (such as $0 = 0$).

Examples

Example 1

Solve by using the substitution method.

$x + 4y = -11$

$3x - 2y = -5$

Isolate x in the first equation: $x = -4y - 11$
Substitute into the second equation.

$3(-4y - 11) - 2y = -5$ Solve the equation.

$-12y - 33 - 2y = -5$

$-14y = 28$

$y = -2$

$x = -4y - 11$ Substitute $y = -2$.

$x = -4(-2) - 11$ Solve for x.

$x = -3$

The ordered pair $(-3, -2)$ checks in the original equations. The solution set is $\{(-3, -2)\}$.

Example 2

Solve by using the substitution method.

$3x + y = 4$

$-6x - 2y = 2$

Isolate y in the first equation: $y = -3x + 4$
Substitute into the second equation.

$-6x - 2(-3x + 4) = 2$

$-6x + 6x - 8 = 2$

$-8 = 2$ Contradiction

The system is inconsistent and has no solution, { }.

Example 3

Solve by using the substitution method.

$y = x + 2$ y is already isolated.

$x - y = -2$

$x - (x + 2) = -2$ Substitute $y = x + 2$ into the second equation.

$x - x - 2 = -2$

$-2 = -2$ Identity

The equations are dependent. The solution set is all points on the line $y = x + 2$ or $\{(x, y) \mid y = x + 2\}$.

Section 4.3 Solving Systems of Equations by the Addition Method

Key Concepts

Solving a System of Linear Equations by Using the Addition Method:

1. Write both equations in standard form: $Ax + By = C$
2. Clear fractions or decimals (optional).
3. Multiply one or both equations by a nonzero constant to create opposite coefficients for one of the variables.
4. Add the equations to eliminate one variable.
5. Solve for the remaining variable.
6. Substitute the known value into one of the original equations to solve for the other variable.
7. Check the ordered pair in both equations.

Examples

Example 1

Solve by using the addition method.

$$5x = -4y - 7 \qquad \text{Write the first equation in standard form.}$$
$$6x - 3y = 15$$

$$5x + 4y = -7 \xrightarrow{\text{Multiply by 3.}} 15x + 12y = -21$$
$$6x - 3y = 15 \xrightarrow{\text{Multiply by 4.}} 24x - 12y = 60$$
$$39x = 39$$
$$x = 1$$

$$5x = -4y - 7$$
$$5(1) = -4y - 7$$
$$5 = -4y - 7$$
$$12 = -4y$$
$$-3 = y$$

The ordered pair $(1, -3)$ checks in both original equations. The solution set is $\{(1, -3)\}$.

Section 4.4 Applications of Linear Equations in Two Variables

Examples

Example 1

A riverboat travels 36 mi with the current in 2 hr. The return trip takes 3 hr against the current. Find the speed of the current and the speed of the boat in still water.

Let x represent the speed of the boat in still water.
Let y represent the speed of the current.

	Distance	Rate	Time
Against current	36	$x - y$	3
With current	36	$x + y$	2

Distance = (rate)(time)

$$36 = (x - y) \cdot 3 \longrightarrow 36 = 3x - 3y$$
$$36 = (x + y) \cdot 2 \longrightarrow 36 = 2x + 2y$$

$$36 = 3x - 3y \xrightarrow{\text{Multiply by 2.}} 72 = 6x - 6y$$
$$36 = 2x + 2y \xrightarrow{\text{Multiply by 3.}} 108 = 6x + 6y$$
$$180 = 12x$$
$$15 = x$$

$$36 = 2(15) + 2y$$
$$36 = 30 + 2y$$
$$6 = 2y$$
$$3 = y$$

The speed of the boat in still water is 15 mph, and the speed of the current is 3 mph.

Example 2

Diane borrows a total of \$15,000. Part of the money is borrowed from a lender that charges 8% simple interest. She borrows the rest of the money from her mother and will pay back the money at 5% simple interest. If the total interest after 1 year is \$900, how much did she borrow from each source?

	8%	5%	Total
Principal	x	y	15,000
Interest	$0.08x$	$0.05y$	900

$$x + y = 15{,}000$$
$$0.08x + 0.05y = 900$$

Substitute $x = 15{,}000 - y$ into the second equation.

$$0.08(15{,}000 - y) + 0.05y = 900$$
$$1200 - 0.08y + 0.05y = 900$$
$$1200 - 0.03y = 900$$
$$-0.03y = -300$$
$$y = 10{,}000$$

$$x = 15{,}000 - 10{,}000$$
$$= 5{,}000$$

The amount borrowed at 8% is \$5,000.
The amount borrowed from her mother is \$10,000.

Section 4.5 Systems of Linear Equations in Three Variables

Key Concepts

A **linear equation in three variables** can be written in the form $Ax + By + Cz = D$, where A, B, and C are not all zero. The graph of a linear equation in three variables is a plane in space.

A solution to a system of linear equations in three variables is an **ordered triple** that satisfies each equation. Graphically, a solution is a point of intersection among three planes.

A system of linear equations in three variables may have one unique solution, infinitely many solutions (dependent equations), or no solution (inconsistent system).

Examples

Example 1

$\boxed{A}\quad x + 2y - z = 4$

$\boxed{B}\quad 3x - y + z = 5$

$\boxed{C}\quad 2x + 3y + 2z = 7$

$\boxed{A}$ and $\boxed{B}$

$$\begin{aligned} x + 2y - z &= 4 \\ 3x - y + z &= 5 \\ \hline 4x + y \quad &= 9 \quad \boxed{D} \end{aligned}$$

$2 \cdot \boxed{A}$ and $\boxed{C}$

$$\begin{aligned} 2x + 4y - 2z &= 8 \\ 2x + 3y + 2z &= 7 \\ \hline 4x + 7y \quad &= 15 \quad \boxed{E} \end{aligned}$$

$\boxed{D}\quad 4x + y = 9 \xrightarrow{\text{Multiply by } -1.} -4x - y = -9$

$\boxed{E}\quad 4x + 7y = 15 \longrightarrow 4x + 7y = 15$

$$\begin{aligned} 6y &= 6 \\ y &= 1 \end{aligned}$$

Substitute $y = 1$ into either equation $\boxed{D}$ or $\boxed{E}$.

$\boxed{D}\quad 4x + (1) = 9$

$$\begin{aligned} 4x &= 8 \\ x &= 2 \end{aligned}$$

Substitute $x = 2$ and $y = 1$ into equation $\boxed{A}$, $\boxed{B}$, or $\boxed{C}$.

$\boxed{A}\quad (2) + 2(1) - z = 4$

$$\begin{aligned} -z &= 0 \\ z &= 0 \end{aligned}$$

The solution set is $\{(2, 1, 0)\}$.

Section 4.6 Applications of Systems of Linear Equations in Three Variables

Key Concepts

In application problems where there are three unknowns, it is often useful to set up a system of linear equations in three variables.

With three variables, three independent relationships among x, y, and z are required.

Example

Example 1

In a triangle, the middle angle measures 55° more than the smallest angle. The largest angle measures 10° more than the sum of the other two angles. Find the measures of the angles.

Let x = measure of the smallest angle

Let y = measure of the middle angle

Let z = measure of the largest angle

First recall that the sum of the angles in a triangle is 180°.

standard form

$$x + y + z = 180 \longrightarrow x + y + z = 180 \quad \boxed{A}$$
$$y = x + 55 \longrightarrow -x + y = 55 \quad \boxed{B}$$
$$z = x + y + 10 \longrightarrow -x - y + z = 10 \quad \boxed{C}$$

$$\boxed{A} \quad x + y + z = 180$$
$$\boxed{B} \quad -x + y = 55$$
$$2y + z = 235 \quad \boxed{D}$$

$$\boxed{A} \quad x + y + z = 180$$
$$\boxed{C} \quad -x - y + z = 10$$
$$2z = 190 \quad \boxed{E}$$
$$z = 95$$

From $\boxed{D}$: $2y + z = 235$
$$2y + 95 = 235$$
$$y = 70$$

From $\boxed{B}$: $-x + y = 55$
$$-x + 70 = 55$$
$$x = 15$$

Solving the system yields $x = 15$, $y = 70$, and $z = 95$.

The measures of the three angles are and 15°, 70°, and 95°.

Chapter 4 Review Exercises

Section 4.1

For Exercises 1–4, determine if the ordered pair is a solution to the system.

1. $x - 4y = -4$ $(4, 2)$
$x + 2y = 8$ Yes

2. $x - 6y = 6$ $(12, 1)$
$-x + y = 4$ No

3. $3x + y = 9$ $(1, 3)$
$y = 3$ No

4. $2x - y = 8$ $(2, -4)$
$x = 2$ Yes

For Exercises 5–10, identify whether the system represents intersecting lines, parallel lines, or coinciding lines by comparing slopes and *y*-intercepts.

5. $y = -\frac{1}{2}x + 4$
$y = x - 1$
Intersecting lines (The lines have different slopes.)

6. $y = -3x + 4$
$y = 3x + 4$
Intersecting lines (The lines have different slopes.)

7. $y = -\frac{4}{7}x + 3$
$y = -\frac{4}{7}x - 5$
Parallel lines (The lines have the same slope but different *y*-intercepts.)

8. $y = 5x - 3$
$y = \frac{1}{5}x - 3$
Intersecting lines (The lines have different slopes.)

9. $y = 9x - 2$
$9x - y = 2$
Coinciding lines (The lines have the same slope and same *y*-intercept.)

10. $x = -5$
$y = 2$
Intersecting lines (The lines have different slopes.)

For Exercises 11–18, solve the system by graphing. For systems that do not have one unique solution, also state the number of solutions and whether the system is inconsistent or the equations are dependent.

11. $y = -\frac{2}{3}x - 2$
$-x + 3y = -6$
$\{(0, -2)\}$

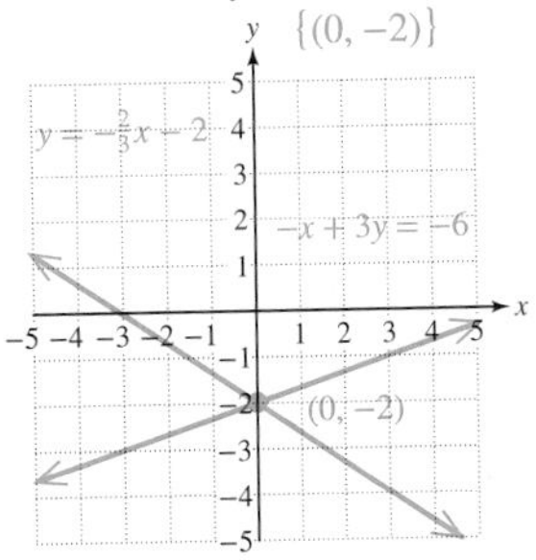

12. $y = -2x - 1$ $\{(-2, 3)\}$
$x + 2y = 4$

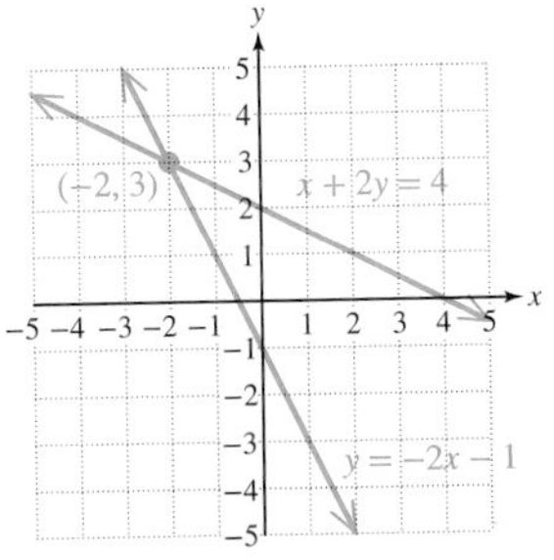

13. $4x = -2y + 10$
$2x + y = 5$

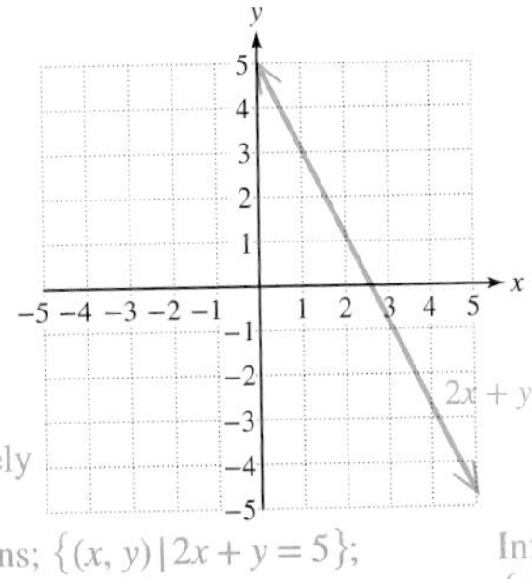

Infinitely many solutions; $\{(x, y) \mid 2x + y = 5\}$; dependent equations

14. $10y = 2x - 10$
$-x + 5y = -5$

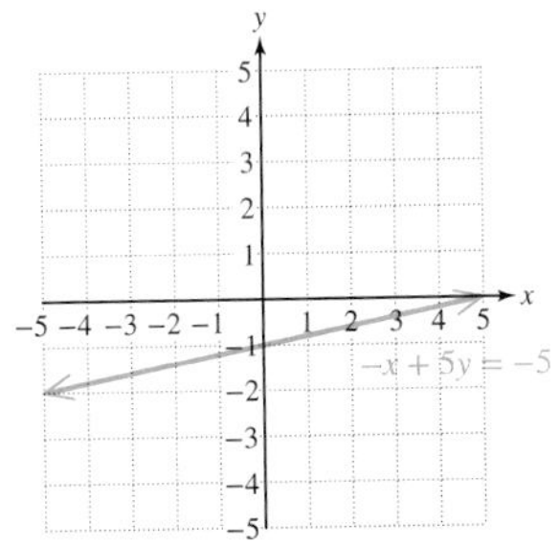

Infinitely many solutions; $\{(x, y) \mid -x + 5y = -5\}$; dependent equations

15. $6x - 3y = 9$
$y = -1$ $\{(1, -1)\}$

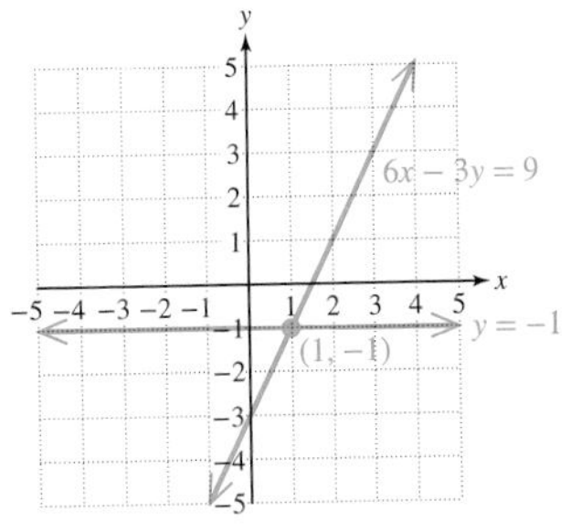

16. $5x + y = -3$
$x = -1$ $\{(-1, 2)\}$

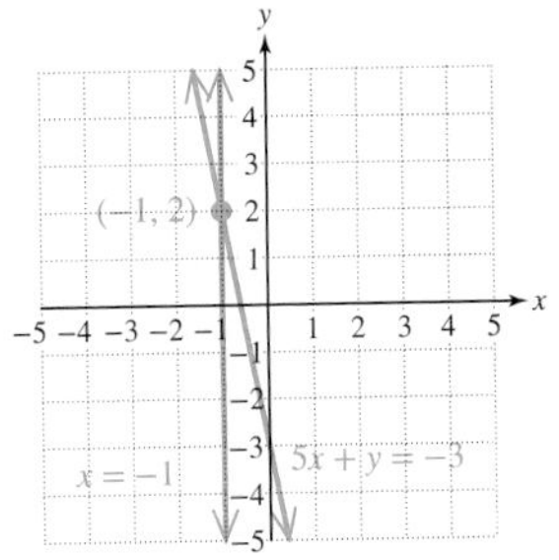

17. $x - 7y = 14$
$-2x + 14y = 14$

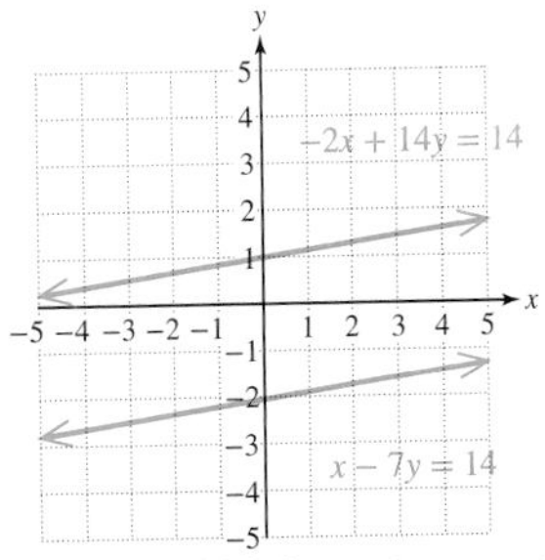

No solution; { }; inconsistent system

18. $y = -5x + 4$
$10x + 2y = -4$

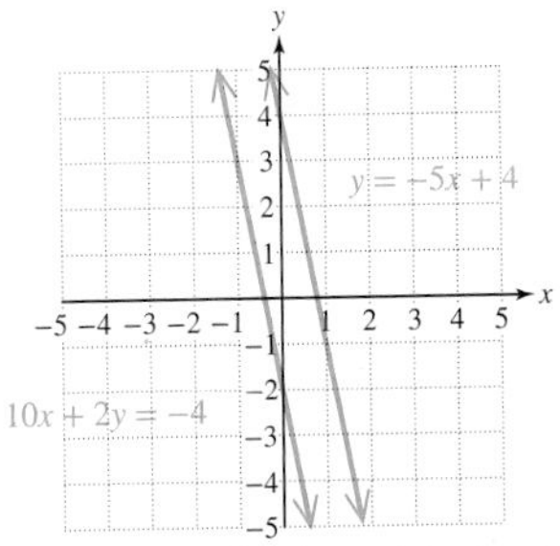

No solution; { }; inconsistent system

Section 4.2

19. One phone company charges \$0.15 a minute for calls but adds a \$3.90 charge each month. Another company does not have a monthly fee but charges \$0.25 per minute. The cost per month, y_1 (in \$) for the first company is given by the equation:

$y_1 = 0.15x + 3.90$ where *x* represents the number of minutes used.

The cost per month, y_2, (in \$) for the second company is given by the equation:

$y_2 = 0.25x$ where *x* represents the number of minutes used. Using 39 minutes per month, the cost per month for each company is \$9.75.

Find the number of minutes at which the cost per month for each company is the same.

For Exercises 20–23, solve each system using the substitution method.

20. $6x + y = 2$ $\left\{\left(\frac{2}{3}, -2\right)\right\}$
$y = 3x - 4$

21. $2x + 3y = -5$ $\{(-4, 1)\}$
$x = y - 5$

22. $2x + 6y = 10$ $\{\ \}$
$x = -3y + 6$

23. $4x + 2y = 4$ Infinitely many solutions; $\{(x, y) \mid y = -2x + 2\}$
$y = -2x + 2$

24. Given the system: $x + 2y = 11$
$5x + 4y = 40$

a. Which variable from which equation is easiest to isolate and why? x in the first equation is easiest to isolate because its coefficient is 1.

b. Solve the system using the substitution method. $\left\{\left(6, \frac{5}{2}\right)\right\}$

25. Given the system: $4x - 3y = 9$
$2x + y = 12$

a. Which variable from which equation is easiest to isolate and why? y in the second equation is easiest to isolate because its coefficient is 1.

b. Solve the system using the substitution method. $\left\{\left(\frac{9}{2}, 3\right)\right\}$

For Exercises 26–29, solve each system using the substitution method.

26. $3x - 2y = 23$ $\{(5, -4)\}$
$x + 5y = -15$

27. $x + 5y = 20$ $\{(0, 4)\}$
$3x + 2y = 8$

28. $x - 3y = 9$ Infinitely many solutions; $\{(x, y) \mid x - 3y = 9\}$
$5x - 15y = 45$

29. $-3x + y = 15$ $\{\ \}$
$6x - 2y = 12$

30. The difference of two positive numbers is 42. The larger number is 2 more than 6 times the smaller number. Find the numbers. The numbers are 50 and 8.

31. In a right triangle, one of the acute angles is 8° less than the other acute angle. Find the measure of each acute angle. The angles are 41° and 49°.

32. Two angles are supplementary. One angle measures 14° less than two times the other angle. Find the measure of each angle. The angles are $115\frac{1}{3}°$ and $64\frac{2}{3}°$.

Section 4.3

33. Given the system. $-2x + 7y = 30$
$4x + 5y = 16$

a. Which variable, x or y, is easier to eliminate using the addition method? (Answers may vary.)

b. Solve the system using the addition method. $\{(-1, 4)\}$

34. Given the system: $3x - 5y = 1$
$2x - y = -4$

a. Which variable, x or y, is easier to eliminate using the addition method? (Answers may vary.)

b. Solve the system using the addition method. $\{(-3, -2)\}$

35. Given the system: $9x - 2y = 14$
$4x + 3y = 14$

a. Which variable, x or y, is easier to eliminate using the addition method? (Answers may vary.)

b. Solve the system using the addition method. $\{(2, 2)\}$

For Exercises 36–43, solve each system using the addition method.

36. $2x + 3y = 1$ $\{(2, -1)\}$
$x - 2y = 4$

37. $x + 3y = 0$ $\{(-6, 2)\}$
$-3x - 10y = -2$

38. $8x + 8 = -6y + 6$
$10x = 9y - 8$ $\left\{\left(-\frac{1}{2}, \frac{1}{3}\right)\right\}$

39. $12x = 5y + 5$
$5y = -1 - 4x$ $\left\{\left(\frac{1}{4}, -\frac{2}{5}\right)\right\}$

40. $-4x - 6y = -2$ Infinitely many solutions; $\{(x, y) \mid -4x - 6y = -2\}$
$6x + 9y = 3$

41. $-8x - 4y = 16$ $\{\ \}$
$10x + 5y = 5$

42. $\frac{1}{2}x - \frac{3}{4}y = -\frac{1}{2}$
$\frac{1}{3}x + y = -\frac{10}{3}$
$\{(-4, -2)\}$

43. $0.5x - 0.2y = 0.5$
$0.4x + 0.7y = 0.4$
$\{(1, 0)\}$

44. Given the system: $4x + 9y = -7$
$y = 2x - 13$

a. Which method would you choose to solve the system, the substitution method or the addition method? Explain your choice. Use the substitution method because y is already isolated in the second equation.

b. Solve the system $\{(5, -3)\}$

45. Given the system: $5x - 8y = -2$
$3x - 7y = 1$

a. Which method would you choose to solve the system, the substitution method or the addition method? Explain your choice. Use the addition method. The substitution method would be cumbersome because isolating either variable from either equation would result in fractional coefficients.

b. Solve the system $\{(-2, -1)\}$

Section 4.4

46. Zoo Miami charges \$19.95 for adult admission and \$15.95 for children under 13. The total bill before tax for a school group of 60 people is \$989. How many adults and how many children were admitted? There were 8 adult tickets and 52 children's tickets sold.

47. As part of his retirement strategy Winston plans to invest \$600,000 in two different funds. He projects that the high-risk investments should return, over time, about 12% per year, while the low-risk investments should return about 4% per year. If he wants a supplemental income of \$30,000 a year, how should he divide his investments? He should invest \$75,000 at 12% and \$525,000 at 4%.

48. Suppose that whole milk with 4% fat is mixed with 1% low fat milk to make a 2% reduced fat milk. How much of the whole milk should be mixed with the low fat milk to make 60 gal of 2% reduced fat milk? 20 gal of whole milk should be mixed with 40 gal of low fat milk.

49. A boat travels 80 mi downstream with the current in 4 hr and 80 mi upstream against the current in 5 hr. Find the speed of the current and the speed of the boat in still water. The speed of the boat is 18 mph, and that of the current is 2 mph.

50. A plane travels 870 mi against the wind in 3 hr. Traveling with the wind, the plane travels 700 mi in 2 hr. Find the speed of the plane in still air and the speed of the wind. The plane's speed in still air is 320 mph. The wind speed is 30 mph.

51. At a sports arena, the total cost of a soft drink and a hot dog is \$8.00. The price of the hot dog is \$1.00 more than the cost of the soft drink. Find the cost of a soft drink and the cost of a hot dog. A hot dog costs \$4.50 and a drink costs \$3.50.

52. Ray played two rounds of golf at Pebble Beach for a total score of 154. If his score in the second round is 10 more than his score in the first round, find the scores for each round. The score was 72 on the first round and 82 on the second round.

© Royalty Free/Corbis RF

Section 4.5

For Exercises 53–58, solve the systems of equations. If a system does not have a unique solution, state whether the system is inconsistent or the equations are dependent.

53. $$\begin{aligned} 5x + 5y + 5z &= 30 \\ -x + y + z &= 2 \\ 10x + 6y - 2z &= 4 \end{aligned}$$
$\{(2, -1, 5)\}$

54. $$\begin{aligned} 5x + 3y - z &= 5 \\ x + 2y + z &= 6 \\ -x - 2y - z &= 8 \end{aligned}$$
Inconsistent system

55. $$\begin{aligned} x + y + z &= 4 \\ -x - 2y - 3z &= -6 \\ 2x + 4y + 6z &= 12 \end{aligned}$$
Dependent equations

56. $$\begin{aligned} 3x \qquad\quad + 4z &= 5 \\ 2y + 3z &= 2 \\ 2x - 5y \qquad &= 8 \end{aligned}$$
$\{(-1, -2, 2)\}$

57. $$\begin{aligned} 3(x - y) &= -1 - 5z - y \\ 3y + 6 &= 2z + x \\ 5x + 1 &= 3(z - y) - y \end{aligned}$$
$\{(1, -3, -2)\}$

58. $$\begin{aligned} 2a &= -3c - 2 \\ 2b - 8 &= 5c \\ 7a + 3b &= 5 \end{aligned}$$
$\{(-1, 4, 0)\}$

Section 4.6

59. The perimeter of a right triangle is 30 ft. One leg is 2 ft longer than twice the shortest leg. The hypotenuse is 2 ft less than 3 times the shortest leg. Find the lengths of the sides of this triangle. 5 ft, 12 ft, and 13 ft

60. Three pumps are working to drain a construction site. Working together, the pumps can drain 950 gal/hr of water. The slowest pump drains 150 gal/hr less than the fastest pump. The fastest pump drains 150 gal/hr less than the sum of the other two pumps. How many gallons can each pump drain per hour? The pumps can drain 250, 300, and 400 gal/hr.

61. Theresa had \$12,000 to invest among three mutual funds. Fund A had a 5% yield for the year. Fund B had a 3.5% yield, and Fund C lost 2% for the year. She invested three times as much in Fund A as in Fund C. If she gained \$400 in 1 year, how much was invested in each fund? She invested \$6000 in Fund A, \$4000 in Fund B, and \$2000 in Fund C.

62. In a triangle, the largest angle measures 76° more than the sum of the other two angles. The middle angle measures 3 times the smallest angle. Find the measure of each angle. The angles are 13°, 39°, and 128°.

Chapter 4 Test

1. Write each line in slope-intercept form. Then determine if the lines represent intersecting lines, parallel lines, or coinciding lines.

$$5x + 2y = -6 \quad y = -\frac{5}{2}x - 3$$

$$-\frac{5}{2}x - \quad y = -3 \quad y = -\frac{5}{2}x + 3$$

Parallel lines

For Exercises 2–3, solve each system by graphing.

2. $y = 2x - 4$

$-2x + 3y = 0$

$\{(3, 2)\}$

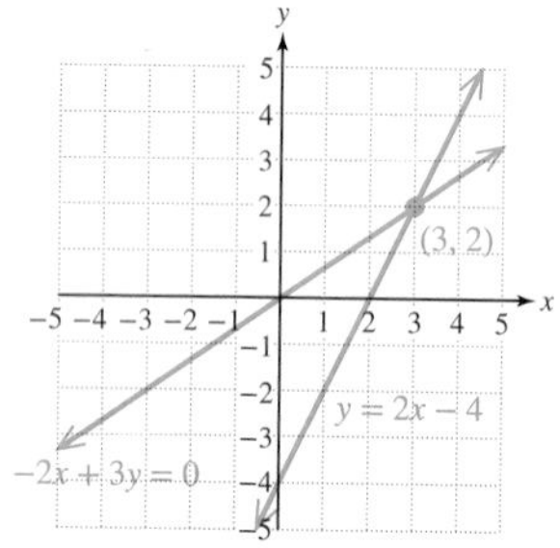

3. $2x + 4y = 12$

$2y - 6 = -x$

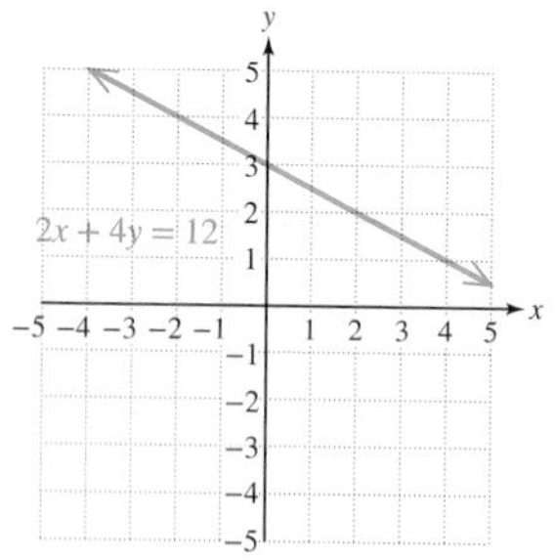

Infinitely many solutions; $\{(x, y) \mid 2x + 4y = 12\}$

4. Solve the system using the substitution method.

$x = 5y - 2$

$2x + y = -4 \quad \{(-2, 0)\}$

5. In an early WNBA (basketball) season, the league's leading scorer was Sheryl Swoopes from the Houston Comets. Swoopes scored 17 points more than the second leading scorer, Lauren Jackson from the Seattle Storm. Together they scored a total of 1211 points. How many points did each player score? Swoopes scored 614 points and Jackson scored 597.

6. Solve the system using the addition method.

$3x - 6y = 8 \quad \left\{\left(2, -\frac{1}{3}\right)\right\}$

$2x + 3y = 3$

7. How many milliliters of a 50% acid solution and how many milliliters of a 20% acid solution must be mixed to produce 36 mL of a 30% acid solution? 12 mL of the 50% acid solution should be mixed with 24 mL of the 20% solution.

8. a. How many solutions does a system of two linear equations have if the equations represent parallel lines? No solution

b. How many solutions does a system of two linear equations have if the equations represent coinciding lines? Infinitely many solutions

c. How many solutions does a system of two linear equations have if the equations represent intersecting lines? One solution

For Exercises 9–14, solve each system using any method.

9. $\frac{1}{3}x + y = \frac{7}{3}$

$x = \frac{3}{2}y - 11$

$\{(-5, 4)\}$

10. $2x - 12 = y$

$2x - \frac{1}{2}y = x + 5$

$\{\ \}$

11. $3x - 4y = 29 \quad \{(3, -5)\}$

$2x + 5y = -19$

12. $2x = 6y - 14 \quad \{(-1, 2)\}$

$2y = 3 - x$

13. $-0.25x - 0.05y = 0.2$

$10x + \quad 2y = -8$

Infinitely many solutions; $\{(x, y) \mid 10x + 2y = -8\}$

14. $3x + 3y = -2y - 7 \quad \{(1, -2)\}$

$-3y = 10 - 4x$

15. Latrell buys four CDs and two DVDs for \$54 from the sale rack. Kendra buys two CDs and three DVDs from the same rack for \$49. What is the price per CD and the price per DVD? CDs cost \$8 each and DVDs cost \$11 each.

16. The cost to ride a certain trolley one way is \$2.25. Kelly and Hazel had to buy eight tickets for their group.

a. What was the total amount of money required? \$18 was required.

b. Kelly and Hazel had only quarters and \$1 bills. They also determined that they used twice as many quarters as \$1 bills. How many quarters and how many \$1 bills did they use? They used 24 quarters and 12 \$1 bills.

17. Suppose a total of \$5000 is borrowed from two different loans. One loan charges 10% simple interest, and the other charges 8% simple interest. How much was borrowed at each rate if \$424 in interest is charged at the end of 1 year? \$1200 was borrowed at 10%, and \$3800 was borrowed at 8%.

18. Mark needs to move to a new apartment and is trying to find the most affordable moving truck. He will only need the truck for one day. After checking the AAA Movers website, he finds that he can rent a 10-ft truck for \$20.95 a day plus \$1.89 per mile. He then checks the website of a local moving company and finds the charge to be \$37.95 a day plus \$1.19 per mile for the same size truck. Determine the number of miles for which the cost to rent from either company would be the same. Round the answer to the nearest mile. They would be the same cost for a distance of approximately 24 mi.

19. A plane travels 910 mi in 2 hr against the wind and 1090 mi in 2 hr with the same wind. Find the speed of the plane in still air and the speed of the wind. The plane travels 500 mph in still air, and the wind speed is 45 mph.

20. The number of calories in a piece of cake is 20 less than 3 times the number of calories in a scoop of ice cream. Together, the cake and ice cream have 460 calories. How many calories are in each? The cake has 340 calories, and the ice cream has 120 calories.

© McGraw-Hill Education/Jill Braaten

21. How much 10% acid solution should be mixed with a 25% acid solution to create 100 mL of a 16% acid solution? 60 mL of 10% solution and 40 mL of 25% solution

For Exercises 22–24, solve the system of equations.

22. $2x + 2y + 4z = -6$
$3x + y + 2z = 29$
$x - y - z = 44$ $\{(16, -37, 9)\}$

23. $2(x + z) = 6 + x - 3y$
$2x = 11 + y - z$
$x + 2(y + z) = 8$ $\{(2, -2, 5)\}$

24. $3x - 4y = 6 - 2z$
$x - 3y + 2z = 9$
$2x = y - 1$ $\{\ \}$

25. The perimeter of a triangle is 43 ft. The shortest side is one-third the length of the middle side. The longest side is 3 feet more than four times the shortest side.Find the lengths of the three sides. The sides are 5 ft, 15 ft, and 23 ft.

26. Bennet invested a total of \$11,500 among three mutual funds. At the end of one year, Fund A had a 6% yield, Fund B had an 8% yield, and Fund C lost 5%. Twice as much money was invested in Fund B as in Fund C. At the end of one year, the total gain was \$550. How much was invested in each fund? \$5500 was invested in Fund A. \$4000 was invested in Fund B, and \$2000 was invested in Fund C.

27. Working together, Joanne, Kent, and Geoff can process 504 orders per day for their business. Kent can process 20 more orders per day than Joanne can process. Geoff can process 104 fewer orders per day than Kent and Joanne combined. Find the number of orders that each person can process per day. Joanne can process 142 orders, Kent can process 162 orders, and Geoff can process 200 orders.

Chapters 1–4 Cumulative Review Exercises

1. Simplify.

$$\frac{|2 - 5| + 10 \div 2 + 3}{\sqrt{10^2 - 8^2}} \quad \frac{11}{6}$$

2. Solve for x. $\frac{1}{3}x - \frac{3}{4} = \frac{1}{2}(x + 2)$ $\left\{-\frac{21}{2}\right\}$

3. Solve for a. $-4(a + 3) + 2 = -5(a + 1) + a$ $\{\ \}$

4. Solve for y. $3x - 2y = 6$ $y = \frac{3}{2}x - 3$

5. Solve for x. $z = \frac{x - m}{5}$ $x = 5z + m$

6. Solve for z. Graph the solution set on a number line and write the solution in interval notation.

$$-2(3z + 1) \le 5(z - 3) + 10$$

$\left[\frac{3}{11}, \infty\right)$

7. The largest angle in a triangle is 110°. Of the remaining two angles, one is 4° less than the other angle. Find the measure of the three angles. The angles are 37°, 33°, and 110°.

8. Two hikers start at opposite ends of an 18-mi trail and walk toward each other. One hiker walks predominately down hill and averages 2 mph faster than the other hiker. Find the average rate of each hiker if they meet in 3 hr.

The rates of the hikers are 2 mph and 4 mph.

9. Jesse Ventura became the 38th governor of Minnesota by receiving 37% of the votes. If approximately 2,060,000 votes were cast, how many did Mr. Ventura get?

Jesse Ventura received approximately 762,200 votes.

10. The YMCA wants to raise \$2500 for its summer program for disadvantaged children. If the YMCA has already raised \$900, what percent of its goal has been achieved?

36% of the goal has been achieved.

11. Two angles are complementary. One angle measures 17° more than the other angle. Find the measure of each angle. The angles are 36.5° and 53.5°.

12. Find the slope and y-intercept of the line $5x + 3y = -6$. Slope: $-\frac{5}{3}$; y-intercept: $(0, -2)$

13. The slope of a given line is $-\frac{2}{3}$.

a. What is the slope of a line parallel to the given line? $-\frac{2}{3}$

b. What is the slope of a line perpendicular to the given line? $\frac{3}{2}$

14. Find an equation of the line passing through the point $(2, -3)$ and having a slope of -3. Write the final answer in slope-intercept form. $y = -3x + 3$

15. Sketch the following equations on the same graph.

a. $2x + 5y = 10$

b. $2y = 4$

c. Find the point of intersection and check the solution in each equation.

$\{(0, 2)\}$

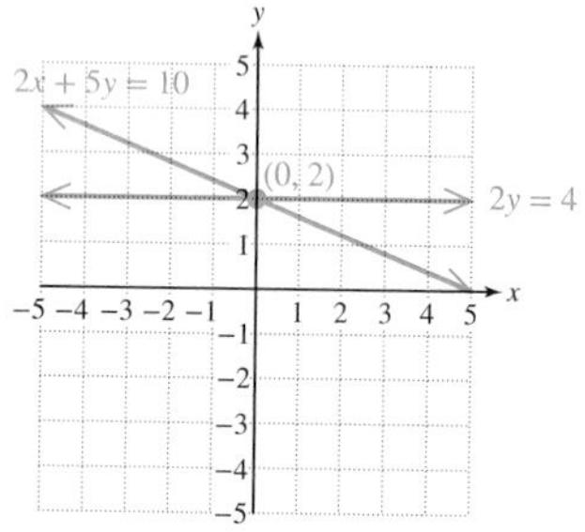

16. Solve the system of equations by using the substitution method.

$$2x + 5y = 10$$
$$2y = 4$$

$\{(0, 2)\}$

17. How many gallons of a 15% antifreeze solution should be mixed with a 60% antifreeze solution to produce 60 gal of a 45% antifreeze solution? 20 gal of the 15% solution should be mixed with 40 gal of the 60% solution.

18. Use a system of linear equations to solve for x and y. x is 27°; y is 63°

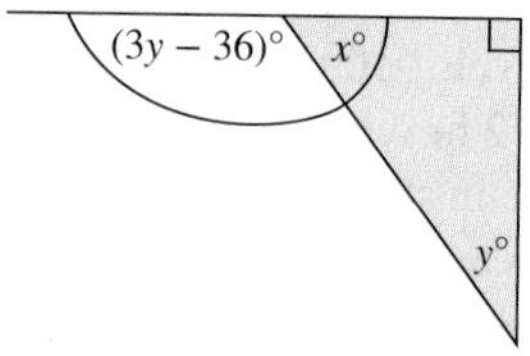

19. In 1920, the average speed for the winner of the Indianapolis 500 car race was 88.6 mph. In 1990, a track record was reached with the speed of 186.0 mph.

a. Find the slope of the line shown in the figure. Round to one decimal place. 1.4

b. Interpret the meaning of the slope in the context of this problem. Between 1920 and 1990, the winning speed in the Indianapolis 500 increased on average by 1.4 mph per year.

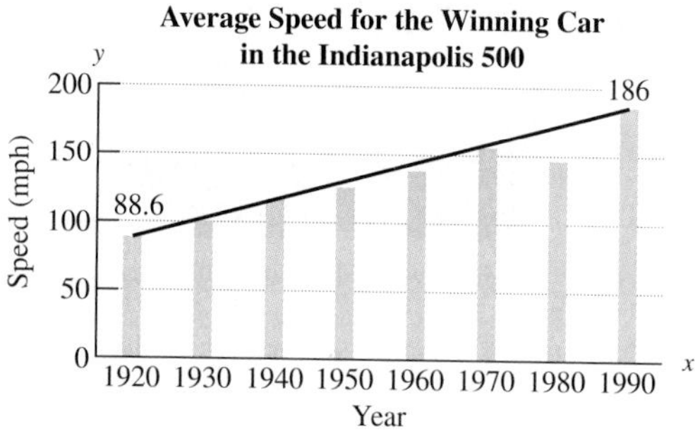

20. Solve the system.

$$x + 3y + z = 5$$
$$2x + 4y - z = -2$$
$$6x + 2y + 5z = 26$$

$\{(1, 0, 4)\}$

Polynomials and Properties of Exponents

5

CHAPTER OUTLINE

Mathematics to Compute Cost

Trevor is a dance instructor and wants to host a one-day dance event. He has a fixed cost of \$200 to rent the dance studio. In addition, to host the event, he has the following variable costs, which depend on the number of participants.

- \$1.00 per person for coffee and breakfast snacks
- \$7.00 per person for lunch
- \$1.20 per person for a step-sheet booklet

If n represents the number of participants, then Trevor's cost for the event is given by

$$\text{Cost} = 1.00n + 7.00n + 1.20n + 200$$

This expression is called a **polynomial**. Terms of a polynomial are separated by addition, and sometimes a polynomial can be simplified by adding ***like* terms**. In this case, the terms containing the variable n are *like* terms. Thus, the polynomial representing cost can be simplified as

$$\begin{aligned}\text{Cost} &= (1.00 + 7.00 + 1.20)n + 200\\ &= 9.20n + 200\end{aligned}$$

The terms $1.00n$, $7.00n$, and $1.20n$ are combined to form $9.20n$ because we're effectively consolidating the costs for breakfast, lunch, and the booklet into one overall cost per person.

As you study polynomials in this chapter, you will encounter other applications including those involving profit and cost.

© McGraw-Hill Education/John Flournoy

Section 5.1 Multiplying and Dividing Expressions with Common Bases

Concepts

1. Review of Exponential Notation
2. Evaluating Expressions with Exponents
3. Multiplying and Dividing Expressions with Common Bases
4. Simplifying Expressions with Exponents
5. Applications of Exponents

1. Review of Exponential Notation

Recall that an **exponent** is used to show repeated multiplication of the **base**.

Definition of b^n

Let b represent any real number and n represent a positive integer. Then,

$$b^n = \underbrace{b \cdot b \cdot b \cdot b \cdot \ldots b}_{n \text{ factors of } b}$$

Classroom Example: p. 349, Exercise 2

Example 1 Evaluating Expressions with Exponents

For each expression, identify the exponent and base. Then evaluate the expression.

a. 6^2 **b.** $\left(-\frac{1}{2}\right)^3$ **c.** 0.8^4

Solution:

Expression	Base	Exponent	Result
a. 6^2	6	2	$(6)(6) = 36$
b. $\left(-\frac{1}{2}\right)^3$	$-\frac{1}{2}$	3	$\left(-\frac{1}{2}\right)\left(-\frac{1}{2}\right)\left(-\frac{1}{2}\right) = -\frac{1}{8}$
c. 0.8^4	0.8	4	$(0.8)(0.8)(0.8)(0.8) = 0.4096$

Skill Practice For each expression, identify the base and exponent.

1. 8^3 **2.** $\left(-\frac{1}{4}\right)^2$ **3.** 0.2^4

Note that if no exponent is explicitly written for an expression, then the expression has an implied exponent of 1. For example, $x = x^1$.

Consider an expression such as $3y^6$. The factor 3 has an exponent of 1, and the factor y has an exponent of 6. That is, the expression $3y^6$ is interpreted as 3^1y^6.

2. Evaluating Expressions with Exponents

Particular care must be taken when evaluating exponential expressions involving negative numbers. An exponential expression with a negative base is written with parentheses around the base, such as $(-3)^2$.

To evaluate $(-3)^2$, we have: $(-3)^2 = (-3)(-3) = 9$

If no parentheses are present, the expression -3^2 is the *opposite* of 3^2, or equivalently, $-1 \cdot 3^2$.

$$-3^2 = -1(3^2) = -1(3)(3) = -9$$

Answers

1. Base 8; exponent 3
2. Base $-\frac{1}{4}$; exponent 2
3. Base 0.2; exponent 4

Example 2 Evaluating Expressions with Exponents

Classroom Examples: p. 349, Exercises 28 and 30

Evaluate each expression.

a. -5^4 **b.** $(-5)^4$ **c.** $(-0.2)^3$ **d.** -0.2^3

Solution:

a. -5^4

$= -1 \cdot 5^4$ — 5 is the base with exponent 4.

$= -1 \cdot 5 \cdot 5 \cdot 5 \cdot 5$ — Multiply −1 by four factors of 5.

$= -625$

b. $(-5)^4$

$= (-5)(-5)(-5)(-5)$ — Parentheses indicate that −5 is the base with exponent 4.

$= 625$ — Multiply four factors of −5.

c. $(-0.2)^3$ — Parentheses indicate that −0.2 is the base with exponent 3.

$= (-0.2)(-0.2)(-0.2)$ — Multiply three factors of −0.2.

$= -0.008$

d. -0.2^3

$= -1 \cdot 0.2^3$ — 0.2 is the base with exponent 3.

$= -1(0.2)(0.2)(0.2)$ — Multiply −1 by three factors of 0.2.

$= -0.008$

Skill Practice Evaluate each expression.

4. -2^4 **5.** $(-2)^4$ **6.** $(-0.1)^3$ **7.** -0.1^3

Example 3 Evaluating Expressions with Exponents

Classroom Examples: p. 350, Exercises 52 and 56

Evaluate each expression for $a = 2$ and $b = -3$.

a. $5a^2$ **b.** $(5a)^2$ **c.** $5ab^2$ **d.** $(b + a)^2$

Solution:

a. $5a^2$

$= 5(\ )^2$ — Use parentheses to substitute a number for a variable.

$= 5(2)^2$ — Substitute $a = 2$.

$= 5(4)$ — Simplify exponents before multiplying.

$= 20$

b. $(5a)^2$

$= [5(\ )]^2$ — Use parentheses to substitute a number for a variable. The original parentheses are replaced with brackets.

$= [5(2)]^2$ — Substitute $a = 2$.

$= (10)^2$ — Simplify inside the parentheses first.

$= 100$

Answers

4. −16 **5.** 16
6. −0.001 **7.** −0.001

Avoiding Mistakes

In the expression $5ab^2$, the exponent, 2, applies only to the variable *b*. The constant 5 and the variable *a* both have an implied exponent of 1.

c. $5ab^2$

$= 5(2)(-3)^2$	Substitute $a = 2$, $b = -3$.
$= 5(2)(9)$	Simplify exponents before multiplying.
$= 90$	Multiply.

Avoiding Mistakes

Be sure to follow the order of operations. In Example 3(d), it would be incorrect to square the terms within the parentheses before adding.

d. $(b + a)^2$

$= [(-3) + (2)]^2$	Substitute $b = -3$ and $a = 2$.
$= (-1)^2$	Simplify within the parentheses first.
$= 1$	

Skill Practice Evaluate each expression for $x = 2$ and $y = -5$.

8. $6x^2$ **9.** $(6x)^2$ **10.** $2xy^2$ **11.** $(y - x)^2$

3. Multiplying and Dividing Expressions with Common Bases

In this section, we investigate the effect of multiplying or dividing two quantities with the same base. For example, consider the expressions: x^5x^2 and $\frac{x^5}{x^2}$. Simplifying each expression, we have:

$$x^5x^2 = (x \cdot x \cdot x \cdot x \cdot x)(x \cdot x) = \overbrace{x \cdot x \cdot x \cdot x \cdot x \cdot x \cdot x}^{\text{7 factors of } x} = x^7$$

$$\frac{x^5}{x^2} = \frac{x \cdot x \cdot x \cdot \cancel{x} \cdot \cancel{x}}{\cancel{x} \cdot \cancel{x}} = \frac{x \cdot x \cdot x}{1} = x^3$$

These examples suggest that to multiply two quantities with the same base, we add the exponents. To divide two quantities with the same base, we subtract the exponent in the denominator from the exponent in the numerator. These rules are stated formally in the following two properties.

Multiplication of Expressions with Like Bases

Assume that *b* is a real number and that *m* and *n* represent positive integers. Then,

$$b^mb^n = b^{m+n}$$

Division of Expressions with Like Bases

Assume that $b \neq 0$ is a real number and that *m* and *n* represent positive integers. Then,

$$\frac{b^m}{b^n} = b^{m-n}$$

Answers

8. 24 **9.** 144 **10.** 100
11. 49

Example 4 **Simplifying Expressions with Exponents**

Classroom Examples: p. 350, Exercises 68 and 70

Simplify the expressions. **a.** w^3w^4 **b.** $2^3 \cdot 2^4$

Solution:

a. w^3w^4 $(w \cdot w \cdot w)(w \cdot w \cdot w \cdot w)$

$= w^{3+4}$ To multiply expressions with like bases, add the exponents.

$= w^7$

b. $2^3 \cdot 2^4$ $(2 \cdot 2 \cdot 2)(2 \cdot 2 \cdot 2 \cdot 2)$

$= 2^{3+4}$ To multiply expressions with like bases, add the exponents (the base is unchanged).

$= 2^7$ or 128

Avoiding Mistakes

When we multiply expressions with like bases, we add the exponents. The base does not change. In Example 4(b), notice that the base 2 does not change. $2^3 \cdot 2^4 = 2^7$.

Skill Practice Simplify the expressions.

12. q^4q^8 **13.** $8^4 \cdot 8^8$

Example 5 **Simplifying Expressions with Exponents**

Classroom Examples: p. 350, Exercises 80 and 86

Simplify the expressions. **a.** $\frac{t^6}{t^4}$ **b.** $\frac{5^6}{5^4}$

Solution:

a. $\frac{t^6}{t^4}$ $\frac{t \cdot t \cdot t \cdot t \cdot t \cdot t}{t \cdot t \cdot t \cdot t}$

$= t^{6-4}$ To divide expressions with like bases, subtract the exponents.

$= t^2$

b. $\frac{5^6}{5^4}$ $\frac{5 \cdot 5 \cdot 5 \cdot 5 \cdot 5 \cdot 5}{5 \cdot 5 \cdot 5 \cdot 5}$

$= 5^{6-4}$ To divide expressions with like bases, subtract the exponents (the base is unchanged).

$= 5^2$ or 25

Skill Practice Simplify the expressions.

14. $\frac{y^{15}}{y^8}$ **15.** $\frac{3^{15}}{3^8}$

Answers

12. q^{12} **13.** 8^{12}

14. y^7 **15.** 3^7

Classroom Example: p. 350, Exercise 90

Example 6 **Simplifying Expressions with Exponents**

Simplify the expressions. **a.** $\dfrac{z^4z^5}{z^3}$ **b.** $\dfrac{10^7}{10^2 \cdot 10}$

Solution:

a. $\dfrac{z^4z^5}{z^3}$

$= \dfrac{z^{4+5}}{z^3}$ Add the exponents in the numerator (the base is unchanged).

$= \dfrac{z^9}{z^3}$

$= z^{9-3}$ Subtract the exponents.

$= z^6$

b. $\dfrac{10^7}{10^2 \cdot 10}$

$= \dfrac{10^7}{10^2 \cdot 10^1}$ Note that 10 is equivalent to 10^1.

$= \dfrac{10^7}{10^{2+1}}$ Add the exponents in the denominator (the base is unchanged).

$= \dfrac{10^7}{10^3}$

$= 10^{7-3}$ Subtract the exponents.

$= 10^4$ or 10,000 Simplify.

Skill Practice Simplify the expressions.

16. $\dfrac{a^3a^8}{a^7}$ **17.** $\dfrac{5^9}{5^2 \cdot 5^5}$

4. Simplifying Expressions with Exponents

Classroom Examples: pp. 350–351, Exercises 98 and 106

Example 7 **Simplifying Expressions with Exponents**

Use the commutative and associative properties of real numbers and the properties of exponents to simplify the expressions.

a. $(-3p^2q^4)(2pq^5)$ **b.** $\dfrac{16w^9z^3}{4w^8z}$

Solution:

a. $(-3p^2q^4)(2pq^5)$

$= (-3 \cdot 2)(p^2p)(q^4q^5)$ Apply the associative and commutative properties of multiplication to group coefficients and like bases.

$= (-3 \cdot 2)p^{2+1}q^{4+5}$ Add the exponents when multiplying expressions with like bases.

$= -6p^3q^9$ Simplify.

Avoiding Mistakes

To simplify the expression in Example 7(a) we multiply the coefficients. However, to multiply expressions with like bases, we add the exponents.

Answers

16. a^4 **17.** 5^2 or 25

b. $\dfrac{16w^9z^3}{4w^8z}$

$= \left(\dfrac{16}{4}\right)\left(\dfrac{w^9}{w^8}\right)\left(\dfrac{z^3}{z}\right)$ Group coefficients and like bases.

$= 4w^{9-8}z^{3-1}$ Subtract the exponents when dividing expressions with like bases.

$= 4wz^2$ Simplify.

Avoiding Mistakes

In Example 7(b) we divide the coefficients. However, to divide expressions with like bases, we subtract the exponents.

Skill Practice Simplify the expressions.

18. $(-4x^2y^3)(3x^5y^7)$ **19.** $\dfrac{81x^4y^7}{9xy^3}$

5. Applications of Exponents

Simple interest on an investment or loan is computed by the formula $I = Prt$, where P is the amount of principal, r is the annual interest rate, and t is the time in years. Simple interest is based only on the original principal. However, in most day-to-day applications, the interest computed on money invested or borrowed is compound interest. **Compound interest** is computed on the original principal and on the interest already accrued.

Suppose \$1000 is invested at 8% interest for 3 years. Compare the total amount in the account if the money earns simple interest versus if the interest is compounded annually.

Simple Interest

The simple interest earned is given by $I = Prt$

$$= (\$1000)(0.08)(3)$$
$$= \$240$$

The total amount, A, at the end of 3 years is $A = P + I$

$$= \$1000 + \$240$$
$$= \$1240$$

Compound Annual Interest

The total amount, A, in an account earning compound annual interest may be computed using the following formula:

$A = P(1 + r)^t$ where P is the amount of principal, r is the annual interest rate (expressed in decimal form), and t is the number of years.

For example, for \$1000 invested at 8% interest compounded annually for 3 years, we have $P = 1000$, $r = 0.08$, and $t = 3$.

$$A = P(1 + r)^t$$
$$A = 1000(1 + 0.08)^3$$
$$= 1000(1.08)^3$$
$$= 1000(1.259712)$$
$$= 1259.712$$

Rounding to the nearest cent, we have $A = \$1259.71$.

Answers

18. $-12x^7y^{10}$ **19.** $9x^3y^4$

Classroom Example: p. 351, Exercise 116

Example 8 Using Exponents in an Application

Find the amount in an account after 8 years if the initial investment is \$7000, invested at 2.25% interest compounded annually.

Solution:

Identify the values for each variable.

$P = 7000$

$r = 0.0225$ Note that the decimal form of a percent is used for calculations.

$t = 8$

$A = P(1 + r)^t$	
$= 7000(1 + 0.0225)^8$	Substitute.
$= 7000(1.0225)^8$	Simplify inside the parentheses.
$\approx 7000(1.194831142)$	Approximate $(1.0225)^8$.
≈ 8363.82	Multiply (round to the nearest cent).

The amount in the account after 8 years is \$8363.82.

Skill Practice

20. Find the amount in an account after 3 years if the initial investment is \$4000 invested at 5% interest compounded annually.

Answer

20. \$4630.50

Calculator Connections

Topic: Review of Evaluating Exponential Expressions on a Calculator

In Example 8, it was necessary to evaluate the expression $(1.0225)^8$. Recall that the ^ or y^x key may be used to enter expressions with exponents.

Scientific Calculator

Enter: 1.0225 y^x 8 = **Result:** 1.194831142

Graphing Calculator

```
1.0225^8
          1.194831142
```

Calculator Exercises

Use a calculator to evaluate the expressions.

1. $(1.06)^5$ 1.338225578 **2.** $(1.02)^{40}$ 2.208039664 **3.** $5000(1.06)^5$ 6691.127888

4. $2000(1.02)^{40}$ 4416.079327 **5.** $3000(1 + 0.06)^2$ 3370.8 **6.** $1000(1 + 0.05)^3$ 1157.625

Section 5.1 Practice Exercises

For this exercise set, assume all variables represent nonzero real numbers.

For additional exercises, see Classroom Activities 5.1A–5.1D in the *Student's Resource Manual* at www.mhhe.com/moh.

Vocabulary and Key Concepts

1. **a.** A(n) exponent is used to show repeated multiplication of the base.

   b. Given the expression b^n, the value b is the base and n is the exponent.

   c. Given the expression x, the value of the exponent on x is understood to be 1.

   d. The formula to compute simple interest is $I = Prt$.

   e. Interest that is computed on the original principal and on the accrued interest is called compound interest.

Concept 1: Review of Exponential Notation

For Exercises 2–13, identify the base and the exponent. **(See Example 1.)**

2. c^3 Base: c; exponent: 3

3. x^4 Base: x; exponent: 4

4. 5^2 Base: 5; exponent: 2

5. 3^5 Base: 3; exponent: 5

6. $(-4)^8$ Base: -4; exponent: 8

7. $(-1)^4$ Base: -1; exponent: 4

8. x Base: x; exponent: 1

9. 13 Base: 13; exponent: 1

10. -4^2 Base: 4; exponent: 2

11. -10^3 Base: 10; exponent: 3

12. $-y^5$ Base: y; exponent: 5

13. $-t^6$ Base: t; exponent: 6

14. What base corresponds to the exponent 5 in the expression $x^3y^5z^2$? y

15. What base corresponds to the exponent 2 in the expression w^3v^2? v

16. What is the exponent for the factor of 2 in the expression $2x^3$? 1

17. What is the exponent for the factor of p in the expression pq^7? 1

For Exercises 18–26, write the expression using exponents.

18. $(4n)(4n)(4n)$ $(4n)^3$

19. $(-6b)(-6b)$ $(-6b)^2$

20. $4 \cdot n \cdot n \cdot n$ $4n^3$

21. $-6 \cdot b \cdot b$ $-6b^2$

22. $(x - 5)(x - 5)(x - 5)$ $(x-5)^3$

23. $(y + 2)(y + 2)(y + 2)(y + 2)$ $(y+2)^4$

24. $\dfrac{4}{x \cdot x \cdot x \cdot x \cdot x}$ $\dfrac{4}{x^5}$

25. $\dfrac{-2}{t \cdot t \cdot t}$ $\dfrac{-2}{t^3}$

26. $\dfrac{5 \cdot x \cdot x \cdot x}{(y-7)(y-7)}$ $\dfrac{5x^3}{(y-7)^2}$

Concept 2: Evaluating Expressions with Exponents

For Exercises 27–34, evaluate the two expressions and compare the answers. Do the expressions have the same value? **(See Example 2.)**

27. -5^2 and $(-5)^2$ No; $-5^2 = -25$ and $(-5)^2 = 25$

28. -3^4 and $(-3)^4$ No; $-3^4 = -81$ and $(-3)^4 = 81$

29. -2^5 and $(-2)^5$ Yes; -32

30. -5^3 and $(-5)^3$ Yes; -125

31. $\left(\dfrac{1}{2}\right)^3$ and $\dfrac{1}{2^3}$ Yes; $\dfrac{1}{8}$

32. $\left(\dfrac{1}{5}\right)^2$ and $\dfrac{1}{5^2}$ Yes; $\dfrac{1}{25}$

33. $-(-2)^4$ and $-(2)^4$ Yes; -16

34. $-(-3)^3$ and $-(3)^3$ No; $-(-3)^3 = 27$ and $-(3)^3 = -27$

For Exercises 35–42, evaluate each expression. **(See Example 2.)**

35. 16^1 16

36. 20^1 20

37. $(-1)^{21}$ -1

38. $(-1)^{30}$ 1

39. $\left(-\dfrac{1}{3}\right)^2$ $\dfrac{1}{9}$

40. $\left(-\dfrac{1}{4}\right)^3$ $-\dfrac{1}{64}$

41. $-\left(\dfrac{2}{5}\right)^2$ $-\dfrac{4}{25}$

42. $-\left(\dfrac{3}{5}\right)^2$ $-\dfrac{9}{25}$

For Exercises 43–50, simplify using the order of operations.

43. $3 \cdot 2^4$ 48 **44.** $2 \cdot 0^5$ 0 **45.** $-4(-1)^7$ 4 **46.** $-3(-1)^4$ −3

47. $6^2 - 3^3$ 9 **48.** $4^3 + 2^3$ 72 **49.** $2 \cdot 3^2 + 4 \cdot 2^3$ 50 **50.** $6^2 - 3 \cdot 1^3$ 33

For Exercises 51–62, evaluate each expression for $a = -4$ and $b = 5$. **(See Example 3.)**

51. $-4b^2$ −100 **52.** $3a^2$ 48 **53.** $(-4b)^2$ 400 **54.** $(3a)^2$ 144

55. $(a + b)^2$ 1 **56.** $(a - b)^2$ 81 **57.** $a^2 + 2ab + b^2$ 1 **58.** $a^2 - 2ab + b^2$ 81

59. $-10ab^2$ 1000 **60.** $-6a^3b$ 1920 **61.** $-10a^2b$ −800 **62.** $-a^2b$ −80

Concept 3: Multiplying and Dividing Expressions with Common Bases

63. Expand the following expressions first. Then simplify using exponents.

a. $x^4 \cdot x^3$ $(x \cdot x \cdot x \cdot x)(x \cdot x \cdot x) = x^7$

b. $5^4 \cdot 5^3$ $(5 \cdot 5 \cdot 5 \cdot 5)(5 \cdot 5 \cdot 5) = 5^7$

64. Expand the following expressions first. Then simplify using exponents.

a. $y^2 \cdot y^4$ $(y \cdot y)(y \cdot y \cdot y \cdot y) = y^6$

b. $3^2 \cdot 3^4$ $(3 \cdot 3)(3 \cdot 3 \cdot 3 \cdot 3) = 3^6$

For Exercises 65–76, simplify each expression. Write the answers in exponent form. **(See Example 4.)**

65. z^5z^3 z^8 **66.** w^4w^7 w^{11} **67.** $a \cdot a^8$ a^9 **68.** p^4p p^5

69. $4^5 \cdot 4^9$ 4^{14} **70.** $6^7 \cdot 6^5$ 6^{12} **71.** $\left(\frac{2}{3}\right)^3\left(\frac{2}{3}\right)$ $\left(\frac{2}{3}\right)^4$ **72.** $\left(\frac{1}{x}\right)\left(\frac{1}{x}\right)^2$ $\left(\frac{1}{x}\right)^3$

73. $c^5c^2c^7$ c^{14} **74.** $b^7b^2b^8$ b^{17} **75.** $x \cdot x^4 \cdot x^{10} \cdot x^3$ x^{18} **76.** $z^7 \cdot z^{11} \cdot z^{60} \cdot z$ z^{79}

77. Expand the expressions. Then simplify.

a. $\frac{p^8}{p^3}$ $\frac{p \cdot p \cdot p \cdot p \cdot p \cdot p \cdot p \cdot p}{p \cdot p \cdot p} = p^5$

b. $\frac{8^8}{8^3}$ $\frac{8 \cdot 8 \cdot 8 \cdot 8 \cdot 8 \cdot 8 \cdot 8 \cdot 8}{8 \cdot 8 \cdot 8} = 8^5$

78. Expand the expressions. Then simplify.

a. $\frac{w^5}{w^2}$ $\frac{w \cdot w \cdot w \cdot w \cdot w}{w \cdot w} = w^3$

b. $\frac{4^5}{4^2}$ $\frac{4 \cdot 4 \cdot 4 \cdot 4 \cdot 4}{4 \cdot 4} = 4^3$

For Exercises 79–94, simplify each expression. Write the answers in exponent form. **(See Examples 5–6.)**

79. $\frac{x^8}{x^6}$ x^2 **80.** $\frac{z^5}{z^4}$ z **81.** $\frac{a^{10}}{a}$ a^9 **82.** $\frac{b^{12}}{b}$ b^{11}

83. $\frac{7^{13}}{7^6}$ 7^7 **84.** $\frac{2^6}{2^4}$ 2^2 **85.** $\frac{5^8}{5}$ 5^7 **86.** $\frac{3^5}{3}$ 3^4

87. $\frac{y^{13}}{y^{12}}$ y **88.** $\frac{w^7}{w^6}$ w **89.** $\frac{h^3h^8}{h^7}$ h^4 **90.** $\frac{n^5n^4}{n^2}$ n^7

91. $\frac{7^2 \cdot 7^6}{7}$ 7^7 **92.** $\frac{5^3 \cdot 5^8}{5}$ 5^{10} **93.** $\frac{10^{20}}{10^3 \cdot 10^8}$ 10^9 **94.** $\frac{3^{15}}{3^2 \cdot 3^{10}}$ 3^3

Concept 4: Simplifying Expressions with Exponents (Mixed Exercises)

For Exercises 95–114, use the commutative and associative properties of real numbers and the properties of exponents to simplify. **(See Example 7.)**

95. $(2x^3)(3x^4)$ $6x^7$ **96.** $(10y)(2y^3)$ $20y^4$ **97.** $(5a^2b)(8a^3b^4)$ $40a^5b^5$ **98.** $(10xy^3)(3x^4y)$ $30x^5y^4$

99. $s^3 \cdot t^5 \cdot t \cdot t^{10} \cdot s^6$ s^9t^{16} **100.** $c \cdot c^4 \cdot d^2 \cdot c^3 \cdot d^3$ c^8d^5 **101.** $(-2v^2)(3v)(5v^5)$ $-30v^8$ **102.** $(10q^5)(-3q^8)(q)$ $-30q^{14}$

103. $\left(\frac{2}{3}m^{13}n^{8}\right)(24m^{7}n^{2})$ $16m^{20}n^{10}$

104. $\left(\frac{1}{4}c^{6}d^{6}\right)(28c^{2}d^{7})$ $7c^{8}d^{13}$

105. $\frac{14c^4d^5}{7c^3d}$ $2cd^4$

106. $\frac{36h^5k^2}{9h^3k}$ $4h^2k$

107. $\frac{z^3z^{11}}{z^4z^6}$ z^4

108. $\frac{w^{12}w^2}{w^4w^5}$ w^5

109. $\frac{25h^3jk^5}{12h^2k}$ $\frac{25hjk^4}{12}$

110. $\frac{15m^5np^{12}}{4mp^9}$ $\frac{15m^4np^3}{4}$

111. $(-4p^6q^8r^4)(2pqr^2)$ $-8p^7q^9r^6$

112. $(-5a^4bc)(-10a^2b)$ $50a^6b^2c$

113. $\frac{-12s^2tu^3}{4su^2}$ $-3stu$

114. $\frac{15w^5x^{10}y^3}{-15w^4x}$ $-wx^9y^3$

Concept 5: Applications of Exponents

Use the formula $A = P(1 + r)^t$ for Exercises 115– 118. **(See Example 8.)**

115. Find the amount in an account after 2 years if the initial investment is $5000, invested at 7% interest compounded annually. $5724.50

116. Find the amount in an account after 5 years if the initial investment is $2000, invested at 4% interest compounded annually. $2433.31

117. Find the amount in an account after 3 years if the initial investment is $4000, invested at 6% interest compounded annually. $4764.06

118. Find the amount in an account after 4 years if the initial investment is $10,000, invested at 5% interest compounded annually. $12,155.06

For Exercises 119–122, use appropriate geometry formulas.

119. Find the area of the pizza shown in the figure. Round to the nearest square inch. 201 in.^{2}

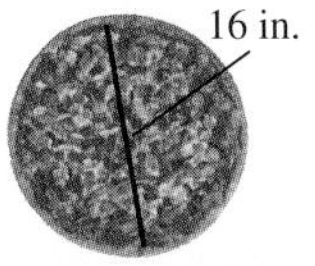

© Brand X Pictures/Alamy RF

120. Find the volume of the sphere shown in the figure. Round to the nearest cubic centimeter. 113 cm^3

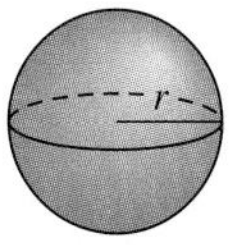

$r = 3$ cm

121. Find the volume of a spherical balloon that is 8 in. in diameter. Round to the nearest cubic inch. 268 in.^{3}

122. Find the area of a circular pool 50 ft in diameter. Round to the nearest square foot. 1963 ft^2

Expanding Your Skills

For Exercises 123–130, simplify each expression using the addition or subtraction rules of exponents. Assume that a, b, m, and n represent positive integers.

123. x^nx^{n+1} x^{2n+1}

124. y^ay^{2a} y^{3a}

125. $p^{3m+5}p^{-m-2}$ p^{2m+3}

126. $q^{4b-3}q^{-4b+4}$ q

127. $\frac{z^{b+1}}{z^b}$ z

128. $\frac{w^{5n+3}}{w^{2n}}$ w^{3n+3}

129. $\frac{r^{3a+3}}{r^{3a}}$ r^3

130. $\frac{t^{3+2m}}{t^{2m}}$ t^3

Section 5.2 More Properties of Exponents

Concepts

1. **Power Rule for Exponents**
2. **The Properties $(ab)^m = a^m b^m$ and $\left(\frac{a}{b}\right)^m = \frac{a^m}{b^m}$**

1. Power Rule for Exponents

The expression $(x^2)^3$ indicates that the quantity x^2 is cubed.

$$(x^2)^3 = (x^2)(x^2)(x^2) = (x \cdot x)(x \cdot x)(x \cdot x) = x^6$$

From this example, it appears that to raise a base to successive powers, we multiply the exponents and leave the base unchanged. This is stated formally as the power rule for exponents.

Power Rule for Exponents

Assume that b is a real number and that m and n represent positive integers. Then,

$$(b^m)^n = b^{m \cdot n}$$

Classroom Examples: p. 355, Exercises 12 and 22

Example 1 **Simplifying Expressions with Exponents**

Simplify the expressions.

a. $(s^4)^2$ **b.** $(3^4)^2$ **c.** $(x^2x^5)^4$

Solution:

a. $(s^4)^2$

$= s^{4 \cdot 2}$ Multiply exponents (the base is unchanged).

$= s^8$

b. $(3^4)^2$

$= 3^{4 \cdot 2}$ Multiply exponents (the base is unchanged).

$= 3^8$ or 6561

c. $(x^2x^5)^4$

$= (x^7)^4$ Simplify inside the parentheses by adding exponents.

$= x^{7 \cdot 4}$ Multiply exponents (the base is unchanged).

$= x^{28}$

Skill Practice Simplify the expressions.

1. $(y^3)^5$ **2.** $(2^8)^{10}$ **3.** $(q^5q^4)^3$

2. The Properties $(ab)^m = a^m b^m$ and $\left(\frac{a}{b}\right)^m = \frac{a^m}{b^m}$

Consider the following expressions and their simplified forms:

$$(xy)^3 = (xy)(xy)(xy) = (x \cdot x \cdot x)(y \cdot y \cdot y) = x^3y^3$$

$$\left(\frac{x}{y}\right)^3 = \left(\frac{x}{y}\right)\left(\frac{x}{y}\right)\left(\frac{x}{y}\right) = \left(\frac{x \cdot x \cdot x}{y \cdot y \cdot y}\right) = \frac{x^3}{y^3}$$

The expressions are simplified using the commutative and associative properties of multiplication. The simplified forms for each expression could have been reached in one step by applying the exponent to each factor inside the parentheses.

Answers

1. y^{15} **2.** 2^{80} **3.** q^{27}

Power of a Product and Power of a Quotient

Assume that a and b are real numbers. Let m represent a positive integer. Then,

$$(ab)^m = a^m b^m$$

$$\left(\frac{a}{b}\right)^m = \frac{a^m}{b^m}, \quad b \neq 0$$

Avoiding Mistakes

The power rule of exponents can be applied to a product of bases but in general cannot be applied to a sum or difference of bases.

$$(ab)^n = a^n b^n$$

but $(a + b)^n \neq a^n + b^n$

Applying these properties of exponents, we have

$$(xy)^3 = x^3y^3 \quad \text{and} \quad \left(\frac{x}{y}\right)^3 = \frac{x^3}{y^3}$$

Example 2 Simplifying Expressions with Exponents

Simplify the expressions.

a. $(-2xyz)^4$ **b.** $(5x^2y^7)^3$ **c.** $\left(\frac{2}{5}\right)^3$ **d.** $\left(\frac{1}{3xy^4}\right)^2$

Solution:

a. $(-2xyz)^4$

$= (-2)^4x^4y^4z^4$ Raise each factor within parentheses to the fourth power.

$= 16x^4y^4z^4$

b. $(5x^2y^7)^3$

$= 5^3(x^2)^3(y^7)^3$ Raise each factor within parentheses to the third power.

$= 125x^6y^{21}$ Multiply exponents and simplify.

c. $\left(\frac{2}{5}\right)^3$

$= \frac{(2)^3}{(5)^3}$ Raise each factor within parentheses to the third power.

$= \frac{8}{125}$ Simplify.

d. $\left(\frac{1}{3xy^4}\right)^2$

$= \frac{1^2}{3^2x^2(y^4)^2}$ Square each factor within parentheses.

$= \frac{1}{9x^2y^8}$ Multiply exponents and simplify.

Classroom Examples: p. 356, Exercises 28 and 32

Instructor Note: Remind students that they can write exponents of 1 where appropriate to avoid confusion. For example, $(5x^2y^7)^3 = (5^1x^2y^7)^3$.

Skill Practice Simplify the expressions.

4. $(3abc)^5$ **5.** $(-2t^2w^4)^3$ **6.** $\left(\frac{3}{4}\right)^3$ **7.** $\left(\frac{2x^3}{y^5}\right)^2$

Answers

4. $3^5a^5b^5c^5$ or $243a^5b^5c^5$
5. $-8t^6w^{12}$ **6.** $\frac{27}{64}$ **7.** $\frac{4x^6}{y^{10}}$

The properties of exponents can be used along with the properties of real numbers to simplify complicated expressions.

Classroom Example: p. 356, Exercise 56

Example 3 Simplifying Expressions with Exponents

Simplify the expression. $\dfrac{(x^2)^6(x^3)}{(x^7)^2}$

Solution:

$\dfrac{(x^2)^6(x^3)}{(x^7)^2}$	Clear parentheses by applying the power rule.
$=\dfrac{x^{2\cdot 6}x^3}{x^{7\cdot 2}}$	Multiply exponents.
$=\dfrac{x^{12}x^3}{x^{14}}$	
$=\dfrac{x^{12+3}}{x^{14}}$	Add exponents in the numerator.
$=\dfrac{x^{15}}{x^{14}}$	
$=x^{15-14}$	Subtract exponents.
$=x$	Simplify.

Skill Practice Simplify the expression.

8. $\dfrac{(k^5)^2k^8}{(k^2)^4}$

Classroom Example: p. 356, Exercise 60

Example 4 Simplifying Expressions with Exponents

Simplify the expression. $(3cd^2)(2cd^3)^3$

Solution:

$(3cd^2)(2cd^3)^3$	Clear parentheses by applying the power rule.
$=3cd^2\cdot 2^3c^3d^9$	Raise each factor in the second parentheses to the third power.
$=3\cdot 2^3cc^3d^2d^9$	Group like factors.
$=3\cdot 8c^{1+3}d^{2+9}$	Add exponents on like bases.
$=24c^4d^{11}$	Simplify.

Skill Practice Simplify the expression.

9. $(4x^4y)(2x^3y^4)^4$

Answers

8. k^{10} **9.** $64x^{16}y^{17}$

Example 5 Simplifying Expressions with Exponents

Classroom Example: p. 356, Exercise 68

Simplify the expression. $\left(\dfrac{x^7yz^4}{8xz^3}\right)^2$

Solution:

$$\left(\frac{x^7yz^4}{8xz^3}\right)^2$$

$$= \left(\frac{x^{7-1}yz^{4-3}}{8}\right)^2$$ First simplify inside the parentheses by subtracting exponents on like bases.

$$= \left(\frac{x^6yz}{8}\right)^2$$

$$= \frac{(x^6)^2y^2z^2}{8^2}$$ Apply the power rule of exponents.

$$= \frac{x^{12}y^2z^2}{64}$$

Skill Practice Simplify the expression.

10. $\left(\dfrac{w^2xy^4}{6xy^3}\right)^2$

Answer

10. $\dfrac{w^4y^2}{36}$

Section 5.2 Practice Exercises

For this exercise set assume all variables represent nonzero real numbers.

For additional exercises, see Classroom Activity 5.2A in the *Student's Resource Manual* at www.mhhe.com/moh.

Review Exercises

For Exercises 1–8, simplify.

1. $4^2 \cdot 4^7$ 4^9
2. $5^8 \cdot 5^3 \cdot 5$ 5^{12}
3. $a^{13} \cdot a \cdot a^6$ a^{20}
4. $y^{14}y^3$ y^{17}
5. $\dfrac{d^{13}d}{d^5}$ d^9
6. $\dfrac{3^8 \cdot 3}{3^2}$ 3^7
7. $\dfrac{7^{11}}{7^5}$ 7^6
8. $\dfrac{z^4}{z^3}$ z
9. Explain when to add exponents versus when to multiply exponents. When multiplying expressions with the same base, add the exponents. When raising an expression with an exponent to a power, multiply the exponents.
10. Explain when to add exponents versus when to subtract exponents. When multiplying expressions with the same base, add the exponents. When dividing expressions with the same base, subtract the exponents.

Concept 1: Power Rule for Exponents

For Exercises 11–22, simplify and write answers in exponent form. **(See Example 1.)**

11. $(5^3)^4$ 5^{12}
12. $(2^8)^7$ 2^{56}
13. $(12^3)^2$ 12^6
14. $(6^4)^4$ 6^{16}
15. $(y^7)^2$ y^{14}
16. $(z^6)^4$ z^{24}
17. $(w^5)^5$ w^{25}
18. $(t^3)^6$ t^{18}
19. $(a^2a^4)^6$ a^{36}
20. $(z \cdot z^3)^2$ z^8
21. $(y^3y^4)^2$ y^{14}
22. $(w^5w)^4$ w^{24}

23. Evaluate the two expressions and compare the answers: $(2^2)^3$ and $(2^3)^2$ They are both equal to 2^6.

24. Evaluate the two expressions and compare the answers: $(4^4)^2$ and $(4^2)^4$ They are both equal to 4^8.

25. Evaluate the two expressions and compare the answers. Which expression is greater? Why?

4^{3^2} and $(4^3)^2$

$4^{3^2} = 4^9$; $(4^3)^2 = 4^6$; the expression 4^{3^2} is greater than $(4^3)^2$.

26. Evaluate the two expressions and compare the answers. Which expression is greater? Why?

3^{5^2} and $(3^5)^2$

$3^{5^2} = 3^{25}$; $(3^5)^2 = 3^{10}$; the expression 3^{5^2} is greater than $(3^5)^2$.

Concept 2: The Properties $(ab)^m = a^m b^m$ and $\left(\frac{a}{b}\right)^m = \frac{a^m}{b^m}$

For Exercises 27–42, use the appropriate property to clear the parentheses. **(See Example 2.)**

27. $(5w)^2$ $25w^2$

28. $(4y)^3$ $64y^3$

29. $(srt)^4$ $s^4r^4t^4$

30. $(wxy)^6$ $w^6x^6y^6$

31. $\left(\frac{2}{r}\right)^4$ $\frac{16}{r^4}$

32. $\left(\frac{1}{t}\right)^8$ $\frac{1}{t^8}$

33. $\left(\frac{x}{y}\right)^5$ $\frac{x^5}{y^5}$

34. $\left(\frac{w}{z}\right)^7$ $\frac{w^7}{z^7}$

35. $(-3a)^4$ $81a^4$

36. $(2x)^5$ $32x^5$

37. $(-3abc)^3$ $-27a^3b^3c^3$

38. $(-5xyz)^2$ $25x^2y^2z^2$

39. $\left(-\frac{4}{x}\right)^3$ $-\frac{64}{x^3}$

40. $\left(-\frac{1}{w}\right)^4$ $\frac{1}{w^4}$

41. $\left(-\frac{a}{b}\right)^2$ $\frac{a^2}{b^2}$

42. $\left(-\frac{r}{s}\right)^3$ $-\frac{r^3}{s^3}$

Mixed Exercises

For Exercises 43–74, simplify. **(See Examples 3–5.)**

43. $(6u^2v^4)^3$ $6^3u^6v^{12}$ or $216u^6v^{12}$

44. $(3a^5b^2)^6$ $3^6a^{30}b^{12}$ or $729a^{30}b^{12}$

45. $5(x^2y)^4$ $5x^8y^4$

46. $18(u^3v^4)^2$ $18u^6v^8$

47. $(-h^4)^7$ $-h^{28}$

48. $(-k^6)^3$ $-k^{18}$

49. $(-m^2)^6$ m^{12}

50. $(-n^3)^8$ n^{24}

51. $\left(\frac{4}{rs^4}\right)^5$ $\frac{4^5}{r^5s^{20}}$ or $\frac{1024}{r^5s^{20}}$

52. $\left(\frac{2}{h^7k}\right)^3$ $\frac{8}{h^{21}k^3}$

53. $\left(\frac{3p}{q^3}\right)^5$ $\frac{3^5p^5}{q^{15}}$ or $\frac{243p^5}{q^{15}}$

54. $\left(\frac{5x^2}{y^3}\right)^4$ $\frac{5^4x^8}{y^{12}}$ or $\frac{625x^8}{y^{12}}$

55. $\frac{y^8(y^3)^4}{(y^2)^3}$ y^{14}

56. $\frac{(w^3)^2(w^4)^5}{(w^4)^2}$ w^{18}

57. $(x^2)^5(x^3)^7$ x^{31}

58. $(y^3)^4(y^2)^5$ y^{22}

59. $(2a^2b)^3(5a^4b^3)^2$ $200a^{14}b^9$

60. $(4c^3d^5)^2(3cd^3)^2$ $144c^8d^{16}$

61. $(-2p^2q^4)^4$ $16p^8q^{16}$

62. $(-7x^4y^5)^2$ $49x^8y^{10}$

63. $(-m^7n^3)^5$ $-m^{35}n^{15}$

64. $(-a^3b^6)^7$ $-a^{21}b^{42}$

65. $\frac{(5a^3b)^4(a^2b)^4}{(5ab)^2}$ $25a^{18}b^6$

66. $\frac{(6s^3)^2(s^4t^5)^2}{(3s^4t^2)^2}$ $4s^6t^6$

67. $\left(\frac{2c^3d^4}{3c^2d}\right)^2$ $\frac{4c^2d^6}{9}$

68. $\left(\frac{x^3y^5z}{5xy^2}\right)^2$ $\frac{x^4y^6z^2}{25}$

69. $(2c^3d^2)^5\left(\frac{c^6d^8}{4c^2d}\right)^3$ $\frac{c^{27}d^{31}}{2}$

70. $\left(\frac{s^5t^6}{2s^2t}\right)^2(10s^3t^3)^2$ $25s^{12}t^{16}$

71. $\left(\frac{-3a^3b}{c^2}\right)^3$ $-\frac{27a^9b^3}{c^6}$

72. $\left(\frac{-4x^2}{y^4z}\right)^3$ $-\frac{64x^6}{y^{12}z^3}$

73. $\frac{(-8b^6)^2(b^3)^5}{4b}$ $16b^{26}$

74. $\frac{(-6a^2)^2(a^3)^4}{9a}$ $4a^{15}$

Expanding Your Skills

For Exercises 75–82, simplify each expression. Assume that a, b, m, n, and x represent positive integers.

75. $(x^m)^2$ x^{2m}

76. $(y^3)^n$ y^{3n}

77. $(5a^{2n})^3$ $125a^{6n}$

78. $(3b^4)^m$ 3^mb^{4m}

79. $\left(\frac{m^2}{n^3}\right)^b$ $\frac{m^{2b}}{n^{3b}}$

80. $\left(\frac{x^5}{y^3}\right)^m$ $\frac{x^{5m}}{y^{3m}}$

81. $\left(\frac{3a^3}{5b^4}\right)^n$ $\frac{3^na^{3n}}{5^nb^{4n}}$

82. $\left(\frac{4m^6}{3n^2}\right)^x$ $\frac{4^xm^{6x}}{3^xn^{2x}}$

Definitions of b^0 and b^{-n}

Section 5.3

Concepts

1. Definition of b^0
2. Definition of b^{-n}
3. Properties of Integer Exponents: A Summary

We have learned several rules that enable us to manipulate expressions containing *positive* integer exponents. In this section, we present definitions that can be used to simplify expressions with negative exponents or with an exponent of zero.

1. Definition of b^0

To begin, consider the following pattern.

$3^3 = 27$
Divide by 3.
$3^2 = 9$
Divide by 3.
$3^1 = 3$
Divide by 3.
$3^0 = 1$

As the exponents decrease by 1, the resulting expressions are divided by 3.

For the pattern to continue, we define $3^0 = 1$.

This pattern suggests that we should define an expression with a zero exponent as follows.

Definition of b^0

Let b be a nonzero real number. Then, $b^0 = 1$.

Note: The value of 0^0 is not defined by this definition because the base b must not equal zero.

Example 1 Simplifying Expressions with a Zero Exponent

Classroom Examples: p. 364, Exercises 14, 18, and 24

Simplify. Assume that $z \neq 0$.

a. 4^0 **b.** $(-4)^0$ **c.** -4^0

d. z^0 **e.** $-4z^0$ **f.** $(4z)^0$

Solution:

a. $4^0 = 1$ By definition

b. $(-4)^0 = 1$ By definition

c. $-4^0 = -1 \cdot 4^0 = -1 \cdot 1 = -1$ The exponent 0 applies only to 4.

d. $z^0 = 1$ By definition

e. $-4z^0 = -4 \cdot z^0 = -4 \cdot 1 = -4$ The exponent 0 applies only to z.

f. $(4z)^0 = 1$ The parentheses indicate that the exponent, 0, applies to both factors 4 and z.

Skill Practice Evaluate the expressions. Assume that $x \neq 0$ and $y \neq 0$.

1. 7^0 **2.** $(-7)^0$ **3.** -5^0

4. y^0 **5.** $-2x^0$ **6.** $(2x)^0$

Answers

1. 1 **2.** 1 **3.** –1
4. 1 **5.** –2 **6.** 1

The definition of b^0 is consistent with the other properties of exponents learned thus far. For example, we know that $1 = \frac{5^3}{5^3}$. If we subtract exponents, the result is 5^0.

Subtract exponents.

$$1 = \frac{5^3}{5^3} = 5^{3-3} = 5^0$$ Therefore, 5^0 must be defined as 1.

2. Definition of b^{-n}

To understand the concept of a *negative* exponent, consider the following pattern.

$3^3 = 27$

Divide by 3.

$3^2 = 9$

Divide by 3.

$3^1 = 3$

Divide by 3.

$3^0 = 1$

Divide by 3.

As the exponents decrease by 1, the resulting expressions are divided by 3.

$3^{-1} = \frac{1}{3}$ ← For the pattern to continue, we define $3^{-1} = \frac{1}{3^1} = \frac{1}{3}$.

$3^{-2} = \frac{1}{9}$ ← For the pattern to continue, we define $3^{-2} = \frac{1}{3^2} = \frac{1}{9}$.

$3^{-3} = \frac{1}{27}$ ← For the pattern to continue, we define $3^{-3} = \frac{1}{3^3} = \frac{1}{27}$.

This pattern suggests that $3^{-n} = \frac{1}{3^n}$ for all integers, n. In general, we have the following definition involving negative exponents.

Definition of b^{-n}

Let n be an integer and b be a nonzero real number. Then,

$$b^{-n} = \left(\frac{1}{b}\right)^n \quad \text{or} \quad \frac{1}{b^n}$$

The definition of b^{-n} implies that to evaluate b^{-n}, take the reciprocal of the base and change the sign of the exponent.

Change the sign of the exponent.

$$4^{-2} = \left(\frac{1}{4}\right)^2 \quad \text{or} \quad \frac{1}{4^2}$$

Reciprocal of the base

Change the sign of the exponent.

$$\left(\frac{a}{b}\right)^{-n} = \left(\frac{b}{a}\right)^n$$

Reciprocal of the base

Example 2 Simplifying Expressions with Negative Exponents

Classroom Examples: pp. 364–365, Exercises 34 and 44

Simplify. Assume that $c \neq 0$.

a. c^{-3} **b.** 5^{-1} **c.** $(-3)^{-4}$

Solution:

a. $c^{-3} = \dfrac{1}{c^3}$ By definition

b. $5^{-1} = \dfrac{1}{5^1}$ By definition

$= \dfrac{1}{5}$ Simplify.

Avoiding Mistakes

A negative exponent does *not* affect the sign of the base.

c. $(-3)^{-4} = \dfrac{1}{(-3)^4}$ The base is -3 and must be enclosed in parentheses.

$= \dfrac{1}{81}$ Simplify. Note that $(-3)^4 = (-3)(-3)(-3)(-3) = 81$.

Skill Practice Simplify. Assume that $p \neq 0$.

7. p^{-4} **8.** 3^{-3} **9.** $(-5)^{-2}$

Example 3 Simplifying Expressions with Negative Exponents

Classroom Examples: pp. 364–365, Exercises 30 and 46

Simplify. Assume that $y \neq 0$.

a. $\left(\dfrac{1}{6}\right)^{-2}$ **b.** $\left(-\dfrac{3}{5}\right)^{-3}$ **c.** $\dfrac{1}{y^{-5}}$

Solution:

a. $\left(\dfrac{1}{6}\right)^{-2} = 6^2$ Take the reciprocal of the base, and change the sign of the exponent.

$= 36$ Simplify.

b. $\left(-\dfrac{3}{5}\right)^{-3} = \left(-\dfrac{5}{3}\right)^3$ Take the reciprocal of the base, and change the sign of the exponent.

$= -\dfrac{125}{27}$ Simplify.

c. $\dfrac{1}{y^{-5}} = \left(\dfrac{1}{y}\right)^{-5}$ Apply the power of a quotient rule.

$= (y)^5$ Take the reciprocal of the base, and change the sign of the exponent.

$= y^5$

TIP: Example 3(c) illustrates that $\dfrac{1}{b^{-n}} = b^n$, for $b \neq 0$.

Skill Practice Simplify. Assume that $w \neq 0$.

10. $\left(\dfrac{1}{3}\right)^{-1}$ **11.** $\left(-\dfrac{2}{5}\right)^{-2}$ **12.** $\dfrac{1}{w^{-7}}$

Answers

7. $\dfrac{1}{p^4}$ **8.** $\dfrac{1}{3^3}$ or $\dfrac{1}{27}$

9. $\dfrac{1}{(-5)^2}$ or $\dfrac{1}{25}$ **10.** 3

11. $\dfrac{25}{4}$ **12.** w^7

Classroom Examples: pp. 364–365, Exercises 36, 38, and 42

Example 4 **Simplifying Expressions with Negative Exponents**

Simplify. Assume that $x \neq 0$.

a. $(5x)^{-3}$ **b.** $5x^{-3}$ **c.** $-5x^{-3}$

Solution:

a. $(5x)^{-3} = \left(\dfrac{1}{5x}\right)^3$ Take the reciprocal of the base, and change the sign of the exponent.

$= \dfrac{(1)^3}{(5x)^3}$ Apply the exponent of 3 to each factor within parentheses.

$= \dfrac{1}{125x^3}$ Simplify.

b. $5x^{-3} = 5 \cdot x^{-3}$ Note that the exponent, -3, applies only to x.

$= 5 \cdot \dfrac{1}{x^3}$ Rewrite x^{-3} as $\dfrac{1}{x^3}$.

$= \dfrac{5}{x^3}$ Multiply.

c. $-5x^{-3} = -5 \cdot x^{-3}$ Note that the exponent, -3, applies only to x, and that -5 is a coefficient.

$= -5 \cdot \dfrac{1}{x^3}$ Rewrite x^{-3} as $\dfrac{1}{x^3}$.

$= -\dfrac{5}{x^3}$ Multiply.

Skill Practice Simplify. Assume that $w \neq 0$.

13. $(2w)^{-4}$ **14.** $2w^{-4}$ **15.** $-2w^{-4}$

It is important to note that the definition of b^{-n} is consistent with the other properties of exponents learned thus far. For example, consider the expression

$$\frac{x^4}{x^7} = \frac{\cancel{x} \cdot \cancel{x} \cdot \cancel{x} \cdot \cancel{x}}{\cancel{x} \cdot \cancel{x} \cdot \cancel{x} \cdot \cancel{x} \cdot x \cdot x \cdot x} = \frac{1}{x^3}$$

Subtract exponents.

By subtracting exponents, we have $\dfrac{x^4}{x^7} = x^{4-7} = x^{-3}$

Hence, $x^{-3} = \dfrac{1}{x^3}$.

3. Properties of Integer Exponents: A Summary

The definitions of b^0 and b^{-n} enable us to extend the properties of exponents. These are summarized in Table 5-1.

Answers

13. $\dfrac{1}{16w^4}$ **14.** $\dfrac{2}{w^4}$

15. $-\dfrac{2}{w^4}$

Table 5-1

Properties of Integer Exponents Assume that a and b are real numbers ($b \neq 0$) and that m and n represent integers.		
Property	**Example**	**Details/Notes**
Multiplication of Expressions with Like Bases $b^m b^n = b^{m+n}$	$b^2 b^4 = b^{2+4} = b^6$	$b^2 b^4 = (b \cdot b)(b \cdot b \cdot b \cdot b) = b^6$
Division of Expressions with Like Bases $\frac{b^m}{b^n} = b^{m-n}$	$\frac{b^5}{b^2} = b^{5-2} = b^3$	$\frac{b^5}{b^2} = \frac{\not{b} \cdot \not{b} \cdot b \cdot b \cdot b}{\not{b} \cdot \not{b}} = b^3$
The Power Rule $(b^m)^n = b^{m \cdot n}$	$(b^4)^2 = b^{4 \cdot 2} = b^8$	$(b^4)^2 = (b \cdot b \cdot b \cdot b)(b \cdot b \cdot b \cdot b) = b^8$
Power of a Product $(ab)^m = a^m b^m$	$(ab)^3 = a^3 b^3$	$(ab)^3 = (ab)(ab)(ab)$ $= (a \cdot a \cdot a)(b \cdot b \cdot b) = a^3 b^3$
Power of a Quotient $\left(\frac{a}{b}\right)^m = \frac{a^m}{b^m}$	$\left(\frac{a}{b}\right)^3 = \frac{a^3}{b^3}$	$\left(\frac{a}{b}\right)^3 = \left(\frac{a}{b}\right)\left(\frac{a}{b}\right)\left(\frac{a}{b}\right) = \frac{a \cdot a \cdot a}{b \cdot b \cdot b} = \frac{a^3}{b^3}$

Definitions Assume that b is a real number ($b \neq 0$) and that n represents an integer.		
Definition	**Example**	**Details/Notes**
$b^0 = 1$	$(4)^0 = 1$	Any nonzero quantity raised to the zero power equals 1.
$b^{-n} = \left(\frac{1}{b}\right)^n = \frac{1}{b^n}$	$b^{-5} = \left(\frac{1}{b}\right)^5 = \frac{1}{b^5}$	To simplify a negative exponent, take the reciprocal of the base and make the exponent positive.

Example 5 Simplifying Expressions with Exponents

Classroom Example: p. 365, Exercise 74

Simplify the expressions. Write the answers with positive exponents only. Assume all variables are nonzero.

a. $\frac{a^3 b^{-2}}{c^{-5}}$ **b.** $\frac{x^2 x^{-7}}{x^3}$ **c.** $\frac{z^2}{w^{-4} w^4 z^{-8}}$

Solution:

a. $\frac{a^3 b^{-2}}{c^{-5}}$

$= \frac{a^3}{1} \cdot \frac{b^{-2}}{1} \cdot \frac{1}{c^{-5}}$

$= \frac{a^3}{1} \cdot \frac{1}{b^2} \cdot \frac{c^5}{1}$ Simplify negative exponents.

$= \frac{a^3 c^5}{b^2}$ Multiply.

b. $\dfrac{x^2x^{-7}}{x^3}$

$= \dfrac{x^{2+(-7)}}{x^3}$ Add the exponents in the numerator.

$= \dfrac{x^{-5}}{x^3}$ Simplify.

$= x^{-5-3}$ Subtract the exponents.

$= x^{-8}$

$= \dfrac{1}{x^8}$ Simplify the negative exponent.

c. $\dfrac{z^2}{w^{-4}w^4z^{-8}}$

$= \dfrac{z^2}{w^{-4+4}z^{-8}}$ Add the exponents in the denominator.

$= \dfrac{z^2}{w^0z^{-8}}$

$= \dfrac{z^2}{(1)z^{-8}}$ Recall that $w^0 = 1$.

$= z^{2-(-8)}$ Subtract the exponents.

$= z^{10}$ Simplify.

Skill Practice Simplify the expressions. Assume all variables are nonzero.

16. $\dfrac{x^{-6}}{y^4z^{-8}}$ **17.** $\dfrac{x^3x^{-8}}{x^4}$ **18.** $\dfrac{p^3}{w^7w^{-7}z^{-2}}$

Classroom Examples: p. 365, Exercises 82 and 92

Example 6 Simplifying Expressions with Exponents

Simplify the expressions. Write the answers with positive exponents only. Assume that all variables are nonzero.

a. $(-4ab^{-2})^{-3}$ **b.** $\left(\dfrac{2p^{-4}q^3}{5p^2q}\right)^{-2}$

Solution:

a. $(-4ab^{-2})^{-3}$

$= (-4)^{-3}a^{-3}(b^{-2})^{-3}$ Apply the power rule of exponents.

$= (-4)^{-3}a^{-3}b^6$

$= \dfrac{1}{(-4)^3} \cdot \dfrac{1}{a^3} \cdot b^6$ Simplify the negative exponents.

$= \dfrac{1}{-64} \cdot \dfrac{1}{a^3} \cdot b^6$ Simplify.

$= -\dfrac{b^6}{64a^3}$ Multiply fractions.

Answers

16. $\dfrac{z^8}{y^4x^6}$ **17.** $\dfrac{1}{x^9}$ **18.** p^3z^2

b. $\left(\dfrac{2p^{-4}q^3}{5p^2q}\right)^{-2}$ First simplify within the parentheses.

$= \left(\dfrac{2p^{-4-2}q^{3-1}}{5}\right)^{-2}$ Divide expressions with like bases by subtracting exponents.

$= \left(\dfrac{2p^{-6}q^2}{5}\right)^{-2}$ Simplify.

$= \dfrac{(2p^{-6}q^2)^{-2}}{(5)^{-2}}$ Apply the power rule of a quotient.

$= \dfrac{2^{-2}(p^{-6})^{-2}(q^2)^{-2}}{5^{-2}}$ Apply the power rule of a product.

$= \dfrac{2^{-2}p^{12}q^{-4}}{5^{-2}}$ Simplify.

$= \dfrac{5^2p^{12}}{2^2q^4}$ Simplify the negative exponents.

$= \dfrac{25p^{12}}{4q^4}$ Simplify.

TIP: For Example 6(b), the power rule of exponents can be performed first. In that case, the second step would be

$$\frac{2^{-2}p^8q^{-6}}{5^{-2}p^{-4}q^{-2}}$$

Skill Practice Simplify the expressions. Assume all variables are nonzero.

19. $(-5x^{-2}y^3)^{-2}$ **20.** $\left(\dfrac{3x^{-3}y^{-2}}{4xy^{-3}}\right)^{-2}$

Example 7 Simplifying an Expression with Exponents

Classroom Example: p. 365, Exercise 96

Simplify the expression $2^{-1} + 3^{-1} + 5^0$. Write the answer with positive exponents only.

Solution:

$2^{-1} + 3^{-1} + 5^0$

$= \dfrac{1}{2} + \dfrac{1}{3} + 1$ Simplify negative exponents. Simplify $5^0 = 1$.

$= \dfrac{3}{6} + \dfrac{2}{6} + \dfrac{6}{6}$ The least common denominator is 6.

$= \dfrac{11}{6}$ Simplify.

Skill Practice Simplify the expressions.

21. $2^{-1} + 4^{-2} + 3^0$

Answers

19. $\dfrac{x^4}{25y^6}$ **20.** $\dfrac{16x^8}{9y^2}$ **21.** $\dfrac{25}{16}$

Section 5.3 Practice Exercises

For this exercise set, assume all variables represent nonzero real numbers.

For additional exercises, see Classroom Activities 5.3A–5.3B in the *Student's Resource Manual* at www.mhhe.com/moh.

Study Skills Exercise

To help you remember the properties of exponents, write them on 3 × 5 cards. On each card, write a property on one side and an example using that property on the other side. Keep these cards with you, and when you have a spare moment (such as waiting at the doctor's office), pull out these cards and go over the properties.

Vocabulary and Key Concepts

1. **a.** The expression b^0 is defined to be ____ provided that $b \neq 0$. 1

   b. The expression b^{-n} is defined as ____ provided that $b \neq 0$. $\left(\frac{1}{b}\right)^n$ or $\frac{1}{b^n}$

Review Exercises

For Exercises 2–9, simplify.

2. b^3b^8 b^{11}

3. c^7c^2 c^9

4. $\dfrac{x^6}{x^2}$ x^4

5. $\dfrac{y^9}{y^8}$ y

6. $\dfrac{9^4 \cdot 9^8}{9}$ 9^{11}

7. $\dfrac{3^{14}}{3^3 \cdot 3^5}$ 3^6 or 729

8. $(6ab^3c^2)^5$ $6^5a^5b^{15}c^{10}$ or $7776a^5b^{15}c^{10}$

9. $(7w^7z^2)^4$ $7^4w^{28}z^8$ or $2401w^{28}z^8$

Concept 1: Definition of b^0

10. Simplify.

a. 8^0 1 **b.** $\dfrac{8^4}{8^4}$ 1

11. Simplify.

a. d^0 1 **b.** $\dfrac{d^3}{d^3}$ 1

12. Simplify.

a. m^0 1 **b.** $\dfrac{m^5}{m^5}$ 1

For Exercises 13–24, simplify. **(See Example 1.)**

13. p^0 1

14. k^0 1

15. 5^0 1

16. 2^0 1

17. -4^0 −1

18. -1^0 −1

19. $(-6)^0$ 1

20. $(-2)^0$ 1

21. $(8x)^0$ 1

22. $(-3y^3)^0$ 1

23. $-7x^0$ −7

24. $6y^0$ 6

Concept 2: Definition of b^{-n}

25. Simplify and write the answers with positive exponents.

a. t^{-5} $\frac{1}{t^5}$ **b.** $\dfrac{t^3}{t^8}$ $\frac{1}{t^5}$

26. Simplify and write the answers with positive exponents.

a. 4^{-3} $\frac{1}{4^3}$ **b.** $\dfrac{4^2}{4^5}$ $\frac{1}{4^3}$

For Exercises 27–46, simplify. **(See Examples 2–4.)**

27. $\left(\dfrac{2}{7}\right)^{-3}$ $\frac{343}{8}$

28. $\left(\dfrac{5}{4}\right)^{-1}$ $\frac{4}{5}$

29. $\left(-\dfrac{1}{5}\right)^{-2}$ 25

30. $\left(-\dfrac{1}{3}\right)^{-3}$ −27

31. a^{-3} $\frac{1}{a^3}$

32. c^{-5} $\frac{1}{c^5}$

33. 12^{-1} $\frac{1}{12}$

34. 4^{-2} $\frac{1}{16}$

35. $(4b)^{-2}$ $\frac{1}{16b^2}$

36. $(3z)^{-1}$ $\frac{1}{3z}$

37. $6x^{-2}$ $\frac{6}{x^2}$

38. $7y^{-1}$ $\frac{7}{y}$

Writing · Translating Expression · Geometry · Scientific Calculator · Video

39. $(-8)^{-2}$ $\frac{1}{64}$ 40. -8^{-2} $-\frac{1}{64}$ 41. $-3y^{-4}$ $-\frac{3}{y^4}$ 42. $-6a^{-2}$ $-\frac{6}{a^2}$

43. $(-t)^{-3}$ $-\frac{1}{t^3}$ 44. $(-r)^{-5}$ $-\frac{1}{r^5}$ 45. $\frac{1}{a^{-5}}$ a^5 46. $\frac{1}{b^{-6}}$ b^6

Concept 3: Properties of Integer Exponents: A Summary

For Exercises 47–50, correct the statement.

47. $\frac{x^4}{x^{-6}} = x^{4-6} = x^{-2}$ $\frac{x^4}{x^{-6}} = x^{4-(-6)} = x^{10}$

48. $\frac{y^5}{y^{-3}} = y^{5-3} = y^2$ $\frac{y^5}{y^{-3}} = y^{5-(-3)} = y^8$

49. $2a^{-3} = \frac{1}{2a^3}$ $2a^{-3} = 2 \cdot \frac{1}{a^3} = \frac{2}{a^3}$

50. $5b^{-2} = \frac{1}{5b^2}$ $5b^{-2} = 5 \cdot \frac{1}{b^2} = \frac{5}{b^2}$

Mixed Exercises

For Exercises 51–94, simplify each expression. Write the answer with positive exponents only. **(See Examples 5–6.)**

51. $x^{-8}x^4$ $\frac{1}{x^4}$ 52. s^5s^{-6} $\frac{1}{s}$ 53. $a^{-8}a^8$ 1 54. q^3q^{-3} 1

55. $y^{17}y^{-13}$ y^4 56. $b^{20}b^{-14}$ b^6 57. $(m^{-6}n^9)^3$ $\frac{n^{27}}{m^{18}}$ 58. $(c^4d^{-5})^{-2}$ $\frac{d^{10}}{c^8}$

59. $(-3j^{-5}k^6)^4$ $\frac{81k^{24}}{j^{20}}$ 60. $(6xy^{-11})^{-3}$ $\frac{y^{33}}{6^3x^3}$ or $\frac{y^{33}}{216x^3}$ 61. $\frac{p^3}{p^9}$ $\frac{1}{p^6}$ 62. $\frac{q^2}{q^{10}}$ $\frac{1}{q^8}$

63. $\frac{r^{-5}}{r^{-2}}$ $\frac{1}{r^3}$ 64. $\frac{u^{-2}}{u^{-6}}$ u^4 65. $\frac{a^2}{a^{-6}}$ a^8 66. $\frac{p^3}{p^{-5}}$ p^8

67. $\frac{y^{-2}}{y^6}$ $\frac{1}{y^8}$ 68. $\frac{s^{-4}}{s^3}$ $\frac{1}{s^7}$ 69. $\frac{7^3}{7^2 \cdot 7^8}$ $\frac{1}{7^7}$ 70. $\frac{3^4 \cdot 3}{3^7}$ $\frac{1}{9}$

71. $\frac{a^2a}{a^3}$ 1 72. $\frac{t^5}{t^2t^3}$ 1 73. $\frac{a^{-1}b^2}{a^3b^8}$ $\frac{1}{a^4b^6}$ 74. $\frac{k^{-4}h^{-1}}{k^6h}$ $\frac{1}{k^{10}h^2}$

75. $\frac{w^{-8}(w^2)^{-5}}{w^3}$ $\frac{1}{w^{21}}$ 76. $\frac{p^2p^{-7}}{(p^2)^3}$ $\frac{1}{p^{11}}$ 77. $\frac{3^{-2}}{3}$ $\frac{1}{27}$ 78. $\frac{5^{-1}}{5}$ $\frac{1}{25}$

79. $\left(\frac{p^{-1}q^5}{p^{-6}}\right)^0$ 1 80. $\left(\frac{ab^{-4}}{a^{-5}}\right)^0$ 1 81. $(8x^3y^0)^{-2}$ $\frac{1}{64x^6}$ 82. $(3u^2v^0)^{-3}$ $\frac{1}{27u^6}$

83. $(-8y^{-12})(2y^{16}z^{-2})$ $-\frac{16y^4}{z^2}$ 84. $(5p^{-2}q^5)(-2p^{-4}q^{-1})$ $-\frac{10q^4}{p^6}$ 85. $\frac{-18a^{10}b^6}{108a^{-2}b^6}$ $-\frac{a^{12}}{6}$ 86. $\frac{-35x^{-4}y^{-3}}{-21x^2y^{-3}}$ $\frac{5}{3x^6}$

87. $\frac{(-4c^{12}d^7)^2}{(5c^{-3}d^{10})^{-1}}$ $80c^{21}d^{24}$ 88. $\frac{(s^3t^{-2})^4}{(3s^{-4}t^6)^{-2}}$ $9s^4t^4$ 89. $\frac{(2x^3y^2)^{-3}}{(3x^2y^4)^{-2}}$ $\frac{9y^2}{8x^5}$ 90. $\frac{(5p^4q)^{-3}}{(p^3q^5)^{-4}}$ $\frac{q^{17}}{125}$

91. $\left(\frac{5cd^{-3}}{10d^5}\right)^{-2}$ $\frac{4d^{16}}{c^2}$ 92. $\left(\frac{4m^{10}n^4}{2m^{12}n^{-2}}\right)^{-1}$ $\frac{m^2}{2n^6}$ 93. $(2xy^3)\left(\frac{9xy}{4x^3y^2}\right)$ $\frac{9y^2}{2x}$ 94. $(-3a^3)\left(\frac{ab}{27a^4b^2}\right)$ $-\frac{1}{9b}$

For Exercises 95–102, simplify. **(See Example 7.)**

95. $5^{-1} + 2^{-2}$ $\frac{9}{20}$ 96. $4^{-2} + 8^{-1}$ $\frac{3}{16}$ 97. $10^0 - 10^{-1}$ $\frac{9}{10}$ 98. $3^0 - 3^{-2}$ $\frac{8}{9}$

99. $2^{-2} + 1^{-2}$ $\frac{5}{4}$ 100. $4^{-1} + 8^{-1}$ $\frac{3}{8}$ 101. $4 \cdot 5^0 - 2 \cdot 3^{-1}$ $\frac{10}{3}$ 102. $2 \cdot 4^0 - 3 \cdot 4^{-1}$ $\frac{5}{4}$

Expanding Your Skills

For Exercises 103–106, determine the missing exponent.

103. $\dfrac{y^4y^{\square}}{y^{-2}} = y^8$ 2

104. $\dfrac{x^4x^{\square}}{x^{-1}} = x^9$ 4

105. $\dfrac{w^{-9}}{w^{\square}} = w^2$ −11

106. $\dfrac{a^{-2}}{a^{\square}} = a^6$ −8

Problem Recognition Exercises

Properties of Exponents

For Exercises 1–40, simplify completely. Assume that all variables represent nonzero real numbers.

1. t^3t^5 t^8

2. 2^32^5 2^8 or 256

3. $\dfrac{y^7}{y^2}$ y^5

4. $\dfrac{p^9}{p^3}$ p^6

5. $(r^2s^4)^2$ r^4s^8

6. $(ab^3c^2)^3$ $a^3b^9c^6$

7. $\dfrac{w^4}{w^{-2}}$ w^6

8. $\dfrac{m^{-14}}{m^2}$ $\dfrac{1}{m^{16}}$

9. $\dfrac{y^{-7}x^4}{z^{-3}}$ $\dfrac{x^4z^3}{y^7}$

10. $\dfrac{a^3b^{-6}}{c^{-8}}$ $\dfrac{a^3c^8}{b^6}$

11. $\dfrac{x^4x^{-3}}{x^{-5}}$ x^6

12. $\dfrac{y^{-4}}{y^7y^{-1}}$ $\dfrac{1}{y^{10}}$

13. $\dfrac{t^{-2}t^4}{t^8t^{-1}}$ $\dfrac{1}{t^5}$

14. $\dfrac{w^8w^{-5}}{w^{-2}w^{-2}}$ w^7

15. $\dfrac{1}{p^{-6}p^{-8}p^{-1}}$ p^{15}

16. p^6p^8p p^{15}

17. $\dfrac{v^9}{v^{11}}$ $\dfrac{1}{v^2}$

18. $(c^5d^4)^{10}$ $c^{50}d^{40}$

19. $\left(\dfrac{1}{2}\right)^{-1} + \left(\dfrac{1}{3}\right)^0$ 3

20. $\left(\dfrac{1}{4}\right)^0 - \left(\dfrac{1}{5}\right)^{-1}$ −4

21. $(2^5b^{-3})^{-3}$ $\dfrac{b^9}{2^{15}}$

22. $(3^{-2}y^3)^{-2}$ $\dfrac{81}{y^6}$

23. $\left(\dfrac{3x}{2y}\right)^{-4}$ $\dfrac{16y^4}{81x^4}$

24. $\left(\dfrac{6c}{5d^3}\right)^{-2}$ $\dfrac{25d^6}{36c^2}$

25. $(3ab^2)(a^2b)^3$ $3a^7b^5$

26. $(4x^2y^3)^3(xy^2)$ $64x^7y^{11}$

27. $\left(\dfrac{xy^2}{x^3y}\right)^4$ $\dfrac{y^4}{x^8}$

28. $\left(\dfrac{a^3b}{a^5b^3}\right)^5$ $\dfrac{1}{a^{10}b^{10}}$

29. $\dfrac{(t^{-2})^3}{t^{-4}}$ $\dfrac{1}{t^2}$

30. $\dfrac{(p^3)^{-4}}{p^{-5}}$ $\dfrac{1}{p^7}$

31. $\left(\dfrac{2w^2x^3}{3y^0}\right)^3$ $\dfrac{8w^6x^9}{27}$

32. $\left(\dfrac{5a^0b^4}{4c^3}\right)^2$ $\dfrac{25b^8}{16c^6}$

33. $\dfrac{q^3r^{-2}}{s^{-1}t^5}$ $\dfrac{q^3s}{r^2t^5}$

34. $\dfrac{n^{-3}m^2}{p^{-3}q^{-1}}$ $\dfrac{m^2p^3q}{n^3}$

35. $\dfrac{(y^{-3})^2(y^5)}{(y^{-3})^{-4}}$ $\dfrac{1}{y^{13}}$

36. $\dfrac{(w^2)^{-4}(w^{-2})}{(w^5)^{-4}}$ w^{10}

37. $\left(\dfrac{-2a^2b^{-3}}{a^{-4}b^{-5}}\right)^{-3}$ $-\dfrac{1}{8a^{18}b^6}$

38. $\left(\dfrac{-3x^{-4}y^3}{2x^5y^{-2}}\right)^{-2}$ $\dfrac{4x^{18}}{9y^{10}}$

39. $(5h^{-2}k^0)^3(5k^{-2})^{-4}$ $\dfrac{k^8}{5h^6}$

40. $(6m^3n^{-5})^{-4}(6m^0n^{-2})^5$ $\dfrac{6n^{10}}{m^{12}}$

Scientific Notation

Section 5.4

Concepts

1. **Writing Numbers in Scientific Notation**
2. **Writing Numbers in Standard Form**
3. **Multiplying and Dividing Numbers in Scientific Notation**

1. Writing Numbers in Scientific Notation

In many applications in mathematics, it is necessary to work with very large or very small numbers. For example, the number of movie tickets sold in the United States recently is estimated to be 1,500,000,000. The weight of a flea is approximately 0.00066 lb. To avoid writing numerous zeros in very large or small numbers, scientific notation was devised as a shortcut.

The principle behind scientific notation is to use a power of 10 to express the magnitude of the number. For example, the numbers 4000 and 0.07 can be written as:

$$4000 = 4 \times 1000 \quad = 4 \times 10^3$$

$$0.07 = 7.0 \times 0.01 = 7.0 \times 10^{-2} \qquad \text{Note that } 10^{-2} = \frac{1}{100} = 0.01$$

Definition of Scientific Notation

A positive number expressed in the form: $a \times 10^n$, where $1 \le a < 10$ and n is an integer, is said to be written in **scientific notation.**

To write a positive number in scientific notation, we apply the following guidelines:

1. Move the decimal point so that its new location is to the right of the first nonzero digit. The number should now be greater than or equal to 1 but less than 10. Count the number of places that the decimal point is moved.
2. If the original number is *large* (greater than or equal to 10), use the number of places the decimal point was moved as a *positive* power of 10.

$$450{,}000 = 4.5 \times 100{,}000 = 4.5 \times 10^5$$

5 places

3. If the original number is *small* (between 0 and 1), use the number of places the decimal point was moved as a *negative* power of 10.

$$0.0002 = 2.0 \times 0.0001 = 2.0 \times 10^{-4}$$

4 places

4. If the original number is greater than or equal to 1 but less than 10, use 0 as the power of 10.

$7.592 = 7.592 \times 10^0$ *Note*: A number between 1 and 10 is seldom written in scientific notation.

5. If the original number is negative, then $-10 < a \le -1$.

$$-450{,}000 = -4.5 \times 100{,}000 = -4.5 \times 10^5$$

5 places

Classroom Examples: p. 371, Exercises 22 and 26

Example 1 Writing Numbers in Scientific Notation

Write the numbers in scientific notation.

a. 53,000 **b.** 0.00053

Solution:

a. $53{,}000. = 5.3 \times 10^4$

To write 53,000 in scientific notation, the decimal point must be moved four places to the left. Because 53,000 is larger than 10, a *positive* power of 10 is used.

b. $0.00053 = 5.3 \times 10^{-4}$

To write 0.00053 in scientific notation, the decimal point must be moved four places to the right. Because 0.00053 is between 0 and 1, a *negative* power of 10 is used.

Skill Practice Write the numbers in scientific notation.

1. 175,000,000 **2.** 0.000005

Classroom Examples: p. 371, Exercises 30 and 32

Example 2 Writing Numbers in Scientific Notation

Write the numbers in scientific notation.

a. The number of movie tickets sold in the United States for a recent year is estimated to be 1,500,000,000.

b. The weight of a flea is approximately 0.00066 lb.

c. The temperature on a January day in Fargo dropped to −43°F.

d. A bench is 8.2 ft long.

Solution:

a. $1{,}500{,}000{,}000 = 1.5 \times 10^9$

b. $0.00066 \text{ lb} = 6.6 \times 10^{-4} \text{ lb}$

c. $-43°\text{F} = -4.3 \times 10^1 \text{ °F}$

d. $8.2 \text{ ft} = 8.2 \times 10^0 \text{ ft}$

Skill Practice Write the numbers in scientific notation.

3. In the year 2011, the population of the Earth was approximately 7,000,000,000.

4. The weight of a grain of salt is approximately 0.000002 ounce.

2. Writing Numbers in Standard Form

Classroom Examples: p. 372, Exercises 40 and 50

Example 3 Writing Numbers in Standard Form

Write the numbers in standard form.

a. The mass of a proton is approximately 1.67×10^{-24} g.

b. The "nearby" star Vega is approximately 1.552×10^{14} miles from Earth.

Solution:

a. $1.67 \times 10^{-24} \text{ g} = 0.000\,000\,000\,000\,000\,000\,000\,001\,67 \text{ g}$

Because the power of 10 is negative, the value of 1.67×10^{-24} is a decimal number between 0 and 1. Move the decimal point 24 places to the *left*.

b. $1.552 \times 10^{14} \text{ miles} = 155{,}200{,}000{,}000{,}000 \text{ miles}$

Because the power of 10 is a positive integer, the value of 1.552×10^{14} is a large number greater than 10. Move the decimal point 14 places to the *right*.

Answers

1. 1.75×10^8 **2.** 5×10^{-6}

3. 7×10^9 **4.** 2×10^{-6} oz

Skill Practice Write the numbers in standard form.

5. The probability of winning the California Super Lotto Jackpot is 5.5×10^{-8}.
6. The Sun's mass is 2×10^{30} kilograms.

3. Multiplying and Dividing Numbers in Scientific Notation

To multiply or divide two numbers in scientific notation, use the commutative and associative properties of multiplication to group the powers of 10. For example:

$$400 \times 2000 = (4 \times 10^2)(2 \times 10^3) = (4 \cdot 2) \times (10^2 \cdot 10^3) = 8 \times 10^5$$

$$\frac{0.00054}{150} = \frac{5.4 \times 10^{-4}}{1.5 \times 10^2} = \left(\frac{5.4}{1.5}\right) \times \left(\frac{10^{-4}}{10^2}\right) = 3.6 \times 10^{-6}$$

Example 4 Multiplying and Dividing Numbers in Scientific Notation

Classroom Examples: p. 372, Exercises 54 and 68

Multiply or divide as indicated.

a. $(8.7 \times 10^4)(2.5 \times 10^{-12})$ **b.** $\dfrac{4.25 \times 10^{13}}{8.5 \times 10^{-2}}$

Solution:

a. $(8.7 \times 10^4)(2.5 \times 10^{-12})$

$= (8.7 \cdot 2.5) \times (10^4 \cdot 10^{-12})$ Regroup factors using the commutative and associative properties of multiplication.

$= 21.75 \times 10^{-8}$ The number 21.75 is not in proper scientific notation because 21.75 is not between 1 and 10.

$= (2.175 \times 10^1) \times 10^{-8}$ Rewrite 21.75 as 2.175×10^1.

$= 2.175 \times (10^1 \times 10^{-8})$ Associative property of multiplication

$= 2.175 \times 10^{-7}$ Simplify.

b. $\dfrac{4.25 \times 10^{13}}{8.5 \times 10^{-2}}$

$= \left(\dfrac{4.25}{8.5}\right) \times \left(\dfrac{10^{13}}{10^{-2}}\right)$ Regroup factors using the commutative and associative properties.

$= 0.5 \times 10^{15}$ The number 0.5×10^{15} is not in proper scientific notation because 0.5 is not between 1 and 10.

$= (5.0 \times 10^{-1}) \times 10^{15}$ Rewrite 0.5 as 5.0×10^{-1}.

$= 5.0 \times (10^{-1} \times 10^{15})$ Associative property of multiplication

$= 5.0 \times 10^{14}$ Simplify.

Skill Practice Multiply or divide as indicated.

7. $(7 \times 10^5)(5 \times 10^3)$
8. $\dfrac{1 \times 10^{-2}}{4 \times 10^{-7}}$

Answers

5. 0.000 000 055
6. 2,000,000,000,000,000,000,000,000,000,000
7. 3.5×10^9
8. 2.5×10^4

Calculator Connections

Topic: Using Scientific Notation

Both scientific and graphing calculators can perform calculations involving numbers written in scientific notation. Most calculators use an [EE] key or an [EXP] key to enter the power of 10.

Scientific Calculator

Enter: 2.7 [EE] 5 [=] or 2.7 [EXP] 5 [=] **Result:** 270000

Enter: 7.1 [EE] 3 [+○-] [=] or 7.1 [EXP] 3 [+○-] [=] **Result:** 0.0071

Graphing Calculator

```
2.7E5
              270000
7.1E-3
               .0071
```

We recommend that you use parentheses to enclose each number written in scientific notation when performing calculations. Try using your calculator to perform the calculations from Example 4.

a. $(8.7 \times 10^4)(2.5 \times 10^{-12})$ **b.** $\dfrac{4.25 \times 10^{13}}{8.5 \times 10^{-2}}$

Scientific Calculator

Enter: [(] 8.7 [EE] 4 [)] [×] [(] 2.5 [EE] 12 [+○-] [)] [=] **Result:** 0.000000218

Enter: [(] 4.25 [EE] 13 [)] [÷] [(] 8.5 [EE] 2 [+○-] [)] [=] **Result:** 5E14

Notice that the answer to part (b) is shown on the calculator in scientific notation. The calculator does not have enough room to display 14 zeros. Also notice that the calculator rounds the answer to part (a). The exact answer is 2.175×10^{-7} or 0.0000002175.

Graphing Calculator

```
(8.7E4)*(2.5E-12
)
            2.175E-7
(4.25E13)/(8.5E-
2)
                5E14
```

Avoiding Mistakes

A display of 5E14 on a calculator does not mean 5^{14}. It is scientific notation and means 5×10^{14}.

Calculator Exercises

Use a calculator to perform the indicated operations:

1. $(5.2 \times 10^6)(4.6 \times 10^{-3})$ 23,920
2. $(2.19 \times 10^{-8})(7.84 \times 10^{-4})$ 1.71696×10^{-11}
3. $\dfrac{4.76 \times 10^{-5}}{2.38 \times 10^9}$ 2×10^{-14}
4. $\dfrac{8.5 \times 10^4}{4.0 \times 10^{-1}}$ 212,500
5. $\dfrac{(9.6 \times 10^7)(4.0 \times 10^{-3})}{2.0 \times 10^{-2}}$ 19,200,000
6. $\dfrac{(5.0 \times 10^{-12})(6.4 \times 10^{-5})}{(1.6 \times 10^{-8})(4.0 \times 10^2)}$ 5×10^{-11}

Section 5.4 Practice Exercises

For additional exercises, see Classroom Activities 5.4A–5.4B in the *Student's Resource Manual* at www.mhhe.com/moh.

Vocabulary and Key Concepts

1. A positive number expressed in the form $a \times 10^n$, where $1 \le a < 10$ and n is an integer is said to be written in scientific notation.

Review Exercises

For Exercises 2–13, simplify each expression. Assume all variables represent nonzero real numbers.

2. a^3a^{-4} $\frac{1}{a}$

3. b^5b^8 b^{13}

4. $10^3 \cdot 10^{-4}$ $\frac{1}{10}$

5. $10^5 \cdot 10^8$ 10^{13}

6. $\frac{x^3}{x^6}$ $\frac{1}{x^3}$

7. $\frac{y^2}{y^7}$ $\frac{1}{y^5}$

8. $(c^4d^2)^3$ $c^{12}d^6$

9. $(x^5y^{-3})^4$ $\frac{x^{20}}{y^{12}}$

10. $\frac{z^9z^4}{z^3}$ z^{10}

11. $\frac{w^{-2}w^5}{w^{-1}}$ w^4

12. $\frac{10^9 \cdot 10^4}{10^3}$ 10^{10}

13. $\frac{10^{-2} \cdot 10^5}{10^{-1}}$ 10^4

Concept 1: Writing Numbers in Scientific Notation

14. Explain how scientific notation might be valuable in studying astronomy. Answers may vary.
For example: Scientific notation would be helpful in writing the distance between Earth and the stars or planets.

15. Explain how you would write the number 0.000 000 000 23 in scientific notation. Move the decimal point between the 2 and 3 and multiply by 10^{-10}; 2.3×10^{-10}.

16. Explain how you would write the number 23,000,000,000,000 in scientific notation. Move the decimal point between the 2 and 3 and multiply by 10^{13}; 2.3×10^{13}.

For Exercises 17–28, write the number in scientific notation. **(See Example 1.)**

17. 50,000 5×10^4

18. 900,000 9×10^5

19. 208,000 2.08×10^5

20. 420,000,000 4.2×10^8

21. 6,010,000 6.01×10^6

22. 75,000 7.5×10^4

23. 0.000008 8×10^{-6}

24. 0.003 3×10^{-3}

25. 0.000125 1.25×10^{-4}

26. 0.00000025 2.5×10^{-7}

27. 0.006708 6.708×10^{-3}

28. 0.02004 2.004×10^{-2}

For Exercises 29–34, write each number in scientific notation. **(See Example 2.)**

29. The mass of a proton is approximately 0.000 000 000 000 000 000 000 0017 g. 1.7×10^{-24} g

30. The total combined salaries of the president, vice president, senators, and representatives of the United States federal government is approximately \$85,000,000. \$$8.5 \times 10^7$

31. A renowned foundation has over \$27,000,000,000 from which it makes contributions to global charities. \$$2.7 \times 10^{10}$

32. One gram is equivalent to 0.0035 oz. 3.5×10^{-3} oz

33. One of the world's largest tanker disasters spilled 68,000,000 gal of oil off Portsall, France, causing widespread environmental damage over 100 miles of Brittany coast. 6.8×10^7 gal; 1×10^2 miles

34. The human heart pumps about 2100 gal of blood per day. That means that it pumps approximately 767,000 gal per year. 2.1×10^3 gal; 7.67×10^5 gal

Writing | Translating Expression | Geometry | Scientific Calculator | Video

Concept 2: Writing Numbers in Standard Form

35. Explain how you would write the number 3.1×10^{-9} in standard form. Move the decimal point nine places to the left; 0.000 000 0031.

36. Explain how you would write the number 3.1×10^{9} in standard form. Move the decimal point nine places to the right; 3,100,000,000.

For Exercises 37–52, write each number in standard form. **(See Example 3.)**

37. 5×10^{-5} 0.00005

38. 2×10^{-7} 0.0000002

39. 2.8×10^{3} 2800

40. 9.1×10^{6} 9,100,000

41. 6.03×10^{-4} 0.000603

42. 7.01×10^{-3} 0.00701

43. 2.4×10^{6} 2,400,000

44. 3.1×10^{4} 31,000

45. 1.9×10^{-2} 0.019

46. 2.8×10^{-6} 0.0000028

47. 7.032×10^{3} 7032

48. 8.205×10^{2} 820.5

49. One picogram (pg) is equal to 1×10^{-12} g. 0.000 000 000 001 g

50. A nanometer (nm) is approximately 3.94×10^{-8} in. 0.000 000 0394 in.

51. A normal diet contains between 1.6×10^{3} Cal and 2.8×10^{3} Cal per day. 1600 Cal and 2800 Cal

52. The total land area of Texas is approximately 2.62×10^{5} square miles. 262,000 square miles

© Ryan McVay/Getty Images RF

Concept 3: Multiplying and Dividing Numbers in Scientific Notation

For Exercises 53–72, multiply or divide as indicated. Write the answers in scientific notation. **(See Example 4.)**

53. $(2.5 \times 10^{6})(2 \times 10^{-2})$ 5×10^{4}

54. $(2 \times 10^{-7})(3 \times 10^{13})$ 6×10^{6}

55. $(1.2 \times 10^{4})(3 \times 10^{7})$ 3.6×10^{11}

56. $(3.2 \times 10^{-3})(2.5 \times 10^{8})$ 8×10^{5}

57. $\dfrac{7.7 \times 10^{6}}{3.5 \times 10^{2}}$ 2.2×10^{4}

58. $\dfrac{9.5 \times 10^{11}}{1.9 \times 10^{3}}$ 5×10^{8}

59. $\dfrac{9 \times 10^{-6}}{4 \times 10^{7}}$ 2.25×10^{-13}

60. $\dfrac{7 \times 10^{-2}}{5 \times 10^{9}}$ 1.4×10^{-11}

61. $80{,}000{,}000{,}000 \times 4000$ 3.2×10^{14}

62. 0.0006×0.03 1.8×10^{-5}

63. $(3.2 \times 10^{-4})(7.6 \times 10^{-7})$ 2.432×10^{-10}

64. $(5.9 \times 10^{12})(3.6 \times 10^{9})$ 2.124×10^{22}

65. $\dfrac{210{,}000{,}000{,}000}{0.007}$ 3×10^{13}

66. $\dfrac{160{,}000{,}000{,}000{,}000}{0.00008}$ 2×10^{18}

67. $\dfrac{5.7 \times 10^{-2}}{9.5 \times 10^{-8}}$ 6×10^{5}

68. $\dfrac{2.72 \times 10^{-6}}{6.8 \times 10^{-4}}$ 4×10^{-3}

69. $6{,}000{,}000{,}000 \times 0.0000000023$ 1.38×10^{1}

70. $0.000055 \times 40{,}000$ 2.2×10^{0}

71. $\dfrac{0.0000000003}{6000}$ 5×10^{-14}

72. $\dfrac{420{,}000}{0.0000021}$ 2×10^{11}

Mixed Exercises

73. If a piece of paper is 3×10^{-3} in. thick, how thick is a stack of 1.25×10^{3} pieces of paper? 3.75 in.

74. A box of staples contains 5×10^{3} staples and weighs 15 oz. How much does one staple weigh? Write your answer in scientific notation. 3×10^{-3} oz

75. At one time, Bill Gates owned approximately 1,100,000,000 shares of Microsoft stock. If the stock price was \$27 per share, how much was Bill Gates' stock worth? $\$2.97 \times 10^{10}$

76. A state lottery had a jackpot of $\$5.2 \times 10^7$. This week the winner was a group of office employees that included 13 people. How much would each person receive? $\$4 \times 10^6$ or \$4,000,000

77. Dinosaurs became extinct about 65 million years ago.

a. Write the number 65 million in scientific notation. 6.5×10^7

b. How many days is 65 million years? 2.3725×10^{10} days

c. How many hours is 65 million years? 5.694×10^{11} hr

d. How many seconds is 65 million years? 2.04984×10^{15} sec

78. The Earth is 150,000,000 km from the Sun.

a. Write the number 150,000,000 in scientific notation. 1.5×10^8

b. There are 1000 m in a kilometer. How many meters is the Earth from the Sun? 1.5×10^{11} m

c. There are 100 cm in a meter. How many centimeters is the Earth from the Sun? 1.5×10^{13} cm

Addition and Subtraction of Polynomials

Section 5.5

Concepts

1. Introduction to Polynomials
2. Addition of Polynomials
3. Subtraction of Polynomials
4. Polynomials and Applications to Geometry

1. Introduction to Polynomials

One commonly used algebraic expression is called a polynomial. A **polynomial** in one variable, x, is defined as a single term or a sum of terms of the form ax^n, where a is a real number and the exponent, n, is a nonnegative integer. For each term, a is called the **coefficient**, and n is called the **degree of the term**. For example:

Term (Expressed in the Form ax^n)	Coefficient	Degree
$-12z^7$	-12	7
$x^3 \rightarrow$ rewrite as $1x^3$	1	3
$10w \rightarrow$ rewrite as $10w^1$	10	1
$7 \rightarrow$ rewrite as $7x^0$	7	0

If a polynomial has exactly one term, it is categorized as a **monomial**. A two-term polynomial is called a **binomial**, and a three-term polynomial is called a **trinomial**. Usually the terms of a polynomial are written in descending order according to degree. The term with highest degree is called the **leading term**, and its coefficient is called the **leading coefficient**. The **degree of a polynomial** is the greatest degree of all of its terms. A polynomial in one variable is written in **descending order** if the term with highest degree is written first, followed by the term of next highest degree and so on. Thus, for a polynomial written in descending order, the leading term determines the degree of the polynomial.

Instructor Note: Ask students why a constant has degree 0.

	Expression	Descending Order	Leading Coefficient	Degree of Polynomial
Monomials	$-3x^4$	$-3x^4$	-3	4
	17	17	17	0
Binomials	$4y^3 - 6y^5$	$-6y^5 + 4y^3$	-6	5
	$\frac{1}{2} - \frac{1}{4}c$	$-\frac{1}{4}c + \frac{1}{2}$	$-\frac{1}{4}$	1
Trinomials	$4p - 3p^3 + 8p^6$	$8p^6 - 3p^3 + 4p$	8	6
	$7a^4 - 1.2a^8 + 3a^3$	$-1.2a^8 + 7a^4 + 3a^3$	-1.2	8

Classroom Example: p. 380, Exercise 14

Example 1 Identifying the Parts of a Polynomial

Given the polynomial: $3a - 2a^4 + 6 - a^3$

a. List the terms of the polynomial, and state the coefficient and degree of each term.

b. Write the polynomial in descending order.

c. State the degree of the polynomial and the leading coefficient.

d. Evaluate the polynomial for $a = -2$.

Solution:

a. term: $3a$ coefficient: 3 degree: 1

term: $-2a^4$ coefficient: -2 degree: 4

term: 6 coefficient: 6 degree: 0

term: $-a^3$ coefficient: -1 degree: 3

b. $-2a^4 - a^3 + 3a + 6$

c. The degree of the polynomial is 4 and the leading coefficient is -2.

d. $-2a^4 - a^3 + 3a + 6$

$= -2(-2)^4 - (-2)^3 + 3(-2) + 6$ Substitute -2 for the variable, a. Remember to use parentheses when replacing a variable.

$= -2(16) - (-8) + 3(-2) + 6$ Simplify exponents first.

$= -32 - (-8) + (-6) + 6$ Perform multiplication before addition and subtraction.

$= -24$ Simplify.

Skill Practice

1. Given the polynomial: $5x^3 - x + 8x^4 + 3x^2$

a. Write the polynomial in descending order.

b. State the degree of the polynomial.

c. State the coefficient of the leading term.

d. Evaluate the polynomial for $x = -1$.

Polynomials may have more than one variable. In such a case, the degree of a term is the sum of the exponents of the variables contained in the term. For example, the term, $32x^2y^5z$, has degree 8 because the exponents applied to x, y, and z are 2, 5, and 1, respectively. The following polynomial has a degree of 11 because the highest degree of its terms is 11.

$$\underset{\text{degree } 8}{32x^2y^5z} - \underset{\text{degree } 4}{2x^3y} + \underset{\text{degree } 11}{2x^2yz^8} + \underset{\text{degree } 0}{7}$$

Answers

1. a. $8x^4 + 5x^3 + 3x^2 - x$
b. 4 **c.** 8 **d.** 7

2. Addition of Polynomials

Recall that two terms are *like* terms if they each have the same variables, and the corresponding variables are raised to the same powers.

Like Terms: $3x^2, -7x^2$ (Same exponents; Same variables) $\quad -5yz^3, yz^3$ (Same exponents; Same variables)

Unlike Terms: $9z^2, 12z^6$ (Different exponents) $\quad \frac{1}{3}w^6, \frac{2}{5}p^6$ (Different variables) $\quad 4y, 7$ (Different variables)

Avoiding Mistakes

Note that when adding terms, the exponents do *not* change.

$$2x^3 + 3x^3 \neq 5x^6$$

Recall that the distributive property is used to add or subtract *like* terms. For example,

$3x^2 + 9x^2 - 2x^2$

$= (3 + 9 - 2)x^2$ Apply the distributive property.

$= (10)x^2$ Simplify.

$= 10x^2$

Example 2 Adding Polynomials

Classroom Example: p. 380, Exercise 26

Add the polynomials. $3x^2y + 5x^2y$

Solution:

$3x^2y + 5x^2y$ The terms are *like* terms.

$= (3 + 5)x^2y$ Apply the distributive property.

$= (8)x^2y$

$= 8x^2y$ Simplify.

Skill Practice Add the polynomials.

2. $13a^2b^3 + 2a^2b^3$

It is the distributive property that enables us to add *like* terms. We shorten the process by adding the coefficients of *like* terms.

Example 3 Adding Polynomials

Classroom Example: p. 380, Exercise 28

Add the polynomials. $(-3c^3 + 5c^2 - 7c) + (11c^3 + 6c^2 + 3)$

Solution:

$(-3c^3 + 5c^2 - 7c) + (11c^3 + 6c^2 + 3)$

$= -3c^3 + 11c^3 + 5c^2 + 6c^2 - 7c + 3$ Clear parentheses, and group *like* terms.

$= 8c^3 + 11c^2 - 7c + 3$ Combine *like* terms.

Avoiding Mistakes

When *adding* like terms, the exponents do not change.

Answer

2. $15a^2b^3$

TIP: Polynomials can also be added by combining *like* terms in columns. The sum of the polynomials from Example 3 is shown here.

$$\begin{array}{r} -3c^3 + 5c^2 - 7c + 0 \\ + 11c^3 + 6c^2 + 0c + 3 \\ \hline 8c^3 + 11c^2 - 7c + 3 \end{array}$$

Place holders such as 0 and 0c may be used to help line up *like* terms.

Skill Practice Add the polynomials.

3. $(7q^2 - 2q + 4) + (5q^2 + 6q - 9)$

Classroom Example: p. 380, Exercise 30

Example 4 **Adding Polynomials**

Add the polynomials. $(4w^2 - 2x) + (3w^2 - 4x^2 + 6x)$

Solution:

$(4w^2 - 2x) + (3w^2 - 4x^2 + 6x)$

$= 4w^2 + 3w^2 - 4x^2 - 2x + 6x$ Clear parentheses and group *like* terms.

$= 7w^2 - 4x^2 + 4x$

Skill Practice Add the polynomials.

4. $(5x^2 - 4xy + y^2) + (-3x^2 - 5y^2)$

3. Subtraction of Polynomials

Subtraction of two polynomials requires us to find the opposite of the polynomial being subtracted. To find the opposite of a polynomial, take the opposite of each term. This is equivalent to multiplying the polynomial by -1.

Classroom Example: p. 381, Exercise 46

Example 5 **Finding the Opposite of a Polynomial**

Find the opposite of the polynomials.

a. $5x$ **b.** $3a - 4b - c$ **c.** $5.5y^4 - 2.4y^3 + 1.1y$

Solution:

	Expression	Opposite	Simplified Form
a.	$5x$	$-(5x)$	$-5x$
b.	$3a - 4b - c$	$-(3a - 4b - c)$	$-3a + 4b + c$
c.	$5.5y^4 - 2.4y^3 + 1.1y$	$-(5.5y^4 - 2.4y^3 + 1.1y)$	$-5.5y^4 + 2.4y^3 - 1.1y$

TIP: Notice that the sign of each term is changed when finding the opposite of a polynomial.

Skill Practice Find the opposite of the polynomials.

5. $x - 3$ 6. $3y^2 - 2xy + 6x + 2$ 7. $-2.1w^3 + 4.9w^2 - 1.9w$

Subtraction of two polynomials is similar to subtracting real numbers. Add the opposite of the second polynomial to the first polynomial.

Answers

3. $12q^2 + 4q - 5$
4. $2x^2 - 4xy - 4y^2$
5. $-x + 3$
6. $-3y^2 + 2xy - 6x - 2$
7. $2.1w^3 - 4.9w^2 + 1.9w$

Subtraction of Polynomials

If A and B are polynomials, then $A - B = A + (-B)$.

Example 6 Subtracting Polynomials

Classroom Example: p. 381, Exercise 58

Subtract the polynomials. $(-4p^4 + 5p^2 - 3) - (11p^2 + 4p - 6)$

Solution:

$(-4p^4 + 5p^2 - 3) - (11p^2 + 4p - 6)$

$= (-4p^4 + 5p^2 - 3) + (-11p^2 - 4p + 6)$ — Add the opposite of the second polynomial.

$= -4p^4 + 5p^2 - 11p^2 - 4p - 3 + 6$ — Group *like* terms.

$= -4p^4 - 6p^2 - 4p + 3$ — Combine *like* terms.

TIP: Two polynomials can also be subtracted in columns by adding the opposite of the second polynomial to the first polynomial. Place holders (shown in red) may be used to help line up *like* terms.

$$\begin{array}{r} -4p^4 + 0p^3 + 5p^2 + 0p - 3 \\ -(0p^4 + 0p^3 + 11p^2 + 4p - 6) \\ \hline \end{array} \xrightarrow{\text{Add the opposite}} \begin{array}{r} -4p^4 + 0p^3 + 5p^2 + 0p - 3 \\ + -0p^4 - 0p^3 - 11p^2 - 4p + 6 \\ \hline -4p^4 \qquad - 6p^2 - 4p + 3 \end{array}$$

The difference of the polynomials is $-4p^4 - 6p^2 - 4p + 3$.

Skill Practice Subtract the polynomials.

8. $(x^2 + 3x - 2) - (4x^2 + 6x + 1)$

Example 7 Subtracting Polynomials

Classroom Example: p. 381, Exercise 60

Subtract the polynomials. $(a^2 - 2ab + 7b^2) - (-8a^2 - 6ab + 2b^2)$

Solution:

$(a^2 - 2ab + 7b^2) - (-8a^2 - 6ab + 2b^2)$

$= (a^2 - 2ab + 7b^2) + (8a^2 + 6ab - 2b^2)$ — Add the opposite of the second polynomial.

$= a^2 + 8a^2 - 2ab + 6ab + 7b^2 - 2b^2$ — Group *like* terms.

$= 9a^2 + 4ab + 5b^2$ — Combine *like* terms.

Skill Practice Subtract the polynomials.

9. $(-3y^2 + xy + 2x^2) - (-2y^2 - 3xy - 8x^2)$

In Example 8, we illustrate the subtraction of polynomials by first clearing parentheses and then combining *like* terms.

Answers

8. $-3x^2 - 3x - 3$
9. $-y^2 + 4xy + 10x^2$

Classroom Example: p. 381, Exercise 72

Example 8 **Subtracting Polynomials**

Subtract $\frac{1}{3}t^4 + \frac{1}{2}t^2$ from $t^2 - 4$, and simplify the result.

Solution:

To subtract a from b, we write $b - a$. Thus, to subtract $\overbrace{\frac{1}{3}t^4 + \frac{1}{2}t^2}^{a}$ from $\overbrace{t^2 - 4}^{b}$, we have

$$\overbrace{(t^2 - 4)}^{b} - \overbrace{\left(\frac{1}{3}t^4 + \frac{1}{2}t^2\right)}^{a}$$

$= t^2 - 4 - \frac{1}{3}t^4 - \frac{1}{2}t^2$ Apply the distributive property to clear parentheses.

$= -\frac{1}{3}t^4 + t^2 - \frac{1}{2}t^2 - 4$ Group *like* terms in descending order.

$= -\frac{1}{3}t^4 + \frac{2}{2}t^2 - \frac{1}{2}t^2 - 4$ The t^2-terms are the only *like* terms. Get a common denominator for the t^2-terms.

$= -\frac{1}{3}t^4 + \frac{1}{2}t^2 - 4$ Add *like* terms.

Avoiding Mistakes

Example 8 involves subtracting two *expressions*. This is not an equation. Therefore, we cannot clear fractions.

Skill Practice

10. Subtract $\frac{3}{4}x^2 + \frac{2}{5}$ from $x^2 + 3x$.

4. Polynomials and Applications to Geometry

Classroom Example: p. 382, Exercise 76

Example 9 **Subtracting Polynomials in Geometry**

If the perimeter of the triangle in Figure 5-1 can be represented by the polynomial $2x^2 + 5x + 6$, find a polynomial that represents the length of the missing side.

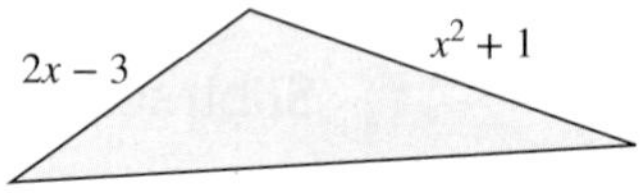

Figure 5-1

Solution:

The missing side of the triangle can be found by subtracting the sum of the two known sides from the perimeter.

$$\begin{pmatrix}\text{Length}\\ \text{of missing}\\ \text{side}\end{pmatrix} = (\text{perimeter}) - \begin{pmatrix}\text{sum of the}\\ \text{two known sides}\end{pmatrix}$$

$$\begin{pmatrix}\text{Length}\\ \text{of missing}\\ \text{side}\end{pmatrix} = (2x^2 + 5x + 6) - [(2x - 3) + (x^2 + 1)]$$

Answer

10. $\frac{1}{4}x^2 + 3x - \frac{2}{5}$

$= 2x^2 + 5x + 6 - [2x - 3 + x^2 + 1]$	Clear inner parentheses.
$= 2x^2 + 5x + 6 - (x^2 + 2x - 2)$	Combine *like* terms within [ ].
$= 2x^2 + 5x + 6 - x^2 - 2x + 2$	Apply the distributive property.
$= 2x^2 - x^2 + 5x - 2x + 6 + 2$	Group *like* terms.
$= x^2 + 3x + 8$	Combine *like* terms.

The polynomial $x^2 + 3x + 8$ represents the length of the missing side.

Skill Practice

11. If the perimeter of the triangle is represented by the polynomial $6x - 9$, find the polynomial that represents the missing side.

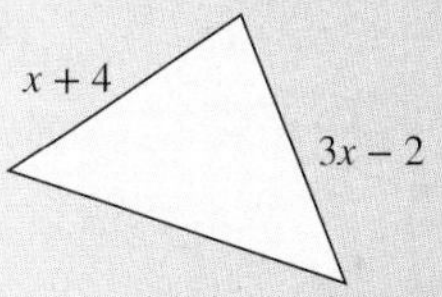

Answer

11. $2x - 11$

Section 5.5 Practice Exercises

For additional exercises, see Classroom Activities 5.5A–5.5C in the *Student's Resource Manual* at www.mhhe.com/moh.

Vocabulary and Key Concepts

1. a. A polynomial is a single term or a sum of terms.

b. For the term ax^n, a is called the coefficient and n is called the degree of the term.

c. Given the term x, the coefficient of the term is 1.

d. A monomial is a polynomial with exactly one term(s).

e. A binomial is a polynomial with exactly two terms.

f. A trinomial is a polynomial with exactly three terms.

g. The term with the highest degree is called the leading term and its coefficient is called the leading coefficient.

h. The degree of a polynomial is the greatest degree of all of its terms.

i. The degree of a nonzero constant such as 5 is zero.

Review Exercises

For Exercises 2–7, simplify each expression.

2. $\dfrac{p^3 \cdot 4p}{p^2}$ $4p^2$

3. $(3x)^2(5x^{-4})$ $\dfrac{45}{x^2}$

4. $(6y^{-3})(2y^9)$ $12y^6$

5. $\dfrac{8t^{-6}}{4t^{-2}}$ $\dfrac{2}{t^4}$

6. $\dfrac{8^3 \cdot 8^{-4}}{8^{-2} \cdot 8^6}$ $\dfrac{1}{8^5}$

7. $\dfrac{3^4 \cdot 3^{-8}}{3^{12} \cdot 3^{-4}}$ $\dfrac{1}{3^{12}}$

8. Explain the difference between 3×10^7 and 3^7. 3×10^7 is in scientific notation in which 10 is raised to the seventh power. 3^7 is not in scientific notation and 3 is being raised to the seventh power.

9. Explain the difference between 4×10^{-2} and 4^{-2}. 4×10^{-2} is in scientific notation in which 10 is raised to the -2 power. 4^{-2} is not in scientific notation and 4 is being raised to the -2 power.

Concept 1: Introduction to Polynomials

For Exercises 10–12,

a. write the polynomial in descending order.

b. identify the leading coefficient.

c. identify the degree of the polynomial. **(See Example 1.)**

10. $10 - 8a - a^3 + 2a^2 + a^5$
a. $a^5 - a^3 + 2a^2 - 8a + 10$ b. 1 c. 5

11. $6 + 7x^2 - 7x^5 + 9x$
a. $-7x^5 + 7x^2 + 9x + 6$ b. -7 c. 5

12. $\frac{1}{2}y + y^2 - 12y^4 + y^3 - 6$
a. $-12y^4 + y^3 + y^2 + \frac{1}{2}y - 6$ b. -12 c. 4

For Exercises 13–22, categorize each expression as a monomial, a binomial, or a trinomial. Then evaluate the polynomial given $x = -3$, $y = 2$, and $z = -1$. **(See Example 1.)**

13. $10x^2 + 5x$
Binomial; 75

14. $7z + 13z^2 - 15$
Trinomial; -9

15. $6x^2$
Monomial; 54

16. 9
Monomial; 9

17. $2y - y^4$
Binomial; -12

18. $7x + 2$
Binomial; -19

19. $2y^4 - 3y + 1$
Trinomial; 27

20. 23
Monomial; 23

21. $-32xyz$
Monomial; -192

22. $y^4 - x^2$
Binomial; 7

Concept 2: Addition of Polynomials

23. Explain why the terms $3x$ and $3x^2$ are not *like* terms. The exponents on the x-factors are different.

24. Explain why the terms $4w^3$ and $4z^3$ are not *like* terms. The variables are different.

For Exercises 25–42, add the polynomials. **(See Examples 2–4.)**

25. $23x^2y + 12x^2y$ $35x^2y$

26. $-5ab^3 + 17ab^3$ $12ab^3$

27. $3b^5d^2 + (5b^5d^2 - 9d)$ $8b^5d^2 - 9d$

28. $4c^2d^3 + (3cd - 10c^2d^3)$ $-6c^2d^3 + 3cd$

29. $(7y^2 + 2y - 9) + (-3y^2 - y)$ $4y^2 + y - 9$

30. $(-3w^2 + 4w - 6) + (5w^2 + 2)$ $2w^2 + 4w - 4$

31. $(5x + 3x^2 - x^3) + (2x^2 + 4x - 10)$
$-x^3 + 5x^2 + 9x - 10$

32. $(t^2 - 4t + t^4) + (3t^4 + 2t + 6)$ $4t^4 + t^2 - 2t + 6$

33. $(6.1y + 3.2x) + (4.8y - 3.2x)$ $10.9y$

34. $(2.7m - 0.5h) + (-3.2m + 0.2h)$ $-0.5m - 0.3h$

35.
$$\begin{array}{rr} & 6a + 2b - 5c \\ + & \underline{-2a - 2b - 3c} \end{array}$$
$4a - 8c$

36.
$$\begin{array}{rr} & -13x + 5y + 10z \\ + & \underline{-3x - 3y + 2z} \end{array}$$
$-16x + 2y + 12z$

37. $\left(\frac{2}{5}a + \frac{1}{4}b - \frac{5}{6}\right) + \left(\frac{3}{5}a - \frac{3}{4}b - \frac{7}{6}\right)$ $a - \frac{1}{2}b - 2$

38. $\left(\frac{5}{9}x + \frac{1}{10}y\right) + \left(-\frac{4}{9}x + \frac{3}{10}y\right)$ $\frac{1}{9}x + \frac{2}{5}y$

39. $\left(z - \frac{8}{3}\right) + \left(\frac{4}{3}z^2 - z + 1\right)$ $\frac{4}{3}z^2 - \frac{5}{3}$

40. $\left(-\frac{7}{5}r + 1\right) + \left(-\frac{3}{5}r^2 + \frac{7}{5}r + 1\right)$ $-\frac{3}{5}r^2 + 2$

41.
$$\begin{array}{rr} & 7.9t^3 \qquad\quad + 2.6t - 1.1 \\ + & \underline{-3.4t^2 + 3.4t - 3.1} \end{array}$$
$7.9t^3 - 3.4t^2 + 6t - 4.2$

42.
$$\begin{array}{rr} & 0.34y^2 \qquad\quad + 1.23 \\ + & \underline{3.42y - 7.56} \end{array}$$
$0.34y^2 + 3.42y - 6.33$

Concept 3: Subtraction of Polynomials

For Exercises 43–48, find the opposite of each polynomial. **(See Example 5.)**

43. $4h - 5$ $\quad -4h + 5$

44. $5k - 12$ $\quad -5k + 12$

45. $-2.3m^2 + 3.1m - 1.5$ $\quad 2.3m^2 - 3.1m + 1.5$

46. $-11.8n^2 - 6.7n + 9.3$ $\quad 11.8n^2 + 6.7n - 9.3$

47. $3v^3 + 5v^2 + 10v + 22$ $\quad -3v^3 - 5v^2 - 10v - 22$

48. $7u^4 + 3v^2 + 17$ $\quad -7u^4 - 3v^2 - 17$

For Exercises 49–68, subtract the polynomials. **(See Examples 6–7.)**

49. $4a^3b^2 - 12a^3b^2$ $\quad -8a^3b^2$

50. $5yz^4 - 14yz^4$ $\quad -9yz^4$

51. $-32x^3 - 21x^3$ $\quad -53x^3$

52. $-23c^5 - 12c^5$ $\quad -35c^5$

53. $(7a - 7) - (12a - 4)$ $\quad -5a - 3$

54. $(4x + 3v) - (-3x + v)$ $\quad 7x + 2v$

55.
$$\begin{array}{r} 4k + 3 \\ \underline{-(-12k - 6)} \\ 16k + 9 \end{array}$$

56.
$$\begin{array}{r} 3h - 15 \\ \underline{-(8h + 13)} \\ -5h - 28 \end{array}$$

57. $25m^4 - (23m^4 + 14m)$ $\quad 2m^4 - 14m$

58. $3x^2 - (-x^2 - 12)$ $\quad 4x^2 + 12$

59. $(5s^2 - 3st - 2t^2) - (2s^2 + st + t^2)$ $\quad 3s^2 - 4st - 3t^2$

60. $(6k^2 + 2kp + p^2) - (3k^2 - 6kp + 2p^2)$ $\quad 3k^2 + 8kp - p^2$

61.
$$\begin{array}{r} 10r - 6s + 2t \\ \underline{-(12r - 3s - t)} \\ -2r - 3s + 3t \end{array}$$

62.
$$\begin{array}{r} a - 14b + 7c \\ \underline{-(-3a - 8b + 2c)} \\ 4a - 6b + 5c \end{array}$$

63. $\left(\frac{7}{8}x + \frac{2}{3}y - \frac{3}{10}\right) - \left(\frac{1}{8}x + \frac{1}{3}y\right)$ $\quad \frac{3}{4}x + \frac{1}{3}y - \frac{3}{10}$

64. $\left(r - \frac{1}{12}s\right) - \left(\frac{1}{2}r - \frac{5}{12}s - \frac{4}{11}\right)$ $\quad \frac{1}{2}r + \frac{1}{3}s + \frac{4}{11}$

65. $\left(\frac{2}{3}h^2 - \frac{1}{5}h - \frac{3}{4}\right) - \left(\frac{4}{3}h^2 - \frac{4}{5}h + \frac{7}{4}\right)$ $\quad -\frac{2}{3}h^2 + \frac{3}{5}h - \frac{5}{2}$

66. $\left(\frac{3}{8}p^3 - \frac{5}{7}p^2 - \frac{2}{5}\right) - \left(\frac{5}{8}p^3 - \frac{2}{7}p^2 + \frac{7}{5}\right)$ $\quad -\frac{1}{4}p^3 - \frac{3}{7}p^2 - \frac{9}{5}$

67.
$$\begin{array}{r} 4.5x^4 - 3.1x^2 \qquad\quad - 6.7 \\ \underline{-(2.1x^4 \qquad\quad + 4.4x + 1.2)} \\ 2.4x^4 - 3.1x^2 - 4.4x - 7.9 \end{array}$$

68.
$$\begin{array}{r} 1.3c^2 \qquad\quad + 4.8 \\ \underline{-\ (4.3c^2 - 2c - 2.2)} \\ -3c^2 + 2c + 7 \end{array}$$

69. Find the difference of $(4b^3 + 6b - 7)$ and $(-12b^2 + 11b + 5)$. $\quad 4b^3 + 12b^2 - 5b - 12$

70. Find the difference of $(-5y^2 + 3y - 21)$ and $(-4y^2 - 5y + 23)$. $\quad -y^2 + 8y - 44$

71. Subtract $\left(\frac{3}{2}x^2 - 5x\right)$ from $(-2x^2 - 11)$. **(See Example 8.)** $\quad -\frac{7}{2}x^2 + 5x - 11$

72. Subtract $\left(a^5 - \frac{1}{3}a^3 + 5a\right)$ from $\left(\frac{3}{4}a^5 + \frac{1}{2}a^4 + 6a\right)$. $\quad -\frac{1}{4}a^5 + \frac{1}{2}a^4 + \frac{1}{3}a^3 + a$

Concept 4: Polynomials and Applications to Geometry

73. Find a polynomial that represents the perimeter of the figure. $\quad 4y^3 + 2y^2 + 2$

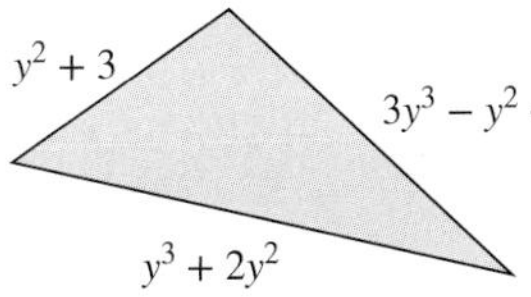

74. Find a polynomial that represents the perimeter of the figure. $\quad 9t^3 + t^2$

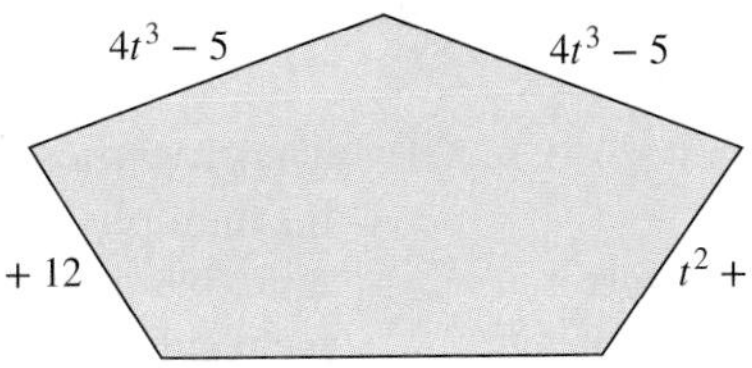

75. If the perimeter of the figure can be represented by the polynomial $5a^2 - 2a + 1$, find a polynomial that represents the length of the missing side. **(See Example 9.)** $3a^2 - 3a + 5$

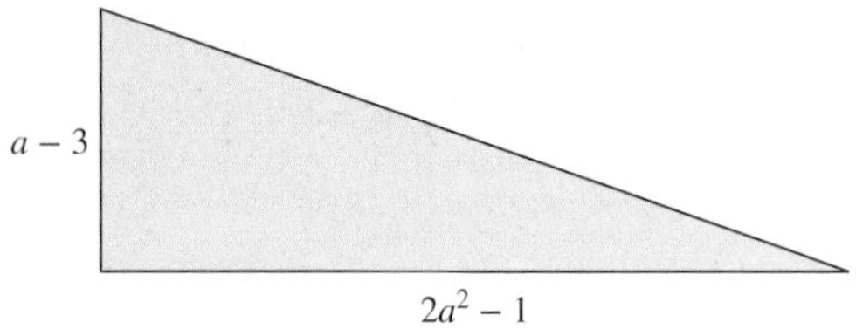

76. If the perimeter of the figure can be represented by the polynomial $6w^3 - 2w - 3$, find a polynomial that represents the length of the missing side. $4w^3 - 6w^2 - 2w$

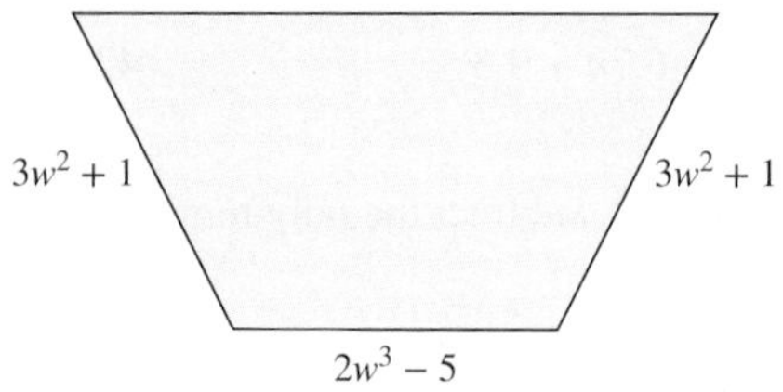

Mixed Exercises

For Exercises 77–92, perform the indicated operation.

77. $(2ab^2 + 9a^2b) + (7ab^2 - 3ab + 7a^2b)$ $9ab^2 - 3ab + 16a^2b$

78. $(8x^2y - 3xy - 6xy^2) + (3x^2y - 12xy)$ $11x^2y - 15xy - 6xy^2$

79.
$$\begin{array}{rl} & 4z^5 \qquad + z^3 - 3z + 13 \\ -(& \quad - z^4 - 8z^3 \qquad + 15) \end{array}$$
$4z^5 + z^4 + 9z^3 - 3z - 2$

80.
$$\begin{array}{rl} & -15t^4 \qquad - 23t^2 + 16t \\ -(& \qquad 21t^3 + 18t^2 + \quad t) \end{array}$$
$-15t^4 - 21t^3 - 41t^2 + 15t$

81. $(9x^4 + 2x^3 - x + 5) + (9x^3 - 3x^2 + 8x + 3) - (7x^4 - x + 12)$ $2x^4 + 11x^3 - 3x^2 + 8x - 4$

82. $(-6y^3 - 9y^2 + 23) - (7y^2 + 2y - 11) + (3y^3 - 25)$ $-3y^3 - 16y^2 - 2y + 9$

83. $(0.2w^2 + 3w + 1.3) - (w^3 - 0.7w + 2)$ $-w^3 + 0.2w^2 + 3.7w - 0.7$

84. $(8.1u^3 - 5.2u^2 + 4) + (2.8u^3 + 6.3u - 7)$ $10.9u^3 - 5.2u^2 + 6.3u - 3$

85. $(7p^2q - 3pq^2) - (8p^2q + pq) + (4pq - pq^2)$ $-p^2q - 4pq^2 + 3pq$

86. $(12c^2d - 2cd + 8cd^2) - (-c^2d + 4cd) - (5cd - 2cd^2)$ $13c^2d - 11cd + 10cd^2$

87. $(5x - 2x^3) + (2x^3 - 5x)$ 0

88. $(p^2 - 4p + 2) - (2 + p^2 - 4p)$ 0

89.
$$\begin{array}{rl} & 2a^2b - 4ab + \ ab^2 \\ -(& 2a^2b + \ ab - 5ab^2) \end{array}$$
$-5ab + 6ab^2$

90.
$$\begin{array}{rl} & -3xy + \ 7xy^2 + 5x^2y \\ +(& -8xy - 11xy^2 + 3x^2y) \end{array}$$
$-11xy - 4xy^2 + 8x^2y$

91. $[(3y^2 - 5y) - (2y^2 + y - 1)] + (10y^2 - 4y - 5)$ $11y^2 - 10y - 4$

92. $(12c^3 - 5c^2 - 2c) + [(7c^3 - 2c^2 + c) - (4c^3 + 4c)]$ $15c^3 - 7c^2 - 5c$

Expanding Your Skills

93. Write a binomial of degree 3. (Answers may vary.) For example: $x^3 + 6$

94. Write a trinomial of degree 6. (Answers may vary.) For example: $5x^6 + x - 4$

95. Write a monomial of degree 5. (Answers may vary.) For example: $8x^5$

96. Write a monomial of degree 1. (Answers may vary.) For example: $3x$

97. Write a trinomial with the leading coefficient –6. (Answers may vary.) For example: $-6x^2 + 2x + 5$

98. Write a binomial with the leading coefficient 13. (Answers may vary.) For example: $13x + 7$

Section 5.6 Multiplication of Polynomials and Special Products

Concepts

1. Multiplication of Polynomials
2. Special Case Products: Difference of Squares and Perfect Square Trinomials
3. Applications to Geometry

1. Multiplication of Polynomials

The properties of exponents can be used to simplify many algebraic expressions including the multiplication of monomials. To multiply monomials, first use the associative and commutative properties of multiplication to group coefficients and like bases. Then simplify the result by using the properties of exponents.

Example 1 **Multiplying Monomials**

Classroom Example: p. 389, Exercise 18

Multiply the monomials.

a. $(3x^4)(4x^2)$ **b.** $(-4c^5d)(2c^2d^3e)$ **c.** $\left(\frac{1}{3}a^4b^3\right)\left(\frac{3}{4}b^7\right)$

Solution:

a. $(3x^4)(4x^2)$

$= (3 \cdot 4)(x^4x^2)$ Group coefficients and like bases.

$= 12x^6$ Multiply the coefficients and add the exponents on x.

b. $(-4c^5d)(2c^2d^3e)$

$= (-4 \cdot 2)(c^5c^2)(dd^3)(e)$ Group coefficients and like bases.

$= -8c^7d^4e$ Simplify.

c. $\left(\frac{1}{3}a^4b^3\right)\left(\frac{3}{4}b^7\right)$

$= \left(\frac{1}{3} \cdot \frac{3}{4}\right)(a^4)(b^3b^7)$ Group coefficients and like bases.

$= \frac{1}{4}a^4b^{10}$ Simplify.

Skill Practice Multiply the monomials.

1. $(-5y)(6y^3)$ **2.** $(7x^2y)(-2x^3y^4)$ **3.** $\left(\frac{2}{5}w^5z^3\right)\left(\frac{15}{4}w^4\right)$

The distributive property is used to multiply polynomials: $a(b + c) = ab + ac$.

Example 2 **Multiplying a Polynomial by a Monomial**

Classroom Example: p. 389, Exercise 24

Multiply the polynomials.

a. $2t(4t - 3)$ **b.** $-3a^2\left(-4a^2 + 2a - \frac{1}{3}\right)$

Solution:

a. $2t(4t - 3)$

$= (2t)(4t) + (2t)(-3)$ Apply the distributive property by multiplying each term by $2t$.

$= 8t^2 - 6t$ Simplify each term.

b. $-3a^2\left(-4a^2 + 2a - \frac{1}{3}\right)$

$= (-3a^2)(-4a^2) + (-3a^2)(2a) + (-3a^2)\left(-\frac{1}{3}\right)$ Apply the distributive property by multiplying each term by $-3a^2$.

$= 12a^4 - 6a^3 + a^2$ Simplify each term.

Answers

1. $-30y^4$
2. $-14x^5y^5$
3. $\frac{3}{2}w^9z^3$

Skill Practice Multiply the polynomials.

4. $-4a(5a - 3)$ **5.** $-4p\left(2p^2 - 6p + \frac{1}{4}\right)$

Thus far, we have illustrated polynomial multiplication involving monomials. Next, the distributive property will be used to multiply polynomials with more than one term.

$$(x + 3)(x + 5) = x(x + 5) + 3(x + 5)$$ Apply the distributive property.

$$= x(x + 5) + 3(x + 5)$$ Apply the distributive property again.

$$= (x)(x) + (x)(5) + (3)(x) + (3)(5)$$

$$= x^2 + 5x + 3x + 15$$

$$= x^2 + 8x + 15$$ Combine *like* terms.

Note: Using the distributive property results in multiplying each term of the first polynomial by each term of the second polynomial.

$$(x + 3)(x + 5) = (x)(x) + (x)(5) + (3)(x) + (3)(5)$$
$$= x^2 + 5x + 3x + 15$$
$$= x^2 + 8x + 15$$

Classroom Example: p. 389, Exercise 30

Example 3 Multiplying a Polynomial by a Polynomial

Multiply the polynomials. $(c - 7)(c + 2)$

Solution:

$(c - 7)(c + 2)$ Multiply each term in the first polynomial by each term in the second. That is, apply the distributive property.

$$= (c)(c) + (c)(2) + (-7)(c) + (-7)(2)$$

$$= c^2 + 2c - 7c - 14$$ Simplify.

$$= c^2 - 5c - 14$$ Combine *like* terms.

Instructor Note: Mention to students that the product $(c - 7)(c + 2)$ requires multiple applications of the distributive property. First distribute c, then distribute -7.

TIP: Notice that the product of two *binomials* equals the sum of the products of the **F**irst terms, the **O**uter terms, the **I**nner terms, and the **L**ast terms. The acronym **FOIL** (First Outer Inner Last) can be used as a memory device to multiply two binomials.

Outer terms, First terms, Inner terms, Last terms

	First		Outer		Inner		Last
$(c - 7)(c + 2)$ =	$(c)(c)$	+	$(c)(2)$	+	$(-7)(c)$	+	$(-7)(2)$
=	c^2	+	$2c$	−	$7c$	−	14

$$= c^2 - 5c - 14$$

Skill Practice Multiply the polynomials.

6. $(x + 2)(x + 8)$

Answers

4. $-20a^2 + 12a$
5. $-8p^3 + 24p^2 - p$
6. $x^2 + 10x + 16$

Example 4 Multiplying a Polynomial by a Polynomial

Multiply the polynomials. $(y - 2)(3y^2 + y - 5)$

Solution:

$(y - 2)(3y^2 + y - 5)$ Multiply each term in the first polynomial by each term in the second.

$= (y)(3y^2) + (y)(y) + (y)(-5) + (-2)(3y^2) + (-2)(y) + (-2)(-5)$

$= 3y^3 + y^2 - 5y - 6y^2 - 2y + 10$ Simplify each term.

$= 3y^3 - 5y^2 - 7y + 10$ Combine *like* terms.

TIP: Multiplication of polynomials can be performed vertically by a process similar to column multiplication of real numbers. For example,

$$\begin{array}{r} 235 \\ \times \quad 21 \\ \hline 235 \\ 4700 \\ \hline 4935 \end{array} \qquad \begin{array}{rrrr} & 3y^2 & +\ y & -\ 5 \\ \times & & y & -\ 2 \\ \hline & -6y^2 & -\ 2y & +\ 10 \\ 3y^3 & +\ y^2 & -\ 5y & +\ 0 \\ \hline 3y^3 & -\ 5y^2 & -\ 7y & +\ 10 \end{array}$$

Note: When multiplying by the column method, it is important to *align like* terms vertically before adding terms.

Skill Practice Multiply the polynomials.

7. $(2y + 4)(3y^2 - 5y + 2)$

Classroom Example: p. 389, Exercise 44

Avoiding Mistakes

It is important to note that the acronym FOIL does not apply to Example 4 because the product does not involve two binomials.

Example 5 Multiplying Polynomials

Multiply the polynomials. $2(10x + 3y)(2x - 4y)$

Solution:

$2(10x + 3y)(2x - 4y)$ In this case we are multiplying three polynomials—a monomial times two binomials. The associative property of multiplication enables us to choose which two polynomials to multiply first.

$= 2[(10x + 3y)(2x - 4y)]$ First we will multiply the binomials. Multiply each term in the first binomial by each term in the second binomial. That is, apply the distributive property.

$= 2[(10x)(2x) + (10x)(-4y) + (3y)(2x) + (3y)(-4y)]$

$= 2[20x^2 - 40xy + 6xy - 12y^2]$ Simplify each term.

$= 2(20x^2 - 34xy - 12y^2)$ Combine *like* terms.

$= 40x^2 - 68xy - 24y^2$ Multiply by 2 using the distributive property.

Skill Practice Multiply.

8. $3(4a - 3c)(5a - 2c)$

Classroom Example: p. 389, Exercise 42

TIP: When multiplying three polynomials, first multiply two of the polynomials. Then multiply the result by the third polynomial.

Answers

7. $6y^3 + 2y^2 - 16y + 8$

8. $60a^2 - 69ac + 18c^2$

2. Special Case Products: Difference of Squares and Perfect Square Trinomials

In some cases the product of two binomials takes on a special pattern.

I. The first special case occurs when multiplying the sum and difference of the same two terms. For example:

$(2x + 3)(2x - 3)$

$= 4x^2 - 6x + 6x - 9$

$= 4x^2 - 9$

Notice that the middle terms are opposites. This leaves only the difference between the square of the first term and the square of the second term. For this reason, the product is called a *difference of squares*.

Note: The binomials $2x + 3$ and $2x - 3$ are called **conjugates**. In one expression, $2x$ and 3 are added, and in the other, $2x$ and 3 are subtracted.

II. The second special case involves the square of a binomial. For example:

$(3x + 7)^2$

$= (3x + 7)(3x + 7)$

$= 9x^2 + 21x + 21x + 49$

$= 9x^2 + 42x + 49$

$= (3x)^2 + 2(3x)(7) + (7)^2$

When squaring a binomial, the product will be a trinomial called a *perfect square trinomial.* The first and third terms are formed by squaring each term of the binomial. The middle term equals twice the product of the terms in the binomial.

Note: The expression $(3x - 7)^2$ also expands to a perfect square trinomial, but the middle term will be negative:

$$(3x - 7)(3x - 7) = 9x^2 - 21x - 21x + 49 = 9x^2 - 42x + 49$$

Special Case Product Formulas

1. $(a + b)(a - b) = a^2 - b^2$ The product is called a **difference of squares**.
2. $(a + b)^2 = a^2 + 2ab + b^2$, $(a - b)^2 = a^2 - 2ab + b^2$ The product is called a **perfect square trinomial**.

Instructor Note: Have students substitute some numbers to confirm that $(a + b)^2 \neq a^2 + b^2$.

You should become familiar with these special case products because they will be used again in the next chapter to factor polynomials.

Classroom Examples: p. 390, Exercises 56 and 62

TIP: The product of two conjugates can be checked by applying the distributive property:

$(x - 9)(x + 9)$

$= x^2 + 9x - 9x - 81$

$= x^2 - 81$

Example 6 Multiplying Conjugates

Multiply the conjugates.

a. $(x - 9)(x + 9)$ **b.** $\left(\frac{1}{2}p + 6\right)\left(\frac{1}{2}p - 6\right)$

Solution:

a. $(x - 9)(x + 9)$ Apply the formula: $(a + b)(a - b) = a^2 - b^2$

$a^2 - b^2$

$= (x)^2 - (9)^2$ Substitute $a = x$ and $b = 9$.

$= x^2 - 81$

b. $\left(\frac{1}{2}p + 6\right)\left(\frac{1}{2}p - 6\right)$ Apply the formula: $(a + b)(a - b) = a^2 - b^2$

$a^2 - b^2$

$= \left(\frac{1}{2}p\right)^2 - (6)^2$ Substitute $a = \frac{1}{2}p$ and $b = 6$.

$= \frac{1}{4}p^2 - 36$ Simplify each term.

Skill Practice Multiply the conjugates.

9. $(a + 7)(a - 7)$ **10.** $\left(\frac{4}{5}x - 10\right)\left(\frac{4}{5}x + 10\right)$

Example 7 Squaring Binomials

Classroom Examples: p. 390, Exercises 72 and 74

Square the binomials.

a. $(3w - 4)^2$ **b.** $(5x^2 + 2)^2$

Solution:

a. $(3w - 4)^2$ Apply the formula: $(a - b)^2 = a^2 - 2ab + b^2$

$a^2 - 2ab + b^2$

$= (3w)^2 - 2(3w)(4) + (4)^2$ Substitute $a = 3w$, $b = 4$.

$= 9w^2 - 24w + 16$ Simplify each term.

TIP: The square of a binomial can be checked by explicitly writing the product of the two binomials and applying the distributive property:

$$(3w - 4)^2 = (3w - 4)(3w - 4) = 9w^2 - 12w - 12w + 16$$
$$= 9w^2 - 24w + 16$$

b. $(5x^2 + 2)^2$ Apply the formula: $(a + b)^2 = a^2 + 2ab + b^2$

$a^2 + 2ab + b^2$

$= (5x^2)^2 + 2(5x^2)(2) + (2)^2$ Substitute $a = 5x^2$, $b = 2$.

$= 25x^4 + 20x^2 + 4$ Simplify each term.

Avoiding Mistakes

The property for squaring two factors is different than the property for squaring two terms: $(ab)^2 = a^2b^2$ but $(a + b)^2 = a^2 + 2ab + b^2$

Skill Practice Square the binomials.

11. $(2x + 3)^2$ **12.** $(5c^2 - 6)^2$

Answers

9. $a^2 - 49$
10. $\frac{16}{25}x^2 - 100$
11. $4x^2 + 12x + 9$
12. $25c^4 - 60c^2 + 36$

3. Applications to Geometry

Classroom Example: p. 391, Exercise 86

Example 8 Using Special Case Products in an Application of Geometry

Find a polynomial that represents the volume of the cube (Figure 5-2).

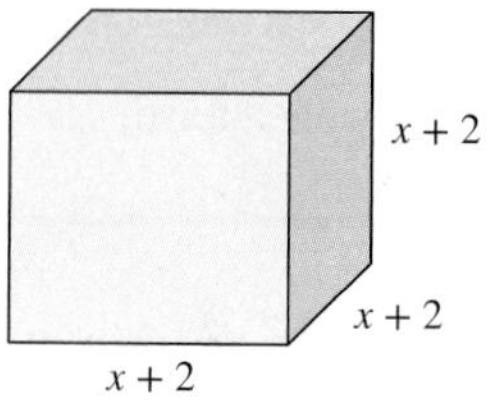

Figure 5-2

Solution:

$$\text{Volume} = (\text{length})(\text{width})(\text{height})$$

$$V = (x + 2)(x + 2)(x + 2) \quad \text{or} \quad V = (x + 2)^3$$

To expand $(x + 2)(x + 2)(x + 2)$, multiply the first two factors. Then multiply the result by the last factor.

$$V = \underbrace{(x + 2)(x + 2)}(x + 2)$$
$$= (x^2 + 4x + 4)(x + 2)$$

TIP: $(x + 2)(x + 2) = (x + 2)^2$ and results in a perfect square trinomial.
$$(x + 2)^2 = (x)^2 + 2(x)(2) + (2)^2$$
$$= x^2 + 4x + 4$$

$$= (x^2)(x) + (x^2)(2) + (4x)(x) + (4x)(2) + (4)(x) + (4)(2)$$ Apply the distributive property.

$$= x^3 + 2x^2 + 4x^2 + 8x + 4x + 8$$ Group *like* terms.

$$= x^3 + 6x^2 + 12x + 8$$ Combine *like* terms.

The volume of the cube can be represented by

$$V = (x + 2)^3 = x^3 + 6x^2 + 12x + 8$$

Skill Practice

13. Find the polynomial that represents the volume of the cube.

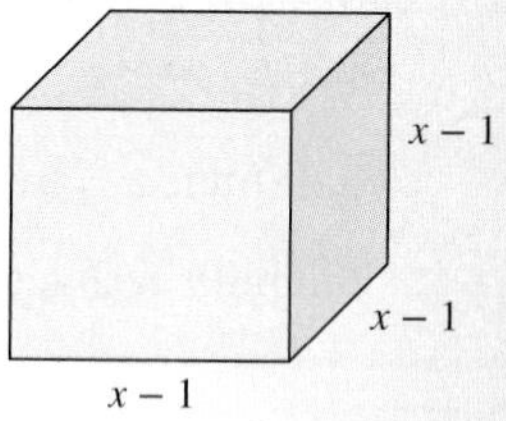

Answer

13. The volume of the cube can be represented by $x^3 - 3x^2 + 3x - 1$.

Section 5.6 Practice Exercises

For additional exercises, see Classroom Activities 5.6A–5.6B in the *Student's Resource Manual* at www.mhhe.com/moh.

Vocabulary and Key Concepts

1. **a.** The conjugate of $5 + 2x$ is $\underline{5 - 2x}$.

   b. When two conjugates are multiplied the resulting binomial is a difference of $\underline{\text{squares}}$. This is given by the formula $(a + b)(a - b) = \underline{a^2 - b^2}$.

   c. When a binomial is squared, the resulting trinomial is a $\underline{\text{perfect}}$ square trinomial. This is given by the formula $(a + b)^2 = \underline{a^2 + 2ab + b^2}$.

Review Exercises

For Exercises 2–9, simplify each expression (if possible).

2. $4x + 5x$ $9x$

3. $2y^2 - 4y^2$ $-2y^2$

4. $(4x)(5x)$ $20x^2$

5. $(2y^2)(-4y^2)$ $-8y^4$

6. $-5a^3b - 2a^3b$ $-7a^3b$

7. $7uvw^2 + uvw^2$ $8uvw^2$

8. $(-5a^3b)(-2a^3b)$ $10a^6b^2$

9. $(7uvw^2)(uvw^2)$ $7u^2v^2w^4$

Concept 1: Multiplication of Polynomials

For Exercises 10–18, multiply the expressions. **(See Example 1.)**

10. $8(4x)$ $32x$

11. $-2(6y)$ $-12y$

12. $-10(5z)$ $-50z$

13. $7(3p)$ $21p$

14. $(x^{10})(4x^3)$ $4x^{13}$

15. $(a^{13}b^4)(12ab^4)$ $12a^{14}b^8$

16. $(4m^3n^7)(-3m^6n)$ $-12m^9n^8$

17. $(2c^7d)(-c^3d^{11})$ $-2c^{10}d^{12}$

18. $(-5u^2v)(-8u^3v^2)$ $40u^5v^3$

For Exercises 19–54, multiply the polynomials. **(See Examples 2–5.)**

19. $8pq(2pq - 3p + 5q)$
$16p^2q^2 - 24p^2q + 40pq^2$

20. $5ab(2ab + 6a - 3b)$
$10a^2b^2 + 30a^2b - 15ab^2$

21. $(k^2 - 13k - 6)(-4k)$
$-4k^3 + 52k^2 + 24k$

22. $(h^2 + 5h - 12)(-2h)$
$-2h^3 - 10h^2 + 24h$

23. $-15pq(3p^2 + p^3q^2 - 2q)$
$-45p^3q - 15p^4q^3 + 30pq^2$

24. $-4u^2v(2u - 5uv^3 + v)$
$-8u^3v + 20u^3v^4 - 4u^2v^2$

25. $(y + 10)(y + 9)$
$y^2 + 19y + 90$

26. $(x + 5)(x + 6)$
$x^2 + 11x + 30$

27. $(m - 12)(m - 2)$
$m^2 - 14m + 24$

28. $(n - 7)(n - 2)$
$n^2 - 9n + 14$

29. $(3p - 2)(4p + 1)$
$12p^2 - 5p - 2$

30. $(7q + 11)(q - 5)$
$7q^2 - 24q - 55$

31. $(8 - 4w)(-3w + 2)$
$12w^2 - 32w + 16$

32. $(-6z + 10)(4 - 2z)$
$12z^2 - 44z + 40$

33. $(p - 3w)(p - 11w)$
$p^2 - 14pw + 33w^2$

34. $(y - 7x)(y - 10x)$
$y^2 - 17xy + 70x^2$

35. $(6x - 1)(2x + 5)$
$12x^2 + 28x - 5$

36. $(3x + 7)(x - 8)$
$3x^2 - 17x - 56$

37. $(4a - 9)(1.5a - 2)$
$6a^2 - 21.5a + 18$

38. $(2.1y - 0.5)(y + 3)$
$2.1y^2 + 5.8y - 1.5$

39. $(3t - 7)(1 + 3t^2)$
$9t^3 - 21t^2 + 3t - 7$

40. $(2 - 5w)(2w^2 - 5)$
$-10w^3 + 4w^2 + 25w - 10$

41. $3(3m + 4n)(m + 2n)$
$9m^2 + 30mn + 24n^2$

42. $2(7y + z)(3y + 5z)$
$42y^2 + 76yz + 10z^2$

43. $(5s + 3)(s^2 + s - 2)$
$5s^3 + 8s^2 - 7s - 6$

44. $(t - 4)(2t^2 - t + 6)$
$2t^3 - 9t^2 + 10t - 24$

45. $(3w - 2)(9w^2 + 6w + 4)$
$27w^3 - 8$

46. $(z + 5)(z^2 - 5z + 25)$
$z^3 + 125$

47. $(p^2 + p - 5)(p^2 + 4p - 1)$
$p^4 + 5p^3 - 2p^2 - 21p + 5$

48. $(-x^2 - 2x + 4)(x^2 + 2x - 6)$
$-x^4 - 4x^3 + 6x^2 + 20x - 24$

49.
$$\begin{array}{r} 3a^2 - 4a + 9 \\ \times \quad\quad 2a - 5 \\ \hline \end{array}$$
$6a^3 - 23a^2 + 38a - 45$

50.
$$\begin{array}{r} 7x^2 - 3x - 4 \\ \times \quad\quad 5x + 1 \\ \hline \end{array}$$
$35x^3 - 8x^2 - 23x - 4$

51.
$$\begin{array}{r} 4x^2 - 12xy + 9y^2 \\ \times \quad\quad 2x - 3y \\ \hline \end{array}$$
$8x^3 - 36x^2y + 54xy^2 - 27y^3$

52.
$$\begin{array}{r} 25a^2 + 10ab + b^2 \\ \times \quad\quad 5a + b \\ \hline \end{array}$$
$125a^3 + 75a^2b + 15ab^2 + b^3$

53.
$$\begin{array}{r} 6x + \ 2y \\ \times\ 0.2x + 1.2y \\ \hline \end{array}$$
$1.2x^2 + 7.6xy + 2.4y^2$

54.
$$\begin{array}{r} 4.5a + \ 2b \\ \times \quad 2a - 1.8b \\ \hline \end{array}$$
$9a^2 - 4.1ab - 3.6b^2$

Concept 2: Special Case Products: Difference of Squares and Perfect Square Trinomials

For Exercises 55–66, multiply the conjugates. **(See Example 6.)**

55. $(y-6)(y+6)$
y^2-36

56. $(x+3)(x-3)$
x^2-9

57. $(3a-4b)(3a+4b)$
$9a^2-16b^2$

58. $(5y+7x)(5y-7x)$
$25y^2-49x^2$

59. $(9k+6)(9k-6)$
$81k^2-36$

60. $(2h-5)(2h+5)$
$4h^2-25$

61. $\left(\frac{2}{3}t-3\right)\left(\frac{2}{3}t+3\right)$
$\frac{4}{9}t^2-9$

62. $\left(\frac{1}{4}r-1\right)\left(\frac{1}{4}r+1\right)$
$\frac{1}{16}r^2-1$

63. $(u^3+5v)(u^3-5v)$
u^6-25v^2

64. $(8w^2-x)(8w^2+x)$
$64w^4-x^2$

65. $\left(\frac{2}{3}-p\right)\left(\frac{2}{3}+p\right)$
$\frac{4}{9}-p^2$

66. $\left(\frac{1}{8}-q\right)\left(\frac{1}{8}+q\right)$
$\frac{1}{64}-q^2$

For Exercises 67–78, square the binomials. **(See Example 7.)**

67. $(a+5)^2$
$a^2+10a+25$

68. $(a-3)^2$
a^2-6a+9

69. $(x-y)^2$
$x^2-2xy+y^2$

70. $(x+y)^2$
$x^2+2xy+y^2$

71. $(2c+5)^2$
$4c^2+20c+25$

72. $(5d-9)^2$
$25d^2-90d+81$

73. $(3t^2-4s)^2$
$9t^4-24st^2+16s^2$

74. $(u^2+4v)^2$
$u^4+8u^2v+16v^2$

75. $(7-t)^2$
$t^2-14t+49$

76. $(4+w)^2$
$w^2+8w+16$

77. $(3+4q)^2$
$16q^2+24q+9$

78. $(2-3b)^2$
$9b^2-12b+4$

79. **a.** Evaluate $(2+4)^2$ by working within the parentheses first. 36

b. Evaluate 2^2+4^2. 20

c. Compare the answers to parts (a) and (b) and make a conjecture about $(a+b)^2$ and a^2+b^2.
$(a+b)^2 \neq a^2+b^2$ in general.

80. **a.** Evaluate $(6-5)^2$ by working within the parentheses first. 1

b. Evaluate 6^2-5^2. 11

c. Compare the answers to parts (a) and (b) and make a conjecture about $(a-b)^2$ and a^2-b^2.
$(a-b)^2 \neq a^2-b^2$ in general.

Concept 3: Applications to Geometry

81. Find a polynomial expression that represents the area of the rectangle shown in the figure.
$4x^2-25$

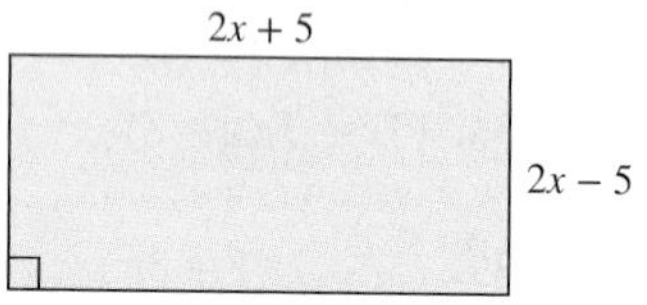

82. Find a polynomial expression that represents the area of the rectangle shown in the figure.
$36-y^2$

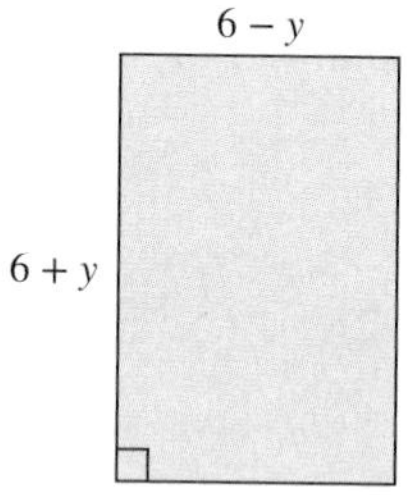

83. Find a polynomial expression that represents the area of the square shown in the figure.
$16p^2+40p+25$

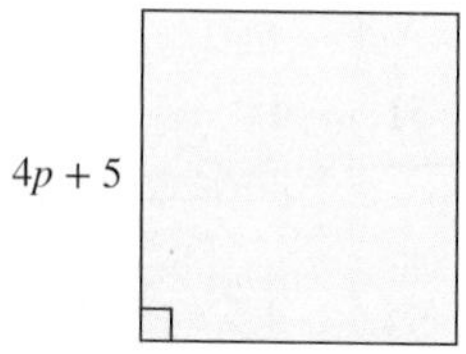

84. Find a polynomial expression that represents the area of the square shown in the figure.
$49q^2-42q+9$

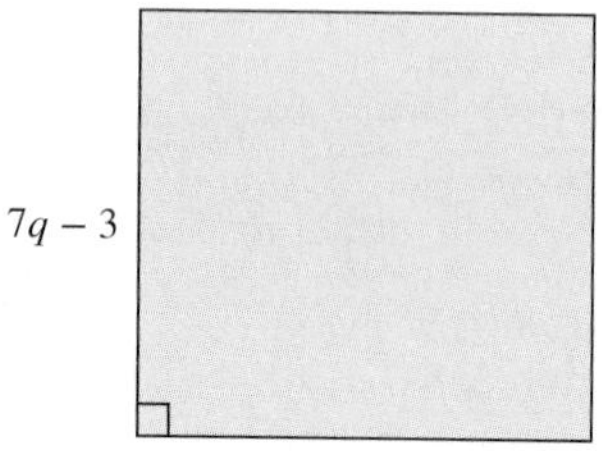

85. Find a polynomial that represents the volume of the cube shown in the figure. **(See Example 8.)**

(Recall: $V = s^3$) $27p^3 - 135p^2 + 225p - 125$

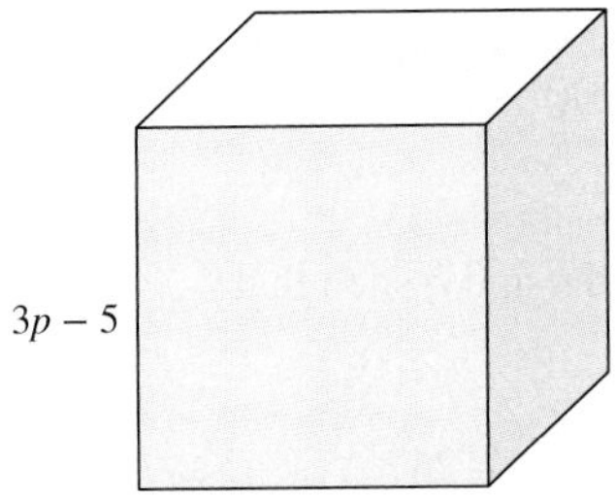

86. Find a polynomial that represents the volume of the rectangular solid shown in the figure.

(Recall: $V = lwh$) $r^3 - 15r^2 + 63r - 49$

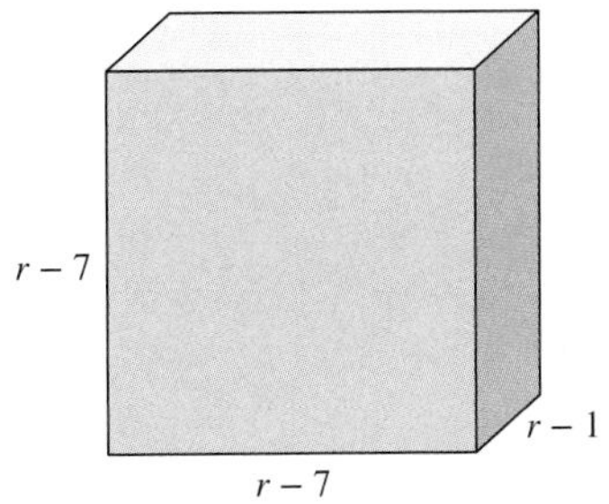

87. Find a polynomial that represents the area of the triangle shown in the figure.

(Recall: $A = \frac{1}{2}bh$) $15a^5 - 6a^2$

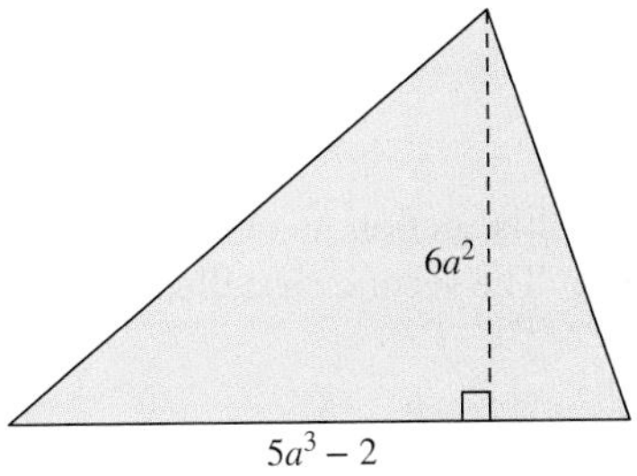

88. Find a polynomial that represents the area of the triangle shown in the figure. $3t^3 - 12t$

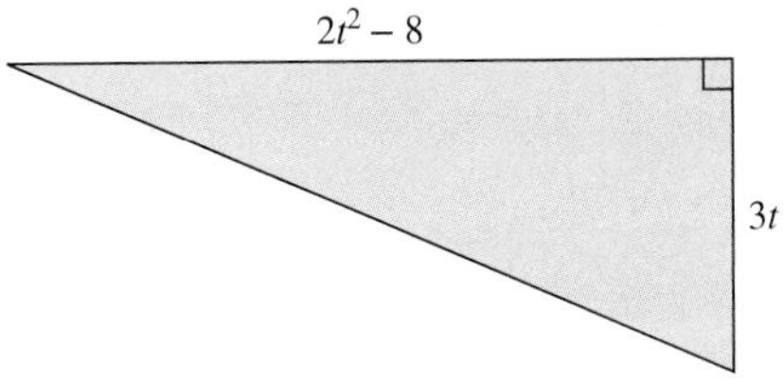

Mixed Exercises

For Exercises 89–118, multiply the expressions.

89. $(7x + y)(7x - y)$ $49x^2 - y^2$

90. $(9w - 4z)(9w + 4z)$ $81w^2 - 16z^2$

91. $(5s + 3t)^2$ $25s^2 + 30st + 9t^2$

92. $(5s - 3t)^2$ $25s^2 - 30st + 9t^2$

93. $(7x - 3y)(3x - 8y)$ $21x^2 - 65xy + 24y^2$

94. $(5a - 4b)(2a - b)$ $10a^2 - 13ab + 4b^2$

95. $\left(\frac{2}{3}t + 2\right)(3t + 4)$ $2t^2 + \frac{26}{3}t + 8$

96. $\left(\frac{1}{5}s + 6\right)(5s - 3)$ $s^2 + \frac{147}{5}s - 18$

97. $-5(3x + 5)(2x - 1)$ $-30x^2 - 35x + 25$

98. $-4(2k - 5)(4k - 3)$ $-32k^2 + 104k - 60$

99. $(3a - 2)(5a + 1 + 2a^2)$ $6a^3 + 11a^2 - 7a - 2$

100. $(u + 4)(2 - 3u + u^2)$ $u^3 + u^2 - 10u + 8$

101. $(y^2 + 2y + 4)(y - 5)$ $y^3 - 3y^2 - 6y - 20$

102. $(w^2 - w + 6)(w + 2)$ $w^3 + w^2 + 4w + 12$

103. $\left(\frac{1}{3}m - n\right)^2$ $\frac{1}{9}m^2 - \frac{2}{3}mn + n^2$

104. $\left(\frac{2}{5}p - q\right)^2$ $\frac{4}{25}p^2 - \frac{4}{5}pq + q^2$

105. $6w^2(7w - 14)$ $42w^3 - 84w^2$

106. $4v^3(v + 12)$ $4v^4 + 48v^3$

107. $(4y - 8.1)(4y + 8.1)$ $16y^2 - 65.61$

108. $(2h + 2.7)(2h - 2.7)$ $4h^2 - 7.29$

109. $(3c^2 + 4)(7c^2 - 8)$ $21c^4 + 4c^2 - 32$

110. $(5k^3 - 9)(k^3 - 2)$ $5k^6 - 19k^3 + 18$

111. $(3.1x + 4.5)^2$ $9.61x^2 + 27.9x + 20.25$

112. $(2.5y + 1.1)^2$ $6.25y^2 + 5.5y + 1.21$

113. $(k - 4)^3$ $k^3 - 12k^2 + 48k - 64$

114. $(h + 3)^3$ $h^3 + 9h^2 + 27h + 27$

115. $(5x + 3)^3$ $125x^3 + 225x^2 + 135x + 27$

116. $(2a - 4)^3$ $8a^3 - 48a^2 + 96a - 64$

117. $(y^2 + 2y + 1)(2y^2 - y + 3)$ $2y^4 + 3y^3 + 3y^2 + 5y + 3$

118. $(2w^2 - w - 5)(3w^2 + 2w + 1)$ $6w^4 + w^3 - 15w^2 - 11w - 5$

Expanding Your Skills

For Exercises 119–122, multiply the expressions containing more than two factors.

119. $2a(3a - 4)(a + 5)$ $6a^3 + 22a^2 - 40a$

120. $5x(x + 2)(6x - 1)$ $30x^3 + 55x^2 - 10x$

121. $(x - 3)(2x + 1)(x - 4)$ $2x^3 - 13x^2 + 17x + 12$

122. $(y - 2)(2y - 3)(y + 3)$ $2y^3 - y^2 - 15y + 18$

123. What binomial when multiplied by $(3x + 5)$ will produce a product of $6x^2 - 11x - 35$? [*Hint:* Let the quantity $(a + b)$ represent the unknown binomial.] Then find a and b such that $(3x + 5)(a + b) = 6x^2 - 11x - 35$. $2x - 7$

124. What binomial when multiplied by $(2x - 4)$ will produce a product of $2x^2 + 8x - 24$? $x + 6$

For Exercises 125–127, determine the values of k that would create a perfect square trinomial.

125. $x^2 + kx + 25$ $k = 10$ or -10

126. $w^2 + kw + 9$ $k = 6$ or -6

127. $a^2 + ka + 16$ $k = 8$ or -8

Section 5.7 Division of Polynomials

Concepts

1. Division by a Monomial
2. Long Division
3. Synthetic Division

Division of polynomials will be presented in this section as two separate cases: The first case illustrates division by a monomial divisor. The second case illustrates long division by a polynomial with two or more terms.

1. Division by a Monomial

To divide a polynomial by a monomial, divide each individual term in the polynomial by the divisor and simplify the result.

Dividing a Polynomial by a Monomial

If a, b, and c are polynomials such that $c \neq 0$, then

$$\frac{a+b}{c} = \frac{a}{c} + \frac{b}{c} \qquad \text{Similarly,} \qquad \frac{a-b}{c} = \frac{a}{c} - \frac{b}{c}$$

Classroom Examples: p. 401, Exercises 12 and 22

Example 1 Dividing a Polynomial by a Monomial

Divide the polynomials.

a. $\dfrac{5a^3 - 10a^2 + 20}{5a}$ **b.** $(12y^2z^3 - 15yz^2 + 6y^2z) \div (-6y^2z)$

Solution:

a. $\dfrac{5a^3 - 10a^2 + 20}{5a}$

$= \dfrac{5a^3}{5a} - \dfrac{10a^2}{5a} + \dfrac{20}{5a}$ Divide each term in the numerator by $5a$.

$= a^2 - 2a + \dfrac{4}{a}$ Simplify each term using the properties of exponents.

b. $(12y^2z^3 - 15yz^2 + 6y^2z) \div (-6y^2z)$

$$= \frac{12y^2z^3 - 15yz^2 + 6y^2z}{-6y^2z}$$

$$= \frac{12y^2z^3}{-6y^2z} - \frac{15yz^2}{-6y^2z} + \frac{6y^2z}{-6y^2z} \qquad \text{Divide each term by } -6y^2z.$$

$$= -2z^2 + \frac{5z}{2y} - 1 \qquad \text{Simplify each term.}$$

Instructor Note: In Example 1(b), mention to students that the third term in the quotient is −1 not 0.

Skill Practice Divide the polynomials.

1. $(36a^4 - 48a^3 + 12a^2) \div (6a^3)$

2. $\dfrac{-15x^3y^4 + 25x^2y^3 - 5xy^2}{-5xy^2}$

2. Long Division

If the divisor has two or more terms, a *long division* process similar to the division of real numbers is used. Take a minute to review the long division process for real numbers by dividing 2273 by 5.

$$\begin{array}{r} 454 \leftarrow \text{Quotient} \\ 5\overline{)2273} \\ \underline{-20} \\ 27 \\ \underline{-25} \\ 23 \\ \underline{-20} \\ 3 \leftarrow \text{Remainder} \end{array}$$

Therefore, $2273 \div 5 = 454\frac{3}{5}$.

A similar procedure is used for long division of polynomials as shown in Example 2.

Example 2 **Using Long Division to Divide Polynomials**

Classroom Example: p. 401, Exercise 28

Divide the polynomials using long division. $(2x^2 - x + 3) \div (x - 3)$

Solution:

$x - 3\overline{)2x^2 - x + 3}$

Divide the leading term in the dividend by the leading term in the divisor.

$$\frac{2x^2}{x} = 2x$$

This is the first term in the quotient.

$$\begin{array}{r} 2x\phantom{{}-x+3} \\ x - 3\overline{)2x^2 - x + 3} \\ -(\underline{2x^2 - 6x})\phantom{{}+3} \end{array}$$

Multiply $2x$ by the divisor: $2x(x - 3) = 2x^2 - 6x$ and subtract the result.

TIP: Recall that taking the opposite of a polynomial changes the sign of each term of the polynomial.

Answers

1. $6a - 8 + \dfrac{2}{a}$

2. $3x^2y^2 - 5xy + 1$

$$\begin{array}{r} 2x \\ x-3\overline{)2x^2 - x + 3} \\ \underline{-2x^2 + 6x} \\ 5x \end{array}$$

Subtract the quantity $2x^2 - 6x$. To do this, add the opposite.

$$\begin{array}{r} 2x + 5 \\ x-3\overline{)2x^2 - x + 3} \\ \underline{-2x^2 + 6x} \\ 5x + 3 \end{array}$$

Bring down the next column, and repeat the process.

Divide the leading term by x: $(5x)/x = 5$

Place 5 in the quotient.

$$\begin{array}{r} 2x + 5 \\ x-3\overline{)2x^2 - x + 3} \\ \underline{-2x^2 + 6x} \\ 5x + 3 \\ \underline{-(5x - 15)} \end{array}$$

Multiply the divisor by 5: $5(x - 3) = 5x - 15$

Subtract the result.

$$\begin{array}{r} 2x + 5 \\ x-3\overline{)2x^2 - x + 3} \\ \underline{-2x^2 + 6x} \\ 5x + 3 \\ \underline{-5x + 15} \\ 18 \end{array}$$

Subtract the quantity $5x - 15$ by adding the opposite.

The remainder is 18.

Summary:

The quotient is	$2x + 5$
The remainder is	18
The divisor is	$x - 3$
The dividend is	$2x^2 - x + 3$

The solution to a long division problem is usually written in the form:

$$\text{quotient} + \frac{\text{remainder}}{\text{divisor}}$$

Hence,

$$(2x^2 - x + 3) \div (x - 3) = 2x + 5 + \frac{18}{x - 3}$$

Skill Practice Divide the polynomials using long division.

3. $(3x^2 + 2x - 5) \div (x + 2)$

The division of polynomials can be checked in the same fashion as the division of real numbers. To check Example 2, we use the **division algorithm**:

$$\text{Dividend} = (\text{divisor})(\text{quotient}) + \text{remainder}$$

$$2x^2 - x + 3 \stackrel{?}{=} (x - 3)(2x + 5) + (18)$$

$$\stackrel{?}{=} 2x^2 + 5x - 6x - 15 + (18)$$

$$= 2x^2 - x + 3 \checkmark$$

Answer

3. $3x - 4 + \dfrac{3}{x + 2}$

Example 3 Using Long Division to Divide Polynomials

Classroom Example: p. 401, Exercise 36

Divide the polynomials using long division: $(3w^3 + 26w^2 - 3) \div (3w - 1)$

Solution:

First note that the dividend has a missing power of w and can be written as $3w^3 + 26w^2 + 0w - 3$. The term $0w$ is a place holder for the missing term. It is helpful to use the place holder to keep the powers of w lined up.

$$\begin{array}{r} w^2 \qquad\qquad\qquad \\ 3w-1\overline{)3w^3 + 26w^2 + 0w - 3} \\ -(\underline{3w^3 - \quad w^2}) \qquad\qquad \end{array}$$

Divide $3w^3 \div 3w = w^2$. This is the first term of the quotient.
Then multiply $w^2(3w - 1) = 3w^3 - w^2$.

$$\begin{array}{r} w^2 \qquad\qquad\qquad \\ 3w-1\overline{)3w^3 + 26w^2 + 0w - 3} \\ \underline{-3w^3 + \quad w^2} \qquad\qquad \\ 27w^2 + 0w \qquad \end{array}$$

Subtract by adding the opposite.

Bring down the next column, and repeat the process.

$$\begin{array}{r} w^2 + 9w \qquad\quad \\ 3w-1\overline{)3w^3 + 26w^2 + 0w - 3} \\ \underline{-3w^3 + \quad w^2} \qquad\qquad \\ 27w^2 + 0w \qquad \\ -(\underline{27w^2 - 9w}) \qquad \end{array}$$

Divide $27w^2$ by the leading term in the divisor. $27w^2 \div 3w = 9w$.
Place $9w$ in the quotient.
Multiply $9w(3w - 1) = 27w^2 - 9w$.

$$\begin{array}{r} w^2 + 9w \qquad\quad \\ 3w-1\overline{)3w^3 + 26w^2 + 0w - 3} \\ \underline{-3w^3 + \quad w^2} \qquad\qquad \\ 27w^2 + 0w \qquad \\ \underline{-27w^2 + 9w} \qquad \\ 9w - 3 \end{array}$$

Subtract by adding the opposite.

Bring down the next column, and repeat the process.

$$\begin{array}{r} w^2 + 9w + 3 \quad \\ 3w-1\overline{)3w^3 + 26w^2 + 0w - 3} \\ \underline{-3w^3 + \quad w^2} \qquad\qquad \\ 27w^2 + 0w \qquad \\ \underline{-27w^2 + 9w} \qquad \\ 9w - 3 \\ -(\underline{9w - 3}) \end{array}$$

Divide $9w$ by the leading term in the divisor. $9w \div 3w = 3$.
Place 3 in the quotient.
Multiply $3(3w - 1) = 9w - 3$.

$$\begin{array}{r} w^2 + 9w + 3 \quad \\ 3w-1\overline{)3w^3 + 26w^2 + 0w - 3} \\ \underline{-3w^3 + \quad w^2} \qquad\qquad \\ 27w^2 + 0w \qquad \\ \underline{-27w^2 + 9w} \qquad \\ 9w - 3 \\ \underline{-9w + 3} \\ 0 \end{array}$$

Subtract by adding the opposite.

The remainder is 0.

The quotient is $w^2 + 9w + 3$, and the remainder is 0.

Skill Practice Divide the polynomials using long division.

4. $\dfrac{9x^3 + 11x + 10}{3x + 2}$

Answer

4. $3x^2 - 2x + 5$

In Example 3, the remainder is zero. Therefore, we say that $3w - 1$ divides evenly into $3w^3 + 26w^2 - 3$. For this reason, the divisor and quotient are factors of $3w^3 + 26w^2 - 3$. To check, we have

$$\text{Dividend} = (\text{divisor})(\text{quotient}) + \text{remainder}$$

$$\begin{aligned} 3w^3 + 26w^2 - 3 &\stackrel{?}{=} (3w - 1)(w^2 + 9w + 3) + 0 \\ &\stackrel{?}{=} 3w^3 + 27w^2 + 9w - w^2 - 9w - 3 \\ &= 3w^3 + 26w^2 - 3 \; \checkmark \end{aligned}$$

Classroom Example: p. 401, Exercise 48

Example 4 Using Long Division to Divide Polynomials

Divide the polynomials using long division.

$$\frac{2y + y^4 - 5}{1 + y^2}$$

Solution:

First note that both the dividend and divisor should be written in descending order:

$$\frac{y^4 + 2y - 5}{y^2 + 1}$$

Also note that the dividend and the divisor have missing powers of y. Leave place holders.

$$y^2 + 0y + 1\overline{)y^4 + 0y^3 + 0y^2 + 2y - 5}$$

$$\begin{array}{r} y^2 \\ y^2 + 0y + 1\overline{)y^4 + 0y^3 + 0y^2 + 2y - 5} \\ \underline{-(y^4 + 0y^3 + y^2)} \end{array}$$

Divide $y^4 \div y^2 = y^2$. This is the first term of the quotient.

Multiply $y^2(y^2 + 0y + 1) = y^4 + 0y^3 + y^2$.

$$\begin{array}{r} y^2 \\ y^2 + 0y + 1\overline{)y^4 + 0y^3 + 0y^2 + 2y - 5} \\ \underline{-y^4 - 0y^3 - y^2} \\ -y^2 + 2y - 5 \end{array}$$

Subtract by adding the opposite.

Bring down the next columns.

$$\begin{array}{r} y^2 - 1 \\ y^2 + 0y + 1\overline{)y^4 + 0y^3 + 0y^2 + 2y - 5} \\ \underline{-y^4 - 0y^3 - y^2} \\ -y^2 + 2y - 5 \\ \underline{-(-y^2 - 0y - 1)} \end{array}$$

Divide $-y^2 \div y^2 = -1$.

Multiply $-1(y^2 + 0y + 1) = -y^2 - 0y - 1$.

$$\begin{array}{r} y^2 - 1 \\ y^2 + 0y + 1\overline{)y^4 + 0y^3 + 0y^2 + 2y - 5} \\ \underline{-y^4 - 0y^3 - \; y^2} \\ -y^2 + 2y - 5 \\ \underline{y^2 + 0y + 1} \\ 2y - 4 \end{array}$$

Subtract by adding the opposite.

Remainder

Therefore, $\dfrac{y^4 + 2y - 5}{y^2 + 1} = y^2 - 1 + \dfrac{2y - 4}{y^2 + 1}$.

Skill Practice Divide the polynomials using long division.

5. $(4 - x^2 + x^3) \div (2 + x^2)$

Answer

5. $x - 1 + \dfrac{-2x + 6}{x^2 + 2}$

Classroom Examples: p. 402, Exercises 74 and 76

Example 5 Determining Whether Long Division Is Necessary

Determine whether long division is necessary for each division of polynomials.

a. $\dfrac{2p^5 - 8p^4 + 4p - 16}{p^2 - 2p + 1}$ **b.** $\dfrac{2p^5 - 8p^4 + 4p - 16}{2p^2}$

c. $(3z^3 - 5z^2 + 10) \div (15z^3)$ **d.** $(3z^3 - 5z^2 + 10) \div (3z + 1)$

Solution:

- Long division is used when the divisor has *two or more terms.*
- If the divisor has *one term,* then divide each term in the dividend by the monomial divisor.

a. $\dfrac{2p^5 - 8p^4 + 4p - 16}{p^2 - 2p + 1}$ The divisor has three terms. Use long division.

b. $\dfrac{2p^5 - 8p^4 + 4p - 16}{2p^2}$ The divisor has one term. Long division is not necessary.

c. $(3z^3 - 5z^2 + 10) \div (15z^3)$ The divisor has one term. Long division is not necessary.

d. $(3z^3 - 5z^2 + 10) \div (3z + 1)$ The divisor has two terms. Use long division.

Skill Practice Divide the polynomials using the appropriate method of division.

6. $\dfrac{6x^3 - x^2 + 3x - 5}{2x + 3}$ **7.** $\dfrac{9w^3 - 18w^2 + 6w + 12}{3w}$

3. Synthetic Division

In this section, we introduced the process of long division to divide two polynomials. Next, we will learn another technique called **synthetic division** to divide two polynomials. Synthetic division can be used when dividing a polynomial by a first-degree divisor of the form $x - r$, where r is a constant. Synthetic division is considered a "shortcut" because it uses the coefficients of the divisor and dividend without writing the variables.

Consider dividing the polynomials $(3x^2 - 14x - 10) \div (x - 2)$.

$$\begin{array}{r} 3x - 8 \\ x - 2\overline{)3x^2 - 14x - 10} \\ -(3x^2 - 6x) \\ \hline -8x - 10 \\ -(-8x + 16) \\ \hline -26 \end{array}$$

Answers

6. $3x^2 - 5x + 9 + \dfrac{-32}{2x + 3}$

7. $3w^2 - 6w + 2 + \dfrac{4}{w}$

First note that the divisor $x - 2$ is in the form $x - r$, where $r = 2$. Therefore, synthetic division can be used to find the quotient and remainder.

Step 1: Write the value of r in a box.

Step 2: Write the coefficients of the dividend to the right of the box.

Step 3: Skip a line and draw a horizontal line below the list of coefficients.

Step 4: Bring down the leading coefficient from the dividend and write it below the line.

$$\begin{array}{r|rrr} 2 & 3 & -14 & -10 \\ & & & \\ \hline & 3 & & \end{array}$$

Step 5: Multiply the value of r by the number below the line ($2 \times 3 = 6$). Write the result in the next column above the line.

Step 6: Add the numbers in the column above the line ($-14 + 6$), and write the result below the line.

$$\begin{array}{r|rrr} 2 & 3 & -14 & -10 \\ & & 6 & \\ \hline & 3 & -8 & \end{array}$$

Repeat steps 5 and 6 until all columns have been completed.

Step 7: To get the final result, we use the numbers below the line. The number in the last column is the remainder. The other numbers are the coefficients of the quotient.

$$\begin{array}{r|rrr} 2 & 3 & -14 & -10 \\ & & 6 & -16 \\ \hline & 3 & -8 & \boxed{-26} \end{array}$$

A box is usually drawn around the remainder.

Quotient: $3x - 8$, remainder: -26

The degree of the quotient will always be 1 less than that of the dividend. Because the dividend is a second-degree polynomial, the quotient will be a first-degree polynomial. In this case, the quotient is $3x - 8$ and the remainder is -26.

Classroom Example: p. 402, Exercise 62

Example 6 Using Synthetic Division to Divide Polynomials

Divide the polynomials $(5x + 4x^3 - 6 + x^4) \div (x + 3)$ by using synthetic division.

Solution:

As with long division, the terms of the dividend and divisor should be written in descending order. Furthermore, missing powers must be accounted for by using placeholders (shown here in red).

$$5x + 4x^3 - 6 + x^4$$
$$= x^4 + 4x^3 + 0x^2 + 5x - 6$$

To use synthetic division, the divisor must be in the form $(x - r)$. The divisor $x + 3$ can be written as $x - (-3)$. Hence, $r = -3$.

Avoiding Mistakes

It is important to check that the divisor is in the form $(x - r)$ before applying synthetic division. The variable x in the divisor must be of first degree, and its coefficient must be 1.

Step 1: Write the value of r in a box.

Step 2: Write the coefficients of the dividend to the right of the box.

$$\begin{array}{r|rrrrr} -3 & 1 & 4 & 0 & 5 & -6 \\ & & & & & \\ \hline & 1 & & & & \end{array}$$

Step 3: Skip a line and draw a horizontal line below the list of coefficients.

Step 4: Bring down the leading coefficient from the dividend and write it below the line.

Instructor Note: Emphasize to the student that the divisor must be in the form $x - r$.

Step 5: Multiply the value of r by the number below the line ($-3 \times 1 = -3$). Write the result in the next column above the line.

Step 6: Add the numbers in the column above the line: $4 + (-3) = 1$.

$$\begin{array}{r|rrrrr} -3 & 1 & 4 & 0 & 5 & -6 \\ & & -3 & & & \\ \hline & 1 & 1 & & & \end{array}$$

Repeat steps 5 and 6:

$$\begin{array}{r|rrrrr} -3 & 1 & 4 & 0 & 5 & -6 \\ & & -3 & -3 & 9 & -42 \\ \hline & 1 & 1 & -3 & 14 & \boxed{-48} \end{array}$$

1: x^3-term coefficient; 1: x^2-term coefficient; -3: x-term coefficient; 14: constant; -48: remainder

The quotient is $x^3 + x^2 - 3x + 14$.

The remainder is -48.

The answer is $x^3 + x^2 - 3x + 14 + \dfrac{-48}{x+3}$.

Skill Practice Divide the polynomials by using synthetic division.

8. $(5y^2 + 2y^3 - 5) \div (y + 2)$

TIP: It is interesting to compare the long division process to the synthetic division process. For Example 5, long division is shown on the left, and synthetic division is shown on the right. Notice that the same pattern of coefficients used in long division appears in the synthetic division process.

$$\begin{array}{r}
x^3 + x^2 - 3x + 14 \\
x + 3\overline{)x^4 + 4x^3 + 0x^2 + 5x - 6} \\
\underline{-(x^4 + 3x^3)} \qquad\qquad\qquad \\
x^3 + 0x^2 \qquad\qquad \\
\underline{-(x^3 + 3x^2)} \qquad\qquad \\
-3x^2 + 5x \qquad \\
\underline{-(-3x^2 - 9x)} \qquad \\
14x - 6 \\
\underline{-(14x + 42)} \\
-48
\end{array}$$

$$\begin{array}{r|rrrrr} -3 & 1 & 4 & 0 & 5 & -6 \\ & & -3 & -3 & 9 & -42 \\ \hline & 1 & 1 & -3 & 14 & \boxed{-48} \\ & x^3 & x^2 & x & \text{constant} & \text{remainder} \end{array}$$

Quotient: $x^3 + x^2 - 3x + 14$
Remainder: -48

Answer

8. $2y^2 + y - 2 + \dfrac{-1}{y+2}$

Classroom Example: p. 402, Exercise 66

Example 7 Using Synthetic Division to Divide Polynomials

Divide the polynomials by using synthetic division. $(p^4 - 81) \div (p - 3)$

Solution:

$(p^4 - 81) \div (p - 3)$

$(p^4 + 0p^3 + 0p^2 + 0p - 81) \div (p - 3)$ Insert placeholders (red) for missing powers of p.

$$\begin{array}{r|rrrrr} 3 & 1 & 0 & 0 & 0 & -81 \\ & & 3 & 9 & 27 & 81 \\ \hline & 1 & 3 & 9 & 27 & \boxed{0} \end{array}$$

Quotient: $p^3 + 3p^2 + 9p + 27$

Remainder: 0

The answer is $p^3 + 3p^2 + 9p + 27$.

Skill Practice Divide the polynomials by using synthetic division.

9. $(x^3 + 1) \div (x + 1)$

Answer

9. $x^2 - x + 1$

Section 5.7 Practice Exercises

Vocabulary and Key Concepts

For additional exercises, see Classroom Activities 5.7A–5.7C in the *Student's Resource Manual* at www.mhhe.com/moh.

1. a. The __division__ algorithm states that: Dividend = (divisor)(__quotient__) + (__remainder__).

b. __Synthetic__ division or long division can be used when dividing a polynomial by a divisor of the form $x - r$, where r is a constant.

Review Exercises

2. a. Add. $(3x + 1) + (2x - 5)$ $5x - 4$

b. Multiply. $(3x + 1)(2x - 5)$ $6x^2 - 13x - 5$

3. a. Subtract. $(a - 10b) - (5a + b)$ $-4a - 11b$

b. Multiply. $(a - 10b)(5a + b)$ $5a^2 - 49ab - 10b^2$

4. a. Subtract. $(2y^2 + 1) - (y^2 - 5y + 1)$ $y^2 + 5y$

b. Multiply. $(2y^2 + 1)(y^2 - 5y + 1)$ $2y^4 - 10y^3 + 3y^2 - 5y + 1$

5. a. Add. $(x^2 - x) + (6x^2 + x + 2)$ $7x^2 + 2$

b. Multiply. $(x^2 - x)(6x^2 + x + 2)$ $6x^4 - 5x^3 + x^2 - 2x$

For Exercises 6–8, answers may vary.

6. Write an example of a product of two binomials and simplify. For example: $(2y + 3)(y - 5) = 2y^2 - 7y - 15$

7. Write an example of the square of a binomial and simplify. For example: $(5y + 1)^2 = 25y^2 + 10y + 1$

8. Write an example of the product of conjugates and simplify. For example: $(6p - 1)(6p + 1) = 36p^2 - 1$

Concept 1: Division by a Monomial

For Exercises 9–24, divide the polynomials. Check your answer by multiplication. **(See Example 1.)**

9. $\dfrac{16t^4 - 4t^2 + 20t}{-4t}$ $-4t^3 + t - 5$

10. $\dfrac{2x^3 + 8x^2 - 2x}{-2x}$ $-x^2 - 4x + 1$

11. $(36y + 24y^2 + 6y^3) \div (3y)$ $12 + 8y + 2y^2$

12. $(6p^2 - 18p^4 + 30p^5) \div (6p)$ $p - 3p^3 + 5p^4$

13. $(4x^3y + 12x^2y^2 - 4xy^3) \div (4xy)$ $x^2 + 3xy - y^2$

14. $(25m^5n - 10m^4n + m^3n) \div (5m^3n)$ $5m^2 - 2m + \dfrac{1}{5}$

15. $(-8y^4 - 12y^3 + 32y^2) \div (-4y^2)$ $2y^2 + 3y - 8$

16. $(12y^5 - 8y^6 + 16y^4 - 10y^3) \div (2y^3)$ $6y^2 - 4y^3 + 8y - 5$

17. $(3p^4 - 6p^3 + 2p^2 - p) \div (-6p)$ $-\dfrac{1}{2}p^3 + p^2 - \dfrac{1}{3}p + \dfrac{1}{6}$

18. $(-4q^3 + 8q^2 - q) \div (-12q)$ $\dfrac{1}{3}q^2 - \dfrac{2}{3}q + \dfrac{1}{12}$

19. $(a^3 + 5a^2 + a - 5) \div (a)$ $a^2 + 5a + 1 - \dfrac{5}{a}$

20. $(2m^5 - 3m^4 + m^3 - m^2 + 9m) \div (m^2)$ $2m^3 - 3m^2 + m - 1 + \dfrac{9}{m}$

21. $\dfrac{6s^3t^5 - 8s^2t^4 + 10st^2}{-2st^4}$ $-3s^2t + 4s - \dfrac{5}{t^2}$

22. $\dfrac{-8r^4w^2 - 4r^3w + 2w^3}{-4r^3w}$ $2rw + 1 - \dfrac{w^2}{2r^3}$

23. $(8p^4q^7 - 9p^5q^6 - 11p^3q - 4) \div (p^2q)$ $8p^2q^6 - 9p^3q^5 - 11p - \dfrac{4}{p^2q}$

24. $(20a^5b^5 - 20a^3b^2 + 5a^2b + 6) \div (a^2b)$ $20a^3b^4 - 20ab + 5 + \dfrac{6}{a^2b}$

Concept 2: Long Division

25. a. Divide $(2x^3 - 7x^2 + 5x - 1) \div (x - 2)$ and identify the divisor, quotient, and remainder.
Divisor: $(x - 2)$; quotient: $(2x^2 - 3x - 1)$; remainder: (-3)

b. Explain how to check by using multiplication.
Multiply the quotient and the divisor, then add the remainder. The result should equal the dividend.

26. a. Divide $(x^3 + 4x^2 + 7x - 3) \div (x + 3)$ and identify the divisor, quotient, and remainder.
Divisor: $(x + 3)$; quotient: $(x^2 + x + 4)$; remainder: (-15)

b. Explain how to check by using multiplication.
Multiply the quotient and the divisor, then add the remainder. The result should equal the dividend.

For Exercises 27–48, divide the polynomials by using long division. Check your answer by multiplication. **(See Examples 2–4.)**

27. $(x^2 + 11x + 19) \div (x + 4)$ $x + 7 + \dfrac{-9}{x+4}$

28. $(x^3 - 7x^2 - 13x + 3) \div (x + 2)$ $x^2 - 9x + 5 + \dfrac{-7}{x+2}$

29. $(3y^3 - 7y^2 - 4y + 3) \div (y - 3)$ $3y^2 + 2y + 2 + \dfrac{9}{y-3}$

30. $(z^3 - 2z^2 + 2z - 5) \div (z - 4)$ $z^2 + 2z + 10 + \dfrac{35}{z-4}$

31. $(-12a^2 + 77a - 121) \div (3a - 11)$ $-4a + 11$

32. $(28x^2 - 29x + 6) \div (4x - 3)$ $7x - 2$

33. $(9y + 18y^2 - 20) \div (3y + 4)$ $6y - 5$

34. $(-2y + 3y^2 - 1) \div (y - 1)$ $3y + 1$

35. $(18x^3 + 7x + 12) \div (3x - 2)$ $6x^2 + 4x + 5 + \dfrac{22}{3x-2}$

36. $(8x^3 - 6x + 22) \div (2x - 1)$ $4x^2 + 2x - 2 + \dfrac{20}{2x-1}$

37. $(8a^3 + 1) \div (2a + 1)$ $4a^2 - 2a + 1$

38. $(81x^4 - 1) \div (3x + 1)$ $27x^3 - 9x^2 + 3x - 1$

39. $(x^4 - x^3 - x^2 + 4x - 2) \div (x^2 + x - 1)$ $x^2 - 2x + 2$

40. $(2a^5 - 7a^4 + 11a^3 - 22a^2 + 29a - 10) \div (2a^2 - 5a + 2)$ $a^3 - a^2 + 2a - 5$

41. $(2x^3 - 10x + x^4 - 25) \div (x^2 - 5)$ $x^2 + 2x + 5$

42. $(-5x^3 + x^4 - 4 - 10x) \div (x^2 + 2)$ $x^2 - 5x - 2$

43. $(x^4 - 3x^2 + 10) \div (x^2 - 2)$ $x^2 - 1 + \dfrac{8}{x^2-2}$

44. $(3y^4 - 25y^2 - 18) \div (y^2 - 3)$ $3y^2 - 16 + \dfrac{-66}{y^2-3}$

45. $(n^4 - 16) \div (n - 2)$ $n^3 + 2n^2 + 4n + 8$

46. $(m^3 + 27) \div (m + 3)$ $m^2 - 3m + 9$

47. $\dfrac{3y^4 + 2y + 3}{1 + y^2}$ $3y^2 - 3 + \dfrac{2y+6}{y^2+1}$

48. $\dfrac{2x^4 + 6x + 4}{2 + x^2}$ $2x^2 - 4 + \dfrac{6x+12}{x^2+2}$

Concept 3: Synthetic Division

49. Explain the conditions under which you may use synthetic division to divide polynomials. The divisor must be of the form $x - r$.

50. Can synthetic division be used directly to divide $(4x^4 + 3x^3 - 7x + 9)$ by $(2x + 5)$? Explain why or why not. No. The divisor is not of the form $x - r$.

51. Can synthetic division be used to divide $(6x^5 - 3x^2 + 2x - 14)$ by $(x^2 - 3)$? Explain why or why not. No. The divisor is not of the form $x - r$.

52. Can synthetic division be used to divide $(3x^4 - x + 1)$ by $(x - 5)$? Explain why or why not. Yes, the divisor is of the form $x - r$.

53. The following table represents the result of a synthetic division.

5	1	−2	−4	3
		5	15	55
	1	3	11	58

Use x as the variable.

a. Identify the divisor. $x - 5$

b. Identify the quotient. $x^2 + 3x + 11$

c. Identify the remainder. 58

54. The following table represents the result of a synthetic division.

−2	2	3	0	−1	6
		−4	2	−4	10
	2	−1	2	−5	16

Use x as the variable.

a. Identify the divisor. $x + 2$

b. Identify the quotient. $2x^3 - x^2 + 2x - 5$

c. Identify the remainder. 16

For Exercises 55–70, divide by using synthetic division. Check your answer by multiplication. **(See Examples 6–7.)**

55. $(x^2 - 2x - 48) \div (x - 8)$ $x + 6$

56. $(x^2 - 4x - 12) \div (x - 6)$ $x + 2$

57. $(t^2 - 3t - 4) \div (t + 1)$ $t - 4$

58. $(h^2 + 7h + 12) \div (h + 3)$ $h + 4$

59. $(5y^2 + 5y + 1) \div (y - 1)$ $5y + 10 + \frac{11}{y-1}$

60. $(3w^2 + w - 5) \div (w + 2)$ $3w - 5 + \frac{5}{w+2}$

61. $(3 + 7y^2 - 4y + 3y^3) \div (y + 3)$ $3y^2 - 2y + 2 + \frac{-3}{y+3}$

62. $(2z - 2z^2 + z^3 - 5) \div (z + 3)$ $z^2 - 5z + 17 + \frac{-56}{z+3}$

63. $(x^3 - 3x^2 + 4) \div (x - 2)$ $x^2 - x - 2$

64. $(3y^4 - 25y^2 - 18) \div (y - 3)$ $3y^3 + 9y^2 + 2y + 6$

65. $(a^5 - 32) \div (a - 2)$ $a^4 + 2a^3 + 4a^2 + 8a + 16$

66. $(b^3 + 27) \div (b + 3)$ $b^2 - 3b + 9$

67. $(x^3 - 216) \div (x - 6)$ $x^2 + 6x + 36$

68. $(y^4 - 16) \div (y + 2)$ $y^3 - 2y^2 + 4y - 8$

69. $(4w^4 - w^2 + 6w - 3) \div \left(w - \frac{1}{2}\right)$ $4w^3 + 2w^2 + 6$

70. $(-12y^4 - 5y^3 - y^2 + y + 3) \div \left(y + \frac{3}{4}\right)$ $-12y^3 + 4y^2 - 4y + 4$

Mixed Exercises

For Exercises 71– 82, divide the polynomials by using an appropriate method. **(See Examples 5.)**

71. $(-x^3 - 8x^2 - 3x - 2) \div (x + 4)$ $-x^2 - 4x + 13 + \frac{-54}{x+4}$

72. $(8xy^2 - 9x^2y + 6x^2y^2) \div (x^2y^2)$ $\frac{8}{x} - \frac{9}{y} + 6$

73. $(22x^2 - 11x + 33) \div (11x)$ $2x - 1 + \frac{3}{x}$

74. $(2m^3 - 4m^2 + 5m - 33) \div (m - 3)$ $2m^2 + 2m + 11$

75. $(12y^3 - 17y^2 + 30y - 10) \div (3y^2 - 2y + 5)$ $4y - 3 + \frac{4y+5}{3y^2 - 2y + 5}$

76. $(90h^{12} - 63h^9 + 45h^8 - 36h^7) \div (9h^9)$ $10h^3 - 7 + \frac{5}{h} - \frac{4}{h^2}$

77. $(4x^4 + 6x^3 + 3x - 1) \div (2x^2 + 1)$ $2x^2 + 3x - 1$

78. $(y^4 - 3y^3 - 5y^2 - 2y + 5) \div (y + 2)$ $y^3 - 5y^2 + 5y - 12 + \frac{29}{y+2}$

79. $(16k^{11} - 32k^{10} + 8k^8 - 40k^4) \div (8k^8)$ $2k^3 - 4k^2 + 1 - \frac{5}{k^4}$

80. $(4m^3 - 18m^2 + 22m - 10) \div (2m^2 - 4m + 3)$ $2m - 5 + \frac{-4m+5}{2m^2 - 4m + 3}$

81. $(5x^3 + 9x^2 + 10x) \div (5x^2)$ $x + \frac{9}{5} + \frac{2}{x}$

82. $(15k^4 + 3k^3 + 4k^2 + 4) \div (3k^2 - 1)$ $5k^2 + k + 3 + \frac{k+7}{3k^2 - 1}$

Problem Recognition Exercises

Operations on Polynomials

For Exercises 1–40, perform the indicated operations and simplify.

1. **a.** $6x^2 + 2x^2$ a. $8x^2$
b. $(6x^2)(2x^2)$ b. $12x^4$

2. **a.** $8y^3 + y^3$ a. $9y^3$
b. $(8y^3)(y^3)$ b. $8y^6$

3. **a.** $(4x + y)^2$
b. $(4xy)^2$ a. $16x^2 + 8xy + y^2$ b. $16x^2y^2$

4. **a.** $(2a + b)^2$
b. $(2ab)^2$ a. $4a^2 + 4ab + b^2$ b. $4a^2b^2$

5. **a.** $(2x + 3) + (4x - 2)$
b. $(2x + 3)(4x - 2)$
a. $6x + 1$ b. $8x^2 + 8x - 6$

6. **a.** $(5m^2 + 1) + (m^2 + m)$
b. $(5m^2 + 1)(m^2 + m)$
a. $6m^2 + m + 1$ b. $5m^4 + 5m^3 + m^2 + m$

7. **a.** $(3z + 2)^2$
b. $(3z + 2)(3z - 2)$
a. $9z^2 + 12z + 4$ b. $9z^2 - 4$

8. **a.** $(6y - 7)^2$
b. $(6y - 7)(6y + 7)$
a. $36y^2 - 84y + 49$ b. $36y^2 - 49$

9. **a.** $(2x - 4)(x^2 - 2x + 3)$
b. $(2x - 4) + (x^2 - 2x + 3)$
a. $2x^3 - 8x^2 + 14x - 12$ b. $x^2 - 1$

10. **a.** $(3y^2 + 8)(-y^2 - 4)$
b. $(3y^2 + 8) - (-y^2 - 4)$
a. $-3y^4 - 20y^2 - 32$ b. $4y^2 + 12$

11. **a.** $x + x$ a. $2x$
b. $x \cdot x$ b. x^2

12. **a.** $2c + 2c$ a. $4c$
b. $2c \cdot 2c$ b. $4c^2$

13. $(7mn)^2$ $49m^2n^2$

14. $(8pq)^2$ $64p^2q^2$

15. $(-2x^4 - 6x^3 + 8x^2) \div (2x^2)$ $-x^2 - 3x + 4$

16. $(-15m^3 + 12m^2 - 3m) \div (-3m)$ $5m^2 - 4m + 1$

17. $(m^3 - 4m^2 - 6) - (3m^2 + 7m) + (-m^3 - 9m + 6)$
$-7m^2 - 16m$

18. $(n^4 + 2n^2 - 3n) + (4n^2 + 2n - 1) - (4n^5 + 6n - 3)$
$-4n^5 + n^4 + 6n^2 - 7n + 2$

19. $(8x^3 + 2x + 6) \div (x - 2)$ $8x^2 + 16x + 34 + \dfrac{74}{x - 2}$

20. $(-4x^3 + 2x^2 - 5) \div (x - 3)$ $-4x^2 - 10x - 30 + \dfrac{-95}{x - 3}$

21. $(2x - y)(3x^2 + 4xy - y^2)$ $6x^3 + 5x^2y - 6xy^2 + y^3$

22. $(3a + b)(2a^2 - ab + 2b^2)$ $6a^3 - a^2b + 5ab^2 + 2b^3$

23. $(x + y^2)(x^2 - xy^2 + y^4)$ $x^3 + y^6$

24. $(m^2 + 1)(m^4 - m^2 + 1)$ $m^6 + 1$

25. $(a^2 + 2b) - (a^2 - 2b)$
$4b$

26. $(y^3 - 6z) - (y^3 + 6z)$
$-12z$

27. $(a^3 + 2b)(a^3 - 2b)$
$a^6 - 4b^2$

28. $(y^3 - 6z)(y^3 + 6z)$
$y^6 - 36z^2$

29. $\dfrac{8p^2 + 4p - 6}{2p - 1}$
$4p + 4 + \dfrac{-2}{2p - 1}$

30. $\dfrac{4v^2 - 8v + 8}{2v + 3}$
$2v - 7 + \dfrac{29}{2v + 3}$

31. $\dfrac{12x^3y^7}{3xy^5}$ $4x^2y^2$

32. $\dfrac{-18p^2q^4}{2pq^3}$ $-9pq$

33. $\left(\dfrac{3}{7}x - \dfrac{1}{2}\right)\left(\dfrac{3}{7}x + \dfrac{1}{2}\right)$
$\dfrac{9}{49}x^2 - \dfrac{1}{4}$

34. $\left(\dfrac{2}{5}y + \dfrac{4}{3}\right)\left(\dfrac{2}{5}y - \dfrac{4}{3}\right)$
$\dfrac{4}{25}y^2 - \dfrac{16}{9}$

35. $\left(\dfrac{1}{9}x^3 + \dfrac{2}{3}x^2 + \dfrac{1}{6}x - 3\right) - \left(\dfrac{4}{3}x^3 + \dfrac{1}{9}x^2 + \dfrac{2}{3}x + 1\right)$
$-\dfrac{11}{9}x^3 + \dfrac{5}{9}x^2 - \dfrac{1}{2}x - 4$

36. $\left(\dfrac{1}{10}y^2 - \dfrac{3}{5}y - \dfrac{1}{15}\right) - \left(\dfrac{7}{5}y^2 + \dfrac{3}{10}y - \dfrac{1}{3}\right)$
$-\dfrac{13}{10}y^2 - \dfrac{9}{10}y + \dfrac{4}{15}$

37. $(0.05x^2 - 0.16x - 0.75) + (1.25x^2 - 0.14x + 0.25)$
$1.3x^2 - 0.3x - 0.5$

38. $(1.6w^3 + 2.8w + 6.1) + (3.4w^3 - 4.1w^2 - 7.3)$ $5w^3 - 4.1w^2 + 2.8w - 1.2$

39. $(3x^2y)(-2xy^5)$ $-6x^3y^6$

40. $(10ab^4)(5a^3b^2)$ $50a^4b^6$

Group Activity

The Pythagorean Theorem and a Geometric "Proof"

Estimated Time: 25–30 minutes

Group Size: 2

Right triangles occur in many applications of mathematics. By definition, a right triangle is a triangle that contains a 90° angle. The two shorter sides in a right triangle are referred to as the "legs," and the longest side is called the "hypotenuse." In the triangle shown, the legs are labeled as a and b, and the hypotenuse is labeled as c.

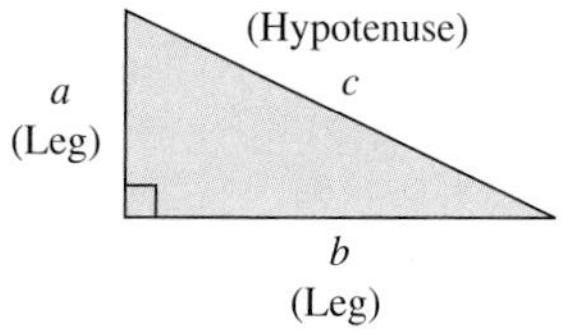

Right triangles have an important property that the sum of the squares of the two legs of a right triangle equals the square of the hypotenuse. This fact is referred to as the Pythagorean theorem. In symbols, the Pythagorean theorem is stated as:

$$a^2 + b^2 = c^2$$

1. The following triangles are right triangles. Verify that $a^2 + b^2 = c^2$. (The units may be left off when performing these calculations.)

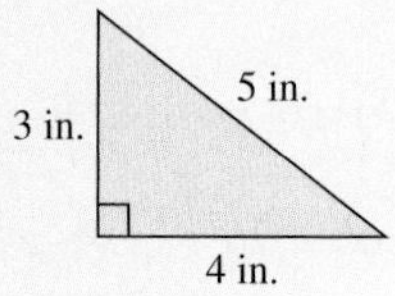

$a = 3$

$b = 4$

$c = 5$

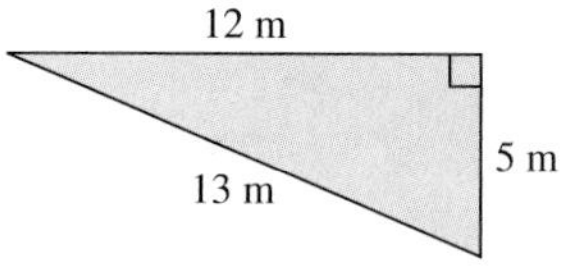

$a =$ ______

$b =$ ______

$c =$ ______

$$a^2 + b^2 = c^2$$
$$(3)^2 + (4)^2 \stackrel{?}{=} (5)^2$$
$$9 + 16 = 25 \checkmark$$

$$a^2 + b^2 = c^2$$
$$(\_\_\_)^2 + (\_\_\_)^2 \stackrel{?}{=} (\_\_\_)^2$$
$$\_\_\_ + \_\_\_ = \_\_\_ \checkmark$$

2. The following geometric "proof" of the Pythagorean theorem uses addition, subtraction, and multiplication of polynomials. Consider the square figure. The length of each side of the large outer square is $(a + b)$. Therefore, the area of the large outer square is $(a + b)^2$.

   The area of the large outer square can also be found by adding the area of the inner square (pictured in light gray) plus the area of the four right triangles (pictured in dark gray).

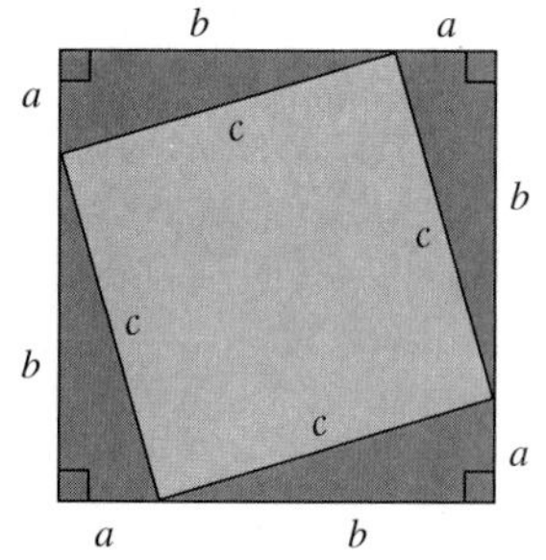

Area of inner square: c^2 Area of the four right triangles: $4 \cdot (\frac{1}{2}\, a\, b)$

½ Base · Height

3. Now equate the two expressions representing the area of the large outer square:

$$\begin{pmatrix}\text{Area of outer}\\ \text{square}\end{pmatrix} = \begin{pmatrix}\text{area of inner}\\ \text{square}\end{pmatrix} + \begin{pmatrix}\text{4 times the area}\\ \text{of the right triangles}\end{pmatrix}$$

$(a + b)^2 = c^2 + 4 \cdot (\frac{1}{2}ab)$;

$a^2 + 2ab + b^2 = c^2 + 2ab$;

$a^2 + b^2 = c^2$

__________ = __________ + __________

__________ = __________ + __________ ← Clear parentheses on both sides of the equation.

__________ = __________ ← Subtract $2ab$ from both sides.

Chapter 5 Summary

Section 5.1 Multiplying and Dividing Expressions with Common Bases

Key Concepts

Definition

$b^n = \underbrace{b \cdot b \cdot b \cdot b \cdot \ldots b}_{n \text{ factors of } b}$ $\quad$ b is the base, n is the exponent

Multiplying Like Bases

$b^m b^n = b^{m+n}$ $\quad$ (m, n positive integers)

Dividing Like Bases

$\dfrac{b^m}{b^n} = b^{m-n}$ $\quad$ ($b \neq 0$, m, n, positive integers)

Examples

Example 1

$3^4 = 3 \cdot 3 \cdot 3 \cdot 3 = 81$ $\quad$ 3 is the base
4 is the exponent

Example 2

Compare: $(-5)^2$ versus -5^2

$(-5)^2 = (-5)(-5) = 25$

versus

$-5^2 = -1(5^2) = -1(5)(5) = -25$

Example 3

Simplify: $x^3 \cdot x^4 \cdot x^2 \cdot x = x^{3+4+2+1} = x^{10}$

Example 4

Simplify: $\dfrac{c^4 d^{10}}{cd^5} = c^{4-1}d^{10-5} = c^3 d^5$

Section 5.2 More Properties of Exponents

Key Concepts

Power Rule for Exponents

$(b^m)^n = b^{mn}$ $\quad$ ($b \neq 0$, m, n positive integers)

Power of a Product and Power of a Quotient

Assume m and n are positive integers and a and b are real numbers where $b \neq 0$.
Then,

$(ab)^m = a^m b^m$ $\quad$ and $\quad$ $\left(\dfrac{a}{b}\right)^m = \dfrac{a^m}{b^m}$

Examples

Example 1

Simplify: $(x^4)^5 = x^{20}$

Example 2

Simplify: $(4uv^2)^3 = 4^3u^3(v^2)^3 = 64u^3v^6$

Example 3

Simplify: $\left(\dfrac{p^5q^3}{5pq^2}\right)^2 = \left(\dfrac{p^{5-1}q^{3-2}}{5}\right)^2 = \left(\dfrac{p^4q}{5}\right)^2$

$= \dfrac{(p^4)^2(q)^2}{(5)^2} = \dfrac{p^8q^2}{25}$

Section 5.3 Definitions of b^0 and b^{-n}

Key Concepts

Definitions

If b is a nonzero real number and n is an integer, then:

1. $b^0 = 1$

2. $b^{-n} = \left(\frac{1}{b}\right)^n = \frac{1}{b^n}$

Examples

Example 1

Simplify: $4^0 = 1$

Example 2

Simplify: $y^{-7} = \frac{1}{y^7}$

Example 3

Simplify: $\frac{8a^0b^{-2}}{c^{-5}d}$

$$= \frac{8(1)c^5}{b^2d} = \frac{8c^5}{b^2d}$$

Section 5.4 Scientific Notation

Key Concepts

A positive number written in **scientific notation** is expressed in the form:

$a \times 10^n$ where $1 \le a < 10$ and n is an integer.

$35{,}000 = 3.5 \times 10^4$

$0.000\,000\,548 = 5.48 \times 10^{-7}$

Examples

Example 1

Multiply: $(3.5 \times 10^4)(2 \times 10^{-6})$

$$= 7 \times 10^{-2}$$

Example 2

Divide: $\frac{2.1 \times 10^{-9}}{8.4 \times 10^3} = 0.25 \times 10^{-9-3}$

$$= 0.25 \times 10^{-12}$$

$$= (2.5 \times 10^{-1}) \times 10^{-12}$$

$$= 2.5 \times 10^{-13}$$

Section 5.5 Addition and Subtraction of Polynomials

Key Concepts

A **polynomial** in one variable is a sum of terms of the form ax^n, where a is a real number and the exponent, n, is a nonnegative integer. For each term, a is called the **coefficient** of the term and n is the **degree of the term**. The term with highest degree is the **leading term**, and its coefficient is called the **leading coefficient**. The **degree of the polynomial** is the largest degree of all its terms.

To add or subtract polynomials, add or subtract *like* terms.

Examples

Example 1

Given: $4x^5 - 8x^3 + 9x - 5$

Coefficients of each term: 4, −8, 9, −5

Degree of each term: 5, 3, 1, 0

Leading term: $4x^5$

Leading coefficient: 4

Degree of polynomial: 5

Example 2

Perform the indicated operations:

$$(2x^4 - 5x^3 + 1) - (x^4 + 3) + (x^3 - 4x - 7)$$
$$= 2x^4 - 5x^3 + 1 - x^4 - 3 + x^3 - 4x - 7$$
$$= 2x^4 - x^4 - 5x^3 + x^3 - 4x + 1 - 3 - 7$$
$$= x^4 - 4x^3 - 4x - 9$$

Section 5.6 Multiplication of Polynomials and Special Products

Key Concepts

Multiplying Monomials

Use the commutative and associative properties of multiplication to group coefficients and like bases.

Multiplying Polynomials

Multiply each term in the first polynomial by each term in the second polynomial.

Product of Conjugates

The product of conjugates results in a **difference of squares**.

$(a + b)(a - b) = a^2 - b^2$

Square of a Binomial

The square of a binomial results in a **perfect square trinomial**.

$(a + b)^2 = a^2 + 2ab + b^2$

$(a - b)^2 = a^2 - 2ab + b^2$

Examples

Example 1

Multiply: $(5a^2b)(-2ab^3)$

$$= [5\cdot(-2)](a^2a)(bb^3)$$
$$= -10a^3b^4$$

Example 2

Multiply: $(x - 2)(3x^2 - 4x + 11)$

$$= 3x^3 - 4x^2 + 11x - 6x^2 + 8x - 22$$
$$= 3x^3 - 10x^2 + 19x - 22$$

Example 3

Multiply: $(3w - 4v)(3w + 4v)$

$$= (3w)^2 - (4v)^2$$
$$= 9w^2 - 16v^2$$

Example 4

Multiply: $(5c - 8d)^2$

$$= (5c)^2 - 2(5c)(8d) + (8d)^2$$
$$= 25c^2 - 80cd + 64d^2$$

Section 5.7 Division of Polynomials

Key Concepts

Division of Polynomials

1. Division by a monomial, use the properties:

$$\frac{a+b}{c}=\frac{a}{c}+\frac{b}{c} \quad \text{and} \quad \frac{a-b}{c}=\frac{a}{c}-\frac{b}{c}$$

2. If the divisor has more than one term, use long division.

3. If the divisor is of the form $x - r$, then synthetic division may be used.

Examples

Example 1

Divide: $\dfrac{-3x^2 - 6x + 9}{-3x}$

$$= \frac{-3x^2}{-3x} - \frac{6x}{-3x} + \frac{9}{-3x}$$

$$= x + 2 - \frac{3}{x}$$

Example 2

Divide: $(3x^2 - 5x + 1) \div (x + 2)$

$$\begin{array}{r} 3x - 11 \\ x+2\overline{)3x^2 - 5x + 1} \\ -(3x^2 + 6x) \\ \hline -11x + 1 \\ -(-11x - 22) \\ \hline 23 \end{array}$$

$$3x - 11 + \frac{23}{x+2}$$

Example 3

Divide: $(4x^3 - 2x - 5) \div (x - 1)$

$$\begin{array}{r|rrrr} 1 & 4 & 0 & -2 & -5 \\ & & 4 & 4 & 2 \\ \hline & 4 & 4 & 2 & -3 \end{array}$$

$$4x^2 + 4x + 2 + \frac{-3}{x-1}$$

Chapter 5 Review Exercises

Section 5.1

For Exercises 1–4, identify the base and the exponent.

1. 5^3 Base: 5; exponent: 3

2. x^4 Base: x; exponent: 4

3. $(-2)^0$ Base: -2; exponent: 0

4. y Base: y; exponent: 1

5. Evaluate the expressions.

a. 6^2 36 **b.** $(-6)^2$ 36 **c.** -6^2 -36

6. Evaluate the expressions.

a. 4^3 64 **b.** $(-4)^3$ -64 **c.** -4^3 -64

For Exercises 7–18, simplify and write the answers in exponent form. Assume that all variables represent nonzero real numbers.

7. $5^3 \cdot 5^{10}$ 5^{13}

8. a^7a^4 a^{11}

9. $x \cdot x^6 \cdot x^2$ x^9

10. $6^3 \cdot 6 \cdot 6^5$ 6^9

11. $\dfrac{10^7}{10^4}$ 10^3

12. $\dfrac{y^{14}}{y^8}$ y^6

13. $\dfrac{b^9}{b}$ b^8

14. $\dfrac{7^8}{7}$ 7^7

15. $\dfrac{k^2k^3}{k^4}$ k

16. $\dfrac{8^4 \cdot 8^7}{8^{11}}$ 1

17. $\dfrac{2^8 \cdot 2^{10}}{2^3 \cdot 2^7}$ 2^8

18. $\dfrac{q^3q^{12}}{qq^8}$ q^6

19. Explain why $2^2 \cdot 4^4$ does *not* equal 8^6.
Exponents are added only when multiplying factors with the same base. In such a case, the base does not change.

20. Explain why $\frac{10^5}{5^2}$ does *not* equal 2^3.
Exponents are subtracted only when dividing factors with the same base. In such a case, the base does not change.

For Exercises 21–22, use the formula

$$A = P(1 + r)^t$$

21. Find the amount in an account after 3 years if the initial investment is \$6000, invested at 6% interest compounded annually. \$7146.10

22. Find the amount in an account after 2 years if the initial investment is \$20,000, invested at 5% interest compounded annually. \$22,050

Section 5.2

For Exercises 23–40, simplify each expression. Write the answer in exponent form. Assume all variables represent nonzero real numbers.

23. $(7^3)^4$ 7^{12}

24. $(c^2)^6$ c^{12}

25. $(p^4p^2)^3$ p^{18}

26. $(9^5 \cdot 9^2)^4$ 9^{28}

27. $\left(\frac{a}{b}\right)^2$ $\frac{a^2}{b^2}$

28. $\left(\frac{1}{3}\right)^4$ $\frac{1}{3^4}$

29. $\left(\frac{5}{c^2d^5}\right)^2$ $\frac{5^2}{c^4d^{10}}$

30. $\left(-\frac{m^2}{4n^6}\right)^5$ $-\frac{m^{10}}{4^5n^{30}}$

31. $(2ab^2)^4$ $2^4a^4b^8$

32. $(-x^7y)^2$ $x^{14}y^2$

33. $\left(\frac{-3x^3}{5y^2z}\right)^3$ $-\frac{3^3x^9}{5^3y^6z^3}$

34. $\left(\frac{r^3}{s^2t^6}\right)^5$ $\frac{r^{15}}{s^{10}t^{30}}$

35. $\frac{a^4(a^2)^8}{(a^3)^3}$ a^{11}

36. $\frac{(8^3)^4 \cdot 8^{10}}{(8^4)^5}$ 8^2

37. $\frac{(4h^2k)^2(h^3k)^4}{(2hk^3)^2}$ $4h^{14}$

38. $\frac{(p^3q)^3(2p^2q^4)^4}{(8p)(pq^3)^2}$ $2p^{14}q^{13}$

39. $\left(\frac{2x^4y^3}{4xy^2}\right)^2$ $\frac{x^6y^2}{4}$

40. $\left(\frac{a^4b^6}{ab^4}\right)^3$ a^9b^6

Section 5.3

For Exercises 41–62, simplify each expression. Write the answers with positive exponents. Assume all variables represent nonzero real numbers.

41. 8^0 1

42. $(-b)^0$ 1

43. $-x^0$ -1

44. 1^0 1

45. $2y^0$ 2

46. $(2y)^0$ 1

47. z^{-5} $\frac{1}{z^5}$

48. 10^{-4} $\frac{1}{10^4}$

49. $(6a)^{-2}$ $\frac{1}{36a^2}$

50. $6a^{-2}$ $\frac{6}{a^2}$

51. $4^0 + 4^{-2}$ $\frac{17}{16}$

52. $9^{-1} + 9^0$ $\frac{10}{9}$

53. $t^{-6}t^{-2}$ $\frac{1}{t^8}$

54. r^8r^{-9} $\frac{1}{r}$

55. $\frac{12x^{-2}y^3}{6x^4y^{-4}}$ $\frac{2y^7}{x^6}$

56. $\frac{8ab^{-3}c^0}{10a^{-5}b^{-4}c^{-1}}$ $\frac{4a^6bc}{5}$

57. $(-2m^2n^{-4})^{-4}$ $\frac{n^{16}}{16m^8}$

58. $(3u^{-5}v^2)^{-3}$ $\frac{u^{15}}{27v^6}$

59. $\frac{(k^{-6})^{-2}(k^3)}{5k^{-6}k^0}$ $\frac{k^{21}}{5}$

60. $\frac{(3h)^{-2}(h^{-5})^{-3}}{h^{-4}h^8}$ $\frac{h^9}{9}$

61. $2 \cdot 3^{-1} - 6^{-1}$ $\frac{1}{2}$

62. $2^{-1} - 2^{-2} + 2^0$ $\frac{5}{4}$

Section 5.4

63. Write the numbers in scientific notation.

a. In a recent year there were 97,400,000 packages of M&Ms sold in the United States. 9.74×10^7

b. The thickness of a piece of paper is 0.0042 in. 4.2×10^{-3} in.

64. Write the numbers in standard form.

a. A pH of 10 means the hydrogen ion concentration is 1×10^{-10} units. 0.000 000 0001

b. A fundraising event for neurospinal research raised $\$2.56 \times 10^5$. \$256,000

For Exercises 65–68, perform the indicated operations. Write the answers in scientific notation.

65. $(41 \times 10^{-6})(2.3 \times 10^{11})$ 9.43×10^5

66. $\frac{9.3 \times 10^3}{6 \times 10^{-7}}$ 1.55×10^{10}

67. $\frac{2000}{0.000008}$ 2.5×10^8

68. $(0.000078)(21{,}000{,}000)$ 1.638×10^3

69. Use your calculator to evaluate 5^{20}. Why is scientific notation necessary on your calculator to express the answer? $\approx 9.5367 \times 10^{13}$. This number has too many digits to fit on most calculator displays.

70. Use your calculator to evaluate $(0.4)^{30}$. Why is scientific notation necessary on your calculator to express the answer? $\approx 1.1529 \times 10^{-12}$. This number has too many digits to fit on most calculator displays.

71. The average distance between the Earth and Sun is 9.3×10^7 mi.

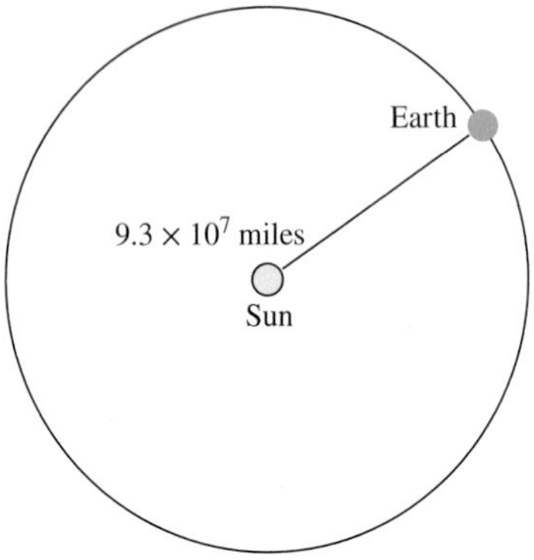

a. If the Earth's orbit is approximated by a circle, find the total distance the Earth travels around the Sun in one orbit. (*Hint:* The circumference of a circle is given by $C = 2\pi r$.) Express the answer in scientific notation.
$\approx 5.84 \times 10^8$ mi

b. If the Earth makes one complete trip around the Sun in 1 year (365 days = 8.76×10^3 hr), find the average speed that the Earth travels around the Sun in miles per hour. Express the answer in scientific notation.
$\approx 6.67 \times 10^4$ mph

72. The average distance between the planet Mercury and the Sun is 3.6×10^7 mi.

a. If Mercury's orbit is approximated by a circle, find the total distance Mercury travels around the Sun in one orbit. (*Hint:* The circumference of a circle is given by $C = 2\pi r$.) Express the answer in scientific notation. $\approx 2.26 \times 10^8$ mi

b. If Mercury makes one complete trip around the Sun in 88 days (2.112×10^3 hr), find the average speed that Mercury travels around the Sun in miles per hour. Express the answer in scientific notation.
$\approx 1.07 \times 10^5$ mph

Section 5.5

73. For the polynomial $7x^4 - x + 6$

a. Classify as a monomial, a binomial, or a trinomial. Trinomial

b. Identify the degree of the polynomial. 4

c. Identify the leading coefficient. 7

74. For the polynomial $2y^3 - 5y^7$

a. Classify as a monomial, a binomial, or a trinomial. Binomial

b. Identify the degree of the polynomial. 7

c. Identify the leading coefficient. -5

For Exercises 75–80, add or subtract as indicated.

75. $(4x + 2) + (3x - 5)$ $7x - 3$

76. $(7y^2 - 11y - 6) - (8y^2 + 3y - 4)$ $-y^2 - 14y - 2$

77. $(9a^2 - 6) - (-5a^2 + 2a)$ $14a^2 - 2a - 6$

78. $\left(5x^3 - \frac{1}{4}x^2 + \frac{5}{8}x + 2\right) + \left(\frac{5}{2}x^3 + \frac{1}{2}x^2 - \frac{1}{8}x\right)$
$\frac{15}{2}x^3 + \frac{1}{4}x^2 + \frac{1}{2}x + 2$

79. $$\begin{array}{rrrrr} & 8w^4 & & -6w & +3 \\ + & 2w^4 & +2w^3 & -w & +1 \\ \hline \end{array}$$
$10w^4 + 2w^3 - 7w + 4$

80. $$\begin{array}{rrrrrr} & -0.02b^5 & +b^4 & & -0.7b & +0.3 \\ + & 0.03b^5 & & -0.1b^3 & +b & +0.03 \\ \hline \end{array}$$
$0.01b^5 + b^4 - 0.1b^3 + 0.3b + 0.33$

81. Subtract $(9x^2 + 4x + 6)$ from $(7x^2 - 5x)$.
$-2x^2 - 9x - 6$

82. Find the difference of $(x^2 - 5x - 3)$ and $(6x^2 + 4x + 9)$. $-5x^2 - 9x - 12$

83. Write a trinomial of degree 2 with a leading coefficient of -5. (Answers may vary.)
For example, $-5x^2 + 2x - 4$

84. Write a binomial of degree 5 with leading coefficient 6. (Answers may vary.)
For example, $6x^5 + 8$

85. Find a polynomial that represents the perimeter of the given rectangle. $6w + 6$

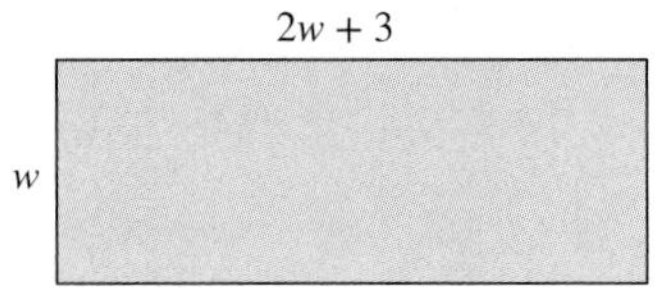

Section 5.6

For Exercises 86–103, multiply the expressions.

86. $(25x^4y^3)(-3x^2y)$
$-75x^6y^4$

87. $(9a^6)(2a^2b^4)$
$18a^8b^4$

88. $5c(3c^3 - 7c + 5)$
$15c^4 - 35c^2 + 25c$

89. $(x^2 + 5x - 3)(-2x)$
$-2x^3 - 10x^2 + 6x$

90. $(5k - 4)(k + 1)$
$5k^2 + k - 4$

91. $(4t - 1)(5t + 2)$
$20t^2 + 3t - 2$

92. $(q + 8)(6q - 1)$
$6q^2 + 47q - 8$

93. $(2a - 6)(a + 5)$
$2a^2 + 4a - 30$

94. $\left(7a + \frac{1}{2}\right)^2$
$49a^2 + 7a + \frac{1}{4}$

95. $(b - 4)^2$
$b^2 - 8b + 16$

96. $(4p^2 + 6p + 9)(2p - 3)$ $8p^3 - 27$

97. $(2w - 1)(-w^2 - 3w - 4)$ $-2w^3 - 5w^2 - 5w + 4$

98. $$\begin{array}{rr} & 2x^2 - 3x + 4 \\ \times & 2x - 1 \\ \hline \end{array}$$
$4x^3 - 8x^2 + 11x - 4$

99. $$\begin{array}{rr} & 4a^2 + a - 5 \\ \times & 3a + 2 \\ \hline \end{array}$$
$12a^3 + 11a^2 - 13a - 10$

100. $(b - 4)(b + 4)$ $b^2 - 16$

101. $\left(\frac{1}{3}r^4 - s^2\right)\left(\frac{1}{3}r^4 + s^2\right)$ $\frac{1}{9}r^8 - s^4$

102. $(-7z^2 + 6)^2$ $49z^4 - 84z^2 + 36$

103. $(2h + 3)(h^4 - h^3 + h^2 - h + 1)$ $2h^5 + h^4 - h^3 + h^2 - h + 3$

104. Find a polynomial that represents the area of the given rectangle. $2x^2 + 3x - 20$

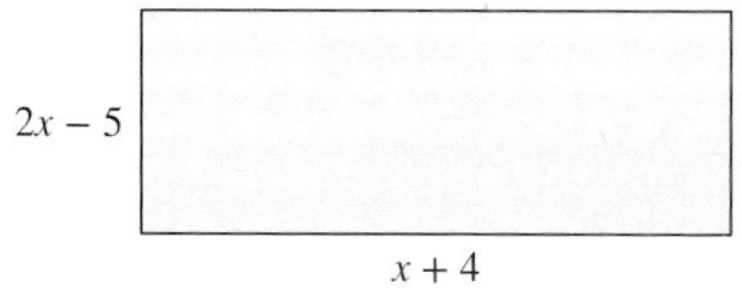

Section 5.7

For Exercises 105–117, divide the polynomials.

105. $\dfrac{20y^3 - 10y^2}{5y}$ $4y^2 - 2y$

106. $(18a^3b^2 - 9a^2b - 27ab^2) \div 9ab$ $2a^2b - a - 3b$

107. $(12x^4 - 8x^3 + 4x^2) \div (-4x^2)$ $-3x^2 + 2x - 1$

108. $\dfrac{10z^7w^4 - 15z^3w^2 - 20zw}{-20z^2w}$ $-\frac{z^5w^3}{2} + \frac{3zw}{4} + \frac{1}{z}$

109. $\dfrac{x^2 + 7x + 10}{x + 5}$ $x + 2$

110. $(2t^2 + t - 10) \div (t - 2)$ $2t + 5$

111. $(2p^2 + p - 16) \div (2p + 7)$ $p - 3 + \frac{5}{2p + 7}$

112. $\dfrac{5a^2 + 27a - 22}{5a - 3}$ $a + 6 + \frac{-4}{5a - 3}$

113. $\dfrac{b^3 - 125}{b - 5}$ $b^2 + 5b + 25$

114. $(z^3 + 4z^2 + 5z + 20) \div (5 + z^2)$ $z + 4$

115. $(y^4 - 4y^3 + 5y^2 - 3y + 2) \div (y^2 + 3)$ $y^2 - 4y + 2 + \frac{9y - 4}{y^2 + 3}$

116. $(3t^4 - 8t^3 + t^2 - 4t - 5) \div (3t^2 + t + 1)$ $t^2 - 3t + 1 + \frac{-2t - 6}{3t^2 + t + 1}$

117. $\dfrac{2w^4 + w^3 + 4w - 3}{2w^2 - w + 3}$ $w^2 + w - 1$

Chapter 5 Test

Assume all variables represent nonzero real numbers.

1. Expand the expression using the definition of exponents, then simplify: $\dfrac{3^4 \cdot 3^3}{3^6}$ $\frac{(3 \cdot 3 \cdot 3 \cdot 3) \cdot (3 \cdot 3 \cdot 3)}{3 \cdot 3 \cdot 3 \cdot 3 \cdot 3 \cdot 3} = 3$

For Exercises 2–13, simplify each expression. Write the answer with positive exponents only.

2. $9^5 \cdot 9$ 9^6

3. $\dfrac{q^{10}}{q^2}$ q^8

4. $(-7)^0$ 1

5. c^{-3} $\frac{1}{c^3}$

6. $3^0 + 2^{-1} - 4^{-1}$ $\frac{5}{4}$

7. $4 \cdot 8^{-1} + 16^0$ $\frac{3}{2}$

8. $(3a^2b)^3$ $27a^6b^3$

9. $\left(\dfrac{2x}{y^3}\right)^4$ $\frac{16x^4}{y^{12}}$

10. $\dfrac{14^3 \cdot 14^9}{14^{10} \cdot 14}$ 14

11. $\dfrac{(s^2t)^3(7s^4t)^4}{(7s^2t^3)^2}$ $49s^{18}t$

12. $(2a^0b^{-6})^2$ $\frac{4}{b^{12}}$

13. $\left(\dfrac{6a^{-5}b}{8ab^{-2}}\right)^{-2}$ $\frac{16a^{12}}{9b^6}$

14. a. Write the number in scientific notation: 43,000,000,000 4.3×10^{10}

b. Write the number in standard form: 5.6×10^{-6} 0.000 0056

15. Multiply: $(1.2 \times 10^6)(7 \times 10^{-15})$ 8.4×10^{-9}

16. Divide: $\dfrac{60{,}000}{0.008}$ 7.5×10^6

17. The average amount of water flowing over Niagara Falls is 1.68×10^5 m^3/min.

a. How many cubic meters of water flow over the falls in one day? 2.4192×10^8 m^3

b. How many cubic meters of water flow over the falls in one year? 8.83008×10^{10} m^3

© Alberto Fresco/Alamy RF

18. Write the polynomial in descending order: $4x + 5x^3 - 7x^2 + 11$ $5x^3 - 7x^2 + 4x + 11$

a. Identify the degree of the polynomial. 3

b. Identify the leading coefficient of the polynomial. 5

For Exercises 19–28, perform the indicated operations.

19. $(5t^4 - 2t^2 - 17) + (12t^3 + 2t^2 + 7t - 2)$ $5t^4 + 12t^3 + 7t - 19$

20. $(7w^2 - 11w - 6) + (8w^2 + 3w + 4) - (-9w^2 - 5w + 2)$ $24w^2 - 3w - 4$

21. $-2x^3(5x^2 + x - 15)$ $-10x^5 - 2x^4 + 30x^3$

22. $(4a - 3)(2a - 1)$ $8a^2 - 10a + 3$

23. $(4y - 5)(y^2 - 5y + 3)$ $4y^3 - 25y^2 + 37y - 15$

24. $(2 + 3b)(2 - 3b)$ $4 - 9b^2$

25. $(5z - 6)^2$ $25z^2 - 60z + 36$

26. $(5x + 3)(3x - 2)$ $15x^2 - x - 6$

27. $(2x^2 + 5x) - (6x^2 - 7)$ $-4x^2 + 5x + 7$

28. $(y^2 - 5y + 2)(y - 6)$ $y^3 - 11y^2 + 32y - 12$

29. Subtract $(3x^2 - 5x^3 + 2x)$ from $(10x^3 - 4x^2 + 1)$. $15x^3 - 7x^2 - 2x + 1$

30. Find the perimeter and the area of the rectangle shown in the figure. Perimeter: $12x - 2$; area: $5x^2 - 13x - 6$

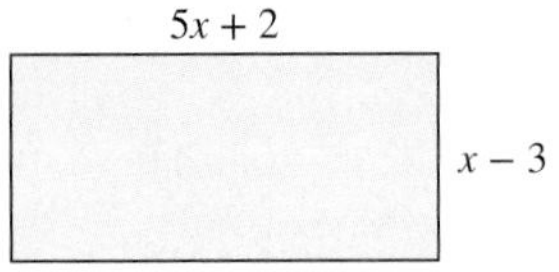

For Exercises 31–35, divide the polynomials.

31. $(-12x^8 + x^6 - 8x^3) \div (4x^2)$ $-3x^6 + \frac{x^4}{4} - 2x$

32. $\dfrac{16a^3b - 2a^2b^2 + 8ab}{-4ab}$ $-4a^2 + \frac{ab}{2} - 2$

33. $\dfrac{2y^2 - 13y + 21}{y - 3}$ $2y - 7$

34. $(-5w^2 + 2w^3 - 2w + 5) \div (2w + 3)$ $w^2 - 4w + 5 + \frac{-10}{2w + 3}$

35. $\dfrac{3x^4 + x^3 + 4x - 33}{x^2 + 4}$ $3x^2 + x - 12 + \frac{15}{x^2 + 4}$

Chapters 1–5 Cumulative Review Exercises

For Exercises 1–2, simplify completely.

1. $-5 - \frac{1}{2}[4 - 3(-7)]$ $-\frac{35}{2}$

2. $|-3^2 + 5|$ 4

3. Translate the phrase into a mathematical expression and simplify:

The difference of the square of five and the square root of four. $5^2 - \sqrt{4}$; 23

4. Solve for x: $\frac{1}{2}(x - 6) + \frac{2}{3} = \frac{1}{4}x$ $\left\{\frac{28}{3}\right\}$

5. Solve for y: $-2y - 3 = -5(y - 1) + 3y$ { }

6. For a point in a rectangular coordinate system, in which quadrant are both the x- and y-coordinates negative? Quadrant III

7. For a point in a rectangular coordinate system, on which axis is the x-coordinate zero and the y-coordinate nonzero? y-axis

8. In a triangle, one angle measures 23° more than the smallest angle. The third angle measures 10° more than the sum of the other two angles. Find the measure of each angle. The measures are 31°, 54°, 95°.

9. A snow storm lasts for 9 hr and dumps snow at a rate of $1\frac{1}{2}$ in./hr. If there was already 6 in. of snow on the ground before the storm, the snow depth is given by the equation:

$y = \frac{3}{2}x + 6$ where y is the snow depth in inches and $x \geq 0$ is the time in hours after the storm began.

a. Find the snow depth after 4 hr. 12 in.

b. Find the snow depth at the end of the storm. 19.5 in.

c. How long had it snowed when the total depth of snow was $14\frac{1}{4}$ in.? 5.5 hr

© Brand X Photography/Veer RF

10. Solve the system of equations. {(−3, 4)}

$$5x + 3y = -3$$
$$3x + 2y = -1$$

11. Solve the inequality. Graph the solution set on the real number line and express the solution in interval notation. $2 - 3(2x + 4) \le -2x - (x - 5)$

$[-5, \infty)$

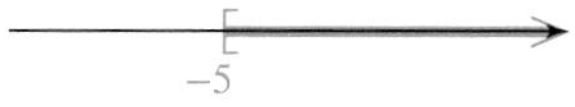

For Exercises 12–15, perform the indicated operations.

12. $(2x^2 + 3x - 7) - (-3x^2 + 12x + 8)$ $5x^2 - 9x - 15$

13. $(2y + 3z)(-y - 5z)$ $-2y^2 - 13yz - 15z^2$

14. $(4t - 3)^2$ $16t^2 - 24t + 9$

15. $\left(\frac{2}{5}a + \frac{1}{3}\right)\left(\frac{2}{5}a - \frac{1}{3}\right)$ $\frac{4}{25}a^2 - \frac{1}{9}$

For Exercises 16–17, divide the polynomials.

16. $(12a^4b^3 - 6a^2b^2 + 3ab) \div (-3ab)$

$-4a^3b^2 + 2ab - 1$

17. $\dfrac{4m^3 - 5m + 2}{m - 2}$ $4m^2 + 8m + 11 + \dfrac{24}{m - 2}$

For Exercises 18–19, use the properties of exponents to simplify the expressions. Write the answers with positive exponents only. Assume all variables represent nonzero real numbers.

18. $\left(\dfrac{2c^2d^4}{8cd^6}\right)^2$ $\dfrac{c^2}{16d^4}$

19. $\dfrac{10a^{-2}b^{-3}}{5a^0b^{-6}}$ $\dfrac{2b^3}{a^2}$

20. Perform the indicated operations, and write the final answer in scientific notation. 4.1×10^3

$$\frac{8.2 \times 10^{-2}}{2 \times 10^{-5}}$$

Factoring Polynomials

6

CHAPTER OUTLINE

Mathematics in the Workplace

Suppose that you are the manager of a laboratory that produces prototype electronics. This week you are tasked with producing 6 laptops over a 6-day period. With these constraints, you could produce 1 laptop per day for 6 days, 2 laptops per day for 3 days, 3 laptops per day for 2 days, or 6 laptops all in 1 day.

Any of these combinations will accomplish your task.

© Henrik Jonsson/Getty Images RF

Laptops per day	Number of days	Total number of laptops
1	6	6
2	3	6
3	2	6
6	1	6

The word **factor** is Latin for "maker." In this example, the numbers 1, 2, 3, and 6 are **factors** of 6 because they *make* a 6 by using multiplication. In other words, we can multiply each of the numbers 1, 2, 3, and 6 by another factor to produce 6. In essence, *factoring* is the process of breaking numbers or expressions into the elements that made them via multiplication.

Factoring (finding the factors) is used extensively in algebra to make expressions easier to use. In this chapter you will learn how to factor both numerical values and polynomials.

Section 6.1 Greatest Common Factor and Factoring by Grouping

Concepts

1. Identifying the Greatest Common Factor
2. Factoring out the Greatest Common Factor
3. Factoring out a Negative Factor
4. Factoring out a Binomial Factor
5. Factoring by Grouping

1. Identifying the Greatest Common Factor

We have already learned how to multiply two or more polynomials. We now devote our study to a related operation called **factoring**. To factor an integer means to write the integer as a product of two or more integers. To factor a polynomial means to express the polynomial as a product of two or more polynomials.

In the product $2 \cdot 5 = 10$, for example, 2 and 5 are factors of 10.

In the product $(3x + 4)(2x - 1) = 6x^2 + 5x - 4$, the quantities $(3x + 4)$ and $(2x - 1)$ are factors of $6x^2 + 5x - 4$.

We begin our study of factoring by factoring integers. The number 20, for example, can be factored as $1 \cdot 20$ or $2 \cdot 10$ or $4 \cdot 5$ or $2 \cdot 2 \cdot 5$. The product $2 \cdot 2 \cdot 5$ (or equivalently $2^2 \cdot 5$) consists only of prime numbers and is called the **prime factorization**.

The **greatest common factor** (denoted **GCF**) of two or more integers is the largest factor common to each integer. To find the greatest common factor of two or more integers, it is often helpful to express the numbers as a product of prime factors as shown in the next example.

Classroom Example: p. 424, Exercise 6

Example 1 Identifying the Greatest Common Factor

Find the greatest common factor.

a. 24 and 36 **b.** 105, 40, and 60

Solution:

First find the prime factorization of each number. Then find the product of common factors.

a.

$$\begin{array}{r|l} 2 & 24 \\ 2 & 12 \\ 2 & 6 \\ & 3 \end{array} \qquad \begin{array}{r|l} 2 & 36 \\ 2 & 18 \\ 3 & 9 \\ & 3 \end{array}$$

Factors of 24 = $2 \cdot 2 \cdot 2 \cdot 3$

Factors of 36 = $2 \cdot 2 \cdot 3 \cdot 3$

Common factors are circled.

The numbers 24 and 36 share two factors of 2 and one factor of 3. Therefore, the greatest common factor is $2 \cdot 2 \cdot 3 = 12$.

b.

$$\begin{array}{r|l} 5 & 105 \\ 3 & 21 \\ & 7 \end{array} \qquad \begin{array}{r|l} 5 & 40 \\ 2 & 8 \\ 2 & 4 \\ & 2 \end{array} \qquad \begin{array}{r|l} 5 & 60 \\ 3 & 12 \\ 2 & 4 \\ & 2 \end{array}$$

Factors of 105 = $3 \cdot 7 \cdot 5$

Factors of 40 = $2 \cdot 2 \cdot 2 \cdot 5$

Factors of 60 = $2 \cdot 2 \cdot 3 \cdot 5$

The greatest common factor is 5.

Skill Practice Find the GCF.

1. 12 and 20 **2.** 45, 75, and 30

Answers

1. 4 **2.** 15

In Example 2, we find the greatest common factor of two or more variable terms.

Example 2 Identifying the Greatest Common Factor

Classroom Example: p. 424, Exercise 10

Find the GCF among each group of terms.

a. $7x^3, 14x^2, 21x^4$ **b.** $15a^4b, 25a^3b^2$

Solution:

List the factors of each term.

a. $7x^3 = 7 \cdot x \cdot x \cdot x$

$14x^2 = 2 \cdot 7 \cdot x \cdot x$

$21x^4 = 3 \cdot 7 \cdot x \cdot x \cdot x \cdot x$

The GCF is $7x^2$.

b. $15a^4b = 3 \cdot 5 \cdot a \cdot a \cdot a \cdot a \cdot b$

$25a^3b^2 = 5 \cdot 5 \cdot a \cdot a \cdot a \cdot b \cdot b$

The GCF is $5a^3b$.

TIP: Notice in Example 2(b) the expressions $15a^4b$ and $25a^3b^2$ share factors of 5, a, and b. The GCF is the product of the common factors, where each factor is raised to the lowest power to which it occurs in all the original expressions.

$15a^4b = 3^1 \cdot 5^1a^4b^1$, $25a^3b^2 = 5^2a^3b^2$

Lowest power of 5 is 1: 5^1

Lowest power of a is 3: a^3

Lowest power of b is 1: b^1

The GCF is $5a^3b$.

Skill Practice Find the GCF.

3. $10z^3, 15z^5, 40z$ **4.** $6w^3y^5, 21w^4y^2$

Example 3 Identifying the Greatest Common Factor

Classroom Example: p. 424, Exercise 12

Find the GCF of the terms $8c^2d^7e$ and $6c^3d^4$.

Solution:

$8c^2d^7e = 2^3c^2d^7e$, $6c^3d^4 = 2 \cdot 3c^3d^4$ — The common factors are 2, c, and d.

The lowest power of 2 is 1: 2^1

The lowest power of c is 2: c^2

The lowest power of d is 4: d^4

The GCF is $2c^2d^4$.

Skill Practice Find the GCF.

5. $9m^2np^8, 15n^4p^5$

Sometimes polynomials share a common binomial factor, as shown in Example 4.

Answers

3. $5z$ **4.** $3w^3y^2$

5. $3np^5$

Classroom Example: p. 424, Exercise 14

Example 4 **Identifying the Greatest Common Binomial Factor**

Find the greatest common factor of the terms $3x(a + b)$ and $2y(a + b)$.

Solution:

$$\left.\begin{array}{l} 3x(a+b) \\ 2y(a+b) \end{array}\right\}$$ The only common factor is the binomial $(a + b)$. The GCF is $(a + b)$.

Skill Practice Find the GCF.

6. $a(x + 2)$ and $b(x + 2)$

2. Factoring out the Greatest Common Factor

The process of factoring a polynomial is the reverse process of multiplying polynomials. Both operations use the distributive property: $ab + ac = a(b + c)$.

Multiply

$$5y(y^2 + 3y + 1) = 5y(y^2) + 5y(3y) + 5y(1)$$
$$= 5y^3 + 15y^2 + 5y$$

Factor

$$5y^3 + 15y^2 + 5y = 5y(y^2) + 5y(3y) + 5y(1)$$
$$= 5y(y^2 + 3y + 1)$$

Factoring out the Greatest Common Factor

Step 1 Identify the GCF of all terms of the polynomial.
Step 2 Write each term as the product of the GCF and another factor.
Step 3 Use the distributive property to remove the GCF.
Note: To check the factorization, multiply the polynomials to remove parentheses.

Classroom Examples: p. 424, Exercises 18 and 22

Example 5 **Factoring out the Greatest Common Factor**

Factor out the GCF.

a. $4x - 20$ **b.** $6w^2 + 3w$

Instructor Note: Tell students that an expression is factored only if the GCF has been removed. The expression $2(2x - 10)$ is not factored completely.

Solution:

a. $4x - 20$ The GCF is 4.

$= 4(x) - 4(5)$ Write each term as the product of the GCF and another factor.

$= 4(x - 5)$ Use the distributive property to factor out the GCF.

TIP: Any factoring problem can be checked by multiplying the factors:

Check: $4(x - 5) = 4x - 20$ ✓

Answer

6. $(x + 2)$

b. $6w^2 + 3w$ — The GCF is $3w$.

$= 3w(2w) + 3w(1)$ — Write each term as the product of $3w$ and another factor.

$= 3w(2w + 1)$ — Use the distributive property to factor out the GCF.

Check: $3w(2w + 1) = 6w^2 + 3w$ ✓

Avoiding Mistakes

In Example 5(b), the GCF, $3w$, is equal to one of the terms of the polynomial. In such a case, you must leave a 1 in place of that term after the GCF is factored out.

Skill Practice Factor out the GCF.

7. $6w + 18$ **8.** $21m^3 - 7m$

Example 6 Factoring out the Greatest Common Factor

Classroom Examples: p. 424, Exercises 24 and 34

Factor out the GCF.

a. $15y^3 + 12y^4$ **b.** $9a^4b - 18a^5b + 27a^6b$

Solution:

a. $15y^3 + 12y^4$ — The GCF is $3y^3$.

$= 3y^3(5) + 3y^3(4y)$ — Write each term as the product of $3y^3$ and another factor.

$= 3y^3(5 + 4y)$ — Use the distributive property to factor out the GCF.

Check: $3y^3(5 + 4y) = 15y^3 + 12y^4$ ✓

TIP: When factoring out the GCF from a polynomial, the terms within parentheses are found by dividing the original terms by the GCF. For example:

$15y^3 + 12y^4$ The GCF is $3y^3$.

$$\frac{15y^3}{3y^3} = 5 \quad \text{and} \quad \frac{12y^4}{3y^3} = 4y$$

Thus, $15y^3 + 12y^4 = 3y^3(5 + 4y)$

b. $9a^4b - 18a^5b + 27a^6b$ — The GCF is $9a^4b$.

$= 9a^4b(1) - 9a^4b(2a) + 9a^4b(3a^2)$ — Write each term as the product of $9a^4b$ and another factor.

$= 9a^4b(1 - 2a + 3a^2)$ — Use the distributive property to factor out the GCF.

Check: $9a^4b(1 - 2a + 3a^2)$

$= 9a^4b - 18a^5b + 27a^6b$ ✓

Avoiding Mistakes

The GCF is $9a^4b$, not $3a^4b$. The expression $3a^4b(3 - 6a + 9a^2)$ is not factored completely.

Skill Practice Factor out the GCF.

9. $9y^2 - 6y^5$ **10.** $50s^3t - 40st^2 + 10st$

The greatest common factor of the polynomial $2x + 5y$ is 1. If we factor out the GCF, we have $1(2x + 5y)$. A polynomial whose only factors are itself and 1 is called a **prime polynomial**.

Answers

7. $6(w + 3)$
8. $7m(3m^2 - 1)$
9. $3y^2(3 - 2y^3)$
10. $10st(5s^2 - 4t + 1)$

Instructor Note: Remind students that first we put the polynomial in descending order, then determine if the leading coefficient is negative.

3. Factoring out a Negative Factor

Usually it is advantageous to factor out the *opposite* of the GCF when the leading coefficient of the polynomial is negative. This is demonstrated in Example 7. Notice that this *changes the signs* of the remaining terms inside the parentheses.

Classroom Example: p. 424, Exercise 42

Example 7 Factoring out a Negative Factor

Factor out -3 from the polynomial $-3x^2 + 6x - 33$.

Solution:

$-3x^2 + 6x - 33$ The GCF is 3. However, in this case, we will factor out the *opposite* of the GCF, -3.

$= -3(x^2) + (-3)(-2x) + (-3)(11)$ Write each term as the product of -3 and another factor.

$= -3[x^2 + (-2x) + 11]$ Factor out -3.

$= -3(x^2 - 2x + 11)$ Simplify. Notice that each sign within the trinomial has changed.

Check: $-3(x^2 - 2x + 11) = -3x^2 + 6x - 33$ ✓

Skill Practice Factor out -2 from the polynomial.

11. $-2x^2 - 10x + 16$

Classroom Example: p. 424, Exercise 44

Example 8 Factoring out a Negative Factor

Factor out the quantity $-4pq$ from the polynomial $-12p^3q - 8p^2q^2 + 4pq^3$.

Solution:

$-12p^3q - 8p^2q^2 + 4pq^3$ The GCF is $4pq$. However, in this case, we will factor out the *opposite* of the GCF, $-4pq$.

$= -4pq(3p^2) + (-4pq)(2pq) + (-4pq)(-q^2)$ Write each term as the product of $-4pq$ and another factor.

$= -4pq[3p^2 + 2pq + (-q^2)]$ Factor out $-4pq$. Notice that each sign within the trinomial has changed.

$= -4pq(3p^2 + 2pq - q^2)$ To verify that this is the correct factorization and that the signs are correct, multiply the factors.

Check: $-4pq(3p^2 + 2pq - q^2) = -12p^3q - 8p^2q^2 + 4pq^3$ ✓

Skill Practice Factor out $-5xy$ from the polynomial.

12. $-10x^2y + 5xy - 15xy^2$

4. Factoring out a Binomial Factor

The distributive property can also be used to factor out a common factor that consists of more than one term, as shown in Example 9.

Answers

11. $-2(x^2 + 5x - 8)$
12. $-5xy(2x - 1 + 3y)$

Example 9 **Factoring out a Binomial Factor**

Classroom Example: p. 424, Exercise 48

Factor out the GCF. $2w(x + 3) - 5(x + 3)$

Solution:

$2w(x + 3) - 5(x + 3)$ The greatest common factor is the quantity $(x + 3)$.

$= (x + 3)(2w - 5)$ Use the distributive property to factor out the GCF.

Skill Practice Factor out the GCF.

13. $8y(a + b) + 9(a + b)$

5. Factoring by Grouping

When two binomials are multiplied, the product before simplifying contains four terms. For example:

$$(x + 4)(3a + 2b) = (x + 4)(3a) + (x + 4)(2b)$$
$$= (x + 4)(3a) + (x + 4)(2b)$$
$$= 3ax + 12a + 2bx + 8b$$

In Example 10, we learn how to reverse this process. That is, given a four-term polynomial, we will factor it as a product of two binomials. The process is called *factoring by grouping*.

Factoring by Grouping

To factor a four-term polynomial by grouping:

Step 1 Identify and factor out the GCF from all four terms.

Step 2 Factor out the GCF from the first pair of terms. Factor out the GCF from the second pair of terms. (Sometimes it is necessary to factor out the opposite of the GCF.)

Step 3 If the two terms share a common binomial factor, factor out the binomial factor.

Example 10 **Factoring by Grouping**

Classroom Example: p. 425, Exercise 58

Factor by grouping. $3ax + 12a + 2bx + 8b$

Solution:

$3ax + 12a + 2bx + 8b$ **Step 1:** Identify and factor out the GCF from all four terms. In this case, the GCF is 1.

$= 3ax + 12a \;\vdots\; + 2bx + 8b$ Group the first pair of terms and the second pair of terms.

Answer

13. $(a + b)(8y + 9)$

$= 3a(x + 4) + 2b(x + 4)$ **Step 2:** Factor out the GCF from each pair of terms. *Note:* The two terms now share a common binomial factor of $(x + 4)$.

$= (x + 4)(3a + 2b)$ **Step 3:** Factor out the common binomial factor.

Check: $(x + 4)(3a + 2b) = 3ax + 2bx + 12a + 8b$ ✓

Note: Step 2 results in two terms with a common binomial factor. If the two binomials are different, step 3 cannot be performed. In such a case, the original polynomial may not be factorable by grouping, or different pairs of terms may need to be grouped and inspected.

Skill Practice Factor by grouping.

14. $5x + 10y + ax + 2ay$

TIP: One frequently asked question when factoring is whether the order can be switched between the factors. The answer is yes. Because multiplication is commutative, the order in which the factors are written does not matter.

$$(x + 4)(3a + 2b) = (3a + 2b)(x + 4)$$

Classroom Example: p. 425, Exercise 60

Example 11 Factoring by Grouping

Factor by grouping. $ax + ay - x - y$

Solution:

$ax + ay - x - y$ **Step 1:** Identify and factor out the GCF from all four terms. In this case, the GCF is 1.

$= ax + ay \mid - x - y$ Group the first pair of terms and the second pair of terms.

$= a(x + y) - 1(x + y)$ **Step 2:** Factor out a from the first pair of terms.

Factor out -1 from the second pair of terms. (This causes sign changes within the second parentheses.) The terms in parentheses now match.

$= (x + y)(a - 1)$ **Step 3:** Factor out the common binomial factor.

Check: $(x + y)(a - 1) = x(a) + x(-1) + y(a) + y(-1)$

$= ax - x + ay - y$ ✓

Avoiding Mistakes

In step 2, the expression $a(x + y) - (x + y)$ is not yet factored completely because it is a *difference,* not a product. To factor the expression, you must carry it one step further.

$a(x + y) - 1(x + y)$

$= (x + y)(a - 1)$

The factored form must be represented as a product.

Skill Practice Factor by grouping.

15. $tu - tv - u + v$

Answers

14. $(x + 2y)(5 + a)$

15. $(u - v)(t - 1)$

Example 12 **Factoring by Grouping**

Factor by grouping. $16w^4 - 40w^3 - 12w^2 + 30w$

Solution:

$16w^4 - 40w^3 - 12w^2 + 30w$

$= 2w[8w^3 - 20w^2 - 6w + 15]$

Step 1: Identify and factor out the GCF from all four terms. In this case, the GCF is $2w$.

$= 2w[8w^3 - 20w^2 \,\vdots\, - 6w + 15]$

Group the first pair of terms and the second pair of terms.

$= 2w[4w^2(2w - 5) - 3(2w - 5)]$

Step 2: Factor out $4w^2$ from the first pair of terms.

Factor out −3 from the second pair of terms. (This causes sign changes within the second parentheses.) The terms in parentheses now match.

$= 2w[(2w - 5)(4w^2 - 3)]$

Step 3: Factor out the common binomial factor.

$= 2w(2w - 5)(4w^2 - 3)$

Skill Practice Factor by grouping.

16. $3ab^2 + 6b^2 - 12ab - 24b$

Classroom Example: p. 425, Exercise 74

Answer

16. $3b(a + 2)(b - 4)$

Section 6.1 Practice Exercises

For additional exercises, see Classroom Activities 6.1A–6.1B in the *Student's Resource Manual* at www.mhhe.com/moh.

Study Skills Exercise

The final exam is just around the corner. Your old tests and quizzes provide good material to study for the final exam. Use your old tests to make a list of the chapters on which you need to concentrate. Ask your professor for help if there are still concepts that you do not understand.

Vocabulary and Key Concepts

1. **a.** Factoring a polynomial means to write it as a __product__ of two or more polynomials.

   b. The prime factorization of a number consists of only __prime__ factors.

   c. The __greatest__ __common__ __factor__ (GCF) of two or more integers is the largest whole number that is a factor of each integer.

   d. A polynomial whose only factors are 1 and itself is called a __prime__ polynomial.

   e. The first step toward factoring a polynomial is to factor out the __greatest__ __common__ __factor (GCF)__.

   f. To factor a four-term polynomial, we try the process of factoring by __grouping__.

Concept 1: Identifying the Greatest Common Factor

2. List all the factors of 24. 1, 2, 3, 4, 6, 8, 12, 24

For Exercises 3–14, identify the greatest common factor. **(See Examples 1–4.)**

3. 28, 63 7
4. 24, 40 8
5. 42, 30, 60 6
6. 20, 52, 32 4
7. $3xy$, $7y$ y
8. $10mn$, $11n$ n
9. $12w^3z$, $16w^2z$ $4w^2z$
10. $20cd$, $15c^3d$ $5cd$
11. $8x^3y^4z^2$, $12xy^5z^4$, $6x^2y^8z^3$ $2xy^4z^2$
12. $15r^2s^2t^5$, $5r^3s^4t^3$, $30r^4s^3t^2$ $5r^2s^2t^2$
13. $7(x-y)$, $9(x-y)$ $(x-y)$
14. $(2a-b)$, $3(2a-b)$ $(2a-b)$

Concept 2: Factoring out the Greatest Common Factor

15. a. Use the distributive property to multiply $3(x-2y)$. $3x-6y$

b. Use the distributive property to factor $3x-6y$. $3(x-2y)$

16. a. Use the distributive property to multiply $a^2(5a+b)$. $5a^3+a^2b$

b. Use the distributive property to factor $5a^3+a^2b$. $a^2(5a+b)$

For Exercises 17–36, factor out the GCF. **(See Examples 5–6.)**

17. $4p+12$ $4(p+3)$
18. $3q-15$ $3(q-5)$
19. $5c^2-10c+15$ $5(c^2-2c+3)$
20. $16d^3+24d^2+32d$ $8d(2d^2+3d+4)$
21. x^5+x^3 $x^3(x^2+1)$
22. y^2-y^3 $y^2(1-y)$
23. $t^4-4t+8t^2$ $t(t^3-4+8t)$
24. $7r^3-r^5+r^4$ $r^3(7-r^2+r)$
25. $2ab+4a^3b$ $2ab(1+2a^2)$
26. $5u^3v^2-5uv$ $5uv(u^2v-1)$
27. $38x^2y-19x^2y^4$ $19x^2y(2-y^3)$
28. $100a^5b^3+16a^2b$ $4a^2b(25a^3b^2+4)$
29. $6x^3y^5-18xy^9z$ $6xy^5(x^2-3y^4z)$
30. $15mp^7q^4+12m^4q^3$ $3mq^3(5p^7q+4m^3)$
31. $5+7y^3$ The expression is prime because it is not factorable.
32. $w^3-5u^3v^2$ The expression is prime because it is not factorable.
33. $42p^3q^2+14pq^2-7p^4q^4$ $7pq^2(6p^2+2-p^3q^2)$
34. $8m^2n^3-24m^2n^2+4m^3n$ $4m^2n(2n^2-6n+m)$
35. $t^5+2rt^3-3t^4+4r^2t^2$ $t^2(t^3+2rt-3t^2+4r^2)$
36. $u^2v+5u^3v^2-2u^2+8uv$ $u(uv+5u^2v^2-2u+8v)$

Concept 3: Factoring out a Negative Factor

37. For the polynomial $-2x^3-4x^2+8x$

a. Factor out $-2x$. $-2x(x^2+2x-4)$

b. Factor out $2x$. $2x(-x^2-2x+4)$

38. For the polynomial $-9y^5+3y^3-12y$

a. Factor out $-3y$. $-3y(3y^4-y^2+4)$

b. Factor out $3y$. $3y(-3y^4+y^2-4)$

39. Factor out -1 from the polynomial. $-8t^2-9t-2$ $-1(8t^2+9t+2)$

40. Factor out -1 from the polynomial. $-6x^3-2x-5$ $-1(6x^3+2x+5)$

For Exercises 41–46, factor out the opposite of the greatest common factor. **(See Examples 7–8.)**

41. $-15p^3-30p^2$ $-15p^2(p+2)$
42. $-24m^3-12m^4$ $-12m^3(2+m)$
43. $-3m^4n^2+6m^2n-9mn^2$ $-3mn(m^3n-2m+3n)$
44. $-12p^3t+2p^2t^3+6pt^2$ $-2pt(6p^2-pt^2-3t)$
45. $-7x-6y-2z$ $-1(7x+6y+2z)$
46. $-4a+5b-c$ $-1(4a-5b+c)$

Concept 4: Factoring out a Binomial Factor

For Exercises 47–52, factor out the GCF. **(See Example 9.)**

47. $13(a+6)-4b(a+6)$ $(a+6)(13-4b)$
48. $7(x^2+1)-y(x^2+1)$ $(x^2+1)(7-y)$
49. $8v(w^2-2)+(w^2-2)$ $(w^2-2)(8v+1)$
50. $t(r+2)+(r+2)$ $(r+2)(t+1)$
51. $21x(x+3)+7x^2(x+3)$ $7x(x+3)^2$
52. $5y^3(y-2)-15y(y-2)$ $5y(y-2)(y^2-3)$

Concept 5: Factoring by Grouping

For Exercises 53–72, factor by grouping. **(See Examples 10–11.)**

53. $8a^2 - 4ab + 6ac - 3bc$
$(2a - b)(4a + 3c)$

54. $4x^3 + 3x^2y + 4xy^2 + 3y^3$
$(4x + 3y)(x^2 + y^2)$

55. $3q + 3p + qr + pr$
$(q + p)(3 + r)$

56. $xy - xz + 7y - 7z$
$(y - z)(x + 7)$

57. $6x^2 + 3x + 4x + 2$
$(2x + 1)(3x + 2)$

58. $4y^2 + 8y + 7y + 14$
$(y + 2)(4y + 7)$

59. $2t^2 + 6t - t - 3$
$(t + 3)(2t - 1)$

60. $2p^2 - p - 2p + 1$
$(2p - 1)(p - 1)$

61. $6y^2 - 2y - 9y + 3$
$(3y - 1)(2y - 3)$

62. $5a^2 + 30a - 2a - 12$
$(a + 6)(5a - 2)$

63. $b^4 + b^3 - 4b - 4$
$(b + 1)(b^3 - 4)$

64. $8w^5 + 12w^2 - 10w^3 - 15$
$(2w^3 + 3)(4w^2 - 5)$

65. $3j^2k + 15k + j^2 + 5$
$(j^2 + 5)(3k + 1)$

66. $2ab^2 - 6ac + b^2 - 3c$
$(b^2 - 3c)(2a + 1)$

67. $14w^6x^6 + 7w^6 - 2x^6 - 1$
$(2x^6 + 1)(7w^6 - 1)$

68. $18p^4x - 4x - 9p^5 + 2p$
$(9p^4 - 2)(2x - p)$

69. $ay + bx + by + ax$
(*Hint:* Rearrange the terms.)
$(y + x)(a + b)$

70. $2c + 3ay + ac + 6y$
$(c + 3y)(2 + a)$

71. $vw^2 - 3 + w - 3wv$
$(vw + 1)(w - 3)$

72. $2x^2 + 6m + 12 + x^2m$
$(m + 2)(6 + x^2)$

Mixed Exercises

For Exercises 73–78, factor out the GCF first. Then factor by grouping. **(See Example 12.)**

73. $15x^4 + 15x^2y^2 + 10x^3y + 10xy^3$
$5x(x^2 + y^2)(3x + 2y)$

74. $2a^3b - 4a^2b + 32ab - 64b$
$2b(a - 2)(a^2 + 16)$

75. $4abx - 4b^2x - 4ab + 4b^2$
$4b(a - b)(x - 1)$

76. $p^2q - pq^2 - rp^2q + rpq^2$
$pq(p - q)(1 - r)$

77. $6st^2 - 18st - 6t^4 + 18t^3$
$6t(t - 3)(s - t^2)$

78. $15j^3 - 10j^2k - 15j^2k^2 + 10jk^3$
$5j(3j - 2k)(j - k^2)$

79. The formula $P = 2l + 2w$ represents the perimeter, P, of a rectangle given the length, l, and the width, w. Factor out the GCF and write an equivalent formula in factored form.
$P = 2(l + w)$

80. The formula $P = 2a + 2b$ represents the perimeter, P, of a parallelogram given the base, b, and an adjacent side, a. Factor out the GCF and write an equivalent formula in factored form.
$P = 2(a + b)$

81. The formula $S = 2\pi r^2 + 2\pi rh$ represents the surface area, S, of a cylinder with radius, r, and height, h. Factor out the GCF and write an equivalent formula in factored form.
$S = 2\pi r(r + h)$

82. The formula $A = P + Prt$ represents the total amount of money, A, in an account that earns simple interest at a rate, r, for t years. Factor out the GCF and write an equivalent formula in factored form.
$A = P(1 + rt)$

Expanding Your Skills

83. Factor out $\frac{1}{7}$ from $\frac{1}{7}x^2 + \frac{3}{7}x - \frac{5}{7}$. $\frac{1}{7}(x^2 + 3x - 5)$

84. Factor out $\frac{1}{5}$ from $\frac{6}{5}y^2 - \frac{4}{5}y + \frac{1}{5}$. $\frac{1}{5}(6y^2 - 4y + 1)$

85. Factor out $\frac{1}{4}$ from $\frac{5}{4}w^2 + \frac{3}{4}w + \frac{9}{4}$. $\frac{1}{4}(5w^2 + 3w + 9)$

86. Factor out $\frac{1}{6}$ from $\frac{1}{6}p^2 - \frac{3}{6}p + \frac{5}{6}$. $\frac{1}{6}(p^2 - 3p + 5)$

87. Write a polynomial that has a GCF of $3x$. (Answers may vary.) For example: $6x^2 + 9x$

88. Write a polynomial that has a GCF of $7y$. (Answers may vary.) For example: $14y - 21y^3 + 7y^2$

89. Write a polynomial that has a GCF of $4p^2q$. (Answers may vary.)
For example: $16p^4q^2 + 8p^3q - 4p^2q$

90. Write a polynomial that has a GCF of $2ab^2$. (Answers may vary.) For example: $18a^2b^3 - 2ab^2$

Section 6.2 Factoring Trinomials of the Form $x^2 + bx + c$

Concept

1. **Factoring Trinomials with a Leading Coefficient of 1**

1. Factoring Trinomials with a Leading Coefficient of 1

We have already learned how to multiply two binomials. We also saw that such a product often results in a trinomial. For example:

$$(x+3)(x+7) = \underbrace{x^2}_{\text{Product of first terms}} + \underbrace{7x + 3x}_{\text{Sum of products of inner terms and outer terms}} + \underbrace{21}_{\text{Product of last terms}} = x^2 + 10x + 21$$

In this section, we want to reverse the process. That is, given a trinomial, we want to *factor* it as a product of two binomials. In particular, we begin our study with the case in which a trinomial has a leading coefficient of 1.

Consider the quadratic trinomial $x^2 + bx + c$. To produce a leading term of x^2, we can construct binomials of the form $(x + \quad)(x + \quad)$. The remaining terms can be obtained from two integers, p and q, whose product is c and whose sum is b.

Factors of c

$$x^2 + bx + c = (x + p)(x + q) = x^2 + qx + px + pq$$
$$= x^2 + \underbrace{(q + p)}_{\text{Sum} = b}x + \underbrace{pq}_{\text{Product} = c}$$

This process is demonstrated in Example 1.

Classroom Example: p. 430, Exercise 8

Example 1 Factoring a Trinomial of the Form $x^2 + bx + c$

Factor. $x^2 + 4x - 45$

Solution:

$x^2 + 4x - 45 = (x + \square)(x + \square)$ The product of the first terms in the binomials must equal the leading term of the trinomial $x \cdot x = x^2$.

We must fill in the blanks with two integers whose product is -45 and whose sum is 4. The factors must have opposite signs to produce a negative product. The possible factorizations of -45 are:

Product = −45	Sum
$-1 \cdot 45$	44
$-3 \cdot 15$	12
$-5 \cdot 9$	4
$-9 \cdot 5$	−4
$-15 \cdot 3$	−12
$-45 \cdot 1$	−44

$x^2 + 4x - 45 = (x + \square)(x + \square)$

$= [x + (-5)](x + 9)$ Fill in the blanks with −5 and 9.

$= (x - 5)(x + 9)$ Factored form

Check:
$(x - 5)(x + 9) = x^2 + 9x - 5x - 45$
$= x^2 + 4x - 45$ ✓

Skill Practice Factor.

1. $x^2 - 5x - 14$

Multiplication of polynomials is a commutative operation. Therefore, in Example 1, we can express the factorization as $(x - 5)(x + 9)$ or as $(x + 9)(x - 5)$.

Example 2 Factoring a Trinomial of the Form $x^2 + bx + c$

Classroom Example: p. 430, Exercise 14

Factor. $w^2 - 15w + 50$

Solution:

$w^2 - 15w + 50 = (w + \square)(w + \square)$ The product $w \cdot w = w^2$.

Find two integers whose product is 50 and whose sum is −15. To form a positive product, the factors must be either both positive or both negative. The sum must be negative, so we will choose negative factors of 50.

Product = 50	Sum
(−1)(−50)	−51
(−2)(−25)	−27
(−5)(−10)	−15

$w^2 - 15w + 50 = (w + \square)(w + \square)$

$= [w + (-5)][w + (-10)]$

$= (w - 5)(w - 10)$ Factored form

Check:
$(w - 5)(w - 10) = w^2 - 10w - 5w + 50$
$= w^2 - 15w + 50$ ✓

Skill Practice Factor.

2. $z^2 - 16z + 48$

TIP: Practice will help you become proficient in factoring polynomials. As you do your homework, keep these important guidelines in mind:

- To factor a trinomial, write the trinomial in descending order such as $x^2 + bx + c$.
- For all factoring problems, always factor out the GCF from all terms first.

Answers

1. $(x - 7)(x + 2)$
2. $(z - 4)(z - 12)$

Furthermore, we offer the following rules for determining the signs within the binomial factors.

Sign Rules for Factoring Trinomials

Given the trinomial $x^2 + bx + c$, the signs within the binomial factors are determined as follows:

Case 1 If c is *positive*, then the signs in the binomials must be the same (either both positive or both negative). The correct choice is determined by the middle term. If the middle term is positive, then both signs must be positive. If the middle term is negative, then both signs must be negative.

c is positive.	c is positive.
$x^2 + 6x + 8$	$x^2 - 6x + 8$
$(x + 2)(x + 4)$	$(x - 2)(x - 4)$
Same signs	Same signs

Case 2 If c is *negative*, then the signs in the binomials must be different.

c is negative.	c is negative.
$x^2 + 2x - 35$	$x^2 - 2x - 35$
$(x + 7)(x - 5)$	$(x - 7)(x + 5)$
Different signs	Different signs

Classroom Examples: p. 431, Exercises 32 and 40

Example 3 Factoring Trinomials

Factor. **a.** $-8p - 48 + p^2$ **b.** $-40t - 30t^2 + 10t^3$

Solution:

a. $-8p - 48 + p^2$

$= p^2 - 8p - 48$ Write in descending order.

$= (p \quad \square)(p \quad \square)$ Find two integers whose product is -48 and whose sum is -8. The numbers are -12 and 4.

$= (p - 12)(p + 4)$ Factored form

b. $-40t - 30t^2 + 10t^3$

$= 10t^3 - 30t^2 - 40t$ Write in descending order.

$= 10t(t^2 - 3t - 4)$ Factor out the GCF.

$= 10t(t \quad \square)(t \quad \square)$ Find two integers whose product is -4 and whose sum is -3. The numbers are -4 and 1.

$= 10t(t - 4)(t + 1)$ Factored form

Skill Practice Factor.

3. $-5w + w^2 - 6$ **4.** $30y^3 + 2y^4 + 112y^2$

Answers

3. $(w - 6)(w + 1)$
4. $2y^2(y + 8)(y + 7)$

Example 4 Factoring Trinomials

Factor. **a.** $-a^2 + 6a - 8$ **b.** $-2c^2 - 22cd - 60d^2$

Solution:

a. $-a^2 + 6a - 8$

$= -1(a^2 - 6a + 8)$ — It is generally easier to factor a trinomial with a *positive* leading coefficient. Therefore, we will factor out −1 from all terms.

$= -1(a \;\square)(a \;\square)$ — Find two integers whose product is 8 and whose sum is −6. The numbers are −4 and −2.

$= -1(a - 4)(a - 2)$

$= -(a - 4)(a - 2)$

b. $-2c^2 - 22cd - 60d^2$

$= -2(c^2 + 11cd + 30d^2)$ — Factor out −2.

$= -2(c \;\square d)(c \;\square d)$ — Notice that the second pair of terms has a factor of d. This will produce a product of d^2.

$= -2(c + 5d)(c + 6d)$ — Find two integers whose product is 30 and whose sum is 11. The numbers are 5 and 6.

Skill Practice Factor.

5. $-x^2 + x + 12$ **6.** $-3a^2 + 15ab - 12b^2$

Classroom Examples: p. 431, Exercises 44 and 46

Avoiding Mistakes

Recall that factoring out −1 from a polynomial changes the signs of all terms within parentheses.

Instructor Note: Show students how a sign difference between two expressions can affect the factors used.

1. $x^2 - 10x + 24$, $x^2 - 10x - 24$
2. $x^2 - 5x + 6$, $x^2 - 5x - 6$
3. $x^2 - 13x + 30$, $x^2 - 13x - 30$

To factor a trinomial of the form $x^2 + bx + c$, we must find two integers whose product is c and whose sum is b. If no such integers exist, then the trinomial is prime.

Example 5 Factoring Trinomials

Factor. $x^2 - 13x + 14$

Solution:

$x^2 - 13x + 14$ — The trinomial is in descending order. The GCF is 1.

$= (x \;\square)(x \;\square)$ — Find two integers whose product is 14 and whose sum is −13. No such integers exist.

The trinomial $x^2 - 13x + 14$ is prime.

Skill Practice Factor.

7. $x^2 - 7x + 28$

Classroom Example: p. 430, Exercise 18

Answers

5. $-(x - 4)(x + 3)$
6. $-3(a - b)(a - 4b)$
7. Prime

Section 6.2 Practice Exercises

Vocabulary and Key Concepts

For additional exercises, see Classroom Activity 6.2A in the *Student's Resource Manual* at www.mhhe.com/moh.

1. **a.** Given a trinomial $x^2 + bx + c$, if c is positive, then the signs in the binomial factors are either both ___positive___ or both negative.

   b. Given a trinomial $x^2 + bx + c$, if c is negative, then the signs in the binomial factors are (choose one: both positive, both negative, different). different

   c. Which is the correct factored form of $x^2 - 7x - 44$? The product $(x + 4)(x - 11)$ or $(x - 11)(x + 4)$? Both are correct.

   d. Which is the complete factorization of $3x^2 + 24x + 36$? The product $(3x + 6)(x + 6)$ or $3(x + 6)(x + 2)$? $3(x + 6)(x + 2)$

Review Exercises

For Exercises 2–6, factor completely.

2. $9a^6b^3 - 27a^3b^6 - 3a^2b^2$ $3a^2b^2(3a^4b - 9ab^4 - 1)$
3. $3t(t - 5) - 6(t - 5)$ $3(t - 5)(t - 2)$
4. $4(3x - 2) + 8x(3x - 2)$ $4(3x - 2)(1 + 2x)$
5. $ax + 2bx - 5a - 10b$ $(a + 2b)(x - 5)$
6. $m^2 - mx - 3pm + 3px$ $(m - x)(m - 3p)$

Concept 1: Factoring Trinomials with a Leading Coefficient of 1

Animation

For Exercises 7–20, factor completely. **(See Examples 1, 2, and 5.)**

7. $x^2 + 10x + 16$ $(x + 8)(x + 2)$
8. $y^2 + 18y + 80$ $(y + 10)(y + 8)$
9. $z^2 - 11z + 18$ $(z - 9)(z - 2)$
10. $w^2 - 7w + 12$ $(w - 3)(w - 4)$
11. $z^2 - 3z - 18$ $(z - 6)(z + 3)$
12. $w^2 + 4w - 12$ $(w + 6)(w - 2)$
13. $p^2 - 3p - 40$ $(p - 8)(p + 5)$
14. $a^2 - 10a + 9$ $(a - 9)(a - 1)$
15. $t^2 + 6t - 40$ $(t + 10)(t - 4)$
16. $m^2 - 12m + 11$ $(m - 11)(m - 1)$
17. $x^2 - 3x + 20$ Prime
18. $y^2 + 6y + 18$ Prime
19. $n^2 + 8n + 16$ $(n + 4)^2$
20. $v^2 + 10v + 25$ $(v + 5)^2$

For Exercises 21–24, assume that b and c represent positive integers.

21. When factoring a polynomial of the form $x^2 + bx + c$, pick an appropriate combination of signs. a

    a. (+)(+) **b.** (−)(−) **c.** (+)(−)

22. When factoring a polynomial of the form $x^2 + bx - c$, pick an appropriate combination of signs. c

    a. (+)(+) **b.** (−)(−) **c.** (+)(−)

23. When factoring a polynomial of the form $x^2 - bx - c$, pick an appropriate combination of signs. c

    a. (+)(+) **b.** (−)(−) **c.** (+)(−)

24. When factoring a polynomial of the form $x^2 - bx + c$, pick an appropriate combination of signs. b

    a. (+)(+) **b.** (−)(−) **c.** (+)(−)

25. Which is the correct factorization of $y^2 - y - 12$, the product $(y - 4)(y + 3)$ or $(y + 3)(y - 4)$? Explain.
    They are both correct because multiplication of polynomials is a commutative operation.

26. Which is the correct factorization of $x^2 + 14x + 13$, the product $(x + 13)(x + 1)$ or $(x + 1)(x + 13)$? Explain.
They are both correct because multiplication of polynomials is a commutative operation.

27. Which is the correct factorization of $w^2 + 2w + 1$, the product $(w + 1)(w + 1)$ or $(w + 1)^2$? Explain.
The expressions are equal and both are correct.

28. Which is the correct factorization of $z^2 - 4z + 4$, the product $(z - 2)(z - 2)$ or $(z - 2)^2$? Explain.
The expressions are equal and both are correct.

29. In what order should a trinomial be written before attempting to factor it?
It should be written in descending order.

30. Once a polynomial is written in descending order, what is the next step to factor the polynomial?
Factor out the greatest common factor (GCF) from all terms.

For Exercises 31–66, factor completely. Be sure to factor out the GCF when necessary. **(See Examples 3–4.)**

31. $-13x + x^2 - 30$
$(x - 15)(x + 2)$

32. $12y - 160 + y^2$
$(y + 20)(y - 8)$

33. $-18w + 65 + w^2$
$(w - 13)(w - 5)$

34. $17t + t^2 + 72$
$(t + 8)(t + 9)$

35. $22t + t^2 + 72$
$(t + 18)(t + 4)$

36. $10q - 1200 + q^2$
$(q - 30)(q + 40)$

37. $3x^2 - 30x - 72$
$3(x - 12)(x + 2)$

38. $2z^2 + 4z - 198$
$2(z + 11)(z - 9)$

39. $8p^3 - 40p^2 + 32p$
$8p(p - 1)(p - 4)$

40. $5w^4 - 35w^3 + 50w^2$
$5w^2(w - 2)(w - 5)$

41. $y^4z^2 - 12y^3z^2 + 36y^2z^2$
$y^2z^2(y - 6)(y - 6)$ or $y^2z^2(y - 6)^2$

42. $t^4u^2 + 6t^3u^2 + 9t^2u^2$
$t^2u^2(t + 3)(t + 3)$ or $t^2u^2(t + 3)^2$

43. $-x^2 + 10x - 24$
$-(x - 4)(x - 6)$

44. $-y^2 - 12y - 35$
$-(y + 5)(y + 7)$

45. $-5a^2 + 5ax + 30x^2$
$-5(a - 3x)(a + 2x)$

46. $-2m^2 + 10mn + 12n^2$
$-2(m + n)(m - 6n)$

47. $-4 - 2c^2 - 6c$
$-2(c + 2)(c + 1)$

48. $-40d - 30 - 10d^2$
$-10(d + 3)(d + 1)$

49. $x^3y^3 - 19x^2y^3 + 60xy^3$
$xy^3(x - 4)(x - 15)$

50. $y^2z^5 + 17yz^5 + 60z^5$
$z^5(y + 5)(y + 12)$

51. $12p^2 - 96p + 84$
$12(p - 7)(p - 1)$

52. $5w^2 - 40w - 45$
$5(w - 9)(w + 1)$

53. $-2m^2 + 22m - 20$
$-2(m - 10)(m - 1)$

54. $-3x^2 - 36x - 81$
$-3(x + 9)(x + 3)$

55. $c^2 + 6cd + 5d^2$ $(c + 5d)(c + d)$

56. $x^2 + 8xy + 12y^2$ $(x + 6y)(x + 2y)$

57. $a^2 - 9ab + 14b^2$ $(a - 2b)(a - 7b)$

58. $m^2 - 15mn + 44n^2$
$(m - 4n)(m - 11n)$

59. $a^2 + 4a + 18$ Prime

60. $b^2 - 6a + 15$ Prime

61. $2q + q^2 - 63$ $(q - 7)(q + 9)$

62. $-32 - 4t + t^2$ $(t - 8)(t + 4)$

63. $x^2 + 20x + 100$ $(x + 10)^2$

64. $z^2 - 24z + 144$ $(z - 12)^2$

65. $t^2 + 18t - 40$ $(t + 20)(t - 2)$

66. $d^2 + 2d - 99$ $(d + 11)(d - 9)$

67. A student factored a trinomial as $(2x - 4)(x - 3)$. The instructor did not give full credit. Why? The student forgot to factor out the GCF before factoring the trinomial further. The polynomial is not factored completely, because $(2x - 4)$ has a common factor of 2.

68. A student factored a trinomial as $(y + 2)(5y - 15)$. The instructor did not give full credit. Why? The student forgot to factor out the GCF before factoring the trinomial further. The polynomial is not factored completely, because $(5y - 15)$ has a common factor of 5.

69. What polynomial factors as $(x - 4)(x + 13)$? $x^2 + 9x - 52$

70. What polynomial factors as $(q - 7)(q + 10)$? $q^2 + 3q - 70$

71. Raul purchased a parcel of land in the country. The given expressions represent the lengths of the boundary lines of his property.

a. Write the perimeter of the land as a polynomial in simplified form. $3x^2 + 9x - 12$

b. Write the polynomial from part (a) in factored form. $3(x + 4)(x - 1)$

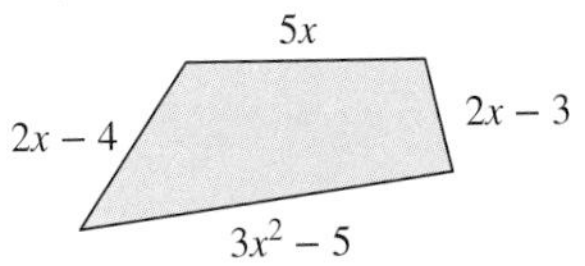

72. Jamison painted a mural in the shape of a triangle on the wall of a building. The given expressions represent the lengths of the sides of the triangle.

a. Write the perimeter of the triangle as a polynomial in simplified form. $2y^2 + 12y + 16$

b. Write the polynomial in factored form.
$2(y + 4)(y + 2)$

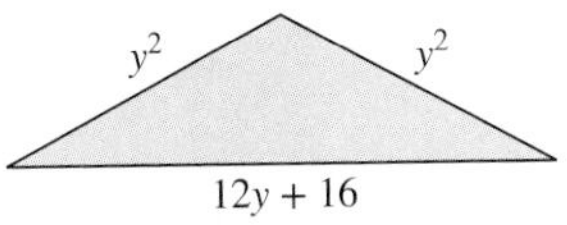

Expanding Your Skills

For Exercises 73–76, factor completely.

73. $x^4 + 10x^2 + 9$ $(x^2 + 1)(x^2 + 9)$

74. $y^4 + 4y^2 - 21$ $(y^2 - 3)(y^2 + 7)$

75. $w^4 + 2w^2 - 15$ $(w^2 + 5)(w^2 - 3)$

76. $p^4 - 13p^2 + 40$ $(p^2 - 8)(p^2 - 5)$

77. Find all integers, b, that make the trinomial $x^2 + bx + 6$ factorable. 7, 5, −7, −5

78. Find all integers, b, that make the trinomial $x^2 + bx + 10$ factorable. 11, 7, −11, −7

79. Find a value of c that makes the trinomial $x^2 + 6x + c$ factorable. For example: $c = -16$

80. Find a value of c that makes the trinomial $x^2 + 8x + c$ factorable. For example: $c = 7$

Section 6.3 Factoring Trinomials: Trial-and-Error Method

Concept

1. Factoring Trinomials by the Trial-and-Error Method

In this section we will learn how to factor a trinomial of the form $ax^2 + bx + c = 0$ (where $a \neq 0$). The method presented here is called the trial-and-error method.

1. Factoring Trinomials by the Trial-and-Error Method

To understand the basis of factoring trinomials of the form $ax^2 + bx + c$, first consider the multiplication of two binomials:

Product of $2 \cdot 1$ Product of $3 \cdot 2$

$$(2x + 3)(1x + 2) = 2x^2 + \mathbf{4x + 3x} + 6 = 2x^2 + 7x + 6$$

Sum of products of inner terms and outer terms

To factor the trinomial, $2x^2 + 7x + 6$, this operation is reversed.

Factors of 2

$$2x^2 + 7x + 6 = (\square x \quad \square)(\square x \quad \square)$$

Factors of 6

We need to fill in the blanks so that the product of the first terms in the binomials is $2x^2$ and the product of the last terms in the binomials is 6. Furthermore, the factors of $2x^2$ and 6 must be chosen so that the sum of the products of the inner terms and outer terms equals $7x$.

To produce the product $2x^2$, we might try the factors $2x$ and x within the binomials:

$$(2x \quad \square)(x \quad \square)$$

To produce a product of 6, the remaining terms in the binomials must either both be positive or both be negative. To produce a positive middle term, we will try positive factors of 6 in the remaining blanks until the correct product is found. The possibilities are $1 \cdot 6$, $2 \cdot 3$, $6 \cdot 1$, and $3 \cdot 2$.

$(2x + 1)(x + 6) = 2x^2 + 12x + 1x + 6 = 2x^2 + 13x + 6$ Wrong middle term

$(2x + 2)(x + 3) = 2x^2 + 6x + 2x + 6 = 2x^2 + 8x + 6$ Wrong middle term

$(2x + 6)(x + 1) = 2x^2 + 2x + 6x + 6 = 2x^2 + 8x + 6$ Wrong middle term

$(2x + 3)(x + 2) = 2x^2 + 4x + 3x + 6 = 2x^2 + 7x + 6$ Correct!

The correct factorization of $2x^2 + 7x + 6$ is $(2x + 3)(x + 2)$. ✓

As this example shows, we factor a trinomial of the form $ax^2 + bx + c$ by shuffling the factors of a and c within the binomials until the correct product is obtained. However, sometimes it is not necessary to test all the possible combinations of factors. In the previous example, the GCF of the original trinomial is 1. Therefore, any binomial factor whose terms share a common factor *greater than 1* does not need to be considered. In this case, the possibilities $(2x + 2)(x + 3)$ and $(2x + 6)(x + 1)$ cannot work.

$$\underbrace{(2x + 2)}_{\text{Common factor of 2}}(x + 3) \qquad \underbrace{(2x + 6)}_{\text{Common factor of 2}}(x + 1)$$

Trial-and-Error Method to Factor $ax^2 + bx + c$

Step 1 Factor out the GCF.

Step 2 List all pairs of positive factors of a and pairs of positive factors of c. Consider the reverse order for one of the lists of factors.

Step 3 Construct two binomials of the form:

Factors of a

$$(\square x \quad \square)(\square x \quad \square)$$

Factors of c

Step 4 Test each combination of factors and signs until the correct product is found.

Step 5 If no combination of factors produces the correct product, the trinomial cannot be factored further and is a *prime polynomial*.

Before we begin Example 1, keep these two important guidelines in mind:

- For any factoring problem you encounter, always factor out the GCF from all terms first.
- To factor a trinomial, write the trinomial in the form $ax^2 + bx + c$.

Example 1 Factoring a Trinomial by the Trial-and-Error Method

Classroom Example: p. 439, Exercise 14

Factor the trinomial by the trial-and-error method. $10x^2 + 11x + 1$

Solution:

$10x^2 + 11x + 1$ **Step 1:** Factor out the GCF from all terms. In this case, the GCF is 1.

The trinomial is written in the form $ax^2 + bx + c$.

To factor $10x^2 + 11x + 1$, two binomials must be constructed in the form:

Factors of 10

$$(\square x \quad \square)(\square x \quad \square)$$

Factors of 1

Step 2: To produce the product $10x^2$, we might try $5x$ and $2x$, or $10x$ and $1x$. To produce a product of 1, we will try the factors $(1)(1)$ and $(-1)(-1)$.

Step 3: Construct all possible binomial factors using different combinations of the factors of $10x^2$ and 1.

$(5x + 1)(2x + 1) = 10x^2 + 5x + 2x + 1 = 10x^2 + 7x + 1$ Wrong middle term

$(5x - 1)(2x - 1) = 10x^2 - 5x - 2x + 1 = 10x^2 - 7x + 1$ Wrong middle term

Because the numbers 1 and −1 did not produce the correct trinomial when coupled with 5*x* and 2*x*, try using 10*x* and 1*x*.

$(10x - 1)(1x - 1) = 10x^2 - 10x - 1x + 1 = 10x^2 - 11x + 1$ Wrong sign on the middle term

$(10x + 1)(1x + 1) = 10x^2 + 10x + 1x + 1 = 10x^2 + 11x + 1$ Correct!

Therefore, $10x^2 + 11x + 1 = (10x + 1)(x + 1)$.

Skill Practice Factor using the trial-and-error method.

1. $3b^2 + 8b + 4$

In Example 1, the factors of 1 must have the same signs to produce a positive product. Therefore, the binomial factors must both be sums or both be differences. Determining the correct signs is an important aspect of factoring trinomials. We suggest the following guidelines:

Sign Rules for the Trial-and-Error Method

Given the trinomial $ax^2 + bx + c$, $(a > 0)$, the signs can be determined as follows:

- If *c is positive*, then the signs in the binomials must be the same (either both positive or both negative). The correct choice is determined by the middle term. If the middle term is positive, then both signs must be positive. If the middle term is negative, then both signs must be negative.

  c is positive → $20x^2 + 43x + 21$, $(4x + 3)(5x + 7)$ — Same signs

  c is positive → $20x^2 - 43x + 21$, $(4x - 3)(5x - 7)$ — Same signs

- If *c is negative*, then the signs in the binomial must be different. The middle term in the trinomial determines which factor gets the positive sign and which gets the negative sign.

  c is negative → $x^2 + 3x - 28$, $(x + 7)(x - 4)$ — Different signs

  c is negative → $x^2 - 3x - 28$, $(x - 7)(x + 4)$ — Different signs

TIP: Look at the sign on the third term. If it is a sum, the signs will be the same in the two binomials. If it is a difference, the signs in the two binomials will be different: sum–same sign; difference–different signs.

Answer

1. $(3b + 2)(b + 2)$

Classroom Example: p. 439, Exercise 20

Example 2 Factoring a Trinomial by the Trial-and-Error Method

Factor the trinomial. $13y - 6 + 8y^2$

Solution:

$13y - 6 + 8y^2$

$= 8y^2 + 13y - 6$ Write the polynomial in descending order.

$(\square y \quad \square)(\square y \quad \square)$ **Step 1:** The GCF is 1.

Step 2: List the positive factors of 8 and positive factors of 6. Consider the reverse order in one list of factors.

Factors of 8	Factors of 6
$1 \cdot 8$	$1 \cdot 6$
$2 \cdot 4$	$2 \cdot 3$
	$3 \cdot 2$ (reverse order)
	$6 \cdot 1$ (reverse order)

Step 3: Construct all possible binomial factors using different combinations of the factors of 8 and 6.

$(1y \quad 1)(8y \quad 6)$
$(1y \quad 3)(8y \quad 2)$
$(2y \quad 1)(4y \quad 6)$
$(2y \quad 2)(4y \quad 3)$
$(2y \quad 3)(4y \quad 2)$
$(2y \quad 6)(4y \quad 1)$

Without regard to signs, these factorizations cannot work because the red terms in the binomials share a common factor greater than 1.

Test the remaining factorizations. Keep in mind that to produce a product of -6, the signs within the parentheses must be opposite (one positive and one negative). Also, the sum of the products of the inner terms and outer terms must be combined to form $13y$.

$(1y \quad 6)(8y \quad 1)$ *Incorrect.* Wrong middle term.
Regardless of the signs, the product of inner terms, $48y$, and the product of outer terms, $1y$, cannot be combined to form the middle term $13y$.

$(1y \quad 2)(8y \quad 3)$ *Correct.* The terms $16y$ and $3y$ can be combined to form the middle term $13y$, provided the signs are applied correctly. We require $+16y$ and $-3y$.

The correct factorization of $8y^2 + 13y - 6$ is $(y + 2)(8y - 3)$.

Skill Practice Factor.

2. $-25w + 6w^2 + 4$

Remember that the first step in any factoring problem is to remove the GCF. By removing the GCF, the remaining terms of the trinomial will have smaller coefficients.

Answer

2. $(6w - 1)(w - 4)$

Classroom Example: p. 440, Exercise 32

Example 3 Factoring a Trinomial by the Trial-and-Error Method

Factor the trinomial by the trial-and-error method. $40x^3 - 104x^2 + 10x$

Solution:

$40x^3 - 104x^2 + 10x$

$= 2x(20x^2 - 52x + 5)$ **Step 1:** The GCF is $2x$.

$= 2x(\square x \quad \square)(\square x \quad \square)$ **Step 2:** List the factors of 20 and factors of 5. Consider the reverse order in one list of factors.

Factors of 20	Factors of 5
$1 \cdot 20$	$1 \cdot 5$
$2 \cdot 10$	$5 \cdot 1$
$4 \cdot 5$	

Step 3: Construct all possible binomial factors using different combinations of the factors of 20 and factors of 5. The signs in the parentheses must both be negative.

> **TIP:** Notice that when the GCF, $2x$, is removed from the original trinomial, the new trinomial has smaller coefficients. This makes the factoring process simpler. It is easier to list the factors of 20 and 5 than the factors of 40 and 10.

$= 2x(1x - 1)(20x - 5)$
$= 2x(2x - 1)(10x - 5)$
$= 2x(4x - 1)(5x - 5)$

Incorrect. Once the GCF has been removed from the original polynomial, the binomial factors cannot contain a GCF greater than 1.

$= 2x(1x - 5)(20x - 1)$ *Incorrect.* Wrong middle term.

$2x(x - 5)(20x - 1)$
$= 2x(20x^2 - 1x - 100x + 5)$
$= 2x(20x^2 - 101x + 5)$

$= 2x(4x - 5)(5x - 1)$ *Incorrect.* Wrong middle term.

$2x(4x - 5)(5x - 1)$
$= 2x(20x^2 - 4x - 25x + 5)$
$= 2x(20x^2 - 29x + 5)$

$= 2x(2x - 5)(10x - 1)$ *Correct.*

$2x(2x - 5)(10x - 1)$
$= 2x(20x^2 - 2x - 50x + 5)$
$= 2x(20x^2 - 52x + 5)$
$= 40x^3 - 104x^2 + 10x$

The correct factorization is $2x(2x - 5)(10x - 1)$.

Skill Practice Factor.

3. $8t^3 + 38t^2 + 24t$

Often it is easier to factor a trinomial when the leading coefficient is positive. If the leading coefficient is negative, consider factoring out the opposite of the GCF.

Answer

3. $2t(4t + 3)(t + 4)$

Example 4 Factoring a Trinomial by the Trial-and-Error Method

Classroom Example: p. 440, Exercise 36

Factor. $-45x^2 - 3xy + 18y^2$

Solution:

$-45x^2 - 3xy + 18y^2$

$= -3(15x^2 + xy - 6y^2)$ **Step 1:** Factor out −3 to make the leading coefficient positive.

$= -3(\square x \quad \square y)(\square x \quad \square y)$ **Step 2:** List the factors of 15 and 6.

Factors of 15	Factors of 6
$1 \cdot 15$	$1 \cdot 6$
$3 \cdot 5$	$2 \cdot 3$
	$3 \cdot 2$
	$6 \cdot 1$

Step 3: We will construct all binomial combinations, without regard to signs first.

$-3(x \quad y)(15x \quad 6y)$
$-3(x \quad 2y)(15x \quad 3y)$
$-3(3x \quad 3y)(5x \quad 2y)$
$-3(3x \quad 6y)(5x \quad y)$

Incorrect. These combinations cannot work because the binomials in red each contain a common factor.

Test the remaining factorizations. The signs within parentheses must be opposite to produce a product of $-6y^2$. Also, the sum of the products of the inner terms and outer terms must be combined to form $1xy$.

$-3(x \quad 3y)(15x \quad 2y)$ *Incorrect.* Regardless of signs, $45xy$ and $2xy$ cannot be combined to equal xy.

$-3(x \quad 6y)(15x \quad y)$ *Incorrect.* Regardless of signs, $90xy$ and xy cannot be combined to equal xy.

$-3(3x \quad y)(5x \quad 6y)$ *Incorrect.* Regardless of signs, $5xy$ and $18xy$ cannot be combined to equal xy.

$-3(3x \quad 2y)(5x \quad 3y)$ *Correct.* The terms $10xy$ and $9xy$ can be combined to form xy provided that the signs are applied correctly. We require $10xy$ and $-9xy$.

$-3(3x + 2y)(5x - 3y)$ Factored form

Avoiding Mistakes

Do not forget to write the GCF in the final answer.

Skill Practice Factor.

4. $-4x^2 + 26xy - 40y^2$

Recall that a prime polynomial is a polynomial whose only factors are itself and 1. Not every trinomial is factorable by the methods presented in this text.

Answer

4. $-2(2x - 5y)(x - 4y)$

Classroom Example: p. 440, Exercise 52

Example 5 Factoring a Trinomial by the Trial-and-Error Method

Factor the trinomial by the trial-and-error method. $2p^2 - 8p + 3$

Solution:

$2p^2 - 8p + 3$ — **Step 1:** The GCF is 1.

$= (1p \quad \square)(2p \quad \square)$ — **Step 2:** List the factors of 2 and the factors of 3.

Factors of 2	Factors of 3
$1 \cdot 2$	$1 \cdot 3$
	$3 \cdot 1$

Step 3: Construct all possible binomial factors using different combinations of the factors of 2 and 3. Because the third term in the trinomial is positive, both signs in the binomial must be the same. Because the middle term coefficient is negative, both signs will be negative.

$(p - 1)(2p - 3) = 2p^2 - 3p - 2p + 3$

$= 2p^2 - 5p + 3$ *Incorrect.* Wrong middle term.

$(p - 3)(2p - 1) = 2p^2 - p - 6p + 3$

$= 2p^2 - 7p + 3$ *Incorrect.* Wrong middle term.

None of the combinations of factors results in the correct product. Therefore, the polynomial $2p^2 - 8p + 3$ is prime and cannot be factored further.

Skill Practice Factor.

5. $3a^2 + a + 4$

In Example 6, we use the trial-and-error method to factor a higher degree trinomial into two binomial factors.

Classroom Example: p. 440, Exercise 38

Example 6 Factoring a Higher Degree Trinomial

Factor the trinomial. $3x^4 + 8x^2 + 5$

Solution:

$3x^4 + 8x^2 + 5$ — **Step 1:** The GCF is 1.

$= (\square x^2 + \square)(\square x^2 + \square)$ — **Step 2:** To produce the product $3x^4$, we must use $3x^2$ and $1x^2$. To produce a product of 5, we will try the factors (1)(5) and (5)(1).

Step 3: Construct all possible binomial factors using the combinations of factors of $3x^4$ and 5.

$(3x^2 + 1)(x^2 + 5) = 3x^4 + 15x^2 + 1x^2 + 5 = 3x^4 + 16x^2 + 5$ Wrong middle term.

$(3x^2 + 5)(x^2 + 1) = 3x^4 + 3x^2 + 5x^2 + 5 = 3x^4 + 8x^2 + 5$ Correct!

Therefore, $3x^4 + 8x^2 + 5 = (3x^2 + 5)(x^2 + 1)$.

Skill Practice Factor.

6. $2y^4 - y^2 - 15$

Answers

5. Prime **6.** $(y^2 - 3)(2y^2 + 5)$

Section 6.3 Practice Exercises

For additional exercises, see Classroom Activity 6.3A in the *Student's Resource Manual* at www.mhhe.com/moh.

Vocabulary and Key Concepts

1. **a.** Which is the correct factored form of $2x^2 - 5x - 12$, the product $(2x + 3)(x - 4)$ or $(x - 4)(2x + 3)$?
   Both are correct.

   b. Which is the complete factorization of $6x^2 - 4x - 10$, the product $(3x - 5)(2x + 2)$ or $2(3x - 5)(x + 1)$?
   $2(3x - 5)(x + 1)$

Review Exercises

For Exercises 2–6, factor completely.

2. $5uv^2 - 10u^2v + 25u^2v^2$
   $5uv(v - 2u + 5uv)$
3. $mn - m - 2n + 2$
   $(n - 1)(m - 2)$
4. $5x - 10 - xy + 2y$
   $(x - 2)(5 - y)$
5. $6a^2 - 30a - 84$
   $6(a - 7)(a + 2)$
6. $10b^2 + 20b - 240$
   $10(b + 6)(b - 4)$

Concept 1: Factoring Trinomials by the Trial-and-Error Method

For Exercises 7–10, assume a, b, and c represent positive integers.

7. When factoring a polynomial of the form $ax^2 + bx + c$, pick an appropriate combination of signs. a
   a. (+)(+)
   b. (−)(−)
   c. (+)(−)

8. When factoring a polynomial of the form $ax^2 - bx - c$, pick an appropriate combination of signs. c
   a. (+)(+)
   b. (−)(−)
   c. (+)(−)

9. When factoring a polynomial of the form $ax^2 - bx + c$, pick an appropriate combination of signs. b
   a. (+)(+)
   b. (−)(−)
   c. (+)(−)

10. When factoring a polynomial of the form $ax^2 + bx - c$, pick an appropriate combination of signs. c
   a. (+)(+)
   b. (−)(−)
   c. (+)(−)

For Exercises 11–28, factor completely by using the trial-and-error method. **(See Examples 1, 2, and 5.)**

11. $3n^2 + 13n + 4$
   $(3n + 1)(n + 4)$
12. $2w^2 + 5w - 3$
   $(2w - 1)(w + 3)$
13. $2y^2 - 3y - 2$
   $(2y + 1)(y - 2)$
14. $2a^2 + 7a + 6$
   $(2a + 3)(a + 2)$
15. $5x^2 - 14x - 3$
   $(5x + 1)(x - 3)$
16. $7y^2 + 9y - 10$
   $(7y - 5)(y + 2)$
17. $12c^2 - 5c - 2$
   $(4c + 1)(3c - 2)$
18. $6z^2 + z - 12$
   $(3z - 4)(2z + 3)$
19. $-12 + 10w^2 + 37w$
   $(10w - 3)(w + 4)$
20. $-10 + 10p^2 + 21p$
   $(2p + 5)(5p - 2)$
21. $-5q - 6 + 6q^2$
   $(3q + 2)(2q - 3)$
22. $17a - 2 + 3a^2$
   Prime
23. $6b - 23 + 4b^2$
   Prime
24. $8 + 7x^2 - 18x$
   $(7x - 4)(x - 2)$
25. $-8 + 25m^2 - 10m$
   $(5m + 2)(5m - 4)$
26. $8q^2 + 31q - 4$
   $(8q - 1)(q + 4)$
27. $6y^2 + 19xy - 20x^2$
   $(6y - 5x)(y + 4x)$
28. $12y^2 - 73yz + 6z^2$
   $(12y - z)(y - 6z)$

For Exercises 29–36, factor completely. Be sure to factor out the GCF first. **(See Examples 3–4.)**

29. $2m^2 - 12m - 80$
$2(m + 4)(m - 10)$

30. $3c^2 - 33c + 72$
$3(c - 8)(c - 3)$

31. $2y^5 + 13y^4 + 6y^3$
$y^3(2y + 1)(y + 6)$

32. $3u^8 - 13u^7 + 4u^6$
$u^6(3u - 1)(u - 4)$

33. $-a^2 - 15a + 34$
$-(a + 17)(a - 2)$

34. $-x^2 - 7x - 10$
$-(x + 2)(x + 5)$

35. $-80m^2 + 100mp + 30p^2$
$-10(4m + p)(2m - 3p)$

36. $-60w^2 - 550wz + 500z^2$
$-10(w + 10z)(6w - 5z)$

For Exercises 37–42, factor the higher degree polynomial. **(See Example 6.)**

37. $x^4 + 10x^2 + 9$
$(x^2 + 1)(x^2 + 9)$

38. $y^4 + 4y^2 - 21$
$(y^2 - 3)(y^2 + 7)$

39. $w^4 + 2w^2 - 15$
$(w^2 + 5)(w^2 - 3)$

40. $p^4 - 13p^2 + 40$
$(p^2 - 8)(p^2 - 5)$

41. $2x^4 - 7x^2 - 15$
$(2x^2 + 3)(x^2 - 5)$

42. $5y^4 + 11y^2 + 2$
$(5y^2 + 1)(y^2 + 2)$

Mixed Exercises

For Exercises 43–82, factor each trinomial completely.

43. $20z - 18 - 2z^2$
$-2(z - 9)(z - 1)$

44. $25t - 5t^2 - 30$
$-5(t - 2)(t - 3)$

45. $42 - 13q + q^2$
$(q - 7)(q - 6)$

46. $-5w - 24 + w^2$
$(w - 8)(w + 3)$

47. $6t^2 + 7t - 3$
$(2t + 3)(3t - 1)$

48. $4p^2 - 9p + 2$
$(4p - 1)(p - 2)$

49. $4m^2 - 20m + 25$
$(2m - 5)^2$

50. $16r^2 + 24r + 9$
$(4r + 3)^2$

51. $5c^2 - c + 2$
Prime

52. $7s^2 + 2s + 9$
Prime

53. $6x^2 - 19xy + 10y^2$
$(2x - 5y)(3x - 2y)$

54. $15p^2 + pq - 2q^2$
$(3p - q)(5p + 2q)$

55. $12m^2 + 11mn - 5n^2$
$(4m + 5n)(3m - n)$

56. $4a^2 + 5ab - 6b^2$
$(4a - 3b)(a + 2b)$

57. $30r^2 + 5r - 10$
$5(3r + 2)(2r - 1)$

58. $36x^2 - 18x - 4$
$2(6x + 1)(3x - 2)$

59. $4s^2 - 8st + t^2$
Prime

60. $6u^2 - 10uv + 5v^2$
Prime

61. $10t^2 - 23t - 5$
$(2t - 5)(5t + 1)$

62. $16n^2 + 14n + 3$
$(8n + 3)(2n + 1)$

63. $14w^2 + 13w - 12$
$(7w - 4)(2w + 3)$

64. $12x^2 - 16x + 5$
$(6x - 5)(2x - 1)$

65. $a^2 - 10a - 24$
$(a - 12)(a + 2)$

66. $b^2 + 6b - 7$
$(b + 7)(b - 1)$

67. $x^2 + 9xy + 20y^2$
$(x + 5y)(x + 4y)$

68. $p^2 - 13pq + 36q^2$
$(p - 9q)(p - 4q)$

69. $a^2 + 21ab + 20b^2$
$(a + 20b)(a + b)$

70. $x^2 - 17xy - 18y^2$
$(x - 18y)(x + y)$

71. $t^2 - 10t + 21$
$(t - 7)(t - 3)$

72. $z^2 - 15z + 36$
$(z - 12)(z - 3)$

73. $5d^3 + 3d^2 - 10d$
$d(5d^2 + 3d - 10)$

74. $3y^3 - y^2 + 12y$
$y(3y^2 - y + 12)$

75. $4b^3 - 4b^2 - 80b$
$4b(b - 5)(b + 4)$

76. $2w^2 + 20w + 42$
$2(w + 7)(w + 3)$

77. $x^2y^2 - 13xy^2 + 30y^2$
$y^2(x - 3)(x - 10)$

78. $p^2q^2 - 14pq^2 + 33q^2$
$q^2(p - 3)(p - 11)$

79. $-12u^3 - 22u^2 + 20u$
$-2u(2u + 5)(3u - 2)$

80. $-18z^4 + 15z^3 + 12z^2$
$-3z^2(3z - 4)(2z + 1)$

81. $8x^4 + 14x^2 + 3$
$(2x^2 + 3)(4x^2 + 1)$

82. $6y^4 - 5y^2 - 4$
$(3y^2 - 4)(2y^2 + 1)$

83. A rock is thrown straight upward from the top of a 40-ft building. Its height in feet after t seconds is given by the polynomial $-16t^2 + 12t + 40$.

a. Calculate the height of the rock after 1 sec. ($t = 1$) 36 ft

b. Write $-16t^2 + 12t + 40$ in factored form. Then evaluate the factored form of the polynomial for $t = 1$. Is the result the same as from part (a)?
$-4(4t + 5)(t - 2)$; Yes

84. A baseball is thrown straight downward from the top of a 120-ft building. Its height in feet after t seconds is given by $-16t^2 - 8t + 120$.

a. Calculate the height of the ball after 2 sec. ($t = 2$) 40 ft

b. Write $-16t^2 - 8t + 120$ in factored form. Then evaluate the factored form of the polynomial for $t = 2$. Is the result the same as from part (a)?
$-8(2t - 5)(t + 3)$; Yes

Expanding Your Skills

For Exercises 85–88, the two trinomials look similar but differ by one sign. Factor each trinomial and see how their factored forms differ.

85. **a.** $x^2 - 10x - 24$ $(x - 12)(x + 2)$

b. $x^2 - 10x + 24$ $(x - 6)(x - 4)$

86. **a.** $x^2 - 13x - 30$ $(x - 15)(x + 2)$

b. $x^2 - 13x + 30$ $(x - 10)(x - 3)$

87. **a.** $x^2 - 5x - 6$ $(x - 6)(x + 1)$

b. $x^2 - 5x + 6$ $(x - 2)(x - 3)$

88. **a.** $x^2 - 10x + 9$ $(x - 9)(x - 1)$

b. $x^2 + 10x + 9$ $(x + 9)(x + 1)$

Factoring Trinomials: AC-Method

Section 6.4

Concept

1. Factoring Trinomials by the AC-Method

We have already learned how to factor a trinomial of the form $ax^2 + bx + c = 0$ with a leading coefficient of 1. Then we learned the trial-and-error method to factor the more general case in which the leading coefficient is any integer. In this section, we provide an alternative method to factor trinomials, called the ac-method.

1. Factoring Trinomials by the AC-Method

The product of two binomials results in a four-term expression that can sometimes be simplified to a trinomial. To factor the trinomial, we want to reverse the process.

Multiply:

Multiply the binomials. Add the middle terms.

$$(2x + 3)(x + 2) = \longrightarrow 2x^2 + 4x + 3x + 6 = \longrightarrow 2x^2 + 7x + 6$$

Factor:

$$2x^2 + 7x + 6 = \longrightarrow 2x^2 + 4x + 3x + 6 = \longrightarrow (2x + 3)(x + 2)$$

Rewrite the middle term as a sum or difference of terms. Factor by grouping.

To factor a quadratic trinomial, $ax^2 + bx + c$, by the ac-method, we rewrite the middle term, bx, as a sum or difference of terms. The goal is to produce a four-term polynomial that can be factored by grouping. The process is outlined as follows.

AC-Method: Factoring $ax^2 + bx + c$ ($a \neq 0$)

Step 1 Factor out the GCF from all terms.

Step 2 Multiply the coefficients of the first and last terms (ac).

Step 3 Find two integers whose product is ac and whose sum is b. (If no pair of integers can be found, then the trinomial cannot be factored further and is a *prime polynomial.*)

Step 4 Rewrite the middle term, bx, as the sum of two terms whose coefficients are the integers found in step 3.

Step 5 Factor the polynomial by grouping.

Instructor Note: Tell students that we use the phrase *prime polynomial* to mean that a polynomial is not factorable over the *integers*.

The ac-method for factoring trinomials is illustrated in Example 1. However, before we begin, keep these two important guidelines in mind:

- For any factoring problem you encounter, always factor out the GCF from all terms first.
- To factor a trinomial, write the trinomial in the form $ax^2 + bx + c$.

Classroom Example: p. 446, Exercise 14

Example 1 Factoring a Trinomial by the AC-Method

Factor the trinomial by the ac-method. $2x^2 + 7x + 6$

Solution:

$2x^2 + 7x + 6$

Step 1: Factor out the GCF from all terms. In this case, the GCF is 1. The trinomial is written in the form $ax^2 + bx + c$.

$a = 2, b = 7, c = 6$

Step 2: Find the product $ac = (2)(6) = 12$.

12	12
$1 \cdot 12$	$(-1)(-12)$
$2 \cdot 6$	$(-2)(-6)$
$3 \cdot 4$	$(-3)(-4)$

Step 3: List all factors of ac and search for the pair whose sum equals the value of b. That is, list the factors of 12 and find the pair whose sum equals 7.

The numbers 3 and 4 satisfy both conditions: $3 \cdot 4 = 12$ and $3 + 4 = 7$.

$2x^2 + 7x + 6$

$= 2x^2 + 3x + 4x + 6$

Step 4: Write the middle term of the trinomial as the sum of two terms whose coefficients are the selected pair of numbers: 3 and 4.

$= 2x^2 + 3x \,\vdots\, + 4x + 6$

Step 5: Factor by grouping.

$= x(2x + 3) + 2(2x + 3)$

$= (2x + 3)(x + 2)$

<u>Check</u>: $(2x + 3)(x + 2) = 2x^2 + 4x + 3x + 6$

$= 2x^2 + 7x + 6$ ✓

Skill Practice Factor by the ac-method.

1. $2x^2 + 5x + 3$

TIP: One frequently asked question is whether the order matters when we rewrite the middle term of the trinomial as two terms (step 4). The answer is no. From the previous example, the two middle terms in step 4 could have been reversed to obtain the same result:

$$\begin{aligned} &2x^2 + 7x + 6 \\ &= 2x^2 + 4x + 3x + 6 \\ &= 2x(x + 2) + 3(x + 2) \\ &= (x + 2)(2x + 3) \end{aligned}$$

This example also points out that the order in which two factors are written does not matter. The expression $(x + 2)(2x + 3)$ is equivalent to $(2x + 3)(x + 2)$ because multiplication is a commutative operation.

Answer

1. $(x + 1)(2x + 3)$

Example 2 Factoring a Trinomial by the AC-Method

Classroom Example: p. 446, Exercise 28

Factor the trinomial by the ac-method. $-2x + 8x^2 - 3$

Solution:

$-2x + 8x^2 - 3$ First rewrite the polynomial in the form $ax^2 + bx + c$.

$= 8x^2 - 2x - 3$ **Step 1:** The GCF is 1.

$a = 8, b = -2, c = -3$ **Step 2:** Find the product $ac = (8)(-3) = -24$.

−24	−24
$-1 \cdot 24$	$-24 \cdot 1$
$-2 \cdot 12$	$-12 \cdot 2$
$-3 \cdot 8$	$-8 \cdot 3$
$-4 \cdot 6$	$-6 \cdot 4$

Step 3: List all the factors of −24 and find the pair of factors whose sum equals −2.

The numbers −6 and 4 satisfy both conditions: $(-6)(4) = -24$ and $-6 + 4 = -2$.

$= 8x^2 - 2x - 3$ **Step 4:** Write the middle term of the trinomial as two terms whose coefficients are the selected pair of numbers, −6 and 4.

$= 8x^2 - 6x + 4x - 3$

$= 8x^2 - 6x \mid + 4x - 3$ **Step 5:** Factor by grouping.

$= 2x(4x - 3) + 1(4x - 3)$

$= (4x - 3)(2x + 1)$

Check: $(4x - 3)(2x + 1) = 8x^2 + 4x - 6x - 3$

$= 8x^2 - 2x - 3$ ✓

Skill Practice Factor by the ac-method.

2. $13w + 6w^2 + 6$

Example 3 Factoring a Trinomial by the AC-Method

Classroom Example: p. 446, Exercise 38

Factor the trinomial by the ac-method. $10x^3 - 85x^2 + 105x$

Solution:

$10x^3 - 85x^2 + 105x$ **Step 1:** Factor out the GCF of $5x$.

$= 5x(2x^2 - 17x + 21)$ The trinomial is in the form $ax^2 + bx + c$.

$a = 2, b = -17, c = 21$ **Step 2:** Find the product $ac = (2)(21) = 42$.

42	42
$1 \cdot 42$	$(-1)(-42)$
$2 \cdot 21$	$(-2)(-21)$
$3 \cdot 14$	$(-3)(-14)$
$6 \cdot 7$	$(-6)(-7)$

Step 3: List all the factors of 42 and find the pair whose sum equals −17.

The numbers −3 and −14 satisfy both conditions: $(-3)(-14) = 42$ and $-3 + (-14) = -17$.

Answer

2. $(2w + 3)(3w + 2)$

$= 5x(2x^2 - 17x + 21)$

Step 4: Write the middle term of the trinomial as two terms whose coefficients are the selected pair of numbers, −3 and −14.

$= 5x(2x^2 - 3x - 14x + 21)$

$= 5x(2x^2 - 3x \mid - 14x + 21)$

Step 5: Factor by grouping.

$= 5x[x(2x - 3) - 7(2x - 3)]$

$= 5x(2x - 3)(x - 7)$

Avoiding Mistakes

Be sure to bring down the GCF in each successive step as you factor.

TIP: Notice when the GCF is removed from the original trinomial, the new trinomial has smaller coefficients. This makes the factoring process simpler because the product ac is smaller. It is much easier to list the factors of 42 than the factors of 1050.

Original trinomial	With the GCF factored out
$10x^3 - 85x^2 + 105x$	$5x(2x^2 - 17x + 21)$
$ac = (10)(105) = 1050$	$ac = (2)(21) = 42$

Skill Practice Factor by the ac-method.

3. $9y^3 - 30y^2 + 24y$

In most cases, it is easier to factor a trinomial with a positive leading coefficient.

Classroom Example: p. 446, Exercise 36

Example 4 Factoring a Trinomial by the AC-Method

Factor the trinomial by the ac-method. $-18x^2 + 21xy + 15y^2$

Solution:

$-18x^2 + 21xy + 15y^2$

$= -3(6x^2 - 7xy - 5y^2)$

Step 1: Factor out the GCF.

Factor out −3 to make the leading term positive.

Step 2: The product $ac = (6)(-5) = -30$.

Step 3: The numbers −10 and 3 have a product of −30 and a sum of −7.

$= -3[6x^2 - 10xy + 3xy - 5y^2]$

Step 4: Rewrite the middle term, $-7xy$ as $-10xy + 3xy$.

$= -3[6x^2 - 10xy \mid + 3xy - 5y^2]$

Step 5: Factor by grouping.

$= -3[2x(3x - 5y) + y(3x - 5y)]$

$= -3(3x - 5y)(2x + y)$ Factored form

Skill Practice Factor.

4. $-8x^2 - 8xy + 30y^2$

Answers

3. $3y(3y - 4)(y - 2)$

4. $-2(2x - 3y)(2x + 5y)$

Recall that a prime polynomial is a polynomial whose only factors are itself and 1. It also should be noted that not every trinomial is factorable by the methods presented in this text.

Example 5 **Factoring a Trinomial by the AC-Method**

Classroom Example: p. 446, Exercise 26

Factor the trinomial by the ac-method. $2p^2 - 8p + 3$

Solution:

$2p^2 - 8p + 3$ **Step 1:** The GCF is 1.

Step 2: The product $ac = 6$.

Step 3: List the factors of 6. Notice that no pair of factors has a sum of -8. Therefore, the trinomial cannot be factored.

6	6
$1 \cdot 6$	$(-1)(-6)$
$2 \cdot 3$	$(-2)(-3)$

The trinomial $2p^2 - 8p + 3$ is a prime polynomial.

Skill Practice Factor.

5. $4x^2 + 5x + 2$

In Example 6, we use the ac-method to factor a higher degree trinomial.

Example 6 **Factoring a Higher Degree Trinomial**

Classroom Example: p. 446, Exercise 42

Factor the trinomial by the ac-method. $2x^4 + 5x^2 + 2$

Solution:

$2x^4 + 5x^2 + 2$ **Step 1:** The GCF is 1.

$a = 2, b = 5, c = 2$ **Step 2:** Find the product $ac = (2)(2) = 4$.

Step 3: The numbers 1 and 4 have a product of 4 and a sum of 5.

$2x^4 + x^2 + 4x^2 + 2$ **Step 4:** Rewrite the middle term, $5x^2$, as $x^2 + 4x^2$.

$2x^4 + x^2 \,\vdots\, + 4x^2 + 2$ **Step 5:** Factor by grouping.

$x^2(2x^2 + 1) + 2(2x^2 + 1)$

$(2x^2 + 1)(x^2 + 2)$ Factored form

Skill Practice Factor.

6. $3y^4 + 2y^2 - 8$

Answers

5. Prime

6. $(3y^2 - 4)(y^2 + 2)$

Section 6.4 Practice Exercises

For additional exercises, see Classroom Activity 6.4A in the *Student's Resource Manual* at www.mhhe.com/moh.

Vocabulary and Key Concepts

1. **a.** Which is the correct factored form of $10x^2 - 13x - 3$? The product $(5x + 1)(2x - 3)$ or $(2x - 3)(5x + 1)$?
   Both are correct.

   b. Which is the complete factorization of $12x^2 - 15x - 18$? The product $(4x + 3)(3x - 6)$ or $3(4x + 3)(x - 2)$?
   $3(4x + 3)(x - 2)$

Review Exercises

For Exercises 2–4, factor completely.

2. $5x(x - 2) - 2(x - 2)$ $(x - 2)(5x - 2)$

3. $8(y + 5) + 9y(y + 5)$ $(y + 5)(8 + 9y)$

4. $6ab + 24b - 12a - 48$ $6(a + 4)(b - 2)$

Concept 1: Factoring Trinomials by the AC-Method

For Exercises 5–12, find the pair of integers whose product and sum are given.

5. Product: 12 Sum: 13 12, 1

6. Product: 12 Sum: 7 3, 4

7. Product: 8 Sum: −9 −8, −1

8. Product: −4 Sum: −3 −4, 1

9. Product: −20 Sum: 1 5, −4

10. Product: −6 Sum: −1 −3, 2

11. Product: −18 Sum: 7 9, −2

12. Product: −72 Sum: −6 −12, 6

For Exercises 13–30, factor the trinomials using the ac-method. **(See Examples 1, 2, and 5.)**

13. $3x^2 + 13x + 4$ $(x + 4)(3x + 1)$

14. $2y^2 + 7y + 6$ $(2y + 3)(y + 2)$

15. $4w^2 - 9w + 2$ $(w - 2)(4w - 1)$

16. $2p^2 - 3p - 2$ $(p - 2)(2p + 1)$

17. $x^2 + 7x - 18$ $(x + 9)(x - 2)$

18. $y^2 - 6y - 40$ $(y - 10)(y + 4)$

19. $2m^2 + 5m - 3$ $(m + 3)(2m - 1)$

20. $6n^2 + 7n - 3$ $(2n + 3)(3n - 1)$

21. $8k^2 - 6k - 9$ $(4k + 3)(2k - 3)$

22. $9h^2 - 3h - 2$ $(3h - 2)(3h + 1)$

23. $4k^2 - 20k + 25$ $(2k - 5)^2$

24. $16h^2 + 24h + 9$ $(4h + 3)^2$

25. $5x^2 + x + 7$ Prime

26. $4y^2 - y + 2$ Prime

27. $10 + 9z^2 - 21z$ $(3z - 5)(3z - 2)$

28. $13x + 4x^2 - 12$
$(4x - 3)(x + 4)$

29. $12y^2 + 8yz - 15z^2$
$(6y - 5z)(2y + 3z)$

30. $20a^2 + 3ab - 9b^2$
$(5a - 3b)(4a + 3b)$

For Exercises 31–38, factor completely. Be sure to factor out the GCF first. **(See Examples 3–4.)**

31. $50y + 24 + 14y^2$
$2(7y + 4)(y + 3)$

32. $-24 + 10w + 4w^2$
$2(2w - 3)(w + 4)$

33. $-15w^2 + 22w + 5$
$-(3w - 5)(5w + 1)$

34. $-16z^2 + 34z + 15$
$-(8z + 3)(2z - 5)$

35. $-12x^2 + 20xy - 8y^2$
$-4(x - y)(3x - 2y)$

36. $-6p^2 - 21pq - 9q^2$
$-3(2p + q)(p + 3q)$

37. $18y^3 + 60y^2 + 42y$
$6y(y + 1)(3y + 7)$

38. $8t^3 - 4t^2 - 40t$
$4t(2t - 5)(t + 2)$

For Exercises 39–44, factor the higher degree polynomial. **(See Example 6.)**

39. $a^4 + 5a^2 + 6$
$(a^2 + 2)(a^2 + 3)$

40. $y^4 - 2y^2 - 35$
$(y^2 + 5)(y^2 - 7)$

41. $6x^4 - x^2 - 15$
$(3x^2 - 5)(2x^2 + 3)$

42. $8t^4 + 2t^2 - 3$
$(4t^2 + 3)(2t^2 - 1)$

43. $8p^4 + 37p^2 - 15$
$(8p^2 - 3)(p^2 + 5)$

44. $2a^4 + 11a^2 + 14$
$(2a^2 + 7)(a^2 + 2)$

Mixed Exercises

For Exercises 45–80, factor completely.

45. $20p^2 - 19p + 3$ $(5p - 1)(4p - 3)$

46. $4p^2 + 5pq - 6q^2$ $(p + 2q)(4p - 3q)$

47. $6u^2 - 19uv + 10v^2$ $(3u - 2v)(2u - 5v)$

48. $15m^2 + mn - 2n^2$ $(5m + 2n)(3m - n)$

49. $12a^2 + 11ab - 5b^2$ $(4a + 5b)(3a - b)$

50. $3r^2 - rs - 14s^2$ $(r + 2s)(3r - 7s)$

51. $3h^2 + 19hk - 14k^2$ $(h + 7k)(3h - 2k)$

52. $2u^2 + uv - 15v^2$ $(2u - 5v)(u + 3v)$

53. $2x^2 - 13xy + y^2$ Prime

54. $3p^2 + 20pq - q^2$ Prime

55. $3 - 14z + 16z^2$ $(2z - 1)(8z - 3)$

56. $10w + 1 + 16w^2$ $(8w + 1)(2w + 1)$

57. $b^2 + 16 - 8b$ $(b - 4)^2$

58. $1 + q^2 - 2q$ $(q - 1)^2$

59. $25x - 5x^2 - 30$ $-5(x - 2)(x - 3)$

60. $20a - 18 - 2a^2$ $-2(a - 1)(a - 9)$

61. $-6 - t + t^2$ $(t - 3)(t + 2)$

62. $-6 + m + m^2$ $(m + 3)(m - 2)$

63. $v^2 + 2v + 15$ Prime

64. $x^2 - x - 1$ Prime

65. $72x^2 + 18x - 2$ $2(12x - 1)(3x + 1)$

66. $20y^2 - 78y - 8$ $2(10y + 1)(y - 4)$

67. $p^3 - 6p^2 - 27p$ $p(p + 3)(p - 9)$

68. $w^5 - 11w^4 + 28w^3$ $w^3(w - 4)(w - 7)$

69. $3x^3 + 10x^2 + 7x$ $x(3x + 7)(x + 1)$

70. $4r^3 + 3r^2 - 10r$ $r(4r - 5)(r + 2)$

71. $2p^3 - 38p^2 + 120p$ $2p(p - 15)(p - 4)$

72. $4q^3 - 4q^2 - 80q$ $4q(q - 5)(q + 4)$

73. $x^2y^2 + 14x^2y + 33x^2$ $x^2(y + 3)(y + 11)$

74. $a^2b^2 + 13ab^2 + 30b^2$ $b^2(a + 10)(a + 3)$

75. $-k^2 - 7k - 10$ $-(k + 2)(k + 5)$

76. $-m^2 - 15m + 34$ $-(m - 2)(m + 17)$

77. $-3n^2 - 3n + 90$ $-3(n + 6)(n - 5)$

78. $-2h^2 + 28h - 90$ $-2(h - 9)(h - 5)$

79. $x^4 - 7x^2 + 10$ $(x^2 - 2)(x^2 - 5)$

80. $m^4 + 10m^2 + 21$ $(m^2 + 3)(m^2 + 7)$

81. Is the expression $(2x + 4)(x - 7)$ factored completely? Explain why or why not.
No. $(2x + 4)$ contains a common factor of 2.

82. Is the expression $(3x + 1)(5x - 10)$ factored completely? Explain why or why not.
No. $(5x - 10)$ contains a common factor of 5.

83. Colleen noticed that the number of tables placed in her restaurant affects the number of customers who eat at the restaurant. The number of customers each night is given by $-2x^2 + 40x - 72$, where x is the number of tables set up in the room, and $2 \le x \le 18$.

a. Calculate the number of customers when there are 10 tables set up. $(x = 10)$
128 customers

b. Write $-2x^2 + 40x - 72$ in factored form. Then evaluate the factored form of the polynomial for $x = 10$. Is the result the same as from part (a)? $-2(x - 18)(x - 2)$; 128; Yes

84. Roland sells cases for smartphones online. He noticed that for every dollar he discounts the price, he sells two more cases per week. His income in dollars each week is given by $-2d^2 + 30d + 200$, where d is the dollar amount of the discount in price.

a. Calculate his income if the discount is \$2. $(d = 2)$ \$252

b. Write $-2d^2 + 30d + 200$ in factored form. Then evaluate the factored form of the polynomial for $d = 2$. Is the result the same as from part (a)?
$-2(d - 20)(d + 5)$; 252; Yes

85. A formula for finding the sum of the first n even integers is given by $n^2 + n$.

a. Find the sum of the first 6 even integers $(2 + 4 + 6 + 8 + 10 + 12)$ by evaluating the expression for $n = 6$. 42

b. Write the polynomial in factored form. Then evaluate the factored form of the expression for $n = 6$. Is the result the same as part (a)?
$n(n + 1)$; 42; Yes

86. A formula for finding the sum of the squares of the first n integers is given by $\frac{2n^3 + 3n^2 + n}{6}$.

a. Find the sum of the squares of the first 4 integers $(1^2 + 2^2 + 3^2 + 4^2)$ by evaluating the expression for $n = 4$. 30

b. Write the polynomial in the numerator of the expression in factored form. Then evaluate the factored form of the expression for $n = 4$. Is the result the same as part (a)?
$\frac{n(n + 1)(2n + 1)}{6}$; 30; Yes

Section 6.5 Difference of Squares and Perfect Square Trinomials

Concepts

1. Factoring a Difference of Squares
2. Factoring Perfect Square Trinomials

1. Factoring a Difference of Squares

Up to this point, we have learned several methods of factoring, including:

- Factoring out the greatest common factor from a polynomial
- Factoring a four-term polynomial by grouping
- Factoring trinomials by the ac-method or by the trial-and-error method

In this section, we will learn to factor polynomials that fit two special case patterns: a difference of squares, and a perfect square trinomial. First recall that the product of two conjugates results in a **difference of squares**:

$$(a + b)(a - b) = a^2 - b^2$$

Therefore, to factor a difference of squares, the process is reversed. Identify a and b and construct the conjugate factors.

Factored Form of a Difference of Squares

$$a^2 - b^2 = (a + b)(a - b)$$

To help recognize a difference of squares, we recommend that you become familiar with the first several perfect squares.

Perfect Squares	Perfect Squares	Perfect Squares
$1 = (1)^2$	$36 = (6)^2$	$121 = (11)^2$
$4 = (2)^2$	$49 = (7)^2$	$144 = (12)^2$
$9 = (3)^2$	$64 = (8)^2$	$169 = (13)^2$
$16 = (4)^2$	$81 = (9)^2$	$196 = (14)^2$
$25 = (5)^2$	$100 = (10)^2$	$225 = (15)^2$

It is also important to recognize that a variable expression is a perfect square if its exponent is a multiple of 2. For example:

Perfect Squares
$x^2 = (x)^2$
$x^4 = (x^2)^2$
$x^6 = (x^3)^2$
$x^8 = (x^4)^2$
$x^{10} = (x^5)^2$

Example 1 **Factoring Differences of Squares**

Classroom Examples: p. 453, Exercises 16 and 18

Factor the binomials.

a. $y^2 - 25$ **b.** $49s^2 - 4t^4$ **c.** $18w^2z - 2z$

Solution:

a. $y^2 - 25$ — The binomial is a difference of squares.

$= (y)^2 - (5)^2$ — Write in the form: $a^2 - b^2$, where $a = y$, $b = 5$.

$= (y + 5)(y - 5)$ — Factor as $(a + b)(a - b)$.

b. $49s^2 - 4t^4$ — The binomial is a difference of squares.

$= (7s)^2 - (2t^2)^2$ — Write in the form $a^2 - b^2$, where $a = 7s$ and $b = 2t^2$.

$= (7s + 2t^2)(7s - 2t^2)$ — Factor as $(a + b)(a - b)$.

c. $18w^2z - 2z$ — The GCF is $2z$.

$= 2z(9w^2 - 1)$ — $(9w^2 - 1)$ is a difference of squares.

$= 2z[(3w)^2 - (1)^2]$ — Write in the form: $a^2 - b^2$, where $a = 3w$, $b = 1$.

$= 2z(3w - 1)(3w + 1)$ — Factor as $(a - b)(a + b)$.

TIP: Recall that multiplication is commutative. Therefore,

$a^2 - b^2 = (a + b)(a - b)$

or $(a - b)(a + b)$.

Skill Practice Factor the binomials.

1. $a^2 - 64$ **2.** $25q^2 - 49w^2$ **3.** $98m^3n - 50mn$

The difference of squares $a^2 - b^2$ factors as $(a + b)(a - b)$. However, the *sum* of squares is not factorable.

Sum of Squares

Suppose a and b have no common factors. Then the **sum of squares** $a^2 + b^2$ is *not* factorable over the real numbers.

That is, $a^2 + b^2$ is prime over the real numbers.

To see why $a^2 + b^2$ is not factorable, consider the product of binomials:

$(a + b)(a - b) = a^2 - b^2$ — Wrong sign

$(a + b)(a + b) = a^2 + 2ab + b^2$ — Wrong middle term

$(a - b)(a - b) = a^2 - 2ab + b^2$ — Wrong middle term

After exhausting all possibilities, we see that if a and b share no common factors, then the sum of squares $a^2 + b^2$ is a prime polynomial.

Example 2 **Factoring Binomials**

Classroom Example: p. 453, Exercise 24

Factor the binomials, if possible. **a.** $p^2 - 9$ **b.** $p^2 + 9$

Solution:

a. $p^2 - 9$ — Difference of squares

$= (p - 3)(p + 3)$ — Factor as $a^2 - b^2 = (a - b)(a + b)$.

b. $p^2 + 9$ — Sum of squares

Prime (cannot be factored)

Answers

1. $(a + 8)(a - 8)$
2. $(5q + 7w)(5q - 7w)$
3. $2mn(7m + 5)(7m - 5)$

Skill Practice Factor the binomials, if possible.

4. $t^2 - 144$ **5.** $t^2 + 144$

Some factoring problems require several steps. Always be sure to factor completely.

Classroom Example: p. 453, Exercise 36

Example 3 Factoring a Difference of Squares

Factor completely. $w^4 - 81$

Solution:

$w^4 - 81$ The GCF is 1. $w^4 - 81$ is a difference of squares.

$= (w^2)^2 - (9)^2$ Write in the form: $a^2 - b^2$, where $a = w^2$, $b = 9$.

$= (w^2 + 9)(w^2 - 9)$ Factor as $(a + b)(a - b)$.

$= (w^2 + 9)(w + 3)(w - 3)$ Note that $w^2 - 9$ can be factored further as a difference of squares. (The binomial $w^2 + 9$ is a sum of squares and cannot be factored further.)

Skill Practice Factor completely.

6. $y^4 - 1$

Classroom Example: p. 453, Exercise 40

Example 4 Factoring a Polynomial

Factor completely. $y^3 - 5y^2 - 4y + 20$

Solution:

$y^3 - 5y^2 - 4y + 20$ The GCF is 1. The polynomial has four terms. Factor by grouping.

$= y^3 - 5y^2 \,\vdots\, - 4y + 20$

$= y^2(y - 5) - 4(y - 5)$

$= (y - 5)(y^2 - 4)$ The expression $y^2 - 4$ is a difference of squares and can be factored further as $(y - 2)(y + 2)$.

$= (y - 5)(y - 2)(y + 2)$

Check: $(y - 5)(y - 2)(y + 2) = (y - 5)(y^2 - 2y + 2y - 4)$

$= (y - 5)(y^2 - 4)$

$= (y^3 - 4y - 5y^2 + 20)$

$= y^3 - 5y^2 - 4y + 20$ ✓

Skill Practice Factor completely.

7. $p^3 + 7p^2 - 9p - 63$

2. Factoring Perfect Square Trinomials

Recall that the square of a binomial always results in a **perfect square trinomial**.

$$(a + b)^2 = (a + b)(a + b) \xrightarrow{\text{Multiply.}} = a^2 + 2ab + b^2$$

$$(a - b)^2 = (a - b)(a - b) \xrightarrow{\text{Multiply.}} = a^2 - 2ab + b^2$$

Answers

4. $(t - 12)(t + 12)$
5. Prime
6. $(y + 1)(y - 1)(y^2 + 1)$
7. $(p - 3)(p + 3)(p + 7)$

For example, $(3x + 5)^2 = (3x)^2 + 2(3x)(5) + (5)^2$

$= 9x^2 + 30x + 25$ (perfect square trinomial)

We now want to reverse this process by factoring a perfect square trinomial. The trial-and-error method or the ac-method can always be used; however, if we recognize the pattern for a perfect square trinomial, we can use one of the following formulas to reach a quick solution.

Factored Form of a Perfect Square Trinomial

$$a^2 + 2ab + b^2 = (a + b)^2$$
$$a^2 - 2ab + b^2 = (a - b)^2$$

For example, $4x^2 + 36x + 81$ is a perfect square trinomial with $a = 2x$ and $b = 9$. Therefore, it factors as

$$4x^2 + 36x + 81 = (2x)^2 + 2(2x)(9) + (9)^2 = (2x + 9)^2$$
$$a^2 \quad + \quad 2(a)(b) + (b)^2 = (a + b)^2$$

To apply the formula to factor a perfect square trinomial, we must first be sure that the trinomial is indeed a perfect square trinomial.

Checking for a Perfect Square Trinomial

Step 1 Determine whether the first and third terms are both perfect squares and have positive coefficients.

Step 2 If this is the case, identify a and b and determine if the middle term equals $2ab$ or $-2ab$.

Example 5 Factoring Perfect Square Trinomials

Classroom Examples: p. 454, Exercises 52 and 54

Factor the trinomials completely.

a. $x^2 + 14x + 49$ **b.** $25y^2 - 20y + 4$

Solution:

a. $x^2 + 14x + 49$ The GCF is 1.

- The first and third terms are positive.
- The first term is a perfect square: $x^2 = (x)^2$.
- The third term is a perfect square: $49 = (7)^2$.
- The middle term is twice the product of x and 7: $14x = 2(x)(7)$.

Perfect squares

$x^2 + 14x + 49$

$= (x)^2 + 2(x)(7) + (7)^2$ The trinomial is in the form $a^2 + 2ab + b^2$, where $a = x$ and $b = 7$.

$= (x + 7)^2$ Factor as $(a + b)^2$.

TIP: The sign of the middle term in a perfect square trinomial determines the sign within the binomial of the factored form.

$$a^2 + 2ab + b^2 = (a + b)^2$$
$$a^2 - 2ab + b^2 = (a - b)^2$$

b. $25y^2 - 20y + 4$ — The GCF is 1.

Perfect squares

- The first and third terms are positive.
- The first term is a perfect square: $25y^2 = (5y)^2$.
- The third term is a perfect square: $4 = (2)^2$.
- In the middle: $-20y = -2(5y)(2)$

$$25y^2 - 20y + 4$$
$$= (5y)^2 - 2(5y)(2) + (2)^2$$
$$= (5y - 2)^2$$

Factor as $(a - b)^2$.

Skill Practice Factor completely.

8. $x^2 - 6x + 9$ **9.** $81w^2 + 72w + 16$

Classroom Examples: p. 454, Exercises 60 and 62

Example 6 Factoring Perfect Square Trinomials

Factor the trinomials completely.

a. $18c^3 - 48c^2d + 32cd^2$ **b.** $5w^2 + 50w + 45$

Solution:

a. $18c^3 - 48c^2d + 32cd^2$

$$= 2c(9c^2 - 24cd + 16d^2)$$

The GCF is $2c$.

Perfect squares

$$= 2c(9c^2 - 24cd + 16d^2)$$

- The first and third terms are positive.
- The first term is a perfect square: $9c^2 = (3c)^2$.
- The third term is a perfect square: $16d^2 = (4d)^2$.
- In the middle: $-24cd = -2(3c)(4d)$

$$= 2c[(3c)^2 - 2(3c)(4d) + (4d)^2]$$
$$= 2c(3c - 4d)^2$$

Factor as $(a - b)^2$.

b. $5w^2 + 50w + 45$

$$= 5(w^2 + 10w + 9)$$

The GCF is 5.

Perfect squares

The first and third terms are perfect squares.

$$w^2 = (w)^2 \quad \text{and} \quad 9 = (3)^2$$

$$= 5(w^2 + 10w + 9)$$

However, the middle term is not 2 times the product of w and 3.

$$10w \neq 2(w)(3)$$

Therefore, this is not a perfect square trinomial.

$$= 5(w + 9)(w + 1)$$

To factor, use the trial-and-error method.

TIP: If you do not recognize that a trinomial is a perfect square trinomial, you can still use the trial-and-error method or ac-method to factor it.

Skill Practice Factor completely.

10. $5z^3 + 20z^2w + 20zw^2$ **11.** $40x^2 + 130x + 90$

Answers

8. $(x - 3)^2$
9. $(9w + 4)^2$
10. $5z(z + 2w)^2$
11. $10(4x + 9)(x + 1)$

Section 6.5 Practice Exercises

For additional exercises, see Classroom Activities 6.5A–6.5B in the *Student's Resource Manual* at www.mhhe.com/moh.

Vocabulary and Key Concepts

1. a. The binomial $x^2 - 16$ is an example of a difference of squares. After factoring out the GCF, we factor a difference of squares $a^2 - b^2$ as $(a + b)(a - b)$.

   b. The binomial $y^2 + 121$ is an example of a sum of squares.

   c. A sum of squares with greatest common factor 1 (is/is not) factorable over the real numbers. is not

   d. The square of a binomial always results in a perfect square trinomial.

   e. A perfect square trinomial $a^2 + 2ab + b^2$ factors as $(a + b)^2$. Likewise, $a^2 - 2ab + b^2$ factors as $(a - b)^2$.

Review Exercises

For Exercises 2–10, factor completely.

2. $3x^2 + x - 10$ $(3x - 5)(x + 2)$
3. $6x^2 - 17x + 5$ $(3x - 1)(2x - 5)$
4. $6a^2b + 3a^3b$ $3a^2b(2 + a)$
5. $15x^2y^5 - 10xy^6$ $5xy^5(3x - 2y)$
6. $5p^2q + 20p^2 - 3pq - 12p$ $p(5p - 3)(q + 4)$
7. $ax + ab - 6x - 6b$ $(x + b)(a - 6)$
8. $-6x + 5 + x^2$ $(x - 1)(x - 5)$
9. $6y - 40 + y^2$ $(y + 10)(y - 4)$
10. $a^2 + 7a + 1$ Prime

Concept 1: Factoring a Difference of Squares

11. What binomial factors as $(x - 5)(x + 5)$? $x^2 - 25$
12. What binomial factors as $(n - 3)(n + 3)$? $n^2 - 9$
13. What binomial factors as $(2p - 3q)(2p + 3q)$? $4p^2 - 9q^2$
14. What binomial factors as $(7x - 4y)(7x + 4y)$? $49x^2 - 16y^2$

For Exercises 15–38, factor each binomial completely. **(See Examples 1–3.)**

15. $x^2 - 36$ $(x - 6)(x + 6)$
16. $r^2 - 81$ $(r - 9)(r + 9)$
17. $3w^2 - 300$ $3(w + 10)(w - 10)$
18. $t^3 - 49t$ $t(t + 7)(t - 7)$
19. $4a^2 - 121b^2$ $(2a - 11b)(2a + 11b)$
20. $9x^2 - y^2$ $(3x - y)(3x + y)$
21. $49m^2 - 16n^2$ $(7m - 4n)(7m + 4n)$
22. $100a^2 - 49b^2$ $(10a - 7b)(10a + 7b)$
23. $9q^2 + 16$ Prime
24. $36 + s^2$ Prime
25. $y^2 - 4z^2$ $(y + 2z)(y - 2z)$
26. $b^2 - 144c^2$ $(b + 12c)(b - 12c)$
27. $a^2 - b^4$ $(a - b^2)(a + b^2)$
28. $y^4 - x^2$ $(y^2 - x)(y^2 + x)$
29. $25p^2q^2 - 1$ $(5pq - 1)(5pq + 1)$
30. $81s^2t^2 - 1$ $(9st - 1)(9st + 1)$
31. $c^2 - \frac{1}{25}$ $\left(c - \frac{1}{5}\right)\left(c + \frac{1}{5}\right)$
32. $z^2 - \frac{1}{4}$ $\left(z - \frac{1}{2}\right)\left(z + \frac{1}{2}\right)$
33. $50 - 32t^2$ $2(5 - 4t)(5 + 4t)$
34. $63 - 7h^2$ $7(3 - h)(3 + h)$
35. $x^4 - 256$ $(x + 4)(x - 4)(x^2 + 16)$
36. $y^4 - 625$ $(y + 5)(y - 5)(y^2 + 25)$
37. $16 - z^4$ $(2 - z)(2 + z)(4 + z^2)$
38. $81 - a^4$ $(3 - a)(3 + a)(9 + a^2)$

For Exercises 39–46, factor each polynomial completely. **(See Example 4.)**

39. $x^3 + 5x^2 - 9x - 45$ $(x + 5)(x + 3)(x - 3)$
40. $y^3 + 6y^2 - 4y - 24$ $(y + 6)(y + 2)(y - 2)$
41. $c^3 - c^2 - 25c + 25$ $(c - 1)(c + 5)(c - 5)$
42. $t^3 + 2t^2 - 16t - 32$ $(t + 2)(t + 4)(t - 4)$
43. $2x^2 - 18 + x^2y - 9y$ $(x + 3)(x - 3)(2 + y)$
44. $5a^2 - 5 + a^2b - b$ $(a + 1)(a - 1)(5 + b)$
45. $x^2y^2 - 9x^2 - 4y^2 + 36$ $(y + 3)(y - 3)(x + 2)(x - 2)$
46. $w^2z^2 - w^2 - 25z^2 + 25$ $(z + 1)(z - 1)(w + 5)(w - 5)$

Concept 2: Factoring Perfect Square Trinomials

47. Multiply. $(3x + 5)^2$ $9x^2 + 30x + 25$
48. Multiply. $(2y - 7)^2$ $4y^2 - 28y + 49$

49. **a.** Which trinomial is a perfect square trinomial? $x^2 + 4x + 4$ or $x^2 + 5x + 4$
a. $x^2 + 4x + 4$ is a perfect square trinomial.
b. Factor the trinomials from part (a).
b. $x^2 + 4x + 4 = (x + 2)^2$; $x^2 + 5x + 4 = (x + 1)(x + 4)$

50. **a.** Which trinomial is a perfect square trinomial? $x^2 + 13x + 36$ or $x^2 + 12x + 36$
a. $x^2 + 12x + 36$ is a perfect square trinomial.
b. Factor the trinomials from part (a).
b. $x^2 + 13x + 36 = (x + 9)(x + 4)$; $x^2 + 12x + 36 = (x + 6)^2$

For Exercises 51–68, factor completely. (*Hint:* Look for the pattern of a perfect square trinomial.) **(See Examples 5–6.)**

51. $x^2 + 18x + 81$
$(x + 9)^2$

52. $y^2 - 8y + 16$
$(y - 4)^2$

53. $25z^2 - 20z + 4$
$(5z - 2)^2$

54. $36p^2 + 60p + 25$
$(6p + 5)^2$

55. $49a^2 + 42ab + 9b^2$
$(7a + 3b)^2$

56. $25m^2 - 30mn + 9n^2$
$(5m - 3n)^2$

57. $-2y + y^2 + 1$
$(y - 1)^2$

58. $4 + w^2 - 4w$
$(w - 2)^2$

59. $80z^2 + 120zw + 45w^2$
$5(4z + 3w)^2$

60. $36p^2 - 24pq + 4q^2$
$4(3p - q)^2$

61. $9y^2 + 78y + 25$
$(3y + 25)(3y + 1)$

62. $4y^2 + 20y + 9$
$(2y + 9)(2y + 1)$

63. $2a^2 - 20a + 50$
$2(a - 5)^2$

64. $3t^2 + 18t + 27$
$3(t + 3)^2$

65. $4x^2 + x + 9$
Prime

66. $c^2 - 4c + 16$
Prime

67. $4x^2 + 4xy + y^2$
$(2x + y)^2$

68. $100y^2 + 20yz + z^2$
$(10y + z)^2$

69. The volume of the box shown is given as $3x^3 - 6x^2 + 3x$. Write the polynomial in factored form.
$3x(x - 1)^2$

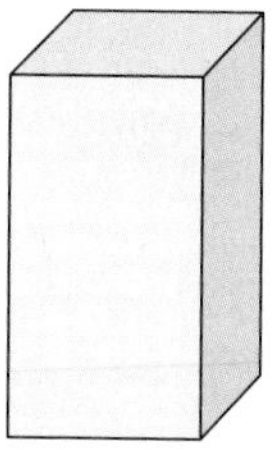

70. The volume of the box shown is given as $20y^3 + 20y^2 + 5y$. Write the polynomial in factored form.
$5y(2y + 1)^2$

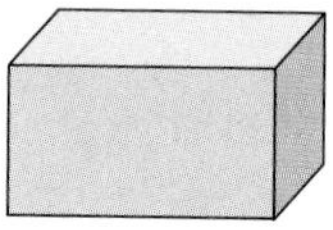

Expanding Your Skills

For Exercises 71–78, factor the difference of squares.

71. $(y - 3)^2 - 9$
$y(y - 6)$

72. $(x - 2)^2 - 4$
$x(x - 4)$

73. $(2p + 1)^2 - 36$
$(2p - 5)(2p + 7)$

74. $(4q + 3)^2 - 25$
$8(2q - 1)(q + 2)$

75. $16 - (t + 2)^2$
$(-t + 2)(t + 6)$ or $-(t - 2)(t + 6)$

76. $81 - (a + 5)^2$
$(-a + 4)(a + 14)$ or $-(a - 4)(a + 14)$

77. $(2a - 5)^2 - 100b^2$
$(2a - 5 + 10b)(2a - 5 - 10b)$

78. $(3k + 7)^2 - 49m^2$
$(3k + 7 + 7m)(3k + 7 - 7m)$

79. **a.** Write a polynomial that represents the area of the shaded region in the figure.
$a^2 - b^2$
b. Factor the expression from part (a).
$(a - b)(a + b)$

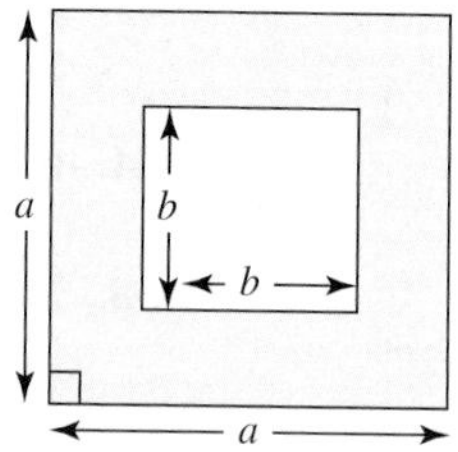

80. **a.** Write a polynomial that represents the area of the shaded region in the figure. $g^2 - h^2$
b. Factor the expression from part (a).
$(g - h)(g + h)$

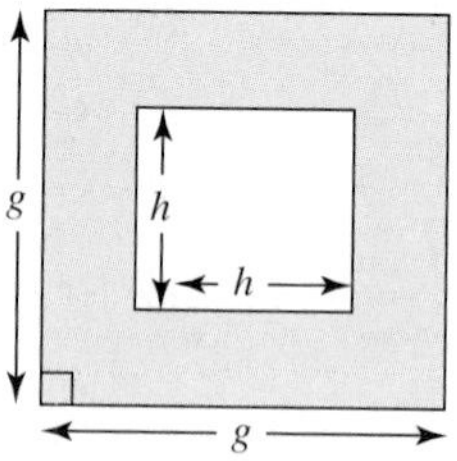

Section 6.6 Sum and Difference of Cubes

Concepts

1. Factoring a Sum or Difference of Cubes
2. Factoring Binomials: A Summary

1. Factoring a Sum or Difference of Cubes

A binomial $a^2 - b^2$ is a difference of squares and can be factored as $(a - b)(a + b)$. Furthermore, if a and b share no common factors, then a sum of squares $a^2 + b^2$ is not factorable over the real numbers. In this section, we will learn that both a difference of cubes, $a^3 - b^3$, and a sum of cubes, $a^3 + b^3$, are factorable.

Factored Form of a Sum or Difference of Cubes

Sum of Cubes: $a^3 + b^3 = (a + b)(a^2 - ab + b^2)$

Difference of Cubes: $a^3 - b^3 = (a - b)(a^2 + ab + b^2)$

Multiplication can be used to confirm the formulas for factoring a sum or difference of cubes:

$$(a + b)(a^2 - ab + b^2) = a^3 - \cancel{a^2b} + \cancel{ab^2} + \cancel{a^2b} - \cancel{ab^2} + b^3 = a^3 + b^3 \checkmark$$

$$(a - b)(a^2 + ab + b^2) = a^3 + \cancel{a^2b} + \cancel{ab^2} - \cancel{a^2b} - \cancel{ab^2} - b^3 = a^3 - b^3 \checkmark$$

To help you remember the formulas for factoring a sum or difference of cubes, keep the following guidelines in mind:

- The factored form is the product of a binomial and a trinomial.
- The first and third terms in the trinomial are the squares of the terms within the binomial factor.
- Without regard to signs, the middle term in the trinomial is the product of terms in the binomial factor.

Square the first term of the binomial. Product of terms in the binomial

$$x^3 + 8 = (x)^3 + (2)^3 = (x + 2)[(x)^2 - (x)(2) + (2)^2]$$

Square the last term of the binomial.

- The sign within the binomial factor is the same as the sign of the original binomial.
- The first and third terms in the trinomial are always positive.
- The sign of the middle term in the trinomial is opposite the sign within the binomial.

TIP: To help remember the placement of the signs in factoring the sum or difference of cubes, remember SOAP: **S**ame sign, **O**pposite signs, **A**lways **P**ositive.

Same sign Positive

$$x^3 + 8 = (x)^3 + (2)^3 = (x + 2)[(x)^2 - (x)(2) + (2)^2]$$

Opposite signs

To help you recognize a sum or difference of cubes, we recommend that you familiarize yourself with the first several perfect cubes:

Perfect Cubes	Perfect Cubes
$1 = (1)^3$	$216 = (6)^3$
$8 = (2)^3$	$343 = (7)^3$
$27 = (3)^3$	$512 = (8)^3$
$64 = (4)^3$	$729 = (9)^3$
$125 = (5)^3$	$1000 = (10)^3$

It is also helpful to recognize that a variable expression is a perfect cube if its exponent is a multiple of 3. For example:

Perfect Cubes
$x^3 = (x)^3$
$x^6 = (x^2)^3$
$x^9 = (x^3)^3$
$x^{12} = (x^4)^3$

Classroom Example: p. 459, Exercise 16

Example 1 **Factoring a Sum of Cubes**

Factor. $w^3 + 64$

Solution:

$w^3 + 64$ — w^3 and 64 are perfect cubes.

$= (w)^3 + (4)^3$ — Write as $a^3 + b^3$, where $a = w$, $b = 4$.

$a^3 + b^3 = (a + b)(a^2 - ab + b^2)$ — Apply the formula for a sum of cubes.

$(w)^3 + (4)^3 = (w + 4)[(w)^2 - (w)(4) + (4)^2]$

$= (w + 4)(w^2 - 4w + 16)$ — Simplify.

Skill Practice Factor.

1. $p^3 + 125$

Classroom Example: p. 459, Exercise 26

Example 2 **Factoring a Difference of Cubes**

Factor. $27p^3 - 1000q^3$

Solution:

$27p^3 - 1000q^3$ — $27p^3$ and $1000q^3$ are perfect cubes.

$= (3p)^3 - (10q)^3$ — Write as $a^3 - b^3$, where $a = 3p$, $b = 10q$.

$a^3 - b^3 = (a - b)(a^2 + ab + b^2)$ — Apply the formula for a difference of cubes.

$(3p)^3 - (10q)^3 = (3p - 10q)[(3p)^2 + (3p)(10q) + (10q)^2]$

$= (3p - 10q)(9p^2 + 30pq + 100q^2)$ — Simplify.

Skill Practice Factor.

2. $8y^3 - 27z^3$

2. Factoring Binomials: A Summary

After removing the GCF, the next step in any factoring problem is to recognize what type of pattern it follows. Exponents that are divisible by 2 are perfect squares and those divisible by 3 are perfect cubes. The formulas for factoring binomials are summarized in the following box:

Factored Forms of Binomials

Difference of Squares: $a^2 - b^2 = (a + b)(a - b)$

Difference of Cubes: $a^3 - b^3 = (a - b)(a^2 + ab + b^2)$

Sum of Cubes: $a^3 + b^3 = (a + b)(a^2 - ab + b^2)$

Classroom Examples: p. 460, Exercises 48 and 52

Example 3 **Factoring Binomials**

Factor completely.

a. $27y^3 + 1$ **b.** $\frac{1}{25}m^2 - \frac{1}{4}$ **c.** $z^6 - 8w^3$

Answers

1. $(p + 5)(p^2 - 5p + 25)$
2. $(2y - 3z)(4y^2 + 6yz + 9z^2)$

Solution:

a. $27y^3 + 1$ Sum of cubes: $27y^3 = (3y)^3$ and $1 = (1)^3$.

$= (3y)^3 + (1)^3$ Write as $a^3 + b^3$, where $a = 3y$ and $b = 1$.

$= (3y + 1)[(3y)^2 - (3y)(1) + (1)^2]$ Apply the formula $a^3 + b^3 = (a + b)(a^2 - ab + b^2)$.

$= (3y + 1)(9y^2 - 3y + 1)$ Simplify.

b. $\frac{1}{25}m^2 - \frac{1}{4}$ Difference of squares

$= \left(\frac{1}{5}m\right)^2 - \left(\frac{1}{2}\right)^2$ Write as $a^2 - b^2$, where $a = \frac{1}{5}m$ and $b = \frac{1}{2}$.

$= \left(\frac{1}{5}m + \frac{1}{2}\right)\left(\frac{1}{5}m - \frac{1}{2}\right)$ Apply the formula $a^2 - b^2 = (a + b)(a - b)$.

c. $z^6 - 8w^3$ Difference of cubes: $z^6 = (z^2)^3$ and $8w^3 = (2w)^3$

$= (z^2)^3 - (2w)^3$ Write as $a^3 - b^3$, where $a = z^2$ and $b = 2w$.

$= (z^2 - 2w)[(z^2)^2 + (z^2)(2w) + (2w)^2]$ Apply the formula $a^3 - b^3 = (a - b)(a^2 + ab + b^2)$.

$= (z^2 - 2w)(z^4 + 2z^2w + 4w^2)$ Simplify.

Each factorization in this example can be checked by multiplying.

Skill Practice Factor completely.

3. $1000x^3 + 1$ **4.** $25p^2 - \frac{1}{9}$ **5.** $27a^6 - b^3$

Some factoring problems require more than one method of factoring. In general, when factoring a polynomial, be sure to factor completely.

Example 4 Factoring a Polynomial

Classroom Example: p. 460, Exercise 58

Factor completely. $3y^4 - 48$

Solution:

$3y^4 - 48$

$= 3(y^4 - 16)$ Factor out the GCF. The binomial is a difference of squares.

$= 3[(y^2)^2 - (4)^2]$ Write as $a^2 - b^2$, where $a = y^2$ and $b = 4$.

$= 3(y^2 + 4)(y^2 - 4)$ Apply the formula $a^2 - b^2 = (a + b)(a - b)$.

$y^2 + 4$ is a sum of squares and cannot be factored.

$= 3(y^2 + 4)(y + 2)(y - 2)$ $y^2 - 4$ is a difference of squares and can be factored further.

Skill Practice Factor completely.

6. $2x^4 - 2$

Answers

3. $(10x + 1)(100x^2 - 10x + 1)$

4. $\left(5p - \frac{1}{3}\right)\left(5p + \frac{1}{3}\right)$

5. $(3a^2 - b)(9a^4 + 3a^2b + b^2)$

6. $2(x^2 + 1)(x - 1)(x + 1)$

Classroom Example: p. 460, Exercise 64

Example 5 **Factoring a Polynomial**

Factor completely. $4x^3 + 4x^2 - 25x - 25$

Solution:

$4x^3 + 4x^2 - 25x - 25$ — The GCF is 1.

$= 4x^3 + 4x^2 \mid - 25x - 25$ — The polynomial has four terms. Factor by grouping.

$= 4x^2(x + 1) - 25(x + 1)$

$= (x + 1)(4x^2 - 25)$ — $4x^2 - 25$ is a difference of squares.

$= (x + 1)(2x + 5)(2x - 5)$

Skill Practice Factor completely.

7. $x^3 + 6x^2 - 4x - 24$

Classroom Example: p. 460, Exercise 50

Example 6 **Factoring a Binomial**

Factor the binomial $x^6 - y^6$ as

a. A difference of cubes **b.** A difference of squares

Notice that the expressions x^6 and y^6 are both perfect squares and perfect cubes because both exponents are multiples of 2 and of 3. Consequently, $x^6 - y^6$ can be factored initially as either the difference of squares or as the difference of cubes.

Solution:

a. $x^6 - y^6$

Difference of cubes

$= (x^2)^3 - (y^2)^3$ — Write as $a^3 - b^3$, where $a = x^2$ and $b = y^2$.

$= (x^2 - y^2)[(x^2)^2 + (x^2)(y^2) + (y^2)^2]$ — Apply the formula $a^3 - b^3 = (a - b)(a^2 + ab + b^2)$.

$= (x^2 - y^2)(x^4 + x^2y^2 + y^4)$ — Factor $x^2 - y^2$ as a difference of squares.

$= (x + y)(x - y)(x^4 + x^2y^2 + y^4)$

Avoiding Mistakes

The trinomial $x^4 + x^2y^2 + y^4$ cannot be factored further with the techniques presented in this chapter.

b. $x^6 - y^6$

Difference of squares

$= (x^3)^2 - (y^3)^2$ — Write as $a^2 - b^2$, where $a = x^3$ and $b = y^3$.

$= (x^3 + y^3)(x^3 - y^3)$ — Apply the formula $a^2 - b^2 = (a + b)(a - b)$.

Sum of cubes — Factor $x^3 + y^3$ as a sum of cubes.

Difference of cubes — Factor $x^3 - y^3$ as a difference of cubes.

$= (x + y)(x^2 - xy + y^2)(x - y)(x^2 + xy + y^2)$

Answer

7. $(x + 6)(x + 2)(x - 2)$

In a case such as this, it is recommended that you factor the expression as a difference of squares first because it factors more completely into polynomials of lower degree.

$$x^6 - y^6 = (x + y)(x^2 - xy + y^2)(x - y)(x^2 + xy + y^2)$$

Skill Practice Factor completely.

8. $z^6 - 64$

Answer

8. $(z + 2)(z - 2)(z^2 + 2z + 4)(z^2 - 2z + 4)$

Section 6.6 Practice Exercises

For additional exercises, see Classroom Activities 6.6A–6.6B in the *Student's Resource Manual* at www.mhhe.com/moh.

Vocabulary and Key Concepts

1. a. The binomial $x^3 + 27$ is an example of a ___sum___ of ___cubes___.

b. The binomial $c^3 - 8$ is an example of a ___difference___ of ___cubes___.

c. A difference of cubes $a^3 - b^3$ factors as $(a - b)(a^2 + ab + b^2)$.

d. A sum of cubes $a^3 + b^3$ factors as $(a + b)(a^2 - ab + b^2)$.

Review Exercises

For Exercises 2–10, factor completely.

2. $600 - 6x^2$
$6(10 - x)(10 + x)$

3. $20 - 5t^2$
$5(2 - t)(2 + t)$

4. $ax + bx + 5a + 5b$
$(a + b)(x + 5)$

5. $2t + 2u + st + su$
$(t + u)(2 + s)$

6. $5y^2 + 13y - 6$
$(5y - 2)(y + 3)$

7. $3v^2 + 5v - 12$
$(3v - 4)(v + 3)$

8. $40a^3b^3 - 16a^2b^2 + 24a^3b$
$8a^2b(5ab^2 - 2b + 3a)$

9. $-c^2 - 10c - 25$
$-(c + 5)^2$

10. $-z^2 + 6z - 9$
$-(z - 3)^2$

Concept 1: Factoring a Sum or Difference of Cubes

11. Identify the expressions that are perfect cubes:
$x^3, 8, 9, y^6, a^4, b^2, 3p^3, 27q^3, w^{12}, r^3s^6$
$x^3, 8, y^6, 27q^3, w^{12}, r^3s^6$

12. Identify the expressions that are perfect cubes:
$z^9, -81, 30, 8, 6x^3, y^{15}, 27a^3, b^2, p^3q^2, -1$
$z^9, 8, y^{15}, 27a^3, -1$

13. Identify the expressions that are perfect cubes:
$36, t^3, -1, 27, a^3b^6, -9, 125, -8x^2, y^6, 25$
$t^3, -1, 27, a^3b^6, 125, y^6$

14. Identify the expressions that are perfect cubes:
$343, 15b^3, z^3, w^{12}, -p^9, -1000, a^2b^3, 3x^3, -8, 60$
$343, z^3, w^{12}, -p^9, -1000, -8$

For Exercises 15–30, factor the sums or differences of cubes. **(See Examples 1–2.)**

15. $y^3 - 8$
$(y - 2)(y^2 + 2y + 4)$

16. $x^3 + 27$
$(x + 3)(x^2 - 3x + 9)$

17. $1 - p^3$
$(1 - p)(1 + p + p^2)$

18. $q^3 + 1$
$(q + 1)(q^2 - q + 1)$

19. $w^3 + 64$
$(w + 4)(w^2 - 4w + 16)$

20. $8 - t^3$
$(2 - t)(4 + 2t + t^2)$

21. $x^3 - 1000y^3$
$(x - 10y)(x^2 + 10xy + 100y^2)$

22. $8r^3 - 27t^3$
$(2r - 3t)(4r^2 + 6rt + 9t^2)$

23. $64t^3 + 1$
$(4t + 1)(16t^2 - 4t + 1)$

24. $125r^3 + 1$
$(5r + 1)(25r^2 - 5r + 1)$

25. $1000a^3 + 27$
$(10a + 3)(100a^2 - 30a + 9)$

26. $216b^3 - 125$
$(6b - 5)(36b^2 + 30b + 25)$

27. $n^3 - \frac{1}{8}$
$\left(n - \frac{1}{2}\right)\left(n^2 + \frac{1}{2}n + \frac{1}{4}\right)$

28. $\frac{8}{27} + m^3$
$\left(\frac{2}{3} + m\right)\left(\frac{4}{9} - \frac{2}{3}m + m^2\right)$

29. $125x^3 + 8y^3$
$(5x + 2y)(25x^2 - 10xy + 4y^2)$

30. $27t^3 + 64u^3$
$(3t + 4u)(9t^2 - 12tu + 16u^2)$

Concept 2: Factoring Binomials: A Summary

For Exercises 31–66, factor completely. **(See Examples 3–6.)**

31. $x^4 - 4$ $(x^2 - 2)(x^2 + 2)$

32. $b^4 - 25$ $(b^2 - 5)(b^2 + 5)$

33. $a^2 + 9$ Prime

34. $w^2 + 36$ Prime

35. $t^3 + 64$ $(t + 4)(t^2 - 4t + 16)$

36. $u^3 + 27$ $(u + 3)(u^2 - 3u + 9)$

37. $g^3 - 4$ Prime

38. $h^3 - 25$ Prime

39. $4b^3 + 108$ $4(b + 3)(b^2 - 3b + 9)$

40. $3c^3 - 24$ $3(c - 2)(c^2 + 2c + 4)$

41. $5p^2 - 125$ $5(p - 5)(p + 5)$

42. $2q^4 - 8$ $2(q^2 - 2)(q^2 + 2)$

43. $\frac{1}{64} - 8h^3$ $(\frac{1}{4} - 2h)(\frac{1}{16} + \frac{1}{2}h + 4h^2)$

44. $\frac{1}{125} + k^6$ $(\frac{1}{5} + k^2)(\frac{1}{25} - \frac{1}{5}k^2 + k^4)$

45. $x^4 - 16$ $(x - 2)(x + 2)(x^2 + 4)$

46. $p^4 - 81$ $(p - 3)(p + 3)(p^2 + 9)$

47. $\frac{4}{9}x^2 - w^2$ $\left(\frac{2}{3}x - w\right)\left(\frac{2}{3}x + w\right)$

48. $\frac{16}{25}y^2 - x^2$ $\left(\frac{4}{5}y - x\right)\left(\frac{4}{5}y + x\right)$

49. $q^6 - 64$ $(q - 2)(q^2 + 2q + 4)(q + 2)(q^2 - 2q + 4)$

50. $a^6 - 1$ $(a - 1)(a^2 + a + 1)$ $(a + 1)(a^2 - a + 1)$

(*Hint:* Factor using the difference of squares first.)

51. $x^9 + 64y^3$ $(x^3 + 4y)(x^6 - 4x^3y + 16y^2)$

52. $125w^3 - z^9$ $(5w - z^3)(25w^2 + 5wz^3 + z^6)$

53. $2x^3 + 3x^2 - 2x - 3$ $(2x + 3)(x - 1)(x + 1)$

54. $3x^3 + x^2 - 12x - 4$ $(3x + 1)(x - 2)(x + 2)$

55. $16x^4 - y^4$ $(2x - y)(2x + y)(4x^2 + y^2)$

56. $1 - t^4$ $(1 - t)(1 + t)(1 + t^2)$

57. $81y^4 - 16$ $(3y - 2)(3y + 2)(9y^2 + 4)$

58. $u^5 - 256u$ $u(u - 4)(u + 4)(u^2 + 16)$

59. $a^3 + b^6$ $(a + b^2)(a^2 - ab^2 + b^4)$

60. $u^6 - v^3$ $(u^2 - v)(u^4 + u^2v + v^2)$

61. $x^4 - y^4$ $(x^2 + y^2)(x - y)(x + y)$

62. $a^4 - b^4$ $(a^2 + b^2)(a - b)(a + b)$

63. $k^3 + 4k^2 - 9k - 36$ $(k + 4)(k - 3)(k + 3)$

64. $w^3 - 2w^2 - 4w + 8$ $(w - 2)^2(w + 2)$

65. $2t^3 - 10t^2 - 2t + 10$ $2(t - 5)(t - 1)(t + 1)$

66. $9a^3 + 27a^2 - 4a - 12$ $(a + 3)(3a - 2)(3a + 2)$

Expanding Your Skills

For Exercises 67–70, factor completely.

67. $\frac{64}{125}p^3 - \frac{1}{8}q^3$ $\left(\frac{4}{5}p - \frac{1}{2}q\right)\left(\frac{16}{25}p^2 + \frac{2}{5}pq + \frac{1}{4}q^2\right)$

68. $\frac{1}{1000}r^3 + \frac{8}{27}s^3$ $\left(\frac{1}{10}r + \frac{2}{3}s\right)\left(\frac{1}{100}r^2 - \frac{1}{15}rs + \frac{4}{9}s^2\right)$

69. $a^{12} + b^{12}$ $(a^4 + b^4)(a^8 - a^4b^4 + b^8)$

70. $a^9 - b^9$ $(a - b)(a^2 + ab + b^2)(a^6 + a^3b^3 + b^6)$

Use Exercises 71–72 to investigate the relationship between division and factoring.

71. **a.** Use long division to divide $x^3 - 8$ by $(x - 2)$. The quotient is $x^2 + 2x + 4$.

b. Factor $x^3 - 8$. $(x - 2)(x^2 + 2x + 4)$

72. **a.** Use long division to divide $y^3 + 27$ by $(y + 3)$. The quotient is $y^2 - 3y + 9$.

b. Factor $y^3 + 27$. $(y + 3)(y^2 - 3y + 9)$

73. What trinomial multiplied by $(x - 4)$ gives a difference of cubes? $x^2 + 4x + 16$

74. What trinomial multiplied by $(p + 5)$ gives a sum of cubes? $p^2 - 5p + 25$

75. Write a binomial that when multiplied by $(4x^2 - 2x + 1)$ produces a sum of cubes. $2x + 1$

76. Write a binomial that when multiplied by $(9y^2 + 15y + 25)$ produces a difference of cubes. $3y - 5$

Problem Recognition Exercises

Factoring Strategy

Factoring Strategy

Step 1 Factor out the GCF.

Step 2 Identify whether the polynomial has two terms, three terms, or more than three terms.

Step 3 If the polynomial has more than three terms, try factoring by grouping.

Step 4 If the polynomial has three terms, check first for a perfect square trinomial. Otherwise, factor the trinomial with the trial-and-error method or the ac-method.

Step 5 If the polynomial has two terms, determine if it fits the pattern for

- A difference of squares: $a^2 - b^2 = (a - b)(a + b)$
- A sum of squares: $a^2 + b^2$ is prime.
- A difference of cubes: $a^3 - b^3 = (a - b)(a^2 + ab + b^2)$
- A sum of cubes: $a^3 + b^3 = (a + b)(a^2 - ab + b^2)$

Step 6 Be sure to factor the polynomial completely.

Step 7 Check by multiplying.

1. What is meant by a prime polynomial? A prime polynomial cannot be factored further.

2. What is the first step in factoring any polynomial? Factor out the GCF.

3. When factoring a binomial, what patterns can you look for? Look for a difference of squares: $a^2 - b^2$, a difference of cubes: $a^3 - b^3$, or a sum of cubes: $a^3 + b^3$.

4. What technique should be considered when factoring a four-term polynomial? Grouping

For Exercises 5–73,

a. Factor out the GCF from each polynomial. Then identify the category in which the remaining polynomial best fits. Choose from

- difference of squares
- sum of squares
- difference of cubes
- sum of cubes
- trinomial (perfect square trinomial)
- trinomial (nonperfect square trinomial)
- four terms-grouping
- none of these

Instructor Note: The following exercises involve a sum or difference of cubes: 10, 12, 13, 18, 23, 28, 29.

b. Factor the polynomial completely.

5. $2a^2 - 162$ a. Difference of squares b. $2(a - 9)(a + 9)$

6. $y^2 + 4y + 3$ a. Nonperfect square trinomial b. $(y + 3)(y + 1)$

7. $6w^2 - 6w$ a. None of these b. $6w(w - 1)$

8. $16z^4 - 81$ a. Difference of squares b. $(2z + 3)(2z - 3)(4z^2 + 9)$

9. $3t^2 + 13t + 4$ a. Nonperfect square trinomial b. $(3t + 1)(t + 4)$

10. $5r^3 + 5$ a. Sum of cubes b. $5(r + 1)(r^2 - r + 1)$

11. $3ac + ad - 3bc - bd$ a. Four terms-grouping b. $(3c + d)(a - b)$

12. $x^3 - 125$ a. Difference of cubes b. $(x - 5)(x^2 + 5x + 25)$

13. $y^3 + 8$ a. Sum of cubes b. $(y + 2)(y^2 - 2y + 4)$

14. $7p^2 - 29p + 4$ a. Nonperfect square trinomial b. $(7p - 1)(p - 4)$

15. $3q^2 - 9q - 12$ a. Nonperfect square trinomial b. $3(q - 4)(q + 1)$

16. $-2x^2 + 8x - 8$ a. Perfect square trinomial b. $-2(x - 2)^2$

17. $18a^2 + 12a$
a. None of these
b. $6a(3a + 2)$

18. $54 - 2y^3$
a. Difference of cubes
b. $2(3 - y)(9 + 3y + y^2)$

19. $4t^2 - 100$
a. Difference of squares
b. $4(t - 5)(t + 5)$

20. $4t^2 - 31t - 8$
a. Nonperfect square trinomial
b. $(4t + 1)(t - 8)$

21. $10c^2 + 10c + 10$
a. Nonperfect square trinomial
b. $10(c^2 + c + 1)$

22. $2xw - 10x + 3yw - 15y$
a. Four terms-grouping
b. $(w - 5)(2x + 3y)$

23. $x^3 + 0.001$
a. Sum of cubes
b. $(x + 0.1)(x^2 - 0.1x + 0.01)$

24. $4q^2 - 9$
a. Difference of squares
b. $(2q - 3)(2q + 3)$

25. $64 + 16k + k^2$
a. Perfect square trinomial
b. $(8 + k)^2$

26. $s^2t + 5t + 6s^2 + 30$
a. Four terms-grouping
b. $(t + 6)(s^2 + 5)$

27. $2x^2 + 2x - xy - y$
a. Four terms-grouping
b. $(x + 1)(2x - y)$

28. $w^3 + y^3$
a. Sum of cubes
b. $(w + y)(w^2 - wy + y^2)$

29. $a^3 - c^3$
a. Difference of cubes
b. $(a - c)(a^2 + ac + c^2)$

30. $3y^2 + y + 1$
a. Nonperfect square trinomial
b. Prime

31. $c^2 + 8c + 9$
a. Nonperfect square trinomial
b. Prime

32. $a^2 + 2a + 1$
a. Perfect square trinomial
b. $(a + 1)^2$

33. $b^2 + 10b + 25$
a. Perfect square trinomial
b. $(b + 5)^2$

34. $-t^2 - 4t + 32$
a. Nonperfect square trinomial
b. $-(t + 8)(t - 4)$

35. $-p^3 - 5p^2 - 4p$
a. Nonperfect square trinomial
b. $-p(p + 4)(p + 1)$

36. $x^2y^2 - 49$
a. Difference of squares
b. $(xy - 7)(xy + 7)$

37. $6x^2 - 21x - 45$
a. Nonperfect square trinomial
b. $3(2x + 3)(x - 5)$

38. $20y^2 - 14y + 2$
a. Nonperfect square trinomial
b. $2(5y - 1)(2y - 1)$

39. $5a^2bc^3 - 7abc^2$
a. None of these
b. $abc^2(5ac - 7)$

40. $8a^2 - 50$
a. Differenc of squares
b. $2(2a - 5)(2a + 5)$

41. $t^2 + 2t - 63$
a. Nonperfect square trinomial
b. $(t + 9)(t - 7)$

42. $b^2 + 2b - 80$
a. Nonperfect square trinomial
b. $(b + 10)(b - 8)$

43. $ab + ay - b^2 - by$
a. Four terms-grouping
b. $(b + y)(a - b)$

44. $6x^3y^4 + 3x^2y^5$
a. None of these
b. $3x^2y^4(2x + y)$

45. $14u^2 - 11uv + 2v^2$
a. Nonperfect square trinomial
b. $(7u - 2v)(2u - v)$

46. $9p^2 - 36pq + 4q^2$
a. Nonperfect square trinomial
b. Prime

47. $4q^2 - 8q - 6$
a. Nonperfect square trinomial
b. $2(2q^2 - 4q - 3)$

48. $9w^2 + 3w - 15$
a. Nonperfect square trinomial
b. $3(3w^2 + w - 5)$

49. $9m^2 + 16n^2$
a. Sum of squares
b. Prime

50. $5b^2 - 30b + 45$
a. Perfect square trinomial
b. $5(b - 3)^2$

51. $6r^2 + 11r + 3$
a. Nonperfect square trinomial
b. $(3r + 1)(2r + 3)$

52. $4s^2 + 4s - 15$
a. Nonperfect square trinomial
b. $(2s - 3)(2s + 5)$

53. $16a^4 - 1$
a. Difference of squares
b. $(2a - 1)(2a + 1)(4a^2 + 1)$

54. $p^3 + p^2c - 9p - 9c$
a. Four terms-grouping
b. $(p + c)(p - 3)(p + 3)$

55. $81u^2 - 90uv + 25v^2$
a. Perfect square trinomial
b. $(9u - 5v)^2$

56. $4x^2 + 16$
a. Sum of squares
b. $4(x^2 + 4)$

57. $x^2 - 5x - 6$
a. Nonperfect square trinomial
b. $(x - 6)(x + 1)$

58. $q^2 + q - 7$
a. Nonperfect square trinomial
b. Prime

59. $2ax - 6ay + 4bx - 12by$
a. Four terms-grouping
b. $2(x - 3y)(a + 2b)$

60. $8m^3 - 10m^2 - 3m$
a. Nonperfect square trinomial
b. $m(4m + 1)(2m - 3)$

61. $21x^4y + 41x^3y + 10x^2y$
a. Nonperfect square trinomial
b. $x^2y(3x + 5)(7x + 2)$

62. $2m^4 - 128$
a. Difference of squares
b. $2(m^2 - 8)(m^2 + 8)$

63. $8uv - 6u + 12v - 9$
a. Four terms-grouping
b. $(4v - 3)(2u + 3)$

64. $4t^2 - 20t + st - 5s$
a. Four terms-grouping
b. $(t - 5)(4t + s)$

65. $12x^2 - 12x + 3$
a. Perfect square trinomial
b. $3(2x - 1)^2$

66. $p^2 + 2pq + q^2$
a. Perfect square trinomial
b. $(p + q)^2$

67. $6n^3 + 5n^2 - 4n$
a. Nonperfect square trinomial
b. $n(2n - 1)(3n + 4)$

68. $4k^3 + 4k^2 - 3k$
a. Nonperfect square trinomial
b. $k(2k - 1)(2k + 3)$

69. $64 - y^2$
a. Difference of squares
b. $(8 - y)(8 + y)$

70. $36b - b^3$
a. Difference of squares
b. $b(6 - b)(6 + b)$

71. $b^2 - 4b + 10$
a. Nonperfect square trinomial
b. Prime

72. $y^2 + 6y + 8$
a. Nonperfect square trinomial
b. $(y + 4)(y + 2)$

73. $c^4 - 12c^2 + 20$
a. Nonperfect square trinomial
b. $(c^2 - 10)(c^2 - 2)$

Section 6.7 Solving Equations Using the Zero Product Rule

Concepts

1. Definition of a Quadratic Equation
2. Zero Product Rule
3. Solving Equations by Factoring

1. Definition of a Quadratic Equation

We have already learned to solve linear equations in one variable. These are equations of the form $ax + b = c$ $(a \neq 0)$. A linear equation in one variable is sometimes called a first-degree polynomial equation because the highest degree of all its terms is 1. A second-degree polynomial equation in one variable is called a quadratic equation.

A Quadratic Equation in One Variable

If a, b, and c are real numbers such that $a \neq 0$, then a **quadratic equation** is an equation that can be written in the form

$$ax^2 + bx + c = 0$$

The following equations are quadratic because they can each be written in the form $ax^2 + bx + c = 0$, $(a \neq 0)$.

$$-4x^2 + 4x = 1 \qquad x(x-2) = 3 \qquad (x-4)(x+4) = 9$$

$$-4x^2 + 4x - 1 = 0 \qquad x^2 - 2x = 3 \qquad x^2 - 16 = 9$$

$$x^2 - 2x - 3 = 0 \qquad x^2 - 25 = 0$$

$$x^2 + 0x - 25 = 0$$

2. Zero Product Rule

One method for solving a quadratic equation is to factor and apply the zero product rule. The **zero product rule** states that if the product of two factors is zero, then one or both of its factors is zero.

Zero Product Rule

If $ab = 0$, then $a = 0$ or $b = 0$.

Example 1 Applying the Zero Product Rule

Classroom Example: p. 468, Exercise 14

Solve the equation by using the zero product rule. $(x-4)(x+3) = 0$

Solution:

$(x-4)(x+3) = 0$	Apply the zero product rule.
$x - 4 = 0$ or $x + 3 = 0$	Set each factor equal to zero.
$x = 4$ or $x = -3$	Solve each equation for x.

Check: $x = 4$

$(4-4)(4+3) \stackrel{?}{=} 0$

$(0)(7) \stackrel{?}{=} 0$ ✓

Check: $x = -3$

$(-3-4)(-3+3) \stackrel{?}{=} 0$

$(-7)(0) \stackrel{?}{=} 0$ ✓

The solution set is $\{4, -3\}$.

Skill Practice Solve.

1. $(x+1)(x-8) = 0$

Answer

1. $\{-1, 8\}$

Classroom Example: p. 468, Exercise 20

Example 2 **Applying the Zero Product Rule**

Solve the equation by using the zero product rule. $(x+8)(4x+1)=0$

Solution:

$(x+8)(4x+1)=0$	Apply the zero product rule.
$x+8=0$ or $4x+1=0$	Set each factor equal to zero.
$x=-8$ or $4x=-1$	Solve each equation for x.
$x=-8$ or $x=-\frac{1}{4}$	The solutions check in the original equation.

The solution set is $\left\{-8, -\frac{1}{4}\right\}$.

Skill Practice Solve.

2. $(4x-5)(x+6)=0$

Classroom Example: p. 468, Exercise 22

Example 3 **Applying the Zero Product Rule**

Solve the equation using the zero product rule. $x(3x-7)=0$

Solution:

$x(3x-7)=0$	Apply the zero product rule.
$x=0$ or $3x-7=0$	Set each factor equal to zero.
$x=0$ or $3x=7$	Solve each equation for x.
$x=0$ or $x=\frac{7}{3}$	The solutions check in the original equation.

The solution set is $\left\{0, \frac{7}{3}\right\}$.

Skill Practice Solve.

3. $x(4x+9)=0$

3. Solving Equations by Factoring

Quadratic equations, like linear equations, arise in many applications in mathematics, science, and business. The following steps summarize the factoring method for solving a quadratic equation.

Solving a Quadratic Equation by Factoring

Step 1 Write the equation in the form: $ax^2+bx+c=0$.

Step 2 Factor the quadratic expression completely.

Step 3 Apply the zero product rule. That is, set each factor equal to zero and solve the resulting equations.

Note: The solution(s) found in step 3 may be checked by substitution in the original equation.

Answers

2. $\left\{\frac{5}{4}, -6\right\}$ **3.** $\left\{0, -\frac{9}{4}\right\}$

Example 4 **Solving a Quadratic Equation**

Solve the quadratic equation. $2x^2 - 9x = 5$

Solution:

$2x^2 - 9x = 5$

$2x^2 - 9x - 5 = 0$ Write the equation in the form $ax^2 + bx + c = 0$.

$(2x + 1)(x - 5) = 0$ Factor the polynomial completely.

$2x + 1 = 0$ or $x - 5 = 0$ Set each factor equal to zero.

$2x = -1$ or $x = 5$ Solve each equation.

$x = -\frac{1}{2}$ or $x = 5$

Check: $x = -\frac{1}{2}$

$$2x^2 - 9x = 5$$
$$2\left(-\frac{1}{2}\right)^2 - 9\left(-\frac{1}{2}\right) \stackrel{?}{=} 5$$
$$2\left(\frac{1}{4}\right) + \frac{9}{2} \stackrel{?}{=} 5$$
$$\frac{1}{2} + \frac{9}{2} \stackrel{?}{=} 5$$
$$\frac{10}{2} \stackrel{?}{=} 5 \checkmark$$

Check: $x = 5$

$$2x^2 - 9x = 5$$
$$2(5)^2 - 9(5) \stackrel{?}{=} 5$$
$$2(25) - 45 \stackrel{?}{=} 5$$
$$50 - 45 \stackrel{?}{=} 5 \checkmark$$

The solution set is $\left\{-\frac{1}{2}, 5\right\}$.

Skill Practice Solve the quadratic equation.

4. $2y^2 + 19y = -24$

Classroom Example: p. 468, Exercise 30

Instructor Note: Show students why $2x^2 - 9x = 5$ cannot be solved as:

$$2x^2 - 9x = 5$$
$$x(2x - 9) = 5$$
$$x = 5 \quad \text{or} \quad 2x - 9 = 5$$

Example 5 **Solving a Quadratic Equation**

Solve the quadratic equation. $4x^2 + 24x = 0$

Solution:

$4x^2 + 24x = 0$ The equation is already in the form $ax^2 + bx + c = 0$. (Note that $c = 0$.)

$4x(x + 6) = 0$ Factor completely.

$4x = 0$ or $x + 6 = 0$ Set each factor equal to zero.

$x = 0$ or $x = -6$ The solutions check in the original equation.

The solution set is $\{0, -6\}$.

Skill Practice Solve the quadratic equation.

5. $5s^2 = 45$

Classroom Example: p. 468, Exercise 46

Answers

4. $\left\{-8, -\frac{3}{2}\right\}$ 5. $\{3, -3\}$

Classroom Example: p. 468, Exercise 54

Example 6 **Solving a Quadratic Equation**

Solve the quadratic equation. $5x(5x+2) = 10x + 9$

Solution:

$5x(5x+2) = 10x + 9$	
$25x^2 + 10x = 10x + 9$	Clear parentheses.
$25x^2 + 10x - 10x - 9 = 0$	Set the equation equal to zero.
$25x^2 - 9 = 0$	The equation is in the form $ax^2 + bx + c = 0$. (Note that $b = 0$.)
$(5x-3)(5x+3) = 0$	Factor completely.
$5x - 3 = 0$ or $5x + 3 = 0$	Set each factor equal to zero.
$5x = 3$ or $5x = -3$	Solve each equation.
$\dfrac{5x}{5} = \dfrac{3}{5}$ or $\dfrac{5x}{5} = \dfrac{-3}{5}$	
$x = \dfrac{3}{5}$ or $x = -\dfrac{3}{5}$	The solutions check in the original equation.

The solution set is $\left\{\dfrac{3}{5}, -\dfrac{3}{5}\right\}$.

Skill Practice Solve the quadratic equation.

6. $4z(z+3) = 4z + 5$

The zero product rule can be used to solve higher degree polynomial equations provided the equations can be set to zero and written in factored form.

Classroom Example: p. 468, Exercise 38

Example 7 **Solving a Higher Degree Polynomial Equation**

Solve the equation. $-6(y+3)(y-5)(2y+7) = 0$

Solution:

$-6(y+3)(y-5)(2y+7) = 0$

The equation is already in factored form and equal to zero.

Set each factor equal to zero.

Solve each equation for y.

$-6 \neq 0$	or	$y + 3 = 0$	or	$y - 5 = 0$	or	$2y + 7 = 0$
No solution,		$y = -3$	or	$y = 5$	or	$y = -\dfrac{7}{2}$

Notice that when the constant factor is set equal to zero, the result is a contradiction, $-6 = 0$. The constant factor does not produce a solution to the equation. Therefore, the solution set is $\{-3, 5, -\frac{7}{2}\}$. Each solution can be checked in the original equation.

Answer

6. $\left\{-\dfrac{5}{2}, \dfrac{1}{2}\right\}$

Skill Practice Solve the equation.

7. $5(p-4)(p+7)(2p-9)=0$

Example 8 **Solving a Higher Degree Polynomial Equation**

Classroom Example: p. 469, Exercise 68

Solve the equation. $w^3+5w^2-9w-45=0$

Solution:

$w^3+5w^2-9w-45=0$ This is a higher degree polynomial equation.

$w^3+5w^2 \mid -9w-45=0$ The equation is already set equal to zero. Now factor.

$w^2(w+5)-9(w+5)=0$
$(w+5)(w^2-9)=0$ Because there are four terms, try factoring by grouping.

$(w+5)(w-3)(w+3)=0$ w^2-9 is a difference of squares and can be factored further.

$w+5=0$ or $w-3=0$ or $w+3=0$ Set each factor equal to zero.

$w=-5$ or $w=3$ or $w=-3$ Solve each equation.

The solution set is $\{-5, 3, -3\}$. Each solution checks in the original equation.

Skill Practice Solve the equation.

8. $x^3+3x^2-4x-12=0$

Answers

7. $\left\{4, -7, \frac{9}{2}\right\}$ 8. $\{-2, -3, 2\}$

Section 6.7 Practice Exercises

For additional exercises, see Classroom Activities 6.7A–6.7B in the *Student's Resource Manual* at www.mhhe.com/moh.

Vocabulary and Key Concepts

1. **a.** An equation that can be written in the form $ax^2+bx+c=0$, $(a \neq 0)$, is called a quadratic equation.

   b. The zero product rule states that if $ab=0$, then $a=$ 0 or $b=$ 0.

Review Exercises

For Exercises 2–7, factor completely.

2. $6a-8-3ab+4b$ $(3a-4)(2-b)$
3. $4b^2-44b+120$ $4(b-5)(b-6)$
4. $8u^2v^2-4uv$ $4uv(2uv-1)$
5. $3x^2+10x-8$ $(3x-2)(x+4)$
6. $3h^2-75$ $3(h-5)(h+5)$
7. $4x^2+16y^2$ $4(x^2+4y^2)$

Concept 1: Definition of a Quadratic Equation

For Exercises 8–13, identify the equations as linear, quadratic, or neither.

8. $4 - 5x = 0$ Linear

9. $5x^3 + 2 = 0$ Neither

10. $3x - 6x^2 = 0$ Quadratic

11. $1 - x + 2x^2 = 0$ Quadratic

12. $7x^4 + 8 = 0$ Neither

13. $3x + 2 = 0$ Linear

Concept 2: Zero Product Rule

For Exercises 14–22, solve each equation using the zero product rule. **(See Examples 1–3.)**

14. $(x - 5)(x + 1) = 0$ $\{5, -1\}$

15. $(x + 3)(x - 1) = 0$ $\{-3, 1\}$

16. $(3x - 2)(3x + 2) = 0$ $\left\{\frac{2}{3}, -\frac{2}{3}\right\}$

17. $(2x - 7)(2x + 7) = 0$ $\left\{\frac{7}{2}, -\frac{7}{2}\right\}$

18. $2(x - 7)(x - 7) = 0$ $\{7\}$

19. $3(x + 5)(x + 5) = 0$ $\{-5\}$

20. $(3x - 2)(2x - 3) = 0$ $\left\{\frac{2}{3}, \frac{3}{2}\right\}$

21. $x(5x - 1) = 0$ $\left\{0, \frac{1}{5}\right\}$

22. $x(3x + 8) = 0$ $\left\{0, -\frac{8}{3}\right\}$

23. For a quadratic equation of the form $ax^2 + bx + c = 0$, what must be done before applying the zero product rule? The polynomial must be factored completely.

24. What are the requirements needed to use the zero product rule to solve a quadratic equation or higher degree polynomial equation? The equation must have one side equal to zero and the other side factored completely.

Concept 3: Solving Equations by Factoring

For Exercises 25–72, solve each equation. **(See Examples 4–8.)**

25. $p^2 - 2p - 15 = 0$ $\{5, -3\}$

26. $y^2 - 7y - 8 = 0$ $\{8, -1\}$

27. $z^2 + 10z - 24 = 0$ $\{-12, 2\}$

28. $w^2 - 10w + 16 = 0$ $\{8, 2\}$

29. $2q^2 - 7q = 4$ $\left\{4, -\frac{1}{2}\right\}$

30. $4x^2 - 11x = 3$ $\left\{-\frac{1}{4}, 3\right\}$

31. $0 = 9x^2 - 4$ $\left\{\frac{2}{3}, -\frac{2}{3}\right\}$

32. $4a^2 - 49 = 0$ $\left\{\frac{7}{2}, -\frac{7}{2}\right\}$

33. $2k^2 - 28k + 96 = 0$ $\{6, 8\}$

34. $0 = 2t^2 + 20t + 50$ $\{-5\}$

35. $0 = 2m^3 - 5m^2 - 12m$ $\left\{0, -\frac{3}{2}, 4\right\}$

36. $3n^3 + 4n^2 + n = 0$ $\left\{0, -\frac{1}{3}, -1\right\}$

37. $5(3p + 1)(p - 3)(p + 6) = 0$ $\left\{-\frac{1}{3}, 3, -6\right\}$

38. $4(2x - 1)(x - 10)(x + 7) = 0$ $\left\{\frac{1}{2}, 10, -7\right\}$

39. $x(x - 4)(2x + 3) = 0$ $\left\{0, 4, -\frac{3}{2}\right\}$

40. $x(3x + 1)(x + 1) = 0$ $\left\{0, -\frac{1}{3}, -1\right\}$

41. $-5x(2x + 9)(x - 11) = 0$ $\left\{0, -\frac{9}{2}, 11\right\}$

42. $-3x(x + 7)(3x - 5) = 0$ $\left\{0, -7, \frac{5}{3}\right\}$

43. $x^3 - 16x = 0$ $\{0, 4, -4\}$

44. $t^3 - 36t = 0$ $\{0, 6, -6\}$

45. $3x^2 + 18x = 0$ $\{-6, 0\}$

46. $2y^2 - 20y = 0$ $\{0, 10\}$

47. $16m^2 = 9$ $\left\{\frac{3}{4}, -\frac{3}{4}\right\}$

48. $9n^2 = 1$ $\left\{\frac{1}{3}, -\frac{1}{3}\right\}$

49. $2y^3 + 14y^2 = -20y$ $\{0, -5, -2\}$

50. $3d^3 - 6d^2 = 24d$ $\{0, -2, 4\}$

51. $5t - 2(t - 7) = 0$ $\left\{-\frac{14}{3}\right\}$

52. $8h = 5(h - 9) + 6$ $\{-13\}$

53. $2c(c - 8) = -30$ $\{5, 3\}$

54. $3q(q - 3) = 12$ $\{-1, 4\}$

55. $b^3 = -4b^2 - 4b$ $\{0, -2\}$

56. $x^3 + 36x = 12x^2$ $\{0, 6\}$

57. $3(a^2 + 2a) = 2a^2 - 9$ $\{-3\}$

58. $9(k - 1) = -4k^2$ $\left\{\frac{3}{4}, -3\right\}$

59. $2n(n + 2) = 6$ $\{-3, 1\}$

60. $3p(p - 1) = 18$ $\{3, -2\}$

61. $x(2x + 5) - 1 = 2x^2 + 3x + 2$ $\left\{\frac{3}{2}\right\}$

62. $3z(z - 2) - z = 3z^2 + 4$ $\left\{-\frac{4}{7}\right\}$

63. $27q^2 = 9q$ $\left\{0, \frac{1}{3}\right\}$

64. $21w^2 = 14w$ $\left\{0, \frac{2}{3}\right\}$

65. $3(c^2 - 2c) = 0$ $\{0, 2\}$

66. $2(4d^2 + d) = 0$ $\left\{0, -\frac{1}{4}\right\}$

67. $y^3 - 3y^2 - 4y + 12 = 0$ $\{3, -2, 2\}$

68. $t^3 + 2t^2 - 16t - 32 = 0$ $\{-2, 4, -4\}$

69. $(x - 1)(x + 2) = 18$ $\{-5, 4\}$

70. $(w + 5)(w - 3) = 20$ $\{-7, 5\}$

71. $(p + 2)(p + 3) = 1 - p$ $\{-5, -1\}$

72. $(k - 6)(k - 1) = -k - 2$ $\{4, 2\}$

Problem Recognition Exercises

Polynomial Expressions Versus Polynomial Equations

For Exercises 1–36, factor the expressions and solve the equations.

1. a. $x^2 + 6x - 7$ $(x + 7)(x - 1)$
b. $x^2 + 6x - 7 = 0$ $\{-7, 1\}$

2. a. $c^2 + 8c + 12$ $(c + 6)(c + 2)$
b. $c^2 + 8c + 12 = 0$ $\{-6, -2\}$

3. a. $2y^2 + 7y + 3$ $(2y + 1)(y + 3)$
b. $2y^2 + 7y + 3 = 0$ $\left\{-\frac{1}{2}, -3\right\}$

4. a. $3x^2 - 8x + 5$ $(3x - 5)(x - 1)$
b. $3x^2 - 8x + 5 = 0$ $\left\{\frac{5}{3}, 1\right\}$

5. a. $5q^2 + q - 4 = 0$ $\left\{\frac{4}{5}, -1\right\}$
b. $5q^2 + q - 4$ $(5q - 4)(q + 1)$

6. a. $6a^2 - 7a - 3 = 0$ $\left\{-\frac{1}{3}, \frac{3}{2}\right\}$
b. $6a^2 - 7a - 3$ $(3a + 1)(2a - 3)$

7. a. $a^2 - 64 = 0$ $\{-8, 8\}$
b. $a^2 - 64$ $(a + 8)(a - 8)$

8. a. $v^2 - 100 = 0$ $\{-10, 10\}$
b. $v^2 - 100$ $(v + 10)(v - 10)$

9. a. $4b^2 - 81$ $(2b + 9)(2b - 9)$
b. $4b^2 - 81 = 0$ $\left\{-\frac{9}{2}, \frac{9}{2}\right\}$

10. a. $36t^2 - 49$ $(6t + 7)(6t - 7)$
b. $36t^2 - 49 = 0$ $\left\{-\frac{7}{6}, \frac{7}{6}\right\}$

11. a. $8x^2 + 16x + 6 = 0$ $\left\{-\frac{3}{2}, -\frac{1}{2}\right\}$
b. $8x^2 + 16x + 6$ $2(2x + 3)(2x + 1)$

12. a. $12y^2 + 40y + 32 = 0$ $\left\{-\frac{4}{3}, -2\right\}$
b. $12y^2 + 40y + 32$ $4(3y + 4)(y + 2)$

13. a. $x^3 - 8x^2 - 20x$ $x(x - 10)(x + 2)$
b. $x^3 - 8x^2 - 20x = 0$ $\{0, 10, -2\}$

14. a. $k^3 + 5k^2 - 14k$ $k(k + 7)(k - 2)$
b. $k^3 + 5k^2 - 14k = 0$ $\{0, -7, 2\}$

15. a. $b^3 + b^2 - 9b - 9 = 0$ $\{-1, 3, -3\}$
b. $b^3 + b^2 - 9b - 9$ $(b + 1)(b - 3)(b + 3)$

16. a. $x^3 - 8x^2 - 4x + 32 = 0$ $\{8, -2, 2\}$
b. $x^3 - 8x^2 - 4x + 32$ $(x - 8)(x + 2)(x - 2)$

17. $2s^2 - 6s + rs - 3r$ $(s - 3)(2s + r)$

18. $6t^2 + 3t + 10tu + 5u$ $(2t + 1)(3t + 5u)$

19. $8x^3 - 2x = 0$ $\left\{-\frac{1}{2}, 0, \frac{1}{2}\right\}$

20. $2b^3 - 50b = 0$ $\{-5, 0, 5\}$

21. $2x^3 - 4x^2 + 2x = 0$ $\{0, 1\}$

22. $3t^3 + 18t^2 + 27t = 0$ $\{-3, 0\}$

23. $7c^2 - 2c + 3 = 7(c^2 + c)$ $\left\{\frac{1}{3}\right\}$

24. $3z(2z + 4) = -7 + 6z^2$ $\left\{-\frac{7}{12}\right\}$

25. $8w^3 + 27$ $(2w + 3)(4w^2 - 6w + 9)$

26. $1000q^3 - 1$ $(10q - 1)(100q^2 + 10q + 1)$

27. $5z^2 + 2z = 7$ $\left\{-\frac{7}{5}, 1\right\}$

28. $4h^2 + 25h = -6$ $\left\{-6, -\frac{1}{4}\right\}$

29. $3b(b + 6) = b - 10$ $\left\{-\frac{2}{3}, -5\right\}$

30. $3y^2 + 1 = y(y - 3)$ $\left\{-1, -\frac{1}{2}\right\}$

31. $5(2x - 3) - 2(3x + 1) = 4 - 3x$ $\{3\}$

32. $11 - 6a = -4(2a - 3) - 1$ $\{0\}$

33. $4s^2 = 64$ $\{-4, 4\}$

34. $81v^2 = 36$ $\left\{-\frac{2}{3}, \frac{2}{3}\right\}$

35. $(x - 3)(x - 4) = 6$ $\{1, 6\}$

36. $(x + 5)(x + 9) = 21$ $\{-2, -12\}$

Section 6.8 Applications of Quadratic Equations

Concepts

1. Applications of Quadratic Equations
2. Pythagorean Theorem

1. Applications of Quadratic Equations

In this section we solve applications using the Problem-Solving Strategies for Word Problems.

Classroom Example: p. 474, Exercise 16

Example 1 Translating to a Quadratic Equation

The product of two consecutive integers is 14 more than 6 times the smaller integer.

Solution:

Let x represent the first (smaller) integer.

Then $x + 1$ represents the second (larger) integer. — Label the variables.

(Smaller integer)(larger integer) = 6 · (smaller integer) + 14 — Verbal model

$x(x + 1) = 6(x) + 14$ — Algebraic equation

$x^2 + x = 6x + 14$ — Simplify.

$x^2 + x - 6x - 14 = 0$ — Set one side of the equation equal to zero.

$x^2 - 5x - 14 = 0$

$(x - 7)(x + 2) = 0$ — Factor.

$x - 7 = 0$ or $x + 2 = 0$ — Set each factor equal to zero.

$x = 7$ or $x = -2$ — Solve for x.

Recall that x represents the smaller integer. Therefore, there are two possibilities for the pairs of consecutive integers.

If $x = 7$, then the larger integer is $x + 1$ or $7 + 1 = 8$.

If $x = -2$, then the larger integer is $x + 1$ or $-2 + 1 = -1$.

The integers are 7 and 8, or -2 and -1.

Skill Practice

1. The product of two consecutive odd integers is 9 more than 10 times the smaller integer. Find the pair of integers.

Classroom Example: p. 475, Exercise 18

Example 2 Using a Quadratic Equation in a Geometry Application

A rectangular sign has an area of 40 ft^2. If the width is 3 feet shorter than the length, what are the dimensions of the sign?

Label the variables.

Figure 6-1

Solution:

Let x represent the length of the sign. Then $x - 3$ represents the width (Figure 6-1).

The problem gives information about the length of the sides and about the area. Therefore, we can form a relationship by using the formula for the area of a rectangle.

Answer

1. The integers are 9 and 11 or −1 and 1.

$A = l \cdot w$	Area equals length times width.
$40 = x(x - 3)$	Set up an algebraic equation.
$40 = x^2 - 3x$	Clear parentheses.
$0 = x^2 - 3x - 40$	Write the equation in the form, $ax^2 + bx + c = 0$.
$0 = (x - 8)(x + 5)$	Factor.
$0 = x - 8$ or $0 = x + 5$	Set each factor equal to zero.
$8 = x$ or $-5 \neq x$	Because x represents the length of a rectangle, reject the negative solution.

The variable x represents the length of the sign. The length is 8 ft.

The expression $x - 3$ represents the width. The width is 8 ft − 3 ft, or 5 ft.

Skill Practice

2. The length of a rectangle is 5 ft more than the width. The area is 36 ft^2. Find the length and width.

Example 3 Using a Quadratic Equation in an Application

Classroom Example: p. 475, Exercise 28

Animation

A stone is dropped off a 64-ft cliff and falls into the ocean below. The height of the stone above sea level is given by the equation

$h = -16t^2 + 64$ where h is the stone's height in feet, and t is the time in seconds.

Find the time required for the stone to hit the water.

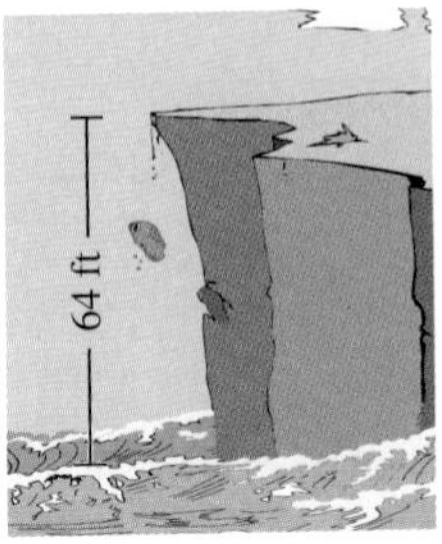

Solution:

When the stone hits the water, its height is zero. Therefore, substitute $h = 0$ into the equation.

$h = -16t^2 + 64$	The equation is quadratic.
$0 = -16t^2 + 64$	Substitute $h = 0$.
$0 = -16(t^2 - 4)$	Factor out the GCF.
$0 = -16(t - 2)(t + 2)$	Factor as a difference of squares.
$-16 \neq 0$ or $t - 2 = 0$ or $t + 2 = 0$	Set each factor to zero.
No solution, $t = 2$ or $t \neq -2$	Solve for t.

The negative value of t is rejected because the stone cannot fall for a negative time. Therefore, the stone hits the water after 2 sec.

Skill Practice

3. An object is launched into the air from the ground and its height is given by $h = -16t^2 + 144t$, where h is the height in feet after t seconds. Find the time required for the object to hit the ground.

Answers

2. The width is 4 ft, and the length is 9 ft.
3. The object hits the ground in 9 sec.

2. Pythagorean Theorem

Recall that a right triangle is a triangle that contains a 90° angle. Furthermore, the sum of the squares of the two legs (the shorter sides) of a right triangle equals the square of the hypotenuse (the longest side). This important fact is known as the Pythagorean theorem. The Pythagorean theorem is an enduring landmark of mathematical history from which many mathematical ideas have been built. Although the theorem is named after Pythagoras (sixth century B.C.E.), a Greek mathematician and philosopher, it is thought that the ancient Babylonians were familiar with the principle more than a thousand years earlier.

For the right triangle shown in Figure 6-2, the **Pythagorean theorem** is stated as:

$$a^2 + b^2 = c^2$$

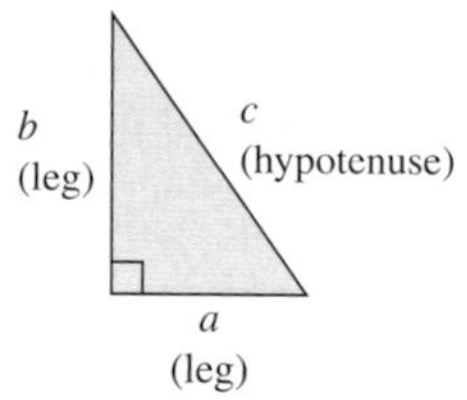

Figure 6-2

In this formula, a and b are the legs of the right triangle and c is the hypotenuse. Notice that the hypotenuse is the longest side of the right triangle and is opposite the 90° angle.

The triangle shown below is a right triangle. Notice that the lengths of the sides satisfy the Pythagorean theorem.

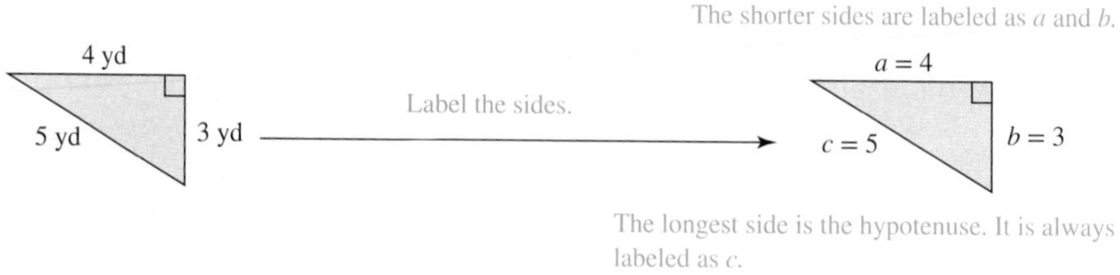

$a^2 + b^2 = c^2$	Apply the Pythagorean theorem.
$(4)^2 + (3)^2 = (5)^2$	Substitute $a = 4$, $b = 3$, and $c = 5$.
$16 + 9 = 25$	
$25 = 25$ ✓	

Classroom Example: p. 476, Exercise 32

Example 4 Applying the Pythagorean Theorem

Find the length of the missing side of the right triangle.

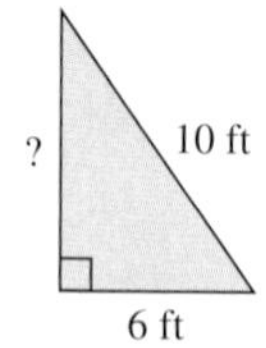

Solution:

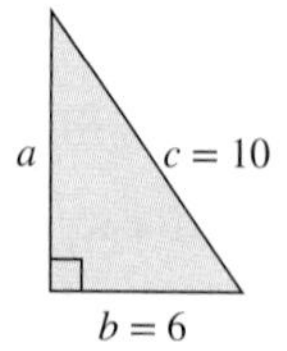

Label the triangle.

$a^2 + b^2 = c^2$	Apply the Pythagorean theorem.
$a^2 + 6^2 = 10^2$	Substitute $b = 6$ and $c = 10$.
$a^2 + 36 = 100$	Simplify. The equation is quadratic.

$a^2 + 36 - 100 = 100 - 100$	Subtract 100 from both sides.
$a^2 - 64 = 0$	One side is now equal to zero.
$(a + 8)(a - 8) = 0$	Factor.
$a + 8 = 0$ or $a - 8 = 0$	Set each factor equal to zero.
$\cancel{a = -8}$ or $a = 8$	Because x represents the length of a side of a triangle, reject the negative solution.

The third side is 8 ft.

Skill Practice

4. Find the length of the missing side.

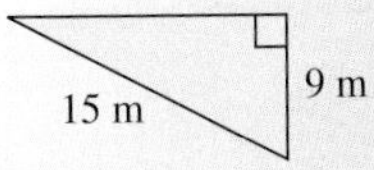

Example 5 **Using a Quadratic Equation in an Application**

Classroom Example: p. 476, Exercise 40

A 13-ft board is used as a ramp to unload furniture off a loading platform. If the distance between the top of the board and the ground is 7 ft less than the distance between the bottom of the board and the base of the platform, find both distances.

Solution:

Let x represent the distance between the bottom of the board and the base of the platform. Then $x - 7$ represents the distance between the top of the board and the ground (Figure 6-3).

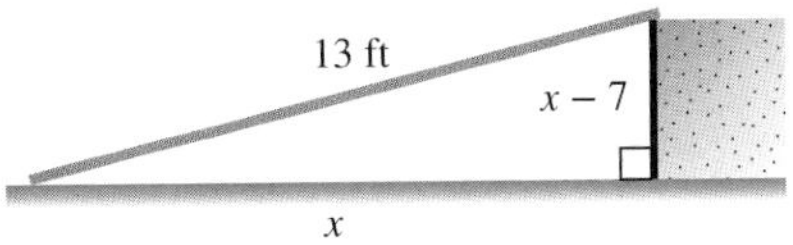

Figure 6-3

$a^2 + b^2 = c^2$	Pythagorean theorem
$x^2 + (x - 7)^2 = (13)^2$	
$x^2 + (x)^2 - 2(x)(7) + (7)^2 = 169$	
$x^2 + x^2 - 14x + 49 = 169$	
$2x^2 - 14x + 49 = 169$	Combine *like* terms.
$2x^2 - 14x + 49 - 169 = 169 - 169$	Set the equation equal to zero.
$2x^2 - 14x - 120 = 0$	Write the equation in the form $ax^2 + bx + c = 0$.
$2(x^2 - 7x - 60) = 0$	Factor.
$2(x - 12)(x + 5) = 0$	
$\cancel{2 = 0}$ or $x - 12 = 0$ or $x + 5 = 0$	Set each factor equal to zero.
$x = 12$ or $\cancel{x = -5}$	Solve both equations for x.

Avoiding Mistakes

Recall that the square of a binomial results in a perfect square trinomial.

$$(a - b)^2 = a^2 - 2ab + b^2$$
$$(x - 7)^2 = x^2 - 2(x)(7) + 7^2$$
$$= x^2 - 14x + 49$$

Don't forget the middle term.

Answer

4. The length of the third side is 12 m.

Recall that x represents the distance between the bottom of the board and the base of the platform. We reject the negative value of x because a distance cannot be negative. Therefore, the distance between the bottom of the board and the base of the platform is 12 ft. The distance between the top of the board and the ground is $x - 7 = 5$ ft.

Skill Practice

5. A 5-yd ladder leans against a wall. The distance from the bottom of the wall to the top of the ladder is 1 yd more than the distance from the bottom of the wall to the bottom of the ladder. Find both distances.

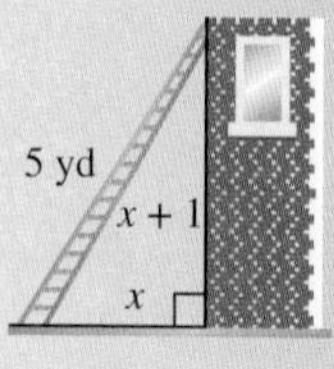

Answer

5. The distance along the wall to the top of the ladder is 4 yd. The distance on the ground from the ladder to the wall is 3 yd.

Section 6.8 Practice Exercises

For additional exercises, see Classroom Activities 6.8A–6.8B in the *Student's Resource Manual* at www.mhhe.com/moh.

Vocabulary and Key Concepts

1. a. If x is the smaller of two consecutive integers, then $\underline{x + 1}$ represents the next greater integer.

b. If x is the smaller of two consecutive odd integers, then $\underline{x + 2}$ represents the next greater odd integer.

c. If x is the smaller of two consecutive even integers, then $\underline{x + 2}$ represents the next greater even integer.

d. The area of a rectangle of length L and width W is given by $A = \underline{LW}$.

e. The area of a triangle with base b and height h is given by the formula $A = \underline{\frac{1}{2}bh}$.

f. Given a right triangle with legs a and b and hypotenuse c, the Pythagorean theorem is stated as $\underline{a^2 + b^2 = c^2}$.

Review Exercises

For Exercises 2–7, solve the quadratic equations.

2. $(6x + 1)(x + 4) = 0$ $\left\{-\frac{1}{6}, -4\right\}$

3. $9x(3x + 2) = 0$ $\left\{0, -\frac{2}{3}\right\}$

4. $4x^2 - 1 = 0$ $\left\{-\frac{1}{2}, \frac{1}{2}\right\}$

5. $x^2 - 5x = 6$ $\{6, -1\}$

6. $x(x - 20) = -100$ $\{10\}$

7. $6x^2 - 7x - 10 = 0$ $\left\{-\frac{5}{6}, 2\right\}$

8. Explain what is wrong with the following logic.

$$(x - 3)(x + 2) = 5$$
$$x - 3 = 5 \quad \text{or} \quad x + 2 = 5$$

A factored expression must be set equal to zero to use the zero product rule.

Concept 1: Applications of Quadratic Equations

9. If eleven is added to the square of a number, the result is sixty. Find all such numbers.
The numbers are 7 and −7.

10. If a number is added to two times its square, the result is thirty-six. Find all such numbers.
The numbers are $-\frac{9}{2}$ and 4.

11. If twelve is added to six times a number, the result is twenty-eight less than the square of the number. Find all such numbers.
The numbers are 10 and −4.

12. The square of a number is equal to twenty more than the number. Find all such numbers.
The numbers are 5 and −4.

13. The product of two consecutive odd integers is sixty-three. Find all such integers. **(See Example 1.)**
The numbers are −9 and −7, or 7 and 9.

14. The product of two consecutive even integers is forty-eight. Find all such integers.
The numbers are 6 and 8, or −8 and −6.

15. The sum of the squares of two consecutive integers is sixty-one. Find all such integers.
The numbers are 5 and 6, or −6 and −5.

16. The sum of the squares of two consecutive even integers is fifty-two. Find all such integers.
The numbers are 4 and 6 or −6 and −4.

17. *Las Meninas* (Spanish for *The Maids of Honor*) is a famous painting by Spanish painter Diego Velázquez. This work is regarded as one of the most important paintings in Western art history. The height of the painting is approximately 2 ft more than its width. If the total area is 99 ft^2, determine the dimensions of the painting. **(See Example 2.)** The height of the painting is 11 ft and the width is 9 ft.

18. The width of a rectangular painting is 2 in. less than the length. The area is 120 $in.^2$ Find the length and width. The painting has length 12 in. and width 10 in.

© IT Stock Free/Alamy RF

19. The width of a rectangular slab of concrete is 3 m less than the length. The area is 28 m^2.

  a. What are the dimensions of the rectangle? The slab is 7 m by 4 m.

  b. What is the perimeter of the rectangle? The perimeter is 22 m.

20. The width of a rectangular picture is 7 in. less than the length. The area of the picture is 78 $in.^2$

  a. What are the dimensions of the picture? The picture is 13 in. by 6 in.

  b. What is the perimeter of the picture? The perimeter is 38 in.

21. The base of a triangle is 3 ft more than the height. If the area is 14 ft^2, find the base and the height. The base is 7 ft and the height is 4 ft.

22. The height of a triangle is 15 cm more than the base. If the area is 125 cm^2, find the base and the height. The base is 10 cm and the height is 25 cm.

23. The height of a triangle is 7 cm less than 3 times the base. If the area is 20 cm^2, find the base and the height. The base is 5 cm and the height is 8 cm.

24. The base of a triangle is 2 ft less than 4 times the height. If the area is 6 ft^2, find the base and the height. The base is 6 ft and the height is 2 ft.

25. In a physics experiment, a ball is dropped off a 144-ft platform. The height of the ball above the ground is given by the equation

$h = -16t^2 + 144$ where h is the ball's height in feet, and t is the time in seconds after the ball is dropped ($t \geq 0$).

Find the time required for the ball to hit the ground. (*Hint:* Let $h = 0$.) **(See Example 3.)** The ball hits the ground in 3 sec.

26. A stone is dropped off a 256-ft cliff. The height of the stone above the ground is given by the equation

$h = -16t^2 + 256$ where h is the stone's height in feet, and t is the time in seconds after the stone is dropped ($t \geq 0$).

Animation

Find the time required for the stone to hit the ground. The stone hits the ground in 4 sec.

27. An object is shot straight up into the air from ground level with an initial speed of 24 ft/sec. The height of the object (in feet) is given by the equation

$h = -16t^2 + 24t$ where t is the time in seconds after launch ($t \geq 0$).

Find the time(s) when the object is at ground level. The object is at ground level at 0 sec and 1.5 sec.

28. A rocket is launched straight up into the air from the ground with initial speed of 64 ft/sec. The height of the rocket (in feet) is given by the equation

$h = -16t^2 + 64t$ where t is the time in seconds after launch ($t \geq 0$).

Find the time(s) when the rocket is at ground level. The rocket is at ground level at 0 sec and 4 sec.

Concept 2: Pythagorean Theorem

29. Sketch a right triangle and label the sides with the words *leg* and *hypotenuse*.

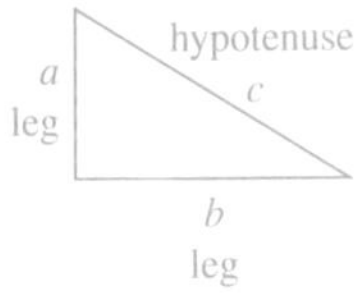

30. State the Pythagorean theorem. Given a right triangle with legs a and b and hypotenuse c, then $a^2 + b^2 = c^2$.

For Exercises 31–34, find the length of the missing side of the right triangle. **(See Example 4.)**

31.

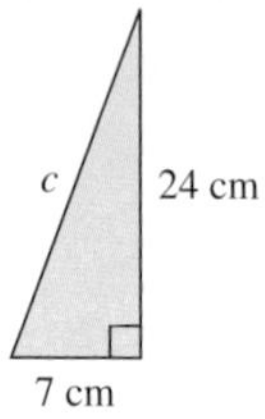

$c = 25$ cm

32.

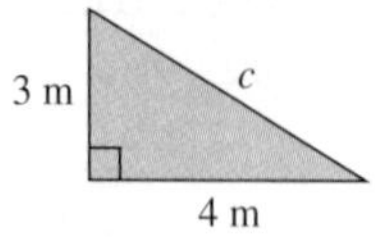

$c = 5$ m

33.

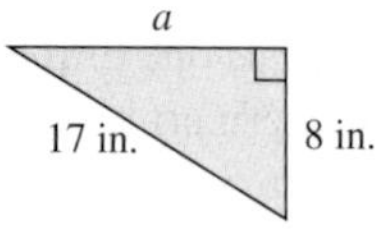

$a = 15$ in.

34.

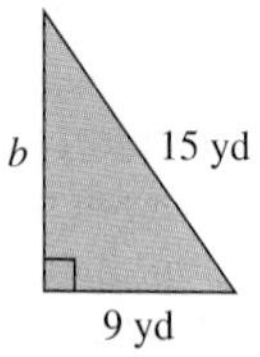

$b = 12$ yd

35. Find the length of the supporting brace. The brace is 20 in. long.

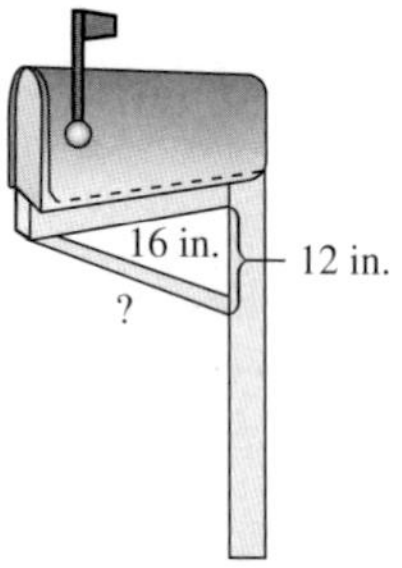

36. Find the height of the airplane above the ground. The height is 9 km.

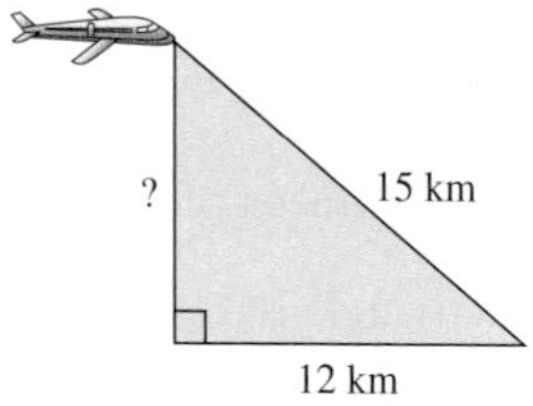

37. Darcy holds the end of a kite string 3 ft (1 yd) off the ground and wants to estimate the height of the kite. Her friend Jenna is 24 yd away from her, standing directly under the kite as shown in the figure. If Darcy has 30 yd of string out, find the height of the kite (ignore the sag in the string). The kite is 19 yd high.

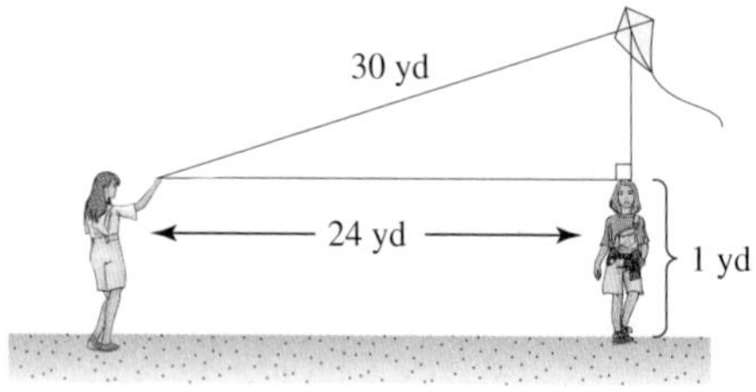

38. Two cars leave the same point at the same time, one traveling north and the other traveling east. After an hour, one car has traveled 48 mi and the other has traveled 64 mi. How many miles apart were they at that time? They were 80 mi apart.

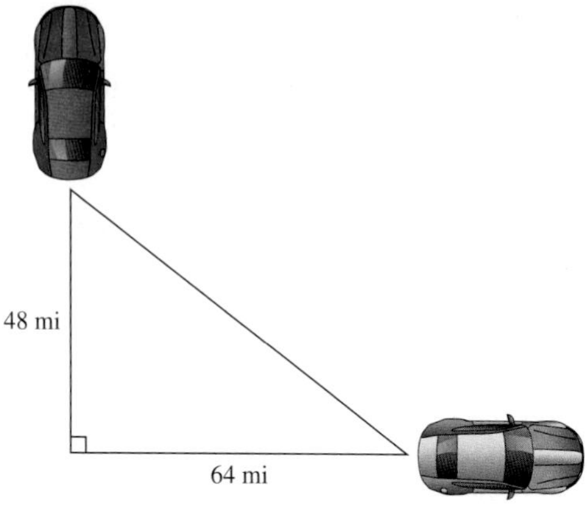

39. A 17-ft ladder rests against the side of a house. The distance between the top of the ladder and the ground is 7 ft more than the distance between the base of the ladder and the bottom of the house. Find both distances. **(See Example 5.)** The bottom of the ladder is 8 ft from the house. The distance from the top of the ladder to the ground is 15 ft.

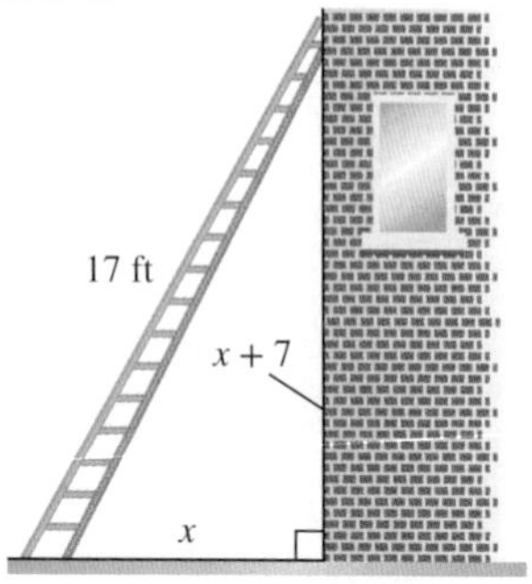

40. Two boats leave a marina. One travels east, and the other travels south. After 30 min, the second boat has traveled 1 mi farther than the first boat and the distance between the boats is 5 mi. Find the distance each boat traveled. The first boat traveled 3 mi; the second boat traveled 4 mi.

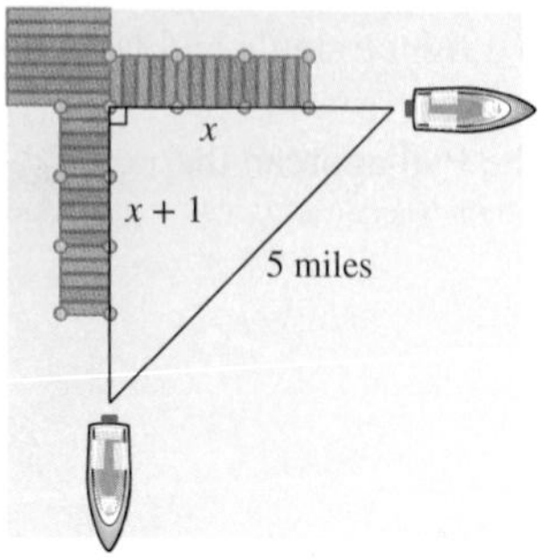

41. One leg of a right triangle is 4 m less than the hypotenuse. The other leg is 2 m less than the hypotenuse. Find the length of the hypotenuse.
The hypotenuse is 10 m.

42. The longer leg of a right triangle is 1 cm less than twice the shorter leg. The hypotenuse is 1 cm greater than twice the shorter leg. Find the length of the shorter leg. The shorter leg is 8 cm.

Group Activity

Building a Factoring Test

Estimated Time: 30–45 minutes

Answers will vary throughout this exercise.

Group Size: 3

In this activity, each group will make a test for this chapter. Then the groups will trade papers and take the test.

For Exercises 1–8, write a polynomial that has the given conditions. Do not use reference materials such as the textbook or your notes.

1. A trinomial with a GCF not equal to 1. The GCF should include a constant and at least one variable. **1.** ____________

2. A four-term polynomial that is factorable by grouping. **2.** ____________

3. A factorable trinomial with a leading coefficient of 1. (The trinomial should factor as a product of two binomials.) **3.** ____________

4. A factorable trinomial with a leading coefficient not equal to 1. (The trinomial should factor as a product of two binomials.) **4.** ____________

5. A trinomial that requires the GCF to be removed. The resulting trinomial should factor as a product of two binomials. **5.** ____________

6. A difference of squares. **6.** ____________

7. A difference of cubes. **7.** ____________

8. A sum of cubes. **8.** ____________

9. Write a quadratic *equation* that has solution set $\{4, -7\}$. **9.** ____________

10. Write a quadratic *equation* that has solution set $\left\{0, -\frac{2}{3}\right\}$. **10.** ____________

Chapter 6 Summary

Section 6.1 Greatest Common Factor and Factoring by Grouping

Key Concepts

The **greatest common factor** (GCF) is the greatest factor common to all terms of a polynomial. To factor out the GCF from a polynomial, use the distributive property.

A four-term polynomial may be factorable by grouping.

Steps to Factoring by Grouping

1. Identify and factor out the GCF from all four terms.
2. Factor out the GCF from the first pair of terms. Factor out the GCF or its opposite from the second pair of terms.
3. If the two terms share a common binomial factor, factor out the binomial factor.

Examples

Example 1

$3x(a + b) - 5(a + b)$ Greatest common factor is $(a + b)$.

$= (a + b)(3x - 5)$

Example 2

$60xa - 30xb - 80ya + 40yb$

$= 10[6xa - 3xb - 8ya + 4yb]$ Factor out the GCF.

$= 10[3x(2a - b) - 4y(2a - b)]$ Factor by grouping.

$= 10(2a - b)(3x - 4y)$

Section 6.2 Factoring Trinomials of the Form $x^2 + bx + c$

Key Concepts

Factoring a Trinomial with a Leading Coefficient of 1

A trinomial of the form $x^2 + bx + c$ factors as

$$x^2 + bx + c = (x \;\square)(x \;\square)$$

where the remaining terms are given by two integers whose product is c and whose sum is b.

Example

Example 1

$x^2 - 14x + 45$ The integers -5 and -9 have a product of 45 and a sum of -14.

$= (x \;\square)(x \;\square)$

$= (x - 5)(x - 9)$

Section 6.3 Factoring Trinomials: Trial-and-Error Method

Key Concepts

Trial-and-Error Method for Factoring Trinomials in the Form $ax^2 + bx + c$ (where $a \neq 0$)

1. Factor out the GCF from all terms.
2. List the pairs of factors of a and the pairs of factors of c. Consider the reverse order in one of the lists.
3. Construct two binomials of the form

Factors of a

$$(\square x \quad \square)(\square x \quad \square)$$

Factors of c

4. Test each combination of factors and signs until the product forms the correct trinomial.
5. If no combination of factors produces the correct product, then the trinomial is prime.

Example

Example 1

$10y^2 + 35y - 20$

$= 5(2y^2 + 7y - 4)$

The pairs of factors of 2 are: $2 \cdot 1$

The pairs of factors of -4 are:

$-1(4)$	$1(-4)$
$-2(2)$	$2(-2)$
$-4(1)$	$4(-1)$

$(2y - 2)(y + 2) = 2y^2 + 2y - 4$ No

$(2y - 4)(y + 1) = 2y^2 - 2y - 4$ No

$(2y + 1)(y - 4) = 2y^2 - 7y - 4$ No

$(2y + 2)(y - 2) = 2y^2 - 2y - 4$ No

$(2y + 4)(y - 1) = 2y^2 + 2y - 4$ No

$(2y - 1)(y + 4) = 2y^2 + 7y - 4$ Yes

$10y^2 + 35y - 20 = 5(2y - 1)(y + 4)$

Section 6.4 Factoring Trinomials: AC-Method

Key Concepts

AC-Method for Factoring Trinomials of the Form $ax^2 + bx + c$ (where $a \neq 0$)

1. Factor out the GCF from all terms.
2. Find the product ac.
3. Find two integers whose product is ac and whose sum is b. (If no pair of integers can be found, then the trinomial is prime.)
4. Rewrite the middle term (bx) as the sum of two terms whose coefficients are the integers found in step 3.
5. Factor the polynomial by grouping.

Example

Example 1

$10y^2 + 35y - 20$

$= 5(2y^2 + 7y - 4)$ First factor out the GCF.

Identify the product $ac = (2)(-4) = -8$.

Find two integers whose product is -8 and whose sum is 7. The numbers are 8 and -1.

$5[2y^2 + 8y - 1y - 4]$

$= 5[2y(y + 4) - 1(y + 4)]$

$= 5(y + 4)(2y - 1)$

Section 6.5 Difference of Squares and Perfect Square Trinomials

Key Concepts

Factoring a Difference of Squares

$a^2 - b^2 = (a + b)(a - b)$

Factoring a Perfect Square Trinomial

The factored form of a **perfect square trinomial** is the square of a binomial:

$a^2 + 2ab + b^2 = (a + b)^2$

$a^2 - 2ab + b^2 = (a - b)^2$

Examples

Example 1

$25z^2 - 4y^2$

$= (5z + 2y)(5z - 2y)$

Example 2

Factor: $25y^2 + 10y + 1$

$= (5y)^2 + 2(5y)(1) + (1)^2$

$= (5y + 1)^2$

Section 6.6 Sum and Difference of Cubes

Key Concepts

Factoring a Sum or Difference of Cubes

$a^3 + b^3 = (a + b)(a^2 - ab + b^2)$

$a^3 - b^3 = (a - b)(a^2 + ab + b^2)$

Examples

Example 1

$x^6 + 8y^3$

$= (x^2)^3 + (2y)^3$

$= (x^2 + 2y)(x^4 - 2x^2y + 4y^2)$

Example 2

$m^3 - 64$

$= (m)^3 - (4)^3$

$= (m - 4)(m^2 + 4m + 16)$

Section 6.7 Solving Equations Using the Zero Product Rule

Key Concepts

An equation of the form $ax^2 + bx + c = 0$, where $a \neq 0$, is a **quadratic equation**.

The zero product rule states that if $ab = 0$, then $a = 0$ or $b = 0$. The zero product rule can be used to solve a quadratic equation or a higher degree polynomial equation that is factored and set to zero.

Examples

Example 1

The equation $2x^2 - 17x + 30 = 0$ is a quadratic equation.

Example 2

$3w(w - 4)(2w + 1) = 0$

$3w = 0$ or $w - 4 = 0$ or $2w + 1 = 0$

$w = 0$ or $w = 4$ or $w = -\frac{1}{2}$

The solution set is $\left\{0, 4, -\frac{1}{2}\right\}$.

Example 3

$4x^2 = 34x - 60$

$4x^2 - 34x + 60 = 0$

$2(2x^2 - 17x + 30) = 0$

$2(2x - 5)(x - 6) = 0$

$2 \neq 0$ or $2x - 5 = 0$ or $x - 6 = 0$

$x = \frac{5}{2}$ or $x = 6$

The solution set is $\left\{\frac{5}{2}, 6\right\}$.

Section 6.8 Applications of Quadratic Equations

Key Concepts

Use the zero product rule to solve applications.

Some applications involve the Pythagorean theorem.

$a^2 + b^2 = c^2$

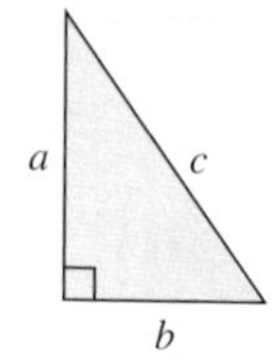

Examples

Example 1

Find two consecutive integers such that the sum of their squares is 61.

Let x represent one integer.
Let $x + 1$ represent the next consecutive integer.

$$x^2 + (x + 1)^2 = 61$$
$$x^2 + x^2 + 2x + 1 = 61$$
$$2x^2 + 2x - 60 = 0$$
$$2(x^2 + x - 30) = 0$$
$$2(x - 5)(x + 6) = 0$$
$$x = 5 \quad \text{or} \quad x = -6$$

If $x = 5$, then the next consecutive integer is 6.
If $x = -6$, then the next consecutive integer is -5.

The integers are 5 and 6, or -6 and -5.

Example 2

Find the length of the missing side.

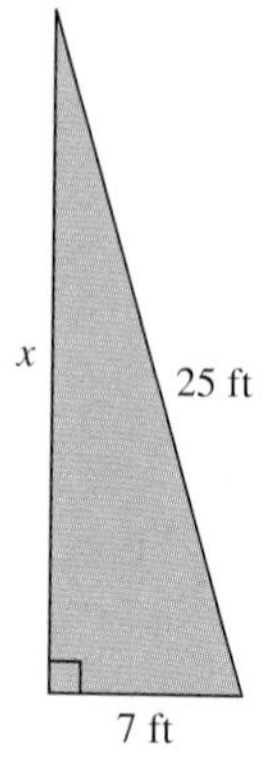

$$x^2 + (7)^2 = (25)^2$$
$$x^2 + 49 = 625$$
$$x^2 - 576 = 0$$
$$(x - 24)(x + 24) = 0$$
$$x = 24 \quad \text{or} \quad \cancel{x = -24}$$

The length of the side is 24 ft.

Chapter 6 Review Exercises

Section 6.1

For Exercises 1–4, identify the greatest common factor for each group of terms.

1. $15a^2b^4, 30a^3b, 9a^5b^3$ $3a^2b$
2. $3(x + 5), x(x + 5)$ $x + 5$
3. $2c^3(3c - 5), 4c(3c - 5)$ $2c(3c - 5)$
4. $-2wyz, -4xyz$ $-2yz$ or $2yz$

For Exercises 5–10, factor out the greatest common factor.

5. $6x^2 + 2x^4 - 8x$ $2x(3x + x^3 - 4)$
6. $11w^3y^3 - 44w^2y^5$ $11w^2y^3(w - 4y^2)$
7. $-t^2 + 5t$ $t(-t + 5)$ or $-t(t - 5)$
8. $-6u^2 - u$ $u(-6u - 1)$ or $-u(6u + 1)$
9. $3b(b + 2) - 7(b + 2)$ $(b + 2)(3b - 7)$
10. $2(5x + 9) + 8x(5x + 9)$ $2(5x + 9)(1 + 4x)$

For Exercises 11–14, factor by grouping.

11. $7w^2 + 14w + wb + 2b$ $(w + 2)(7w + b)$
12. $b^2 - 2b + yb - 2y$ $(b - 2)(b + y)$
13. $60y^2 - 45y - 12y + 9$ $3(4y - 3)(5y - 1)$
14. $6a - 3a^2 - 2ab + a^2b$ $a(2 - a)(3 - b)$

Section 6.2

For Exercises 15–24, factor completely.

15. $x^2 - 10x + 21$ $(x - 3)(x - 7)$
16. $y^2 - 19y + 88$ $(y - 8)(y - 11)$
17. $-6z + z^2 - 72$ $(z - 12)(z + 6)$
18. $-39 + q^2 - 10q$ $(q - 13)(q + 3)$
19. $3p^2w + 36pw + 60w$ $3w(p + 10)(p + 2)$
20. $2m^4 + 26m^3 + 80m^2$ $2m^2(m + 8)(m + 5)$
21. $-t^2 + 10t - 16$ $-(t - 8)(t - 2)$
22. $-w^2 - w + 20$ $-(w - 4)(w + 5)$
23. $a^2 + 12ab + 11b^2$ $(a + b)(a + 11b)$
24. $c^2 - 3cd - 18d^2$ $(c - 6d)(c + 3d)$

Section 6.3

For Exercises 25–28, assume that a, b, and c represent positive integers.

25. When factoring a polynomial of the form $ax^2 - bx - c$, should the signs of the binomials be both positive, both negative, or different? Different
26. When factoring a polynomial of the form $ax^2 - bx + c$, should the signs of the binomials be both positive, both negative, or different? Both negative
27. When factoring a polynomial of the form $ax^2 + bx + c$, should the signs of the binomials be both positive, both negative, or different? Both positive
28. When factoring a polynomial of the form $ax^2 + bx - c$, should the signs of the binomials be both positive, both negative, or different? Different

For Exercises 29–42, factor each trinomial using the trial-and-error method.

29. $2y^2 - 5y - 12$ $(2y + 3)(y - 4)$
30. $4w^2 - 5w - 6$ $(4w + 3)(w - 2)$
31. $10z^2 + 29z + 10$ $(2z + 5)(5z + 2)$
32. $8z^2 + 6z - 9$ $(4z - 3)(2z + 3)$
33. $2p^2 - 5p + 1$ Prime
34. $5r^2 - 3r + 7$ Prime
35. $10w^2 - 60w - 270$ $10(w - 9)(w + 3)$
36. $-3y^2 + 18y + 48$ $-3(y - 8)(y + 2)$
37. $9c^2 - 30cd + 25d^2$ $(3c - 5d)^2$
38. $x^2 + 12x + 36$ $(x + 6)^2$
39. $6g^2 + 7gh + 2h^2$ $(3g + 2h)(2g + h)$
40. $12m^2 - 32mn + 5n^2$ $(6m - n)(2m - 5n)$
41. $v^4 - 2v^2 - 3$ $(v^2 + 1)(v^2 - 3)$
42. $x^4 + 7x^2 + 10$ $(x^2 + 5)(x^2 + 2)$

Section 6.4

For Exercises 43–44, find a pair of integers whose product and sum are given.

43. Product: -5 sum: 4 $5, -1$
44. Product: 15 sum: -8 $-3, -5$

For Exercises 45–58, factor each trinomial using the ac-method.

45. $3c^2 - 5c - 2$ $(c - 2)(3c + 1)$
46. $4y^2 + 13y + 3$ $(y + 3)(4y + 1)$
47. $t^2 + 13tw + 12w^2$ $(t + 12w)(t + w)$
48. $4x^4 + 17x^2 - 15$ $(4x^2 - 3)(x^2 + 5)$
49. $w^4 + 7w^2 + 10$ $(w^2 + 5)(w^2 + 2)$
50. $p^2 - 8pq + 15q^2$ $(p - 3q)(p - 5q)$
51. $-40v^2 - 22v + 6$ $-2(4v + 3)(5v - 1)$
52. $40s^2 + 30s - 100$ $10(4s - 5)(s + 2)$
53. $a^3b - 10a^2b^2 + 24ab^3$ $ab(a - 6b)(a - 4b)$
54. $2z^6 + 8z^5 - 42z^4$ $2z^4(z + 7)(z - 3)$

55. $m + 9m^2 - 2$
Prime

56. $2 + 6p^2 + 19p$
Prime

57. $49x^2 + 140x + 100$
$(7x + 10)^2$

58. $9w^2 - 6wz + z^2$
$(3w - z)^2$

Section 6.5

For Exercises 59–60, write the formula to factor each binomial, if possible.

59. $a^2 - b^2$
$(a - b)(a + b)$

60. $a^2 + b^2$
Prime

For Exercises 61–76, factor completely.

61. $a^2 - 49$
$(a - 7)(a + 7)$

62. $d^2 - 64$
$(d - 8)(d + 8)$

63. $100 - 81t^2$
$(10 - 9t)(10 + 9t)$

64. $4 - 25k^2$
$(2 - 5k)(2 + 5k)$

65. $x^2 + 16$
Prime

66. $y^2 + 121$
Prime

67. $y^2 + 12y + 36$
$(y + 6)^2$

68. $t^2 + 16t + 64$
$(t + 8)^2$

69. $9a^2 - 12a + 4$
$(3a - 2)^2$

70. $25x^2 - 40x + 16$
$(5x - 4)^2$

71. $-3v^2 - 12v - 12$
$-3(v + 2)^2$

72. $-2x^2 + 20x - 50$
$-2(x - 5)^2$

73. $2c^4 - 18$
$2(c^2 - 3)(c^2 + 3)$

74. $72x^2 - 2y^2$
$2(6x - y)(6x + y)$

75. $p^3 + 3p^2 - 16p - 48$
$(p + 3)(p - 4)(p + 4)$

76. $4k - 8 - k^3 + 2k^2$
$(k - 2)(2 - k)(2 + k)$
or $-(k - 2)^2(2 + k)$

Section 6.6

For Exercises 77–78, write the formula to factor each binomial, if possible.

77. $a^3 + b^3$
$(a + b)(a^2 - ab + b^2)$

78. $a^3 - b^3$
$(a - b)(a^2 + ab + b^2)$

For Exercises 79–92, factor completely.

79. $64 + a^3$
$(4 + a)(16 - 4a + a^2)$

80. $125 - b^3$
$(5 - b)(25 + 5b + b^2)$

81. $p^6 + 8$
$(p^2 + 2)(p^4 - 2p^2 + 4)$

82. $q^6 - \frac{1}{27}$
$\left(q^2 - \frac{1}{3}\right)\left(q^4 + \frac{1}{3}q^2 + \frac{1}{9}\right)$

83. $6x^3 - 48$
$6(x - 2)(x^2 + 2x + 4)$

84. $7y^3 + 7$
$7(y + 1)(y^2 - y + 1)$

85. $x^3 - 36x$
$x(x - 6)(x + 6)$

86. $q^4 - 64q$
$q(q - 4)(q^2 + 4q + 16)$

87. $8h^2 + 20$
$4(2h^2 + 5)$

88. $m^2 - 8m$
$m(m - 8)$

89. $x^3 + 4x^2 - x - 4$
$(x + 4)(x + 1)(x - 1)$

90. $5p^4q - 20q^3$
$5q(p^2 - 2q)(p^2 + 2q)$

91. $8n + n^4$
$n(2 + n)(4 - 2n + n^2)$

92. $14m^3 - 14$
$14(m - 1)(m^2 + m + 1)$

Section 6.7

93. For which of the following equations can the zero product rule be applied directly? Explain.
$(x - 3)(2x + 1) = 0$ or $(x - 3)(2x + 1) = 6$
$(x - 3)(2x + 1) = 0$ can be solved directly by the zero product rule because it is a product of factors set equal to zero.

For Exercises 94–109, solve each equation using the zero product rule.

94. $(4x - 1)(3x + 2) = 0$ $\left\{\frac{1}{4}, -\frac{2}{3}\right\}$

95. $(a - 9)(2a - 1) = 0$ $\left\{9, \frac{1}{2}\right\}$

96. $3w(w + 3)(5w + 2) = 0$ $\left\{0, -3, -\frac{2}{5}\right\}$

97. $6u(u - 7)(4u - 9) = 0$ $\left\{0, 7, \frac{9}{4}\right\}$

98. $7k^2 - 9k - 10 = 0$ $\left\{-\frac{5}{7}, 2\right\}$

99. $4h^2 - 23h - 6 = 0$ $\left\{-\frac{1}{4}, 6\right\}$

100. $q^2 - 144 = 0$
$\{12, -12\}$

101. $r^2 = 25$
$\{5, -5\}$

102. $5v^2 - v = 0$ $\left\{0, \frac{1}{5}\right\}$

103. $x(x - 6) = -8$
$\{4, 2\}$

104. $36t^2 + 60t = -25$ $\left\{-\frac{5}{6}\right\}$

105. $9s^2 + 12s = -4$
$\left\{-\frac{2}{3}\right\}$

106. $3(y^2 + 4) = 20y$
$\left\{\frac{2}{3}, 6\right\}$

107. $2(p^2 - 66) = -13p$
$\left\{\frac{11}{2}, -12\right\}$

108. $2y^3 - 18y^2 = -28y$
$\{0, 7, 2\}$

109. $x^3 - 4x = 0$
$\{0, 2, -2\}$

Section 6.8

110. The base of a parallelogram is 1 ft longer than twice the height. If the area is 78 ft², find the base and height of the parallelogram.
The height is 6 ft, and the base is 13 ft.

111. A ball is tossed into the air from ground level with initial speed of 16 ft/sec. The height of the ball is given by the equation

$$h = -16t^2 + 16t \quad (t \geq 0)$$

where h is the ball's height in feet, and t is the time in seconds.

Find the time(s) when the ball is at ground level.
The ball is at ground level at 0 and 1 sec.

112. Find the length of the ramp.
The ramp is 13 ft long.

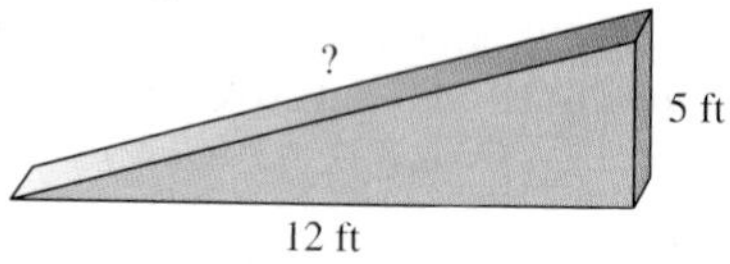

113. A right triangle has one leg that is 2 ft longer than the other leg. The hypotenuse is 2 ft less than twice the shorter leg. Find the lengths of all sides of the triangle.
The legs are 6 ft and 8 ft; the hypotenuse is 10 ft.

114. If the square of a number is subtracted from 60, the result is −4. Find all such numbers.
The numbers are −8 and 8.

115. The product of two consecutive integers is 44 more than 14 times their sum. Find all such integers.
The numbers are 29 and 30, or −2 and −1.

116. The base of a triangle is 1 m longer than twice the height. If the area of the triangle is 18 m^2, find the base and height.
The height is 4 m, and the base is 9 m.

Chapter 6 Test

1. Factor out the GCF. $15x^4 - 3x + 6x^3$
$3x(5x^3 - 1 + 2x^2)$

2. Factor by grouping. $7a - 35 - a^2 + 5a$
$(a - 5)(7 - a)$

3. Factor the trinomial. $6w^2 - 43w + 7$
$(6w - 1)(w - 7)$

4. Factor the difference of squares. $169 - p^2$
$(13 - p)(13 + p)$

5. Factor the perfect square trinomial. $q^2 - 16q + 64$ $(q - 8)^2$

6. Factor the sum of cubes. $8 + t^3$
$(2 + t)(4 - 2t + t^2)$

For Exercises 7–26, factor completely.

7. $a^2 + 12a + 32$
$(a + 4)(a + 8)$

8. $x^2 + x - 42$
$(x + 7)(x - 6)$

9. $2y^2 - 17y + 8$
$(2y - 1)(y - 8)$

10. $6z^2 + 19z + 8$
$(2z + 1)(3z + 8)$

11. $9t^2 - 100$
$(3t - 10)(3t + 10)$

12. $v^2 - 81$
$(v + 9)(v - 9)$

13. $3a^2 + 27ab + 54b^2$
$3(a + 6b)(a + 3b)$

14. $c^4 - 1$
$(c - 1)(c + 1)(c^2 + 1)$

15. $xy - 7x + 3y - 21$
$(y - 7)(x + 3)$

16. $49 + p^2$ Prime

17. $-10u^2 + 30u - 20$
$-10(u - 2)(u - 1)$

18. $12t^2 - 75$
$3(2t - 5)(2t + 5)$

19. $5y^2 - 50y + 125$
$5(y - 5)^2$

20. $21q^2 + 14q$
$7q(3q + 2)$

21. $2x^3 + x^2 - 8x - 4$
$(2x + 1)(x - 2)(x + 2)$

22. $y^3 - 125$
$(y - 5)(y^2 + 5y + 25)$

23. $m^2n^2 - 81$
$(mn - 9)(mn + 9)$

24. $16a^2 - 64b^2$
$16(a - 2b)(a + 2b)$

25. $64x^3 - 27y^6$
$(4x - 3y^2)(16x^2 + 12xy^2 + 9y^4)$

26. $3x^2y - 6xy - 24y$
$3y(x - 4)(x + 2)$

For Exercises 27–31, solve the equation.

27. $(2x - 3)(x + 5) = 0$ $\left\{\frac{3}{2}, -5\right\}$

28. $x^2 - 7x = 0$ $\{0, 7\}$

29. $x^2 - 6x = 16$ $\{8, -2\}$

30. $x(5x + 4) = 1$ $\left\{\frac{1}{5}, -1\right\}$

31. $y^3 + 10y^2 - 9y - 90 = 0$
$\{3, -3, -10\}$

32. A tennis court has an area of 312 yd^2. If the length is 2 yd more than twice the width, find the dimensions of the court.
The tennis court is 12 yd by 26 yd.

33. The product of two consecutive odd integers is 35. Find the integers.
The two integers are 5 and 7, or −5 and −7.

34. The height of a triangle is 5 in. less than the length of the base. The area is 42 in^2. Find the base and the height of the triangle.
The base is 12 in., and the height is 7 in.

35. The hypotenuse of a right triangle is 2 ft less than three times the shorter leg. The longer leg is 3 ft less than three times the shorter leg. Find the length of the shorter leg. The shorter leg is 5 ft.

36. A stone is dropped off a 64-ft cliff. The height of the stone above the ground is given in the equation

$h = -16t^2 + 64$ where h is the stone's height in feet, and t is the time in seconds after the stone is dropped ($t \geq 0$).

Find the time required for the stone to hit the ground. The stone hits the ground in 2 sec.

Chapters 1–6 Cumulative Review Exercises

1. Simplify. $\dfrac{|4 - 25 \div (-5) \cdot 2|}{\sqrt{8^2 + 6^2}}$ $\frac{7}{5}$

2. Solve. $5 - 2(t + 4) = 3t + 12$ $\{-3\}$

3. Solve for y. $3x - 2y = 8$ $y = \frac{3}{2}x - 4$

4. A child's piggy bank has 17 coins in quarters and dimes. The number of dimes is three less than the number of quarters. How many of each type of coin is in the piggy bank?
There are 10 quarters and 7 dimes.

© Ryan McVay/Getty Images RF

5. Solve the inequality. Graph the solution on a number line and write the solution set in interval notation. $[-4, \infty)$

$$-\frac{5}{12}x \le \frac{5}{3}$$

6. Given the equation $y = x + 4$,

   a. Is the equation linear? Yes

   b. Identify the slope. 1

   c. Identify the y-intercept. $(0, 4)$

   d. Identify the x-intercept. $(-4, 0)$

   e. Graph the line

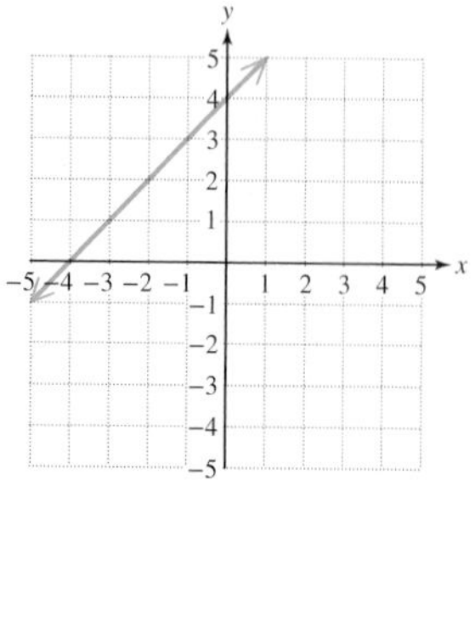

7. Consider the equation $x = 5$,

   a. Does the equation represent a horizontal or vertical line? Vertical line

   b. Determine the slope of the line, if it exists. Undefined

   c. Identify the x-intercept, if it exists. $(5, 0)$

   d. Identify the y-intercept, if it exists. Does not exist

8. Find an equation of the line passing through the point $(-3, 5)$ and having a slope of 3. Write the final answer in slope-intercept form. $y = 3x + 14$

9. Solve the system. $2x - 3y = 4$ $\{(5, 2)\}$
$5x - 6y = 13$

For Exercises 10–13, perform the indicated operations.

10. $2\left(\frac{1}{3}y^3 - \frac{3}{2}y^2 - 7\right) - \left(\frac{2}{3}y^3 + \frac{1}{2}y^2 + 5y\right)$
$-\frac{7}{2}y^2 - 5y - 14$

11. $(4p^2 - 5p - 1)(2p - 3)$ $8p^3 - 22p^2 + 13p + 3$

12. $(2w - 7)^2$ $4w^2 - 28w + 49$

13. $(r^4 + 2r^3 - 5r + 1) \div (r - 3)$ $r^3 + 5r^2 + 15r + 40 + \frac{121}{r - 3}$

14. Simplify. $\dfrac{c^{12}c^{-5}}{c^3}$ c^4

15. Simplify. $\left(\dfrac{6a^2b^{-4}}{2a^4b^{-5}}\right)^{-2}$ $\frac{a^4}{9b^2}$

16. Divide. Write the final answer in scientific notation. $\dfrac{8 \times 10^{-3}}{5 \times 10^{-6}}$ 1.6×10^3

For Exercises 17–19, factor completely.

17. $w^4 - 16$ $(w - 2)(w + 2)(w^2 + 4)$

18. $2ax + 10bx - 3ya - 15yb$ $(a + 5b)(2x - 3y)$

19. $4x^2 - 8x - 5$ $(2x - 5)(2x + 1)$

20. Solve. $4x(2x - 1)(x + 5) = 0$ $\left\{0, \frac{1}{2}, -5\right\}$

Rational Expressions and Equations

7

CHAPTER OUTLINE

Mathematics in Purchasing Land

Suppose you want to purchase a parcel of land in a remote area. The current owner has a large amount of acreage that she plans to divide into n smaller lots for sale. Her total acreage is worth \$120,000 and the smaller lots are of equal size. Thus, the cost (in dollars) of an individual lot is given by:

$$\frac{120{,}000}{n}$$

© AlinaMD/Shutterstock RF

This fraction is called a **rational expression**, because it consists of a polynomial in the numerator and a nonzero polynomial in the denominator.

The cost to purchase an individual lot also includes closing costs. If closing costs are \$5600, then the total cost (in dollars) to purchase one lot is given by:

$$\frac{120{,}000}{n} + 5600$$

This expression can be simplified by combining the two terms into a single rational expression. In this chapter we will learn how to perform operations on rational expressions and see numerous applications of their use.

Section 7.1 Introduction to Rational Expressions

Concepts

1. Definition of a Rational Expression
2. Evaluating Rational Expressions
3. Restricted Values of a Rational Expression
4. Simplifying Rational Expressions
5. Simplifying a Ratio of −1

1. Definition of a Rational Expression

We define a rational number as the ratio of two integers, $\frac{p}{q}$, where $q \neq 0$.

Examples of rational numbers: $\frac{2}{3}, -\frac{1}{5}, 9$

In a similar way, we define a **rational expression** as the ratio of two polynomials, $\frac{p}{q}$, where $q \neq 0$.

Examples of rational expressions: $\frac{3x-6}{x^2-4}, \frac{3}{4}, \frac{6r^5+2r}{7r^3}$

2. Evaluating Rational Expressions

Classroom Examples: p. 495, Exercises 6 and 10

Example 1 Evaluating Rational Expressions

Evaluate the rational expression (if possible) for the given values of x. $\frac{x}{x-3}$

a. $x = 6$ **b.** $x = -3$ **c.** $x = 0$ **d.** $x = 3$

Solution:

Substitute the given value for the variable. Use the order of operations to simplify.

Instructor Note: Memory Device: Zero **under** the line is **un**defined.

a. $\frac{x}{x-3}$

$\frac{(6)}{(6)-3}$ Substitute $x = 6$.

$= \frac{6}{3}$

$= 2$

b. $\frac{x}{x-3}$

$\frac{(-3)}{(-3)-3}$ Substitute $x = -3$.

$= \frac{-3}{-6}$

$= \frac{1}{2}$

c. $\frac{x}{x-3}$

$\frac{(0)}{(0)-3}$ Substitute $x = 0$.

$= \frac{0}{-3}$

$= 0$

d. $\frac{x}{x-3}$

$\frac{(3)}{(3)-3}$ Substitute $x = 3$.

$= \frac{3}{0}$ Undefined.

Recall that division by zero is undefined.

Avoiding Mistakes

The numerator is 0 and the denominator is nonzero. Therefore, the fraction is equal to 0.

Avoiding Mistakes

The denominator is 0, therefore the fraction is undefined.

Skill Practice Evaluate the expression for the given values of x. $\frac{x-3}{x+5}$

1. $x = 2$ **2.** $x = 0$ **3.** $x = 3$ **4.** $x = -5$

Answers

1. $-\frac{1}{7}$ **2.** $-\frac{3}{5}$

3. 0 **4.** Undefined

3. Restricted Values of a Rational Expression

From Example 1 we see that not all values of x can be substituted into a rational expression. The values that make the denominator zero must be restricted.

The expression $\frac{x}{x-3}$ is undefined for $x = 3$, so we call $x = 3$ a restricted value.

Restricted values of a rational expression are all values that make the expression undefined, that is, make the denominator equal to zero.

Finding the Restricted Values of a Rational Expression

- Set the denominator equal to zero and solve the resulting equation.
- The restricted values are the solutions to the equation.

Example 2 Finding the Restricted Values of Rational Expressions

Classroom Examples: p. 496, Exercises 14 and 24

Identify the restricted values for each expression.

a. $\frac{y-3}{2y+7}$ **b.** $\frac{-5}{x}$

Solution:

a. $\frac{y-3}{2y+7}$

$2y + 7 = 0$ Set the denominator equal to zero.

$2y = -7$ Solve the equation.

$\frac{2y}{2} = \frac{-7}{2}$

$y = -\frac{7}{2}$ The restricted value is $y = -\frac{7}{2}$.

b. $\frac{-5}{x}$

$x = 0$ Set the denominator equal to zero.

The restricted value is $x = 0$.

Skill Practice Identify the restricted values.

5. $\frac{a+2}{2a-8}$ **6.** $\frac{2}{t}$

Instructor Note: Ask the students to find the restricted values of a rational expression that has no variable in the denominator.

For example: $\frac{3x+7}{8}$

Answers

5. $a = 4$ **6.** $t = 0$

Classroom Examples: p. 496, Exercises 18 and 20

Example 3 **Finding the Restricted Values of Rational Expressions**

Identify the restricted values for each expression.

a. $\dfrac{a+10}{a^2-25}$ **b.** $\dfrac{2x^3+5}{x^2+9}$

Solution:

a. $\dfrac{a+10}{a^2-25}$

$a^2 - 25 = 0$ Set the denominator equal to zero. The equation is quadratic.

$(a-5)(a+5) = 0$ Factor.

$a - 5 = 0$ or $a + 5 = 0$ Set each factor equal to zero.

$a = 5$ or $a = -5$

The restricted values are $a = 5$ and $a = -5$.

b. $\dfrac{2x^3+5}{x^2+9}$

$x^2 + 9 = 0$

$x^2 = -9$

The quantity x^2 cannot be negative for any real number, x. The denominator $x^2 + 9$ is the sum of two nonnegative values, and thus cannot equal zero. Therefore, there are no restricted values.

Skill Practice Identify the restricted values.

7. $\dfrac{w-4}{w^2-9}$ **8.** $\dfrac{8}{z^4+1}$

4. Simplifying Rational Expressions

Instructor Note: Remind students that we can reduce common factors, but not terms. We know that $\frac{33}{3} = 11$. If we rewrite as $\frac{30+3}{3}$ it is incorrect to write $\frac{30+\cancel{3}}{\cancel{3}}$.

In many cases, it is advantageous to simplify or reduce a fraction to lowest terms. The same is true for rational expressions.

The method for simplifying rational expressions mirrors the process for simplifying fractions. In each case, factor the numerator and denominator. Common factors in the numerator and denominator form a ratio of 1 and can be reduced.

Simplifying a fraction: $\dfrac{21}{35} \xrightarrow{\text{Factor}} \dfrac{3\cdot 7}{5\cdot 7} = \dfrac{3}{5}\cdot\dfrac{\cancelto{1}{7}}{\cancel{7}} = \dfrac{3}{5}\cdot(1) = \dfrac{3}{5}$

Simplifying a rational expression: $\dfrac{2x-6}{x^2-9} \xrightarrow{\text{Factor}} \dfrac{2(x-3)}{(x+3)(x-3)} = \dfrac{2}{(x+3)}\cdot\dfrac{\cancelto{1}{(x-3)}}{\cancel{(x-3)}} = \dfrac{2}{(x+3)}(1)$

$= \dfrac{2}{x+3}$

Informally, to simplify a rational expression, we simplify the ratio of common factors to 1. Formally, this is accomplished by applying the fundamental principle of rational expressions.

Answers

7. $w = 3, w = -3$

8. There are no restricted values.

Fundamental Principle of Rational Expressions

Let p, q, and r represent polynomials where $q \neq 0$ and $r \neq 0$. Then

$$\frac{pr}{qr} = \frac{p}{q} \cdot \frac{r}{r} = \frac{p}{q} \cdot 1 = \frac{p}{q}$$

TIP: In practice we often shorten the process to reduce a rational expression by dividing out common factors.

$$\frac{p \cdot \overset{1}{\cancel{r}}}{q \cdot \cancel{r}} = \frac{p}{q}$$

Example 4 **Simplifying a Rational Expression**

Classroom Example: p. 497, Exercise 40

Given the expression $\dfrac{2p - 14}{p^2 - 49}$

a. Factor the numerator and denominator.

b. Identify the restricted values.

c. Simplify the rational expression.

Solution:

a. $\dfrac{2p - 14}{p^2 - 49}$ — Factor out the GCF in the numerator.

$= \dfrac{2(p - 7)}{(p + 7)(p - 7)}$ — Factor the denominator as a difference of squares.

b. $(p + 7)(p - 7) = 0$ — To find the restricted values, set the denominator equal to zero. The equation is quadratic.

$p + 7 = 0$ or $p - 7 = 0$ — Set each factor equal to 0.

$p = -7$ or $p = 7$ — The restricted values are -7 and 7.

Avoiding Mistakes

The restricted values of a rational expression are always determined *before* simplifying the expression.

c. $\dfrac{2\overset{1}{\cancel{(p - 7)}}}{(p + 7)\cancel{(p - 7)}}$ — Simplify the ratio of common factors to 1.

$= \dfrac{2}{p + 7}$ (provided $p \neq 7$ and $p \neq -7$)

Skill Practice Given $\dfrac{5z + 25}{z^2 + 3z - 10}$

9. Factor the numerator and the denominator.

10. Identify the restricted values. **11.** Simplify the rational expression.

In Example 4, it is important to note that the expressions

$$\frac{2p - 14}{p^2 - 49} \quad \text{and} \quad \frac{2}{p + 7}$$

are equal for all values of p that make each expression a real number. Therefore,

$$\frac{2p - 14}{p^2 - 49} = \frac{2}{p + 7}$$

for all values of p except $p = 7$ and $p = -7$. (At $p = 7$ and $p = -7$, the original expression is undefined.) This is why the restricted values are determined before the expression is simplified.

Answers

9. $\dfrac{5(z + 5)}{(z + 5)(z - 2)}$

10. $z = -5, z = 2$

11. $\dfrac{5}{z - 2}$ $(z \neq 2, z \neq -5)$

From this point forward, we will write statements of equality between two rational expressions with the assumption that they are equal for all values of the variable for which each expression is defined.

Classroom Example: p. 497, Exercise 44

Example 5 Simplifying a Rational Expression

Simplify the rational expression. $\dfrac{18a^4}{9a^5}$

Solution:

$$\frac{18a^4}{9a^5}$$

$$= \frac{2 \cdot 3 \cdot 3 \cdot a \cdot a \cdot a \cdot a}{3 \cdot 3 \cdot a \cdot a \cdot a \cdot a \cdot a}$$ Factor the numerator and denominator.

$$= \frac{2 \cdot \overset{1}{\cancel{(3 \cdot 3 \cdot a \cdot a \cdot a \cdot a)}}}{\cancel{(3 \cdot 3 \cdot a \cdot a \cdot a \cdot a)} \cdot a}$$ Simplify common factors.

$$= \frac{2}{a}$$

TIP: The expression $\dfrac{18a^4}{9a^5}$ can also be simplified using the properties of exponents.

$$\frac{18a^4}{9a^5} = 2a^{4-5} = 2a^{-1} = \frac{2}{a}$$

Skill Practice Simplify the rational expression.

12. $\dfrac{15q^3}{9q^2}$

Classroom Example: p. 497, Exercise 58

Example 6 Simplifying a Rational Expression

Simplify the rational expression. $\dfrac{2c - 8}{10c^2 - 80c + 160}$

Solution:

$$\frac{2c - 8}{10c^2 - 80c + 160}$$

$$= \frac{2(c - 4)}{10(c^2 - 8c + 16)}$$ Factor out the GCF.

$$= \frac{2(c - 4)}{10(c - 4)^2}$$ Factor the denominator.

$$= \frac{\overset{1}{\cancel{2}}\overset{1}{\cancel{(c - 4)}}}{2 \cdot 5\cancel{(c - 4)}(c - 4)}$$ Simplify the ratio of common factors to 1.

$$= \frac{1}{5(c - 4)}$$

Avoiding Mistakes

Given the expression

$$\frac{2c - 8}{10c^2 - 80c + 160}$$

do not be tempted to reduce before factoring. The terms $2c$ and $10c^2$ cannot be "canceled" because they are *terms* not factors.

The numerator and denominator must be in factored form before simplifying.

Skill Practice Simplify the rational expression.

13. $\dfrac{x^2 - 1}{2x^2 - x - 3}$

Answers

12. $\dfrac{5q}{3}$ **13.** $\dfrac{x - 1}{2x - 3}$

The process to simplify a rational expression is based on the identity property of multiplication. Therefore, this process applies only to factors (remember that factors are multiplied). For example:

$$\frac{3x}{3y} = \frac{3 \cdot x}{3 \cdot y} = \frac{\overset{1}{\cancel{3}}}{\cancel{3}} \cdot \frac{x}{y} = 1 \cdot \frac{x}{y} = \frac{x}{y}$$

Simplify

Terms that are added or subtracted cannot be reduced to lowest terms. For example:

$$\frac{x+3}{y+3}$$

Cannot be simplified

The objective of simplifying a rational expression is to create an equivalent expression that is simpler to use. Consider the rational expression from Example 6 in its original form and in its reduced form. If we substitute a value c into each expression, we see that the reduced form is easier to evaluate. For example, substitute $c = 3$:

	Original Expression	Simplified Expression
	$\frac{2c-8}{10c^2-80c+160}$	$\frac{1}{5(c-4)}$
Substitute $c = 3$	$= \frac{2(3)-8}{10(3)^2-80(3)+160}$	$= \frac{1}{5(3-4)}$
	$= \frac{6-8}{10(9)-240+160}$	$= \frac{1}{5(-1)}$
	$= \frac{-2}{90-240+160}$	$= -\frac{1}{5}$
	$= \frac{-2}{10}$ or $-\frac{1}{5}$	

5. Simplifying a Ratio of −1

When two factors are identical in the numerator and denominator, they form a ratio of 1 and can be reduced. Sometimes we encounter two factors that are *opposites* and form a ratio of −1. For example:

Simplified Form	Details/Notes
$\frac{-5}{5} = -1$	The ratio of a number and its opposite is −1.
$\frac{100}{-100} = -1$	The ratio of a number and its opposite is −1.
$\frac{x+7}{-x-7} = -1$	$\frac{x+7}{-x-7} = \frac{x+7}{-1(x+7)} = \frac{\overset{1}{\cancel{x+7}}}{-1(\cancel{x+7})} = \frac{1}{-1} = -1$ (factor out −1)
$\frac{2-x}{x-2} = -1$	$\frac{2-x}{x-2} = \frac{-1(-2+x)}{x-2} = \frac{-1(\overset{1}{\cancel{x-2}})}{\cancel{x-2}} = \frac{-1}{1} = -1$

Recognizing factors that are opposites is useful when simplifying rational expressions.

Avoiding Mistakes

While the expression $2 - x$ and $x - 2$ are opposites, the expressions $2 - x$ and $2 + x$ are *not*. Therefore, $\frac{2-x}{2+x}$ does not simplify to −1.

Classroom Example: p. 497, Exercise 80

Example 7 **Simplifying a Rational Expression**

Simplify the rational expression. $\dfrac{3c-3d}{d-c}$

Solution:

$\dfrac{3c-3d}{d-c}$

$=\dfrac{3(c-d)}{d-c}$ Factor the numerator and denominator.

Notice that $(c-d)$ and $(d-c)$ are opposites and form a ratio of -1.

$=\dfrac{3\overset{-1}{\cancel{(c-d)}}}{\cancel{d-c}}$ Details: $\dfrac{3(c-d)}{d-c}=\dfrac{3(-1)(-c+d)}{d-c}=\dfrac{-3(d-c)}{d-c)}=-3$

$=3(-1)$

$=-3$

Skill Practice Simplify the rational expression.

14. $\dfrac{2t-12}{6-t}$

TIP: It is important to recognize that a rational expression can be written in several equivalent forms. In particular, two numbers with opposite signs form a negative quotient. Therefore, a number such as $-\frac{3}{4}$ can be written as:

$$-\frac{3}{4} \quad \text{or} \quad \frac{-3}{4} \quad \text{or} \quad \frac{3}{-4}$$

The negative sign can be written in the numerator, in the denominator, or out in front of the fraction. We demonstrate this concept in Example 8.

Classroom Example: p. 497, Exercises 86

Example 8 **Simplifying a Rational Expression**

Simplify the rational expression. $\dfrac{5-y}{y^2-25}$

Solution:

$\dfrac{5-y}{y^2-25}$

$=\dfrac{5-y}{(y-5)(y+5)}$ Factor the numerator and denominator.

Notice that $5-y$ and $y-5$ are opposites and form a ratio of -1.

Answer

14. -2

$$= \frac{\overset{-1}{\cancel{5-y}}}{\cancel{(y-5)}(y+5)} \qquad \underline{\text{Details:}}\ \frac{5-y}{(y-5)(y+5)} = \frac{-1(-5+y)}{(y-5)(y+5)}$$

$$= \frac{-1(y-5)}{(y-5)(y+5)} = \frac{-1}{y+5}$$

$$= \frac{-1}{y+5} \quad \text{or} \quad \frac{1}{-(y+5)} \quad \text{or} \quad -\frac{1}{y+5}$$

Skill Practice Simplify the rational expression.

15. $\dfrac{b-a}{a^2-b^2}$

Answer

15. $-\dfrac{1}{a+b}$

Section 7.1 Practice Exercises

For additional exercises, see Classroom Activities 7.1A–7.1B in the *Student's Resource Manual* at www.mhhe.com/moh.

Study Skills Exercise

Write an example of how to simplify (reduce) a fraction, multiply two fractions, divide two fractions, add two fractions, and subtract two fractions. Then as you learn about rational expressions, compare the operations on rational expressions with those on fractions. This is a great place to use 3 × 5 cards again. Write an example of an operation with fractions on one side and the same operation with rational expressions on the other side.

Vocabulary and Key Concepts

1. a. A __rational__ expression is the ratio of two polynomials, $\frac{p}{q}$, where $q \neq 0$.

b. Restricted values of a rational expression are all values that make the __denominator__ equal to __zero__.

c. For polynomials p, q, and r, where ($q \neq 0$ and $r \neq 0$), $\dfrac{pr}{qr} =$ __$\frac{p}{q}$__.

d. The ratio $\dfrac{a-b}{a-b} =$ __1__ whereas the ratio $\dfrac{a-b}{b-a} =$ __−1__ provided that $a \neq b$.

Concept 2: Evaluating Rational Expressions

For Exercises 2–10, substitute the given number into the expression and simplify (if possible). **(See Example 1.)**

2. $\dfrac{5}{y-4}$; $y = 6$ $\quad \frac{5}{2}$

3. $\dfrac{t-2}{t^2-4t+8}$; $t = 2$ $\quad 0$

4. $\dfrac{4x}{x-7}$; $x = 8$ $\quad 32$

5. $\dfrac{1}{x-6}$; $x = -2$ $\quad -\frac{1}{8}$

6. $\dfrac{w-10}{w+6}$; $w = 0$ $\quad -\frac{5}{3}$

7. $\dfrac{w-4}{2w+8}$; $w = 0$ $\quad -\frac{1}{2}$

8. $\dfrac{y-8}{2y^2+y-1}$; $y = 8$ $\quad 0$

9. $\dfrac{(a-7)(a+1)}{(a-2)(a+5)}$; $a = 2$ $\quad$ Undefined

10. $\dfrac{(a+4)(a+1)}{(a-4)(a-1)}$; $a = 1$ $\quad$ Undefined

11. A bicyclist rides 24 mi against a wind and returns 24 mi with the same wind. His average speed for the return trip traveling with the wind is 8 mph faster than his speed going out against the wind. If x represents the bicyclist's speed going out against the wind, then the total time, t, required for the round trip is given by

$$t = \frac{24}{x} + \frac{24}{x+8} \quad \text{where } t \text{ is measured in hours.}$$

© Royalty Free/Corbis RF

a. Find the time required for the round trip if the cyclist rides 12 mph against the wind. $3\frac{1}{5}$ hr or 3.2 hr

b. Find the time required for the round trip if the cyclist rides 24 mph against the wind. $1\frac{3}{4}$ hr or 1.75 hr

12. The manufacturer of mountain bikes has a fixed cost of \$56,000, plus a variable cost of \$140 per bike. The average cost per bike, y (in dollars), is given by the equation:

$$y = \frac{56{,}000 + 140x}{x} \quad \text{where } x \text{ represents the number of bikes produced.}$$

a. Find the average cost per bike if the manufacturer produces 1000 bikes. \$196

b. Find the average cost per bike if the manufacturer produces 2000 bikes. \$168

c. Find the average cost per bike if the manufacturer produces 10,000 bikes. \$145.80

© Jeff Maloney/Getty Images RF

Concept 3: Restricted Values of a Rational Expression

For Exercises 13–24, identify the restricted values. **(See Examples 2–3.)**

13. $\frac{5}{k+2}$ $k = -2$

14. $\frac{-3}{h-4}$ $h = 4$

15. $\frac{x+5}{(2x-5)(x+8)}$ $x = \frac{5}{2}, x = -8$

16. $\frac{4y+1}{(3y+7)(y+3)}$ $y = -\frac{7}{3}, y = -3$

17. $\frac{m+12}{m^2+5m+6}$ $m = -2, m = -3$

18. $\frac{c-11}{c^2-5c-6}$ $c = 6, c = -1$

19. $\frac{x-4}{x^2+9}$ There are no restricted values.

20. $\frac{x+1}{x^2+4}$ There are no restricted values.

21. $\frac{y^2-y-12}{12}$ There are no restricted values.

22. $\frac{z^2+10z+9}{9}$ There are no restricted values.

23. $\frac{t-5}{t}$ $t = 0$

24. $\frac{2w+7}{w}$ $w = 0$

25. Construct a rational expression that is undefined for $x = 2$. (Answers will vary.) For example: $\frac{1}{x-2}$

26. Construct a rational expression that is undefined for $x = 5$. (Answers will vary.) For example: $\frac{1}{x-5}$

27. Construct a rational expression that is undefined for $x = -3$ and $x = 7$. (Answers will vary.) For example: $\frac{1}{(x+3)(x-7)}$

28. Construct a rational expression that is undefined for $x = -1$ and $x = 4$. (Answers will vary.) For example: $\frac{1}{(x+1)(x-4)}$

29. Evaluate the expressions for $x = -1$.

a. $\frac{3x^2-2x-1}{6x^2-7x-3}$ $\frac{2}{5}$ **b.** $\frac{x-1}{2x-3}$ $\frac{2}{5}$

30. Evaluate the expressions for $x = 4$.

a. $\frac{(x+5)^2}{x^2+6x+5}$ $\frac{9}{5}$ **b.** $\frac{x+5}{x+1}$ $\frac{9}{5}$

31. Evaluate the expressions for $x = 1$.

a. $\frac{5x+5}{x^2-1}$ Undefined **b.** $\frac{5}{x-1}$ Undefined

32. Evaluate the expressions for $x = -3$.

a. $\frac{2x^2-4x-6}{2x^2-18}$ Undefined **b.** $\frac{x+1}{x+3}$ Undefined

Concept 4: Simplifying Rational Expressions

For Exercises 33–42,

a. Identify the restricted values. **b.** Simplify the rational expression. **(See Example 4.)**

33. $\dfrac{3y+6}{6y+12}$ a. $y=-2$ b. $\dfrac{1}{2}$

34. $\dfrac{8x-8}{4x-4}$ a. $x=1$ b. 2

35. $\dfrac{t^2-1}{t+1}$ a. $t=-1$ b. $t-1$

36. $\dfrac{r^2-4}{r-2}$ a. $r=2$ b. $r+2$

37. $\dfrac{7w}{21w^2-35w}$ a. $w=0$, $w=\dfrac{5}{3}$ b. $\dfrac{1}{3w-5}$

38. $\dfrac{12a^2}{24a^2-18a}$ a. $a=0$, $a=\dfrac{3}{4}$ b. $\dfrac{2a}{4a-3}$

39. $\dfrac{9x^2-4}{6x+4}$ a. $x=-\dfrac{2}{3}$ b. $\dfrac{3x-2}{2}$

40. $\dfrac{8n-20}{4n^2-25}$ a. $n=\dfrac{5}{2}$, $n=-\dfrac{5}{2}$ b. $\dfrac{4}{2n+5}$

41. $\dfrac{a^2+3a-10}{a^2+a-6}$ a. $a=-3$, $a=2$ b. $\dfrac{a+5}{a+3}$

42. $\dfrac{t^2+3t-10}{t^2+t-20}$ a. $t=-5$, $t=4$ b. $\dfrac{t-2}{t-4}$

For Exercises 43–72, simplify the rational expression. **(See Examples 5–6.)**

43. $\dfrac{7b^2}{21b}$ $\dfrac{b}{3}$

44. $\dfrac{15c^3}{3c^5}$ $\dfrac{5}{c^2}$

45. $\dfrac{-24x^2y^5z}{8xy^4z^3}$ $-\dfrac{3xy}{z^2}$

46. $\dfrac{60rs^4t^2}{-12r^4s^2t^3}$ $-\dfrac{5s^2}{r^3t}$

47. $\dfrac{(p-3)(p+5)}{(p+5)(p+4)}$ $\dfrac{p-3}{p+4}$

48. $\dfrac{(c+4)(c-1)}{(c+4)(c+2)}$ $\dfrac{c-1}{c+2}$

49. $\dfrac{m+11}{4(m+11)(m-11)}$ $\dfrac{1}{4(m-11)}$

50. $\dfrac{n-7}{9(n+2)(n-7)}$ $\dfrac{1}{9(n+2)}$

51. $\dfrac{x(2x+1)^2}{4x^3(2x+1)}$ $\dfrac{2x+1}{4x^2}$

52. $\dfrac{(p+2)(p-3)^4}{(p+2)^2(p-3)^2}$ $\dfrac{(p-3)^2}{p+2}$

53. $\dfrac{5}{20a-25}$ $\dfrac{1}{4a-5}$

54. $\dfrac{7}{14c-21}$ $\dfrac{1}{2c-3}$

55. $\dfrac{3x^2-6x}{9xy+18x}$ $\dfrac{x-2}{3(y+2)}$

56. $\dfrac{6p^2+12p}{2pq-4p}$ $\dfrac{3(p+2)}{q-2}$

57. $\dfrac{2x+4}{x^2-3x-10}$ $\dfrac{2}{x-5}$

58. $\dfrac{5z+15}{z^2-4z-21}$ $\dfrac{5}{z-7}$

59. $\dfrac{a^2-49}{a-7}$ $a+7$

60. $\dfrac{b^2-64}{b-8}$ $b+8$

61. $\dfrac{q^2+25}{q+5}$ Cannot simplify

62. $\dfrac{r^2+36}{r+6}$ Cannot simplify

63. $\dfrac{y^2+6y+9}{2y^2+y-15}$ $\dfrac{y+3}{2y-5}$

64. $\dfrac{h^2+h-6}{h^2+2h-8}$ $\dfrac{h+3}{h+4}$

65. $\dfrac{5q^2+5}{q^4-1}$ $\dfrac{5}{(q+1)(q-1)}$

66. $\dfrac{4t^2+16}{t^4-16}$ $\dfrac{4}{(t-2)(t+2)}$

67. $\dfrac{ac-ad+2bc-2bd}{2ac+ad+4bc+2bd}$ (*Hint*: Factor by grouping.) $\dfrac{c-d}{2c+d}$

68. $\dfrac{3pr-ps-3qr+qs}{3pr-ps+3qr-qs}$ (*Hint*: Factor by grouping.) $\dfrac{p-q}{p+q}$

69. $\dfrac{5x^3+4x^2-45x-36}{x^2-9}$ $5x+4$

70. $\dfrac{x^2-1}{ax^3-bx^2-ax+b}$ $\dfrac{1}{ax-b}$

71. $\dfrac{2x^2-xy-3y^2}{2x^2-11xy+12y^2}$ $\dfrac{x+y}{x-4y}$

72. $\dfrac{2c^2+cd-d^2}{5c^2+3cd-2d^2}$ $\dfrac{2c-d}{5c-2d}$

Concept 5: Simplifying a Ratio of −1

73. What is the relationship between $x-2$ and $2-x$? They are opposites.

74. What is the relationship between $w+p$ and $-w-p$? They are opposites.

For Exercises 75–86, simplify the rational expressions. **(See Examples 7–8.)**

75. $\dfrac{x-5}{5-x}$ -1

76. $\dfrac{8-p}{p-8}$ -1

77. $\dfrac{-4-y}{4+y}$ -1

78. $\dfrac{z+10}{-z-10}$ -1

79. $\dfrac{3y-6}{12-6y}$ $-\dfrac{1}{2}$

80. $\dfrac{4q-4}{12-12q}$ $-\dfrac{1}{3}$

81. $\dfrac{k+5}{5-k}$ Cannot simplify

82. $\dfrac{2+n}{2-n}$ Cannot simplify

83. $\dfrac{10x-12}{10x+12}$ $\dfrac{5x-6}{5x+6}$

84. $\dfrac{4t-16}{16+4t}$ $\dfrac{t-4}{4+t}$

85. $\dfrac{x^2-x-12}{16-x^2}$ $-\dfrac{x+3}{4+x}$

86. $\dfrac{49-b^2}{b^2-10b+21}$ $-\dfrac{7+b}{b-3}$

Mixed Exercises

For Exercises 87–100, simplify the rational expressions.

87. $\dfrac{3x^2 + 7x - 6}{x^2 + 7x + 12}$ $\dfrac{3x-2}{x+4}$

88. $\dfrac{y^2 - 5y - 14}{2y^2 - y - 10}$ $\dfrac{y-7}{2y-5}$

89. $\dfrac{3(m-2)}{6(2-m)}$ $-\dfrac{1}{2}$

90. $\dfrac{8(1-x)}{4(x-1)}$ -2

91. $\dfrac{w^2 - 4}{8 - 4w}$ $-\dfrac{w+2}{4}$

92. $\dfrac{15 - 3x}{x^2 - 25}$ $-\dfrac{3}{x+5}$

93. $\dfrac{18st^5}{12st^3}$ $\dfrac{3t^2}{2}$

94. $\dfrac{20a^4b^2}{25ab^2}$ $\dfrac{4a^3}{5}$

95. $\dfrac{4r^2 - 4rs + s^2}{s^2 - 4r^2}$ $-\dfrac{2r-s}{s+2r}$

96. $\dfrac{y^2 - 9z^2}{3z^2 + 2yz - y^2}$ $-\dfrac{y+3z}{z+y}$

97. $\dfrac{3y - 3x}{2x^2 - 4xy + 2y^2}$ $-\dfrac{3}{2(x-y)}$

98. $\dfrac{49p^2 - 28pq + 4q^2}{4q - 14p}$ $-\dfrac{7p-2q}{2}$

99. $\dfrac{2t^2 - 3t}{2t^4 - 13t^3 + 15t^2}$ $\dfrac{1}{t(t-5)}$

100. $\dfrac{4m^3 + 3m^2}{4m^3 + 7m^2 + 3m}$ $\dfrac{m}{m+1}$

Expanding Your Skills

For Exercises 101–104, factor and simplify.

101. $\dfrac{w^3 - 8}{w^2 + 2w + 4}$ $w - 2$

102. $\dfrac{y^3 + 27}{y^2 - 3y + 9}$ $y + 3$

103. $\dfrac{z^2 - 16}{z^3 - 64}$ $\dfrac{z+4}{z^2+4z+16}$

104. $\dfrac{x^2 - 25}{x^3 + 125}$ $\dfrac{x-5}{x^2-5x+25}$

Section 7.2 Multiplication and Division of Rational Expressions

Concepts

1. Multiplication of Rational Expressions
2. Division of Rational Expressions

1. Multiplication of Rational Expressions

Recall that to multiply fractions, we multiply the numerators and multiply the denominators. The same is true for multiplying rational expressions.

> **Multiplication of Rational Expressions**
>
> Let p, q, r, and s represent polynomials, such that $q \neq 0$, $s \neq 0$. Then,
>
> $$\frac{p}{q} \cdot \frac{r}{s} = \frac{pr}{qs}$$

For example:

Multiply the Fractions	Multiply the Rational Expressions
$\dfrac{2}{3} \cdot \dfrac{5}{7} = \dfrac{10}{21}$	$\dfrac{2x}{3y} \cdot \dfrac{5z}{7} = \dfrac{10xz}{21y}$

Sometimes it is possible to simplify a ratio of common factors to 1 *before* multiplying. To do so, we must first factor the numerators and denominators of each fraction.

$$\frac{15}{14} \cdot \frac{21}{10} = \frac{3 \cdot \overset{1}{\cancel{5}}}{2 \cdot \cancel{7}} \cdot \frac{3 \cdot \overset{1}{\cancel{7}}}{2 \cdot \cancel{5}} = \frac{9}{4}$$

The same process is also used to multiply rational expressions.

Multiplying Rational Expressions

Step 1 Factor the numerators and denominators of all rational expressions.

Step 2 Simplify the ratios of common factors to 1 and opposite factors to -1.

Step 3 Multiply the remaining factors in the numerator, and multiply the remaining factors in the denominator.

Example 1 Multiplying Rational Expressions

Classroom Example: p. 503, Exercise 10

Multiply. $\dfrac{5a^2b}{2} \cdot \dfrac{6a}{10b}$

Solution:

$$\frac{5a^2b}{2} \cdot \frac{6a}{10b}$$

$$= \frac{5 \cdot a \cdot a \cdot b}{2} \cdot \frac{2 \cdot 3 \cdot a}{2 \cdot 5 \cdot b} \qquad \text{Factor into prime factors.}$$

$$= \frac{\overset{1}{\cancel{5}} \cdot a \cdot a \cdot \overset{1}{\cancel{b}}}{2} \cdot \frac{\overset{1}{\cancel{2}} \cdot 3 \cdot a}{\cancel{2} \cdot \cancel{5} \cdot \cancel{b}} \qquad \text{Simplify.}$$

$$= \frac{3a^3}{2} \qquad \text{Multiply remaining factors.}$$

Skill Practice Multiply.

1. $\dfrac{7a}{3b} \cdot \dfrac{15b}{14a^2}$

Example 2 Multiplying Rational Expressions

Classroom Example: p. 503, Exercise 16

Multiply. $\dfrac{3c - 3d}{6c} \cdot \dfrac{2}{c^2 - d^2}$

Solution:

$$\frac{3c - 3d}{6c} \cdot \frac{2}{c^2 - d^2}$$

$$= \frac{3(c - d)}{2 \cdot 3 \cdot c} \cdot \frac{2}{(c - d)(c + d)} \qquad \text{Factor.}$$

$$= \frac{\overset{1}{\cancel{3}}\overset{1}{\cancel{(c - d)}}}{\cancel{2} \cdot \cancel{3} \cdot c} \cdot \frac{\overset{1}{\cancel{2}}}{\cancel{(c - d)}(c + d)} \qquad \text{Simplify.}$$

$$= \frac{1}{c(c + d)} \qquad \text{Multiply remaining factors.}$$

Avoiding Mistakes

If all the factors in the numerator reduce to a ratio of 1, a factor of 1 is left in the numerator.

Skill Practice Multiply.

2. $\dfrac{4x - 8}{x + 6} \cdot \dfrac{x^2 + 6x}{2x}$

Answers

1. $\dfrac{5}{2a}$ 2. $2(x - 2)$

Classroom Example: p. 503, Exercise 20

Example 3 Multiplying Rational Expressions

Multiply. $\frac{35-5x}{5x+5} \cdot \frac{x^2+5x+4}{x^2-49}$

Solution:

$$\frac{35-5x}{5x+5} \cdot \frac{x^2+5x+4}{x^2-49}$$

$$= \frac{5(7-x)}{5(x+1)} \cdot \frac{(x+4)(x+1)}{(x-7)(x+7)}$$ Factor the numerators and denominators completely.

$$= \frac{\overset{1}{\cancel{5}}\overset{-1}{\cancel{(7-x)}}}{\cancel{5}\cancel{(x+1)}} \cdot \frac{(x+4)\overset{1}{\cancel{(x+1)}}}{\cancel{(x-7)}(x+7)}$$ Simplify the ratios of common factors to 1 or −1.

TIP: The ratio $\frac{7-x}{x-7} = -1$ because $7 - x$ and $x - 7$ are opposites.

$$= \frac{-1(x+4)}{x+7}$$ Multiply remaining factors.

$$= \frac{-(x+4)}{x+7} \quad \text{or} \quad \frac{x+4}{-(x+7)} \quad \text{or} \quad -\frac{x+4}{x+7}$$

Skill Practice Multiply.

3. $\frac{p^2+4p+3}{5p+10} \cdot \frac{p^2-p-6}{9-p^2}$

2. Division of Rational Expressions

Recall that to divide two fractions, multiply the first fraction by the reciprocal of the second.

$$\frac{21}{10} \div \frac{49}{15} \xrightarrow[\text{of the second fraction}]{\text{multiply by the reciprocal}} \frac{21}{10} \cdot \frac{15}{49} \xrightarrow{\text{factor}} \frac{3 \cdot \overset{1}{\cancel{7}}}{2 \cdot \cancel{5}} \cdot \frac{3 \cdot \overset{1}{\cancel{5}}}{\cancel{7} \cdot 7} = \frac{9}{14}$$

The same process is used to divide rational expressions.

Division of Rational Expressions

Let p, q, r, and s represent polynomials, such that $q \neq 0$, $r \neq 0$, $s \neq 0$. Then,

$$\frac{p}{q} \div \frac{r}{s} = \frac{p}{q} \cdot \frac{s}{r} = \frac{ps}{qr}$$

Classroom Example: p. 504, Exercise 32

Example 4 Dividing Rational Expressions

Divide. $\frac{5t-15}{2} \div \frac{t^2-9}{10}$

Solution:

$$\frac{5t-15}{2} \div \frac{t^2-9}{10}$$

Avoiding Mistakes

When dividing rational expressions, take the reciprocal of the second fraction and change to multiplication *before* reducing like factors.

$$= \frac{5t-15}{2} \cdot \frac{10}{t^2-9}$$ Multiply the first fraction by the reciprocal of the second.

Answer

3. $\frac{-(p+1)}{5}$ or $\frac{p+1}{-5}$ or $-\frac{p+1}{5}$

$= \dfrac{5(t-3)}{2} \cdot \dfrac{2 \cdot 5}{(t-3)(t+3)}$ Factor each polynomial.

$= \dfrac{5\overset{1}{\cancel{(t-3)}}}{\cancel{2}} \cdot \dfrac{\overset{1}{\cancel{2}} \cdot 5}{\cancel{(t-3)}(t+3)}$ Simplify the ratio of common factors to 1.

$= \dfrac{25}{t+3}$

Skill Practice Divide.

4. $\dfrac{7y-14}{y+1} \div \dfrac{y^2+2y-8}{2y+2}$

Example 5 **Dividing Rational Expressions**

Classroom Example: p. 504, Exercise 38

Divide. $\dfrac{p^2-11p+30}{10p^2-250} \div \dfrac{30p-5p^2}{2p+4}$

Solution:

$\dfrac{p^2-11p+30}{10p^2-250} \div \dfrac{30p-5p^2}{2p+4}$

$= \dfrac{p^2-11p+30}{10p^2-250} \cdot \dfrac{2p+4}{30p-5p^2}$ Multiply the first fraction by the reciprocal of the second.

$= \dfrac{(p-5)(p-6)}{2 \cdot 5(p-5)(p+5)} \cdot \dfrac{2(p+2)}{5p(6-p)}$

Factor the trinomial.
$p^2-11p+30 = (p-5)(p-6)$

Factor out the GCF.
$2p+4 = 2(p+2)$

Factor out the GCF. Then factor the difference of squares.
$10p^2-250 = 10(p^2-25)$
$= 2 \cdot 5(p-5)(p+5)$

Factor out the GCF.
$30p-5p^2 = 5p(6-p)$

$= \dfrac{\overset{1}{\cancel{(p-5)}}\overset{-1}{\cancel{(p-6)}}}{\cancel{2} \cdot 5\cancel{(p-5)}(p+5)} \cdot \dfrac{\overset{1}{\cancel{2}}(p+2)}{5p\cancel{(6-p)}}$ Simplify the ratio of common factors to 1 or −1.

$= -\dfrac{(p+2)}{25p(p+5)}$

Skill Practice Divide.

5. $\dfrac{4x^2-9}{2x^2-x-3} \div \dfrac{20x+30}{x^2+7x+6}$

Answers

4. $\dfrac{14}{y+4}$ 5. $\dfrac{x+6}{10}$

Classroom Example: p. 504, Exercise 28

Example 6 **Dividing Rational Expressions**

Divide. $\dfrac{\dfrac{3x}{4y}}{\dfrac{5x}{6y}}$

Solution:

$\dfrac{\dfrac{3x}{4y}}{\dfrac{5x}{6y}}$ ← This fraction bar denotes division (÷).

$= \dfrac{3x}{4y} \div \dfrac{5x}{6y}$

$= \dfrac{3x}{4y} \cdot \dfrac{6y}{5x}$ Multiply by the reciprocal of the second fraction.

$= \dfrac{3 \cdot \overset{1}{\cancel{x}}}{\cancel{2} \cdot 2 \cdot \cancel{y}} \cdot \dfrac{\overset{1}{\cancel{2}} \cdot 3 \cdot \overset{1}{\cancel{y}}}{5 \cdot \cancel{x}}$ Simplify the ratio of common factors to 1.

$= \dfrac{9}{10}$

Skill Practice Divide.

6. $\dfrac{\dfrac{a^3b}{9c}}{\dfrac{4ab}{3c^3}}$

Sometimes multiplication and division of rational expressions appear in the same problem. In such a case, apply the order of operations by multiplying or dividing in order from left to right.

Classroom Example: p. 505, Exercise 66

Example 7 **Multiplying and Dividing Rational Expressions**

Perform the indicated operations. $\dfrac{4}{c^2-9} \div \dfrac{6}{c-3} \cdot \dfrac{3c}{8}$

Solution:

In this example, division occurs first, before multiplication. Parentheses may be inserted to reinforce the proper order.

$\left(\dfrac{4}{c^2-9} \div \dfrac{6}{c-3}\right) \cdot \dfrac{3c}{8}$

$= \left(\dfrac{4}{c^2-9} \cdot \dfrac{c-3}{6}\right) \cdot \dfrac{3c}{8}$ Multiply the first fraction by the reciprocal of the second.

Answer

6. $\dfrac{a^2c^2}{12}$

$$= \left(\frac{2 \cdot 2}{(c-3)(c+3)} \cdot \frac{c-3}{2 \cdot 3}\right) \cdot \frac{3 \cdot c}{2 \cdot 2 \cdot 2}$$

Now that each operation is written as multiplication, factor the polynomials and reduce the common factors.

$$= \frac{\overset{1}{\cancel{2}} \cdot \overset{1}{\cancel{2}}}{\cancel{(c-3)}(c+3)} \cdot \frac{\overset{1}{\cancel{(c-3)}}}{2 \cdot \cancel{3}} \cdot \frac{\overset{1}{\cancel{3}} \cdot c}{\cancel{2} \cdot \cancel{2} \cdot 2}$$

$$= \frac{c}{4(c+3)}$$

Simplify.

Skill Practice Perform the indicated operations.

7. $\dfrac{v}{v+2} \div \dfrac{5v^2}{v^2-4} \cdot \dfrac{v}{10}$

Answer

7. $\dfrac{v-2}{50}$

Section 7.2 Practice Exercises

For additional exercises, see Classroom Activities 7.2A–7.2B in the *Student's Resource Manual* at www.mhhe.com/moh.

Review Exercises

For Exercises 1–8, multiply or divide the fractions.

1. $\dfrac{3}{5} \cdot \dfrac{1}{2}$ $\quad \dfrac{3}{10}$

2. $\dfrac{6}{7} \cdot \dfrac{5}{12}$ $\quad \dfrac{5}{14}$

3. $\dfrac{3}{4} \div \dfrac{3}{8}$ $\quad 2$

4. $\dfrac{18}{5} \div \dfrac{2}{5}$ $\quad 9$

5. $6 \cdot \dfrac{5}{12}$ $\quad \dfrac{5}{2}$

6. $\dfrac{7}{25} \cdot 5$ $\quad \dfrac{7}{5}$

7. $\dfrac{\frac{21}{4}}{\frac{7}{5}}$ $\quad \dfrac{15}{4}$

8. $\dfrac{\frac{9}{2}}{\frac{3}{4}}$ $\quad 6$

Concept 1: Multiplication of Rational Expressions

For Exercises 9–24, multiply. **(See Examples 1–3.)**

9. $\dfrac{2xy}{5x^2} \cdot \dfrac{15}{4y}$ $\quad \dfrac{3}{2x}$

10. $\dfrac{7s}{t^2} \cdot \dfrac{t^2}{14s^2}$ $\quad \dfrac{1}{2s}$

11. $\dfrac{6x^3}{9x^6y^2} \cdot \dfrac{18x^4y^7}{4y}$ $\quad 3xy^4$

12. $\dfrac{10a^2b}{15b^2} \cdot \dfrac{30b}{2a^3}$ $\quad \dfrac{10}{a}$

13. $\dfrac{4x-24}{20x} \cdot \dfrac{5x}{8}$ $\quad \dfrac{x-6}{8}$

14. $\dfrac{5a+20}{a} \cdot \dfrac{3a}{10}$ $\quad \dfrac{3(a+4)}{2}$

15. $\dfrac{3y+18}{y^2} \cdot \dfrac{4y}{6y+36}$ $\quad \dfrac{2}{y}$

16. $\dfrac{2p-4}{6p} \cdot \dfrac{4p^2}{8p-16}$ $\quad \dfrac{p}{6}$

17. $\dfrac{10}{2-a} \cdot \dfrac{a-2}{16}$ $\quad -\dfrac{5}{8}$

18. $\dfrac{w-3}{6} \cdot \dfrac{20}{3-w}$ $\quad -\dfrac{10}{3}$

19. $\dfrac{b^2-a^2}{a-b} \cdot \dfrac{a}{a^2-ab}$ $\quad -\dfrac{b+a}{a-b}$

20. $\dfrac{(x-y)^2}{x^2+xy} \cdot \dfrac{x}{y-x}$ $\quad -\dfrac{x-y}{x+y}$

21. $\dfrac{y^2+2y+1}{5y-10} \cdot \dfrac{y^2-3y+2}{y^2-1}$ $\quad \dfrac{y+1}{5}$

22. $\dfrac{6a^2-6}{a^2+6a+5} \cdot \dfrac{a^2+5a}{12a}$ $\quad \dfrac{a-1}{2}$

23. $\dfrac{10x}{2x^2+3x+1} \cdot \dfrac{x^2+7x+6}{5x}$ $\quad \dfrac{2(x+6)}{2x+1}$

24. $\dfrac{p-3}{p^2+p-12} \cdot \dfrac{4p+16}{p+1}$ $\quad \dfrac{4}{p+1}$

Concept 2: Division of Rational Expressions

For Exercises 25–38, divide. **(See Examples 4–6.)**

25. $\dfrac{4x}{7y} \div \dfrac{2x^2}{21xy}$ $\quad 6$

26. $\dfrac{6cd}{5d^2} \div \dfrac{8c^3}{10d}$ $\quad \dfrac{3}{2c^2}$

27. $\dfrac{\dfrac{8m^4n^5}{5n^6}}{\dfrac{24mn}{15m^3}}$ $\quad \dfrac{m^6}{n^2}$

28. $\dfrac{\dfrac{10a^3b}{3a}}{\dfrac{5b}{9ab}}$ $\quad 6a^3b$

29. $\dfrac{4a+12}{6a-18} \div \dfrac{3a+9}{5a-15}$ $\quad \dfrac{10}{9}$

30. $\dfrac{8m-16}{3m+3} \div \dfrac{5m-10}{2m+2}$ $\quad \dfrac{16}{15}$

31. $\dfrac{3x-21}{6x^2-42x} \div \dfrac{7}{12x}$ $\quad \dfrac{6}{7}$

32. $\dfrac{4a^2-4a}{9a-9} \div \dfrac{5}{12a}$ $\quad \dfrac{16a^2}{15}$

33. $\dfrac{m^2-n^2}{9} \div \dfrac{3n-3m}{27m}$ $\quad -m(m+n)$

34. $\dfrac{9-t^2}{15t+15} \div \dfrac{t-3}{5t}$ $\quad -\dfrac{t(3+t)}{3(t+1)}$

35. $\dfrac{3p+4q}{p^2+4pq+4q^2} \div \dfrac{4}{p+2q}$ $\quad \dfrac{3p+4q}{4(p+2q)}$

36. $\dfrac{x^2+2xy+y^2}{2x-y} \div \dfrac{x+y}{5}$ $\quad \dfrac{5(x+y)}{2x-y}$

37. $\dfrac{p^2-2p-3}{p^2-p-6} \div \dfrac{p^2-1}{p^2+2p}$ $\quad \dfrac{p}{p-1}$

38. $\dfrac{4t^2-1}{t^2-5t} \div \dfrac{2t^2+5t+2}{t^2-3t-10}$ $\quad \dfrac{2t-1}{t}$

Mixed Exercises

For Exercises 39–64, multiply or divide as indicated.

39. $(w+3) \cdot \dfrac{w}{2w^2+5w-3}$ $\quad \dfrac{w}{2w-1}$

40. $\dfrac{5t+1}{5t^2-31t+6} \cdot (t-6)$ $\quad \dfrac{5t+1}{5t-1}$

41. $(r-5) \cdot \dfrac{4r}{2r^2-7r-15}$ $\quad \dfrac{4r}{2r+3}$

42. $\dfrac{q+1}{5q^2-28q-12} \cdot (5q+2)$ $\quad \dfrac{q+1}{q-6}$

43. $\dfrac{\dfrac{5t-10}{12}}{\dfrac{4t-8}{8}}$ $\quad \dfrac{5}{6}$

44. $\dfrac{\dfrac{6m+6}{5}}{\dfrac{3m+3}{10}}$ $\quad 4$

45. $\dfrac{2a^2+13a-24}{8a-12} \div (a+8)$ $\quad \dfrac{1}{4}$

46. $\dfrac{3y^2+20y-7}{5y+35} \div (3y-1)$ $\quad \dfrac{1}{5}$

47. $\dfrac{y^2+5y-36}{y^2-2y-8} \cdot \dfrac{y+2}{y-6}$ $\quad \dfrac{y+9}{y-6}$

48. $\dfrac{z^2-11z+28}{z-1} \cdot \dfrac{z+1}{z^2-6z-7}$ $\quad \dfrac{z-4}{z-1}$

49. $\dfrac{2t^2+t-1}{t^2+3t+2} \cdot \dfrac{t+2}{2t-1}$ $\quad 1$

50. $\dfrac{3p^2-2p-8}{3p^2-5p-12} \cdot \dfrac{p-3}{p-2}$ $\quad 1$

51. $(5t-1) \div \dfrac{5t^2+9t-2}{3t+8}$ $\quad \dfrac{3t+8}{t+2}$

52. $(2q-3) \div \dfrac{2q^2+5q-12}{q-7}$ $\quad \dfrac{q-7}{q+4}$

53. $\dfrac{x^2+2x-3}{x^2-3x+2} \cdot \dfrac{x^2+2x-8}{x^2+4x+3}$ $\quad \dfrac{x+4}{x+1}$

54. $\dfrac{y^2+y-12}{y^2-y-20} \cdot \dfrac{y^2+y-30}{y^2-2y-3}$ $\quad \dfrac{y+6}{y+1}$

55. $\dfrac{\dfrac{w^2-6w+9}{8}}{\dfrac{9-w^2}{4w+12}}$ $\quad -\dfrac{w-3}{2}$

56. $\dfrac{\dfrac{p^2-6p+8}{24}}{\dfrac{16-p^2}{6p+6}}$ $\quad -\dfrac{(p-2)(p+1)}{4(4+p)}$

57. $\dfrac{5k^2+7k+2}{k^2+5k+4} \div \dfrac{5k^2+17k+6}{k^2+10k+24}$ $\quad \dfrac{k+6}{k+3}$

58. $\dfrac{4h^2-5h+1}{h^2+h-2} \div \dfrac{6h^2-7h+2}{2h^2+3h-2}$ $\quad \dfrac{4h-1}{3h-2}$

59. $\dfrac{ax+a+bx+b}{2x^2+4x+2} \cdot \dfrac{4x+4}{a^2+ab}$ $\quad \dfrac{2}{a}$

60. $\dfrac{3my+9m+ny+3n}{9m^2+6mn+n^2} \cdot \dfrac{30m+10n}{5y^2+15y}$ $\quad \dfrac{2}{y}$

61. $\dfrac{y^4 - 1}{2y^2 - 3y + 1} \div \dfrac{2y^2 + 2}{8y^2 - 4y}$ $2y(y+1)$

62. $\dfrac{x^4 - 16}{6x^2 + 24} \div \dfrac{x^2 - 2x}{3x}$ $\dfrac{x+2}{2}$

63. $\dfrac{x^2 - xy - 2y^2}{x + 2y} \div \dfrac{x^2 - 4xy + 4y^2}{x^2 - 4y^2}$ $x + y$

64. $\dfrac{4m^2 - 4mn - 3n^2}{8m^2 - 18n^2} \div \dfrac{3m + 3n}{6m^2 + 15mn + 9n^2}$ $\dfrac{2m+n}{2}$

For Exercises 65–70, multiply or divide as indicated. **(See Example 7.)**

65. $\dfrac{y^3 - 3y^2 + 4y - 12}{y^4 - 16} \cdot \dfrac{3y^2 + 5y - 2}{3y^2 - 10y + 3} \div \dfrac{3}{6y - 12}$ 2

66. $\dfrac{x^2 - 25}{3x^2 + 3xy} \cdot \dfrac{x^2 + 4x + xy + 4y}{x^2 + 9x + 20} \div \dfrac{x - 5}{x}$ $\dfrac{1}{3}$

67. $\dfrac{a^2 - 5a}{a^2 + 7a + 12} \div \dfrac{a^3 - 7a^2 + 10a}{a^2 + 9a + 18} \div \dfrac{a + 6}{a + 4}$ $\dfrac{1}{a-2}$

68. $\dfrac{t^2 + t - 2}{t^2 + 5t + 6} \div \dfrac{t - 1}{t} \div \dfrac{5t - 5}{t + 3}$ $\dfrac{t}{5(t-1)}$

69. $\dfrac{p^3 - q^3}{p - q} \cdot \dfrac{p + q}{2p^2 + 2pq + 2q^2}$ $\dfrac{p+q}{2}$

70. $\dfrac{r^3 + s^3}{r - s} \div \dfrac{r^2 + 2rs + s^2}{r^2 - s^2}$ $r^2 - rs + s^2$

Least Common Denominator

Section 7.3

Concepts

1. Least Common Denominator
2. Writing Rational Expressions with the Least Common Denominator

1. Least Common Denominator

We have already learned how to simplify, multiply, and divide rational expressions. Our next goal is to add and subtract rational expressions. As with fractions, rational expressions may be added or subtracted only if they have the same denominator.

The **least common denominator (LCD)** of two or more rational expressions is defined as the least common multiple of the denominators. For example, consider the fractions $\frac{1}{20}$ and $\frac{1}{8}$. By inspection, you can probably see that the least common denominator is 40. To understand why, find the prime factorization of both denominators:

$$20 = 2^2 \cdot 5 \quad \text{and} \quad 8 = 2^3$$

A common multiple of 20 and 8 must be a multiple of 5, a multiple of 2^2, and a multiple of 2^3. However, any number that is a multiple of $2^3 = 8$ is automatically a multiple of $2^2 = 4$. Therefore, it is sufficient to construct the least common denominator as the product of unique prime factors, in which each factor is raised to its highest power.

$$\text{The LCD of } \frac{1}{20} \text{ and } \frac{1}{8} \text{ is } 2^3 \cdot 5 = 40.$$

Finding the Least Common Denominator of Two or More Rational Expressions

Step 1 Factor all denominators completely.

Step 2 The LCD is the product of unique prime factors from the denominators, in which each factor is raised to the highest power to which it appears in any denominator.

Classroom Example: p. 510, Exercise 20

Example 1 Finding the Least Common Denominator

Find the LCD of the rational expressions.

a. $\dfrac{5}{14}; \dfrac{3}{49}; \dfrac{1}{8}$ **b.** $\dfrac{5}{3x^2z}; \dfrac{7}{x^5y^3}$

Solution:

a. $\dfrac{5}{14}; \dfrac{3}{49}; \dfrac{1}{8}$

$= \dfrac{5}{2 \cdot 7}; \dfrac{3}{7^2}; \dfrac{1}{2^3}$ Factor the denominators.

The LCD is $7^2 \cdot 2^3 = 392$. The LCD is the product of unique factors, each raised to its highest power.

b. $\dfrac{5}{3x^2z}; \dfrac{7}{x^5y^3}$

$= \dfrac{5}{3 \cdot x^2 \cdot z^1}; \dfrac{7}{x^5 \cdot y^3}$ The denominators are in factored form.

The LCD is the product of $3 \cdot x^5 \cdot y^3 \cdot z^1$ or simply $3x^5y^3z$.

Skill Practice Find the LCD for each set of expressions.

1. $\dfrac{3}{8}; \dfrac{7}{10}; \dfrac{1}{15}$ **2.** $\dfrac{1}{5a^3b^2}; \dfrac{1}{10a^4b}$

Classroom Examples: p. 510, Exercises 26 and 28

Example 2 Finding the Least Common Denominator

Find the LCD for each pair of rational expressions.

a. $\dfrac{a+b}{a^2-25}; \dfrac{1}{2a-10}$ **b.** $\dfrac{x-5}{x^2-2x}; \dfrac{1}{x^2-4x+4}$

Solution:

a. $\dfrac{a+b}{a^2-25}; \dfrac{1}{2a-10}$

$= \dfrac{a+b}{(a-5)(a+5)}; \dfrac{1}{2(a-5)}$ Factor the denominators.

The LCD is $2(a-5)(a+5)$. The LCD is the product of unique factors, each raised to its highest power.

b. $\dfrac{x-5}{x^2-2x}; \dfrac{1}{x^2-4x+4}$

$= \dfrac{x-5}{x(x-2)}; \dfrac{1}{(x-2)^2}$ Factor the denominators.

The LCD is $x(x-2)^2$. The LCD is the product of unique factors, each raised to its highest power.

Answers

1. 120
2. $10a^4b^2$

Skill Practice Find the LCD.

3. $\dfrac{x}{x^2 - 16}; \dfrac{2}{3x + 12}$ **4.** $\dfrac{6}{t^2 + 5t - 14}; \dfrac{8}{t^2 - 3t + 2}$

2. Writing Rational Expressions with the Least Common Denominator

To add or subtract two rational expressions, the expressions must have the same denominator. Therefore, we must first practice the skill of converting each rational expression into an equivalent expression with the LCD as its denominator.

Writing Equivalent Fractions with Common Denominators

Step 1 Identify the LCD for the expressions.

Step 2 Multiply the numerator and denominator of each fraction by the factors from the LCD that are missing from the original denominators.

Example 3 Converting to the Least Common Denominator

Classroom Examples: p. 510, Exercises 34 and 40

Find the LCD of each pair of rational expressions. Then convert each expression to an equivalent fraction with the denominator equal to the LCD.

a. $\dfrac{3}{2ab}; \dfrac{6}{5a^2}$ **b.** $\dfrac{4}{x + 1}; \dfrac{7}{x - 4}$

Solution:

a. $\dfrac{3}{2ab}; \dfrac{6}{5a^2}$ The LCD is $10a^2b$.

$$\frac{3}{2ab} = \frac{3 \cdot 5a}{2ab \cdot 5a} = \frac{15a}{10a^2b}$$

The first expression is missing the factor $5a$ from the denominator.

$$\frac{6}{5a^2} = \frac{6 \cdot 2b}{5a^2 \cdot 2b} = \frac{12b}{10a^2b}$$

The second expression is missing the factor $2b$ from the denominator.

b. $\dfrac{4}{x + 1}; \dfrac{7}{x - 4}$ The LCD is $(x + 1)(x - 4)$.

$$\frac{4}{x + 1} = \frac{4(x - 4)}{(x + 1)(x - 4)} = \frac{4x - 16}{(x + 1)(x - 4)}$$

The first expression is missing the factor $(x - 4)$ from the denominator.

$$\frac{7}{x - 4} = \frac{7(x + 1)}{(x - 4)(x + 1)} = \frac{7x + 7}{(x - 4)(x + 1)}$$

The second expression is missing the factor $(x + 1)$ from the denominator.

Skill Practice For each pair of expressions, find the LCD, and then convert each expression to an equivalent fraction with the denominator equal to the LCD.

5. $\dfrac{2}{rs^2}; \dfrac{-1}{r^3s}$ **6.** $\dfrac{5}{x - 3}; \dfrac{x}{x + 1}$

Answers

3. $3(x - 4)(x + 4)$

4. $(t + 7)(t - 2)(t - 1)$

5. $\dfrac{2}{rs^2} = \dfrac{2r^2}{r^3s^2}; \dfrac{-1}{r^3s} = \dfrac{-s}{r^3s^2}$

6. $\dfrac{5}{x - 3} = \dfrac{5x + 5}{(x - 3)(x + 1)}$

$\dfrac{x}{x + 1} = \dfrac{x^2 - 3x}{(x + 1)(x - 3)}$

Classroom Example: p. 511, Exercise 46

Example 4 Converting to the Least Common Denominator

Find the LCD of the pair of rational expressions. Then convert each expression to an equivalent fraction with the denominator equal to the LCD.

$$\frac{w+2}{w^2-w-12}; \frac{1}{w^2-9}$$

Solution:

$$\frac{w+2}{w^2-w-12}; \frac{1}{w^2-9}$$

To find the LCD, factor each denominator.

$$\frac{w+2}{(w-4)(w+3)}; \frac{1}{(w-3)(w+3)}$$

The LCD is $(w-4)(w+3)(w-3)$.

$$\frac{w+2}{(w-4)(w+3)} = \frac{(w+2)(w-3)}{(w-4)(w+3)(w-3)}$$

The first expression is missing the factor $(w-3)$ from the denominator.

$$= \frac{w^2-w-6}{(w-4)(w+3)(w-3)}$$

$$\frac{1}{(w-3)(w+3)} = \frac{1(w-4)}{(w-3)(w+3)(w-4)}$$

The second expression is missing the factor $(w-4)$ from the denominator.

$$= \frac{w-4}{(w-3)(w+3)(w-4)}$$

Skill Practice Find the LCD. Then convert each expression to an equivalent expression with the denominator equal to the LCD.

7. $\frac{z}{z^2-4}; \frac{-3}{z^2-z-2}$

Classroom Example: p. 511, Exercise 48

TIP: In Example 5, the expressions

$$\frac{3}{x-7} \text{ and } \frac{1}{7-x}$$

have opposite factors in the denominators. In such a case, you do not need to include *both* factors in the LCD.

Example 5 Converting to the Least Common Denominator

Convert each expression to an equivalent expression with the denominator equal to the LCD.

$$\frac{3}{x-7} \quad \text{and} \quad \frac{1}{7-x}$$

Solution:

Notice that the expressions $x-7$ and $7-x$ are opposites and differ by a factor of -1. Therefore, we may use either $x-7$ or $7-x$ as a common denominator. Each case is shown below.

Converting to the Denominator $x-7$

$$\frac{3}{x-7}; \frac{1}{7-x}$$

Leave the first fraction unchanged because it has the desired LCD.

$$\frac{1}{7-x} = \frac{(-1)1}{(-1)(7-x)}$$

Multiply the *second* rational expression by the ratio $\frac{-1}{-1}$ to change its denominator to $x-7$.

$$= \frac{-1}{-7+x}$$

Apply the distributive property.

$$= \frac{-1}{x-7}$$

Answer

7. $\frac{z^2+z}{(z-2)(z+2)(z+1)}; \frac{-3z-6}{(z-2)(z+2)(z+1)}$

Converting to the Denominator $7 - x$

$\frac{3}{x-7}; \frac{1}{7-x}$ Leave the second fraction unchanged because it has the desired LCD.

$\frac{3}{x-7} = \frac{(-1)3}{(-1)(x-7)};$ Multiply the *first* rational expression by the ratio $\frac{-1}{-1}$ to change its denominator to $7 - x$.

$= \frac{-3}{-x+7}$ Apply the distributive property.

$= \frac{-3}{7-x}$

Skill Practice

8. a. Find the LCD of the expressions. $\frac{9}{w-2}; \frac{11}{2-w}$

b. Convert each expression to an equivalent fraction with denominator equal to the LCD.

Answers

8. a. The LCD is $(w - 2)$ or $(2 - w)$.

b. $\frac{9}{w-2} = \frac{9}{w-2}$; $\frac{11}{2-w} = \frac{-11}{w-2}$

or

$\frac{9}{w-2} = \frac{-9}{2-w}$; $\frac{11}{2-w} = \frac{11}{2-w}$

Section 7.3 Practice Exercises

For additional exercises, see Classroom Activities 7.3A–7.3C in the *Student's Resource Manual* at www.mhhe.com/moh.

Vocabulary and Key Concepts

1. The least common denominator (LCD) of two rational expressions is defined as the least common __multiple__ of the __denominators__.

Review Exercises

2. Evaluate the expression for the given values of x. $\frac{2x}{x+5}$

a. $x = 1$ $\frac{1}{3}$ b. $x = 5$ 1 c. $x = -5$ Undefined

For Exercises 3–4, identify the restricted values. Then simplify the expression.

3. $\frac{3x+3}{5x^2-5}$ $x = 1, x = -1; \frac{3}{5(x-1)}$

4. $\frac{x+2}{x^2-3x-10}$ $x = -2, x = 5; \frac{1}{x-5}$

For Exercises 5–8, multiply or divide as indicated.

5. $\frac{a+3}{a+7} \cdot \frac{a^2+3a-10}{a^2+a-6}$ $\frac{a+5}{a+7}$

6. $\frac{6(a+2b)}{2(a-3b)} \cdot \frac{4(a+3b)(a-3b)}{9(a+2b)(a-2b)}$ $\frac{4(a+3b)}{3(a-2b)}$

7. $\frac{16y^2}{9y+36} \div \frac{8y^3}{3y+12}$ $\frac{2}{3y}$

8. $\frac{5w^2+6w+1}{w^2+5w+6} \div (5w+1)$ $\frac{w+1}{(w+2)(w+3)}$

9. Which of the expressions are equivalent to $-\frac{5}{x-3}$? Circle all that apply.

a. $\frac{-5}{x-3}$ b. $\frac{5}{-x+3}$ c. $\frac{5}{3-x}$ d. $\frac{5}{-(x-3)}$ a, b, c, d

10. Which of the expressions are equivalent to $\frac{4-a}{6}$? Circle all that apply.

a. $\frac{a-4}{-6}$ **b.** $\frac{a-4}{6}$ **c.** $\frac{-(4-a)}{-6}$ **d.** $-\frac{a-4}{6}$ a, c, d

Concept 1: Least Common Denominator

11. Explain why the least common denominator of $\frac{1}{x^3}$, $\frac{1}{x^5}$, and $\frac{1}{x^4}$ is x^5.
x^5 is the greatest power of x that appears in any denominator.

12. Explain why the least common denominator of $\frac{2}{y^3}$, $\frac{9}{y^6}$, and $\frac{4}{y^5}$ is y^6.
y^6 is the greatest power of y that appears in any denominator.

For Exercises 13–30, identify the LCD. **(See Examples 1–2.)**

13. $\frac{4}{15}; \frac{5}{9}$ 45

14. $\frac{7}{12}; \frac{1}{18}$ 36

15. $\frac{1}{16}; \frac{1}{4}; \frac{1}{6}$ 48

16. $\frac{1}{2}; \frac{11}{12}; \frac{3}{8}$ 24

17. $\frac{1}{7}; \frac{2}{9}$ 63

18. $\frac{2}{3}; \frac{5}{8}$ 24

19. $\frac{1}{3x^2y}; \frac{8}{9xy^3}$ $9x^2y^3$

20. $\frac{5}{2a^4b^2}; \frac{1}{8ab^3}$ $8a^4b^3$

21. $\frac{6}{w^2}; \frac{7}{y}$ w^2y

22. $\frac{2}{r}; \frac{3}{s^2}$ rs^2

23. $\frac{p}{(p+3)(p-1)}; \frac{2}{(p+3)(p+2)}$ $(p+3)(p-1)(p+2)$

24. $\frac{6}{(q+4)(q-4)}; \frac{q^2}{(q+1)(q+4)}$ $(q+4)(q-4)(q+1)$

25. $\frac{7}{3t(t+1)}; \frac{10t}{9(t+1)^2}$ $9t(t+1)^2$

26. $\frac{13x}{15(x-1)^2}; \frac{5}{3x(x-1)}$ $15x(x-1)^2$

27. $\frac{y}{y^2-4}; \frac{3y}{y^2+5y+6}$ $(y-2)(y+2)(y+3)$

28. $\frac{4}{w^2-3w+2}; \frac{w}{w^2-4}$ $(w-1)(w-2)(w+2)$

29. $\frac{5}{3-x}; \frac{7}{x-3}$ $3-x$ or $x-3$

30. $\frac{4}{x-6}; \frac{9}{6-x}$ $x-6$ or $6-x$

31. Explain why a common denominator of

$$\frac{b+1}{b-1} \quad \text{and} \quad \frac{b}{1-b}$$

could be either $(b-1)$ or $(1-b)$.
Because $(b-1)$ and $(1-b)$ are opposites, they differ by a factor of -1.

32. Explain why a common denominator of

$$\frac{1}{6-t} \quad \text{and} \quad \frac{t}{t-6}$$

could be either $(6-t)$ or $(t-6)$.
Because $(6-t)$ and $(t-6)$ are opposites, they differ by a factor of -1.

Concept 2: Writing Rational Expressions with the Least Common Denominator

For Exercises 33–56, find the LCD. Then convert each expression to an equivalent expression with the denominator equal to the LCD. **(See Examples 3–5.)**

33. $\frac{6}{5x^2}; \frac{1}{x}$ $\frac{6}{5x^2}; \frac{5x}{5x^2}$

34. $\frac{3}{y}; \frac{7}{9y^2}$ $\frac{27y}{9y^2}; \frac{7}{9y^2}$

35. $\frac{4}{5x^2}; \frac{y}{6x^3}$ $\frac{24x}{30x^3}; \frac{5y}{30x^3}$

36. $\frac{3}{15b^2}; \frac{c}{3b^2}$ $\frac{3}{15b^2}; \frac{5c}{15b^2}$

37. $\frac{5}{6a^2b}; \frac{a}{12b}$ $\frac{10}{12a^2b}; \frac{a^3}{12a^2b}$

38. $\frac{x}{15y^2}; \frac{y}{5xy}$ $\frac{x^2}{15xy^2}; \frac{3y^2}{15xy^2}$

39. $\frac{6}{m+4}; \frac{3}{m-1}$ $\frac{6m-6}{(m+4)(m-1)}; \frac{3m+12}{(m+4)(m-1)}$

40. $\frac{3}{n-5}; \frac{7}{n+2}$ $\frac{3n+6}{(n-5)(n+2)}; \frac{7n-35}{(n-5)(n+2)}$

41. $\frac{6}{2x-5}; \frac{1}{x+3}$ $\frac{6x+18}{(2x-5)(x+3)}; \frac{2x-5}{(2x-5)(x+3)}$

42. $\frac{4}{m+3}; \frac{-3}{5m+1}$ $\frac{20m+4}{(m+3)(5m+1)}; \frac{-3m-9}{(m+3)(5m+1)}$

43. $\frac{6}{(w+3)(w-8)}; \frac{w}{(w-8)(w+1)}$ $\frac{6w+6}{(w+3)(w-8)(w+1)}; \frac{w^2+3w}{(w+3)(w-8)(w+1)}$

44. $\frac{t}{(t+2)(t+12)}; \frac{18}{(t-2)(t+2)}$ $\frac{t^2-2t}{(t+2)(t-2)(t+12)}; \frac{18t+216}{(t+2)(t-2)(t+12)}$

45. $\dfrac{6p}{p^2-4};\ \dfrac{3}{p^2+4p+4}$ $\quad\dfrac{6p^2+12p}{(p-2)(p+2)^2};\ \dfrac{3p-6}{(p-2)(p+2)^2}$

46. $\dfrac{5}{t^2-6t+9};\ \dfrac{t}{t^2-9}$ $\quad\dfrac{5t+15}{(t-3)^2(t+3)};\ \dfrac{t^2-3t}{(t-3)^2(t+3)}$

47. $\dfrac{1}{a-4};\ \dfrac{a}{4-a}$ $\quad\dfrac{1}{a-4};\ \dfrac{-a}{a-4}$ or $\dfrac{-1}{4-a};\ \dfrac{a}{4-a}$

48. $\dfrac{3b}{2b-5};\ \dfrac{2b}{5-2b}$ $\quad\dfrac{3b}{2b-5};\ \dfrac{-2b}{2b-5}$ or $\dfrac{-3b}{5-2b};\ \dfrac{2b}{5-2b}$

49. $\dfrac{4}{x-7};\ \dfrac{y}{14-2x}$ $\quad\dfrac{8}{2(x-7)};\ \dfrac{-y}{2(x-7)}$ or $\dfrac{-8}{2(7-x)};\ \dfrac{y}{2(7-x)}$

50. $\dfrac{4}{3x-15};\ \dfrac{z}{5-x}$ $\quad\dfrac{4}{3(x-5)};\ \dfrac{-3z}{3(x-5)}$ or $\dfrac{-4}{3(5-x)};\ \dfrac{3z}{3(5-x)}$

51. $\dfrac{1}{a+b};\ \dfrac{6}{-a-b}$ $\quad\dfrac{1}{a+b};\ \dfrac{-6}{a+b}$ or $\dfrac{-1}{-a-b};\ \dfrac{6}{-a-b}$

52. $\dfrac{p}{-q-8};\ \dfrac{1}{q+8}$ $\quad\dfrac{p}{-q-8};\ \dfrac{-1}{-q-8}$ or $\dfrac{-p}{q+8};\ \dfrac{1}{q+8}$

53. $\dfrac{-3}{24y+8};\ \dfrac{5}{18y+6}$ $\quad\dfrac{-9}{24(3y+1)};\ \dfrac{20}{24(3y+1)}$

54. $\dfrac{r}{10r+5};\ \dfrac{2}{16r+8}$ $\quad\dfrac{8r}{40(2r+1)};\ \dfrac{10}{40(2r+1)}$

55. $\dfrac{3}{5z};\ \dfrac{1}{z+4}$ $\quad\dfrac{3z+12}{5z(z+4)};\ \dfrac{5z}{5z(z+4)}$

56. $\dfrac{-1}{4a-8};\ \dfrac{5}{4a}$ $\quad\dfrac{-a}{4a(a-2)};\ \dfrac{5a-10}{4a(a-2)}$

Expanding Your Skills

For Exercises 57–60, find the LCD. Then convert each expression to an equivalent expression with the denominator equal to the LCD.

57. $\dfrac{z}{z^2+9z+14};\ \dfrac{-3z}{z^2+10z+21};\ \dfrac{5}{z^2+5z+6}$ $\quad\dfrac{z^2+3z}{(z+2)(z+7)(z+3)};\ \dfrac{-3z^2-6z}{(z+2)(z+7)(z+3)};\ \dfrac{5z+35}{(z+2)(z+7)(z+3)}$

58. $\dfrac{6}{w^2-3w-4};\ \dfrac{1}{w^2+6w+5};\ \dfrac{-9w}{w^2+w-20}$ $\quad\dfrac{6w+30}{(w-4)(w+1)(w+5)};\ \dfrac{w-4}{(w-4)(w+1)(w+5)};\ \dfrac{-9w^2-9w}{(w-4)(w+1)(w+5)}$

59. $\dfrac{3}{p^3-8};\ \dfrac{p}{p^2-4};\ \dfrac{5p}{p^2+2p+4}$ $\quad\dfrac{3p+6}{(p-2)(p^2+2p+4)(p+2)};\ \dfrac{p^3+2p^2+4p}{(p-2)(p^2+2p+4)(p+2)};\ \dfrac{5p^3-20p}{(p-2)(p^2+2p+4)(p+2)}$

60. $\dfrac{7}{n^3+125};\ \dfrac{n}{n^2-25};\ \dfrac{12}{n^2-5n+25}$ $\quad\dfrac{7n-35}{(n+5)(n^2-5n+25)(n-5)};\ \dfrac{n^3-5n^2+25n}{(n+5)(n^2-5n+25)(n-5)};\ \dfrac{12n^2-300}{(n+5)(n^2-5n+25)(n-5)}$

Addition and Subtraction of Rational Expressions

Section 7.4

Concepts

1. Addition and Subtraction of Rational Expressions with the Same Denominator
2. Addition and Subtraction of Rational Expressions with Different Denominators
3. Using Rational Expressions in Translations

1. Addition and Subtraction of Rational Expressions with the Same Denominator

To add or subtract rational expressions, the expressions must have the same denominator. As with fractions, we add or subtract rational expressions with the same denominator by combining the terms in the numerator and then writing the result over the common denominator. Then, if possible, simplify the expression.

Addition and Subtraction of Rational Expressions

Let p, q, and r represent polynomials where $q \neq 0$. Then,

1. $\dfrac{p}{q}+\dfrac{r}{q}=\dfrac{p+r}{q}$ **2.** $\dfrac{p}{q}-\dfrac{r}{q}=\dfrac{p-r}{q}$

Classroom Example: p. 518, Exercises 8 and 12

Example 1 **Adding and Subtracting Rational Expressions with the Same Denominator**

Add or subtract as indicated. **a.** $\frac{1}{12}+\frac{7}{12}$ **b.** $\frac{2}{5p}-\frac{7}{5p}$

Solution:

a. $\frac{1}{12}+\frac{7}{12}$ The fractions have the same denominator.

$=\frac{1+7}{12}$ Add the terms in the numerators, and write the result over the common denominator.

$=\frac{8}{12}$

$=\frac{2}{3}$ Simplify.

b. $\frac{2}{5p}-\frac{7}{5p}$ The rational expressions have the same denominator.

$=\frac{2-7}{5p}$ Subtract the terms in the numerators, and write the result over the common denominator.

$=\frac{-5}{5p}$

$=\frac{\cancel{-5}^{-1}}{\cancel{5}p}$ Simplify.

$=-\frac{1}{p}$

Skill Practice Add or subtract as indicated.

1. $\frac{3}{14}+\frac{4}{14}$ **2.** $\frac{2}{7d}-\frac{9}{7d}$

Classroom Example: p. 518, Exercise 18

Example 2 **Adding and Subtracting Rational Expressions with the Same Denominator**

Add or subtract as indicated.

a. $\frac{2}{3d+5}+\frac{7d}{3d+5}$ **b.** $\frac{x^2}{x-3}-\frac{-5x+24}{x-3}$

Solution:

a. $\frac{2}{3d+5}+\frac{7d}{3d+5}$ The rational expressions have the same denominator.

$=\frac{2+7d}{3d+5}$ Add the terms in the numerators, and write the result over the common denominator.

$=\frac{7d+2}{3d+5}$ Because the numerator and denominator share no common factors, the expression is in lowest terms.

Answers

1. $\frac{1}{2}$ **2.** $-\frac{1}{d}$

b. $\dfrac{x^2}{x-3} - \dfrac{-5x+24}{x-3}$ The rational expressions have the same denominator.

$= \dfrac{x^2 - (-5x+24)}{x-3}$ Subtract the terms in the numerators, and write the result over the common denominator.

$= \dfrac{x^2+5x-24}{x-3}$ Simplify the numerator.

$= \dfrac{(x+8)(x-3)}{(x-3)}$ Factor the numerator and denominator to determine if the rational expression can be simplified.

$= \dfrac{(x+8)\overset{1}{\cancel{(x-3)}}}{\cancel{(x-3)}}$ Simplify.

$= x+8$

Avoiding Mistakes

When subtracting rational expressions, use parentheses to group the terms in the numerator that follow the subtraction sign. This will help you remember to apply the distributive property.

Instructor Note: Have students consider the alternative method for subtraction. Rewrite as addition and change the signs of the numerator in the second fraction.

$\dfrac{x^2}{x-3} - \dfrac{-5x+24}{x-3}$ becomes

$\dfrac{x^2}{x-3} + \dfrac{5x-24}{x-3}$

Skill Practice Add or subtract as indicated.

3. $\dfrac{x^2+2}{x+3} + \dfrac{4x+1}{x+3}$ **4.** $\dfrac{4t-9}{2t+1} - \dfrac{t-5}{2t+1}$

2. Addition and Subtraction of Rational Expressions with Different Denominators

To add or subtract two rational expressions with unlike denominators, we must convert the expressions to equivalent expressions with the same denominator. For example, consider adding

$$\frac{1}{10} + \frac{12}{5y}$$

The LCD is $10y$. For each expression, identify the factors from the LCD that are missing from the denominator. Then multiply the numerator and denominator of the expression by the missing factor(s).

$$\underbrace{\frac{1}{10}}_{\text{Missing } y} + \underbrace{\frac{12}{5y}}_{\text{Missing } 2}$$

$= \dfrac{1 \cdot y}{10 \cdot y} + \dfrac{12 \cdot 2}{5y \cdot 2}$

$= \dfrac{y}{10y} + \dfrac{24}{10y}$ The rational expressions now have the same denominators.

$= \dfrac{y+24}{10y}$ Add the numerators.

After successfully adding or subtracting two rational expressions, always check to see if the final answer is simplified. If necessary, factor the numerator and denominator, and reduce common factors. The expression

$$\frac{y+24}{10y}$$

is in lowest terms because the numerator and denominator do not share any common factors.

Avoiding Mistakes

In the expression $\frac{y+24}{10y}$, notice that you cannot reduce the 24 and 10 because 24 is not a factor in the numerator, it is a term. Only factors can be reduced—not terms.

Answers

3. $x+1$ **4.** $\dfrac{3t-4}{2t+1}$

Adding or Subtracting Rational Expressions

Step 1 Factor the denominators of each rational expression.

Step 2 Identify the LCD.

Step 3 Rewrite each rational expression as an equivalent expression with the LCD as its denominator.

Step 4 Add or subtract the numerators, and write the result over the common denominator.

Step 5 Simplify.

Classroom Example: p. 519, Exercise 32

Example 3 Subtracting Rational Expressions with Different Denominators

Subtract. $\dfrac{4}{7k} - \dfrac{3}{k^2}$

Solution:

$\dfrac{4}{7k} - \dfrac{3}{k^2}$ **Step 1:** The denominators are already factored.

Step 2: The LCD is $7k^2$.

$= \dfrac{4 \cdot k}{7k \cdot k} - \dfrac{3 \cdot 7}{k^2 \cdot 7}$ **Step 3:** Write each expression with the LCD.

$= \dfrac{4k}{7k^2} - \dfrac{21}{7k^2}$

$= \dfrac{4k - 21}{7k^2}$ **Step 4:** Subtract the numerators, and write the result over the LCD.

Step 5: The expression is in lowest terms because the numerator and denominator share no common factors.

Avoiding Mistakes

Do not reduce after rewriting the individual fractions with the LCD. You will revert back to the original expression.

Skill Practice Subtract.

5. $\dfrac{4}{3x} - \dfrac{1}{2x^2}$

Classroom Example: p. 519, Exercise 42

Example 4 Subtracting Rational Expressions with Different Denominators

Subtract. $\dfrac{2q - 4}{3} - \dfrac{q + 1}{2}$

Solution:

$\dfrac{2q - 4}{3} - \dfrac{q + 1}{2}$ **Step 1:** The denominators are already factored.

Step 2: The LCD is 6.

$= \dfrac{2(2q - 4)}{2 \cdot 3} - \dfrac{3(q + 1)}{3 \cdot 2}$ **Step 3:** Write each expression with the LCD.

Answer

5. $\dfrac{8x - 3}{6x^2}$

$= \dfrac{2(2q-4)-3(q+1)}{6}$ **Step 4:** Subtract the numerators, and write the result over the LCD.

$= \dfrac{4q-8-3q-3}{6}$

$= \dfrac{q-11}{6}$ **Step 5:** The expression is in lowest terms because the numerator and denominator share no common factors.

Skill Practice Subtract.

6. $\dfrac{t}{12} - \dfrac{t-2}{4}$

Example 5 Adding Rational Expressions with Different Denominators

Classroom Example: p. 519, Exercise 40

Add. $\dfrac{1}{x-5} + \dfrac{-10}{x^2-25}$

Solution:

$\dfrac{1}{x-5} + \dfrac{-10}{x^2-25}$

$= \dfrac{1}{x-5} + \dfrac{-10}{(x-5)(x+5)}$ **Step 1:** Factor the denominators.

Step 2: The LCD is $(x-5)(x+5)$.

$= \dfrac{1(x+5)}{(x-5)(x+5)} + \dfrac{-10}{(x-5)(x+5)}$ **Step 3:** Write each expression with the LCD.

$= \dfrac{1(x+5)+(-10)}{(x-5)(x+5)}$ **Step 4:** Add the numerators, and write the result over the LCD.

$= \dfrac{x+5-10}{(x-5)(x+5)}$

$= \dfrac{\overset{1}{\cancel{x-5}}}{\cancel{(x-5)}(x+5)}$ **Step 5:** Simplify.

$= \dfrac{1}{x+5}$

Skill Practice Add.

7. $\dfrac{1}{x-4} + \dfrac{-8}{x^2-16}$

Answers

6. $\dfrac{-t+3}{6}$ **7.** $\dfrac{1}{x+4}$

Classroom Example: p. 520, Exercise 68

Example 6 Subtracting Rational Expressions with Different Denominators

Subtract. $\frac{p+2}{p-1}-\frac{2}{p+6}-\frac{14}{p^2+5p-6}$

Solution:

$$\frac{p+2}{p-1}-\frac{2}{p+6}-\frac{14}{p^2+5p-6}$$

$$=\frac{p+2}{p-1}-\frac{2}{p+6}-\frac{14}{(p-1)(p+6)}$$

Step 1: Factor the denominators.

Step 2: The LCD is $(p-1)(p+6)$.

Step 3: Write each expression with the LCD.

$$=\frac{(p+2)(p+6)}{(p-1)(p+6)}-\frac{2(p-1)}{(p+6)(p-1)}-\frac{14}{(p-1)(p+6)}$$

$$=\frac{(p+2)(p+6)-2(p-1)-14}{(p-1)(p+6)}$$

Step 4: Combine the numerators, and write the result over the LCD.

$$=\frac{p^2+6p+2p+12-2p+2-14}{(p-1)(p+6)}$$

Step 5: Clear parentheses in the numerator.

$$=\frac{p^2+6p}{(p-1)(p+6)}$$

Combine *like* terms.

$$=\frac{p(p+6)}{(p-1)(p+6)}$$

Factor the numerator to determine if the expression is in lowest terms.

$$=\frac{p\overset{1}{\cancel{(p+6)}}}{(p-1)\cancel{(p+6)}}$$

Simplify.

$$=\frac{p}{p-1}$$

Skill Practice Subtract.

8. $\frac{2y}{y-1}-\frac{1}{y}-\frac{2y+1}{y^2-y}$

When the denominators of two rational expressions are opposites, we can produce identical denominators by multiplying one of the expressions by the ratio $\frac{-1}{-1}$. This is demonstrated in Example 7.

Classroom Example: p. 519, Exercise 52

Example 7 Adding Rational Expressions with Different Denominators

Add the rational expressions. $\frac{1}{d-7}+\frac{5}{7-d}$

Answer

8. $\frac{2y-3}{y-1}$

Solution:

$\dfrac{1}{d-7}+\dfrac{5}{7-d}$ — The expressions $d-7$ and $7-d$ are opposites and differ by a factor of -1. Therefore, multiply the numerator and denominator of *either* expression by -1 to obtain a common denominator.

$=\dfrac{1}{d-7}+\dfrac{(-1)5}{(-1)(7-d)}$ — Note that $-1(7-d)=-7+d$ or $d-7$.

$=\dfrac{1}{d-7}+\dfrac{-5}{d-7}$ — Simplify.

$=\dfrac{1+(-5)}{d-7}$ — Add the terms in the numerators, and write the result over the common denominator.

$=\dfrac{-4}{d-7}$

Skill Practice Add.

9. $\dfrac{3}{p-8}+\dfrac{1}{8-p}$

3. Using Rational Expressions in Translations

Example 8 Using Rational Expressions in Translations

Classroom Example: p. 520, Exercise 80

Write the English phrase as a mathematical expression. Then simplify by combining the rational expressions.

The difference of the reciprocal of n and the quotient of n and 3

Solution:

The difference of the reciprocal of n and the quotient of n and 3

The difference of

$$\left(\frac{1}{n}\right)-\left(\frac{n}{3}\right)$$

The reciprocal of n — The quotient of n and 3

$\dfrac{1}{n}-\dfrac{n}{3}$ — The LCD is $3n$.

$=\dfrac{3\cdot 1}{3\cdot n}-\dfrac{n\cdot n}{3\cdot n}$ — Write each expression with the LCD.

$=\dfrac{3-n^2}{3n}$ — Subtract the numerators.

Skill Practice Write the English phrase as a mathematical expression. Then simplify by combining the rational expressions.

10. The sum of 1 and the quotient of 2 and a

Answers

9. $\dfrac{2}{p-8}$ or $\dfrac{-2}{8-p}$

10. $1+\dfrac{2}{a}$; $\dfrac{a+2}{a}$

Section 7.4 Practice Exercises

For additional exercises, see Classroom Activities 7.4A–7.4B in the *Student's Resource Manual* at www.mhhe.com/moh.

Review Exercises

1. For the rational expression $\dfrac{x^2 - 4x - 5}{x^2 - 7x + 10}$

   a. Find the value of the expression (if possible) when $x = 0, 1, -1, 2,$ and 5. $-\frac{1}{2}, -2, 0,$ undefined, undefined

   b. Factor the denominator and identify the restricted values. $(x-5)(x-2); x = 5, x = 2$

   c. Simplify the expression. $\dfrac{x+1}{x-2}$

2. For the rational expression $\dfrac{a^2 + a - 2}{a^2 - 4a - 12}$

   a. Find the value of the expression (if possible) when $a = 0, 1, -2, 2,$ and 6. $\frac{1}{6}$, 0, undefined, $-\frac{1}{4}$, undefined

   b. Factor the denominator, and identify the restricted values. $(a-6)(a+2); a = 6, a = -2$

   c. Simplify the expression. $\dfrac{a-1}{a-6}$

For Exercises 3–4, multiply or divide as indicated.

3. $\dfrac{2x^2 - x - 3}{2x^2 - 3x - 9} \div \dfrac{x^2 - 1}{4x + 6}$ $\dfrac{2(2x-3)}{(x-3)(x-1)}$

4. $\dfrac{6t - 1}{5t - 30} \cdot \dfrac{10t - 25}{2t^2 - 3t - 5}$ $\dfrac{6t-1}{(t+1)(t-6)}$

Concept 1: Addition and Subtraction of Rational Expressions with the Same Denominator

For Exercises 5–26, add or subtract the expressions with the same denominators as indicated. **(See Examples 1–2.)**

5. $\dfrac{7}{8} + \dfrac{3}{8}$ $\dfrac{5}{4}$

6. $\dfrac{1}{3} + \dfrac{7}{3}$ $\dfrac{8}{3}$

7. $\dfrac{9}{16} - \dfrac{3}{16}$ $\dfrac{3}{8}$

8. $\dfrac{14}{15} - \dfrac{4}{15}$ $\dfrac{2}{3}$

9. $\dfrac{5a}{a+2} - \dfrac{3a-4}{a+2}$ 2

10. $\dfrac{2b}{b-3} - \dfrac{b-9}{b-3}$ $\dfrac{b+9}{b-3}$

11. $\dfrac{5c}{c+6} + \dfrac{30}{c+6}$ 5

12. $\dfrac{12}{2+d} + \dfrac{6d}{2+d}$ 6

13. $\dfrac{5}{t-8} - \dfrac{2t+1}{t-8}$ $\dfrac{-2(t-2)}{t-8}$

14. $\dfrac{7p+1}{2p+1} - \dfrac{p-4}{2p+1}$ $\dfrac{6p+5}{2p+1}$

15. $\dfrac{9x^2}{3x-7} - \dfrac{49}{3x-7}$ $3x+7$

16. $\dfrac{4w^2}{2w-1} - \dfrac{1}{2w-1}$ $2w+1$

17. $\dfrac{m^2}{m+5} + \dfrac{10m+25}{m+5}$ $m+5$

18. $\dfrac{k^2}{k-3} - \dfrac{6k-9}{k-3}$ $k-3$

19. $\dfrac{2a}{a+2} + \dfrac{4}{a+2}$ 2

20. $\dfrac{5b}{b+4} + \dfrac{20}{b+4}$ 5

21. $\dfrac{x^2}{x+5} - \dfrac{25}{x+5}$ $x-5$

22. $\dfrac{y^2}{y-7} - \dfrac{49}{y-7}$ $y+7$

23. $\dfrac{r}{r^2+3r+2} + \dfrac{2}{r^2+3r+2}$ $\dfrac{1}{r+1}$

24. $\dfrac{x}{x^2-x-12} - \dfrac{4}{x^2-x-12}$ $\dfrac{1}{x+3}$

25. $\dfrac{1}{3y^2+22y+7} - \dfrac{-3y}{3y^2+22y+7}$ $\dfrac{1}{y+7}$

26. $\dfrac{5}{2x^2+13x+20} + \dfrac{2x}{2x^2+13x+20}$ $\dfrac{1}{x+4}$

For Exercises 27–28, find an expression that represents the perimeter of the figure (assume that $x > 0$, $y > 0$, and $t > 0$).

27.

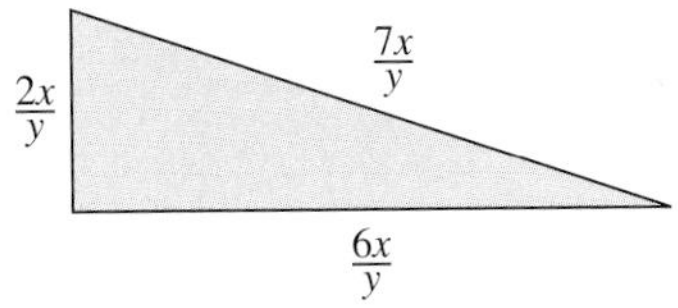

$\frac{15x}{y}$

28.

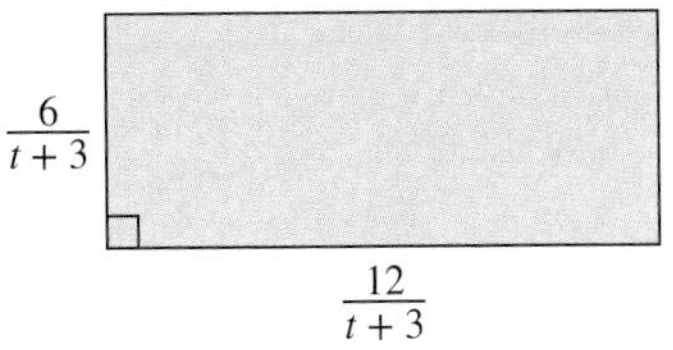

$\frac{36}{t+3}$

Concept 2: Addition and Subtraction of Rational Expressions with Different Denominators

For Exercises 29–70, add or subtract the expressions with different denominators as indicated. **(See Examples 3–7.)**

29. $\frac{5}{4} + \frac{3}{2a}$ $\quad \frac{5a+6}{4a}$

30. $\frac{11}{6p} + \frac{-7}{4p}$ $\quad \frac{1}{12p}$

31. $\frac{4}{5xy^3} + \frac{2x}{15y^2}$ $\quad \frac{2(6+x^2y)}{15xy^3}$

32. $\frac{5}{3a^2b} - \frac{7}{6b^2}$ $\quad \frac{10b-7a^2}{6a^2b^2}$

33. $\frac{2}{s^3t^3} - \frac{3}{s^4t}$ $\quad \frac{2s-3t^2}{s^4t^3}$

34. $\frac{1}{p^2q} - \frac{2}{pq^3}$ $\quad \frac{q^2-2p}{p^2q^3}$

35. $\frac{z}{3z-9} - \frac{z-2}{z-3}$ $\quad -\frac{2}{3}$

36. $\frac{3w-8}{2w-4} - \frac{w-3}{w-2}$ $\quad \frac{1}{2}$

37. $\frac{5}{a+1} + \frac{4}{3a+3}$ $\quad \frac{19}{3(a+1)}$

38. $\frac{2}{c-4} + \frac{1}{5c-20}$ $\quad \frac{11}{5(c-4)}$

39. $\frac{k}{k^2-9} - \frac{4}{k-3}$ $\quad \frac{-3(k+4)}{(k-3)(k+3)}$

40. $\frac{7}{h+2} + \frac{2h-3}{h^2-4}$ $\quad \frac{9h-17}{(h-2)(h+2)}$

41. $\frac{3a-7}{6a+10} - \frac{10}{3a^2+5a}$ $\quad \frac{a-4}{2a}$

42. $\frac{k+2}{8k} - \frac{3-k}{12k}$ $\quad \frac{5}{24}$

43. $\frac{x}{x-4} + \frac{3}{x+1}$ $\quad \frac{(x+6)(x-2)}{(x-4)(x+1)}$

44. $\frac{4}{y-3} + \frac{y}{y-5}$ $\quad \frac{(y+5)(y-4)}{(y-5)(y-3)}$

45. $\frac{3x}{x^2+6x+9} + \frac{x}{x^2+5x+6}$ $\quad \frac{x(4x+9)}{(x+3)^2(x+2)}$

46. $\frac{7x}{x^2+2xy+y^2} + \frac{3x}{x^2+xy}$ $\quad \frac{10x+3y}{(x+y)^2}$

47. $\frac{p}{3} - \frac{4p-1}{-3}$ $\quad \frac{5p-1}{3}$ or $\frac{-5p+1}{-3}$

48. $\frac{r}{7} - \frac{r-5}{-7}$ $\quad \frac{2r-5}{7}$ or $\frac{-2r+5}{-7}$

49. $\frac{8}{x-3} - \frac{1}{3-x}$ $\quad \frac{9}{x-3}$ or $\frac{-9}{3-x}$

50. $\frac{5y}{y-1} - \frac{3y}{1-y}$ $\quad \frac{8y}{y-1}$ or $\frac{-8y}{1-y}$

51. $\frac{4n}{n-8} - \frac{2n-1}{8-n}$ $\quad \frac{6n-1}{n-8}$ or $\frac{-6n+1}{8-n}$

52. $\frac{m}{m-2} - \frac{3m+1}{2-m}$ $\quad \frac{4m+1}{m-2}$ or $\frac{-4m-1}{2-m}$

53. $\frac{5}{x} + \frac{3}{x+2}$ $\quad \frac{2(4x+5)}{x(x+2)}$

54. $\frac{6}{y-1} + \frac{9}{y}$ $\quad \frac{3(5y-3)}{y(y-1)}$

55. $\frac{y}{4y+2} + \frac{3y}{6y+3}$ $\quad \frac{3y}{2(2y+1)}$

56. $\frac{4}{q^2-2q} - \frac{5}{3q-6}$ $\quad \frac{12-5q}{3q(q-2)}$

57. $\frac{4w}{w^2+2w-3} + \frac{2}{1-w}$ $\quad \frac{2(w-3)}{(w+3)(w-1)}$

58. $\frac{z-23}{z^2-z-20} - \frac{2}{5-z}$ $\quad \frac{3}{z+4}$

59. $\frac{3a-8}{a^2-5a+6} + \frac{a+2}{a^2-6a+8}$ $\quad \frac{4a-13}{(a-3)(a-4)}$

60. $\frac{3b+5}{b^2+4b+3} + \frac{-b+5}{b^2+2b-3}$ $\quad \frac{2b}{(b+1)(b-1)}$

61. $\frac{4x}{x^2+4x-5} - \frac{x}{x^2+10x+25}$ $\quad \frac{3x(x+7)}{(x+5)^2(x-1)}$

62. $\frac{x}{x^2+5x+4} - \frac{2x}{x^2+8x+16}$ $\quad \frac{-x(x-2)}{(x+1)(x+4)^2}$

63. $\frac{3y}{2y^2-y-1} - \frac{4y}{2y^2-7y-4}$ $\quad \frac{-y(y+8)}{(2y+1)(y-1)(y-4)}$

64. $\frac{5}{6y^2-7y-3} + \frac{4y}{3y^2+4y+1}$ $\quad \frac{8y^2-7y+5}{(3y+1)(2y-3)(y+1)}$

65. $\dfrac{3}{2p-1} - \dfrac{4p+4}{4p^2-1}$ $\quad \dfrac{1}{2p+1}$

66. $\dfrac{1}{3q-2} - \dfrac{6q+4}{9q^2-4}$ $\quad \dfrac{-1}{3q-2}$

67. $\dfrac{m}{m+n} - \dfrac{m}{m-n} + \dfrac{1}{m^2-n^2}$ $\quad \dfrac{-2mn+1}{(m+n)(m-n)}$

68. $\dfrac{x}{x+y} - \dfrac{2xy}{x^2-y^2} + \dfrac{y}{x-y}$ $\quad \dfrac{x-y}{x+y}$

69. $\dfrac{2}{a+b} + \dfrac{2}{a-b} - \dfrac{4a}{a^2-b^2}$ $\quad 0$

70. $\dfrac{-2x}{x^2-y^2} + \dfrac{1}{x+y} - \dfrac{1}{x-y}$ $\quad \dfrac{-2}{x-y}$

For Exercises 71–72, find an expression that represents the perimeter of the figure (assume that $x > 0$ and $t > 0$).

71.

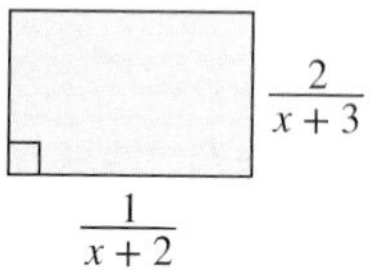

$\dfrac{2(3x+7)}{(x+3)(x+2)}$

72.

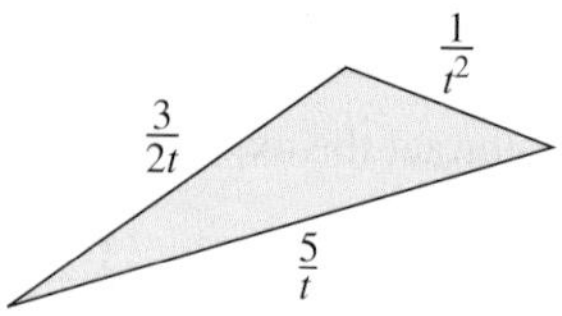

$\dfrac{13t+2}{2t^2}$

Concept 3: Using Rational Expressions in Translations

73. Let a number be represented by n. Write the reciprocal of n. $\quad \dfrac{1}{n}$

74. Write the reciprocal of the sum of a number and 6. $\quad \dfrac{1}{n+6}$

75. Write the quotient of 5 and the sum of a number and 2. $\quad \dfrac{5}{n+2}$

76. Write the quotient of 12 and p. $\quad \dfrac{12}{p}$

For Exercises 77–80, translate the English phrases into algebraic expressions. Then simplify by combining the rational expressions. **(See Example 8.)**

77. The sum of a number and the quantity seven times the reciprocal of the number. $\quad n + \left(7 \cdot \dfrac{1}{n}\right); \dfrac{n^2+7}{n}$

78. The sum of a number and the quantity five times the reciprocal of the number. $\quad n + \left(5 \cdot \dfrac{1}{n}\right); \dfrac{n^2+5}{n}$

79. The difference of the reciprocal of n and the quotient of 2 and n. $\quad \dfrac{1}{n} - \dfrac{2}{n}; -\dfrac{1}{n}$

80. The difference of the reciprocal of m and the quotient of $3m$ and 7. $\quad \dfrac{1}{m} - \dfrac{3m}{7}; \dfrac{7-3m^2}{7m}$

Expanding Your Skills

For Exercises 81–86, perform the indicated operations.

81. $\dfrac{-3}{w^3+27} - \dfrac{1}{w^2-9}$ $\quad \dfrac{-w^2}{(w+3)(w-3)(w^2-3w+9)}$

82. $\dfrac{m}{m^3-1} + \dfrac{1}{(m-1)^2}$ $\quad \dfrac{2m^2+1}{(m-1)^2(m^2+m+1)}$

83. $\dfrac{2p}{p^2+5p+6} - \dfrac{p+1}{p^2+2p-3} + \dfrac{3}{p^2+p-2}$ $\quad \dfrac{p^2-2p+7}{(p+2)(p+3)(p-1)}$

84. $\dfrac{3t}{8t^2+2t-1} - \dfrac{5t}{2t^2-9t-5} + \dfrac{2}{4t^2-21t+5}$ $\quad \dfrac{-17t^2-6t+2}{(2t+1)(4t-1)(t-5)}$

85. $\dfrac{3m}{m^2+3m-10} + \dfrac{5}{4-2m} - \dfrac{1}{m+5}$ $\quad \dfrac{-m-21}{2(m+5)(m-2)}$ or $\dfrac{m+21}{2(m+5)(2-m)}$

86. $\dfrac{2n}{3n^2-8n-3} + \dfrac{1}{6-2n} - \dfrac{3}{3n+1}$ $\quad \dfrac{-5n+17}{2(3n+1)(n-3)}$ or $\dfrac{5n-17}{2(3n+1)(3-n)}$

For Exercises 87–90, simplify by applying the order of operations.

87. $\left(\dfrac{2}{k+1}+3\right)\left(\dfrac{k+1}{4k+7}\right)$ $\quad \dfrac{3k+5}{4k+7}$

88. $\left(\dfrac{p+1}{3p+4}\right)\left(\dfrac{1}{p+1}+2\right)$ $\quad \dfrac{2p+3}{3p+4}$

89. $\left(\dfrac{1}{10a}-\dfrac{b}{10a^2}\right) \div \left(\dfrac{1}{10}-\dfrac{b}{10a}\right)$ $\quad \dfrac{1}{a}$

90. $\left(\dfrac{1}{2m}+\dfrac{n}{2m^2}\right) \div \left(\dfrac{1}{4}+\dfrac{n}{4m}\right)$ $\quad \dfrac{2}{m}$

Problem Recognition Exercises

Operations on Rational Expressions

We have learned how to simplify, add, subtract, multiply, and divide rational expressions. The procedure for each operation is different, and it takes considerable practice to determine the correct method to apply for a given problem. The following review exercises give you the opportunity to practice the specific techniques for simplifying rational expressions.

For Exercises 1–20, perform any indicated operations, and simplify the expression.

1. $\dfrac{5}{3x+1} - \dfrac{2x-4}{3x+1}$ $\quad \dfrac{-2x+9}{3x+1}$

2. $\dfrac{\dfrac{w+1}{w^2-16}}{\dfrac{w+1}{w+4}}$ $\quad \dfrac{1}{w-4}$

3. $\dfrac{3}{y} \cdot \dfrac{y^2-5y}{6y-9}$ $\quad \dfrac{y-5}{2y-3}$

4. $\dfrac{-1}{x+3} + \dfrac{2}{2x-1}$ $\quad \dfrac{7}{(x+3)(2x-1)}$

5. $\dfrac{x-9}{9x-x^2}$ $\quad -\dfrac{1}{x}$

6. $\dfrac{1}{p} - \dfrac{3}{p^2+3p} + \dfrac{p}{3p+9}$ $\quad \dfrac{1}{3}$

7. $\dfrac{c^2+5c+6}{c^2+c-2} \div \dfrac{c}{c-1}$ $\quad \dfrac{c+3}{c}$

8. $\dfrac{2x^2-5x-3}{x^2-9} \cdot \dfrac{x^2+6x+9}{10x+5}$ $\quad \dfrac{x+3}{5}$

9. $\dfrac{6a^2b^3}{72ab^7c}$ $\quad \dfrac{a}{12b^4c}$

10. $\dfrac{2a}{a+b} - \dfrac{b}{a-b} - \dfrac{-4ab}{a^2-b^2}$ $\quad \dfrac{2a-b}{a-b}$

11. $\dfrac{p^2+10pq+25q^2}{p^2+6pq+5q^2} \div \dfrac{10p+50q}{2p^2-2q^2}$ $\quad \dfrac{p-q}{5}$

12. $\dfrac{3k-8}{k-5} + \dfrac{k-12}{k-5}$ $\quad 4$

13. $\dfrac{20x^2+10x}{4x^3+4x^2+x}$ $\quad \dfrac{10}{2x+1}$

14. $\dfrac{w^2-81}{w^2+10w+9} \cdot \dfrac{w^2+w+2zw+2z}{w^2-9w+zw-9z}$ $\quad \dfrac{w+2z}{w+z}$

15. $\dfrac{8x^2-18x-5}{4x^2-25} \div \dfrac{4x^2-11x-3}{3x-9}$ $\quad \dfrac{3}{2x+5}$

16. $\dfrac{xy+7x+5y+35}{x^2+ax+5x+5a}$ $\quad \dfrac{y+7}{x+a}$

17. $\dfrac{a}{a^2-9} - \dfrac{3}{6a-18}$ $\quad \dfrac{1}{2(a+3)}$

18. $\dfrac{4}{y^2-36} + \dfrac{2}{y^2-4y-12}$ $\quad \dfrac{2(3y+10)}{(y-6)(y+6)(y+2)}$

19. $(t^2+5t-24)\left(\dfrac{t+8}{t-3}\right)$ $\quad (t+8)^2$

20. $\dfrac{6b^2-7b-10}{b-2}$ $\quad 6b+5$

Section 7.5 Complex Fractions

Concepts

1. Simplifying Complex Fractions (Method I)
2. Simplifying Complex Fractions (Method II)

1. Simplifying Complex Fractions (Method I)

A **complex fraction** is an expression containing one or more fractions in the numerator, denominator, or both. For example,

$$\frac{\frac{1}{ab}}{\frac{2}{b}} \quad \text{and} \quad \frac{1+\frac{3}{4}-\frac{1}{6}}{\frac{1}{2}+\frac{1}{3}}$$

are complex fractions.

Two methods will be presented to simplify complex fractions. The first method (Method I) follows the order of operations to simplify the numerator and denominator separately before dividing. The process is summarized as follows.

Simplifying a Complex Fraction (Method I)

Step 1 Add or subtract expressions in the numerator to form a single fraction. Add or subtract expressions in the denominator to form a single fraction.

Step 2 Divide the rational expressions from step 1 by multiplying the numerator of the complex fraction by the reciprocal of the denominator of the complex fraction.

Step 3 Simplify to lowest terms if possible.

Classroom Example: p. 528, Exercise 12

Example 1 Simplifying a Complex Fraction (Method I)

Simplify the expression. $\dfrac{\frac{1}{ab}}{\frac{2}{b}}$

Solution:

Step 1: The numerator and denominator of the complex fraction are already single fractions.

$\dfrac{\frac{1}{ab}}{\frac{2}{b}}$ ← This fraction bar denotes division (÷).

$= \dfrac{1}{ab} \div \dfrac{2}{b}$

$= \dfrac{1}{ab} \cdot \dfrac{b}{2}$ **Step 2:** Multiply the numerator of the complex fraction by the reciprocal of $\frac{2}{b}$, which is $\frac{b}{2}$.

$= \dfrac{1}{a\cancel{b}} \cdot \dfrac{\cancel{b}}{2}$ **Step 3:** Reduce common factors and simplify.

$= \dfrac{1}{2a}$

Skill Practice Simplify the expression.

1. $\dfrac{\dfrac{6x}{y}}{\dfrac{9}{2y}}$

Sometimes it is necessary to simplify the numerator and denominator of a complex fraction before the division can be performed. This is illustrated in Example 2.

Example 2 Simplifying a Complex Fraction (Method I)

Classroom Example: p. 528, Exercise 16

Simplify the expression. $\dfrac{1+\dfrac{3}{4}-\dfrac{1}{6}}{\dfrac{1}{2}+\dfrac{1}{3}}$

Solution:

$$\dfrac{1+\dfrac{3}{4}-\dfrac{1}{6}}{\dfrac{1}{2}+\dfrac{1}{3}}$$

Step 1: Combine fractions in the numerator and denominator separately.

$$=\dfrac{1\cdot\dfrac{12}{12}+\dfrac{3}{4}\cdot\dfrac{3}{3}-\dfrac{1}{6}\cdot\dfrac{2}{2}}{\dfrac{1}{2}\cdot\dfrac{3}{3}+\dfrac{1}{3}\cdot\dfrac{2}{2}}$$

The LCD in the numerator is 12.
The LCD in the denominator is 6.

$$=\dfrac{\dfrac{12}{12}+\dfrac{9}{12}-\dfrac{2}{12}}{\dfrac{3}{6}+\dfrac{2}{6}}$$

$$=\dfrac{\dfrac{19}{12}}{\dfrac{5}{6}}$$

Form a single fraction in the numerator and in the denominator.

$$=\dfrac{19}{\cancel{12}_{2}}\cdot\dfrac{\cancel{6}^{1}}{5}$$

Step 2: Multiply the numerator by the reciprocal of the denominator.

$$=\dfrac{19}{10}$$

Step 3: Simplify.

Skill Practice Simplify the expression.

2. $\dfrac{\dfrac{3}{4}-\dfrac{1}{6}+2}{\dfrac{1}{3}+\dfrac{1}{2}}$

Answers

1. $\dfrac{4x}{3}$ 2. $\dfrac{31}{10}$

Classroom Example: p. 528, Exercise 24

Example 3 Simplifying a Complex Fraction (Method I)

Simplify the expression. $\dfrac{\dfrac{1}{x}+\dfrac{1}{y}}{x-\dfrac{y^2}{x}}$

Solution:

$$\frac{\dfrac{1}{x}+\dfrac{1}{y}}{x-\dfrac{y^2}{x}}$$

The LCD in the numerator is xy.
The LCD in the denominator is x.

$$=\frac{\dfrac{1\cdot y}{x\cdot y}+\dfrac{1\cdot x}{y\cdot x}}{\dfrac{x\cdot x}{1\cdot x}-\dfrac{y^2}{x}}$$

Rewrite the expressions using common denominators.

$$=\frac{\dfrac{y}{xy}+\dfrac{x}{xy}}{\dfrac{x^2}{x}-\dfrac{y^2}{x}}$$

$$=\frac{\dfrac{y+x}{xy}}{\dfrac{x^2-y^2}{x}}$$

Form single fractions in the numerator and denominator.

$$=\frac{y+x}{xy}\cdot\frac{x}{x^2-y^2}$$

Multiply the numerator by the reciprocal of the denominator.

$$=\frac{\overset{1}{\cancel{y+x}}}{\cancel{x}y}\cdot\frac{\overset{1}{\cancel{x}}}{\cancel{(x+y)}(x-y)}$$

Factor and reduce. Note that $(y+x)=(x+y)$.

$$=\frac{1}{y(x-y)}$$

Simplify.

Skill Practice Simplify the expression.

3. $\dfrac{1-\dfrac{1}{p}}{\dfrac{p}{w}+\dfrac{w}{p}}$

2. Simplifying Complex Fractions (Method II)

We will now simplify the expressions from Examples 2 and 3 again using a second method to simplify complex fractions (Method II). Recall that multiplying the numerator and denominator of a rational expression by the same quantity does not change the value of the expression because we are multiplying by a number equivalent to 1. This is the basis for Method II.

Answer

3. $\dfrac{w(p-1)}{p^2+w^2}$

Simplifying a Complex Fraction (Method II)

Step 1 Multiply the numerator and denominator of the complex fraction by the LCD of *all* individual fractions within the expression.

Step 2 Apply the distributive property, and simplify the numerator and denominator.

Step 3 Simplify to lowest terms if possible.

Example 4 Simplifying a Complex Fraction (Method II)

Classroom Example: p. 528, Exercise 16

Simplify the expression. $\dfrac{1+\dfrac{3}{4}-\dfrac{1}{6}}{\dfrac{1}{2}+\dfrac{1}{3}}$

Solution:

$$\dfrac{1+\dfrac{3}{4}-\dfrac{1}{6}}{\dfrac{1}{2}+\dfrac{1}{3}}$$

The LCD of the expressions $1, \frac{3}{4}, \frac{1}{6}, \frac{1}{2}$, and $\frac{1}{3}$ is 12.

$$=\dfrac{12\left(1+\dfrac{3}{4}-\dfrac{1}{6}\right)}{12\left(\dfrac{1}{2}+\dfrac{1}{3}\right)}$$

Step 1: Multiply the numerator and denominator of the complex fraction by 12.

TIP: In step 1, we multiply the original expression by $\frac{12}{12}$, which equals 1.

$$=\dfrac{12\cdot 1+12\cdot\dfrac{3}{4}-12\cdot\dfrac{1}{6}}{12\cdot\dfrac{1}{2}+12\cdot\dfrac{1}{3}}$$

Step 2: Apply the distributive property.

$$=\dfrac{12\cdot 1+\overset{3}{\cancel{12}}\cdot\dfrac{3}{\cancel{4}}-\overset{2}{\cancel{12}}\cdot\dfrac{1}{\cancel{6}}}{\overset{6}{\cancel{12}}\cdot\dfrac{1}{\cancel{2}}+\overset{4}{\cancel{12}}\cdot\dfrac{1}{\cancel{3}}}$$

Simplify each term.

$$=\dfrac{12+9-2}{6+4}$$

$$=\dfrac{19}{10}$$

Step 3: Simplify. This is the same result as in Example 2.

Skill Practice Simplify the expression.

4. $\dfrac{1-\dfrac{3}{5}}{\dfrac{1}{4}-\dfrac{7}{10}+1}$

Answer

4. $\dfrac{8}{11}$

Classroom Example: p. 528, Exercise 26

Example 5 Simplifying a Complex Fraction (Method II)

Simplify the expression. $\dfrac{\dfrac{1}{x}+\dfrac{1}{y}}{x-\dfrac{y^2}{x}}$

Solution:

$\dfrac{\dfrac{1}{x}+\dfrac{1}{y}}{x-\dfrac{y^2}{x}}$ The LCD of the expressions $\frac{1}{x}$, $\frac{1}{y}$, x, and $\frac{y^2}{x}$ is xy.

$= \dfrac{xy\left(\dfrac{1}{x}+\dfrac{1}{y}\right)}{xy\left(x-\dfrac{y^2}{x}\right)}$ **Step 1:** Multiply numerator and denominator of the complex fraction by xy.

$= \dfrac{xy \cdot \dfrac{1}{x} + xy \cdot \dfrac{1}{y}}{xy \cdot x - xy \cdot \dfrac{y^2}{x}}$ **Step 2:** Apply the distributive property, and simplify each term.

$= \dfrac{y+x}{x^2y - y^3}$

$= \dfrac{y+x}{y(x^2-y^2)}$ **Step 3:** Factor completely, and reduce common factors.

$= \dfrac{\overset{1}{\cancel{y+x}}}{y\cancel{(x+y)}(x-y)}$ Note that $(y+x) = (x+y)$.

$= \dfrac{1}{y(x-y)}$ This is the same result as in Example 3.

Skill Practice Simplify the expression.

5. $\dfrac{\dfrac{z}{3}-\dfrac{3}{z}}{1+\dfrac{3}{z}}$

Answer

5. $\dfrac{z-3}{3}$

Example 6 Simplifying a Complex Fraction (Method II)

Classroom Example: p. 528, Exercise 28

Simplify the expression. $\dfrac{\dfrac{1}{k+1}-1}{\dfrac{1}{k+1}+1}$

Solution:

$\dfrac{\dfrac{1}{k+1}-1}{\dfrac{1}{k+1}+1}$ The LCD of $\dfrac{1}{k+1}$ and 1 is $(k+1)$.

$= \dfrac{(k+1)\left(\dfrac{1}{k+1}-1\right)}{(k+1)\left(\dfrac{1}{k+1}+1\right)}$ **Step 1:** Multiply numerator and denominator of the complex fraction by $(k+1)$.

$= \dfrac{(k+1)\cdot\dfrac{1}{(k+1)}-(k+1)\cdot 1}{(k+1)\cdot\dfrac{1}{(k+1)}+(k+1)\cdot 1}$ **Step 2:** Apply the distributive property.

$= \dfrac{1-(k+1)}{1+(k+1)}$ Simplify.

$= \dfrac{1-k-1}{1+k+1}$

$= \dfrac{-k}{k+2}$ **Step 3:** The expression is already in lowest terms.

Skill Practice Simplify the expression.

6. $\dfrac{\dfrac{4}{p-3}+1}{1+\dfrac{2}{p-3}}$

Answer

6. $\dfrac{p+1}{p-1}$

Section 7.5 Practice Exercises

For additional exercises, see Classroom Activities 7.5A–7.5B in the *Student's Resource Manual* at www.mhhe.com/moh.

Vocabulary and Key Concepts

1. A __complex__ fraction is an expression containing one or more fractions in the numerator, denominator, or both.

Review Exercises

For Exercises 2–3, simplify the expression.

2. $\dfrac{y(2y+9)}{y^2(2y+9)}$ $\dfrac{1}{y}$

3. $\dfrac{a+5}{2a^2+7a-15}$ $\dfrac{1}{2a-3}$

For Exercises 4–6, perform the indicated operations.

4. $\dfrac{2}{w-2}+\dfrac{3}{w}$ $\quad \dfrac{5w-6}{w(w-2)}$

5. $\dfrac{6}{5}-\dfrac{3}{5k-10}$ $\quad \dfrac{3(2k-5)}{5(k-2)}$

6. $\dfrac{x^2-2xy+y^2}{x^4-y^4}\div\dfrac{3x^2y-3xy^2}{x^2+y^2}$ $\quad \dfrac{1}{3xy(x+y)}$

Concepts 1–2: Simplifying Complex Fractions (Methods I and II)

For Exercises 7–34, simplify the complex fractions using either method. **(See Examples 1–6.)**

7. $\dfrac{\frac{7}{18y}}{\frac{2}{9}}$ $\quad \dfrac{7}{4y}$

8. $\dfrac{\frac{a^2}{2a-3}}{\frac{5a}{8a-12}}$ $\quad \dfrac{4a}{5}$

9. $\dfrac{\frac{3x+2y}{2y}}{\frac{6x+4y}{2}}$ $\quad \dfrac{1}{2y}$

10. $\dfrac{\frac{2x-10}{4}}{\frac{x^2-5x}{3x}}$ $\quad \dfrac{3}{2}$

11. $\dfrac{\frac{8a^4b^3}{3c}}{\frac{a^7b^2}{9c}}$ $\quad \dfrac{24b}{a^3}$

12. $\dfrac{\frac{12x^2}{5y}}{\frac{8x^6}{9y^2}}$ $\quad \dfrac{27y}{10x^4}$

13. $\dfrac{\frac{4r^3s}{t^5}}{\frac{2s^7}{r^2t^9}}$ $\quad \dfrac{2r^5t^4}{s^6}$

14. $\dfrac{\frac{5p^4q}{w^4}}{\frac{10p^2}{qw^2}}$ $\quad \dfrac{p^2q^2}{2w^2}$

15. $\dfrac{\frac{1}{8}+\frac{4}{3}}{\frac{1}{2}-\frac{5}{12}}$ $\quad \dfrac{35}{2}$

16. $\dfrac{\frac{8}{9}-\frac{1}{3}}{\frac{7}{6}+\frac{1}{9}}$ $\quad \dfrac{10}{23}$

17. $\dfrac{\frac{1}{h}+\frac{1}{k}}{\frac{1}{hk}}$ $\quad k+h$

18. $\dfrac{\frac{1}{b}+1}{\frac{1}{b}}$ $\quad 1+b$

19. $\dfrac{\frac{n+1}{n^2-9}}{\frac{2}{n+3}}$ $\quad \dfrac{n+1}{2(n-3)}$

20. $\dfrac{\frac{5}{k-5}}{\frac{k+1}{k^2-25}}$ $\quad \dfrac{5(k+5)}{k+1}$

21. $\dfrac{2+\frac{1}{x}}{4+\frac{1}{x}}$ $\quad \dfrac{2x+1}{4x+1}$

22. $\dfrac{6+\frac{6}{k}}{1+\frac{1}{k}}$ $\quad 6$

23. $\dfrac{\frac{m}{7}-\frac{7}{m}}{\frac{1}{7}+\frac{1}{m}}$ $\quad m-7$

24. $\dfrac{\frac{2}{p}+\frac{p}{2}}{\frac{p}{3}-\frac{3}{p}}$ $\quad \dfrac{3(4+p^2)}{2(p-3)(p+3)}$

25. $\dfrac{\frac{1}{5}-\frac{1}{y}}{\frac{7}{10}+\frac{1}{y^2}}$ $\quad \dfrac{2y(y-5)}{7y^2+10}$

26. $\dfrac{\frac{1}{m^2}+\frac{2}{3}}{\frac{1}{m}-\frac{5}{6}}$ $\quad \dfrac{2(3+2m^2)}{m(6-5m)}$

27. $\dfrac{\frac{8}{a+4}+2}{\frac{12}{a+4}-2}$ $\quad -\dfrac{a+8}{a-2}$ or $\dfrac{a+8}{2-a}$

28. $\dfrac{\frac{2}{w+1}+3}{\frac{3}{w+1}+4}$ $\quad \dfrac{3w+5}{4w+7}$

29. $\dfrac{1-\frac{4}{t^2}}{1-\frac{2}{t}-\frac{8}{t^2}}$ $\quad \dfrac{t-2}{t-4}$

30. $\dfrac{1-\frac{9}{p^2}}{1-\frac{1}{p}-\frac{6}{p^2}}$ $\quad \dfrac{p+3}{p+2}$

31. $\dfrac{t+4+\frac{3}{t}}{t-4-\frac{5}{t}}$ $\quad \dfrac{t+3}{t-5}$

32. $\dfrac{\frac{9}{4m}+\frac{9}{2m^2}}{\frac{3}{2}+\frac{3}{m}}$ $\quad \dfrac{3}{2m}$

33. $\dfrac{\frac{1}{k-6}-1}{\frac{2}{k-6}-2}$ $\quad \dfrac{1}{2}$

34. $\dfrac{\frac{3}{y-3}+4}{8+\frac{6}{y-3}}$ $\quad \dfrac{1}{2}$

For Exercises 35–38, write the English phrases as algebraic expressions. Then simplify the expressions.

35. The sum of one-half and two-thirds, divided by five $\quad \dfrac{\frac{1}{2}+\frac{2}{3}}{5}; \dfrac{7}{30}$

36. The quotient of ten and the difference of two-fifths and one-fourth $\quad \dfrac{10}{\frac{2}{5}-\frac{1}{4}}; \dfrac{200}{3}$

37. The quotient of three and the sum of two-thirds and three-fourths $\quad \dfrac{3}{\frac{2}{3}+\frac{3}{4}}; \dfrac{36}{17}$

38. The difference of three-fifths and one-half, divided by four $\quad \dfrac{\frac{3}{5}-\frac{1}{2}}{4}; \dfrac{1}{40}$

39. In electronics, resistors oppose the flow of current. For two resistors in parallel, the total resistance is given by

$$R = \frac{1}{\dfrac{1}{R_1} + \dfrac{1}{R_2}}$$

© S. Meltzer/PhotoLink/ Getty Images RF

a. Find the total resistance if $R_1 = 2\ \Omega$ (ohms) and $R_2 = 3\ \Omega$. $\frac{6}{5}\ \Omega$

b. Find the total resistance if $R_1 = 10\ \Omega$ and $R_2 = 15\ \Omega$. $6\ \Omega$

40. Suppose that Joëlle makes a round trip to a location that is d miles away. If the average rate going to the location is r_1 and the average rate on the return trip is given by r_2, the average rate of the entire trip, R, is given by

$$R = \frac{2d}{\dfrac{d}{r_1} + \dfrac{d}{r_2}}$$

a. Find the average rate of a trip to a destination 30 mi away when the average rate going there is 60 mph and the average rate returning home is 45 mph. (Round to the nearest tenth of a mile per hour.)
51.4 mph average

b. Find the average rate of a trip to a destination that is 50 mi away if the driver travels at the same rates as in part (a). (Round to the nearest tenth of a mile per hour.)
51.4 mph

c. Compare your answers from parts (a) and (b) and explain the results in the context of the problem.
Because the rates going to and leaving from the destination are the same, the average rate is unchanged. The average rate is not affected by the distance traveled.

Expanding Your Skills

For Exercises 41–50, simplify the complex fractions using either method.

41. $\dfrac{x^{-1} - y^{-1}}{x^{-2} - y^{-2}}$ $\dfrac{xy}{y+x}$

42. $\dfrac{a^{-2} - 1}{a^{-1} - 1}$ $\dfrac{1+a}{a}$

43. $\dfrac{2x^{-1} + 8y^{-1}}{4x^{-1}}$ $\dfrac{y+4x}{2y}$
$\left(\textit{Hint}: 2x^{-1} = \dfrac{2}{x}\right)$

44. $\dfrac{6a^{-1} + 4b^{-1}}{8b^{-1}}$ $\dfrac{3b+2a}{4a}$

45. $\dfrac{(mn)^{-2}}{m^{-2} + n^{-2}}$ $\dfrac{1}{n^2+m^2}$

46. $\dfrac{(xy)^{-1}}{2x^{-1} + 3y^{-1}}$ $\dfrac{1}{2y+3x}$

47. $\dfrac{\dfrac{1}{z^2 - 9} + \dfrac{2}{z+3}}{\dfrac{3}{z-3}}$ $\dfrac{2z-5}{3(z+3)}$

48. $\dfrac{\dfrac{5}{w^2 - 25} - \dfrac{3}{w+5}}{\dfrac{4}{w-5}}$ $\dfrac{-3w+20}{4(w+5)}$

49. $\dfrac{\dfrac{2}{x-1} + 2}{\dfrac{2}{x+1} - 2}$ $-\dfrac{x+1}{x-1}$ or $\dfrac{x+1}{1-x}$

50. $\dfrac{\dfrac{1}{y-3} + 1}{\dfrac{2}{y+3} - 1}$ $-\dfrac{(y+3)(y-2)}{(y+1)(y-3)}$

For Exercises 51–52, simplify the complex fractions. (*Hint:* Use the order of operations and begin with the fraction on the lower right.)

51. $1 + \dfrac{1}{1+1}$ $\dfrac{3}{2}$

52. $1 + \dfrac{1}{1 + \dfrac{1}{1+1}}$ $\dfrac{5}{3}$

Section 7.6 Rational Equations

Concepts

1. Introduction to Rational Equations
2. Solving Rational Equations
3. Solving Formulas Involving Rational Expressions

1. Introduction to Rational Equations

Thus far we have studied two specific types of equations in one variable: linear equations and quadratic equations. Recall,

$ax + b = c$, where $a \neq 0$, is a **linear equation**.

$ax^2 + bx + c = 0$, where $a \neq 0$, is a **quadratic equation**.

We will now study another type of equation called a rational equation.

Definition of a Rational Equation

An equation with one or more rational expressions is called a **rational equation**.

The following equations are rational equations:

$$\frac{1}{x} + \frac{1}{3} = \frac{5}{6} \qquad \frac{6}{t^2 - 7t + 12} + \frac{2t}{t-3} = \frac{3t}{t-4}$$

To understand the process of solving a rational equation, first review the process of clearing fractions. We can clear the fractions in an equation by multiplying both sides of the equation by the LCD of all terms.

Classroom Example: p. 538, Exercise 12

Example 1 Solving an Equation Containing Fractions

Solve. $\frac{y}{2} + \frac{y}{4} = 6$

Solution:

$\frac{y}{2} + \frac{y}{4} = 6$ The LCD of all terms in the equation is 4.

$4\left(\frac{y}{2} + \frac{y}{4}\right) = 4(6)$ Multiply both sides of the equation by 4 to clear fractions.

$\overset{2}{\cancel{4}} \cdot \frac{y}{2} + \overset{1}{\cancel{4}} \cdot \frac{y}{\cancel{4}} = 4(6)$ Apply the distributive property.

$2y + y = 24$ Clear fractions.

$3y = 24$ Solve the resulting equation (linear).

$y = 8$

Check: $\frac{y}{2} + \frac{y}{4} = 6$

$\frac{(8)}{2} + \frac{(8)}{4} \stackrel{?}{=} 6$

$4 + 2 \stackrel{?}{=} 6$

$6 \stackrel{?}{=} 6$ ✓ (True)

The solution set is $\{8\}$.

Skill Practice Solve the equation.

1. $\frac{t}{5} - \frac{t}{4} = 2$

2. Solving Rational Equations

The same process of clearing fractions is used to solve rational equations when variables are present in the denominator. However, variables in the denominator make it necessary to take note of the restricted values.

Example 2 **Solving a Rational Equation**

Classroom Example: p. 538, Exercise 26

Solve the equation. $\frac{x+1}{x} + \frac{1}{3} = \frac{5}{6}$

Solution:

$$\frac{x+1}{x} + \frac{1}{3} = \frac{5}{6}$$ The LCD of all the expressions is $6x$. The restricted value is $x = 0$.

TIP: The restricted value tells us that $x = 0$ is *not* a possible solution to the equation.

$$6x \cdot \left(\frac{x+1}{x} + \frac{1}{3}\right) = 6x \cdot \left(\frac{5}{6}\right)$$ Multiply by the LCD.

$$\overset{1}{6\cancel{x}} \cdot \left(\frac{x+1}{\cancel{x}}\right) + \overset{2}{\cancel{6}x} \cdot \left(\frac{1}{\cancel{3}}\right) = \overset{1}{\cancel{6}x} \cdot \left(\frac{5}{\cancel{6}}\right)$$ Apply the distributive property.

$$6(x+1) + 2x = 5x$$ Clear fractions.

$$6x + 6 + 2x = 5x$$ Solve the resulting equation.

$$8x + 6 = 5x$$

$$3x = -6$$

$$x = -2$$ -2 is not a restricted value.

Check:
$$\frac{x+1}{x} + \frac{1}{3} = \frac{5}{6}$$
$$\frac{(-2)+1}{(-2)} + \frac{1}{3} \stackrel{?}{=} \frac{5}{6}$$
$$\frac{-1}{-2} + \frac{1}{3} \stackrel{?}{=} \frac{5}{6}$$
$$\frac{1}{2} + \frac{1}{3} \stackrel{?}{=} \frac{5}{6}$$
$$\frac{3}{6} + \frac{2}{6} \stackrel{?}{=} \frac{5}{6}$$
$$\frac{5}{6} \stackrel{?}{=} \frac{5}{6} \checkmark \text{ (True)}$$

The solution set is $\{-2\}$.

Skill Practice Solve the equation.

2. $\frac{3}{4} + \frac{5+a}{a} = \frac{1}{2}$

Answers

1. $\{-40\}$ 2. $\{-4\}$

Classroom Example: p. 539, Exercise 32

Example 3 Solving a Rational Equation

Solve the equation. $1 + \frac{3a}{a-2} = \frac{6}{a-2}$

Solution:

$$1 + \frac{3a}{a-2} = \frac{6}{a-2}$$

The LCD of all the expressions is $a - 2$. The restricted value is $a = 2$.

$$(a-2)\left(1 + \frac{3a}{a-2}\right) = (a-2)\left(\frac{6}{a-2}\right)$$

Multiply by the LCD.

$$(a-2)1 + (a-2)\left(\frac{3a}{a-2}\right) = (a-2)\left(\frac{6}{a-2}\right)$$

Apply the distributive property.

$$a - 2 + 3a = 6$$

Solve the resulting equation (linear).

$$4a - 2 = 6$$

$$4a = 8$$

$$a = 2$$

2 is a restricted value.

Check: $1 + \frac{3a}{a-2} = \frac{6}{a-2}$

$$1 + \frac{3(2)}{(2)-2} \stackrel{?}{=} \frac{6}{(2)-2}$$

$$1 + \frac{6}{0} \stackrel{?}{=} \frac{6}{0}$$

The denominator is 0 when $a = 2$.

Because the value $a = 2$ makes the denominator zero in one (or more) of the rational expressions within the equation, the equation is undefined for $a = 2$. No other potential solutions exist for the equation, therefore, the solution set is { }.

Skill Practice Solve the equation.

3. $\frac{x}{x+1} - 2 = \frac{-1}{x+1}$

Instructor Note: Have students explain the difference between

$$\frac{2}{x+3} + \frac{5}{x+2}$$

and

$$\frac{2}{x+3} = \frac{5}{x+2}$$

Examples 1–3 show that the steps to solve a rational equation mirror the process of clearing fractions. However, there is one significant difference. The solutions of a rational equation must not make the denominator equal to zero for any expression within the equation.

Answer

3. { } (The value −1 does not check.)

The steps to solve a rational equation are summarized as follows.

Solving a Rational Equation

Step 1 Factor the denominators of all rational expressions. Identify the restricted values.

Step 2 Identify the LCD of all expressions in the equation.

Step 3 Multiply both sides of the equation by the LCD.

Step 4 Solve the resulting equation.

Step 5 Check potential solutions in the original equation.

After multiplying by the LCD and then simplifying, the rational equation will be either a linear equation or higher degree equation.

Example 4 Solving a Rational Equation

Classroom Example: p. 538, Exercise 24

Solve the equation. $1 - \frac{4}{p} = -\frac{3}{p^2}$

Solution:

$$1 - \frac{4}{p} = -\frac{3}{p^2}$$

Step 1: The denominators are already factored. The restricted value is $p = 0$.

Step 2: The LCD of all expressions is p^2.

$$p^2\left(1 - \frac{4}{p}\right) = p^2\left(-\frac{3}{p^2}\right)$$

Step 3: Multiply by the LCD.

$$p^2(1) - \overset{p}{\cancel{p^2}}\left(\frac{4}{\cancel{p}}\right) = \overset{1}{\cancel{p^2}}\left(-\frac{3}{\cancel{p^2}}\right)$$

Apply the distributive property.

$$p^2 - 4p = -3$$

Step 4: Solve the resulting quadratic equation.

$$p^2 - 4p + 3 = 0$$

$$(p - 3)(p - 1) = 0$$

Set the equation equal to zero and factor.

$$p - 3 = 0 \quad \text{or} \quad p - 1 = 0$$

Set each factor equal to zero.

$$p = 3 \quad \text{or} \quad p = 1$$

3 and 1 are not restricted values.

Step 5: Check: $p = 3$

$$1 - \frac{4}{p} = -\frac{3}{p^2}$$

$$1 - \frac{4}{(3)} \stackrel{?}{=} -\frac{3}{(3)^2}$$

$$\frac{3}{3} - \frac{4}{3} \stackrel{?}{=} -\frac{3}{9}$$

$$-\frac{1}{3} \stackrel{?}{=} -\frac{1}{3} \checkmark$$

Check: $p = 1$

$$1 - \frac{4}{p} = -\frac{3}{p^2}$$

$$1 - \frac{4}{(1)} \stackrel{?}{=} -\frac{3}{(1)^2}$$

$$1 - 4 \stackrel{?}{=} -3$$

$$-3 \stackrel{?}{=} -3 \checkmark$$

The solution set is $\{3, 1\}$.

Skill Practice Solve the equation.

4. $\frac{z}{2} - \frac{1}{2z} = \frac{12}{z}$

Answer

4. $\{5, -5\}$

Classroom Example: p. 539, Exercise 42

Example 5 Solving a Rational Equation

Solve the equation. $\dfrac{6}{t^2 - 7t + 12} + \dfrac{2t}{t-3} = \dfrac{3t}{t-4}$

Solution:

$$\frac{6}{t^2 - 7t + 12} + \frac{2t}{t-3} = \frac{3t}{t-4}$$

$$\frac{6}{(t-3)(t-4)} + \frac{2t}{t-3} = \frac{3t}{t-4}$$

Step 1: Factor the denominators. The restricted values are $t = 3$ and $t = 4$.

Step 2: The LCD is $(t-3)(t-4)$.

Step 3: Multiply by the LCD on both sides.

$$(t-3)(t-4)\left[\frac{6}{(t-3)(t-4)} + \frac{2t}{t-3}\right] = (t-3)(t-4)\left(\frac{3t}{t-4}\right)$$

$$(t-3)(t-4)\left[\frac{6}{(t-3)(t-4)}\right] + (t-3)(t-4)\left(\frac{2t}{t-3}\right) = (t-3)(t-4)\left(\frac{3t}{t-4}\right)$$

$6 + 2t(t-4) = 3t(t-3)$

$6 + 2t^2 - 8t = 3t^2 - 9t$

Step 4: Solve the resulting equation.

$0 = 3t^2 - 2t^2 - 9t + 8t - 6$

Because the resulting equation is quadratic, set the equation equal to zero and factor.

$0 = t^2 - t - 6$

$0 = (t-3)(t+2)$

$t - 3 = 0$ or $t + 2 = 0$ Set each factor equal to zero.

$t = 3$ or $t = -2$

3 is a restricted value, but −2 is not restricted.

Step 5: Check the potential solutions in the original equation.

Check: $t = 3$

3 cannot be a solution to the equation because it will make the denominator zero in the original equation.

$$\frac{6}{t^2 - 7t + 12} + \frac{2t}{t-3} = \frac{3t}{t-4}$$

$$\frac{6}{(3)^2 - 7(3) + 12} + \frac{2(3)}{(3)-3} \stackrel{?}{=} \frac{3(3)}{(3)-4}$$

$$\frac{6}{0} + \frac{6}{0} \stackrel{?}{=} \frac{9}{-1}$$

Zero in the denominator

Check: $t = -2$

$$\frac{6}{t^2 - 7t + 12} + \frac{2t}{t-3} = \frac{3t}{t-4}$$

$$\frac{6}{(-2)^2 - 7(-2) + 12} + \frac{2(-2)}{(-2)-3} \stackrel{?}{=} \frac{3(-2)}{(-2)-4}$$

$$\frac{6}{4 + 14 + 12} + \frac{-4}{-5} \stackrel{?}{=} \frac{-6}{-6}$$

$$\frac{6}{30} + \frac{4}{5} \stackrel{?}{=} 1$$

$$\frac{1}{5} + \frac{4}{5} \stackrel{?}{=} 1 \checkmark \text{ (True)}$$

$t = -2$ is a solution.

The solution set is $\{-2\}$.

Skill Practice Solve the equation.

5. $\dfrac{-8}{x^2 + 6x + 8} + \dfrac{x}{x+4} = \dfrac{2}{x+2}$

Answer

5. $\{4\}$ (The value −4 does not check.)

Example 6 **Translating to a Rational Equation**

Classroom Example: p. 539, Exercise 48

Ten times the reciprocal of a number is added to four. The result is equal to the quotient of twenty-two and the number. Find the number.

Solution:

Let x represent the number.

$$\underset{\text{is added to four}}{4} + \underset{\text{10 times the reciprocal of a number}}{10\left(\frac{1}{x}\right)} \underset{\text{the result is equal to}}{=} \underset{\text{the quotient of 22 and the number}}{\frac{22}{x}}$$

$4 + \frac{10}{x} = \frac{22}{x}$ **Step 1:** The denominators are already factored. The restricted value is $x = 0$.

Step 2: The LCD is x.

$x\left(4 + \frac{10}{x}\right) = x\left(\frac{22}{x}\right)$ **Step 3:** Multiply both sides by the LCD.

$4x + 10 = 22$ Apply the distributive property.

$4x = 12$ **Step 4:** Solve the resulting linear equation.

$x = 3$ is a potential solution. **Step 5:** 3 is not a restricted value. Substituting $x = 3$ into the original equation verifies that it is a solution.

The number is 3.

Skill Practice

6. The quotient of ten and a number is two less than four times the reciprocal of the number. Find the number.

3. Solving Formulas Involving Rational Expressions

A rational equation may have more than one variable. To solve for a specific variable within a rational equation, we can still apply the principle of clearing fractions.

Answer

6. The number is −3.

Classroom Example: p. 539, Exercise 54

Example 7 Solving Formulas Involving Rational Equations

Solve for k. $F = \dfrac{ma}{k}$

Solution:

To solve for k, we must clear fractions so that k no longer appears in the denominator.

$$F = \frac{ma}{k}$$ The LCD is k.

$$k \cdot (F) = k \cdot \left(\frac{ma}{k}\right)$$ Multiply both sides of the equation by the LCD.

$$kF = ma$$ Clear fractions.

$$\frac{kF}{F} = \frac{ma}{F}$$ Divide both sides by F.

$$k = \frac{ma}{F}$$

Skill Practice

7. Solve for t. $C = \dfrac{rt}{d}$

Classroom Example: p. 539, Exercise 56

Example 8 Solving Formulas Involving Rational Equations

A formula to find the height of a trapezoid given its area and the lengths of the two parallel sides is $h = \dfrac{2A}{B + b}$. Solve for b, the length of one of the parallel sides.

Solution:

To solve for b, we must clear fractions so that b no longer appears in the denominator.

$$h = \frac{2A}{B + b}$$ The LCD is $(B + b)$.

Avoiding Mistakes

Algebra is case-sensitive. The variables B and b represent different values.

$$h(B + b) = \left(\frac{2A}{B + b}\right) \cdot (B + b)$$ Multiply both sides of the equation by the LCD.

$$hB + hb = 2A$$ Apply the distributive property.

$$hb = 2A - hB$$ Subtract hB from both sides to isolate the b term.

$$\frac{hb}{h} = \frac{2A - hB}{h}$$ Divide by h.

$$b = \frac{2A - hB}{h}$$

Skill Practice

8. Solve the formula for x. $y = \dfrac{3}{x - 2}$

Answers

7. $t = \dfrac{Cd}{r}$

8. $x = \dfrac{3 + 2y}{y}$ or $x = \dfrac{3}{y} + 2$

TIP: The solution to Example 8 can be written in several forms. The quantity

$$\frac{2A - hB}{h}$$

can be left as a single rational expression or can be split into two fractions and simplified.

$$b = \frac{2A - hB}{h} = \frac{2A}{h} - \frac{hB}{h} = \frac{2A}{h} - B$$

Example 9 Solving Formulas Involving Rational Equations

Classroom Example: p. 539, Exercise 64

Solve for z. $\quad y = \frac{x - z}{x + z}$

Solution:

To solve for z, we must clear fractions so that z no longer appears in the denominator.

$y = \frac{x - z}{x + z}$	LCD is $(x + z)$.
$y(x + z) = \left(\frac{x - z}{x + z}\right)(x + z)$	Multiply both sides of the equation by the LCD.
$yx + yz = x - z$	Apply the distributive property.
$yz + z = x - yx$	Collect z terms on one side of the equation and collect terms not containing z on the other side.
$z(y + 1) = x - yx$	Factor out z.
$z = \frac{x - yx}{y + 1}$	Divide by $y + 1$ to solve for z.

Skill Practice

9. Solve for h. $\quad \frac{b}{x} = \frac{a}{h} + 1$

Answer

9. $h = \frac{ax}{b - x}$ or $\frac{-ax}{x - b}$

Section 7.6 Practice Exercises

For additional exercises, see Classroom Activities 7.6A–7.6B in the *Student's Resource Manual* at www.mhhe.com/moh.

Vocabulary and Key Concepts

1. a. The equation $4x + 7 = -18$ is an example of a ___linear___ equation, whereas $3y^2 - 4y - 7 = 0$ is an example of a ___quadratic___ equation.

b. The equation $\frac{6}{x + 2} + \frac{1}{4} = \frac{2}{3}$ is an example of a ___rational___ equation.

c. After solving a rational equation, check each potential solution to determine if it makes the ___denominator___ equal to zero in one or more of the rational expressions. If so, that potential solution is not part of the solution set.

Review Exercises

For Exercises 2–7, perform the indicated operations.

2. $\frac{2}{x-3} - \frac{3}{x^2-x-6}$ $\frac{2x+1}{(x-3)(x+2)}$

3. $\frac{2x-6}{4x^2+7x-2} \div \frac{x^2-5x+6}{x^2-4}$ $\frac{2}{4x-1}$

4. $\frac{2y}{y-3} + \frac{4}{y^2-9}$ $\frac{2(y+2)(y+1)}{(y-3)(y+3)}$

5. $\frac{h - \frac{1}{h}}{\frac{1}{5} - \frac{1}{5h}}$ $5(h+1)$

6. $\frac{w-4}{w^2-9} \cdot \frac{w-3}{w^2-8w+16}$ $\frac{1}{(w+3)(w-4)}$

7. $1 + \frac{1}{x} - \frac{12}{x^2}$ $\frac{(x+4)(x-3)}{x^2}$

Concept 1: Introduction to Rational Equations

For Exercises 8–13, solve the equations by first clearing the fractions. **(See Example 1.)**

8. $\frac{1}{3}z + \frac{2}{3} = -2z + 10$ $\{4\}$

9. $\frac{5}{2} + \frac{1}{2}b = 5 - \frac{1}{3}b$ $\{3\}$

10. $\frac{3}{2}p + \frac{1}{3} = \frac{2p-3}{4}$ $\left\{-\frac{13}{12}\right\}$

11. $\frac{5}{3} - \frac{1}{6}k = \frac{3k+5}{4}$ $\left\{\frac{5}{11}\right\}$

12. $\frac{2x-3}{4} + \frac{9}{10} = \frac{x}{5}$ $\left\{-\frac{1}{2}\right\}$

13. $\frac{4y+2}{3} - \frac{7}{6} = -\frac{y}{6}$ $\left\{\frac{1}{3}\right\}$

Concept 2: Solving Rational Equations

14. For the equation

$$\frac{1}{w} - \frac{1}{2} = -\frac{1}{4}$$

a. Identify the restricted values. $w = 0$

b. Identify the LCD of the fractions in the equation. $4w$

c. Solve the equation. $\{4\}$

15. For the equation

$$\frac{3}{z} - \frac{4}{5} = -\frac{1}{5}$$

a. Identify the restricted values. $z = 0$

b. Identify the LCD of the fractions in the equation. $5z$

c. Solve the equation. $\{5\}$

16. Identify the LCD of all the denominators in the equation.

$$\frac{x+1}{x^2+2x-3} = \frac{1}{x+3} - \frac{1}{x-1}$$ $(x+3)(x-1)$

For Exercises 17–46, solve the equations. **(See Examples 2–5.)**

17. $\frac{1}{8} = \frac{3}{5} + \frac{5}{y}$ $\left\{-\frac{200}{19}\right\}$

18. $\frac{2}{7} - \frac{1}{x} = \frac{2}{3}$ $\left\{-\frac{21}{8}\right\}$

19. $\frac{7}{4a} = \frac{3}{a-5}$ $\{-7\}$

20. $\frac{2}{x+4} = \frac{5}{3x}$ $\{20\}$

21. $\frac{5}{6x} + \frac{7}{x} = 1$ $\left\{\frac{47}{6}\right\}$

22. $\frac{14}{3x} - \frac{5}{x} = 2$ $\left\{-\frac{1}{6}\right\}$

23. $1 - \frac{2}{y} = \frac{3}{y^2}$ $\{3, -1\}$

24. $1 - \frac{2}{m} = \frac{8}{m^2}$ $\{4, -2\}$

25. $\frac{a+1}{a} = 1 + \frac{a-2}{2a}$ $\{4\}$

26. $\frac{7b-4}{5b} = \frac{9}{5} - \frac{4}{b}$ $\{8\}$

27. $\frac{w}{5} - \frac{w+3}{w} = -\frac{3}{w}$ $\{5\}$ (The value 0 does not check.)

28. $\frac{t}{12} + \frac{t+3}{3t} = \frac{1}{t}$ $\{-4\}$ (The value 0 does not check.)

29. $\dfrac{2}{m+3} = \dfrac{5}{4m+12} - \dfrac{3}{8}$ $\{-5\}$

30. $\dfrac{2}{4n-4} - \dfrac{7}{4} = \dfrac{-3}{n-1}$ $\{3\}$

31. $\dfrac{p}{p-4} - 5 = \dfrac{4}{p-4}$ { } (The value 4 does not check.)

32. $\dfrac{-5}{q+5} = \dfrac{q}{q+5} + 2$ { } (The value −5 does not check.)

33. $\dfrac{2t}{t+2} - 2 = \dfrac{t-8}{t+2}$ $\{4\}$

34. $\dfrac{4w}{w-3} - 3 = \dfrac{3w-1}{w-3}$ $\{5\}$

35. $\dfrac{x^2-x}{x-2} = \dfrac{12}{x-2}$ $\{4, -3\}$

36. $\dfrac{x^2+9}{x+4} = \dfrac{-10x}{x+4}$ $\{-9, -1\}$

37. $\dfrac{x^2+3x}{x-1} = \dfrac{4}{x-1}$ $\{-4\}$ (The value 1 does not check.)

38. $\dfrac{2x^2-21}{2x-3} = \dfrac{-11x}{2x-3}$ $\{-7\}$ (The value $\frac{3}{2}$ does not check.)

39. $\dfrac{2x}{x+4} - \dfrac{8}{x-4} = \dfrac{2x^2+32}{x^2-16}$ { } (The value −4 does not check.)

40. $\dfrac{4x}{x+3} - \dfrac{12}{x-3} = \dfrac{4x^2+36}{x^2-9}$ { } (The value −3 does not check.)

41. $\dfrac{x}{x+6} = \dfrac{72}{x^2-36} + 4$ $\{4\}$ (The value −6 does not check.)

42. $\dfrac{y}{y+4} = \dfrac{32}{y^2-16} + 3$ $\{2\}$ (The value −4 does not check.)

43. $\dfrac{5}{3x-3} - \dfrac{2}{x-2} = \dfrac{7}{x^2-3x+2}$ $\{-25\}$

44. $\dfrac{6}{5a+10} - \dfrac{1}{a-5} = \dfrac{4}{a^2-3a-10}$ $\{60\}$

45. $\dfrac{w}{w-3} = \dfrac{17}{w^2-7w+12} + \dfrac{1}{w-4}$ $\{-2, 7\}$

46. $\dfrac{y}{y+6} = \dfrac{-6}{y^2+7y+6} + \dfrac{2}{y+1}$ $\{-2, 3\}$

For Exercises 47–50, translate to a rational equation and solve. **(See Example 6.)**

47. The reciprocal of a number is added to three. The result is the quotient of 25 and the number. Find the number. The number is 8.

48. The difference of three and the reciprocal of a number is equal to the quotient of 20 and the number. Find the number. The number is 7.

49. If a number added to five is divided by the difference of the number and two, the result is three-fourths. Find the number. The number is −26.

50. If twice a number added to three is divided by the number plus one, the result is three-halves. Find the number. The number is −3.

Concept 3: Solving Formulas Involving Rational Expressions

For Exercises 51–68, solve for the indicated variable. **(See Examples 7–9.)**

51. $K = \dfrac{ma}{F}$ for m $m = \dfrac{FK}{a}$

52. $K = \dfrac{ma}{F}$ for a $a = \dfrac{FK}{m}$

53. $K = \dfrac{IR}{E}$ for E $E = \dfrac{IR}{K}$

54. $K = \dfrac{IR}{E}$ for R $R = \dfrac{KE}{I}$

55. $I = \dfrac{E}{R+r}$ for R $R = \dfrac{E-Ir}{I}$ or $R = \dfrac{E}{I} - r$

56. $I = \dfrac{E}{R+r}$ for r $r = \dfrac{E-IR}{I}$ or $r = \dfrac{E}{I} - R$

57. $h = \dfrac{2A}{B+b}$ for B $B = \dfrac{2A-hb}{h}$ or $B = \dfrac{2A}{h} - b$

58. $\dfrac{C}{\pi r} = 2$ for r $r = \dfrac{C}{2\pi}$

59. $\dfrac{V}{\pi h} = r^2$ for h $h = \dfrac{V}{r^2\pi}$

60. $\dfrac{V}{lw} = h$ for w $w = \dfrac{V}{lh}$

61. $x = \dfrac{at+b}{t}$ for t $t = \dfrac{b}{x-a}$ or $t = \dfrac{-b}{a-x}$

62. $\dfrac{T+mf}{m} = g$ for m $m = \dfrac{T}{g-f}$ or $m = \dfrac{-T}{f-g}$

63. $\dfrac{x-y}{xy} = z$ for x $x = \dfrac{y}{1-yz}$ or $x = \dfrac{-y}{yz-1}$

64. $\dfrac{w-n}{wn} = P$ for w $w = \dfrac{n}{1-Pn}$ or $w = \dfrac{-n}{Pn-1}$

65. $a + b = \dfrac{2A}{h}$ for h $h = \dfrac{2A}{a+b}$

66. $1 + rt = \dfrac{A}{P}$ for P $P = \dfrac{A}{1+rt}$

67. $\dfrac{1}{R} = \dfrac{1}{R_1} + \dfrac{1}{R_2}$ for R $R = \dfrac{R_1R_2}{R_2+R_1}$

68. $\dfrac{b+a}{ab} = \dfrac{1}{f}$ for b $b = \dfrac{fa}{a-f}$ or $b = \dfrac{-fa}{f-a}$

Problem Recognition Exercises

Comparing Rational Equations and Rational Expressions

Often adding or subtracting rational expressions is confused with solving rational equations. When adding rational expressions, we combine the terms to simplify the expression. When solving an equation, we clear the fractions and find numerical solutions, if possible. Both processes begin with finding the LCD, but the LCD is used differently in each process. Compare these two examples.

Example 1:

Add. $\frac{4}{x}+\frac{x}{3}$ (The LCD is $3x$.)

$=\frac{3}{3}\cdot\left(\frac{4}{x}\right)+\left(\frac{x}{3}\right)\cdot\frac{x}{x}$

$=\frac{12}{3x}+\frac{x^2}{3x}$

$=\frac{12+x^2}{3x}$ The answer is a rational expression.

Example 2:

Solve. $\frac{4}{x}+\frac{x}{3}=-\frac{8}{3}$ (The LCD is $3x$.)

$\frac{3x}{1}\left(\frac{4}{x}+\frac{x}{3}\right)=\frac{3x}{1}\left(-\frac{8}{3}\right)$

$12+x^2=-8x$

$x^2+8x+12=0$

$(x+2)(x+6)=0$

$x+2=0$ or $x+6=0$

$x=-2$ or $x=-6$ The answer is the set $\{-2,-6\}$.

For Exercises 1–20, solve the equations and simplify the expressions.

1. $\frac{y}{2y+4}-\frac{2}{y^2+2y}$ $\frac{y-2}{2y}$

2. $\frac{1}{x+2}+2=\frac{x+11}{x+2}$ $\{6\}$

3. $\frac{5t}{2}-\frac{t-2}{3}=5$ $\{2\}$

4. $3-\frac{2}{a-5}$ $\frac{3a-17}{a-5}$

5. $\frac{7}{6p^2}+\frac{2}{9p}+\frac{1}{3p^2}$ $\frac{4p+27}{18p^2}$

6. $\frac{3b}{b+1}-\frac{2b}{b-1}$ $\frac{b(b-5)}{(b-1)(b+1)}$

7. $4+\frac{2}{h-3}=5$ $\{5\}$

8. $\frac{2}{w+1}+\frac{3}{(w+1)^2}$ $\frac{2w+5}{(w+1)^2}$

9. $\frac{1}{x-6}-\frac{3}{x^2-6x}=\frac{4}{x}$ $\{7\}$

10. $\frac{3}{m}-\frac{6}{5}=-\frac{3}{m}$ $\{5\}$

11. $\frac{7}{2x+2}+\frac{3x}{4x+4}$ $\frac{3x+14}{4(x+1)}$

12. $\frac{10}{2t-1}-1=\frac{t}{2t-1}$ $\left\{\frac{11}{3}\right\}$

13. $\frac{3}{5x}+\frac{7}{2x}=1$ $\left\{\frac{41}{10}\right\}$

14. $\frac{7}{t^2-5t}-\frac{3}{t-5}$ $\frac{7-3t}{t(t-5)}$

15. $\frac{5}{2a-1}+4$ $\frac{8a+1}{2a-1}$

16. $p-\frac{5p}{p-2}=-\frac{10}{p-2}$
$\{5\}$ (The value 2 does not check.)

17. $\frac{3}{u}+\frac{12}{u^2-3u}=\frac{u+1}{u-3}$
$\{-1\}$ (The value 3 does not check.)

18. $\frac{5}{4k}-\frac{2}{6k}$ $\frac{11}{12k}$

19. $\frac{-2h}{h^2-9}+\frac{3}{h-3}$ $\frac{h+9}{(h-3)(h+3)}$

20. $\frac{3y}{y^2-5y+4}=\frac{2}{y-4}+\frac{3}{y-1}$ $\{7\}$

Applications of Rational Equations and Proportions

Section 7.7

Concepts

1. Solving Proportions
2. Applications of Proportions and Similar Triangles
3. Distance, Rate, and Time Applications
4. Work Applications

1. Solving Proportions

In this section, we look at how rational equations can be used to solve a variety of applications. The first type of rational equation that will be applied is called a proportion.

Definition of Ratio and Proportion

1. The **ratio** of a to b is $\frac{a}{b}$ $(b \neq 0)$ and can also be expressed as $a{:}b$ or $a \div b$.
2. An equation that equates two ratios or rates is called a **proportion**. Therefore, if $b \neq 0$ and $d \neq 0$, then $\frac{a}{b} = \frac{c}{d}$ is a proportion.

A proportion can be solved by multiplying both sides of the equation by the LCD and clearing fractions.

Example 1 Solving a Proportion

Classroom Example: p. 548, Exercise 10

Solve the proportion. $\frac{3}{11} = \frac{123}{w}$

Solution:

$\frac{3}{11} = \frac{123}{w}$ The LCD is $11w$.

$11w\left(\frac{3}{11}\right) = 11w\left(\frac{123}{w}\right)$ Multiply by the LCD and clear fractions.

$3w = 11 \cdot 123$ Solve the resulting equation (linear).

$3w = 1353$

$\frac{3w}{3} = \frac{1353}{3}$

$w = 451$

Check: $w = 451$

$\frac{3}{11} = \frac{123}{w}$

$\frac{3}{11} \stackrel{?}{=} \frac{123}{(451)}$

The solution set is {451}.

$\frac{3}{11} \stackrel{?}{=} \frac{3}{11}$ ✓ (True) Simplify to lowest terms.

Skill Practice Solve the proportion.

1. $\frac{10}{b} = \frac{2}{33}$

Answer

1. {165}

2. Applications of Proportions and Similar Triangles

Classroom Example: p. 549, Exercise 28

Example 2 Using a Proportion in an Application

For a recent year, the population of Alabama was approximately 4.2 million. At that time, Alabama had seven representatives in the U.S. House of Representatives. In the same year, North Carolina had a population of approximately 7.2 million. If representation in the House is based on population in equal proportions for each state, how many representatives did North Carolina have?

© Brand X Pictures/ PunchStock RF

Solution:

Let x represent the number of representatives for North Carolina.

Set up a proportion by writing two equivalent ratios.

$$\frac{\text{Population of Alabama}}{\text{number of representatives}} \rightarrow \frac{4.2}{7} = \frac{7.2}{x} \leftarrow \frac{\text{Population of North Carolina}}{\text{number of representatives}}$$

$$\frac{4.2}{7} = \frac{7.2}{x}$$

$$7x \cdot \frac{4.2}{7} = 7x \cdot \frac{7.2}{x}$$ Multiply by the LCD, $7x$.

$$4.2x = (7.2)(7)$$ Solve the resulting linear equation.

$$4.2x = 50.4$$

$$\frac{4.2x}{4.2} = \frac{50.4}{4.2}$$

$$x = 12$$ North Carolina had 12 representatives.

TIP: The equation from Example 2 could have been solved by first equating the cross products:

$$\frac{4.2}{7} \times \frac{7.2}{x}$$

$$4.2x = (7.2)(7)$$

$$4.2x = 50.4$$

$$x = 12$$

Skill Practice

2. A university has a ratio of students to faculty of 105 to 2. If the student population at the university is 15,750, how many faculty members are needed?

Proportions are used in geometry with **similar triangles**. Two triangles are similar if their angles have equal measure. In such a case, the lengths of the corresponding sides are proportional. In Figure 7-1, triangle ABC is similar to triangle XYZ. Therefore, the following ratios are equivalent.

$$\frac{a}{x} = \frac{b}{y} = \frac{c}{z}$$

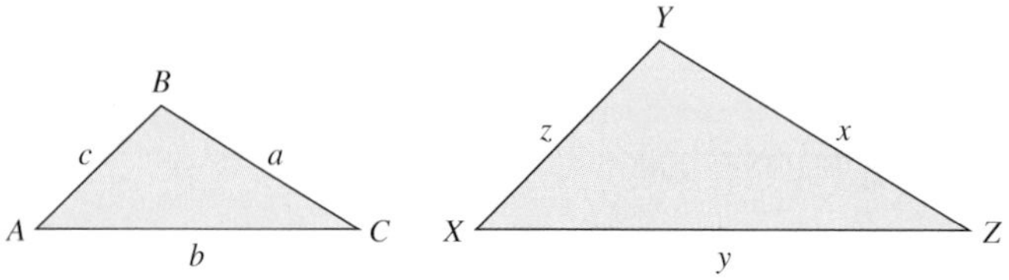

Figure 7-1

Answer

2. 300 faculty members are needed.

Example 3 Using Similar Triangles to Find an Unknown Side in a Triangle

Classroom Example: p. 549, Exercise 34

In Figure 7-2, triangle XYZ is similar to triangle ABC.

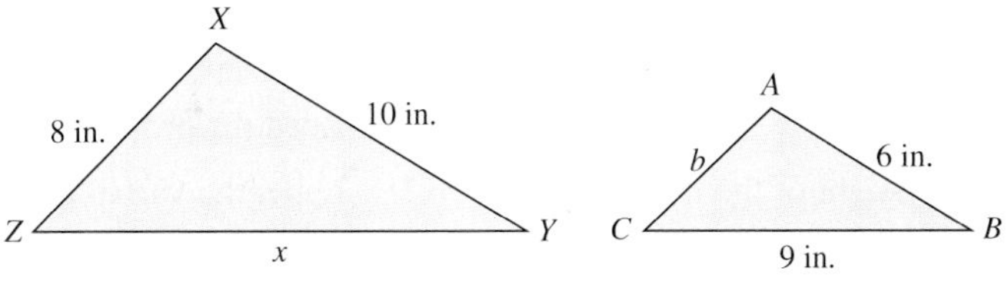

Figure 7-2

a. Solve for x. **b.** Solve for b.

Solution:

a. The lengths of the upper right sides of the triangles are given. These form a known ratio of $\frac{10}{6}$. Because the triangles are similar, the ratio of the other corresponding sides must also be equal to $\frac{10}{6}$. To solve for x, we have

$$\frac{\text{Bottom side from large triangle}}{\text{bottom side from small triangle}} \rightarrow \frac{x}{9 \text{ in.}} = \frac{10 \text{ in.}}{6 \text{ in.}} \leftarrow \frac{\text{Right side from large triangle}}{\text{right side from small triangle}}$$

$$\frac{x}{9} = \frac{10}{6} \qquad \text{The LCD is 18.}$$

$$\overset{2}{\cancel{18}} \cdot \left(\frac{x}{\cancel{9}}\right) = \overset{3}{\cancel{18}} \cdot \left(\frac{10}{\cancel{6}}\right) \qquad \text{Multiply by the LCD.}$$

$$2x = 30 \qquad \text{Clear fractions.}$$

$$x = 15 \qquad \text{Divide by 2.}$$

The length of side x is 15 in.

b. To solve for b, the ratio of the upper left sides of the triangles must equal $\frac{10}{6}$.

$$\frac{\text{Left side from large triangle}}{\text{left side from small triangle}} \rightarrow \frac{8 \text{ in.}}{b} = \frac{10 \text{ in.}}{6 \text{ in.}} \leftarrow \frac{\text{Right side from large triangle}}{\text{right side from small triangle}}$$

$$\frac{8}{b} = \frac{10}{6} \qquad \text{The LCD is } 6b.$$

$$6\cancel{b} \cdot \left(\frac{8}{\cancel{b}}\right) = \cancel{6}b \cdot \left(\frac{10}{\cancel{6}}\right) \qquad \text{Multiply by the LCD.}$$

$$48 = 10b \qquad \text{Clear fractions.}$$

$$\frac{48}{10} = \frac{10b}{10}$$

$$4.8 = b$$

The length of side b is 4.8 in.

Skill Practice

3. Triangle ABC is similar to triangle XYZ. Solve for the lengths of the missing sides.

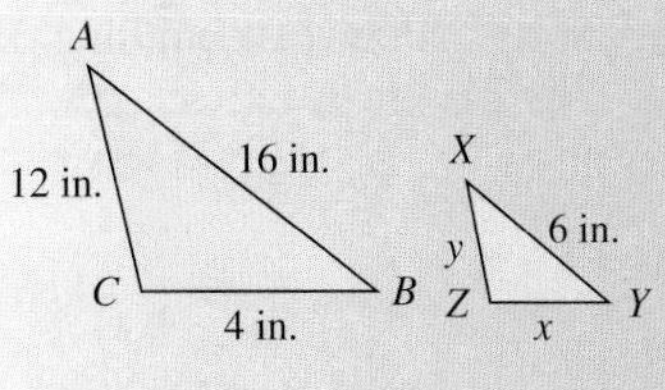

Answer

3. $x = 1.5$ in., and $y = 4.5$ in.

Classroom Example: p. 550, Exercise 38

Example 4 Using Similar Triangles in an Application

A tree that is 20 ft from a house is to be cut down. Use the following information and similar triangles to find the height of the tree to determine if it will hit the house.

The shadow cast by a yardstick is 2 ft long. The shadow cast by the tree is 11 ft long.

Solution: **Step 1:** Read the problem.

Let x represent the height of the tree. **Step 2:** Label the variables.

We will assume that the measurements were taken at the same time of day. Therefore, the angle of the Sun is the same on both objects, and we can set up similar triangles (Figure 7-3).

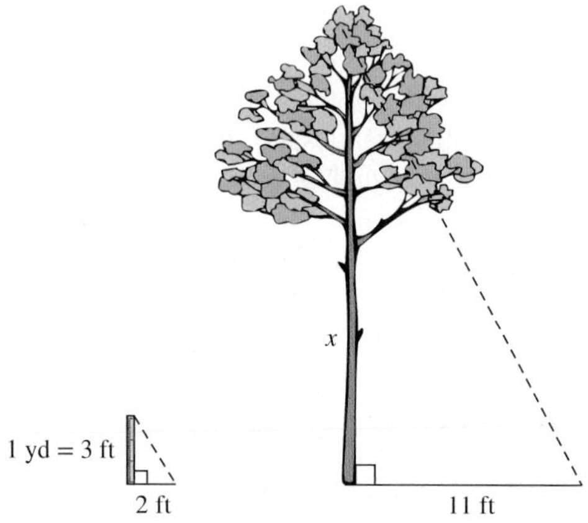

Figure 7-3

Step 3: Create a verbal model.

Height of yardstick / height of tree → $\dfrac{3 \text{ ft}}{x} = \dfrac{2 \text{ ft}}{11 \text{ ft}}$ ← Length of yardstick's shadow / length of tree's shadow

$$\frac{3}{x} = \frac{2}{11}$$

Step 4: Write a mathematical equation.

$$11x\left(\frac{3}{x}\right) = \left(\frac{2}{11}\right)11x$$

Step 5: Multiply by the LCD.

$$33 = 2x$$

Solve the equation.

$$\frac{33}{2} = \frac{2x}{2}$$

$$16.5 = x$$

Step 6: Interpret the results, and write the answer in words.

The tree is 16.5 ft high. The tree is less than 20 ft high so it will not hit the house.

Skill Practice

4. The Sun casts a 3.2-ft shadow of a 6-ft man. At the same time, the Sun casts a 80-ft shadow of a building. How tall is the building?

Answer

4. The building is 150 ft tall.

3. Distance, Rate, and Time Applications

In Examples 5 and 6, we use the familiar relationship among the variables distance, rate, and time. Recall that $d = rt$.

Example 5 **Using a Rational Equation in a Distance, Rate, and Time Application**

Classroom Example: p. 550, Exercise 42

A small plane flies 440 mi with the wind from Memphis, TN, to Oklahoma City, OK. In the same amount of time, the plane flies 340 miles against the wind from Oklahoma City to Little Rock, AR (see Figure 7-4). If the wind speed is 30 mph, find the speed of the plane in still air.

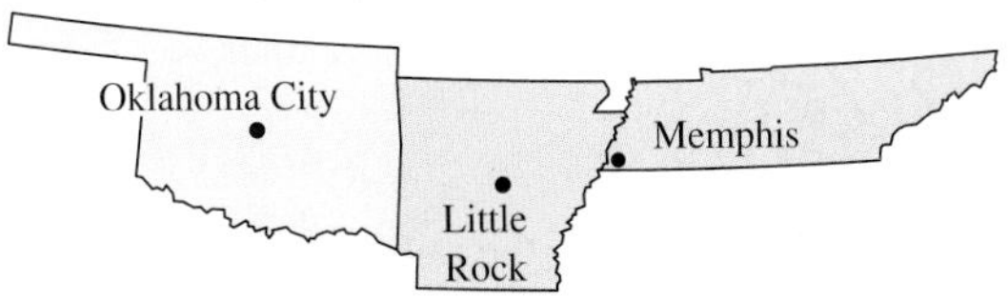

Figure 7-4

Solution:

Let x represent the speed of the plane in still air.

Then $x + 30$ is the speed of the plane with the wind.

$x - 30$ is the speed of the plane against the wind.

Organize the given information in a chart.

	Distance	Rate	Time
With the wind	440	$x + 30$	$\frac{440}{x+30}$
Against the wind	340	$x - 30$	$\frac{340}{x-30}$

Because $d = rt$, then $t = \frac{d}{r}$

The plane travels with the wind for the same amount of time as it travels against the wind, so we can equate the two expressions for time.

$$\begin{pmatrix}\text{Time with}\\ \text{the wind}\end{pmatrix} = \begin{pmatrix}\text{time against}\\ \text{the wind}\end{pmatrix}$$

$$\frac{440}{x+30} = \frac{340}{x-30}$$

The LCD is $(x + 30)(x - 30)$.

$$\cancel{(x+30)}(x-30) \cdot \frac{440}{\cancel{x+30}} = (x+30)\cancel{(x-30)} \cdot \frac{340}{\cancel{x-30}}$$

$$440(x - 30) = 340(x + 30)$$

$$440x - 13{,}200 = 340x + 10{,}200$$

Solve the resulting linear equation.

$$100x = 23{,}400$$

$$x = 234$$

The plane's speed in still air is 234 mph.

TIP: The equation

$$\frac{440}{x+30} = \frac{340}{x-30}$$

is a proportion. The fractions can also be cleared by equating the cross products.

$$\frac{440}{x+30} \times \frac{340}{x-30}$$

$$440(x - 30) = 340(x + 30)$$

Skill Practice

5. Alison paddles her kayak in a river where the current is 2 mph. She can paddle 20 mi with the current in the same amount of time that she can paddle 10 mi against the current. Find the speed of the kayak in still water.

Classroom Example: p. 551, Exercise 48

Example 6 Using a Rational Equation in a Distance, Rate, and Time Application

A motorist drives 100 mi between two cities in a bad rainstorm. For the return trip in sunny weather, she averages 10 mph faster and takes $\frac{1}{2}$ hr less time. Find the average speed of the motorist in the rainstorm and in sunny weather.

Solution:

Let x represent the motorist's speed during the rain.

Then $x + 10$ represents the speed in sunny weather.

	Distance	Rate	Time
Trip during rainstorm	100	x	$\frac{100}{x}$
Trip during sunny weather	100	$x+10$	$\frac{100}{x+10}$

Because $d = rt$, then $t = \frac{d}{r}$

Because the same distance is traveled in $\frac{1}{2}$ hr less time, the difference between the time of the trip during the rainstorm and the time during sunny weather is $\frac{1}{2}$ hr.

$$\begin{pmatrix}\text{Time during}\\\text{the rainstorm}\end{pmatrix} - \begin{pmatrix}\text{time during}\\\text{sunny weather}\end{pmatrix} = \left(\frac{1}{2}\text{ hr}\right) \quad \text{Verbal model}$$

$$\frac{100}{x} - \frac{100}{x+10} = \frac{1}{2} \quad \text{Mathematical equation}$$

$$2x(x+10)\left(\frac{100}{x} - \frac{100}{x+10}\right) = 2x(x+10)\left(\frac{1}{2}\right) \quad \text{Multiply by the LCD.}$$

$$2x(x+10)\left(\frac{100}{x}\right) - 2x(x+10)\left(\frac{100}{x+10}\right) = 2x(x+10)\left(\frac{1}{2}\right) \quad \text{Apply the distributive property.}$$

$$200(x+10) - 200x = x(x+10) \quad \text{Clear fractions.}$$

$$200x + 2000 - 200x = x^2 + 10x \quad \text{Solve the resulting equation (quadratic).}$$

$$2000 = x^2 + 10x$$

$$0 = x^2 + 10x - 2000 \quad \text{Set the equation equal to zero.}$$

$$0 = (x - 40)(x + 50) \quad \text{Factor.}$$

$$x = 40 \quad \text{or} \quad x = -50$$

Avoiding Mistakes

The equation

$$\frac{100}{x} - \frac{100}{x+10} = \frac{1}{2}$$

is not a proportion because the left-hand side has more than one fraction. Do not try to multiply the cross products. Instead, multiply by the LCD to clear fractions.

Answer

5. The speed of the kayak is 6 mph.

Because a rate of speed cannot be negative, reject $x = -50$. Therefore, the speed of the motorist in the rainstorm is 40 mph. Because $x + 10 = 40 + 10 = 50$, the average speed for the return trip in sunny weather is 50 mph.

Skill Practice

6. Harley rode his mountain bike 12 mi to the top of a mountain and the same distance back down. His speed going up was 8 mph slower than coming down. The ride up took 2 hr longer than the ride coming down. Find his speed in each direction.

4. Work Applications

Example 7 demonstrates how work rates are related to a portion of a job that can be completed in one unit of time.

Example 7 Using a Rational Equation in a Work Problem

Classroom Example: p. 551, Exercise 52

A new printing press can print the morning edition in 2 hr, whereas the old printer requires 4 hr. How long would it take to print the morning edition if both printers work together?

© Getty Images RF

Solution:

One method to solve this problem is to add rates.

Let x represent the time required for both printers working together to complete the job.

$$\begin{pmatrix}\text{Rate}\\ \text{of old printer}\end{pmatrix} + \begin{pmatrix}\text{rate}\\ \text{of new printer}\end{pmatrix} = \begin{pmatrix}\text{rate of}\\ \text{both working together}\end{pmatrix}$$

$$\frac{1\text{ job}}{4\text{ hr}} + \frac{1\text{ job}}{2\text{ hr}} = \frac{1\text{ job}}{x\text{ hr}}$$

$$\frac{1}{4} + \frac{1}{2} = \frac{1}{x}$$

$$4x\left(\frac{1}{4} + \frac{1}{2}\right) = 4x\left(\frac{1}{x}\right)$$ The LCD is $4x$.

$$\overset{1}{\cancel{4}}x \cdot \frac{1}{4} + \overset{2}{\cancel{4}}x \cdot \frac{1}{2} = 4\overset{1}{\cancel{x}} \cdot \frac{1}{\cancel{x}}$$ Apply the distributive property.

$$x + 2x = 4$$ Solve the resulting linear equation.

$$3x = 4$$

$$x = \frac{4}{3}$$ The time required to print the morning edition using both printers is $1\frac{1}{3}$ hr.

Skill Practice

7. The computer at a bank can process and prepare the bank statements in 30 hr. A new faster computer can do the job in 20 hr. If the bank uses both computers together, how long will it take to process the statements?

Answers

6. Uphill speed was 4 mph; downhill speed was 12 mph.
7. 12 hr

An alternative approach to Example 7 is to determine the portion of the job that each printer can complete in 1 hr and extend that rate to the portion of the job completed in x hours.

- The old printer can perform the job in 4 hr. Therefore, it completes $\frac{1}{4}$ of the job in 1 hr and $\frac{1}{4}x$ jobs in x hours.
- The new printer can perform the job in 2 hr. Therefore, it completes $\frac{1}{2}$ of the job in 1 hr and $\frac{1}{2}x$ jobs in x hours.

The sum of the portions of the job completed by each printer must equal one whole job.

$$\begin{pmatrix}\text{Portion of job}\\ \text{completed by}\\ \text{old printer}\end{pmatrix} + \begin{pmatrix}\text{portion of job}\\ \text{completed by}\\ \text{new printer}\end{pmatrix} = \begin{pmatrix}1\\ \text{whole}\\ \text{job}\end{pmatrix}$$

$\frac{1}{4}x + \frac{1}{2}x = 1$ The LCD is 4.

$4\left(\frac{1}{4}x + \frac{1}{2}x\right) = 4(1)$ Multiply by the LCD.

$x + 2x = 4$ Solve the resulting linear equation.

$3x = 4$

$x = \frac{4}{3}$ The time required using both printers is $1\frac{1}{3}$ hr.

Section 7.7 Practice Exercises

For additional exercises, see Classroom Activities 7.7A–7.7C in the *Student's Resource Manual* at www.mhhe.com/moh.

Vocabulary and Key Concepts

1. a. An equation that equates two ratios is called a proportion.

b. Given similar triangles, the lengths of corresponding sides are proportional.

Review Exercises

For Exercises 2–7, determine whether each of the following is an equation or an expression. If it is an equation, solve it. If it is an expression, perform the indicated operation.

2. $\frac{b}{5} + 3 = 9$ Equation; {30}

3. $\frac{m}{m-1} - \frac{2}{m+3}$ Expression; $\frac{m^2+m+2}{(m-1)(m+3)}$

4. $\frac{2}{a+5} + \frac{5}{a^2-25}$ Expression; $\frac{2a-5}{(a+5)(a-5)}$

5. $\frac{3y+6}{20} \div \frac{4y+8}{8}$ Expression; $\frac{3}{10}$

6. $\frac{z^2+z}{24} \cdot \frac{8}{z+1}$ Expression; $\frac{z}{3}$

7. $\frac{3}{p+3} = \frac{12p+19}{p^2+7p+12} - \frac{5}{p+4}$ Equation; {2}

8. Determine whether 1 is a solution to the equation. $\frac{1}{x-1} + \frac{1}{2} = \frac{2}{x^2-1}$ No

Concept 1: Solving Proportions

For Exercises 9–22, solve the proportions. **(See Example 1.)**

9. $\frac{8}{5} = \frac{152}{p}$ {95}

10. $\frac{6}{7} = \frac{96}{y}$ {112}

11. $\frac{19}{76} = \frac{z}{4}$ {1}

12. $\frac{15}{135} = \frac{w}{9}$ {1}

13. $\frac{5}{3} = \frac{a}{8}$ $\left\{\frac{40}{3}\right\}$

14. $\frac{b}{14} = \frac{3}{8}$ $\left\{\frac{21}{4}\right\}$

15. $\frac{2}{1.9} = \frac{x}{38}$ {40}

16. $\frac{16}{1.3} = \frac{30}{p}$ {2.4375}

17. $\frac{y+1}{2y} = \frac{2}{3}$ {3}

18. $\frac{w-2}{4w} = \frac{1}{6}$ {6}

19. $\frac{9}{2z-1} = \frac{3}{z}$ {−1}

20. $\frac{1}{t} = \frac{1}{4-t}$ {2}

21. $\frac{8}{9a-1} = \frac{5}{3a+2}$ {1}

22. $\frac{4p+1}{3} = \frac{2p-5}{6}$ $\left\{-\frac{7}{6}\right\}$

23. Charles' law describes the relationship between the initial and final temperature and volume of a gas held at a constant pressure.

$$\frac{V_i}{V_f} = \frac{T_i}{T_f}$$

a. Solve the equation for V_f. $V_f = \frac{V_i T_f}{T_i}$

b. Solve the equation for T_f. $T_f = \frac{T_i V_f}{V_i}$

24. The relationship between the area, height, and base of a triangle is given by the proportion

$$\frac{A}{b} = \frac{h}{2}$$

a. Solve the equation for A. $A = \frac{hb}{2}$

b. Solve the equation for b. $b = \frac{2A}{h}$

Concept 2: Applications of Proportions and Similar Triangles

For Exercises 25–32, solve using proportions.

25. Toni drives her car 132 mi on the highway on 4 gal of gas. At this rate how many miles can she drive on 9 gal of gas? **(See Example 2.)** Toni can drive 297 mi on 9 gal of gas.

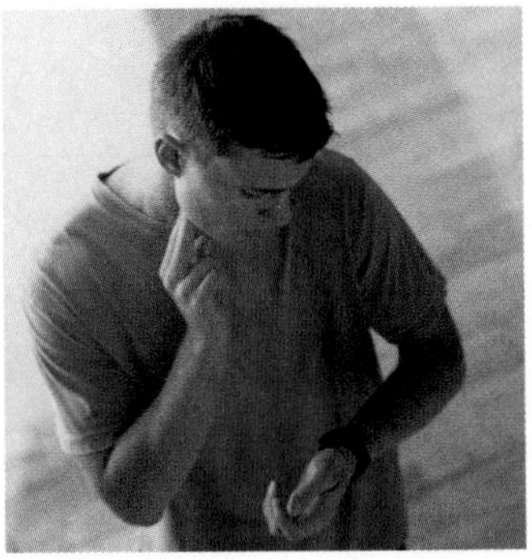

© Duncan Smith/Getty Images RF

26. Tim takes his pulse for 10 sec and counts 12 beats. How many beats per minute is this? This is 72 beats/min.

27. It is recommended that 7.8 mL of Grow-It-Right plant food be mixed with 2 L of water for feeding house plants. How much plant food should be mixed with 1 gal of water to maintain the same concentration? (1 gal ≈ 3.8 L.) Express the answer in milliliters. Mix 14.82 mL of plant food.

28. According to the website for the state of Virginia, 0.8 million tons of clothing is reused or recycled out of 7 million tons of clothing discarded. If 17.5 million tons of clothing is discarded, how many tons will be reused or recycled? 2 million tons of clothing will be reused or recycled.

29. Andrew is on a low-carbohydrate diet. If his diet book tells him that an 8-oz serving of pineapple contains 19.2 g of carbohydrate, how many grams of carbohydrate does a 5-oz serving contain? 5 oz contains 12 g of carbohydrate.

30. Cooking oatmeal requires 1 cup of water for every $\frac{1}{2}$ cup of oats. How many cups of water will be required for $\frac{3}{4}$ cup of oats? 1.5 cups of water will be necessary.

31. According to a building code, a wheelchair ramp must be at least 12 ft long for each foot of height. If the height of a newly constructed ramp is to be $1\frac{2}{3}$ ft, find the minimum acceptable length. The minimum length is 20 ft.

32. A map has a scale of 50 mi/in. If two cities measure 6.5 in. apart, how many miles does this represent? This represents 325 mi.

For Exercises 33–36, triangle ABC is similar to triangle XYZ. Solve for x and y. **(See Example 3.)**

33.

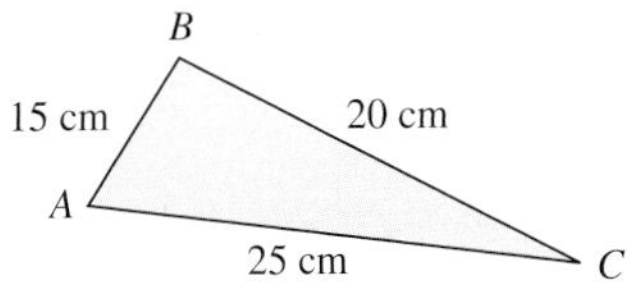

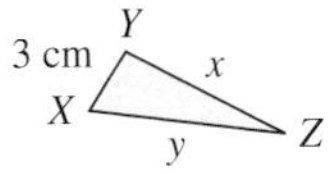

$x = 4$ cm; $y = 5$ cm

34.

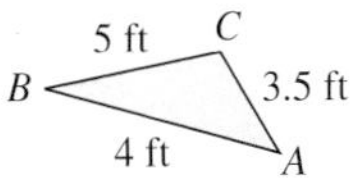

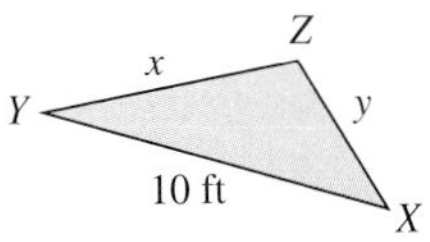

$x = 12.5$ ft.; $y = 8.75$ ft

35.

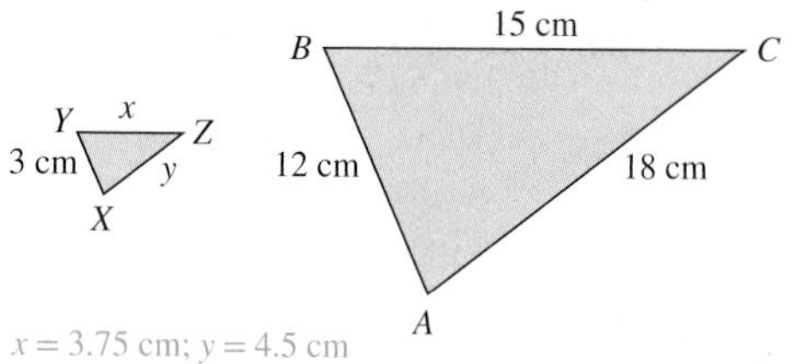

$x = 3.75$ cm; $y = 4.5$ cm

36.

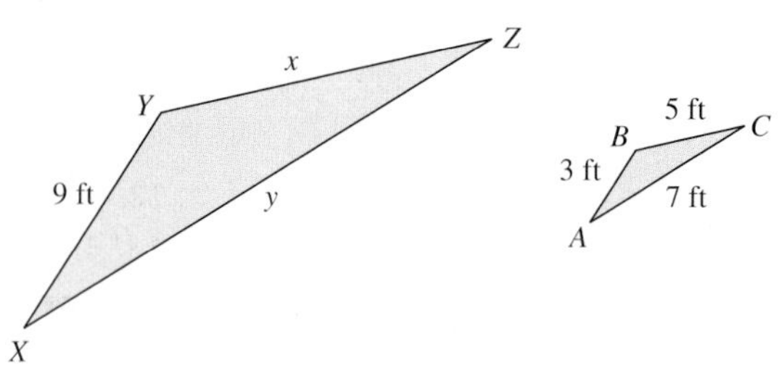

$x = 15$ ft; $y = 21$ ft

37. To estimate the height of a light pole, a mathematics student measures the length of a shadow cast by a meterstick and the length of the shadow cast by the light pole. Find the height of the light pole. **(See Example 4.)** The height of the pole is 7 m.

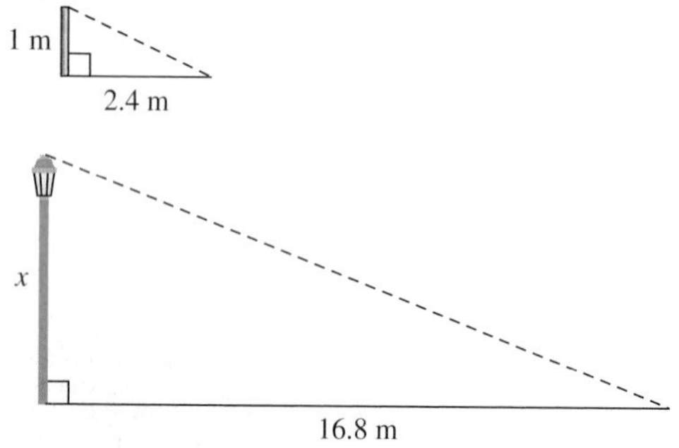

38. To estimate the height of a building, a student measures the length of a shadow cast by a yardstick and the length of the shadow cast by the building. Find the height of the building. The height is 36 ft.

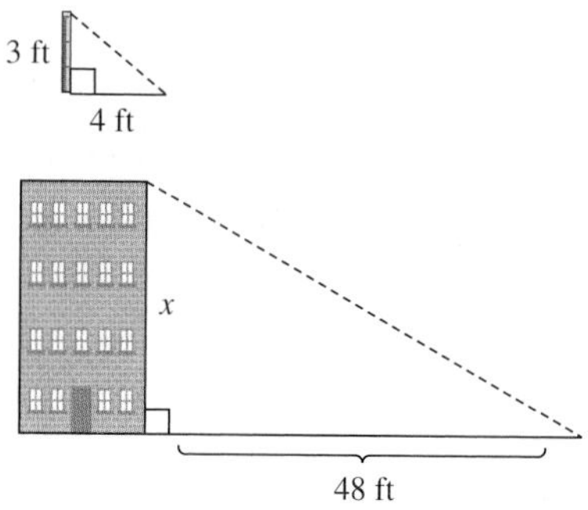

39. A 6-ft-tall man standing 54 ft from a light post casts an 18-ft shadow. What is the height of the light post? The light post is 24 ft high.

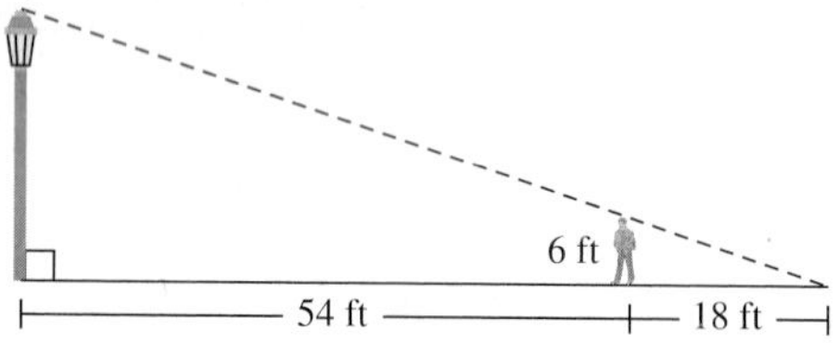

40. For a science project at school, a student must measure the height of a tree. The student measures the length of the shadow of the tree and then measures the length of the shadow cast by a yardstick. Find the height of the tree. The tree is 36 ft high.

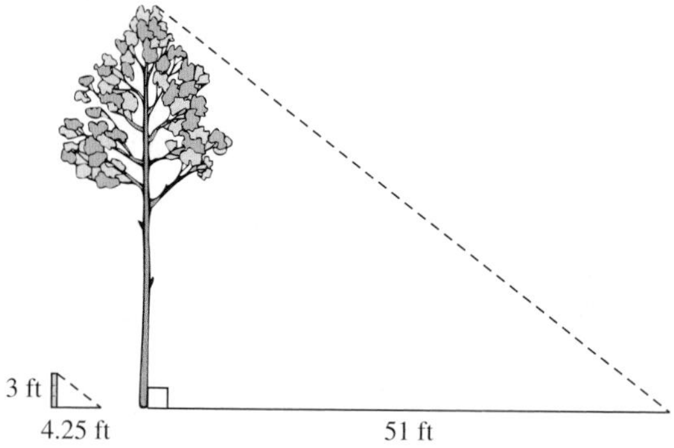

Concept 3: Distance, Rate, and Time Applications

41. A boat travels 54 mi upstream against the current in the same amount of time it takes to travel 66 mi downstream with the current. If the current is 2 mph, what is the speed of the boat in still water? (Use $t = \frac{d}{r}$ to complete the table.) **(See Example 5.)** The speed of the boat is 20 mph.

	Distance	Rate	Time
With the current (downstream)			
Against the current (upstream)			

42. A plane flies 630 mi with the wind in the same amount of time that it takes to fly 455 mi against the wind. If this plane flies at the rate of 217 mph in still air, what is the speed of the wind? (Use $t = \frac{d}{r}$ to complete the table.) The wind speed is 35 mph.

	Distance	Rate	Time
With the wind			
Against the wind			

43. The jet stream is a fast-flowing air current found in the atmosphere at around 36,000 ft above the surface of the Earth. During one summer day, the speed of the jet stream is 35 mph. A plane flying with the jet stream can fly 700 mi in the same amount of time that it would take to fly 500 mi against the jet stream. What is the speed of the plane in still air? The plane flies 210 mph in still air.

44. A fishing boat travels 9 mi downstream with the current in the same amount of time that it travels 3 mi upstream against the current. If the speed of the current is 6 mph, what is the speed at which the boat travels in still water? The speed of the boat in still water is 12 mph.

© PhotoLink/Getty Images RF

45. An athlete in training rides his bike 20 mi and then immediately follows with a 10-mi run. The total workout takes him 2.5 hr. He also knows that he bikes about twice as fast as he runs. Determine his biking speed and his running speed. He runs 8 mph and bikes 16 mph.

46. Devon can cross-country ski 5 km/hr faster than his sister Shanelle. Devon skis 45 km in the same amount of time Shanelle skis 30 km. Find their speeds. Shanelle skis 10 km/hr and Devon skis 15 km/hr.

47. Floyd can walk 2 mph faster than his wife, Rachel. It takes Rachel 3 hr longer than Floyd to hike a 12-mi trail through a park. Find their speeds. **(See Example 6.)** Floyd walks 4 mph and Rachel walks 2 mph.

48. Janine bikes 3 mph faster than her sister, Jessica. Janine can ride 36 mi in 1 hr less time than Jessica can ride the same distance. Find each of their speeds. Janine's speed is 12 mph and Jessica's is 9 mph.

49. Sergio rode his bike 4 mi. Then he got a flat tire and had to walk back 4 mi. It took him 1 hr longer to walk than it did to ride. If his rate walking was 9 mph less than his rate riding, find the two rates. Sergio rode 12 mph and walked 3 mph.

50. Amber jogs 10 km in $\frac{3}{4}$ hr less time than she can walk the same distance. If her walking rate is 3 km/hr less than her jogging rate, find her rates jogging and walking (in km/hr). Amber jogs 8 km/hr and walks 5 km/hr.

Concept 4: Work Applications

51. If the cold-water faucet is left on, the sink will fill in 10 min. If the hot-water faucet is left on, the sink will fill in 12 min. How long would it take to fill the sink if both faucets are left on? **(See Example 7.)** $5\frac{5}{11}$ $(5.\overline{45})$ min

Animation

52. The CUT-IT-OUT lawn mowing company consists of two people: Tina and Bill. If Tina cuts a lawn by herself, she can do it in 4 hr. If Bill cuts the same lawn himself, it takes him an hour longer than Tina. How long would it take them if they worked together? $2\frac{2}{9}$ $(2.\overline{2})$ hr

53. A manuscript needs to be printed. One printer can do the job in 50 min, and another printer can do the job in 40 min. How long would it take if both printers were used? $22\frac{2}{9}$ $(22.\overline{2})$ min

54. A pump can empty a small pond in 4 hr. Another more efficient pump can do the job in 3 hr. How long would it take to empty the pond if both pumps were used? $1\frac{5}{7}$ (approximately 1.7) hr

55. A pipe can fill a reservoir in 16 hr. A drainage pipe can drain the reservoir in 24 hr. How long would it take to fill the reservoir if the drainage pipe were left open by mistake? (*Hint:* The rate at which water drains should be negative.) 48 hr

56. A hole in the bottom of a child's plastic swimming pool can drain the pool in 60 min. If the pool had no hole, a hose could fill the pool in 40 min. How long would it take the hose to fill the pool with the hole? 120 min

57. Tim and Al are bricklayers. Tim can construct an outdoor grill in 5 days. If Al helps Tim, they can build it in only 2 days. How long would it take Al to build the grill alone? $3\frac{1}{3}$ $(3.\overline{3})$ days

58. Norma is a new and inexperienced secretary. It takes her 3 hr to prepare a mailing. If her boss helps her, the mailing can be completed in 1 hr. How long would it take the boss to do the job by herself? $1\frac{1}{2}$ (1.5) hr

Expanding Your Skills

For Exercises 59–62, solve using proportions.

59. The ratio of smokers to nonsmokers in a restaurant is 2 to 7. There are 100 more nonsmokers than smokers. How many smokers and nonsmokers are in the restaurant? There are 40 smokers and 140 nonsmokers.

60. The ratio of fiction to nonfiction books sold in a bookstore is 5 to 3. One week there were 180 more fiction books sold than nonfiction. Find the number of fiction and nonfiction books sold during that week. There are 450 fiction and 270 nonfiction books sold.

61. There are 440 students attending a biology lecture. The ratio of male to female students at the lecture is 6 to 5. How many men and women are attending the lecture? There are 240 men and 200 women.

62. The ratio of dogs to cats at the humane society is 5 to 8. The total number of dogs and cats is 650. How many dogs and how many cats are at the humane society? There are 250 dogs and 400 cats.

Group Activity

Computing Monthly Mortgage Payments

Materials: A calculator

Estimated Time: 15–20 minutes

Group Size: 3

When a person borrows money to buy a house, the bank usually requires a down payment of between 0% and 20% of the cost of the house. The bank then issues a loan for the remaining balance on the house. The loan to buy a house is called a *mortgage.* Monthly payments are made to pay off the mortgage over a period of years.

A formula to calculate the monthly payment, P, for a loan is given by:

$$P = \frac{\dfrac{Ar}{12}}{1 - \dfrac{1}{\left(1 + \dfrac{r}{12}\right)^{12t}}}$$

where
P is the monthly payment
A is the original amount of the mortgage
r is the annual interest rate written as a decimal
t is the term of the loan in years

Suppose a person wants to buy a $200,000 house. The bank requires a down payment of 20%, and the loan is issued for 30 years at 7.5% interest for 30 years.

1. Find the amount of the down payment. ____$40,000____

2. Find the amount of the mortgage. ____$160,000____

3. Find the monthly payment (to the nearest cent). ____$1118.74____

4. Multiply the monthly payment found in question 3 by the total number of months in a 30-year period. Interpret what this value means in the context of the problem.
$402,746.40; This is the total amount owed to the bank.

5. How much total interest was paid on the loan for the house? ____$242,746.40____

6. What was the total amount paid to the bank (include the down payment). ____$442,746.40____

Chapter 7 Summary

Section 7.1 Introduction to Rational Expressions

Key Concepts

A **rational expression** is a ratio of the form $\frac{p}{q}$ where p and q are polynomials and $q \neq 0$.

Restricted values of a rational expression are those values that, when substituted for the variable, make the expression undefined. To find restricted values, set the denominator equal to 0 and solve the equation.

Simplifying a Rational Expression

Factor the numerator and denominator completely, and reduce factors whose ratio is equal to 1 or to -1. A rational expression written in lowest terms will still have the same restricted values as the original expression.

Examples

Example 1

$\dfrac{x+2}{x^2-5x-14}$ is a rational expression.

Example 2

To find the restricted values of $\dfrac{x+2}{x^2-5x-14}$ factor the denominator: $\dfrac{x+2}{(x+2)(x-7)}$

The restricted values are $x=-2$ and $x=7$.

Example 3

Simplify the rational expression. $\dfrac{x+2}{x^2-5x-14}$

$\dfrac{\overset{1}{\cancel{x+2}}}{(\cancel{x+2})(x-7)}$ Simplify.

$= \dfrac{1}{x-7}$ (provided $x \neq 7, x \neq -2$).

Section 7.2 Multiplication and Division of Rational Expressions

Key Concepts

Multiplying Rational Expressions

Multiply the numerators and multiply the denominators. That is, if $q \neq 0$ and $s \neq 0$, then

$$\frac{p}{q} \cdot \frac{r}{s} = \frac{pr}{qs}$$

Factor the numerator and denominator completely. Then reduce factors whose ratio is 1 or -1.

Examples

Example 1

Multiply. $\dfrac{b^2-a^2}{a^2-2ab+b^2} \cdot \dfrac{a^2-3ab+2b^2}{2a+2b}$

$$= \frac{\overset{-1}{\cancel{(b-a)}}\overset{1}{\cancel{(b+a)}}}{\cancel{(a-b)}\cancel{(a-b)}} \cdot \frac{(a-2b)\overset{1}{\cancel{(a-b)}}}{2\cancel{(a+b)}}$$

$$= -\frac{a-2b}{2} \quad \text{or} \quad \frac{2b-a}{2}$$

Dividing Rational Expressions

Multiply the first expression by the reciprocal of the second expression. That is, for $q \neq 0$, $r \neq 0$, and $s \neq 0$,

$$\frac{p}{q} \div \frac{r}{s} = \frac{p}{q} \cdot \frac{s}{r} = \frac{ps}{qr}$$

Example 2

Divide. $\frac{x-2}{15} \div \frac{x^2+2x-8}{20x}$

$$= \frac{x-2}{15} \cdot \frac{20x}{x^2+2x-8}$$

$$= \frac{\overset{1}{\cancel{(x-2)}}}{\underset{3}{\cancel{15}}} \cdot \frac{\overset{4}{\cancel{20}}x}{\underset{1}{\cancel{(x-2)}}(x+4)}$$

$$= \frac{4x}{3(x+4)}$$

Section 7.3 Least Common Denominator

Key Concepts

Finding the Least Common Denominator (LCD) of Two or More Rational Expressions

1. Factor all denominators completely.
2. The LCD is the product of unique factors from the denominators, where each factor is raised to its highest power.

Examples

Example 1

Identify the LCD. $\frac{1}{8x^3y^2z}$; $\frac{5}{6xy^4}$

1. Write the denominators as a product of prime factors:

$$\frac{1}{2^3x^3y^2z}; \frac{5}{2 \cdot 3xy^4}$$

2. The LCD is $2^3 \cdot 3x^3y^4z$ or $24x^3y^4z$

Converting a Rational Expression to an Equivalent Expression with a Different Denominator

Multiply numerator and denominator of the rational expression by the missing factors necessary to create the desired denominator.

Example 2

Convert $\frac{-3}{x-2}$ to an equivalent expression with the indicated denominator:

$$\frac{-3}{x-2} = \frac{}{5(x-2)(x+2)}$$

Multiply numerator and denominator by the missing factors from the denominator.

$$\frac{-3 \cdot 5(x+2)}{(x-2) \cdot 5(x+2)} = \frac{-15x-30}{5(x-2)(x+2)}$$

Section 7.4 Addition and Subtraction of Rational Expressions

Key Concepts

To add or subtract rational expressions, the expressions must have the same denominator.

Steps to Add or Subtract Rational Expressions

1. Factor the denominators of each rational expression.
2. Identify the LCD.
3. Rewrite each rational expression as an equivalent expression with the LCD as its denominator.
4. Add or subtract the numerators, and write the result over the common denominator.
5. Simplify.

Example

Example 1

Add. $\dfrac{c-2}{c+1}+\dfrac{12c-3}{2c^2-c-3}$

$$=\frac{c-2}{c+1}+\frac{12c-3}{(2c-3)(c+1)}$$

The LCD is $(2c-3)(c+1)$.

$$=\frac{(2c-3)(c-2)}{(2c-3)(c+1)}+\frac{12c-3}{(2c-3)(c+1)}$$

$$=\frac{2c^2-4c-3c+6+12c-3}{(2c-3)(c+1)}$$

$$=\frac{2c^2+5c+3}{(2c-3)(c+1)}$$

$$=\frac{(2c+3)\cancel{(c+1)}}{(2c-3)\cancel{(c+1)}}=\frac{2c+3}{2c-3}$$

Section 7.5 Complex Fractions

Key Concepts

Complex fractions can be simplified by using Method I or Method II.

Method I

1. Add or subtract expressions in the numerator to form a single fraction. Add or subtract expressions in the denominator to form a single fraction.
2. Divide the rational expressions from step 1 by multiplying the numerator of the complex fraction by the reciprocal of the denominator of the complex fraction.
3. Simplify to lowest terms, if possible.

Examples

Example 1

Simplify. $\dfrac{1-\dfrac{4}{w^2}}{1-\dfrac{1}{w}-\dfrac{6}{w^2}}=\dfrac{1\cdot\dfrac{w^2}{w^2}-\dfrac{4}{w^2}}{1\cdot\dfrac{w^2}{w^2}-\dfrac{1}{w}\cdot\dfrac{w}{w}-\dfrac{6}{w^2}}$

$$=\frac{\dfrac{w^2}{w^2}-\dfrac{4}{w^2}}{\dfrac{w^2}{w^2}-\dfrac{w}{w^2}-\dfrac{6}{w^2}}=\frac{\dfrac{w^2-4}{w^2}}{\dfrac{w^2-w-6}{w^2}}$$

$$=\frac{w^2-4}{w^2}\cdot\frac{w^2}{w^2-w-6}$$

$$=\frac{(w-2)\overset{1}{\cancel{(w+2)}}}{\cancel{w^2}}\cdot\frac{\overset{1}{\cancel{w^2}}}{(w-3)\cancel{(w+2)}}$$

$$=\frac{w-2}{w-3}$$

Method II

1. Multiply the numerator and denominator of the complex fraction by the LCD of all individual fractions within the expression.
2. Apply the distributive property, and simplify the result.
3. Simplify to lowest terms, if possible.

Example 2

Simplify. $\dfrac{1-\dfrac{4}{w^2}}{1-\dfrac{1}{w}-\dfrac{6}{w^2}} = \dfrac{w^2\left(1-\dfrac{4}{w^2}\right)}{w^2\left(1-\dfrac{1}{w}-\dfrac{6}{w^2}\right)}$

$$= \frac{w^2-4}{w^2-w-6} = \frac{(w-2)\overset{1}{\cancel{(w+2)}}}{(w-3)\cancel{(w+2)}}$$

$$= \frac{w-2}{w-3}$$

Section 7.6 Rational Equations

Key Concepts

An equation with one or more rational expressions is called a **rational equation**.

Steps to Solve a Rational Equation

1. Factor the denominators of all rational expressions. Identify the restricted values.
2. Identify the LCD of all expressions in the equation.
3. Multiply both sides of the equation by the LCD.
4. Solve the resulting equation.
5. Check each potential solution in the original equation.

Examples

Example 1

Solve. $\dfrac{1}{w} - \dfrac{1}{2w-1} = \dfrac{-2w}{2w-1}$ The restricted values are $w = 0$ and $w = \frac{1}{2}$.

The LCD is $w(2w-1)$.

$$\cancel{w}(2w-1)\frac{1}{\cancel{w}} - w\cancel{(2w-1)}\frac{1}{\cancel{2w-1}}$$

$$= w\cancel{(2w-1)}\frac{-2w}{\cancel{2w-1}}$$

$$(2w-1)(1) - w(1) = w(-2w)$$

$$2w - 1 - w = -2w^2 \quad \text{Quadratic equation}$$

$$2w^2 + w - 1 = 0$$

$$(2w-1)(w+1) = 0$$

$w \cancel{=} \frac{1}{2}$ or $w = -1$

Does not check. Checks.

The solution set is $\{-1\}$.

Example 2

Solve for I. $q = \dfrac{VQ}{I}$

$$I \cdot q = \frac{VQ}{\cancel{I}} \cdot \cancel{I}$$

$$Iq = VQ$$

$$I = \frac{VQ}{q}$$

Section 7.7 Applications of Rational Equations and Proportions

Key Concepts and Examples

Solving Proportions

An equation that equates two rates or ratios is called a **proportion**:

$$\frac{a}{b} = \frac{c}{d} \quad (b \neq 0, d \neq 0)$$

To solve a proportion, multiply both sides of the equation by the LCD.

Examples

Example 1

A 90-g serving of a particular ice cream contains 10 g of fat. How much fat does 400 g of the same ice cream contain?

$$\frac{10 \text{ g fat}}{90 \text{ g ice cream}} = \frac{x \text{ grams fat}}{400 \text{ g ice cream}}$$

$$\frac{10}{90} = \frac{x}{400} \qquad \text{The LCD is 3600.}$$

$$\overset{40}{\cancel{3600}} \cdot \left(\frac{10}{\cancel{90}}\right) = \left(\frac{x}{\cancel{400}}\right) \cdot \overset{9}{\cancel{3600}}$$

$$400 = 9x$$

$$x = \frac{400}{9} \approx 44.4 \text{ g}$$

Examples 2 and 3 give applications of rational equations.

Example 2

Two cars travel from Los Angeles to Las Vegas. One car travels an average of 8 mph faster than the other car. If the faster car travels 189 mi in the same amount of time that the slower car travels 165 mi, what is the average speed of each car?

Let r represent the speed of the slower car.
Let $r + 8$ represent the speed of the faster car.

	Distance	Rate	Time
Slower car	165	r	$\frac{165}{r}$
Faster car	189	$r+8$	$\frac{189}{r+8}$

$$\frac{165}{r} = \frac{189}{r+8}$$

$$165(r+8) = 189r$$

$$165r + 1320 = 189r$$

$$1320 = 24r$$

$$55 = r$$

The slower car travels 55 mph, and the faster car travels $55 + 8 = 63$ mph.

Example 3

Beth and Cecelia have a house cleaning business. Beth can clean a particular house in 5 hr by herself. Cecelia can clean the same house in 4 hr. How long would it take if they cleaned the house together?

Let x be the number of hours it takes for both Beth and Cecelia to clean the house.

Beth's rate is $\frac{1 \text{ job}}{5 \text{ hr}}$. Cecelia's rate is $\frac{1 \text{ job}}{4 \text{ hr}}$.

The rate together is $\frac{1 \text{ job}}{x \text{ hr}}$.

$$\frac{1}{5} + \frac{1}{4} = \frac{1}{x} \qquad \text{Add the rates.}$$

$$20x\left(\frac{1}{5} + \frac{1}{4}\right) = 20x\left(\frac{1}{x}\right)$$

$$4x + 5x = 20$$

$$9x = 20$$

$$x = \frac{20}{9}$$

It takes $\frac{20}{9}$ hr or $2\frac{2}{9}$ hr working together.

Chapter 7 Review Exercises

Section 7.1

1. For the rational expression $\frac{t-2}{t+9}$

a. Evaluate the expression (if possible) for $t = 0, 1, 2, -3, -9$ $-\frac{2}{9}, -\frac{1}{10}, 0, -\frac{5}{6}$, undefined

b. Identify the restricted values. $t = -9$

2. For the rational expression $\frac{k+1}{k-5}$

a. Evaluate the expression for $k = 0, 1, 5, -1, -2$
$-\frac{1}{5}, -\frac{1}{2}$, undefined, $0, \frac{1}{7}$

b. Identify the restricted values. $k = 5$

3. Which of the rational expressions are equal to -1? a, c, d

a. $\frac{2-x}{x-2}$ b. $\frac{x-5}{x+5}$

c. $\frac{-x-7}{x+7}$ d. $\frac{x^2-4}{4-x^2}$

For Exercises 4–13, identify the restricted values. Then simplify the expressions.

4. $\frac{x-3}{(2x-5)(x-3)}$ $x = \frac{5}{2}, x = 3$; $\frac{1}{2x-5}$

5. $\frac{h+7}{(3h+1)(h+7)}$ $h = -\frac{1}{3}, h = -7$; $\frac{1}{3h+1}$

6. $\frac{4a^2+7a-2}{a^2-4}$ $a = 2, a = -2$; $\frac{4a-1}{a-2}$

7. $\frac{2w^2+11w+12}{w^2-16}$ $w = 4, w = -4$; $\frac{2w+3}{w-4}$

8. $\frac{z^2-4z}{8-2z}$ $z = 4$; $-\frac{z}{2}$

9. $\frac{15-3k}{2k^2-10k}$ $k = 0, k = 5$; $-\frac{3}{2k}$

10. $\frac{2b^2+4b-6}{4b+12}$ $b = -3$; $\frac{b-1}{2}$

11. $\frac{3m^2-12m-15}{9m+9}$ $m = -1$; $\frac{m-5}{3}$

12. $\frac{n+3}{n^2+6n+9}$ $n = -3$; $\frac{1}{n+3}$

13. $\frac{p+7}{p^2+14p+49}$ $p = -7$; $\frac{1}{p+7}$

Section 7.2

For Exercises 14–27, multiply or divide as indicated.

14. $\frac{3y^3}{3y-6} \cdot \frac{y-2}{y}$ y^2

15. $\frac{2u+10}{u} \cdot \frac{u^3}{4u+20}$ $\frac{u^2}{2}$

16. $\frac{11}{v-2} \cdot \frac{2v^2-8}{22}$ $v+2$

17. $\frac{8}{x^2-25} \cdot \frac{3x+15}{16}$ $\frac{3}{2(x-5)}$

18. $\frac{4c^2+4c}{c^2-25} \div \frac{8c}{c^2-5c}$ $\frac{c(c+1)}{2(c+5)}$

19. $\frac{q^2-5q+6}{2q+4} \div \frac{2q-6}{q+2}$ $\frac{q-2}{4}$

20. $\left(\frac{-2t}{t+1}\right)(t^2-4t-5)$ $-2t(t-5)$

21. $(s^2-6s+8)\left(\frac{4s}{s-2}\right)$ $4s(s-4)$

22. $\dfrac{\frac{a^2+5a+1}{7a-7}}{\frac{a^2+5a+1}{a-1}}$ $\frac{1}{7}$

23. $\dfrac{\frac{n^2+n+1}{n^2-4}}{\frac{n^2+n+1}{n+2}}$ $\frac{1}{n-2}$

24. $\frac{5h^2-6h+1}{h^2-1} \div \frac{16h^2-9}{4h^2+7h+3} \cdot \frac{3-4h}{30h-6}$ $-\frac{1}{6}$

25. $\frac{3m-3}{6m^2+18m+12} \cdot \frac{2m^2-8}{m^2-3m+2} \div \frac{m+3}{m+1}$ $\frac{1}{m+3}$

26. $\frac{x-2}{x^2-3x-18} \cdot \frac{6-x}{x^2-4}$ $\frac{-1}{(x+3)(x+2)}$

27. $\frac{4y^2-1}{1+2y} \div \frac{y^2-4y-5}{5-y}$ $-\frac{2y-1}{y+1}$

Section 7.3

28. Determine the LCD.

$$\frac{6}{n^2-9}; \frac{5}{n^2-n-6}$$

LCD $= (n+3)(n-3)(n+2)$

29. Determine the LCD.

$$\frac{8}{m^2-16}; \frac{7}{m^2-m-12}$$

LCD $= (m+4)(m-4)(m+3)$

30. State two possible LCDs that could be used to add the fractions. $c-2$ or $2-c$

$$\frac{7}{c-2} + \frac{4}{2-c}$$

31. State two possible LCDs that could be used to subtract the fractions. $3-x$ or $x-3$

$$\frac{10}{3-x} - \frac{5}{x-3}$$

For Exercises 32–37, write each fraction as an equivalent fraction with the LCD as its denominator.

32. $\dfrac{2}{5a}; \dfrac{3}{10b}$ $\dfrac{4b}{10ab}; \dfrac{3a}{10ab}$

33. $\dfrac{7}{4x}; \dfrac{11}{6y}$ $\dfrac{21y}{12xy}; \dfrac{22x}{12xy}$

34. $\dfrac{1}{x^2y^4}; \dfrac{3}{xy^5}$ $\dfrac{y}{x^2y^5}; \dfrac{3x}{x^2y^5}$

35. $\dfrac{5}{ab^3}; \dfrac{3}{ac^2}$ $\dfrac{5c^2}{ab^3c^2}; \dfrac{3b^3}{ab^3c^2}$

36. $\dfrac{5}{p+2}; \dfrac{p}{p-4}$ $\dfrac{5p-20}{(p+2)(p-4)}; \dfrac{p^2+2p}{(p+2)(p-4)}$

37. $\dfrac{6}{q}; \dfrac{1}{q+8}$ $\dfrac{6q+48}{q(q+8)}; \dfrac{q}{q(q+8)}$

Section 7.4

For Exercises 38–49, add or subtract as indicated.

38. $\dfrac{h+3}{h+1} + \dfrac{h-1}{h+1}$ 2

39. $\dfrac{b-6}{b-2} + \dfrac{b+2}{b-2}$ 2

40. $\dfrac{a^2}{a-5} - \dfrac{25}{a-5}$ $a+5$

41. $\dfrac{x^2}{x+7} - \dfrac{49}{x+7}$ $x-7$

42. $\dfrac{y}{y^2-81} + \dfrac{2}{9-y}$ $\dfrac{-y-18}{(y-9)(y+9)}$ or $\dfrac{y+18}{(9-y)(y+9)}$

43. $\dfrac{3}{4-t^2} + \dfrac{t}{2-t}$ $\dfrac{t^2+2t+3}{(2-t)(2+t)}$

44. $\dfrac{4}{3m} - \dfrac{1}{m+2}$ $\dfrac{m+8}{3m(m+2)}$

45. $\dfrac{5}{2r+12} - \dfrac{1}{r}$ $\dfrac{3(r-4)}{2r(r+6)}$

46. $\dfrac{4p}{p^2+6p+5} - \dfrac{3p}{p^2+5p+4}$ $\dfrac{p}{(p+4)(p+5)}$

47. $\dfrac{3q}{q^2+7q+10} - \dfrac{2q}{q^2+6q+8}$ $\dfrac{q}{(q+5)(q+4)}$

48. $\dfrac{1}{h} + \dfrac{h}{2h+4} - \dfrac{2}{h^2+2h}$ $\dfrac{1}{2}$

49. $\dfrac{x}{3x+9} - \dfrac{3}{x^2+3x} + \dfrac{1}{x}$ $\dfrac{1}{3}$

Section 7.5

For Exercises 50–57, simplify the complex fractions.

50. $\dfrac{\dfrac{a-4}{3}}{\dfrac{a-2}{3}}$ $\dfrac{a-4}{a-2}$

51. $\dfrac{\dfrac{z+5}{z}}{\dfrac{z-5}{3}}$ $\dfrac{3(z+5)}{z(z-5)}$

52. $\dfrac{\dfrac{2-3w}{2}}{\dfrac{2}{w}-3}$ $\dfrac{w}{2}$

53. $\dfrac{\dfrac{2}{y}+6}{\dfrac{3y+1}{4}}$ $\dfrac{8}{y}$

54. $\dfrac{\dfrac{y}{x}-\dfrac{x}{y}}{\dfrac{1}{x}+\dfrac{1}{y}}$ $y-x$

55. $\dfrac{\dfrac{b}{a}-\dfrac{a}{b}}{\dfrac{1}{b}-\dfrac{1}{a}}$ $-(b+a)$

56. $\dfrac{\dfrac{6}{p+2}+4}{\dfrac{8}{p+2}-4}$ $-\dfrac{2p+7}{2p}$

57. $\dfrac{\dfrac{25}{k+5}+5}{\dfrac{5}{k+5}-5}$ $-\dfrac{k+10}{k+4}$

Section 7.6

For Exercises 58–65, solve the equations.

58. $\dfrac{2}{x} + \dfrac{1}{2} = \dfrac{1}{4}$ $\{-8\}$

59. $\dfrac{1}{y} + \dfrac{3}{4} = \dfrac{1}{4}$ $\{-2\}$

60. $\dfrac{2}{h-2} + 1 = \dfrac{h}{h+2}$ $\{0\}$

61. $\dfrac{w}{w-1} = \dfrac{3}{w+1} + 1$ $\{2\}$

62. $\dfrac{t+1}{3} - \dfrac{t-1}{6} = \dfrac{1}{6}$ $\{-2\}$

63. $\dfrac{w+1}{w-3} - \dfrac{3}{w} = \dfrac{12}{w^2-3w}$ $\{-1\}$ (The value 3 does not check.)

64. $\dfrac{1}{z+2} = \dfrac{4}{z^2-4} - \dfrac{1}{z-2}$ { } (The value 2 does not check.)

65. $\dfrac{y+1}{y+3} = \dfrac{y^2-11y}{y^2+y-6} - \dfrac{y-3}{y-2}$ $\{-11, 1\}$

66. Four times a number is added to 5. The sum is then divided by 6. The result is $\frac{7}{2}$. Find the number. The number is 4.

67. Solve the formula $\dfrac{V}{h} = \dfrac{\pi r^2}{3}$ for h. $h = \dfrac{3V}{\pi r^2}$

68. Solve the formula $\dfrac{A}{b} = \dfrac{h}{2}$ for b. $b = \dfrac{2A}{h}$

Section 7.7

For Exercises 69–70, solve the proportions.

69. $\dfrac{m+2}{8} = \dfrac{m}{3}$ $\left\{\dfrac{6}{5}\right\}$

70. $\dfrac{12}{a} = \dfrac{5}{8}$ $\left\{\dfrac{96}{5}\right\}$

71. A bag of popcorn states that it contains 4 g of fat per serving. If a serving is 2 oz, how many grams of fat are in a 5-oz bag? It contains 10 g of fat.

72. Bud goes 10 mph faster on his motorcycle than Ed goes on his motorcycle. If Bud travels 105 mi in the same amount of time that Ed travels 90 mi, what are the rates of the two bikers?
Ed travels 60 mph, and Bud travels 70 mph.

© Glow Images RF

73. There are two pumps set up to fill a small swimming pool. One pump takes 24 min by itself to fill the pool, but the other takes 56 min by itself. How long would it take if both pumps work together?
Together the pumps would fill the pool in 16.8 min.

74. Triangle XYZ is similar to triangle ABC. Find the values of x and b. $x = 11$; $b = 26$

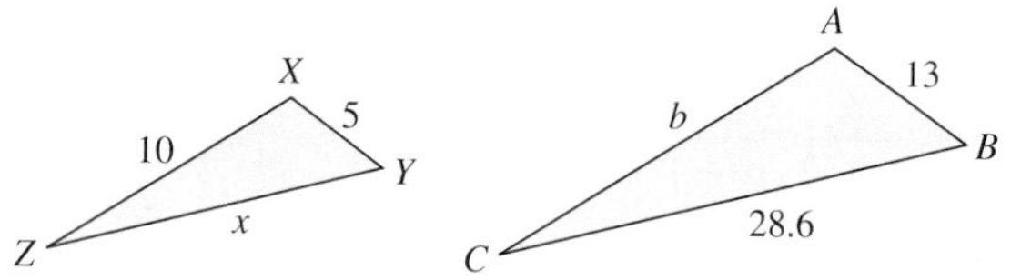

Chapter 7 Test

For Exercises 1–2,

a. Identify the restricted values.

b. Simplify the rational expression.

1. $\dfrac{5(x-2)(x+1)}{30(2-x)}$ a. $x = 2$ b. $-\dfrac{x+1}{6}$

2. $\dfrac{7a^2 - 42a}{a^3 - 4a^2 - 12a}$ a. $a = 6, a = -2, a = 0$ b. $\dfrac{7}{a+2}$

3. Identify the rational expressions that are equal to -1. b, c, d

a. $\dfrac{x+4}{x-4}$ **b.** $\dfrac{7-2x}{2x-7}$

c. $\dfrac{9x^2+16}{-9x^2-16}$ **d.** $-\dfrac{x+5}{x+5}$

4. Find the LCD of the following pairs of rational expressions.

a. $\dfrac{x}{3(x+3)}; \dfrac{7}{5(x+3)}$ $15(x+3)$ **b.** $\dfrac{-2}{3x^2y}; \dfrac{4}{xy^2}$ $3x^2y^2$

For Exercises 5–11, perform the indicated operation.

5. $\dfrac{2}{y^2+4y+3} + \dfrac{1}{3y+9}$ $\dfrac{y+7}{3(y+3)(y+1)}$

6. $\dfrac{9-b^2}{5b+15} \div \dfrac{b-3}{b+3}$ $-\dfrac{b+3}{5}$

7. $\dfrac{w^2-4w}{w^2-8w+16} \cdot \dfrac{w-4}{w^2+w}$ $\dfrac{1}{w+1}$

8. $\dfrac{t}{t-2} - \dfrac{8}{t^2-4}$ $\dfrac{t+4}{t+2}$

9. $\dfrac{1}{x+4} + \dfrac{2}{x^2+2x-8} + \dfrac{x}{x-2}$ $\dfrac{x(x+5)}{(x+4)(x-2)}$

10. $\dfrac{2y}{y-6} - \dfrac{7}{6-y}$ $\dfrac{2y+7}{y-6}$ or $\dfrac{-2y-7}{6-y}$

11. $\dfrac{1-\dfrac{4}{m}}{m-\dfrac{16}{m}}$ $\dfrac{1}{m+4}$

For Exercises 12–16, solve the equation.

12. $\dfrac{3}{a} + \dfrac{5}{2} = \dfrac{7}{a}$ $\left\{\dfrac{8}{5}\right\}$

13. $\dfrac{p}{p-1} + \dfrac{1}{p} = \dfrac{p^2+1}{p^2-p}$ $\{2\}$

14. $\dfrac{3}{c-2} - \dfrac{1}{c+1} = \dfrac{7}{c^2-c-2}$ $\{1\}$

15. $\dfrac{4x}{x-4} = 3 + \dfrac{16}{x-4}$ { } (The value 4 does not check.)

16. $\dfrac{y^2+7y}{y-2} - \dfrac{36}{2y-4} = 4$ $\{-5\}$ (The value 2 does not check.)

17. Solve the formula $\dfrac{C}{2} = \dfrac{A}{r}$ for r. $r = \dfrac{2A}{C}$

18. Solve the proportion.

$$\frac{y+7}{-4} = \frac{1}{4} \quad \{-8\}$$

19. A recipe for vegetable soup calls for $\frac{1}{2}$ cup of carrots for six servings. How many cups of carrots are needed to prepare 15 servings?
$1\frac{1}{4}$ (1.25) cups of carrots

20. A motorboat can travel 28 mi downstream in the same amount of time as it can travel 18 mi upstream. Find the speed of the current if the boat can travel 23 mph in still water.
The speed of the current is 5 mph.

21. Two printers working together can complete a job in 2 hr. If one printer requires 6 hr to do the job alone, how many hours would the second printer need to complete the job alone? It would take the second printer 3 hr to do the job working alone.

22. Triangle XYZ is similar to triangle ABC. Find the values of a and b. $a = 5.6$; $b = 12$

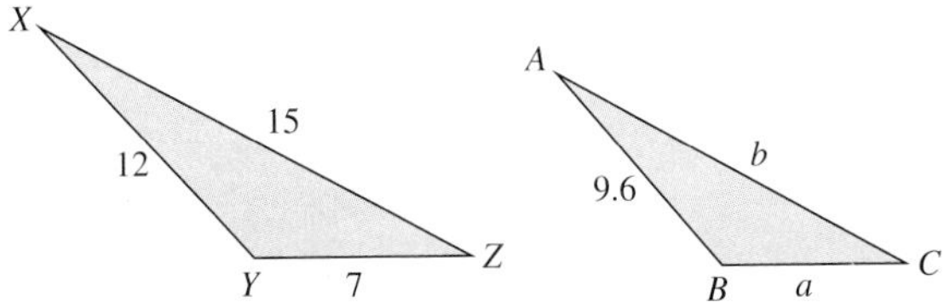

Chapters 1–7 Cumulative Review Exercises

For Exercises 1–2, simplify completely.

1. $\left(\frac{1}{2}\right)^{-4} + 2^4$ 32

2. $|3 - 5| + |-2 + 7|$ 7

3. Solve. $\frac{1}{2} - \frac{3}{4}(y - 1) = \frac{5}{12}$ $\left\{\frac{10}{9}\right\}$

4. Complete the table.

Set-Builder Notation	Graph	Interval Notation
$\{x \mid x \geq -1\}$		$[-1, \infty)$
$\{x \mid x < 5\}$		$(-\infty, 5)$

5. The perimeter of a rectangular swimming pool is 104 m. The length is 1 m more than twice the width. Find the length and width.
The width is 17 m and the length is 35 m.

6. The height of a triangle is 2 in. less than the base. The area is 40 in.^{2} Find the base and height of the triangle. The base is 10 in. and the height is 8 in.

7. Simplify. $\left(\frac{4x^{-1}y^{-2}}{z^4}\right)^{-2}(2y^{-1}z^3)^3$ $\frac{x^2yz^{17}}{2}$

8. The length and width of a rectangle are given in terms of x.

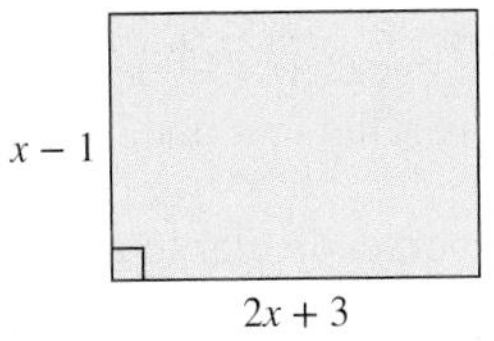

a. Write a polynomial that represents the perimeter of the rectangle. $6x + 4$

b. Write a polynomial that represents the area of the rectangle. $2x^2 + x - 3$

9. Factor completely. $25x^2 - 30x + 9$ $(5x - 3)^2$

10. Factor completely. $10cd + 5d - 6c - 3$
$(2c + 1)(5d - 3)$

11. Identify the restricted values of the expression.

$$\frac{x+3}{(x-5)(2x+1)} \quad x = 5, x = -\frac{1}{2}$$

12. Solve the system.

$$x + 2y = -7 \quad \{(1, -4)\}$$
$$6x + 3y = -6$$

13. Divide. $\frac{2x - 6}{x^2 - 16} \div \frac{10x^2 - 90}{x^2 - x - 12}$ $\frac{1}{5(x + 4)}$

14. Simplify.

$$\frac{\frac{3}{4}-\frac{1}{x}}{\frac{1}{3x}-\frac{1}{4}}$$ -3

15. Solve. $\frac{7}{y^2-4}=\frac{3}{y-2}+\frac{2}{y+2}$ $\{1\}$

16. Solve the proportion.

$$\frac{2b-5}{6}=\frac{4b}{7}$$ $\left\{-\frac{7}{2}\right\}$

17. Determine the x- and y-intercepts.

a. $-2x+4y=8$ x-intercept: $(-4, 0)$; y-intercept: $(0, 2)$

b. $y=5x$ x-intercept: $(0,0)$; y-intercept: $(0,0)$

18. Determine the slope

a. of the line containing the points $(0, -6)$ and $(-5, 1)$. $m=-\frac{7}{5}$

b. of the line $y=-\frac{2}{3}x-6$. $m=-\frac{2}{3}$

c. of a line parallel to a line having a slope of 4. $m=4$

d. of a line perpendicular to a line having a slope of 4. $m=-\frac{1}{4}$

19. Find an equation of a line passing through the point $(1, 2)$ and having a slope of 5. Write the answer in slope-intercept form. $y=5x-3$

20. A group of teenagers buys 2 large popcorns and 6 drinks at the movie theater for \$27. A couple buys 1 large popcorn and 2 drinks for \$10.50. Find the price for 1 large popcorn and the price for 1 drink. One large popcorn costs \$4.50, and one drink costs \$3.00.

© BananaStock/PunchStock RF

Relations and Functions

8

CHAPTER OUTLINE

Mathematics in Communication

Imagine that every time you call your friend's cell phone your call is sent to a wrong device, and a different person answers the call. Suppose that one time you reach a single mother in Alabama, another time perhaps a small-business owner in Georgia, and the next time a person in Kansas.

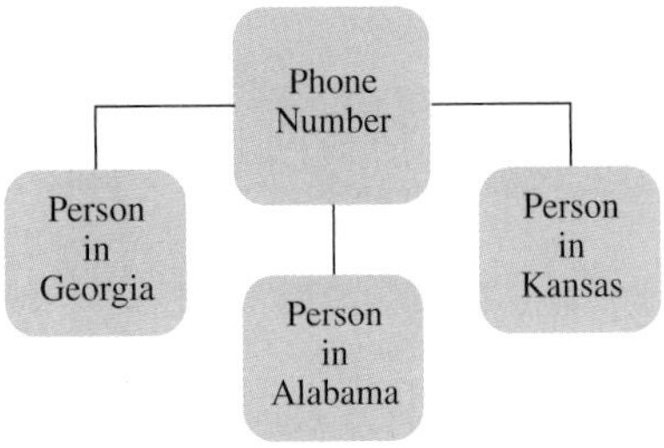

This sort of haphazard relationship between a phone number and a target would create chaos and seriously compromise the future of your cell phone provider. Instead, when we dial 10 digits on our phone we know that the call will be routed to *only one* person's device—the person to whom the phone number is registered.

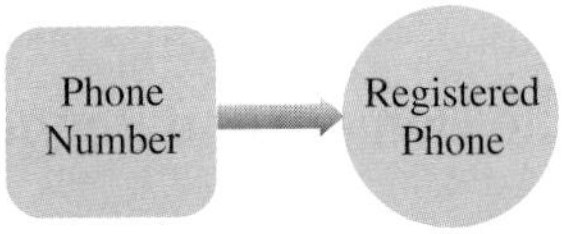

This example illustrates the importance of a **function**. That is, every item in a first set of items (in this case, a phone number being dialed) is associated with one and only one element in a second set of items (in this case, the phone of the proper recipient). Functions are relationships that take an input value and perform an operation on that value to produce a unique and predictable output value. The study of relations and functions begins this chapter and provides the springboard for mathematics at the next level.

Section 8.1 Introduction to Relations

Concepts

1. Definition of a Relation
2. Domain and Range of a Relation
3. Applications Involving Relations

1. Definition of a Relation

In many naturally occurring phenomena, two variables may be linked by some other type of relationship. Table 8-1 shows a correspondence between the length of a woman's femur and her height. (The femur is the large bone in the thigh attached to the knee and hip.)

Table 8-1

Length of Femur (cm) x	Height (in.) y		Ordered Pair
45.5	65.5	⟶	(45.5, 65.5)
48.2	68.0	⟶	(48.2, 68.0)
41.8	62.2	⟶	(41.8, 62.2)
46.0	66.0	⟶	(46.0, 66.0)
50.4	70.0	⟶	(50.4, 70.0)

Each data point from Table 8-1 may be represented as an ordered pair. In this case, the first value represents the length of a woman's femur and the second, the woman's height. The set of ordered pairs {(45.5, 65.5), (48.2, 68.0), (41.8, 62.2), (46.0, 66.0), (50.4, 70.0)} defines a relation between femur length and height.

2. Domain and Range of a Relation

Instructor Note: To help students remember domain and range, "D" is earlier in the alphabet than "R," just as *x* is earlier in the alphabet than *y*.

Definition of Relation in *x* and *y*

A set of ordered pairs (x, y) is called a **relation in *x* and *y***. Furthermore,

- The set of first components in the ordered pairs is called the **domain of the relation**.
- The set of second components in the ordered pairs is called the **range of the relation**.

Classroom Example: p. 569, Exercise 4

Example 1 Finding the Domain and Range of a Relation

Find the domain and range of the relation linking the length of a woman's femur to her height {(45.5, 65.5), (48.2, 68.0), (41.8, 62.2), (46.0, 66.0), (50.4, 70.0)}.

Solution:

Domain:	{45.5, 48.2, 41.8, 46.0, 50.4}	Set of first components
Range:	{65.5, 68.0, 62.2, 66.0, 70.0}	Set of second components

Skill Practice Find the domain and range of the relation.

1. $\left\{(0, 0), (-8, 4), \left(\frac{1}{2}, 1\right), (-3, 4), (-8, 0)\right\}$

The x and y components that constitute the ordered pairs in a relation do not need to be numerical. This is demonstrated in Example 2.

Answer

1. Domain: $\left\{0, -8, \frac{1}{2}, -3\right\}$; range: {0, 4, 1}

Example 2 Writing a Relation and Finding Its Domain and Range

Classroom Example: p. 569, Exercise 6

Table 8-2 gives five states in the United States and the corresponding number of representatives in the House of Representatives for a recent year.

a. The data in the table define a relation. Write a list of ordered pairs for this relation.

b. Write the domain and range.

Table 8-2

State x	Number of Representatives y
Alabama	7
California	53
Colorado	7
Florida	27
Kansas	4

Solution:

a. {(Alabama, 7), (California, 53), (Colorado, 7), (Florida, 27), (Kansas, 4)}

b. Domain: {Alabama, California, Colorado, Florida, Kansas}

Range: {7, 53, 27, 4} (*Note:* The element 7 is not listed twice.)

Skill Practice The table depicts six types of animals and their average longevity.

2. Write the ordered pairs indicated by the relation in the table.
3. Find the domain and range of the relation.

Animal x	Longevity (Years) y
Bear	22.5
Cat	11
Cow	20.5
Deer	12.5
Dog	11
Elephant	35

A relation may consist of a finite number of ordered pairs or an infinite number of ordered pairs. Furthermore, a relation may be defined by several different methods.

- A relation may be defined as a set of ordered pairs.

$$\{(1, 2), (-3, 4), (1, -4), (3, 4)\}$$

- A relation may be defined by a correspondence (Figure 8-1). The corresponding ordered pairs are $\{(1, 2), (1, -4), (-3, 4), (3, 4)\}$.

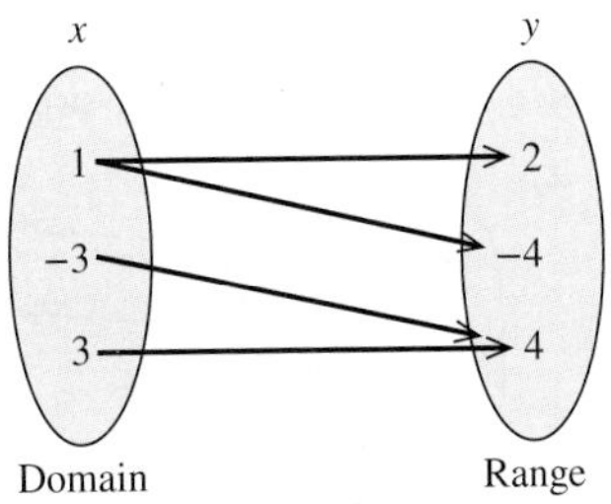

Figure 8-1

- A relation may be defined by a graph (Figure 8-2). The corresponding ordered pairs are $\{(1, 2), (-3, 4), (1, -4), (3, 4)\}$.

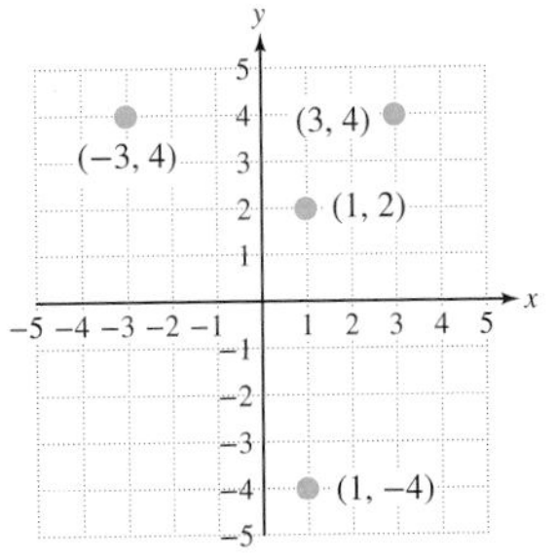

Figure 8-2

Answers

2. {(Bear, 22.5), (Cat, 11), (Cow, 20.5), (Deer, 12.5), (Dog, 11), (Elephant, 35)}
3. Domain: {Bear, Cat, Cow, Deer, Dog, Elephant}; range: {22.5, 11, 20.5, 12.5, 35}

- A relation may be expressed by an equation such as $x = y^2$. The solutions to this equation define an infinite set of ordered pairs of the form $\{(x, y) \mid x = y^2\}$. The solutions can also be represented by a graph in a rectangular coordinate system (Figure 8-3).

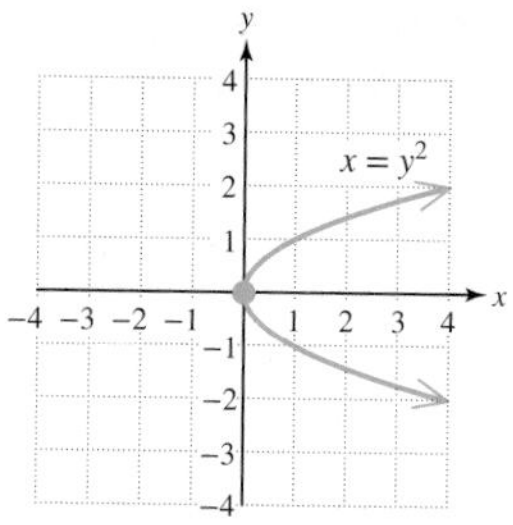

Figure 8-3

Classroom Examples: pp. 569–570, Exercises 8 and 14

Example 3 Finding the Domain and Range of a Relation

Write the relation as a set of ordered pairs. Then find the domain and range.

a.

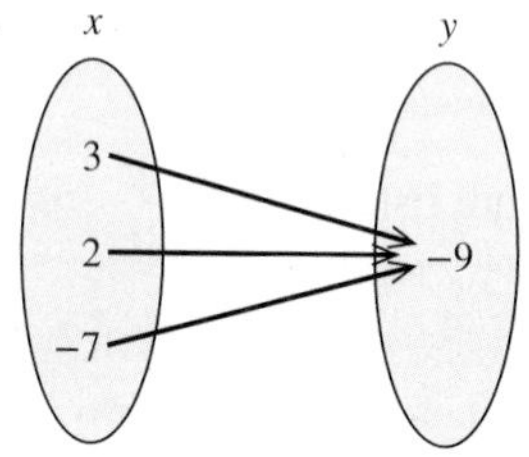

b.

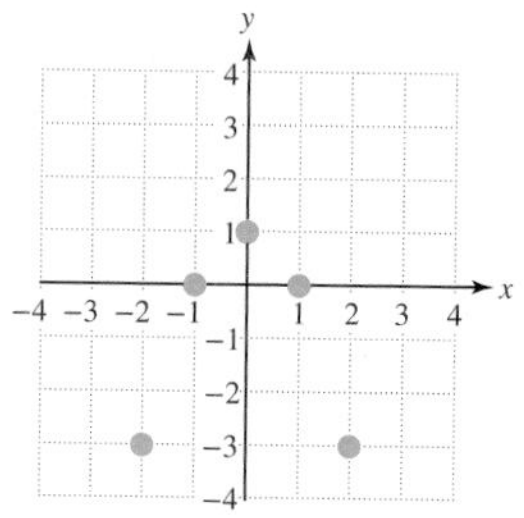

Solution:

a. From the figure, the relation defines the set of ordered pairs:
$\{(3, -9), (2, -9), (-7, -9)\}$

Domain: $\{3, 2, -7\}$

Range: $\{-9\}$

b. The points in the graph make up the set of ordered pairs:
$\{(-2, -3), (-1, 0), (0, 1), (1, 0), (2, -3)\}$

Domain: $\{-2, -1, 0, 1, 2\}$

Range: $\{-3, 0, 1\}$

Skill Practice Find the domain and range of the relations.

4.

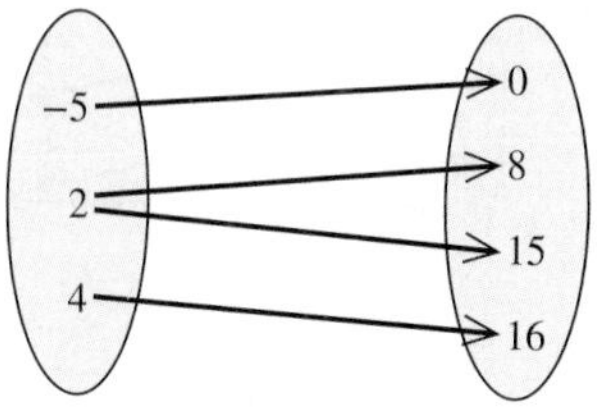

5.

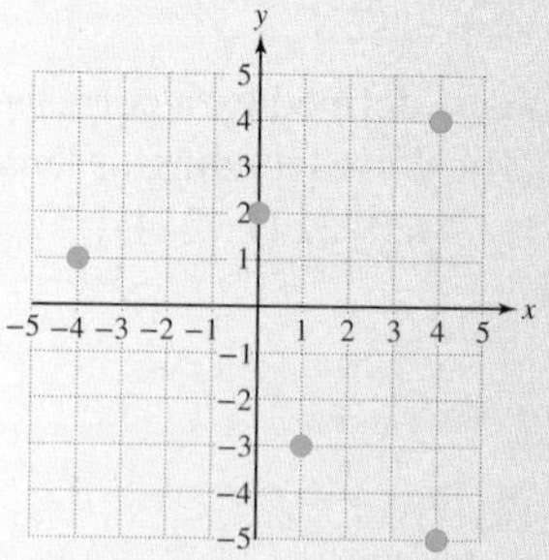

Answers

4. Domain: {−5, 2, 4}; range: {0, 8, 15, 16}
5. Domain: {−4, 0, 1, 4}; range: {−5, −3, 1, 2, 4}

Example 4 Finding the Domain and Range of a Relation

Classroom Examples: pp. 570–571, Exercises 16 and 26

Use interval notation to express the domain and range of the relation.

a.

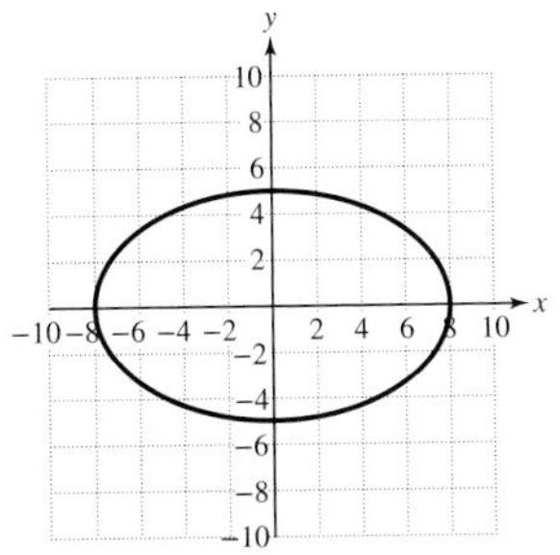

b.

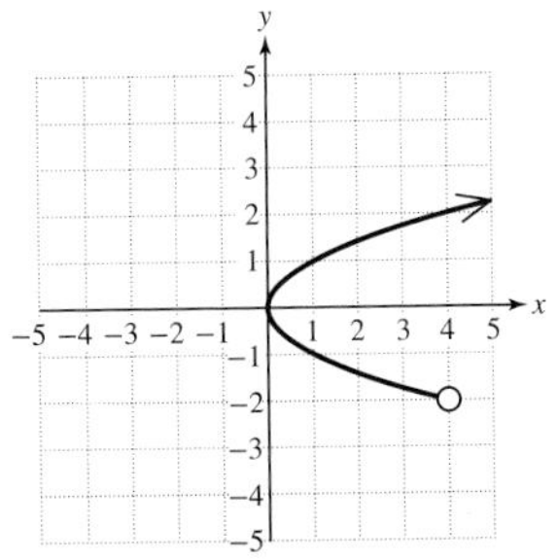

Solution:

a.

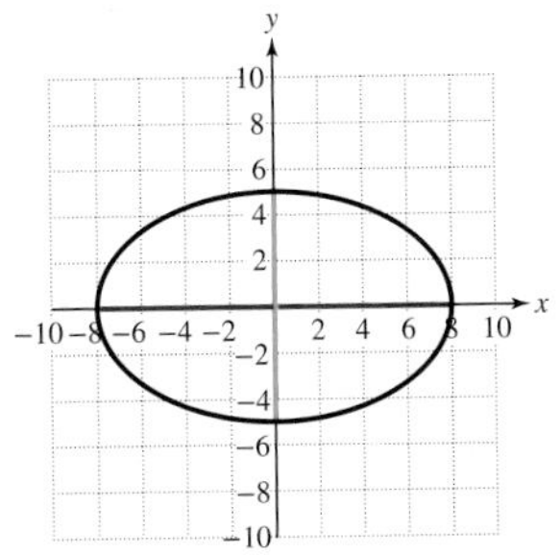

The domain consists of an infinite number of x values extending from -8 to 8 (shown in red). The range consists of all y values from -5 to 5 (shown in blue). Thus, the domain and range must be expressed in set-builder notation or in interval notation.

Domain: $[-8, 8]$

Range: $[-5, 5]$

b.

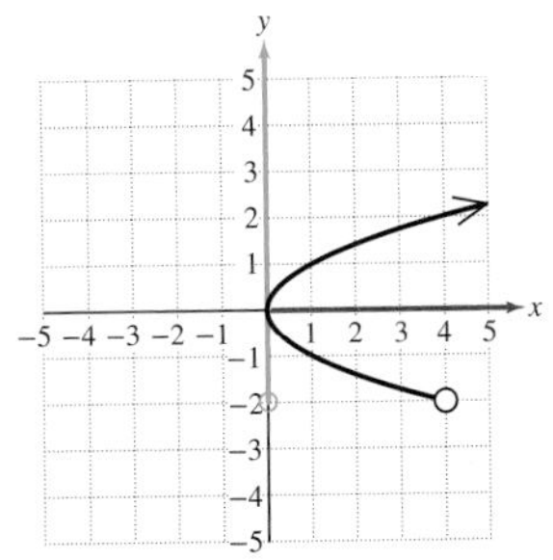

The arrow on the curve indicates that the graph extends infinitely far up and to the right. The open circle means that the graph will end at the point $(4, -2)$, but not include that point.

Domain: $[0, \infty)$

Range: $(-2, \infty)$

Skill Practice Use interval notation to express the domain and range of the relations.

6.

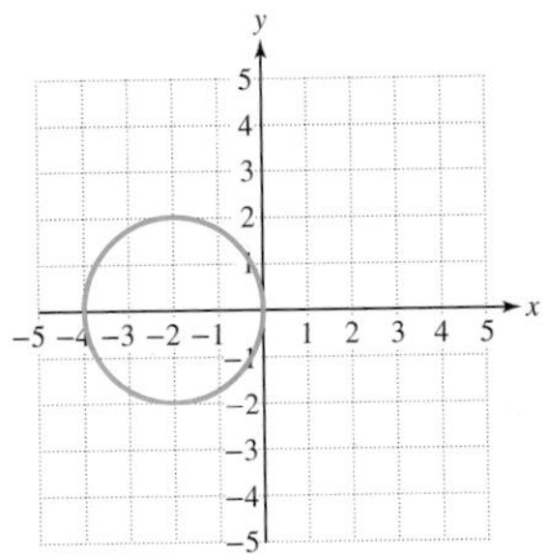

7.

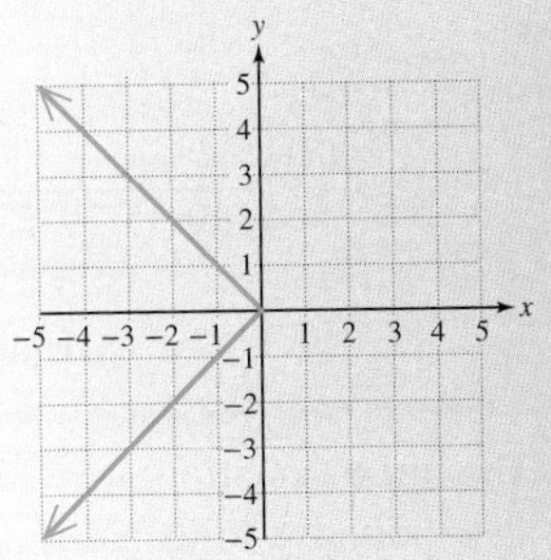

Answers

6. Domain: $[-4, 0]$
Range: $[-2, 2]$

7. Domain: $(-\infty, 0]$
Range: $(-\infty, \infty)$

3. Applications Involving Relations

Classroom Example: p. 572, Exercise 34

Table 8-3

Length of Femur (cm) x	Height (in.) y
45.5	65.5
48.2	68.0
41.8	62.2
46.0	66.0
50.4	70.0

Example 5 Analyzing a Relation

The data in Table 8-3 depict the length of a woman's femur and her corresponding height. Based on these data, a forensics specialist can find a linear relationship between height y (in inches) and femur length x (in centimeters):

$$y = 0.91x + 24 \qquad 40 \le x \le 55$$

From this type of relationship, the height of a woman can be inferred based on skeletal remains.

a. Find the height of a woman whose femur is 46.0 cm.

b. Find the height of a woman whose femur is 51.0 cm.

c. Why is the domain restricted to $40 \le x \le 55$?

Solution:

a. $y = 0.91x + 24$

$= 0.91(46.0) + 24$ Substitute $x = 46.0$ cm.

$= 65.86$ The woman is approximately 65.9 in. tall.

b. $y = 0.91x + 24$

$= 0.91(51.0) + 24$ Substitute $x = 51.0$ cm.

$= 70.41$ The woman is approximately 70.4 in. tall.

c. The domain restricts femur length to values between 40 cm and 55 cm inclusive. These values are within the normal lengths for an adult female and are in the proximity of the observed data (Figure 8-4).

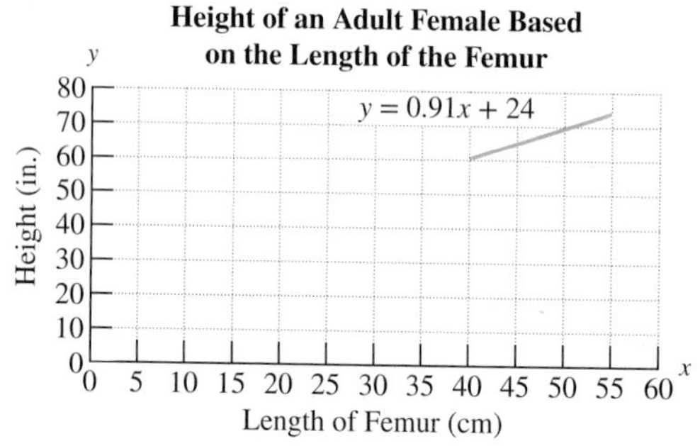

Figure 8-4

Skill Practice The linear equation, $y = -0.014x + 64.5$, for $1500 \le x \le 4000$, relates the weight of a car, x (in pounds), to its gas mileage, y (in mpg).

8. Find the gas mileage in miles per gallon for a car weighing 2550 lb.

9. Find the gas mileage for a car weighing 2850 lb.

10. Why is the domain restricted to $1500 \le x \le 4000$?

Answers

8. 28.8 mpg **9.** 24.6 mpg

10. The relation is valid only for cars weighing between 1500 lb and 4000 lb, inclusive.

Section 8.1 Practice Exercises

For additional exercises, see Classroom Activities 8.1A–8.1B in the *Student's Resource Manual* at www.mhhe.com/moh.

Vocabulary and Key Concepts

1. **a.** A set of ordered pairs (x, y) is called a ___relation___ in x and y.

   b. The ___domain___ of a relation is the set of first components in the ordered pairs.

   c. The ___range___ of a relation is the set of second components in the ordered pairs.

Concept 2: Domain and Range of a Relation

2. Explain how to determine the domain and range of a relation represented by a set of ordered pairs.
   The domain is the set consisting of the first coordinates of the ordered pairs. The range is the set consisting of the second coordinates of the ordered pairs.

For Exercises 3–14,

a. Write the relation as a set of ordered pairs.

b. Determine the domain and range. **(See Examples 1–3.)**

3.

Region	Number living in poverty (thousands)
Northeast	54.1
Midwest	65.6
South	110.7
West	70.7

a. {(Northeast, 54.1), (Midwest, 65.6), (South, 110.7), (West, 70.7)}
b. Domain: {Northeast, Midwest, South, West}; Range: {54.1, 65.6, 110.7, 70.7}

4.

x	y
0	3
−2	$\frac{1}{2}$
−7	1
−2	8
5	1

a. $\{(0, 3), (-2, \frac{1}{2}), (-7, 1), (-2, 8), (5, 1)\}$
b. Domain: $\{0, -2, -7, 5\}$; range: $\{3, \frac{1}{2}, 1, 8\}$

5.

Country	Year of First Man or Woman in Space
USSR	1961
USA	1962
Poland	1978
Vietnam	1980
Cuba	1980

a. {(USSR, 1961), (USA, 1962), (Poland, 1978), (Vietnam, 1980), (Cuba, 1980)}
b. Domain: {USSR, USA, Poland, Vietnam, Cuba}; range: {1961, 1962, 1978, 1980}

6.

State, x	Year of Statehood, y
Maine	1820
Nebraska	1823
Utah	1847
Hawaii	1959
Alaska	1959

a. {(Maine, 1820), (Nebraska, 1823), (Utah, 1847), (Hawaii, 1959), (Alaska, 1959)}
b. Domain: {Maine, Nebraska, Utah, Hawaii, Alaska}; range: {1820, 1823, 1847, 1959}

7.

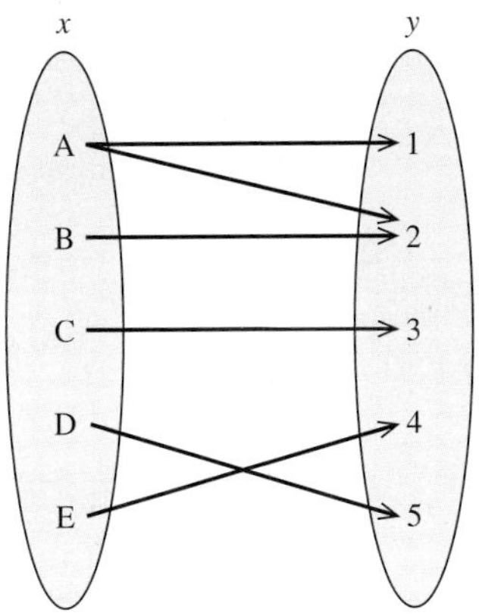

a. {(A, 1), (A, 2), (B, 2), (C, 3), (D, 5), (E, 4)}
b. Domain: {A, B, C, D, E}; range: {1, 2, 3, 4, 5}

8.

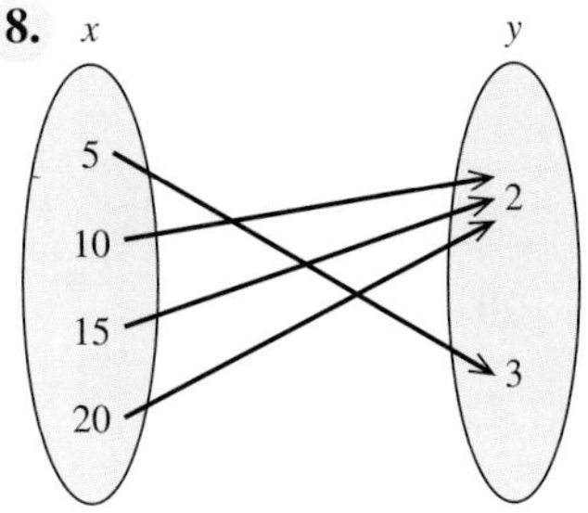

a. {(5, 3), (10, 2), (15, 2), (20, 2)}
b. Domain: {5, 10, 15, 20}; range: {2, 3}

9.

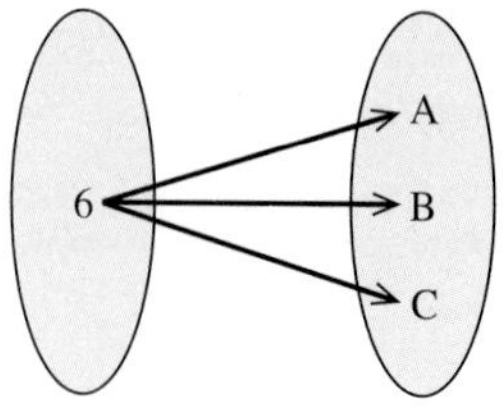

a. {(6, A), (6, B), (6, C)}
b. Domain: {6}; range: {A, B, C}

10.

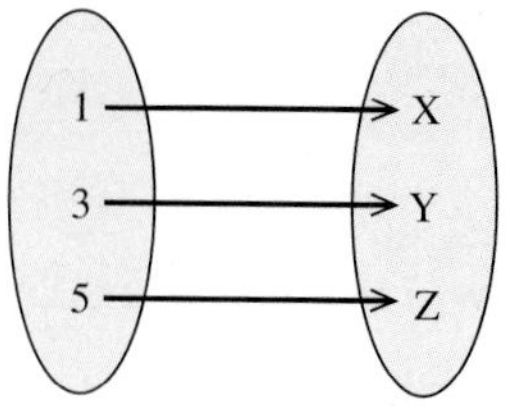

a. {(1, X), (3, Y), (5, Z)}
b. Domain: {1, 3, 5}; range: {X, Y, Z}

11.

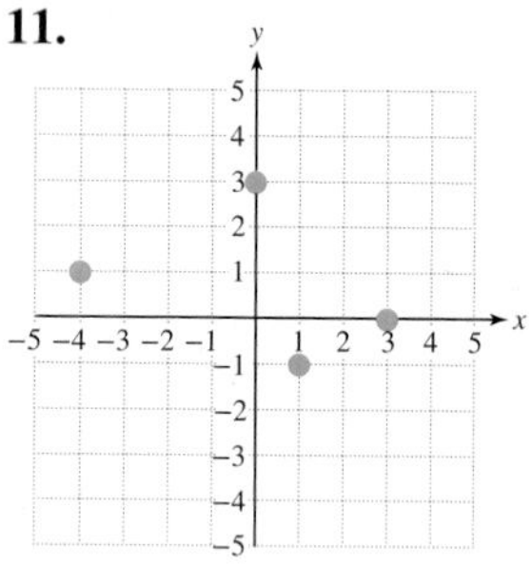

a. {(−4, 1), (0, 3), (1, −1), (3, 0)}
b. Domain: {−4, 0, 1, 3}; range: {−1, 0, 1, 3}

12.

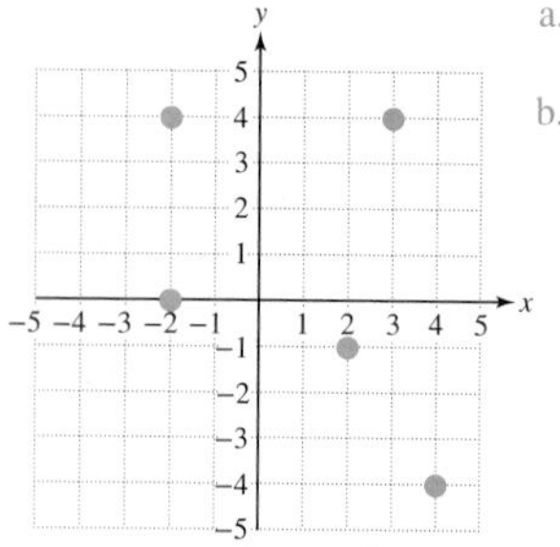

a. {(−2, 0), (−2, 4), (2, −1), (3, 4), (4, −4)}
b. Domain: {−2, 2, 3, 4}; range: {−4, −1, 0, 4}

13.

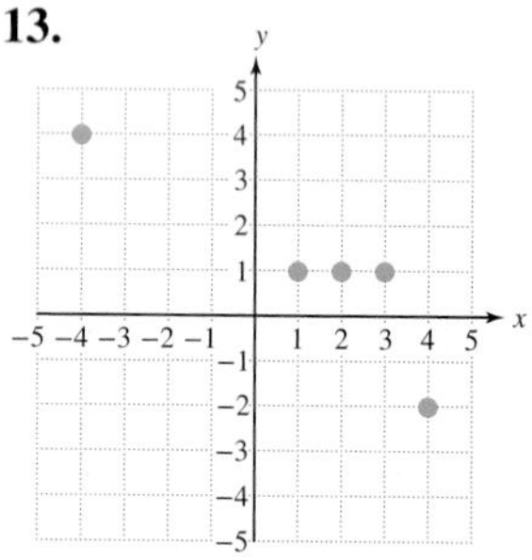

a. {(−4, 4), (1, 1), (2, 1), (3, 1), (4, −2)}
b. Domain: {−4, 1, 2, 3, 4}; range: {−2, 1, 4}

14.

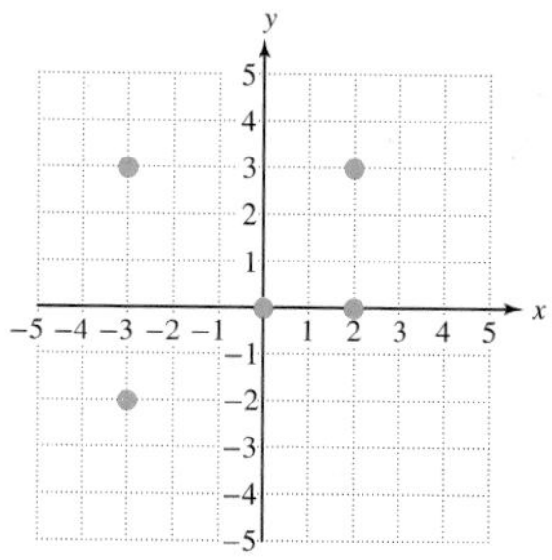

a. {(−3, 3), (−3, −2), (0, 0), (2, 0), (2, 3)}
b. Domain: {−3, 0, 2}; range: {−2, 0, 3}

For Exercises 15–30, find the domain and range of the relations. Use interval notation where appropriate. **(See Example 4.)**

15.

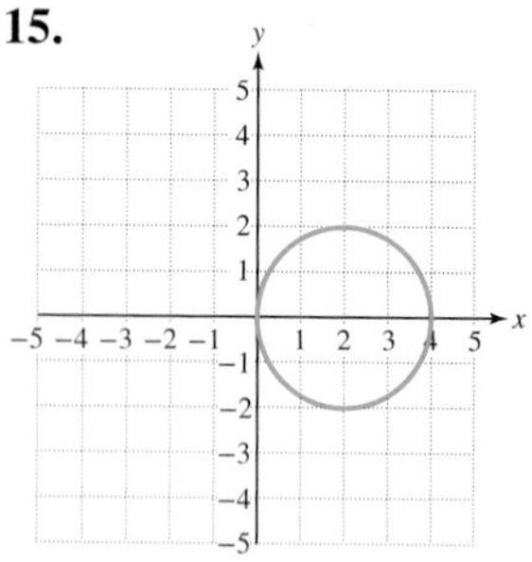

Domain: [0, 4]; range: [−2, 2]

16.

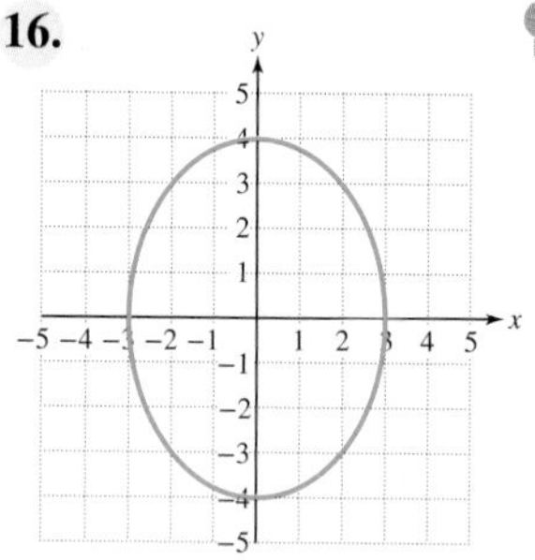

Domain: [−3, 3]; range: [−4, 4]

17.

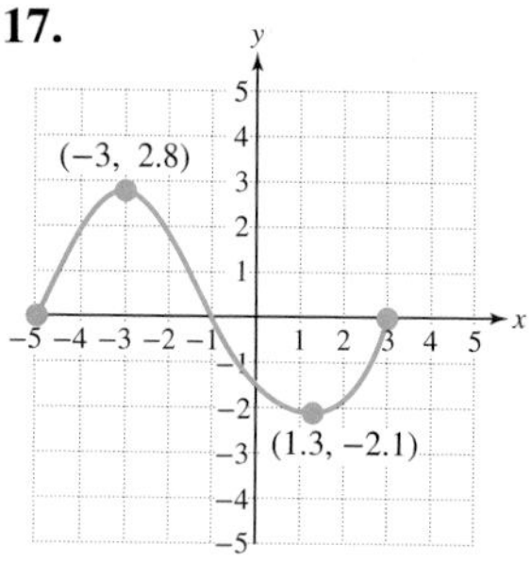

Domain: [−5, 3]; range: [−2.1, 2.8]

18.

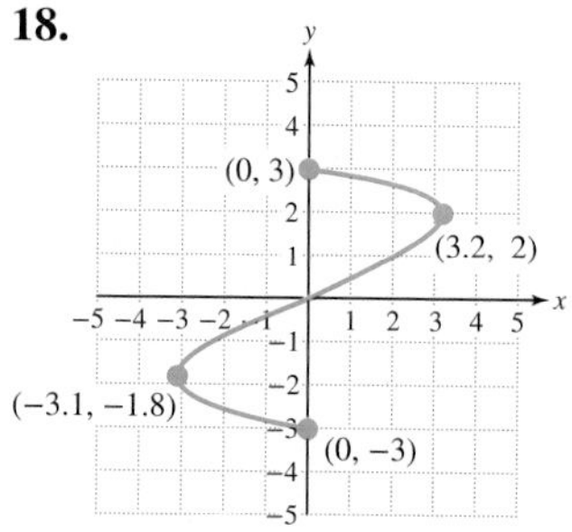

Domain: [−3.1, 3.2]; range: [−3, 3]

19.

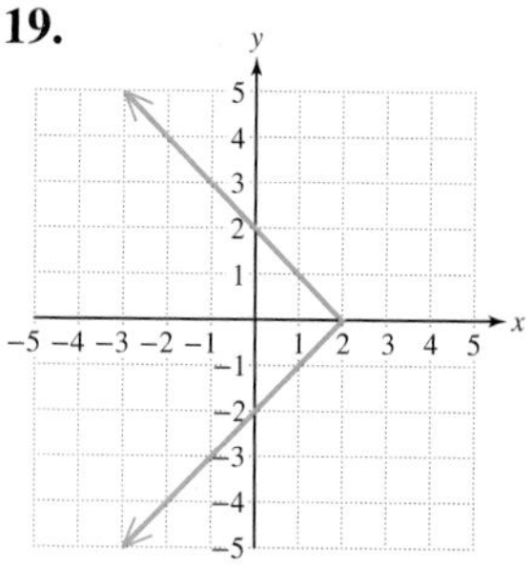

Domain: $(-\infty, 2]$; range: $(-\infty, \infty)$

20.

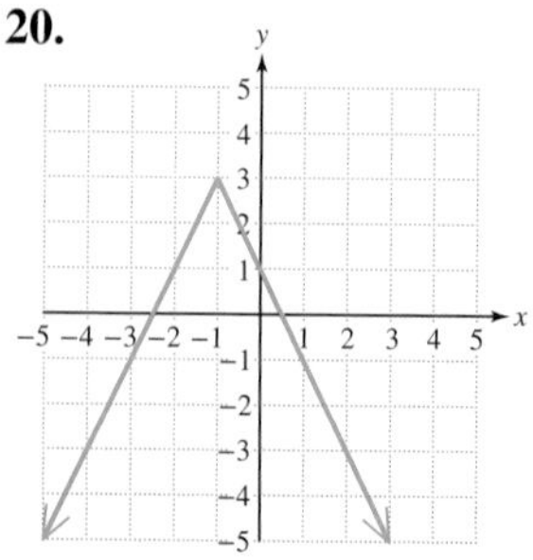

Domain: $(-\infty, \infty)$; range: $(-\infty, 3]$

21.

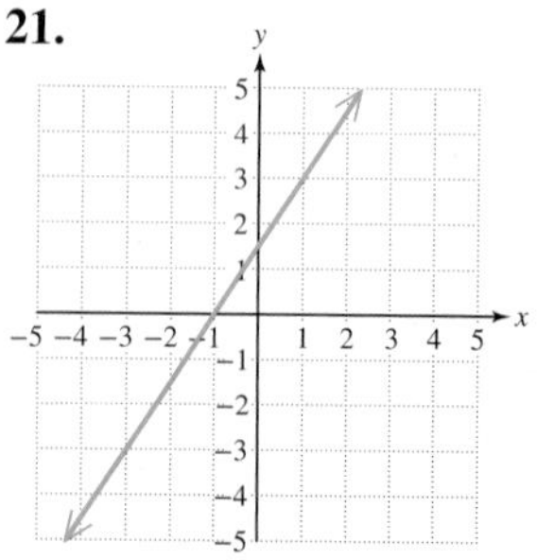

Domain: $(-\infty, \infty)$; range: $(-\infty, \infty)$

22.

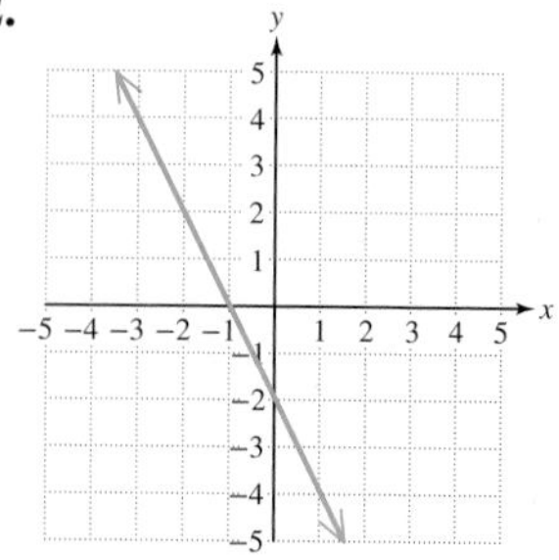

Domain: $(-\infty, \infty)$; range: $(-\infty, \infty)$

23.

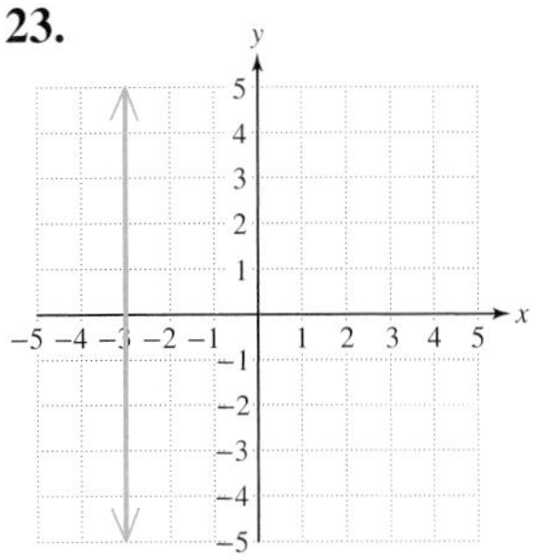

Domain: {−3}; range: (−∞, ∞)

24.

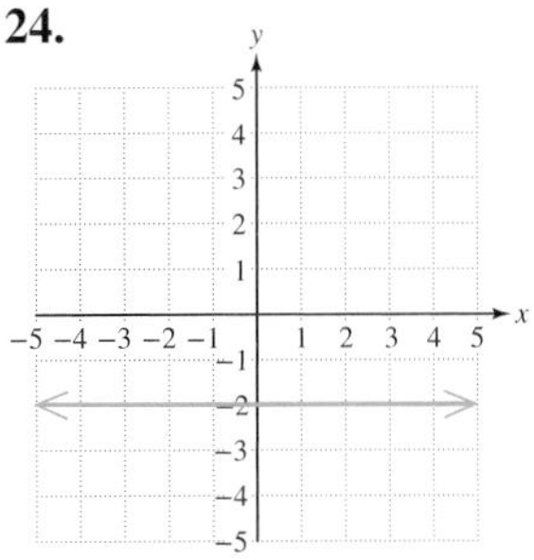

Domain: (−∞, ∞); range: {−2}

25.

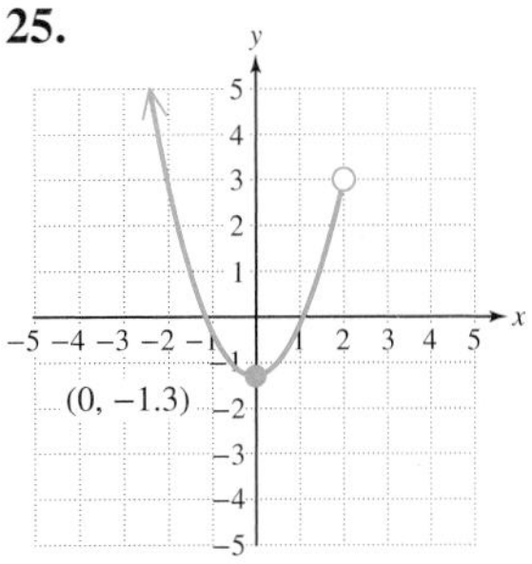

Domain: (−∞, 2); range: [−1.3, ∞)

26.

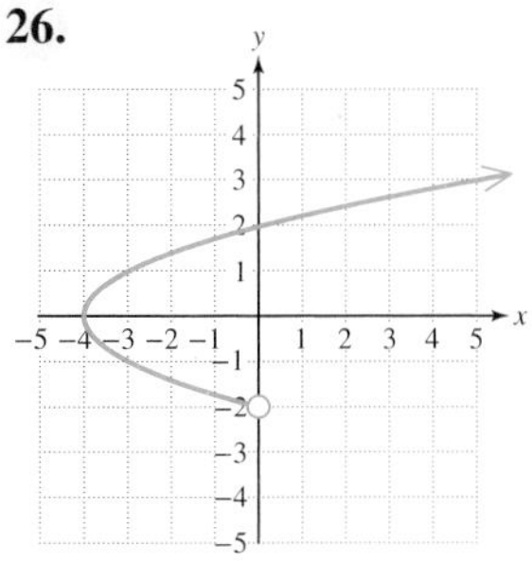

Domain: [−4, ∞); range: (−2, ∞)

27.

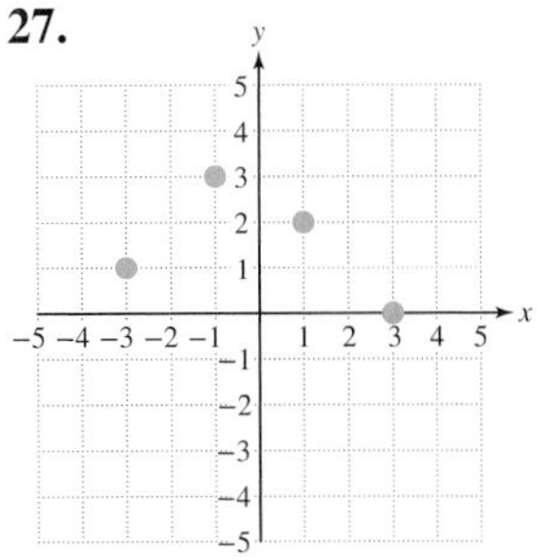

Domain: {−3, −1, 1, 3}; range: {0, 1, 2, 3}

28.

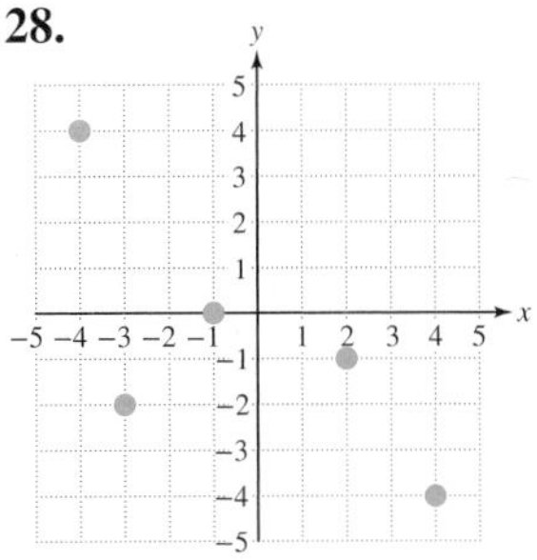

Domain: {−4, −3, −1, 2, 4}; range: {−4, −2, −1, 0, 4}

29.

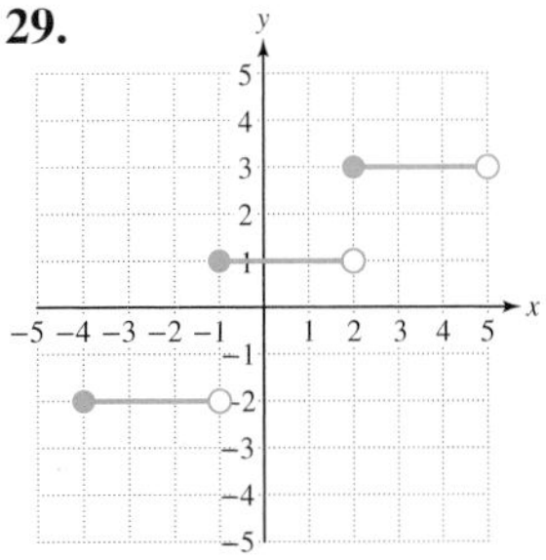

Domain: [−4, 5); range: {−2, 1, 3}

30.

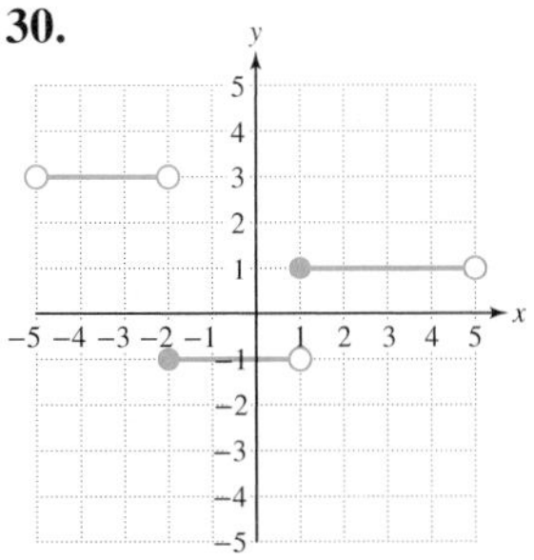

Domain: (−5, 5); range: {−1, 1, 3}

Concept 3: Applications Involving Relations

31. The table gives a relation between the month of the year and the average precipitation for that month for Miami, Florida. **(See Example 5.)**

Month x	Precipitation (in.) y	Month x	Precipitation (in.) y
Jan.	2.01	July	5.70
Feb.	2.08	Aug.	7.58
Mar.	2.39	Sept.	7.63
Apr.	2.85	Oct.	5.64
May	6.21	Nov.	2.66
June	9.33	Dec.	1.83

Source: U.S. National Oceanic and Atmospheric Administration

a. What is the range element corresponding to April? 2.85

b. What is the range element corresponding to June? 9.33

c. Which element in the domain corresponds to the least value in the range? Dec.

d. Complete the ordered pair: (, 2.66) Nov.

e. Complete the ordered pair: (Sept.,) 7.63

f. What is the domain of this relation? {Jan., Feb., Mar., Apr., May, June, July, Aug., Sept., Oct., Nov., Dec.}

32. The table gives a relation between a person's age and the person's maximum recommended heart rate.

Age (years) x	Maximum Recommended Heart Rate (Beats per Minute) y
20	200
30	190
40	180
50	170
60	160

a. What is the domain? {20, 30, 40, 50, 60}

b. What is the range? {200, 190, 180, 170, 160}

c. The range element 200 corresponds to what element in the domain? 20

d. Complete the ordered pair: (50,) 170

e. Complete the ordered pair: (, 190) 30

33. The population of Canada y (in millions) can be approximated by the relation $y = 0.276x + 31$, where x represents the number of years since 2000.

a. Approximate the population of Canada in the year 2009. 33.484 million or 33,484,000

b. In what year did the population of Canada reach approximately 35,140,000? The year 2015

34. The world record times for women's track and field events are shown in the table. The women's world record time y (in seconds) required to run x meters can be approximated by the relation $y = 0.159x - 10.79$.

Distance (m)	Time (sec)	Winner's Name and Country
100	10.49	Florence Griffith Joyner (United States)
200	21.34	Florence Griffith Joyner (United States)
400	47.60	Marita Koch (East Germany)
800	113.28	Jarmila Kratochvilova (Czechoslovakia)
1000	148.98	Svetlana Masterkova (Russia)
1500	230.07	Genzebe Dibaba (Ethiopia)

a. Predict the time required for a 500-m race. 68.71 sec

b. Use this model to predict the time for a 1000-m race. Is this value exactly the same as the data value given in the table? Explain. 148.21 sec. The time is not exactly the same because the equation represents approximate times.

Expanding Your Skills

35. a. Define a relation with four ordered pairs such that the first element of the ordered pair is the name of a friend and the second element is your friend's place of birth.
For example: {(Julie, New York), (Peggy, Florida), (Stephen, Kansas), (Pat, New York)}

b. State the domain and range of this relation.
Domain: {Julie, Peggy, Stephen, Pat}; range: {New York, Florida, Kansas}

36. a. Define a relation with four ordered pairs such that the first element is a state and the second element is its capital. For example: {(Michigan, Lansing), (Florida, Tallahassee), (Texas, Austin), (New York, Albany)}

b. State the domain and range of this relation. Domain: {Michigan, Florida, Texas, New York}; range: {Lansing, Tallahassee, Austin, Albany}

37. Use a mathematical equation to define a relation whose second component y is 1 less than 2 times the first component x. $y = 2x - 1$

38. Use a mathematical equation to define a relation whose second component y is 3 more than the first component x. $y = x + 3$

39. Use a mathematical equation to define a relation whose second component y is the square of the first component x. $y = x^2$

40. Use a mathematical equation to define a relation whose second component y is one-fourth the first component x. $y = \frac{1}{4}x$

Introduction to Functions

Section 8.2

Concepts

1. Definition of a Function
2. Vertical Line Test
3. Function Notation
4. Finding Function Values from a Graph
5. Domain of a Function

1. Definition of a Function

In this section, we introduce a special type of relation called a function.

Definition of a Function

Given a relation in x and y, we say "y is a **function** of x" if, for each element x in the domain, there is exactly one value of y in the range.

Note: This means that no two ordered pairs may have the same first coordinate and different second coordinates.

To understand the difference between a relation that is a function and a relation that is not a function, consider Example 1.

Example 1 Determining Whether a Relation Is a Function

Classroom Examples: p. 580 Exercises 6 and 10

Determine which of the relations define y as a function of x.

a. **b.** **c.**

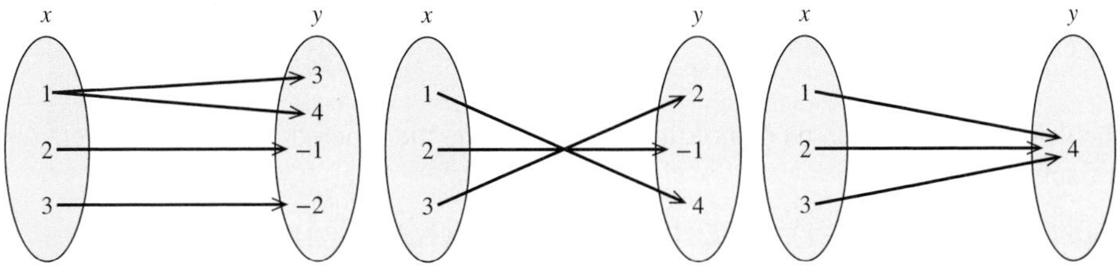

Solution:

a. This relation is defined by the set of ordered pairs

same x

$$\{(1, 3), (1, 4), (2, -1), (3, -2)\}$$

different y-values

When $x = 1$, there are *two* possible range elements: $y = 3$ and $y = 4$. Therefore, this relation is *not* a function.

b. This relation is defined by the set of ordered pairs $\{(1, 4), (2, -1), (3, 2)\}$.

Notice that no two ordered pairs have the same value of x but different values of y. Therefore, this relation *is* a function.

c. This relation is defined by the set of ordered pairs $\{(1, 4), (2, 4), (3, 4)\}$.

Notice that no two ordered pairs have the same value of x but different values of y. Therefore, this relation *is* a function.

Instructor Note: Explain that a function can have the same y-coordinate with different x-coordinates, but not have the same x-coordinate with different y-coordinates.

Skill Practice Determine if the relation defines y as a function of x.

1.

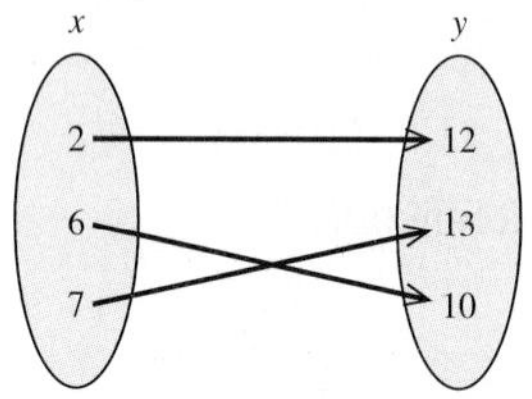

2. $\{(4, 2), (-5, 4), (0, 0), (8, 4)\}$

3. $\{(-1, 6), (8, 9), (-1, 4), (-3, 10)\}$

2. Vertical Line Test

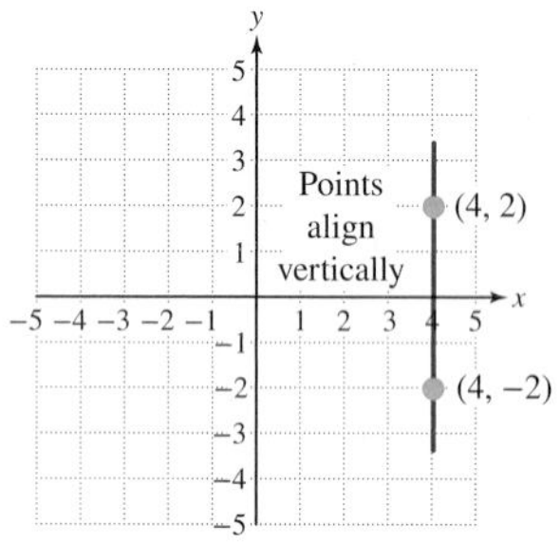

Figure 8-5

A relation that is not a function has at least one domain element x paired with more than one range value y. For example, the set $\{(4, 2), (4, -2)\}$ does not define a function because two different y values correspond to the same x. These two points are aligned vertically in the xy-plane, and a vertical line drawn through one point also intersects the other point (see Figure 8-5). If a vertical line drawn through a graph of a relation intersects the graph in more than one point, the relation cannot be a function. This idea is stated formally as the **vertical line test**.

The Vertical Line Test

Consider a relation defined by a set of points (x, y) in a rectangular coordinate system. The graph defines y as a function of x if no vertical line intersects the graph in more than one point.

The vertical line test can be demonstrated by graphing the ordered pairs from the relations in Example 1.

a. $\{(1, 3), (1, 4), (2, -1), (3, -2)\}$

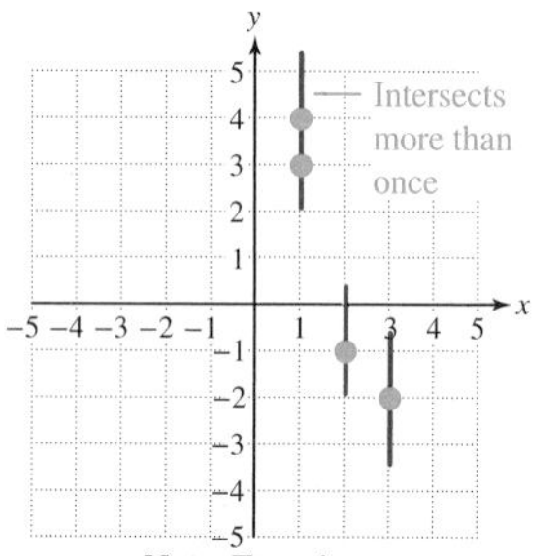

Not a Function
A vertical line intersects in more than one point.

b. $\{(1, 4), (2, -1), (3, 2)\}$

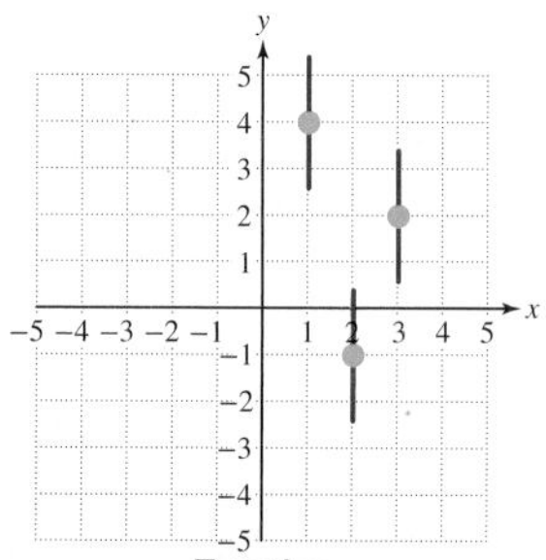

Function
No vertical line intersects more than once.

Classroom Examples: p. 581, Exercises 12 and 16

Example 2 Using the Vertical Line Test

Use the vertical line test to determine whether the relations define y as a function of x.

a.

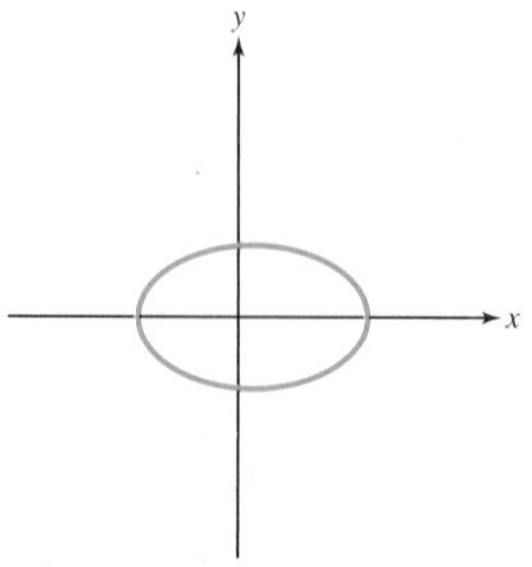

b.

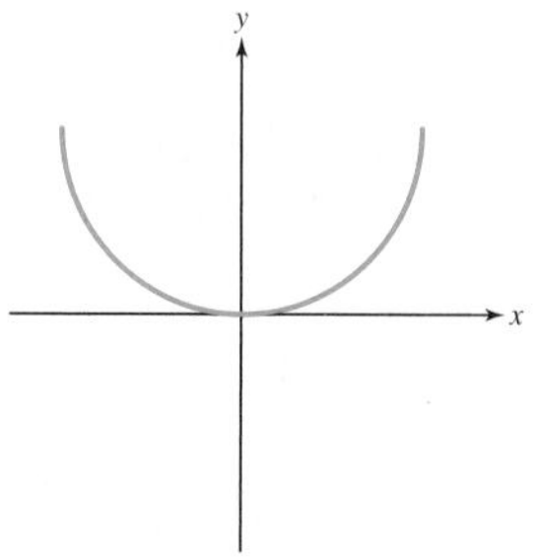

Answers

1. Yes **2.** Yes **3.** No

Solution:

a.

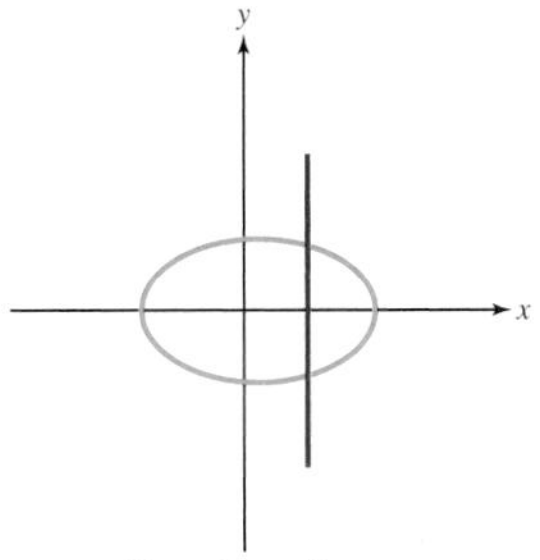

Not a Function
A vertical line intersects in more than one point.

b.

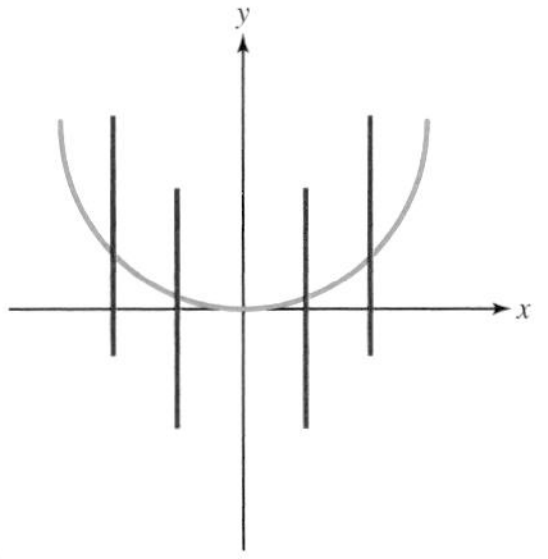

Function
No vertical line intersects in more than one point.

Skill Practice Use the vertical line test to determine whether the relations define y as a function of x.

4.

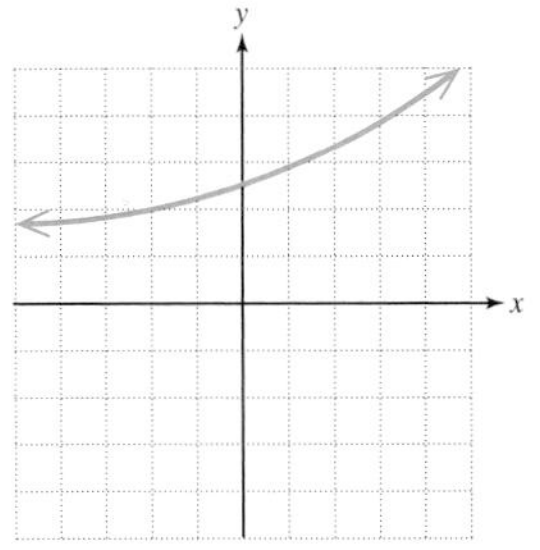

5.

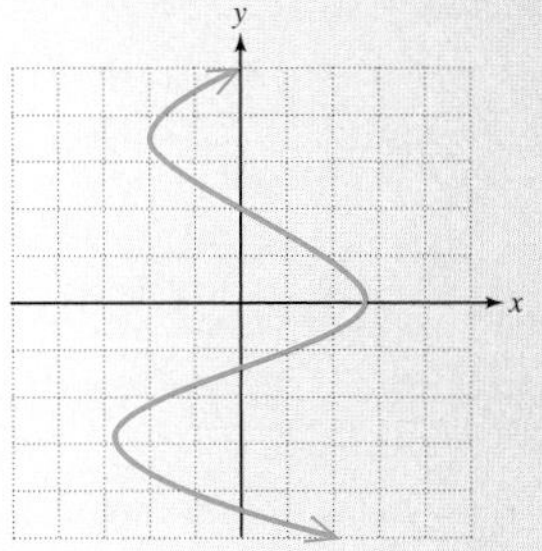

3. Function Notation

A function is defined as a relation with the added restriction that each value in the domain must have only one corresponding y value in the range. In mathematics, functions are often given by rules or equations to define the relationship between two or more variables. For example, the equation $y = 2x$ defines the set of ordered pairs such that the y value is twice the x value.

When a function is defined by an equation, we often use **function notation**. For example, the equation $y = 2x$ may be written in function notation as

$f(x) = 2x$
- f is the name of the function.
- x is an input value from the domain of the function.
- $f(x)$ is the function value (y value) corresponding to x.

The notation $f(x)$ is read as "f of x" or "the value of the function f at x."

Avoiding Mistakes
Be sure to note that $f(x)$ is *not* $f \cdot x$.

A function may be evaluated at different values of x by substituting x values from the domain into the function. For example, to evaluate the function defined by $f(x) = 2x$ at $x = 5$, substitute $x = 5$ into the function.

$$f(x) = 2x$$
$$\downarrow \qquad \downarrow$$
$$f(5) = 2(5)$$
$$f(5) = 10$$

TIP: $f(5) = 10$ can be interpreted as the ordered pair $(5, 10)$.

Answers
4. Yes **5.** No

Thus, when $x = 5$, the corresponding function value is 10. We say:

- f of 5 is 10.
- f at 5 is 10.
- f evaluated at 5 is 10.

The names of functions are often given by either lowercase or uppercase letters, such as f, g, h, p, K, and M. The input variable may also be a letter other than x. For example, $y = P(t)$ might represent population as a function of time.

Classroom Examples: p. 581, Exercises 22 and 26

Example 3 Evaluating a Function

Given the function defined by $g(x) = \frac{1}{2}x - 1$, find the function values.

a. $g(0)$ **b.** $g(2)$ **c.** $g(4)$ **d.** $g(-2)$

Solution:

a. $g(x) = \frac{1}{2}x - 1$

$$g(0) = \frac{1}{2}(0) - 1$$
$$= 0 - 1$$
$$= -1$$

We say that "g of 0 is -1." This is equivalent to the ordered pair $(0, -1)$.

b. $g(x) = \frac{1}{2}x - 1$

$$g(2) = \frac{1}{2}(2) - 1$$
$$= 1 - 1$$
$$= 0$$

We say that "g of 2 is 0." This is equivalent to the ordered pair $(2, 0)$.

c. $g(x) = \frac{1}{2}x - 1$

$$g(4) = \frac{1}{2}(4) - 1$$
$$= 2 - 1$$
$$= 1$$

We say that "g of 4 is 1." This is equivalent to the ordered pair $(4, 1)$.

d. $g(x) = \frac{1}{2}x - 1$

$$g(-2) = \frac{1}{2}(-2) - 1$$
$$= -1 - 1$$
$$= -2$$

We say that "g of -2 is -2." This is equivalent to the ordered pair $(-2, -2)$.

Skill Practice Given the function defined by $f(x) = -2x - 3$, find the function values.

6. $f(1)$ **7.** $f(0)$ **8.** $f(-3)$ **9.** $f\left(\frac{1}{2}\right)$

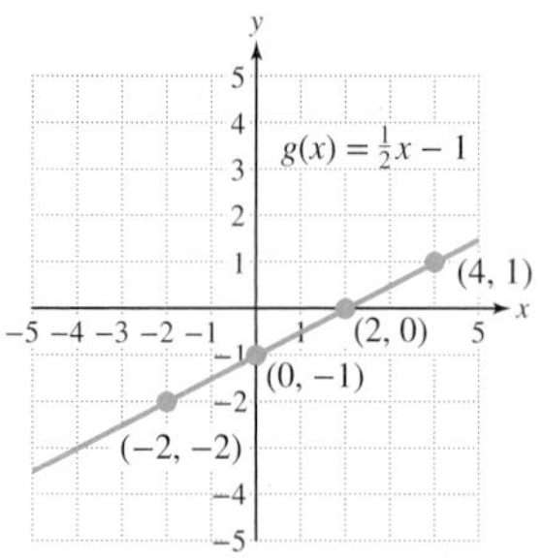

Figure 8-6

In Example 3, notice that $g(0)$, $g(2)$, $g(4)$, and $g(-2)$ correspond to the ordered pairs $(0, -1)$, $(2, 0)$, $(4, 1)$, and $(-2, -2)$. In the graph, these points "line up." The graph of *all* ordered pairs defined by this function is a line with a slope of $\frac{1}{2}$ and y-intercept of $(0, -1)$ (Figure 8-6). This should not be surprising because the function defined by $g(x) = \frac{1}{2}x - 1$ is equivalent to $y = \frac{1}{2}x - 1$.

Answers

6. −5 **7.** −3 **8.** 3 **9.** −4

Calculator Connections

Topic: Using the *Table* and *Value* Features

The values of $g(x)$ in Example 3 can be found using a *Table* feature. First enter the equation of the function as

$$Y_1 = \frac{1}{2}x - 1$$

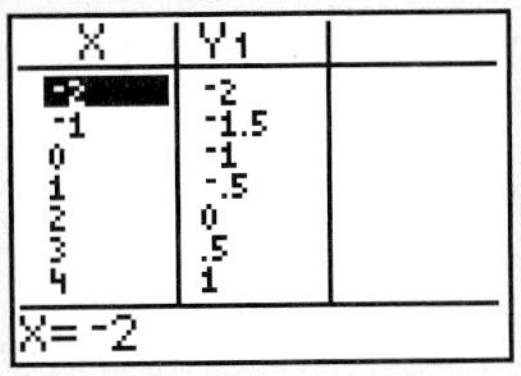

Function values can also be evaluated by using a *Value* feature. The value of $g(4)$ is shown here.

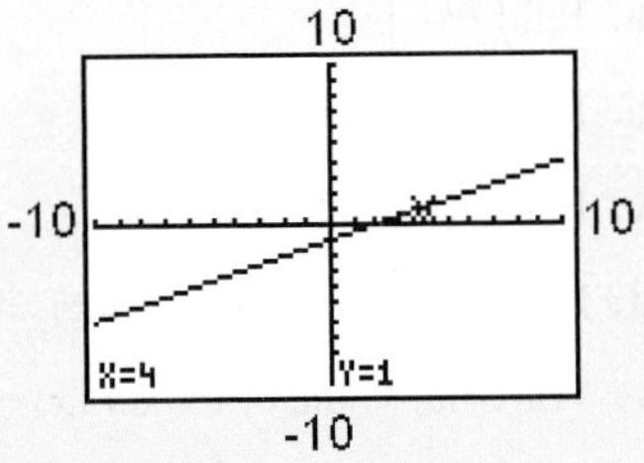

A function may be evaluated at numerical values or at algebraic expressions, as shown in Example 4.

Example 4 **Evaluating Functions**

Classroom Examples: p. 581, Exercises 28 and 42

Given the functions defined by $f(x) = x^2 - 2x$ and $g(x) = 3x + 5$, find the function values.

a. $f(t)$ **b.** $g(w + 4)$ **c.** $f(-t)$

Solution:

a. $f(x) = x^2 - 2x$

$f(t) = (t)^2 - 2(t)$ Substitute $x = t$ for all values of x in the function.

$= t^2 - 2t$ Simplify.

b. $g(x) = 3x + 5$

$g(w + 4) = 3(w + 4) + 5$ Substitute $x = w + 4$ for all values of x in the function.

$= 3w + 12 + 5$

$= 3w + 17$ Simplify.

c. $f(x) = x^2 - 2x$ Substitute $-t$ for x.

$f(-t) = (-t)^2 - 2(-t)$

$= t^2 + 2t$ Simplify.

Skill Practice Given the function defined by $g(x) = 4x - 3$, find the function values.

10. $g(a)$ **11.** $g(x + h)$ **12.** $g(-x)$

Answers

10. $4a - 3$ **11.** $4x + 4h - 3$

12. $-4x - 3$

4. Finding Function Values from a Graph

We can find function values by looking at the graph of a function. The value of $f(a)$ refers to the y-coordinate of a point with x-coordinate a.

Classroom Example: p. 582, Exercise 62

Example 5 **Finding Function Values from a Graph**

Consider the function pictured in Figure 8-7.

a. Find $h(-1)$.

b. Find $h(2)$.

Animation

c. Find $h(5)$.

d. For what value of x is $h(x) = 3$?

e. For what values of x is $h(x) = 0$?

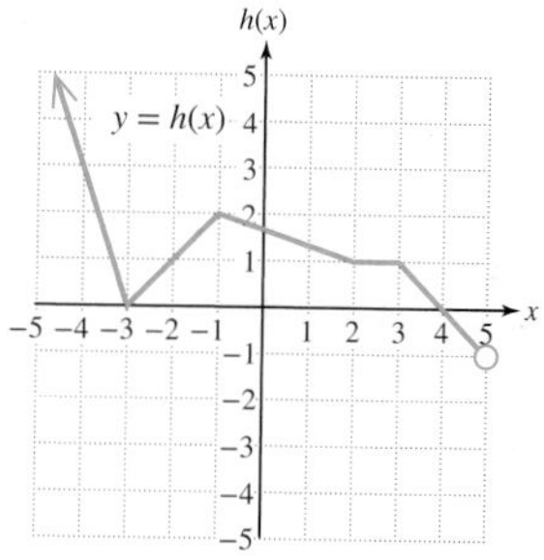

Figure 8-7

Solution:

a. $h(-1) = 2$ — From the graph, when $x = -1$, the function value (y value) is 2. This corresponds to the ordered pair $(-1, 2)$.

b. $h(2) = 1$ — From the graph, when $x = 2$, the function value (y value) is 1. This corresponds to the ordered pair $(2, 1)$.

c. $h(5)$ is not defined. — The open dot at $(5, -1)$ indicates that 5 is not in the domain.

d. $h(x) = 3$ for $x = -4$ — We want to find the x value(s) that correspond to a function value (y value) of 3. This corresponds to the ordered pair $(-4, 3)$.

e. $h(x) = 0$ for $x = -3$ and $x = 4$ — We want to find the x value(s) that correspond to a function value (y value) of 0. These correspond to the ordered pairs $(-3, 0)$ and $(4, 0)$.

Skill Practice Refer to the function graphed here.

13. Find $f(0)$.

14. Find $f(-2)$.

15. Find $f(5)$.

16. For what value(s) of x is $f(x) = 0$?

17. For what value(s) of x is $f(x) = -4$?

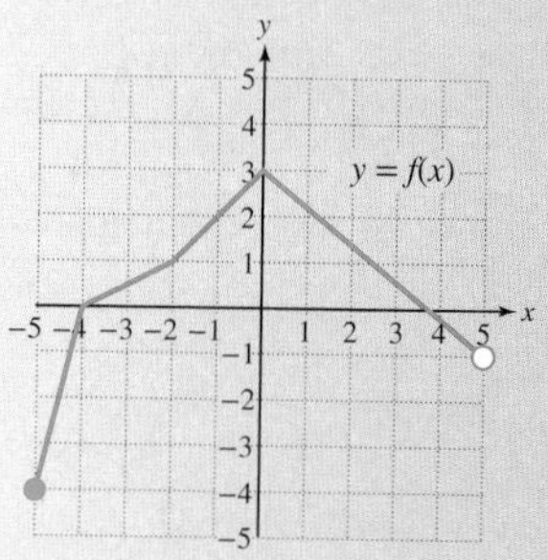

5. Domain of a Function

A function is a relation, and it is often necessary to determine its domain and range. Consider a function defined by the equation $y = f(x)$. The **domain** of f is the set of all x values that when substituted into the function produce a real number. The **range** of f is the set of all y values corresponding to the values of x in the domain.

To find the domain of a function defined by $y = f(x)$, keep these guidelines in mind.

- Exclude values of x that make the denominator of a fraction zero.
- Exclude values of x that make the expression within a square root negative.

Answers

13. 3 **14.** 1
15. not defined
16. $x = -4$ and $x = 4$
17. $x = -5$

Example 6 Finding the Domain of a Function

Write the domain in interval notation.

a. $f(x) = \dfrac{x+7}{2x-1}$ **b.** $h(x) = \dfrac{x-4}{x^2+9}$

c. $k(t) = \sqrt{t+4}$ **d.** $g(t) = t^2 - 3t$

Solution:

a. $f(x) = \dfrac{x+7}{2x-1}$ will not be a real number when the denominator is zero, that is, when

$$2x - 1 = 0$$
$$2x = 1$$
$$x = \frac{1}{2}$$

The value $x = \frac{1}{2}$ must be *excluded* from the domain.

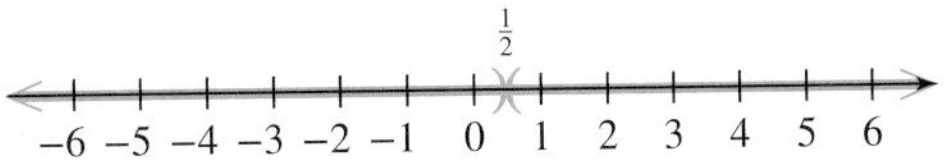

The number line indicates that the domain consists of two intervals, $(-\infty, \frac{1}{2})$ and $(\frac{1}{2}, \infty)$. We use the notation $\cup$ to combine the two intervals. The symbol $\cup$ stands for union. The union of two intervals consists of all the numbers in the first interval, along with all the numbers in the second interval.

Interval notation: $\left(-\infty, \dfrac{1}{2}\right) \cup \left(\dfrac{1}{2}, \infty\right)$

b. For $h(x) = \dfrac{x-4}{x^2+9}$ the quantity x^2 is greater than or equal to 0 for all real numbers x, and the number 9 is positive. The sum $x^2 + 9$ must be *positive* for all real numbers x. The denominator will never be zero; therefore, the domain is the set of all real numbers.

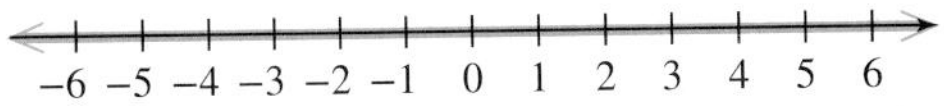

Interval notation: $(-\infty, \infty)$

c. The value of the function defined by $k(t) = \sqrt{t+4}$ will not be a real number when the expression within the square root is negative. Therefore, the domain is the set of all t values that make $t + 4$ greater than or equal to zero.

$$t + 4 \geq 0$$
$$t \geq -4$$

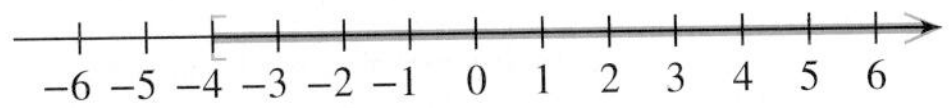

Interval notation: $[-4, \infty)$

d. The function defined by $g(t) = t^2 - 3t$ has no restrictions on its domain because any real number substituted for t will produce a real number. The domain is the set of all real numbers.

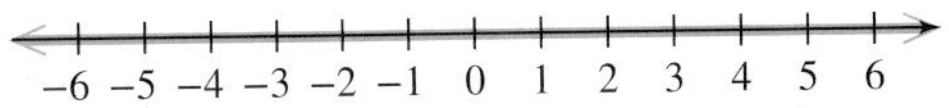

Interval notation: $(-\infty, \infty)$

Skill Practice Write the domain in interval notation.

18. $f(x) = \dfrac{2x+1}{x-9}$ **19.** $k(x) = \dfrac{-5}{4x^2+1}$

20. $g(x) = \sqrt{x-2}$ **21.** $h(x) = x + 6$

Classroom Examples: pp. 583–584, Exercises 80, 86, and 94

Instructor Note: Example 6 shows students that they can find the domain of a function without needing its graph. If you want to emphasize the graphical relationship, show the students the graphs of these functions in class. Or have the students graph the functions on a graphing calculator.

Answers

18. $(-\infty, 9) \cup (9, \infty)$ **19.** $(-\infty, \infty)$
20. $[2, \infty)$ **21.** $(-\infty, \infty)$

Section 8.2 Practice Exercises

Vocabulary and Key Concepts

For additional exercises, see Classroom Activities 8.2A–8.2D in the *Student's Resource Manual* at www.mhhe.com/moh.

1. **a.** Given a relation in x and y, we say that y is a ___function___ of x if for each element x in the domain, there is exactly one value of y in the range.

   b. If a ___vertical___ line intersects the graph of a relation in more than one point, the relation is not a function.

   c. Function notation for the equation $y = 2x + 1$ is $f(x) =$ ___$2x+1$___.

   d. Given a function defined by $y = f(x)$, the set of all ___x values___ that produce a real number when substituted into a function is called the domain of the function.

   e. The set of all ___y values___ corresponding to x values in the domain is called the range of a function.

   f. To find the domain of a function defined by $y = f(x)$, exclude any values of x that make the ___denominator___ of a fraction equal to zero.

   g. To find the domain of a function defined by $y = f(x)$, exclude any values of x that make the expression within a square root ___negative___.

Review Exercises

For Exercises 2–4, **a.** write the relation as a set of ordered pairs, **b.** identify the domain, and **c.** identify the range.

2.

Parent, x	Child, y
Kevin	Kayla
Kevin	Kira
Kathleen	Katie
Kathleen	Kira

a. {(Kevin, Kayla), (Kevin, Kira), (Kathleen, Katie), (Kathleen, Kira)}
b. {Kevin, Kathleen}
c. {Kayla, Katie, Kira}

3.

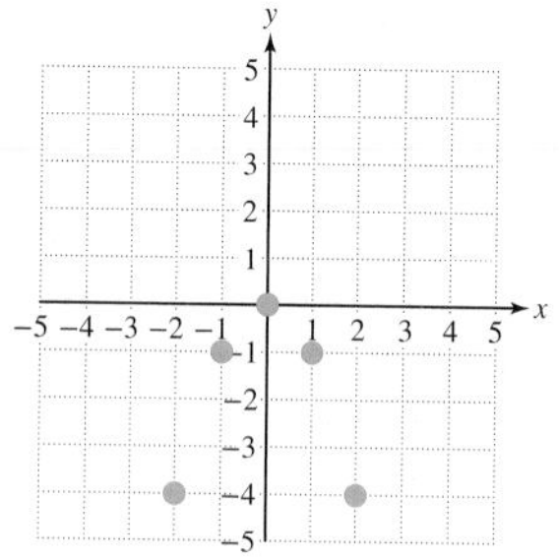

a. $\{(-2, -4), (-1, -1), (0, 0), (1, -1), (2, -4)\}$
b. $\{-2, -1, 0, 1, 2\}$ c. $\{-4, -1, 0\}$

4.

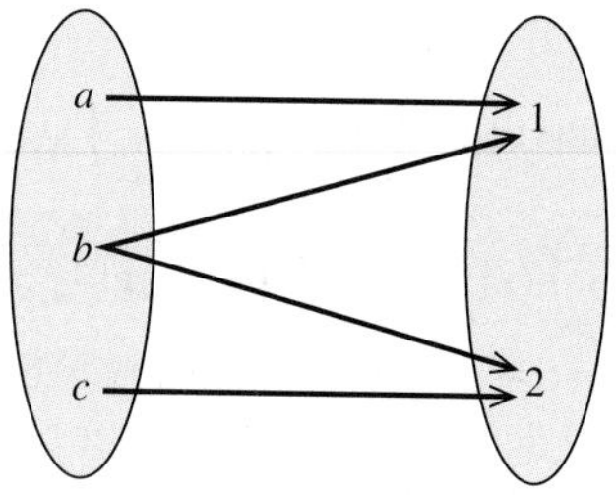

a. $\{(a, 1), (b, 1), (b, 2), (c, 2)\}$
b. $\{a, b, c\}$ c. $\{1, 2\}$

Concept 1: Definition of a Function

For Exercises 5–10, determine if the relation defines y as a function of x. **(See Example 1.)**

5.

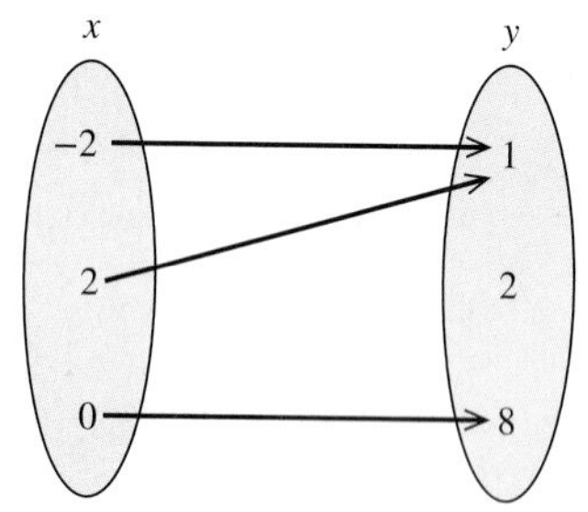

Function

6.

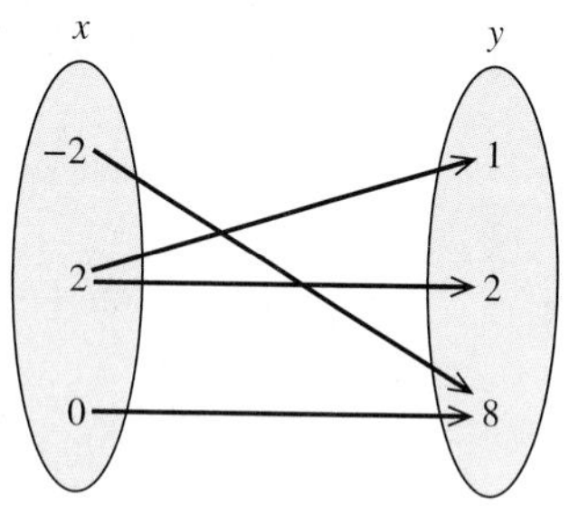

Not a function

7.

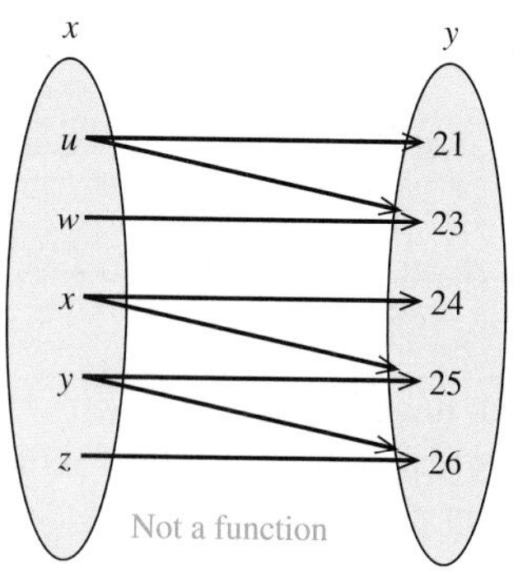

Not a function

8.

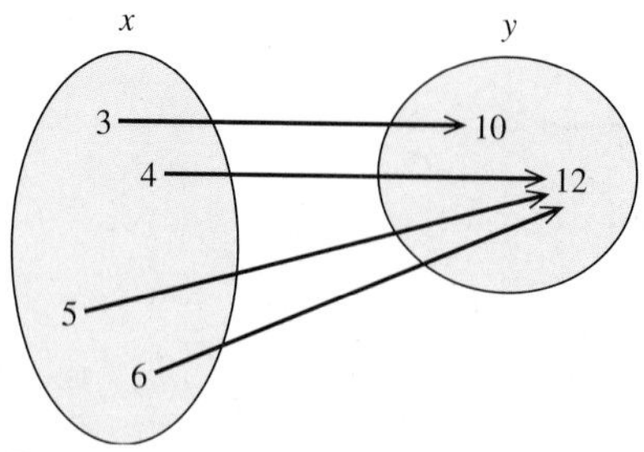

Function

9. $\{(1, 2), (3, 4), (5, 4), (-9, 3)\}$

Function

10. $\left\{(0, -1.1), \left(\frac{1}{2}, 8\right), (1.1, 8), \left(4, \frac{1}{2}\right)\right\}$

Function

Concept 2: Vertical Line Test

For Exercises 11–16, use the vertical line test to determine whether the relation defines y as a function of x. **(See Example 2.)**

11.

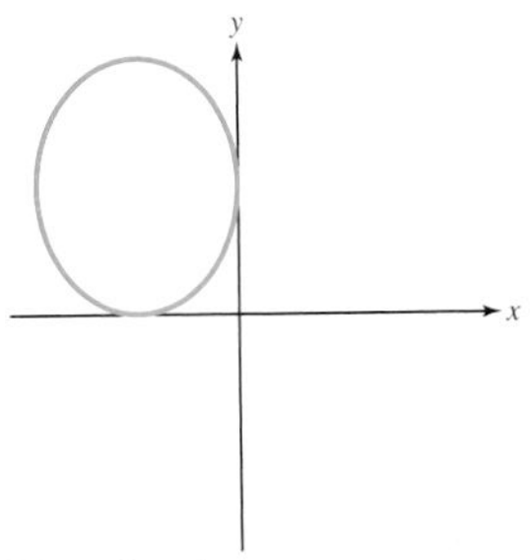

Not a function

12.

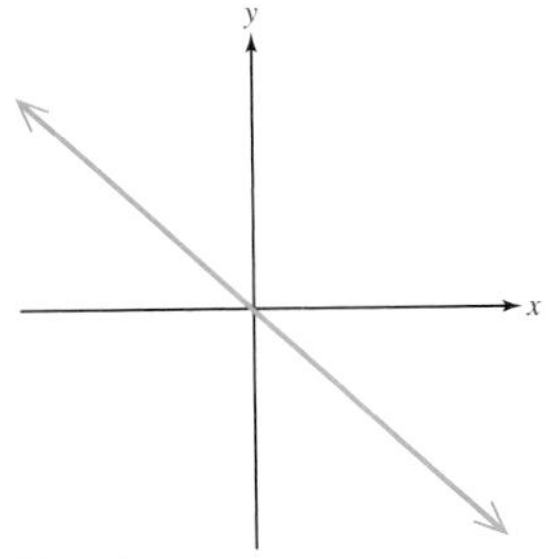

Function

13.

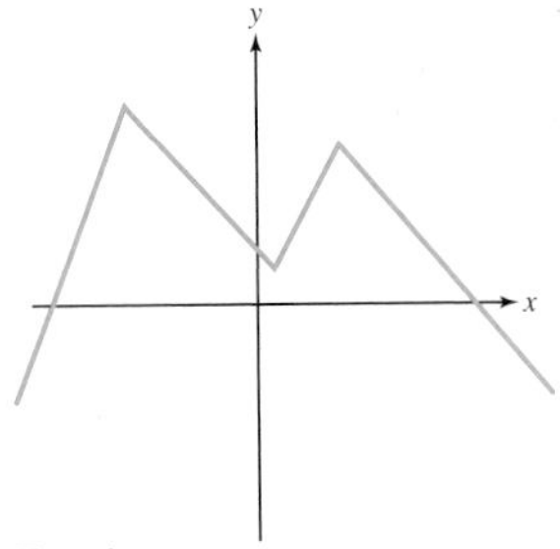

Function

14.

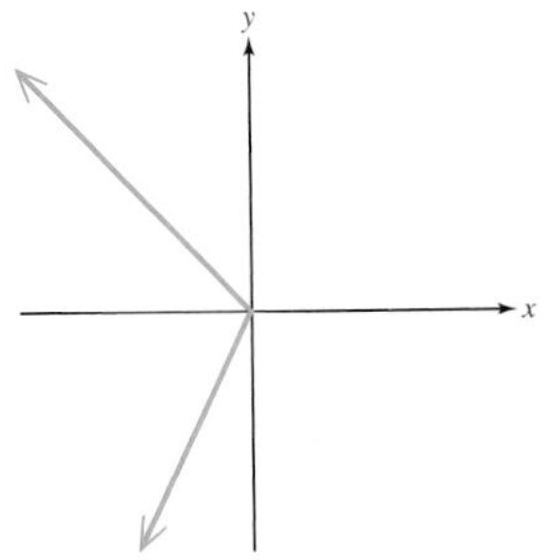

Not a function

15.

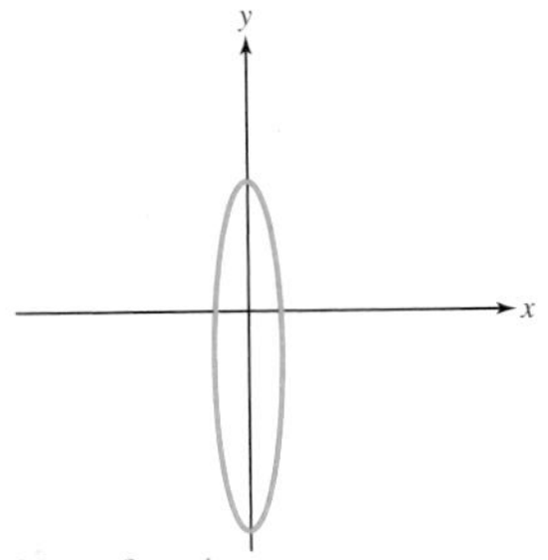

Not a function

16.

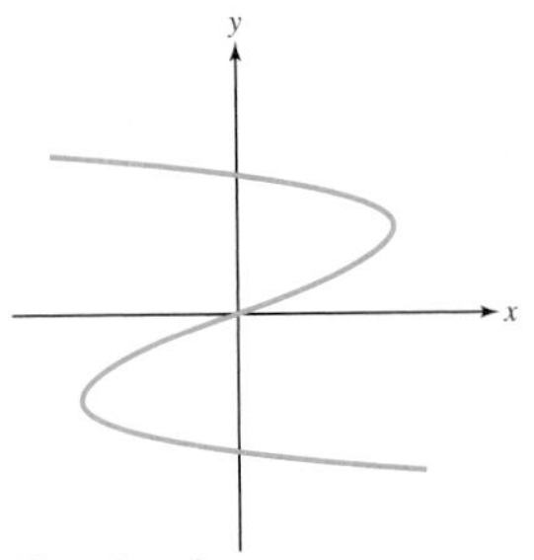

Not a function

Concept 3: Function Notation

For Exercises 17–20, consider a function defined by $y = f(x)$.

17. Interpret the meaning of $f(2) = 5$.
When x is 2, the function value y is 5.

18. Interpret the meaning of $f(-7) = 8$.
When x is -7, the function value y is 8.

19. Write the ordered pair represented by $f(0) = -2$.
$(0, -2)$

20. Write the ordered pair represented by $f(-10) = 11$.
$(-10, 11)$

Consider the functions defined by $f(x) = 6x - 2$, $g(x) = -x^2 - 4x + 1$, $h(x) = 7$, and $k(x) = |x - 2|$. For Exercises 21–52, find the following. **(See Examples 3–4.)**

21. $g(2)$ -11
22. $k(2)$ 0
23. $g(0)$ 1
24. $h(0)$ 7
25. $k(0)$ 2
26. $f(0)$ -2
27. $f(t)$ $6t - 2$
28. $g(a)$ $-a^2 - 4a + 1$
29. $h(u)$ 7
30. $k(v)$ $|v - 2|$
31. $g(-3)$ 4
32. $h(-5)$ 7
33. $k(-2)$ 4
34. $f(-6)$ -38
35. $f(x + 1)$ $6x + 4$
36. $h(x + 1)$ 7
37. $g(2x)$ $-4x^2 - 8x + 1$
38. $k(x - 3)$ $|x - 5|$
39. $g(-\pi)$ $-\pi^2 + 4\pi + 1$
40. $g(a^2)$ $-a^4 - 4a^2 + 1$
41. $h(a + b)$ 7
42. $f(x + h)$ $6x + 6h - 2$
43. $f(-a)$ $-6a - 2$
44. $g(-b)$ $-b^2 + 4b + 1$
45. $k(-c)$ $|-c - 2|$
46. $h(-x)$ 7
47. $f\left(\frac{1}{2}\right)$ 1
48. $g\left(\frac{1}{4}\right)$ $-\frac{1}{16}$
49. $h\left(\frac{1}{7}\right)$ 7
50. $k\left(\frac{3}{2}\right)$ $\frac{1}{2}$
51. $f(-2.8)$ -18.8
52. $k(-5.4)$ 7.4

Consider the functions $p = \{(\frac{1}{2}, 6), (2, -7), (1, 0), (3, 2\pi)\}$ and $q = \{(6, 4), (2, -5), (\frac{3}{4}, \frac{1}{5}), (0, 9)\}$. For Exercises 53–60, find the function values.

53. $p(2)$ -7
54. $p(1)$ 0
55. $p(3)$ 2π
56. $p\left(\frac{1}{2}\right)$ 6
57. $q(2)$ -5
58. $q\left(\frac{3}{4}\right)$ $\frac{1}{5}$
59. $q(6)$ 4
60. $q(0)$ 9

Concept 4: Finding Function Values from a Graph

61. The graph of $y = f(x)$ is given. **(See Example 5.)**

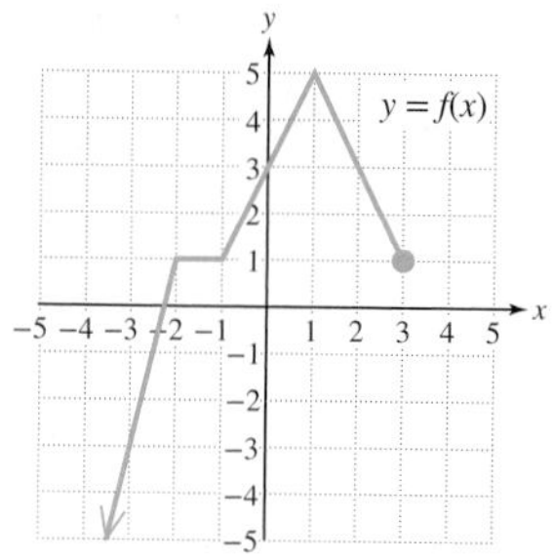

a. Find $f(0)$. 3

b. Find $f(3)$. 1

c. Find $f(-2)$. 1

d. For what value(s) of x is $f(x) = -3$? $x = -3$

e. For what value(s) of x is $f(x) = 3$? $x = 0, x = 2$

f. Write the domain of f. $(-\infty, 3]$

g. Write the range of f. $(-\infty, 5]$

62. The graph of $y = g(x)$ is given.

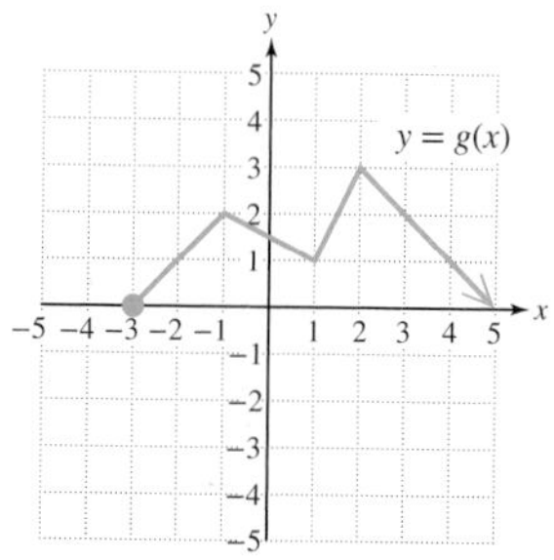

a. Find $g(-1)$. 2

b. Find $g(1)$. 1

c. Find $g(4)$. 1

d. For what value(s) of x is $g(x) = 3$? $x = 2$

e. For what value(s) of x is $g(x) = 0$? $x = -3, x = 5$

f. Write the domain of g. $[-3, \infty)$

g. Write the range of g. $(-\infty, 3]$

63. The graph of $y = H(x)$ is given.

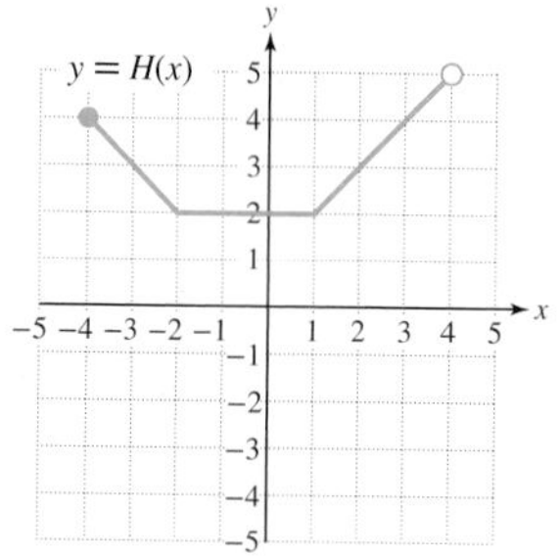

a. Find $H(-3)$. 3

b. Find $H(4)$.
$H(4)$ is not defined because 4 is not in the domain of H.

c. Find $H(3)$. 4

d. For what value(s) of x is $H(x) = 3$?
$x = -3$ and $x = 2$

e. For what value(s) of x is $H(x) = 2$?
All x on the interval $[-2, 1]$

f. Write the domain of H. $[-4, 4)$

g. Write the range of H. $[2, 5)$

64. The graph of $y = K(x)$ is given.

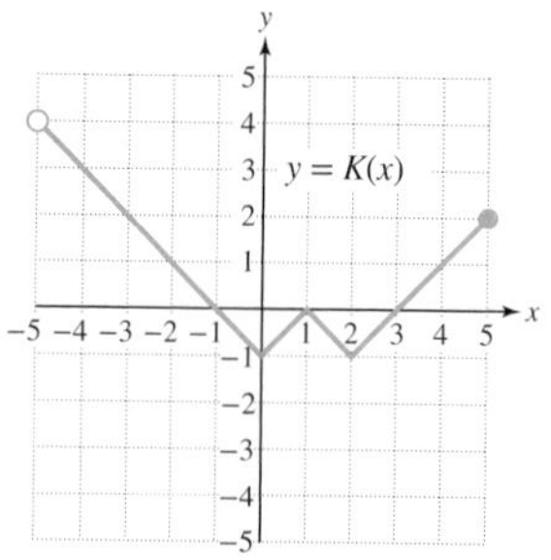

a. Find $K(0)$. -1

b. Find $K(-5)$.
$K(-5)$ is not defined because -5 is not in the domain of K.

c. Find $K(1)$. 0

d. For what value(s) of x is $K(x) = 0$?
$x = -1, x = 1$, and $x = 3$

e. For what value(s) of x is $K(x) = 3$? $x = -4$

f. Write the domain of K. $(-5, 5]$

g. Write the range of K. $[-1, 4)$

65. The graph of $y = p(x)$ is given.

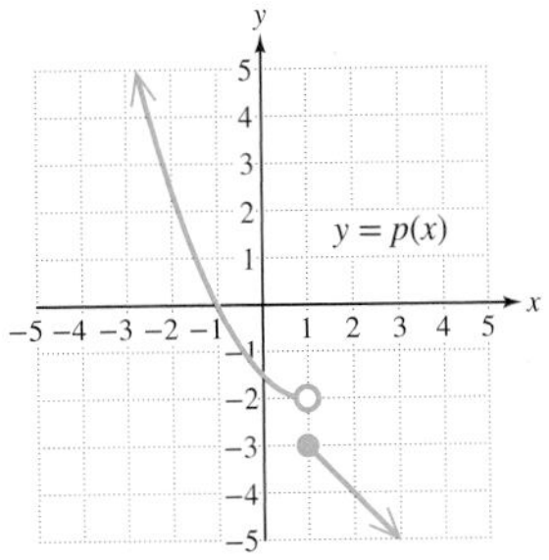

a. Find $p(2)$. -4

b. Find $p(-1)$. 0

c. Find $p(1)$. -3

d. For what value(s) of x is $p(x) = 0$? $x = -1$

e. For what value(s) of x is $p(x) = -2$? There are no such values of x.

f. Write the domain of p. $(-\infty, \infty)$

g. Write the range of p. $(-\infty, -3] \cup (-2, \infty)$

66. The graph of $y = q(x)$ is given.

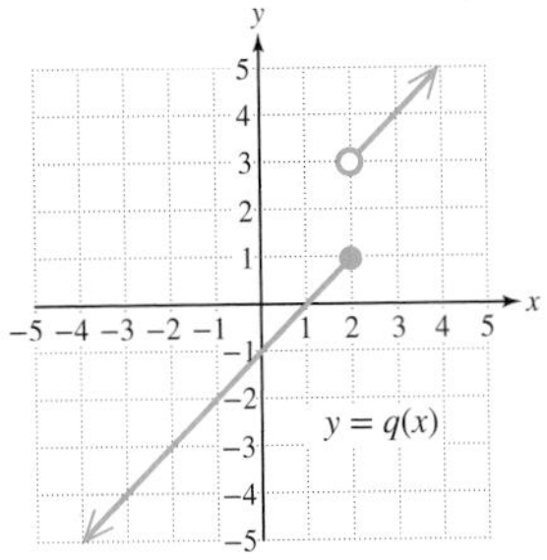

a. Find $q(3)$. 4

b. Find $q(-1)$. -2

c. Find $q(2)$. 1

d. For what value(s) of x is $q(x) = -4$? $x = -3$

e. For what value(s) of x is $q(x) = 3$? There are no such values of x.

f. Write the domain of q. $(-\infty, \infty)$

g. Write the range of q. $(-\infty, 1] \cup (3, \infty)$

For Exercises 67–76, refer to the functions $y = f(x)$ and $y = g(x)$, defined as follows:

$$f = \{(-3, 5), (-7, -3), (-\tfrac{3}{2}, 4), (1.2, 5)\}$$
$$g = \{(0, 6), (2, 6), (6, 0), (1, 0)\}$$

67. Identify the domain of f. $\{-3, -7, -\frac{3}{2}, 1.2\}$

68. Identify the range of f. $\{5, -3, 4\}$

69. Identify the range of g. $\{6, 0\}$

70. Identify the domain of g. $\{0, 2, 6, 1\}$

71. For what value(s) of x is $f(x) = 5$? $x = -3$ and $x = 1.2$

72. For what value(s) of x is $f(x) = -3$? $x = -7$

73. For what value(s) of x is $g(x) = 0$? $x = 6$ and $x = 1$

74. For what value(s) of x is $g(x) = 6$? $x = 0$ and $x = 2$

75. Find $f(-7)$. -3

76. Find $g(0)$. 6

Concept 5: Domain of a Function

77. Explain how to determine the domain of the function defined by $f(x) = \dfrac{x+6}{x-2}$. The domain is the set of all real numbers for which the denominator is not zero. Set the denominator equal to zero, and solve the resulting equation. The solution(s) to the equation must be excluded from the domain. In this case, setting $x - 2 = 0$ indicates that $x = 2$ must be excluded from the domain. The domain is $(-\infty, 2) \cup (2, \infty)$.

78. Explain how to determine the domain of the function defined by $g(x) = \sqrt{x-3}$. The domain is the set of all real numbers for which $x - 3$ is nonnegative. Set the quantity $x - 3 \geq 0$ and solve the inequality. The solution set for the inequality is the domain of the function. Thus, the domain is $[3, \infty)$.

For Exercises 79–94, find the domain. Write the answer in interval notation. **(See Example 6.)**

79. $k(x) = \dfrac{x-3}{x+6}$ $(-\infty, -6) \cup (-6, \infty)$

80. $m(x) = \dfrac{x-1}{x-4}$ $(-\infty, 4) \cup (4, \infty)$

81. $f(t) = \dfrac{5}{t}$ $(-\infty, 0) \cup (0, \infty)$

82. $g(t) = \dfrac{t-7}{t}$ $(-\infty, 0) \cup (0, \infty)$

83. $h(p) = \dfrac{p-4}{p^2+1}$ $(-\infty, \infty)$

84. $n(p) = \dfrac{p+8}{p^2+2}$ $(-\infty, \infty)$

85. $h(t) = \sqrt{t+7}$ $[-7, \infty)$

86. $k(t) = \sqrt{t-5}$ $[5, \infty)$

87. $f(a) = \sqrt{a - 3}$ $[3, \infty)$

88. $g(a) = \sqrt{a + 2}$ $[-2, \infty)$

89. $m(x) = \sqrt{1 - 2x}$ $(-\infty, \frac{1}{2}]$

90. $n(x) = \sqrt{12 - 6x}$ $(-\infty, 2]$

91. $p(t) = 2t^2 + t - 1$ $(-\infty, \infty)$

92. $q(t) = t^3 + t - 1$ $(-\infty, \infty)$

93. $f(x) = x + 6$ $(-\infty, \infty)$

94. $g(x) = 8x - \pi$ $(-\infty, \infty)$

Mixed Exercises

95. The height (in feet) of a ball that is dropped from an 80-ft building is given by $h(t) = -16t^2 + 80$, where t is the time in seconds after the ball is dropped.

a. Find $h(1)$ and $h(1.5)$. $h(1) = 64$ and $h(1.5) = 44$

b. Interpret the meaning of the function values found in part (a). $h(1) = 64$ means that after 1 sec, the height of the ball is 64 ft. $h(1.5) = 44$ means that after 1.5 sec, the height of the ball is 44 ft.

96. A ball is dropped from a 50-m building. The height (in meters) after t sec is given by $h(t) = -4.9t^2 + 50$.

a. Find $h(1)$ and $h(1.5)$. $h(1) = 45.1$ and $h(1.5) = 38.975$

b. Interpret the meaning of the function values found in part (a). $h(1) = 45.1$ means that after 1 sec, the height of the ball is 45.1 m. $h(1.5) = 38.975$ means that after 1.5 sec, the height of the ball is 38.975 m.

97. If Alicia rides a bike at an average speed of 11.5 mph, the distance that she rides can be represented by $d(t) = 11.5t$, where t is the time in hours.

a. Find $d(1)$ and $d(1.5)$. $d(1) = 11.5$ and $d(1.5) = 17.25$

b. Interpret the meaning of the function values found in part (a). $d(1) = 11.5$ means that after 1 hr, the distance traveled is 11.5 mi. $d(1.5) = 17.25$ means that after 1.5 hr, the distance traveled is 17.25 mi.

98. Brian's score on an exam is a function of the number of hours he spends studying. The function defined by $P(x) = \dfrac{100x^2}{50 + x^2}$ $(x \geq 0)$ indicates that he will achieve a score of $P\%$ if he studies for x hours.

Evaluate $P(0)$, $P(5)$, $P(10)$, $P(15)$, $P(20)$, and $P(25)$ and confirm the values on the graph. (Round to one decimal place.) Interpret $P(25)$ in the context of this problem.

$P(0) = 0\%$
$P(5) \approx 33.3\%$
$P(10) \approx 66.7\%$
$P(15) \approx 81.8\%$
$P(20) \approx 88.9\%$
$P(25) \approx 92.6\%$. If Brian studies 25 hr he will get a score of 92.6%.

Student Score (Percent) as a Function of Study Time

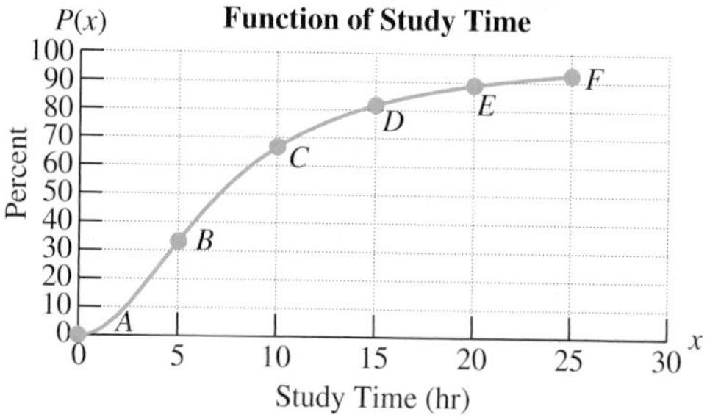

For Exercises 99–102, write a function defined by $y = f(x)$ subject to the conditions given.

99. The value of $f(x)$ is three more than two times x. $f(x) = 2x + 3$

100. The value of $f(x)$ is four less than the square of x. $f(x) = x^2 - 4$

101. The value of $f(x)$ is ten less than the absolute value of x. $f(x) = |x| - 10$

102. The value of $f(x)$ is sixteen times the square root of x. $f(x) = 16\sqrt{x}$

Expanding Your Skills

For Exercises 103–104, write the domain in interval notation.

103. $q(x) = \dfrac{2}{\sqrt{x + 2}}$ $(-2, \infty)$

104. $p(x) = \dfrac{8}{\sqrt{x - 4}}$ $(4, \infty)$

Graphing Calculator Exercises

105. Graph $k(t) = \sqrt{t - 5}$. Use the graph to support your answer to Exercise 86.

106. Graph $h(t) = \sqrt{t + 7}$. Use the graph to support your answer to Exercise 85.

Graphs of Functions

Section 8.3

Concepts

1. Linear and Constant Functions
2. Graphs of Basic Functions
3. Definition of a Quadratic Function
4. Finding the x- and y-Intercepts of a Graph Defined by $y = f(x)$

1. Linear and Constant Functions

A function may be expressed as a mathematical equation that relates two or more variables. In this section, we will look at several elementary functions.

Recall that the graph of an equation $y = k$, where k is a constant, is a horizontal line. In function notation, this can be written as $f(x) = k$. For example, the graph of the function defined by $f(x) = 3$ is a horizontal line, as shown in Figure 8-8.

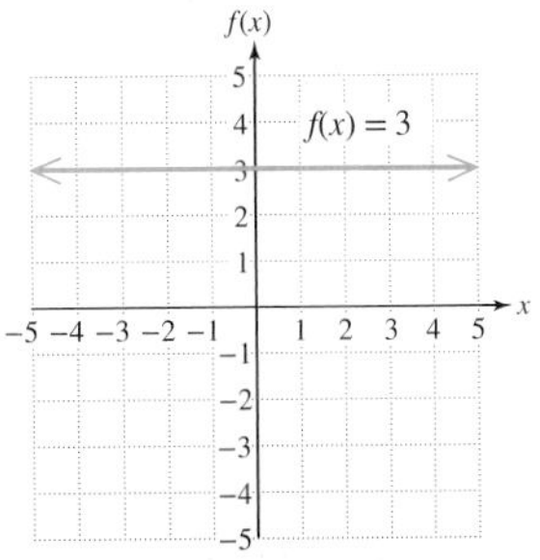

Figure 8-8

We say that a function defined by $f(x) = k$ is a constant function because for any value of x, the function value is constant.

An equation of the form $y = mx + b$ is represented graphically by a line with slope m and y-intercept $(0, b)$. In function notation, this may be written as $f(x) = mx + b$. A function in this form is called a linear function. For example, the function defined by $f(x) = 2x - 3$ is a linear function with slope $m = 2$ and y-intercept $(0, -3)$ (Figure 8-9).

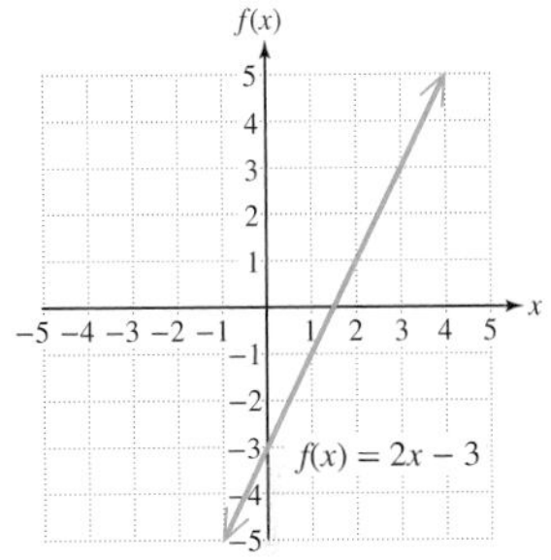

Figure 8-9

Linear Functions and Constant Functions

Let m and b represent real numbers such that $m \neq 0$. Then

A function that can be written in the form $f(x) = mx + b$ is a **linear function**.
A function that can be written in the form $f(x) = b$ is a **constant function**.

Note: The graphs of linear and constant functions are lines.

2. Graphs of Basic Functions

At this point, we are able to recognize the equations and graphs of linear and constant functions. In addition to linear and constant functions, the following equations define six basic functions that will be encountered in the study of algebra:

Equation		Function Notation	Type of Function
$y = x$		$f(x) = x$	Identity function
$y = x^2$		$f(x) = x^2$	Quadratic function
$y = x^3$	equivalent function notation →	$f(x) = x^3$	Cubic function
$y = \lvert x \rvert$		$f(x) = \lvert x \rvert$	Absolute value function
$y = \sqrt{x}$		$f(x) = \sqrt{x}$	Square root function
$y = \dfrac{1}{x}$		$f(x) = \dfrac{1}{x}$	Reciprocal function

The graph of the function defined by $f(x) = x$ is linear, with slope $m = 1$ and y-intercept (0, 0) (Figure 8-10).

To determine the shapes of the other basic functions, we can plot several points to establish the pattern of the graph. Analyzing the equation itself may also provide insight to the domain, range, and shape of the graph. To demonstrate this, we will graph $f(x) = x^2$ and $g(x) = \frac{1}{x}$.

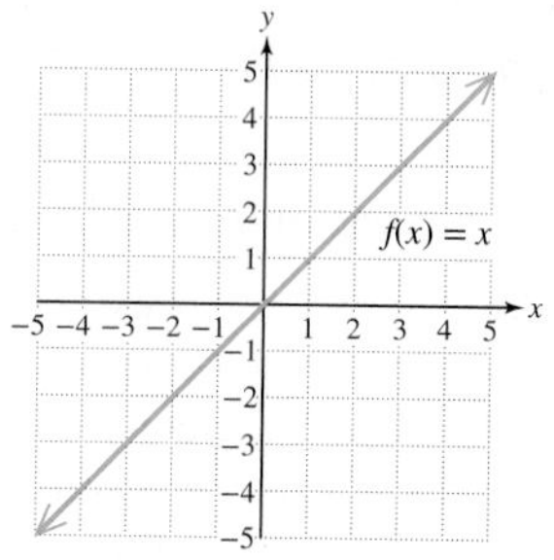

Figure 8-10

Classroom Example: p. 593, Exercise 12

Example 1 Graphing Basic Functions

Graph the function defined by $f(x) = x^2$.

Solution:

The domain of the function given by $f(x) = x^2$ (or equivalently $y = x^2$) is all real numbers.

To graph the function, choose arbitrary values of x within the domain of the function. Be sure to choose values of x that are positive and values that are negative to determine the behavior of the function to the right and left of the origin (Table 8-4). The graph of $f(x) = x^2$ is shown in Figure 8-11.

The function values are equated to the square of x, so $f(x)$ will always be greater than or equal to zero. Hence, the y-coordinates on the graph will never be negative. The range of the function is $[0, \infty)$. The arrows on each branch of the graph imply that the pattern continues indefinitely.

Table 8-4

x	$f(x) = x^2$
0	0
1	1
2	4
3	9
−1	1
−2	4
−3	9

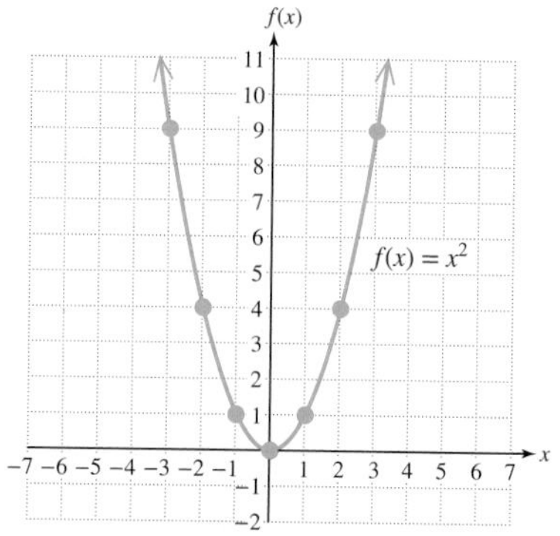

Figure 8-11

Skill Practice

1. Graph $f(x) = -x^2$ by first making a table of points.

Answer

1.

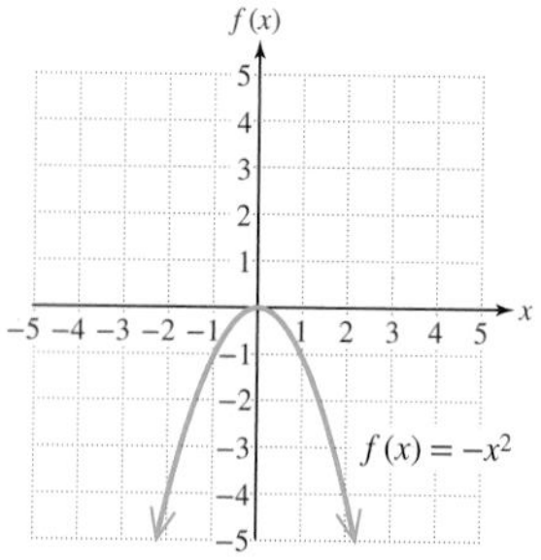

Example 2 Graphing Basic Functions

Classroom Example: p. 593, Exercise 16

Graph the function defined by $g(x) = \frac{1}{x}$.

Solution:

$g(x) = \frac{1}{x}$ Notice that $x = 0$ is not in the domain of the function. From the equation $y = \frac{1}{x}$, the y values will be the reciprocal of the x-values. The graph defined by $g(x) = \frac{1}{x}$ is shown in Figure 8-12.

x	$g(x) = \frac{1}{x}$
1	1
2	$\frac{1}{2}$
3	$\frac{1}{3}$
−1	−1
−2	$-\frac{1}{2}$
−3	$-\frac{1}{3}$

x	$g(x) = \frac{1}{x}$
$\frac{1}{2}$	2
$\frac{1}{3}$	3
$\frac{1}{4}$	4
$-\frac{1}{2}$	−2
$-\frac{1}{3}$	−3
$-\frac{1}{4}$	−4

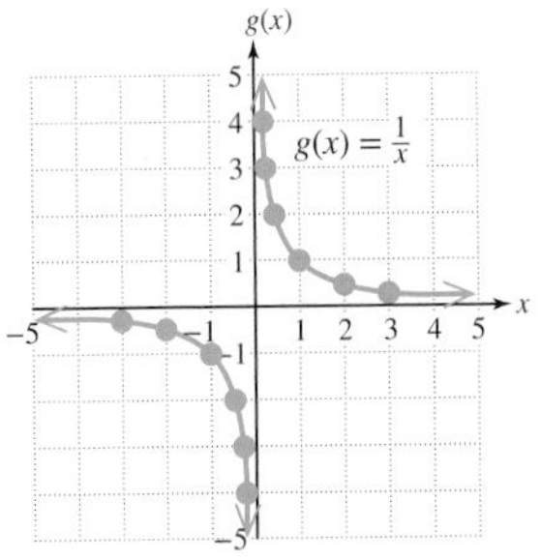

Figure 8-12

Notice that as x approaches ∞ and $-\infty$, the y values approach zero, and the graph approaches the x-axis. In this case, the x-axis is called a *horizontal asymptote*. Similarly, the graph of the function approaches the y-axis as x gets close to zero. In this case, the y-axis is called a *vertical asymptote*.

Skill Practice

2. Graph $h(x) = |x| - 1$ by first making a table of points.

Calculator Connections

Topic: Graphing Nonlinear Functions

To enter a function, let $f(x) = y$. That is, to graph $f(x) = x^2$, enter $Y_1 = x^2$.

To graph $g(x) = \frac{1}{x}$, enter $Y_1 = 1/x$.

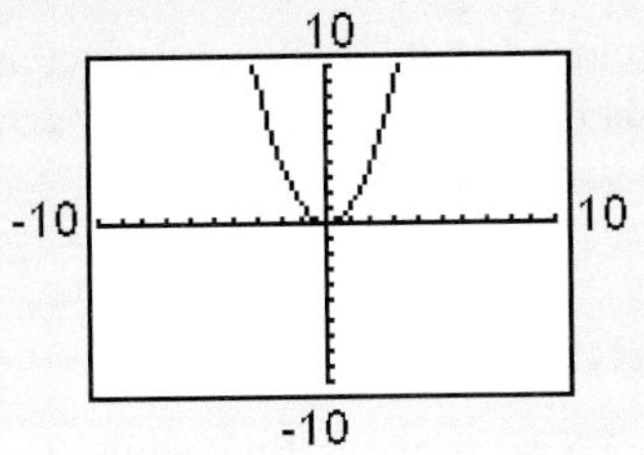

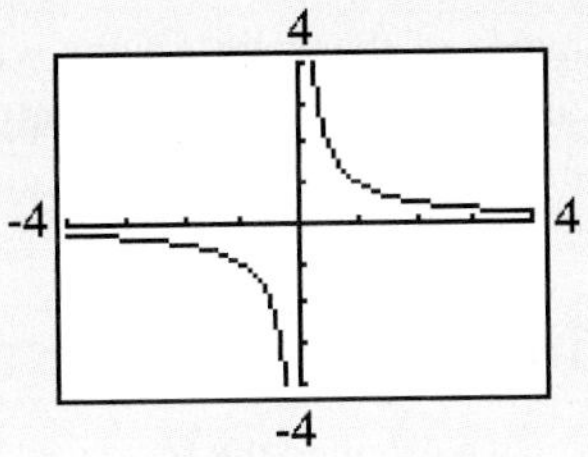

Answer

2.

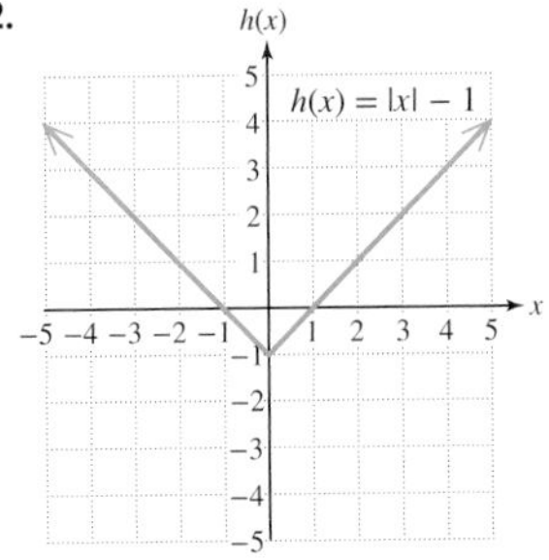

Summary of Six Basic Functions and Their Graphs

Function	Graph	Domain and Range
1. $f(x) = x$ Identity function	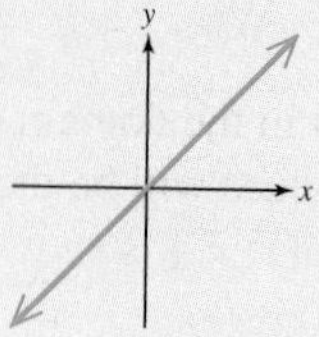	Domain $(-\infty, \infty)$ Range $(-\infty, \infty)$
2. $f(x) = x^2$ Quadratic function	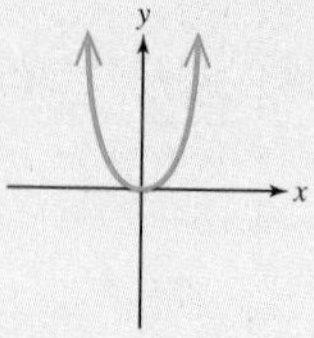	Domain $(-\infty, \infty)$ Range $[0, \infty)$
3. $f(x) = x^3$ Cubic function	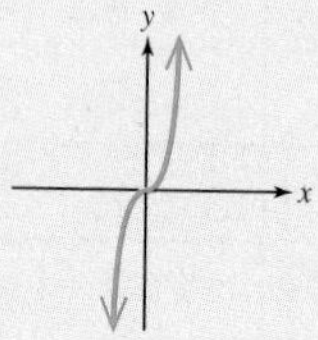	Domain $(-\infty, \infty)$ Range $(-\infty, \infty)$
4. $f(x) = \lvert x \rvert$ Absolute value function	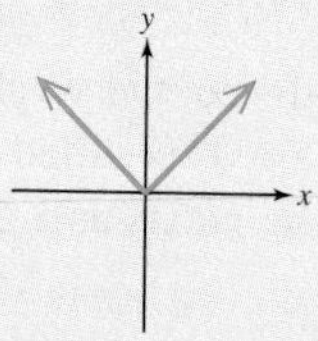	Domain $(-\infty, \infty)$ Range $[0, \infty)$
5. $f(x) = \sqrt{x}$ Square root function	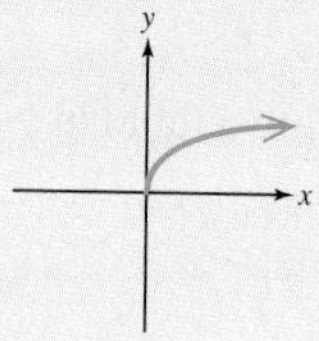	Domain $[0, \infty)$ Range $[0, \infty)$
6. $f(x) = \dfrac{1}{x}$ Reciprocal function	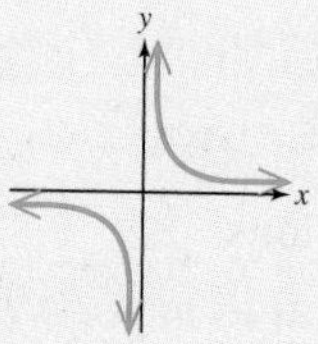	Domain $(-\infty, 0) \cup (0, \infty)$ Range $(-\infty, 0) \cup (0, \infty)$

TIP: Recall that the symbol $\cup$ means the combination (or union) of the two intervals.

The shapes of these six graphs will be developed in the homework exercises. These functions are used often in the study of algebra. Therefore, we recommend that you associate an equation with its graph and commit each to memory.

3. Definition of a Quadratic Function

In Example 1 we graphed the function defined by $f(x) = x^2$ by plotting points. This function belongs to a special category called quadratic functions.

Definition of a Quadratic Function

A **quadratic function** is a function defined by

$f(x) = ax^2 + bx + c$ where a, b, and c are real numbers and $a \neq 0$.

The graph of a quadratic function is in the shape of a **parabola**. The leading coefficient, a, determines the direction of the parabola.

- If $a > 0$, then the parabola opens upward, and the vertex is the minimum point on the parabola. For example, the graph of $f(x) = x^2$ is shown in Figure 8-13.
- If $a < 0$, then the parabola opens downward, and the vertex is the maximum point on the parabola. For example, the graph of $f(x) = -x^2$ is shown in Figure 8-14.

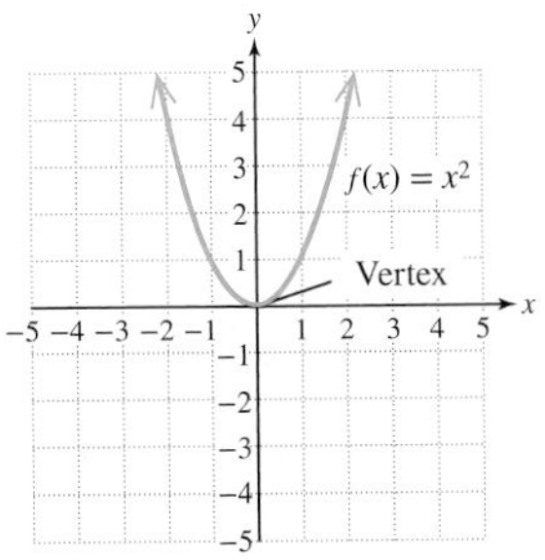

Figure 8-13

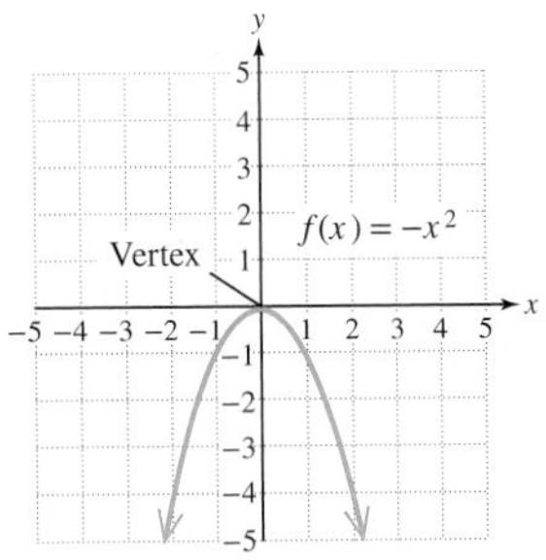

Figure 8-14

Example 3 Identifying Functions

Classroom Examples: p. 594, Exercises 18, 20, 22, and 28

Identify each function as linear, constant, quadratic, or none of these.

a. $f(x) = -4$ **b.** $f(x) = x^2 + 3x + 2$ **c.** $f(x) = 7 - 2x$

d. $f(x) = \dfrac{4x + 8}{8}$ **e.** $f(x) = \dfrac{6}{x} + 2$

Solution:

a. $f(x) = -4$ is a constant function. It is in the form $f(x) = b$, where $b = -4$.

b. $f(x) = x^2 + 3x + 2$ is a quadratic function. It is in the form $f(x) = ax^2 + bx + c$, where $a \neq 0$.

c. $f(x) = 7 - 2x$ is linear. Writing it in the form $f(x) = mx + b$, we get $f(x) = -2x + 7$, where $m = -2$ and $b = 7$.

d. $f(x) = \dfrac{4x + 8}{8}$ is linear. Writing it in the form $f(x) = mx + b$, we get

$$f(x) = \frac{4x}{8} + \frac{8}{8}$$

$$= \frac{1}{2}x + 1, \text{ where } m = \frac{1}{2} \text{ and } b = 1.$$

e. $f(x) = \dfrac{6}{x} + 2$ fits none of these categories because the variable is in the denominator.

Skill Practice Identify each function as constant, linear, quadratic, or none of these.

3. $m(x) = -2x^2 - 3x + 7$ **4.** $n(x) = -6$

5. $W(x) = \dfrac{4}{3}x - \dfrac{1}{2}$ **6.** $R(x) = \dfrac{4}{3x} - \dfrac{1}{2}$

Answers

3. Quadratic
4. Constant
5. Linear
6. None of these

4. Finding the x- and y-Intercepts of a Graph Defined by $y = f(x)$

We have already learned that to find an x-intercept, we substitute $y = 0$ and solve the equation for x. Using function notation, this is equivalent to finding the real solutions of the equation $f(x) = 0$. To find the y-intercept, substitute $x = 0$ and solve the equation for y. In function notation, this is equivalent to finding $f(0)$.

Finding Intercepts Using Function Notation

Given a function defined by $y = f(x)$,

Step 1 The x-intercepts are the real solutions to the equation $f(x) = 0$.

Step 2 The y-intercept is given by $f(0)$.

Classroom Example: p. 594, Exercise 32

Example 4 Finding x- and y-Intercepts

Given the function defined by $f(x) = 2x - 4$:

a. Find the x-intercept(s).

b. Find the y-intercept.

c. Graph the function.

Solution:

a. To find the x-intercept(s), find the real solutions to the equation $f(x) = 0$.

$f(x) = 2x - 4$

$0 = 2x - 4$ Substitute $f(x) = 0$.

$4 = 2x$

$2 = x$ The x-intercept is $(2, 0)$.

b. To find the y-intercept, evaluate $f(0)$.

$f(0) = 2(0) - 4$ Substitute $x = 0$.

$f(0) = -4$ The y-intercept is $(0, -4)$.

c. This function is linear, with a y-intercept of $(0, -4)$, an x-intercept of $(2, 0)$, and a slope of 2 (Figure 8-15).

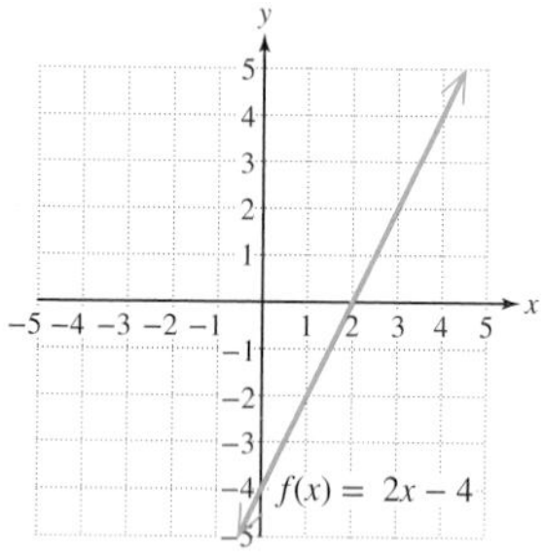

Figure 8-15

Skill Practice Consider $f(x) = -5x + 1$.

7. Find the x-intercept.

8. Find the y-intercept.

9. Graph the function.

Answers

7. $(\frac{1}{5}, 0)$ **8.** $(0, 1)$

9.

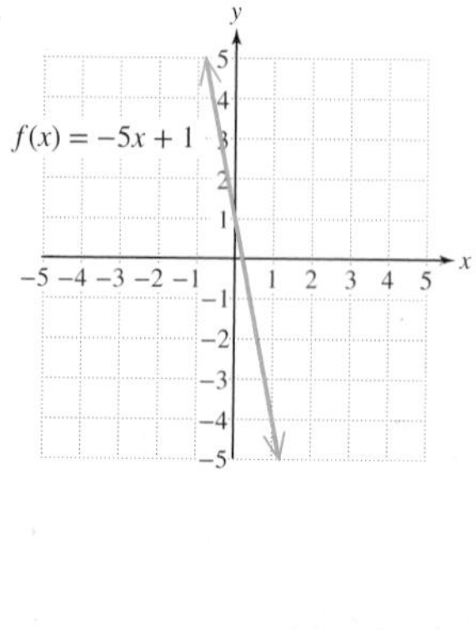

Calculator Connections

Topic: Finding *x*- and *y*-Intercepts

Refer to Example 4 with $f(x) = 2x - 4$. To find the *y*-intercept, let $x = 0$. We can do this using the *Value* key.

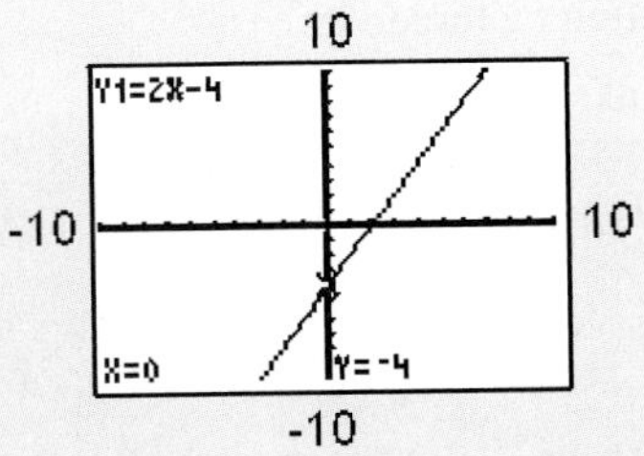

To find the *x*-intercept, use the *Zero* feature. To use this feature you must give bounds for the *x*-intercept. To find a left bound, place the curser to the left of the *x*-intercept and press Enter. For the right bound, place the curser to the right of the *x*-intercept and press Enter.

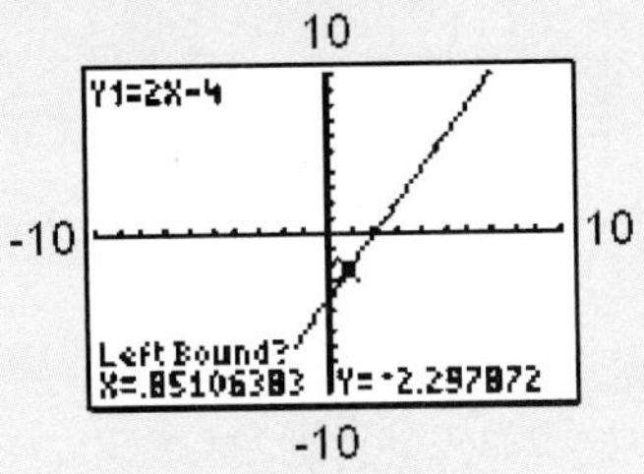

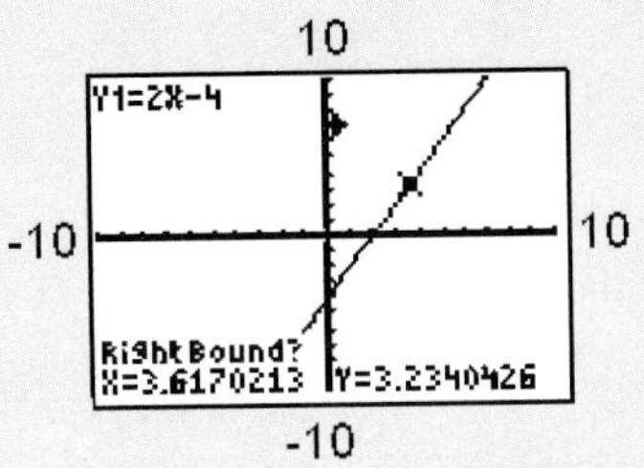

Then make a guess by placing the curser near the *x*-intercept. Press Enter and the *x*-intercept will be displayed.

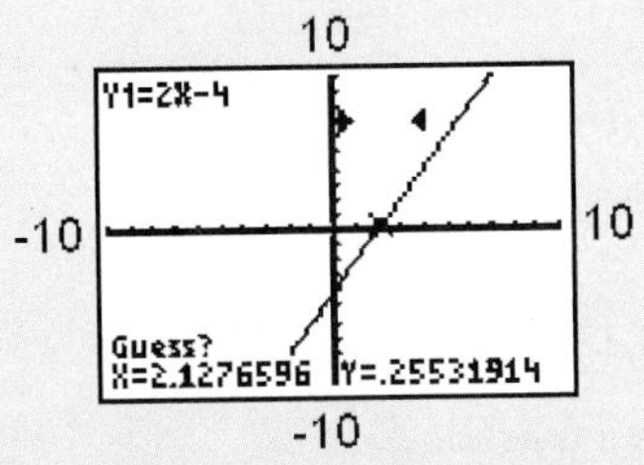

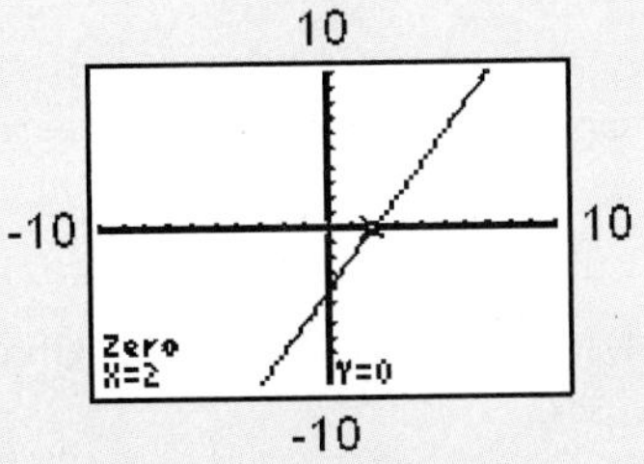

Example 5 Finding *x*- and *y*-Intercepts

Classroom Example: p. 595, Exercise 42

For the function pictured in Figure 8-16, estimate

a. The real values of *x* for which $f(x) = 0$.

b. The value of $f(0)$.

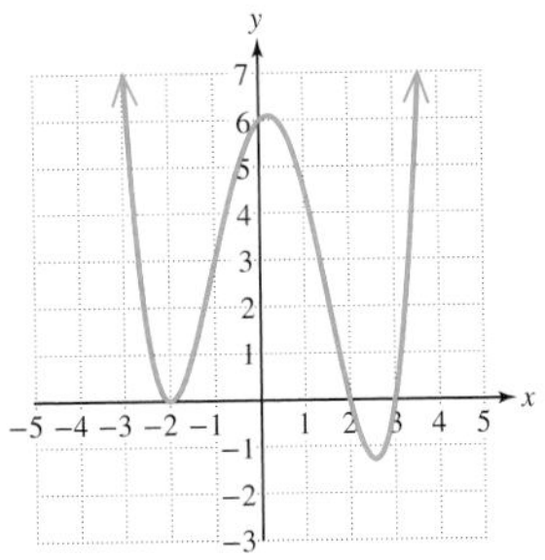

Figure 8-16

Solution:

a. The real values of x for which $f(x) = 0$ are the x-intercepts of the function. For this graph, the x-intercepts are located at $x = -2$, $x = 2$, and $x = 3$.

b. The value of $f(0)$ is the value of y at $x = 0$. That is, $f(0)$ is the y-intercept, $f(0) = 6$.

Skill Practice Use the function pictured.

10. a. Estimate the real value(s) of x for which $f(x) = 0$.

b. Estimate the value of $f(0)$.

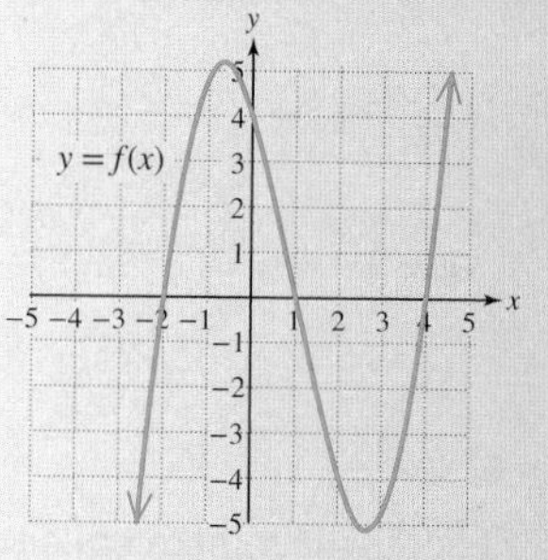

Answer

10. a. $x = -2$, $x = 1$, and $x = 4$
b. $f(0) = 4$

Section 8.3 Practice Exercises

For additional exercises, see Classroom Activities 8.3A–8.3D in the *Student's Resource Manual* at www.mhhe.com/moh.

Vocabulary and Key Concepts

1. a. A function that can be written in the form $f(x) = mx + b$, $m \neq 0$, is a ___linear___ function.

b. A function that can be written in the form $f(x) = b$ is a ___constant___ function.

c. A function that can be written in the form $f(x) = ax^2 + bx + c$, $a \neq 0$, is a ___quadratic___ function.

d. The graph of a quadratic function is in the shape of a ___parabola___.

e. To find the x-intercept(s) of a graph defined by $y = f(x)$, find the real solutions to the equation $f(x) =$ ___0___.

f. To find the ___y___-intercept of a graph defined by $y = f(x)$, evaluate $f(0)$.

Review Exercises

2. Given: $g = \{(6, 1), (5, 2), (4, 3), (3, 4)\}$

a. Is this relation a function? Yes

b. Write the domain. $\{6, 5, 4, 3\}$

c. Write the range. $\{1, 2, 3, 4\}$

3. Given: $f = \{(7, 3), (2, 3), (-5, 3)\}$

a. Is this relation a function? Yes

b. Write the domain. $\{7, 2, -5\}$

c. Write the range. $\{3\}$

4. Given: $f(x) = \sqrt{x + 4}$

a. Evaluate $f(0)$, $f(-3)$, $f(-4)$, and $f(-5)$, if possible. $f(0) = 2$, $f(-3) = 1$, $f(-4) = 0$, and $f(-5)$ cannot be evaluated because $x = -5$ is not in the domain of f.

b. Write the domain of f in interval notation. $[-4, \infty)$

5. The force (measured in pounds) to stretch a certain spring x inches is given by $f(x) = 3x$. Evaluate $f(3)$ and $f(10)$, and interpret the results in the context of this problem. $f(3) = 9$ means that 9 lb of force is required to stretch the spring 3 in. $f(10) = 30$ means that 30 lb of force is required to stretch the spring 10 in.

6. The velocity (in feet per second) of a falling object is given by $V(t) = -32t$, where t is the time in seconds after the object was released. Evaluate $V(2)$ and interpret the results in the context of this problem.
$V(2) = -64$ means that 2 sec after release, the object is falling at 64 ft/sec.

Concept 1: Linear and Constant Functions

7. Fill in the blank with the word *vertical* or *horizontal*. The graph of a constant function is a _____ line.
horizontal

8. For the linear function defined by $f(x) = mx + b$, identify the slope and y-intercept.
m is the slope, and $(0, b)$ is the y-intercept.

9. Graph the constant function $f(x) = 2$. Then use the graph to identify the domain and range of f. Domain $(-\infty, \infty)$; range $\{2\}$

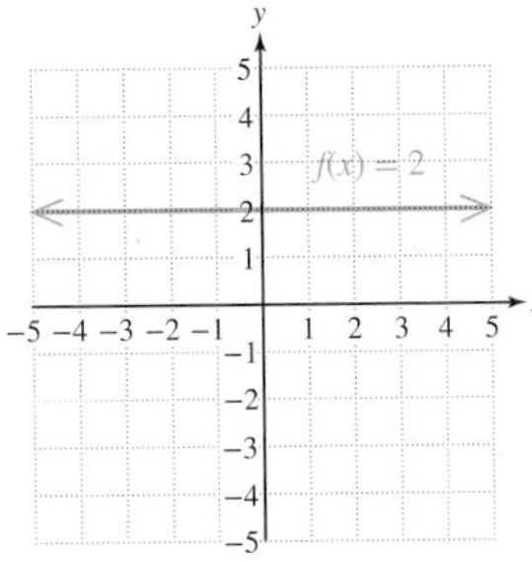

10. Graph the linear function $g(x) = -2x + 1$. Then use the graph to identify the domain and range of g. Domain $(-\infty, \infty)$; range $(-\infty, \infty)$

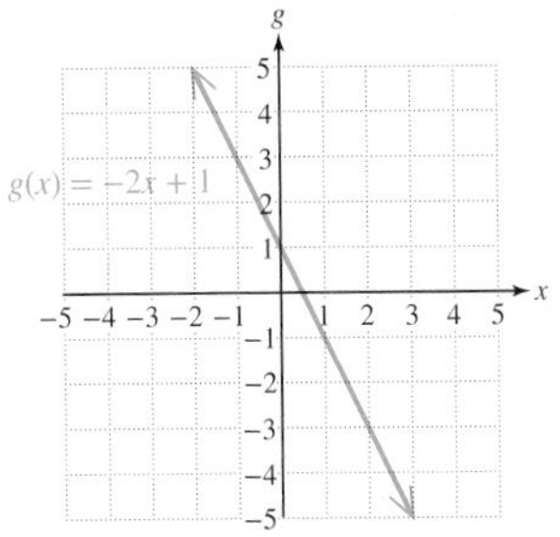

Concept 2: Graphs of Basic Functions

For Exercises 11–16, sketch a graph by completing the table and plotting the points. **(See Examples 1–2.)**

11. $f(x) = \dfrac{1}{x}$

x	$f(x)$
-2	$-\frac{1}{2}$
-1	-1
$-\frac{1}{2}$	-2
$-\frac{1}{4}$	-4

x	$f(x)$
$\frac{1}{4}$	4
$\frac{1}{2}$	2
1	1
2	$\frac{1}{2}$

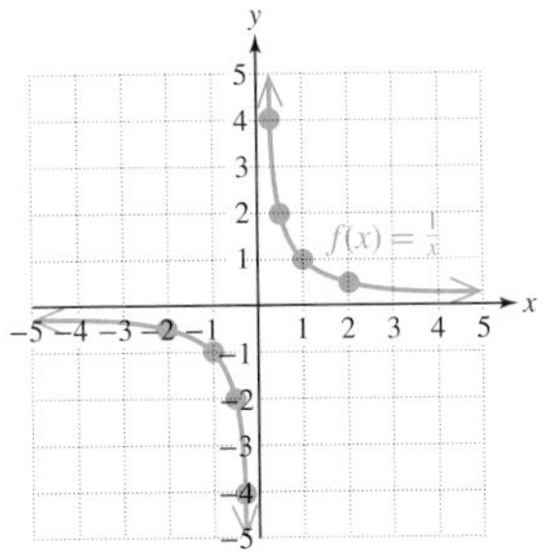

12. $g(x) = |x|$

x	$g(x)$
-2	2
-1	1
0	0
1	1
2	2

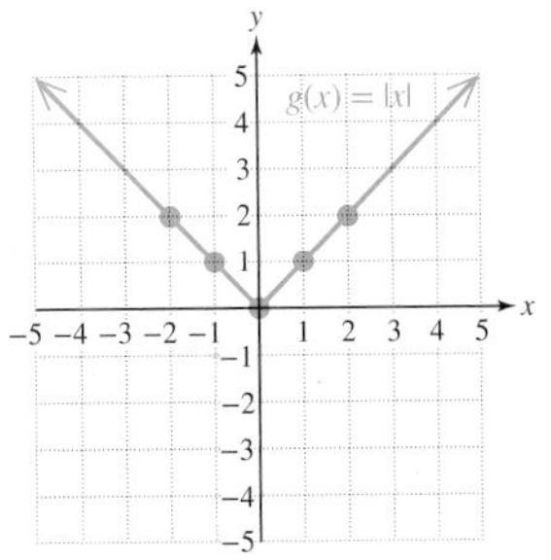

13. $h(x) = x^3$

x	$h(x)$
-2	-8
-1	-1
0	0
1	1
2	8

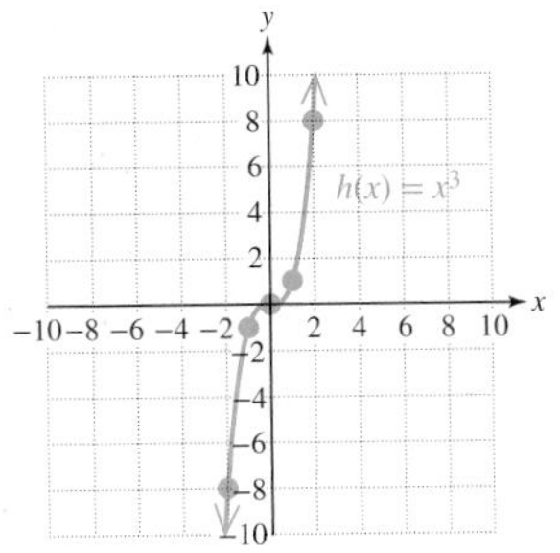

14. $k(x) = x$

x	$k(x)$
-2	-2
-1	-1
0	0
1	1
2	2

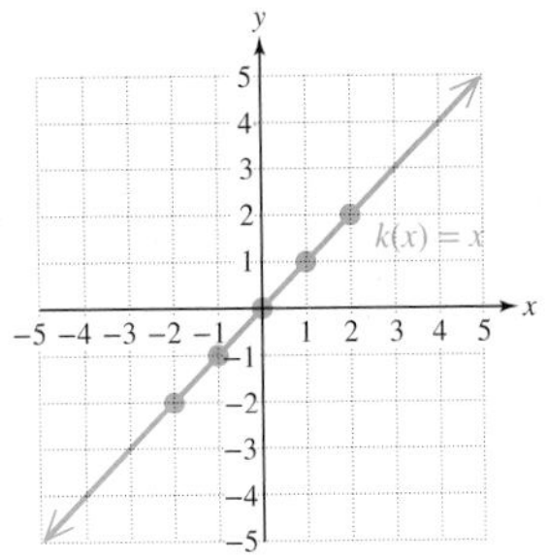

15. $q(x) = x^2$

x	$q(x)$
-2	4
-1	1
0	0
1	1
2	4

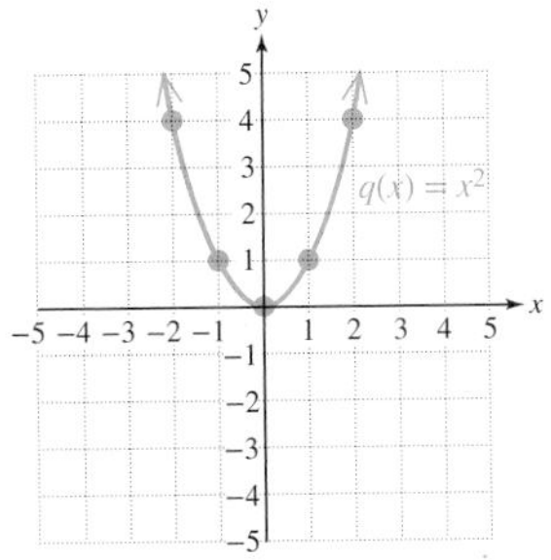

16. $p(x) = \sqrt{x}$

x	$p(x)$
0	0
1	1
4	2
9	3
16	4

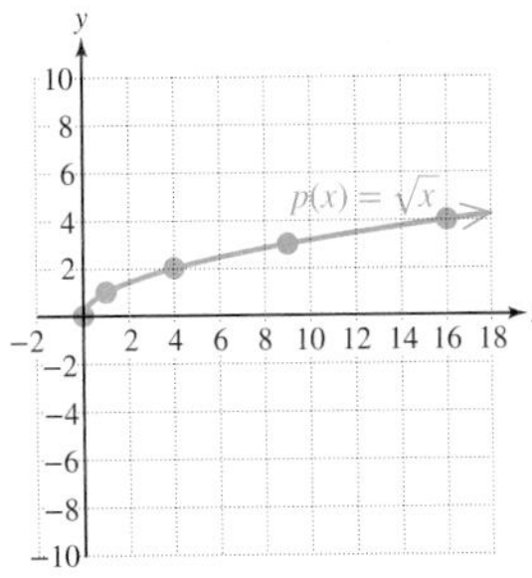

Concept 3: Definition of a Quadratic Function

For Exercises 17–28, determine if the function is constant, linear, quadratic, or none of these. **(See Example 3.)**

17. $f(x) = 2x^2 + 3x + 1$
Quadratic

18. $g(x) = -x^2 + 4x + 12$
Quadratic

19. $k(x) = -3x - 7$
Linear

20. $h(x) = -x - 3$
Linear

21. $m(x) = \dfrac{4}{3}$
Constant

22. $n(x) = 0.8$
Constant

23. $p(x) = \dfrac{2}{3x} + \dfrac{1}{4}$
None of these

24. $Q(x) = \dfrac{1}{5x} - 3$
None of these

25. $t(x) = \dfrac{2}{3}x + \dfrac{1}{4}$
Linear

26. $r(x) = \dfrac{1}{5}x - 3$
Linear

27. $w(x) = \sqrt{4 - x}$
None of these

28. $T(x) = -|x + 10|$
None of these

Concept 4: Finding the *x*- and *y*-Intercepts of a Graph Defined by *y* = *f*(*x*)

For Exercises 29–36, find the *x*- and *y*-intercepts, and graph the function. **(See Example 4.)**

29. $f(x) = 5x - 10$

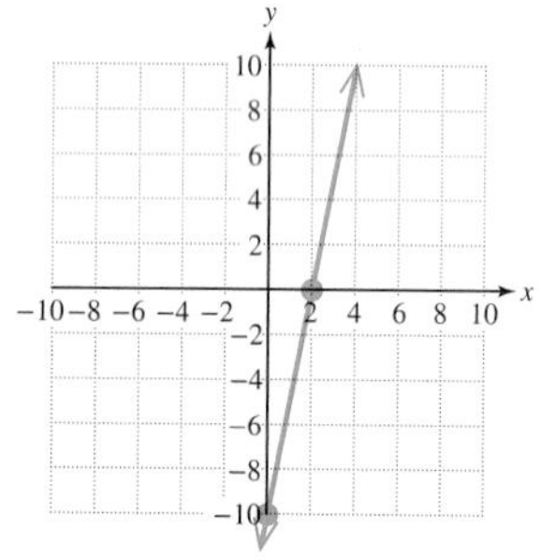

x-intercept: (2, 0); *y*-intercept: (0, −10)

30. $f(x) = -3x + 12$

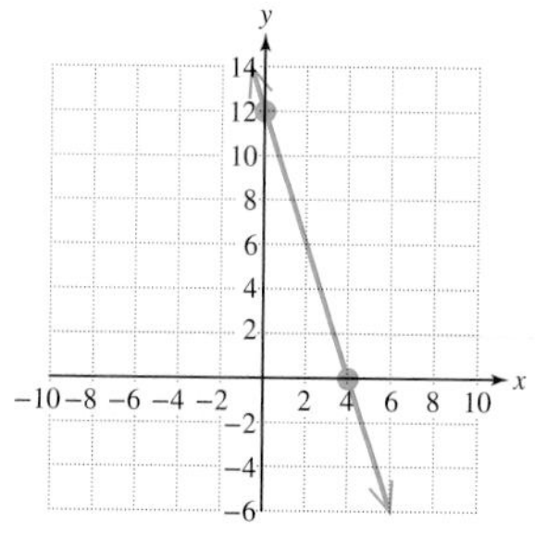

x-intercept: (4, 0); *y*-intercept: (0, 12)

31. $g(x) = -6x + 5$

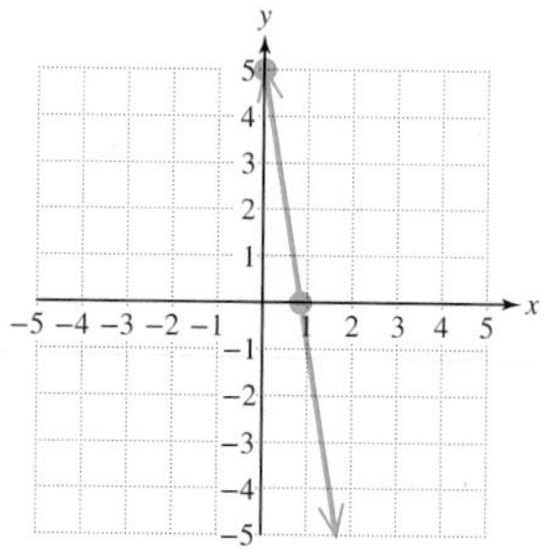

x-intercept: $\left(\frac{5}{6}, 0\right)$; *y*-intercept: (0, 5)

32. $h(x) = 2x + 9$

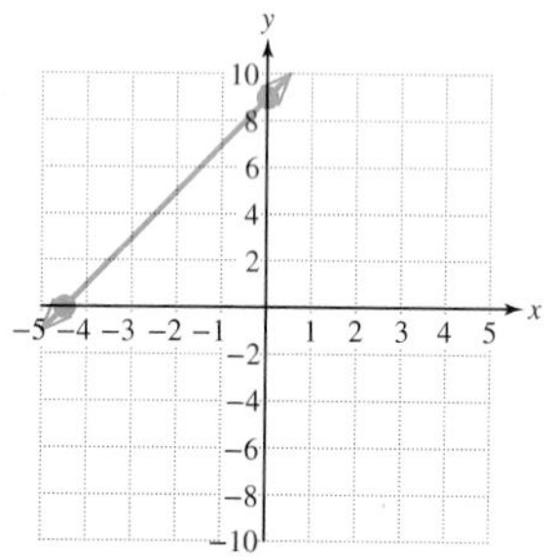

x-intercept: $\left(-\frac{9}{2}, 0\right)$; *y*-intercept: (0, 9)

33. $f(x) = 18$

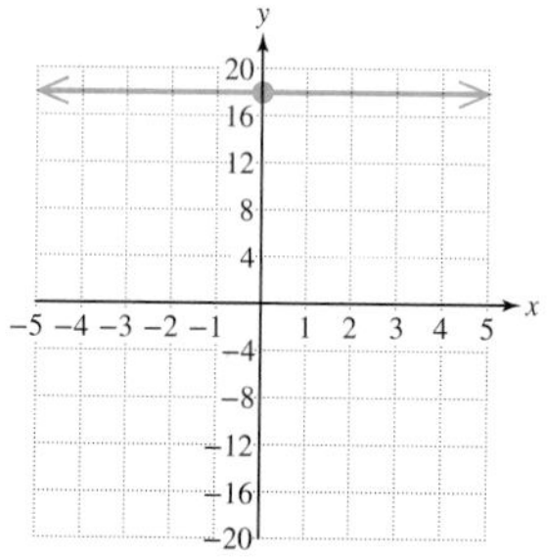

x-intercept: none; *y*-intercept: (0, 18)

34. $g(x) = -7$

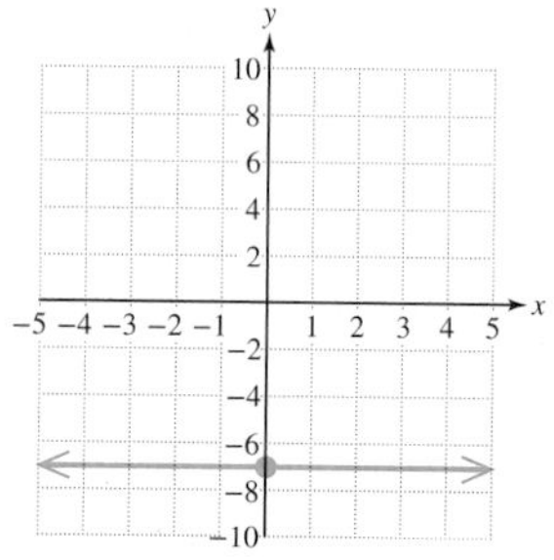

x-intercept: none; *y*-intercept: (0, −7)

35. $g(x) = \dfrac{2}{3}x + 2$

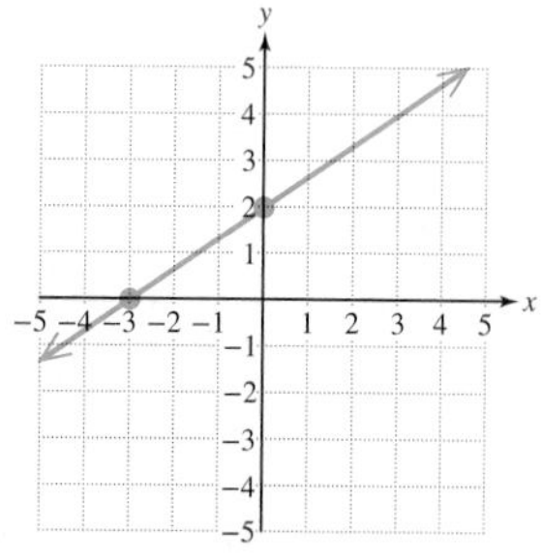

x-intercept: (−3, 0); *y*-intercept: (0, 2)

36. $h(x) = -\dfrac{3}{5}x - 3$

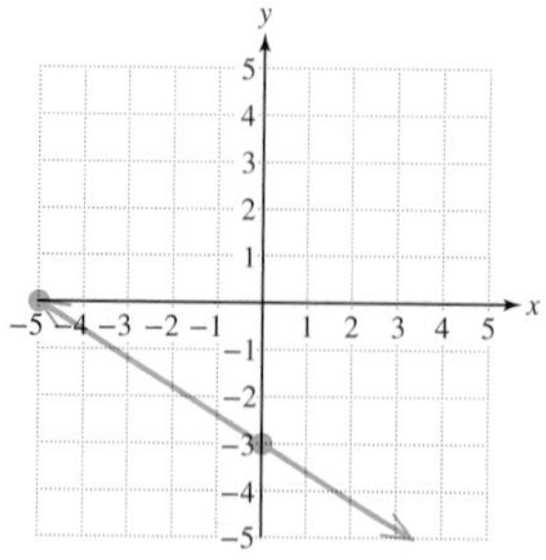

x-intercept: (−5, 0); *y*-intercept: (0, −3)

For Exercises 37–42, use the graph to estimate

a. The real values of x for which $f(x) = 0$. **b.** The value of $f(0)$. **(See Example 5.)**

37.

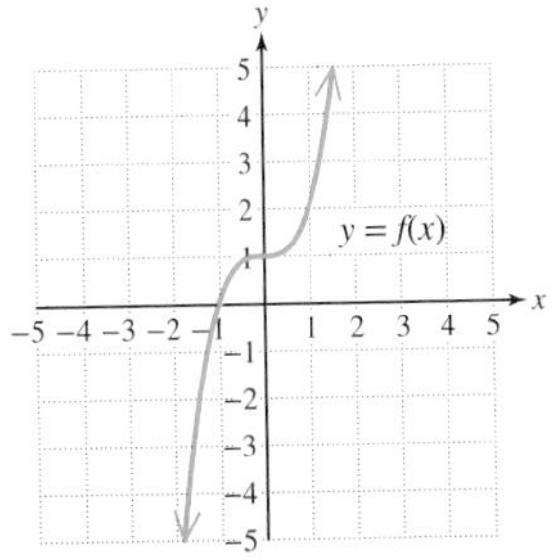

a. $x = -1$
b. $f(0) = 1$

38.

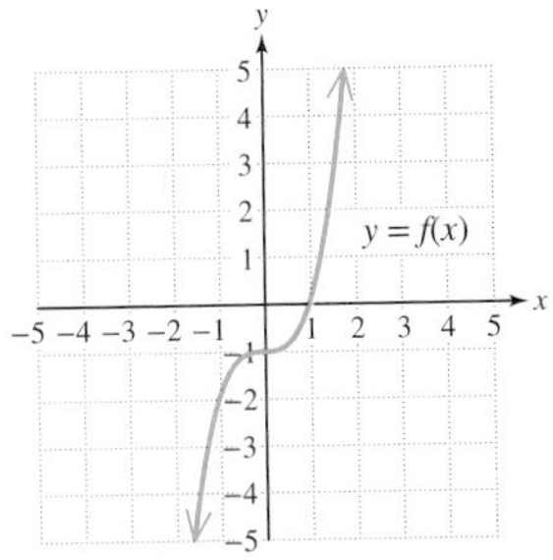

a. $x = 1$
b. $f(0) = -1$

39.

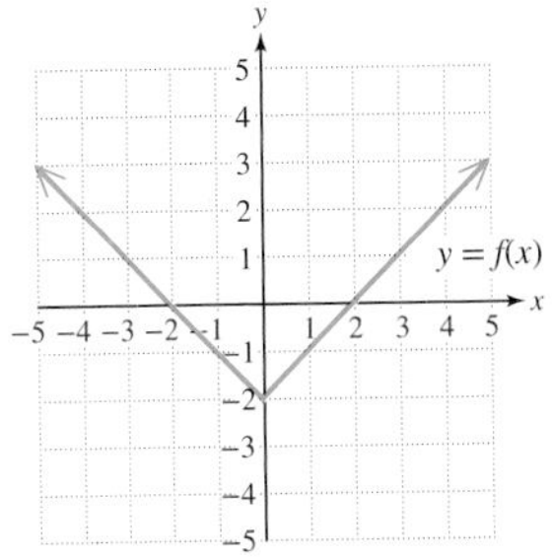

a. $x = -2$ and $x = 2$ b. $f(0) = -2$

40.

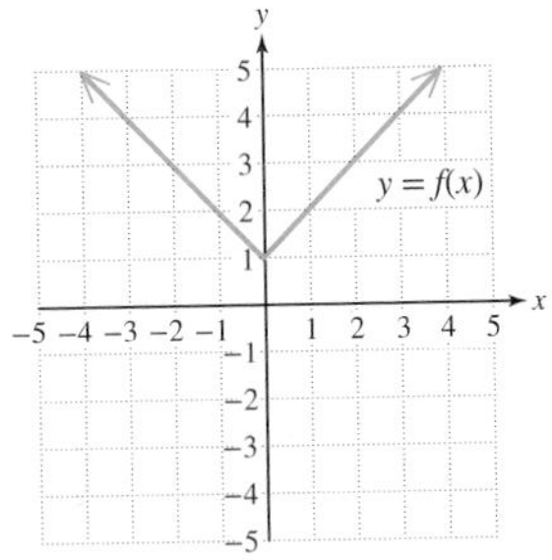

a. None
b. $f(0) = 1$

41.

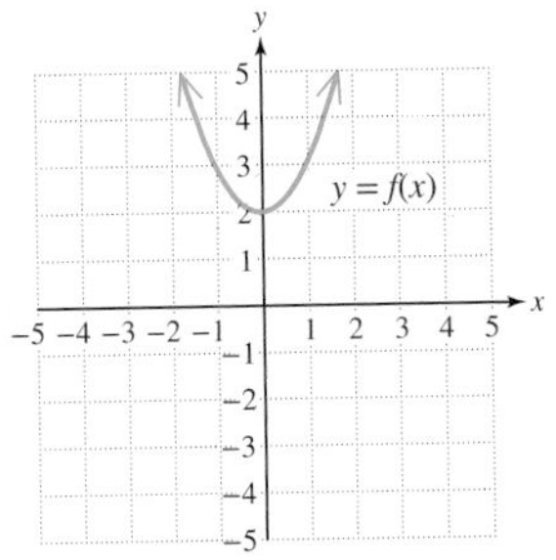

a. None
b. $f(0) = 2$

42.

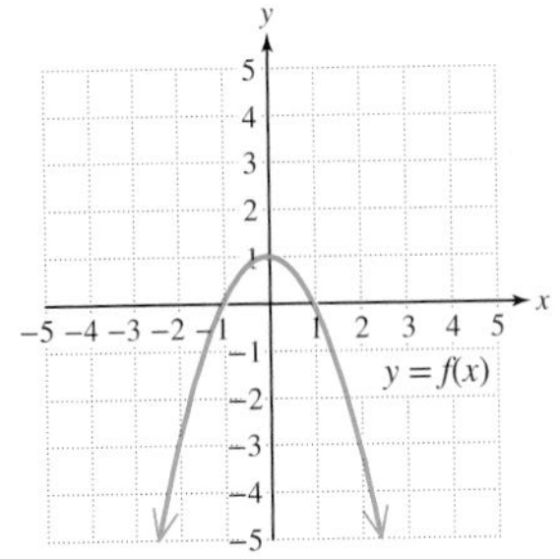

a. $x = 1$ and $x = -1$
b. $f(0) = 1$

Mixed Exercises

For Exercises 43–52,

a. Identify the domain of the function.

b. Identify the y-intercept.

c. Match the function with its graph by recognizing the basic shape of the graph and using the results from parts (a) and (b). Plot additional points if necessary.

43. $q(x) = 2x^2$
a. $(-\infty, \infty)$ b. $(0, 0)$ c. vi

44. $p(x) = -2x^2 + 1$
a. $(-\infty, \infty)$ b. $(0, 1)$ c. iii

45. $h(x) = x^3 + 1$
a. $(-\infty, \infty)$ b. $(0, 1)$ c. viii

46. $k(x) = x^3 - 2$
a. $(-\infty, \infty)$ b. $(0, -2)$ c. v

47. $r(x) = \sqrt{x + 1}$
a. $[-1, \infty)$ b. $(0, 1)$ c. vii

48. $s(x) = \sqrt{x + 4}$
a. $[-4, \infty)$ b. $(0, 2)$ c. i

49. $f(x) = \dfrac{1}{x - 3}$
a. $(-\infty, 3) \cup (3, \infty)$ b. $\left(0, -\dfrac{1}{3}\right)$ c. ii

50. $g(x) = \dfrac{1}{x + 1}$
a. $(-\infty, -1) \cup (-1, \infty)$ b. $(0, 1)$ c. x

51. $k(x) = |x + 2|$
a. $(-\infty, \infty)$ b. $(0, 2)$ c. iv

52. $h(x) = |x - 1| + 2$
a. $(-\infty, \infty)$ b. $(0, 3)$ c. ix

i.

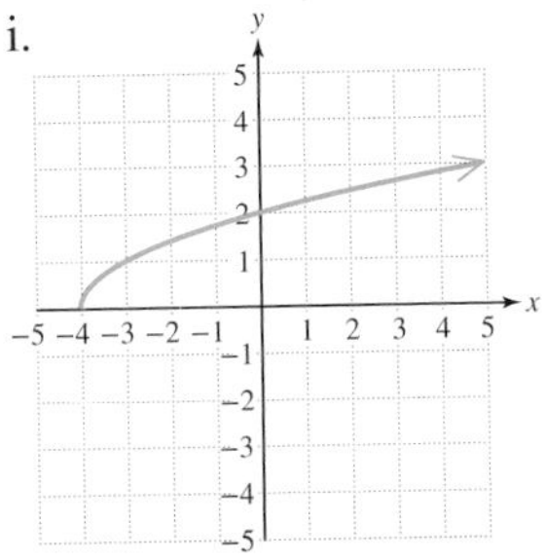

ii.

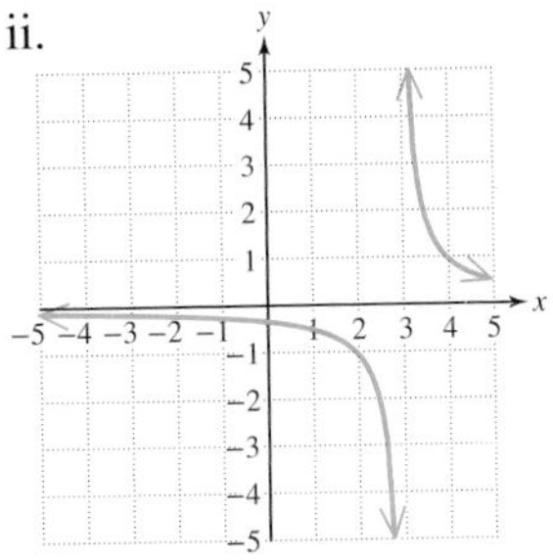

iii.

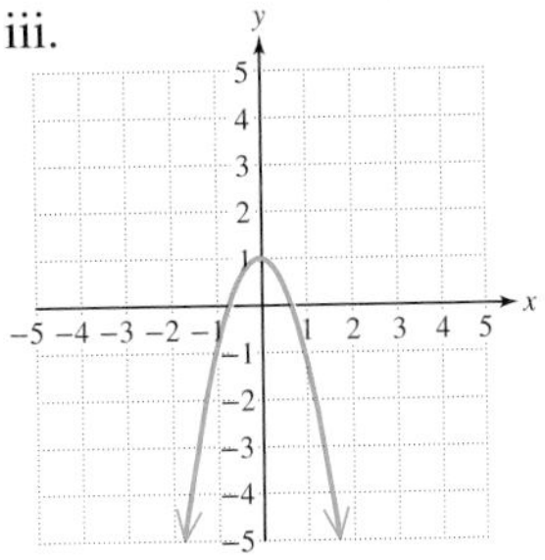

iv.

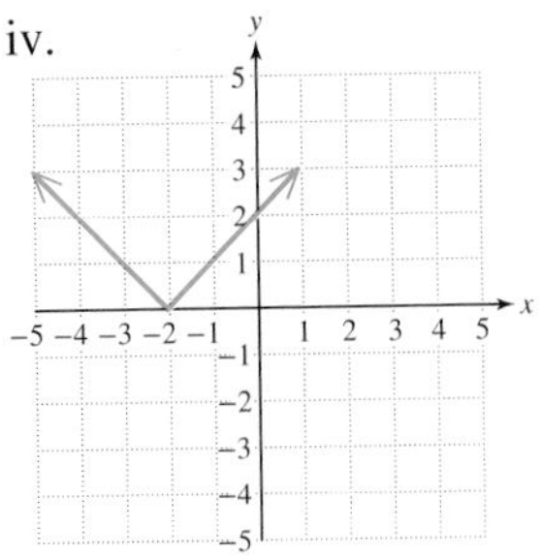

v.
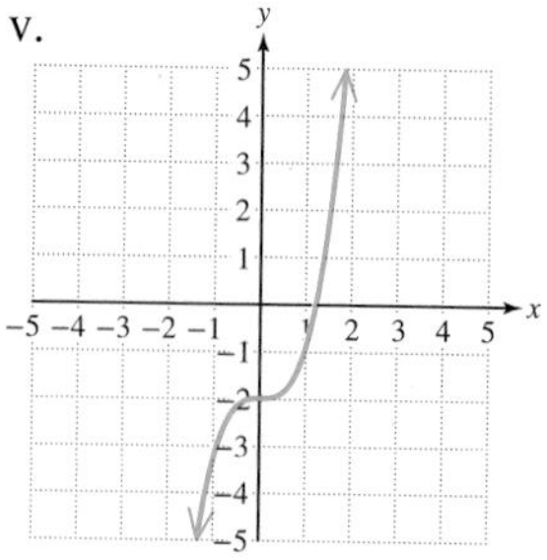

vi.
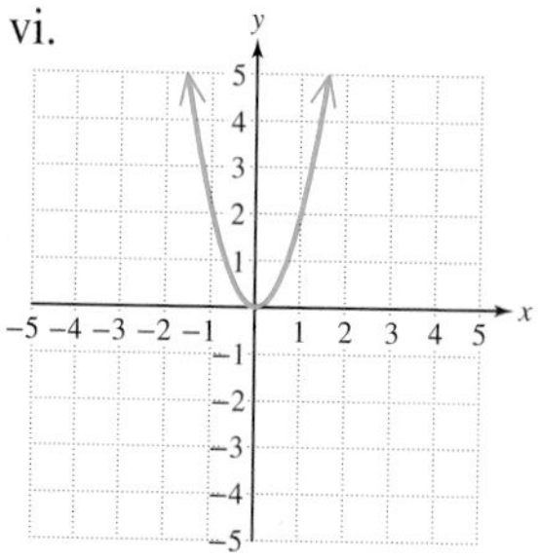

vii.
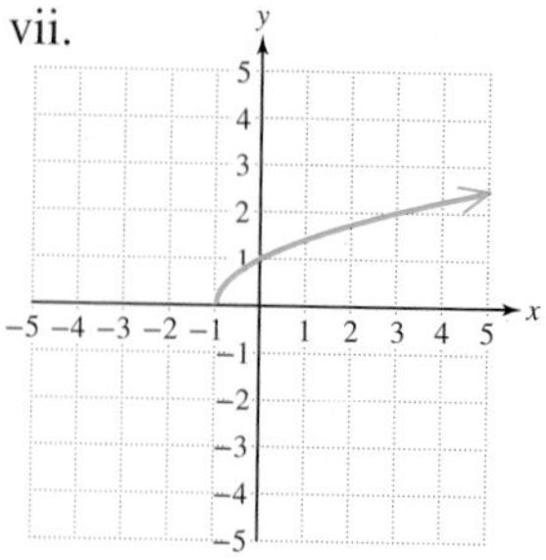

viii.
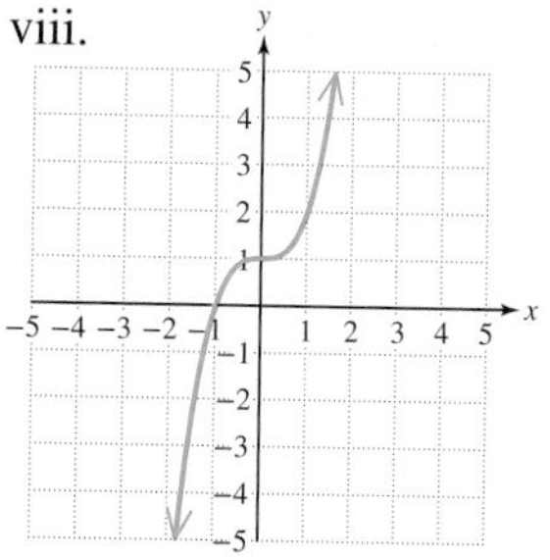

ix.
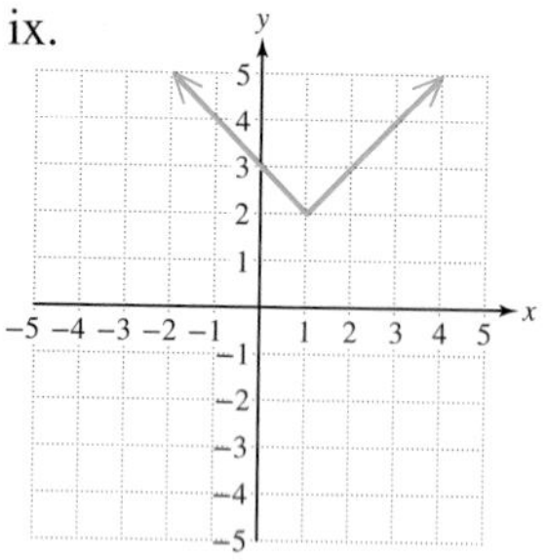

x.
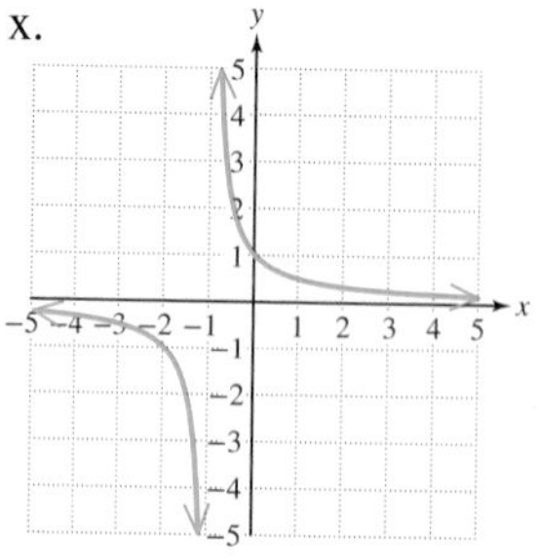

53. Suppose that a student has an 80% average on all of her chapter tests in her Intermediate Algebra class. This counts as $\frac{3}{4}$ of the student's overall grade. The final exam grade counts as the remaining $\frac{1}{4}$ of the student's overall grade. The student's overall course grade, $G(x)$, can be computed by

$$G(x) = \frac{3}{4}(80) + \frac{1}{4}x, \text{ where } x \text{ is the student's grade on the final exam.}$$

a. Is this function linear, quadratic, or neither? Linear

b. Evaluate $G(90)$ and interpret its meaning in the context of the problem. $G(90) = 82.5$. This means that if the student gets a 90% score on her final exam, then her overall course average is 82.5%.

c. Evaluate $G(50)$ and interpret its meaning in the context of the problem. $G(50) = 72.5$. This means that if the student gets a 50% score on her final exam, then her overall course average is 72.5%.

54. The median weekly earnings, $E(x)$ in dollars, for women 16 yr and older working full time can be approximated by $E(x) = 0.14x^2 + 7.8x + 540$. For this function, x represents the number of years since 2000. (*Source:* U.S. Department of Labor)

a. Is this function linear, quadratic, or neither? Quadratic

b. Evaluate $E(5)$ and interpret its meaning in the context of this problem. $E(5) = 582.5$; This means that for $x = 5$ (the year 2005), the median weekly earnings for women was $582.50

c. Evaluate $E(10)$ and interpret its meaning in the context of this problem. $E(10) = 632$; This means that for $x = 10$ (the year 2010), the median weekly earnings for women was $632.

For Exercises 55–60, write a function defined by $y = f(x)$ under the given conditions.

55. The value of $f(x)$ is two more than the square of x. $f(x) = x^2 + 2$

56. The value of $f(x)$ is the square of the sum of two and x. $f(x) = (x + 2)^2$

57. The function f is a constant function passing through the point (4, 3). $f(x) = 3$

58. The function f is a constant function with y-intercept (0, 5). $f(x) = 5$

59. The function f is a linear function with slope $\frac{1}{2}$ and y-intercept (0, −2). $f(x) = \frac{1}{2}x - 2$

60. The function f is a linear function with slope −4 and y-intercept $(0, \frac{1}{3})$. $f(x) = -4x + \frac{1}{3}$

Graphing Calculator Exercises

For Exercises 61–66, use a graphing calculator to graph the basic functions. Verify your answers from the Summary of Six Basic Functions and Their Graphs.

61. $f(x) = x$

62. $f(x) = x^2$

63. $f(x) = x^3$

64. $f(x) = |x|$

65. $f(x) = \sqrt{x}$

66. $f(x) = \frac{1}{x}$

For Exercises 67–70, find the x- and y-intercepts using a graphing calculator and the *Value* and *Zero* features.

67. $y = -\frac{1}{8}x + 1$
x-intercept: (8, 0)
y-intercept: (0, 1)

68. $y = -\frac{1}{2}x - 3$
x-intercept: (−6, 0)
y-intercept: (0, −3)

69. $y = \frac{4}{5}x + 4$
x-intercept: (−5, 0)
y-intercept: (0, 4)

70. $y = \frac{7}{2}x - 7$
x-intercept: (2, 0)
y-intercept: (0, −7)

Problem Recognition Exercises

Characteristics of Relations

Exercises 1–15 refer to the sets of points (x, y) described in a–h.

a. $\{(0, 8), (1, 4), (\frac{1}{2}, 4), (-3, 5), (2, 1)\}$

b. $\{(-6, 4), (2, 3), (-9, 6), (2, 1), (0, 10)\}$

c. $c(x) = 3x^2 - 2x - 1$

d. $d(x) = 5x - 9$

e.

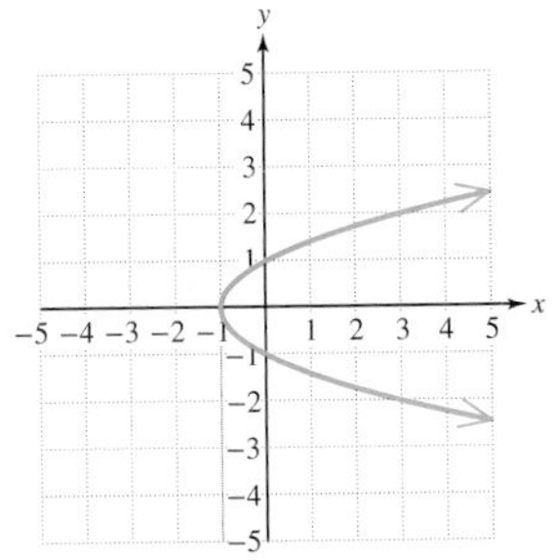

f.

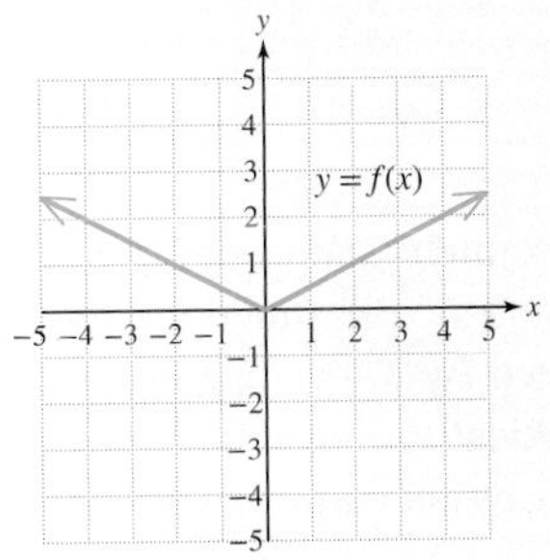

g.

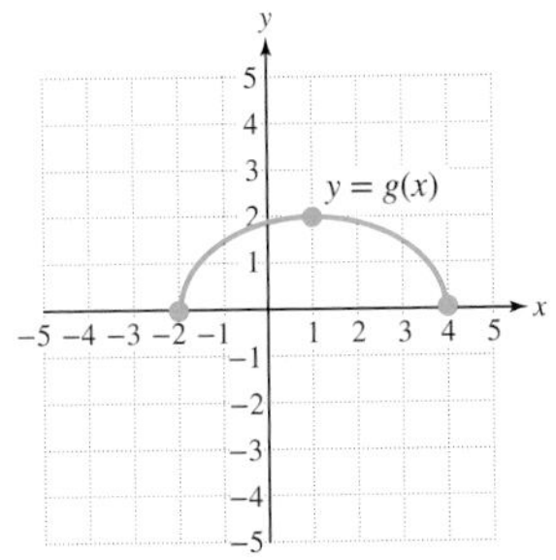

h.

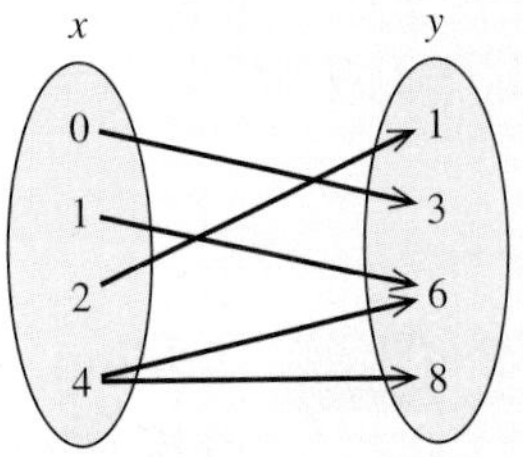

1. Which relations define y as a function of x?
a, c, d, f, g

2. Which relations contain the point (2, 1)?
a, b, d, f, h

3. Use relation (c) to find $c(-1)$.
4

4. Use relation (f) to find $f(-4)$.
2

5. Find the domain of relation (a).
$\{0, 1, \frac{1}{2}, -3, 2\}$

6. Find the range of relation (b).
{4, 3, 6, 1, 10}

7. Find the domain of relation (g).
$[-2, 4]$

8. Find the range of relation (f).
$[0, \infty)$

9. Use relation (h) to complete the ordered pair (__, 3).
0

10. Find the x-intercept(s) of the graph of relation (d). $\left(\frac{9}{5}, 0\right)$

11. Find the y-intercept(s) of the graph shown in relation (e).
(0, −1), (0, 1)

12. Use relation (g) to determine the value of x such that $g(x) = 2$.
1

13. Which relation describes a quadratic function?
c

14. Which relation describes a linear function?
d

15. Use relation (d) to find the value of x such that $d(x) = 6$.
3

Section 8.4 Algebra of Functions and Composition

Objectives

1. Algebra of Functions
2. Composition of Functions
3. Operations on Functions

1. Algebra of Functions

Addition, subtraction, multiplication, and division can be used to create a new function from two or more functions. The domain of the new function will be the intersection of the domains of the original functions.

Instructor Note: Ask students why we make the restriction that $g(x) \neq 0$.

Sum, Difference, Product, and Quotient of Functions

Given two functions f and g, the functions $f + g, f - g, f \cdot g$, and $\frac{f}{g}$ are defined as

$$(f + g)(x) = f(x) + g(x)$$
$$(f - g)(x) = f(x) - g(x)$$
$$(f \cdot g)(x) = f(x) \cdot g(x)$$
$$\left(\frac{f}{g}\right)(x) = \frac{f(x)}{g(x)} \quad \text{provided } g(x) \neq 0$$

For example, suppose $f(x) = |x|$ and $g(x) = 3$. Taking the sum of the functions produces a new function denoted by $f + g$. In this case, $(f + g)(x) = |x| + 3$. Graphically, the y values of the function $f + g$ are given by the sum of the corresponding y values of f and g. This is depicted in Figure 8-17. The function $f + g$ appears in red. In particular, notice that $(f + g)(2) = f(2) + g(2) = 2 + 3 = 5$.

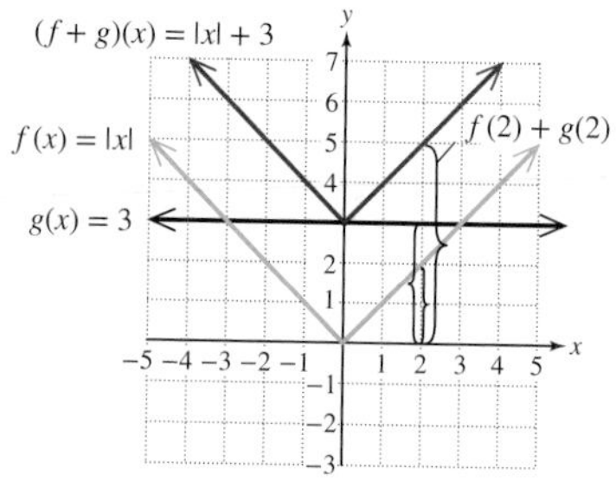

Figure 8-17

Classroom Examples: p. 602, Exercises 4, 6, 10, and 12

Example 1 Adding, Subtracting, Multiplying and Dividing Functions

Given: $g(x) = 4x \quad h(x) = x^2 - 3x \quad k(x) = x - 2$

a. Find $(g + h)(x)$. **b.** Find $(h - g)(x)$.

c. Find $(g \cdot k)(x)$. **d.** Find $\left(\frac{k}{h}\right)(x)$.

Solution:

a. $(g + h)(x) = g(x) + h(x)$

$= (4x) + (x^2 - 3x)$

$= 4x + x^2 - 3x$

$= x^2 + x$ Simplify.

b. $(h - g)(x) = h(x) - g(x)$

$= (x^2 - 3x) - (4x)$

$= x^2 - 3x - 4x$

$= x^2 - 7x$ Simplify.

c. $(g \cdot k)(x) = g(x) \cdot k(x)$

$= (4x)(x - 2)$

$= 4x^2 - 8x$ Simplify.

d. $\left(\frac{k}{h}\right)(x) = \frac{k(x)}{h(x)}$

$= \frac{x - 2}{x^2 - 3x}$ From the denominator we have $x^2 - 3x \neq 0$ or, equivalently, $x(x - 3) \neq 0$. Hence, $x \neq 3$ and $x \neq 0$.

Skill Practice Given $f(x) = x - 1$, $g(x) = 5x^2 + x$, and $h(x) = x^2$, find

1. $(f + g)(x)$ **2.** $(g - f)(x)$ **3.** $(g \cdot h)(x)$ **4.** $\left(\frac{f}{h}\right)(x)$

2. Composition of Functions

Composition of Functions

The **composition** of f and g, denoted $f \circ g$, is defined by the rule

$(f \circ g)(x) = f(g(x))$ provided that $g(x)$ is in the domain of f

Note: $f \circ g$ is read as "f of g" or "f compose g."

For example, given $f(x) = 2x - 3$ and $g(x) = x + 5$, we have

$(f \circ g)(x) = f(g(x))$

$= f(x + 5)$ Substitute $g(x) = x + 5$ into the function f.

$= 2(x + 5) - 3$

$= 2x + 10 - 3$

$= 2x + 7$

In this composition, the function g is the innermost operation and acts on x first. Then the output value of function g becomes the domain element of the function f, as shown in the figure.

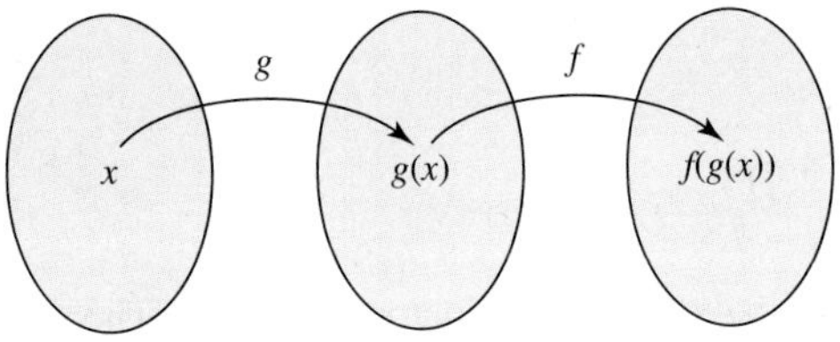

Example 2 Composing Functions

Given: $f(x) = x - 5$, $g(x) = x^2$, and $n(x) = \sqrt{x + 2}$, find

a. $(f \circ g)(x)$

b. $(g \circ f)(x)$

c. $(n \circ f)(x)$

Classroom Example: p. 602, Exercise 20

Answers

1. $5x^2 + 2x - 1$ **2.** $5x^2 + 1$

3. $5x^4 + x^3$ **4.** $\frac{x - 1}{x^2}, x \neq 0$

Solution:

a. $(f \circ g)(x) = f(g(x))$

$= f(x^2)$ Evaluate the function f at x^2.

$= (x^2) - 5$ Replace x by x^2 in function f.

$= x^2 - 5$

TIP: Examples 2(a) and 2(b) illustrate that the order in which two functions are composed may result in different functions. That is, $f \circ g$ does not necessarily equal $g \circ f$.

b. $(g \circ f)(x) = g(f(x))$

$= g(x - 5)$ Evaluate the function g at $(x - 5)$.

$= (x - 5)^2$ Replace x by $(x - 5)$ in function g.

$= x^2 - 10x + 25$ Simplify.

c. $(n \circ f)(x) = n(f(x))$

$= n(x - 5)$ Evaluate the function n at $x - 5$.

$= \sqrt{(x - 5) + 2}$ Replace x by the quantity $(x - 5)$ in function n.

$= \sqrt{x - 3}$

Skill Practice Given $f(x) = 2x^2$, $g(x) = x + 3$, and $h(x) = \sqrt{x - 1}$, find

5. $(f \circ g)(x)$ **6.** $(g \circ f)(x)$ **7.** $(h \circ g)(x)$

3. Operations on Functions

Classroom Examples: p. 603, Exercises 36 and 42

Example 3 Combining Functions

Given the functions defined by $f(x) = x - 7$ and $h(x) = 2x^3$, find the function values, if possible.

a. $(f \cdot h)(3)$ b. $\left(\frac{h}{f}\right)(7)$ c. $(h \circ f)(2)$

Solution:

a. $(f \cdot h)(3) = f(3) \cdot h(3)$ $(f \cdot h)(3)$ is a product (not a composition).

$= (3 - 7) \cdot 2(3)^3$

$= (-4) \cdot 2(27)$

$= -216$

b. $\left(\frac{h}{f}\right)(7) = \frac{h(7)}{f(7)} = \frac{2(7)^3}{7 - 7}$

The value $x = 7$ will make the denominator equal to 0. Therefore, $\left(\frac{h}{f}\right)(7)$ is undefined.

c. $(h \circ f)(2) = h(f(2))$ Evaluate $f(2)$ first. $f(2) = 2 - 7 = -5$

$= h(-5)$ Substitute the result into function h.

$= 2(-5)^3$

$= 2(-125)$

$= -250$

Instructor Note: For a class that has some advanced students, it can be useful to have them consider the question: What two functions could be composed to form a third? For example, how could we define $g(x)$ and $h(x)$ so that $(g \circ h)(x) = f(x)$ when $f(x) = \sqrt{x + 2}$? If students can see that $h(x) = x + 2$ and $g(x) = \sqrt{x}$, then the chain rule in calculus will be easier to grasp.

Answers

5. $2x^2 + 12x + 18$ **6.** $2x^2 + 3$
7. $\sqrt{x + 2}$

Skill Practice Given $h(x) = x + 4$ and $k(x) = x^2 - 3$, find

8. $(h \cdot k)(-2)$ **9.** $\left(\frac{k}{h}\right)(-4)$ **10.** $(k \circ h)(1)$

Example 4 Finding Function Values from a Graph

Classroom Examples: p. 603, Exercises 50, 58, and 60

For the functions f and g pictured, find the function values if possible.

a. $g(2)$

b. $(f - g)(-3)$

c. $\left(\frac{g}{f}\right)(5)$

d. $(f \circ g)(4)$

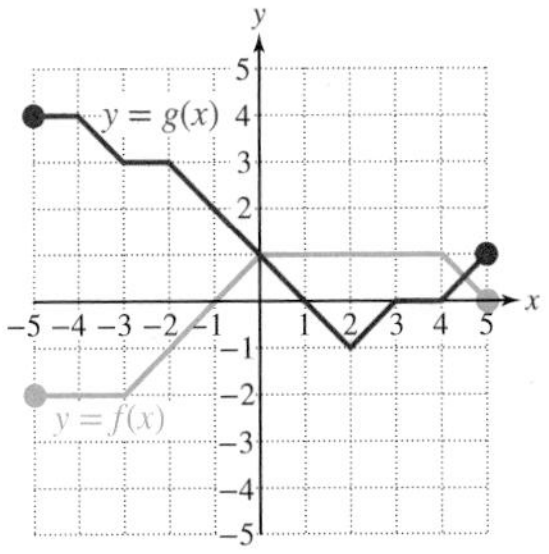

Solution:

a. $g(2) = -1$

The value $g(2)$ represents the y value of $y = g(x)$ (the red graph) when $x = 2$. Because the point $(2, -1)$ lies on the graph, $g(2) = -1$.

b. $(f - g)(-3) = f(-3) - g(-3)$ Evaluate the difference of $f(-3)$ and $g(-3)$.

$= -2 - (3)$ Estimate function values from the graph.

$= -5$

c. $\left(\frac{g}{f}\right)(5) = \frac{g(5)}{f(5)}$ Evaluate the quotient of $g(5)$ and $f(5)$.

$= \frac{1}{0}$ (undefined)

The function $\frac{g}{f}$ is undefined at 5 because the denominator is zero.

d. $(f \circ g)(4) = f(g(4))$ From the red graph, find the value of $g(4)$ first. We see that $g(4) = 0$.

$= f(0)$ From the blue graph, find the value of f at $x = 0$.

$= 1$

Skill Practice Find the values from the graph.

11. $g(3)$

12. $(f + g)(-4)$

13. $\left(\frac{f}{g}\right)(2)$

14. $(g \circ f)(-2)$

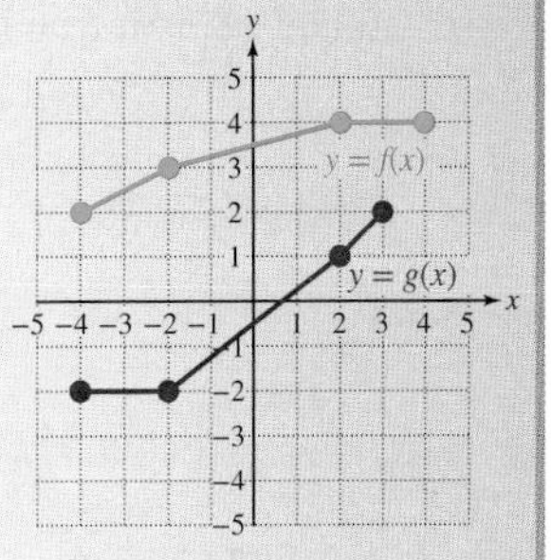

Answers

8. 2 **9.** undefined **10.** 22

11. 2 **12.** 0 **13.** 4 **14.** 2

Section 8.4 Practice Exercises

For additional exercises, see Classroom Activities 8.4A–8.4C in the *Student's Resource Manual* at www.mhhe.com/moh.

Vocabulary and Key Concepts

1. **a.** Given the functions f and g, the function $(f+g)(x) =$ ____$f(x)$____ $+$ ____$g(x)$____.

b. Given the functions f and g, the function $\left(\frac{f}{g}\right)(x) = \frac{f(x)}{\square}$, provided ____$g(x)$; $g(x)$____ $\neq 0$.

c. The composition of functions f and g is defined by the rule $(f \circ g)(x) =$ ____$f(g(x))$____.

Concept 1: Algebra of Functions

2. Given $f(x) = x^2$ and $g(x) = 2x - 3$, find

a. $f(-2)$ 4 **b.** $g(-2)$ −7 **c.** $(f+g)(-2)$ −3

For Exercises 3–14, refer to the functions defined below.

$$f(x) = x + 4 \qquad g(x) = 2x^2 + 4x \qquad h(x) = x^2 + 1 \qquad k(x) = \frac{1}{x}$$

Find the indicated functions. **(See Example 1.)**

3. $(f+g)(x)$
$(f+g)(x) = 2x^2 + 5x + 4$

4. $(f-g)(x)$
$(f-g)(x) = -2x^2 - 3x + 4$

5. $(g-f)(x)$
$(g-f)(x) = 2x^2 + 3x - 4$

6. $(f+h)(x)$
$(f+h)(x) = x^2 + x + 5$

7. $(f \cdot h)(x)$
$(f \cdot h)(x) = x^3 + 4x^2 + x + 4$

8. $(h \cdot k)(x)$
$(h \cdot k)(x) = \frac{x^2+1}{x}, x \neq 0$

9. $(g \cdot f)(x)$
$(g \cdot f)(x) = 2x^3 + 12x^2 + 16x$

10. $(f \cdot k)(x)$
$(f \cdot k)(x) = \frac{x+4}{x}, x \neq 0$

11. $\left(\frac{h}{f}\right)(x)$
$\left(\frac{h}{f}\right)(x) = \frac{x^2+1}{x+4}, x \neq -4$

12. $\left(\frac{g}{f}\right)(x)$
$\left(\frac{g}{f}\right)(x) = \frac{2x^2+4x}{x+4}, x \neq -4$

13. $\left(\frac{f}{g}\right)(x)$
$\left(\frac{f}{g}\right)(x) = \frac{x+4}{2x^2+4x}, x \neq 0, x \neq -2$

14. $\left(\frac{f}{h}\right)(x)$
$\left(\frac{f}{h}\right)(x) = \frac{x+4}{x^2+1}$

Concept 2: Composition of Functions

For Exercises 15–22, find the indicated functions. Use f, g, h, and k as defined in Exercises 3–14. **(See Example 2.)**

Animation

15. $(f \circ g)(x)$
$(f \circ g)(x) = 2x^2 + 4x + 4$

16. $(f \circ k)(x)$ $(f \circ k)(x) = \frac{1}{x} + 4, x \neq 0$

17. $(g \circ f)(x)$
$(g \circ f)(x) = 2x^2 + 20x + 48$

18. $(k \circ f)(x)$ $(k \circ f)(x) = \frac{1}{x+4}, x \neq -4$

19. $(k \circ h)(x)$ $(k \circ h)(x) = \frac{1}{x^2+1}$

20. $(h \circ k)(x)$
$(h \circ k)(x) = \frac{1}{x^2} + 1, x \neq 0$

21. $(k \circ g)(x)$
$(k \circ g)(x) = \frac{1}{2x^2+4x}, x \neq 0, x \neq -2$

22. $(g \circ k)(x)$ $(g \circ k)(x) = \frac{2}{x^2} + \frac{4}{x}, x \neq 0$

23. Based on your answers to Exercises 15 and 17, is it true in general that $(f \circ g)(x) = (g \circ f)(x)$? No

24. Based on your answers to Exercises 16 and 18, is it true in general that $(f \circ k)(x) = (k \circ f)(x)$? No

For Exercises 25–28, find $(f \circ g)(x)$ and $(g \circ f)(x)$.

25. $f(x) = x^2 - 3x + 1$, $g(x) = 5x$
$(f \circ g)(x) = 25x^2 - 15x + 1$;
$(g \circ f)(x) = 5x^2 - 15x + 5$

26. $f(x) = 3x^2 + 8$, $g(x) = 2x - 4$
$(f \circ g)(x) = 12x^2 - 48x + 56$;
$(g \circ f)(x) = 6x^2 + 12$

27. $f(x) = |x|$, $g(x) = x^3 - 1$
$(f \circ g)(x) = |x^3 - 1|$;
$(g \circ f)(x) = |x|^3 - 1$

28. $f(x) = \dfrac{1}{x+2}$, $g(x) = |x + 2|$
$(f \circ g)(x) = \dfrac{1}{|x+2| + 2}$;
$(g \circ f)(x) = \left|\dfrac{1}{x+2} + 2\right|$ or $\left|\dfrac{2x+5}{x+2}\right|$, $x \neq -2$

29. For $h(x) = 5x - 4$, find $(h \circ h)(x)$.
$(h \circ h)(x) = 25x - 24$

30. For $k(x) = -x^2 + 1$, find $(k \circ k)(x)$.
$(k \circ k)(x) = -x^4 + 2x^2$

Concept 3: Operations on Functions

For Exercises 31–46, refer to the functions defined below.

$$m(x) = x^3 \qquad n(x) = x - 3 \qquad r(x) = \sqrt{x+4} \qquad p(x) = \frac{1}{x+2}$$

Find each function value if possible. **(See Example 3.)**

31. $(m \cdot r)(0)$ 0

32. $(n \cdot p)(0)$ $-\frac{3}{2}$

33. $(m + r)(-4)$ -64

34. $(n - m)(4)$ -63

35. $(r \circ n)(3)$ 2

36. $(n \circ r)(5)$ 0

37. $(p \circ m)(-1)$ 1

38. $(m \circ n)(5)$ 8

39. $(m \circ p)(2)$ $\frac{1}{64}$

40. $(r \circ m)(2)$ $\sqrt{12}$ or $2\sqrt{3}$

41. $(r + p)(-3)$ 0

42. $(n + p)(-2)$ Undefined

43. $(m \circ p)(-2)$ Not a real number

44. $(r \circ m)(-2)$ Not a real number

45. $\left(\frac{r}{n}\right)(12)$ $\frac{4}{9}$

46. $\left(\frac{n}{m}\right)(2)$ $-\frac{1}{8}$

For Exercises 47–64, approximate each function value from the graph, if possible. **(See Example 4.)**

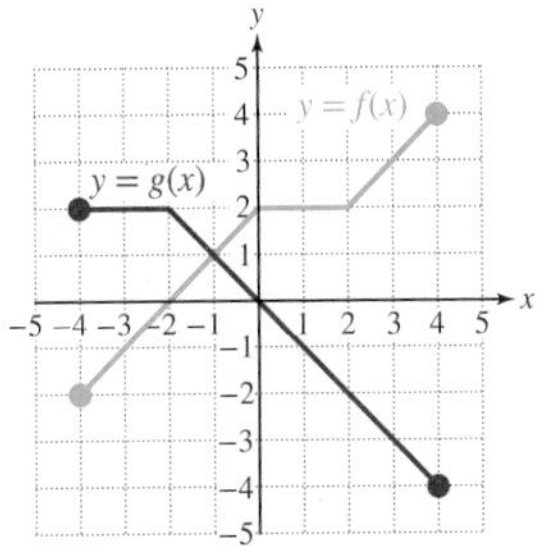

47. $f(-4)$ -2

48. $f(1)$ 2

49. $g(-2)$ 2

50. $g(3)$ -3

51. $(f + g)(2)$ 0

52. $(g - f)(3)$ -6

53. $(f \cdot g)(-1)$ 1

54. $(g \cdot f)(-4)$ -4

55. $\left(\frac{g}{f}\right)(0)$ 0

56. $\left(\frac{f}{g}\right)(-2)$ 0

57. $\left(\frac{f}{g}\right)(0)$ Undefined

58. $\left(\frac{g}{f}\right)(-2)$ Undefined

59. $(g \circ f)(-1)$ -1

60. $(f \circ g)(0)$ 2

61. $(f \circ g)(-4)$ 2

62. $(g \circ f)(-4)$ 2

63. $(g \circ g)(2)$ 2

64. $(f \circ f)(-2)$ 2

For Exercises 65–80, approximate each function value from the graph, if possible. **(See Example 4.)**

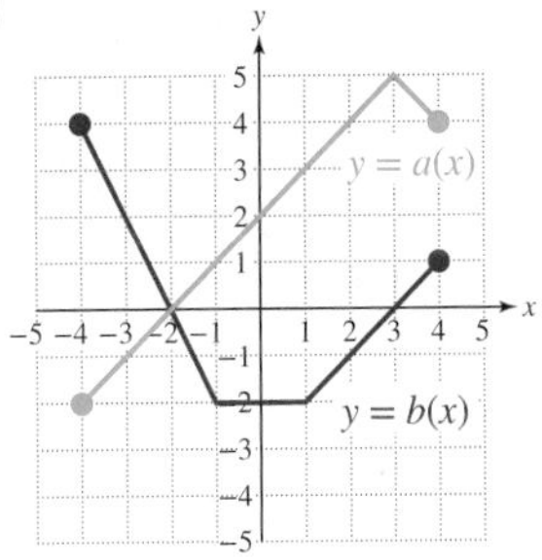

65. $a(-3)$ -1

66. $a(1)$ 3

67. $b(-1)$ -2

68. $b(3)$ 0

69. $(a - b)(-1)$ 3

70. $(a + b)(0)$ 0

71. $(b \cdot a)(1)$ -6

72. $(a \cdot b)(2)$ -4

73. $(b \circ a)(0)$ -1

74. $(a \circ b)(-2)$ 2

75. $(a \circ b)(-4)$ 4

76. $(b \circ a)(-3)$ -2

77. $\left(\frac{b}{a}\right)(3)$ 0

78. $\left(\frac{a}{b}\right)(4)$ 4

79. $(a \circ a)(-2)$ 2

80. $(b \circ b)(1)$ 0

81. The cost in dollars of producing x toy cars is $C(x) = 2.2x + 1$. The revenue for selling x toy cars is $R(x) = 5.98x$. To calculate profit, subtract the cost from the revenue.

a. Write and simplify a function P that represents profit in terms of x. $P(x) = 3.78x - 1$

b. Find the profit of producing 50 toy cars. \$188

82. The cost in dollars of producing x lawn chairs is $C(x) = 2.5x + 10.1$. The revenue for selling x lawn chairs is $R(x) = 6.99x$. To calculate profit, subtract the cost from the revenue.

a. Write and simplify a function P that represents profit in terms of x. $P(x) = 4.49x - 10.1$

b. Find the profit in producing 100 lawn chairs. \$438.90

83. The functions defined by $D(t) = 0.925t + 26.958$ and $R(t) = 0.725t + 20.558$ approximate the amount of child support (in billions of dollars) that was due $D(t)$ and the amount of child support actually received $R(t)$ in the United States for a selected number of years. In each case, $t = 0$ represents the first year of the study.

Difference Between Child Support Due and Child Support Paid, United States

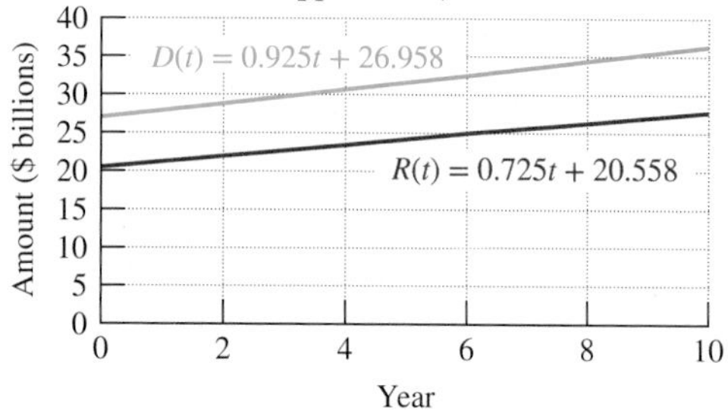

Source: U.S. Bureau of the Census

a. Find the function defined by $F(t) = D(t) - R(t)$. What does $F(t)$ represent in the context of this problem? $F(t) = 0.2t + 6.4$; $F(t)$ represents the amount of child support (in billion dollars) not paid for year t.

b. Find $F(4)$. What does this function value represent in the context of this problem? $F(4) = 7.2$ means that in year 4, \$7.2 billion of child support was not paid.

84. The rural and urban populations in the South (in the United States) between the years 1900 and 1970 can be modeled by the following:

$$r(t) = -3.497t^2 + 266.2t + 20{,}220$$

$$u(t) = 0.0566t^3 + 0.952t^2 + 177.8t + 4593$$

The variable t represents the number of years since 1900, $r(t)$ represents the rural population in thousands, and $u(t)$ represents the urban population in thousands.

Rural and Urban Populations in the South, United States, 1900–1970

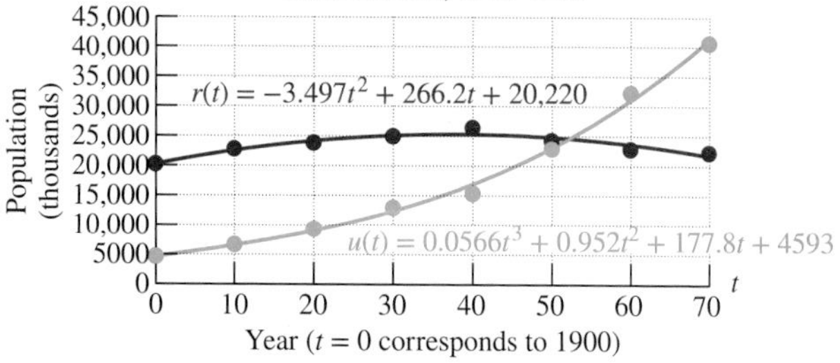

Source: Historical Abstract of the United States

a. Find the function defined by $T(t) = r(t) + u(t)$. What does $T(t)$ represent in the context of this problem? $T(t) = 0.0566t^3 - 2.545t^2 + 444t + 24{,}813$; $T(t)$ is the total population of the South (in thousands) for year t.

b. Use the function T to approximate the total population in the South for the year 1940. 42,123.4 thousand

85. Joe rides a bicycle and his wheels revolve at 80 revolutions per minute (rpm). Therefore, the total number of revolutions, r, is given by $r(t) = 80t$, where t is the time in minutes. For each revolution of the wheels of the bike, he travels approximately 7 ft. Therefore, the total distance he travels $D(r)$ (in feet) depends on the total number of revolutions, r, according to the function $D(r) = 7r$.

a. Find $(D \circ r)(t)$ and interpret its meaning in the context of this problem. $(D \circ r)(t) = 560t$; This function represents the total distance Joe travels as a function of time that he rides.

b. Find Joe's total distance in feet after 10 min. 5600 ft

86. The area of a square is given by the function $a(x) = x^2$, where x is the length of the sides of the square. If carpeting costs \$9.95 per square yard, then the cost $C(a)$ (in dollars) to carpet a square room is given by $C(a) = 9.95a$, where a is the area of the room in square yards.

a. Find $(C \circ a)(x)$ and interpret its meaning in the context of this problem. $(C \circ a)(x) = 9.95x^2$; This function represents the total cost to carpet a square room where the dimensions of the room are x yd by x yd.

b. Find the cost to carpet a square room if its floor dimensions are 15 yd by 15 yd. \$2238.75

Variation

Section 8.5

Concepts

1. Definition of Direct and Inverse Variation
2. Translations Involving Variation
3. Applications of Variation

1. Definition of Direct and Inverse Variation

In this section, we introduce the concept of variation. Direct and inverse variation models can show how one quantity varies in proportion to another.

Definition of Direct and Inverse Variation

Let k be a nonzero constant real number. Then,

1. y varies **directly** as x.
   y is directly proportional to x. $\Big\}\ y = kx$

2. y varies **inversely** as x.
   y is inversely proportional to x. $\Big\}\ y = \dfrac{k}{x}$

Note: The value of k is called the constant of variation.

For a car traveling 30 mph, the equation $d = 30t$ indicates that the distance traveled is *directly proportional* to the time of travel. For positive values of k, when two variables are directly related, as one variable increases, the other variable will also increase. Likewise, if one variable decreases, the other will decrease. In the equation $d = 30t$, the longer the time of the trip, the greater the distance traveled. The shorter the time of the trip, the shorter the distance traveled.

For positive values of k, when two positive variables are *inversely related,* as one variable increases, the other will decrease, and vice versa. Consider a car traveling between Toronto and Montreal, a distance of 500 km. The time required to make the trip is inversely proportional to the speed of travel: $t = 500/r$. As the rate of speed, r, increases, the quotient $500/r$ will decrease. Thus, the time will decrease. Similarly, as the rate of speed decreases, the trip will take longer.

2. Translations Involving Variation

The first step in using a variation model is to write an English phrase as an equivalent mathematical equation.

Example 1 Translating to a Variation Model

Classroom Examples: p. 611, Exercises 12 and 14

Write each expression as an equivalent mathematical model.

a. The circumference of a circle varies directly as the radius.

b. At a constant temperature, the volume of a gas varies inversely as the pressure.

c. The length of time of a meeting is directly proportional to the *square* of the number of people present.

Solution:

a. Let C represent circumference and r represent radius. The variables are directly related, so use the model $C = kr$.

b. Let V represent volume and P represent pressure. Because the variables are inversely related, use the model $V = \frac{k}{P}$.

c. Let t represent time, and let N be the number of people present at a meeting. Because t is directly related to N^2, use the model $t = kN^2$.

Skill Practice Write each expression as an equivalent mathematical model.

1. The distance, d, driven in a particular time varies directly with the speed of the car, s.
2. The weight of an individual kitten, w, varies inversely with the number of kittens in the litter, n.
3. The value of v varies inversely as the square root of b.

Sometimes a variable varies directly as the product of two or more other variables. In this case, we have joint variation.

Definition of Joint Variation

Let k be a nonzero constant real number. Then the following statements are equivalent:

y varies **jointly** as w and z.
y is jointly proportional to w and z.
} $y = kwz$

Classroom Examples: p. 611, Exercises 18 and 22

Example 2 Translating to a Variation Model

Write each expression as an equivalent mathematical model.

a. y varies jointly as u and the square root of v.

b. The gravitational force of attraction between two planets varies jointly as the product of their masses and inversely as the square of the distance between them.

Solution:

a. $y = ku\sqrt{v}$

b. Let m_1 and m_2 represent the masses of the two planets. Let F represent the gravitational force of attraction and d represent the distance between the planets.

The variation model is: $F = \dfrac{km_1m_2}{d^2}$

Skill Practice Write each expression as an equivalent mathematical model.

4. The value of q varies jointly as u and v.
5. The value of x varies directly as the square of y and inversely as z.

Answers

1. $d = ks$
2. $w = \dfrac{k}{n}$
3. $v = \dfrac{k}{\sqrt{b}}$
4. $q = kuv$
5. $x = \dfrac{ky^2}{z}$

3. Applications of Variation

Consider the variation models $y = kx$ and $y = \frac{k}{x}$. In either case, if values for x and y are known, we can solve for k. Once k is known, we can use the variation equation to find y if x is known, or to find x if y is known. This concept is the basis for solving many applications involving variation.

Finding a Variation Model

Step 1 Write a general variation model that relates the variables given in the problem. Let k represent the constant of variation.

Step 2 Solve for k by substituting known values of the variables into the model from step 1.

Step 3 Substitute the value of k into the original variation model from step 1.

Example 3 **Solving an Application Involving Direct Variation**

Classroom Examples: p. 611, Exercises 24 and 32

The variable z varies directly as w. When w is 16, z is 56.

a. Write a variation model for this situation. Use k as the constant of variation.

b. Solve for the constant of variation.

c. Find the value of z when w is 84.

Solution:

a. $z = kw$

b. $z = kw$

$56 = k(16)$ Substitute known values for z and w. Then solve for the unknown value of k.

$\frac{56}{16} = \frac{k(16)}{16}$ To isolate k, divide both sides by 16.

$\frac{7}{2} = k$ Simplify $\frac{56}{16}$ to $\frac{7}{2}$.

c. With the value of k known, the variation model can now be written as:

$z = \frac{7}{2}w$

$z = \frac{7}{2}(84)$ To find z when $w = 84$, substitute $w = 84$ into the equation.

$z = 294$

Skill Practice The variable t varies directly as the square of v. When v is 8, t is 32.

6. Write a variation model for this relationship.

7. Solve for the constant of variation.

8. Find t when $v = 10$.

Answers

6. $t = kv^2$ **7.** $\frac{1}{2}$ **8.** 50

Classroom Example: p. 612 Exercise 42

Example 4 **Solving an Application Involving Direct Variation**

The speed of a racing canoe in still water varies directly as the square root of the length of the canoe.

a. If a 16-ft canoe can travel 6.2 mph in still water, find a variation model that relates the speed of a canoe to its length.

b. Find the speed of a 25-ft canoe.

Animation

Solution:

a. Let s represent the speed of the canoe and L represent the length. The general variation model is $s = k\sqrt{L}$. To solve for k, substitute the known values for s and L.

$$s = k\sqrt{L}$$

$$6.2 = k\sqrt{16} \qquad \text{Substitute } s = 6.2 \text{ mph and } L = 16 \text{ ft.}$$

$$6.2 = k \cdot 4$$

$$\frac{6.2}{4} = \frac{4k}{4} \qquad \text{Solve for } k.$$

$$k = 1.55$$

$$s = 1.55\sqrt{L} \qquad \text{Substitute } k = 1.55 \text{ into the model } s = k\sqrt{L}.$$

b. $s = 1.55\sqrt{L}$

$$= 1.55\sqrt{25} \qquad \text{Find the speed when } L = 25 \text{ ft.}$$

$$= 7.75 \text{ mph} \qquad \text{The speed is 7.75 mph.}$$

Skill Practice

9. The amount of water needed by a mountain hiker varies directly as the time spent hiking. The hiker needs 2.4 L for a 4-hr hike. How much water will be needed for a 5-hr hike?

Classroom Example: p. 613, Exercise 50

Example 5 **Solving an Application Involving Inverse Variation**

The loudness of sound measured in decibels (dB) varies inversely as the square of the distance between the listener and the source of the sound. If the loudness of sound is 17.92 dB at a distance of 10 ft from a home theater speaker, what is the decibel level 20 ft from the speaker?

Solution:

Let L represent the loudness of sound in decibels and d represent the distance in feet. The inverse relationship between decibel level and the square of the distance is modeled by

$$L = \frac{k}{d^2}$$

$$17.92 = \frac{k}{(10)^2} \qquad \text{Substitute } L = 17.92 \text{ dB and } d = 10 \text{ ft.}$$

Answer

9. 3 L

$$17.92 = \frac{k}{100}$$

$$(17.92)100 = \frac{k}{100} \cdot 100$$ Solve for k (clear fractions).

$$k = 1792$$

$$L = \frac{1792}{d^2}$$ Substitute $k = 1792$ into the original model $L = \frac{k}{d^2}$.

With the value of k known, we can find L for any value of d.

$$L = \frac{1792}{(20)^2}$$ Find the loudness when $d = 20$ ft.

$$= 4.48 \text{ dB}$$ The loudness is 4.48 dB.

Notice that the loudness of sound is 17.92 dB at a distance 10 ft from the speaker. When the distance from the speaker is increased to 20 ft, the decibel level decreases to 4.48 dB. This is consistent with an inverse relationship. For $k > 0$, as one variable is increased, the other is decreased. It also seems reasonable that the farther one moves away from the source of a sound, the softer the sound becomes.

Skill Practice

10. The yield on a bond varies inversely as the price. The yield on a particular bond is 5% when the price is \$100. Find the yield when the price is \$125.

Example 6 Solving an Application Involving Joint Variation

Classroom Example: p. 613, Exercise 58

The kinetic energy of an object varies jointly as the weight of the object at sea level and as the square of its velocity. During a hurricane, a 0.5-lb stone traveling at 60 mph has 81 J (joules) of kinetic energy. Suppose the wind speed doubles to 120 mph. Find the kinetic energy.

Solution:

Let E represent the kinetic energy, let w represent the weight, and let v represent the velocity of the stone. The variation model is

$$E = kwv^2$$

$$81 = k(0.5)(60)^2$$ Substitute $E = 81$ J, $w = 0.5$ lb, and $v = 60$ mph.

$$81 = k(0.5)(3600)$$ Simplify exponents.

$$81 = k(1800)$$

$$\frac{81}{1800} = \frac{k(1800)}{1800}$$ Divide by 1800.

$$0.045 = k$$ Solve for k.

Answer

10. 4%

With the value of k known, the model $E = kwv^2$ can now be written as $E = 0.045wv^2$. We now find the kinetic energy of a 0.5-lb stone traveling at 120 mph.

$$E = 0.045(0.5)(120)^2$$
$$= 324$$

The kinetic energy of a 0.5-lb stone traveling 120 mph is 324 J.

Skill Practice

11. The amount of simple interest earned in an account varies jointly as the interest rate and time of the investment. An account earns \$72 in 4 years at 2% interest. How much interest would be earned in 3 years at a rate of 5%?

In Example 6, when the velocity increased by 2 times, the kinetic energy increased by 4 times (note that $324 \text{ J} = 4 \cdot 81 \text{ J}$). This factor of 4 occurs because the kinetic energy is proportional to the *square* of the velocity. When the velocity increased by 2 times, the kinetic energy increased by 2^2 times.

Answer

11. \$135

Section 8.5 Practice Exercises

For additional exercises, see Classroom Activities 8.5A–8.5C in the *Student's Resource Manual* at www.mhhe.com/moh.

Vocabulary and Key Concepts

1. **a.** Let k be a nonzero constant. If y varies directly as x, then $y =$ ___kx___, where k is the constant of variation.

b. Let k be a nonzero constant. If y varies inversely as x, then $y =$ ___$\frac{k}{x}$___, where k is the constant of variation.

c. Let k be a nonzero constant. If y varies jointly as x and w, then $y =$ ___kxw___, where k is the constant of variation.

Review Exercises

For Exercises 2–7, refer to the functions defined below.

$$f(x) = x^2 \qquad g(x) = x - 2 \qquad h(x) = \sqrt{2 - x}$$

Find the indicated functions or function values.

2. $(f + g)(2)$ 4

3. $(f \circ g)(x)$ $x^2 - 4x + 4$

4. $(g - f)(3)$ -8

5. $(g \circ f)(x)$ $x^2 - 2$

6. $(f \cdot g)(x)$ $x^3 - 2x^2$

7. $\left(\frac{g}{h}\right)(1)$ -1

Concept 1: Definition of Direct and Inverse Variation

8. In the equation $r = kt$, does r vary directly or inversely as t? Directly

9. In the equation $w = \frac{k}{v}$, does w vary directly or inversely as v? Inversely

10. In the equation $P = \frac{k \cdot c}{v}$, does P vary directly or inversely as v? Inversely

Concept 2: Translations Involving Variation

For Exercises 11–22, write a variation model. Use k as the constant of variation. **(See Examples 1–2.)**

11. T varies directly as q. $T = kq$

12. W varies directly as z. $W = kz$

13. b varies inversely as c. $b = \frac{k}{c}$

14. m varies inversely as t. $m = \frac{k}{t}$

15. Q is directly proportional to x and inversely proportional to y. $Q = \frac{kx}{y}$

16. d is directly proportional to p and inversely proportional to n. $d = \frac{kp}{n}$

17. c varies jointly as s and t. $c = kst$

18. w varies jointly as p and f. $w = kpf$

19. L varies jointly as w and the square root of v. $L = kw\sqrt{v}$

20. q varies jointly as v and the cube root of w. $q = kv\sqrt[3]{w}$

21. x varies directly as the square of y and inversely as z. $x = \frac{ky^2}{z}$

22. a varies directly as n and inversely as the square of d. $a = \frac{kn}{d^2}$

Concept 3: Applications of Variation

For Exercises 23–28, find the constant of variation, k. **(See Example 3.)**

23. y varies directly as x and when x is 4, y is 18. $k = \frac{9}{2}$

24. m varies directly as x and when x is 8, m is 22. $k = \frac{11}{4}$

25. p varies inversely as q and when q is 16, p is 32. $k = 512$

26. T varies inversely as x and when x is 40, T is 200. $k = 8000$

27. y varies jointly as w and v. When w is 50 and v is 0.1, y is 8.75. $k = 1.75$

28. N varies jointly as t and p. When t is 1 and p is 7.5, N is 330. $k = 44$

For Exercises 29–40, solve for the indicated variable. **(See Example 3.)**

29. x varies directly as p. If $x = 50$ when $p = 10$, find x when p is 14. $x = 70$

30. y is directly proportional to z. If $y = 12$ when $z = 36$, find y when z is 21. $y = 7$

31. b is inversely proportional to c. If b is 4 when c is 3, find b when $c = 2$. $b = 6$

32. q varies inversely as w. If q is 8 when w is 50, find q when w is 125. $q = 3.2$

33. Z varies directly as the square of w. If $Z = 14$ when $w = 4$, find Z when $w = 8$. $Z = 56$

34. m varies directly as the square of x. If $m = 200$ when $x = 20$, find m when x is 32. $m = 512$

35. Q varies inversely as the square of p. If $Q = 4$ when $p = 3$, find Q when $p = 2$. $Q = 9$

36. z is inversely proportional to the square of t. If $z = 15$ when $t = 4$, find z when $t = 10$. $z = 2.4$

37. L varies jointly as a and the square root of b. If $L = 72$ when $a = 8$ and $b = 9$, find L when $a = \frac{1}{2}$ and $b = 36$. $L = 9$

38. Y varies jointly as the cube of x and the square root of w. $Y = 128$ when $x = 2$ and $w = 16$. Find Y when $x = \frac{1}{2}$ and $w = 64$. $Y = 4$

39. B varies directly as m and inversely as n. $B = 20$ when $m = 10$ and $n = 3$. Find B when $m = 15$ and $n = 12$. $B = \frac{15}{2}$

40. R varies directly as s and inversely as t. $R = 14$ when $s = 2$ and $t = 9$. Find R when $s = 4$ and $t = 3$. $R = 84$

For Exercises 41–58, use a variation model to solve for the unknown value. **(See Examples 4–6.)**

41. The weight of a person's heart varies directly as the person's actual weight. For a 150-lb man, his heart would weigh 0.75 lb.

a. Approximate the weight of a 184-lb man's heart. The heart weighs 0.92 lb.

b. How much does your heart weigh? Answers will vary.

42. The number of calories, C, in beer varies directly with the number of ounces, n. If 12 oz of beer contains 153 calories, how many calories are in 40 oz of beer? There are 510 calories in 40 oz of beer.

43. The amount of medicine that a physician prescribes for a patient varies directly as the weight of the patient. A physician prescribes 3 g of a medicine for a 150-lb person.

a. How many grams should be prescribed for a 180-lb person? 3.6 g

b. How many grams should be prescribed for a 225-lb person? 4.5 g

c. How many grams should be prescribed for a 120-lb person? 2.4 g

© Sean Justice/Corbis RF

44. The number of turkeys needed for a banquet is directly proportional to the number of guests that must be fed. Master Chef Rico knows that he needs to cook 3 turkeys to feed 42 guests.

a. How many turkeys should he cook to feed 70 guests? 5 turkeys

b. How many turkeys should he cook to feed 140 guests? 10 turkeys

c. How many turkeys should be cooked to feed 700 guests at an inaugural ball? 50 turkeys

d. How many turkeys should be cooked for a wedding with 100 guests? 8 turkeys; Note that the answer was rounded up, because it would be better for the chef to have too much food than too little.

© BananaStock/PunchStock RF

45. The unit cost of producing CDs is inversely proportional to the number of CDs produced. If 5000 CDs are produced, the cost per CD is \$0.48.

a. What would be the unit cost if 6000 CDs were produced? \$0.40

b. What would be the unit cost if 8000 CDs were produced? \$0.30

c. What would be the unit cost if 2400 CDs were produced? \$1.00

46. An author self-publishes a book and finds that the number of books she can sell per month varies inversely as the price of the book. The author can sell 1500 books per month when the price is set at \$8 per book.

a. How many books would she expect to sell if the price were \$12? 1000 books

b. How many books would she expect to sell if the price were \$15? 800 books

c. How many books would she expect to sell if the price were \$6? 2000 books

47. The amount of pollution entering the atmosphere over a given time varies directly as the number of people living in an area. If 80,000 people create 56,800 tons of pollutants, how many tons enter the atmosphere in a city with a population of 500,000? 355,000 tons

© Patrick Clark/Getty Images RF

48. The area of a picture projected on a wall varies directly as the square of the distance from the projector to the wall. If a 10-ft distance produces a 16-ft^2 picture, what is the area of a picture produced when the projection unit is moved to a distance 20 ft from the wall? 64 ft^2

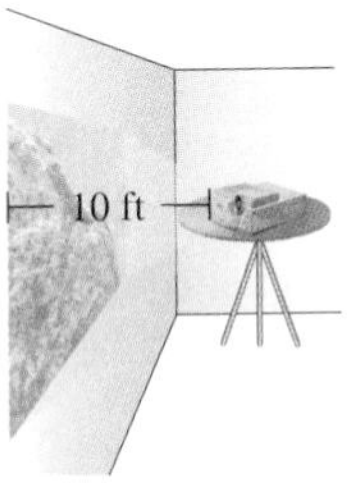

49. The stopping distance of a car varies directly as the square of the speed of the car. If a car traveling 40 mph has a stopping distance of 109 ft, find the stopping distance of a car that travels 25 mph. (Round the answer to one decimal place.) 42.6 ft

50. The intensity of a light source varies inversely as the square of the distance from the source. If the intensity of a light bulb is 400 lumen/m^2 (lux) at a distance of 5 m, determine the intensity at 8 m.

156.25 lumen/m^2

51. The power in an electric circuit varies jointly as the current and the square of the resistance. If the power is 144 W (watts) when the current is 4 A (amperes) and the resistance is 6 Ω (ohms), find the power when the current is 3 A and the resistance is 10 Ω. 300 W

52. Some body-builders claim that, within safe limits, the number of repetitions that a person can complete on a given weight-lifting exercise is inversely proportional to the amount of weight lifted. Roxanne can bench press 45 lb for 15 repetitions.

a. How many repetitions can Roxanne bench with 60 lb of weight? 11 repetitions

b. How many repetitions can Roxanne bench with 75 lb of weight? 9 repetitions

c. How many repetitions can Roxanne bench with 100 lb of weight? 6 repetitions

53. The current in a wire varies directly as the voltage and inversely as the resistance. If the current is 9 A when the voltage is 90 V (volts) and the resistance is 10 Ω, find the current when the voltage is 185 V and the resistance is 10 Ω. 18.5 A

54. The resistance of a wire varies directly as its length and inversely as the square of its diameter. A 40-ft wire 0.1 in. in diameter has a resistance of 4 Ω. What is the resistance of a 50-ft wire with a diameter of 0.2 in.? 1.25 Ω

55. The weight of a medicine ball varies directly as the cube of its radius. A ball with a radius of 3 in. weighs 4.32 lb. How much would a medicine ball weigh if its radius is 5 in.? 20 lb

56. The area of an equilateral triangle varies directly as the square of the length of the sides. For an equilateral triangle with 7-cm sides, the area is 21.22 cm^2. What is the area of an equilateral triangle with 17-cm sides? Round to the nearest whole unit. 125 cm^2

57. The amount of simple interest earned in an account varies jointly as the amount of principal invested and the amount of time the money is invested. If $2500 in principal earns $500 in interest after 4 years, then how much interest will be earned on $7000 invested for 10 years? $3500

58. The amount of simple interest earned in an account varies jointly as the amount of principal invested and the amount of time the money is invested. If $6000 in principal earns $840 in interest after 2 years, then how much interest will be earned on $4500 invested for 8 years? $2520

Group Activity

Deciphering a Coded Message

Materials: A calculator

Estimated time: 20–25 minutes

Group Size: 4 (two pairs)

Cryptography is the study of coding and decoding messages. One type of coding process assigns a number to each letter of the alphabet and to the space character. For example:

A	B	C	D	E	F	G	H	I	J	K	L	M	N
1	2	3	4	5	6	7	8	9	10	11	12	13	14

O	P	Q	R	S	T	U	V	W	X	Y	Z	space
15	16	17	18	19	20	21	22	23	24	25	26	27

According to the numbers assigned to each letter, the message "*Decimals have a point*" would be coded as follows:

D	E	C	I	M	A	L	S	_	H	A	V	E	_	A	_	P	O	I	N	T
4	5	3	9	13	1	12	19	27	8	1	22	5	27	1	27	16	15	9	14	20

Now suppose each letter is encoded by applying a function such as $f(x) = 2x + 5$, where x is the numerical value of each letter. For example:

The letter "a" would be coded as: $f(1) = 2(1) + 5 = 7$

The letter "b" would be coded as: $f(2) = 2(2) + 5 = 9$

Using this encoding function, we have

Message:	D	E	C	I	M	A	L	S	_	H	A	V	E	_	A	_	P	O	I	N	T
Original:	4	5	3	9	13	1	12	19	27	8	1	22	5	27	1	27	16	15	9	14	20
Coded Form:	13	15	11	23	31	7	29	43	59	21	7	49	15	59	7	59	37	35	23	33	45

To decode this message, the receiver would need to reverse the operations assigned by $f(x) = 2x + 5$. Since the function f multiplies x by 2 and then adds 5, we can reverse this process by subtracting 5 and dividing by 2. This is represented by $g(x) = \frac{x-5}{2}$.

1. a. One pair of students will encode the follow message according to $f(x) = 4x + 2$.

MATH IS THE KEY TO THE SCIENCES

54, 6, 82, 34, 110, 38, 78, 110, 82, 34, 22, 110, 46, 22, 102, 110, 82, 62, 110, 82, 34, 22, 110, 78, 14, 38, 22, 58, 14, 22, 78

b. The second pair of students will encode the follow message according to $f(x) = 3x - 1$.

MATH IS NOT A SPECTATOR SPORT

38, 2, 59, 23, 80, 26, 56, 80, 41, 44, 59, 80, 2, 80, 56, 47, 14, 8, 59, 2, 59, 44, 53, 80, 56, 47, 44, 53, 59

2. With each message encoded, the pairs will exchange papers. Each pair will then decode the message.

Instructor Note: This activity would be a great place to use the Table feature on a graphing calculator.

Chapter 8 Summary

Section 8.1 Introduction to Relations

Key Concepts

A set of ordered pairs (x, y) is called a **relation in x and y**.

The **domain** of a relation is the set of first components in the ordered pairs in the relation. The **range** of a relation is the set of second components in the ordered pairs.

Examples

Example 1

Let $A = \{(0, 0), (1, 1), (2, 4), (3, 9), (-1, 1), (-2, 4)\}$.

Domain of A: $\{0, 1, 2, 3, -1, -2\}$

Range of A: $\{0, 1, 4, 9\}$

Example 2

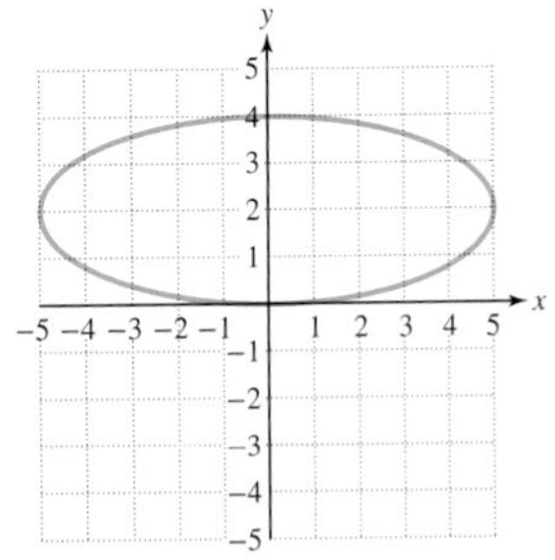

Domain: $[-5, 5]$
Range: $[0, 4]$

Section 8.2 Introduction to Functions

Key Concepts

Given a relation in x and y, we say "y is a **function** of x" if, for each element x in the domain, there is exactly one value of y in the range.

Note: This means that no two ordered pairs may have the same first coordinate and different second coordinates.

The Vertical Line Test for Functions

Consider a relation defined by a set of points (x, y) in a rectangular coordinate system. The graph defines y as a function of x if no vertical line intersects the graph in more than one point.

Examples

Example 1

Function $\{(1, 3), (2, 5), (6, 3)\}$

Not a function $\{(1, 3), (2, 5), (1, 4)\}$

same x

different y

Example 2

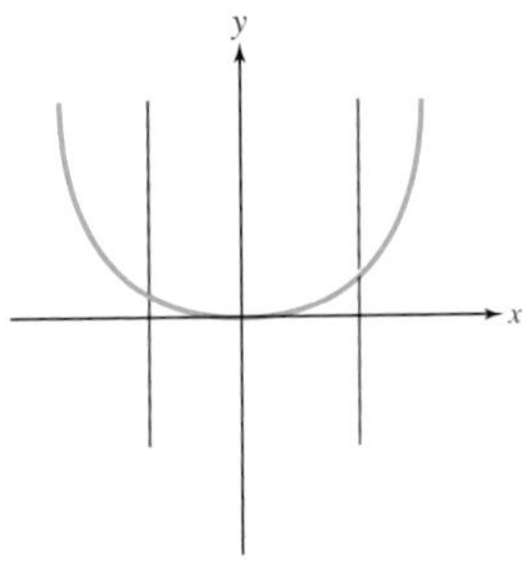

Function

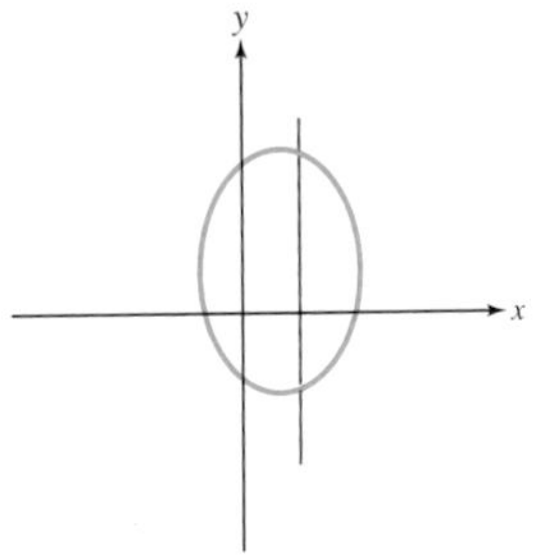

Not a function

Function Notation

$f(x)$ is the value of the function f at x.

Example 3

Given $f(x) = -3x^2 + 5x$, find $f(-2)$.

$$f(-2) = -3(-2)^2 + 5(-2)$$
$$= -12 - 10$$
$$= -22$$

The domain of a function defined by $y = f(x)$ is the set of x values that when substituted into the function produce a real number. In particular,

- Exclude values of x that make the denominator of a fraction zero.
- Exclude values of x that make the expression within a square root negative.

Example 4

Find the domain.

1. $f(x) = \dfrac{x+4}{x-5}$; Domain: $(-\infty, 5) \cup (5, \infty)$
2. $f(x) = \sqrt{x-3}$; Domain: $[3, \infty)$
3. $f(x) = 3x^2 - 5$; Domain: $(-\infty, \infty)$

Section 8.3 Graphs of Functions

Key Concepts

A function defined by $f(x) = mx + b$ $(m \neq 0)$ is a **linear function**. Its graph is a line with slope m and y-intercept $(0, b)$.

A function defined by $f(x) = k$ is a **constant function**. Its graph is a horizontal line.

A function defined by $f(x) = ax^2 + bx + c$ $(a \neq 0)$ is a **quadratic function**. Its graph is a **parabola**.

Graphs of basic functions:

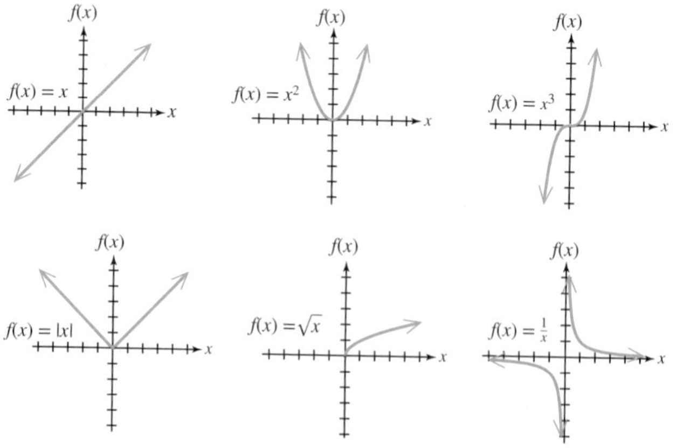

The x-intercepts of a function are determined by finding the real solutions to the equation $f(x) = 0$.

The y-intercept of a function is at $f(0)$.

Examples

Example 1

$f(x) = 2x - 3$

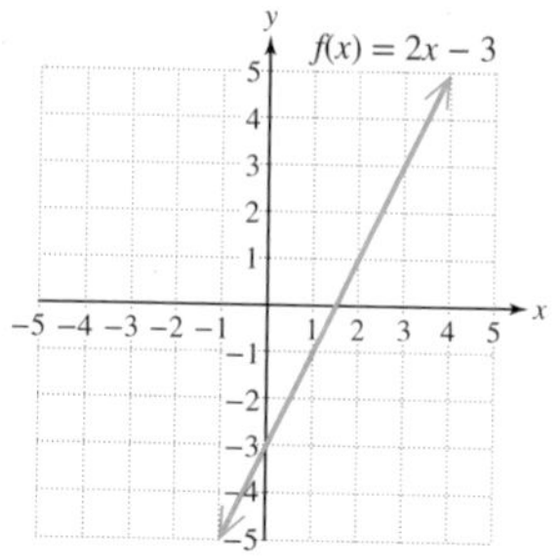

Linear function

$f(x) = 3$

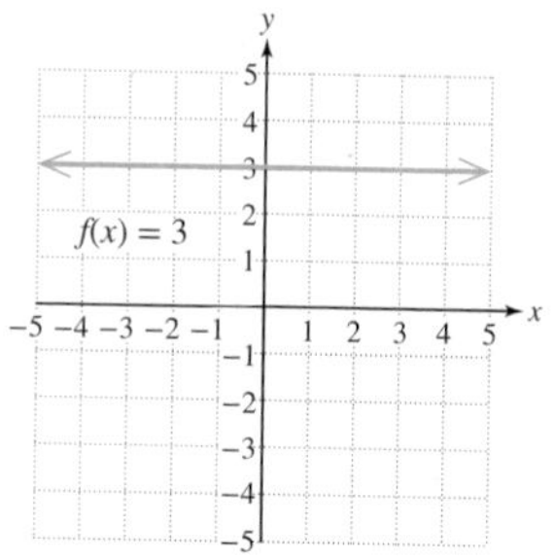

Constant function

Example 2

Find the x- and y-intercepts for the function pictured.

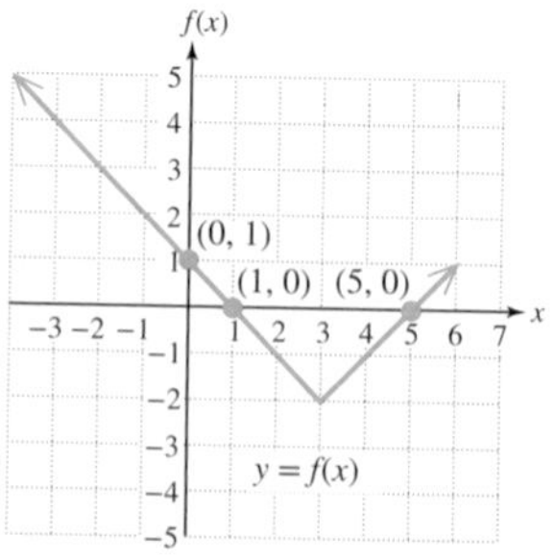

$f(x) = 0$, when $x = 1$ and $x = 5$.
The x-intercepts are $(1, 0)$ and $(5, 0)$.

$f(0) = 1$. The y-intercept is $(0, 1)$.

Section 8.4 Algebra of Functions and Composition

Key Concepts

The Algebra of Functions

Given two functions f and g, the functions $f+g, f-g, f\cdot g$, and $\frac{f}{g}$ are defined as

$(f+g)(x) = f(x) + g(x)$

$(f-g)(x) = f(x) - g(x)$

$(f\cdot g)(x) = f(x)\cdot g(x)$

$\left(\frac{f}{g}\right)(x) = \frac{f(x)}{g(x)}$ provided $g(x) \neq 0$

Composition of Functions

The **composition** of f and g, denoted $f \circ g$, is defined by the rule

$(f \circ g)(x) = f(g(x))$ provided that $g(x)$ is in the domain of f

Examples

Example 1

Let $g(x) = 5x + 1$ and $h(x) = x^3$. Find:

1. $(g + h)(3) = g(3) + h(3) = 16 + 27 = 43$
2. $(g \cdot h)(-1) = g(-1) \cdot h(-1) = (-4) \cdot (-1) = 4$
3. $(g - h)(x) = 5x + 1 - x^3$
4. $\left(\frac{g}{h}\right)(x) = \frac{5x+1}{x^3}, x \neq 0$

Example 2

Find $(f \circ g)(x)$ given the functions defined by $f(x) = 4x + 3$ and $g(x) = 7x$.

$$\begin{aligned}(f \circ g)(x) &= f(g(x)) \\ &= f(7x) \\ &= 4(7x) + 3 \\ &= 28x + 3\end{aligned}$$

Section 8.5 Variation

Key Concepts

Direct Variation

y varies directly as x.
y is directly proportional to x. } $y = kx$

Inverse Variation

y varies inversely as x.
y is inversely proportional to x. } $y = \frac{k}{x}$

Examples

Example 1

t varies directly as the square root of x.

$t = k\sqrt{x}$

Example 2

W is inversely proportional to the cube of x.

$W = \frac{k}{x^3}$

Joint Variation

$\left.\begin{array}{l} y \text{ varies jointly as } w \text{ and } z. \\ y \text{ is jointly proportional to } w \text{ and } z. \end{array}\right\}$ $y = kwz$

Steps to Find a Variation Model

1. Write a general variation model that relates the variables given in the problem. Let k represent the constant of variation.
2. Solve for k by substituting known values of the variables into the model from step 1.
3. Substitute the value of k into the original variation model from step 1.

Example 3

y is jointly proportional to x and to the square of z.

$y = kxz^2$

Example 4

C varies directly as the square root of d and inversely as t. If $C = 12$ when d is 9 and t is 6, find C if d is 16 and t is 12.

Step 1. $C = \dfrac{k\sqrt{d}}{t}$

Step 2. $12 = \dfrac{k\sqrt{9}}{6} \Rightarrow 12 = \dfrac{k \cdot 3}{6} \Rightarrow k = 24$

Step 3. $C = \dfrac{24\sqrt{d}}{t} \Rightarrow C = \dfrac{24\sqrt{16}}{12} \Rightarrow C = 8$

Chapter 8 Review Exercises

Section 8.1

For Exercises 1–4, find the domain and range.

1. $\left\{\left(\frac{1}{3}, 10\right), \left(6, -\frac{1}{2}\right), \left(\frac{1}{4}, 4\right), \left(7, \frac{2}{5}\right)\right\}$ Domain: $\left\{\frac{1}{3}, 6, \frac{1}{4}, 7\right\}$; range: $\left\{10, -\frac{1}{2}, 4, \frac{2}{5}\right\}$

2.

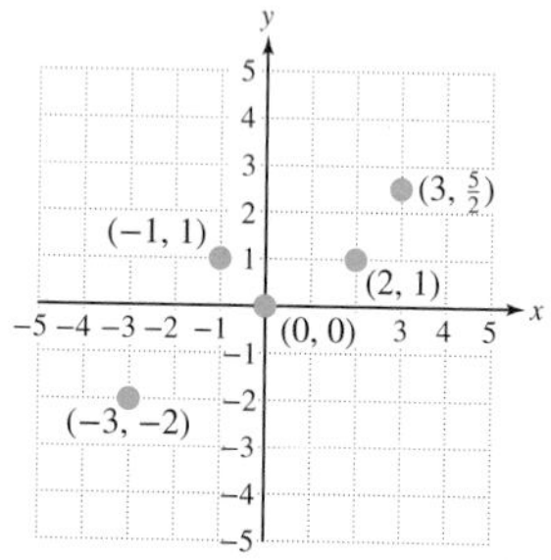

Domain: $\{-3, -1, 0, 2, 3\}$; range: $\left\{-2, 0, 1, \frac{5}{2}\right\}$

3.

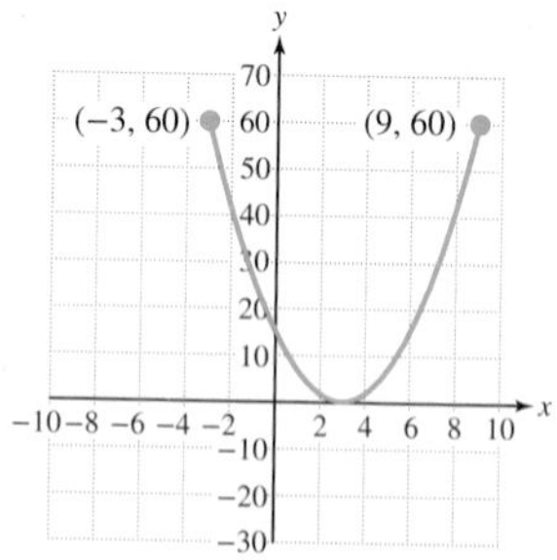

Domain: $[-3, 9]$; range: $[0, 60]$

4.

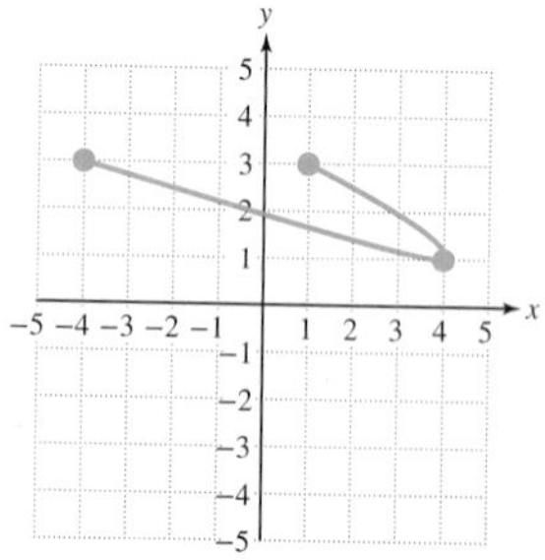

Domain: $[-4, 4]$; range: $[1, 3]$

Section 8.2

5. Sketch a relation that is *not* a function. (Answers may vary.)

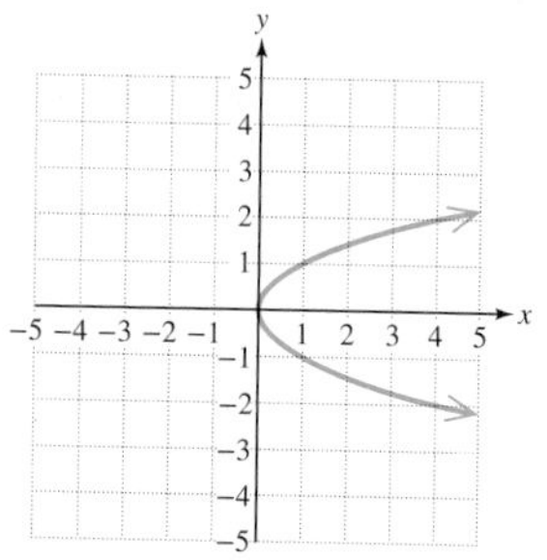

6. Sketch a relation that *is* a function. (Answers may vary.)

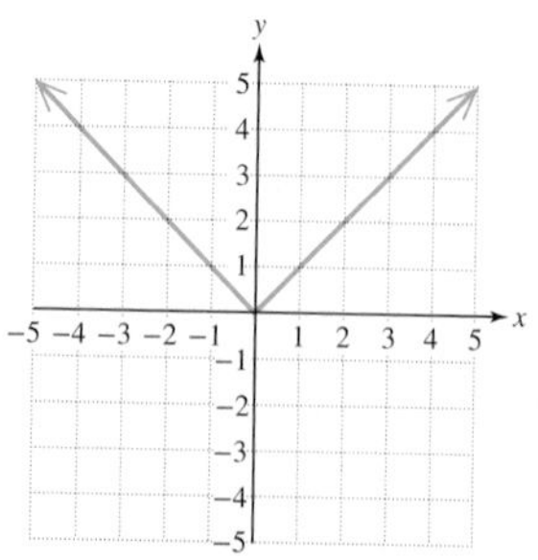

For Exercises 7–12:

a. Determine whether the relation defines y as a function of x.

b. Find the domain.

c. Find the range.

7.

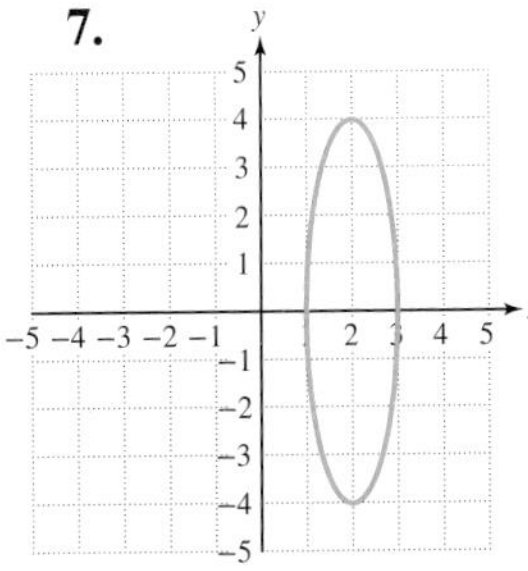

a. Not a function
b. $[1, 3]$ c. $[-4, 4]$

8.

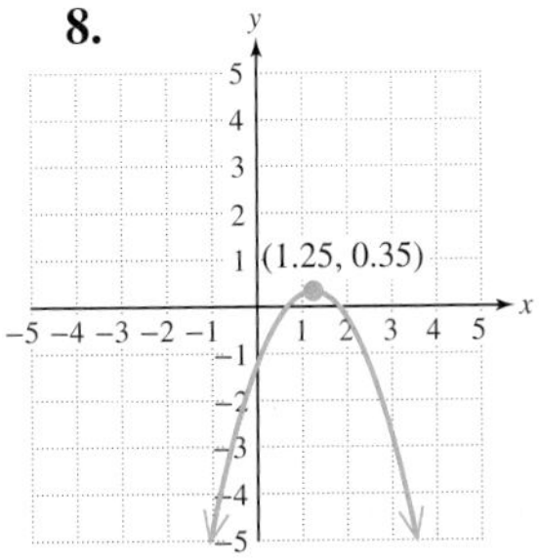

a. Function
b. $(-\infty, \infty)$ c. $(-\infty, 0.35]$

9. $\{(1, 3), (2, 3), (3, 3), (4, 3)\}$ a. Function b. $\{1, 2, 3, 4\}$ c. $\{3\}$

10. $\{(0, 2), (0, 3), (4, 4), (0, 5)\}$ a. Not a function b. $\{0, 4\}$ c. $\{2, 3, 4, 5\}$

11.

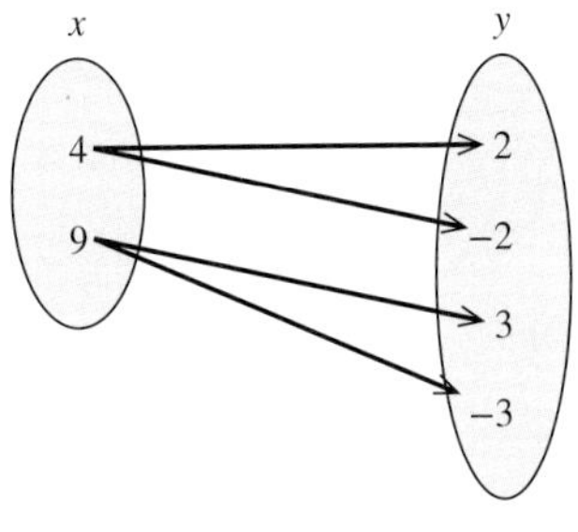

a. Not a function
b. $\{4, 9\}$
c. $\{2, -2, 3, -3\}$

12.

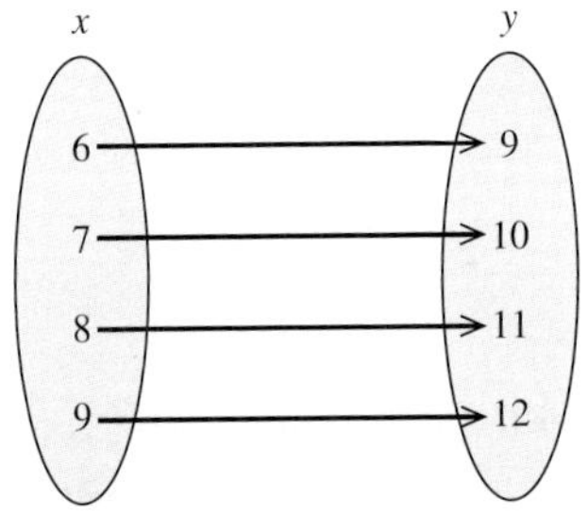

a. Function
b. $\{6, 7, 8, 9\}$
c. $\{9, 10, 11, 12\}$

For Exercises 13–20, find the function values given $f(x) = 6x^2 - 4$.

13. $f(0)$ -4

14. $f(1)$ 2

15. $f(-1)$ 2

16. $f(t)$ $6t^2 - 4$

17. $f(b)$ $6b^2 - 4$

18. $f(\pi)$ $6\pi^2 - 4$

19. $f(a)$ $6a^2 - 4$

20. $f(-2)$ 20

For Exercises 21–24, write the domain of each function in interval notation.

21. $g(x) = 7x^3 + 1$
$(-\infty, \infty)$

22. $h(x) = \dfrac{x + 10}{x - 11}$
$(-\infty, 11) \cup (11, \infty)$

23. $k(x) = \sqrt{x - 8}$
$[8, \infty)$

24. $w(x) = \sqrt{x + 2}$
$[-2, \infty)$

25. Anita is a waitress and makes \$12.50 per hour plus tips. Her tips average \$5 per table. In one 8-hr shift, Anita's total pay $p(x)$ can be described by $p(x) = 100 + 5x$, where x represents the number of tables she waits on. Determine how much Anita will earn if she waits on

a. 10 tables \$150
b. 15 tables \$175
c. 20 tables \$200

Section 8.3

For Exercises 26–31, sketch the functions from memory.

26. $h(x) = x$

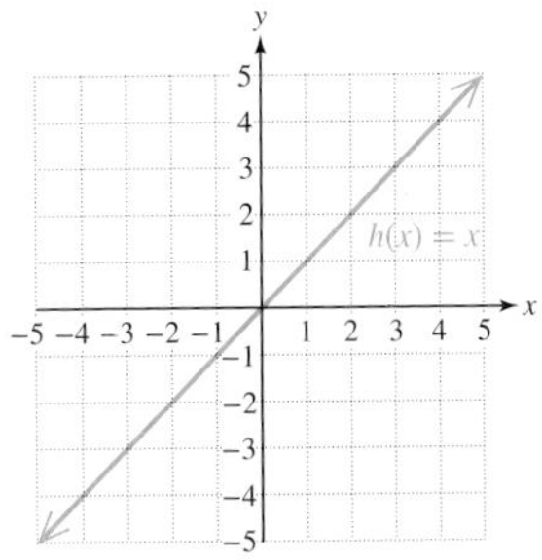

27. $f(x) = x^2$

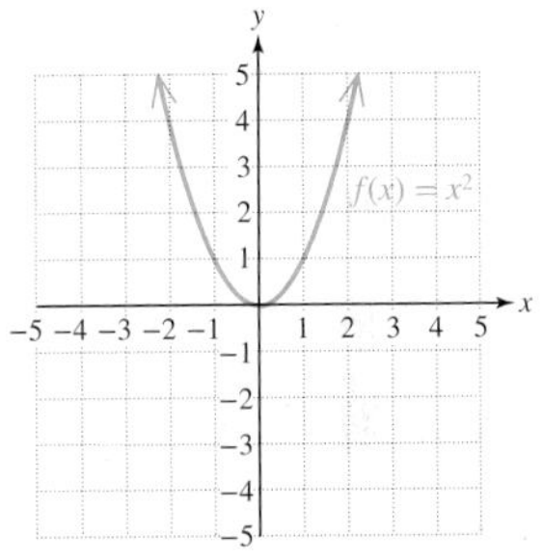

28. $g(x) = x^3$

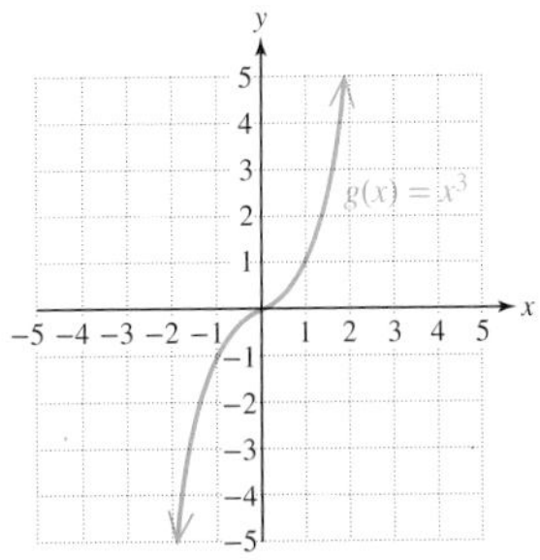

29. $w(x) = |x|$

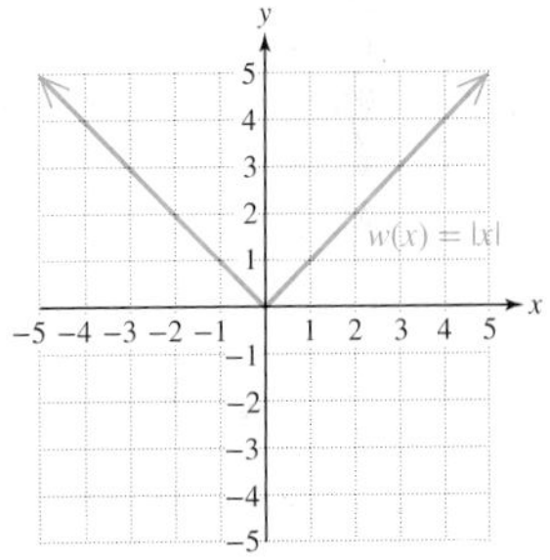

30. $s(x) = \sqrt{x}$

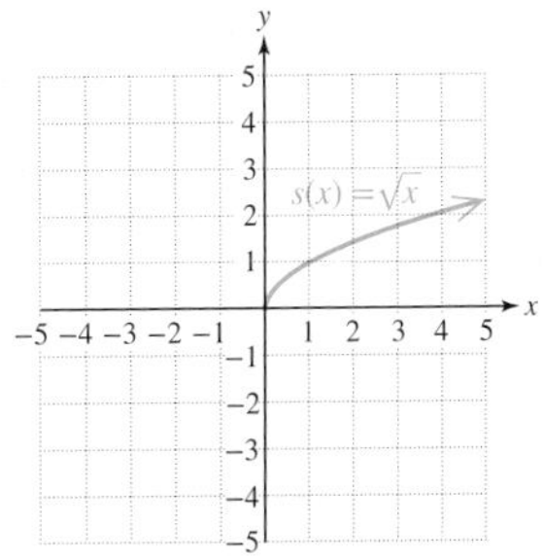

31. $r(x) = \dfrac{1}{x}$

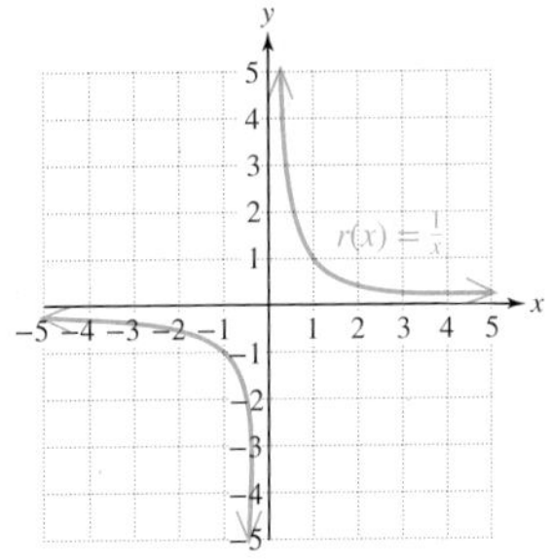

For Exercises 32–33, sketch the functions.

32. $q(x) = 3$

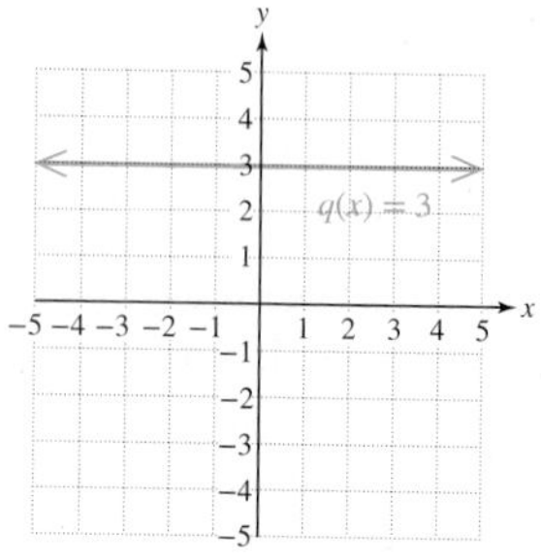

33. $k(x) = 2x + 1$

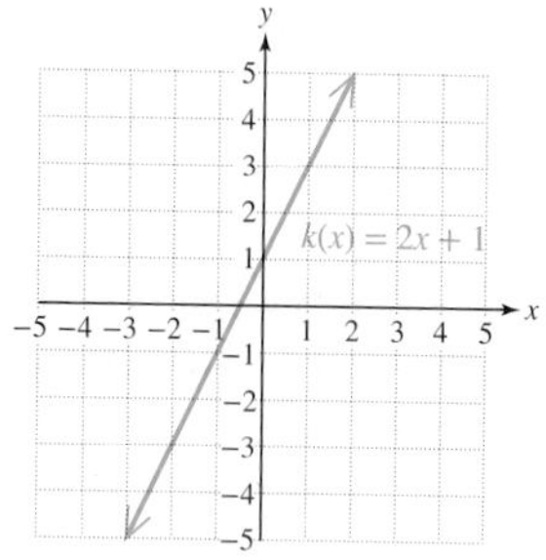

34. Given: $s(x) = (x - 2)^2$

a. Find $s(4)$, $s(-3)$, $s(2)$, $s(1)$, and $s(0)$.
$s(4) = 4$, $s(-3) = 25$, $s(2) = 0$, $s(1) = 1$, $s(0) = 4$

b. What is the domain of s?
$(-\infty, \infty)$

35. Given: $r(x) = 2\sqrt{x - 4}$

a. Find $r(2)$, $r(4)$, $r(5)$, and $r(8)$.
$r(2)$ is not a real number, $r(4) = 0$, $r(5) = 2$, $r(8) = 4$

b. What is the domain of r?
$[4, \infty)$

36. Given: $h(x) = \dfrac{3}{x - 3}$

a. Find $h(-3)$, $h(0)$, $h(2)$, and $h(5)$.
$h(-3) = -\frac{1}{2}$, $h(0) = -1$, $h(2) = -3$, $h(5) = \frac{3}{2}$

b. What is the domain of h?
$(-\infty, 3) \cup (3, \infty)$

37. Given: $k(x) = -|x + 3|$

a. Find $k(-5)$, $k(-4)$, $k(-3)$, and $k(2)$.
$k(-5) = -2$, $k(-4) = -1$, $k(-3) = 0$, $k(2) = -5$

b. What is the domain of k?
$(-\infty, \infty)$

For Exercises 38–39, find the x- and y-intercepts.

38. $p(x) = 4x - 7$ x-intercept: $\left(\frac{7}{4}, 0\right)$; y-intercept: $(0, -7)$

39. $q(x) = -2x + 9$ x-intercept: $\left(\frac{9}{2}, 0\right)$; y-intercept: $(0, 9)$

40. The function defined by $b(t) = 1.64t + 28.3$ represents the per capita consumption of bottled water in the United States since 2010. The values of $b(t)$ are measured in gallons, and $t = 0$ corresponds to the year 2010. (*Source:* U.S. Department of Agriculture)

a. Evaluate $b(0)$ and $b(5)$ and interpret the results in the context of this problem. $b(0) = 28.3$.
In 2010 consumption was 28.3 gal of bottled water per capita. $b(5) = 36.5$. In 2015 consumption was 36.5 gal of bottled water per capita.

b. Determine the slope and interpret its meaning in the context of this problem.
$m = 1.64$. Consumption increased at a rate of 1.64 gal/year.

For Exercises 41–46, refer to the graph.

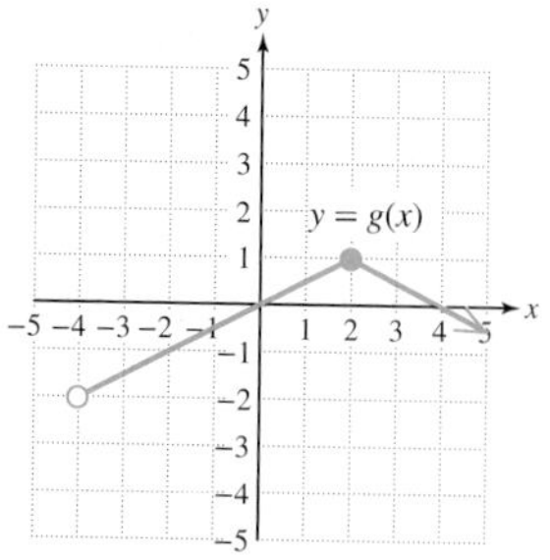

41. Find $g(-2)$. -1

42. Find $g(4)$. 0

43. For what value(s) of x is $g(x) = 0$? $x = 0$ and $x = 4$

44. For what value(s) of x is $g(x) = 4$?
There are no values of x for which $g(x) = 4$.

45. Write the domain of g. $(-4, \infty)$

46. Write the range of g. $(-\infty, 1]$

Section 8.4

For Exercises 47–54, refer to the functions defined here.

$$f(x) = x - 7 \qquad g(x) = -2x^3 - 8x$$
$$m(x) = x^2 \qquad n(x) = \frac{1}{x - 2}$$

Find the indicated functions.

47. $(f - g)(x)$
$(f - g)(x) = 2x^3 + 9x - 7$

48. $(f + g)(x)$
$(f + g)(x) = -2x^3 - 7x - 7$

49. $(f \cdot n)(x)$
$(f \cdot n)(x) = \dfrac{x - 7}{x - 2}, x \neq 2$

50. $(f \cdot m)(x)$
$(f \cdot m)(x) = x^3 - 7x^2$

51. $\left(\dfrac{f}{g}\right)(x)$
$\left(\dfrac{f}{g}\right)(x) = \dfrac{x - 7}{-2x^3 - 8x}, x \neq 0$

52. $\left(\dfrac{g}{f}\right)(x)$
$\left(\dfrac{g}{f}\right)(x) = \dfrac{-2x^3 - 8x}{x - 7}, x \neq 7$

53. $(m \circ f)(x)$
$(m \circ f)(x) = (x - 7)^2$ or $x^2 - 14x + 49$

54. $(n \circ f)(x)$
$(n \circ f)(x) = \dfrac{1}{x - 9}, x \neq 9$

For Exercises 55–58, refer to the functions defined for Exercises 47–54. Find the function values, if possible.

55. $(m \circ g)(-1)$ 100

56. $(n \circ g)(-1)$ $\frac{1}{8}$

57. $(f \circ g)(4)$ -167

58. $(g \circ f)(8)$ -10

59. Given: $f(x) = 2x + 1$ and $g(x) = x^2$

a. Find $(g \circ f)(x)$. $(2x + 1)^2$ or $4x^2 + 4x + 1$

b. Find $(f \circ g)(x)$. $2x^2 + 1$

c. Based on your answers to part (a), is $f \circ g$ equal to $g \circ f$? No, $f \circ g \neq g \circ f$

For Exercises 60–65, refer to the graph. Approximate the function values, if possible.

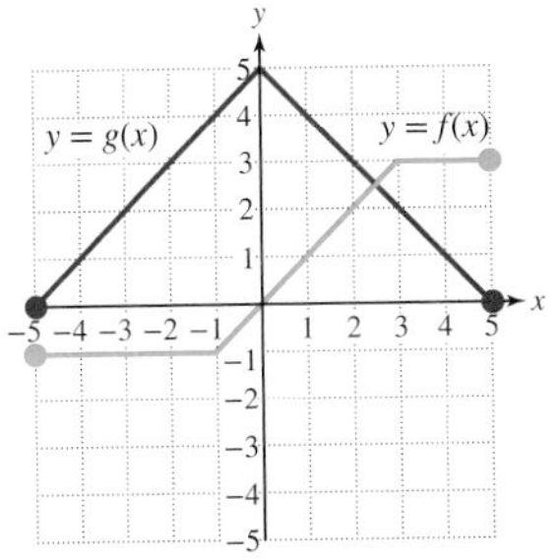

60. $\left(\frac{f}{g}\right)(1)$ $\frac{1}{4}$

61. $(f \cdot g)(-2)$ -3

62. $(f+g)(-4)$ 0

63. $(f-g)(2)$ -1

64. $(g \circ f)(-3)$ 4

65. $(f \circ g)(4)$ 1

Section 8.5

66. The force F applied to a spring varies directly with the distance d that the spring is stretched.

a. Write a variation model using k as the constant of variation. $F = kd$

b. When 6 lb of force is applied, the spring stretches 2 ft. Find k. $k = 3$

c. How much force is required to stretch the spring 4.2 ft? 12.6 lb

67. Suppose y varies inversely with the cube of x, and $y = 9$ when $x = 2$. Find y when $x = 3$. $y = \frac{8}{3}$

68. Suppose y varies jointly with x and the square root of z, and $y = 3$ when $x = 3$ and $z = 4$. Find y when $x = 8$ and $z = 9$. $y = 12$

69. The distance, d, that one can see to the horizon varies directly as the square root of the height above sea level. If a person 25 m above sea level can see 30 km, how far can a person see if she is 64 m above sea level? 48 km

Chapter 8 Test

For Exercises 1–2, **a.** determine if the relation defines y as a function of x, **b.** identify the domain, and **c.** identify the range.

1.

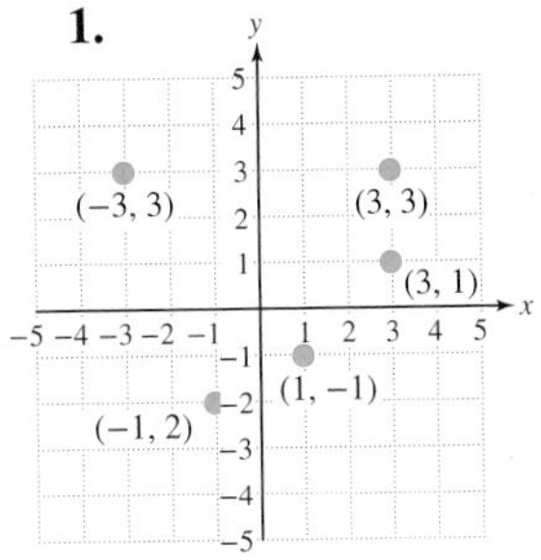

a. Not a function
b. $\{-3, -1, 1, 3\}$
c. $\{-2, -1, 1, 3\}$

2.

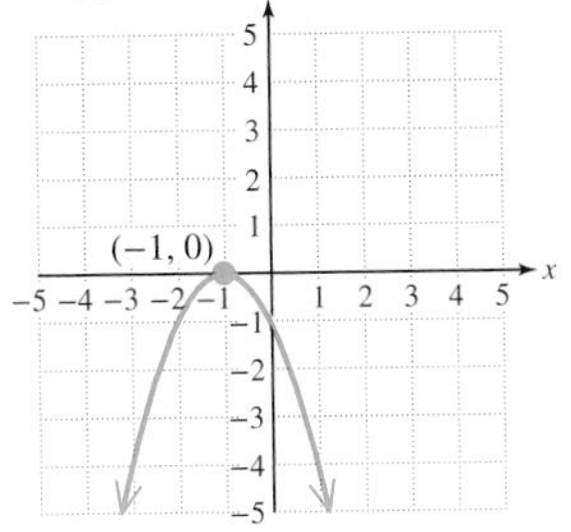

a. Function
b. $(-\infty, \infty)$
c. $(-\infty, 0]$

3. Explain how to find the x- and y-intercepts of the graph defined by $y = f(x)$.
To find the x-intercept(s), solve for the real solutions of the equation $f(x) = 0$. To find the y-intercept, find $f(0)$.

For Exercises 4–7, graph the functions.

4. $f(x) = -3x - 1$

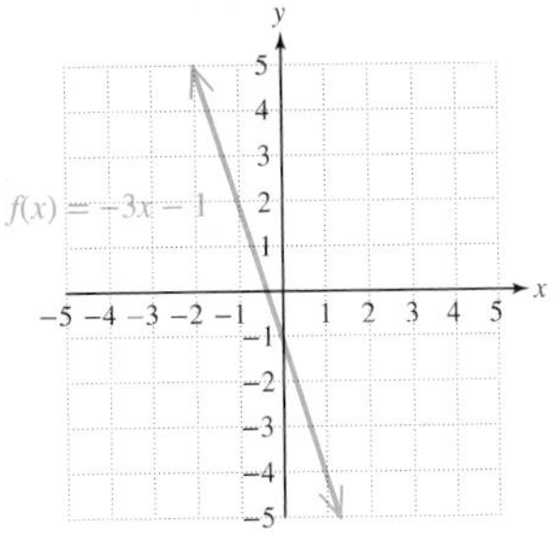

5. $k(x) = -2$

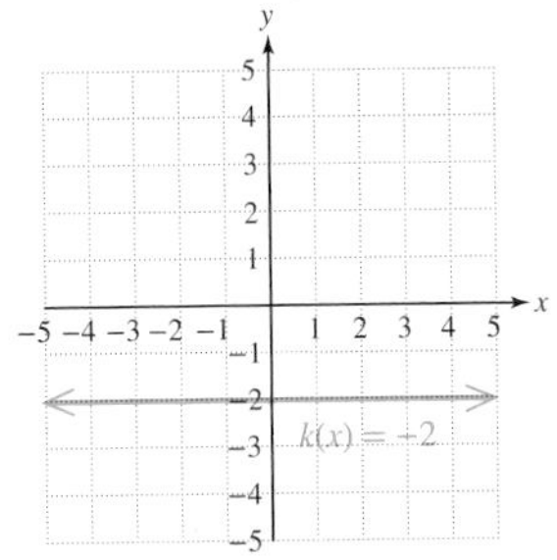

6. $p(x) = x^2$

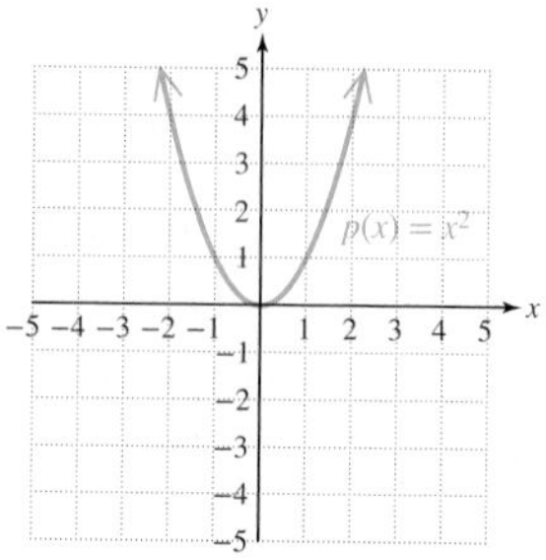

7. $w(x) = |x|$

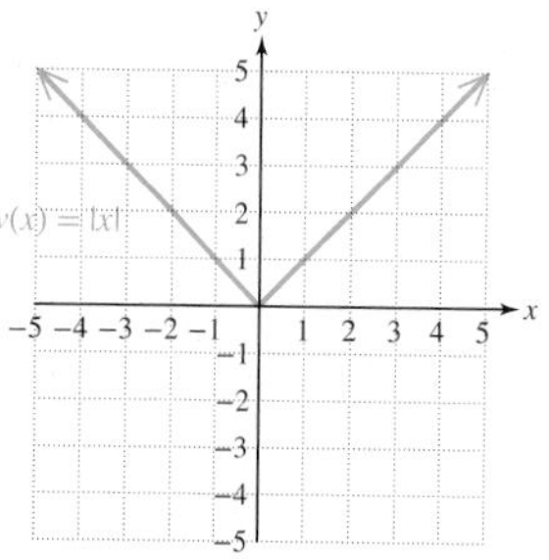

For Exercises 8–10, write the domain in interval notation.

8. $f(x) = \dfrac{x-5}{x+7}$ $(-\infty, -7) \cup (-7, \infty)$

9. $f(x) = \sqrt{x+7}$ $[-7, \infty)$

10. $h(x) = (x+7)(x-5)$ $(-\infty, \infty)$

11. Given: $r(x) = x^2 - 2x + 1$

a. Find $r(-2)$, $r(0)$, and $r(3)$.
$r(-2) = 9$, $r(0) = 1$, $r(3) = 4$

b. What is the domain of r?
$(-\infty, \infty)$

12. The function defined by $s(t) = -0.008t + 0.96$ approximates the per capita consumption of milk per day in the United States, t years after the study began. The values of $s(t)$ are measured in cups. (*Source:* U.S. Department of Agriculture) Evaluate $s(0)$ and $s(20)$ and interpret the results in the context of this problem.
$s(0) = 0.96$. At the beginning of the study (year 0), the per capita consumption was 0.96 c per day. $s(20) = 0.8$. In year 20, the per capita consumption was 0.8 c per day.

For Exercises 13–20, refer to the graph.

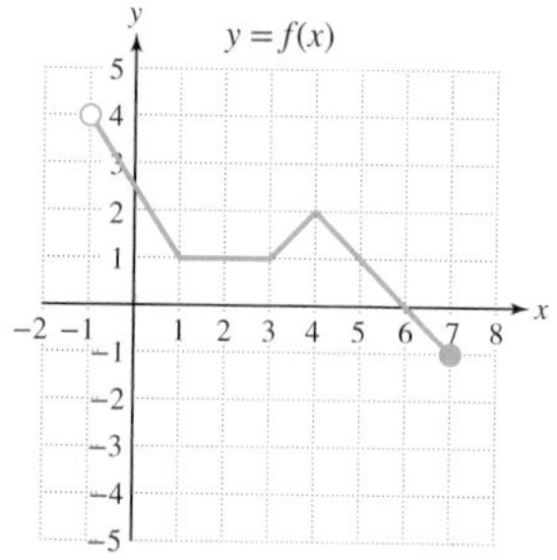

13. Find $f(1)$. 1

14. Find $f(4)$. 2

15. Write the domain of f. $(-1, 7]$

16. Write the range of f. $[-1, 4)$

17. Answer true or false. The value $y = 5$ is in the range of f. False

18. Find the x-intercept. $(6, 0)$

19. For what value(s) of x is $f(x) = 0$? $x = 6$

20. For what value(s) of x is $f(x) = 1$? All x in the interval $[1, 3]$ and $x = 5$

For Exercises 21–24, determine if the function is constant, linear, quadratic, or none of these.

21. $f(x) = -3x^2$
Quadratic

22. $g(x) = -3x$
Linear

23. $h(x) = -3$
Constant

24. $k(x) = -\dfrac{3}{x}$
None of these

25. Find the x- and y-intercepts for $f(x) = \dfrac{3}{4}x + 9$.
x-intercept: $(-12, 0)$; y-intercept: $(0, 9)$

For Exercises 26–34, refer to functions f, g, and h.

$f(x) = x - 4$ $\quad g(x) = x^2 + 2$ $\quad h(x) = \dfrac{1}{x}$

Find the indicated functions or function values.

26. $\left(\dfrac{f}{g}\right)(x)$ $\left(\dfrac{f}{g}\right)(x) = \dfrac{x-4}{x^2+2}$

27. $(h \cdot g)(x)$ $(h \cdot g)(x) = \dfrac{x^2+2}{x}, x \neq 0$

28. $(g \circ f)(x)$ $(g \circ f)(x) = x^2 - 8x + 18$

29. $(h \circ f)(x)$ $(h \circ f)(x) = \dfrac{1}{x-4}, x \neq 4$

30. $(f - g)(7)$ -48

31. $(h + f)(2)$ $-\dfrac{3}{2}$

32. $(h \circ g)(4)$ $\dfrac{1}{18}$

33. $(g \circ f)(0)$ 18

34. $\left(\dfrac{g}{f}\right)(x)$ $\left(\dfrac{g}{f}\right)(x) = \dfrac{x^2+2}{x-4}, x \neq 4$

35. The amount of medication prescribed for a patient varies directly as the patient's weight. If a 160-lb person is prescribed 6 mL of a medicine, how much medicine would be prescribed for a 220-lb person? 8.25 mL

36. The number of drinks sold at a concession stand varies inversely as price. If the price is set at \$1.25 per drink, then 400 drinks are sold. If the price is set at \$2.50 per drink, then how many drinks are sold? 200 drinks are sold.

Chapters 1–8 Cumulative Review Exercises

For Exercises 1–2, simplify the expression.

1. $\dfrac{5-2^3 \div 4+7}{-1-3(4-1)}$ -1

2. $4[-3x-5(y-2x)+3]-7(6y+x)$
$21x-62y+12$

For Exercises 3–4, solve the equation.

3. $\dfrac{2x-3}{6}-\dfrac{x+1}{4}=-2$ $\{-15\}$

4. $w-(3+2w)+5=-w-5$ $\{\ \}$

5. Solve the inequality. $-3x+2 \le 11$ $[-3, \infty)$

6. Find the x- and y-intercepts of $3x-5y=10$. Then graph the line. x-intercept: $\left(\frac{10}{3}, 0\right)$
y-intercept: $(0, -2)$

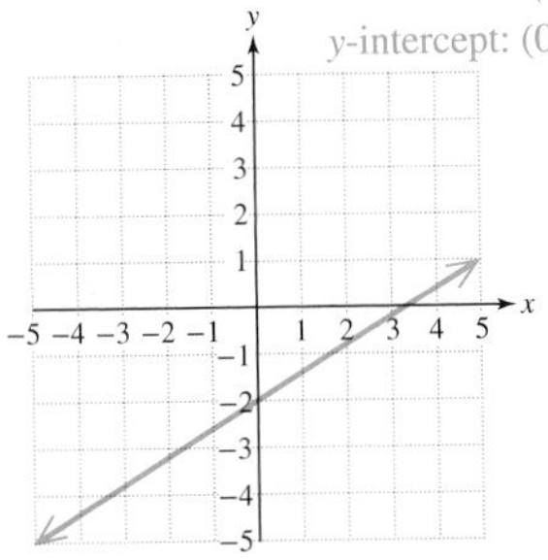

7. Find the slope of the line that passes through the point $(4, -5)$ and $(-6, -3)$. $m=-\frac{1}{5}$

8. Find the slope of the line $5x-2y=-10$. $m=\frac{5}{2}$

For Exercises 9–10, solve the system of equations.

9. $4x-y=9$ $\{(2, -1)\}$
$x+2y=0$

10. $x-2y+z=1$
$3x+y-2z=-22$
$4x+z=-11$
$\{(-4, 0, 5)\}$

11. Simplify. $\left(\dfrac{3x^2y}{9x^3y^{-2}}\right)^{-2}$ $\dfrac{9x^2}{y^6}$

For Exercises 12–13, perform the indicated operations.

12. $(5x^2-6x)+(-2x+7)$ $5x^2-8x+7$

13. $(5x^2-6x)(-2x+7)$ $-10x^3+47x^2-42x$

For Exercises 14–15, factor completely.

14. $2x^2+7x+3$ $(2x+1)(x+3)$

15. $5x^2-80$ $5(x-4)(x+4)$

16. Add. $\dfrac{5}{x-5}+\dfrac{x}{x+1}$ $\dfrac{x^2+5}{(x-5)(x+1)}$

17. Divide. $\dfrac{x^2+3x}{x-2} \div \dfrac{x^4+3x^3}{x^2-4}$ $\dfrac{x+2}{x^2}$

18. Determine the domain and range of the function.
$\{(2, 4), (-1, 4), (9, 2), (-6, 8)\}$
Domain: $\{2, -1, 9, -6\}$
Range: $\{4, 2, 8\}$

19. Determine the domain of $f(x)=\dfrac{x-5}{x}$.
$(-\infty, 0) \cup (0, \infty)$

20. Find $(f \circ g)(x)$ for $f(x)=x^2-6$ and $g(x)=x+1$.
$(f \circ g)(x)=x^2+2x-5$

More Equations and Inequalities

9

CHAPTER OUTLINE

Mathematics in Manufacturing

When a company manufactures a product, the goal is to obtain maximum profit at minimum cost. However, the production process is often limited by certain constraints such as the amount of labor available, the capacity of machinery, and the amount of money available for the company to invest in the process. To determine the optimal production parameters for a manufacturing process, mathematicians use **linear inequalities in two variables** and a process called linear programming.

© zhanglianxun/Getty Images RF

To understand the concept of a linear inequality in two variables, suppose that Morgan tutors algebra and physics and that he has exactly 15 hr of time available. Let x represent the amount of time he spends tutoring algebra, and let y represent the amount of time he spends tutoring physics. Then the inequality $x + y \leq 15$ represents the distribution of his time tutoring. Furthermore, since Morgan cannot tutor for a negative period of time, we also have $x \geq 0$ and $y \geq 0$. The solution set to the three inequalities is the set of points in the first quadrant on and below the line $x + y = 15$. For example, the point (5, 8) means that Morgan tutored 5 hr of algebra and 8 hr of physics.

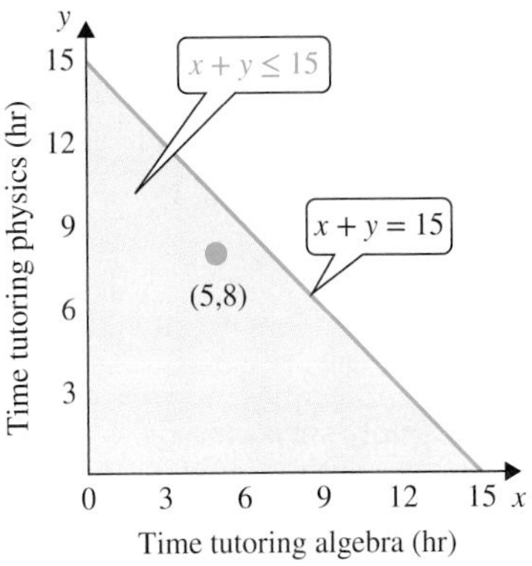

Section 9.1 Compound Inequalities

Concepts

1. Union and Intersection of Sets
2. Solving Compound Inequalities: And
3. Solving Inequalities of the Form $a < x < b$
4. Solving Compound Inequalities: Or
5. Applications of Compound Inequalities

1. Union and Intersection of Sets

We have already learned how to graph linear inequalities and to express the solution sets in interval notation and in set-builder notation. Now we will solve **compound inequalities** that involve the union or intersection of two or more inequalities.

Definition of *A* Union *B* and *A* Intersection *B*

The **union** of sets A and B, denoted $A \cup B$, is the set of elements that belong to set A or to set B or to both sets A and B.

The **intersection** of two sets A and B, denoted $A \cap B$, is the set of elements common to both A and B.

The concepts of the union and intersection of two sets are illustrated in Figures 9-1 and 9-2.

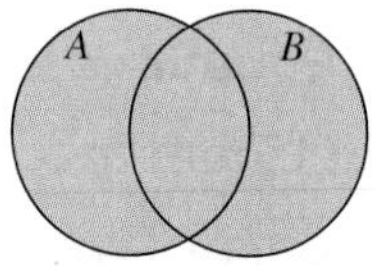

$A \cup B$
A union B
The elements in A *or* B *or* both

Figure 9-1

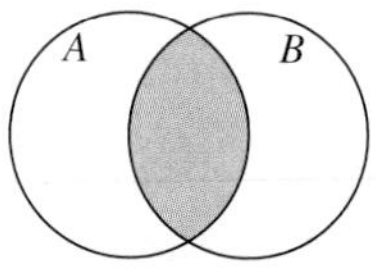

$A \cap B$
A intersection B
The elements in A *and* B

Figure 9-2

Classroom Example: p. 635, Exercise 8

Example 1 Finding the Union and Intersection of Sets

Given the sets: $A = \{a, b, c, d, e, f\}$ $B = \{a, c, e, g, i, k\}$ $C = \{g, h, i, j, k\}$

Find: **a.** $A \cup B$ **b.** $A \cap B$ **c.** $A \cap C$

Solution:

a. $A \cup B = \{a, b, c, d, e, f, g, i, k\}$

The union of A and B includes all the elements of A along with all the elements of B. Notice that the elements a, c, and e are not listed twice.

b. $A \cap B = \{a, c, e\}$

The intersection of A and B includes only those elements that are common to both sets.

c. $A \cap C = \{\ \}$ (the empty set)

Because A and C share no common elements, the intersection of A and C is the empty set (also called the null set).

TIP: The empty set is denoted by the symbol $\{\ \}$ or by the symbol $\emptyset$.

Skill Practice Given: $A = \{r, s, t, u, v, w\}$ $B = \{s, v, w, y, z\}$ $C = \{x, y, z\}$

Find: **1.** $B \cup C$ **2.** $A \cap B$ **3.** $A \cap C$

Answers

1. $\{s, v, w, x, y, z\}$ **2.** $\{s, v, w\}$ **3.** $\{\ \}$

Example 2 Finding the Union and Intersection of Sets

Classroom Examples: p. 635, Exercises 10 and 12

Given the sets: $A = \{x \mid x < 3\}$ $\quad B = \{x \mid x \geq -2\}$ $\quad C = \{x \mid x \geq 5\}$

Graph the following sets. Then express each set in interval notation.

a. $A \cap B$ **b.** $A \cup C$

Solution:

It is helpful to visualize the graphs of individual sets on the number line before taking the union or intersection.

a. Graph of $A = \{x \mid x < 3\}$

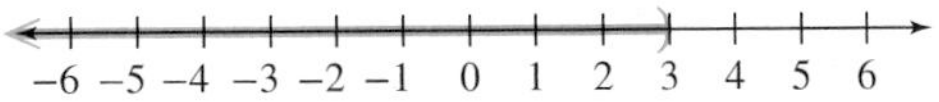

Graph of $B = \{x \mid x \geq -2\}$

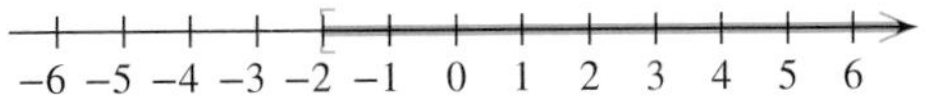

Graph of $A \cap B$ (the "overlap")

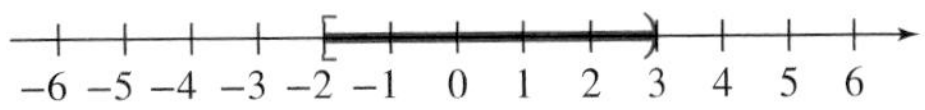

Interval notation: $[-2, 3)$

Note that the set $A \cap B$ represents the real numbers greater than or equal to -2 and less than 3. This relationship can be written more concisely as a compound inequality: $-2 \leq x < 3$. We can interpret this inequality as "x is between -2 and 3, including $x = -2$."

b. Graph of $A = \{x \mid x < 3\}$

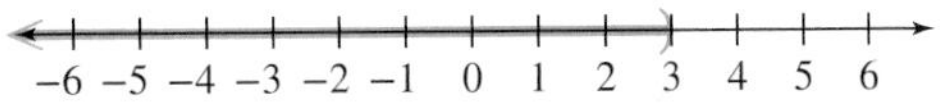

Graph of $C = \{x \mid x \geq 5\}$

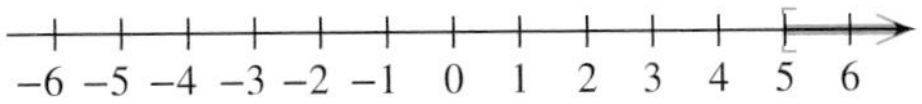

Graph of $A \cup C$

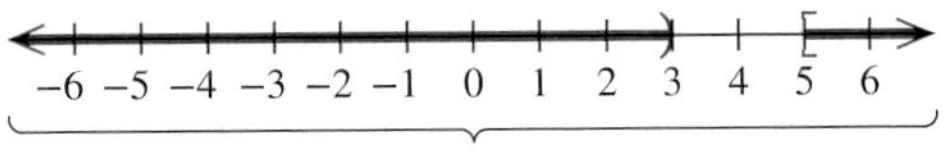

Interval notation: $(-\infty, 3) \cup [5, \infty)$

$A \cup C$ includes all elements from set A along with the elements from set C.

Skill Practice Given the sets: $A = \{x \mid x \geq -1\}$, $B = \{x \mid x < 4\}$, and $C = \{x \mid x \geq 9\}$, determine the union or intersection and express the answer in interval notation.

4. $A \cap B$ **5.** $B \cup C$

In Example 3, we find the union and intersection of sets expressed in interval notation.

Example 3 Finding the Union and Intersection of Two Intervals

Classroom Example: p. 635, Exercise 22

Find the union or intersection as indicated. Write the answer in interval notation.

a. $(-\infty, -2) \cup [-4, 3)$ **b.** $(-\infty, -2) \cap [-4, 3)$

Solution:

a. $(-\infty, -2) \cup [-4, 3)$ To find the union, graph each interval separately. The union is the collection of real numbers that lie in the first interval, the second interval, or both intervals.

Answers

4. $[-1, 4)$ **5.** $(-\infty, 4) \cup [9, \infty)$

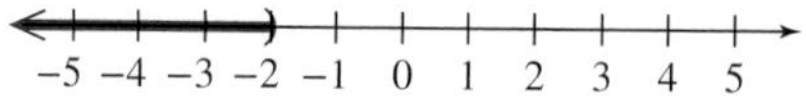

$(-\infty, -2)$

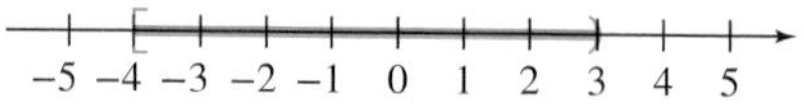

$[-4, 3)$

The union is $(-\infty, 3)$.

The union consists of all real numbers in the red interval along with the real numbers in the blue interval: $(-\infty, 3)$

b. $(-\infty, -2) \cap [-4, 3)$

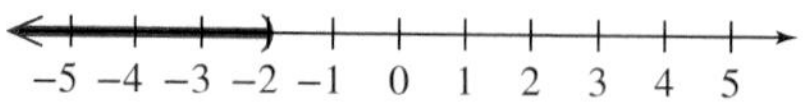

$(-\infty, -2)$

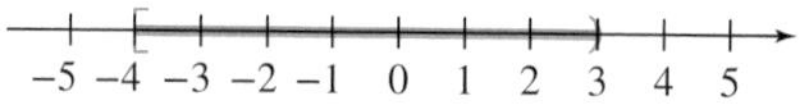

$[-4, 3)$

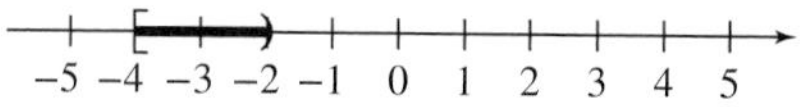

The intersection is the "overlap" of the two intervals: $[-4, -2)$.

The intersection is $[-4, -2)$.

Skill Practice Find the union or intersection. Write the answer in interval notation.

6. $(-\infty, -5] \cup (-7, 0)$ **7.** $(-\infty, -5] \cap (-7, 0)$

2. Solving Compound Inequalities: And

The solution to two inequalities joined by the word *and* is the intersection of their solution sets. For example, to play in a golf tournament for juniors, a child's age x must be at least 8 yr and not more than 16 yr. This is translated as $x \geq 8$ and $x \leq 16$. The word "and" joins the two inequalities and implies that we want the intersection of the individual solution sets.

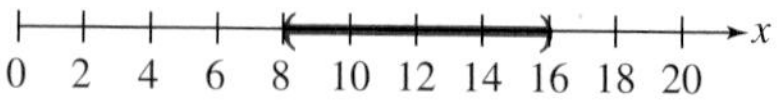

Solving a Compound Inequality: And

Step 1 Solve and graph each inequality separately.

Step 2 If the inequalities are joined by the word *and*, find the intersection of the two solution sets.

Step 3 Express the solution set in interval notation or in set-builder notation.

As you work through the examples in this section, remember that multiplying or dividing an inequality by a negative factor reverses the direction of the inequality sign.

Classroom Example: p. 635, Exercise 28

Instructor Note: If students are struggling with the issue of when to reverse the inequality symbol, some examples using numbers may help:

$2 < 5$ but $-2 > -5$
$-4 < -2$ but $4 > 2$

Answers
6. $(-\infty, 0)$ **7.** $(-7, -5]$

Example 4 Solving a Compound Inequality: And

Solve the compound inequality.

$$-2x < 6 \quad \text{and} \quad x + 5 \leq 7$$

Solution:

$-2x < 6$	and	$x + 5 \leq 7$	Solve each inequality separately.
$\dfrac{-2x}{-2} > \dfrac{6}{-2}$	and	$x \leq 2$	Reverse the first inequality sign.
$x > -3$	and	$x \leq 2$	

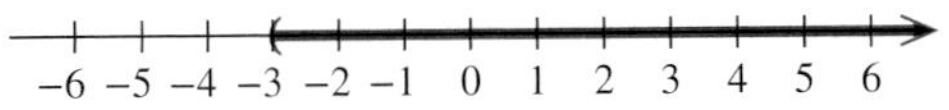

$\{x \mid x > -3\}$

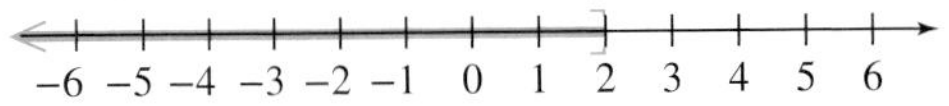

$\{x \mid x \le 2\}$

Identify the intersection of the solution sets: $\{x \mid -3 < x \le 2\}$

The solution is $\{x \mid -3 < x \le 2\}$, or equivalently in interval notation, $(-3, 2]$.

Skill Practice Solve the compound inequality.

8. $5x + 2 \ge -8$ and $-4x > -24$

Example 5 Solving a Compound Inequality: And

Classroom Example: p. 635, Exercise 36

Solve the compound inequality.

$$4.4a + 3.1 < -12.3 \quad \text{and} \quad -2.8a + 9.1 < -6.3$$

Solution:

$$4.4a + 3.1 < -12.3 \quad \text{and} \quad -2.8a + 9.1 < -6.3$$

$$4.4a < -15.4 \quad \text{and} \quad -2.8a < -15.4$$

Solve each inequality separately.

$$\frac{4.4a}{4.4} < \frac{-15.4}{4.4} \quad \text{and} \quad \frac{-2.8a}{-2.8} > \frac{-15.4}{-2.8}$$

Reverse the second inequality sign.

$$a < -3.5 \quad \text{and} \quad a > 5.5$$

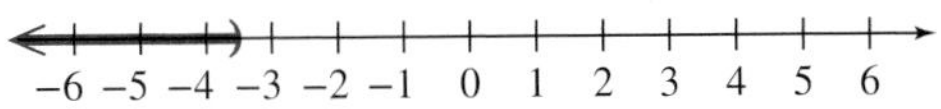

$\{a \mid a < -3.5\}$

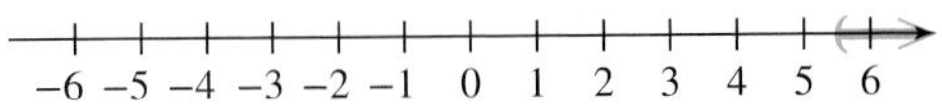

$\{a \mid a > 5.5\}$

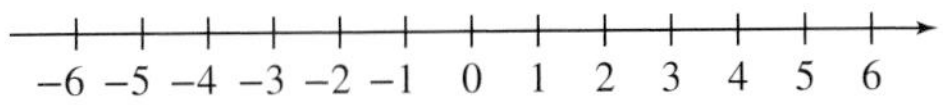

The intersection of the solution sets is the empty set: { }

There are no real numbers that are simultaneously less than -3.5 and greater than 5.5. There is no solution.

The solution set is { }.

Skill Practice Solve the compound inequality.

9. $3.2y - 2.4 > 16.8$ and $-4.1y \ge 8.2$

Answers

8. $\{x \mid -2 \le x < 6\}$; $[-2, 6)$

9. { }

Classroom Example: p. 635, Exercise 34

Example 6 Solving a Compound Inequality: And

Solve the compound inequality.

$$-\frac{2}{3}x \le 6 \quad \text{and} \quad -\frac{1}{2}x < 1$$

Solution:

$$-\frac{2}{3}x \le 6 \qquad \text{and} \qquad -\frac{1}{2}x < 1$$

$$-\frac{3}{2}\left(-\frac{2}{3}x\right) \ge -\frac{3}{2}(6) \qquad \text{and} \qquad -2\left(-\frac{1}{2}x\right) > -2(1)$$

Solve each inequality separately.

$$x \ge -9 \qquad \text{and} \qquad x > -2$$

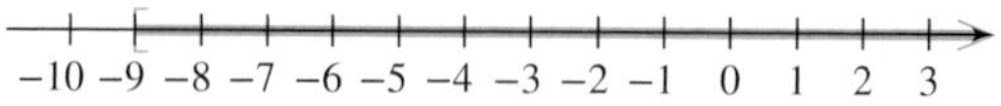

$\{x \mid x \ge -9\}$

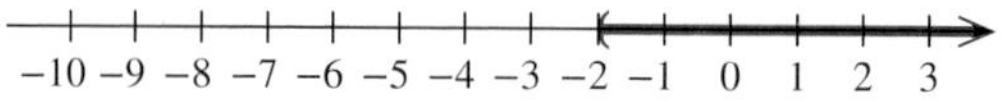

$\{x \mid x > -2\}$

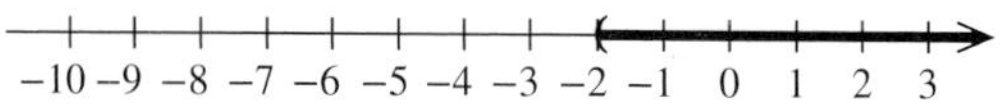

Identify the intersection of the solution sets: $\{x \mid x > -2\}$

The solution set is $\{x \mid x > -2\}$, or in interval notation, $(-2, \infty)$.

Skill Practice Solve the compound inequality.

10. $-\frac{1}{4}z < \frac{5}{8}$ and $\frac{1}{2}z + 1 \ge 3$

3. Solving Inequalities of the Form $a < x < b$

Instructor Note: Remind students that a "three-part" inequality is used to imply that x is *between* two values. Show them why the following statements fail to do this.

$-5 > x < 4$
$-6 < x > 8$
$5 < x < -2$

An inequality of the form $a < x < b$ is a type of compound inequality, one that defines two simultaneous conditions on x.

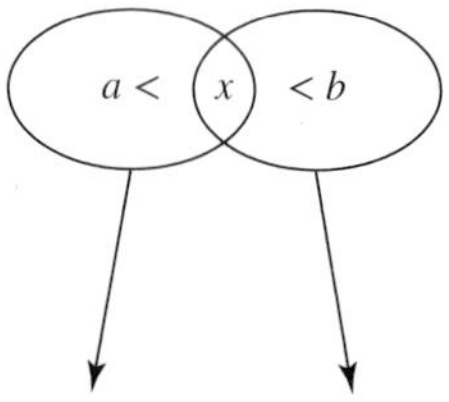

$a < x$ *and* $x < b$

The solution set to the compound inequality $a < x < b$ is the *intersection* of the solution sets to the inequalities $a < x$ and $x < b$.

Classroom Example: p. 636, Exercise 44

Example 7 Solving an Inequality of the Form $a < x < b$

Solve the inequality. $-4 < 3x + 5 \le 10$

Solution:

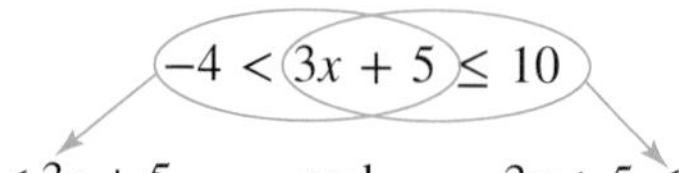

$-4 < 3x + 5 \qquad \text{and} \qquad 3x + 5 \le 10$

Set up the intersection of two inequalities.

Answer

10. $\{z \mid z \ge 4\}$; $[4, \infty)$

$-9 < 3x$	and	$3x \le 5$	Solve each inequality.
$\dfrac{-9}{3} < \dfrac{3x}{3}$	and	$\dfrac{3x}{3} \le \dfrac{5}{3}$	
$-3 < x$	and	$x \le \dfrac{5}{3}$	Recall $-3 < x$ is the same as $x > -3$.
	$-3 < x \le \dfrac{5}{3}$		Identify the intersection of the solution sets.

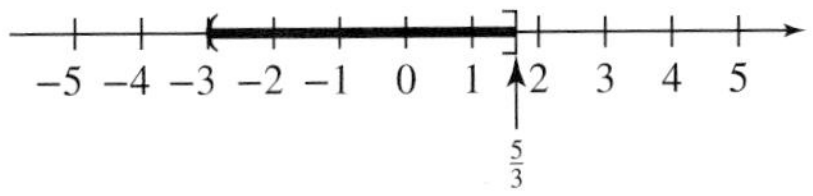

The solution is $\{x \mid -3 < x \le \frac{5}{3}\}$, or equivalently in interval notation, $(-3, \frac{5}{3}]$.

Skill Practice Solve the inequality.

11. $-6 \le 2x - 5 < 1$

To solve an inequality of the form $a < x < b$, we can also work with the inequality as a "three-part" inequality and isolate x. This is demonstrated in Example 8.

Example 8 **Solving an Inequality of the Form $a < x < b$**

Classroom Example: p. 636, Exercise 48

Solve the inequality. $2 \ge \dfrac{p-2}{-3} \ge -1$

Solution:

$2 \ge \dfrac{p-2}{-3} \ge -1$	Isolate the variable in the middle part.
$-3(2) \le -3\left(\dfrac{p-2}{-3}\right) \le -3(-1)$	Multiply all three parts by -3. Remember to reverse the inequality signs.
$-6 \le p - 2 \le 3$	Simplify.
$-6 + 2 \le p - 2 + 2 \le 3 + 2$	Add 2 to all three parts to isolate p.
$-4 \le p \le 5$	

The solution is $\{p \mid -4 \le p \le 5\}$, or equivalently in interval notation $[-4, 5]$.

Skill Practice Solve the inequality.

12. $8 > \dfrac{t+4}{-2} > -5$

4. Solving Compound Inequalities: Or

In Examples 9 and 10, we solve compound inequalities that involve inequalities joined by the word "or." In such a case, the solution to the compound inequality is the union of the solution sets of the individual inequalities.

Answers

11. $\{x \mid -\frac{1}{2} \le x < 3\}$; $[-\frac{1}{2}, 3)$

12. $\{t \mid -20 < t < 6\}$; $(-20, 6)$

For example, a resting heart rate x is potentially abnormal if it is below 50 beats per minute or above 100 beats per minute.

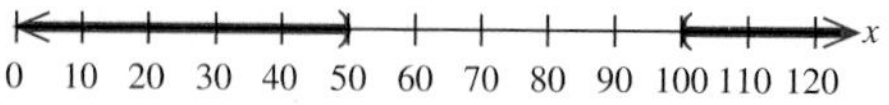

Solving a Compound Inequality: Or

Step 1 Solve and graph each inequality separately.

Step 2 If the inequalities are joined by the word *or*, find the union of the two solution sets.

Step 3 Express the solution set in interval notation or in set-builder notation.

Classroom Example: p. 636, Exercise 56

Example 9 Solving a Compound Inequality: Or

Solve the compound inequality. $-3y - 5 > 4$ or $4 - y \leq 6$

Solution:

$-3y - 5 > 4$ or $4 - y \leq 6$

$-3y > 9$ or $-y \leq 2$ Solve each inequality separately.

$\dfrac{-3y}{-3} < \dfrac{9}{-3}$ or $\dfrac{-y}{-1} \geq \dfrac{2}{-1}$ Reverse the inequality signs.

$y < -3$ or $y \geq -2$

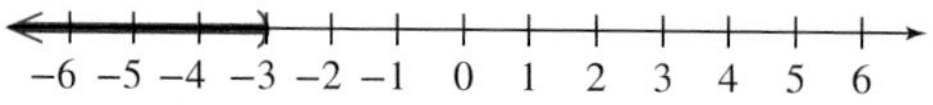

$\{y \mid y < -3\}$

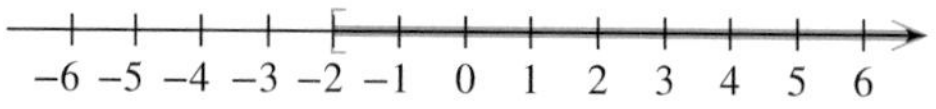

$\{y \mid y \geq -2\}$

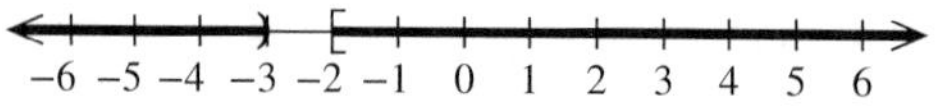

Identify the union of the solution sets: $\{y \mid y < -3 \text{ or } y \geq -2\}$

The solution is $\{y \mid y < -3 \text{ or } y \geq -2\}$ or, equivalently in interval notation, $(-\infty, -3) \cup [-2, \infty)$.

Skill Practice Solve the compound inequality.

13. $-10t - 8 \geq 12$ or $3t - 6 > 3$

Answer

13. $\{t \mid t \leq -2 \text{ or } t > 3\}$; $(-\infty, -2] \cup (3, \infty)$

Example 10 **Solving a Compound Inequality: Or**

Solve the compound inequality. $4x + 3 < 16$ or $-2x < 3$

Solution:

$$4x + 3 < 16 \quad \text{or} \quad -2x < 3$$

$$4x < 13 \quad \text{or} \quad x > -\frac{3}{2}$$ Solve each inequality separately.

$$x < \frac{13}{4} \quad \text{or} \quad x > -\frac{3}{2}$$

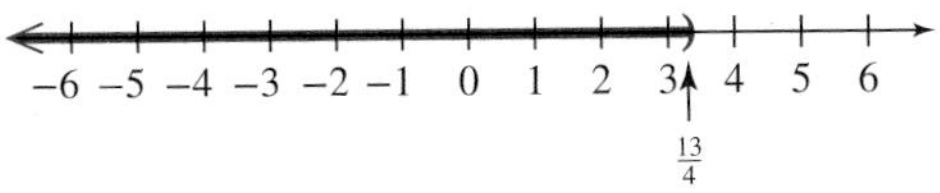

$\{x \mid x < \frac{13}{4}\}$

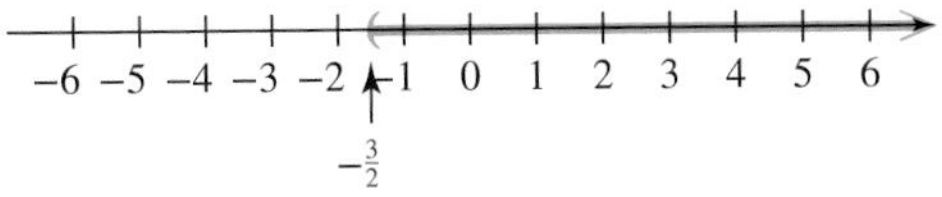

$\{x \mid x > -\frac{3}{2}\}$

Identify the union of the solution sets.

The union of the solution sets is $\{x \mid x$ is a real number$\}$, or equivalently, $(-\infty, \infty)$.

Skill Practice Solve the compound inequality.

14. $x - 7 > -2$ or $-6x > -48$

Classroom Example: p. 636, Exercise 62

5. Applications of Compound Inequalities

Compound inequalities are used in many applications, as shown in Examples 11 and 12.

Example 11 **Translating Compound Inequalities**

The normal level of thyroid-stimulating hormone (TSH) for adults ranges from 0.4 to 4.8 microunits per milliliter (μU/mL), inclusive. Let x represent the amount of TSH measured in microunits per milliliter.

a. Write an inequality representing the normal range of TSH.

b. Write a compound inequality representing abnormal TSH levels.

Solution:

a. $0.4 \le x \le 4.8$ **b.** $x < 0.4$ or $x > 4.8$

Skill Practice The length of a normal human pregnancy, w, is from 37 to 41 weeks, inclusive.

15. Write an inequality representing the normal length of a pregnancy.

16. Write a compound inequality representing an abnormal length for a pregnancy.

Classroom Example: p. 637, Exercise 76

Answers

14. $\{x \mid x$ is a real number$\}$; $(-\infty, \infty)$

15. $37 \le w \le 41$

16. $w < 37$ or $w > 41$

TIP:

- In mathematics, the word "between" means strictly between two values. That is, the endpoints are *excluded*.
  Example: x is between 4 and 10 $\Rightarrow$ (4, 10).
- If the word "inclusive" is added to the statement, then we *include* the endpoints.
  Example: x is between 4 and 10, inclusive $\Rightarrow$ [4, 10].

Classroom Example: p. 637, Exercise 80

Example 12 Translating and Solving a Compound Inequality

The sum of a number and 4 is between −5 and 12. Find all such numbers.

Solution:

Let x represent a number.

$-5 < x + 4 < 12$ Translate the inequality.

$-5 - 4 < x + 4 - 4 < 12 - 4$ Subtract 4 from all three parts of the inequality.

$-9 < x < 8$

The number may be any real number between −9 and 8: $\{x \mid -9 < x < 8\}$.

Skill Practice

17. The sum of twice a number and 11 is between 21 and 31. Find all such numbers.

Answer

17. Any real number between 5 and 10: $\{x \mid 5 < x < 10\}$

Section 9.1 Practice Exercises

For additional exercises, see Classroom Activities 9.1A–9.1D in the *Student's Resource Manual* at www.mhhe.com/moh.

Vocabulary and Key Concepts

1. a. The __union__ of two sets A and B, denoted by __$A \cup B$__, is the set of elements that belong to A or B or both A and B.

b. The __intersection__ of two sets A and B, denoted by __$A \cap B$__, is the set of elements common to both A and B.

c. The solution set to the compound inequality $x < c$ and $x > d$ is the (union/intersection) of the solution sets of the individual inequalities. intersection

d. The compound inequality $a < x$ and $x < b$ can be written as the three-part inequality __$a < x < b$__.

e. The solution set to the compound inequality $x < a$ or $x > b$ is the (union/intersection) of the solution sets of the individual inequalities. union

Review Exercises

For Exercises 2–6, solve the linear inequality. Write the solution in interval notation.

2. $-6u + 8 > 2$ $(-\infty, 1)$

3. $2 - 3z \geq -4$ $(-\infty, 2]$

4. $-12 \leq \frac{3}{4}p$ $[-16, \infty)$

5. $5 > \frac{1}{3}w$ $(-\infty, 15)$

6. $-3x + 5 < -2x + 1$ $(4, \infty)$

Writing Translating Expression Geometry Scientific Calculator Video

Concept 1: Union and Intersection of Sets

7. Given $M = \{-3, -1, 1, 3, 5\}$ and $N = \{-4, -3, -2, -1, 0\}$, **(See Example 1.)**

List the elements of the following sets.

a. $M \cap N$ $\{-3, -1\}$ **b.** $M \cup N$ $\{-4, -3, -2, -1, 0, 1, 3, 5\}$

8. Given $P = \{a, b, c, d, e, f, g, h, i\}$ and $Q = \{a, e, i, o, u\}$,

List the elements of the following sets.

a. $P \cap Q$ $\{a, e, i\}$ **b.** $P \cup Q$ $\{a, b, c, d, e, f, g, h, i, o, u\}$

For Exercises 9–20, refer to the sets A, B, C, and D. Determine the union or intersection as indicated. Express the answer in interval notation, if possible. **(See Example 2.)**

$A = \{x \mid x < -4\}$, $B = \{x \mid x > 2\}$, $C = \{x \mid x \geq -7\}$, $D = \{x \mid 0 \leq x < 5\}$

9. $A \cap C$ $[-7, -4)$

10. $B \cap C$ $(2, \infty)$

11. $A \cup B$ $(-\infty, -4) \cup (2, \infty)$

12. $A \cup D$ $(-\infty, -4) \cup [0, 5)$

13. $A \cap B$ $\{\ \}$

14. $A \cap D$ $\{\ \}$

15. $B \cup C$ $[-7, \infty)$

16. $B \cup D$ $[0, \infty)$

17. $C \cap D$ $[0, 5)$

18. $B \cap D$ $(2, 5)$

19. $C \cup D$ $[-7, \infty)$

20. $A \cup C$ $(-\infty, \infty)$

For Exercises 21–26, find the intersection and union of sets as indicated. Write the answers in interval notation. **(See Example 3.)**

21. a. $(-2, 5) \cap [-1, \infty)$ $[-1, 5)$

b. $(-2, 5) \cup [-1, \infty)$ $(-2, \infty)$

22. a. $(-\infty, 4) \cap [-1, 5)$ $[-1, 4)$

b. $(-\infty, 4) \cup [-1, 5)$ $(-\infty, 5)$

23. a. $\left(-\frac{5}{2}, 3\right) \cap \left(-1, \frac{9}{2}\right)$ $(-1, 3)$

b. $\left(-\frac{5}{2}, 3\right) \cup \left(-1, \frac{9}{2}\right)$ $\left(-\frac{5}{2}, \frac{9}{2}\right)$

24. a. $(-3.4, 1.6) \cap (-2.2, 4.1)$ $(-2.2, 1.6)$

b. $(-3.4, 1.6) \cup (-2.2, 4.1)$ $(-3.4, 4.1)$

25. a. $(-4, 5] \cap (0, 2]$ $(0, 2]$

b. $(-4, 5] \cup (0, 2]$ $(-4, 5]$

26. a. $[-1, 5) \cap (0, 3)$ $(0, 3)$

b. $[-1, 5) \cup (0, 3)$ $[-1, 5)$

Concept 2: Solving Compound Inequalities: And

For Exercises 27–36, solve the compound inequality and graph the solution. Write the answer in interval notation. **(See Examples 4–6.)**

27. $y - 7 \geq -9$ and $y + 2 \leq 5$ $[-2, 3]$

28. $a + 6 > -2$ and $5a < 30$ $(-8, 6)$

29. $2t + 7 < 19$ and $5t + 13 > 28$ $(3, 6)$

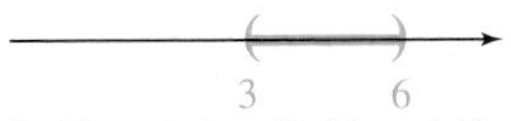

30. $5p + 2p \geq -21$ and $-9p + 3p \geq -24$ $[-3, 4]$

31. $2.1k - 1.1 \leq 0.6k + 1.9$ and $0.3k - 1.1 < -0.1k + 0.9$ $(-\infty, 2]$

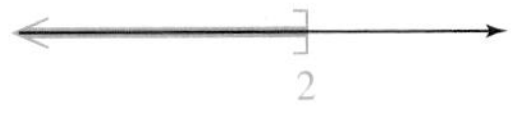

32. $0.6w + 0.1 > 0.3w - 1.1$ and $2.3w + 1.5 \geq 0.3w + 6.5$ $[2.5, \infty)$

33. $\frac{2}{3}(2p - 1) \geq 10$ and $\frac{4}{5}(3p + 4) \geq 20$ $[8, \infty)$

34. $\frac{5}{2}(a + 2) < -6$ and $\frac{3}{4}(a - 2) < 1$ $\left(-\infty, -\frac{22}{5}\right)$

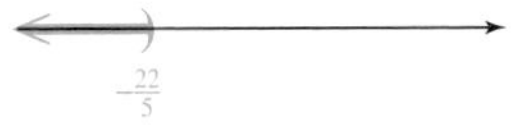

35. $-2 < -x - 12$ and $-14 < 5(x - 3) + 6x$ $\{\ \}$

36. $-8 \geq -3y - 2$ and $3(y - 7) + 16 > 4y$ $\{\ \}$

Concept 3: Solving Inequalities of the Form $a < x < b$

37. Write $-4 \le t < \frac{3}{4}$ as two separate inequalities.
$-4 \le t$ and $t < \frac{3}{4}$

38. Write $-2.8 < y \le 15$ as two separate inequalities.
$-2.8 < y$ and $y \le 15$

39. Explain why $6 < x < 2$ has no solution.
The statement $6 < x < 2$ is equivalent to $6 < x$ and $x < 2$. However, no real number is greater than 6 and also less than 2.

40. Explain why $4 < t < 1$ has no solution.
The statement $4 < t < 1$ is equivalent to $4 < t$ and $t < 1$. However, no real number is greater than 4 and also less than 1.

41. Explain why $-5 > y > -2$ has no solution.
The statement $-5 > y > -2$ is equivalent to $-5 > y$ and $y > -2$. However, no real number is less than -5 and also greater than -2.

42. Explain why $-3 > w > -1$ has no solution.
The statement $-3 > w > -1$ is equivalent to $-3 > w$ and $w > -1$. However, no real number is less than -3 and also greater than -1.

For Exercises 43–54, solve the compound inequality and graph the solution set. Write the answer in interval notation.
(See Examples 7–8.)

43. $0 \le 2b - 5 < 9$ $\left[\frac{5}{2}, 7\right)$

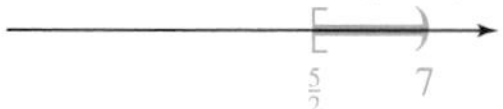

44. $-6 < 3k - 9 \le 0$ $(1, 3]$

45. $-1 < \frac{a}{6} \le 1$ $(-6, 6]$

46. $-3 \le \frac{1}{2}x < 0$ $[-6, 0)$

47. $-\frac{2}{3} < \frac{y-4}{-6} < \frac{1}{3}$ $(2, 8)$

48. $\frac{1}{3} > \frac{t-4}{-3} > -2$ $(3, 10)$

49. $5 \le -3x - 2 \le 8$ $\left[-\frac{10}{3}, -\frac{7}{3}\right]$

50. $-1 < -2x + 4 \le 5$ $\left[-\frac{1}{2}, \frac{5}{2}\right)$

51. $12 > 6x + 3 \ge 0$ $\left[-\frac{1}{2}, \frac{3}{2}\right)$

52. $-4 \ge 2x - 5 > -7$ $\left(-1, \frac{1}{2}\right]$

53. $-0.2 < 2.6 + 7t < 4$ $(-0.4, 0.2)$

54. $-1.5 < 0.1x \le 8.1$ $(-15, 81]$

Concept 4: Solving Compound Inequalities: Or

For Exercises 55–64, solve the compound inequality and graph the solution set. Write the answer in interval notation.
(See Examples 9–10.)

55. $2y - 1 \ge 3$ or $y < -2$

$(-\infty, -2) \cup [2, \infty)$

56. $x < 0$ or $3x + 1 \ge 7$

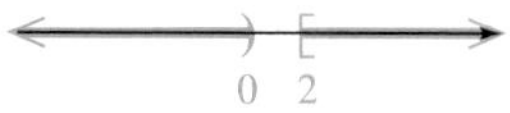

$(-\infty, 0) \cup [2, \infty)$

57. $1 > 6z - 8$ or $8z - 6 \le 10$

$(-\infty, 2]$

58. $22 > 4t - 10$ or $7 > 2t - 5$

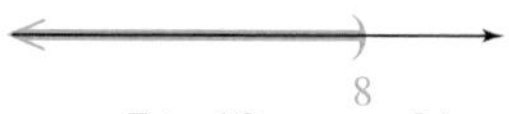

$(-\infty, 8)$

59. $5(x - 1) \ge -5$ or $5 - x \le 11$

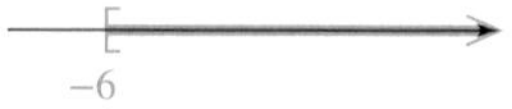

$[-6, \infty)$

60. $-p + 7 \ge 10$ or $3(p - 1) \le 12$ $(-\infty, 5]$

61. $\frac{5}{3}v \le 5$ or $-v - 6 < 1$ $(-\infty, \infty)$

62. $\frac{3}{8}u + 1 > 0$ or $-2u \ge -4$ $(-\infty, \infty)$

63. $0.5w + 5 < 2.5w - 4$ or $0.3w \le -0.1w - 1.6$

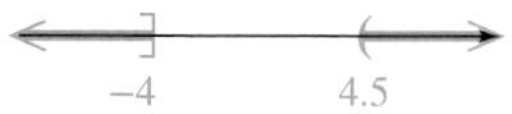

$(-\infty, -4] \cup (4.5, \infty)$

64. $1.25a + 3 \le 0.5a - 6$ or $2.5a - 1 \ge 9 - 1.5a$

$(-\infty, -12] \cup [2.5, \infty)$

Mixed Exercises

For Exercises 65–74, solve the compound inequality. Write the answer in interval notation.

65. **a.** $3x - 5 < 19$ and $-2x + 3 < 23$
$(-10, 8)$

b. $3x - 5 < 19$ or $-2x + 3 < 23$
$(-\infty, \infty)$

66. **a.** $0.5(6x + 8) > 0.8x - 7$ and $4(x + 1) < 7.2$
$(-5, 0.8)$

b. $0.5(6x + 8) > 0.8x - 7$ or $4(x + 1) < 7.2$
$(-\infty, \infty)$

67. **a.** $8x - 4 \ge 6.4$ or $0.3(x + 6) \le -0.6$
$(-\infty, -8] \cup [1.3, \infty)$

b. $8x - 4 \ge 6.4$ and $0.3(x + 6) \le -0.6$
{ }

68. **a.** $-2r + 4 \le -8$ or $3r + 5 \le 8$
$(-\infty, 1] \cup [6, \infty)$

b. $-2r + 4 \le -8$ and $3r + 5 \le 8$
{ }

69. $-4 \le \frac{2-4x}{3} < 8$ $\left(-\frac{11}{2}, \frac{7}{2}\right]$

70. $-1 < \frac{3-x}{2} \le 0$ $[3, 5)$

71. $5 \ge -4(t-3) + 3t$ or $6 < 12t + 8(4-t)$ $\left(-\frac{13}{2}, \infty\right)$

72. $3 > -(w-3) + 4w$ or $-5 \ge -3(w-5) + 6w$ $(-\infty, 0)$

73. $\frac{-x+3}{2} > \frac{4+x}{5}$ or $\frac{1-x}{4} > \frac{2-x}{3}$ $(-\infty, 1) \cup (5, \infty)$

74. $\frac{y-7}{-3} < \frac{1}{4}$ or $\frac{y+1}{-2} > -\frac{1}{3}$ $\left(-\infty, -\frac{1}{3}\right) \cup \left(\frac{25}{4}, \infty\right)$

Concept 5: Applications of Compound Inequalities

75. The normal number of white blood cells for human blood is between 4800 and 10,800 cells per cubic millimeter, inclusive. Let x represent the number of white blood cells per cubic millimeter. **(See Example 11.)**

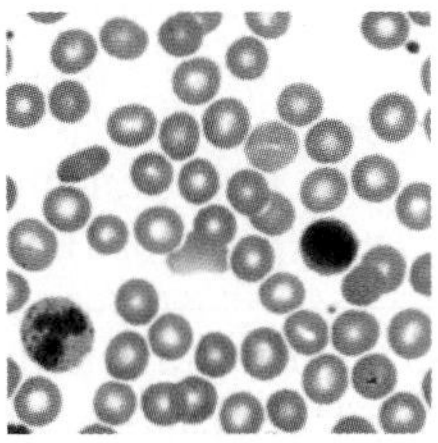

© McGraw-Hill Education/ Dr. Al Telser

a. Write an inequality representing the normal range of white blood cells per cubic millimeter. $4800 \le x \le 10{,}800$

b. Write a compound inequality representing abnormal levels of white blood cells per cubic millimeter. $x < 4800$ or $x > 10{,}800$

76. Normal hemoglobin levels in human blood for adult males are between 13 and 16 grams per deciliter (g/dL), inclusive. Let x represent the level of hemoglobin measured in grams per deciliter.

a. Write an inequality representing normal hemoglobin levels for adult males. $13 \le x \le 16$

b. Write a compound inequality representing abnormal levels of hemoglobin for adult males. $x < 13$ or $x > 16$

77. A polling company estimates that a certain candidate running for office will receive between 44% and 48% of the votes. Let x represent the percentage of votes for this candidate.

a. Write a strict inequality representing the expected percentage of votes for this candidate. $44\% < x < 48\%$

b. Write a compound inequality representing the percentage of votes that would fall outside the polling company's prediction. $x \le 44\%$ or $x \ge 48\%$

78. A machine is calibrated to cut a piece of wood between 2.4 in. thick and 2.6 in. thick. Let x represent the thickness of the wood after it is cut.

a. Write a strict inequality representing the expected range of thickness of the wood after it has been cut. $2.4 < x < 2.6$

b. Write a compound inequality representing the thickness of wood that would fall outside the normal range for this machine. $x \le 2.4$ or $x \ge 2.6$

79. Twice a number is between -3 and 12. Find all such numbers. **(See Example 12.)** All real numbers between $-\frac{3}{2}$ and 6

80. The difference of a number and 6 is between 0 and 8. Find all such numbers. All real numbers between 6 and 14

81. One plus twice a number is either greater than 5 or less than -1. Find all such numbers. All real numbers greater than 2 or less than -1

82. One-third of a number is either less than -2 or greater than 5. Find all such numbers. All real numbers less than -6 or greater than 15

83. Amy knows from reading her syllabus in intermediate algebra that the average of her chapter tests accounts for 80% (0.8) of her overall course grade. She also knows that the final exam counts as 20% (0.2) of her grade. Suppose that the average of Amy's chapter tests is 92%.

a. Determine the range of grades that she would need on her final exam to get an "A" in the class. (Assume that a grade of "A" is obtained if Amy's overall average is 90% or better.)
Amy would need 82% or better on her final exam.

b. Determine the range of grades that Amy would need on her final exam to get a "B" in the class. (Assume that a grade of "B" is obtained if Amy's overall average is at least 80% but less than 90%.)
If Amy scores at least 32% and less than 82% on her final exam she will receive a "B" in the class.

84. Robert knows from reading his syllabus in intermediate algebra that the average of his chapter tests accounts for 60% (0.6) of his overall course grade. He also knows that the final exam counts as 40% (0.4) of his grade. Suppose that the average of Robert's chapter tests is 89%.

a. Determine the range of grades that he would need on his final exam to get an "A" in the class. (Assume that a grade of "A" is obtained if Robert's overall average is 90% or better.)
Robert would need 91.5% or better on his final.

b. Determine the range of grades that Robert would need on his final exam to get a "B" in the class. (Assume that a grade of "B" is obtained if Robert's overall average is at least 80% but less than 90%.)
If Robert scores at least 66.5% and less than 91.5% on his final exam he will receive a "B" in the class.

85. The average high and low temperatures for Vancouver, British Columbia, in January are 5.6°C and 0°C, respectively. The formula relating Celsius temperatures to Fahrenheit temperatures is given by $C = \frac{5}{9}(F - 32)$. Convert the inequality $0.0° \leq C \leq 5.6°$ to an equivalent inequality using Fahrenheit temperatures. $32° \leq F \leq 42.08°$

© BrandX/Punchstock/ Getty Images RF

86. For a day in July, the temperature in Austin, Texas, ranged from 20°C to 29°C. The formula relating Celsius temperatures to Fahrenheit temperatures is given by $C = \frac{5}{9}(F - 32)$. Convert the inequality $20° \leq C \leq 29°$ to an equivalent inequality using Fahrenheit temperatures. $68° \leq F \leq 84.2°$

Section 9.2 Polynomial and Rational Inequalities

Concepts

1. Solving Quadratic and Polynomial Inequalities
2. Solving Rational Inequalities

1. Solving Quadratic and Polynomial Inequalities

In this section, we will expand our study of solving inequalities.

Quadratic inequalities are inequalities that can be written in one of the following forms:

$$ax^2 + bx + c \geq 0 \qquad ax^2 + bx + c \leq 0$$

$$ax^2 + bx + c > 0 \qquad ax^2 + bx + c < 0 \qquad \text{where } a \neq 0$$

Recall that the graph of a quadratic function defined by $f(x) = ax^2 + bx + c$ is a parabola that opens upward or downward.

- The inequality $ax^2 + bx + c > 0$ is asking "For what values of x is the function positive (above the x-axis)?"
- The inequality $ax^2 + bx + c < 0$ is asking "For what values of x is the function negative (below the x-axis)?"

The graph of a quadratic function can be used to answer these questions.

Example 1 Using a Graph to Solve a Quadratic Inequality

Classroom Example: p. 646, Exercise 10

Use the graph of $f(x) = x^2 - 6x + 5$ in Figure 9-3 to solve the inequalities.

a. $x^2 - 6x + 5 < 0$ **b.** $x^2 - 6x + 5 > 0$

Solution:

From Figure 9-3, we see that the graph of $f(x) = x^2 - 6x + 5$ is a parabola opening upward. The function factors as $f(x) = (x - 1)(x - 5)$. The x-intercepts are (1, 0) and (5, 0), and the y-intercept is (0, 5).

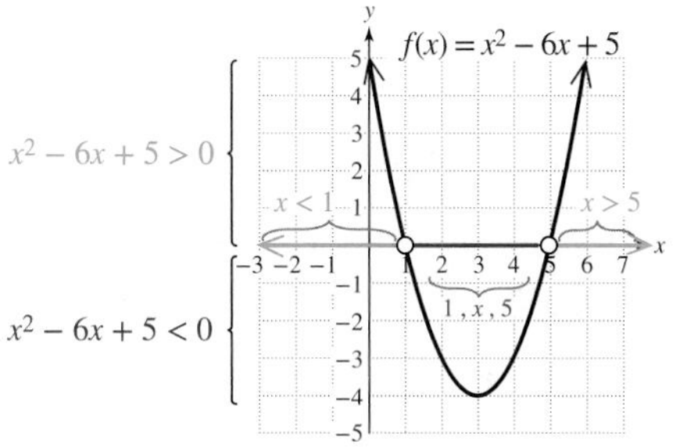

Figure 9-3

a. The solution to $x^2 - 6x + 5 < 0$ is the set of real numbers, x, for which $f(x) < 0$. Graphically, this is the set of all x values corresponding to the points where the parabola is below the x-axis (shown in red).

$$x^2 - 6x + 5 < 0 \quad \text{for } \{x \mid 1 < x < 5\} \text{ or in interval notation, } (1, 5)$$

b. The solution to $x^2 - 6x + 5 > 0$ is the set of real numbers, x, for which $f(x) > 0$. This is the set of x values where the parabola is above the x-axis (shown in blue).

$$x^2 - 6x + 5 > 0 \quad \text{for } \{x \mid x < 1 \text{ or } x > 5\} \quad \text{or} \quad (-\infty, 1) \cup (5, \infty)$$

Skill Practice Refer to the graph of $f(x) = x^2 + 3x - 4$ to solve the inequalities.

1. $x^2 + 3x - 4 > 0$

2. $x^2 + 3x - 4 < 0$

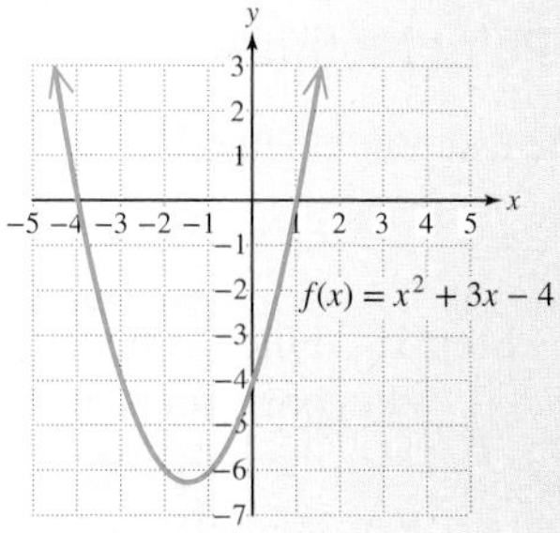

TIP: The inequalities in Example 1 are strict inequalities. Therefore, $x = 1$ and $x = 5$ (where $f(x) = 0$) are not included in the solution set. However, the corresponding inequalities using the symbols $\le$ and $\ge$ *do* include the values where $f(x) = 0$.

The solution to $x^2 - 6x + 5 \le 0$ is $\{x \mid 1 \le x \le 5\}$ or equivalently, $[1, 5]$.

The solution to $x^2 - 6x + 5 \ge 0$ is $\{x \mid x \le 1 \text{ or } x \ge 5\}$ or $(-\infty, 1] \cup [5, \infty)$.

Answers

1. $\{x \mid x < -4 \text{ or } x > 1\}$; $(-\infty, -4) \cup (1, \infty)$

2. $\{x \mid -4 < x < 1\}$; $(-4, 1)$

Notice that $x = 1$ and $x = 5$ are the boundaries of the solution set to the inequalities in Example 1. These values are the solutions to the related equation $x^2 - 6x + 5 = 0$.

Definition of Boundary Points

The **boundary points** of an inequality consist of the real solutions to the related equation and the points where the inequality is undefined.

Testing points on intervals bounded by these points is the basis of the **test point method** to solve inequalities.

Solving Inequalities by Using the Test Point Method

Step 1 Find the boundary points of the inequality.

Step 2 Plot the boundary points on the number line. This divides the number line into intervals.

Step 3 Select a test point from each interval and substitute it into the original inequality.

- If a test point makes the original inequality true, then that interval is part of the solution set.

Step 4 Test the boundary points in the original inequality.

- If the original inequality is strict (< or >), do not include the boundary points in the solution set.
- If the original inequality is defined using ≤ or ≥, then include the boundary points that are defined within the inequality.

Note: Any boundary point that makes an expression within the inequality undefined must *always* be excluded from the solution set.

Classroom Example: p. 646, Exercise 16

Example 2 Solving a Quadratic Inequality by Using the Test Point Method

Solve the inequality by using the test point method. $2x^2 + 5x < 12$

Solution:

$2x^2 + 5x < 12$ **Step 1:** Find the boundary points. Because polynomials are defined for all values of x, the only boundary points are the real solutions to the related equation.

$2x^2 + 5x = 12$ Solve the related equation.

$2x^2 + 5x - 12 = 0$

$(2x - 3)(x + 4) = 0$

$x = \frac{3}{2}$ $x = -4$ The boundary points are $\frac{3}{2}$ and -4.

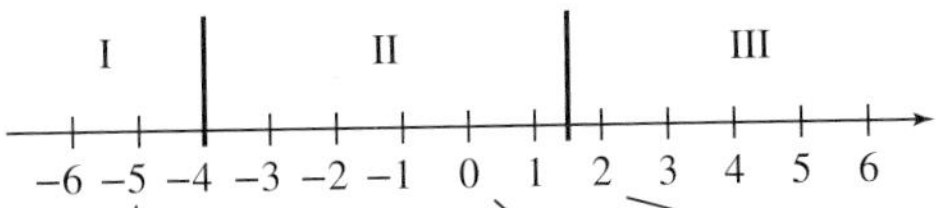

Step 2: Plot the boundary points.

Step 3: Select a test point from each interval.

Test $x = -5$

$$2x^2 + 5x < 12$$
$$2(-5)^2 + 5(-5) \overset{?}{<} 12$$
$$50 - 25 \overset{?}{<} 12$$
$$25 \overset{?}{<} 12 \quad \text{False}$$

Test $x = 0$

$$2x^2 + 5x < 12$$
$$2(0)^2 + 5(0) \overset{?}{<} 12$$
$$0 + 0 \overset{?}{<} 12$$
$$0 \overset{?}{<} 12 \quad \text{True}$$

Test $x = 2$

$$2x^2 + 5x < 12$$
$$2(2)^2 + 5(2) \overset{?}{<} 12$$
$$8 + 10 \overset{?}{<} 12$$
$$18 \overset{?}{<} 12 \quad \text{False}$$

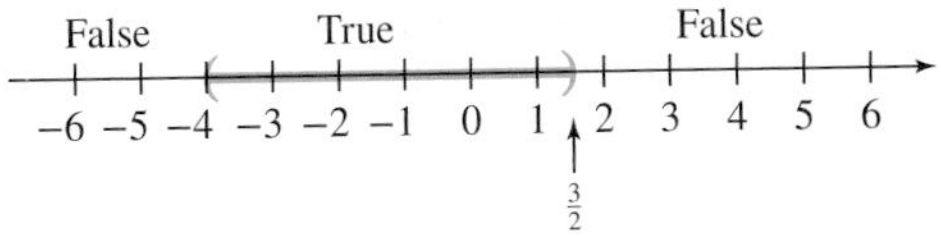

Step 4: Test the boundary points. The strict inequality excludes values of x for which $2x^2 + 5x = 12$. Therefore, the boundary points are *not* included in the solution set.

The solution set is $\{x \mid -4 < x < \frac{3}{2}\}$ or equivalently in interval notation $(-4, \frac{3}{2})$.

Skill Practice Solve the inequality.

3. $x^2 + x > 6$

Calculator Connections

Topic: Analyzing a Quadratic Inequality Graphically

Graph $Y_1 = 2x^2 + 5x$ and $Y_2 = 12$.
Notice that $Y_1 < Y_2$ for $\{x \mid -4 < x < \frac{3}{2}\}$.

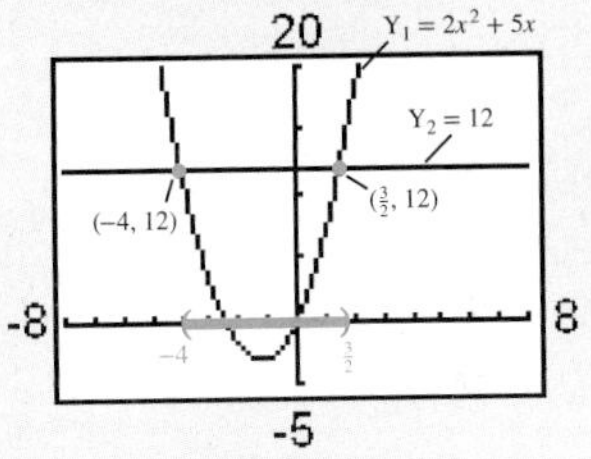

Example 3 Solving a Polynomial Inequality by Using the Test Point Method

Classroom Example: p. 646, Exercise 24

Solve the inequality by using the test point method. $x(x + 4)^2(x - 4) \geq 0$

Solution:

$$x(x + 4)^2(x - 4) \geq 0$$

$$x(x + 4)^2(x - 4) = 0$$ **Step 1:** Find the boundary points.

$$x = 0 \qquad x = -4 \qquad x = 4$$

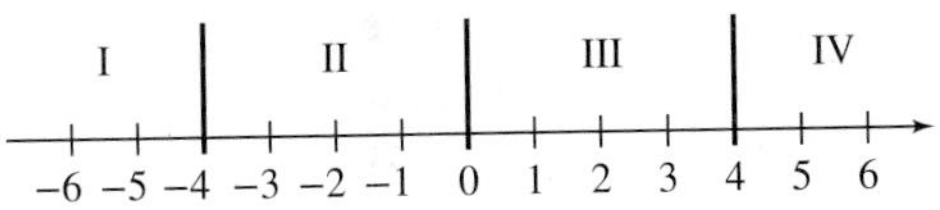

Step 2: Plot the boundary points.

Step 3: Select a test point from each interval.

Test $x = -5$: $-5(-5 + 4)^2(-5 - 4) \overset{?}{\geq} 0$ $\quad 45 \overset{?}{\geq} 0$ True

Test $x = -1$: $-1(-1 + 4)^2(-1 - 4) \overset{?}{\geq} 0$ $\quad 45 \overset{?}{\geq} 0$ True

Test $x = 1$: $1(1 + 4)^2(1 - 4) \overset{?}{\geq} 0$ $\quad -75 \overset{?}{\geq} 0$ False

Test $x = 5$: $5(5 + 4)^2(5 - 4) \overset{?}{\geq} 0$ $\quad 405 \overset{?}{\geq} 0$ True

Answer

3. $(-\infty, -3) \cup (2, \infty)$

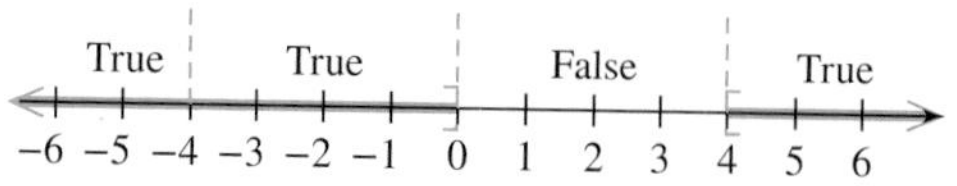

Step 4: The inequality symbol, $\geq$, includes equality. Therefore, include the boundary points in the solution set.

The solution set is $\{x \mid x \leq 0 \text{ and } x \geq 4\}$, or equivalently in interval notation, $(-\infty, 0] \cup [4, \infty)$.

Skill Practice Solve the inequality.

4. $t(t-5)(t+2)^2 > 0$

Calculator Connections

Topic: Analyzing a Polynomial Inequality Graphically

Graph $Y_1 = x(x+4)^2(x-4)$. Y_1 is positive (above the x-axis) for $\{x \mid x \leq 0 \text{ and } x \geq 4\}$ or equivalently $(-\infty, 0] \cup [4, \infty)$.

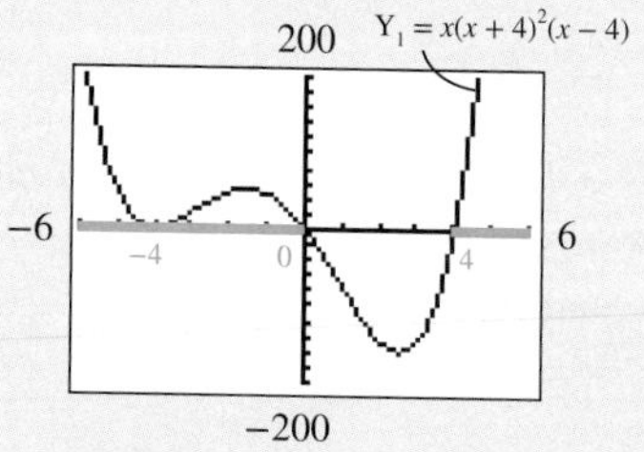

TIP: In Example 3, one side of the inequality is factored, and the other side is zero. For inequalities written in this form, we can use a sign chart to determine the sign of each factor. Then the sign of the product (bottom row) is easily determined.

Sign of x	−	−	+	+
Sign of $(x+4)^2$	+	+	+	+
Sign of $(x-4)$	−	−	−	+
Sign of $x(x+4)^2(x-4)$	+	+	−	+
		−4	0	4

The solution to the inequality $x(x+4)^2(x-4) \geq 0$ includes the intervals for which the product is positive (shown in blue).

The solution is $(-\infty, 0] \cup [4, \infty)$.

2. Solving Rational Inequalities

The test point method can be used to solve rational inequalities. A **rational inequality** is an inequality in which one or more terms is a rational expression. The solution set to a rational inequality must exclude all values of the variable that make the inequality undefined. That is, exclude all values that make the denominator equal to zero for any rational expression in the inequality.

Answer

4. $(-\infty, -2) \cup (-2, 0) \cup (5, \infty)$

Example 4 Solving a Rational Inequality by Using the Test Point Method

Classroom Example: p. 647, Exercise 42

Solve the inequality. $\dfrac{3}{x-1} > 0$

Solution:

$$\frac{3}{x-1} > 0$$

$$\frac{3}{x-1} = 0$$

$$(x-1)\cdot\left(\frac{3}{x-1}\right) = (x-1)\cdot 0$$

$$3 = 0$$

Step 1: Find the boundary points. Note that the inequality is undefined for $x = 1$, so $x = 1$ is a boundary point. To find any other boundary points, solve the related equation.

Clear fractions.

There is no solution to the related equation.

The only boundary point is $x = 1$.

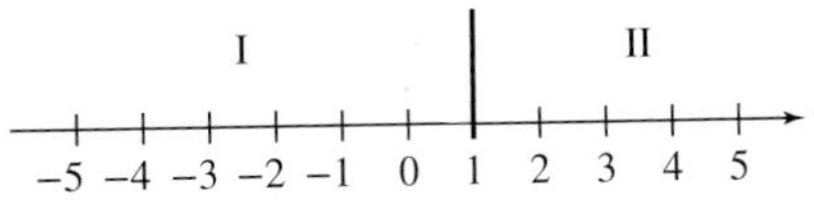

Step 2: Plot boundary points.

Step 3: Select test points.

Test $x = 0$:

$$\frac{3}{(0)-1} \stackrel{?}{>} 0$$

$$\frac{3}{-1} \stackrel{?}{>} 0 \quad \text{False}$$

Test $x = 2$:

$$\frac{3}{(2)-1} \stackrel{?}{>} 0$$

$$\frac{3}{1} > 0 \quad \text{True}$$

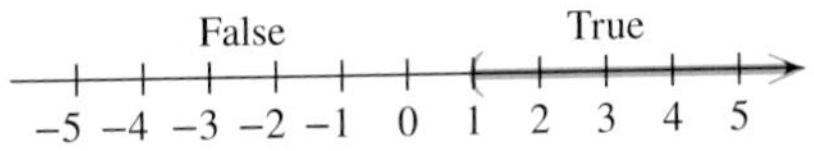

Step 4: The boundary point $x = 1$ cannot be included in the solution set because it is undefined in the original inequality.

The solution is $\{x \mid x > 1\}$ or equivalently in interval notation, $(1, \infty)$.

Skill Practice Solve the inequality.

5. $\dfrac{-5}{y+2} < 0$

TIP: Using a sign chart we see that the quotient of the factors 3 and $(x - 1)$ is positive on the interval $(1, \infty)$.

Therefore, the solution to the inequality $\dfrac{3}{x-1} > 0$ is $(1, \infty)$.

Sign of 3	+	+
Sign of $(x-1)$	−	+
Sign of $\dfrac{3}{x-1}$	−	+
	1 (undefined)	

Answer

5. $(-2, \infty)$

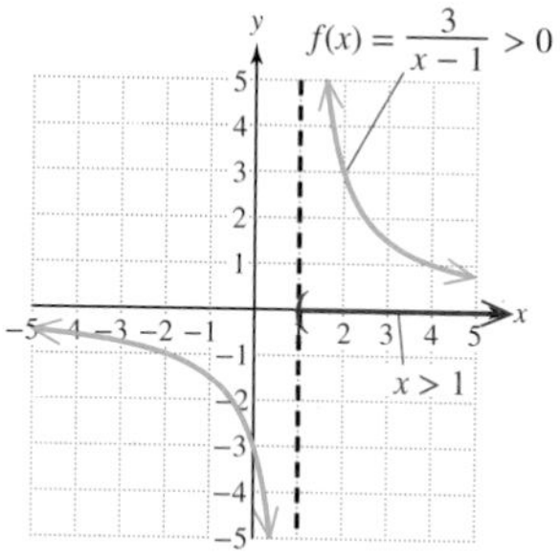

Figure 9-4

The solution to the inequality $\frac{3}{x-1} > 0$ can be confirmed from the graph of the related rational function, $f(x) = \frac{3}{x-1}$ (see Figure 9-4).

- The graph is above the x-axis where $f(x) = \frac{3}{x-1} > 0$ for $x > 1$ (shaded red).
- Also note that $x = 1$ cannot be included in the solution set because 1 is not in the domain of f.

Classroom Example: p. 647, Exercise 52

Example 5 Solving a Rational Inequality by Using the Test Point Method

Solve the inequality by using the test point method. $\frac{x+2}{x-4} \le 3$

Solution:

$$\frac{x+2}{x-4} \le 3$$

Step 1: Find the boundary points. Note that the inequality is undefined for $x = 4$. Therefore, $x = 4$ is automatically a boundary point. To find any other boundary points, solve the related equation.

$$\frac{x+2}{x-4} = 3$$

$$(x-4)\left(\frac{x+2}{x-4}\right) = (x-4)(3)$$ Clear fractions.

$$x + 2 = 3(x - 4)$$ Solve for x.

$$x + 2 = 3x - 12$$

$$-2x = -14$$

$$x = 7$$

The solution to the related equation is $x = 7$, and the inequality is undefined for $x = 4$. Therefore, the boundary points are $x = 4$ and $x = 7$.

Step 2: Plot boundary points.

Step 3: Select test points.

Test $x = 0$

$$\frac{x+2}{x-4} \le 3$$

$$\frac{0+2}{0-4} \overset{?}{\le} 3$$

$$-\frac{1}{2} \overset{?}{\le} 3 \quad \text{True}$$

Test $x = 5$

$$\frac{x+2}{x-4} \le 3$$

$$\frac{5+2}{5-4} \overset{?}{\le} 3$$

$$\frac{7}{1} \overset{?}{\le} 3 \quad \text{False}$$

Test $x = 8$

$$\frac{x+2}{x-4} \le 3$$

$$\frac{8+2}{8-4} \overset{?}{\le} 3$$

$$\frac{10}{4} \overset{?}{\le} 3$$

$$\frac{5}{2} \overset{?}{\le} 3 \quad \text{True}$$

Test $x = 4$:

$\frac{x+2}{x-4} \le 3$

$\frac{4+2}{4-4} \overset{?}{\le} 3$

$\frac{6}{0} \overset{?}{\le} 3$ Undefined

Test $x = 7$:

$\frac{x+2}{x-4} \le 3$

$\frac{7+2}{7-4} \overset{?}{\le} 3$

$\frac{9}{3} \overset{?}{\le} 3$ True

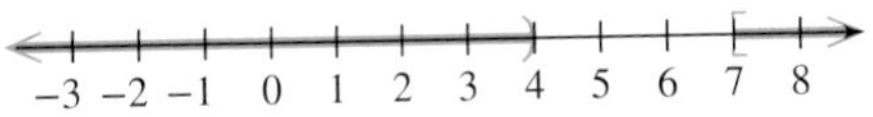

Step 4: Test the boundary points.

The boundary point $x = 4$ cannot be included in the solution set, because it is undefined in the inequality. The boundary point $x = 7$ makes the original inequality true and must be included in the solution set.

The solution is $\{x \mid x < 4 \text{ or } x \ge 7\}$, or equivalently in interval notation, $(-\infty, 4) \cup [7, \infty)$.

Skill Practice Solve the inequality.

6. $\frac{x-5}{x+4} \le -1$

Answer

6. $\left(-4, \frac{1}{2}\right]$

Section 9.2 Practice Exercises

For additional exercises, see Classroom Activities 9.2A–9.2C in the *Student's Resource Manual* at www.mhhe.com/moh.

Vocabulary and Key Concepts

1. **a.** An inequality of the form $ax^2 + bx + c > 0$ or $ax^2 + bx + c < 0$ is an example of a quadratic inequality.

   b. The boundary points of an inequality consist of the real solutions to the related equation and the points where the inequality is undefined.

   c. In solving an inequality by using the test point method, a point is selected from each interval formed by the boundary points and substituted into the original inequality.

   d. If a test point makes the original inequality true, then that interval is part of the solution set.

   e. The inequality $\frac{4}{x+7} > 0$ is an example of a rational inequality.

   f. The solution set to a rational inequality must exclude all values that make the denominator equal to zero for any rational expression in the inequality.

Review Exercises

For Exercises 2–8, solve the compound inequalities. Write the solutions in interval notation.

2. $6x - 10 > 8$ or $8x + 2 < 5$ $\left(-\infty, \frac{3}{8}\right) \cup (3, \infty)$

3. $3(a - 1) + 2 > 0$ or $2a > 5a + 12$ $(-\infty, -4) \cup \left(\frac{1}{3}, \infty\right)$

4. $5(k - 2) > -25$ and $7(1 - k) > 7$ $(-3, 0)$

5. $2y + 4 \ge 10$ and $5y - 3 \le 13$ $\left[3, \frac{16}{5}\right]$

6. $0 < 3(x + 1) \le 4$ $\left(-1, \frac{1}{3}\right]$

7. $6 \ge 4 - 2x \ge -2$ $[-1, 3]$

8. $-4 > 5 - x > -6$ $(9, 11)$

Concept 1: Solving Quadratic and Polynomial Inequalities

For Exercises 9–12, estimate from the graph the intervals for which the inequality is true. **(See Example 1.)**

9.

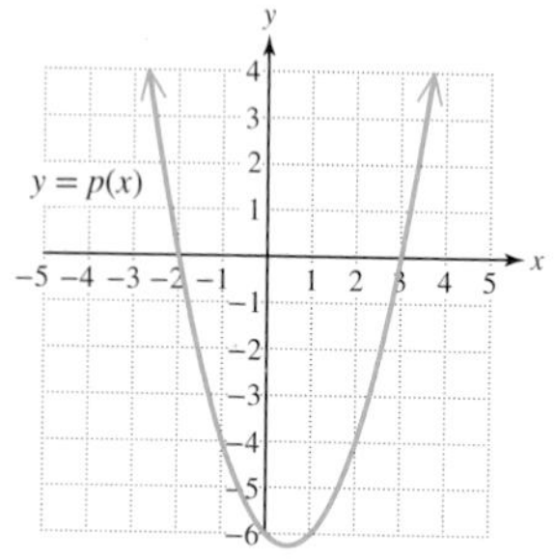

a. $p(x) > 0$ $(-\infty, -2) \cup (3, \infty)$ **b.** $p(x) < 0$ $(-2, 3)$

c. $p(x) \le 0$ $[-2, 3]$ **d.** $p(x) \ge 0$ $(-\infty, -2] \cup [3, \infty)$

10.

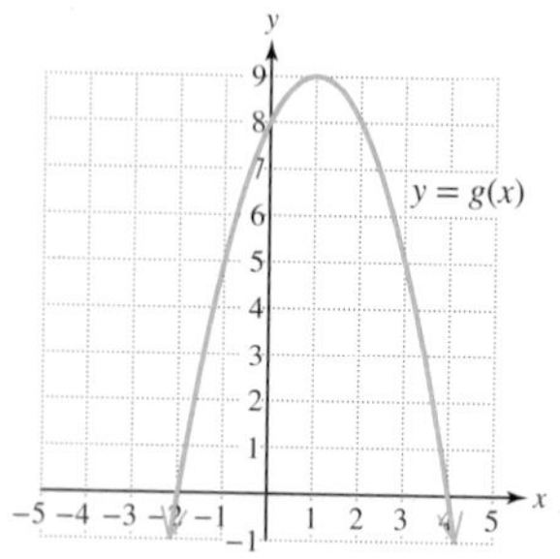

a. $g(x) > 0$ $(-2, 4)$ **b.** $g(x) < 0$ $(-\infty, -2) \cup (4, \infty)$

c. $g(x) \le 0$ $(-\infty, -2] \cup [4, \infty)$ **d.** $g(x) \ge 0$ $[-2, 4]$

11.

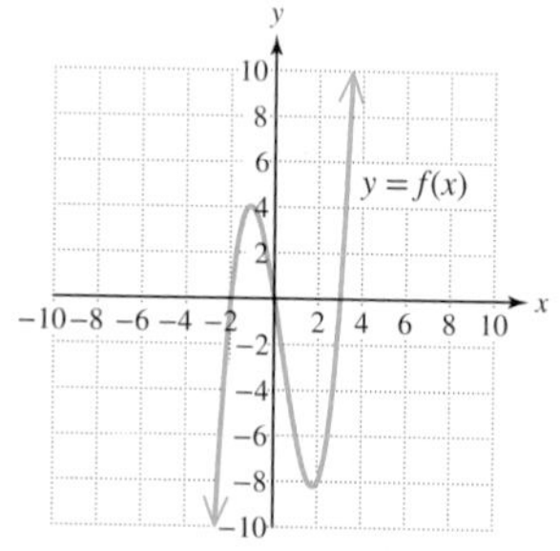

a. $f(x) > 0$ $(-2, 0) \cup (3, \infty)$ **b.** $f(x) < 0$ $(-\infty, -2) \cup (0, 3)$

c. $f(x) \le 0$ $(-\infty, -2] \cup [0, 3]$ **d.** $f(x) \ge 0$ $[-2, 0] \cup [3, \infty]$

12.

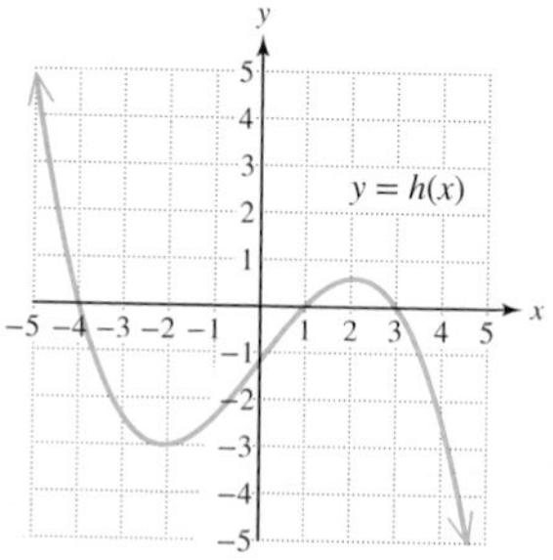

a. $h(x) > 0$ $(-\infty, -4) \cup (1, 3)$ **b.** $h(x) < 0$ $(-4, 1) \cup (3, \infty)$

c. $h(x) \le 0$ $[-4, 1] \cup [3, \infty)$ **d.** $h(x) \ge 0$ $(-\infty, -4) \cup [1, 3]$

For Exercises 13–18, solve the equation and related inequalities. **(See Examples 2–3.)**

13. **a.** $3(4 - x)(2x + 1) = 0$ $\{4, -\frac{1}{2}\}$

b. $3(4 - x)(2x + 1) < 0$ $(-\infty, -\frac{1}{2}) \cup (4, \infty)$

c. $3(4 - x)(2x + 1) > 0$ $(-\frac{1}{2}, 4)$

14. **a.** $5(y + 6)(3 - 5y) = 0$ $\{-6, \frac{3}{5}\}$

b. $5(y + 6)(3 - 5y) < 0$ $(-\infty, -6) \cup (\frac{3}{5}, \infty)$

c. $5(y + 6)(3 - 5y) > 0$ $(-6, \frac{3}{5})$

15. **a.** $x^2 + 7x = 30$ $\{-10, 3\}$

b. $x^2 + 7x < 30$ $(-10, 3)$

c. $x^2 + 7x > 30$ $(-\infty, -10) \cup (3, \infty)$

16. **a.** $q^2 - 4q = 5$ $\{5, -1\}$

b. $q^2 - 4q \le 5$ $[-1, 5]$

c. $q^2 - 4q \ge 5$ $(-\infty, -1] \cup [5, \infty)$

17. **a.** $2p(p - 2) = p + 3$ $\left\{-\frac{1}{2}, 3\right\}$

b. $2p(p - 2) \le p + 3$ $\left[-\frac{1}{2}, 3\right]$

c. $2p(p - 2) \ge p + 3$ $\left(-\infty, -\frac{1}{2}\right] \cup [3, \infty)$

18. **a.** $3w(w + 4) = 10 - w$ $\left\{\frac{2}{3}, -5\right\}$

b. $3w(w + 4) < 10 - w$ $\left(-5, \frac{2}{3}\right)$

c. $3w(w + 4) > 10 - w$ $(-\infty, -5) \cup \left(\frac{2}{3}, \infty\right)$

For Exercises 19–36, solve the polynomial inequality. Write the answer in interval notation. **(See Examples 2–3.)**

19. $(t - 7)(t - 1) < 0$ $(1, 7)$

20. $(p - 4)(p - 2) > 0$ $(-\infty, 2) \cup (4, \infty)$

21. $-6(4 + 2x)(5 - x) > 0$ $(-\infty, -2) \cup (5, \infty)$

22. $-8(2t + 5)(6 - t) < 0$ $\left(-\frac{5}{2}, 6\right)$

23. $m(m + 1)^2(m + 5) \le 0$ $[-5, 0]$

24. $w^2(3 - w)(w + 2) \ge 0$ $[-2, 3]$

25. $a^2 - 12a \le -32$ $[4, 8]$

26. $w^2 + 20w \ge -64$ $(-\infty, -16] \cup [-4, \infty)$

27. $5x^2 - 4x - 1 > 0$ $\left(-\infty, -\frac{1}{5}\right) \cup (1, \infty)$

28. $x^2 + x \le 6$ $[-3, 2]$

29. $b^2 - 121 < 0$ $(-11, 11)$

30. $c^2 - 25 < 0$ $(-5, 5)$

31. $3p(p-2)-3\geq 2p$ $\left(-\infty, -\frac{1}{3}\right] \cup [3, \infty)$

32. $2t(t+3)-t\leq 12$ $\left[-4, \frac{3}{2}\right]$

33. $x^3-x^2\leq 12x$ $(-\infty, -3] \cup [0, 4]$

34. $x^3+36>4x^2+9x$ $(-3, 3) \cup (4, \infty)$

35. $w^3+w^2>4w+4$ $(-2, -1) \cup (2, \infty)$

36. $2p^3-5p^2\leq 3p$ $\left(-\infty, -\frac{1}{2}\right] \cup [0, 3]$

Concept 2: Solving Rational Inequalities

For Exercises 37–40, estimate from the graph the intervals for which the inequality is true.

37.

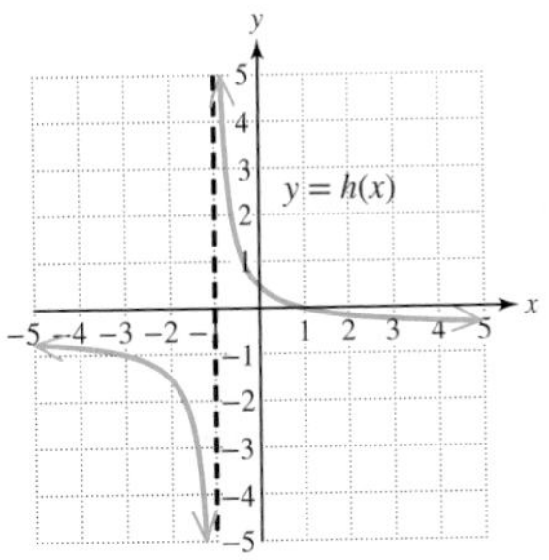

a. $h(x)\geq 0$ $(-1, 1]$

b. $h(x)\leq 0$ $(-\infty, -1) \cup [1, \infty)$

c. $h(x)<0$ $(-\infty, -1) \cup (1, \infty)$

d. $h(x)>0$ $(-1, 1)$

38.

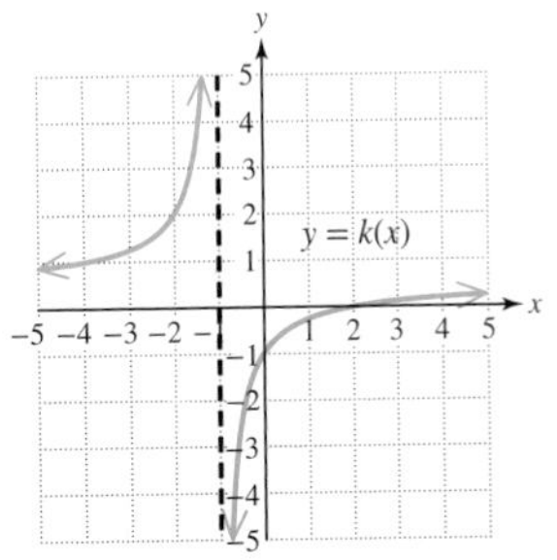

a. $k(x)\leq 0$ $(-1, 2]$

b. $k(x)\geq 0$ $(-\infty, -1) \cup [2, \infty)$

c. $k(x)>0$ $(-\infty, -1) \cup (2, \infty)$

d. $k(x)<0$ $(-1, 2)$

39.

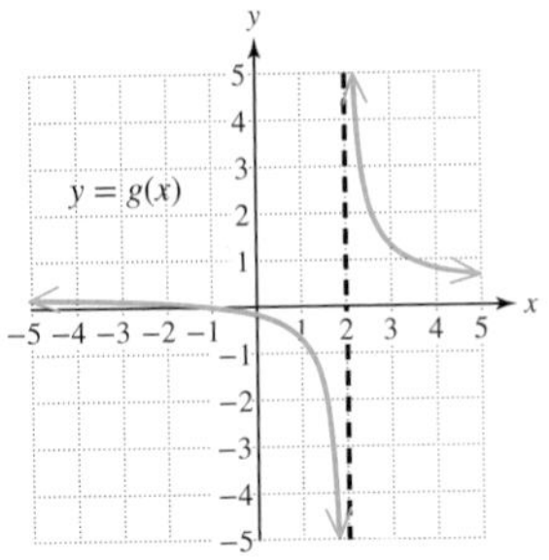

a. $g(x)>0$ $(-\infty, -1) \cup (2, \infty)$

b. $g(x)<0$ $(-1, 2)$

c. $g(x)\leq 0$ $[-1, 2)$

d. $g(x)\geq 0$ $(-\infty, -1] \cup (2, \infty)$

40.

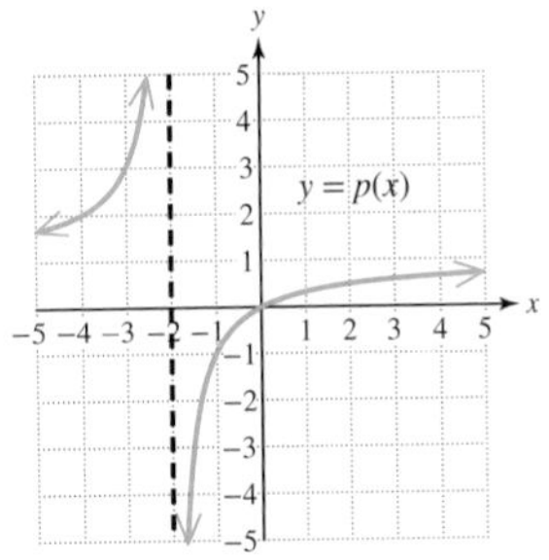

a. $p(x)>0$ $(-\infty, -2) \cup (0, \infty)$

b. $p(x)<0$ $(-2, 0)$

c. $p(x)\leq 0$ $(-2, 0]$

d. $p(x)\geq 0$ $(-\infty, -2) \cup [0, \infty)$

For Exercises 41–44, solve the equation and related inequalities. **(See Examples 4–5.)**

41. a. $\dfrac{10}{x-5}=5$ $\{7\}$

b. $\dfrac{10}{x-5}<5$ $(-\infty, 5) \cup (7, \infty)$

c. $\dfrac{10}{x-5}>5$ $(5, 7)$

42. a. $\dfrac{8}{a+1}=4$ $\{1\}$

b. $\dfrac{8}{a+1}>4$ $(-1, 1)$

c. $\dfrac{8}{a+1}<4$ $(-\infty, -1) \cup (1, \infty)$

43. a. $\dfrac{z+2}{z-6}=-3$ $\{4\}$

b. $\dfrac{z+2}{z-6}\leq -3$ $[4, 6)$

c. $\dfrac{z+2}{z-6}\geq -3$ $(-\infty, 4] \cup (6, \infty)$

44. a. $\dfrac{w-8}{w+6}=2$ $\{-20\}$

b. $\dfrac{w-8}{w+6}\leq 2$ $(-\infty, -20] \cup (-6, \infty)$

c. $\dfrac{w-8}{w+6}\geq 2$ $[-20, -6)$

For Exercises 45–56, solve the rational inequality. Write the answer in interval notation. **(See Examples 4–5.)**

45. $\dfrac{2}{x-1}\geq 0$ $(1, \infty)$

46. $\dfrac{-3}{x+2}\leq 0$ $(-2, \infty)$

47. $\dfrac{b+4}{b-4}>0$ $(-\infty, -4) \cup (4, \infty)$

48. $\dfrac{a+1}{a-3}<0$ $(-1, 3)$

49. $\dfrac{3}{2x-7}<-1$ $\left(2, \frac{7}{2}\right)$

50. $\dfrac{8}{4x+9}>1$ $\left(-\frac{9}{4}, -\frac{1}{4}\right)$

51. $\dfrac{x+1}{x-5}\geq 4$ $(5, 7]$

52. $\dfrac{x-2}{x+6}\leq 5$ $(-\infty, -8] \cup (-6, \infty)$

53. $\dfrac{1}{x}\leq 2$ $(-\infty, 0) \cup \left[\frac{1}{2}, \infty\right)$

54. $\dfrac{1}{x}\geq 3$ $\left(0, \frac{1}{3}\right]$

55. $\dfrac{(x+2)^2}{x}>0$ $(0, \infty)$

56. $\dfrac{(x-3)^2}{x}<0$ $(-\infty, 0)$

Mixed Exercises

For Exercises 57–76, identify the inequality as one of the following types: linear, quadratic, rational, or polynomial (degree > 2). Then solve the inequality and write the answer in interval notation.

57. $2y^2 - 8 \le 24$ Quadratic; $[-4, 4]$

58. $8p^2 - 18 > 0$ Quadratic; $(-\infty, -\frac{3}{2}) \cup (\frac{3}{2}, \infty)$

59. $(5x + 2)^2 > 4$ Quadratic; $\left(-\infty, -\frac{4}{5}\right) \cup (0, \infty)$

60. $(7x - 4)^2 < 9$ Quadratic; $\left(\frac{1}{7}, 1\right)$

61. $4(x - 2) < 6x - 3$ Linear; $(-\frac{5}{2}, \infty)$

62. $-7(3 - y) > 4 + 2y$ Linear; $(5, \infty)$

63. $\dfrac{2x + 3}{x + 1} \le 2$ Rational; $(-\infty, -1)$

64. $\dfrac{5x - 1}{x + 3} \ge 5$ Rational; $(-\infty, -3)$

65. $4x^3 - 40x^2 + 100x > 0$ Polynomial (degree > 2); $(0, 5) \cup (5, \infty)$

66. $2y^3 - 12y^2 + 18y < 0$ Polynomial (degree > 2); $(-\infty, 0)$

67. $2p^3 > 4p^2$ Polynomial (degree > 2); $(2, \infty)$

68. $w^3 \le 5w^2$ Polynomial (degree > 2); $(-\infty, 5]$

69. $-3(x + 4)^2(x - 5) \ge 0$ Polynomial (degree > 2); $(-\infty, 5]$

70. $5x(x - 2)(x - 6)^2 \ge 0$ Polynomial (degree > 2); $(-\infty, 0] \cup [2, \infty]$

71. $x^2 - 4 < 0$ Quadratic; $(-2, 2)$

72. $y^2 - 9 > 0$ Quadratic; $(-\infty, -3) \cup (3, \infty)$

73. $\dfrac{a + 2}{a - 5} \ge 0$ Rational; $(-\infty, -2] \cup (5, \infty)$

74. $\dfrac{t + 1}{t - 2} \le 0$ Rational; $[-1, 2)$

75. $2 \ge t - 3$ Linear; $(-\infty, 5]$

76. $-5p + 8 < p$ Linear; $\left(\frac{4}{3}, \infty\right)$

Expanding Your Skills

The solution to an inequality is often one or more intervals on the real number line. Sometimes, however, the solution to an inequality may be a single point on the number line, the empty set, or the set of all real numbers. We call these "special case" solution sets.

For Exercises 77–92, solve the inequalities involving "special case" solution sets.

77. $x^2 + 10x + 25 \ge 0$ $(-\infty, \infty)$

78. $x^2 + 6x + 9 < 0$ $\{\ \}$

79. $x^2 + 2x + 1 < 0$ $\{\ \}$

80. $x^2 + 8x + 16 \ge 0$ $(-\infty, \infty)$

81. $x^4 + 3x^2 \le 0$ $\{0\}$

82. $x^4 + 2x^2 \le 0$ $\{0\}$

83. $x^2 + 12x + 36 < 0$ $\{\ \}$

84. $x^2 + 12x + 36 \ge 0$ $(-\infty, \infty)$

85. $x^2 + 3x + 5 < 0$ $\{\ \}$

86. $2x^2 + 3x + 3 > 0$ $(-\infty, \infty)$

87. $-5x^2 + x < 1$ $(-\infty, \infty)$

88. $-3x^2 - x > 6$ $\{\ \}$

89. $x^2 + 22x + 121 > 0$ $(-\infty, -11) \cup (-11, \infty)$

90. $y^2 - 24y + 144 > 0$ $(-\infty, 12) \cup (12, \infty)$

91. $4t^2 - 12t \le -9$ $\left\{\frac{3}{2}\right\}$

92. $9y^2 - 30y \le -25$ $\left\{\frac{5}{3}\right\}$

Graphing Calculator Exercises

93. To solve the inequality $\dfrac{x}{x - 2} > 0$ enter Y_1 as $x/(x - 2)$ and determine where the graph is above the x-axis. Write the solution in interval notation. $(-\infty, 0) \cup (2, \infty)$

94. To solve the inequality $\dfrac{x}{x - 2} < 0$ enter Y_1 as $x/(x - 2)$ and determine where the graph is below the x-axis. Write the solution in interval notation. $(0, 2)$

95. To solve the inequality $x^2 - 1 < 0$, enter Y_1 as $x^2 - 1$ and determine where the graph is below the x-axis. Write the solution in interval notation. $(-1, 1)$

96. To solve the inequality $x^2 - 1 > 0$, enter Y_1 as $x^2 - 1$ and determine where the graph is above the x-axis. Write the solution in interval notation. $(-\infty, -1) \cup (1, \infty)$

For Exercises 97–100, determine the solution by graphing the inequalities.

97. $x^2 + 10x + 25 \le 0$ $\{-5\}$

98. $-x^2 + 10x - 25 \ge 0$ $\{5\}$

99. $\dfrac{8}{x^2 + 2} < 0$ $\{\ \}$

100. $\dfrac{-6}{x^2 + 3} > 0$ $\{\ \}$

Absolute Value Equations

Section 9.3

Concepts

1. Solving Absolute Value Equations
2. Solving Equations Containing Two Absolute Values

1. Solving Absolute Value Equations

An equation of the form $|x| = a$ is called an **absolute value equation**. The solution includes all real numbers whose absolute value equals a. For example, the solutions to the equation $|x| = 4$ are 4 as well as -4, because $|4| = 4$ and $|-4| = 4$. A geometric interpretation of the absolute value of a number is its distance from zero on the number line (Figure 9-5). Therefore, the solutions to the equation $|x| = 4$ are the values of x that are 4 units away from zero.

$|x| = 4$

$x = -4$ or $x = 4$

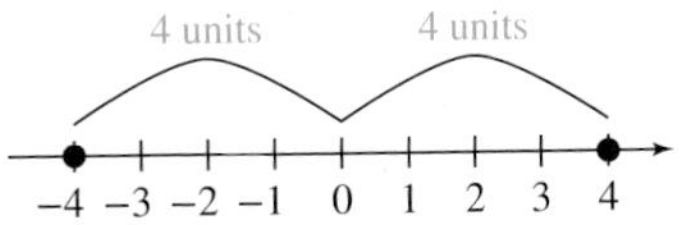

Figure 9-5

Solving Absolute Value Equations of the Form |x| = a

If a is a real number, then

- If $a \geq 0$, the solutions to the equation $|x| = a$ are $x = a$ and $x = -a$.
- If $a < 0$, there is no solution to the equation $|x| = a$.

To solve an absolute value equation of the form $|x| = a$ $(a \geq 0)$, rewrite the equation as $x = a$ or $x = -a$.

Example 1 Solving Absolute Value Equations

Classroom Example: p. 655, Exercises 8, 14, and 16

Solve the absolute value equations.

a. $|x| = 5$ **b.** $|w| - 2 = 12$ **c.** $|p| = 0$ **d.** $|x| = -6$

Solution:

a. $|x| = 5$ The equation is in the form $|x| = a$, where $a = 5$.

$x = 5$ or $x = -5$ Rewrite the equation as $x = a$ or $x = -a$.

The solution set is $\{5, -5\}$.

b. $|w| - 2 = 12$ Isolate the absolute value to write the equation in the form $|x| = a$.

$|w| = 14$

$w = 14$ or $w = -14$ Rewrite the equation as $w = a$ or $w = -a$.

The solution set is $\{14, -14\}$.

c. $|p| = 0$

$p = 0$ or $p = -0$

The solution set is $\{0\}$.

Rewrite as two equations. Notice that the second equation $p = -0$ is the same as the first equation. Intuitively, $p = 0$ is the only number whose absolute value equals 0.

d. $|x| = -6$

No solution, $\{\ \}$

The equation is of the form $|x| = a$, but a is negative. There is no number whose absolute value is negative.

Skill Practice Solve the absolute value equations.

1. $|y| = 7$ **2.** $|v| + 6 = 10$ **3.** $|w| + 3 = 3$ **4.** $|z| = -12$

We have solved absolute value equations of the form $|x| = a$. Notice that x can represent any algebraic quantity. For example, to solve the equation $|2w - 3| = 5$, we still rewrite the absolute value equation as two equations. In this case, we set the quantity $2w - 3$ equal to 5 and to -5, respectively.

$$|2w - 3| = 5$$

$$2w - 3 = 5 \quad \text{or} \quad 2w - 3 = -5$$

Solving an Absolute Value Equation

Step 1 Isolate the absolute value. That is, write the equation in the form $|x| = a$, where a is a real number.

Step 2 If $a < 0$, there is no solution.

Step 3 Otherwise, if $a \geq 0$, rewrite the absolute value equation as $x = a$ or $x = -a$.

Step 4 Solve the individual equations from step 3.

Step 5 Check the answers in the original absolute value equation.

Classroom Example: p. 655, Exercise 18

Example 2 Solving an Absolute Value Equation

Solve the equation. $|2w - 3| = 5$

Solution:

$|2w - 3| = 5$ The equation is already in the form $|x| = a$, where $x = 2w - 3$.

$2w - 3 = 5$ or $2w - 3 = -5$ Rewrite as two equations.

$2w = 8$ or $2w = -2$ Solve each equation.

$w = 4$ or $w = -1$

Answers

1. $\{7, -7\}$
2. $\{4, -4\}$
3. $\{0\}$ **4.** $\{\ \}$

Check: $w = 4$	Check: $w = -1$	Check the solutions in the original equation.
$\lvert 2w - 3\rvert = 5$	$\lvert 2w - 3\rvert = 5$	
$\lvert 2(4) - 3\rvert \stackrel{?}{=} 5$	$\lvert 2(-1) - 3\rvert \stackrel{?}{=} 5$	
$\lvert 8 - 3\rvert \stackrel{?}{=} 5$	$\lvert -2 - 3\rvert \stackrel{?}{=} 5$	
$\lvert 5\rvert \stackrel{?}{=} 5$ ✓	$\lvert -5\rvert \stackrel{?}{=} 5$ ✓	

The solution set is $\{4, -1\}$.

Skill Practice Solve the equation.

5. $|4x + 1| = 9$

Calculator Connections

Topic: Analyzing an Absolute Value Equation Graphically

To confirm the answers to Example 2, graph $Y_1 = \text{abs}(2x - 3)$ and $Y_2 = 5$. The solutions to the equation $|2x - 3| = 5$ are the x-coordinates of the points of intersection $(4, 5)$ and $(-1, 5)$.

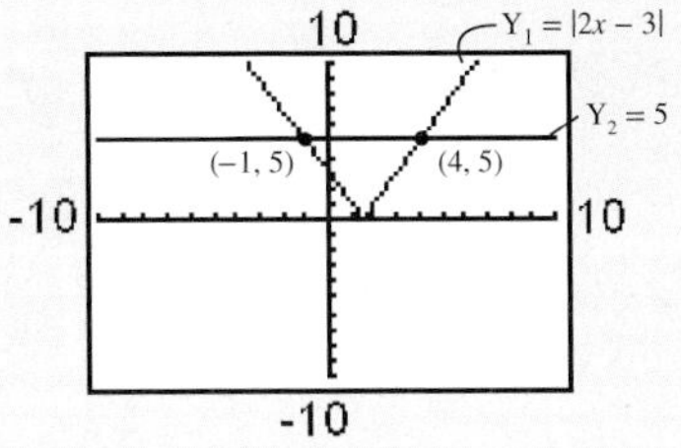

Example 3 Solving an Absolute Value Equation

Solve the equation. $|2c - 5| + 6 = 2$

Classroom Example: p. 655, Exercise 32

Solution:

$|2c - 5| + 6 = 2$

$|2c - 5| = -4$ Isolate the absolute value. The equation is in the form $|x| = a$, where $x = 2c - 5$ and $a = -4$. Because $a < 0$, there is no solution.

No solution, { } There are no numbers c that will make an absolute value equal to a negative number.

Avoiding Mistakes

Always isolate the absolute value first. Otherwise you will get answers that do not check.

Skill Practice Solve the equation.

6. $|3z + 10| + 3 = 1$

Calculator Connections

Topic: Analyzing an Absolute Value Equation with No Solution

To confirm the answer in Example 3, note that the graphs of $Y_1 = \text{abs}(2x - 5) + 6$ and $Y_2 = 2$ do not intersect.

Therefore, there is no solution to the equation $|2x - 5| + 6 = 2$.

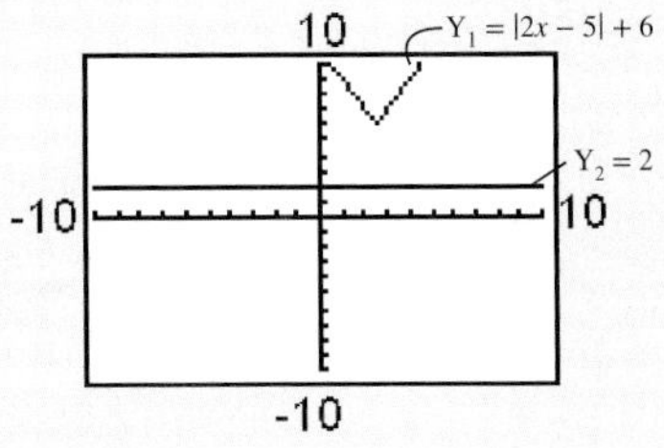

Answers

5. $\left\{2, -\frac{5}{2}\right\}$ **6.** { }

Classroom Example: p. 655, Exercise 38

Example 4 Solving an Absolute Value Equation

Solve the equation. $-2\left|\frac{2}{5}p+3\right|-7=-19$

Solution:

$$-2\left|\frac{2}{5}p+3\right|-7=-19$$

$$-2\left|\frac{2}{5}p+3\right|=-12 \quad \text{Isolate the absolute value.}$$

$$\frac{-2\left|\frac{2}{5}p+3\right|}{-2}=\frac{-12}{-2}$$

$$\left|\frac{2}{5}p+3\right|=6$$

$$\frac{2}{5}p+3=6 \quad \text{or} \quad \frac{2}{5}p+3=-6 \quad \text{Rewrite as two equations.}$$

$$2p+15=30 \quad \text{or} \quad 2p+15=-30 \quad \text{Multiply by 5 to clear fractions.}$$

$$2p=15 \quad \text{or} \quad 2p=-45$$

$$p=\frac{15}{2} \quad \text{or} \quad p=-\frac{45}{2} \quad \text{Both values check in the original equation.}$$

The solution set is $\left\{\frac{15}{2}, -\frac{45}{2}\right\}$.

Skill Practice Solve the equation.

7. $3\left|\frac{3}{2}a+1\right|+2=14$

Classroom Example: p. 655, Exercise 34

Example 5 Solving an Absolute Value Equation

Solve the equation. $6.9=|4.1-p|+6.9$

Solution:

$$6.9=|4.1-p|+6.9$$

$$|4.1-p|+6.9=6.9$$

First write the absolute value on the left. Then subtract 6.9 from both sides to write the equation in the form $|x|=a$.

$$|4.1-p|=0 \quad \text{Isolate the absolute value.}$$

$$4.1-p=0 \quad \text{or} \quad 4.1-p=-0$$

Rewrite as two equations. Notice that the equations are the same.

$$-p=-4.1 \quad \text{Subtract 4.1 from both sides.}$$

$$p=4.1$$

Answer

7. $\left\{2, -\frac{10}{3}\right\}$

Check $p = 4.1$ in the original equation.

Check: $p = 4.1$

$$|4.1 - p| + 6.9 = 6.9$$
$$|4.1 - 4.1| + 6.9 \stackrel{?}{=} 6.9$$
$$|0| + 6.9 \stackrel{?}{=} 6.9$$
$$6.9 \stackrel{?}{=} 6.9 \checkmark$$

The solution set is $\{4.1\}$.

Skill Practice Solve the equation.

8. $-3.5 = |1.2 + x| - 3.5$

2. Solving Equations Containing Two Absolute Values

Some equations have two absolute values such as $|x| = |y|$. If two quantities have the same absolute value, then the quantities are equal or the quantities are opposites.

Equality of Absolute Values

$|x| = |y|$ implies that $x = y$ or $x = -y$.

Example 6 Solving an Equation Having Two Absolute Values

Classroom Example: p. 655, Exercise 42

Solve the equation. $|2w - 3| = |5w + 1|$

Solution:

$$|2w - 3| = |5w + 1|$$

$2w - 3 = 5w + 1$	or	$2w - 3 = -(5w + 1)$	Rewrite as two equations, $x = y$ or $x = -y$.
$2w - 3 = 5w + 1$	or	$2w - 3 = -5w - 1$	Solve for w.
$-3w - 3 = 1$	or	$7w - 3 = -1$	
$-3w = 4$	or	$7w = 2$	
$w = -\frac{4}{3}$	or	$w = \frac{2}{7}$	Both values check in the original equation.

The solution set is $\left\{-\frac{4}{3}, \frac{2}{7}\right\}$.

Avoiding Mistakes

To take the opposite of the quantity $5w + 1$, use parentheses and apply the distributive property.

Skill Practice Solve the equation.

9. $|3 - 2x| = |3x - 1|$

Answers

8. $\{-1.2\}$ **9.** $\left\{\frac{4}{5}, -2\right\}$

Classroom Example: p. 655, Exercise 48

Example 7 **Solving an Equation Having Two Absolute Values**

Solve the equation. $|x-4| = |x+8|$

Solution:

$|x-4| = |x+8|$

$x-4 = x+8$ or $x-4 = -(x+8)$ Rewrite as two equations, $x = y$ or $x = -y$.

$-4 = 8$ or $x-4 = -x-8$ Solve for x.

contradiction

$2x-4=-8$

$2x=-4$

$x=-2$ $x=-2$ checks in the original equation.

The solution set is $\{-2\}$.

Skill Practice Solve the equation.

10. $|4t+3| = |4t-5|$

Calculator Connections

Topic: Analyzing an Absolute Value Equation Graphically

To confirm the answer in Example 7, graph $Y_1 = \text{abs}(x-4)$ and $Y_2 = \text{abs}(x+8)$. There is one point of intersection at $(-2, 6)$. Therefore, the solution to $|x-4| = |x+8|$ is -2.

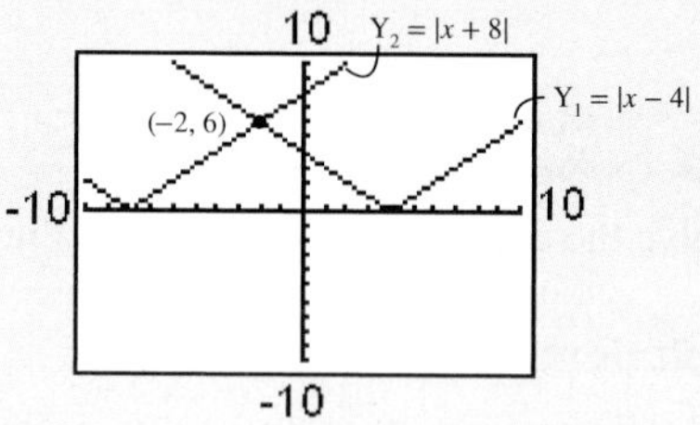

Answer

10. $\left\{\frac{1}{4}\right\}$

Section 9.3 Practice Exercises

For additional exercises, see Classroom Activities 9.3A–9.3B in the *Student's Resource Manual* at www.mhhe.com/moh.

Vocabulary and Key Concepts

1. **a.** An ___absolute___ value equation is an equation of the form $|x| = a$. If a is a positive real number then the solution set is ___$\{a, -a\}$___.

b. What is the first step to solve the absolute value equation $|x| + 5 = 7$? Subtract 5 from both sides.

c. The absolute value equation $|x| = |y|$ implies that $x =$ ___y___ or $x =$ ___$-y$___.

d. The solution set to the equation $|x+4| = -2$ is ___{ }___. The solution set to the equation $|x+4| = 0$ is ___$\{-4\}$___.

Review Exercises

For Exercises 2–6, solve the inequalities. Write the answers in interval notation.

2. $x^2 - 3x - 10 \le 0$ $[-2, 5]$

3. $x^2 - 1 \ge 0$ $(-\infty, -1] \cup [1, \infty)$

4. $\dfrac{4}{y-4} \ge 3$ $\left(4, \dfrac{16}{3}\right]$

5. $\dfrac{3}{t+1} \le 2$ $(-\infty, -1) \cup \left[\dfrac{1}{2}, \infty\right)$

6. $x^3 - 7x^2 - 8x > 0$ $(-1, 0) \cup (8, \infty)$

Writing Translating Expression Geometry Scientific Calculator Video

Concept 1: Solving Absolute Value Equations

For Exercises 7–38, solve the absolute value equations. **(See Examples 1–5.)**

7. $|p| = 7$ $\{7, -7\}$

8. $|q| = 10$ $\{10, -10\}$

9. $|x| + 5 = 11$ $\{6, -6\}$

10. $|x| - 3 = 20$ $\{23, -23\}$

11. $|y| + 8 = 5$ $\{\ \}$

12. $|x| + 12 = 6$ $\{\ \}$

13. $|w| - 3 = -1$ $\{-2, 2\}$

14. $|z| - 14 = -10$ $\{-4, 4\}$

15. $|3q| = 0$ $\{0\}$

16. $|4p| = 0$ $\{0\}$

17. $|3x - 4| = 8$ $\left\{4, -\frac{4}{3}\right\}$

18. $|4x + 1| = 6$ $\left\{\frac{5}{4}, -\frac{7}{4}\right\}$

19. $5 = |2x - 4|$ $\left\{\frac{9}{2}, -\frac{1}{2}\right\}$

20. $10 = |3x + 7|$ $\left\{1, -\frac{17}{3}\right\}$

21. $\left|\frac{7z}{3} - \frac{1}{3}\right| + 3 = 6$ $\left\{\frac{10}{7}, -\frac{8}{7}\right\}$

22. $\left|\frac{w}{2} + \frac{3}{2}\right| - 2 = 7$ $\{15, -21\}$

23. $|0.2x - 3.5| = -5.6$ $\{\ \}$

24. $|1.81 + 2x| = -2.2$ $\{\ \}$

25. $1 = -4 + \left|2 - \frac{1}{4}w\right|$ $\{-12, 28\}$

26. $-12 = -6 - |6 - 2x|$ $\{0, 6\}$

27. $10 = 4 + |2y + 1|$ $\left\{\frac{5}{2}, -\frac{7}{2}\right\}$

28. $-1 = -|5x + 7|$ $\left\{-\frac{6}{5}, -\frac{8}{5}\right\}$

29. $-2|3b - 7| - 9 = -9$ $\left\{\frac{7}{3}\right\}$

30. $-3|5x + 1| + 4 = 4$ $\left\{-\frac{1}{5}\right\}$

31. $-2|x + 3| = 5$ $\{\ \}$

32. $-3|x - 5| = 7$ $\{\ \}$

33. $0 = |6x - 9|$ $\left\{\frac{3}{2}\right\}$

34. $7 = |4k - 6| + 7$ $\left\{\frac{3}{2}\right\}$

35. $\left|-\frac{1}{5} - \frac{1}{2}k\right| = \frac{9}{5}$ $\left\{-4, \frac{16}{5}\right\}$

36. $\left|-\frac{1}{6} - \frac{2}{9}h\right| = \frac{1}{2}$ $\left\{-3, \frac{3}{2}\right\}$

37. $-3|2 - 6x| + 5 = -10$ $\left\{-\frac{1}{2}, \frac{7}{6}\right\}$

38. $5|1 - 2x| - 7 = 3$ $\left\{-\frac{1}{2}, \frac{3}{2}\right\}$

Concept 2: Solving Equations Containing Two Absolute Values

For Exercises 39–56, solve the absolute value equations. **(See Examples 6–7.)**

39. $|4x - 2| = |-8|$ $\left\{\frac{5}{2}, -\frac{3}{2}\right\}$

40. $|3x + 5| = |-5|$ $\left\{0, -\frac{10}{3}\right\}$

41. $|4w + 3| = |2w - 5|$ $\left\{-4, \frac{1}{3}\right\}$

42. $|3y + 1| = |2y - 7|$ $\left\{-8, \frac{6}{5}\right\}$

43. $|2y + 5| = |7 - 2y|$ $\left\{\frac{1}{2}\right\}$

44. $|9a + 5| = |9a - 1|$ $\left\{-\frac{2}{9}\right\}$

45. $\left|\frac{4w - 1}{6}\right| = \left|\frac{2w}{3} + \frac{1}{4}\right|$ $\left\{-\frac{1}{16}\right\}$

46. $\left|\frac{6p + 3}{8}\right| = \left|\frac{3}{4}p - 2\right|$ $\left\{\frac{13}{12}\right\}$

47. $|2h - 6| = |2h + 5|$ $\left\{\frac{1}{4}\right\}$

48. $|6n - 7| = |4 - 6n|$ $\left\{\frac{11}{12}\right\}$

49. $|3.5m - 1.2| = |8.5m + 6|$ $\{-1.44, -0.4\}$

50. $|11.2n + 9| = |7.2n - 2.1|$ $\{-2.775, -0.375\}$

51. $|4x - 3| = -|2x - 1|$ $\{\ \}$

52. $-|3 - 6y| = |8 - 2y|$ $\{\ \}$

53. $|8 - 7w| = |7w - 8|$ $\{w \mid w \text{ is a real number}\}$

54. $|4 - 3z| = |3z - 4|$ $\{z \mid z \text{ is a real number}\}$

55. $|x + 2| + |x - 4| = 0$ $\{\ \}$

56. $|t + 6| + |t - 1| = 0$ $\{\ \}$

Expanding Your Skills

57. Write an absolute value equation whose solution is the set of real numbers 6 units from zero on the number line. $|x| = 6$

58. Write an absolute value equation whose solution is the set of real numbers $\frac{7}{2}$ units from zero on the number line. $|x| = \frac{7}{2}$

59. Write an absolute value equation whose solution is the set of real numbers $\frac{4}{3}$ units from zero on the number line. $|x| = \frac{4}{3}$

60. Write an absolute value equation whose solution is the set of real numbers 9 units from zero on the number line. $|x| = 9$

Graphing Calculator Exercises

For Exercises 61–66, enter the left side of the equation as Y_1 and enter the right side of the equation as Y_2. Then use the *Intersect* feature to approximate the x-values where the two graphs intersect (if they intersect).

61. $|4x - 3| = 5$ $\left\{2, -\frac{1}{2}\right\}$

62. $|x - 4| = 3$ $\{7, 1\}$

63. $|8x + 1| + 8 = 1$ $\{\ \}$

64. $|3x - 2| + 4 = 2$ $\{\ \}$

65. $|x - 3| = |x + 2|$ $\left\{\frac{1}{2}\right\}$

66. $|x + 4| = |x - 2|$ $\{-1\}$

Section 9.4 Absolute Value Inequalities

Concepts

1. Solving Absolute Value Inequalities by Definition
2. Solving Absolute Value Inequalities by the Test Point Method
3. Translating to an Absolute Value Expression

1. Solving Absolute Value Inequalities by Definition

In this section, we will solve absolute value *inequalities*. An inequality in any of the forms $|x| < a$, $|x| \le a$, $|x| > a$, or $|x| \ge a$ is called an **absolute value inequality**.

Recall that an absolute value represents distance from zero on the real number line. Consider the following absolute value equation and inequalities.

1. $|x| = 3$

$x = 3$ or $x = -3$

Solution:

The set of all points 3 units from zero on the number line

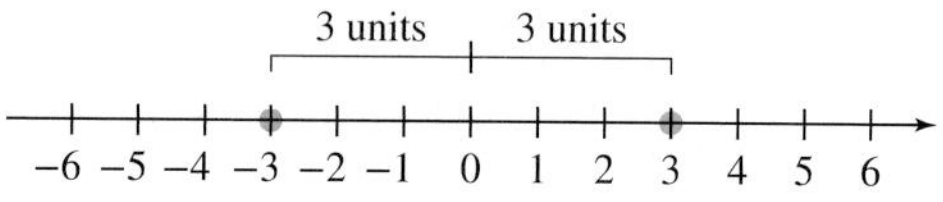

2. $|x| > 3$

$x < -3$ or $x > 3$

Solution:

The set of all points more than 3 units from zero

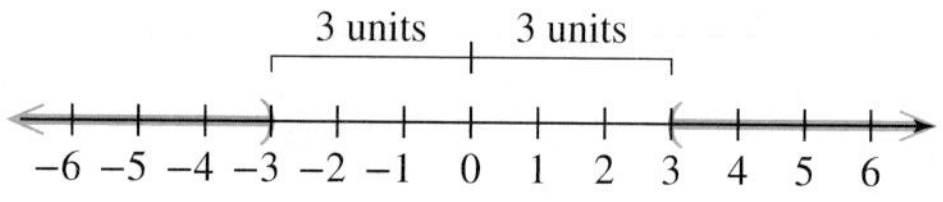

3. $|x| < 3$

$-3 < x < 3$

Solution:

The set of all points less than 3 units from zero

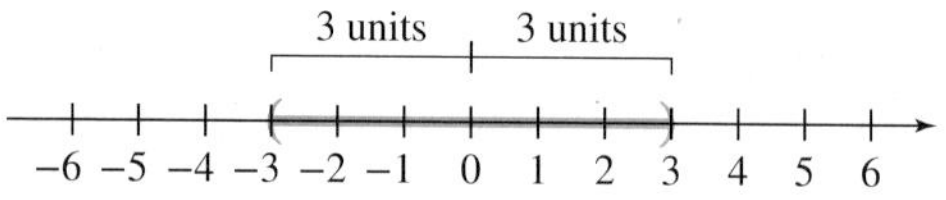

Solving Absolute Value Equations and Inequalities

Let a be a real number such that $a > 0$. Then

Equation/ Inequality	Solution (Equivalent Form)	Graph
$\|x\| = a$	$x = -a$ or $x = a$	
$\|x\| > a$	$x < -a$ or $x > a$	
$\|x\| < a$	$-a < x < a$	

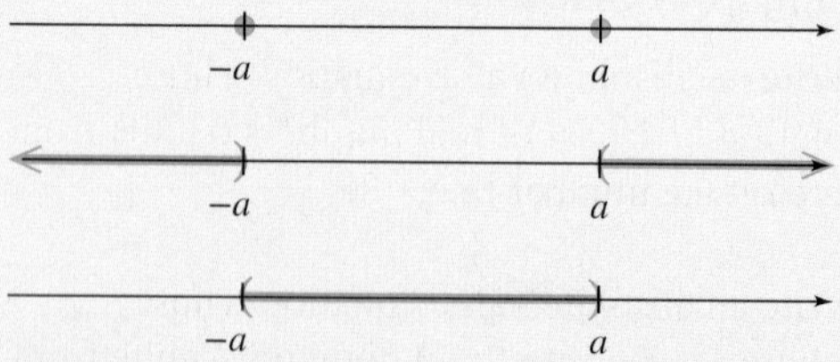

Instructor Note:
$|x| = a$ means that x is "a" units away from 0.
$|x| > a$ means that x is more than "a" units away from 0.
$|x| < a$ means that x is less than "a" units away from 0.

To solve an absolute value inequality, first isolate the absolute value and then rewrite the absolute value inequality in its equivalent form.

Example 1 **Solving an Absolute Value Inequality**

Solve the inequality. $|3w + 1| - 4 < 7$

Solution:

$|3w + 1| - 4 < 7$

$|3w + 1| < 11$ ⟵ Isolate the absolute value first.

The inequality is in the form $|x| < a$, where $x = 3w + 1$.

$-11 < 3w + 1 < 11$ Rewrite in the equivalent form $-a < x < a$.

$-12 < 3w < 10$ Solve for w.

$-4 < w < \frac{10}{3}$

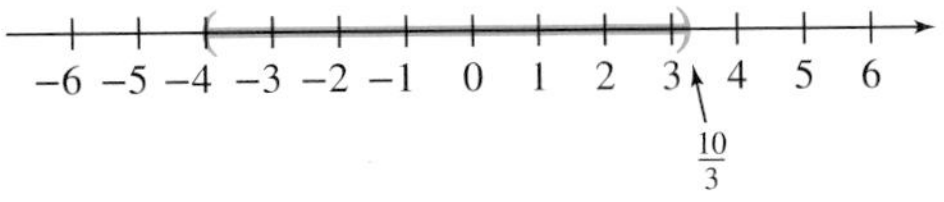

The solution is $\{w \mid -4 < w < \frac{10}{3}\}$, or equivalently in interval notation, $(-4, \frac{10}{3})$.

Skill Practice Solve the inequality. Write the solution in interval notation.

1. $|2t + 5| + 2 \le 11$

Classroom Example: p. 664, Exercise 12

TIP: Recall that a strict inequality (using the symbols > and <) will have parentheses at the endpoints of the interval form of the solution.

Calculator Connections

Topic: Analyzing an Absolute Value Inequality Graphically

To confirm the answer in Example 1, graph $Y_1 = \text{abs}(3x + 1) - 4$ and $Y_2 = 7$. On the given display window, $Y_1 < Y_2$ (Y_1 is below Y_2) for $-4 < x < \frac{10}{3}$.

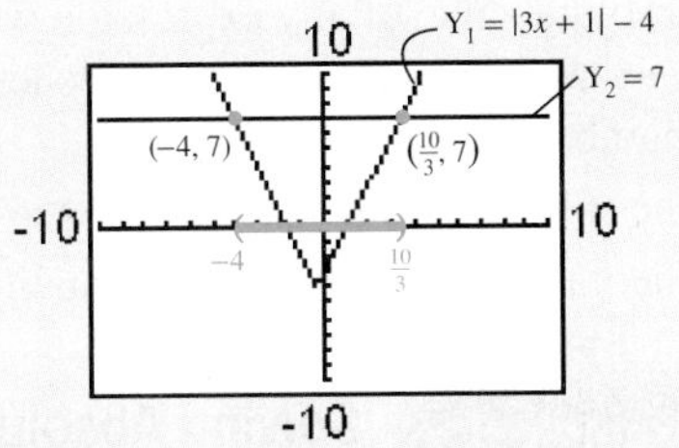

Example 2 **Solving an Absolute Value Inequality**

Solve the inequality. $3 \le 1 + \left|\frac{1}{2}t - 5\right|$

Solution:

$3 \le 1 + \left|\frac{1}{2}t - 5\right|$

$1 + \left|\frac{1}{2}t - 5\right| \ge 3$ Write the inequality with the absolute value on the left.

$\left|\frac{1}{2}t - 5\right| \ge 2$ Isolate the absolute value.

The inequality is in the form $|x| \ge a$, where $x = \frac{1}{2}t - 5$.

$\frac{1}{2}t - 5 \le -2$ or $\frac{1}{2}t - 5 \ge 2$ Rewrite in the equivalent form $x \le -a$ or $x \ge a$.

Classroom Example: p. 664, Exercise 32

TIP: It is generally easier to solve an absolute value inequality if the absolute value appears on the left-hand side of the inequality.

Answer

1. $[-7, 2]$

$\frac{1}{2}t \leq 3$ or $\frac{1}{2}t \geq 7$ Solve the compound inequality.

$2\left(\frac{1}{2}t\right) \leq 2(3)$ or $2\left(\frac{1}{2}t\right) \geq 2(7)$ Clear fractions.

$t \leq 6$ or $t \geq 14$

The solution is $\{t \mid t \leq 6 \text{ or } t \geq 14\}$ or, equivalently in interval notation, $(-\infty, 6] \cup [14, \infty)$.

Skill Practice Solve the inequality. Write the solution in interval notation.

2. $5 < 1 + \left|\frac{1}{3}c - 1\right|$

Calculator Connections

Topic: Analyzing an Absolute Value Inequality Graphically

To confirm the answer in Example 2, graph $Y_1 = \text{abs}((1/2)x - 5) + 1$ and $Y_2 = 3$. On the given display window, $Y_1 \geq Y_2$ for $x \leq 6$ or $x \geq 14$.

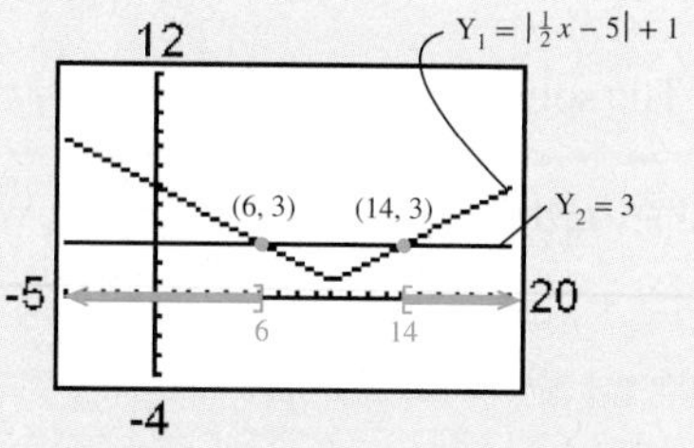

By definition, the absolute value of a real number will always be nonnegative. Therefore, the absolute value of any expression will always be greater than a negative number. Similarly, an absolute value can never be less than a negative number. If a represents a positive real number, then

- The solution to the inequality $|x| > -a$ is all real numbers, $(-\infty, \infty)$.
- There is no solution to the inequality $|x| < -a$.

Classroom Examples: pp. 664–665, Exercises 38 and 40

Example 3 Solving Absolute Value Inequalities

Solve the inequalities.

a. $|3d - 5| + 7 < 4$ **b.** $|3d - 5| + 7 > 4$

Solution:

a. $|3d - 5| + 7 < 4$

$|3d - 5| < -3$

Isolate the absolute value. An absolute value expression cannot be less than a negative number. Therefore, there is no solution.

No solution, { }

b. $|3d - 5| + 7 > 4$

$|3d - 5| > -3$

Isolate the absolute value. The inequality is in the form $|x| > a$, where a is negative. An absolute value of any real number is greater than a negative number. Therefore, the solution is all real numbers.

All real numbers, $(-\infty, \infty)$

Skill Practice Solve the inequalities.

3. $|4p + 2| + 6 < 2$ **4.** $|4p + 2| + 6 > 2$

Answer

2. $(-\infty, -9) \cup (15, \infty)$
3. { }
4. All real numbers; $(-\infty, \infty)$

Calculator Connections

Topic: Analyzing an Absolute Value Inequality Graphically

By graphing $Y_1 = \text{abs}(3x - 5) + 7$ and $Y_2 = 4$ from Example 3, we see that $Y_1 > Y_2$ (Y_1 is above Y_2) for all real numbers x on the given display window.

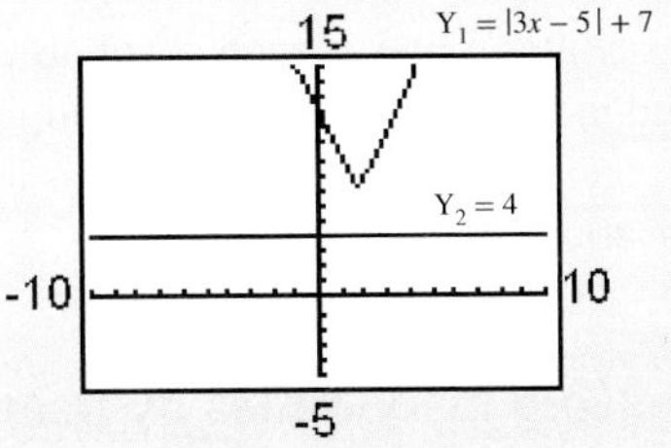

Example 4 Solving Absolute Value Inequalities

Classroom Examples: pp. 664–665, Exercises 26, 42, and 44

Solve the inequalities.

a. $|4x + 2| \geq 0$ **b.** $|4x + 2| > 0$ **c.** $|4x + 2| \leq 0$

Solution:

a. $|4x + 2| \geq 0$ ⟵ The absolute value is already isolated.

The absolute value of any real number is nonnegative. Therefore, the solution is all real numbers, $(-\infty, \infty)$.

b. $|4x + 2| > 0$

An absolute value will be greater than zero at all points *except where it is equal to zero*. That is, the value(s) of x for which $|4x + 2| = 0$ must be excluded from the solution set.

$|4x + 2| = 0$

$4x + 2 = 0$ or $4x + 2 = -0$ The second equation is the same as the first.

$4x = -2$

$x = -\dfrac{1}{2}$ Therefore, exclude $x = -\frac{1}{2}$ from the solution.

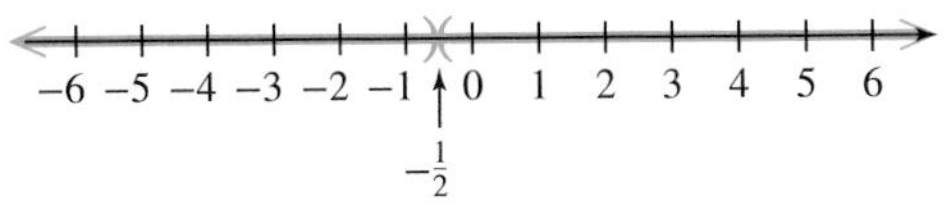

The solution is $\{x \mid x \neq -\frac{1}{2}\}$ or equivalently in interval notation, $(-\infty, -\frac{1}{2}) \cup (-\frac{1}{2}, \infty)$.

c. $|4x + 2| \leq 0$

An absolute value of a number cannot be less than zero. However, it can be *equal* to zero. Therefore, the only solutions to this inequality are the solutions to the related equation:

$|4x + 2| = 0$ From part (b), we see that the solution set is $\left\{-\dfrac{1}{2}\right\}$.

Calculator Connections

Topic: Analyzing an Absolute Value Inequality Graphically

From Example 4, graph $Y_1 = \text{abs}(4x + 2)$. From the graph, $Y_1 = 0$ at $x = -\frac{1}{2}$ (the x-intercept). On the given display window, $Y_1 > 0$ for $x < -\frac{1}{2}$ or $x > -\frac{1}{2}$.

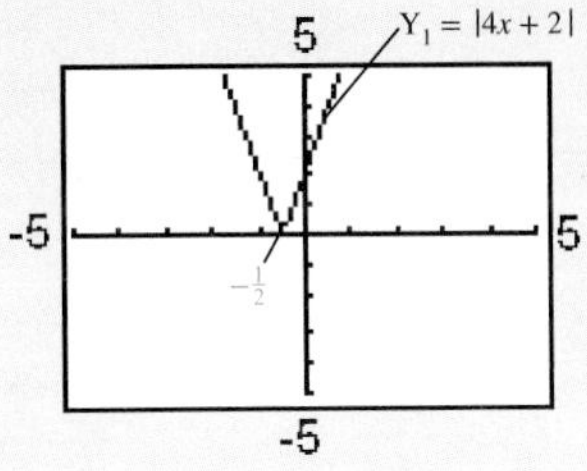

Skill Practice Solve the inequalities.

5. $|3x - 1| \geq 0$ **6.** $|3x - 1| > 0$ **7.** $|3x - 1| \leq 0$

Answers

5. $(-\infty, \infty)$

6. $\left\{x \middle| x \neq \dfrac{1}{3}\right\}$ or $\left(-\infty, \dfrac{1}{3}\right) \cup \left(\dfrac{1}{3}, \infty\right)$

7. $\left\{\dfrac{1}{3}\right\}$

2. Solving Absolute Value Inequalities by the Test Point Method

In Examples 1 and 2, each absolute value inequality was converted to an equivalent compound inequality. However, sometimes students have difficulty setting up the appropriate compound inequality. To avoid this problem, you may want to use the test point method to solve absolute value inequalities.

Solving Inequalities by Using the Test Point Method

Step 1 Find the boundary points of the inequality. (Boundary points are the real solutions to the related equation and points where the inequality is undefined.)

Step 2 Plot the boundary points on the number line. This divides the number line into intervals.

Step 3 Select a test point from each interval and substitute it into the original inequality.

- If a test point makes the original inequality true, then that interval is part of the solution set.

Step 4 Test the boundary points in the original inequality.

- If the original inequality is strict ($<$ or $>$), do not include the boundary points in the solution set.
- If the original inequality is defined using $\le$ or $\ge$, then include the boundary points that are defined within the inequality.

Note: Any boundary point that makes an expression within the inequality undefined must *always* be excluded from the solution set.

To demonstrate the use of the test point method, we will repeat the absolute value inequalities from Examples 1 and 2. Notice that regardless of the method used, the absolute value is always isolated *first* before any further action is taken.

Classroom Example: p. 665, Exercise 48

Example 5 Solving an Absolute Value Inequality by the Test Point Method

Solve the inequality by using the test point method. $|3w+1|-4<7$

Solution:

$|3w+1|-4<7$

$|3w+1|<11$ ← Isolate the absolute value.

$|3w+1|=11$ **Step 1:** Solve the related equation.

$3w+1=11$ or $3w+1=-11$ Write as an equivalent system of two equations.

$3w=10$ or $3w=-12$

$w=\dfrac{10}{3}$ or $w=-4$ These are the only boundary points.

Step 2: Plot the boundary points.

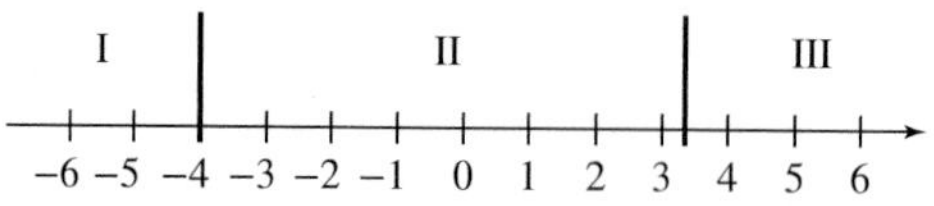

Step 3: Select a test point from each interval.

Test $w = -5$:

$$|3(-5) + 1| - 4 \overset{?}{<} 7$$
$$|-14| - 4 \overset{?}{<} 7$$
$$14 - 4 \overset{?}{<} 7$$
$$10 \overset{?}{<} 7 \quad \text{False}$$

Test $w = 0$:

$$|3(0) + 1| - 4 \overset{?}{<} 7$$
$$|1| - 4 \overset{?}{<} 7$$
$$-3 \overset{?}{<} 7 \quad \text{True}$$

Test $w = 4$:

$$|3(4) + 1| - 4 \overset{?}{<} 7$$
$$|13| - 4 \overset{?}{<} 7$$
$$13 - 4 \overset{?}{<} 7$$
$$9 \overset{?}{<} 7 \quad \text{False}$$

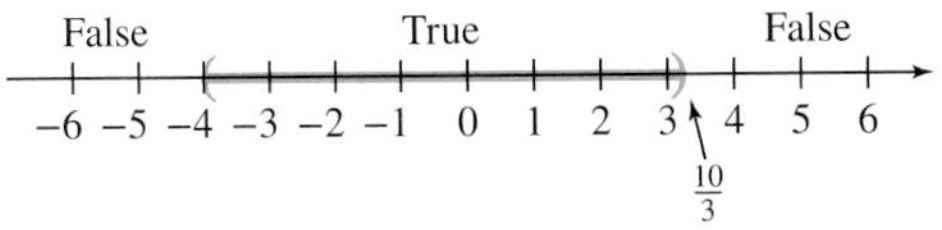

Step 4: Because the original inequality is a strict inequality, the boundary points (where equality occurs) are not included.

The solution is $\{w \mid -4 < w < \frac{10}{3}\}$ or, equivalently in interval notation, $\left(-4, \frac{10}{3}\right)$.

Skill Practice Solve the inequality.

8. $6 + |3t - 4| \le 10$

Example 6 Solving an Absolute Value Inequality by the Test Point Method

Classroom Example: p. 665, Exercise 46

Solve the inequality by using the test point method. $3 \le 1 + \left|\frac{1}{2}t - 5\right|$

Solution:

$$3 \le 1 + \left|\frac{1}{2}t - 5\right|$$

$$1 + \left|\frac{1}{2}t - 5\right| \ge 3$$ Write the inequality with the absolute value on the left.

$$\left|\frac{1}{2}t - 5\right| \ge 2$$ Isolate the absolute value.

$$\left|\frac{1}{2}t - 5\right| = 2$$ **Step 1:** Solve the related equation.

$$\frac{1}{2}t - 5 = 2 \quad \text{or} \quad \frac{1}{2}t - 5 = -2$$ Write as an equivalent system of two equations.

$$\frac{1}{2}t = 7 \quad \text{or} \quad \frac{1}{2}t = 3$$

$$t = 14 \quad \text{or} \quad t = 6$$ These are the boundary points.

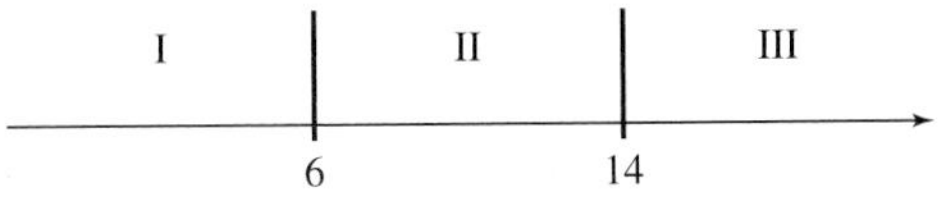

Step 2: Plot the boundary points.

Step 3: Select a test point from each interval.

Answer

8. $\left[0, \frac{8}{3}\right]$

Test $t = 0$:	**Test $t = 10$:**	**Test $t = 16$:**
$3 \overset{?}{\leq} 1 + \left\lvert \frac{1}{2}(0) - 5 \right\rvert$	$3 \overset{?}{\leq} 1 + \left\lvert \frac{1}{2}(10) - 5 \right\rvert$	$3 \overset{?}{\leq} 1 + \left\lvert \frac{1}{2}(16) - 5 \right\rvert$
$3 \overset{?}{\leq} 1 + \lvert 0 - 5 \rvert$	$3 \overset{?}{\leq} 1 + \lvert 5 - 5 \rvert$	$3 \overset{?}{\leq} 1 + \lvert 8 - 5 \rvert$
$3 \overset{?}{\leq} 1 + \lvert -5 \rvert$	$3 \overset{?}{\leq} 1 + \lvert 0 \rvert$	$3 \overset{?}{\leq} 1 + \lvert 3 \rvert$
$3 \overset{?}{\leq} 6$ True	$3 \overset{?}{\leq} 1$ False	$3 \overset{?}{\leq} 4$ True

Step 4: The original inequality uses the sign $\geq$. Therefore, the boundary points (where equality occurs) must be part of the solution set.

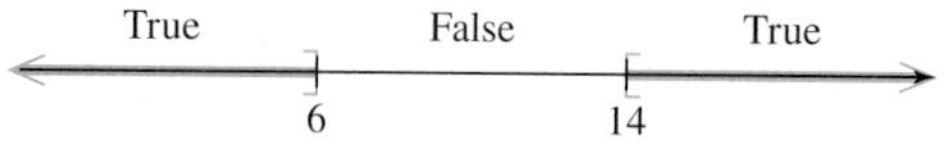

The solution is $\{t \mid t \leq 6 \text{ or } t \geq 14\}$ or, equivalently in interval notation, $(-\infty, 6] \cup [14, \infty)$.

Skill Practice Solve the inequality.

9. $\left\lvert \frac{1}{2}c + 4 \right\rvert + 1 > 6$

3. Translating to an Absolute Value Expression

Absolute value expressions can be used to describe distances. The distance between c and d is given by $\lvert c - d \rvert$. For example, the distance between -2 and 3 on the number line is $\lvert(-2) - 3\rvert = 5$ as expected.

Classroom Example: p. 665, Exercise 52

Example 7 Expressing Distances with Absolute Value

Write an absolute value inequality to represent the following phrases.

a. All real numbers x, whose distance from zero is greater than 5 units

b. All real numbers x, whose distance from -7 is less than 3 units

Solution:

a. All real numbers x, whose distance from zero is greater than 5 units

$\lvert x - 0 \rvert > 5$ or simply $\lvert x \rvert > 5$

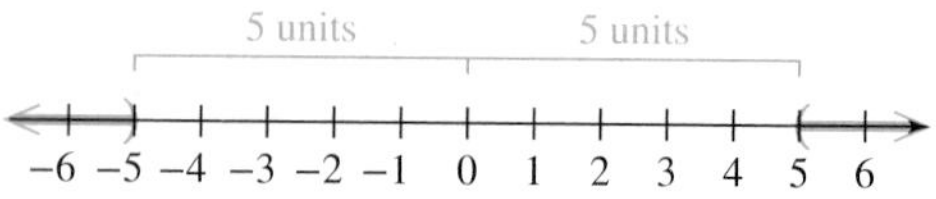

b. All real numbers x, whose distance from -7 is less than 3 units

$\lvert x - (-7) \rvert < 3$ or simply $\lvert x + 7 \rvert < 3$

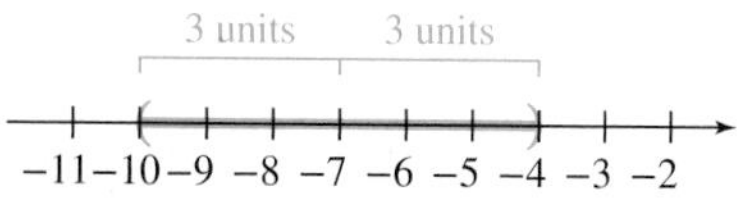

Skill Practice Write an absolute value inequality to represent the following phrases.

10. All real numbers whose distance from zero is greater than 10 units

11. All real numbers whose distance from 4 is less than 6 units

Answers

9. $(-\infty, -18) \cup (2, \infty)$
10. $\lvert x \rvert > 10$
11. $\lvert x - 4 \rvert < 6$

Absolute value expressions can also be used to describe boundaries for measurement error.

Example 8 **Expressing Measurement Error with Absolute Value**

Classroom Example: p. 665, Exercise 56

Latoya measured a certain compound on a scale in the chemistry lab at school. She measured 8 g of the compound, but the scale is only accurate to ±0.1 g. Write an absolute value inequality to express an interval for the true mass, x, of the compound she measured.

Solution:

Because the scale is only accurate to ±0.1 g, the true mass, x, of the compound may deviate by as much as 0.1 g above or below 8 g. This may be expressed as an absolute value inequality:

$|x - 8.0| \leq 0.1$ or equivalently $7.9 \leq x \leq 8.1$

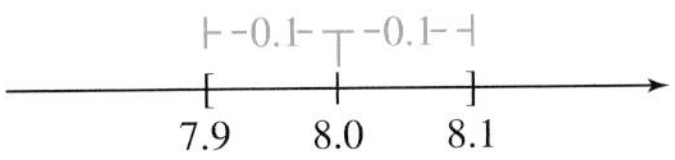

Skill Practice

12. Vonzell molded a piece of metal in her machine shop. She measured the thickness at 12 mm. Her machine is accurate to ±0.05 mm. Write an absolute value inequality to express an interval for the true measurement of the thickness, t, of the metal.

Answer

12. $|t - 12| \leq 0.05$

Section 9.4 Practice Exercises

For additional exercises, see Classroom Activities 9.4A–9.4C in the *Student's Resource Manual* at www.mhhe.com/moh.

Vocabulary and Key Concepts

1. a. If a is a positive real number, then the inequality $|x| < a$ is equivalent to $\underline{-a} < x < \underline{a}$.

   b. If a is a positive real number, then the inequality $|x| > a$ is equivalent to $x < \underline{-a}$ or $x \underline{>} a$.

   c. The solution set to the inquality $|x + 2| < -6$ is $\underline{\{\ \}}$, whereas the solution set to the inequality $|x + 2| > -6$ is $\underline{(-\infty, \infty)}$.

   d. The solution set to the inequality $|x + 4| \leq 0$ (includes/excludes) -4, whereas the solution set to the inequality $|x + 4| < 0$ (includes/excludes) -4. includes; excludes

Review Exercises

For Exercises 2–4, solve the equations.

2. $|10x - 6| = -5$ { }

3. $2 = |5 - 7x| + 1$ $\left\{\frac{4}{7}, \frac{6}{7}\right\}$

4. $|3x - 12| + 4 = 6 - 2$ {4}

For Exercises 5–8, solve the inequality and graph the solution set. Write the solution in interval notation.

5. $-15 < 3w - 6 \leq -9$ $(-3, -1]$

6. $5 - 2y \leq 1$ and $3y + 2 \geq 14$ $[4, \infty)$

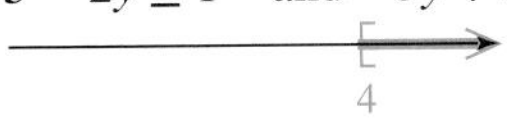

7. $m - 7 \leq -5$ or $m - 7 \geq -10$

$(-\infty, \infty)$

8. $3b - 2 < 7$ or $b - 2 > 4$

$(-\infty, 3) \cup (6, \infty)$

Concepts 1 and 2: Solving Absolute Value Inequalities

For Exercises 9–20, solve the equations and inequalities. For each inequality, graph the solution set and express the solution in interval notation. **(See Examples 1–6.)**

9. **a.** $|x| = 5$ $\{-5, 5\}$
b. $|x| > 5$ $(-\infty, -5) \cup (5, \infty)$
c. $|x| < 5$ $(-5, 5)$

10. **a.** $|a| = 4$ $\{4, -4\}$
b. $|a| > 4$ $(-\infty, -4) \cup (4, \infty)$
c. $|a| < 4$ $(-4, 4)$

11. **a.** $|x - 3| = 7$ $\{10, -4\}$
b. $|x - 3| > 7$ $(-\infty, -4) \cup (10, \infty)$
c. $|x - 3| < 7$ $(-4, 10)$

12. **a.** $|w + 2| = 6$ $\{4, -8\}$
b. $|w + 2| > 6$ $(-\infty, -8) \cup (4, \infty)$
c. $|w + 2| < 6$ $(-8, 4)$

13. **a.** $|p| = -2$ $\{\ \}$
b. $|p| > -2$ $(-\infty, \infty)$
c. $|p| < -2$ $\{\ \}$

14. **a.** $|x| = -14$ $\{\ \}$
b. $|x| > -14$ $(-\infty, \infty)$
c. $|x| < -14$ $\{\ \}$

15. **a.** $|y + 1| = -6$ $\{\ \}$
b. $|y + 1| > -6$ $(-\infty, \infty)$
c. $|y + 1| < -6$ $\{\ \}$

16. **a.** $|z - 4| = -3$ $\{\ \}$
b. $|z - 4| > -3$ $(-\infty, \infty)$
c. $|z - 4| < -3$ $\{\ \}$

17. **a.** $|x| = 0$ $\{0\}$
b. $|x| > 0$ $(-\infty, 0) \cup (0, \infty)$
c. $|x| < 0$ $\{\ \}$

18. **a.** $|p + 3| = 0$ $\{-3\}$
b. $|p + 3| > 0$ $(-\infty, -3) \cup (-3, \infty)$
c. $|p + 3| < 0$ $\{\ \}$

19. **a.** $|k - 7| = 0$ $\{7\}$
b. $|k - 7| > 0$ $(-\infty, 7) \cup (7, \infty)$
c. $|k - 7| < 0$ $\{\ \}$

20. **a.** $|2x + 4| + 3 = 2$ $\{\ \}$
b. $|2x + 4| + 3 > 2$ $\{-\infty, \infty\}$
c. $|2x + 4| + 3 < 2$ $\{\ \}$

For Exercises 21–50, solve the absolute value inequality. Graph the solution set and write the solution in interval notation. **(See Examples 1–6.)**

21. $|x| > 6$ $(-\infty, -6) \cup (6, \infty)$

22. $|x| \leq 6$ $[-6, 6]$

23. $|t| \leq 3$ $[-3, 3]$

24. $|p| > 3$ $(-\infty, -3) \cup (3, \infty)$

25. $|y + 2| \geq 0$ $(-\infty, \infty)$

26. $0 \leq |7n + 2|$ $(-\infty, \infty)$

27. $5 \leq |2x - 1|$ $(-\infty, -2] \cup [3, \infty)$

28. $|x - 2| \geq 7$ $(-\infty, -5] \cup [9, \infty)$

29. $|k - 7| < -3$ $\{\ \}$

30. $|h + 2| < -9$ $\{\ \}$

31. $\left|\dfrac{w - 2}{3}\right| - 3 \leq 1$ $[-10, 14]$

32. $\left|\dfrac{x + 3}{2}\right| - 2 \geq 4$ $(-\infty, -15] \cup [9, \infty)$

33. $12 \leq |9 - 4y| - 2$ $\left(-\infty, -\frac{5}{4}\right] \cup \left[\frac{23}{4}, \infty\right)$

34. $5 > |2m - 7| + 4$ $(3, 4)$

35. $4 > -1 + \left|\dfrac{2x + 1}{4}\right|$ $\left(-\frac{21}{2}, \frac{19}{2}\right)$

36. $9 \geq 2 + \left|\dfrac{x - 4}{5}\right|$ $[-31, 39]$

37. $8 < |4 - 3x| + 12$ $(-\infty, \infty)$

38. $-16 < |5x - 1| - 1$ $(-\infty, \infty)$

39. $5 - |2m + 1| > 5$ $\{ \}$

40. $3 - |5x + 3| > 3$ $\{ \}$

41. $|p + 5| \le 0$ $\{-5\}$

42. $|y + 1| - 4 \le -4$ $\{-1\}$

43. $|z - 6| + 5 > 5$ $(-\infty, 6) \cup (6, \infty)$

44. $|2c - 1| - 4 > -4$ $\left(-\infty, \frac{1}{2}\right) \cup \left(\frac{1}{2}, \infty\right)$

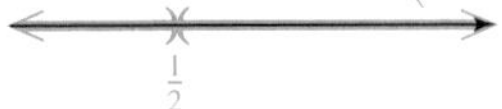

45. $5|2y - 6| + 3 \ge 13$ $(-\infty, 2] \cup [4, \infty)$

46. $7|y + 1| - 3 \ge 11$ $(-\infty, -3] \cup [1, \infty)$

47. $-3|6 - t| + 1 > -5$ $(4, 8)$

48. $-4|8 - x| + 2 > -14$ $(4, 12)$

49. $|0.02x + 0.06| - 0.1 < 0.05$ $(-10.5, 4.5)$

50. $|0.05x - 0.04| - 0.01 < 0.11$ $(-1.6, 3.2)$

Concept 3: Translating to an Absolute Value Expression

For Exercises 51–54, write an absolute value inequality equivalent to the expression given. **(See Example 7.)**

51. All real numbers whose distance from 0 is greater than 7 $|x| > 7$

52. All real numbers whose distance from −3 is less than 4 $|x + 3| < 4$

53. All real numbers whose distance from 2 is at most 13 $|x - 2| \le 13$

54. All real numbers whose distance from 0 is at least 6 $|x| \ge 6$

55. A 32-oz jug of orange juice may not contain exactly 32 oz of juice. The possibility of measurement error exists when the jug is filled in the factory. If the maximum measurement error is ±0.05 oz, write an absolute value inequality representing the range of volumes, x, in which the orange juice jug may be filled. **(See Example 8.)** $|x - 32| \le 0.05$

56. The length of a board is measured to be 32.3 in. The maximum measurement error is ±0.2 in. Write an absolute value inequality that represents the range for the length of the board, x. $|x - 32.3| \le 0.2$

57. A bag of potato chips states that its weight is $6\frac{3}{4}$ oz. The maximum measurement error is $\pm\frac{1}{8}$ oz. Write an absolute value inequality that represents the range for the weight, x, of the bag of chips. $\left|x - 6\frac{3}{4}\right| \le \frac{1}{8}$

58. A $\frac{7}{8}$-in. bolt varies in length by at most $\pm\frac{1}{16}$ in. Write an absolute value inequality that represents the range for the length, x, of the bolt. $\left|x - \frac{7}{8}\right| \le \frac{1}{16}$

59. The width, w, of a bolt is supposed to be 2 cm but may have a 0.01-cm margin of error. Solve $|w - 2| \le 0.01$, and interpret the solution to the inequality in the context of this problem. The solution set is $\{w \mid 1.99 \le w \le 2.01\}$ or equivalently in interval notation, $[1.99, 2.01]$. This means that the actual width of the bolt could be between 1.99 cm and 2.01 cm, inclusive.

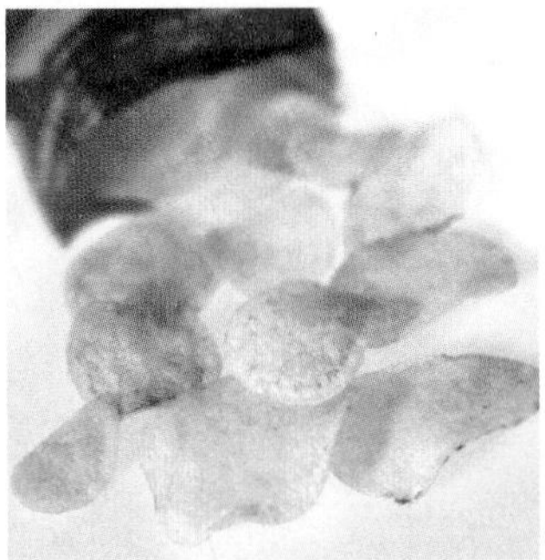

© BananaStock/Punchstock RF

60. In a political poll, the front-runner was projected to receive 53% of the votes with a margin of error of 3%. Solve $|p - 0.53| \le 0.03$ and interpret the solution in the context of this problem.
The solution set is $\{p \mid 0.50 \le p \le 0.56\}$ or equivalently in interval notation $[0.50, 0.56]$. This means that the percentage of votes received by the front-runner was projected to be between 50% and 56%, inclusive.

Expanding Your Skills

For Exercises 61–64, match the graph with the inequality.

61. 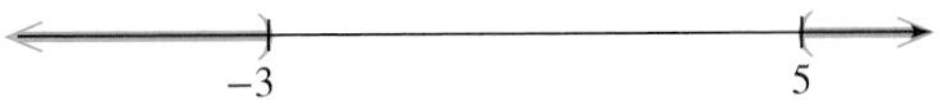

b

62. 

d

63. 

a

64. 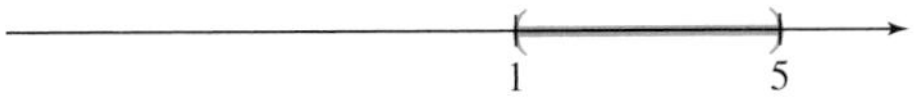

c

a. $|x - 2| < 4$ **b.** $|x - 1| > 4$ **c.** $|x - 3| < 2$ **d.** $|x - 5| > 1$

Graphing Calculator Exercises

To solve an absolute value inequality by using a graphing calculator, let Y_1 equal the left side of the inequality and let Y_2 equal the right side of the inequality. Graph both Y_1 and Y_2 on a standard viewing window and use an *Intersect* feature to approximate the intersection of the graphs. To solve $Y_1 > Y_2$, determine all x-values where the graph of Y_1 is above the graph of Y_2. To solve $Y_1 < Y_2$, determine all x-values where the graph of Y_1 is below the graph of Y_2.

For Exercises 65–74, solve the inequalities using a graphing calculator.

65. $|x+2|>4$ $(-\infty,-6)\cup(2,\infty)$

66. $|3-x|>6$ $(-\infty,-3)\cup(9,\infty)$

67. $\left|\frac{x+1}{3}\right|<2$ $(-7,5)$

68. $\left|\frac{x-1}{4}\right|<1$ $(-3,5)$

69. $|x-5|<-3$ $\{\ \}$

70. $|x+2|<-2$ $\{\ \}$

71. $|2x+5|>-4$ $(-\infty,\infty)$

72. $|1-2x|>-4$ $(-\infty,\infty)$

73. $|6x+1|\le 0$ $\left\{-\frac{1}{6}\right\}$

74. $|3x-4|\le 0$ $\left\{\frac{4}{3}\right\}$

Problem Recognition Exercises

Equations and Inequalities

For Exercises 1–24, identify the category for each equation or inequality (choose from the list here). Then solve the equation or inequality. Express the solution in interval notation where appropriate.

- Linear
- Quadratic
- Polynomial (degree greater than 2)
- Rational
- Absolute value

1. $z^2+10z+9>0$
Quadratic; $(-\infty,-9)\cup(-1,\infty)$

2. $5a-2=6(a+4)$ Linear; $\{-26\}$

3. $\frac{x-4}{2x+4}\ge 1$
Rational; $[-8,-2)$

4. $4x^2-7x=2$
Quadratic; $\{-\frac{1}{4},2\}$

5. $|3x-1|+4<6$
Absolute value; $(-\frac{1}{3},1)$

6. $2t^2-t+1<0$
Quadratic; $\{\ \}$

7. $\frac{1}{2}p-\frac{2}{3}<\frac{1}{6}p-4$
Linear; $(-\infty,-10)$

8. $p^2+3p\le 4$
Quadratic; $[-4,1]$

9. $3y^2+y-2\ge 0$
Quadratic; $(-\infty,-1]\cup[\frac{2}{3},\infty)$

10. $\frac{x+6}{x+4}=7$
Rational; $\{-\frac{11}{3}\}$

11. $3(2x-4)\ge 1-(x-3)$
Linear; $\left[\frac{16}{7},\infty\right)$

12. $|6x+5|+3=2$
Absolute value; $\{\ \}$

13. $(x-3)(2x+1)(x+5)\ge 0$
Polynomial; $[-5,-\frac{1}{2}]\cup[3,\infty)$

14. $-x^2-x-3\le 0$
Quadratic; $(-\infty,\infty)$

15. $\frac{-6}{y-2}<2$
Rational; $(-\infty,-1)\cup(2,\infty)$

16. $x^2-5=4x$
Quadratic; $\{-1,5\}$

17. $\left|\frac{x}{4}+2\right|+6>6$
Absolute value; $(-\infty,-8)\cup(-8,\infty)$

18. $x^2-36<0$
Quadratic; $(-6,6)$

19. $3y^3+5y^2-12y-20=0$
Polynomial; $\{2,-2,-\frac{5}{3}\}$

20. $|8-2x|=16$
Absolute value; $\{12,-4\}$

21. $5b-10-3b=3(b-2)-4$
Linear; $\{0\}$

22. $\frac{x}{x-5}\ge 0$
Rational; $(-\infty,0]\cup(5,\infty)$

23. $|6x+1|=|5+6x|$
Absolute value; $\{-\frac{1}{2}\}$

24. $4x(x-5)^2(2x+3)<0$
Polynomial; $(-\frac{3}{2},0)$

Linear Inequalities and Systems of Linear Inequalities in Two Variables

Section 9.5

Concepts

1. Graphing Linear Inequalities in Two Variables
2. Systems of Linear Inequalities in Two Variables
3. Graphing a Feasible Region

1. Graphing Linear Inequalities in Two Variables

A **linear inequality in two variables** x and y is an inequality that can be written in one of the following forms: $Ax + By < C$, $Ax + By > C$, $Ax + By \le C$, or $Ax + By \ge C$, provided A and B are not both zero.

A solution to a linear inequality in two variables is an ordered pair that makes the inequality true. For example, solutions to the inequality $x + y < 6$ are ordered pairs (x, y) such that the sum of the x- and y-coordinates is less than 6. This inequality has an infinite number of solutions, and therefore it is convenient to express the solution set as a graph.

To graph a linear inequality in two variables, we will follow these steps.

Graphing a Linear Inequality in Two Variables

Step 1 Write the inequality with the y variable isolated, if possible.

Step 2 Graph the related equation. Draw a dashed line if the inequality is strict, $<$ or $>$. Otherwise, draw a solid line.

Step 3 Shade above or below the line as follows:

- Shade *above* the line if the inequality is of the form $y > mx + b$ or $y \ge mx + b$.
- Shade *below* the line if the inequality is of the form $y < mx + b$ or $y \le mx + b$.

Note: A dashed line indicates that the line is *not* included in the solution set. A solid line implies that the line *is* included in the solution set.

This process is demonstrated in Example 1.

Example 1 Graphing a Linear Inequality in Two Variables

Classroom Example: p. 675, Exercise 18

Graph the solution set. $-3x + y \le 1$

Solution:

$-3x + y \le 1$

$y \le 3x + 1$ Solve for y.

Next graph the line defined by the related equation $y = 3x + 1$.

Because the inequality is of the form $y \le mx + b$, the solution to the inequality is the region *below* the line $y = 3x + 1$. So to indicate the solution set, shade the region on and below the line. See Figure 9-6.

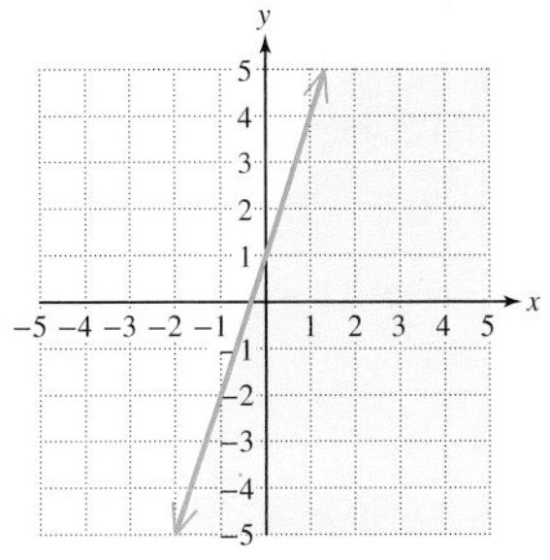

Figure 9-6

Instructor Note: Introduce this concept by asking students to determine if a given ordered pair is a solution to the inequality. For example, ask students to test (3, 1), (−1, 4), and (−4, −1) in Example 1.

Skill Practice Graph the solution set.

1. $2x + y \ge -4$

Answer

1.

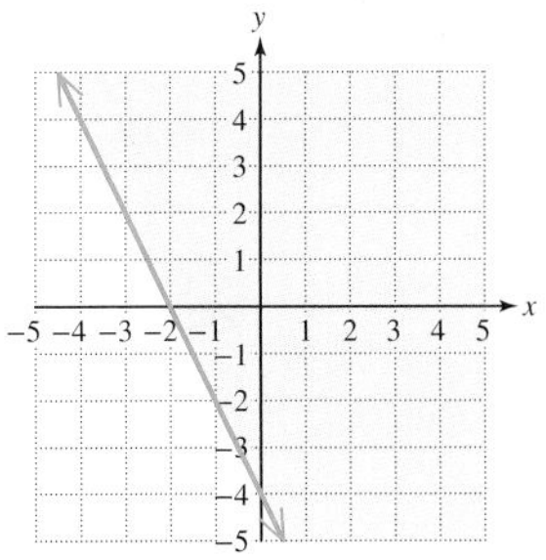

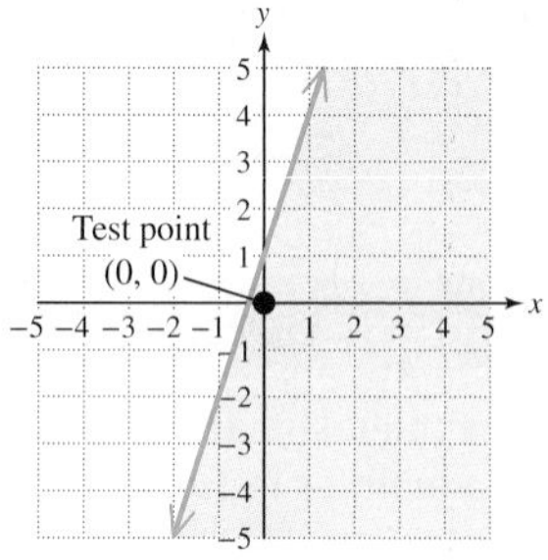

Figure 9-7

After graphing the solution to a linear inequality, we can verify that we have shaded the correct side of the line by using test points. In Example 1, we can pick an arbitrary ordered pair within the shaded region. Then substitute the x- and y-coordinates in the original inequality. If the result is a true statement, then that ordered pair is a solution to the inequality and suggests that other points from the same region are also solutions.

For example, the point (0, 0) lies within the shaded region (Figure 9-7).

$-3x + y \leq 1$ Substitute (0, 0) in the original inequality.

$-3(0) + (0) \overset{?}{\leq} 1$

$0 + 0 \overset{?}{\leq} 1$ ✓ True The point (0, 0) from the shaded region is a solution.

In Example 2, we will graph the solution set to a strict inequality. A strict inequality does not include equality and therefore, is expressed with the symbols < or >. In such a case, the boundary line will be drawn as a dashed line. This indicates that the boundary itself is *not* part of the solution set.

Classroom Example: p. 675, Exercise 24

Example 2 Graphing a Linear Inequality in Two Variables

Graph the solution set. $-4y < 5x$

Solution:

$-4y < 5x$

$\dfrac{-4y}{-4} > \dfrac{5x}{-4}$ Solve for y. Recall that when we divide both sides by a negative number, reverse the inequality sign.

$y > -\dfrac{5}{4}x$

Instructor Note: Consider drawing an analogy between shading the number line when expressing the solution to a single variable inequality versus shading part of a plane for an inequality in two variables.

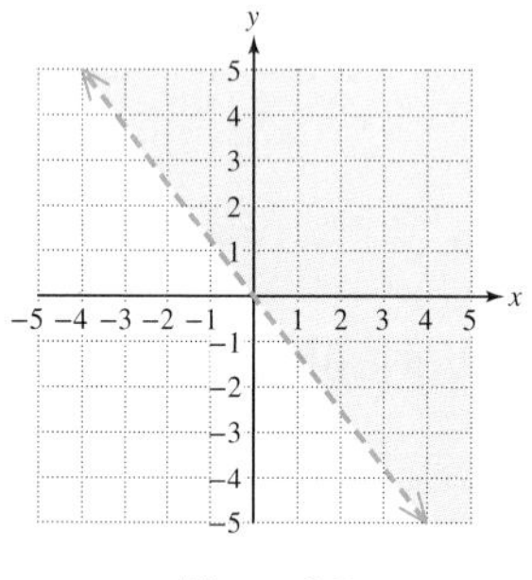

Figure 9-8

Graph the line defined by the related equation, $y = -\frac{5}{4}x$. The boundary line is drawn as a dashed line because the inequality is strict. Also note that the line passes through the origin.

Because the inequality is of the form $y > mx + b$, the solution to the inequality is the region *above* the line. See Figure 9-8.

Skill Practice Graph the solution set.

2. $-3y < x$

Answer

2.

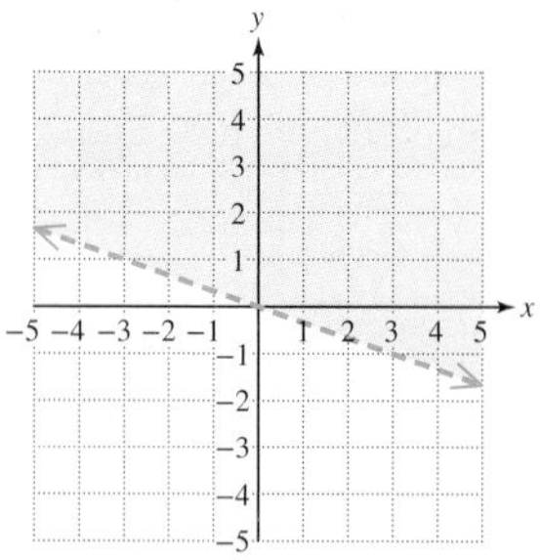

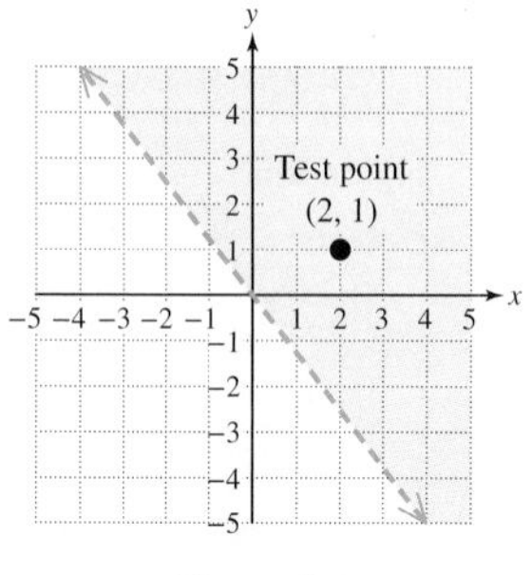

Figure 9-9

In Example 2, we cannot use the origin as a test point, because the point (0, 0) is on the boundary line. Be sure to select a test point strictly within the shaded region. In this case, we choose (2, 1). See Figure 9-9.

$-4y < 5x$ The test point (2, 1) is indeed a solution to the original inequality.

$-4(1) \overset{?}{<} 5(2)$

$-4 \overset{?}{<} 10$ ✓ True

In Example 3, we encounter a situation in which we cannot solve for the y-variable.

Example 3 Graphing a Linear Inequality in Two Variables

Classroom Example: p. 675, Exercise 28

Graph the solution set. $4x \geq -12$

Solution:

$4x \geq -12$

$x \geq -3$

In this inequality, there is no y-variable. However, we can simplify the inequality by solving for x.

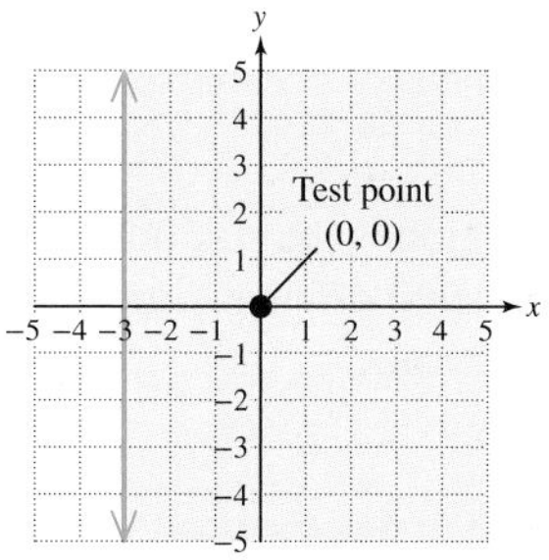

Figure 9-10

Graph the related equation $x = -3$. This is a vertical line. The boundary is drawn as a solid line, because the inequality is not strict, $\geq$.

To shade the appropriate region, refer to the inequality, $x \geq -3$. The points for which x is greater than -3 are to the right of $x = -3$. Therefore, shade the region to the *right* of the line (Figure 9-10).

Selecting a test point such as (0, 0) from the shaded region indicates that we have shaded the correct side of the line.

$4x \geq -12$ Substitute $x = 0$.

$4(0) \overset{?}{\geq} -12$ ✓ True

Skill Practice Graph the solution set.

3. $-2x \geq 2$

2. Systems of Linear Inequalities in Two Variables

Some applications require us to find the solutions to a system of linear inequalities.

Example 4 Graphing a System of Linear Inequalities

Classroom Example: p. 677, Exercise 46

Graph the solution set.

$y > \frac{1}{2}x + 1$

$x + y < 1$

Solution:

Solve each inequality for y.

First inequality

$y > \frac{1}{2}x + 1$

The inequality is of the form $y > mx + b$. Shade *above* the boundary line. See Figure 9-11.

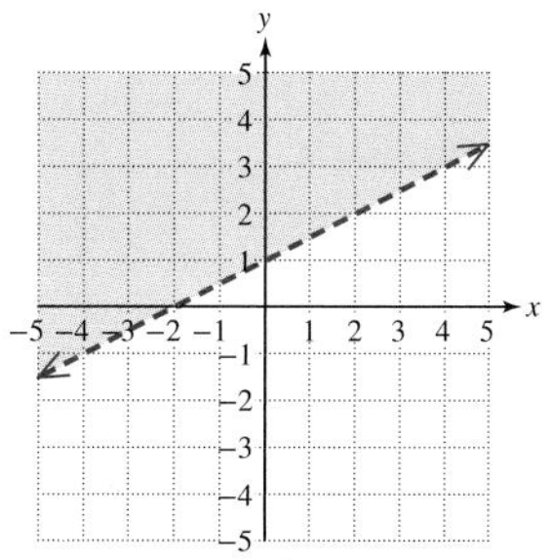

Figure 9-11

Answer

3.

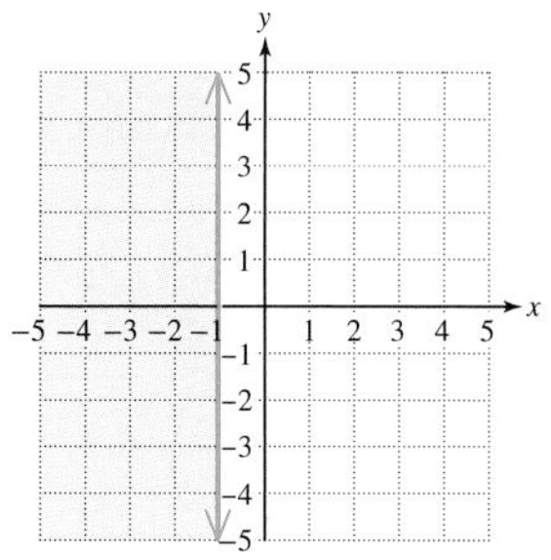

Second inequality

$x + y < 1$

$y < -x + 1$

The inequality is of the form $y < mx + b$. Shade *below* the boundary line. See Figure 9-12.

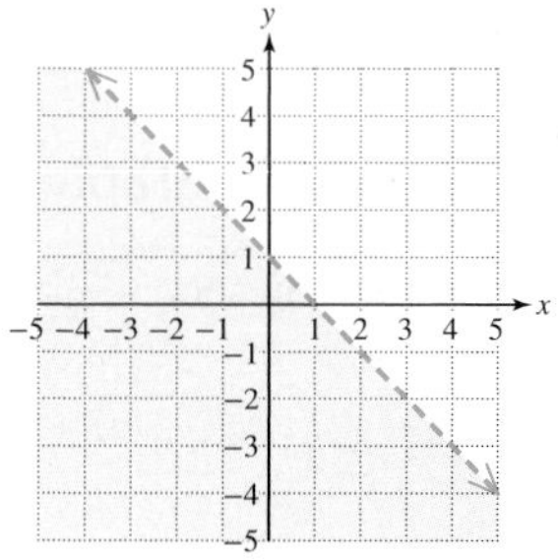

Figure 9-12

The region bounded by the inequalities is the region above the line $y = \frac{1}{2}x + 1$ and below the line $y = -x + 1$. This is the intersection or "overlap" of the two shaded regions (shown in purple in Figure 9-13).

The intersection is the solution set to the system of inequalities. See Figure 9-14.

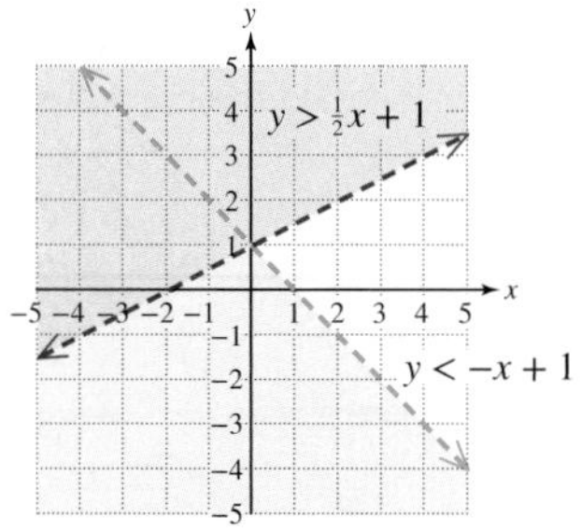

Figure 9-13

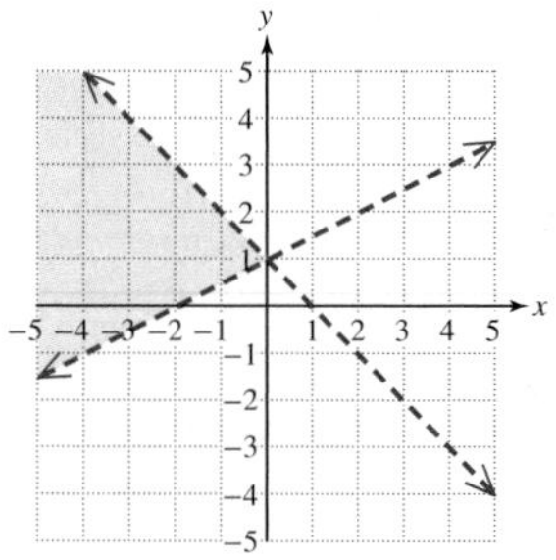

Figure 9-14

Skill Practice Graph the solution set.

4. $x - 3y > 3$

$y < -2x + 4$

Classroom Example: p. 677, Exercise 44

Example 5 Graphing a System of Linear Inequalities

Graph the solution set. $3y \le 6$

$y - x \le 0$

Solution:

First inequality

$3y \le 6$

$y \le 2$

The graph of $y \le 2$ is the region on and below the horizontal line $y = 2$. See Figure 9-15.

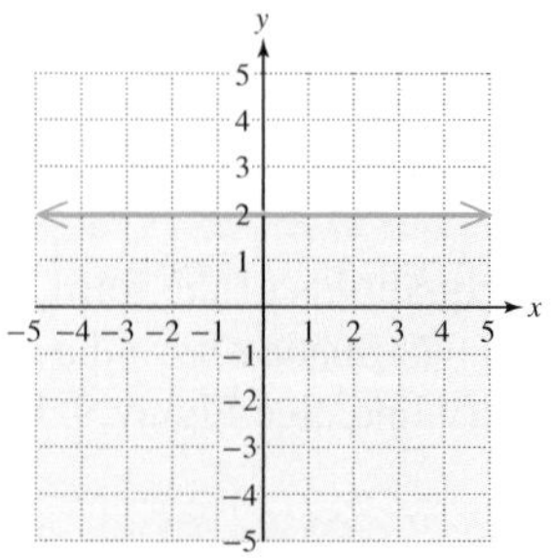

Figure 9-15

Answer

4.

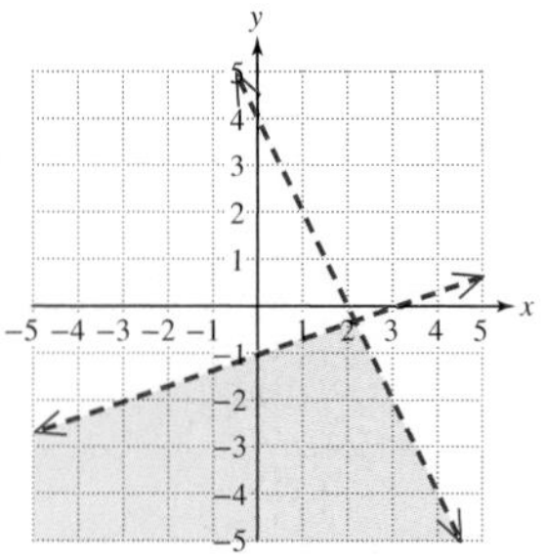

Second inequality

$y - x \le 0$

$y \le x$

The inequality $y \le x$ is of the form $y \le mx + b$. Graph a solid line and shade the region below the line. See Figure 9-16.

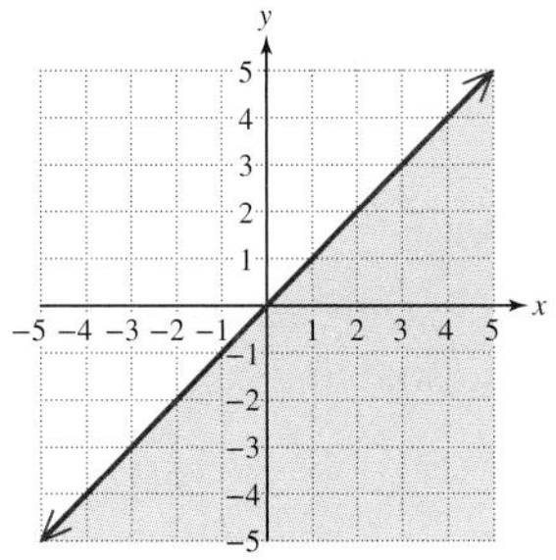

Figure 9-16

The solution to the system of inequalities is the intersection of the shaded regions. Notice that the portions of the lines not bounding the solution are dashed. See Figure 9-17.

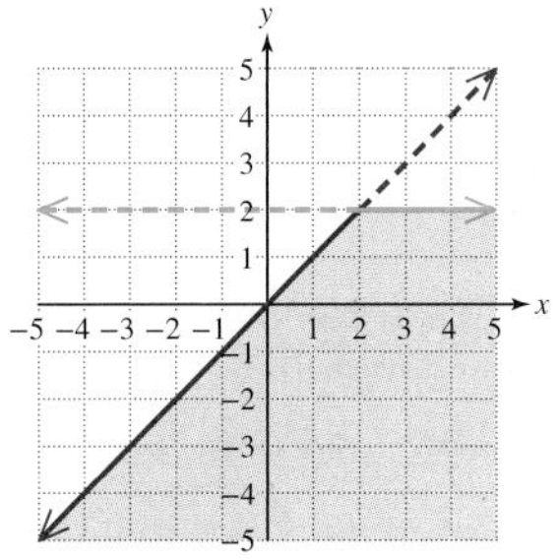

Figure 9-17

Skill Practice Graph the solution set.

5. $2y \le 4$

$y \le x + 1$

Example 6 **Graphing a System of Linear Inequalities**

Classroom Example: p. 677, Exercise 50

Describe the region of the plane defined by the system of inequalities.

$$x \le 0$$
$$y \ge 0$$

Solution:

$x \le 0$ $x \le 0$ for points on the y-axis and in the second and third quadrants.

$y \ge 0$ $y \ge 0$ for points on the x-axis and in the first and second quadrants.

The intersection of these regions is the set of points in the second quadrant (with the boundaries included).

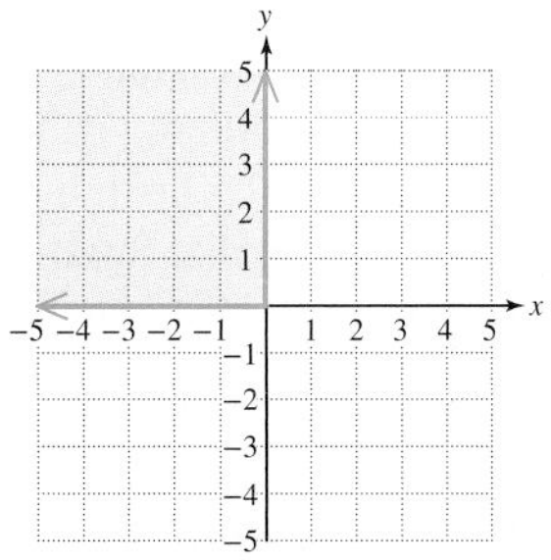

Skill Practice Graph the region defined by the system of inequalities.

6. $x \le 0$

$y \le 0$

3. Graphing a Feasible Region

When two variables are related under certain constraints, a system of linear inequalities can be used to show a region of feasible values for the variables.

The feasible region represents the ordered pairs that are true for each inequality in the system.

Answers

5.

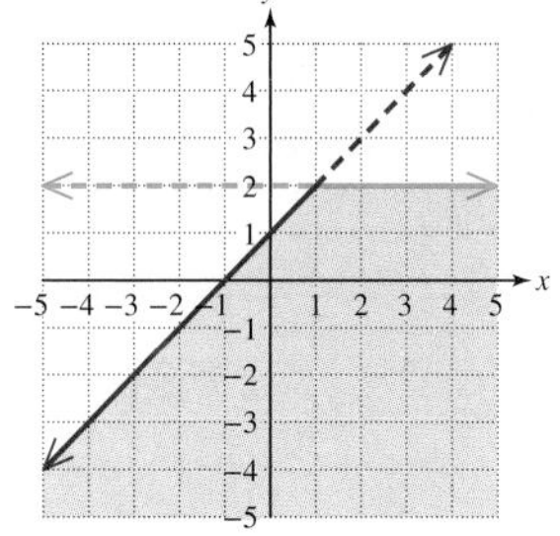

6.

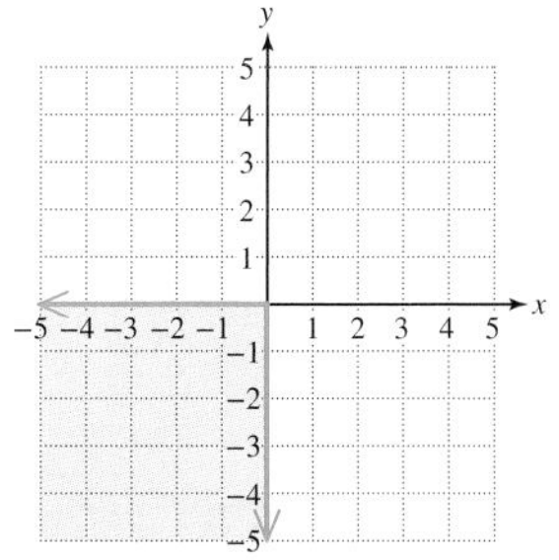

Classroom Example: p. 679, Exercise 62

Example 7 Graphing a Feasible Region

Susan has two tests on Friday: one in chemistry and one in psychology. Because the two classes meet in consecutive hours, she has no study time between tests. Susan estimates that she has a maximum of 12 hr of study time before the tests, and she must divide her time between chemistry and psychology.

Let x represent the number of hours Susan spends studying chemistry.

Let y represent the number of hours Susan spends studying psychology.

a. Find a set of inequalities to describe the constraints on Susan's study time.

b. Graph the constraints to find the feasible region defining Susan's study time.

Solution:

a. Because Susan cannot study chemistry or psychology for a negative period of time, we have $x \geq 0$ and $y \geq 0$. Furthermore, her total time studying cannot exceed 12 hr: $x + y \leq 12$.

A system of inequalities that defines the constraints on Susan's study time is:

$$x \geq 0$$
$$y \geq 0$$
$$x + y \leq 12$$

b. The first two conditions $x \geq 0$ and $y \geq 0$ represent the set of points in the first quadrant. The third condition $x + y \leq 12$ represents the set of points below and including the line $x + y = 12$ (Figure 9-18).

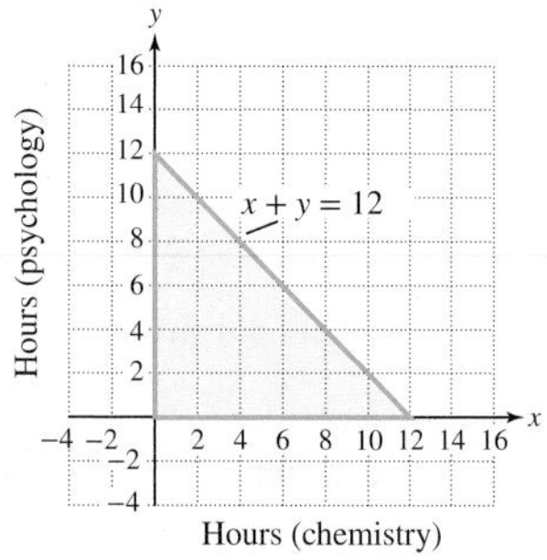

Figure 9-18

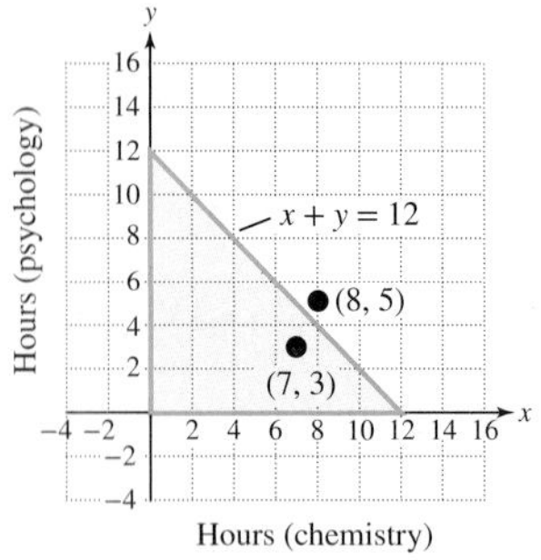

Figure 9-19

Discussion:

1. Refer to the feasible region drawn in Example 7(b). Is the ordered pair (8, 5) part of the feasible region?

No. The ordered pair (8, 5) indicates that Susan spent 8 hr studying chemistry and 5 hr studying psychology. This is a total of 13 hr, which exceeds the constraint that Susan only had 12 hr to study. The point (8, 5) lies outside the feasible region, above the line $x + y = 12$ (Figure 9-19).

2. Is the ordered pair (7, 3) part of the feasible region?

Yes. The ordered pair (7, 3) indicates that Susan spent 7 hr studying chemistry and 3 hr studying psychology.

This point lies within the feasible region and satisfies all three constraints.

$$x \geq 0 \longrightarrow \quad 7 \geq 0 \quad \text{True}$$
$$y \geq 0 \longrightarrow \quad 3 \geq 0 \quad \text{True}$$
$$x + y \leq 12 \longrightarrow (7) + (3) \leq 12 \quad \text{True}$$

Notice that the ordered pair (7, 3) corresponds to a point where Susan is not making full use of the 12 hr of study time.

3. Suppose there was one additional constraint imposed on Susan's study time. She knows she needs to spend at least twice as much time studying chemistry as she does studying psychology. Graph the feasible region with this additional constraint.

Because the time studying chemistry must be at least twice the time studying psychology, we have $x \geq 2y$.

This inequality may also be written as $y \leq \frac{1}{2}x$.

Figure 9-20 shows the first quadrant with the constraint $y \leq \frac{1}{2}x$.

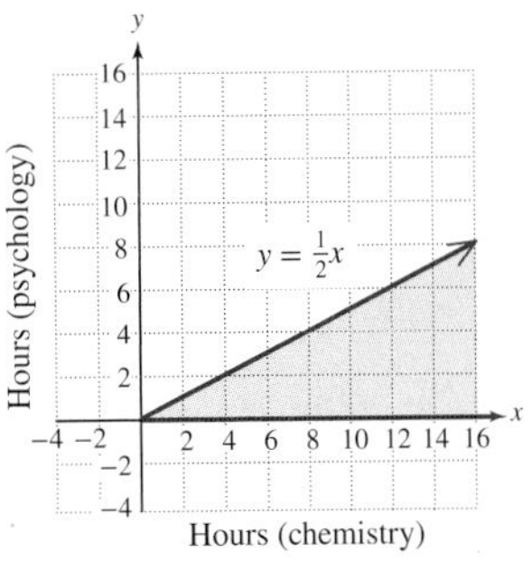

Figure 9-20

4. At what point in the feasible region is Susan making the most efficient use of her time for both classes?

First and foremost, Susan must make use of *all* 12 hr. This occurs for points along the line $x + y = 12$. Susan will also want to study for both classes with approximately twice as much time devoted to chemistry. Therefore, Susan will be deriving the maximum benefit at the point of intersection of the line

$x + y = 12$ and the line $y = \frac{1}{2}x$.

Using the substitution method, replace $y = \frac{1}{2}x$ into the equation $x + y = 12$.

$x + \frac{1}{2}x = 12$

$2x + x = 24$ Clear fractions.

$3x = 24$

$x = 8$ Solve for x.

$y = \dfrac{(8)}{2}$ To solve for y, substitute $x = 8$ into the equation $y = \frac{1}{2}x$.

$y = 4$

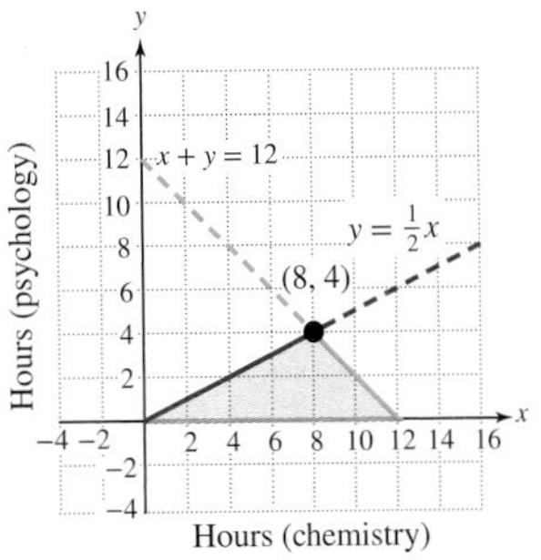

Therefore, Susan should spend 8 hr studying chemistry and 4 hr studying psychology.

Skill Practice

7. A local pet rescue group has a total of 30 cages that can be used to hold cats and dogs. Let x represent the number of cages used for cats, and let y represent the number used for dogs.

a. Write a set of inequalities to express the fact that the number of cat and dog cages cannot be negative.

b. Write an inequality to describe the constraint on the total number of cages for cats and dogs.

c. Graph the system of inequalities to find the feasible region describing the available cages.

Answer

7 a. $x \geq 0$ and $y \geq 0$

b. $x + y \leq 30$

c.

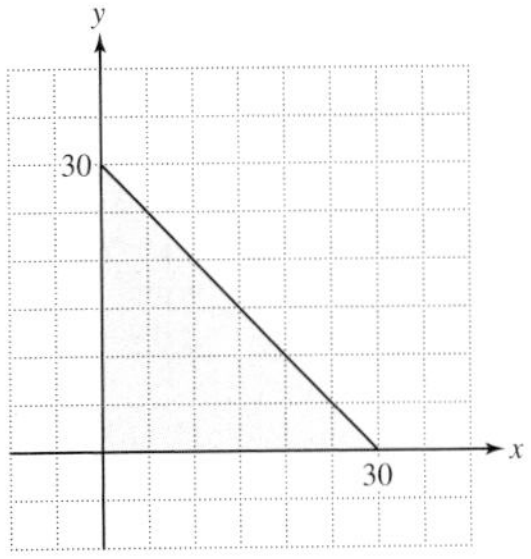

Section 9.5 Practice Exercises

Vocabulary and Key Concepts

For additional exercises, see Classroom Activities 9.5A–9.5C in the *Student's Resource Manual* at www.mhhe.com/moh.

1. **a.** An inequality that can be written in the form $Ax + By > C$ is called a ___linear___ inequality in two variables.

   b. Given the inequality $3x - 4y < 6$, the boundary line $3x - 4y = 6$ (is/is not) included in the solution set. However, given $3x - 4y \le 6$, then the boundary line (is/is not) included in the solution set. is not; is

   c. Given the inequality $5x + y > 5$, the boundary line $5x + y = 5$ should be drawn as a (solid/dashed) line to indicate that the line (is/is not) part of the solution set. dashed; is not

   d. Given the inequality $y \ge -x + 4$, the boundary line $y = -x + 4$ should be drawn as a (solid/dashed) line to indicate that the line (is/is not) part of the solution set. solid; is

Review Exercises

For Exercises 2–5, solve the inequality. Write the solution set in interval notation.

2. $5 < x + 1$ and $-2x + 6 \ge -6$ $(4, 6]$

3. $5 - x \le 4$ and $6 > 3x - 3$ $[1, 3)$

4. $4 - y < 3y + 12$ or $-2(y + 3) \ge 12$
   $(-\infty, -9] \cup (-2, \infty)$

5. $-2x < 4$ or $3x - 1 \le -13$
   $(-\infty, -4] \cup (-2, \infty)$

Concept 1: Graphing Linear Inequalities in Two Variables

For Exercises 6–9, determine if the given point is a solution to the inequality.

6. $2x - y > 8$
   a. $(3, -5)$ Yes
   b. $(-1, -10)$ No
   c. $(4, -2)$ Yes
   d. $(0, 0)$ No

7. $3y + x < 5$
   a. $(-1, 7)$ No
   b. $(5, 0)$ No
   c. $(0, 0)$ Yes
   d. $(2, -3)$ Yes

8. $y \le -2$
   a. $(5, -3)$ Yes
   b. $(-4, -2)$ Yes
   c. $(0, 0)$ No
   d. $(3, 2)$ No

9. $x \ge 5$
   a. $(4, 5)$ No
   b. $(5, -1)$ Yes
   c. $(8, 8)$ Yes
   d. $(0, 0)$ No

10. When should you use a dashed line to graph the solution to a linear inequality?
    Use a dashed line when the inequality is strict ($<$ or $>$).

For Exercises 11–16, decide which inequality symbol should be used ($<, >, \ge, \le$) by looking at the graph.

11.
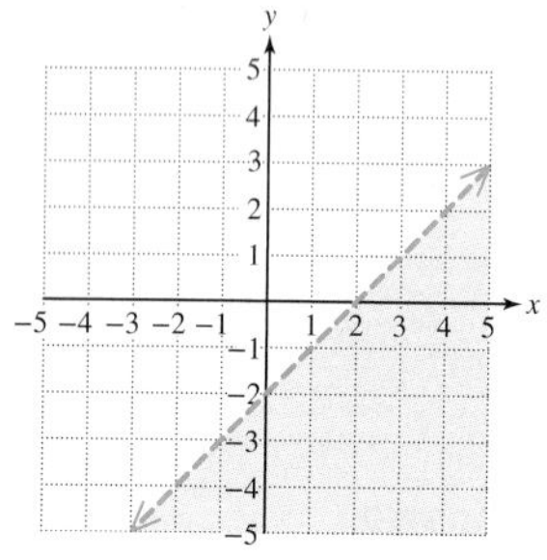
$x - y$ ___>___ 2

12.
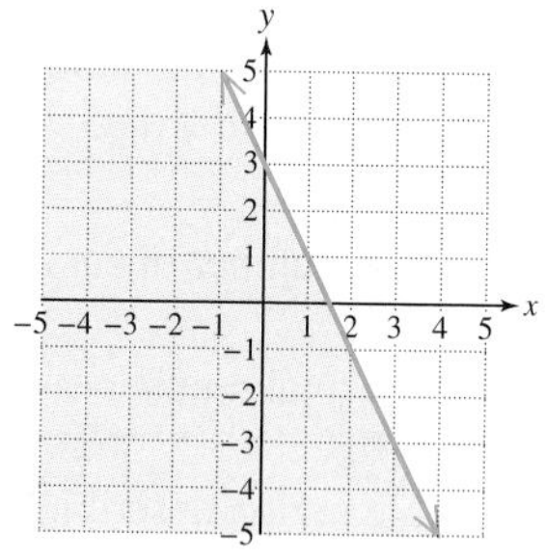
y ___≤___ $-2x + 3$

13.
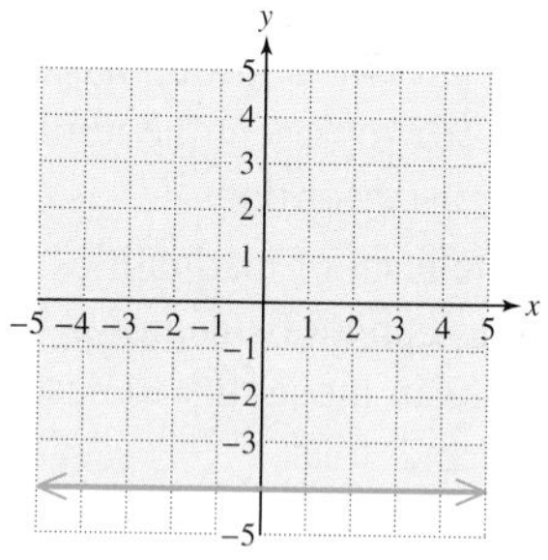
y ___≥___ -4

14.
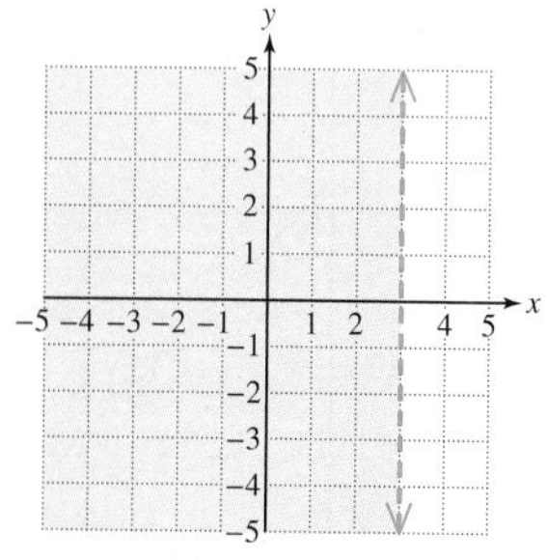
x ___<___ 3

15.
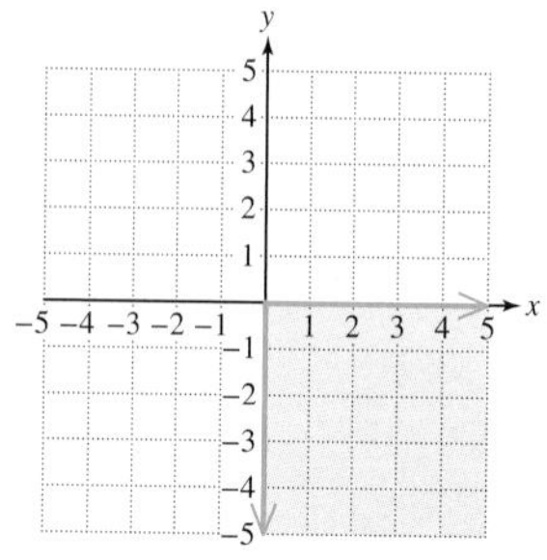
x ___≥___ 0 and y ___≤___ 0

16.
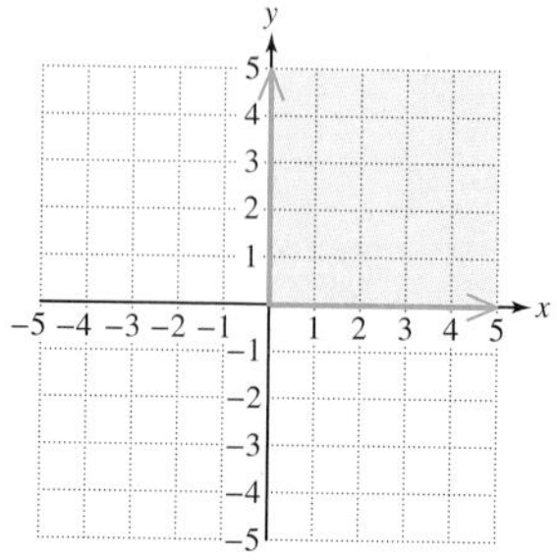
x ___≥___ 0 and y ___≥___ 0

For Exercises 17–40, graph the solution set. **(See Examples 1–3.)**

17. $x - 2y > 4$

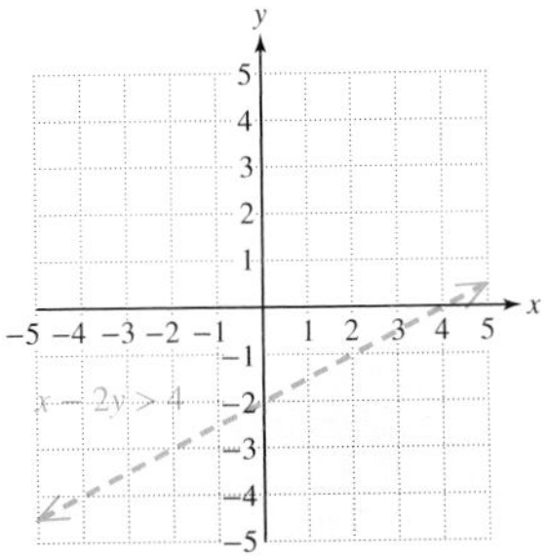

18. $x - 3y \geq 6$

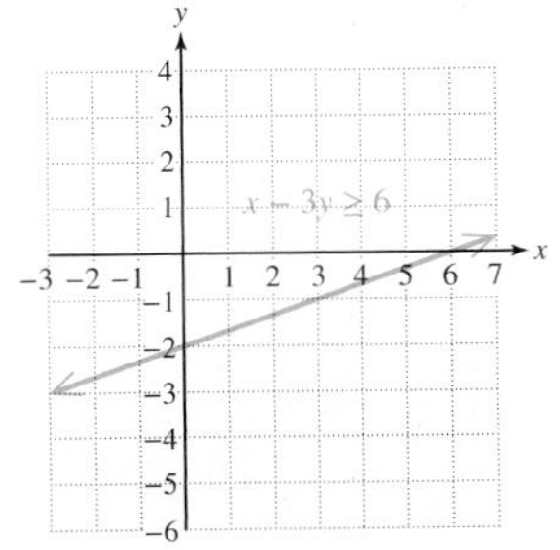

19. $5x - 2y < 10$

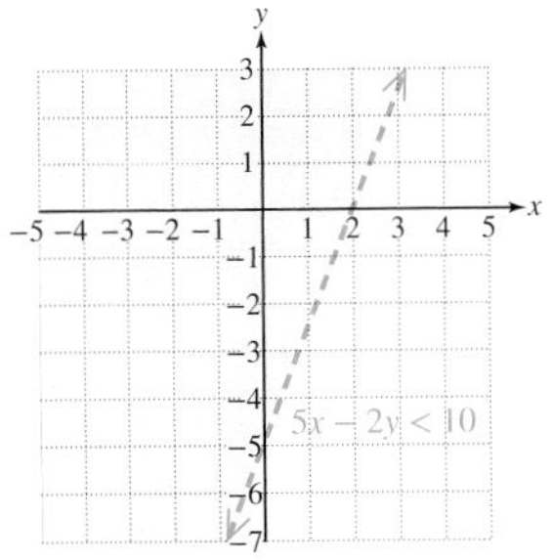

20. $x - 3y < 8$

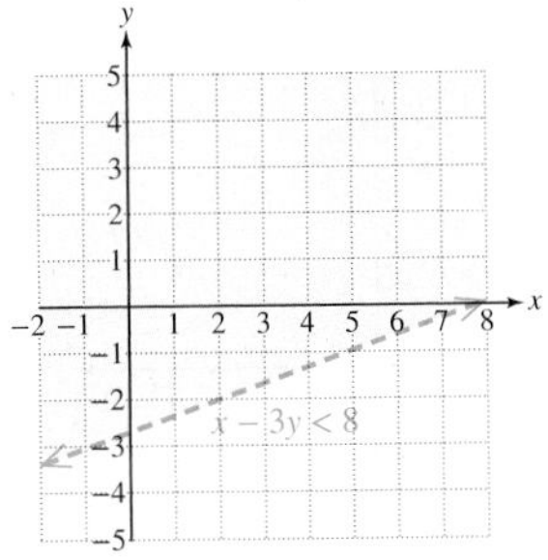

21. $2x \leq -6y + 12$

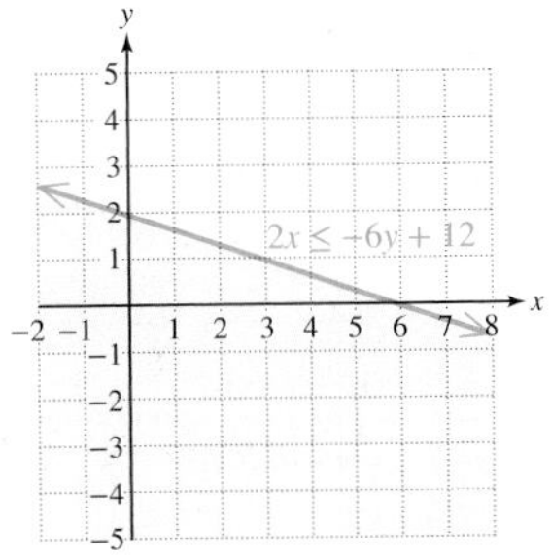

22. $4x < 3y + 12$

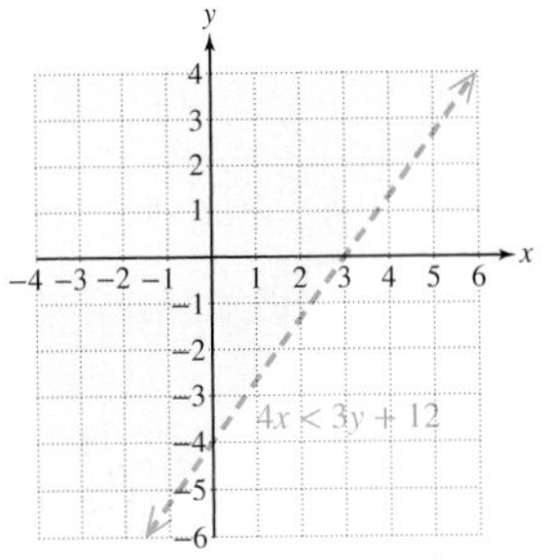

23. $2y \leq 4x$

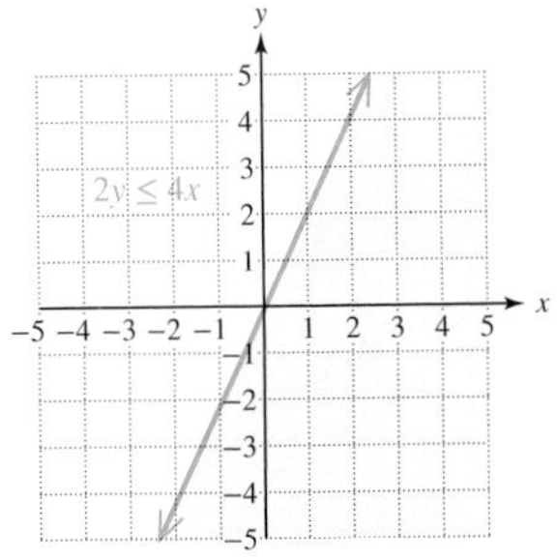

24. $-6x < 2y$

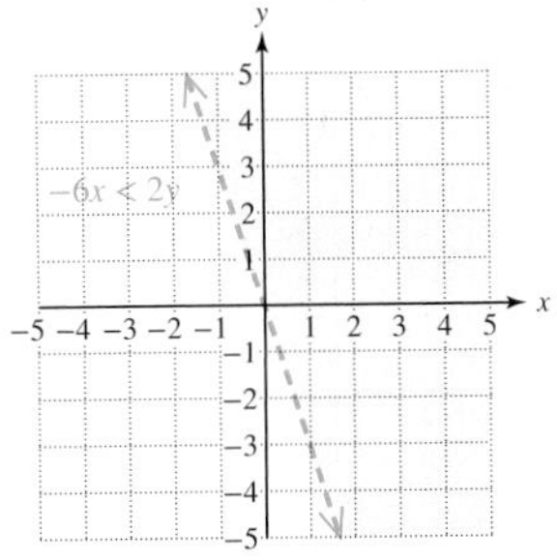

25. $y \geq -2$

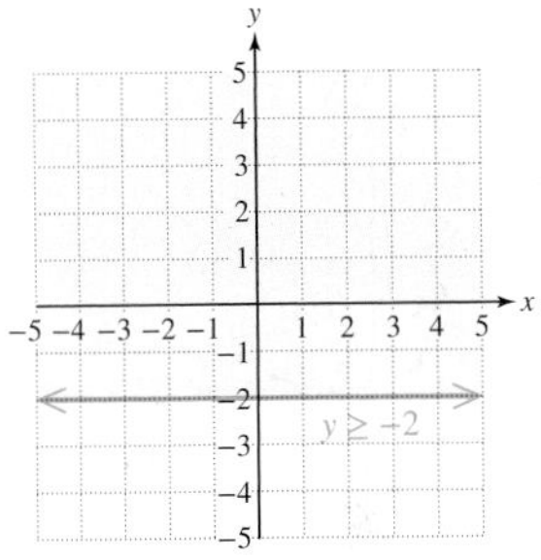

26. $y \geq 5$

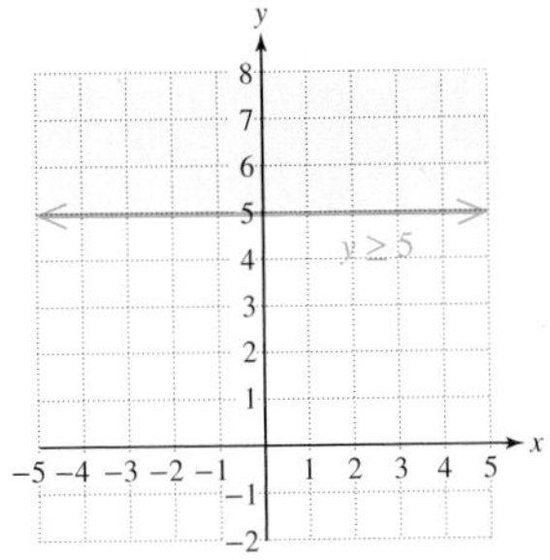

27. $4x < 5$

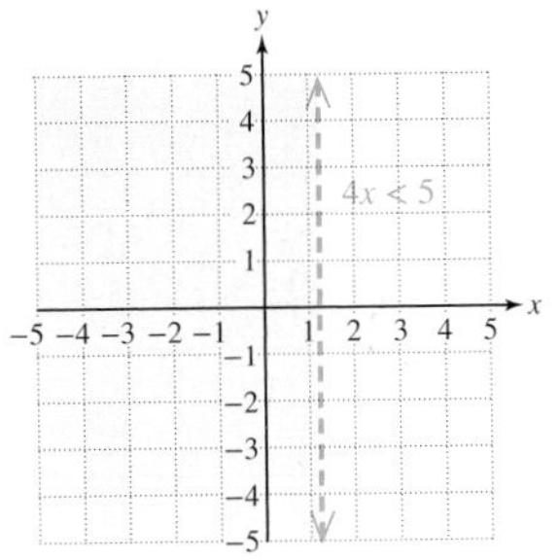

28. $x + 6 < 7$

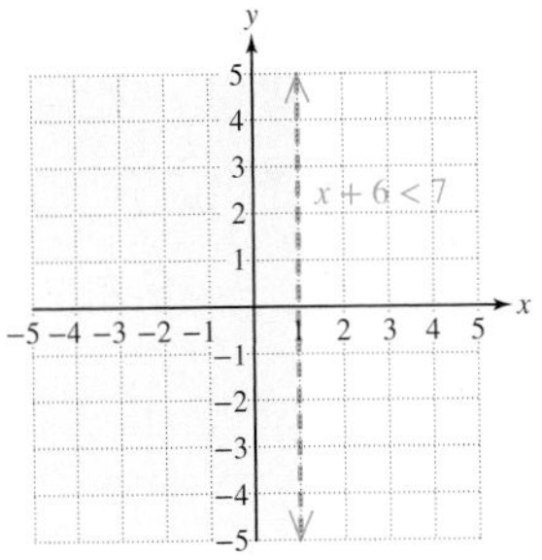

29. $y \geq \frac{2}{5}x - 4$

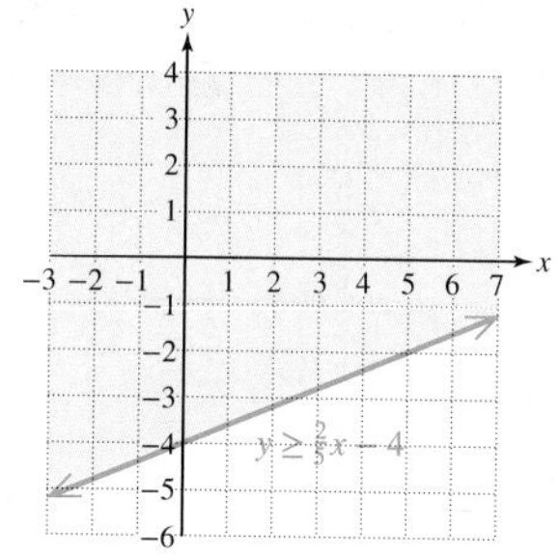

30. $y \geq -\frac{5}{2}x - 4$

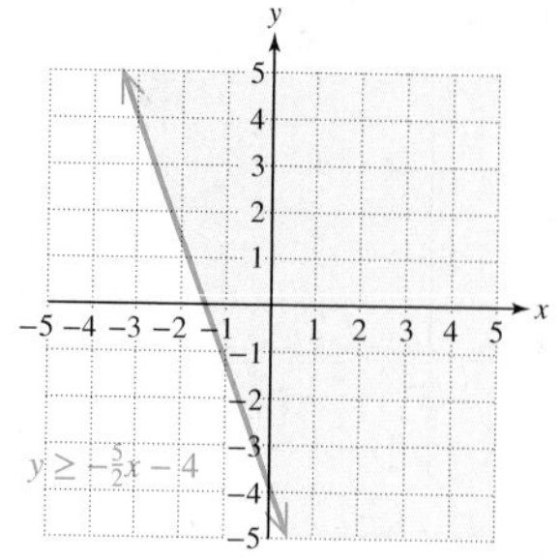

31. $y \leq \frac{1}{3}x + 6$

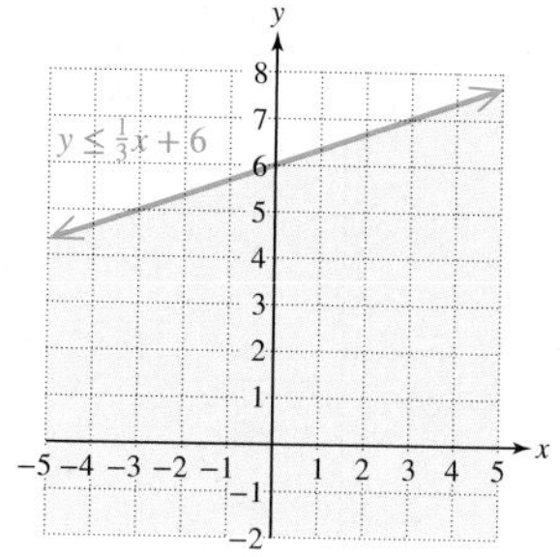

32. $y \leq -\frac{1}{4}x + 2$

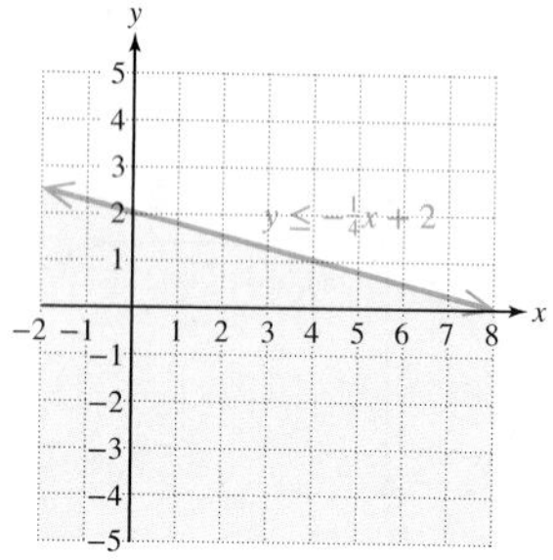

33. $y - 5x > 0$

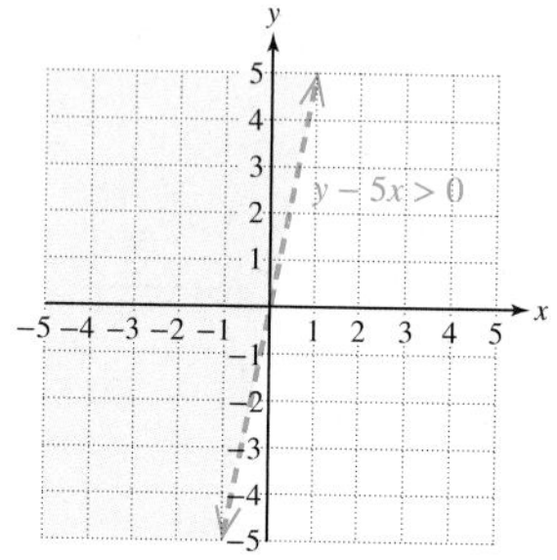

34. $y - \frac{1}{2}x > 0$

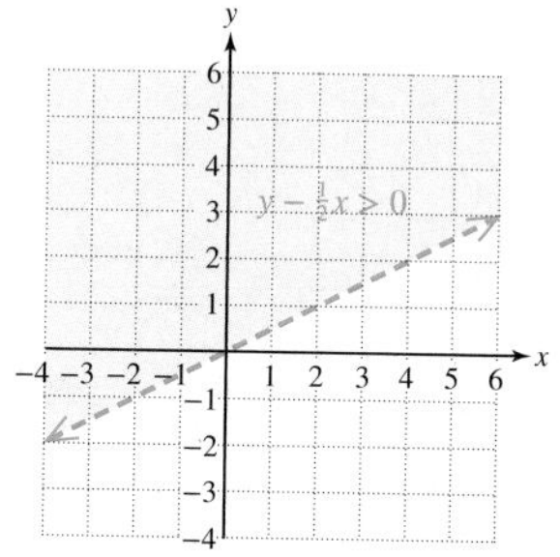

35. $\frac{x}{5} + \frac{y}{4} < 1$

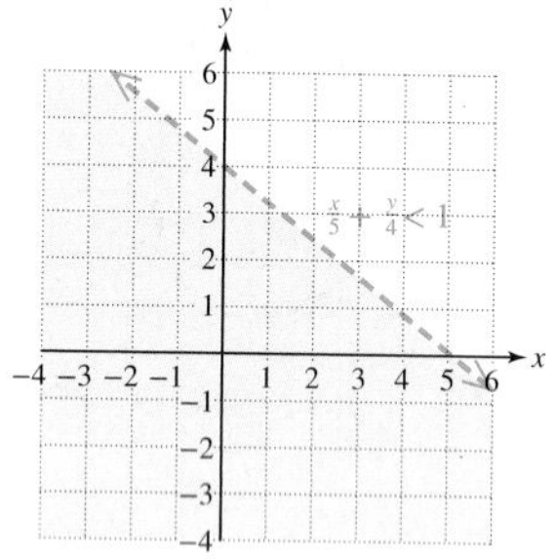

36. $x + \frac{y}{2} \geq 2$

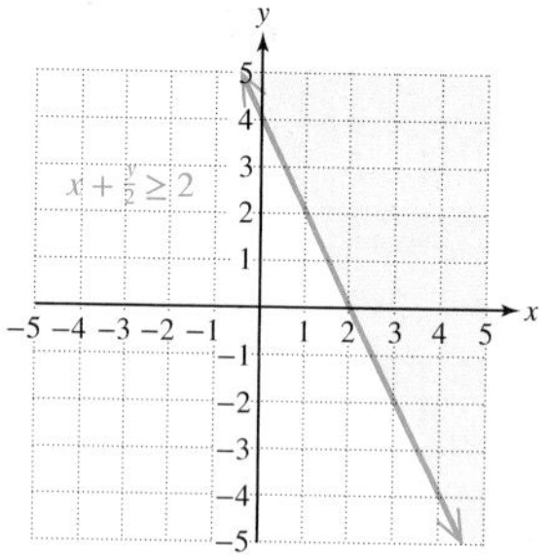

37. $0.1x + 0.2y \leq 0.6$

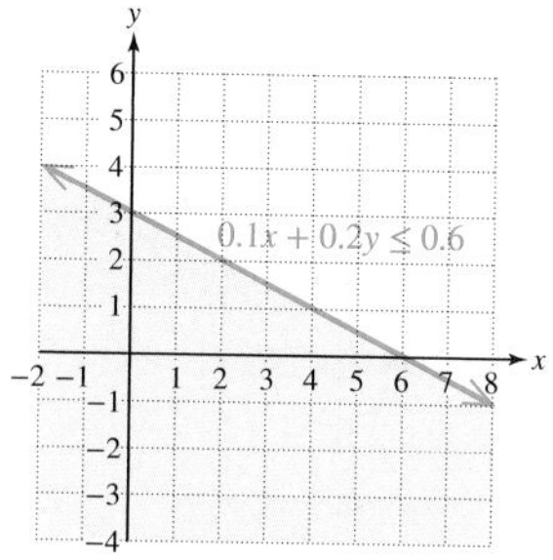

38. $0.3x - 0.2y < 0.6$

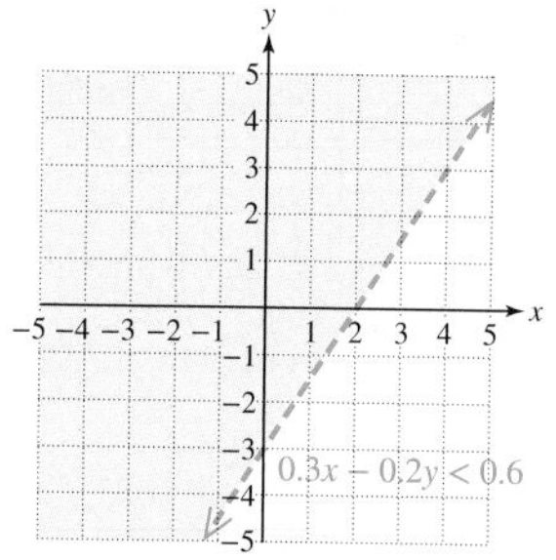

39. $x \leq -\frac{2}{3}y$

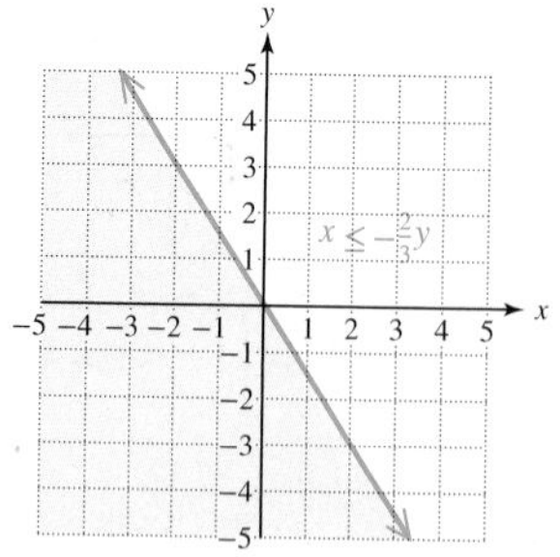

40. $x \geq -\frac{5}{4}y$

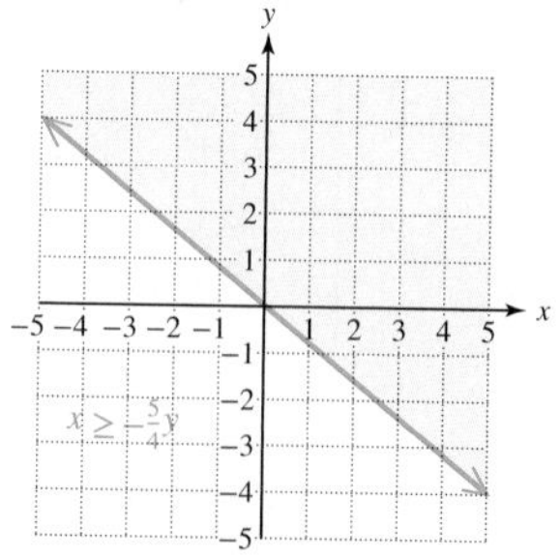

Concept 2: Systems of Linear Inequalities in Two Variables

For Exercises 41–55, graph the solution set. **(See Examples 4–6.)**

41. $y < 4$
$y > -x + 2$

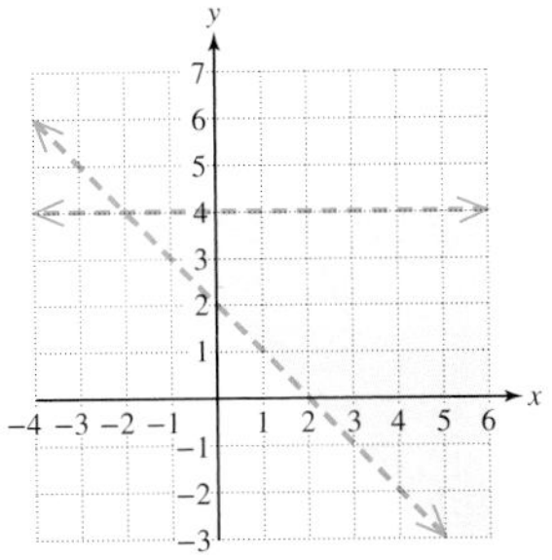

42. $y < 3$
$x + 2y < 6$

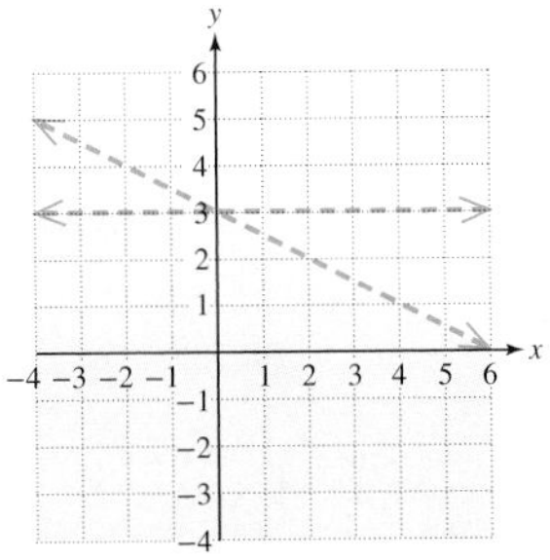

43. $2x + y \leq 5$
$x \geq 3$

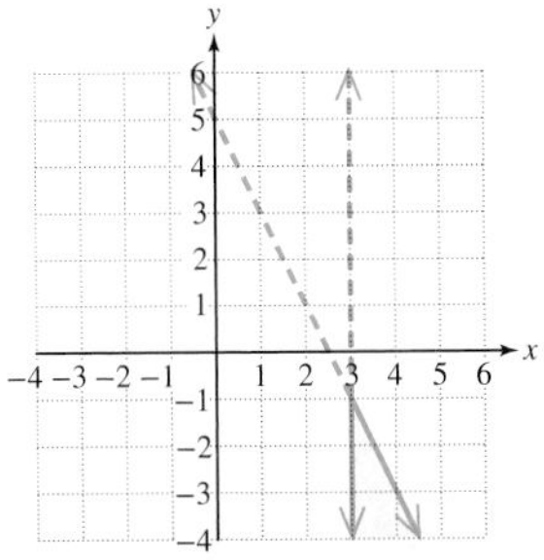

44. $x + 3y \geq 3$
$x \leq -2$

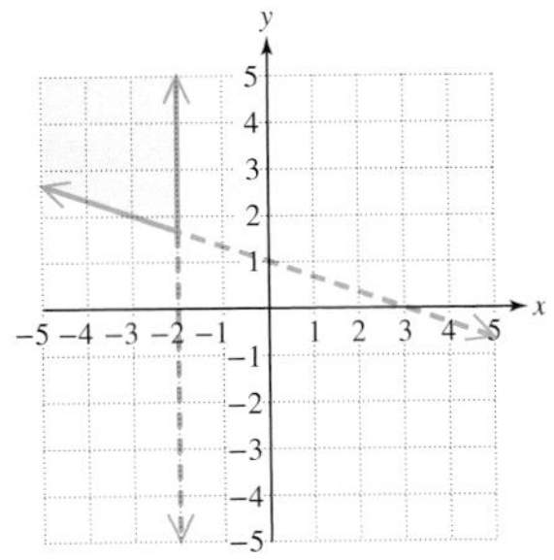

45. $x + y < 3$
$4x + y < 6$

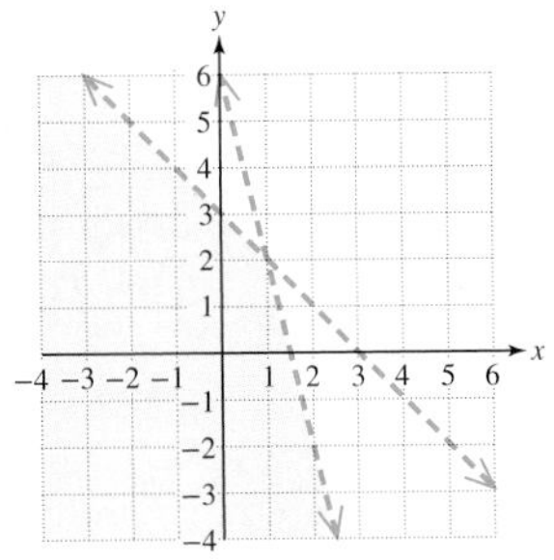

46. $x + y < 4$
$3x + y < 9$

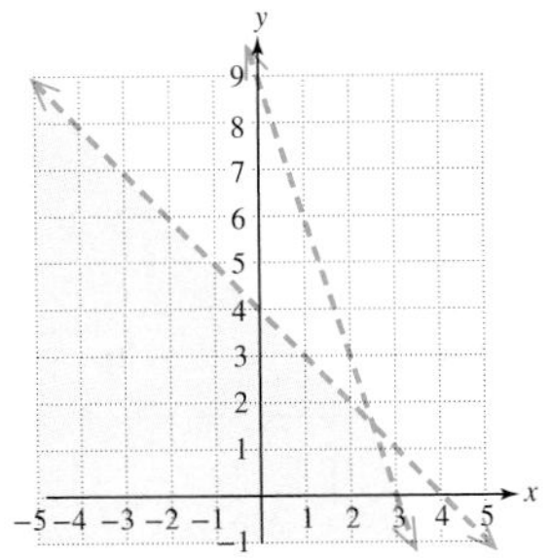

47. $2x - y \leq 2$
$2x + 3y \geq 6$

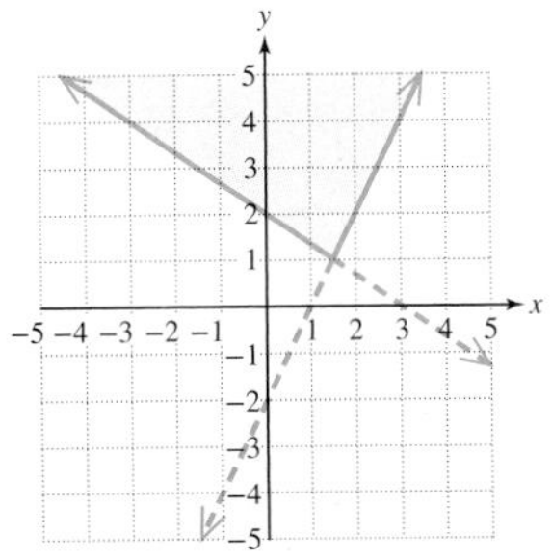

48. $3x + 2y \geq 4$
$x - y \leq 3$

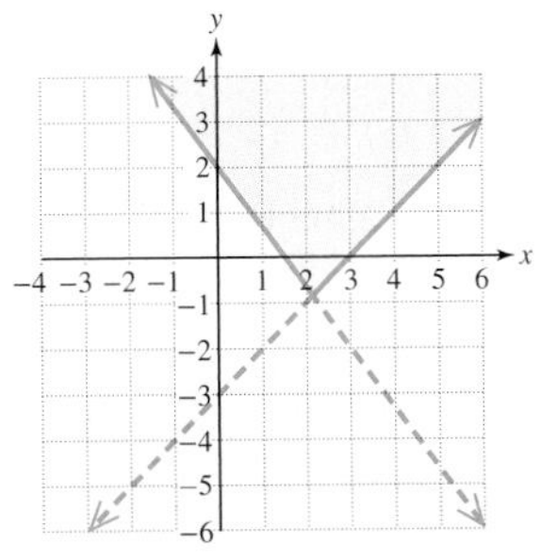

49. $x > 4$
$y < 2$

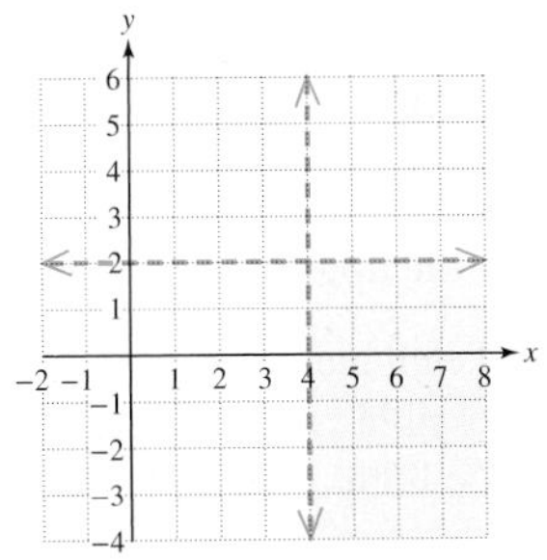

50. $x < 3$
$y > 4$

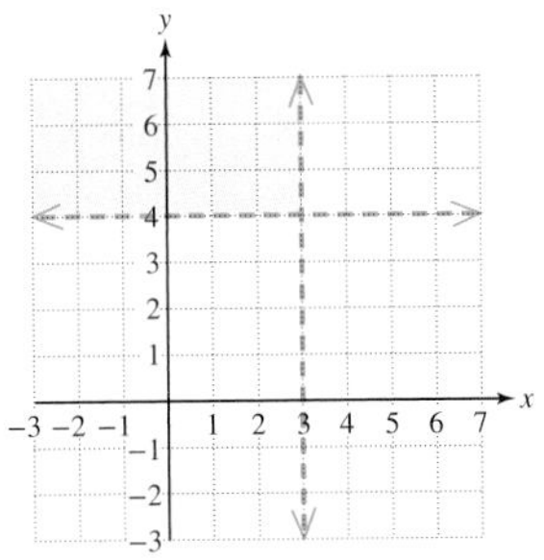

51. $x \leq -2$
$y \leq 0$

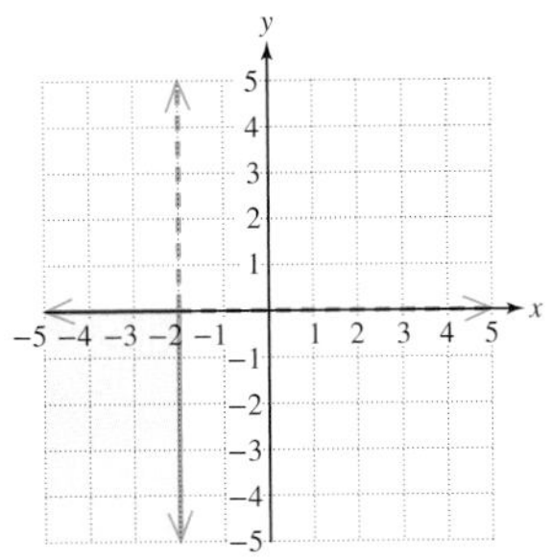

52. $x \geq 0$
$y \geq -3$

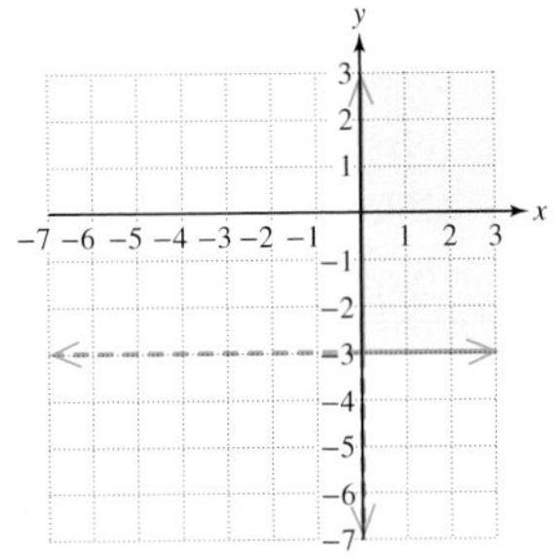

53. $x > 0$
$x + y < 6$

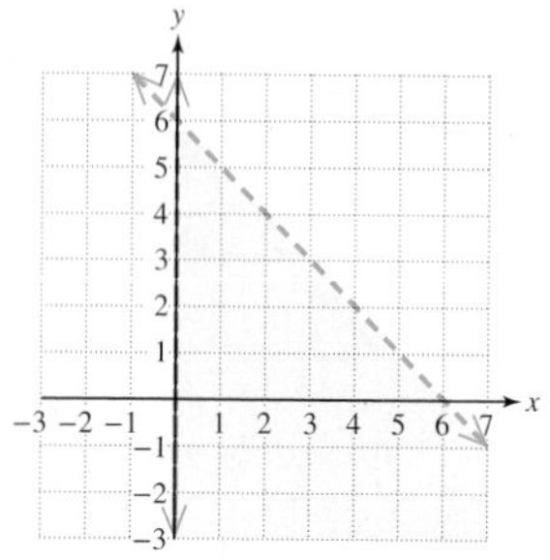

54. $x < 0$
$x + y < 2$

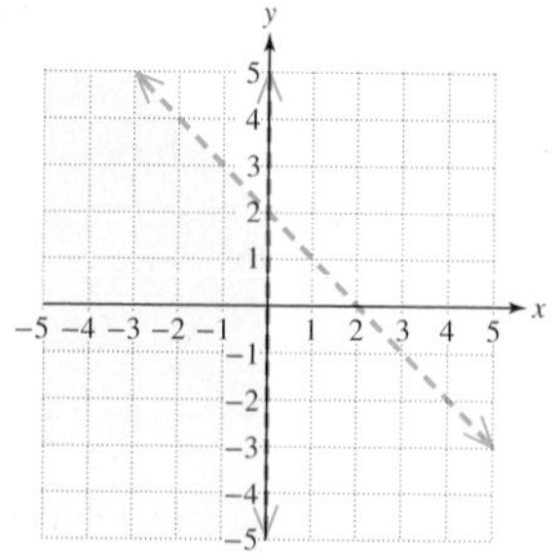

55. $y \geq 0$
$-2x + y \leq -4$

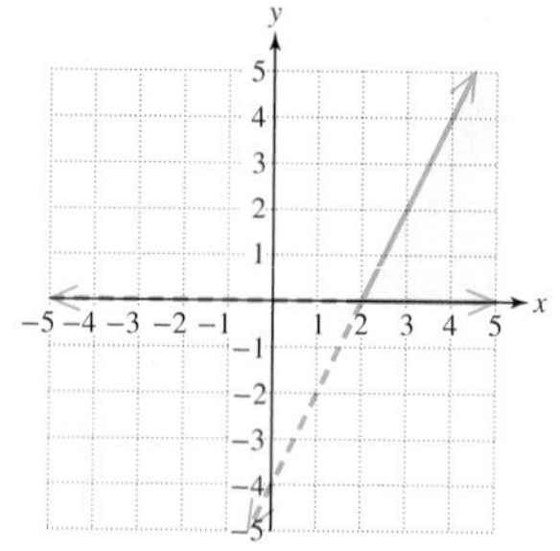

Concept 3: Graphing a Feasible Region

For Exercises 56–59, graph the feasible regions.

56. $x + y \leq 3$ and
$x \geq 0, y \geq 0$

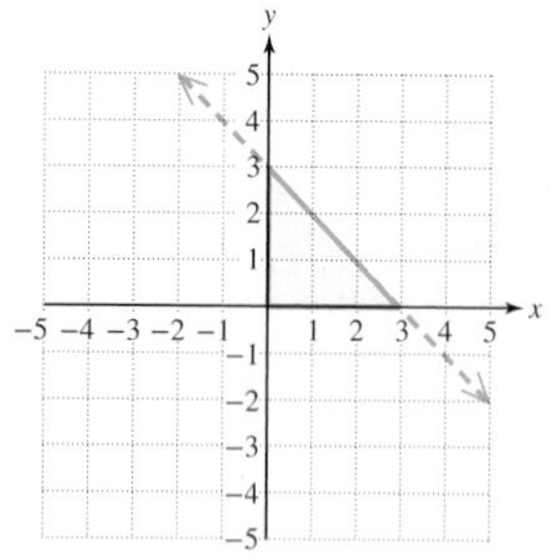

57. $x - y \leq 2$ and
$x \geq 0, y \geq 0$

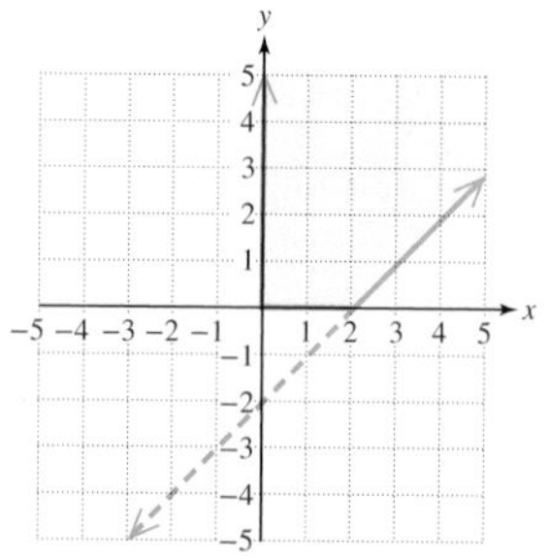

58. $x \geq 0, y \geq 0$
$x + y \leq 8$ and
$3x + 5y \leq 30$

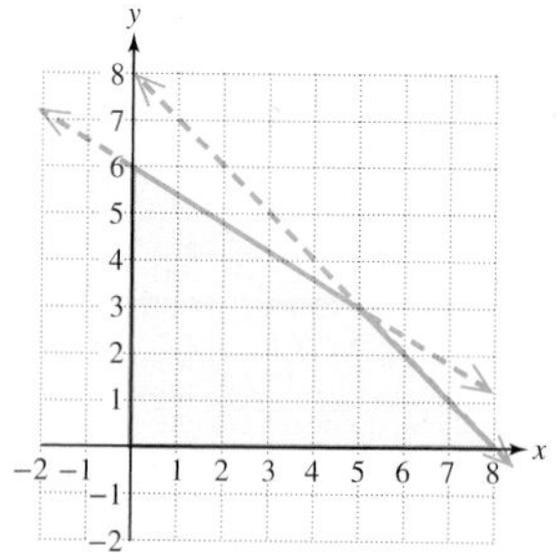

59. $x \geq 0, y \geq 0$
$x + y \leq 5$ and
$x + 2y \leq 6$

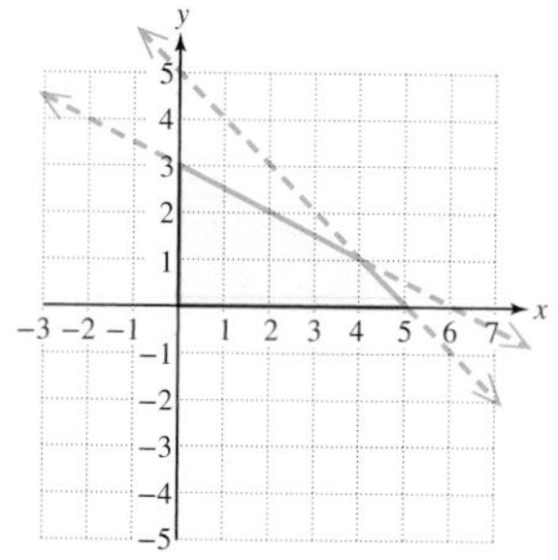

60. Suppose Sue has 50 ft of fencing with which she can build a rectangular dog run. Let x represent the length of the dog run and let y represent the width.

a. Write an inequality representing the fact that the total perimeter of the dog run is at most 50 ft. $2x + 2y \leq 50$

b. Sketch part of the solution set for this inequality that represents all possible values for the length and width of the dog run. (*Hint:* Note that both the length and the width must be positive.)

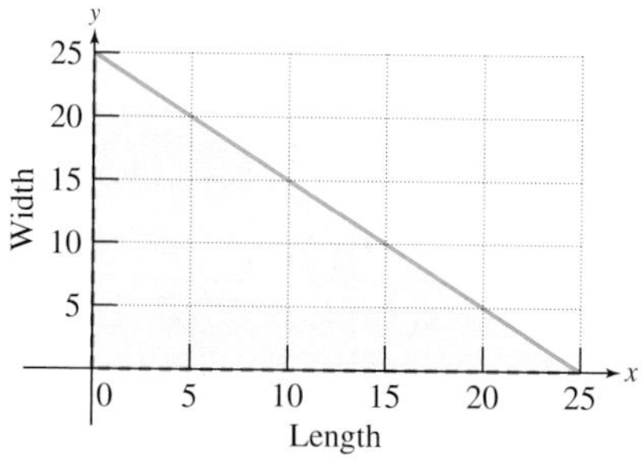

61. Suppose Rick has 40 ft of fencing with which he can build a rectangular garden. Let x represent the length of the garden and let y represent the width.

a. Write an inequality representing the fact that the total perimeter of the garden is at most 40 ft. $2x + 2y \leq 40$

b. Sketch part of the solution set for this inequality that represents all possible values for the length and width of the garden. (*Hint:* Note that both the length and the width must be positive.)

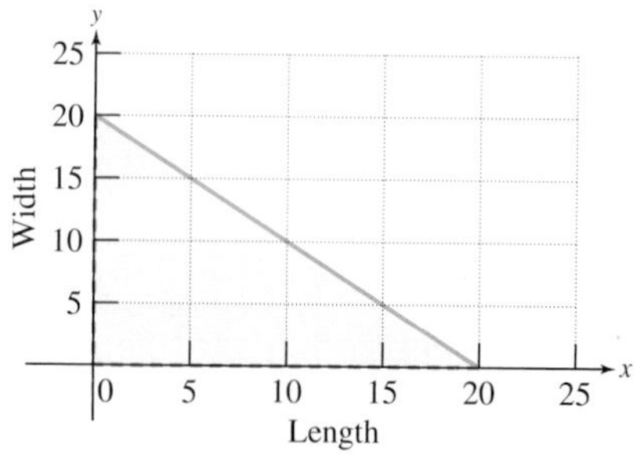

62. A manufacturer produces two models of desks. Model A requires 4 hr to stain and finish and 3 hr to assemble. Model B requires 3 hr to stain and finish and 1 hr to assemble. The total amount of time available for staining and finishing is 24 hr and for assembling is 12 hr. Let x represent the number of Model A desks produced, and let y represent the number of Model B desks produced.

a. Write two inequalities that express the fact that the number of desks to be produced cannot be negative. $x \geq 0, y \geq 0$

b. Write an inequality in terms of the number of Model A and Model B desks that can be produced if the total time for staining and finishing is at most 24 hr. $4x + 3y \leq 24$

c. Write an inequality in terms of the number of Model A and Model B desks that can be produced if the total time for assembly is no more than 12 hr. $3x + y \leq 12$

d. Graph the feasible region formed by graphing the preceding inequalities.

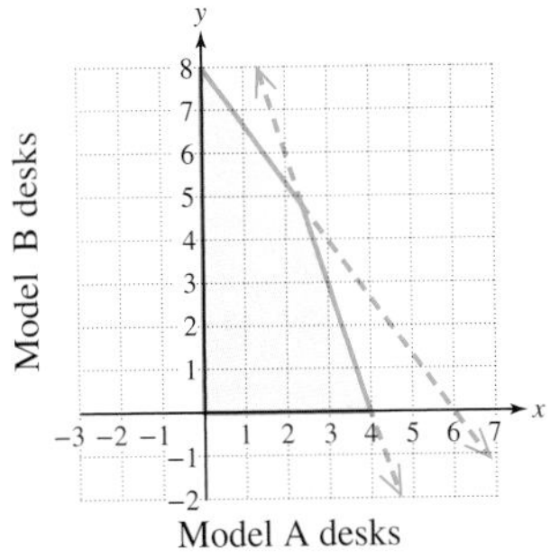

e. Is the point (3, 1) in the feasible region? What does the point (3, 1) represent in the context of this problem? Yes; The point (3, 1) represents 3 Model A desks and 1 Model B desk produced.

f. Is the point (5, 4) in the feasible region? What does the point (5, 4) represent in the context of this problem? No; The point (5, 4) represents 5 Model A desks and 4 Model B desks produced. Producing this combination of desks would exceed the number of available hours for staining and finishing and for assembly.

63. In scheduling two drivers for delivering pizza, James needs to have at least 65 hr scheduled this week. His two drivers, Karen and Todd, are not allowed to get overtime, so each one can work at most 40 hr. Let x represent the number of hours that Karen can be scheduled, and let y represent the number of hours Todd can be scheduled. **(See Example 7.)**

a. Write two inequalities that express the fact that Karen and Todd cannot work a negative number of hours. $x \geq 0, y \geq 0$

b. Write two inequalities that express the fact that neither Karen nor Todd is allowed overtime (i.e., each driver can have at most 40 hr). $x \leq 40, y \leq 40$

c. Write an inequality that expresses the fact that the total number of hours from both Karen and Todd needs to be at least 65 hr. $x + y \geq 65$

d. Graph the feasible region formed by graphing the inequalities.

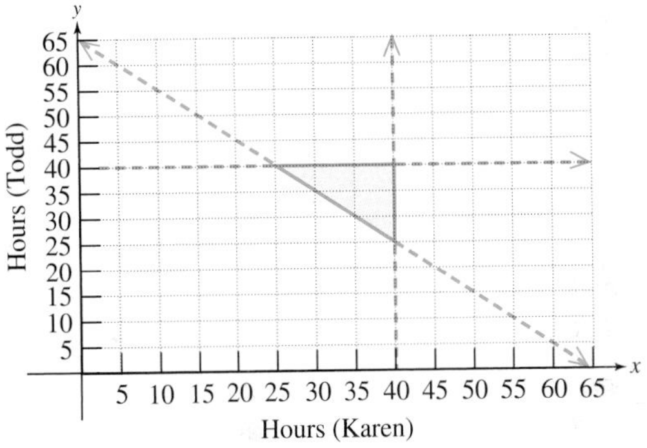

e. Is the point (35, 40) in the feasible region? What does the point (35, 40) represent in the context of this problem? Yes; The point (35, 40) means that Karen works 35 hr and Todd works 40 hr.

f. Is the point (20, 40) in the feasible region? What does the point (20, 40) represent in the context of this problem? No; The point (20, 40) means that Karen works 20 hr and Todd works 40 hr. This does not satisfy the constraint that there must be at least 65 hr total.

Group Activity

Recognizing Inequality Types

Estimated time: 20–25 minutes

Group Size: 3

For each exercise, solve the equation in part (a). Then determine how the solution sets differ for parts (b)–(e). Use interval notation to express your answers to the inequalities.

1. a. $2x - 3 = 15$ $\{9\}$

b. $2x - 3 > 15$ $(9, \infty)$

c. $2x - 3 < 15$ $(-\infty, 9)$

d. $2x - 3 \leq 15$ $(-\infty, 9]$

e. $2x - 3 \geq 15$ $[9, \infty)$

2. a. $|2x - 3| = 15$ $\{-6, 9\}$

b. $|2x - 3| > 15$ $(-\infty, -6) \cup (9, \infty)$

c. $|2x - 3| < 15$ $(-6, 9)$

d. $|2x - 3| \leq 15$ $[-6, 9]$

e. $|2x - 3| \geq 15$ $(-\infty, -6] \cup [9, \infty)$

3. a. $2x^2 - 3 = 15$ $\{-3, 3\}$

b. $2x^2 - 3 > 15$ $(-\infty, -3) \cup (3, \infty)$

c. $2x^2 - 3 < 15$ $(-3, 3)$

d. $2x^2 - 3 \leq 15$ $[-3, 3]$

e. $2x^2 - 3 \geq 15$ $(-\infty, -3] \cup [3, \infty)$

4. a. $\dfrac{3}{x - 6} = 3$ $\{7\}$

b. $\dfrac{3}{x - 6} > 3$ $(6, 7)$

c. $\dfrac{3}{x - 6} < 3$ $(-\infty, 6) \cup (7, \infty)$

d. $\dfrac{3}{x - 6} \leq 3$ $(-\infty, 6) \cup [7, \infty)$

e. $\dfrac{3}{x - 6} \geq 3$ $(6, 7]$

5. a. $x^2 + 12x + 36 = 0$ $\{-6\}$

b. $x^2 + 12x + 36 > 0$ $(-\infty, -6) \cup (-6, \infty)$

c. $x^2 + 12x + 36 < 0$ $\{\ \}$

d. $x^2 + 12x + 36 \leq 0$ $\{-6\}$

e. $x^2 + 12x + 36 \geq 0$ (∞, ∞)

6. a. $|x - 3| = -6$ $\{\ \}$

b. $|x - 3| > -6$ $(-\infty, \infty)$

c. $|x - 3| < -6$ $\{\ \}$

d. $|x - 3| \leq -6$ $\{\ \}$

e. $|x - 3| \geq -6$ $(-\infty, \infty)$

Chapter 9 Summary

Section 9.1 Compound Inequalities

Key Concepts

$A \cup B$ is the **union** of A and B. This is the set of elements that belong to set A or set B or both sets A and B.

$A \cap B$ is the **intersection** of A and B. This is the set of elements common to both A and B.

- Solve two or more inequalities joined by *and* by finding the intersection of their solution sets.
- Solve two or more inequalities joined by *or* by finding the union of their solution sets.

Examples

Example 1

Union

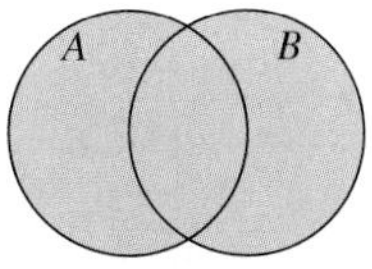

$A \cup B$

Intersection

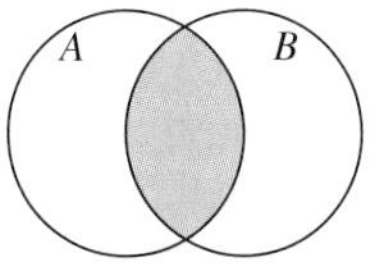

$A \cap B$

Example 2

$-7x + 3 \geq -11$ and $1 - x < 4.5$

$-7x \geq -14$ and $-x < 3.5$

$x \leq 2$ and $x > -3.5$

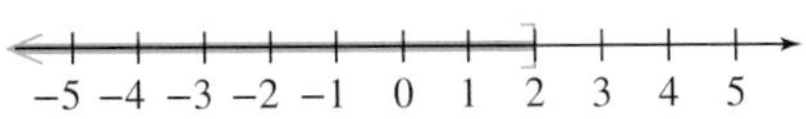

$x \leq 2$

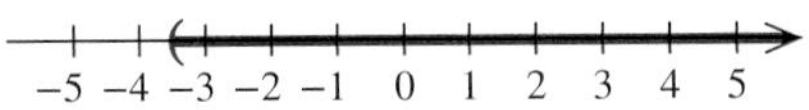

$x > -3.5$

The solution is $\{x \mid -3.5 < x \leq 2\}$ or equivalently $(-3.5, 2]$.

Inequalities of the form $a < x < b$:

The inequality $a < x < b$ is equivalent to the compound inequality $a < x$ and $x < b$.

or, in interval notation, (a, b)

Example 3

$5y + 1 \geq 6$ or $2y - 5 \leq -11$

$5y \geq 5$ or $2y \leq -6$

$y \geq 1$ or $y \leq -3$

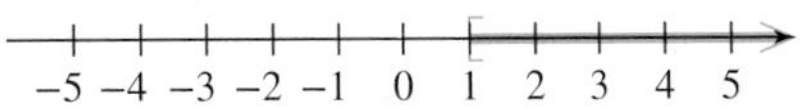

$y \geq 1$

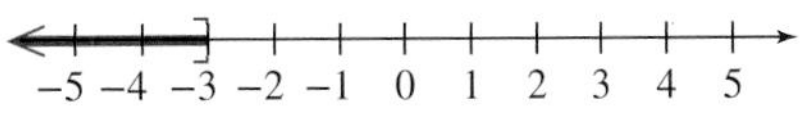

$y \leq -3$

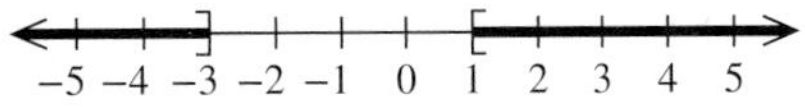

The solution is $\{y \mid y \leq -3 \text{ or } y \geq 1\}$ or equivalently $(-\infty, -3] \cup [1, \infty)$.

Example 4

Solve.

$$-13 \leq 3x - 1 < 5$$

$$-13 + 1 \leq 3x - 1 + 1 < 5 + 1$$

$$-12 \leq 3x < 6$$

$$\frac{-12}{3} \leq \frac{3x}{3} < \frac{6}{3}$$

$$-4 \leq x < 2$$

Interval notation: $[-4, 2)$

Section 9.2 Polynomial and Rational Inequalities

Key Concepts

The Test Point Method to Solve Polynomial and Rational Inequalities

1. Find the boundary points of the inequality. (Boundary points are the real solutions to the related equation and points where the inequality is undefined.)
2. Plot the boundary points on the number line. This divides the number line into intervals.
3. Select a test point from each interval and substitute it into the original inequality.
   - If a test point makes the original inequality true, then that interval is part of the solution set.
4. Test the boundary points in the original inequality.
   - If the original inequality is strict (< or >), do not include the boundary points in the solution set.
   - If the original inequality is defined using ≤ or ≥, then include the boundary points that are defined within the inequality.

Note: Any boundary point that makes an expression within the inequality undefined must *always* be excluded from the solution set.

Example 1

$4x^2 - 7x - 2 < 0$

$(4x + 1)(x - 2) = 0$ Related equation

$4x + 1 = 0 \quad x - 2 = 0$

$x = -\frac{1}{4} \quad x = 2$ The boundaries are $-\frac{1}{4}$ and 2.

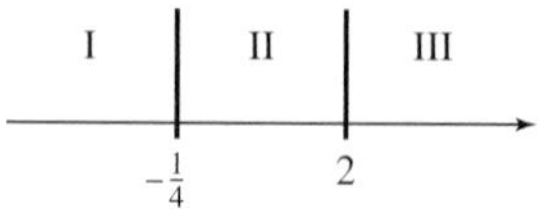

Interval I: Test $x = -1$: $4(-1)^2 - 7(-1) - 2 \overset{?}{<} 0$ False

Interval II: Test $x = 0$: $4(0)^2 - 7(0) - 2 \overset{?}{<} 0$ True

Interval III: Test $x = 3$: $4(3)^2 - 7(3) - 2 \overset{?}{<} 0$ False

The strict inequality excludes the boundary points as solutions.

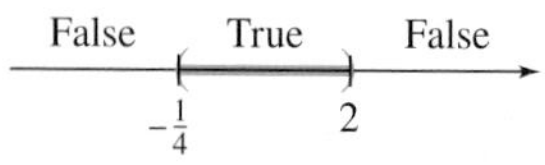

The solution is $\left(-\frac{1}{4}, 2\right)$.

Examples

Example 2

$\frac{28}{2x-3} \le 4$ The inequality is undefined for $x = \frac{3}{2}$. Find other possible boundary points by solving the related equation.

$\frac{28}{2x-3} = 4$ Related equation

$(2x-3) \cdot \frac{28}{2x-3} = (2x-3) \cdot 4$

$28 = 8x - 12$

$40 = 8x$

$x = 5$

The boundaries are $x = \frac{3}{2}$ and $x = 5$.

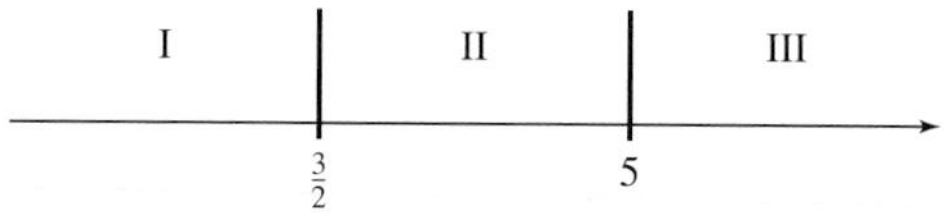

Interval I: Test $x = 1$: $\frac{28}{2(1)-3} \overset{?}{\le} 4$ True

Interval II: Test $x = 2$: $\frac{28}{2(2)-3} \overset{?}{\le} 4$ False

Interval III: Test $x = 6$: $\frac{28}{2(6)-3} \overset{?}{\le} 4$ True

The boundary point $x = \frac{3}{2}$ is not included because $\frac{28}{2x-3}$ is undefined there. The boundary $x = 5$ does check in the original inequality.

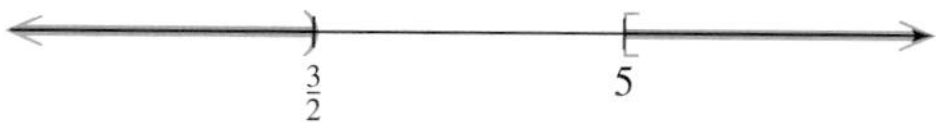

The solution is $(-\infty, \frac{3}{2}) \cup [5, \infty)$.

Section 9.3 Absolute Value Equations

Key Concepts

The equation $|x| = a$ is an absolute value equation. For $a \geq 0$, the solution to the equation $|x| = a$ is $x = a$ or $x = -a$.

Steps to Solve an Absolute Value Equation

1. Isolate the absolute value to write the equation in the form $|x| = a$.
2. If $a < 0$, there is no solution.
3. Otherwise, rewrite the equation $|x| = a$ as $x = a$ or $x = -a$.
4. Solve the equations from step 3.
5. Check answers in the original equation.

The equation $|x| = |y|$ implies $x = y$ or $x = -y$.

Examples

Example 1

$|2x - 3| + 5 = 10$

$|2x - 3| = 5$ Isolate the absolute value.

$2x - 3 = 5$ or $2x - 3 = -5$

$2x = 8$ or $2x = -2$

$x = 4$ or $x = -1$

The solution set is $\{4, -1\}$.

Example 2

$|x + 2| + 5 = 1$

$|x + 2| = -4$ There is no solution, $\{ \}$.

Example 3

$|2x - 1| = |x + 4|$

$2x - 1 = x + 4$ or $2x - 1 = -(x + 4)$

$x = 5$ or $2x - 1 = -x - 4$

or $3x = -3$

or $x = -1$

The solution set is $\{5, -1\}$.

Section 9.4 Absolute Value Inequalities

Key Concepts

Solutions to Absolute Value Inequalities

For $a > 0$, we have:

$|x| > a \Rightarrow x < -a$ or $x > a$

$|x| < a \Rightarrow -a < x < a$

Test Point Method to Solve Inequalities

1. Find the boundary points of the inequality. (Boundary points are the real solutions to the related equation and points where the inequality is undefined.)
2. Plot the boundary points on the number line. This divides the number line into intervals.
3. Select a test point from each interval and substitute it into the original inequality.
   - If a test point makes the original inequality true, then that interval is part of the solution set.
4. Test the boundary points in the original inequality.
   - If the original inequality is strict ($<$ or $>$), do not include the boundary in the solution set.
   - If the original inequality is defined using $\le$ or $\ge$, then include the boundary points that are defined within the inequality.

Note: Any boundary point that makes an expression within the inequality undefined must *always* be excluded from the solution set.

If *a* is *negative* ($a < 0$), then

1. $|x| < a$ has no solution.
2. $|x| > a$ is true for all real numbers.

Examples

Example 1

$$|5x - 2| < 12$$
$$-12 < 5x - 2 < 12$$
$$-10 < 5x < 14$$
$$-2 < x < \frac{14}{5}$$

The solution is $\left(-2, \frac{14}{5}\right)$.

Example 2

$|x - 3| + 2 \ge 7$

$|x - 3| \ge 5$ Isolate the absolute value.

$|x - 3| = 5$ Solve the related equation.

$x - 3 = 5$ or $x - 3 = -5$

$x = 8$ or $x = -2$ Boundary points

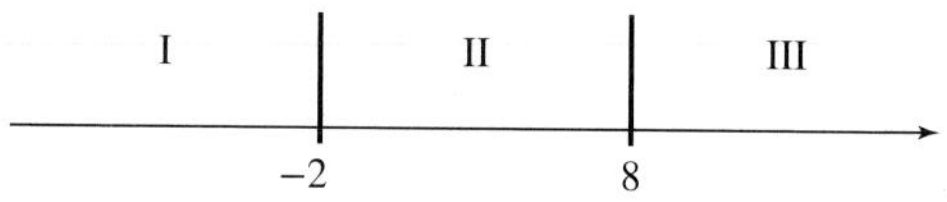

Interval I: Test $x = -3$: $|(-3) - 3| + 2 \overset{?}{\ge} 7$ True

Interval II: Test $x = 0$: $|(0) - 3| + 2 \overset{?}{\ge} 7$ False

Interval III: Test $x = 9$: $|(9) - 3| + 2 \overset{?}{\ge} 7$ True

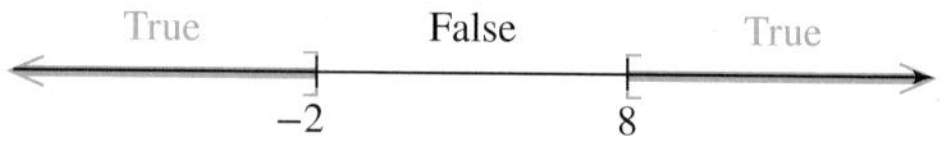

The solution is $(-\infty, -2] \cup [8, \infty)$.

Example 3

$|x + 5| > -2$

The solution is all real numbers because an absolute value will always be greater than a negative number.

$(-\infty, \infty)$

Example 4

$|x + 5| < -2$

There is no solution because an absolute value cannot be less than a negative number.

The solution set is { }.

Section 9.5 Linear Inequalities and Systems of Linear Inequalities in Two Variables

Key Concepts

A **linear inequality in two variables** is an inequality of the form $Ax + By < C$, $Ax + By > C$, $Ax + By \le C$, or $Ax + By \ge C$.

Graphing a Linear Inequality in Two Variables

1. Write the inequality with the y variable isolated, if possible.
2. Graph the related equation. Draw a dashed line if the inequality is strict, $<$ or $>$. Otherwise, draw a solid line.
3. Shade above or below the line according to the following convention.

- Shade *above* the line if the inequality is of the form $y > mx + b$ or $y \ge mx + b$.
- Shade *below* the line if the inequality is of the form $y < mx + b$ or $y \le mx + b$.

You can use test points to check that you have shaded the correct region. Select an ordered pair from the proposed solution set and substitute the values of x and y in the original inequality. If the test point produces a true statement, then you have shaded the correct region.

Graphing a System of Linear Inequalities in Two Variables

Graph each linear inequality in the system. The solution to the system is the intersection of the shaded regions.

Examples

Example 1

Graph the solution to the inequality $2x - y < 4$.

Graph the related equation, $y = 2x - 4$, with a dashed line.

Solve for y: $2x - y < 4$

$$-y < -2x + 4$$

$$y > 2x - 4$$

Shade above the line.

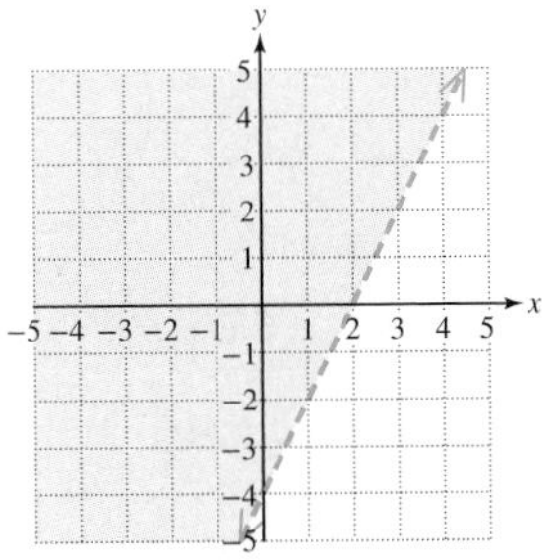

Example 2

Graph.

$x < 0$

$y > 2$

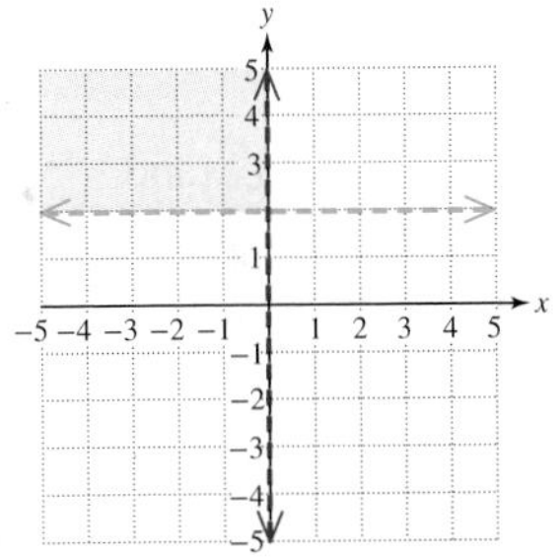

Chapter 9 Review Exercises

Section 9.1

1. Explain the difference between the union and intersection of two sets. You may use the sets C and D in the following diagram to provide an example.

$C \cap D$ is the set of elements common to both sets C and D.

$C \cup D$ is the set of elements in either set C, set D, or both sets.

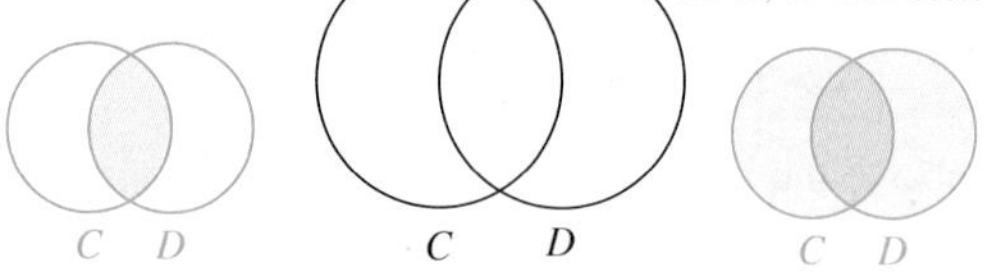

Let $X = \{x \mid x \geq -10\}$, $Y = \{x \mid x < 1\}$, $Z = \{x \mid x > -1\}$, and $W = \{x \mid x \leq -3\}$. For Exercises 2–7, find the intersection or union of the sets X, Y, Z, and W. Write the answers in interval notation.

2. $X \cap Y$ $[-10, 1)$

3. $X \cup Y$ $(-\infty, \infty)$

4. $Y \cup Z$ $(-\infty, \infty)$

5. $Y \cap Z$ $(-1, 1)$

6. $Z \cup W$ $(-\infty, -3] \cup (-1, \infty)$

7. $Z \cap W$ $\{\ \}$

For Exercises 8–13, solve the compound inequalities. Write the solutions in interval notation.

8. $4m > -11$ and $4m - 3 \leq 13$ $\left(-\frac{11}{4}, 4\right]$

9. $4n - 7 < 1$ and $7 + 3n \geq -8$ $[-5, 2)$

10. $\frac{2}{3}t - 3 \leq 1$ or $\frac{3}{4}t - 2 > 7$ $(-\infty, 6] \cup (12, \infty)$

11. $2(3x + 1) < -10$ or $3(2x - 4) \geq 0$ $(-\infty, -2) \cup [2, \infty)$

12. $2 \geq -(b - 2) - 5b \geq -6$ $\left[0, \frac{4}{3}\right]$

13. $-4 \leq \frac{1}{2}(x - 1) < -\frac{3}{2}$ $[-7, -2)$

14. Normal levels of total cholesterol vary according to age. For adults between 25 and 40 yr old, the normal range is generally accepted to be between 140 and 225 mg/dL (milligrams per deciliter), inclusive. Let x represent cholesterol level.

a. Write an inequality representing the normal range for total cholesterol for adults between 25 and 40 yr old. $140 \leq x \leq 225$

b. Write a compound inequality representing abnormal ranges for total cholesterol for adults between 25 and 40 yr old.
$x < 140$ or $x > 225$

15. Normal levels of total cholesterol vary according to age. For adults younger than 25 yr old, the normal range is generally accepted to be between 125 and 200 mg/dL, inclusive. Let x represent cholesterol level.

a. Write an inequality representing the normal range for total cholesterol for adults younger than 25 yr old. $125 \leq x \leq 200$

b. Write a compound inequality representing abnormal ranges for total cholesterol for adults younger than 25 yr old.
$x < 125$ or $x > 200$

Section 9.2

16. Solve the equation and inequalities. How do your answers to parts (a), (b), and (c) relate to the graph of $g(x) = x^2 - 4$?

a. $x^2 - 4 = 0$ $(-2, 0)$ and $(2, 0)$ are the x-intercepts.

b. $x^2 - 4 < 0$
On the interval $(-2, 2)$ the graph is below the x-axis.

c. $x^2 - 4 > 0$
On the intervals $(-\infty, -2)$ and $(2, \infty)$ the graph is above the x-axis.

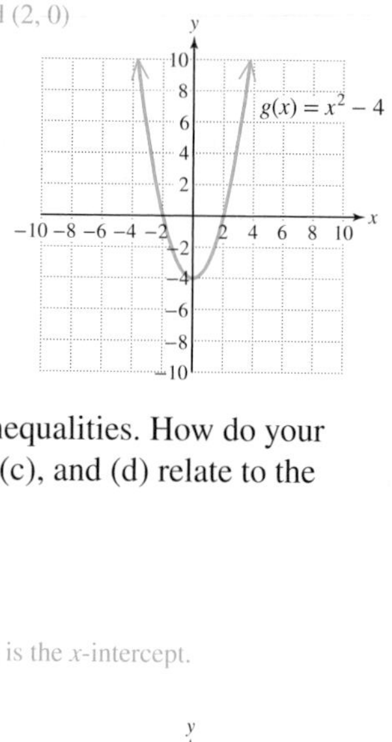

17. Solve the equation and inequalities. How do your answers to parts (a), (b), (c), and (d) relate to the graph of $k(x) = \dfrac{4x}{(x - 2)}$?

a. $\dfrac{4x}{x - 2} = 0$ $x = 0$; $(0, 0)$ is the x-intercept.

b. For which values is $k(x)$ undefined?
$x = 2$ is the vertical asymptote.

c. $\dfrac{4x}{x - 2} \geq 0$
On the intervals $(-\infty, 0]$ and $(2, \infty)$ the graph is on or above the x-axis.

d. $\dfrac{4x}{x - 2} \leq 0$
On the interval $[0, 2)$ the graph is on or below the x-axis.

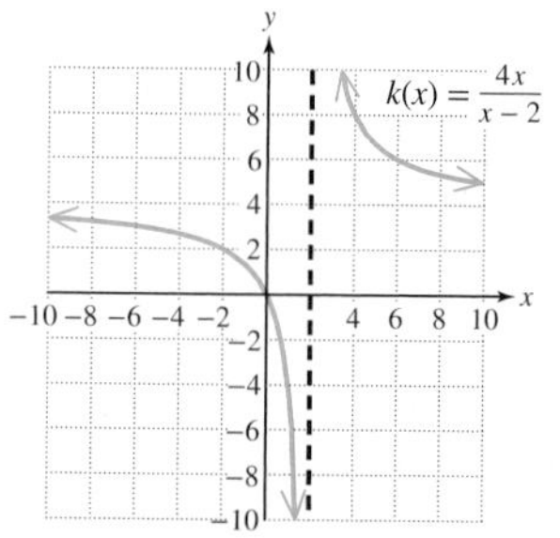

For Exercises 18–29, solve the inequalities. Write the answers in interval notation.

18. $w^2 - 4w - 12 < 0$ $(-2, 6)$

19. $t^2 + 6t + 9 \geq 0$ $(-\infty, \infty)$

20. $\dfrac{12}{x+2} \leq 6$ $(-\infty, -2) \cup [0, \infty)$

21. $\dfrac{8}{p-1} \geq -4$ $(-\infty, -1] \cup (1, \infty)$

22. $3y(y-5)(y+2) > 0$ $(-2, 0) \cup (5, \infty)$

23. $-3c(c+2)(2c-5) < 0$ $(-2, 0) \cup \left(\frac{5}{2}, \infty\right)$

24. $-x^2 - 4x \geq 3$ $[-3, -1]$

25. $y^2 + 4y > 5$ $(-\infty, -5) \cup (1, \infty)$

26. $\dfrac{w+1}{w-3} > 1$ $(3, \infty)$

27. $\dfrac{2a}{a+3} \leq 2$ $(-3, \infty)$

28. $t^2 + 10t + 25 \leq 0$ $\{-5\}$

29. $-x^2 - 4x < 4$ $(-\infty, -2) \cup (-2, \infty)$

Section 9.3

For Exercises 30–41, solve the absolute value equations.

30. $|x| = 10$ $\{10, -10\}$

31. $|x| = 17$ $\{17, -17\}$

32. $|8.7 - 2x| = 6.1$ $\{1.3, 7.4\}$

33. $|5.25 - 5x| = 7.45$ $\{-0.44, 2.54\}$

34. $16 = |x+2| + 9$ $\{5, -9\}$

35. $5 = |x-2| + 4$ $\{3, 1\}$

36. $|4x-1| + 6 = 4$ $\{\ \}$

37. $|3x-1| + 7 = 3$ $\{\ \}$

38. $\left|\dfrac{7x-3}{5}\right| + 4 = 4$ $\left\{\frac{3}{7}\right\}$

39. $\left|\dfrac{4x+5}{-2}\right| - 3 = -3$ $\left\{-\frac{5}{4}\right\}$

40. $|3x-5| = |2x+1|$ $\left\{6, \frac{4}{5}\right\}$

41. $|8x+9| = |8x-1|$ $\left\{-\frac{1}{2}\right\}$

42. Which absolute value expression represents the distance between 3 and −2 on the number line?

$|3 - (-2)|$ $\quad$ $|-2 - 3|$

Both expressions give the distance between 3 and −2.

Section 9.4

43. Write the compound inequality $x < -5$ or $x > 5$ as an absolute value inequality. $|x| > 5$

44. Write the compound inequality $-4 < x < 4$ as an absolute value inequality. $|x| < 4$

For Exercises 45–46, write an absolute value inequality that represents the solution set graphed here.

45. 

$|x| < 6$

46. 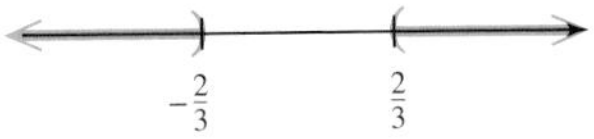

$|x| > \frac{2}{3}$

For Exercises 47–60, solve the absolute value inequalities. Graph each solution set and write the solution in interval notation.

47. $|x+6| \geq 8$ $(-\infty, -14] \cup [2, \infty)$

48. $|x+8| \leq 3$ $[-11, -5]$

49. $2|7x-1| + 4 > 4$ $\left(-\infty, \frac{1}{7}\right) \cup \left(\frac{1}{7}, \infty\right)$

50. $4|5x+1| - 3 > -3$ $\left(-\infty, -\frac{1}{5}\right) \cup \left(-\frac{1}{5}, \infty\right)$

51. $|3x+4| - 6 \leq -4$ $\left[-2, -\frac{2}{3}\right]$

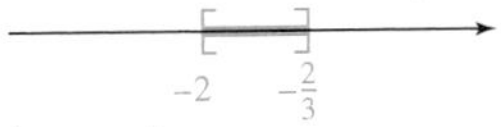

52. $|5x-3| + 3 \leq 6$ $\left[0, \frac{6}{5}\right]$

53. $\left|\dfrac{x}{2} - 6\right| < 5$ $(2, 22)$

54. $\left|\dfrac{x}{3} + 2\right| < 2$ $(-12, 0)$

55. $|4 - 2x| + 8 \geq 8$  $(-\infty, \infty)$

56. $|9 + 3x| + 1 \geq 1$  $(-\infty, \infty)$

57. $-2|5.2x - 7.8| < 13$  $(-\infty, \infty)$

58. $-|2.5x + 15| < 7$  $(-\infty, \infty)$

59. $|3x - 8| < -1$ $\{\ \}$

60. $|x + 5| < -4$ $\{\ \}$

61. State one possible situation in which an absolute value inequality will have no solution. If an absolute value is less than a negative number, there will be no solution.

62. State one possible situation in which an absolute value inequality will have a solution of all real numbers. If an absolute value is greater than a negative number, then all real numbers are solutions.

63. The Neilsen ratings estimated that the percent, p, of the television viewing audience watching a popular reality show was 20% with a 3% margin of error. Solve the inequality $|p - 0.20| \leq 0.03$ and interpret the answer in the context of this problem.
$0.17 \leq p \leq 0.23$ or, equivalently in interval notation, $[0.17, 0.23]$. This means that the actual percentage of viewers is estimated to be between 17% and 23%, inclusive.

64. The length, L, of a screw is supposed to be $3\frac{3}{8}$ in. Due to variation in the production equipment, there is a $\frac{1}{4}$-in. margin of error. Solve the inequality $|L - 3\frac{3}{8}| \le \frac{1}{4}$ and interpret the answer in the context of this problem. $3\frac{1}{8} \le L \le 3\frac{5}{8}$ or, equivalently in interval notation, $[3\frac{1}{8}, 3\frac{5}{8}]$. This means that the actual length of the screw may be between $3\frac{1}{8}$ in. and $3\frac{5}{8}$ in., inclusive.

Section 9.5

For Exercises 65–72, solve the inequalities by graphing.

65. $2x > -y + 5$

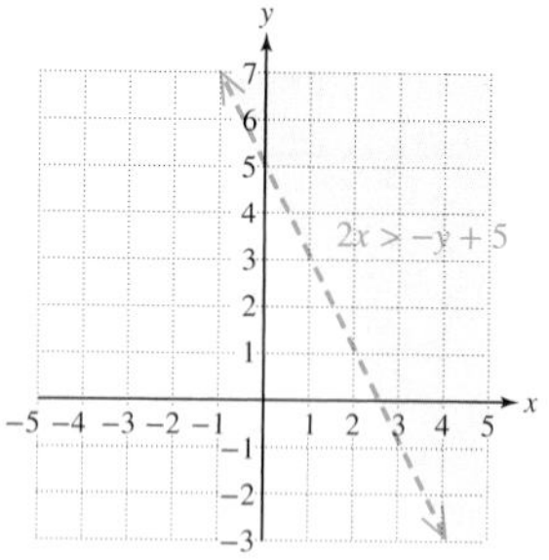

66. $2x \le -8 - 3y$

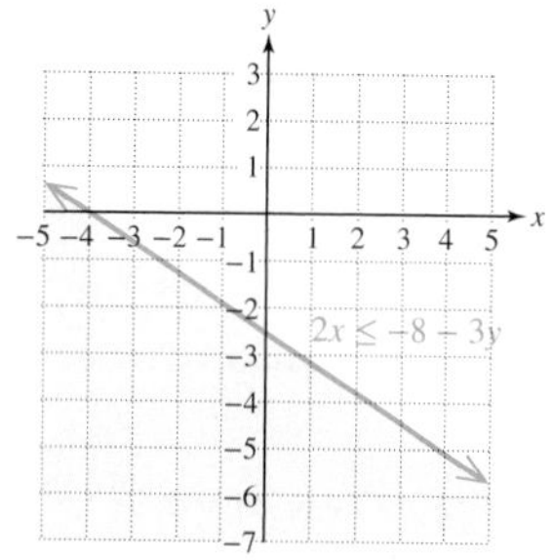

67. $y \ge -\frac{2}{3}x + 3$

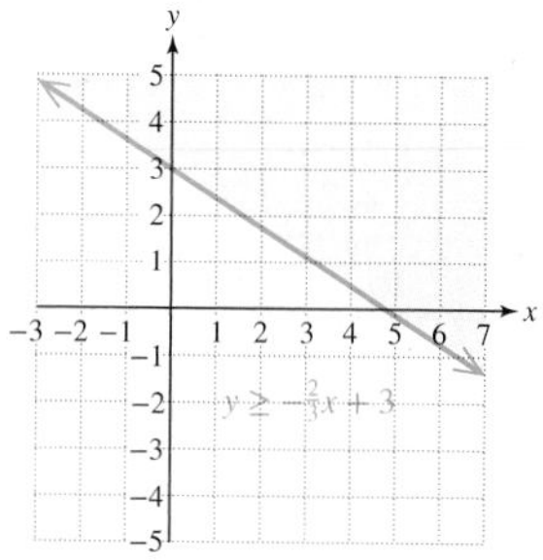

68. $y > \frac{3}{4}x - 2$

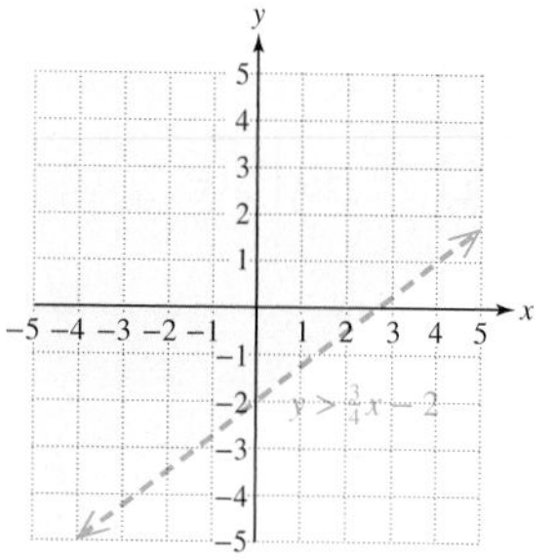

69. $x > -3$

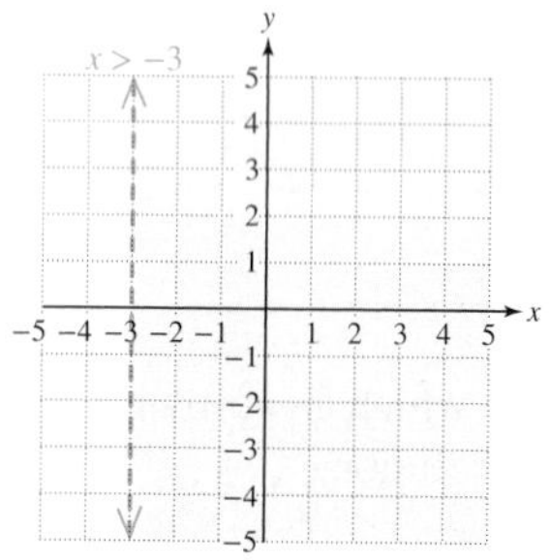

70. $x \le 2$

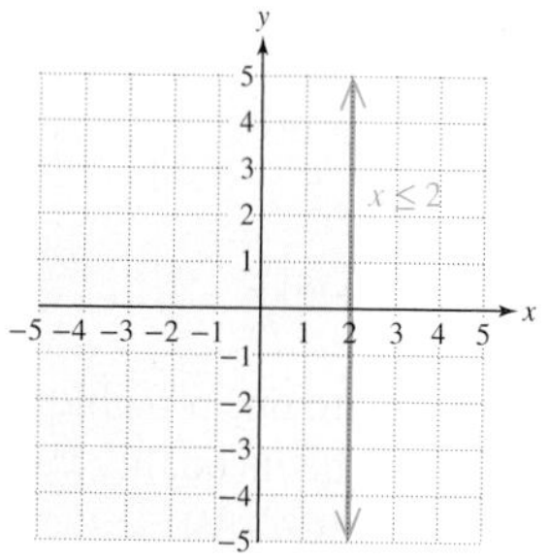

71. $x \ge \frac{1}{2}y$

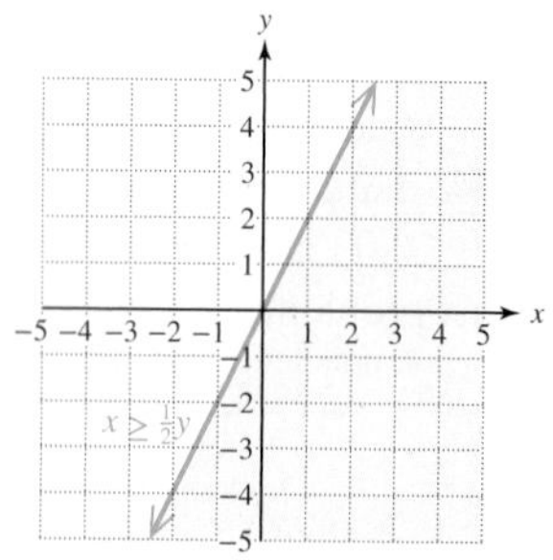

72. $x < \frac{2}{5}y$

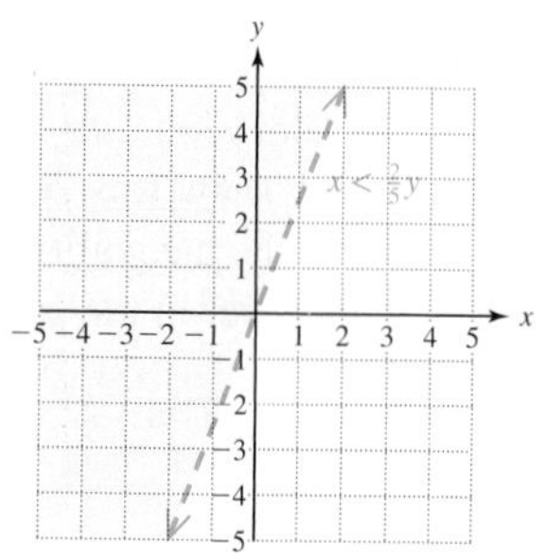

For Exercises 73–76 graph the system of inequalities.

73. $2x - y > -2$

$2x - y \le 2$

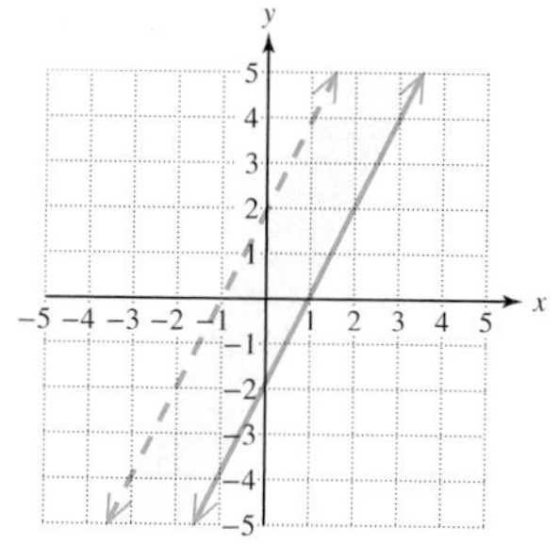

74. $3x + y < 6$

$-3x + y < -2$

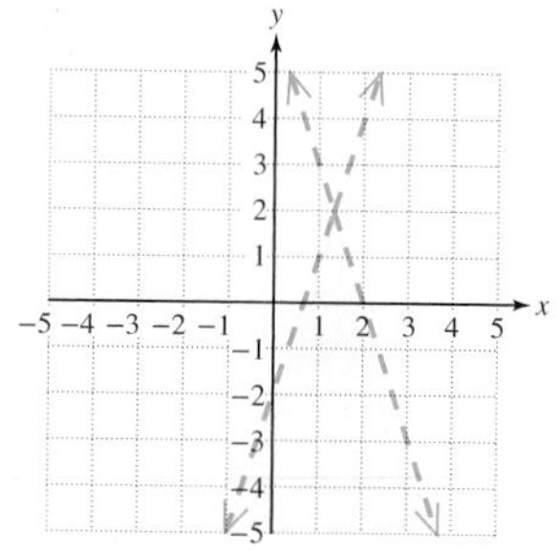

75. $y \ge x$

$y \le -x$

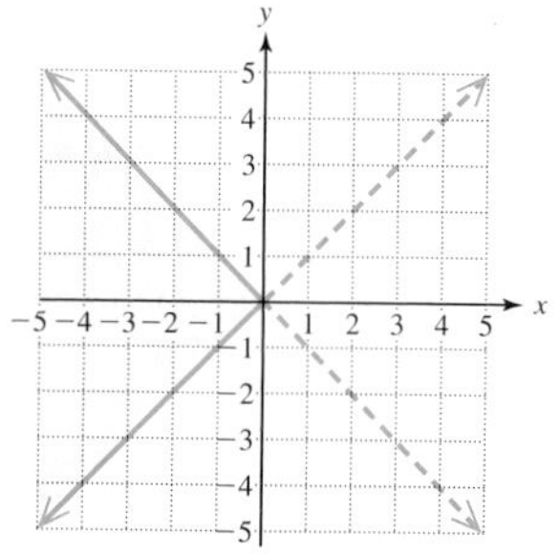

76. $x \ge 0$

$y \ge 0$

$y \le -\frac{2}{3}x + 4$

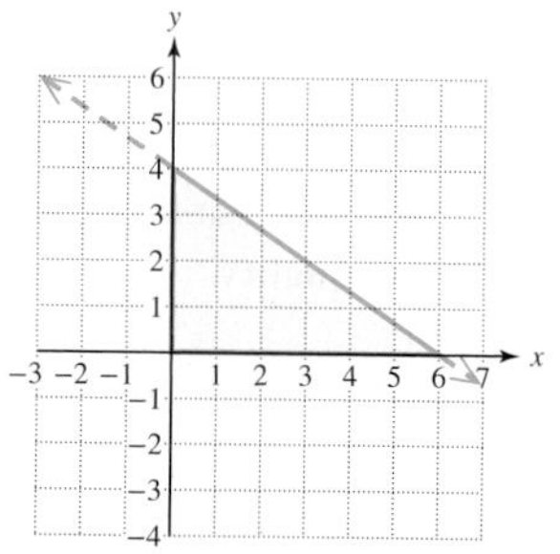

77. Suppose a farmer has 100 acres of land on which to grow oranges and grapefruit. Furthermore, because of demand from his customers, he wants to plant at least 4 times as many acres of orange trees as grapefruit trees.

© Adalberto Rios Lanz/Sexto Sol/Getty Images RF

Let x represent the number of acres of orange trees.

Let y represent the number of acres of grapefruit trees.

a. Write two inequalities that express the fact that the farmer cannot use a negative number of acres to plant orange and grapefruit trees.
$x \geq 0, y \geq 0$

b. Write an inequality that expresses the fact that the total number of acres used for growing orange and grapefruit trees is at most 100.
$x + y \leq 100$

c. Write an inequality that expresses the fact that the farmer wants to plant at least 4 times as many orange trees as grapefruit trees.
$x \geq 4y$

d. Sketch the inequalities in parts (a)–(c) to find the feasible region for the farmer's distribution of orange and grapefruit trees.

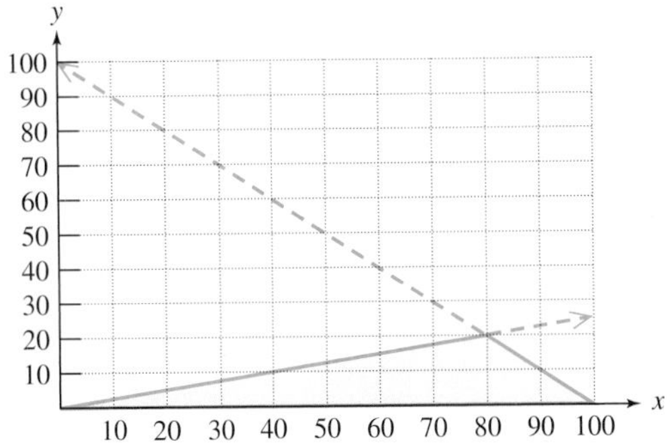

Chapter 9 Test

For Exercises 1–5, solve the compound inequalities. Write the answers in interval notation.

1. $-2 \leq 3x - 1 \leq 5$ $\left[-\frac{1}{3}, 2\right]$

2. $-\frac{3}{5}x - 1 \leq 8$ or $-\frac{2}{3}x \geq 16$
$(-\infty, -24] \cup [-15, \infty)$

3. $-2x - 3 > -3$ and $x + 3 \geq 0$ $[-3, 0)$

4. $5x + 1 \leq 6$ or $2x + 4 > -6$ $(-\infty, \infty)$

5. $2x - 3 > 1$ and $x + 4 < -1$
{ }

6. The normal range in humans of the enzyme adenosine deaminase (ADA), is between 9 and 33 IU (international units), inclusive. Let x represent the ADA level in international units.

a. Write an inequality representing the normal range for ADA. $9 \leq x \leq 33$

b. Write a compound inequality representing abnormal ranges for ADA. $x < 9$ or $x > 33$

For Exercises 7–12, solve the polynomial and rational inequalities.

7. $50 - 2a^2 > 0$
$(-5, 5)$

8. $y^3 + 3y^2 - 4y - 12 < 0$
$(-\infty, -3) \cup (-2, 2)$

9. $5x^2 - 2x + 2 < 0$
{ }

10. $t^2 + 22t + 121 \leq 0$
$\{-11\}$

11. $\frac{2x - 1}{x - 6} \leq 0$ $\left[\frac{1}{2}, 6\right)$

12. $\frac{3}{w + 3} > 2$ $\left(-3, -\frac{3}{2}\right)$

For Exercises 13–14, solve the absolute value equations.

13. $\left|\frac{1}{2}x + 3\right| - 4 = 4$ $\{10, -22\}$

14. $|3x + 4| = |x - 12|$ $\{-8, 2\}$

For Exercises 15–18, solve the absolute value inequalities. Write the answers in interval notation.

15. $|3 - 2x| + 6 < 2$
{ }

16. $|3x - 8| > 9$
$\left(-\infty, -\frac{1}{3}\right) \cup \left(\frac{17}{3}, \infty\right)$

17. $|0.4x + 0.3| - 0.2 < 7$ $(-18.75, 17.25)$

18. $|7 - 3x| + 1 > -3$ $(-\infty, \infty)$

19. The mass of a small piece of metal is measured to be 15.41 g. If the measurement error is at most ± 0.01 g, write an absolute value inequality that represents the possible mass, x, of the piece of metal.
$|x - 15.41| \leq 0.01$

20. Graph the solution to the inequality $2x - 5y \geq 10$.

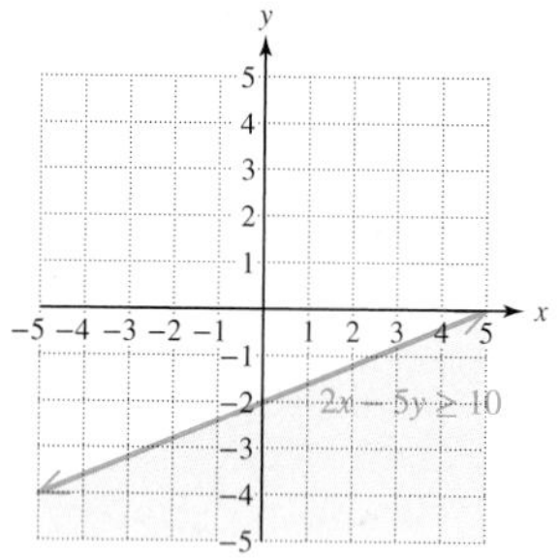

For Exercises 21–22, graph the solution to the system.

21. $x + y < 3$
$3x - 2y > -6$

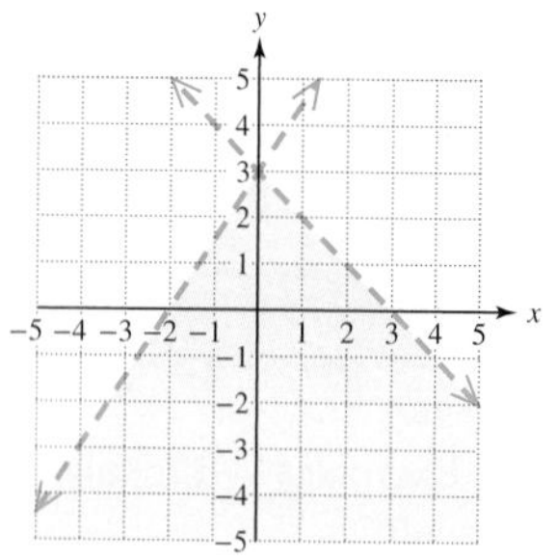

22. $5x \leq 5$
$x + y \leq 0$

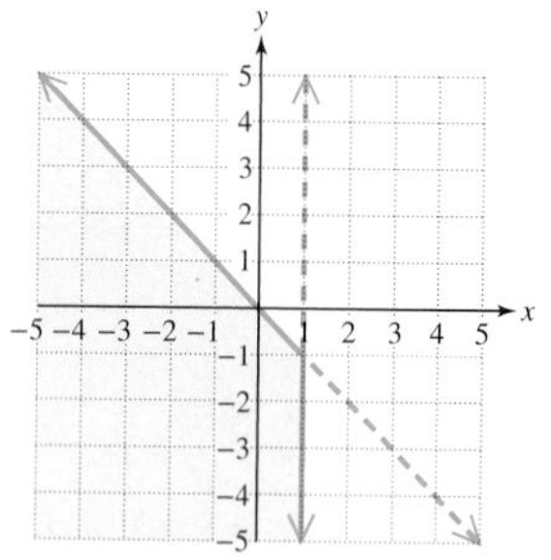

23. After menopause, women are at higher risk for hip fractures as a result of low calcium. As early as their teen years, women need at least 1200 mg of calcium per day (the USDA recommended daily allowance). One 8-oz glass of skim milk contains 300 mg of calcium, and one Antacid (regular strength) contains 400 mg of calcium. Let x represent the number of 8-oz glasses of milk that a woman drinks per day. Let y represent the number of Antacid tablets (regular strength) that a woman takes per day.

a. Write two inequalities that express the fact that the number of glasses of milk and the number of Antacid taken each day cannot be negative.
$x \geq 0, y \geq 0$

b. Write a linear inequality in terms of x and y for which the daily calcium intake is at least 1200 mg. $300x + 400y \geq 1200$

c. Graph the inequalities.

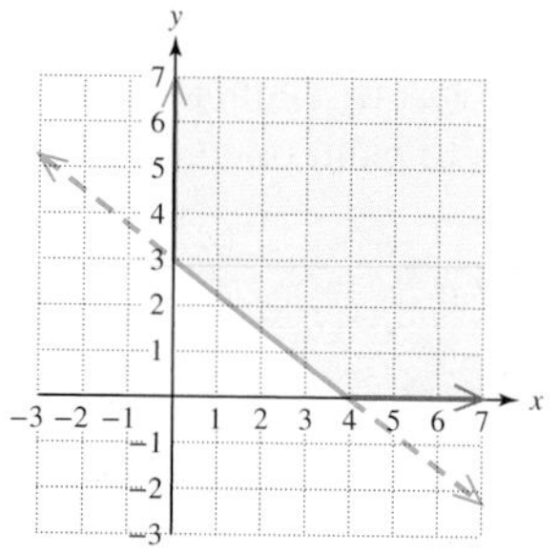

Chapters 1–9 Cumulative Review Exercises

1. Perform the indicated operations.

$$(2x - 3)(x - 4) - (x - 5)^2 \quad x^2 - x - 13$$

2. Solve. $-9m + 3 = 2m(m - 4)$
$\left\{-\frac{3}{2}, 1\right\}$

For Exercises 3–4, solve the equation and inequalities. Write the solutions to the inequalities in interval notation.

3. a. $2|3 - p| - 4 = 2$ $\{0, 6\}$

b. $2|3 - p| - 4 < 2$ $(0, 6)$

c. $2|3 - p| - 4 > 2$ $(-\infty, 0) \cup (6, \infty)$

4. a. $\left|\frac{y-2}{4}\right| - 6 = -3$ $\{14, -10\}$

b. $\left|\frac{y-2}{4}\right| - 6 < -3$ $(-10, 14)$

c. $\left|\frac{y-2}{4}\right| - 6 > -3$ $(-\infty, -10) \cup (14, \infty)$

5. Graph the inequality. $4x - y > 12$

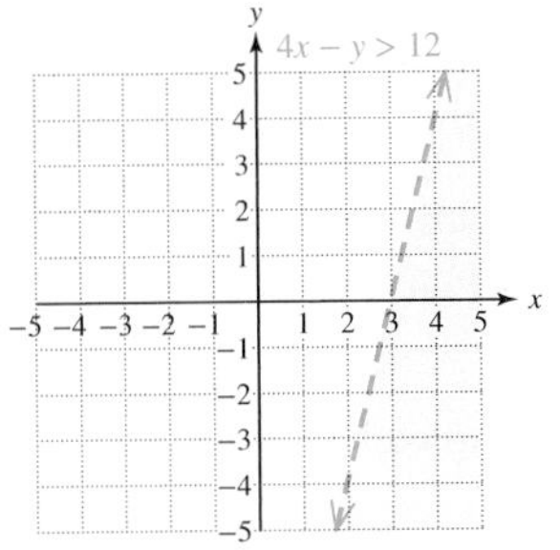

6. The time in minutes required for a rat to run through a maze depends on the number of trials, n, that the rat has practiced.

$$t(n) = \frac{3n + 15}{n + 1} \qquad n \geq 1$$

a. Find $t(1)$, $t(50)$, and $t(500)$, and interpret the results in the context of this problem. Round to 2 decimal places, if necessary.

$t(1) = 9$. After one trial the rat requires 9 min to complete the maze. $t(50) = 3.24$. After 50 trials the rat requires 3.24 min to complete the maze. $t(500) = 3.02$. After 500 trials the rat requires 3.02 min to complete the maze.

b. Does there appear to be a limiting time in which the rat can complete the maze?
The limiting time is 3 min.

c. How many trials are required so that the rat is able to finish the maze in under 5 min?
More than 5 trials

7. a. Solve the inequality. $2x^2 + x - 10 \geq 0$
$\left(-\infty, -\frac{5}{2}\right] \cup [2, \infty)$

b. How does the answer in part (a) relate to the graph of the function $f(x) = 2x^2 + x - 10$?

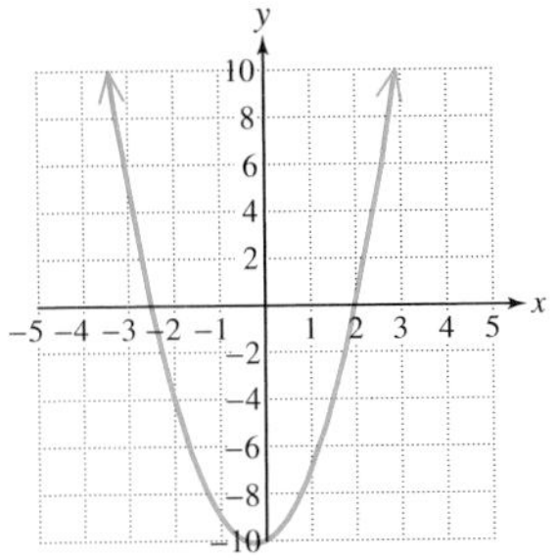

On these intervals, the graph is on or above the x-axis.

8. Graph the solution to the system of inequalities.

$$3x + y \leq -2$$
$$y \geq 1$$

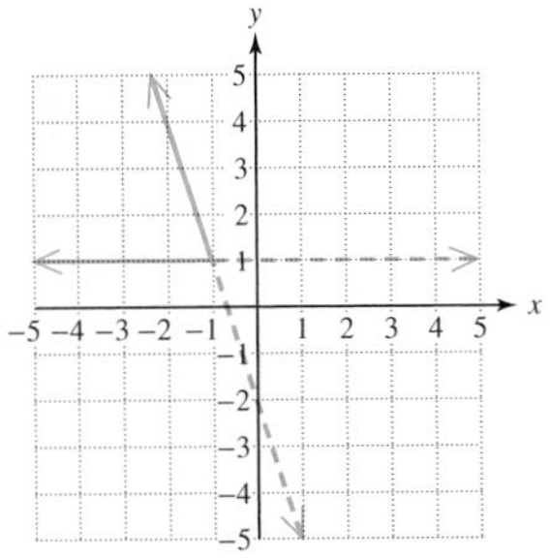

9. Simplify the expression.

$$2 - 3(x - 5) + 2[4 - (2x + 6)]$$

$-7x + 13$

10. a. Divide the polynomials.

$$\frac{2x^4 - x^3 + 5x - 7}{x^2 + 2x - 1}$$

Identify the quotient and remainder.
Quotient: $2x^2 - 5x + 12$; remainder: $-24x + 5$

b. Check your answer by multiplying.

11. The area of a trapezoid is given by $A = \frac{1}{2}h(b_1 + b_2)$.

a. Solve for b_1. $b_1 = \frac{2A - hb_2}{h}$ or $b_1 = \frac{2A}{h} - b_2$

b. Find b_1 when $h = 4$ cm, $b_2 = 6$ cm, and $A = 32\text{ cm}^2$. 10 cm

12. The speed of a car varies inversely as the time to travel a fixed distance. A car traveling the speed limit of 60 mph travels between two points in 10 sec. How fast is a car moving if it takes only 8 sec to cover the same distance? 75 mph

13. Two angles are supplementary. One angle measures 9° more than twice the other angle. Find the measures of the angles. 57°, 123°

14. Chemique invests \$3000 less in an account earning 5% simple interest than she does in an account earning 6.5% simple interest. At the end of one year, she earns a total \$770 in interest. Find the amount invested in each account.
\$8000 in the 6.5% account; \$5000 in the 5% account

15. Determine algebraically whether the lines are parallel, perpendicular, or neither. Neither

$$4x - 2y = 5$$
$$-3x + 6y = 10$$

16. Find the x- and y-intercepts and slope (if they exist) of the lines. Then graph the lines.

a. $3x + 5 = 8$

b. $\frac{1}{2}x + y = 4$

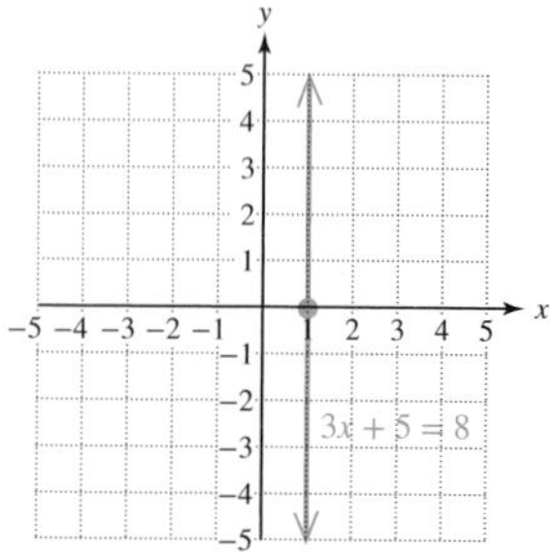

x-intercept (1, 0); no y-intercept; undefined slope

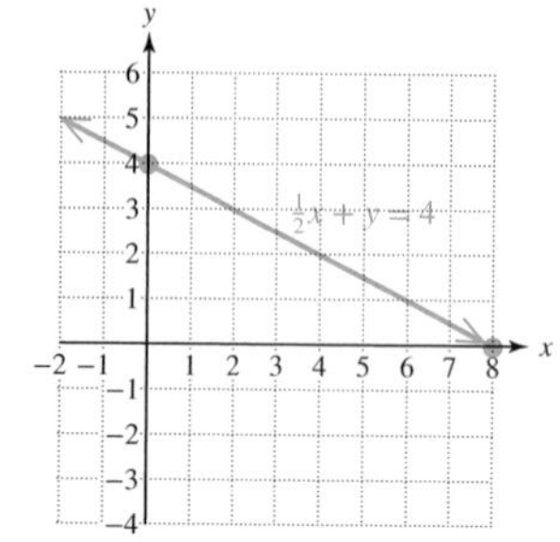

x-intercept (8, 0); y-intercept (0, 4); slope $-\frac{1}{2}$

17. Find an equation of the line with slope $-\frac{2}{3}$ passing through the point (4, −7). Write the final answer in slope-intercept form.
$y = -\frac{2}{3}x - \frac{13}{3}$

18. Solve the system of equations. $\{(-1, 3, -2)\}$

$$3x + y = z + 2$$
$$y = 1 - 2x$$
$$3z = -2y$$

19. Simplify. $\left(\frac{5x^2y^5}{30x^{-2}y^0}\right)^{-1}$ $\frac{6}{x^4y^5}$

20. Against the wind, a plane can travel 6240 mi in 13 hr. On the return trip flying with the same wind, the plane can fly 6240 mi in 12 hr. Find the wind speed and the speed of the plane in still air.
Plane: 500 mph; wind: 20 mph

21. The profit that a company makes manufacturing computer desks is given by

$$P(x) = -\tfrac{1}{5}(x - 20)(x - 650) \qquad x \geq 0$$

where x is the number of desks produced and $P(x)$ is the profit in dollars.

a. Is this function constant, linear, or quadratic?
Quadratic

b. Find $P(0)$ and interpret the result in the context of this problem. $P(0) = -2600$. The company will lose \$2600 if no desks are produced.

c. Find the values of x where $P(x) = 0$. Interpret the results in the context of this problem.
$P(x) = 0$ for $x = 20$ and $x = 650$. The company will break even (\$0 profit) when 20 desks or 650 desks are produced.

22. Factor the expression. $3x^3 - 6x^2 - 12x + 24$
$3(x - 2)^2(x + 2)$

23. Simplify completely. $\frac{x^{-1} - y^{-1}}{y^{-2} - x^{-2}}$ $-\frac{xy}{x + y}$

24. Divide. $\frac{a^3 + 64}{16 - a^2} \div \frac{a^3 - 4a^2 + 16a}{a^2 - 3a - 4}$ $-\frac{a + 1}{a}$

25. Perform the indicated operations.

$$\frac{1}{x^2 - 7x + 10} + \frac{1}{x^2 + 8x - 20}$$

$\frac{2x + 5}{(x - 5)(x - 2)(x + 10)}$

Radicals and Complex Numbers

10

CHAPTER OUTLINE

Mathematics in Architecture

The area A of a triangle can be found if the length of one side (the base b) and the corresponding height h of the triangle are known. $A = \frac{1}{2}bh$

However, if the base and height are not known, but the lengths of the three sides a, b, and c are known, then we can use Heron's formula to find the area of the triangle. Let s represent the semi-perimeter of the triangle.

That is, $s = \frac{1}{2}(a + b + c)$.

Then Heron's formula gives the area A as

$$A = \sqrt{s(s - a)(s - b)(s - c)}$$

The Louvre pyramid, designed by architect I.M. Pei, is a glass structure that serves as the entrance to the Louvre Museum in Paris, France. Each triangular face is made of glass with sides of lengths 108.5 ft, 108.5 ft, and 116 ft. To determine the surface area of glass for each face, we can apply Heron's formula.

$$s = \frac{1}{2}(a + b + c) = \frac{1}{2}(108.5 + 108.5 + 116) = 166.5$$

$$A = \sqrt{s(s - a)(s - b)(s - c)} = \sqrt{166.5(166.5 - 108.5)(166.5 - 108.5)(166.5 - 116)}$$

$$\approx 5318 \text{ ft}^2 \quad \text{Each face is approximately } 5318 \text{ ft}^2 \text{ of glass.}$$

Heron's formula is one application of radicals. In this chapter, we will simplify radical expressions and solve equations containing radicals.

Section 10.1 Definition of an *n*th Root

Concepts

1. Definition of a Square Root
2. Definition of an *n*th Root
3. Roots of Variable Expressions
4. Pythagorean Theorem
5. Radical Functions

1. Definition of a Square Root

The reverse operation to squaring a number is to find its square roots. For example, finding a square root of 36 is equivalent to asking, "when squared, what number equals 36?"

One obvious answer to this question is 6 because $(6)^2 = 36$, but -6 will also work, because $(-6)^2 = 36$.

Definition of a Square Root

b is a **square root** of a if $b^2 = a$.

Classroom Example: p. 702, Exercise 4

Example 1 Identifying Square Roots

Identify the square roots of the real numbers.

a. 25 **b.** 49 **c.** 0 **d.** -9

Solution:

a. 5 is a square root of 25 because $(5)^2 = 25$.

-5 is a square root of 25 because $(-5)^2 = 25$.

b. 7 is a square root of 49 because $(7)^2 = 49$.

-7 is a square root of 49 because $(-7)^2 = 49$.

c. 0 is a square root of 0 because $(0)^2 = 0$.

d. There are no real numbers that when squared will equal a negative number; therefore, there are no real-valued square roots of -9.

Skill Practice Identify the square roots of the real numbers.

1. 64 **2.** 16 **3.** 1 **4.** -100

TIP:

- All positive real numbers have two real-valued square roots (one positive and one negative).
- Zero has only one square root, which is zero itself.
- A negative number has no real-valued square roots.

Recall that the positive square root of a real number can be denoted with a **radical sign** $\sqrt{}$.

Positive and Negative Square Roots

Let a represent a positive real number. Then

1. $\sqrt{a}$ is the *positive* square root of a. The positive square root is also called the **principal square root**.
2. $-\sqrt{a}$ is the *negative* square root of a.
3. $\sqrt{0} = 0$

Answers

1. -8 and 8
2. -4 and 4
3. -1 and 1
4. No real-valued square roots

Example 2 Simplifying Square Roots

Classroom Example: p. 703, Exercise 14

Simplify the square roots.

a. $\sqrt{36}$ **b.** $\sqrt{\frac{4}{9}}$ **c.** $\sqrt{0.04}$

Solution:

a. $\sqrt{36}$ denotes the positive square root of 36.

$\sqrt{36} = 6$ because $(6)^2 = 36$

b. $\sqrt{\frac{4}{9}}$ denotes the positive square root of $\frac{4}{9}$.

$\sqrt{\frac{4}{9}} = \frac{2}{3}$ because $\left(\frac{2}{3}\right)^2 = \frac{4}{9}$

c. $\sqrt{0.04}$ denotes the positive square root of 0.04.

$\sqrt{0.04} = 0.2$ because $(0.2)^2 = 0.04$

Skill Practice Simplify the square roots.

5. $\sqrt{81}$ **6.** $\sqrt{\frac{36}{49}}$ **7.** $\sqrt{0.09}$

The numbers 36, $\frac{4}{9}$, and 0.04 are **perfect squares** because their square roots are rational numbers.

Radicals that cannot be simplified to rational numbers are irrational numbers. Recall that an irrational number cannot be written as a terminating or repeating decimal. For example, the symbol $\sqrt{13}$ is used to represent the *exact* value of the square root of 13. The symbol $\sqrt{42}$ is used to represent the *exact* value of the square root of 42. These values can be approximated by a rational number by using a calculator.

$$\sqrt{13} \approx 3.605551275 \qquad \sqrt{42} \approx 6.480740698$$

Calculator Connections

Topic: Approximating Square Roots

Use a calculator to approximate the values of $\sqrt{13}$ and $\sqrt{42}$.

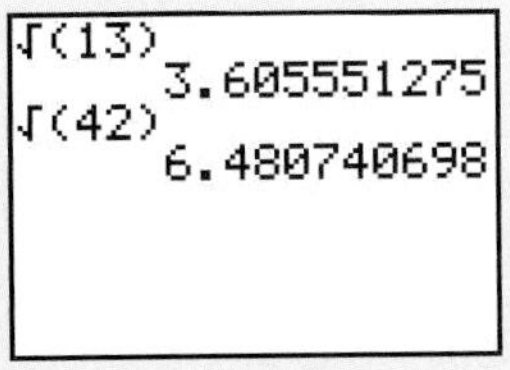

TIP: Before using a calculator to evaluate a square root, try estimating the value first.
$\sqrt{13}$ must be a number between 3 and 4 because $\sqrt{9} < \sqrt{13} < \sqrt{16}$.
$\sqrt{42}$ must be a number between 6 and 7 because $\sqrt{36} < \sqrt{42} < \sqrt{49}$.

A negative number cannot have a real number as a square root because no real number when squared is negative. For example, $\sqrt{-25}$ is *not* a real number because there is no real number b for which $(b)^2 = -25$.

Answers

5. 9 **6.** $\frac{6}{7}$ **7.** 0.3

Classroom Examples: p. 703, Exercises 10, 12, and 18

Example 3 **Simplifying Square Roots**

Simplify the square roots, if possible.

a. $\sqrt{-144}$ **b.** $-\sqrt{144}$ **c.** $\sqrt{-0.01}$ **d.** $-\sqrt{\frac{1}{9}}$

Solution:

a. $\sqrt{-144}$ is *not* a real number. No real number when squared equals -144.

b. $-\sqrt{144}$

$= -1 \cdot \sqrt{144}$

$= -1 \cdot 12$

$= -12$

TIP: For the expression $-\sqrt{144}$, the factor of -1 is *outside* the radical.

c. $\sqrt{-0.01}$ is *not* a real number. No real number when squared equals -0.01.

d. $-\sqrt{\frac{1}{9}}$

$= -1 \cdot \sqrt{\frac{1}{9}}$

$= -1 \cdot \frac{1}{3}$

$= -\frac{1}{3}$

Skill Practice Simplify the square roots, if possible.

8. $\sqrt{-81}$ **9.** $-\sqrt{64}$ **10.** $-\sqrt{0.25}$ **11.** $\sqrt{-\frac{1}{4}}$

2. Definition of an *n*th Root

Finding a square root of a number is the reverse process of squaring a number. This concept can be extended to finding a third root (called a cube root), a fourth root, and in general an ***n*th root**.

Definition of an *n*th Root

b is an nth root of a if $b^n = a$.

Example: 2 is a square root of 4 because 2^2 is 4.

Example: 2 is a third root of 8 because 2^3 is 8.

Example: 2 is a fourth root of 16 because 2^4 is 16.

The radical sign $\sqrt{}$ is used to denote the principal square root of a number. The symbol $\sqrt[n]{}$ is used to denote the principal nth root of a number. In the expression $\sqrt[n]{a}$, n is called the **index** of the radical, and a is called the **radicand**. For a square root, the index is 2, but it is usually not written ($\sqrt[2]{a}$ is denoted simply as $\sqrt{a}$). A radical with an index of 3 is called a **cube root**, denoted by $\sqrt[3]{a}$.

Answers

8. Not a real number **9.** -8
10. -0.5 **11.** Not a real number

Evaluating $\sqrt[n]{a}$

1. If $n > 1$ is an *even* integer and $a > 0$, then $\sqrt[n]{a}$ is the principal (positive) nth root of a. Example: $\sqrt[4]{625} = 5$
2. If $n > 1$ is an *odd* integer, then $\sqrt[n]{a}$ is the nth root of a.
   Example: $\sqrt[3]{8} = 2$, $\sqrt[3]{-8} = -2$
3. If $n > 1$ is an integer, then $\sqrt[n]{0} = 0$.

For the purpose of simplifying nth roots, it is helpful to know numbers that are perfect squares as well as the following common perfect cubes, fourth powers, and fifth powers.

Perfect Cubes	Perfect Fourth Powers	Perfect Fifth Powers
$1^3 = 1$	$1^4 = 1$	$1^5 = 1$
$2^3 = 8$	$2^4 = 16$	$2^5 = 32$
$3^3 = 27$	$3^4 = 81$	$3^5 = 243$
$4^3 = 64$	$4^4 = 256$	$4^5 = 1024$
$5^3 = 125$	$5^4 = 625$	$5^5 = 3125$

Instructor Note: Students are acquainted with the perfect square integers 1, 4, 9, . . . They may need to familiarize themselves with the perfect cubes, 4th powers, etc.

Example 4 Identifying the *n*th Root of a Real Number

Classroom Examples: p. 703, Exercises 24, 32, and 34

Simplify the expressions, if possible.

a. $\sqrt{4}$ **b.** $\sqrt[3]{64}$ **c.** $\sqrt[5]{-32}$ **d.** $\sqrt[4]{81}$

e. $\sqrt[6]{1{,}000{,}000}$ **f.** $\sqrt{-100}$ **g.** $\sqrt[4]{-16}$

Solution:

a. $\sqrt{4} = 2$ because $(2)^2 = 4$

b. $\sqrt[3]{64} = 4$ because $(4)^3 = 64$

c. $\sqrt[5]{-32} = -2$ because $(-2)^5 = -32$

d. $\sqrt[4]{81} = 3$ because $(3)^4 = 81$

e. $\sqrt[6]{1{,}000{,}000} = 10$ because $(10)^6 = 1{,}000{,}000$

f. $\sqrt{-100}$ is not a real number. No real number when squared equals -100.

g. $\sqrt[4]{-16}$ is not a real number. No real number when raised to the fourth power equals -16.

Skill Practice Simplify if possible.

12. $\sqrt[4]{16}$ **13.** $\sqrt[3]{1000}$ **14.** $\sqrt[5]{-1}$ **15.** $\sqrt[5]{32}$

16. $\sqrt[5]{100{,}000}$ **17.** $\sqrt{-36}$ **18.** $\sqrt[3]{-27}$

Calculator Connections

Topic: Approximating *n*th Roots

A calculator can be used to approximate nth roots by using the $\sqrt[x]{\ }$ function. On most calculators, the index is entered first.

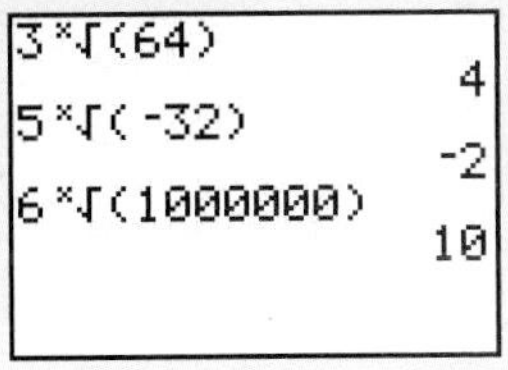

Examples 4(f) and 4(g) illustrate that an nth root of a negative quantity is not a real number if the index is even. This is because no real number raised to an even power is negative.

3. Roots of Variable Expressions

Finding an nth root of a variable expression is similar to finding an nth root of a numerical expression. For roots with an even index, however, particular care must be taken to obtain a nonnegative result.

Answers

12. 2 **13.** 10 **14.** -1
15. 2 **16.** 10
17. Not a real number **18.** -3

Evaluating $\sqrt[n]{a^n}$

1. If n is a positive *odd* integer, then $\sqrt[n]{a^n} = a$.
2. If n is a positive *even* integer, then $\sqrt[n]{a^n} = |a|$.

The absolute value bars are necessary for roots with an even index because the variable a may represent a positive quantity or a negative quantity. By using absolute value bars, $\sqrt[n]{a^n} = |a|$ is nonnegative and represents the principal nth root of a^n.

Classroom Examples: p. 703, Exercises 40 and 42

Example 5 Simplifying Expressions of the Form $\sqrt[n]{a^n}$

Simplify the expressions.

a. $\sqrt[4]{(-3)^4}$ **b.** $\sqrt[5]{(-3)^5}$ **c.** $\sqrt{(x+2)^2}$ **d.** $\sqrt[6]{(a+b)^3}$ **e.** $\sqrt{y^4}$

Solution:

a. $\sqrt[4]{(-3)^4} = |-3| = 3$ — Because this is an *even*-indexed root, absolute value bars are necessary to make the answer positive.

b. $\sqrt[5]{(-3)^5} = -3$ — This is an *odd*-indexed root, so absolute value bars are not necessary.

c. $\sqrt{(x+2)^2} = |x+2|$ — Because this is an *even*-indexed root, absolute value bars are necessary. The sign of the quantity $x+2$ is unknown; however, $|x+2| \geq 0$ regardless of the value of x.

d. $\sqrt[3]{(a+b)^3} = a+b$ — This is an *odd*-indexed root, so absolute value bars are not necessary.

e. $\sqrt{y^4} = \sqrt{(y^2)^2}$

$= |y^2|$ — Because this is an even-indexed root, use absolute value bars.

$= y^2$ — However, because y^2 is nonnegative, the absolute value bars are not necessary.

Skill Practice Simplify the expressions.

19. $\sqrt{(-4)^2}$ **20.** $\sqrt[3]{(-4)^3}$ **21.** $\sqrt{(y+9)^2}$ **22.** $\sqrt[3]{(t+1)^3}$ **23.** $\sqrt[4]{v^8}$

If n is an even integer, then $\sqrt[n]{a^n} = |a|$; however, if the variable a is assumed to be *nonnegative*, then the absolute value bars may be dropped. That is, $\sqrt[n]{a^n} = a$ provided $a \geq 0$. In many examples and exercises, we will make the assumption that the variables within a radical expression are positive real numbers. In such a case, the absolute value bars are not needed to evaluate $\sqrt[n]{a^n}$.

Take a minute to examine the following patterns associated with perfect squares and perfect cubes. In general, any expression raised to an even power is a perfect square. An expression raised to a power that is a multiple of three is a perfect cube.

Perfect Squares	Perfect Cubes
$(x^1)^2 = x^2$	$(x^1)^3 = x^3$
$(x^2)^2 = x^4$	$(x^2)^3 = x^6$
$(x^3)^2 = x^6$	$(x^3)^3 = x^9$
$(x^4)^2 = x^8$	$(x^4)^3 = x^{12}$

These patterns may be extended to higher powers.

Answers

19. 4 **20.** −4 **21.** $|y+9|$
22. $t+1$ **23.** v^2

Example 6 Simplifying *n*th Roots

Simplify the expressions. Assume that all variables are positive real numbers.

a. $\sqrt{y^8}$ **b.** $\sqrt[3]{27a^3}$ **c.** $\sqrt[5]{\dfrac{a^5}{b^5}}$ **d.** $-\sqrt[4]{\dfrac{81x^4y^8}{16}}$

Solution:

a. $\sqrt{y^8} = \sqrt{(y^4)^2}$
$= y^4$

b. $\sqrt[3]{27a^3} = \sqrt[3]{(3a)^3}$
$= 3a$

c. $\sqrt[5]{\dfrac{a^5}{b^5}} = \sqrt[5]{\left(\dfrac{a}{b}\right)^5}$
$= \dfrac{a}{b}$

d. $-\sqrt[4]{\dfrac{81x^4y^8}{16}} = -\sqrt[4]{\left(\dfrac{3xy^2}{2}\right)^4}$
$= -\dfrac{3xy^2}{2}$

Skill Practice Simplify the expressions. Assume all variables represent positive real numbers.

24. $\sqrt{t^6}$ **25.** $\sqrt[3]{64y^{12}}$ **26.** $\sqrt[4]{\dfrac{x^4}{y^4}}$ **27.** $-\sqrt[5]{\dfrac{32a^5}{b^{10}}}$

Classroom Examples: pp. 703–704, Exercises 66 and 70

TIP: In Example 6, the variables are assumed to represent positive numbers. Therefore, absolute value bars are not necessary in the simplified form.

4. Pythagorean Theorem

Given a right triangle with legs of lengths a and b and hypotenuse of length c, the **Pythagorean theorem** can be stated as $a^2 + b^2 = c^2$. See Figure 10-1.

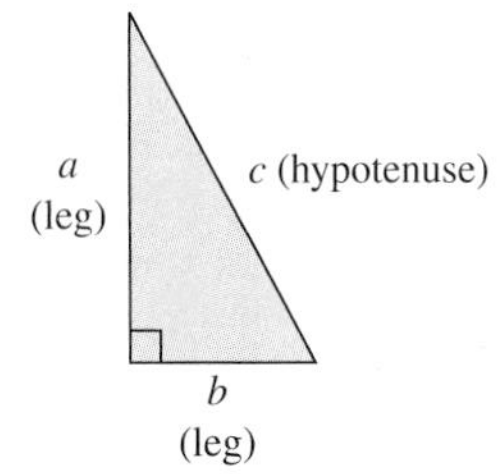

Figure 10-1

Classroom Example: p. 704, Exercise 78

Example 7 Applying the Pythagorean Theorem

Use the Pythagorean theorem and the definition of the principal square root to find the length of the unknown side.

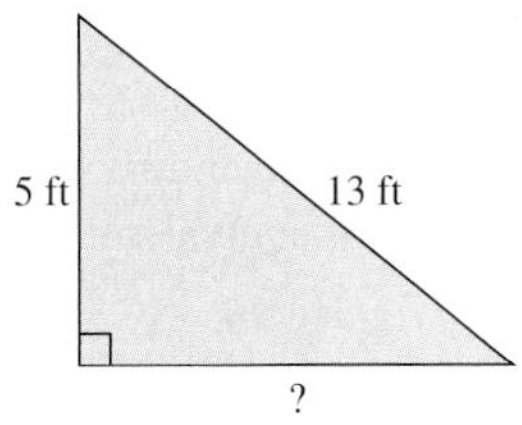

Solution:

Label the sides of the triangle.

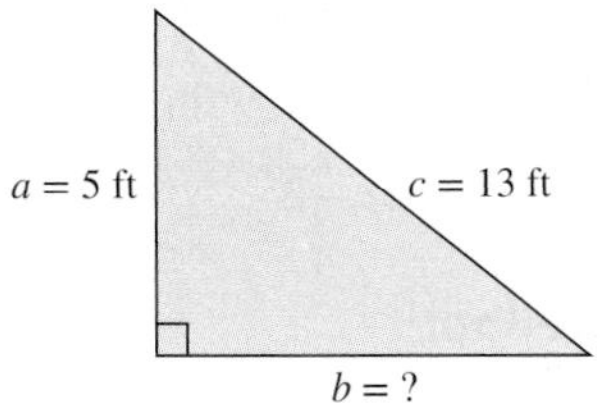

$a^2 + b^2 = c^2$
$(5)^2 + b^2 = (13)^2$ Apply the Pythagorean theorem.

$25 + b^2 = 169$ Simplify.

$b^2 = 169 - 25$ Isolate b^2.

$b^2 = 144$ By definition, b must be one of the square roots of 144. Because b represents the length of a side of a triangle, choose the positive square root of 144.

$b = 12$

The third side is 12 ft long.

Skill Practice

28. Use the Pythagorean theorem and the definition of the principal square root to find the length of the unknown side of the right triangle.

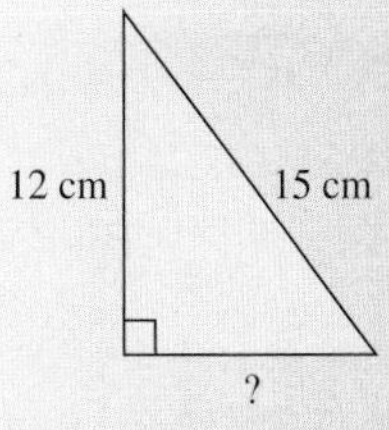

Answers

24. t^3 **25.** $4y^4$ **26.** $\dfrac{x}{y}$

27. $-\dfrac{2a}{b^2}$ **28.** 9 cm

Classroom Example: p. 704, Exercise 80

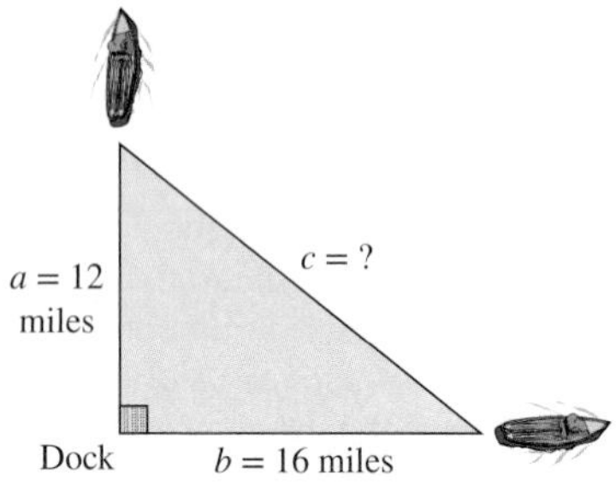

Figure 10-2

Example 8 Applying the Pythagorean Theorem

Two boats leave a dock at 12:00 noon. One travels due north at 6 mph, and the other travels due east at 8 mph (Figure 10-2). How far apart are the two boats after 2 hr?

Solution:

The boat traveling north travels a distance of (6 mph)(2 hr) = 12 mi. The boat traveling east travels a distance of (8 mph)(2 hr) = 16 mi. The course of the boats forms a right triangle where the hypotenuse represents the distance between them.

$a^2 + b^2 = c^2$

$(12)^2 + (16)^2 = c^2$ Apply the Pythagorean theorem.

$144 + 256 = c^2$ Simplify.

$400 = c^2$

$\sqrt{400} = c$ By definition, c must be one of the square roots of 400. Choose the positive square root of 400 to represent the distance between the two boats.

$20 = c$

The boats are 20 mi apart.

Skill Practice

29. Two cars leave from the same place at the same time. One travels west at 40 mph, and the other travels north at 30 mph. How far apart are they after 2 hr?

5. Radical Functions

If n is an integer greater than 1, then a function written in the form $f(x) = \sqrt[n]{x}$ is called a **radical function**. Note that if n is an even integer, then the function will be a real number only if the radicand is nonnegative. Therefore, the domain is restricted to nonnegative real numbers, or equivalently, $[0, \infty)$. If n is an odd integer, then the domain is all real numbers.

Classroom Examples: p. 704, Exercises 86 and 88

Example 9 Determining the Domain of Radical Functions

For each function, write the domain in interval notation.

a. $g(t) = \sqrt[4]{t - 2}$ **b.** $h(a) = \sqrt[3]{a - 3}$ **c.** $k(x) = \sqrt{3 - 5x} + 2$

Solution:

a. $g(t) = \sqrt[4]{t - 2}$ The index is even. The radicand must be nonnegative.

$t - 2 \geq 0$ Set the radicand greater than or equal to zero.

$t \geq 2$ Solve for t.

The domain is $[2, \infty)$.

b. $h(a) = \sqrt[3]{a - 3}$ The index is odd; therefore, the domain is all real numbers.

The domain is $(-\infty, \infty)$.

Answer

29. 100 mi

c. $k(x) = \sqrt{3 - 5x} + 2$ The index is even; therefore, the radicand must be nonnegative.

$3 - 5x \geq 0$ Set the radicand greater than or equal to zero.

$-5x \geq -3$ Solve for x.

$\frac{-5x}{-5} \leq \frac{-3}{-5}$ Reverse the inequality sign.

$x \leq \frac{3}{5}$

The domain is $\left(-\infty, \frac{3}{5}\right]$.

Skill Practice For each function, write the domain in interval notation.

30. $f(x) = \sqrt{x + 5}$ **31.** $g(t) = \sqrt[3]{t - 9}$ **32.** $h(a) = \sqrt{1 - 2a}$

Calculator Connections

Topic: Graphing Radical Functions

We can graph the functions defined in Example 9. The graphs support the answers we obtained for the domain of each function.

$g(t) = \sqrt[4]{t - 2}$

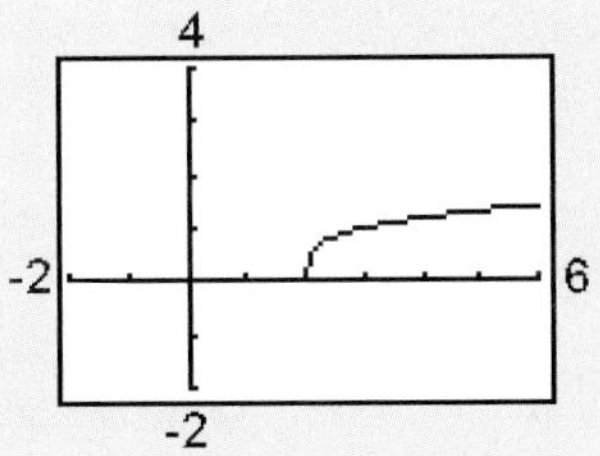

Domain: $[2, \infty)$

$h(a) = \sqrt[3]{a - 3}$

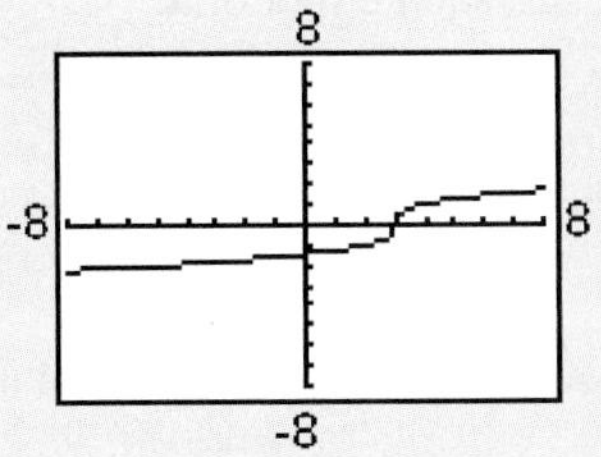

Domain: $(-\infty, \infty)$

$k(x) = \sqrt{3 - 5x} + 2$

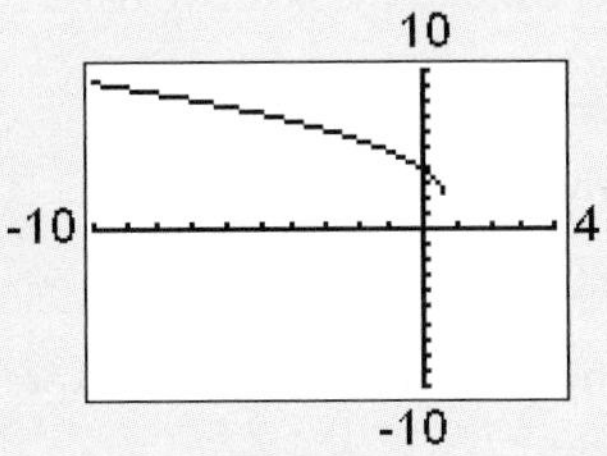

Domain: $\left(-\infty, \frac{3}{5}\right]$

Example 10 Graphing a Radical Function

Classroom Example: p. 705, Exercise 96

Given $f(x) = \sqrt{3 - x}$

a. Write the domain of f in interval notation.

b. Graph f by making a table of ordered pairs.

Solution:

a. $f(x) = \sqrt{3 - x}$

$3 - x \geq 0$ The index is even. The radicand must be greater than or equal to zero.

$-x \geq -3$

$x \leq 3$ Reverse the inequality sign.

The domain is $(-\infty, 3]$.

Answers

30. $[-5, \infty)$ **31.** $(-\infty, \infty)$

32. $\left(-\infty, \frac{1}{2}\right]$

b. Create a table of ordered pairs where x values are taken to be less than or equal to 3.

x	$f(x)$
3	0
2	1
−1	2
−6	3

$f(3) = \sqrt{3-3} = \sqrt{0} = 0$

$f(2) = \sqrt{3-2} = \sqrt{1} = 1$

$f(-1) = \sqrt{3-(-1)} = \sqrt{4} = 2$

$f(-6) = \sqrt{3-(-6)} = \sqrt{9} = 3$

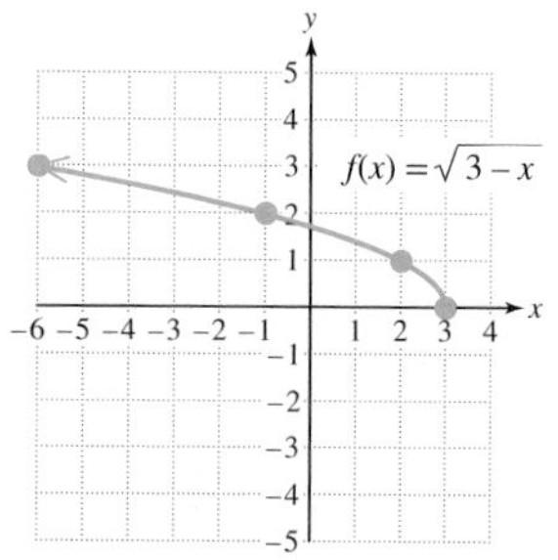

Skill Practice

33. Given $f(x) = \sqrt{x+4}$

a. Write the domain of f in interval notation.

b. Graph f by making a table of ordered pairs.

Answers

33. a. $[-4, \infty)$

b.

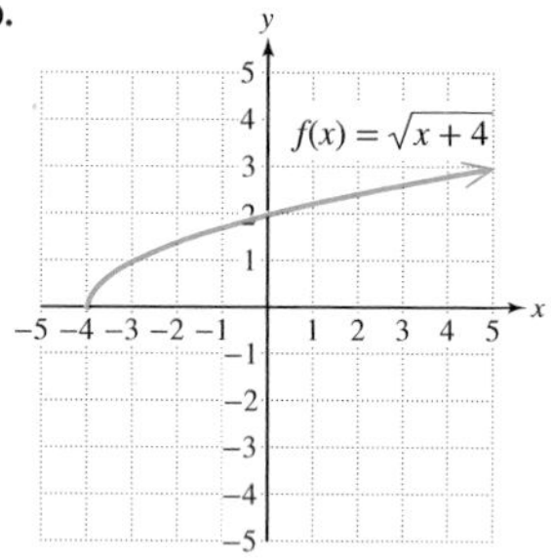

Section 10.1 Practice Exercises

For additional exercises, see Classroom Activities 10.1A–10.1D in the *Student's Resource Manual* at www.mhhe.com/moh.

Vocabulary and Key Concepts

1. **a.** If $b^2 = a$, then ___b___ is a square root of ___a___.

   b. Given $a > 0$, the symbol $\sqrt{a}$ denotes the positive or ___principal___ square root of a.

   c. b is an nth root of a if ___b^n___ = ___a___.

   d. Given the symbol $\sqrt[n]{a}$, the value n is called the ___index___ and a is called the ___radicand___.

   e. The symbol $\sqrt[3]{a}$ denotes the ___cube___ root of a.

   f. The expression $\sqrt{-4}$ (is/is not) a real number. The expression $-\sqrt{4}$ (is/is not) a real number. is not; is

   g. The expression $\sqrt[n]{a^n} = |a|$ if n is (even/odd). The expression $\sqrt[n]{a^n} = a$ if n is (even/odd). even; odd

   h. Given a right triangle with legs a and b and hypotenuse c, the ___Pythagorean___ theorem is stated as $a^2 + b^2 =$ ___c^2___.

   i. In interval notation, the domain of $f(x) = \sqrt{x}$ is ___$[0, \infty)$___, whereas the domain of $g(x) = \sqrt[3]{x}$ is ___$(-\infty, \infty)$___.

   j. Which of the following values of x are *not* in the domain of $h(x) = \sqrt{x+3}$: $x = -5, x = -4, x = -3, x = -2, x = -1, x = 0$? −5 and −4

Concept 1: Definition of a Square Root

2. Simplify the expression $\sqrt[3]{8}$. Explain how you can check your answer. $\sqrt[3]{8} = 2$ because $2^3 = 8$.

3. **a.** Find the square roots of 64. **(See Example 1.)** 8, −8

   b. Find $\sqrt{64}$. 8

   c. Explain the difference between the answers in part (a) and part (b). There are two square roots for every positive number. $\sqrt{64}$ identifies the positive square root.

4. **a.** Find the square roots of 121. 11, −11

   b. Find $\sqrt{121}$. 11

   c. Explain the difference between the answers in part (a) and part (b). There are two square roots for every positive number. $\sqrt{121}$ identifies the positive square root.

5. **a.** What is the principal square root of 81? 9

   b. What is the negative square root of 81? −9

6. **a.** What is the principal square root of 100? 10

   b. What is the negative square root of 100? −10

7. Using the definition of a square root, explain why $\sqrt{-36}$ is not a real number. There is no real number b such that $b^2 = -36$.

For Exercises 8–19, evaluate the roots without using a calculator. Identify those that are not real numbers. **(See Examples 2–3.)**

8. $\sqrt{25}$ 5 **9.** $\sqrt{49}$ 7 **10.** $-\sqrt{25}$ −5 **11.** $-\sqrt{49}$ −7

12. $\sqrt{-25}$ Not a real number **13.** $\sqrt{-49}$ Not a real number **14.** $\sqrt{\frac{100}{121}}$ $\frac{10}{11}$ **15.** $\sqrt{\frac{64}{9}}$ $\frac{8}{3}$

16. $\sqrt{0.64}$ 0.8 **17.** $\sqrt{0.81}$ 0.9 **18.** $-\sqrt{0.0144}$ −0.12 **19.** $-\sqrt{0.16}$ −0.4

Concept 2: Definition of an *n*th Root

20. Using the definition of an *n*th root, explain why $\sqrt[4]{-16}$ is not a real number. There is no real number b such that $b^4 = -16$.

For Exercises 21–38, evaluate the roots without using a calculator. Identify those that are not real numbers. **(See Example 4.)**

21. **a.** $\sqrt{64}$ 8 **b.** $\sqrt[3]{64}$ 4 **c.** $-\sqrt{64}$ −8
d. $-\sqrt[3]{64}$ −4 **e.** $\sqrt{-64}$ Not a real number **f.** $\sqrt[3]{-64}$ −4

22. **a.** $\sqrt{16}$ 4 **b.** $\sqrt[4]{16}$ 2 **c.** $-\sqrt{16}$ −4
d. $-\sqrt[4]{16}$ −2 **e.** $\sqrt{-16}$ Not a real number **f.** $\sqrt[4]{-16}$ Not a real number

23. $\sqrt[3]{-27}$ −3 **24.** $\sqrt[3]{-125}$ −5 **25.** $\sqrt[3]{\frac{1}{8}}$ $\frac{1}{2}$ **26.** $\sqrt[5]{\frac{1}{32}}$ $\frac{1}{2}$

27. $\sqrt[5]{32}$ 2 **28.** $\sqrt[4]{1}$ 1 **29.** $\sqrt[3]{-\frac{125}{64}}$ $-\frac{5}{4}$ **30.** $\sqrt[3]{-\frac{8}{27}}$ $-\frac{2}{3}$

31. $\sqrt[4]{-1}$ Not a real number **32.** $\sqrt[6]{-1}$ Not a real number **33.** $\sqrt[6]{1{,}000{,}000}$ 10 **34.** $\sqrt[4]{10{,}000}$ 10

35. $-\sqrt[3]{0.008}$ −0.2 **36.** $-\sqrt[4]{0.0016}$ −0.2 **37.** $\sqrt[4]{0.0625}$ 0.5 **38.** $\sqrt[3]{0.064}$ 0.4

Concept 3: Roots of Variable Expressions

For Exercises 39–58, simplify the radical expressions. **(See Example 5.)**

39. $\sqrt{a^2}$ $|a|$ **40.** $\sqrt[4]{a^4}$ $|a|$ **41.** $\sqrt[3]{a^3}$ a **42.** $\sqrt[5]{a^5}$ a

43. $\sqrt[6]{a^6}$ $|a|$ **44.** $\sqrt[7]{a^7}$ a **45.** $\sqrt{(x+1)^2}$ $|x+1|$ **46.** $\sqrt[3]{(y+3)^3}$ $y+3$

47. $\sqrt{x^2y^4}$ $|x|y^2$ **48.** $\sqrt[3]{(u+v)^3}$ $u+v$ **49.** $-\sqrt[3]{\frac{x^3}{y^3}}$, $y \neq 0$ $-\frac{x}{y}$ **50.** $\sqrt[4]{\frac{a^4}{b^8}}$, $b \neq 0$ $\frac{|a|}{b^2}$

51. $\frac{2}{\sqrt[4]{x^4}}$, $x \neq 0$ $\frac{2}{|x|}$ **52.** $\sqrt{(-5)^2}$ 5 **53.** $\sqrt[3]{(-92)^3}$ −92 **54.** $\sqrt[6]{(50)^6}$ 50

55. $\sqrt[10]{(-2)^{10}}$ 2 **56.** $\sqrt[5]{(-2)^5}$ −2 **57.** $\sqrt[7]{(-923)^7}$ −923 **58.** $\sqrt[6]{(-417)^6}$ 417

For Exercises 59–74, simplify the expressions. Assume all variables are positive real numbers. **(See Example 6.)**

59. $\sqrt{y^8}$ y^4 **60.** $\sqrt{x^4}$ x^2 **61.** $\sqrt{\frac{a^6}{b^2}}$ $\frac{a^3}{b}$ **62.** $\sqrt{\frac{w^2}{z^4}}$ $\frac{w}{z^2}$

63. $-\sqrt{\frac{25}{q^2}}$ $-\frac{5}{q}$ **64.** $-\sqrt{\frac{p^6}{81}}$ $-\frac{p^3}{9}$ **65.** $\sqrt{9x^2y^4z^2}$ $3xy^2z$ **66.** $\sqrt{4a^4b^2c^6}$ $2a^2bc^3$

67. $\sqrt{\dfrac{h^2k^4}{16}}$ $\dfrac{hk^2}{4}$

68. $\sqrt{\dfrac{4x^2}{y^8}}$ $\dfrac{2x}{y^4}$

69. $-\sqrt[3]{\dfrac{t^3}{27}}$ $-\dfrac{t}{3}$

70. $\sqrt[4]{\dfrac{16}{w^4}}$ $\dfrac{2}{w}$

71. $\sqrt[5]{32y^{10}}$ $2y^2$

72. $\sqrt[3]{64x^6y^3}$ $4x^2y$

73. $\sqrt[6]{64p^{12}q^{18}}$ $2p^2q^3$

74. $\sqrt[4]{16r^{12}s^8}$ $2r^3s^2$

Concept 4: Pythagorean Theorem

For Exercises 75–78, find the length of the third side of each triangle by using the Pythagorean theorem. **(See Example 7.)**

75.

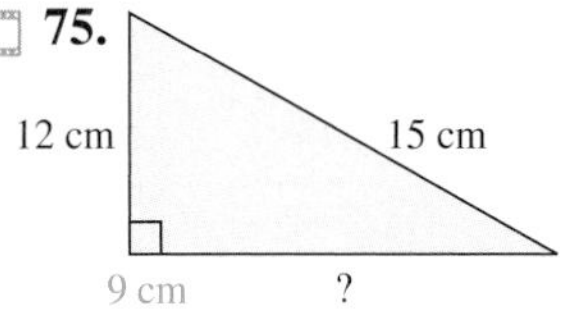

76.

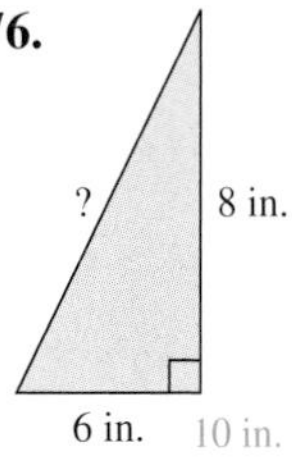

77.

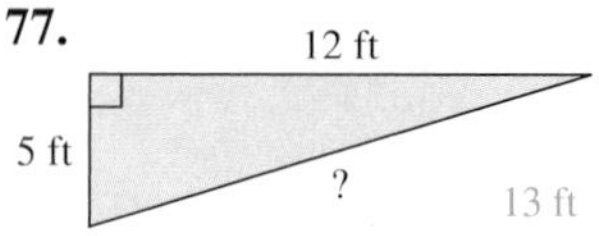

78.

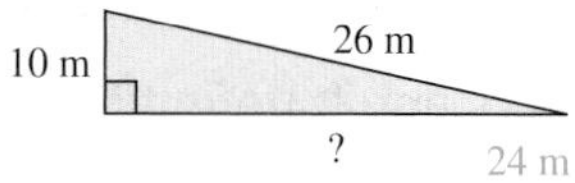

For Exercises 79–82, use the Pythagorean theorem.

79. Roberto and Sherona began running from the same place at the same time. They ran along two different paths that formed right angles with each other. Roberto ran 4 mi and stopped, while Sherona ran 3 mi and stopped. How far apart were they when they stopped? **(See Example 8.)**
They were 5 mi apart.

80. Leine and Laura began hiking from their campground. Laura headed south while Leine headed east. Laura walked 12 mi and Leine walked 5 mi. How far apart were they when they stopped walking? They were 13 mi apart.

81. Two mountain bikers take off from the same place at the same time. One travels north at 4 mph, and the other travels east at 3 mph. How far apart are they after 5 hr? They are 25 mi apart.

82. Professor Ortiz leaves campus on her bike, heading west at 12 ft/sec. Professor Wilson leaves campus at the same time and walks south at 5 ft/sec. How far apart are they after 40 sec? They are 520 ft apart.

Concept 5: Radical Functions

For Exercises 83–86, evaluate the function for the given values of x. Then write the domain of the function in interval notation. **(See Example 9.)**

83. $h(x) = \sqrt{x-2}$
- **a.** $h(0)$ Not a real number
- **b.** $h(1)$ Not a real number
- **c.** $h(2)$ 0
- **d.** $h(3)$ 1
- **e.** $h(6)$ 2

Domain: $[2, \infty)$

84. $k(x) = \sqrt{x+1}$
- **a.** $k(-3)$ Not a real number
- **b.** $k(-2)$ Not a real number
- **c.** $k(-1)$ 0
- **d.** $k(0)$ 1
- **e.** $k(3)$ 2

Domain: $[-1, \infty)$

85. $g(x) = \sqrt[3]{x-2}$
- **a.** $g(-6)$ −2
- **b.** $g(1)$ −1
- **c.** $g(2)$ 0
- **d.** $g(3)$ 1

Domain: $(-\infty, \infty)$

86. $f(x) = \sqrt[3]{x+1}$
- **a.** $f(-9)$ −2
- **b.** $f(-2)$ −1
- **c.** $f(0)$ 1
- **d.** $f(7)$ 2

Domain: $(-\infty, \infty)$

For each function defined in Exercises 87–94, write the domain in interval notation. **(See Example 9.)**

87. $f(x) = \sqrt{5-2x}$ $\left(-\infty, \dfrac{5}{2}\right]$

88. $g(x) = \sqrt{3-4x}$ $\left(-\infty, \dfrac{3}{4}\right]$

89. $k(x) = \sqrt[3]{4x-7}$ $(-\infty, \infty)$

90. $R(x) = \sqrt[3]{x+1}$ $(-\infty, \infty)$

91. $M(x) = \sqrt{x-5} + 3$ $[5, \infty)$

92. $N(x) = \sqrt{x+3} - 1$ $[-3, \infty)$

93. $F(x) = \sqrt[3]{x+7} - 2$ $(-\infty, \infty)$

94. $G(x) = \sqrt[3]{x-10} + 4$ $(-\infty, \infty)$

For Exercises 95–102,

a. Write the domain of f in interval notation.

b. Graph f by making a table of ordered pairs. **(See Example 10.)**

95. $f(x) = \sqrt{1 - x}$

a. $(-\infty, 1]$

b.

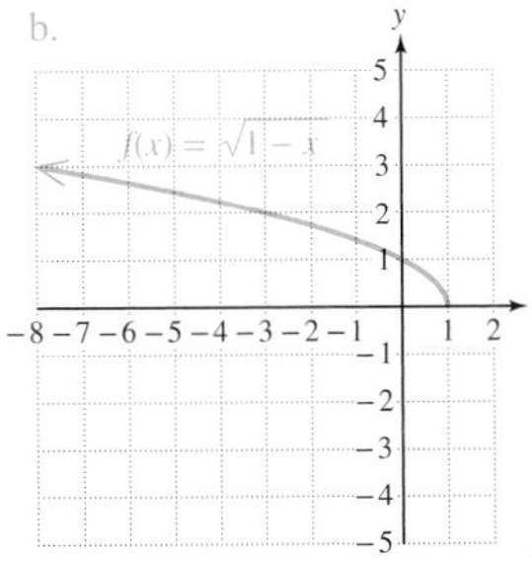

96. $f(x) = \sqrt{2 - x}$

a. $(-\infty, 2]$

b.

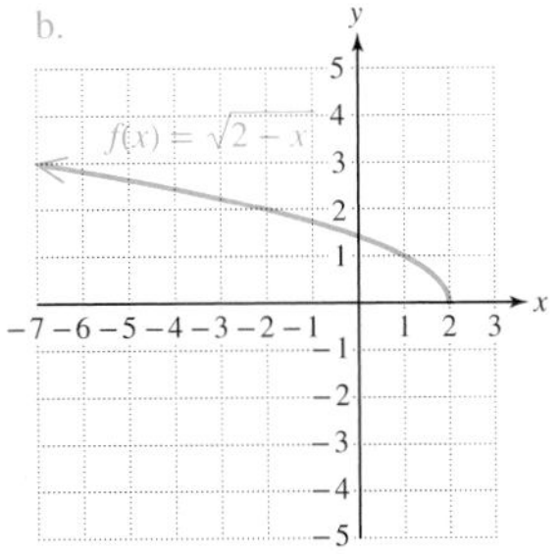

97. $f(x) = \sqrt{x + 3}$

a. $[-3, \infty)$

b.

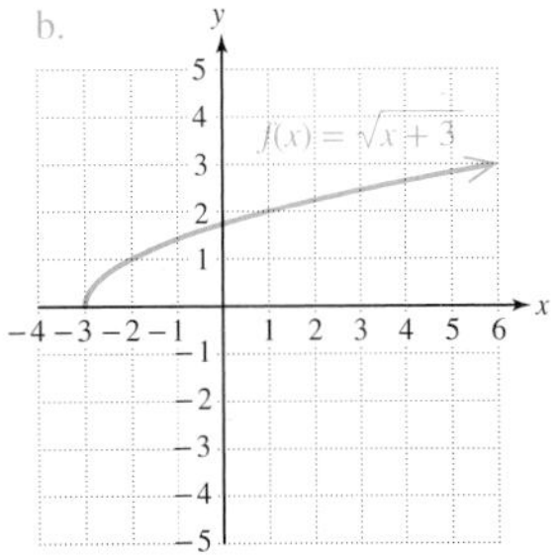

98. $f(x) = \sqrt{x + 1}$

a. $[-1, \infty)$

b.

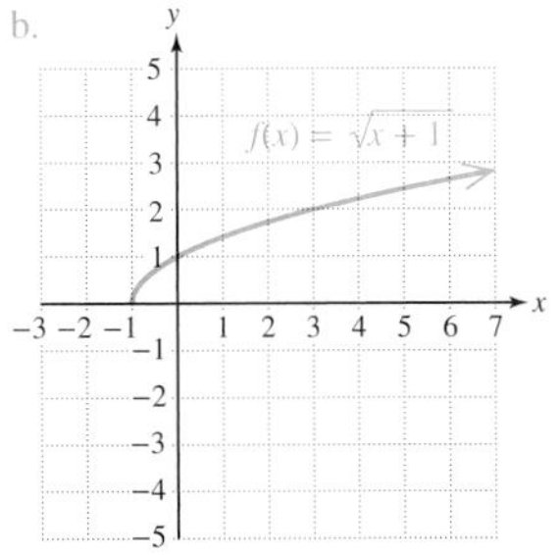

99. $f(x) = \sqrt{x} + 2$

a. $[0, \infty)$

b.

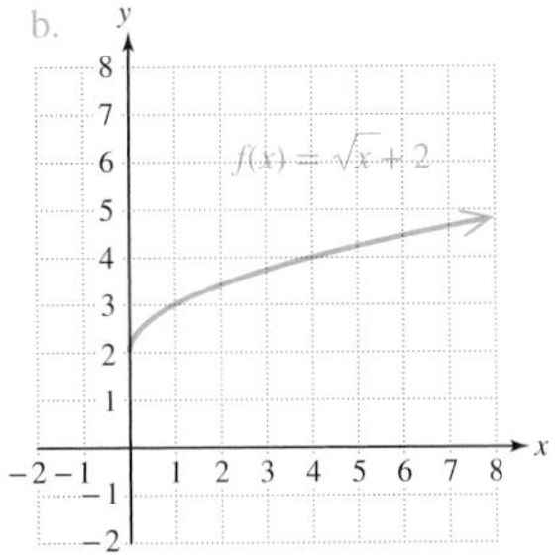

100. $f(x) = \sqrt{x} - 1$

a. $[0, \infty)$

b.

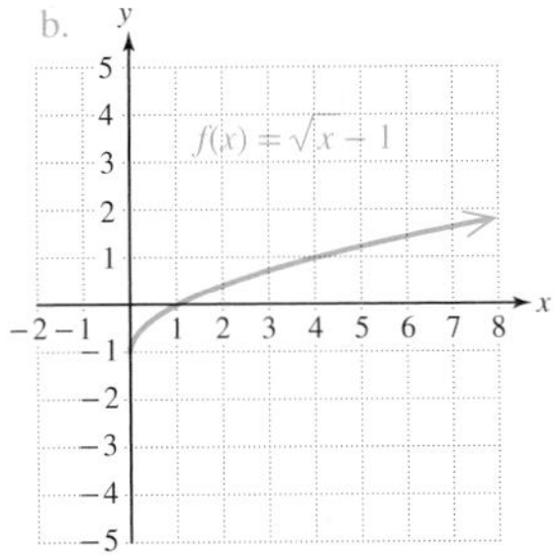

101. $f(x) = \sqrt[3]{x - 1}$

a. $(-\infty, \infty)$

b.

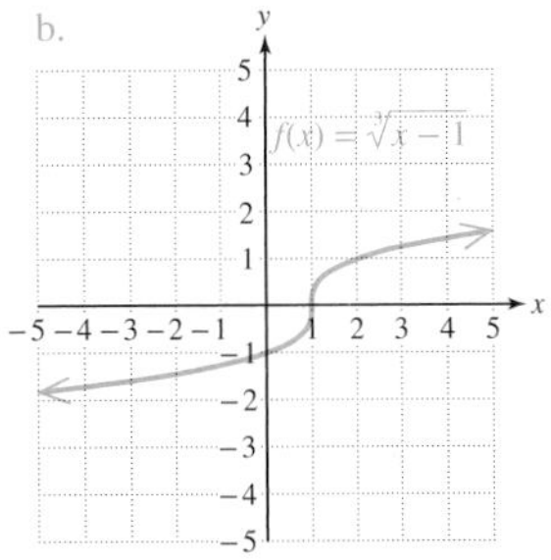

102. $f(x) = \sqrt[3]{x + 2}$

a. $(-\infty, \infty)$

b.

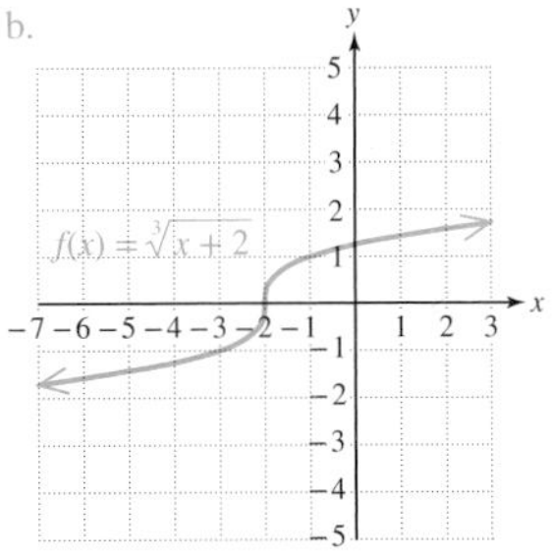

Mixed Exercises

For Exercises 103–106, write the English phrase as an algebraic expression.

103. The sum of q and the square of p $q + p^2$

104. The product of 11 and the cube root of x $11\sqrt[3]{x}$

105. The quotient of 6 and the cube root of x $\frac{6}{\sqrt[3]{x}}$

106. The difference of y and the principal square root of x $y - \sqrt{x}$

107. If a square has an area of 64 in.^{2}, then what are the lengths of the sides? 8 in.

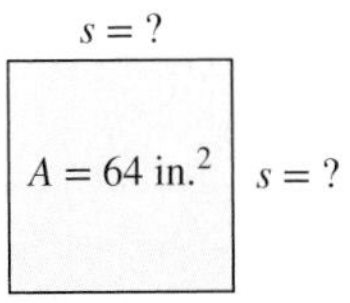

108. If a square has an area of 121 m^2, then what are the lengths of the sides? 11 m

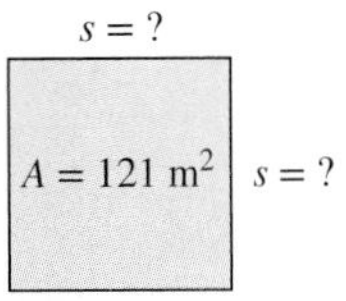

Graphing Calculator Exercises

For Exercises 109–116, use a calculator to evaluate the expressions to four decimal places.

109. $\sqrt{69}$ 8.3066

110. $\sqrt{5798}$ 76.1446

111. $2 + \sqrt[3]{5}$ 3.7100

112. $3 - 2\sqrt[4]{10}$ −0.5566

113. $7\sqrt[4]{25}$ 15.6525

114. $-3\sqrt[3]{9}$ −6.2403

115. $\dfrac{3 - \sqrt{19}}{11}$ −0.1235

116. $\dfrac{5 + 2\sqrt{15}}{12}$ 1.0622

117. Graph $h(x) = \sqrt{x - 2}$. Use the graph to confirm the domain found in Exercise 83.

118. Graph $k(x) = \sqrt{x + 1}$. Use the graph to confirm the domain found in Exercise 84.

119. Graph $g(x) = \sqrt[3]{x - 2}$. Use the graph to confirm the domain found in Exercise 85.

120. Graph $f(x) = \sqrt[3]{x + 1}$. Use the graph to confirm the domain found in Exercise 86.

Section 10.2 Rational Exponents

Concepts

1. Definition of $a^{1/n}$ and $a^{m/n}$
2. Converting Between Rational Exponents and Radical Notation
3. Properties of Rational Exponents
4. Applications Involving Rational Exponents

1. Definition of $a^{1/n}$ and $a^{m/n}$

In this section, the properties for simplifying expressions with integer exponents are expanded to include expressions with rational exponents. We begin by defining expressions of the form $a^{1/n}$.

Definition of $a^{1/n}$

Let a be a real number, and let n be an integer such that $n > 1$. If $\sqrt[n]{a}$ is a real number, then

$$a^{1/n} = \sqrt[n]{a}$$

Classroom Examples: p. 711, Exercises 8, 12, and 16

Example 1 Evaluating Expressions of the Form $a^{1/n}$

Convert the expression to radical form and simplify, if possible.

a. $(-8)^{1/3}$ **b.** $81^{1/4}$ **c.** $-100^{1/2}$ **d.** $(-100)^{1/2}$ **e.** $16^{-1/2}$

Solution:

a. $(-8)^{1/3} = \sqrt[3]{-8} = -2$

b. $81^{1/4} = \sqrt[4]{81} = 3$

c. $-100^{1/2} = -1 \cdot 100^{1/2}$ The exponent applies only to the base of 100.

$= -1\sqrt{100}$

$= -10$

d. $(-100)^{1/2}$ is not a real number because $\sqrt{-100}$ is not a real number.

e. $16^{-1/2} = \dfrac{1}{16^{1/2}}$ Write the expression with a positive exponent. Recall that $b^{-n} = \dfrac{1}{b^n}$.

$= \dfrac{1}{\sqrt{16}}$

$= \dfrac{1}{4}$

Skill Practice Convert the expression to radical form and simplify, if possible.

1. $(-64)^{1/3}$ **2.** $16^{1/4}$ **3.** $-36^{1/2}$ **4.** $(-36)^{1/2}$ **5.** $64^{-1/3}$

If $\sqrt[n]{a}$ is a real number, then we can define an expression of the form $a^{m/n}$ in such a way that the multiplication property of exponents still holds true. For example:

$$16^{3/4} \nearrow (16^{1/4})^3 = (\sqrt[4]{16})^3 = (2)^3 = 8$$

$$16^{3/4} \searrow (16^3)^{1/4} = \sqrt[4]{16^3} = \sqrt[4]{4096} = 8$$

Answers

1. −4 **2.** 2 **3.** −6 **4.** Not a real number **5.** $\frac{1}{4}$

Definition of $a^{m/n}$

Let a be a real number, and let m and n be positive integers such that m and n share no common factors and $n > 1$. If $\sqrt[n]{a}$ is a real number, then

$$a^{m/n} = (a^{1/n})^m = (\sqrt[n]{a})^m \qquad \text{and} \qquad a^{m/n} = (a^m)^{1/n} = \sqrt[n]{a^m}$$

The rational exponent in the expression $a^{m/n}$ is essentially performing two operations. The numerator of the exponent raises the base to the mth power. The denominator takes the nth root.

Example 2 Evaluating Expressions of the Form $a^{m/n}$

Classroom Example: p. 711, Exercise 24

Convert each expression to radical form and simplify.

a. $8^{2/3}$ **b.** $100^{5/2}$ **c.** $\left(\frac{1}{25}\right)^{3/2}$ **d.** $4^{-3/2}$ **e.** $(-81)^{3/4}$

Solution:

a. $8^{2/3} = (\sqrt[3]{8})^2$ Take the cube root of 8 and square the result.

$= (2)^2$ Simplify.

$= 4$

b. $100^{5/2} = (\sqrt{100})^5$ Take the square root of 100 and raise the result to the fifth power.

$= (10)^5$ Simplify.

$= 100{,}000$

c. $\left(\frac{1}{25}\right)^{3/2} = \left(\sqrt{\frac{1}{25}}\right)^3$ Take the square root of $\frac{1}{25}$ and cube the result.

$= \left(\frac{1}{5}\right)^3$ Simplify.

$= \frac{1}{125}$

d. $4^{-3/2} = \left(\frac{1}{4}\right)^{3/2} = \frac{1}{4^{3/2}}$ Write the expression with positive exponents.

$= \frac{1}{(\sqrt{4})^3}$ Take the square root of 4 and cube the result.

$= \frac{1}{2^3}$ Simplify.

$= \frac{1}{8}$

e. $(-81)^{3/4}$ is not a real number because $\sqrt[4]{-81}$ is not a real number.

Calculator Connections

Topic: Evaluating Expressions with Rational Exponents

A calculator can be used to confirm the results of Example 2(a)–2(c).

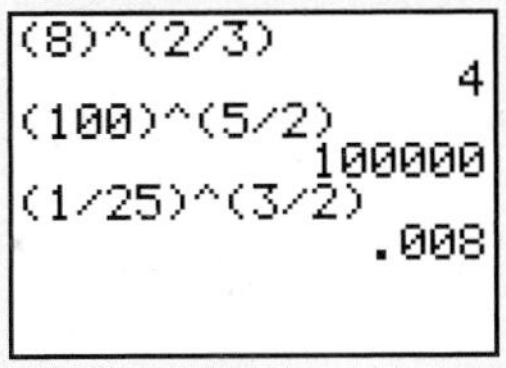

Skill Practice Convert each expression to radical form and simplify.

6. $9^{3/2}$ 7. $8^{5/3}$ 8. $\left(\frac{1}{27}\right)^{4/3}$ 9. $32^{-4/5}$ 10. $(-4)^{3/2}$

2. Converting Between Rational Exponents and Radical Notation

Classroom Examples: p. 711, Exercises 50, 52, and 54

Example 3 Using Radical Notation and Rational Exponents

Convert each expression to radical notation. Assume all variables represent positive real numbers.

a. $a^{3/5}$ b. $5^{1/3}x^{2/3}$ c. $3y^{1/4}$ d. $9z^{-3/4}$

Solution:

a. $a^{3/5} = \sqrt[5]{a^3}$ or $(\sqrt[5]{a})^3$

b. $5^{1/3}x^{2/3} = (5x^2)^{1/3} = \sqrt[3]{5x^2}$

c. $3y^{1/4} = 3\sqrt[4]{y}$ Note that the coefficient 3 is not raised to the $\frac{1}{4}$ power.

d. $9z^{-3/4} = 9 \cdot \dfrac{1}{z^{3/4}} = \dfrac{9}{\sqrt[4]{z^3}}$ Note that the coefficient 9 has an implied exponent of 1, not $-\frac{3}{4}$.

Skill Practice Convert each expression to radical notation. Assume all variables represent positive real numbers.

11. $t^{4/5}$ 12. $2^{1/4}y^{3/4}$ 13. $10p^{1/2}$ 14. $11q^{-2/3}$

Classroom Examples: p. 712, Exercises 60 and 62

Example 4 Using Radical Notation and Rational Exponents

Convert each expression to an equivalent expression by using rational exponents. Assume that all variables represent positive real numbers.

a. $\sqrt[4]{b^3}$ b. $\sqrt{7a}$ c. $7\sqrt{a}$

Solution:

a. $\sqrt[4]{b^3} = b^{3/4}$ b. $\sqrt{7a} = (7a)^{1/2}$ c. $7\sqrt{a} = 7a^{1/2}$

Skill Practice Convert to an equivalent expression using rational exponents. Assume all variables represent positive real numbers.

15. $\sqrt[3]{x^2}$ 16. $\sqrt{5y}$ 17. $5\sqrt{y}$

3. Properties of Rational Exponents

The properties and definitions for simplifying expressions with integer exponents also apply to rational exponents.

Answers

6. 27 7. 32 8. $\frac{1}{81}$
9. $\frac{1}{16}$ 10. Not a real number
11. $\sqrt[5]{t^4}$ 12. $\sqrt[4]{2y^3}$ 13. $10\sqrt{p}$
14. $\dfrac{11}{\sqrt[3]{q^2}}$ 15. $x^{2/3}$ 16. $(5y)^{1/2}$
17. $5y^{1/2}$

Definitions and Properties of Exponents

Let a and b be nonzero real numbers. Let m and n be rational numbers such that a^m, a^n, and b^m are real numbers.

Description	Property	Example
1. Multiplying like bases	$a^m a^n = a^{m+n}$	$x^{1/3}x^{4/3} = x^{5/3}$
2. Dividing like bases	$\frac{a^m}{a^n} = a^{m-n}$	$\frac{x^{3/5}}{x^{1/5}} = x^{2/5}$
3. The power rule	$(a^m)^n = a^{mn}$	$(2^{1/3})^{1/2} = 2^{1/6}$
4. Power of a product	$(ab)^m = a^m b^m$	$(9y)^{1/2} = 9^{1/2}y^{1/2} = 3y^{1/2}$
5. Power of a quotient	$\left(\frac{a}{b}\right)^m = \frac{a^m}{b^m}$	$\left(\frac{4}{25}\right)^{1/2} = \frac{4^{1/2}}{25^{1/2}} = \frac{2}{5}$

Description	Definition	Example
1. Negative exponents	$a^{-m} = \left(\frac{1}{a}\right)^m = \frac{1}{a^m}$	$(8)^{-1/3} = \left(\frac{1}{8}\right)^{1/3} = \frac{1}{2}$
2. Zero exponent	$a^0 = 1$	$5^0 = 1$

Example 5 **Simplifying Expressions with Rational Exponents**

Classroom Examples: p. 712, Exercises 66, 74, and 80

Use the properties of exponents to simplify the expressions. Assume all variables represent positive real numbers.

a. $y^{2/5}y^{3/5}$ **b.** $\frac{6a^{-1/2}}{a^{3/2}}$ **c.** $\left(\frac{s^{1/2}t^{1/3}}{w^{3/4}}\right)^4$

Solution:

a. $y^{2/5}y^{3/5} = y^{(2/5)+(3/5)}$ Multiply like bases by adding exponents.

$= y^{5/5}$ Simplify.

$= y$

b. $\frac{6a^{-1/2}}{a^{3/2}}$

$= 6a^{(-1/2)-(3/2)}$ Divide like bases by subracting exponents.

$= 6a^{-2}$ Simplify: $-\frac{1}{2} - \left(\frac{3}{2}\right) = -\frac{4}{2} = -2$

$= \frac{6}{a^2}$ Simplify the negative exponent.

c. $\left(\frac{s^{1/2}t^{1/3}}{w^{3/4}}\right)^4 = \frac{s^{(1/2)\cdot 4}t^{(1/3)\cdot 4}}{w^{(3/4)\cdot 4}}$ Apply the power rule. Multiply exponents.

$= \frac{s^2t^{4/3}}{w^3}$ Simplify.

Skill Practice Use the properties of exponents to simplify the expressions. Assume all variables represent positive real numbers.

18. $x^{1/2} \cdot x^{3/4}$ **19.** $\frac{4k^{-2/3}}{k^{1/3}}$ **20.** $\left(\frac{a^{1/3}b^{1/2}}{c^{5/8}}\right)^6$

Answers

18. $x^{5/4}$ **19.** $\frac{4}{k}$ **20.** $\frac{a^2b^3}{c^{15/4}}$

4. Applications Involving Rational Exponents

Classroom Example: p. 712, Exercise 90

Example 6 Applying Rational Exponents

Suppose P dollars in principal is invested in an account that earns interest annually. If after t years the investment grows to A dollars, then the annual rate of return r on the investment is given by

$$r = \left(\frac{A}{P}\right)^{1/t} - 1$$

Find the annual rate of return on \$5000 which grew to \$6894.21 after 6 yr.

Solution:

$$r = \left(\frac{A}{P}\right)^{1/t} - 1$$

$$= \left(\frac{6894.21}{5000}\right)^{1/6} - 1 \quad \text{where } A = \$6894.21,\ P = \$5000, \text{ and } t = 6$$

$$\approx 0.055 \text{ or } 5.5\%$$

The annual rate of return is 5.5%.

Skill Practice

21. The formula for the radius of a sphere is

$$r = \left(\frac{3V}{4\pi}\right)^{1/3}$$

where V is the volume. Find the radius of a sphere whose volume is 113.04 in.^{3} (Use 3.14 for π.)

Answer

21. 3 in.

Section 10.2 Practice Exercises

For additional exercises, see Classroom Activities 10.2A–10.2C in the *Student's Resource Manual* at www.mhhe.com/moh.

For the exercises in this set, assume that all variables represent positive real numbers unless otherwise stated.

Vocabulary and Key Concepts

1. **a.** If n is an integer greater than 1, then radical notation for $a^{1/n}$ is ____$\sqrt[n]{a}$____.

   b. Assume that m and n are positive integers that share no common factors and $n > 1$. If $\sqrt[n]{a}$ exists, then in radical notation $a^{m/n} =$ ____$(\sqrt[n]{a})^m$ or $\sqrt[n]{a^m}$____.

   c. The radical notation for $x^{-1/2}$ is ____$\frac{1}{\sqrt{x}}$____.

   d. $8^{1/3} =$ ____2____ and $8^{-1/3} =$ ____. $\frac{1}{2}$

Review Exercises

2. Given $\sqrt[3]{27}$, identify the index and radicand. Index: 3; radicand: 27

For Exercises 3–6, evaluate the radicals.

3. $\sqrt{25}$ 5 **4.** $\sqrt[3]{8}$ 2 **5.** $\sqrt[4]{81}$ 3 **6.** $(\sqrt[4]{16})^3$ 8

Concept 1: Definition of $a^{1/n}$ and $a^{m/n}$

For Exercises 7–18, convert the expressions to radical form and simplify. **(See Example 1.)**

7. $144^{1/2}$ 12 **8.** $16^{1/4}$ 2 **9.** $-144^{1/2}$ −12 **10.** $-16^{1/4}$ −2

11. $(-144)^{1/2}$ Not a real number **12.** $(-16)^{1/4}$ Not a real number **13.** $(-64)^{1/3}$ −4 **14.** $(-32)^{1/5}$ −2

15. $25^{-1/2}$ $\frac{1}{5}$ **16.** $27^{-1/3}$ $\frac{1}{3}$ **17.** $-49^{-1/2}$ $-\frac{1}{7}$ **18.** $-64^{-1/2}$ $-\frac{1}{8}$

19. Explain how to interpret the expression $a^{m/n}$ as a radical. $a^{m/n} = \sqrt[n]{a^m}$; The numerator of the exponent represents the power of the base. The denominator of the exponent represents the index of the radical.

20. Explain why $(\sqrt[3]{8})^4$ is easier to evaluate than $\sqrt[3]{8^4}$.
$(\sqrt[3]{8})^4$ works within the parentheses first. Taking the root first results in a smaller number that must be raised to the fourth power. $\sqrt[3]{8^4}$ takes the fourth power of 8 first. This results in a larger number whose cube root may be difficult to identify.

For Exercises 21–24, simplify the expression, if possible. **(See Example 2.)**

21. a. $16^{3/4}$ 8
b. $-16^{3/4}$ −8
c. $(-16)^{3/4}$ Not a real number
d. $16^{-3/4}$ $\frac{1}{8}$
e. $-16^{-3/4}$ $-\frac{1}{8}$
f. $(-16)^{-3/4}$ Not a real number

22. a. $81^{3/4}$ 27
b. $-81^{3/4}$ −27
c. $(-81)^{3/4}$ Not a real number
d. $81^{-3/4}$ $\frac{1}{27}$
e. $-81^{-3/4}$ $-\frac{1}{27}$
f. $(-81)^{-3/4}$ Not a real number

23. a. $25^{3/2}$ 125
b. $-25^{3/2}$ −125
c. $(-25)^{3/2}$ Not a real number
d. $25^{-3/2}$ $\frac{1}{125}$
e. $-25^{-3/2}$ $-\frac{1}{125}$
f. $(-25)^{-3/2}$ Not a real number

24. a. $4^{3/2}$ 8
b. $-4^{3/2}$ −8
c. $(-4)^{3/2}$ Not a real number
d. $4^{-3/2}$ $\frac{1}{8}$
e. $-4^{-3/2}$ $-\frac{1}{8}$
f. $(-4)^{-3/2}$ Not a real number

For Exercises 25–48, simplify the expression. **(See Example 2.)**

25. $64^{-3/2}$ $\frac{1}{512}$ **26.** $81^{-3/2}$ $\frac{1}{729}$ **27.** $243^{3/5}$ 27 **28.** $1^{5/3}$ 1

29. $-27^{-4/3}$ $-\frac{1}{81}$ **30.** $-16^{-5/4}$ $-\frac{1}{32}$ **31.** $\left(\frac{100}{9}\right)^{-3/2}$ $\frac{27}{1000}$ **32.** $\left(\frac{49}{100}\right)^{-1/2}$ $\frac{10}{7}$

33. $(-4)^{-3/2}$ Not a real number **34.** $(-49)^{-3/2}$ Not a real number **35.** $(-8)^{1/3}$ −2 **36.** $(-9)^{1/2}$ Not a real number

37. $-8^{1/3}$ −2 **38.** $-9^{1/2}$ −3 **39.** $\frac{1}{36^{-1/2}}$ 6 **40.** $\frac{1}{16^{-1/2}}$ 4

41. $\frac{1}{1000^{-1/3}}$ 10 **42.** $\frac{1}{81^{-3/4}}$ 27 **43.** $\left(\frac{1}{8}\right)^{2/3} + \left(\frac{1}{4}\right)^{1/2}$ $\frac{3}{4}$ **44.** $\left(\frac{1}{8}\right)^{-2/3} + \left(\frac{1}{4}\right)^{-1/2}$ 6

45. $\left(\frac{1}{16}\right)^{-3/4} - \left(\frac{1}{49}\right)^{-1/2}$ 1 **46.** $\left(\frac{1}{16}\right)^{1/4} - \left(\frac{1}{49}\right)^{1/2}$ $\frac{5}{14}$ **47.** $\left(\frac{1}{4}\right)^{1/2} + \left(\frac{1}{64}\right)^{-1/3}$ $\frac{9}{2}$ **48.** $\left(\frac{1}{36}\right)^{1/2} + \left(\frac{1}{64}\right)^{-5/6}$ $\frac{193}{6}$

Concept 2: Converting Between Rational Exponents and Radical Notation

For Exercises 49–56, convert each expression to radical notation. **(See Example 3.)**

49. $q^{2/3}$ $\sqrt[3]{q^2}$ **50.** $t^{3/5}$ $\sqrt[5]{t^3}$ **51.** $6y^{3/4}$ $6\sqrt[4]{y^3}$ **52.** $8b^{4/9}$ $8\sqrt[9]{b^4}$

53. $x^{2/3}y^{1/3}$ $\sqrt[3]{x^2y}$ **54.** $c^{2/5}d^{3/5}$ $\sqrt[5]{c^2d^3}$ **55.** $6r^{-2/5}$ $\frac{6}{\sqrt[5]{r^2}}$ **56.** $7x^{-3/4}$ $\frac{7}{\sqrt[4]{x^3}}$

For Exercises 57–64, write each expression by using rational exponents rather than radical notation. **(See Example 4.)**

57. $\sqrt[3]{x}$ $x^{1/3}$ **58.** $\sqrt[4]{a}$ $a^{1/4}$ **59.** $10\sqrt{b}$ $10b^{1/2}$ **60.** $-2\sqrt[3]{t}$ $-2t^{1/3}$

61. $\sqrt[3]{y^2}$ $y^{2/3}$ **62.** $\sqrt[6]{z^5}$ $z^{5/6}$ **63.** $\sqrt[4]{a^2b^3}$ $(a^2b^3)^{1/4}$ **64.** $\sqrt{abc}$ $(abc)^{1/2}$

Concept 3: Properties of Rational Exponents

For Exercises 65–88, simplify the expressions by using the properties of rational exponents. Write the final answers using positive exponents only. **(See Example 5.)**

65. $x^{1/4}x^{-5/4}$ $\frac{1}{x}$ **66.** $2^{2/3}2^{-5/3}$ $\frac{1}{2}$ **67.** $\frac{p^{5/3}}{p^{2/3}}$ p **68.** $\frac{q^{5/4}}{q^{1/4}}$ q

69. $(y^{1/5})^{10}$ y^2 **70.** $(x^{1/2})^8$ x^4 **71.** $6^{-1/5}6^{3/5}$ $6^{2/5}$ **72.** $a^{-1/3}a^{2/3}$ $a^{1/3}$

73. $\frac{4t^{-1/3}}{t^{4/3}}$ $\frac{4}{t^{5/3}}$ **74.** $\frac{5s^{-1/3}}{s^{5/3}}$ $\frac{5}{s^2}$ **75.** $(a^{1/3}a^{1/4})^{12}$ a^7 **76.** $(x^{2/3}x^{1/2})^6$ x^7

77. $(5a^2c^{-1/2}d^{1/2})^2$ $\frac{25a^4d}{c}$ **78.** $(2x^{-1/3}y^2z^{5/3})^3$ $\frac{8y^6z^5}{x}$ **79.** $\left(\frac{x^{-2/3}}{y^{-3/4}}\right)^{12}$ $\frac{y^9}{x^8}$ **80.** $\left(\frac{m^{-1/4}}{n^{-1/2}}\right)^{-4}$ $\frac{m}{n^2}$

81. $\left(\frac{16w^{-2}z}{2wz^{-8}}\right)^{1/3}$ $\frac{2z^3}{w}$ **82.** $\left(\frac{50p^{-1}q}{2pq^{-3}}\right)^{1/2}$ $\frac{5q^2}{p}$ **83.** $(25x^2y^4z^6)^{1/2}$ $5xy^2z^3$ **84.** $(8a^6b^3c^9)^{2/3}$ $4a^4b^2c^6$

85. $(x^2y^{-1/3})^6(x^{1/2}yz^{2/3})^2$ $x^{13}z^{4/3}$ **86.** $(a^{-1/3}b^{1/2})^4(a^{-1/2}b^{3/5})^{10}$ $\frac{b^8}{a^{19/3}}$ **87.** $\left(\frac{x^{3m}y^{2m}}{z^{5m}}\right)^{1/m}$ $\frac{x^3y^2}{z^5}$ **88.** $\left(\frac{a^{4n}b^{3n}}{c^n}\right)^{1/n}$ $\frac{a^4b^3}{c}$

Concept 4: Applications Involving Rational Exponents

89. If P dollars in principal grows to A dollars after t years with annual interest, then the interest rate r is given by $r = \left(\frac{A}{P}\right)^{1/t} - 1$. **(See Example 6.)**

a. In one account, \$10,000 grows to \$16,802 after 5 yr. Compute the interest rate. Round your answer to a tenth of a percent. 10.9%

b. In another account \$10,000 grows to \$18,000 after 7 yr. Compute the interest rate. Round your answer to a tenth of a percent. 8.8%

c. Which account produced a higher average yearly return? The account in part (a).

90. If the area A of a square is known, then the length of its sides, s, can be computed by the formula $s = A^{1/2}$.

a. Compute the length of the sides of a square having an area of 100 in.^{2} 10 in.

b. Compute the length of the sides of a square having an area of 72 in.^{2} Round your answer to the nearest 0.1 in. 8.5 in.

91. The radius r of a sphere of volume V is given by $r = \left(\frac{3V}{4\pi}\right)^{1/3}$. Find the radius of a sphere having a volume of 85 in.^{3} Round your answer to the nearest 0.1 in. 2.7 in.

92. Is $(a + b)^{1/2}$ the same as $a^{1/2} + b^{1/2}$? If not, give a counterexample. Not the same. For example: $(9 + 16)^{1/2} = (25)^{1/2} = 5$
$9^{1/2} + 16^{1/2} = 3 + 4 = 7$

Expanding Your Skills

For Exercises 93–104, write the expression using rational exponents. Then simplify and convert back to radical notation.

Example: $\sqrt[15]{x^{10}} \xrightarrow[\text{exponents}]{\text{Rational}} x^{10/15} \xrightarrow{\text{Simplify}} x^{2/3} \xrightarrow[\text{notation}]{\text{Radical}} \sqrt[3]{x^2}$

93. $\sqrt[6]{y^3}$ $\sqrt{y}$ **94.** $\sqrt[4]{w^2}$ $\sqrt{w}$ **95.** $\sqrt[12]{z^3}$ $\sqrt[4]{z}$ **96.** $\sqrt[18]{t^3}$ $\sqrt[6]{t}$

97. $\sqrt[9]{x^6}$ $\sqrt[3]{x^2}$ **98.** $\sqrt[12]{p^9}$ $\sqrt[4]{p^3}$ **99.** $\sqrt[6]{x^3y^6}$ $y\sqrt{x}$ **100.** $\sqrt[8]{m^2p^8}$ $p\sqrt[4]{m}$

101. $\sqrt{16x^8y^6}$ $4x^4y^3$ **102.** $\sqrt{81a^{12}b^{20}}$ $9a^6b^{10}$ **103.** $\sqrt[3]{8x^3y^2z}$ $2x\sqrt[3]{y^2z}$ **104.** $\sqrt[3]{64m^2n^3p}$ $4n\sqrt[3]{m^2p}$

For Exercises 105–108, write the expression as a single radical.

105. $\sqrt{\sqrt[3]{x}}$ $\sqrt[6]{x}$ **106.** $\sqrt[3]{\sqrt{x}}$ $\sqrt[6]{x}$ **107.** $\sqrt[5]{\sqrt[3]{w}}$ $\sqrt[15]{w}$ **108.** $\sqrt[3]{\sqrt[4]{w}}$ $\sqrt[12]{w}$

For Exercises 109–116, use a calculator to approximate the expressions. Round to four decimal places, if necessary.

109. $9^{1/2}$ 3 **110.** $125^{-1/3}$ 0.2 **111.** $50^{-1/4}$ 0.3761 **112.** $(172)^{3/5}$ 21.9441

113. $\sqrt[3]{5^2}$ 2.9240 **114.** $\sqrt[4]{6^3}$ 3.8337 **115.** $\sqrt{10^3}$ 31.6228 **116.** $\sqrt[3]{16}$ 2.5198

Simplifying Radical Expressions

Section 10.3

Concepts

1. Multiplication Property of Radicals
2. Simplifying Radicals by Using the Multiplication Property of Radicals
3. Simplifying Radicals by Using the Order of Operations

1. Multiplication Property of Radicals

You may have already noticed certain properties of radicals involving a product or quotient.

> **Multiplication Property of Radicals**
>
> Let a and b represent real numbers such that $\sqrt[n]{a}$ and $\sqrt[n]{b}$ are both real. Then
>
> $$\sqrt[n]{ab} = \sqrt[n]{a} \cdot \sqrt[n]{b}$$

The multiplication property of radicals follows from the property of rational exponents.

$$\sqrt[n]{ab} = (ab)^{1/n} = a^{1/n}b^{1/n} = \sqrt[n]{a} \cdot \sqrt[n]{b}$$

The multiplication property of radicals indicates that a product within a radicand can be written as a product of radicals, provided the roots are real numbers. For example:

$$\sqrt{144} = \sqrt{16} \cdot \sqrt{9}$$

The reverse process is also true. A product of radicals can be written as a single radical provided the roots are real numbers and they have the same indices.

$$\sqrt{3} \cdot \sqrt{12} = \sqrt{36}$$

2. Simplifying Radicals by Using the Multiplication Property of Radicals

In algebra, it is customary to simplify radical expressions.

Simplified Form of a Radical

Consider any radical expression where the radicand is written as a product of prime factors. The expression is in *simplified form* if all the following conditions are met:

1. The radicand has no factor raised to a power greater than or equal to the index.
2. The radicand does not contain a fraction.
3. There are no radicals in the denominator of a fraction.

For example, the following radicals are not simplified.

1. The expression $\sqrt[3]{x^5}$ fails condition 1.
2. The expression $\sqrt{\frac{1}{4}}$ fails condition 2.
3. The expression $\frac{1}{\sqrt[3]{8}}$ fails condition 3.

The expressions $\sqrt{x^2}$, $\sqrt{x^4}$, $\sqrt{x^6}$, and $\sqrt{x^8}$ are not simplified because they fail condition 1 (the exponents are not less than the index). However, each radicand is a perfect square and is easily simplified for $x \geq 0$.

$$\sqrt{x^2} = x$$
$$\sqrt{x^4} = x^2$$
$$\sqrt{x^6} = x^3$$
$$\sqrt{x^8} = x^4$$

However, how is an expression such as $\sqrt{x^9}$ simplified? This and many other radical expressions are simplified by using the multiplication property of radicals. We demonstrate the process in Examples 1–4.

Classroom Example: p. 718, Exercise 10

Example 1 **Using the Multiplication Property to Simplify a Radical Expression**

Simplify the expression assuming that $x \geq 0$. $\sqrt{x^9}$

Solution:

The expression $\sqrt{x^9}$ is equivalent to $\sqrt{x^8 \cdot x}$.

$\sqrt{x^9} = \sqrt{x^8 \cdot x}$

$= \sqrt{x^8} \cdot \sqrt{x}$ Apply the multiplication property of radicals.

Note that x^8 is a perfect square because $x^8 = (x^4)^2$.

$= x^4\sqrt{x}$ Simplify.

Instructor Note: Try giving students a visual representation of simplifying a radical.

$\sqrt{x^9}$

$= \sqrt{(x \cdot x) \cdot (x \cdot x) \cdot (x \cdot x) \cdot (x \cdot x) \cdot x}$

$= x^4\sqrt{x}$

Skill Practice Simplify the expression. Assume $a \geq 0$.

1. $\sqrt{a^{11}}$

Answer

1. $a^5\sqrt{a}$

In Example 1, the expression x^9 is not a perfect square. Therefore, to simplify $\sqrt{x^9}$, it was necessary to write the expression as the product of the largest perfect square and a remaining or "left-over" factor: $\sqrt{x^9} = \sqrt{x^8 \cdot x}$. This process also applies to simplifying nth roots, as shown in Example 2.

Example 2 Using the Multiplication Property to Simplify Radical Expressions

Classroom Examples: p. 718, Exercises 14 and 16

Simplify each expression. Assume all variables represent positive real numbers.

a. $\sqrt[4]{b^7}$ **b.** $\sqrt[3]{w^7z^9}$

Solution:

The goal is to rewrite each radicand as the product of the greatest perfect square (perfect cube, perfect fourth power, and so on) and a leftover factor.

a. $\sqrt[4]{b^7} = \sqrt[4]{b^4 \cdot b^3}$ b^4 is the greatest perfect fourth power in the radicand.

$= \sqrt[4]{b^4} \cdot \sqrt[4]{b^3}$ Apply the multiplication property of radicals.

$= b\sqrt[4]{b^3}$ Simplify.

b. $\sqrt[3]{w^7z^9} = \sqrt[3]{(w^6z^9) \cdot (w)}$ w^6z^9 is the greatest perfect cube in the radicand.

$= \sqrt[3]{w^6z^9} \cdot \sqrt[3]{w}$ Apply the multiplication property of radicals.

$= w^2z^3\sqrt[3]{w}$ Simplify.

Skill Practice Simplify the expressions. Assume all variables represent positive real numbers.

2. $\sqrt[4]{v^{25}}$ **3.** $\sqrt[3]{p^{17}q^{10}}$

Each expression in Example 2 involves a radicand that is a product of variable factors. If a numerical factor is present, sometimes it is necessary to factor the coefficient before simplifying the radical.

Example 3 Using the Multiplication Property to Simplify a Radical

Classroom Example: p. 718, Exercise 18

Simplify the expression. $\sqrt{56}$

Solution:

$\sqrt{56} = \sqrt{2^3 \cdot 7}$ Factor the radicand.

$$\begin{array}{r|l} 2 & 56 \\ 2 & 28 \\ 2 & 14 \\ & 7 \end{array}$$

$= \sqrt{(2^2) \cdot (2 \cdot 7)}$ 2^2 is the greatest perfect square in the radicand.

$= \sqrt{2^2} \cdot \sqrt{2 \cdot 7}$ Apply the multiplication property of radicals.

$= 2\sqrt{14}$ Simplify.

TIP: It may be easier to visualize the greatest perfect square factor within the radicand as follows:

$$\sqrt{56} = \sqrt{4 \cdot 14} = \sqrt{4} \cdot \sqrt{14} = 2\sqrt{14}$$

Skill Practice Simplify.

4. $\sqrt{24}$

Answers

2. $v^6\sqrt[4]{v}$ **3.** $p^5q^3\sqrt[3]{p^2q}$ **4.** $2\sqrt{6}$

Calculator Connections

Topic: Verifying a Simplified Radical

A calculator can be used to support the solution to Example 3. The decimal approximation for $\sqrt{56}$ and $2\sqrt{14}$ agree for the first 10 digits. This in itself does not make $\sqrt{56} = 2\sqrt{14}$. It is the multiplication property of radicals that guarantees that the expressions are equal.

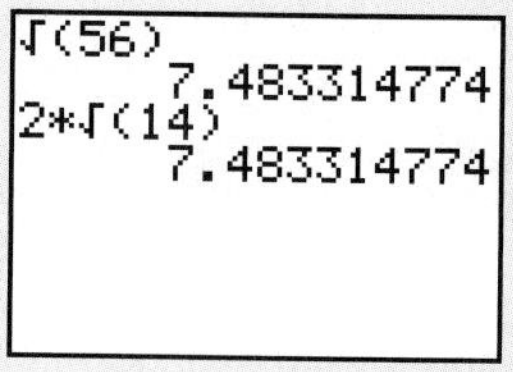

Classroom Example: p. 718, Exercise 22

TIP: The radical can also be simplified as:

$$6\sqrt{50} = 6\sqrt{25 \cdot 2}$$
$$= 6\sqrt{25} \cdot \sqrt{2}$$
$$= 6 \cdot 5\sqrt{2}$$
$$= 30\sqrt{2}$$

Example 4 Using the Multiplication Property to Simplify Radicals

Simplify. $6\sqrt{50}$

Solution:

$6\sqrt{50} = 6\sqrt{5^2 \cdot 2}$ Factor the radicand.

$= 6 \cdot \sqrt{5^2} \cdot \sqrt{2}$ Apply the multiplication property of radicals.

$= 6 \cdot 5 \cdot \sqrt{2}$ Simplify.

$= 30\sqrt{2}$ Simplify.

Skill Practice Simplify.

5. $5\sqrt{18}$

Classroom Example: p. 718, Exercise 32

TIP: In Example 5, the numerical coefficient within the radicand can be written $8 \cdot 5$ because 8 is the greatest perfect cube factor of 40:

$$\sqrt[3]{40x^3y^5z^7} = \sqrt[3]{8 \cdot 5x^3y^5z^7}$$
$$= \sqrt[3]{(8x^3y^3z^6)(5y^2z)}$$
$$= \sqrt[3]{8x^3y^3z^6} \cdot \sqrt[3]{5y^2z}$$
$$= 2xyz^2 \cdot \sqrt[3]{5y^2z}$$

Example 5 Using the Multiplication Property to Simplify Radicals

Simplify the expression. Assume that x, y, and z represent positive real numbers.

$\sqrt[3]{40x^3y^5z^7}$

Solution:

$\sqrt[3]{40x^3y^5z^7}$

$= \sqrt[3]{2^3 5x^3y^5z^7}$ Factor the radicand.

$= \sqrt[3]{(2^3x^3y^3z^6) \cdot (5y^2z)}$ $2^3x^3y^3z^6$ is the greatest perfect cube.

$= \sqrt[3]{2^3x^3y^3z^6} \cdot \sqrt[3]{5y^2z}$ Apply the multiplication property of radicals.

$= 2xyz^2\sqrt[3]{5y^2z}$ Simplify.

$$\begin{array}{r|l} 2 & 40 \\ 2 & 20 \\ 2 & 10 \\ & 5 \end{array}$$

Skill Practice Simplify. Assume that $a > 0$ and $b > 0$.

6. $\sqrt[4]{32a^{10}b^{19}}$

3. Simplifying Radicals by Using the Order of Operations

Often a radical can be simplified by applying the order of operations. In Example 6, the first step will be to simplify the expression within the radicand.

Answers

5. $15\sqrt{2}$ **6.** $2a^2b^4\sqrt[4]{2a^2b^3}$

Example 6 Using the Order of Operations to Simplify Radicals

Classroom Examples: p. 719, Exercises 36 and 40

Use the order of operations to simplify the expressions. Assume $a > 0$.

a. $\sqrt{\dfrac{a^7}{a^3}}$ **b.** $\sqrt[3]{\dfrac{3}{81}}$

Solution:

a. $\sqrt{\dfrac{a^7}{a^3}}$ The radicand contains a fraction. However, the fraction can be reduced to lowest terms.

$= \sqrt{a^4}$

$= a^2$ Simplify the radical.

b. $\sqrt[3]{\dfrac{3}{81}}$ The radical contains a fraction that can be simplified.

$= \sqrt[3]{\dfrac{1}{27}}$ Reduce to lowest terms.

$= \dfrac{1}{3}$ Simplify.

Skill Practice Use the order of operations to simplify the expressions. Assume $v > 0$.

7. $\sqrt{\dfrac{v^{21}}{v^5}}$ **8.** $\sqrt[5]{\dfrac{64}{2}}$

Example 7 Simplifying a Radical Expression

Classroom Example: p. 719, Exercise 42

Simplify. $\dfrac{7\sqrt{50}}{10}$

Solution:

$\dfrac{7\sqrt{50}}{10} = \dfrac{7\sqrt{25 \cdot 2}}{10}$ 25 is the greatest perfect square in the radicand.

$= \dfrac{7 \cdot 5\sqrt{2}}{10}$ Simplify the radical.

$= \dfrac{7 \cdot \overset{1}{\cancel{5}}\sqrt{2}}{\underset{2}{\cancel{10}}}$ Simplify the fraction to lowest terms.

$= \dfrac{7\sqrt{2}}{2}$

Avoiding Mistakes

The expression $\frac{7\sqrt{2}}{2}$ cannot be simplified further because one factor of 2 is in the radicand and the other is outside the radical.

Skill Practice Simplify.

9. $\dfrac{2\sqrt{300}}{30}$

Answers

7. v^8 **8.** 2 **9.** $\dfrac{2\sqrt{3}}{3}$

Section 10.3 Practice Exercises

Study Skills Exercise

For additional exercises, see Classroom Activities 10.3A–10.3B in the *Student's Resource Manual* at www.mhhe.com/moh.

The final exam is just around the corner. Your old tests and quizzes provide good material to study for the final exam. Use your old tests to make a list of the concepts on which you need to concentrate. Ask your professor for help if there are still concepts that you do not understand.

For the exercises in this set, assume that all variables represent positive real numbers unless otherwise stated.

Vocabulary and Key Concepts

1. **a.** The multiplication property of radicals indicates that if $\sqrt[n]{a}$ and $\sqrt[n]{b}$ are real numbers, then $\sqrt[n]{ab}$ = ___$\sqrt[n]{a}$___ · ___$\sqrt[n]{b}$___.

   b. Explain why the following radical is not in simplified form. $\sqrt{x^3}$
   The exponent within the radicand is greater than the index.

   c. The radical expression $\sqrt[3]{x^{10}}$ (is/is not) in simplified form. is not

   d. The radical expression $\sqrt{18}$ simplifies to __$\sqrt{2}$. 3

   e. To simplify the radical expression $\sqrt[3]{t^{14}}$ the radicand is rewritten as $\sqrt[3]{\_\_ \cdot t^2}$. t^{12}

   f. On a calculator, $\sqrt{2}$ is given as 1.414213562. Is this decimal number the exact value of $\sqrt{2}$?
   No. $\sqrt{2}$ is an irrational number and the decimal form is a nonterminating, nonrepeating decimal.

Review Exercises

For Exercises 2–4, simplify the expression. Write the answer with positive exponents only.

2. $(a^2b^{-4})^{1/2}\left(\dfrac{a}{b^{-3}}\right)$ a^2b

3. $\left(\dfrac{p^4}{q^{-6}}\right)^{-1/2} \cdot (p^3q^{-2})$ $\dfrac{p}{q^5}$

4. $(x^{1/3}y^{5/6})^{-6}$ $\dfrac{1}{x^2y^5}$

5. Write $x^{4/7}$ in radical notation. $\sqrt[7]{x^4}$

6. Write $y^{2/5}$ in radical notation. $\sqrt[5]{y^2}$

7. Write $\sqrt{y^9}$ by using rational exponents. $y^{9/2}$

8. Write $\sqrt[3]{x^2}$ by using rational exponents. $x^{2/3}$

Concept 2: Simplifying Radicals by Using the Multiplication Property of Radicals

For Exercises 9–32, simplify the radicals. **(See Examples 1–5.)**

9. $\sqrt{x^5}$ $x^2\sqrt{x}$

10. $\sqrt{p^{15}}$ $p^7\sqrt{p}$

11. $\sqrt[3]{q^7}$ $q^2\sqrt[3]{q}$

12. $\sqrt[3]{r^{17}}$ $r^5\sqrt[3]{r^2}$

13. $\sqrt{a^5b^4}$ $a^2b^2\sqrt{a}$

14. $\sqrt{c^9d^6}$ $c^4d^3\sqrt{c}$

15. $-\sqrt[4]{x^8y^{13}}$ $-x^2y^3\sqrt[4]{y}$

16. $-\sqrt[4]{p^{16}q^{17}}$ $-p^4q^4\sqrt[4]{q}$

17. $\sqrt{28}$ $2\sqrt{7}$

18. $\sqrt{63}$ $3\sqrt{7}$

19. $\sqrt{20}$ $2\sqrt{5}$

20. $\sqrt{50}$ $5\sqrt{2}$

21. $5\sqrt{18}$ $15\sqrt{2}$

22. $2\sqrt{24}$ $4\sqrt{6}$

23. $\sqrt[3]{54}$ $3\sqrt[3]{2}$

24. $\sqrt[3]{250}$ $5\sqrt[3]{2}$

25. $\sqrt{25ab^3}$ $5b\sqrt{ab}$

26. $\sqrt{64m^5n^{20}}$ $8m^2n^{10}\sqrt{m}$

27. $\sqrt[3]{40x^7}$ $2x^2\sqrt[3]{5x}$

28. $\sqrt[3]{81y^{17}}$ $3y^5\sqrt[3]{3y^2}$

29. $\sqrt[3]{-16x^6yz^3}$ $-2x^2z\sqrt[3]{2y}$

30. $\sqrt[3]{-192a^6bc^2}$ $-4a^2\sqrt[3]{3bc^2}$

31. $\sqrt[4]{80w^4z^7}$ $2wz\sqrt[4]{5z^3}$

32. $\sqrt[4]{32p^8qr^5}$ $2p^2r\sqrt[4]{2qr}$

Concept 3: Simplifying Radicals by Using the Order of Operations

For Exercises 33–44, simplify the radical expressions. **(See Examples 6–7.)**

33. $\sqrt{\dfrac{x^3}{x}}$ x

34. $\sqrt{\dfrac{y^5}{y}}$ y^2

35. $\sqrt{\dfrac{p^7}{p^3}}$ p^2

36. $\sqrt{\dfrac{q^{11}}{q^5}}$ q^3

37. $\sqrt{\dfrac{50}{2}}$ 5

38. $\sqrt{\dfrac{98}{2}}$ 7

39. $\sqrt[3]{\dfrac{3}{24}}$ $\dfrac{1}{2}$

40. $\sqrt[3]{\dfrac{2}{250}}$ $\dfrac{1}{5}$

41. $\dfrac{5\sqrt[3]{16}}{6}$ $\dfrac{5\sqrt[3]{2}}{3}$

42. $\dfrac{7\sqrt{18}}{9}$ $\dfrac{7\sqrt{2}}{3}$

43. $\dfrac{5\sqrt[3]{72}}{12}$ $\dfrac{5\sqrt[3]{9}}{6}$

44. $\dfrac{3\sqrt[3]{250}}{10}$ $\dfrac{3\sqrt[3]{2}}{2}$

Mixed Exercises

For Exercises 45–72, simplify the radical expressions.

45. $\sqrt{80}$ $4\sqrt{5}$

46. $\sqrt{108}$ $6\sqrt{3}$

47. $-6\sqrt{75}$ $-30\sqrt{3}$

48. $-8\sqrt{8}$ $-16\sqrt{2}$

49. $\sqrt{25x^4y^3}$ $5x^2y\sqrt{y}$

50. $\sqrt{125p^3q^2}$ $5pq\sqrt{5p}$

51. $\sqrt[3]{27x^2y^3z^4}$ $3yz\sqrt[3]{x^2z}$

52. $\sqrt[3]{108a^3bc^2}$ $3a\sqrt[3]{4bc^2}$

53. $\sqrt{\dfrac{12w^5}{3w}}$ $2w^2$

54. $\sqrt{\dfrac{64x^9}{4x^3}}$ $4x^3$

55. $\sqrt{\dfrac{3y^3}{300y^{15}}}$ $\dfrac{1}{10y^6}$

56. $\sqrt{\dfrac{4h}{100h^5}}$ $\dfrac{1}{5h^2}$

57. $\sqrt[3]{\dfrac{16a^2b}{2a^2b^4}}$ $\dfrac{2}{b}$

58. $\sqrt[3]{\dfrac{-27a^4}{8a}}$ $-\dfrac{3a}{2}$

59. $\sqrt{2^3a^{14}b^8c^{31}d^{22}}$ $2a^7b^4c^{15}d^{11}\sqrt{2c}$

60. $\sqrt{7^5u^{12}v^{20}w^{65}x^{80}}$ $49u^6v^{10}w^{32}x^{40}\sqrt{7w}$

61. $\sqrt[3]{54a^6b^4}$ $3a^2b\sqrt[3]{2b}$

62. $\sqrt[3]{72m^5n^3}$ $2mn\sqrt[3]{9m^2}$

63. $-5a\sqrt{12a^3b^4c}$ $-10a^2b^2\sqrt{3ac}$

64. $-7y\sqrt{75xy^5z^6}$ $-35y^3z^3\sqrt{3xy}$

65. $\sqrt[4]{7x^5y}$ $x\sqrt[4]{7xy}$

66. $\sqrt[4]{10cd^7}$ $d\sqrt[4]{10cd^3}$

67. $\sqrt{54a^4b^2}$ $3a^2b\sqrt{6}$

68. $\sqrt{48r^6s^2}$ $4r^3s\sqrt{3}$

69. $\dfrac{2\sqrt{27}}{3}$ $2\sqrt{3}$

70. $\dfrac{7\sqrt{24}}{2}$ $7\sqrt{6}$

71. $\dfrac{3\sqrt{125}}{20}$ $\dfrac{3\sqrt{5}}{4}$

72. $\dfrac{10\sqrt{63}}{12}$ $\dfrac{5\sqrt{7}}{2}$

For Exercises 73–76, write a mathematical expression for the English phrase and simplify.

73. The quotient of 1 and the cube root of w^6
$\dfrac{1}{\sqrt[3]{w^6}}$ simplifies to $\dfrac{1}{w^2}$

74. The principal square root of the quotient of h^2 and 49
$\sqrt{\dfrac{h^2}{49}}$ simplifies to $\dfrac{h}{7}$

75. The principal square root of the quantity k raised to the third power $\sqrt{k^3}$ simplifies to $k\sqrt{k}$

76. The cube root of $2x^4$
$\sqrt[3]{2x^4}$ simplifies to $x\sqrt[3]{2x}$

For Exercises 77–80, determine the length of the third side of the right triangle. Write the answer as a simplified radical.

77.

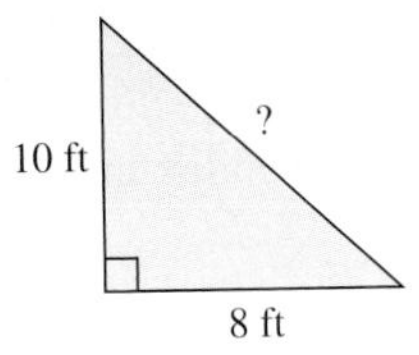

$2\sqrt{41}$ ft

78.

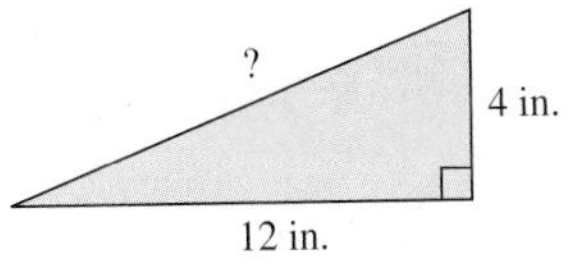

$4\sqrt{10}$ in.

79.

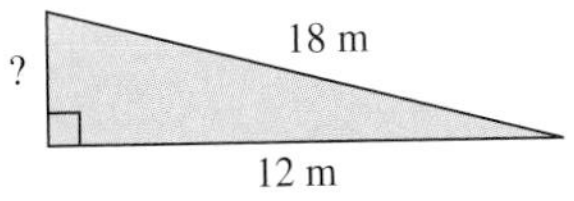

$6\sqrt{5}$ m

80.

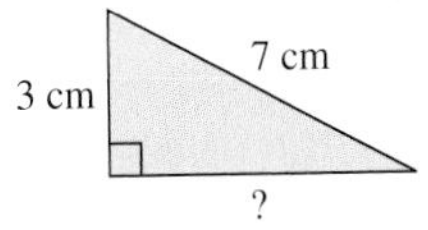

$2\sqrt{10}$ cm

81. On a baseball diamond, the bases are 90 ft apart. Find the exact distance from home plate to second base. Then round to the nearest tenth of a foot.

The distance is $90\sqrt{2}$ ft or approximately 127.3 ft.

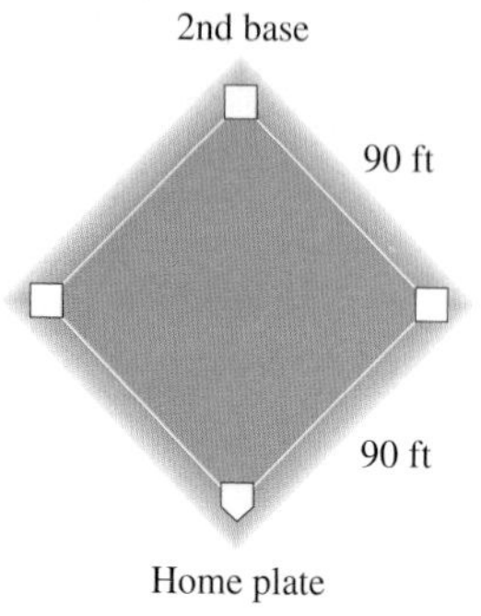

82. Linda is at the beach flying a kite. The kite is directly over a sand castle 60 ft away from Linda. If 100 ft of kite string is out (ignoring any sag in the string), how high is the kite? (Assume that Linda is 5 ft tall.) See figure.

The kite is 85 ft high.

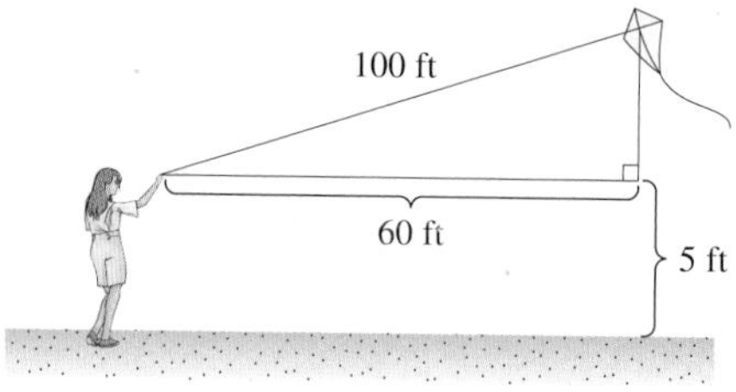

Expanding Your Skills

83. Tom has to travel from town A to town C across a small mountain range. He can travel one of two routes. He can travel on a four-lane highway from A to B and then from B to C at an average speed of 55 mph. Or he can travel on a two-lane road directly from town A to town C, but his average speed will be only 35 mph. If Tom is in a hurry, which route will take him to town C faster?

The path from A to B and B to C is faster.

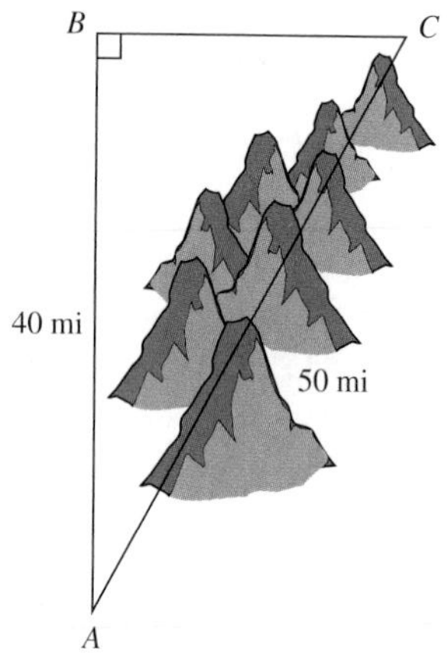

84. One side of a rectangular pasture is 80 ft in length. The diagonal distance is 110 yd. If fencing costs \$3.29 per foot, how much will it cost to fence the pasture?

It will cost approximately \$2633.

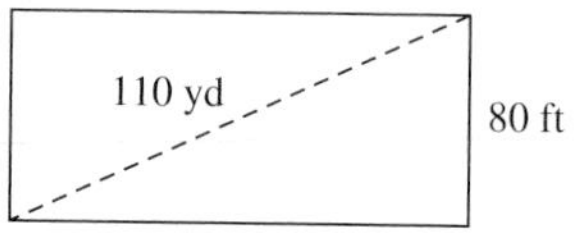

Section 10.4 Addition and Subtraction of Radicals

Concept

1. Addition and Subtraction of Radicals

1. Addition and Subtraction of Radicals

Definition of *Like* Radicals

Two radical terms are called ***like* radicals** if they have the same index and same radicand.

Like radicals can be added or subtracted by using the distributive property.

Same index — Distributive property

$$3\sqrt{x} + 7\sqrt{x} = (3 + 7)\sqrt{x} = 10\sqrt{x}$$

Same radicand

Example 1 **Adding and Subtracting Radicals**

Classroom Example: p. 724, Exercise 20

Add or subtract as indicated.

a. $6\sqrt{11} - 2\sqrt{11}$ **b.** $\sqrt{3} + \sqrt{3}$

Solution:

a. $6\sqrt{11} - 2\sqrt{11}$

$= (6 - 2)\sqrt{11}$ Apply the distributive property.

$= 4\sqrt{11}$ Simplify.

b. $\sqrt{3} + \sqrt{3}$

$= 1\sqrt{3} + 1\sqrt{3}$ Note that $\sqrt{3} = 1\sqrt{3}$.

$= (1 + 1)\sqrt{3}$ Apply the distributive property.

$= 2\sqrt{3}$ Simplify.

Avoiding Mistakes

The process of adding *like* radicals with the distributive property is similar to adding *like* terms. The end result is that the numerical coefficients are added and the radical factor is unchanged.

$$\sqrt{3} + \sqrt{3} = 1\sqrt{3} + 1\sqrt{3} = 2\sqrt{3}$$

Be careful: $\sqrt{3} + \sqrt{3} \neq \sqrt{6}$

In general: $\sqrt{x} + \sqrt{y} \neq \sqrt{x + y}$

Skill Practice Add or subtract as indicated.

1. $5\sqrt{6} - 8\sqrt{6}$ **2.** $\sqrt{10} + \sqrt{10}$

Example 2 **Adding and Subtracting Radicals**

Classroom Example: p. 724, Exercise 30

Add or subtract as indicated.

a. $-2\sqrt[3]{ab} + 7\sqrt[3]{ab} - \sqrt[3]{ab}$ **b.** $\frac{1}{4}x\sqrt{3y} - \frac{3}{2}x\sqrt{3y}$

Solution:

a. $-2\sqrt[3]{ab} + 7\sqrt[3]{ab} - \sqrt[3]{ab}$

$= (-2 + 7 - 1)\sqrt[3]{ab}$ Apply the distributive property.

$= 4\sqrt[3]{ab}$ Simplify.

b. $\frac{1}{4}x\sqrt{3y} - \frac{3}{2}x\sqrt{3y}$

$= \left(\frac{1}{4} - \frac{3}{2}\right)x\sqrt{3y}$ Apply the distributive property.

$= \left(\frac{1}{4} - \frac{6}{4}\right)x\sqrt{3y}$ Get a common denominator.

$= -\frac{5}{4}x\sqrt{3y}$ Simplify.

Answers

1. $-3\sqrt{6}$ **2.** $2\sqrt{10}$

Skill Practice Add or subtract as indicated.

3. $5\sqrt[3]{xy} - 3\sqrt[3]{xy} + 7\sqrt[3]{xy}$

4. $\frac{5}{6}y\sqrt{2} + \frac{1}{4}y\sqrt{2}$

Example 3 shows that it is often necessary to simplify radicals before adding or subtracting.

Classroom Examples: p. 724, Exercises 38 and 60

Example 3 Adding and Subtracting Radicals

Simplify the radicals and add or subtract as indicated. Assume all variables represent positive real numbers.

a. $3\sqrt{8} + \sqrt{2}$ **b.** $8\sqrt{x^3y^2} - 3y\sqrt{x^3}$

c. $\sqrt{50x^2y^5} - 13y\sqrt{2x^2y^3} + xy\sqrt{98y^3}$

Solution:

a. $3\sqrt{8} + \sqrt{2}$ — The radicands are different. Try simplifying the radicals first.

$= 3 \cdot 2\sqrt{2} + \sqrt{2}$ — Simplify: $\sqrt{8} = \sqrt{2^3} = 2\sqrt{2}$

$= 6\sqrt{2} + \sqrt{2}$

$= (6 + 1)\sqrt{2}$ — Apply the distributive property.

$= 7\sqrt{2}$ — Simplify.

b. $8\sqrt{x^3y^2} - 3y\sqrt{x^3}$ — The radicands are different. Simplify the radicals first.

$= 8xy\sqrt{x} - 3xy\sqrt{x}$ — Simplify $\sqrt{x^3y^2} = xy\sqrt{x}$ and $\sqrt{x^3} = x\sqrt{x}$.

$= (8 - 3)xy\sqrt{x}$ — Apply the distributive property.

$= 5xy\sqrt{x}$ — Simplify.

c. $\sqrt{50x^2y^5} - 13y\sqrt{2x^2y^3} + xy\sqrt{98y^3}$ — Simplify each radical.

$$\begin{cases} \sqrt{50x^2y^5} = \sqrt{25 \cdot 2x^2y^5} \\ \quad = 5xy^2\sqrt{2y} \\ -13y\sqrt{2x^2y^3} = -13xy^2\sqrt{2y} \\ xy\sqrt{98y^3} = xy\sqrt{49 \cdot 2y^3} \\ \quad = 7xy^2\sqrt{2y} \end{cases}$$

$= 5xy^2\sqrt{2y} - 13xy^2\sqrt{2y} + 7xy^2\sqrt{2y}$

$= (5 - 13 + 7)xy^2\sqrt{2y}$ — Apply the distributive property.

$= -xy^2\sqrt{2y}$

Skill Practice Simplify the radicals and add or subtract as indicated. Assume all variables represent positive real numbers.

5. $\sqrt{75} + 2\sqrt{3}$

6. $4\sqrt{a^2b} - 6a\sqrt{b}$

7. $-3\sqrt{2y^3} + 5y\sqrt{18y} - 2\sqrt{50y^3}$

Answers

3. $9\sqrt[3]{xy}$ **4.** $\frac{13}{12}y\sqrt{2}$

5. $7\sqrt{3}$ **6.** $-2a\sqrt{b}$

7. $2y\sqrt{2y}$

In some cases, when two radicals are added, the resulting sum is written in factored form. This is demonstrated in Example 4.

Example 4 **Adding Radical Expressions**

Add the radicals. Assume that $x \geq 0$. $3\sqrt{2x^2} + \sqrt{8}$

Solution:

$3\sqrt{2x^2} + \sqrt{8}$

$= 3x\sqrt{2} + 2\sqrt{2}$ Simplify each radical. Notice that the radicands are the same, but the terms are not *like* terms. The first term has a factor of x and the second does not.

$= (3x + 2)\sqrt{2}$ Apply the distributive property. The expression cannot be simplified further because $3x$ and 2 are not *like* terms.

Classroom Example: p. 724, Exercise 58

Skill Practice Add the radicals. Assume that $y \geq 0$.

8. $4\sqrt{45} - \sqrt{5y^4}$

Answer

8. $(12 - y^2)\sqrt{5}$

Section 10.4 Practice Exercises

For additional exercises, see Classroom Activities 10.4A–10.4B in the *Student's Resource Manual* at www.mhhe.com/moh.

For the exercises in this set, assume that all variables represent positive real numbers, unless otherwise stated.

Vocabulary and Key Concepts

1. a. Two radical terms are called *like* radicals if they have the same __index__ and the same __radicand__.

b. The expression $\sqrt{3x} + \sqrt{3x}$ simplifies to __$2\sqrt{3x}$__.

c. The expression $\sqrt{2} + \sqrt{3}$ (can/cannot) be simplified further whereas the expression $\sqrt{2} \cdot \sqrt{3}$ (can/cannot) be simplified further. cannot; can

d. The expression $\sqrt{2} + \sqrt{18}$ simplifies to __$4\sqrt{2}$__.

Review Exercises

For Exercises 2–5, simplify the radicals.

2. $\sqrt[3]{-16s^4t^9}$ $-2st^3\sqrt[3]{2s}$

3. $-\sqrt[4]{x^7y^4}$ $-xy\sqrt[4]{x^3}$

4. $\sqrt{36a^2b^3}$ $6ab\sqrt{b}$

5. $\sqrt[3]{\dfrac{7b^8}{56b^2}}$ $\dfrac{b^2}{2}$

6. Write $(4x^2)^{1/3}$ in radical notation. $\sqrt[3]{4x^2}$

7. Write $\sqrt[4]{x^3y}$ using rational exponents. $(x^3y)^{1/4}$

8. Simplify. $32^{-1/5}$ $\dfrac{1}{2}$

For Exercises 9–10, simplify the expressions. Write the answer with positive exponents only.

9. $y^{2/3}y^{1/4}$ $y^{11/12}$

10. $(x^{1/2}y^{-3/4})^{-4}$ $\dfrac{y^3}{x^2}$

Concept 1: Addition and Subtraction of Radicals

For Exercises 11–12, determine if the radical terms are *like*.

11. **a.** $\sqrt{2}$ and $\sqrt[3]{2}$ Not *like* radicals

b. $\sqrt{2}$ and $3\sqrt{2}$ *Like* radicals

c. $\sqrt{2}$ and $\sqrt{5}$ Not *like* radicals

12. **a.** $7\sqrt[3]{x}$ and $\sqrt[3]{x}$ *Like* radicals

b. $\sqrt[3]{x}$ and $\sqrt[4]{x}$ Not *like* radicals

c. $2\sqrt[4]{x}$ and $x\sqrt[4]{2}$ Not *like* radicals

13. Explain the similarities between the pairs of expressions.

a. $7\sqrt{5} + 4\sqrt{5}$ and $7x + 4x$ Both expressions can be simplified by using the distributive property.

b. $-2\sqrt{6} - 9\sqrt{3}$ and $-2x - 9y$ Neither expression can be simplified because the terms do not contain *like* radicals or *like* terms.

14. Explain the similarities between the pairs of expressions.

a. $-4\sqrt{3} + 5\sqrt{3}$ and $-4z + 5z$ Both expressions can be simplified by using the distributive property.

b. $13\sqrt{7} - 18$ and $13a - 18$ Neither expression can be simplified because the terms do not contain *like* radicals or *like* terms.

For Exercises 15–32, add or subtract the radical expressions, if possible. **(See Examples 1–2.)**

15. $3\sqrt{5} + 6\sqrt{5}$ $9\sqrt{5}$

16. $5\sqrt{a} + 3\sqrt{a}$ $8\sqrt{a}$

17. $3\sqrt[3]{tw} - 2\sqrt[3]{tw} + \sqrt[3]{tw}$ $2\sqrt[3]{tw}$

18. $6\sqrt[3]{7} - 2\sqrt[3]{7} + \sqrt[3]{7}$ $5\sqrt[3]{7}$

19. $6\sqrt{10} - \sqrt{10}$ $5\sqrt{10}$

20. $13\sqrt{11} - \sqrt{11}$ $12\sqrt{11}$

21. $\sqrt[4]{3} + 7\sqrt[4]{3} - \sqrt[4]{14}$ $8\sqrt[4]{3} - \sqrt[4]{14}$

22. $2\sqrt{11} + 3\sqrt{13} + 5\sqrt{11}$ $7\sqrt{11} + 3\sqrt{13}$

23. $8\sqrt{x} + 2\sqrt{y} - 6\sqrt{x}$ $2\sqrt{x} + 2\sqrt{y}$

24. $10\sqrt{10} - 8\sqrt{10} + \sqrt{2}$ $2\sqrt{10} + \sqrt{2}$

25. $\sqrt[3]{ab} + a\sqrt[3]{b}$ Cannot be simplified further

26. $x\sqrt[4]{y} - y\sqrt[4]{x}$ Cannot be simplified further

27. $\sqrt{2t} + \sqrt[3]{2t}$ Cannot be simplified further

28. $\sqrt[4]{5c} + \sqrt[3]{5c}$ Cannot be simplified further

29. $\frac{5}{6}z\sqrt[3]{6} + \frac{7}{9}z\sqrt[3]{6}$ $\frac{29}{18}z\sqrt[3]{6}$

30. $\frac{3}{4}a\sqrt[4]{b} + \frac{1}{6}a\sqrt[4]{b}$ $\frac{11}{12}a\sqrt[4]{b}$

31. $0.81x\sqrt{y} - 0.11x\sqrt{y}$ $0.7x\sqrt{y}$

32. $7.5\sqrt{pq} - 6.3\sqrt{pq}$ $1.2\sqrt{pq}$

33. Explain the process for adding the two radicals. Then find the sum. $3\sqrt{2} + 7\sqrt{50}$
Simplify each radical: $3\sqrt{2} + 35\sqrt{2}$. Then add *like* radicals: $38\sqrt{2}$

34. Explain the process for subtracting two radicals. Then find the difference. $\sqrt{12x} - \sqrt{75x}$
Simplify each radical: $2\sqrt{3x} - 5\sqrt{3x}$. Then subtract *like* radicals: $-3\sqrt{3x}$

For Exercises 35–64, add or subtract the radical expressions as indicated. **(See Examples 3–4.)**

35. $\sqrt{36} + \sqrt{81}$ 15

36. $3\sqrt{80} - 5\sqrt{45}$ $-3\sqrt{5}$

37. $2\sqrt{12} + \sqrt{48}$ $8\sqrt{3}$

38. $5\sqrt{32} + 2\sqrt{50}$ $30\sqrt{2}$

39. $4\sqrt{7} + \sqrt{63} - 2\sqrt{28}$ $3\sqrt{7}$

40. $8\sqrt{3} - 2\sqrt{27} + \sqrt{75}$ $7\sqrt{3}$

41. $5\sqrt{18} + \sqrt{27} - 4\sqrt{50}$ $-5\sqrt{2} + 3\sqrt{3}$

42. $7\sqrt{40} - \sqrt{8} + 4\sqrt{50}$ $14\sqrt{10} + 18\sqrt{2}$

43. $\sqrt[3]{81} - \sqrt[3]{24}$ $\sqrt[3]{3}$

44. $17\sqrt[3]{81} - 2\sqrt[3]{24}$ $47\sqrt[3]{3}$

45. $3\sqrt{2a} - \sqrt{8a} - \sqrt{72a}$ $-5\sqrt{2a}$

46. $\sqrt{12t} - \sqrt{27t} + 5\sqrt{3t}$ $4\sqrt{3t}$

47. $2s^2\sqrt[3]{s^2t^6} + 3t^2\sqrt[3]{8s^8}$ $8s^2t^2\sqrt[3]{s^2}$

48. $4\sqrt[3]{x^4} - 2x\sqrt[3]{x}$ $2x\sqrt[3]{x}$

49. $7\sqrt[3]{x^4} - x\sqrt[3]{x}$ $6x\sqrt[3]{x}$

50. $6\sqrt[3]{y^{10}} - 3y^2\sqrt[3]{y^4}$ $3y^3\sqrt[3]{y}$

51. $5p\sqrt{20p^2} + p^2\sqrt{80}$ $14p^2\sqrt{5}$

52. $2q\sqrt{48q^2} - \sqrt{27q^4}$ $5q^2\sqrt{3}$

53. $\sqrt[3]{a^2b} - \sqrt[3]{8a^2b}$ $-\sqrt[3]{a^2b}$

54. $w\sqrt{80} - 3\sqrt{125w^2}$ $-11w\sqrt{5}$

55. $5x\sqrt{x} + 6\sqrt{x}$ $(5x + 6)\sqrt{x}$

56. $9y^2\sqrt{2} + 4\sqrt{2}$ $(9y^2 + 4)\sqrt{2}$

57. $\sqrt{50x^2} - 3\sqrt{8}$ $(5x - 6)\sqrt{2}$

58. $\sqrt{9x^3} - \sqrt{25x}$ $(3x - 5)\sqrt{x}$

59. $11\sqrt[3]{54cd^3} - 2\sqrt[3]{2cd^3} + d\sqrt[3]{16c}$ $33d\sqrt[3]{2c}$

60. $x\sqrt[3]{64x^5y^2} - x^2\sqrt[3]{x^2y^2} + 5\sqrt[3]{x^8y^2}$ $8x^2\sqrt[3]{x^2y^2}$

61. $\frac{3}{2}ab\sqrt{24a^3} + \frac{4}{3}\sqrt{54a^5b^2} - a^2b\sqrt{150a}$ $2a^2b\sqrt{6a}$

62. $mn\sqrt{72n} + \frac{2}{3}n\sqrt{8m^2n} - \frac{5}{6}\sqrt{50m^2n^3}$ $\frac{19}{6}mn\sqrt{2n}$

63. $x\sqrt[3]{16} - 2\sqrt[3]{27x} + \sqrt[3]{54x^3}$ $5x\sqrt[3]{2} - 6\sqrt[3]{x}$

64. $5\sqrt[4]{y^5} - 2y\sqrt[4]{y} + \sqrt[4]{16y^7}$ $3y\sqrt[4]{y} + 2y\sqrt[4]{y^3}$

Mixed Exercises

For Exercises 65–72, answer true or false. If an answer is false, explain why or give a counterexample.

65. $\sqrt{x} + \sqrt{y} = \sqrt{x+y}$ False; $\sqrt{9} + \sqrt{16} \neq \sqrt{9+16}$; $7 \neq 5$

66. $\sqrt{x} + \sqrt{x} = 2\sqrt{x}$ True

67. $5\sqrt[3]{x} + 2\sqrt[3]{x} = 7\sqrt[3]{x}$ True

68. $6\sqrt{x} + 5\sqrt[3]{x} = 11\sqrt{x}$ False; radicals must have the same index.

69. $\sqrt{y} + \sqrt{y} = \sqrt{2y}$ False; $\sqrt{y} + \sqrt{y} = 2\sqrt{y} \neq \sqrt{2y}$

70. $\sqrt{c^2 + d^2} = c + d$ False; $\sqrt{3^2 + 4^2} \neq 3 + 4$; $5 \neq 7$

71. $2w\sqrt{5} + 4w\sqrt{5} = 6w^2\sqrt{5}$ False; $2w\sqrt{5} + 4w\sqrt{5} = 6w\sqrt{5} \neq 6w^2\sqrt{5}$

72. $7x\sqrt{3} - 2\sqrt{3} = (7x - 2)\sqrt{3}$ True

For Exercises 73–76, write the English phrase as an algebraic expression. Simplify each expression.

73. The sum of the principal square root of 48 and the principal square root of 12 $\sqrt{48} + \sqrt{12}$ simplifies to $6\sqrt{3}$

74. The sum of the cube root of 16 and the cube root of 2 $\sqrt[3]{16} + \sqrt[3]{2}$ simplifies to $3\sqrt[3]{2}$

75. The difference of 5 times the cube root of x^6 and the square of x $5\sqrt[3]{x^6} - x^2$ simplifies to $4x^2$

76. The sum of the cube of y and the principal fourth root of y^{12} $y^3 + \sqrt[4]{y^{12}}$ simplifies to $2y^3$

For Exercises 77–80, write an English phrase that translates the mathematical expression. (Answers may vary.)

77. $\sqrt{18} - 5^2$ The difference of the principal square root of 18 and the square of 5

78. $4^3 - \sqrt[3]{4}$ The difference of the cube of 4 and the cube root of 4

79. $\sqrt[4]{x} + y^3$ The sum of the principal fourth root of x and the cube of y

80. $a^4 + \sqrt{a}$ The sum of the fourth power of a and the principal square root of a

For Exercises 81–82, find the exact value of the perimeter, and then approximate the value to one decimal place.

81.

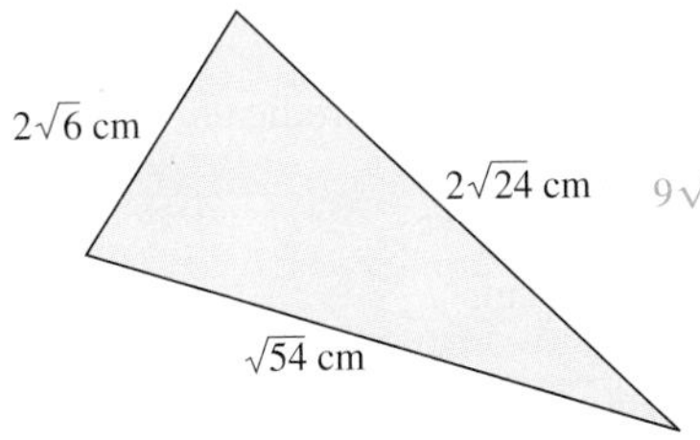

$9\sqrt{6}$ cm ≈ 22.0 cm

82.

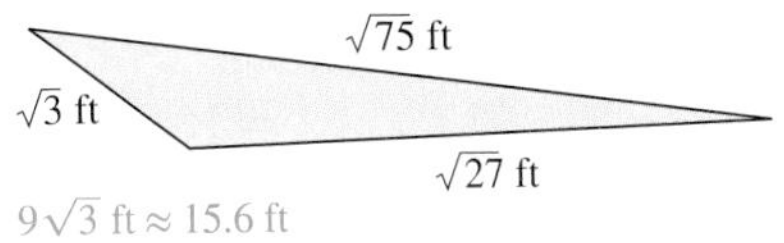

$9\sqrt{3}$ ft ≈ 15.6 ft

83. The figure has perimeter $14\sqrt{2}$ ft. Find the value of x. $x = 2\sqrt{2}$ ft

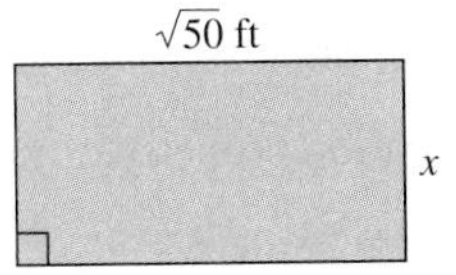

84. The figure has perimeter $12\sqrt{7}$ cm. Find the value of x. $x = 2\sqrt{7}$ cm

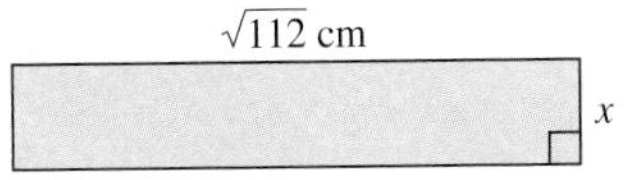

Expanding Your Skills

85. **a.** An irregularly shaped garden is shown in the figure. All distances are expressed in yards. Find the perimeter. (*Hint*: Use the Pythagorean theorem to find the length of each side.) Write the final answer in radical form. $10\sqrt{5}$ yd

b. Approximate your answer to two decimal places. 22.36 yd

c. If edging costs $1.49 per foot and sales tax is 6%, find the total cost of edging the garden. $105.95

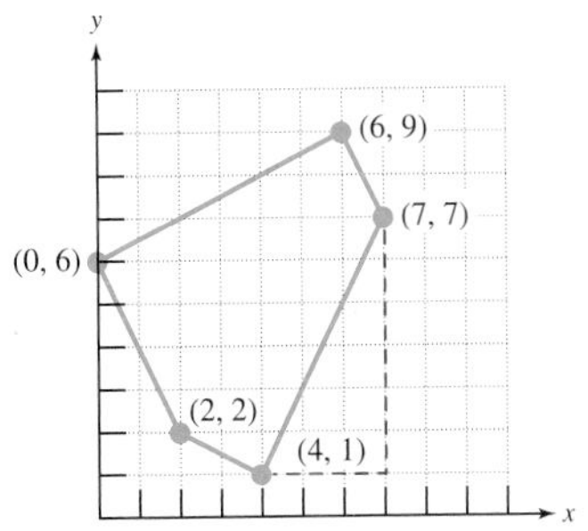

Writing Translating Expression Geometry Scientific Calculator Video

Section 10.5 Multiplication of Radicals

Concepts

1. Multiplication Property of Radicals
2. Expressions of the Form $(\sqrt[n]{a})^n$
3. Special Case Products
4. Multiplying Radicals with Different Indices

1. Multiplication Property of Radicals

In this section, we will learn how to multiply radicals by using the multiplication property of radicals.

The Multiplication Property of Radicals

Let a and b represent real numbers such that $\sqrt[n]{a}$ and $\sqrt[n]{b}$ are both real. Then

$$\sqrt[n]{ab} = \sqrt[n]{a} \cdot \sqrt[n]{b}$$

To multiply two radical expressions, we use the multiplication property of radicals along with the commutative and associative properties of multiplication.

Classroom Examples: p. 732, Exercises 12 and 22

Example 1 Multiplying Radical Expressions

Multiply each expression and simplify the result. Assume all variables represent positive real numbers.

a. $(3\sqrt{2})(5\sqrt{6})$ **b.** $(2x\sqrt{y})(-7\sqrt{xy})$ **c.** $(15c\sqrt[3]{cd})\left(\frac{1}{3}\sqrt[3]{cd^2}\right)$

Solution:

a. $(3\sqrt{2})(5\sqrt{6})$

$= (3 \cdot 5)(\sqrt{2} \cdot \sqrt{6})$ Commutative and associative properties of multiplication

$= 15\sqrt{12}$ Multiplication property of radicals

$= 15\sqrt{2^2 3}$

$= 15 \cdot 2\sqrt{3}$ Simplify the radical.

$= 30\sqrt{3}$

b. $(2x\sqrt{y})(-7\sqrt{xy})$

$= (2x)(-7)(\sqrt{y} \cdot \sqrt{xy})$ Commutative and associative properties of multiplication

$= -14x\sqrt{xy^2}$ Multiplication property of radicals

$= -14xy\sqrt{x}$ Simplify the radical.

c. $(15c\sqrt[3]{cd})\left(\frac{1}{3}\sqrt[3]{cd^2}\right)$

$= \left(15c \cdot \frac{1}{3}\right)(\sqrt[3]{cd} \cdot \sqrt[3]{cd^2})$ Commutative and associative properties of multiplication

$= 5c\sqrt[3]{c^2d^3}$ Multiplication property of radicals

$= 5cd\sqrt[3]{c^2}$ Simplify the radical.

Skill Practice Multiply the expressions and simplify the results. Assume all variables represent positive real numbers.

1. $(4\sqrt{6})(-2\sqrt{3})$
2. $(3ab\sqrt{b})(-2\sqrt{ab})$
3. $(2\sqrt[3]{4ab})(5\sqrt[3]{2a^2b})$

When multiplying radical expressions with more than one term, we use the distributive property.

Example 2 Multiplying Radical Expressions

Classroom Example: p. 732, Exercise 30

Multiply. $3\sqrt{11}(2 + \sqrt{11})$

Solution:

$3\sqrt{11}(2 + \sqrt{11})$

$= 3\sqrt{11} \cdot (2) + 3\sqrt{11} \cdot \sqrt{11}$ Apply the distributive property.

$= 6\sqrt{11} + 3\sqrt{11^2}$ Multiplication property of radicals

$= 6\sqrt{11} + 3 \cdot 11$ Simplify the radical.

$= 6\sqrt{11} + 33$

Skill Practice Multiply.

4. $5\sqrt{5}(2\sqrt{5} - 2)$

Example 3 Multiplying Radical Expressions

Classroom Examples: p. 732, Exercises 36 and 42

Multiply.

a. $(\sqrt{5} + 3\sqrt{2})(2\sqrt{5} - \sqrt{2})$ **b.** $(-10a\sqrt{b} + 7b)(a\sqrt{b} + 2b)$

Solution:

a. $(\sqrt{5} + 3\sqrt{2})(2\sqrt{5} - \sqrt{2})$

$= 2\sqrt{5^2} - \sqrt{10} + 6\sqrt{10} - 3\sqrt{2^2}$ Apply the distributive property.

$= 2 \cdot 5 + 5\sqrt{10} - 3 \cdot 2$ Simplify radicals and combine *like* radicals.

$= 10 + 5\sqrt{10} - 6$

$= 4 + 5\sqrt{10}$ Combine *like* terms.

b. $(-10a\sqrt{b} + 7b)(a\sqrt{b} + 2b)$

$= -10a^2\sqrt{b^2} - 20ab\sqrt{b} + 7ab\sqrt{b} + 14b^2$ Apply the distributive property.

$= -10a^2b - 13ab\sqrt{b} + 14b^2$ Simplify and combine *like* terms.

Answers

1. $-24\sqrt{2}$
2. $-6ab^2\sqrt{a}$
3. $20a\sqrt[3]{b^2}$
4. $50 - 10\sqrt{5}$

Skill Practice Multiply.

5. $(2\sqrt{3} - 3\sqrt{10})(\sqrt{3} + 2\sqrt{10})$ **6.** $(x\sqrt{y} + y)(3x\sqrt{y} - 2y)$

Classroom Example: p. 732, Exercise 44

Example 4 **Multiplying Radical Expressions**

Multiply. $(2\sqrt{x} + \sqrt{y})(6 - \sqrt{x} + 8\sqrt{y})$

Solution:

$(2\sqrt{x} + \sqrt{y})(6 - \sqrt{x} + 8\sqrt{y})$

$= 12\sqrt{x} - 2\sqrt{x^2} + 16\sqrt{xy} + 6\sqrt{y} - \sqrt{xy} + 8\sqrt{y^2}$ Apply the distributive property.

$= 12\sqrt{x} - 2x + 16\sqrt{xy} + 6\sqrt{y} - \sqrt{xy} + 8y$ Simplify the radicals.

$= 12\sqrt{x} - 2x + 15\sqrt{xy} + 6\sqrt{y} + 8y$ Combine *like* terms.

Skill Practice Multiply.

7. $(\sqrt{t} + 3\sqrt{w})(4 - \sqrt{t} - \sqrt{w})$

Instructor Note: Ask students if $(\sqrt{x})^2 = \sqrt{x^2}$ is always true, sometimes true, or never true.

2. Expressions of the Form $(\sqrt[n]{a})^n$

The multiplication property of radicals can be used to simplify an expression of the form $(\sqrt{a})^2$, where $a \geq 0$.

$$(\sqrt{a})^2 = \sqrt{a} \cdot \sqrt{a} = \sqrt{a^2} = a \qquad \text{where } a \geq 0$$

This logic can be applied to nth roots.

- If $\sqrt[n]{a}$ is a real number, then $(\sqrt[n]{a})^n = a$.

Classroom Example: p. 732, Exercise 46

Example 5 **Simplifying Radical Expressions**

Simplify the expressions. Assume all variables represent positive real numbers.

a. $(\sqrt{11})^2$ **b.** $(\sqrt[5]{z})^5$ **c.** $(\sqrt[3]{pq})^3$

Solution:

a. $(\sqrt{11})^2 = 11$ **b.** $(\sqrt[5]{z})^5 = z$ **c.** $(\sqrt[3]{pq})^3 = pq$

Skill Practice Simplify.

8. $(\sqrt{14})^2$ **9.** $(\sqrt[7]{q})^7$ **10.** $(\sqrt[5]{3z})^5$

Answers

5. $-54 + \sqrt{30}$
6. $3x^2y + xy\sqrt{y} - 2y^2$
7. $4\sqrt{t} - t - 4\sqrt{tw} + 12\sqrt{w} - 3w$
8. 14 **9.** q **10.** $3z$

3. Special Case Products

From Examples 2–4, you may have noticed a similarity between multiplying radical expressions and multiplying polynomials.

Recall that the square of a binomial results in a perfect square trinomial:

$$(a+b)^2 = a^2 + 2ab + b^2$$
$$(a-b)^2 = a^2 - 2ab + b^2$$

The same patterns occur when squaring a radical expression with two terms.

Example 6 **Squaring a Two-Term Radical Expression**

Classroom Example: p. 732, Exercise 60

Square the radical expressions. Assume all variables represent positive real numbers.

a. $(\sqrt{d}+3)^2$ **b.** $(5\sqrt{y}-\sqrt{2})^2$

Solution:

a. $(\sqrt{d}+3)^2$ This expression is in the form $(a+b)^2$, where $a=\sqrt{d}$ and $b=3$.

$a^2 + 2ab + b^2$ Apply the formula

$= (\sqrt{d})^2 + 2(\sqrt{d})(3)+(3)^2$ $(a+b)^2 = a^2 + 2ab + b^2$.

$= d + 6\sqrt{d} + 9$ Simplify.

TIP: The product $(\sqrt{d}+3)^2$ can also be found by using the distributive property.

$$(\sqrt{d}+3)^2 = (\sqrt{d}+3)(\sqrt{d}+3)$$

b. $(5\sqrt{y}-\sqrt{2})^2$ This expression is in the form $(a-b)^2$, where $a=5\sqrt{y}$ and $b=\sqrt{2}$.

$a^2 - 2ab + b^2$ Apply the formula

$= (5\sqrt{y})^2 - 2(5\sqrt{y})(\sqrt{2})+(\sqrt{2})^2$ $(a-b)^2 = a^2 - 2ab + b^2$.

$= 25y - 10\sqrt{2y} + 2$ Simplify.

Skill Practice Square the radical expressions. Assume all variables represent positive real numbers.

11. $(\sqrt{a}-5)^2$ **12.** $(4\sqrt{x}+\sqrt{3})^2$

Recall that the product of two conjugate binomials results in a difference of squares.

$$(a+b)(a-b) = a^2 - b^2$$

The same pattern occurs when multiplying two conjugate radical expressions.

Example 7 **Multiplying Conjugate Radical Expressions**

Classroom Example: p. 732, Exercise 62

Multiply the radical expressions. Assume all variables represent positive real numbers.

a. $(\sqrt{3}+2)(\sqrt{3}-2)$ **b.** $\left(\frac{1}{3}\sqrt{s}-\frac{3}{4}\sqrt{t}\right)\left(\frac{1}{3}\sqrt{s}+\frac{3}{4}\sqrt{t}\right)$

Answers

11. $a - 10\sqrt{a} + 25$
12. $16x + 8\sqrt{3x} + 3$

TIP: The product $(\sqrt{3}+2)(\sqrt{3}-2)$ can also be found by using the distributive property.

$$(\sqrt{3}+2)(\sqrt{3}-2)$$

Solution:

a. $(\sqrt{3}+2)(\sqrt{3}-2)$ — The expression is in the form $(a+b)(a-b)$, where $a=\sqrt{3}$ and $b=2$.

$$a^2 - b^2$$

$= (\sqrt{3})^2 - (2)^2$ — Apply the formula $(a+b)(a-b)=a^2-b^2$.

$= 3 - 4$ — Simplify.

$= -1$

b. $\left(\frac{1}{3}\sqrt{s}-\frac{3}{4}\sqrt{t}\right)\left(\frac{1}{3}\sqrt{s}+\frac{3}{4}\sqrt{t}\right)$ — This expression is in the form $(a-b)(a+b)$, where $a=\frac{1}{3}\sqrt{s}$ and $b=\frac{3}{4}\sqrt{t}$.

$$a^2 - b^2$$

$= \left(\frac{1}{3}\sqrt{s}\right)^2 - \left(\frac{3}{4}\sqrt{t}\right)^2$ — Apply the formula $(a+b)(a-b)=a^2-b^2$.

$= \frac{1}{9}s - \frac{9}{16}t$ — Simplify.

Skill Practice Multiply the conjugates. Assume all variables represent positive real numbers.

13. $(\sqrt{5}+3)(\sqrt{5}-3)$ **14.** $\left(\frac{1}{2}\sqrt{a}+\frac{2}{5}\sqrt{b}\right)\cdot\left(\frac{1}{2}\sqrt{a}-\frac{2}{5}\sqrt{b}\right)$

4. Multiplying Radicals with Different Indices

The product of two radicals can be simplified provided the radicals have the same index. If the radicals have different indices, then we can use the properties of rational exponents to obtain a common index.

Classroom Examples: p. 733, Exercises 92 and 98

Example 8 Multiplying Radicals with Different Indices

Multiply the expressions. Write the answers in radical form.

a. $\sqrt[3]{5}\cdot\sqrt[4]{5}$ **b.** $\sqrt[3]{7}\cdot\sqrt{2}$

Solution:

a. $\sqrt[3]{5}\cdot\sqrt[4]{5}$

$= 5^{1/3}5^{1/4}$ — Rewrite each expression with rational exponents.

$= 5^{(1/3)+(1/4)}$ — Because the bases are equal, we can add the exponents.

$= 5^{(4/12)+(3/12)}$ — Write the fractions with a common denominator.

$= 5^{7/12}$ — Simplify the exponent.

$= \sqrt[12]{5^7}$ — Rewrite the expression as a radical.

Answers

13. -4 **14.** $\frac{1}{4}a - \frac{4}{25}b$

b. $\sqrt[3]{7} \cdot \sqrt{2}$

$= 7^{1/3}2^{1/2}$	Rewrite each expression with rational exponents.
$= 7^{2/6}2^{3/6}$	Write the rational exponents with a common denominator.
$= (7^2 2^3)^{1/6}$	Apply the power rule of exponents.
$= \sqrt[6]{7^2 2^3}$	Rewrite the expression as a single radical.
$= \sqrt[6]{392}$	Simplify.

Skill Practice Multiply the expressions. Write the answers in radical form. Assume all variables represent positive real numbers.

15. $\sqrt{x} \cdot \sqrt[3]{x}$ **16.** $\sqrt[4]{a^3} \cdot \sqrt[3]{b}$

Answers
15. $\sqrt[6]{x^5}$ **16.** $\sqrt[12]{a^9b^4}$

Section 10.5 Practice Exercises

For additional exercises, see Classroom Activities 10.5A–10.5B in the *Student's Resource Manual* at www.mhhe.com/moh.

For the exercises in this set, assume that all variables represent positive real numbers, unless otherwise stated.

Vocabulary and Key Concepts

1. a. If $\sqrt[n]{a}$ and $\sqrt[n]{b}$ are real numbers, then $\sqrt[n]{a} \cdot \sqrt[n]{b} =$ ____$\sqrt[n]{ab}$____.

b. If $x \geq 0$, then $\sqrt{x} \cdot \sqrt{x} =$ ____x____.

c. If $\sqrt[n]{a}$ is a real number, then $(\sqrt[n]{a})^n =$ ____a____.

d. Two binomials $(x + \sqrt{2})$ and $(x - \sqrt{2})$ are called ____conjugates____ of each other, and their product is $(x)^2 - (\sqrt{2})^2$.

e. If $m \geq 0$ and $n \geq 0$, then $(\sqrt{m} + \sqrt{n})(\sqrt{m} - \sqrt{n}) =$ ____$m - n$____.

f. Which is the correct simplification of $(\sqrt{c} + 4)^2$?

$c + 16$ or $c + 8\sqrt{c} + 16$ $c + 8\sqrt{c} + 16$

Review Exercises

For Exercises 2–4, simplify the radicals.

2. $\sqrt[3]{-16x^5y^6z^7}$ $-2xy^2z^2\sqrt[3]{2x^2z}$

3. $-\sqrt{20a^2b^3c}$ $-2ab\sqrt{5bc}$

4. $\sqrt{\dfrac{8y^3z^5}{y}}$ $2yz^2\sqrt{2z}$

For Exercises 5–6, simplify the expressions. Write the answer with positive exponents only.

5. $x^{1/3}y^{1/4}x^{-1/6}y^{1/3}$ $x^{1/6}y^{7/12}$

6. $\dfrac{b^{1/4}}{b^{3/2}}$ $\dfrac{1}{b^{5/4}}$

For Exercises 7–8, add or subtract as indicated.

7. $-2\sqrt[3]{7} + 4\sqrt[3]{7}$ $2\sqrt[3]{7}$

8. $4\sqrt{8x^3} - x\sqrt{50x}$ $3x\sqrt{2x}$

Concept 1: Multiplication Property of Radicals

For Exercises 9–44, multiply the radical expressions. **(See Examples 1–4.)**

9. $\sqrt[3]{7}\cdot\sqrt[3]{3}$ $\sqrt[3]{21}$

10. $\sqrt[4]{6}\cdot\sqrt[4]{2}$ $\sqrt[4]{12}$

11. $\sqrt{2}\cdot\sqrt{10}$ $2\sqrt{5}$

12. $\sqrt[3]{4}\cdot\sqrt[3]{12}$ $2\sqrt[3]{6}$

13. $\sqrt[4]{16}\cdot\sqrt[4]{64}$ $4\sqrt[4]{4}$

14. $\sqrt{5x^3}\cdot\sqrt{10x^4}$ $5x^3\sqrt{2x}$

15. $(4\sqrt[3]{4})(2\sqrt[3]{5})$ $8\sqrt[3]{20}$

16. $(2\sqrt{5})(3\sqrt{7})$ $6\sqrt{35}$

17. $(8a\sqrt{b})(-3\sqrt{ab})$ $-24ab\sqrt{a}$

18. $(p\sqrt[4]{q^3})(\sqrt[4]{pq})$ $pq\sqrt[4]{p}$

19. $\sqrt{30}\cdot\sqrt{12}$ $6\sqrt{10}$

20. $\sqrt{20}\cdot\sqrt{54}$ $6\sqrt{30}$

21. $\sqrt{6x}\cdot\sqrt{12x}$ $6x\sqrt{2}$

22. $(\sqrt{3ab^2})(\sqrt{21a^2b})$ $3ab\sqrt{7ab}$

23. $\sqrt{5a^3b^2}\cdot\sqrt{20a^3b^3}$ $10a^3b^2\sqrt{b}$

24. $\sqrt[3]{m^2n^2}\cdot\sqrt[3]{48m^4n^2}$ $2m^2n\sqrt[3]{6n}$

25. $(4\sqrt{3xy^3})(-2\sqrt{6x^3y^2})$ $-24x^2y^2\sqrt{2y}$

26. $(2\sqrt[4]{3x})(4\sqrt[4]{27x^6})$ $24x\sqrt[4]{x^3}$

27. $(\sqrt[3]{4a^2b})(\sqrt[3]{2ab^3})(\sqrt[3]{54a^2b})$ $6ab\sqrt[3]{2a^2b^2}$

28. $(\sqrt[3]{9x^3y})(\sqrt[3]{6xy})(\sqrt[3]{8x^2y^5})$ $6x^2y^2\sqrt[3]{2y}$

29. $\sqrt{3}(4\sqrt{3}-6)$ $12-6\sqrt{3}$

30. $3\sqrt{5}(2\sqrt{5}+4)$ $30+12\sqrt{5}$

31. $\sqrt{2}(\sqrt{6}-\sqrt{3})$ $2\sqrt{3}-\sqrt{6}$

32. $\sqrt{5}(\sqrt{3}+\sqrt{7})$ $\sqrt{15}+\sqrt{35}$

33. $-\frac{1}{3}\sqrt{x}(6\sqrt{x}+7)$ $-2x-\frac{7}{3}\sqrt{x}$

34. $-\frac{1}{2}\sqrt{y}(8-3\sqrt{y})$ $-4\sqrt{y}+\frac{3}{2}y$

35. $(\sqrt{3}+2\sqrt{10})(4\sqrt{3}-\sqrt{10})$ $-8+7\sqrt{30}$

36. $(8\sqrt{7}-\sqrt{5})(\sqrt{7}+3\sqrt{5})$ $41+23\sqrt{35}$

37. $(\sqrt{x}+4)(\sqrt{x}-9)$ $x-5\sqrt{x}-36$

38. $(\sqrt{w}-2)(\sqrt{w}-9)$ $w-11\sqrt{w}+18$

39. $(\sqrt[3]{y}+2)(\sqrt[3]{y}-3)$ $\sqrt[3]{y^2}-\sqrt[3]{y}-6$

40. $(4+\sqrt[5]{p})(5+\sqrt[5]{p})$ $20+9\sqrt[5]{p}+\sqrt[5]{p^2}$

41. $(\sqrt{a}-3\sqrt{b})(9\sqrt{a}-\sqrt{b})$ $9a-28\sqrt{ab}+3b$

42. $(11\sqrt{m}+4\sqrt{n})(\sqrt{m}+\sqrt{n})$ $11m+15\sqrt{mn}+4n$

43. $(\sqrt{p}+2\sqrt{q})(8+3\sqrt{p}-\sqrt{q})$ $8\sqrt{p}+3p+5\sqrt{pq}+16\sqrt{q}-2q$

44. $(5\sqrt{s}-\sqrt{t})(\sqrt{s}+5+6\sqrt{t})$ $5s+25\sqrt{s}+29\sqrt{st}-5\sqrt{t}-6t$

Concept 2: Expressions of the Form $(\sqrt[n]{a})^n$

For Exercises 45–52, simplify the expressions. Assume all variables represent positive real numbers. **(See Example 5.)**

45. $(\sqrt{15})^2$ 15

46. $(\sqrt{58})^2$ 58

47. $(\sqrt{3y})^2$ $3y$

48. $(\sqrt{19yz})^2$ $19yz$

49. $(\sqrt[3]{6})^3$ 6

50. $(\sqrt[5]{24})^5$ 24

51. $\sqrt{709}\cdot\sqrt{709}$ 709

52. $\sqrt{401}\cdot\sqrt{401}$ 401

Concept 3: Special Case Products

53. **a.** Write the formula for the product of two conjugates. $(x+y)(x-y)=$ x^2-y^2

b. Multiply. $(x+5)(x-5)$ x^2-25

54. **a.** Write the formula for squaring a binomial. $(x+y)^2=$ $x^2+2xy+y^2$

b. Multiply. $(x+5)^2$ $x^2+10x+25$

For Exercises 55–66, multiply the radical expressions. **(See Examples 6–7.)**

55. $(\sqrt{13}+4)^2$ $29+8\sqrt{13}$

56. $(6-\sqrt{11})^2$ $47-12\sqrt{11}$

57. $(\sqrt{p}-\sqrt{7})^2$ $p-2\sqrt{7p}+7$

58. $(\sqrt{q}+\sqrt{2})^2$ $q+2\sqrt{2q}+2$

59. $(\sqrt{2a}-3\sqrt{b})^2$ $2a-6\sqrt{2ab}+9b$

60. $(\sqrt{3w}+4\sqrt{z})^2$ $3w+8\sqrt{3wz}+16z$

61. $(\sqrt{3}+x)(\sqrt{3}-x)$ $3-x^2$

62. $(y+\sqrt{6})(y-\sqrt{6})$ y^2-6

63. $(\sqrt{6}+\sqrt{2})(\sqrt{6}-\sqrt{2})$ 4

64. $(\sqrt{15}+\sqrt{5})(\sqrt{15}-\sqrt{5})$ 10

65. $\left(\frac{2}{3}\sqrt{x}+\frac{1}{2}\sqrt{y}\right)\left(\frac{2}{3}\sqrt{x}-\frac{1}{2}\sqrt{y}\right)$ $\frac{4}{9}x-\frac{1}{4}y$

66. $\left(\frac{1}{4}\sqrt{s}+\frac{1}{5}\sqrt{t}\right)\left(\frac{1}{4}\sqrt{s}-\frac{1}{5}\sqrt{t}\right)$ $\frac{1}{16}s-\frac{1}{25}t$

For Exercises 67–68, multiply the expressions.

67. **a.** $(\sqrt{3}+\sqrt{x})(\sqrt{3}-\sqrt{x})$ $3-x$
b. $(\sqrt{3}+\sqrt{x})(\sqrt{3}+\sqrt{x})$ $3+2\sqrt{3x}+x$
c. $(\sqrt{3}-\sqrt{x})(\sqrt{3}-\sqrt{x})$ $3-2\sqrt{3x}+x$

68. **a.** $(\sqrt{5}+\sqrt{y})(\sqrt{5}-\sqrt{y})$ $5-y$
b. $(\sqrt{5}+\sqrt{y})(\sqrt{5}+\sqrt{y})$ $5+2\sqrt{5y}+y$
c. $(\sqrt{5}-\sqrt{y})(\sqrt{5}-\sqrt{y})$ $5-2\sqrt{5y}+y$

Mixed Exercises

For Exercises 69–76, identify each statement as true or false. If an answer is false, explain why.

69. $\sqrt{3}\cdot\sqrt{2}=\sqrt{6}$ True

70. $\sqrt{5}\cdot\sqrt[3]{2}=\sqrt{10}$ False; the radicals have different indices.

71. $(x-\sqrt{5})^2=x-5$ False; $(x-\sqrt{5})^2=x^2-2x\sqrt{5}+5$

72. $3(2\sqrt{5x})=6\sqrt{5x}$ True

73. $5(3\sqrt{4x})=15\sqrt{20x}$ False; 5 is multiplied by 3 only.

74. $\dfrac{\sqrt{5x}}{5}=\sqrt{x}$ False; $\dfrac{\sqrt{5}}{5}\neq 1$

75. $\dfrac{3\sqrt{x}}{3}=\sqrt{x}$ True

76. $(\sqrt{t}-1)(\sqrt{t}+1)=t-1$ True

For Exercises 77–84, perform the indicated operations.

77. $(-\sqrt{6x})^2$ $6x$

78. $(-\sqrt{8a})^2$ $8a$

79. $(\sqrt{3x+1})^2$ $3x+1$

80. $(\sqrt{x-1})^2$ $x-1$

81. $(\sqrt{x+3}-4)^2$ $x+19-8\sqrt{x+3}$

82. $(\sqrt{x+1}+3)^2$ $x+10+6\sqrt{x+1}$

83. $(\sqrt{2t-3}+5)^2$ $2t+10\sqrt{2t-3}+22$

84. $(\sqrt{3w-2}-4)^2$ $3w-8\sqrt{3w-2}+14$

For Exercises 85–88, find the exact area.

85.

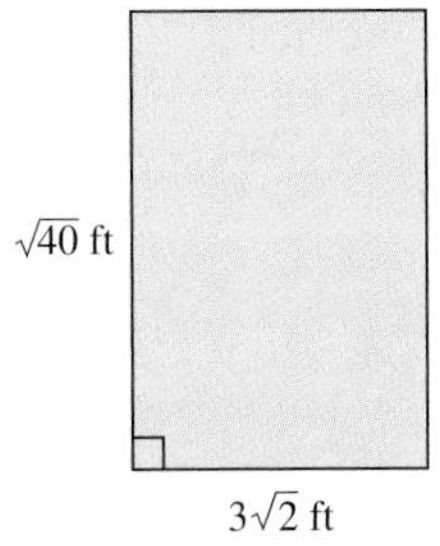

$12\sqrt{5}$ ft²

86.

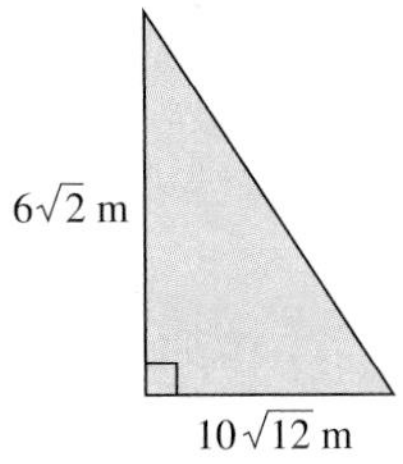

$60\sqrt{6}$ m²

87.

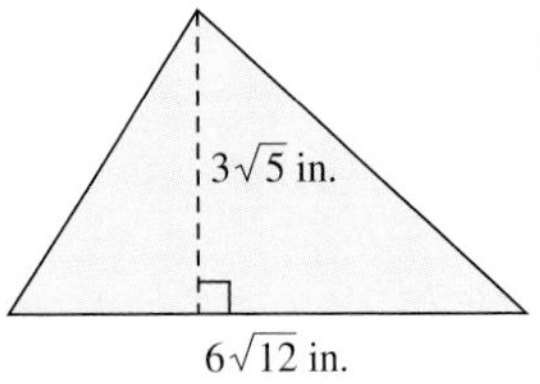

$18\sqrt{15}$ in.²

88.

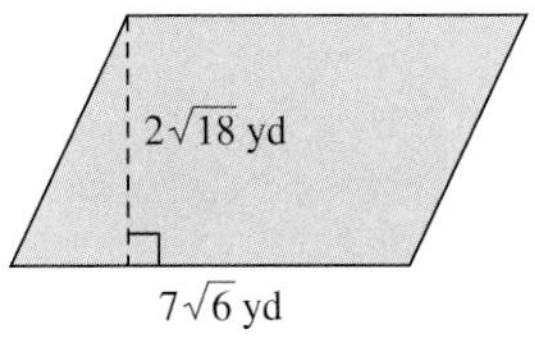

$84\sqrt{3}$ yd²

Concept 4: Multiplying Radicals with Different Indices

For Exercises 89–100, multiply or divide the radicals with different indices. Write the answers in radical form and simplify. **(See Example 8.)**

89. $\sqrt{x}\cdot\sqrt[4]{x}$ $\sqrt[4]{x^3}$

90. $\sqrt[3]{y}\cdot\sqrt{y}$ $\sqrt[6]{y^5}$

91. $\sqrt[5]{2z}\cdot\sqrt[3]{2z}$ $\sqrt[15]{(2z)^8}$

92. $\sqrt[3]{5w}\cdot\sqrt[4]{5w}$ $\sqrt[12]{(5w)^7}$

93. $\sqrt[3]{p^2}\cdot\sqrt{p^3}$ $p^2\sqrt[6]{p}$

94. $\sqrt[4]{q^3}\cdot\sqrt[3]{q^2}$ $q\sqrt[12]{q^5}$

95. $\dfrac{\sqrt{u^3}}{\sqrt[3]{u}}$ $u\sqrt[6]{u}$

96. $\dfrac{\sqrt{v^5}}{\sqrt[4]{v}}$ $v^2\sqrt[4]{v}$

97. $\sqrt[3]{x}\cdot\sqrt[6]{y}$ $\sqrt[6]{x^2y}$

98. $\sqrt{a}\cdot\sqrt[6]{b}$ $\sqrt[6]{a^3b}$

99. $\sqrt[4]{8}\cdot\sqrt{3}$ $\sqrt[4]{2^3\cdot 3^2}$ or $\sqrt[4]{72}$

100. $\sqrt{11}\cdot\sqrt[6]{2}$ $\sqrt[6]{11^3\cdot 2}$ or $\sqrt[6]{2662}$

Expanding Your Skills

For Exercises 101–106, multiply.

101. $\sqrt[3]{2xy}\cdot\sqrt[4]{5xy}$ $\sqrt[12]{2^4 5^3 x^7 y^7}$

102. $\sqrt{6ab}\cdot\sqrt[3]{7ab}$ $\sqrt[6]{2^3 3^3 7^2 a^5 b^5}$

103. $\sqrt[3]{4m^2n}\cdot\sqrt{6mn}$ $2m\sqrt[6]{3^3 2mn^5}$

104. $\sqrt[4]{5xy^3}\cdot\sqrt[3]{10x^2y}$ $y\sqrt[12]{2^4 5^7 x^{11} y}$

105. $(\sqrt[3]{a}+\sqrt[3]{b})(\sqrt[3]{a^2}-\sqrt[3]{ab}+\sqrt[3]{b^2})$ $a+b$

106. $(\sqrt[3]{a}-\sqrt[3]{b})(\sqrt[3]{a^2}+\sqrt[3]{ab}+\sqrt[3]{b^2})$ $a-b$

Problem Recognition Exercises

Simplifying Radical Expressions

For Exercises 1–20, simplify the expressions.

1. **a.** $\sqrt{24}$ $2\sqrt{6}$
b. $\sqrt[3]{24}$ $2\sqrt[3]{3}$

2. **a.** $\sqrt{54}$ $3\sqrt{6}$
b. $\sqrt[3]{54}$ $3\sqrt[3]{2}$

3. **a.** $\sqrt{200y^6}$ $10y^3\sqrt{2}$
b. $\sqrt[3]{200y^6}$ $2y^2\sqrt[3]{25}$

4. **a.** $\sqrt{32z^{15}}$ $4z^7\sqrt{2z}$
b. $\sqrt[3]{32z^{15}}$ $2z^5\sqrt[3]{4}$

5. **a.** $\sqrt{80}$ $4\sqrt{5}$
b. $\sqrt[3]{80}$ $2\sqrt[3]{10}$
c. $\sqrt[4]{80}$ $2\sqrt[4]{5}$

6. **a.** $\sqrt{48}$ $4\sqrt{3}$
b. $\sqrt[3]{48}$ $2\sqrt[3]{6}$
c. $\sqrt[4]{48}$ $2\sqrt[4]{3}$

7. **a.** $\sqrt{x^5y^6}$ $x^2y^3\sqrt{x}$
b. $\sqrt[3]{x^5y^6}$ $xy^2\sqrt[3]{x^2}$
c. $\sqrt[4]{x^5y^6}$ $xy\sqrt[4]{xy^2}$

8. **a.** $\sqrt{a^{10}b^9}$ $a^5b^4\sqrt{b}$
b. $\sqrt[3]{a^{10}b^9}$ $a^3b^3\sqrt[3]{a}$
c. $\sqrt[4]{a^{10}b^9}$ $a^2b^2\sqrt[4]{a^2b}$

9. **a.** $\sqrt[3]{32s^5t^6}$ $2st^2\sqrt[3]{4s^2}$
b. $\sqrt[4]{32s^5t^6}$ $2st\sqrt[4]{2st^2}$
c. $\sqrt[5]{32s^5t^6}$ $2st\sqrt[5]{t}$

10. **a.** $\sqrt[3]{96v^7w^{20}}$ $2v^2w^6\sqrt[3]{12vw^2}$
b. $\sqrt[4]{96v^7w^{20}}$ $2vw^5\sqrt[4]{6v^3}$
c. $\sqrt[5]{96v^7w^{20}}$ $2vw^4\sqrt[5]{3v^2}$

11. **a.** $\sqrt{5} + \sqrt{5}$ $2\sqrt{5}$
b. $\sqrt{5} \cdot \sqrt{5}$ 5

12. **a.** $\sqrt{10} + \sqrt{10}$ $2\sqrt{10}$
b. $\sqrt{10} \cdot \sqrt{10}$ 10

13. **a.** $2\sqrt{6} - 5\sqrt{6}$ $-3\sqrt{6}$
b. $2\sqrt{6} \cdot 5\sqrt{6}$ 60

14. **a.** $3\sqrt{7} - 10\sqrt{7}$ $-7\sqrt{7}$
b. $3\sqrt{7} \cdot 10\sqrt{7}$ 210

15. **a.** $\sqrt{8} + \sqrt{2}$ $3\sqrt{2}$
b. $\sqrt{8} \cdot \sqrt{2}$ 4

16. **a.** $\sqrt{12} + \sqrt{3}$ $3\sqrt{3}$
b. $\sqrt{12} \cdot \sqrt{3}$ 6

17. **a.** $5\sqrt{18} - 4\sqrt{8}$ $7\sqrt{2}$
b. $5\sqrt{18} \cdot 4\sqrt{8}$ 240

18. **a.** $\sqrt{50} - \sqrt{72}$ $-\sqrt{2}$
b. $\sqrt{50} \cdot \sqrt{72}$ 60

19. **a.** $4\sqrt[3]{24} + 6\sqrt[3]{3}$ $14\sqrt[3]{3}$
b. $4\sqrt[3]{24} \cdot 6\sqrt[3]{3}$ $48\sqrt[3]{9}$

20. **a.** $2\sqrt[3]{54} - 5\sqrt[3]{2}$ $\sqrt[3]{2}$
b. $2\sqrt[3]{54} \cdot 5\sqrt[3]{2}$ $30\sqrt[3]{4}$

Section 10.6 Division of Radicals and Rationalization

Concepts

1. Simplified Form of a Radical
2. Division Property of Radicals
3. Rationalizing the Denominator—One Term
4. Rationalizing the Denominator—Two Terms

1. Simplified Form of a Radical

Recall that for a radical expression to be in simplified form the following three conditions must be met.

Simplified Form of a Radical

Consider any radical expression in which the radicand is written as a product of prime factors. The expression is in simplified form if all the following conditions are met:

1. The radicand has no factor raised to a power greater than or equal to the index.
2. The radicand does not contain a fraction.
3. No radicals are in the denominator of a fraction.

In the previous sections, we have concentrated on the first condition in the simplification process. Next, we will demonstrate how to satisfy the second and third conditions involving radicals and fractions.

2. Division Property of Radicals

The multiplication property of radicals makes it possible to write a product within a radical to be separated as a product of radicals. We now state a similar property for radicals involving quotients.

Division Property of Radicals

Let a and b represent real numbers such that $\sqrt[n]{a}$ and $\sqrt[n]{b}$ are both real. Then,

$$\sqrt[n]{\frac{a}{b}} = \frac{\sqrt[n]{a}}{\sqrt[n]{b}} \qquad b \neq 0$$

The division property of radicals indicates that a quotient within a radicand can be written as a quotient of radicals provided the roots are real numbers. For example:

$$\sqrt{\frac{25}{36}} = \frac{\sqrt{25}}{\sqrt{36}}$$

The reverse process is also true. A quotient of radicals can be written as a single radical provided that the roots are real numbers and that they have the same index.

$$\text{Same index} \quad \frac{\sqrt[3]{125}}{\sqrt[3]{8}} = \sqrt[3]{\frac{125}{8}}$$

In Examples 1 and 2, we will apply the division property of radicals to simplify radical expressions.

Example 1 Using the Division Property to Simplify Radicals

Classroom Example: p. 742, Exercise 16

Use the division property of radicals to simplify the expressions. Assume the variables represent positive real numbers.

a. $\sqrt{\frac{a^6}{b^4}}$ **b.** $\sqrt[3]{\frac{81y^5}{x^3}}$

Solution:

a. $\sqrt{\frac{a^6}{b^4}}$ The radicand contains an irreducible fraction.

$= \frac{\sqrt{a^6}}{\sqrt{b^4}}$ Apply the division property to rewrite as a quotient of radicals.

$= \frac{a^3}{b^2}$ Simplify the radicals.

b. $\sqrt[3]{\dfrac{81y^5}{x^3}}$ The radicand contains an irreducible fraction.

$= \dfrac{\sqrt[3]{81y^5}}{\sqrt[3]{x^3}}$ Apply the division property to rewrite as a quotient of radicals.

$= \dfrac{\sqrt[3]{3^4 \cdot y^5}}{\sqrt[3]{x^3}}$ Factor the radicand in the numerator to simplify the radical.

$= \dfrac{3y\sqrt[3]{3y^2}}{x}$ Simplify the radicals in the numerator and the denominator. The expression is simplified because it now satisfies all conditions.

Skill Practice Simplify the expressions.

1. $\sqrt{\dfrac{x^4}{y^{10}}}$ **2.** $\sqrt[3]{\dfrac{w^7}{64}}$

Classroom Example: p. 742, Exercise 22

Example 2 **Using the Division Property to Simplify a Radical**

Use the division property of radicals to simplify the expressions. Assume the variables represent positive real numbers.

$$\frac{\sqrt[4]{8p^7}}{\sqrt[4]{p^3}}$$

Solution:

$\dfrac{\sqrt[4]{8p^7}}{\sqrt[4]{p^3}}$ There is a radical in the denominator of the fraction.

$= \sqrt[4]{\dfrac{8p^7}{p^3}}$ Apply the division property to write the quotient under a single radical.

$= \sqrt[4]{8p^4}$ Simplify the fraction.

$= p\sqrt[4]{8}$ Simplify the radical.

Skill Practice Simplify the expression.

3. $\dfrac{\sqrt[3]{16y^4}}{\sqrt[3]{y}}$

3. Rationalizing the Denominator—One Term

The third condition restricts radicals from the denominator of an expression. The process to remove a radical from the denominator is called **rationalizing the denominator**. In many cases, rationalizing the denominator creates an expression that is computationally simpler. For example,

$$\frac{6}{\sqrt{3}} = 2\sqrt{3} \quad \text{and} \quad \frac{-2}{2+\sqrt{6}} = 2-\sqrt{6}$$

Answers

1. $\dfrac{x^2}{y^5}$ **2.** $\dfrac{w^2\sqrt[3]{w}}{4}$ **3.** $2y\sqrt[3]{2}$

We will demonstrate the process to rationalize the denominator as two separate cases:

- Rationalizing the denominator (one term)
- Rationalizing the denominator (two terms involving square roots)

To begin the first case, recall that the *n*th root of a perfect *n*th power simplifies completely.

$$\sqrt{x^2} = x \qquad x \geq 0$$
$$\sqrt[3]{x^3} = x$$
$$\sqrt[4]{x^4} = x \qquad x \geq 0$$
$$\sqrt[5]{x^5} = x$$
$$\ldots$$

Therefore, to rationalize a radical expression, use the multiplication property of radicals to create an *n*th root of an *n*th power.

Example 3 Rationalizing Radical Expressions

Classroom Example: p. 742, Exercise 26

Fill in the missing radicand to rationalize the radical expressions. Assume all variables represent positive real numbers.

a. $\sqrt{a} \cdot \sqrt{?} = \sqrt{a^2} = a$ **b.** $\sqrt[3]{y} \cdot \sqrt[3]{?} = \sqrt[3]{y^3} = y$

c. $\sqrt[4]{2z^3} \cdot \sqrt[4]{?} = \sqrt[4]{2^4z^4} = 2z$

Solution:

a. $\sqrt{a} \cdot \sqrt{?} = \sqrt{a^2} = a$ What multiplied by $\sqrt{a}$ will equal $\sqrt{a^2}$?

$\sqrt{a} \cdot \sqrt{a} = \sqrt{a^2} = a$

b. $\sqrt[3]{y} \cdot \sqrt[3]{?} = \sqrt[3]{y^3} = y$ What multiplied by $\sqrt[3]{y}$ will equal $\sqrt[3]{y^3}$?

$\sqrt[3]{y} \cdot \sqrt[3]{y^2} = \sqrt[3]{y^3} = y$

c. $\sqrt[4]{2z^3} \cdot \sqrt[4]{?} = \sqrt[4]{2^4z^4} = 2z$ What multiplied by $\sqrt[4]{2z^3}$ will equal $\sqrt[4]{2^4z^4}$?

$\sqrt[4]{2z^3} \cdot \sqrt[4]{2^3z} = \sqrt[4]{2^4z^4} = 2z$

Skill Practice Fill in the missing radicand to rationalize the radical expression.

4. $\sqrt{7} \cdot \sqrt{?}$ **5.** $\sqrt[5]{t^2} \cdot \sqrt[5]{?}$ **6.** $\sqrt[3]{5x^2} \cdot \sqrt[3]{?}$

To rationalize the denominator of an expression with a single radical term in the denominator, we have the following strategy. Multiply the numerator and denominator by an appropriate expression to create an *n*th root of an *n*th power in the denominator.

Answers

4. 7 **5.** t^3 **6.** 5^2x

Classroom Example: p. 742, Exercise 42

Example 4 Rationalizing the Denominator—One Term

Simplify the expression. $\dfrac{5}{\sqrt[3]{a}}$ $a \neq 0$

Solution:

To remove the radical from the denominator, a cube root of a perfect cube is needed in the denominator. Multiply numerator and denominator by $\sqrt[3]{a^2}$ because $\sqrt[3]{a} \cdot \sqrt[3]{a^2} = \sqrt[3]{a^3} = a$.

$$\frac{5}{\sqrt[3]{a}} = \frac{5}{\sqrt[3]{a}} \cdot \frac{\sqrt[3]{a^2}}{\sqrt[3]{a^2}}$$

$$= \frac{5\sqrt[3]{a^2}}{\sqrt[3]{a^3}} \quad \text{Multiply the radicals.}$$

$$= \frac{5\sqrt[3]{a^2}}{a} \quad \text{Simplify.}$$

Skill Practice Simplify the expression. Assume $y > 0$.

7. $\dfrac{2}{\sqrt[4]{y}}$

Note that for $a \neq 0$, the expression $\dfrac{\sqrt[3]{a^2}}{\sqrt[3]{a^2}} = 1$. In Example 4, multiplying the expression $\dfrac{5}{\sqrt[3]{a}}$ by this ratio does not change its value.

Classroom Example: p. 742, Exercise 38

Example 5 Rationalizing the Denominator—One Term

Simplify the expression. $\sqrt{\dfrac{y^5}{7}}$

Solution:

$$\sqrt{\frac{y^5}{7}} \quad \text{The radical contains an irreducible fraction.}$$

$$= \frac{\sqrt{y^5}}{\sqrt{7}} \quad \text{Apply the division property of radicals.}$$

$$= \frac{y^2\sqrt{y}}{\sqrt{7}} \quad \text{Simplify the radical in the numerator.}$$

$$= \frac{y^2\sqrt{y}}{\sqrt{7}} \cdot \frac{\sqrt{7}}{\sqrt{7}} \quad \text{Rationalize the denominator.}$$

Note: $\sqrt{7} \cdot \sqrt{7} = \sqrt{7^2} = 7$

$$= \frac{y^2\sqrt{7y}}{\sqrt{7^2}}$$

$$= \frac{y^2\sqrt{7y}}{7} \quad \text{Simplify.}$$

Avoiding Mistakes

A factor within a radicand cannot be simplified with a factor outside the radicand. For example, $\dfrac{\sqrt{7y}}{7}$ cannot be simplified.

Answer

7. $\dfrac{2\sqrt[4]{y^3}}{y}$

Skill Practice Simplify the expression.

8. $\sqrt{\frac{8}{3}}$

Example 6 Rationalizing the Denominator—One Term

Classroom Example: p. 742, Exercise 52

Simplify the expression. $\frac{15}{\sqrt[3]{25s}}$

Solution:

$\frac{15}{\sqrt[3]{25s}}$

$= \frac{15}{\sqrt[3]{5^2 s}} \cdot \frac{\sqrt[3]{5s^2}}{\sqrt[3]{5s^2}}$ Because $25 = 5^2$, one additional factor of 5 is needed to form a perfect cube. Two additional factors of s are needed to make a perfect cube. Multiply numerator and denominator by $\sqrt[3]{5s^2}$.

$= \frac{15\sqrt[3]{5s^2}}{\sqrt[3]{5^3 s^3}}$

$= \frac{15\sqrt[3]{5s^2}}{5s}$ Simplify the perfect cube.

$= \frac{\overset{3}{\cancel{15}}\sqrt[3]{5s^2}}{\underset{1}{\cancel{5}}s}$ Reduce to lowest terms.

$= \frac{3\sqrt[3]{5s^2}}{s}$

TIP: In the expression $\frac{15\sqrt[3]{5s^2}}{5s}$, the factor of 15 and the factor of 5 may be reduced because both are outside the radical.

$$\frac{15\sqrt[3]{5s^2}}{5s} = \frac{15}{5} \cdot \frac{\sqrt[3]{5s^2}}{s}$$
$$= \frac{3\sqrt[3]{5s^2}}{s}$$

Skill Practice Simplify the expression.

9. $\frac{18}{\sqrt[3]{3y^2}}$

4. Rationalizing the Denominator—Two Terms

Example 7 demonstrates how to rationalize a two-term denominator involving square roots.

First recall from the multiplication of polynomials that the product of two conjugates results in a difference of squares.

$$(a + b)(a - b) = a^2 - b^2$$

If either a or b has a square root factor, the expression will simplify without a radical. That is, the expression is *rationalized.* For example:

$$(2 + \sqrt{6})(2 - \sqrt{6}) = (2)^2 - (\sqrt{6})^2$$
$$= 4 - 6$$
$$= -2$$

Answers

8. $\frac{2\sqrt{6}}{3}$ **9.** $\frac{6\sqrt[3]{9y}}{y}$

Classroom Example: p. 743, Exercise 66

Instructor Note: In Example 7, point out to students that $\frac{(2-\sqrt{6})}{(2-\sqrt{6})}=1$.

Avoiding Mistakes

When constructing the conjugate of an expression, change only the sign between the terms (not the sign of the leading term).

Example 7 Rationalizing the Denominator—Two Terms

Simplify the expression by rationalizing the denominator. $\frac{-2}{2+\sqrt{6}}$

Solution:

$$\frac{-2}{2+\sqrt{6}}$$

$$=\frac{(-2)}{(2+\sqrt{6})}\cdot\frac{(2-\sqrt{6})}{(2-\sqrt{6})}$$ Multiply the numerator and denominator by the conjugate of the denominator.

(conjugates)

$$=\frac{-2(2-\sqrt{6})}{(2)^2-(\sqrt{6})^2}$$ In the denominator, apply the formula $(a+b)(a-b)=a^2-b^2$.

$$=\frac{-2(2-\sqrt{6})}{4-6}$$ Simplify.

$$=\frac{-2(2-\sqrt{6})}{-2}$$

$$=\frac{\cancel{-2}(2-\sqrt{6})}{\cancel{-2}}$$

$$=2-\sqrt{6}$$

Skill Practice Simplify by rationalizing the denominator.

10. $\frac{8}{3+\sqrt{5}}$

Classroom Example: p. 743, Exercise 74

Example 8 Rationalizing the Denominator—Two Terms

Rationalize the denominator. $\frac{4+\sqrt{x}}{\sqrt{x}-7}$

Solution:

$$\frac{(4+\sqrt{x})}{(\sqrt{x}-7)}\cdot\frac{(\sqrt{x}+7)}{(\sqrt{x}+7)}$$ Multiply numerator and denominator by the conjugate of the denominator.

$$=\frac{(4)(\sqrt{x})+(4)(7)+(\sqrt{x})(\sqrt{x})+(\sqrt{x})(7)}{(\sqrt{x})^2-(7)^2}$$ Apply the distributive property.

$$=\frac{4\sqrt{x}+28+x+7\sqrt{x}}{x-49}$$ Multiply the radicals.

$$=\frac{x+11\sqrt{x}+28}{x-49}$$ Simplify.

Skill Practice Rationalize the denominator.

11. $\frac{\sqrt{y}-4}{8-\sqrt{y}}$

Answers

10. $6-2\sqrt{5}$

11. $\frac{y+4\sqrt{y}-32}{64-y}$

Example 9 Rationalizing the Denominator—Two Terms

Classroom Example: p. 743, Exercise 80

Rationalize the denominator. $\dfrac{3\sqrt{2}+2\sqrt{5}}{\sqrt{2}-4\sqrt{5}}$

Solution:

$\dfrac{(3\sqrt{2}+2\sqrt{5})}{(\sqrt{2}-4\sqrt{5})}\cdot\dfrac{(\sqrt{2}+4\sqrt{5})}{(\sqrt{2}+4\sqrt{5})}$ Multiply numerator and denominator by the conjugate of the denominator.

$=\dfrac{(3\sqrt{2})\cdot(\sqrt{2})+(3\sqrt{2})(4\sqrt{5})+(2\sqrt{5})(\sqrt{2})+(2\sqrt{5})(4\sqrt{5})}{(\sqrt{2})^2-(4\sqrt{5})^2}$ Apply the distributive property.

$=\dfrac{6+12\sqrt{10}+2\sqrt{10}+40}{2-80}$ Multiply the radicals.

$=\dfrac{46+14\sqrt{10}}{-78}$ or $-\dfrac{46+14\sqrt{10}}{78}$

$=-\dfrac{\overset{1}{\cancel{2}}(23+7\sqrt{10})}{\underset{39}{\cancel{78}}}$ Factor and simplify.

$=-\dfrac{23+7\sqrt{10}}{39}$

Skill Practice Rationalize the denominator.

12. $\dfrac{5\sqrt{2}-2\sqrt{5}}{\sqrt{2}-\sqrt{5}}$

Answer

12. $-\sqrt{10}$

Section 10.6 Practice Exercises

For additional exercises, see Classroom Activities 10.6A–10.6C in the *Student's Resource Manual* at www.mhhe.com/moh.

For the exercises in this set, assume that all variables represent positive real numbers unless otherwise stated.

Vocabulary and Key Concepts

1. **a.** In the simplified form of a radical expression, no ____radical____ may appear in the denominator of a fraction.

   b. The division property of radicals indicates that if $\sqrt[n]{a}$ and $\sqrt[n]{b}$ are real numbers, then $\sqrt[n]{\dfrac{a}{b}}=\dfrac{\square}{\square}$ provided that $b \neq 0$. $\dfrac{\sqrt[n]{a}}{\sqrt[n]{b}}$

   c. The simplified form of the expression $\sqrt[3]{\dfrac{64}{x^6}}$ is ____$\dfrac{4}{x^2}$____.

   d. The process of removing a radical from the denominator of a fraction is called ____rationalizing____ the denominator.

   e. The expression $\dfrac{\sqrt{3}}{3}$ (is/is not) in simplified form whereas $\dfrac{3}{\sqrt{3}}$ (is/is not) in simplified form. is; is not

   f. To rationalize the denominator for the expression $\dfrac{\sqrt{x}+3}{\sqrt{x}-2}$, multiply numerator and denominator by the conjugate of the ____denominator____.

Review Exercises

2. Simplify. $(4x^2y^4)^{1/2}(64y^{-3})^{1/3}$ $8xy$

For Exercises 3–10, perform the indicated operations.

3. $2y\sqrt{45} + 3\sqrt{20y^2}$ $12y\sqrt{5}$
4. $3x\sqrt{72x} - 9\sqrt{50x^3}$ $-27x\sqrt{2x}$
5. $(-6\sqrt{y} + 3)(3\sqrt{y} + 1)$ $-18y + 3\sqrt{y} + 3$
6. $(\sqrt{w} + 12)(2\sqrt{w} - 4)$ $2w + 20\sqrt{w} - 48$
7. $(8 - \sqrt{t})^2$ $64 - 16\sqrt{t} + t$
8. $(\sqrt{p} + 4)^2$ $p + 8\sqrt{p} + 16$
9. $(\sqrt{2} + \sqrt{7})(\sqrt{2} - \sqrt{7})$ -5
10. $(\sqrt{3} + 5)(\sqrt{3} - 5)$ -22

Concept 2: Division Property of Radicals

For Exercises 11–22, simplify using the division property of radicals. Assume all variables represent positive real numbers. **(See Examples 1–2.)**

11. $\sqrt{\dfrac{49x^4}{y^6}}$ $\dfrac{7x^2}{y^3}$
12. $\sqrt{\dfrac{100p^2}{q^8}}$ $\dfrac{10p}{q^4}$
13. $\sqrt{\dfrac{8a^2}{x^6}}$ $\dfrac{2a\sqrt{2}}{x^3}$
14. $\sqrt{\dfrac{4w^3}{25y^4}}$ $\dfrac{2w\sqrt{w}}{5y^2}$
15. $\sqrt[3]{\dfrac{-16j^3}{k^3}}$ $-\dfrac{2j\sqrt[3]{2}}{k}$
16. $\sqrt[5]{\dfrac{32x}{y^{10}}}$ $\dfrac{2\sqrt[5]{x}}{y^2}$
17. $\dfrac{\sqrt{72ab^5}}{\sqrt{8ab}}$ $3b^2$
18. $\dfrac{\sqrt{6x^3}}{\sqrt{24x}}$ $\dfrac{x}{2}$
19. $\dfrac{\sqrt[4]{3b^3}}{\sqrt[4]{48b^{11}}}$ $\dfrac{1}{2b^2}$
20. $\dfrac{\sqrt[3]{128wz^8}}{\sqrt[3]{2wz^2}}$ $4z^2$
21. $\dfrac{\sqrt{3yz^2}}{\sqrt{w^4}}$ $\dfrac{z\sqrt{3y}}{w^2}$
22. $\dfrac{\sqrt{50x^3z}}{\sqrt{9y^4}}$ $\dfrac{5x\sqrt{2xz}}{3y^2}$

Concept 3: Rationalizing the Denominator—One Term

The radical expressions in Exercises 23–30 have radicals in the denominator. Fill in the missing radicands to rationalize the denominators. **(See Example 3.)**

23. $\dfrac{x}{\sqrt{5}} = \dfrac{x}{\sqrt{5}} \cdot \dfrac{\sqrt{?}}{\sqrt{?}}$ $\dfrac{\sqrt{5}}{\sqrt{5}}$
24. $\dfrac{2}{\sqrt{x}} = \dfrac{2}{\sqrt{x}} \cdot \dfrac{\sqrt{?}}{\sqrt{?}}$ $\dfrac{\sqrt{x}}{\sqrt{x}}$
25. $\dfrac{7}{\sqrt[3]{x}} = \dfrac{7}{\sqrt[3]{x}} \cdot \dfrac{\sqrt[3]{?}}{\sqrt[3]{?}}$ $\dfrac{\sqrt[3]{x^2}}{\sqrt[3]{x^2}}$
26. $\dfrac{5}{\sqrt[4]{y}} = \dfrac{5}{\sqrt[4]{y}} \cdot \dfrac{\sqrt[4]{?}}{\sqrt[4]{?}}$ $\dfrac{\sqrt[4]{y^3}}{\sqrt[4]{y^3}}$
27. $\dfrac{8}{\sqrt{3z}} = \dfrac{8}{\sqrt{3z}} \cdot \dfrac{\sqrt{??}}{\sqrt{??}}$ $\dfrac{\sqrt{3z}}{\sqrt{3z}}$
28. $\dfrac{10}{\sqrt{7w}} = \dfrac{10}{\sqrt{7w}} \cdot \dfrac{\sqrt{??}}{\sqrt{??}}$ $\dfrac{\sqrt{7w}}{\sqrt{7w}}$
29. $\dfrac{1}{\sqrt[4]{8a^2}} = \dfrac{1}{\sqrt[4]{8a^2}} \cdot \dfrac{\sqrt[4]{??}}{\sqrt[4]{??}}$ $\dfrac{\sqrt[4]{2a^2}}{\sqrt[4]{2a^2}}$
30. $\dfrac{1}{\sqrt[3]{9b^2}} = \dfrac{1}{\sqrt[3]{9b^2}} \cdot \dfrac{\sqrt[3]{??}}{\sqrt[3]{??}}$ $\dfrac{\sqrt[3]{3b}}{\sqrt[3]{3b}}$

For Exercises 31–58, rationalize the denominator. **(See Examples 4–6.)**

31. $\dfrac{1}{\sqrt{3}}$ $\dfrac{\sqrt{3}}{3}$
32. $\dfrac{1}{\sqrt{7}}$ $\dfrac{\sqrt{7}}{7}$
33. $\sqrt{\dfrac{1}{x}}$ $\dfrac{\sqrt{x}}{x}$
34. $\sqrt{\dfrac{1}{z}}$ $\dfrac{\sqrt{z}}{z}$
35. $\dfrac{6}{\sqrt{2y}}$ $\dfrac{3\sqrt{2y}}{y}$
36. $\dfrac{9}{\sqrt{3t}}$ $\dfrac{3\sqrt{3t}}{t}$
37. $\sqrt{\dfrac{a^3}{2}}$ $\dfrac{a\sqrt{2a}}{2}$
38. $\sqrt{\dfrac{b^3}{3}}$ $\dfrac{b\sqrt{3b}}{3}$
39. $\dfrac{6}{\sqrt{8}}$ $\dfrac{3\sqrt{2}}{2}$
40. $\dfrac{2}{\sqrt{48}}$ $\dfrac{\sqrt{3}}{6}$
41. $\dfrac{3}{\sqrt[3]{2}}$ $\dfrac{3\sqrt[3]{4}}{2}$
42. $\dfrac{2}{\sqrt[3]{7}}$ $\dfrac{2\sqrt[3]{49}}{7}$
43. $\dfrac{-6}{\sqrt[4]{x}}$ $\dfrac{-6\sqrt[4]{x^3}}{x}$
44. $\dfrac{-2}{\sqrt[5]{y}}$ $\dfrac{-2\sqrt[5]{y^4}}{y}$
45. $\dfrac{7}{\sqrt[3]{4}}$ $\dfrac{7\sqrt[3]{2}}{2}$
46. $\dfrac{1}{\sqrt[3]{9}}$ $\dfrac{\sqrt[3]{3}}{3}$
47. $\sqrt[3]{\dfrac{4}{w^2}}$ $\dfrac{\sqrt[3]{4w}}{w}$
48. $\sqrt[3]{\dfrac{5}{z^2}}$ $\dfrac{\sqrt[3]{5z}}{z}$
49. $\sqrt[4]{\dfrac{16}{3}}$ $\dfrac{2\sqrt[4]{27}}{3}$
50. $\sqrt[4]{\dfrac{81}{8}}$ $\dfrac{3\sqrt[4]{2}}{2}$
51. $\dfrac{2}{\sqrt[3]{4x^2}}$ $\dfrac{\sqrt[3]{2x}}{x}$
52. $\dfrac{6}{\sqrt[3]{3y^2}}$ $\dfrac{2\sqrt[3]{9y}}{y}$
53. $\dfrac{8}{7\sqrt{24}}$ $\dfrac{2\sqrt{6}}{21}$
54. $\dfrac{5}{3\sqrt{50}}$ $\dfrac{\sqrt{2}}{6}$

55. $\dfrac{1}{\sqrt{x^7}}$ $\dfrac{\sqrt{x}}{x^4}$

56. $\dfrac{1}{\sqrt{y^5}}$ $\dfrac{\sqrt{y}}{y^3}$

57. $\dfrac{2}{\sqrt{8x^5}}$ $\dfrac{\sqrt{2x}}{2x^3}$

58. $\dfrac{6}{\sqrt{27t^7}}$ $\dfrac{2\sqrt{3t}}{3t^4}$

Concept 4: Rationalizing the Denominator—Two Terms

59. What is the conjugate of $\sqrt{2} - \sqrt{6}$? $\sqrt{2} + \sqrt{6}$

60. What is the conjugate of $\sqrt{11} + \sqrt{5}$? $\sqrt{11} - \sqrt{5}$

61. What is the conjugate of $\sqrt{x} + 23$? $\sqrt{x} - 23$

62. What is the conjugate of $17 - \sqrt{y}$? $17 + \sqrt{y}$

For Exercises 63–82, rationalize the denominator. **(See Examples 7–9.)**

63. $\dfrac{4}{\sqrt{2} + 3}$ $\dfrac{4\sqrt{2} - 12}{-7}$ or $\dfrac{-4\sqrt{2} + 12}{7}$

64. $\dfrac{6}{4 - \sqrt{3}}$ $\dfrac{24 + 6\sqrt{3}}{13}$

65. $\dfrac{8}{\sqrt{6} - 2}$ $4\sqrt{6} + 8$

66. $\dfrac{-12}{\sqrt{5} - 3}$ $3\sqrt{5} + 9$

67. $\dfrac{\sqrt{7}}{\sqrt{3} + 2}$ $-\sqrt{21} + 2\sqrt{7}$

68. $\dfrac{\sqrt{8}}{\sqrt{3} + 1}$ $\sqrt{6} - \sqrt{2}$

69. $\dfrac{-1}{\sqrt{p} + \sqrt{q}}$ $\dfrac{-\sqrt{p} + \sqrt{q}}{p - q}$

70. $\dfrac{6}{\sqrt{a} - \sqrt{b}}$ $\dfrac{6\sqrt{a} + 6\sqrt{b}}{a - b}$

71. $\dfrac{x - 5}{\sqrt{x} + \sqrt{5}}$ $\sqrt{x} - \sqrt{5}$

72. $\dfrac{y - 2}{\sqrt{y} - \sqrt{2}}$ $\sqrt{y} + \sqrt{2}$

73. $\dfrac{\sqrt{w} + 2}{9 - \sqrt{w}}$ $\dfrac{w + 11\sqrt{w} + 18}{81 - w}$

74. $\dfrac{10 - \sqrt{t}}{\sqrt{t} - 6}$ $\dfrac{-t + 4\sqrt{t} + 60}{t - 36}$

75. $\dfrac{3\sqrt{x} - \sqrt{y}}{\sqrt{y} + \sqrt{x}}$ $\dfrac{4\sqrt{xy} - 3x - y}{y - x}$

76. $\dfrac{2\sqrt{a} + \sqrt{b}}{\sqrt{b} - \sqrt{a}}$ $\dfrac{3\sqrt{ab} + 2a + b}{b - a}$

77. $\dfrac{3\sqrt{10}}{2 + \sqrt{10}}$ $5 - \sqrt{10}$

78. $\dfrac{4\sqrt{7}}{3 + \sqrt{7}}$ $6\sqrt{7} - 14$

79. $\dfrac{2\sqrt{3} + \sqrt{7}}{3\sqrt{3} - \sqrt{7}}$ $\dfrac{5 + \sqrt{21}}{4}$

80. $\dfrac{5\sqrt{2} - \sqrt{5}}{5\sqrt{2} + \sqrt{5}}$ $\dfrac{11 - 2\sqrt{10}}{9}$

81. $\dfrac{\sqrt{5} + 4}{2 - \sqrt{5}}$ $-6\sqrt{5} - 13$

82. $\dfrac{3 + \sqrt{2}}{\sqrt{2} - 5}$ $\dfrac{17 + 8\sqrt{2}}{-23}$ or $\dfrac{-17 - 8\sqrt{2}}{23}$

Mixed Exercises

For Exercises 83–86, write the English phrase as an algebraic expression. Then simplify the expression.

83. 16 divided by the cube root of 4 $\dfrac{16}{\sqrt[3]{4}}$ simplifies to $8\sqrt[3]{2}$

84. 21 divided by the principal fourth root of 27 $\dfrac{21}{\sqrt[4]{27}}$ simplifies to $7\sqrt[4]{3}$

85. 4 divided by the difference of x and the principal square root of 2 $\dfrac{4}{x - \sqrt{2}}$ simplifies to $\dfrac{4x + 4\sqrt{2}}{x^2 - 2}$

86. 8 divided by the sum of y and the principal square root of 3 $\dfrac{8}{y + \sqrt{3}}$ simplifies to $\dfrac{8y - 8\sqrt{3}}{y^2 - 3}$

87. The time $T(x)$ (in seconds) for a pendulum to make one complete swing back and forth is approximated by

$$T(x) = 2\pi\sqrt{\frac{x}{32}}$$

where x is the length of the pendulum in feet.

Determine the exact time required for one swing for a pendulum that is 1 ft long. Then approximate the time to the nearest hundredth of a second.
$\dfrac{\pi\sqrt{2}}{4}$ sec ≈ 1.11 sec

© Jonnie Miles/Getty Images RF

88. An object is dropped off a building x meters tall. The time $T(x)$ (in seconds) required for the object to hit the ground is given by

$$T(x) = \sqrt{\frac{10x}{49}}$$

Find the exact time required for the object to hit the ground if it is dropped off Three First National Plaza in Chicago, a height of 230 m. Then round the time to the nearest hundredth of a second.
$\dfrac{10\sqrt{23}}{7}$ sec ≈ 6.85 sec

For Exercises 89–92, rationalize the denominator.

89. **a.** $\frac{1}{\sqrt{2}}$ $\frac{\sqrt{2}}{2}$ **b.** $\frac{1}{\sqrt[3]{2}}$ $\frac{\sqrt[3]{4}}{2}$

90. **a.** $\frac{1}{\sqrt[3]{x}}$ $\frac{\sqrt[3]{x^2}}{x}$ **b.** $\frac{1}{\sqrt[3]{x^2}}$ $\frac{\sqrt[3]{x}}{x}$

91. **a.** $\frac{1}{\sqrt{5a}}$ $\frac{\sqrt{5a}}{5a}$ **b.** $\frac{1}{\sqrt{5}+a}$ $\frac{\sqrt{5}-a}{5-a^2}$

92. **a.** $\frac{4}{\sqrt{2x}}$ $\frac{2\sqrt{2x}}{x}$ **b.** $\frac{4}{2-\sqrt{x}}$ $\frac{8+4\sqrt{x}}{4-x}$

Expanding Your Skills

For Exercises 93–98, simplify each term of the expression. Then add or subtract as indicated.

93. $\frac{\sqrt{6}}{2}+\frac{1}{\sqrt{6}}$ $\frac{2\sqrt{6}}{3}$

94. $\frac{1}{\sqrt{7}}+\sqrt{7}$ $\frac{8\sqrt{7}}{7}$

95. $\sqrt{15}-\sqrt{\frac{3}{5}}+\sqrt{\frac{5}{3}}$ $\frac{17\sqrt{15}}{15}$

96. $\sqrt{\frac{6}{2}}-\sqrt{12}+\sqrt{\frac{2}{6}}$ $\frac{-2\sqrt{3}}{3}$

97. $\sqrt[3]{25}+\frac{3}{\sqrt[3]{5}}$ $\frac{8\sqrt[3]{25}}{5}$

98. $\frac{1}{\sqrt[3]{4}}+\sqrt[3]{54}$ $\frac{7\sqrt[3]{2}}{2}$

For Exercises 99–106, rationalize the numerator by multiplying both numerator and denominator by the conjugate of the numerator.

99. $\frac{\sqrt{3}+6}{2}$ $\frac{-33}{2\sqrt{3}-12}$

100. $\frac{\sqrt{7}-2}{5}$ $\frac{3}{5\sqrt{7}+10}$

101. $\frac{\sqrt{a}-\sqrt{b}}{\sqrt{a}+\sqrt{b}}$ $\frac{a-b}{a+2\sqrt{ab}+b}$

102. $\frac{\sqrt{p}+\sqrt{q}}{\sqrt{p}-\sqrt{q}}$ $\frac{p-q}{p-2\sqrt{pq}+q}$

103. $\frac{\sqrt{5+3h}-\sqrt{5}}{h}$ $\frac{3}{\sqrt{5+3h}+\sqrt{5}}$

104. $\frac{\sqrt{7+2h}-\sqrt{7}}{h}$ $\frac{2}{\sqrt{7+2h}+\sqrt{7}}$

105. $\frac{\sqrt{4+5h}-2}{h}$ $\frac{5}{\sqrt{4+5h}+2}$

106. $\frac{\sqrt{9+4h}-3}{h}$ $\frac{4}{\sqrt{9+4h}+3}$

Section 10.7 Solving Radical Equations

Concepts

1. Solutions to Radical Equations
2. Solving Radical Equations Involving One Radical
3. Solving Radical Equations Involving More than One Radical
4. Applications of Radical Equations and Functions

1. Solutions to Radical Equations

An equation with one or more radicals containing a variable is called a **radical equation**. For example, $\sqrt[3]{x}=5$ is a radical equation. Recall that $(\sqrt[n]{a})^n = a$, provided $\sqrt[n]{a}$ is a real number. The basis of solving a radical equation is to eliminate the radical by raising both sides of the equation to a power equal to the index of the radical.

To solve the equation $\sqrt[3]{x}=5$, cube both sides of the equation.

$$\sqrt[3]{x}=5$$

$$(\sqrt[3]{x})^3=(5)^3$$

$$x=125$$

By raising each side of a radical equation to a power equal to the index of the radical, a new equation is produced. Note, however, that some of (or all) the solutions to the new equation may *not* be solutions to the original radical equation. For this reason, it is necessary to *check all potential solutions* in the original equation. For example, consider the equation $\sqrt{x}=-7$. This equation has no solution because by definition, the principal square root of x must be a nonnegative number. However, if we square both sides of the equation, it appears as though a solution exists.

Instructor Note: Give students this Memory Device: Extraneous solutions are *Extra* solutions that don't fit the original problem.

$$(\sqrt{x})^2=(-7)^2$$

$x=49$ The value 49 does not check in the original equation $\sqrt{x}=-7$. Therefore, 49 is an **extraneous solution**.

Solving a Radical Equation

Step 1 Isolate the radical. If an equation has more than one radical, choose one of the radicals to isolate.

Step 2 Raise each side of the equation to a power equal to the index of the radical.

Step 3 Solve the resulting equation. If the equation still has a radical, repeat steps 1 and 2.

***Step 4** Check the potential solutions in the original equation.

*In solving radical equations, extraneous solutions *potentially occur* only when each side of the equation is raised to an even power.

2. Solving Radical Equations Involving One Radical

Example 1 Solving an Equation Containing One Radical

Classroom Example: p. 752, Exercise 14

Solve the equation. $\sqrt{p} + 5 = 9$

Solution:

$\sqrt{p} + 5 = 9$

$\sqrt{p} = 4$ Isolate the radical.

$(\sqrt{p})^2 = 4^2$ Because the index is 2, square both sides.

$p = 16$

Check: $p = 16$ Check $p = 16$ as a potential solution.

$\sqrt{p} + 5 = 9$

$\sqrt{16} + 5 \stackrel{?}{=} 9$

$4 + 5 \stackrel{?}{=} 9$ ✓ True, 16 is a solution to the original equation.

The solution set is $\{16\}$.

Skill Practice Solve.

1. $\sqrt{x} - 3 = 2$

Example 2 Solving an Equation Containing One Radical

Classroom Example: p. 752, Exercise 22

Solve the equation. $\sqrt[3]{w - 1} - 2 = 2$

Solution:

$\sqrt[3]{w - 1} - 2 = 2$

$\sqrt[3]{w - 1} = 4$ Isolate the radical.

$(\sqrt[3]{w - 1})^3 = (4)^3$ Because the index is 3, cube both sides.

$w - 1 = 64$ Simplify.

$w = 65$

Answer

1. $\{25\}$

Check: $w = 65$

$\sqrt[3]{65-1} - 2 \stackrel{?}{=} 2$ Check $w = 65$ as a potential solution.

$\sqrt[3]{64} - 2 \stackrel{?}{=} 2$

$4 - 2 \stackrel{?}{=} 2$ ✓ True, 65 is a solution to the original equation.

The solution set is $\{65\}$.

Skill Practice Solve.

2. $\sqrt[3]{t+2} + 5 = 3$

Classroom Example: p. 752, Exercise 30

Example 3 Solving an Equation Containing One Radical

Solve the equation. $7 = (x+3)^{1/4} + 9$

Solution:

$7 = (x+3)^{1/4} + 9$

$7 = \sqrt[4]{x+3} + 9$ Note that $(x+3)^{1/4} = \sqrt[4]{x+3}$.

$-2 = \sqrt[4]{x+3}$ Isolate the radical.

$(-2)^4 = (\sqrt[4]{x+3})^4$ Because the index is 4, raise both sides to the fourth power.

$16 = x + 3$

$x = 13$ Solve for x.

Check: $x = 13$

$7 = \sqrt[4]{x+3} + 9$

$7 \stackrel{?}{=} \sqrt[4]{(13)+3} + 9$

$7 \stackrel{?}{=} \sqrt[4]{16} + 9$

$7 \stackrel{?}{=} 2 + 9$ (false) 13 is *not* a solution to the original equation.

The equation $7 = \sqrt[4]{x+3} + 9$ has no solution.

The solution set is the empty set, { }.

TIP: After isolating the radical in Example 3, the equation shows a fourth root equated to a negative number:

$$-2 = \sqrt[4]{x+3}$$

By definition, a principal fourth root of any real number must be nonnegative. Therefore, there can be no real solution to this equation.

Skill Practice Solve.

3. $3 = 6 + (x-1)^{1/4}$

Classroom Example: p. 752, Exercise 46

Example 4 Solving an Equation Containing One Radical

Solve the equation. $y + 2\sqrt{4y-3} = 3$

Solution:

$y + 2\sqrt{4y-3} = 3$

$2\sqrt{4y-3} = 3 - y$ Isolate the radical term.

$(2\sqrt{4y-3})^2 = (3-y)^2$ Because the index is 2, square both sides.

$4(4y-3) = 9 - 6y + y^2$ Note that $(2\sqrt{4y-3})^2 = 2^2(\sqrt{4y-3})^2$ and $(3-y)^2 = (3-y)(3-y) = 9 - 6y + y^2$.

Answers

2. $\{-10\}$

3. { } (The value 82 does not check.)

$$16y - 12 = 9 - 6y + y^2$$

$$0 = y^2 - 22y + 21$$ The equation is quadratic. Set one side equal to zero. Write the other side in descending order.

$$0 = (y - 21)(y - 1)$$ Factor.

$y - 21 = 0$ or $y - 1 = 0$ Set each factor equal to zero.

$y = 21$ or $y = 1$ Solve.

Check: $y = 21$

$$y + 2\sqrt{4y - 3} = 3$$
$$21 + 2\sqrt{4(21) - 3} \stackrel{?}{=} 3$$
$$21 + 2\sqrt{81} \stackrel{?}{=} 3$$
$$21 + 18 \stackrel{?}{=} 3$$
$$39 \stackrel{?}{=} 3 \text{ False}$$

Check: $y = 1$

$$y + 2\sqrt{4y - 3} = 3$$
$$1 + 2\sqrt{4(1) - 3} \stackrel{?}{=} 3$$
$$1 + 2\sqrt{1} \stackrel{?}{=} 3$$
$$1 + 2 \stackrel{?}{=} 3$$
$$3 \stackrel{?}{=} 3 \checkmark$$

The solution set is {1}. (The value 21 does not check.)

Skill Practice Solve.

4. $2\sqrt{m + 3} - m = 3$

3. Solving Radical Equations Involving More than One Radical

Example 5 **Solving an Equation with Two Radicals**

Classroom Example: p. 752, Exercise 50

Solve the equation. $\sqrt[3]{2x - 4} = \sqrt[3]{1 - 8x}$

Solution:

$$\sqrt[3]{2x - 4} = \sqrt[3]{1 - 8x}$$

$$(\sqrt[3]{2x - 4})^3 = (\sqrt[3]{1 - 8x})^3$$ Because the index is 3, cube both sides.

$$2x - 4 = 1 - 8x$$ Simplify.

$$10x - 4 = 1$$ Solve the resulting equation.

$$10x = 5$$

$$x = \frac{1}{2}$$ Solve for x.

Check: $x = \frac{1}{2}$

$$\sqrt[3]{2x - 4} = \sqrt[3]{1 - 8x}$$
$$\sqrt[3]{2\left(\frac{1}{2}\right) - 4} \stackrel{?}{=} \sqrt[3]{1 - 8\left(\frac{1}{2}\right)}$$
$$\sqrt[3]{1 - 4} \stackrel{?}{=} \sqrt[3]{1 - 4}$$
$$\sqrt[3]{-3} \stackrel{?}{=} \sqrt[3]{-3} \checkmark \text{ (True)}$$

Therefore, $\frac{1}{2}$ is a solution to the original equation.

The solution set is $\left\{\frac{1}{2}\right\}$.

Answer

4. {−3, 1}

Skill Practice Solve.

5. $\sqrt[5]{2y-1} = \sqrt[5]{10y+3}$

Classroom Example: p. 752, Exercise 62

Example 6 Solving an Equation with Two Radicals

Solve the equation. $\sqrt{3m+1} - \sqrt{m+4} = 1$

Solution:

$$\sqrt{3m+1} - \sqrt{m+4} = 1$$

$$\sqrt{3m+1} = \sqrt{m+4} + 1$$ Isolate one of the radicals.

$$(\sqrt{3m+1})^2 = (\sqrt{m+4} + 1)^2$$ Square both sides.

$$3m+1 = m+4+2\sqrt{m+4}+1$$

Note: $(\sqrt{m+4} + 1)^2$

$$= (\sqrt{m+4})^2 + 2(1)\sqrt{m+4} + (1)^2$$

$$= m+4+2\sqrt{m+4}+1$$

TIP: In Example 6, we divided the equation by 2 because all coefficients were divisible by 2. This makes the coefficients smaller before we square both sides of the equation a second time.

$$3m+1 = m+5+2\sqrt{m+4}$$ Combine *like* terms.

$$2m-4 = 2\sqrt{m+4}$$ Isolate the radical again.

$$m-2 = \sqrt{m+4}$$ Divide both sides by 2.

$$(m-2)^2 = (\sqrt{m+4})^2$$ Square both sides again.

$$m^2-4m+4 = m+4$$ The resulting equation is quadratic.

$$m^2-5m = 0$$ Set one side equal to zero.

$$m(m-5) = 0$$ Factor.

$$m = 0 \quad \text{or} \quad m = 5$$

Check: $m = 0$

$$\sqrt{3(0)+1} - \sqrt{(0)+4} \stackrel{?}{=} 1$$

$$\sqrt{1} - \sqrt{4} \stackrel{?}{=} 1$$

$$1 - 2 \stackrel{?}{=} 1 \quad \text{(False)}$$

Check: $m = 5$

$$\sqrt{3(5)+1} - \sqrt{(5)+4} = 1$$

$$\sqrt{16} - \sqrt{9} \stackrel{?}{=} 1$$

$$4 - 3 \stackrel{?}{=} 1 \checkmark$$

The solution set is $\{5\}$. (The value 0 does not check.)

Skill Practice Solve.

6. $\sqrt{3c+1} - \sqrt{c-1} = 2$

Answers

5. $\left\{-\frac{1}{2}\right\}$ **6.** $\{1, 5\}$

Example 7 **Solving an Equation with Two Radicals**

Classroom Example: p. 752, Exercise 54

Solve the equation. $\sqrt{5x+4} = 1 + \sqrt{5x-3}$

Solution:

$\sqrt{5x+4} = 1 + \sqrt{5x-3}$	One radical is already isolated.
$(\sqrt{5x+4})^2 = (1 + \sqrt{5x-3})^2$	Square both sides.
$5x + 4 = 1 + 2\sqrt{5x-3} + 5x - 3$	*Note*: $(1 + \sqrt{5x-3})^2 = (1)^2 + 2(1)\sqrt{5x-3} + (\sqrt{5x-3})^2$
$5x + 4 = 2\sqrt{5x-3} + 5x - 2$	Combine *like* terms.
$4 = 2\sqrt{5x-3} - 2$	Subtract $5x$ from both sides.
$6 = 2\sqrt{5x-3}$	Isolate the radical.
$3 = \sqrt{5x-3}$	Divide both sides by 2.
$(3)^2 = (\sqrt{5x-3})^2$	Square both sides again.
$9 = 5x - 3$	The resulting equation is linear.
$12 = 5x$	Solve for x.
$\frac{12}{5} = x$	Check: $x = \frac{12}{5}$

$$\sqrt{5\left(\frac{12}{5}\right) + 4} \stackrel{?}{=} 1 + \sqrt{5\left(\frac{12}{5}\right) - 3}$$

$$\sqrt{16} \stackrel{?}{=} 1 + \sqrt{9}$$

$$4 \stackrel{?}{=} 1 + 3 \quad ✓ \text{ True}$$

The solution set is $\left\{\frac{12}{5}\right\}$.

Skill Practice Solve.

7. $\sqrt{4x-3} = 2 - \sqrt{4x+1}$

4. Applications of Radical Equations and Functions

Example 8 **Applying a Radical Equation in Geometry**

Classroom Example: p. 753, Exercise 72

For a pyramid with a square base, the length of a side of the base b is given by

$$b = \sqrt{\frac{3V}{h}}$$

where V is the volume and h is the height.

The Pyramid of the Pharaoh Khufu (known as the Great Pyramid) at Giza has a square base (Figure 10-3). If the distance around the bottom of the pyramid is 921.6 m and the height is 146.6 m, what is the volume of the pyramid?

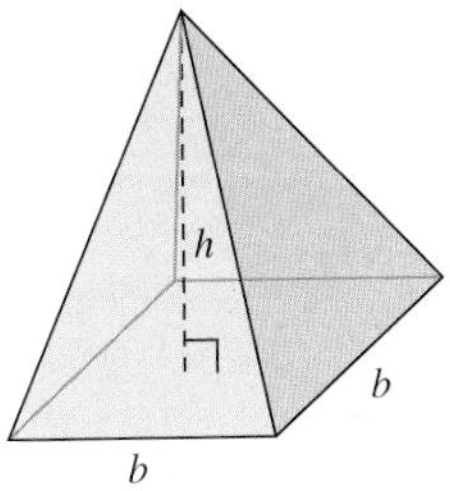

Figure 10-3

Answer

7. $\left\{\frac{3}{4}\right\}$

Solution:

$$b = \sqrt{\frac{3V}{h}}$$

$$b^2 = \left(\sqrt{\frac{3V}{h}}\right)^2 \qquad \text{Because the index is 2, square both sides.}$$

$$b^2 = \frac{3V}{h} \qquad \text{Simplify.}$$

$$b^2 \cdot h = \frac{3V}{\cancel{h}} \cdot \cancel{h} \qquad \text{Multiply both sides by } h.$$

$$b^2h = 3V$$

$$\frac{b^2h}{3} = \frac{3V}{3} \qquad \text{Divide both sides by 3.}$$

$$\frac{b^2h}{3} = V$$

The length of a side b (in meters) is given by $\frac{921.6}{4} = 230.4$ m.

$$\frac{(230.4)^2(146.6)}{3} = V \qquad \text{Substitute } b = 230.4 \text{ and } h = 146.6.$$

$$2{,}594{,}046 \approx V$$

The volume of the Great Pyramid at Giza is approximately 2,594,046 m^3.

Skill Practice

8. The length of the legs, s, of an isosceles right triangle is $s = \sqrt{2A}$, where A is the area. If the legs of the triangle are 9 in., find the area.

Classroom Example: p. 753, Exercise 74

Example 9 Applying a Radical Function

On a certain surface, the speed $s(x)$ (in miles per hour) of a car before the brakes were applied can be approximated from the length of its skid marks x (in feet) by

$$s(x) = 3.8\sqrt{x} \qquad x \geq 0 \quad \text{See Figure 10-4.}$$

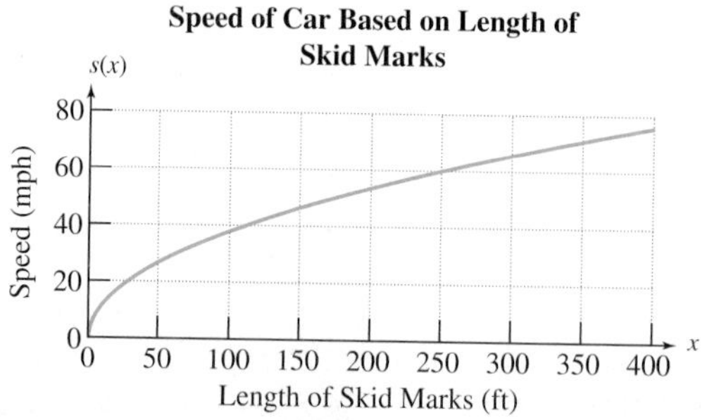

Figure 10-4

a. Find the speed of a car before the brakes were applied if its skid marks are 361 ft long.

b. How long would you expect the skid marks to be if the car had been traveling the speed limit of 50 mph? (Round to the nearest foot.)

Answer

8. 40.5 in.^{2}

Solution:

a. $s(x) = 3.8\sqrt{x}$

$s(361) = 3.8\sqrt{361}$ Substitute $x = 361$.

$= 3.8(19)$

$= 72.2$

If the skid marks are 361 ft, the car was traveling approximately 72.2 mph before the brakes were applied.

b. $s(x) = 3.8\sqrt{x}$

$50 = 3.8\sqrt{x}$ Substitute $s(x) = 50$ and solve for x.

$\frac{50}{3.8} = \sqrt{x}$ Isolate the radical.

$\left(\frac{50}{3.8}\right)^2 = x$

$x \approx 173$

If the car had been going the speed limit (50 mph), then the length of the skid marks would have been approximately 173 ft.

Skill Practice When an object is dropped from a height of 64 ft, the time $t(x)$ (in seconds) it takes to reach a height x (in feet) is given by

$$t(x) = \frac{1}{4}\sqrt{64 - x}$$

9. Find the time to reach a height of 28 ft from the ground.

10. What is the height after 1 sec?

Answers

9. $\frac{3}{2}$ sec **10.** 48 ft

Section 10.7 Practice Exercises

For additional exercises, see Classroom Activities 10.7A–10.7C in the *Student's Resource Manual* at www.mhhe.com/moh.

Vocabulary and Key Concepts

1. a. The equation $\sqrt{x + 5} + 7 = 11$ is an example of a ___radical___ equation.

b. The first step to solve the equation $\sqrt{x + 5} + 7 = 11$ is to ___isolate___ the radical by subtracting ___7___ from both sides of the equation.

c. When solving a radical equation some potential solutions may not check in the original equation. These are called ___extraneous___ solutions.

d. To solve the equation $\sqrt[3]{w - 1} = 5$, raise both sides of the equation to the ___third___ power.

Review Exercises

2. Identify the equation as linear or quadratic. Then solve the equation.

a. $2x + 3 = 23$ Linear; $\{10\}$

b. $2x^2 - 9x = 5$ Quadratic; $\left\{-\frac{1}{2}, 5\right\}$

For Exercises 3–6, simplify the radical expressions. Assume all variables represent positive real numbers.

3. $\sqrt{\dfrac{9w^3}{16}}$ $\dfrac{3w\sqrt{w}}{4}$ **4.** $\sqrt{\dfrac{a^2}{3}}$ $\dfrac{a\sqrt{3}}{3}$ **5.** $\sqrt[3]{54c^4}$ $3c\sqrt[3]{2c}$ **6.** $\sqrt{\dfrac{49}{5t^3}}$ $\dfrac{7\sqrt{5t}}{5t^2}$

For Exercises 7–10, simplify each expression. Assume all radicands represent positive real numbers.

7. $(\sqrt{4x-6})^2$ $4x-6$ **8.** $(\sqrt{5y+2})^2$ $5y+2$ **9.** $(\sqrt[3]{9p+7})^3$ $9p+7$ **10.** $(\sqrt[3]{4t+13})^3$ $4t+13$

Concept 2: Solving Radical Equations Involving One Radical

For Exercises 11–30, solve the equations. **(See Examples 1–3.)**

11. $\sqrt{x}=10$ $\{100\}$ **12.** $\sqrt{y}=7$ $\{49\}$ **13.** $\sqrt{x}+4=6$ $\{4\}$ **14.** $\sqrt{x}+2=8$ $\{36\}$

15. $\sqrt{5y+1}=4$ $\{3\}$ **16.** $\sqrt{9z-5}-2=9$ $\{14\}$ **17.** $6=\sqrt{2z-3}-3$ $\{42\}$ **18.** $4=\sqrt{8+3a}-1$ $\left\{\dfrac{17}{3}\right\}$

19. $\sqrt{x^2+5}=x+1$ $\{2\}$ **20.** $\sqrt{y^2-8}=y-2$ $\{3\}$ **21.** $\sqrt[3]{x-2}-1=2$ $\{29\}$ **22.** $\sqrt[3]{2x-5}-1=1$ $\left\{\dfrac{13}{2}\right\}$

23. $(15-w)^{1/3}+7=2$ $\{140\}$ **24.** $(k+18)^{1/3}+5=3$ $\{-26\}$ **25.** $3+\sqrt{x-16}=0$ { } (The value 25 does not check.) **26.** $12+\sqrt{2x+1}=0$ { } (The value $\frac{143}{2}$ does not check.)

27. $2\sqrt{6a+7}-2a=0$ $\{7\}$ (The value -1 does not check.) **28.** $2\sqrt{3-w}-w=0$ $\{2\}$ (The value -6 does not check.) **29.** $(2x-5)^{1/4}=-1$ { } (The value 3 does not check.) **30.** $(x+16)^{1/4}=-4$ { } (The value 240 does not check.)

For Exercises 31–34, assume all variables represent positive real numbers.

31. Solve for V: $r=\sqrt[3]{\dfrac{3V}{4\pi}}$ $V=\dfrac{4\pi r^3}{3}$ **32.** Solve for V: $r=\sqrt{\dfrac{V}{h\pi}}$ $V=\pi r^2 h$

33. Solve for h^2: $r=\pi\sqrt{r^2+h^2}$ $h^2=\dfrac{r^2-\pi^2r^2}{\pi^2}$ or $h^2=\dfrac{r^2}{\pi^2}-r^2$ **34.** Solve for d: $s=1.3\sqrt{d}$ $d=\dfrac{s^2}{1.69}$

For Exercises 35–40, square the expression as indicated.

35. $(a+5)^2$ $a^2+10a+25$ **36.** $(b+7)^2$ $b^2+14b+49$ **37.** $(\sqrt{5a}-3)^2$ $5a-6\sqrt{5a}+9$

38. $(2+\sqrt{b})^2$ $4+4\sqrt{b}+b$ **39.** $(\sqrt{r-3}+5)^2$ $r+22+10\sqrt{r-3}$ **40.** $(2-\sqrt{2t-4})^2$ $2t-4\sqrt{2t-4}$

For Exercises 41–46, solve the radical equations, if possible. **(See Example 4.)**

41. $\sqrt{a^2+2a+1}=a+5$ $\{-3\}$ **42.** $\sqrt{b^2-5b-8}=b+7$ $\{-3\}$ **43.** $\sqrt{25w^2-2w-3}=5w-4$ { } (The value $\frac{1}{2}$ does not check.)

44. $\sqrt{4p^2-2p+1}=2p-3$ { } (The value $\frac{4}{5}$ does not check.) **45.** $4\sqrt{p-2}-2=-p$ $\{2\}$ (The value 18 does not check.) **46.** $x-3\sqrt{x-5}=5$ $\{5, 14\}$

Concept 3: Solving Radical Equations Involving More than One Radical

For Exercises 47–70, solve the radical equations, if possible. **(See Examples 5–7.)**

47. $\sqrt[4]{h+4}=\sqrt[4]{2h-5}$ $\{9\}$ **48.** $\sqrt[4]{3b+6}=\sqrt[4]{7b-6}$ $\{3\}$ **49.** $\sqrt[3]{5a+3}-\sqrt[3]{a-13}=0$ $\{-4\}$

50. $\sqrt[3]{k-8}-\sqrt[3]{4k+1}=0$ $\{-3\}$ **51.** $\sqrt{5a-9}=\sqrt{5a}-3$ $\left\{\dfrac{9}{5}\right\}$ **52.** $\sqrt{8+b}=2+\sqrt{b}$ $\{1\}$

53. $\sqrt{2h+5}-\sqrt{2h}=1$ $\{2\}$ **54.** $\sqrt{3k-5}-\sqrt{3k}=-1$ $\{3\}$ **55.** $(t-9)^{1/2}-t^{1/2}=3$ { } (The value 9 does not check.)

56. $(y-16)^{1/2}-y^{1/2}=4$ { } (The value 16 does not check.) **57.** $6=\sqrt{x^2+3}-x$ $\left\{-\dfrac{11}{4}\right\}$ **58.** $2=\sqrt{y^2+5}-y$ $\left\{\dfrac{1}{4}\right\}$

59. $\sqrt{3t-7}=2-\sqrt{3t+1}$ { } (The value $\frac{8}{3}$ does not check.) **60.** $\sqrt{p-6}=\sqrt{p+2}-4$ { } (The value 7 does not check.) **61.** $\sqrt{z+1}+\sqrt{2z+3}=1$ $\{-1\}$ (The value 3 does not check.)

62. $\sqrt{2y+6}=\sqrt{7-2y}+1$ $\{\frac{3}{2}\}$ (The value -1 does not check.) **63.** $\sqrt{6m+7}-\sqrt{3m+3}=1$ $\left\{\dfrac{1}{3}, -1\right\}$ **64.** $\sqrt{5w+1}-\sqrt{3w}=1$ $\{0, 3\}$

65. $2 + 2\sqrt{2t+3} + 2\sqrt{3t-5} = 0$ { } (The values 3 and 23 do not check.)

66. $6 + 3\sqrt{3x+1} + 3\sqrt{x-1} = 0$ { } (The values 5 and 1 do not check.)

67. $3\sqrt{y-3} = \sqrt{4y+3}$ {6}

68. $\sqrt{5x-8} = 2\sqrt{x-1}$ {4}

69. $\sqrt{p+7} = \sqrt{2p} + 1$ {2} (The value 18 does not check.)

70. $\sqrt{t} = \sqrt{t-12} + 2$ {16}

Concept 4: Applications of Radical Equations and Functions

71. If an object is dropped from an initial height h, its velocity at impact with the ground is given by

$$v = \sqrt{2gh}$$

where g is the acceleration due to gravity and h is the initial height. **(See Example 8.)**

a. Find the initial height (in feet) of an object if its velocity at impact is 44 ft/sec. (Assume that the acceleration due to gravity is $g = 32$ ft/sec^2.) 30.25 ft

b. Find the initial height (in meters) of an object if its velocity at impact is 26 m/sec. (Assume that the acceleration due to gravity is $g = 9.8$ m/sec^2.) Round to the nearest tenth of a meter. 34.5 m

72. The time T (in seconds) required for a pendulum to make one complete swing back and forth is approximated by

$$T = 2\pi\sqrt{\frac{L}{g}}$$

where g is the acceleration due to gravity and L is the length of the pendulum (in feet).

a. Find the length of a pendulum that requires 1.36 sec to make one complete swing back and forth. (Assume that the acceleration due to gravity is $g = 32$ ft/sec^2.) Round to the nearest tenth of a foot. 1.5 ft

b. Find the time required for a pendulum to complete one swing back and forth if the length of the pendulum is 4 ft. (Assume that the acceleration due to gravity is $g = 32$ ft/sec^2.) Round to the nearest tenth of a second. 2.2 sec

73. The airline cost for x thousand passengers to travel round trip from New York to Atlanta is given by

$$C(x) = \sqrt{0.3x + 1}$$

where $C(x)$ is measured in millions of dollars and $x \geq 0$. **(See Example 9.)**

a. Find the airline's cost for 10,000 passengers ($x = 10$) to travel from New York to Atlanta. \$2 million

b. If the airline charges \$320 per passenger, find the profit made by the airline for flying 10,000 passengers from New York to Atlanta. \$1.2 million

c. Approximate the number of passengers who traveled from New York to Atlanta if the total cost for the airline was \$4 million. 50,000 passengers

74. The time $t(d)$ in seconds it takes an object to drop d meters is given by

$$t(d) = \sqrt{\frac{d}{4.9}}$$

a. Approximate the height of the JP Morgan Chase Tower in Houston if it takes an object 7.89 sec to drop from the top. Round to the nearest meter. 305 m

b. Approximate the height of the Willis Tower in Chicago if it takes an object 9.51 sec to drop from the top. Round to the nearest meter. 443 m

Expanding Your Skills

75. The number of hours needed to cook a turkey that weighs x pounds can be approximated by

$$t(x) = 0.90\sqrt[5]{x^3}$$

where $t(x)$ is the time in hours and x is the weight of the turkey in pounds.

a. Find the weight of a turkey that cooked for 4 hr. Round to the nearest pound. 12 lb

b. Find $t(18)$ and interpret the result. Round to the nearest tenth of an hour. $t(18) = 5.1$. An 18-lb turkey will take about 5.1 hr to cook.

For Exercises 76–79, use the Pythagorean theorem to find a, b, or c.

76. Find b when $a = 2$ and $c = y$. $b = \sqrt{y^2 - 4}$

77. Find b when $a = h$ and $c = 5$. $b = \sqrt{25 - h^2}$

78. Find a when $b = x$ and $c = 8$. $a = \sqrt{64 - x^2}$

79. Find a when $b = 14$ and $c = k$. $a = \sqrt{k^2 - 196}$

Graphing Calculator Exercises

80. Graph Y_1 and Y_2 on a viewing window defined by $-10 \le x \le 40$ and $-5 \le y \le 10$.

$$Y_1 = \sqrt{2x} \quad \text{and} \quad Y_2 = 8$$

Use an *Intersect* feature to approximate the x-coordinate of the point of intersection of the two graphs. How does the point of intersection relate to the solution to the equation $\sqrt{2x} = 8$? The x-coordinate of the point of intersection is the solution to the equation.

81. Graph Y_1 and Y_2 on a viewing window defined by $-10 \le x \le 20$ and $-5 \le y \le 10$.

$$Y_1 = \sqrt{4x} \quad \text{and} \quad Y_2 = 6$$

Use an *Intersect* feature to approximate the x-coordinate of the point of intersection of the two graphs. How does the point of intersection relate to the solution to the equation $\sqrt{4x} = 6$? The x-coordinate of the point of intersection is the solution to the equation.

82. Refer to Exercise 48. Graph Y_1 and Y_2 on a viewing window defined by $-5 \le x \le 20$ and $-1 \le y \le 4$.

$$Y_1 = \sqrt[4]{3x + 6} \quad \text{and} \quad Y_2 = \sqrt[4]{7x - 6}$$

Use an *Intersect* feature to approximate the x-coordinate of the point of intersection of the two graphs to support your solution to Exercise 48.

83. Refer to Exercise 47. Graph Y_1 and Y_2 on a viewing window defined by $-5 \le x \le 20$ and $-1 \le y \le 4$.

$$Y_1 = \sqrt[4]{x + 4} \quad \text{and} \quad Y_2 = \sqrt[4]{2x - 5}$$

Use an *Intersect* feature to approximate the x-coordinate of the point of intersection of the two graphs to support your solution to Exercise 47.

Section 10.8 Complex Numbers

Concepts

1 Definition of *i*
2 Powers of *i*
3 Definition of a Complex Number
4 Addition, Subtraction, and Multiplication of Complex Numbers
5 Division and Simplification of Complex Numbers

1. Definition of *i*

We have already learned that there are no real-valued square roots of a negative number. For example, $\sqrt{-9}$ is not a real number because no real number when squared equals -9. However, the square roots of a negative number are defined over another set of numbers called the **imaginary numbers**. The foundation of the set of imaginary numbers is the definition of the imaginary number i.

Definition of the Imaginary Number *i*

$$i = \sqrt{-1}$$

Note: From the definition of i, it follows that $i^2 = -1$.

Using the imaginary number i, we can define the square root of any negative real number.

Instructor Note: Since $i = \sqrt{-1}$, and $\sqrt{-1}$ is not real, i is not a real number.

Definition of $\sqrt{-b}$ for $b > 0$

Let b be a positive real number. Then $\sqrt{-b} = i\sqrt{b}$.

Example 1 Simplifying Expressions in Terms of i

Classroom Examples: p. 762, Exercises 12, 14, and 16

Simplify the expressions in terms of i.

a. $\sqrt{-64}$ **b.** $\sqrt{-50}$ **c.** $-\sqrt{-4}$ **d.** $\sqrt{-29}$

Solution:

a. $\sqrt{-64} = i\sqrt{64}$
$= 8i$

b. $\sqrt{-50} = i\sqrt{50}$
$= i\sqrt{5^2 \cdot 2}$
$= 5i\sqrt{2}$

c. $-\sqrt{-4} = -1 \cdot \sqrt{-4}$
$= -1 \cdot i\sqrt{4}$
$= -1 \cdot 2i$
$= -2i$

d. $\sqrt{-29} = i\sqrt{29}$

Avoiding Mistakes

In an expression such as $i\sqrt{29}$, the i is often written in front of the square root. The expression $\sqrt{29}i$ is also correct, but may be misinterpreted as $\sqrt{29i}$ (with i incorrectly placed under the radical).

Skill Practice Simplify the expressions in terms of i.

1. $\sqrt{-81}$ **2.** $\sqrt{-20}$ **3.** $-\sqrt{-36}$ **4.** $\sqrt{-7}$

If a and b represent real numbers such that $\sqrt[n]{a}$ and $\sqrt[n]{b}$ are both real, then

$$\sqrt[n]{ab} = \sqrt[n]{a} \cdot \sqrt[n]{b} \quad \text{and} \quad \sqrt[n]{\frac{a}{b}} = \frac{\sqrt[n]{a}}{\sqrt[n]{b}} \quad b \neq 0$$

The conditions that $\sqrt[n]{a}$ and $\sqrt[n]{b}$ must both be real numbers prevent us from applying the multiplication and division properties of radicals for square roots with a negative radicand. Therefore, to multiply or divide radicals with a negative radicand, first write the radical in terms of the imaginary number i. This is demonstrated in Example 2.

Example 2 Simplifying a Product or Quotient in Terms of i

Classroom Examples: p. 762, Exercises 22, 24, and 30

Simplify the expressions.

a. $\dfrac{\sqrt{-100}}{\sqrt{-25}}$ **b.** $\sqrt{-25} \cdot \sqrt{-9}$ **c.** $\sqrt{-5} \cdot \sqrt{-5}$

Answers

1. $9i$ **2.** $2i\sqrt{5}$ **3.** $-6i$ **4.** $i\sqrt{7}$

Solution:

a. $\dfrac{\sqrt{-100}}{\sqrt{-25}}$

$= \dfrac{10i}{5i}$ Simplify each radical in terms of i *before* dividing.

$= 2$

b. $\sqrt{-25} \cdot \sqrt{-9}$

$= 5i \cdot 3i$ Simplify each radical in terms of i first *before* multiplying.

$= 15i^2$ Multiply.

$= 15(-1)$ Recall that $i^2 = -1$.

$= -15$ Simplify.

c. $\sqrt{-5} \cdot \sqrt{-5}$

$= i\sqrt{5} \cdot i\sqrt{5}$

$= i^2 \cdot (\sqrt{5})^2$

$= -1 \cdot 5$

$= -5$

Skill Practice Simplify the expressions.

5. $\dfrac{\sqrt{-36}}{\sqrt{-9}}$ **6.** $\sqrt{-16} \cdot \sqrt{-49}$ **7.** $\sqrt{-2} \cdot \sqrt{-2}$

Avoiding Mistakes

In Example 2, we wrote the radical expressions in terms of i first, before multiplying or dividing. If we had mistakenly applied the multiplication or division property first, we would have obtained an incorrect answer.

Correct: $\sqrt{-25} \cdot \sqrt{-9}$

$= (5i)(3i) = 15i^2$

$= 15(-1) = -15$ ← correct

Be careful: $\sqrt{-25} \cdot \sqrt{-9}$

$\neq \sqrt{225} = 15$ (incorrect answer)

$\sqrt{-25}$ and $\sqrt{-9}$ are not real numbers. Therefore, the multiplication property of radicals cannot be applied.

2. Powers of *i*

From the definition of $i = \sqrt{-1}$, it follows that

$i = i$

$i^2 = -1$

$i^3 = -i$ because $i^3 = i^2 \cdot i = (-1)i = -i$

$i^4 = 1$ because $i^4 = i^2 \cdot i^2 = (-1)(-1) = 1$

$i^5 = i$ because $i^5 = i^4 \cdot i = (1)i = i$

$i^6 = -1$ because $i^6 = i^4 \cdot i^2 = (1)(-1) = -1$

Answers

5. 2 **6.** −28 **7.** −2

This pattern of values $i, -1, -i, 1, i, -1, -i, 1, \ldots$ continues for all subsequent powers of i. Table 10-1 lists several powers of i.

Table 10-1 Powers of *i*

$i^1 = i$	$i^5 = i$	$i^9 = i$
$i^2 = -1$	$i^6 = -1$	$i^{10} = -1$
$i^3 = -i$	$i^7 = -i$	$i^{11} = -i$
$i^4 = 1$	$i^8 = 1$	$i^{12} = 1$

To simplify higher powers of i, we can decompose the expression into multiples of i^4 ($i^4 = 1$) and write the remaining factors as i, i^2, or i^3.

Example 3 Simplifying Powers of *i*

Classroom Examples: p. 762, Exercises 34, 36, and 42

Simplify the powers of i.

a. i^{13} **b.** i^{18} **c.** i^{107} **d.** i^{32}

Solution:

a. $i^{13} = (i^{12}) \cdot (i)$ Write the exponent as a multiple of 4 and a remainder.

$= (i^4)^3 \cdot (i)$

$= (1)^3(i)$ Recall that $i^4 = 1$.

$= i$ Simplify.

b. $i^{18} = (i^{16}) \cdot (i^2)$ Write the exponent as a multiple of 4 and a remainder.

$= (i^4)^4 \cdot (i^2)$

$= (1)^4 \cdot (-1)$ $i^4 = 1$ and $i^2 = -1$

$= -1$ Simplify.

c. $i^{107} = (i^{104}) \cdot (i^3)$ Write the exponent as a multiple of 4 and a remainder.

$= (i^4)^{26}(i^3)$

$= (1)^{26}(-i)$ $i^4 = 1$ and $i^3 = -i$

$= -i$ Simplify.

d. $i^{32} = (i^4)^8$

$= (1)^8$ $i^4 = 1$

$= 1$ Simplify.

Skill Practice Simplify the powers of i.

8. i^{45} **9.** i^{22} **10.** i^{31} **11.** i^{80}

3. Definition of a Complex Number

We have already learned the definitions of the integers, rational numbers, irrational numbers, and real numbers. In this section, we define the complex numbers.

Answers

8. i **9.** -1
10. $-i$ **11.** 1

Definition of a Complex Number

A **complex number** is a number of the form $a + bi$, where a and b are real numbers and $i = \sqrt{-1}$.

Notes:

- If $b = 0$, then the complex number $a + bi$ is a real number.
- If $b \neq 0$, then we say that $a + bi$ is an imaginary number.
- The complex number $a + bi$ is said to be written in standard form. The quantities a and b are called the real and imaginary parts (respectively) of the complex number.
- The complex numbers $a - bi$ and $a + bi$ are called **complex conjugates**.

From the definition of a complex number, it follows that all real numbers are complex numbers and all imaginary numbers are complex numbers. Figure 10-5 illustrates the relationship among the sets of numbers we have learned so far.

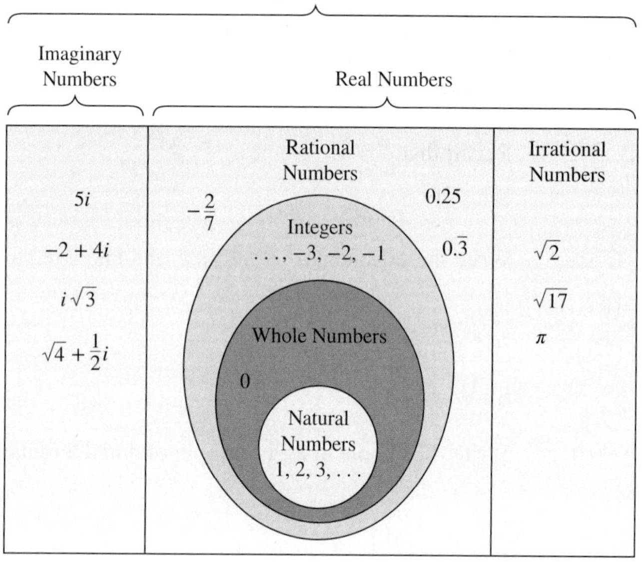

Figure 10-5

Classroom Examples: p. 763, Exercises 46, 48, and 50

Example 4 Identifying the Real and Imaginary Parts of a Complex Number

Identify the real and imaginary parts of the complex numbers.

a. $-8 + 2i$ **b.** $\frac{3}{2}$ **c.** $-1.75i$

Solution:

a. $-8 + 2i$ — -8 is the real part, and 2 is the imaginary part.

b. $\frac{3}{2} = \frac{3}{2} + 0i$ — Rewrite $\frac{3}{2}$ in the form $a + bi$. $\frac{3}{2}$ is the real part, and 0 is the imaginary part.

c. $-1.75i$

$= 0 + -1.75i$ — Rewrite $-1.75i$ in the form $a + bi$. 0 is the real part, and -1.75 is the imaginary part.

Skill Practice Identify the real and imaginary parts of the complex numbers.

12. $22 - 14i$ **13.** -50 **14.** $15i$

TIP: Example 4(b) illustrates that a real number is also a complex number.

$$\frac{3}{2} = \frac{3}{2} + 0i$$

Example 4(c) illustrates that an imaginary number is also a complex number.

$$-1.75i = 0 + -1.75i$$

4. Addition, Subtraction, and Multiplication of Complex Numbers

The operations of addition, subtraction, and multiplication of real numbers also apply to imaginary numbers. To add or subtract complex numbers, combine the real parts and combine the imaginary parts. The commutative, associative, and distributive properties that apply to real numbers also apply to complex numbers.

Example 5 **Adding and Subtracting Complex Numbers**

Classroom Examples: p. 763, Exercises 56 and 58

Add or subtract as indicated. Write the answers in the form $a + bi$.

a. $(1 - 5i) + (-3 + 7i)$ **b.** $\left(-\frac{1}{4} + \frac{3}{5}i\right) - \left(\frac{1}{2} - \frac{1}{10}i\right)$

c. $\sqrt{-8} + \sqrt{-18}$

Solution:

a. $(1 - 5i) + (-3 + 7i) = (1 + -3) + (-5 + 7)i$ (real parts: 1 and −3; imaginary parts: −5i and 7i) Add the real parts. Add the imaginary parts.

$= -2 + 2i$ Simplify.

b. $\left(-\frac{1}{4} + \frac{3}{5}i\right) - \left(\frac{1}{2} - \frac{1}{10}i\right) = -\frac{1}{4} + \frac{3}{5}i - \frac{1}{2} + \frac{1}{10}i$ Apply the distributive property.

$= \left(-\frac{1}{4} - \frac{1}{2}\right) + \left(\frac{3}{5} + \frac{1}{10}\right)i$ Add real parts. Add imaginary parts.

$= \left(-\frac{1}{4} - \frac{2}{4}\right) + \left(\frac{6}{10} + \frac{1}{10}\right)i$ Get common denominators.

$= -\frac{3}{4} + \frac{7}{10}i$ Simplify.

c. $\sqrt{-8} + \sqrt{-18} = 2i\sqrt{2} + 3i\sqrt{2}$ Simplify each radical in terms of i.

$= 5i\sqrt{2}$ Combine *like* radicals.

Skill Practice Perform the indicated operations.

15. $\left(\frac{1}{2} - \frac{1}{4}i\right) + \left(\frac{3}{5} + \frac{2}{3}i\right)$ **16.** $(-6 + 11i) - (-9 - 12i)$ **17.** $\sqrt{-45} - \sqrt{-20}$

Answers

12. real: 22; imaginary: −14
13. real: −50; imaginary: 0
14. real: 0; imaginary: 15
15. $\frac{11}{10} + \frac{5}{12}i$ **16.** $3 + 23i$
17. $i\sqrt{5}$

Classroom Examples: p. 763, Exercises 66 and 68

Example 6 **Multiplying Complex Numbers**

Multiply the complex numbers. Write the answers in the form $a + bi$.

a. $(10 - 5i)(2 + 3i)$ **b.** $(1.2 + 0.5i)(1.2 - 0.5i)$

Solution:

a. $(10 - 5i)(2 + 3i)$

$= (10)(2) + (10)(3i) + (-5i)(2) + (-5i)(3i)$ Apply the distributive property.

$= 20 + 30i - 10i - 15i^2$

$= 20 + 20i - (15)(-1)$ Recall $i^2 = -1$.

$= 20 + 20i + 15$

$= 35 + 20i$ Write in the form $a + bi$.

b. $(1.2 + 0.5i)(1.2 - 0.5i)$

The expressions $(1.2 + 0.5i)$ and $(1.2 - 0.5i)$ are complex conjugates. The product is a difference of squares.

$(a + b)(a - b) = a^2 - b^2$ Apply the formula, where $a = 1.2$ and $b = 0.5i$.

$(1.2 + 0.5i)(1.2 - 0.5i) = (1.2)^2 - (0.5i)^2$

$= 1.44 - 0.25i^2$

$= 1.44 - 0.25(-1)$ Recall $i^2 = -1$.

$= 1.44 + 0.25$

$= 1.69 + 0i$

Skill Practice Multiply.

18. $(4 - 6i)(2 - 3i)$ **19.** $(1.5 + 0.8i)(1.5 - 0.8i)$

5. Division and Simplification of Complex Numbers

The product of a complex number and its complex conjugate is a real number. For example:

$$\begin{aligned}(5 + 3i)(5 - 3i) &= 25 - 9i^2\\ &= 25 - 9(-1)\\ &= 25 + 9\\ &= 34\end{aligned}$$

To divide by a complex number, multiply the numerator and denominator by the complex conjugate of the denominator. This produces a real number in the denominator so that the resulting expression can be written in the form $a + bi$.

Answers

18. $-10 - 24i$ **19.** $2.89 + 0i$

Example 7 **Dividing by a Complex Number**

Divide the complex numbers and write the answer in the form $a + bi$.

$$\frac{4-3i}{5+2i}$$

Solution:

$\frac{4-3i}{5+2i}$ Multiply the numerator and denominator by the complex conjugate of the denominator:

$$\frac{(4-3i)}{(5+2i)} \cdot \frac{(5-2i)}{(5-2i)} = \frac{(4)(5)+(4)(-2i)+(-3i)(5)+(-3i)(-2i)}{(5)^2-(2i)^2}$$

$= \frac{20-8i-15i+6i^2}{25-4i^2}$ Simplify numerator and denominator.

$= \frac{20-23i+6(-1)}{25-4(-1)}$ Recall $i^2 = -1$.

$= \frac{20-23i-6}{25+4}$

$= \frac{14-23i}{29}$ Simplify.

$= \frac{14}{29} - \frac{23}{29}i$ Write in the form $a + bi$.

Skill Practice Divide the complex numbers. Write the answer in the form $a + bi$.

20. $\frac{2+i}{3-2i}$

Classroom Example: p. 763, Exercise 82

Instructor Note: In Example 7 point out that $\frac{(5-2i)}{(5-2i)} = 1$.

TIP: In Example 7, we asked for the answer in the form $a + bi$. However, if the second term is negative, we often leave an answer in terms of subtraction: $\frac{14}{29} - \frac{23}{29}i$. This is the same as $\frac{14}{29} + (-\frac{23}{29}i)$.

Example 8 **Simplifying a Complex Number**

Simplify the complex number. $\frac{6+\sqrt{-18}}{9}$

Solution:

$\frac{6+\sqrt{-18}}{9} = \frac{6+i\sqrt{18}}{9}$ Write the radical in terms of i.

$= \frac{6+3i\sqrt{2}}{9}$ Simplify $\sqrt{18} = 3\sqrt{2}$.

$= \frac{3(2+i\sqrt{2})}{9}$ Factor the numerator.

$= \frac{\overset{1}{\cancel{3}}(2+i\sqrt{2})}{\underset{3}{\cancel{9}}}$ Simplify.

$= \frac{2+i\sqrt{2}}{3}$ or $\frac{2}{3} + \frac{\sqrt{2}}{3}i$ Write in the form $a + bi$.

Skill Practice Simplify the complex number.

21. $\frac{8-\sqrt{-24}}{6}$

Classroom Example: p. 763, Exercise 94

TIP: As an alternative approach in Example 8, the expression $\frac{6+i\sqrt{18}}{9}$ can be written in the form $a + bi$ and then simplified.

$$\frac{6+i\sqrt{18}}{9} = \frac{6}{9} + \frac{3\sqrt{2}}{9}i$$
$$= \frac{2}{3} + \frac{\sqrt{2}}{3}i$$

Answers

20. $\frac{4}{13} + \frac{7}{13}i$

21. $\frac{4-i\sqrt{6}}{3}$ or $\frac{4}{3} - \frac{\sqrt{6}}{3}i$

Section 10.8 Practice Exercises

Vocabulary and Key Concepts

For additional exercises, see Classroom Activities 10.8A–10.8D in the *Student's Resource Manual* at www.mhhe.com/moh.

1. **a.** A square root of a negative number is not a real number, but rather is an ___imaginary___ number.
   b. $i =$ ___$\sqrt{-1}$___, and $i^2 =$ ___-1___.
   c. For a positive number b, the value $\sqrt{-b} =$ ___$i\sqrt{b}$___.
   d. A complex number is a number in the form ___$a + bi$___, where a and b are real numbers and $i =$ ___$\sqrt{-1}$___.
   e. Given a complex number $a + bi$, the value a is called the ___real___ part, and ___b___ is called the imaginary part.
   f. The complex conjugate of $a - bi$ is ___$a + bi$___.
   g. Answer true or false. All real numbers are complex numbers. True
   h. Answer true or false. All imaginary numbers are complex numbers. True

Review Exercises

For Exercises 2–4, perform the indicated operations.

2. $-2\sqrt{5} - 3\sqrt{50} + \sqrt{125}$ $3\sqrt{5} - 15\sqrt{2}$
3. $(3 - \sqrt{x})(3 + \sqrt{x})$ $9 - x$
4. $(\sqrt{5} + \sqrt{2})^2$ $7 + 2\sqrt{10}$

For Exercises 5–7, solve the equations.

5. $\sqrt[3]{3p + 7} - \sqrt[3]{2p - 1} = 0$ $\{-8\}$
6. $\sqrt{9t + 10} + 18 = 10$ { }; (The value 6 does not check.)
7. $\sqrt{4a + 29} = 2\sqrt{a} + 5$ $\left\{\frac{1}{25}\right\}$
8. Rationalize the denominator. $\dfrac{2}{\sqrt{x} - 3}$ $\dfrac{2\sqrt{x} + 6}{x - 9}$

Concept 1: Definition of *i*

9. Simplify the expressions $\sqrt{-1}$ and $-\sqrt{1}$. $\sqrt{-1} = i$ and $-\sqrt{1} = -1$
10. Simplify i^2. $i^2 = -1$

For Exercises 11–30, simplify the expressions. **(See Examples 1–2.)**

11. $\sqrt{-144}$ $12i$
12. $\sqrt{-81}$ $9i$
13. $\sqrt{-3}$ $i\sqrt{3}$
14. $\sqrt{-17}$ $i\sqrt{17}$
15. $-\sqrt{-20}$ $-2i\sqrt{5}$
16. $-\sqrt{-75}$ $-5i\sqrt{3}$
17. $(2\sqrt{-25})(3\sqrt{-4})$ -60
18. $(-4\sqrt{-9})(-3\sqrt{-1})$ -36
19. $7\sqrt{-63} - 4\sqrt{-28}$ $13i\sqrt{7}$
20. $7\sqrt{-3} - 4\sqrt{-27}$ $-5i\sqrt{3}$
21. $\sqrt{-7} \cdot \sqrt{-7}$ -7
22. $\sqrt{-11} \cdot \sqrt{-11}$ -11
23. $\sqrt{-9} \cdot \sqrt{-16}$ -12
24. $\sqrt{-25} \cdot \sqrt{-36}$ -30
25. $\sqrt{-15} \cdot \sqrt{-6}$ $-3\sqrt{10}$
26. $\sqrt{-12} \cdot \sqrt{-50}$ $-10\sqrt{6}$
27. $\dfrac{\sqrt{-50}}{\sqrt{25}}$ $i\sqrt{2}$
28. $\dfrac{\sqrt{-27}}{\sqrt{9}}$ $i\sqrt{3}$
29. $\dfrac{\sqrt{-90}}{\sqrt{-10}}$ 3
30. $\dfrac{\sqrt{-125}}{\sqrt{-45}}$ $\frac{5}{3}$

Concept 2: Powers of *i*

For Exercises 31–42, simplify the powers of i. **(See Example 3.)**

31. i^7 $-i$
32. i^{38} -1
33. i^{64} 1
34. i^{75} $-i$
35. i^{41} i
36. i^{25} i
37. i^{52} 1
38. i^0 1
39. i^{23} $-i$
40. i^{103} $-i$
41. i^6 -1
42. i^{82} -1

Concept 3: Definition of a Complex Number

43. What is the complex conjugate of a complex number $a + bi$? $a - bi$

44. True or false?

a. Every real number is a complex number. True

b. Every complex number is a real number. False

For Exercises 45–52, identify the real and imaginary parts of the complex number. **(See Example 4.)**

45. $-5 + 12i$ Real: -5; imaginary: 12

46. $22 - 16i$ Real: 22; imaginary: -16

47. $-6i$ Real: 0; imaginary: -6

48. $10i$ Real: 0; imaginary: 10

49. 35 Real: 35; imaginary: 0

50. -1 Real: -1; imaginary: 0

51. $\frac{3}{5} + i$ Real: $\frac{3}{5}$; imaginary: 1

52. $-\frac{1}{2} - \frac{1}{4}i$ Real: $-\frac{1}{2}$; imaginary: $-\frac{1}{4}$

Concept 4: Addition, Subtraction, and Multiplication of Complex Numbers

For Exercises 53–76, perform the indicated operations. Write the answer in the form $a + bi$. **(See Examples 5–6.)**

53. $(2 - i) + (5 + 7i)$ $7 + 6i$

54. $(5 - 2i) + (3 + 4i)$ $8 + 2i$

55. $\left(\frac{1}{2} + \frac{2}{3}i\right) - \left(\frac{1}{5} - \frac{5}{6}i\right)$ $\frac{3}{10} + \frac{3}{2}i$

56. $\left(\frac{11}{10} - \frac{7}{5}i\right) - \left(-\frac{2}{5} + \frac{3}{5}i\right)$ $\frac{3}{2} - 2i$

57. $\sqrt{-98} - \sqrt{-8}$ $5i\sqrt{2}$

58. $\sqrt{-75} + \sqrt{-12}$ $7i\sqrt{3}$

59. $(2 + 3i) - (1 - 4i) + (-2 + 3i)$ $-1 + 10i$

60. $(2 + 5i) - (7 - 2i) + (-3 + 4i)$ $-8 + 11i$

61. $(8i)(3i)$ $-24 + 0i$

62. $(2i)(4i)$ $-8 + 0i$

63. $6i(1 - 3i)$ $18 + 6i$

64. $-i(3 + 4i)$ $4 - 3i$

65. $(2 - 10i)(3 + 2i)$ $26 - 26i$

66. $(4 + 7i)(2 - 3i)$ $29 + 2i$

67. $(-5 + 2i)(5 + 2i)$ $-29 + 0i$

68. $(4 - 11i)(4 + 11i)$ $137 + 0i$

69. $(4 + 5i)^2$ $-9 + 40i$

70. $(3 - 2i)^2$ $5 - 12i$

71. $(2 + i)(3 - 2i)(4 + 3i)$ $35 + 20i$

72. $(3 - i)(3 + i)(4 - i)$ $40 - 10i$

73. $(-4 - 6i)^2$ $-20 + 48i$

74. $(-3 - 5i)^2$ $-16 + 30i$

75. $\left(-\frac{1}{2} - \frac{3}{4}i\right)\left(-\frac{1}{2} + \frac{3}{4}i\right)$ $\frac{13}{16} + 0i$

76. $\left(-\frac{2}{3} + \frac{1}{6}i\right)\left(-\frac{2}{3} - \frac{1}{6}i\right)$ $\frac{17}{36} + 0i$

Concept 5: Division and Simplification of Complex Numbers

For Exercises 77–90, divide the complex numbers. Write the answer in the form $a + bi$. **(See Example 7.)**

77. $\frac{2}{1 + 3i}$ $\frac{1}{5} - \frac{3}{5}i$

78. $\frac{-2}{3 + i}$ $-\frac{3}{5} + \frac{1}{5}i$

79. $\frac{-i}{4 - 3i}$ $\frac{3}{25} - \frac{4}{25}i$

80. $\frac{3 - 3i}{1 - i}$ $3 + 0i$

81. $\frac{5 + 2i}{5 - 2i}$ $\frac{21}{29} + \frac{20}{29}i$

82. $\frac{7 + 3i}{4 - 2i}$ $\frac{11}{10} + \frac{13}{10}i$

83. $\frac{3 + 7i}{-2 - 4i}$ $-\frac{17}{10} - \frac{1}{10}i$

84. $\frac{-2 + 9i}{-1 - 4i}$ $-2 - i$

85. $\frac{13i}{-5 - i}$ $-\frac{1}{2} - \frac{5}{2}i$

86. $\frac{15i}{-2 - i}$ $-3 - 6i$

87. $\frac{2 + 3i}{6i}$ $\frac{1}{2} - \frac{1}{3}i$ (*Hint:* Consider multiplying numerator and denominator by i or by $-i$. This will make the denominator a real number.)

88. $\frac{4 - i}{2i}$ $-\frac{1}{2} - 2i$

89. $\frac{-10 + i}{i}$ $1 + 10i$

90. $\frac{-6 - i}{-i}$ $1 - 6i$

For Exercises 91–98, simplify the complex numbers. Write the answer in the form $a + bi$. **(See Example 8.)**

91. $\frac{2 + \sqrt{-16}}{8}$ $\frac{1}{4} + \frac{1}{2}i$

92. $\frac{6 - \sqrt{-4}}{4}$ $\frac{3}{2} - \frac{1}{2}i$

93. $\frac{-6 + \sqrt{-72}}{6}$ $-1 + i\sqrt{2}$

94. $\frac{-20 + \sqrt{-500}}{10}$ $-2 + i\sqrt{5}$

95. $\dfrac{-8-\sqrt{-48}}{4}$ $-2-i\sqrt{3}$

96. $\dfrac{-18-\sqrt{-72}}{3}$ $-6-2i\sqrt{2}$

97. $\dfrac{-5+\sqrt{-50}}{10}$ $-\dfrac{1}{2}+\dfrac{\sqrt{2}}{2}i$

98. $\dfrac{14+\sqrt{-98}}{7}$ $2+i\sqrt{2}$

Expanding Your Skills

For Exercises 99–102, determine if the complex number is a solution to the equation.

99. $x^2-4x+5=0$; $2+i$ Yes

100. $x^2-6x+25=0$; $3-4i$ Yes

101. $x^2+12=0$; $-2i\sqrt{3}$ Yes

102. $x^2+18=0$; $3i\sqrt{2}$ Yes

Group Activity

Margin of Error of Survey Results

Materials: Calculator

Estimated time: 20 minutes

Group Size: 3

Instructor Note: You might want to have students begin collecting data a week or so before assigning this activity.

The members of the class will conduct a survey to estimate the percentage of the college population that answers "yes" to several survey questions.

1. The members of the class will decide on three "Yes or No" questions that they will use to perform a survey. For example, here are some possible questions.

"Do you study more than 10 hr a week?"

"Do you work more than 25 hr a week?"

"Are you taking more than 10 credit hours?"

List the questions here:

a. ______________________________ Answers will vary.

b. ______________________________

c. ______________________________

2. Each student in the class will survey 20 people and record the number of "yes" responses in the table.

Question	Number of "Yes" Responses
1	
2	
3	

3. The instructor will then pool the results obtained from each student to get the total number of people surveyed by the whole class. Record the number of people surveyed (sample size) and the number of "yes" responses for each question in the table. Once the data are entered into the table, compute the percent, p, of "yes" responses in the fourth column. Write this value in decimal form. Round the values of p to three decimal places. (*Note:* For now, leave the last column blank.)

Question	Sample Size	Number of "Yes" Responses	Percent "Yes" Responses, p	Margin of Error, E
1				
2				
3				

4. The value of p represents the percent (written in decimal form) of people in the *sample* who answered "yes." However, the percentage of people in the entire college population who would answer "yes" is unknown. The value of p is only an *estimate*. Statisticians often compute a margin of error associated with such an estimate by using the following formula.

$$E = 1.96\sqrt{\frac{p(1-p)}{n}}$$

where E is the margin of error.
n is the sample size.
p is the percent (in decimal form) of "yes" responses.

Compute the margin of error for each of the three questions. Round the values of E to three decimal places. Record the results in the table.

5. The margin of error computed in step 4 is associated with what statisticians call a 95% level of confidence. To interpret the results, a statistician would say "With 95% confidence, the researcher estimates the percentage of 'yes' responses from the entire college population to be between $p \pm E$."

Interpret the results from each of the three questions.

Chapter 10 Summary

Section 10.1 Definition of an *n*th Root

Key Concepts

b is an **nth root** of a if $b^n = a$.

The expression $\sqrt{a}$ represents the **principal square root** of a.
The expression $\sqrt[n]{a}$ represents the principal nth root of a.

$\sqrt[n]{a^n} = |a|$ if n is even.

$\sqrt[n]{a^n} = a$ if n is odd.

$\sqrt[n]{a}$ is not a real number if $a < 0$ and n is even.

$f(x) = \sqrt[n]{x}$ defines a **radical function**.

The Pythagorean Theorem

$a^2 + b^2 = c^2$

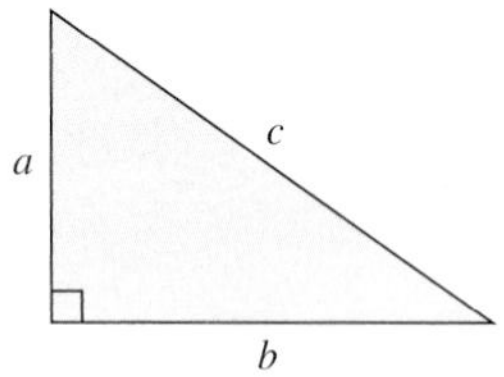

Examples

Example 1

2 is a square root of 4.

-2 is a square root of 4.

-3 is a cube root of -27.

Example 2

$\sqrt{36} = 6 \qquad \sqrt[3]{-64} = -4$

Example 3

$\sqrt[4]{(x+3)^4} = |x+3| \qquad \sqrt[5]{(x+3)^5} = x+3$

Example 4

$\sqrt[4]{-16}$ is not a real number.

Example 5

For $g(x) = \sqrt{x}$ the domain is $[0, \infty)$.
For $h(x) = \sqrt[3]{x}$ the domain is $(-\infty, \infty)$.

Example 6

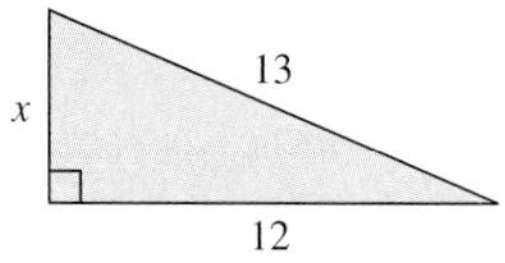

$$x^2 + 12^2 = 13^2$$
$$x^2 + 144 = 169$$
$$x^2 = 25$$
$$x = \sqrt{25}$$
$$x = 5$$

Section 10.2 Rational Exponents

Key Concepts

Let a be a real number and n be an integer such that $n > 1$. If $\sqrt[n]{a}$ exists, then

$$a^{1/n} = \sqrt[n]{a}$$

$$a^{m/n} = \left(\sqrt[n]{a}\right)^m = \sqrt[n]{a^m}$$

All properties of integer exponents hold for rational exponents, provided the roots are real-valued.

Examples

Example 1

$121^{1/2} = \sqrt{121} = 11$

Example 2

$27^{2/3} = \left(\sqrt[3]{27}\right)^2 = (3)^2 = 9$

Example 3

a. $p^{1/3}p^{1/4} = p^{1/3+1/4} = p^{4/12+3/12} = p^{7/12}$

b. $\dfrac{4^{4/3}}{4^{1/3}} = 4^{4/3-1/3} = 4^{3/3} = 4$

c. $\left(y^{-1/2}\right)^6 = y^{(-1/2)(6)} = y^{-3} = \dfrac{1}{y^3}$

Section 10.3 Simplifying Radical Expressions

Key Concepts

Let a and b represent real numbers such that $\sqrt[n]{a}$ and $\sqrt[n]{b}$ are both real. Then,

$\sqrt[n]{ab} = \sqrt[n]{a} \cdot \sqrt[n]{b}$ Multiplication property

A radical expression whose radicand is written as a product of prime factors is in simplified form if all the following conditions are met:

1. The radicand has no factor raised to a power greater than or equal to the index.
2. The radicand does not contain a fraction.
3. No radicals are in the denominator of a fraction.

Examples

Example 1

$$\begin{aligned}\sqrt{12} &= \sqrt{4 \cdot 3}\\ &= \sqrt{4} \cdot \sqrt{3}\\ &= 2\sqrt{3}\end{aligned}$$

Example 2

$$\begin{aligned}&\sqrt[3]{16x^5y^7}\\ &= \sqrt[3]{2^4x^5y^7}\\ &= \sqrt[3]{2^3x^3y^6 \cdot 2x^2y}\\ &= \sqrt[3]{2^3x^3y^6} \cdot \sqrt[3]{2x^2y}\\ &= 2xy^2\sqrt[3]{2x^2y}\end{aligned}$$

Section 10.4 Addition and Subtraction of Radicals

Key Concepts

***Like* radicals** have radical factors with the same index and the same radicand.

Use the distributive property to add and subtract *like* radicals.

Examples

Example 1

$2x\sqrt{7} - 5x\sqrt{7} + x\sqrt{7}$

$= (2 - 5 + 1)x\sqrt{7}$

$= -2x\sqrt{7}$

Example 2

$x\sqrt[4]{16x} - 3\sqrt[4]{x^5}$

$= 2x\sqrt[4]{x} - 3x\sqrt[4]{x}$

$= (2 - 3)x\sqrt[4]{x}$

$= -x\sqrt[4]{x}$

Section 10.5 Multiplication of Radicals

Key Concepts

The Multiplication Property of Radicals

If $\sqrt[n]{a}$ and $\sqrt[n]{b}$ are real numbers, then

$\sqrt[n]{a} \cdot \sqrt[n]{b} = \sqrt[n]{ab}$

To multiply or divide radicals with different indices, convert to rational exponents and use the properties of exponents.

Examples

Example 1

$3\sqrt{2}(\sqrt{2} + 5\sqrt{7} - \sqrt{6})$

$= 3\sqrt{4} + 15\sqrt{14} - 3\sqrt{12}$

$= 3 \cdot 2 + 15\sqrt{14} - 3 \cdot 2\sqrt{3}$

$= 6 + 15\sqrt{14} - 6\sqrt{3}$

Example 2

$\sqrt{p} \cdot \sqrt[5]{p^2}$

$= p^{1/2} \cdot p^{2/5}$

$= p^{5/10} \cdot p^{4/10}$

$= p^{9/10}$

$= \sqrt[10]{p^9}$

Section 10.6 Division of Radicals and Rationalization

Key Concepts

The Division Property of Radicals

If $\sqrt[n]{a}$ and $\sqrt[n]{b}$ are real numbers, then

$$\sqrt[n]{\frac{a}{b}} = \frac{\sqrt[n]{a}}{\sqrt[n]{b}} \qquad b \neq 0$$

The process of removing a radical from the denominator of an expression is called **rationalizing the denominator**.

- Rationalizing a denominator with one term
- Rationalizing a denominator with two terms involving square roots

Examples

Example 1

Simplify.

$$\sqrt{\frac{4x^5}{y^4}}$$

$$= \frac{\sqrt{4x^5}}{\sqrt{y^4}}$$

$$= \frac{2x^2\sqrt{x}}{y^2}$$

Example 2

Rationalize the denominator.

$$\frac{4}{\sqrt[3]{t}}$$

$$= \frac{4}{\sqrt[3]{t}} \cdot \frac{\sqrt[3]{t^2}}{\sqrt[3]{t^2}}$$

$$= \frac{4\sqrt[3]{t^2}}{\sqrt[3]{t^3}} = \frac{4\sqrt[3]{t^2}}{t}$$

Example 3

Rationalize the denominator.

$$\frac{\sqrt{2} - 3\sqrt{x}}{\sqrt{x} - \sqrt{2}}$$

$$= \frac{(\sqrt{2} - 3\sqrt{x})}{(\sqrt{x} - \sqrt{2})} \cdot \frac{(\sqrt{x} + \sqrt{2})}{(\sqrt{x} + \sqrt{2})}$$

$$= \frac{\sqrt{2} \cdot \sqrt{x} + \sqrt{2} \cdot \sqrt{2} - 3\sqrt{x} \cdot \sqrt{x} - 3\sqrt{x} \cdot \sqrt{2}}{(\sqrt{x})^2 - (\sqrt{2})^2}$$

$$= \frac{\sqrt{2x} + 2 - 3x - 3\sqrt{2x}}{x - 2}$$

$$= \frac{-3x - 2\sqrt{2x} + 2}{x - 2}$$

Section 10.7 Solving Radical Equations

Key Concepts

Steps to Solve a Radical Equation

1. Isolate the radical. If an equation has more than one radical, choose one of the radicals to isolate.
2. Raise each side of the equation to a power equal to the index of the radical.
3. Solve the resulting equation. If the equation still has a radical, repeat steps 1 and 2.
4. Check the potential solutions in the original equation.

Example 1

Solve.

$$\sqrt[3]{2x+5}+7=12$$
$$\sqrt[3]{2x+5}=5$$
$$(\sqrt[3]{2x+5})^3=(5)^3$$
$$2x+5=125$$
$$2x=120$$
$$x=60$$

Check:

$$\sqrt[3]{2(60)+5}+7\stackrel{?}{=}12$$
$$\sqrt[3]{125}+7\stackrel{?}{=}12$$
$$5+7\stackrel{?}{=}12 \quad \text{(true)}$$

The solution set is $\{60\}$.

Examples

Example 2

Solve.

$$\sqrt{b-5}-\sqrt{b+3}=2$$
$$\sqrt{b-5}=\sqrt{b+3}+2$$
$$(\sqrt{b-5})^2=(\sqrt{b+3}+2)^2$$
$$b-5=b+3+4\sqrt{b+3}+4$$
$$b-5=b+7+4\sqrt{b+3}$$
$$-12=4\sqrt{b+3}$$
$$-3=\sqrt{b+3}$$
$$(-3)^2=(\sqrt{b+3})^2$$
$$9=b+3$$
$$6=b$$

Check:

$$\sqrt{6-5}-\sqrt{6+3}\stackrel{?}{=}2$$
$$\sqrt{1}-\sqrt{9}\stackrel{?}{=}2$$
$$1-3\stackrel{?}{=}2 \quad \text{(false)}$$

No solution, { }

Section 10.8 Complex Numbers

Key Concepts

$i = \sqrt{-1}$ and $i^2 = -1$

For a real number $b > 0$, $\sqrt{-b} = i\sqrt{b}$

A **complex number** is in the form $a + bi$, where a and b are real numbers. The value a is called the real part, and b is called the imaginary part.

To add or subtract complex numbers, combine the real parts and combine the imaginary parts.

Multiply complex numbers by using the distributive property.

Divide complex numbers by multiplying the numerator and denominator by the **complex conjugate** of the denominator.

Examples

Example 1

$$\sqrt{-4} \cdot \sqrt{-9}$$
$$= (2i)(3i)$$
$$= 6i^2$$
$$= -6$$

Example 2

$$(3 - 5i) - (2 + i) + (3 - 2i)$$
$$= 3 - 5i - 2 - i + 3 - 2i$$
$$= 4 - 8i$$

Example 3

$$(1 + 6i)(2 + 4i)$$
$$= 2 + 4i + 12i + 24i^2$$
$$= 2 + 16i + 24(-1)$$
$$= -22 + 16i$$

Example 4

$$\frac{3}{2 - 5i}$$
$$= \frac{3}{(2 - 5i)} \cdot \frac{(2 + 5i)}{(2 + 5i)}$$
$$= \frac{6 + 15i}{4 - 25i^2}$$
$$= \frac{6 + 15i}{4 + 25}$$
$$= \frac{6 + 15i}{29}$$
$$= \frac{6}{29} + \frac{15}{29}i$$

Chapter 10 Review Exercises

For the exercises in this set, assume that all variables represent positive real numbers unless otherwise stated.

Section 10.1

1. True or false?

a. The principal *n*th root of an even-indexed root is always positive
False; $\sqrt{0} = 0$ is not positive.

b. The principal *n*th root of an odd-indexed root is always positive. False; $\sqrt[3]{-8} = -2$

2. Explain why $\sqrt{(-3)^2} \neq -3$. $\sqrt{(-3)^2} = \sqrt{9} = 3$

3. For $a > 0$ and $b > 0$, are the following statements true or false?

a. $\sqrt{a^2 + b^2} = a + b$ False

b. $\sqrt{(a+b)^2} = a + b$ True

For Exercises 4–6, simplify the radicals.

4. $\sqrt{\dfrac{50}{32}}$ $\dfrac{5}{4}$ **5.** $\sqrt[4]{625}$ 5 **6.** $\sqrt{(-6)^2}$ 6

7. Evaluate the function values for $f(x) = \sqrt{x-1}$.

a. $f(10)$ 3 **b.** $f(1)$ 0 **c.** $f(8)$ $\sqrt{7}$

d. Write the domain of f in interval notation.
$[1, \infty)$

8. Evaluate the function values for $g(t) = \sqrt{5+t}$.

a. $g(-5)$ 0 **b.** $g(-4)$ 1 **c.** $g(4)$ 3

d. Write the domain of g in interval notation
$[-5, \infty)$

9. Write the English expression as an algebraic expression: Four more than the quotient of the cube root of $2x$ and the principal fourth root of $2x$.
$\dfrac{\sqrt[3]{2x}}{\sqrt[4]{2x}} + 4$

For Exercises 10–11, simplify the expression. Assume that x and y represent *any* real number.

10. a. $\sqrt{x^2}$ $|x|$ **b.** $\sqrt[3]{x^3}$ x

c. $\sqrt[4]{x^4}$ $|x|$ **d.** $\sqrt[5]{(x+1)^5}$ $x+1$

11. a. $\sqrt{4y^2}$ $2|y|$ **b.** $\sqrt[3]{27y^3}$ $3y$

c. $\sqrt[100]{y^{100}}$ $|y|$ **d.** $\sqrt[101]{y^{101}}$ y

12. Use the Pythagorean theorem to find the length of the third side of the triangle. 8 cm

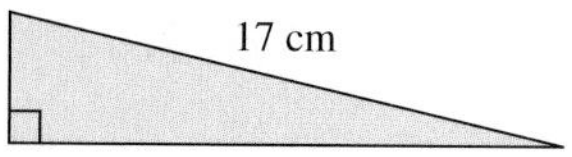

Section 10.2

13. Are the properties of exponents the same for rational exponents and integer exponents? Give an example. (Answers may vary.) Yes, provided the expressions are defined. For example: $x^5 \cdot x^3 = x^8$ and $x^{1/5} \cdot x^{2/5} = x^{3/5}$

14. In the expression $x^{m/n}$ what does n represent?
n represents the root.

15. Explain the process of eliminating a negative exponent from an algebraic expression. Take the reciprocal of the base and change the exponent to positive.

For Exercises 16–21, simplify the expressions. Write the answers with positive exponents only.

16. $(-125)^{1/3}$ -5 **17.** $16^{-1/4}$ $\dfrac{1}{2}$

18. $\left(\dfrac{1}{16}\right)^{-3/4} - \left(\dfrac{1}{8}\right)^{-2/3}$ 4 **19.** $\left(b^{1/2} \cdot b^{1/3}\right)^{12}$ b^{10}

20. $\left(\dfrac{x^{-1/4}y^{-1/3}z^{3/4}}{2^{1/3}x^{-1/3}y^{2/3}}\right)^{-12}$ $\dfrac{16y^{12}}{xz^9}$ **21.** $\left(\dfrac{a^{12}b^{-4}c^7}{a^3b^2c^4}\right)^{1/3}$ $\dfrac{a^3c}{b^2}$

For Exercises 22–23, rewrite the expressions by using rational exponents.

22. $\sqrt[4]{x^3}$ $x^{3/4}$ **23.** $\sqrt[3]{2y^2}$ $(2y^2)^{1/3}$

For Exercises 24–26, use a calculator to approximate the expressions to four decimal places.

24. $10^{1/3}$ 2.1544 **25.** $17.8^{2/3}$ 6.8173 **26.** $\sqrt[5]{147^4}$ 54.1819

Section 10.3

27. List the criteria for a radical expression to be simplified.
a. The radicand has no factor raised to a power greater than or equal to the index.
b. The radicand does not contain a fraction.
c. There are no radicals in the denominator of a fraction.

For Exercises 28–31, simplify the radicals.

28. $\sqrt{108}$ $6\sqrt{3}$ **29.** $\sqrt[4]{x^5yz^4}$ $xz\sqrt[4]{xy}$

30. $-2\sqrt[3]{250a^3b^{10}}$ $-10ab^3\sqrt[3]{2b}$ **31.** $\sqrt[3]{\dfrac{-16a^4}{2ab^3}}$ $-\dfrac{2a}{b}$

32. Write an English phrase that describes the following mathematical expressions: (Answers may vary.)

a. $\sqrt{\frac{2}{x}}$ The principal square root of the quotient of 2 and x

b. $(x+1)^3$ The cube of the sum of x and 1

33. An engineering firm made a mistake when building a $\frac{1}{4}$-mi bridge in the Florida Keys. The bridge was made without adequate expansion joints to prevent buckling during the heat of summer. During mid-June, the bridge expanded 1.5 ft, causing a vertical bulge in the middle. Calculate the height of the bulge h in feet. (*Note:* 1 mi = 5280 ft.) Round to the nearest foot.
31 ft

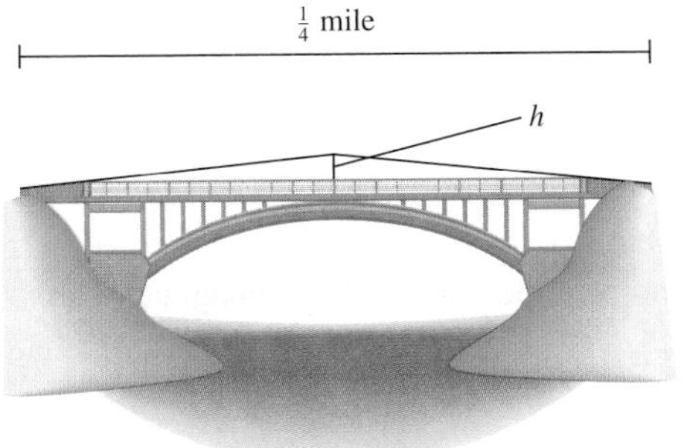

Section 10.4

34. Complete the following statement: Radicals may be added or subtracted if . . .
they are *like* radicals.

For Exercises 35–38, determine whether the radicals may be combined, and explain your answer.

35. $\sqrt[3]{2x} - 2\sqrt{2x}$ Cannot be combined; the indices are different.

36. $2 + \sqrt{x}$ Cannot be combined; one term has a radical, but the other does not.

37. $\sqrt[4]{3xy} + 2\sqrt[4]{3xy}$ Can be combined: $3\sqrt[4]{3xy}$

38. $-4\sqrt{32} + 7\sqrt{50}$ Can be added after simplifying: $19\sqrt{2}$

For Exercises 39–42, add or subtract as indicated.

39. $4\sqrt{7} - 2\sqrt{7} + 3\sqrt{7}$ $5\sqrt{7}$

40. $2\sqrt[3]{64} + 3\sqrt[3]{54} - 16$ $9\sqrt[3]{2} - 8$

41. $\sqrt{50} + 7\sqrt{2} - \sqrt{8}$ $10\sqrt{2}$

42. $x\sqrt[3]{16x^2} - 4\sqrt[3]{2x^5} + 5x\sqrt[3]{54x^2}$ $13x\sqrt[3]{2x^2}$

For Exercises 43–44, answer true or false. If an answer is false, explain why. Assume all variables represent positive real numbers.

43. $5 + 3\sqrt{x} = 8\sqrt{x}$ False; 5 and $3\sqrt{x}$ are not *like* radicals.

44. $\sqrt{y} + \sqrt{y} = \sqrt{2y}$ False; $\sqrt{y} + \sqrt{y} = 2\sqrt{y}$ (add the coefficients).

Section 10.5

For Exercises 45–56, multiply the radicals and simplify the answer.

45. $\sqrt{3} \cdot \sqrt{12}$ 6

46. $\sqrt[4]{4} \cdot \sqrt[4]{8}$ $2\sqrt[4]{2}$

47. $-2\sqrt{3}(\sqrt{7} - 3\sqrt{11})$ $-2\sqrt{21} + 6\sqrt{33}$

48. $-3\sqrt{5}(2\sqrt{3} - \sqrt{5})$ $-6\sqrt{15} + 15$

49. $(2\sqrt{x} - 3)(2\sqrt{x} + 3)$ $4x - 9$

50. $(\sqrt{y} + 4)(\sqrt{y} - 4)$ $y - 16$

51. $(\sqrt{7y} - \sqrt{3x})^2$ $7y - 2\sqrt{21xy} + 3x$

52. $(2\sqrt{3w} + 5)^2$ $12w + 20\sqrt{3w} + 25$

53. $(-\sqrt{z} - \sqrt{6})(2\sqrt{z} + 7\sqrt{6})$ $-2z - 9\sqrt{6z} - 42$

54. $(3\sqrt{a} - \sqrt{5})(\sqrt{a} + 2\sqrt{5})$ $3a + 5\sqrt{5a} - 10$

55. $\sqrt[3]{u} \cdot \sqrt{u^5}$ $u^2\sqrt[6]{u^5}$

56. $\sqrt{2} \cdot \sqrt[4]{w^3}$ $\sqrt[4]{4w^3}$

Section 10.6

For Exercises 57–60, simplify the radicals.

57. $\sqrt{\frac{3y^5}{25x^6}}$ $\frac{y^2\sqrt{3y}}{5x^3}$

58. $\sqrt[3]{\frac{-16x^7y^6}{z^9}}$ $\frac{-2x^2y^2\sqrt[3]{2x}}{z^3}$

59. $\frac{\sqrt{324w^7}}{\sqrt{4w^3}}$ $9w^2$

60. $\frac{\sqrt[3]{3t^{14}}}{\sqrt[3]{192t^2}}$ $\frac{t^4}{4}$

For Exercises 61–68, rationalize the denominator.

61. $\sqrt{\frac{7}{2y}}$ $\frac{\sqrt{14y}}{2y}$

62. $\sqrt{\frac{5}{3w}}$ $\frac{\sqrt{15w}}{3w}$

63. $\frac{4}{\sqrt[3]{9p^2}}$ $\frac{4\sqrt[3]{3p}}{3p}$

64. $\frac{-2}{\sqrt[3]{2x}}$ $-\frac{\sqrt[3]{4x^2}}{x}$

65. $\frac{-5}{\sqrt{15} + \sqrt{10}}$ $\sqrt{10} - \sqrt{15}$

66. $\frac{-6}{\sqrt{7} + \sqrt{5}}$ $3\sqrt{5} - 3\sqrt{7}$

67. $\frac{t - 3}{\sqrt{t} - \sqrt{3}}$ $\sqrt{t} + \sqrt{3}$

68. $\frac{w - 7}{\sqrt{w} - \sqrt{7}}$ $\sqrt{w} + \sqrt{7}$

69. Write the mathematical expression as an English phrase. (Answers may vary.)

$\frac{\sqrt{2}}{x^2}$ The quotient of the principal square root of 2 and the square of x

Section 10.7

Solve the radical equations in Exercises 70–77, if possible.

70. $\sqrt{2y} = 7$ $\left\{\frac{49}{2}\right\}$

71. $\sqrt{a - 6} - 5 = 0$ $\{31\}$

72. $\sqrt[3]{2w - 3} + 5 = 2$ $\{-12\}$

73. $\sqrt[4]{p+12} - \sqrt[4]{5p-16} = 0$ {7}

74. $\sqrt{t} + \sqrt{t-5} = 5$ {9}

75. $\sqrt{8x+1} = -\sqrt{x-13}$
{ } (The value −2 does not check.)

76. $\sqrt{2m^2+4} - \sqrt{9m} = 0$ $\left\{\frac{1}{2}, 4\right\}$

77. $\sqrt{x+2} = 1 - \sqrt{2x+5}$
{−2} (The value 2 does not check.)

78. A tower is supported by stabilizing wires. Find the exact length of each wire, and then round to the nearest tenth of a meter. $6\sqrt{5}$ m ≈ 13.4 m

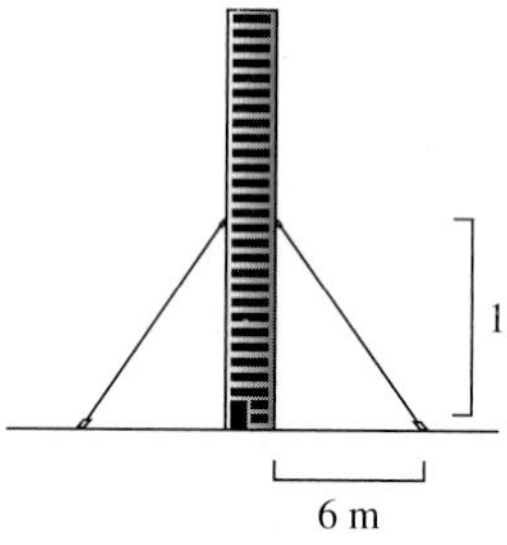

79. The velocity, $v(d)$, of an ocean wave depends on the water depth d as the wave approaches land.

$$v(d) = \sqrt{32d}$$

where $v(d)$ is in feet per second and d is in feet.

a. Find $v(20)$ and interpret its value Round to one decimal place. $v(20) \approx 25.3$ ft/sec. When the water depth is 20 ft, a wave travels about 25.3 ft/sec.

b. Find the depth of the water at a point where a wave is traveling at 16 ft/sec. 8 ft

Section 10.8

80. Define a complex number.
$a + bi$, where a and b are real numbers and $i = \sqrt{-1}$

81. Define an imaginary number. $a + bi$, where $b \neq 0$

82. Describe the first step in the process to simplify the expression.

$$\frac{3}{4+6i}$$

Multiply the numerator and denominator by $4 - 6i$, which is the complex conjugate of the denominator.

For Exercises 83–86, rewrite the expressions in terms of i.

83. $\sqrt{-16}$ $4i$

84. $-\sqrt{-5}$ $-i\sqrt{5}$

85. $\sqrt{-75} \cdot \sqrt{-3}$ -15

86. $\dfrac{-\sqrt{-24}}{\sqrt{6}}$ $-2i$

For Exercises 87–90, simplify the powers of i.

87. i^{38} -1

88. i^{101} i

89. i^{19} $-i$

90. $i^{1000} + i^{1002}$ 0

For Exercises 91–94, perform the indicated operations. Write the final answer in the form $a + bi$.

91. $(-3+i) - (2-4i)$
$-5 + 5i$

92. $(1+6i)(3-i)$
$9 + 17i$

93. $(4-3i)(4+3i)$
$25 + 0i$

94. $(5-i)^2$
$24 - 10i$

For Exercises 95–96, write the expressions in the form $a + bi$, and determine the real and imaginary parts.

95. $\dfrac{17-4i}{-4}$ $-\frac{17}{4} + i$; real part: $-\frac{17}{4}$; imaginary part: 1

96. $\dfrac{-16-8i}{8}$ $-2 - i$; real part: −2; imaginary part: −1

For Exercises 97–100, divide and simplify. Write the final answer in the form $a + bi$.

97. $\dfrac{2-i}{3+2i}$ $\frac{4}{13} - \frac{7}{13}i$

98. $\dfrac{10+5i}{2-i}$ $3 + 4i$

99. $\dfrac{5+3i}{-2i}$ $-\frac{3}{2} + \frac{5}{2}i$

100. $\dfrac{4i}{4-i}$ $-\frac{4}{17} + \frac{16}{17}i$

For Exercises 101–102, simplify the expression.

101. $\dfrac{-8+\sqrt{-40}}{12}$
$-\frac{2}{3} + \frac{\sqrt{10}}{6}i$

102. $\dfrac{6-\sqrt{-144}}{3}$ $2 - 4i$

Chapter 10 Test

1. a. What is the principal square root of 36? 6

b. What is the negative square root of 36? −6

2. Which of the following are real numbers?

a. $-\sqrt{100}$ Real **b.** $\sqrt{-100}$ Not real

c. $-\sqrt[3]{1000}$ Real **d.** $\sqrt[3]{-1000}$ Real

3. Simplify.

a. $\sqrt[3]{y^3}$ y **b.** $\sqrt[4]{y^4}$ $|y|$

For Exercises 4–11, simplify the radicals. Assume that all variables represent positive numbers.

4. $\sqrt[4]{81}$ 3

5. $\sqrt{\dfrac{16}{9}}$ $\frac{4}{3}$

6. $\sqrt[3]{32}$ $2\sqrt[3]{4}$

7. $\sqrt{a^4b^3c^5}$ $a^2bc^2\sqrt{bc}$

8. $\sqrt{18x^5y^3z^4}$ $3x^2yz^2\sqrt{2xy}$

9. $\sqrt{\dfrac{32w^6}{2w}}$ $4w^2\sqrt{w}$

10. $\sqrt[3]{\dfrac{x^6}{125y^3}}$ $\frac{x^2}{5y}$

11. $\dfrac{2\sqrt{72}}{8}$ $\frac{3\sqrt{2}}{2}$

12. a. Evaluate the function values $f(-8)$, $f(-6)$, $f(-4)$, and $f(-2)$ for $f(x) = \sqrt{-2x-4}$.
$f(-8) = 2\sqrt{3}; f(-6) = 2\sqrt{2}; f(-4) = 2; f(-2) = 0$

b. Write the domain of f in interval notation.
$(-\infty, -2]$

13. Use a calculator to evaluate $\dfrac{-3-\sqrt{5}}{17}$ to four decimal places. −0.3080

For Exercises 14–15, simplify the expressions. Assume that all variables represent positive numbers.

14. $-27^{1/3}$ −3

15. $8^{2/3} \cdot \left(\dfrac{25x^4y^6}{z^2}\right)^{1/2}$ $\frac{20x^2y^3}{z}$

For Exercises 16–17, use rational exponents to multiply or divide. Write the final answer in radical form.

16. $\sqrt[6]{7} \cdot \sqrt{y}$ $\sqrt[6]{7y^3}$

17. $\dfrac{\sqrt[3]{10}}{\sqrt[4]{10}}$ $\sqrt[12]{10}$

18. Add or subtract as indicated. $3\sqrt{5}$

$$3\sqrt{5} + 4\sqrt{5} - 2\sqrt{20}$$

For Exercises 19–20, multiply the radicals.

19. $3\sqrt{x}(\sqrt{2} - \sqrt{5})$ $3\sqrt{2x} - 3\sqrt{5x}$

20. $(2\sqrt{5} - 3\sqrt{x})(4\sqrt{5} + \sqrt{x})$ $40 - 10\sqrt{5x} - 3x$

For Exercises 21–22, rationalize the denominator. Assume $x > 0$.

21. $\dfrac{-2}{\sqrt[3]{x}}$ $\frac{-2\sqrt[3]{x^2}}{x}$

22. $\dfrac{\sqrt{x}+2}{3-\sqrt{x}}$ $\frac{x+6+5\sqrt{x}}{9-x}$

23. Rewrite the expressions in terms of i.

a. $\sqrt{-8}$ $2i\sqrt{2}$ **b.** $2\sqrt{-16}$ $8i$ **c.** $\dfrac{2+\sqrt{-8}}{4}$ $\frac{1}{2} + \frac{\sqrt{2}}{2}i$

For Exercises 24–30, perform the indicated operations and simplify completely. Write the final answer in the form $a + bi$.

24. $(3-5i) - (2+6i)$ $1 - 11i$

25. $(4+i)(8+2i)$ $30 + 16i$

26. $\sqrt{-16} \cdot \sqrt{-49}$ −28

27. $(4-7i)^2$ $-33 - 56i$

28. $(2-10i)(2+10i)$ 104

29. $\dfrac{3-2i}{3-4i}$ $\frac{17}{25} + \frac{6}{25}i$

30. $\dfrac{6i}{3-5i}$ $-\frac{15}{17} + \frac{9}{17}i$

31. If the volume V of a sphere is known, the radius of the sphere can be computed by

$$r(V) = \sqrt[3]{\frac{3V}{4\pi}}$$

Find $r(10)$ to two decimal places. Interpret the meaning in the context of the problem.
$r(10) \approx 1.34$; the radius of a sphere of volume 10 cubic units is approximately 1.34 units.

32. A patio 20 ft wide has a slanted roof, as shown in the figure. Find the length of the roof if there is an 8-in. overhang. Round the answer to the nearest foot. 21 ft

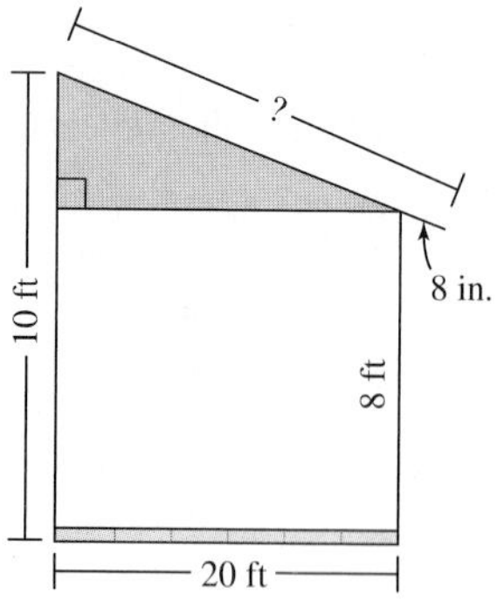

For Exercises 33–35, solve the radical equation.

33. $\sqrt[3]{2x+5} = -3$ $\{-16\}$

34. $\sqrt{5x+8} = \sqrt{5x-1} + 1$ $\left\{\frac{17}{5}\right\}$

35. $\sqrt{t+7} - \sqrt{2t-3} = 2$ $\{2\}$ (The value 42 does not check.)

Chapters 1–10 Cumulative Review Exercises

1. Simplify the expression.
$6^2 - 2[5 - 8(3-1) + 4 \div 2]$ 54

2. Simplify the expression.
$3x - 3(-2x+5) - 4y + 2(3x+5) - y$
$15x - 5y - 5$

3. Solve. $9(2y+8) = 20 - (y+5)$ $\{-3\}$

For Exercises 4–6, solve the inequalities. Write the answers in interval notation, if possible.

4. $2a - 4 < -14$
$(-\infty, -5)$

5. $11 \geq -x + 2 > 5$
$[-9, -3)$

6. $|9 - 4x| + 4 < 2$ $\{\ \}$

7. Write an equation of the line that is parallel to the line $2x + y = 9$ and passes through the point $(3, -1)$. Write the answer in slope-intercept form. $y = -2x + 5$

8. Write an equation of a line parallel to the y-axis passing through the point $(-5, 8)$. $x = -5$

9. Solve the system of equations by using the addition method.

$$2x - 3y = 0$$
$$-4x + 3y = -1$$

$\left\{\left(\frac{1}{2}, \frac{1}{3}\right)\right\}$

10. Determine if $\left(2, -2, \frac{1}{2}\right)$ is a solution to the system.

$$2x + y - 4z = 0$$
$$x - y + 2z = 5$$
$$3x + 2y + 2z = 4$$

$\left(2, -2, \frac{1}{2}\right)$ is not a solution.

11. Bennette and Pepe are landscapers and have to dig a ditch in which to put underground piping for a sprinkler system. Bennette can dig 40 yd of ditch in 3 hr and Pepe can dig 40 yd of ditch in 5 hr. How long will it take them to dig 40 yd together? Together it will take them $1\frac{7}{8}$ hr.

12. Given the function defined by $f(x) = 4x - 2$.

a. Find $f(-2), f(0), f(4)$, and $f(\frac{1}{2})$.
$f(-2) = -10; f(0) = -2; f(4) = 14; f\left(\frac{1}{2}\right) = 0$

b. Write the ordered pairs that correspond to the function values in part (a)
$(-2, -10), (0, -2), (4, 14), \left(\frac{1}{2}, 0\right)$

c. Graph $y = f(x)$.

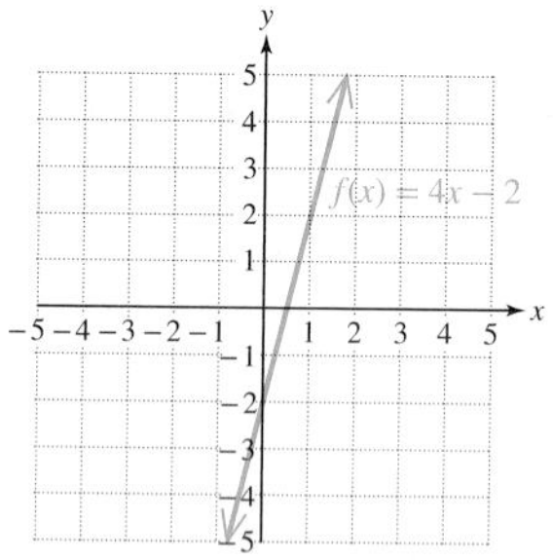

13. Simplify the expression. Write the final answer with positive exponents only. $a^6b^{12}c^4$

$$\left(\frac{a^{3/2}b^{-1/4}c^{1/3}}{ab^{-5/4}c^0}\right)^{12}$$

14. Multiply or divide as indicated, and write the answer in scientific notation.

a. $(3.5 \times 10^7)(4 \times 10^{-12})$ 1.4×10^{-4}

b. $\dfrac{6.28 \times 10^5}{2 \times 10^{-4}}$ 3.14×10^9

15. Multiply the polynomials $(2x + 5)(x - 3)$. What is the degree of the product?
$2x^2 - x - 15$; 2nd degree

16. Perform the indicated operations and simplify.
$\sqrt{3}(\sqrt{5} + \sqrt{6} + \sqrt{3})$ $\sqrt{15} + 3\sqrt{2} + 3$

17. Divide. $(x^2 - x - 12) \div (x + 3)$ $x - 4$

18. Simplify and subtract. $\sqrt[4]{\dfrac{1}{16}} - \sqrt[3]{\dfrac{8}{27}}$ $-\dfrac{1}{6}$

19. Simplify. $\sqrt[3]{\dfrac{54c^4}{cd^3}}$ $\dfrac{3c\sqrt[3]{2}}{d}$

20. Add. $4\sqrt{45b^3} + 5b\sqrt{80b}$ $32b\sqrt{5b}$

21. Divide. $\dfrac{13i}{3 + 2i}$ Write the answer in the form $a + bi$. $2 + 3i$

22. Solve. $\dfrac{5}{y - 2} - \dfrac{3}{y - 4} = \dfrac{6}{y^2 - 6y + 8}$ $\{10\}$

23. Add. $\dfrac{3}{x^2 + 5x} + \dfrac{-2}{x^2 - 25}$ $\dfrac{x - 15}{x(x + 5)(x - 5)}$

24. Divide. $\dfrac{a + 10}{2a^2 - 11a - 6} \div \dfrac{a^2 + 12a + 20}{6 - a}$ $\dfrac{-1}{(2a + 1)(a + 2)}$

25. Perform the indicated operations.
$(-5x^2 - 4x + 8) - (3x - 5)^2$ $-14x^2 + 26x - 17$

26. Simplify. $\dfrac{-4}{\sqrt{3} - \sqrt{5}}$ $2\sqrt{3} + 2\sqrt{5}$

27. Divide. $\dfrac{4}{3 - 5i}$ $\dfrac{6}{17} + \dfrac{10}{17}i$

28. Solve. $12x^2 + 4x - 21 = 0$ $\left\{\dfrac{7}{6}, -\dfrac{3}{2}\right\}$

29. Factor. $x^2 + 6x + 9 - y^2$ $(x + 3 - y)(x + 3 + y)$

30. Factor. $x^6 + 8$ $(x^2 + 2)(x^4 - 2x^2 + 4)$

Quadratic Equations and Functions

11

CHAPTER OUTLINE

Mathematics in Art

A **golden rectangle** is a rectangle in which the ratio of its length L to its width W is equal to the ratio of the sum of its length and width to its length.

$$\frac{L}{W} = \frac{L + W}{L}$$

The values of L and W that meet this condition are said to be in the **golden ratio**. The golden ratio has been studied by artists and art historians for generations because the golden ratio represents an aesthetically pleasing ratio between the length and width of a figure. For example, the face of the Parthenon built in ancient Greece has the dimensions of a golden rectangle.

We can show that the length of a golden rectangle is approximately 1.62 times the width. Substituting 1 for the width, we have the proportion $\frac{L}{1} = \frac{L + 1}{L}$.

Then, clearing fractions and writing the quadratic equation in standard form gives $L^2 - L - 1 = 0$. The expression on the left is not factorable, but fortunately in this chapter, we will learn two techniques to solve a quadratic equation when factoring fails. The positive solution for L in this equation is the golden ratio, $\frac{1 + \sqrt{5}}{2} \approx 1.62$.

© Purestock/SuperStock RF

Section 11.1 Square Root Property and Completing the Square

Concepts

1. Solving Quadratic Equations by Using the Square Root Property
2. Solving Quadratic Equations by Completing the Square
3. Literal Equations

1. Solving Quadratic Equations by Using the Square Root Property

We have already learned how to solve a quadratic equation by factoring and applying the zero product rule. For example:

$$x^2 = 81$$

$$x^2 - 81 = 0 \qquad \text{Set one side equal to zero.}$$

$$(x - 9)(x + 9) = 0 \qquad \text{Factor.}$$

$$x - 9 = 0 \quad \text{or} \quad x + 9 = 0 \qquad \text{Set each factor equal to zero.}$$

$$x = 9 \quad \text{or} \quad x = -9$$

The solution set is $\{9, -9\}$.

It is important to note that the zero product rule can only be used if the equation is factorable. In this section, we will learn a method to solve quadratic equations containing expressions that are both factorable and nonfactorable.

Consider a quadratic equation of the form $x^2 = k$. The solutions are all numbers (real or imaginary) that when squared equal k, so for any nonzero constant k, there will be two solutions, $\sqrt{k}$ or $-\sqrt{k}$. For example:

$$x^2 = 25 \qquad \text{The solutions are 5 and } -5.$$

$$x^2 = -25 \qquad \text{The solutions are } 5i \text{ and } -5i.$$

This principle is stated formally as the **square root property**.

The Square Root Property

For any real number, k, if $x^2 = k$, then $x = \sqrt{k}$ or $x = -\sqrt{k}$.

Note: The solution may also be written as $\pm\sqrt{k}$, read "plus or minus the square root of k."

Classroom Example: p. 787, Exercise 6

Example 1 Solving a Quadratic Equation by Using the Square Root Property

Use the square root property to solve the equation. $4p^2 = 9$

Solution:

$$4p^2 = 9$$

$$p^2 = \frac{9}{4} \qquad \text{Isolate } p^2 \text{ by dividing both sides by 4.}$$

$$p = \pm\sqrt{\frac{9}{4}} \qquad \text{Apply the square root property.}$$

$$p = \pm\frac{3}{2} \qquad \text{Simplify the radical.}$$

The solution set is $\left\{\frac{3}{2}, -\frac{3}{2}\right\}$.

Skill Practice Solve using the square root property.

1. $25a^2 = 16$

For a quadratic equation, $ax^2 + bx + c = 0$, if $b = 0$, then the equation is easily solved by using the square root property. This is demonstrated in Example 2.

Example 2 Solving a Quadratic Equation by Using the Square Root Property

Classroom Example: p. 787, Exercise 8

Use the square root property to solve the equation. $3x^2 + 75 = 0$

Solution:

$3x^2 + 75 = 0$ Rewrite the equation to fit the form $x^2 = k$.

$3x^2 = -75$

$x^2 = -25$ The equation is now in the form $x^2 = k$.

$x = \pm\sqrt{-25}$ Apply the square root property.

$= \pm 5i$

Check: $x = 5i$	Check: $x = -5i$
$3x^2 + 75 = 0$	$3x^2 + 75 = 0$
$3(5i)^2 + 75 \stackrel{?}{=} 0$	$3(-5i)^2 + 75 \stackrel{?}{=} 0$
$3(25i^2) + 75 \stackrel{?}{=} 0$	$3(25i^2) + 75 \stackrel{?}{=} 0$
$3(-25) + 75 \stackrel{?}{=} 0$	$3(-25) + 75 \stackrel{?}{=} 0$
$-75 + 75 \stackrel{?}{=} 0$ ✓	$-75 + 75 \stackrel{?}{=} 0$ ✓

The solution set is $\{\pm 5i\}$.

Avoiding Mistakes

A common mistake is to forget the ± symbol when solving the equation $x^2 = k$:

$x = \pm\sqrt{k}$

Skill Practice Solve using the square root property.

2. $8x^2 + 72 = 0$

Example 3 Solving a Quadratic Equation by Using the Square Root Property

Classroom Example: p. 787, Exercise 12

Use the square root property to solve the equation. $(w + 3)^2 = 20$

Solution:

$(w + 3)^2 = 20$ The equation is in the form $x^2 = k$, where $x = (w + 3)$.

$w + 3 = \pm\sqrt{20}$ Apply the square root property.

$w + 3 = \pm\sqrt{4 \cdot 5}$ Simplify the radical.

$w + 3 = \pm 2\sqrt{5}$

$w = -3 \pm 2\sqrt{5}$ Solve for w.

The solution set is $\{-3 \pm 2\sqrt{5}\}$.

TIP: Recall that $-3 \pm 2\sqrt{5}$ represents two solutions:

$-3 + 2\sqrt{5}$ and $-3 - 2\sqrt{5}$

Skill Practice Solve using the square root property.

3. $(t - 5)^2 = 18$

Answers

1. $\left\{\frac{4}{5}, -\frac{4}{5}\right\}$ **2.** $\{\pm 3i\}$

3. $\{5 \pm 3\sqrt{2}\}$

2. Solving Quadratic Equations by Completing the Square

In Example 3 we used the square root property to solve an equation where the square of a binomial was equal to a constant.

$$\underbrace{(w+3)^2}_{\text{Square of a binomial}} = \underset{\uparrow \text{ Constant}}{20}$$

The square of a binomial is the factored form of a perfect square trinomial. For example:

Perfect Square Trinomial		**Factored Form**
$x^2 + 10x + 25$	⟶	$(x + 5)^2$
$t^2 - 6t + 9$	⟶	$(t - 3)^2$
$p^2 - 14p + 49$	⟶	$(p - 7)^2$

For a perfect square trinomial with a leading coefficient of 1, the constant term is the square of one-half the linear term coefficient. For example:

$$x^2 + 10x + 25$$
$$[\tfrac{1}{2}(10)]^2 \rightarrow 25$$

In general an expression of the form $x^2 + bx + n$ is a perfect square trinomial if $n = (\frac{1}{2}b)^2$. The process to create a perfect square trinomial is called **completing the square**.

Classroom Examples: p. 787, Exercises 28 and 38

Example 4 Completing the Square

Determine the value of n that makes the polynomial a perfect square trinomial. Then factor the expression as the square of a binomial.

a. $x^2 + 12x + n$ **b.** $x^2 - 26x + n$

c. $x^2 + 11x + n$ **d.** $x^2 - \frac{4}{7}x + n$

Solution:

The expressions are in the form $x^2 + bx + n$. The value of n equals the square of one-half the linear term coefficient $(\frac{1}{2}b)^2$.

a. $x^2 + 12x + n$

$x^2 + 12x + 36$ $\quad n = [\frac{1}{2}(12)]^2 = (6)^2 = 36$

$(x + 6)^2$ Factored form

b. $x^2 - 26x + n$

$x^2 - 26x + 169$ $\quad n = [\frac{1}{2}(-26)]^2 = (-13)^2 = 169$

$(x - 13)^2$ Factored form

c. $x^2 + 11x + n$

$x^2 + 11x + \frac{121}{4}$ $\quad n = [\frac{1}{2}(11)]^2 = (\frac{11}{2})^2 = \frac{121}{4}$

$\left(x + \frac{11}{2}\right)^2$ Factored form

d. $x^2 - \frac{4}{7}x + n$

$x^2 - \frac{4}{7}x + \frac{4}{49}$ $\quad n = [\frac{1}{2}(-\frac{4}{7})]^2 = (-\frac{2}{7})^2 = \frac{4}{49}$

$\left(x - \frac{2}{7}\right)^2$ Factored form

Skill Practice Determine the value of n that makes the polynomial a perfect square trinomial. Then factor.

4. $x^2 + 20x + n$ **5.** $y^2 - 16y + n$

6. $a^2 - 15a + n$ **7.** $w^2 + \frac{7}{3}w + n$

The process of completing the square can be used to write a quadratic equation $ax^2 + bx + c = 0$ $(a \neq 0)$ in the form $(x - h)^2 = k$. Then the square root property can be used to solve the equation. The following steps outline the procedure.

Solving a Quadratic Equation $ax^2 + bx + c = 0$ by Completing the Square and Applying the Square Root Property

Step 1 Divide both sides by a to make the leading coefficient 1.

Step 2 Isolate the variable terms on one side of the equation.

Step 3 Complete the square.

- Add the square of one-half the linear term coefficient to both sides, $(\frac{1}{2}b)^2$.
- Factor the resulting perfect square trinomial.

Step 4 Apply the square root property and solve for x.

Example 5 Solving a Quadratic Equation by Completing the Square and Applying the Square Root Property

Classroom Example: p. 788, Exercise 46

Solve by completing the square and applying the square root property.

$$x^2 - 6x + 13 = 0$$

Solution:

$x^2 - 6x + 13 = 0$ **Step 1:** Since the leading coefficient a is equal to 1, we do not have to divide by a. We can proceed to step 2.

$x^2 - 6x = -13$ **Step 2:** Isolate the variable terms on one side.

$x^2 - 6x + 9 = -13 + 9$ **Step 3:** To complete the square, add $[\frac{1}{2}(-6)]^2 = 9$ to both sides of the equation.

$(x - 3)^2 = -4$ Factor the perfect square trinomial.

Instructor Note: It may help if you discuss the connection between degree and the anticipated number of solutions. With degree two, we expect to see two solutions (including multiplicities).

Answers

4. $n = 100$; $(x + 10)^2$
5. $n = 64$; $(y - 8)^2$
6. $n = \frac{225}{4}$; $\left(a - \frac{15}{2}\right)^2$
7. $n = \frac{49}{36}$; $\left(w + \frac{7}{6}\right)^2$

$x - 3 = \pm\sqrt{-4}$	**Step 4:** Apply the square root property.
$x - 3 = \pm 2i$	Simplify the radical.
$x = 3 \pm 2i$	Solve for x.

The solutions are imaginary numbers and can be written as $3 + 2i$ and $3 - 2i$.

The solution set is $\{3 \pm 2i\}$.

Skill Practice Solve by completing the square and applying the square root property.

8. $z^2 - 4z + 26 = 0$

Classroom Example: p. 788, Exercise 54

Example 6 Solving a Quadratic Equation by Completing the Square and Applying the Square Root Property

Solve by completing the square and applying the square root property.

$$2m^2 + 10m = 3$$

Solution:

$2m^2 + 10m = 3$	The variable terms are already isolated on one side of the equation.
$\frac{2m^2}{2} + \frac{10m}{2} = \frac{3}{2}$	Divide by the leading coefficient, 2.
$m^2 + 5m = \frac{3}{2}$	
$m^2 + 5m + \frac{25}{4} = \frac{3}{2} + \frac{25}{4}$	Add $[\frac{1}{2}(5)]^2 = (\frac{5}{2})^2 = \frac{25}{4}$ to both sides.
$\left(m + \frac{5}{2}\right)^2 = \frac{6}{4} + \frac{25}{4}$	Factor the left side and write the terms on the right with a common denominator.
$\left(m + \frac{5}{2}\right)^2 = \frac{31}{4}$	
$m + \frac{5}{2} = \pm\sqrt{\frac{31}{4}}$	Apply the square root property.
$m = -\frac{5}{2} \pm \frac{\sqrt{31}}{2}$	Subtract $\frac{5}{2}$ from both sides and simplify the radical.

The solution set is $\left\{-\frac{5}{2} \pm \frac{\sqrt{31}}{2}\right\}$. The solutions are irrational numbers.

TIP: The solutions to Example 6 can also be written as:

$$\frac{-5 \pm \sqrt{31}}{2}$$

Skill Practice Solve by completing the square and applying the square root property.

9. $4x^2 + 12x = 5$

Answers

8. $\{2 \pm i\sqrt{22}\}$

9. $\left\{-\frac{3}{2} \pm \frac{\sqrt{14}}{2}\right\}$

Example 7 Solving a Quadratic Equation by Completing the Square and Applying the Square Root Property

Solve by completing the square and applying the square root property.

$$2x(2x - 10) = -30 + 6x$$

Solution:

$2x(2x - 10) = -30 + 6x$

$4x^2 - 20x = -30 + 6x$ — Clear parentheses.

$4x^2 - 26x + 30 = 0$ — Write the equation in the form $ax^2 + bx + c = 0$.

$\dfrac{4x^2}{4} - \dfrac{26x}{4} + \dfrac{30}{4} = \dfrac{0}{4}$ — **Step 1:** Divide both sides by the leading coefficient, 4.

$x^2 - \dfrac{13}{2}x + \dfrac{15}{2} = 0$

$x^2 - \dfrac{13}{2}x = -\dfrac{15}{2}$ — **Step 2:** Isolate the variable terms on one side.

$x^2 - \dfrac{13}{2}x + \dfrac{169}{16} = -\dfrac{15}{2} + \dfrac{169}{16}$ — **Step 3:** Add $\left[\frac{1}{2}\left(-\frac{13}{2}\right)\right]^2 = \left(-\frac{13}{4}\right)^2 = \frac{169}{16}$ to both sides.

$\left(x - \dfrac{13}{4}\right)^2 = -\dfrac{120}{16} + \dfrac{169}{16}$ — Factor the perfect square trinomial. Rewrite the right-hand side with a common denominator.

$\left(x - \dfrac{13}{4}\right)^2 = \dfrac{49}{16}$

$x - \dfrac{13}{4} = \pm\sqrt{\dfrac{49}{16}}$ — **Step 4:** Apply the square root property.

$x - \dfrac{13}{4} = \pm\dfrac{7}{4}$ — Simplify the radical.

$x = \dfrac{13}{4} \pm \dfrac{7}{4}$

$x = \dfrac{13}{4} + \dfrac{7}{4} = \dfrac{20}{4} = 5$

$x = \dfrac{13}{4} - \dfrac{7}{4} = \dfrac{6}{4} = \dfrac{3}{2}$

The solution set is $\left\{5, \dfrac{3}{2}\right\}$. The solutions are rational numbers.

Skill Practice Solve by completing the square and applying the square root property.

10. $2y(y - 1) = 3 - y$

Classroom Example: p. 788, Exercise 60

Instructor Note: Dividing through by "a" is a trouble spot for students. Be sure they understand that *all* terms must be divided by "a."

TIP: In general, if the solutions to a quadratic equation are rational numbers, the equation can be solved by factoring and using the zero product rule. Consider the equation from Example 7.

$2x(2x - 10) = -30 + 6x$

$4x^2 - 20x = -30 + 6x$

$4x^2 - 26x + 30 = 0$

$2(2x^2 - 13x + 15) = 0$

$2(x - 5)(2x - 3) = 0$

$x = 5$ or $x = \dfrac{3}{2}$

Avoiding Mistakes

When the solutions are rational, combine the *like* terms. That is, do not leave the solution with the ± sign.

Answer

10. $\left\{\frac{3}{2}, -1\right\}$

3. Literal Equations

Classroom Example: p. 788, Exercise 62

Example 8 Solving a Literal Equation

Ignoring air resistance, the distance d (in meters) that an object falls in t sec is given by the equation

$$d = 4.9t^2 \qquad \text{where } t \geq 0$$

a. Solve the equation for t. Do not rationalize the denominator.

b. Using the equation from part (a), determine the amount of time required for an object to fall 500 m. Round to the nearest second.

Solution:

a. $d = 4.9t^2$

$\frac{d}{4.9} = t^2$ Isolate the quadratic term. The equation is in the form $t^2 = k$.

$t = \pm\sqrt{\frac{d}{4.9}}$ Apply the square root property.

$= \sqrt{\frac{d}{4.9}}$ Because t represents time, $t \geq 0$. We reject the negative solution.

b. $t = \sqrt{\frac{d}{4.9}}$

$= \sqrt{\frac{500}{4.9}}$ Substitute $d = 500$.

$t \approx 10.1$

The object will require approximately 10.1 sec to fall 500 m.

Skill Practice

11. Given $x = 2yz^2$, solve for z where $z > 0$. Do not rationalize the denominator.

12. Use the equation from the previous exercise to find z when $x = 54$ and $y = 3$.

Answers

11. $z = \sqrt{\frac{x}{2y}}$

12. $z = 3$

Section 11.1 Practice Exercises

Vocabulary and Key Concepts

For additional exercises, see Classroom Activities 11.1A–11.1D in the *Student's Resource Manual* at www.mhhe.com/moh.

1. a. The zero product rule states that if $ab = 0$, then $a =$ __0__ or $b =$ __0__.

b. To apply the zero product rule, one side of the equation must be equal to __0__ and the other side must be written in factored form.

c. The square root property states that for any real number k, if $x^2 = k$, then $x =$ __$\sqrt{k}$__ or $x =$ __$-\sqrt{k}$__.

d. To apply the square root property to the equation $t^2 + 2 = 11$, first subtract __2__ from both sides. The solution set is __$\{3, -3\}$__.

e. The process to create a perfect square trinomial is called __completing__ the square.

f. Fill in the blank to complete the square for the trinomial $x^2 + 20x +$ ____100____.

g. To use completing the square to solve the equation $4x^2 + 3x + 5 = 0$, the first step is to divide by ____4____ so that the coefficient of the x^2 term is ____1____.

h. Given the trinomial $y^2 + 8y + 16$, the coefficient of the linear term is ____8____.

Concept 1: Solving Quadratic Equations by Using the Square Root Property

For Exercises 2–21, solve the equations by using the square root property. Write imaginary solutions in the form $a + bi$. **(See Examples 1–3.)**

2. $x^2 = 100$ $\{\pm 10\}$

3. $y^2 = 4$ $\{\pm 2\}$

4. $a^2 = 5$ $\{\pm\sqrt{5}\}$

5. $k^2 - 7 = 0$ $\{\pm\sqrt{7}\}$

6. $4t^2 = 81$ $\left\{\frac{9}{2}, -\frac{9}{2}\right\}$

7. $36u^2 = 121$ $\left\{\frac{11}{6}, -\frac{11}{6}\right\}$

8. $3v^2 + 33 = 0$ $\{\pm i\sqrt{11}\}$

9. $-2m^2 = 50$ $\{\pm 5i\}$

10. $(p - 5)^2 = 9$ $\{8, 2\}$

11. $(q + 3)^2 = 4$ $\{-1, -5\}$

12. $(3x - 2)^2 - 5 = 0$ $\left\{\frac{2 \pm \sqrt{5}}{3}\right\}$

13. $(2y + 3)^2 - 7 = 0$ $\left\{\frac{-3 \pm \sqrt{7}}{2}\right\}$

14. $(h - 4)^2 = -8$ $\{4 \pm 2i\sqrt{2}\}$

15. $(t + 5)^2 = -18$ $\{-5 \pm 3i\sqrt{2}\}$

16. $6p^2 - 3 = 2$ $\left\{\pm\frac{\sqrt{30}}{6}\right\}$

17. $15 = 4 + 3w^2$ $\left\{\pm\frac{\sqrt{33}}{3}\right\}$

18. $\left(x - \frac{3}{2}\right)^2 + \frac{7}{4} = 0$ $\left\{\frac{3}{2} \pm \frac{\sqrt{7}}{2}i\right\}$

19. $\left(m + \frac{4}{5}\right)^2 + \frac{3}{25} = 0$ $\left\{-\frac{4}{5} \pm \frac{\sqrt{3}}{5}i\right\}$

20. $-x^2 + 4 = 13$ $\{3i, -3i\}$

21. $-y^2 - 2 = 14$ $\{4i, -4i\}$

22. Given the equation $x^2 = k$, match the following statements.

a. If $k > 0$, then ____ **i.** there will be one real solution.

b. If $k < 0$, then ____ **ii.** there will be two real solutions.

c. If $k = 0$, then ____ **iii.** there will be two imaginary solutions.

a. ii b. iii c. i

23. State two methods that can be used to solve the equation $x^2 - 36 = 0$. Then solve the equation by using both methods. 1. Factoring and applying the zero product rule. 2. Applying the square root property. $\{\pm 6\}$

24. Explain the difference between solving the equations: $x = \sqrt{16}$ and $x^2 = 16$. The equation $x = \sqrt{16}$ has only one solution, 4, because the symbol $\sqrt{\ }$ gives only the principal square root. The equation $x^2 = 16$ has two solutions, $\pm\sqrt{16}$ that simplify to 4 and -4.

For Exercises 25–26, solve the equations.

25. a. $\sqrt{x} = 4$ $\{16\}$

b. $x^2 = 4$ $\{2, -2\}$

26. a. $\sqrt{y} = 9$ $\{81\}$

b. $y^2 = 9$ $\{3, -3\}$

Concept 2: Solving Quadratic Equations by Completing the Square

For Exercises 27–38, find the value of n so that the expression is a perfect square trinomial. Then factor the trinomial. **(See Example 4.)**

27. $x^2 - 6x + n$ $n = 9$; $(x - 3)^2$

28. $x^2 + 24x + n$ $n = 144$; $(x + 12)^2$

29. $t^2 + 8t + n$ $n = 16$; $(t + 4)^2$

30. $v^2 - 18v + n$ $n = 81$; $(v - 9)^2$

31. $c^2 - c + n$ $n = \frac{1}{4}$; $\left(c - \frac{1}{2}\right)^2$

32. $x^2 + 9x + n$ $n = \frac{81}{4}$; $\left(x + \frac{9}{2}\right)^2$

33. $y^2 + 5y + n$ $n = \frac{25}{4}$; $\left(y + \frac{5}{2}\right)^2$

34. $a^2 - 7a + n$ $n = \frac{49}{4}$; $\left(a - \frac{7}{2}\right)^2$

35. $b^2 + \frac{2}{5}b + n$ $n = \frac{1}{25}$; $\left(b + \frac{1}{5}\right)^2$

36. $m^2 - \frac{2}{7}m + n$ $n = \frac{1}{49}$; $\left(m - \frac{1}{7}\right)^2$

37. $p^2 - \frac{2}{3}p + n$ $n = \frac{1}{9}$; $\left(p - \frac{1}{3}\right)^2$

38. $w^2 + \frac{3}{4}w + n$ $n = \frac{9}{64}$; $\left(w + \frac{3}{8}\right)^2$

39. Summarize the steps used in solving a quadratic equation of the form $ax^2 + bx + c = 0$ by completing the square and applying the square root property. 1. Divide both sides by a to make the leading coefficient 1. 2. Isolate the variable terms on one side of the equation. 3. Complete the square. 4. Apply the square root property and solve for x.

40. What types of quadratic equations can be solved by completing the square and applying the square root property? All quadratic equations

For Exercises 41–60, solve the quadratic equation by completing the square and applying the square root property. Write imaginary solutions in the form $a + bi$. **(See Examples 5–7.)**

41. $t^2 + 8t + 15 = 0$ $\{-3, -5\}$

42. $m^2 + 6m + 8 = 0$ $\{-4, -2\}$

43. $x^2 + 6x = -16$ $\{-3 \pm i\sqrt{7}\}$

44. $x^2 - 4x = -15$ $\{2 \pm i\sqrt{11}\}$

45. $p^2 + 4p + 6 = 0$ $\{-2 \pm i\sqrt{2}\}$

46. $q^2 + 2q + 2 = 0$ $\{-1 \pm i\}$

47. $-3y - 10 = -y^2$ $\{5, -2\}$

48. $-24 = -2y^2 + 2y$ $\{4, -3\}$

49. $2a^2 + 4a + 5 = 0$ $\left\{-1 \pm \frac{\sqrt{6}}{2}i\right\}$

50. $3a^2 + 6a - 7 = 0$ $\left\{-1 \pm \frac{\sqrt{30}}{3}\right\}$

51. $9x^2 - 36x + 40 = 0$ $\left\{2 \pm \frac{2}{3}i\right\}$

52. $9y^2 - 12y + 5 = 0$ $\left\{\frac{2}{3} \pm \frac{1}{3}i\right\}$

53. $25p^2 - 10p = 2$ $\left\{\frac{1}{5} \pm \frac{\sqrt{3}}{5}\right\}$

54. $9n^2 - 6n = 1$ $\left\{\frac{1}{3} \pm \frac{\sqrt{2}}{3}\right\}$

55. $(2w + 5)(w - 1) = 2$ $\left\{-\frac{3}{4} \pm \frac{\sqrt{65}}{4}\right\}$

56. $(3p - 5)(p + 1) = -3$ $\left\{\frac{1}{3} \pm \frac{\sqrt{7}}{3}\right\}$

57. $n(n - 4) = 7$ $\{2 \pm \sqrt{11}\}$

58. $m(m + 10) = 2$ $\{-5 \pm 3\sqrt{3}\}$

59. $2x(x + 6) = 14$ $\{1, -7\}$

60. $3x(x - 2) = 24$ $\{-2, 4\}$

Concept 3: Literal Equations

61. The distance d (in feet) that an object falls in t sec is given by the equation $d = 16t^2$, where $t \geq 0$.

a. Solve the equation for t. **(See Example 8.)** $t = \frac{\sqrt{d}}{4}$

b. Using the equation from part (a), determine the amount of time required for an object to fall 1024 ft. 8 sec

62. The volume V (in cubic inches) of a can that is 4 in. tall is given by the equation $V = 4\pi r^2$, where r is the radius of the can, measured in inches.

a. Solve the equation for r. Do not rationalize the denominator. $r = \frac{1}{2}\sqrt{\frac{V}{\pi}}$

b. Using the equation from part (a), determine the radius of a can with a volume of 12.56 in.^{3} Use 3.14 for π. 1 in.

For Exercises 63–68, solve for the indicated variable.

63. $A = \pi r^2$ for r $(r > 0)$ $r = \sqrt{\frac{A}{\pi}}$ or $r = \frac{\sqrt{A\pi}}{\pi}$

64. $E = mc^2$ for c $(c > 0)$ $c = \sqrt{\frac{E}{m}}$ or $c = \frac{\sqrt{Em}}{m}$

65. $a^2 + b^2 + c^2 = d^2$ for a $(a > 0)$ $a = \sqrt{d^2 - b^2 - c^2}$

66. $a^2 + b^2 = c^2$ for b $(b > 0)$ $b = \sqrt{c^2 - a^2}$

67. $V = \frac{1}{3}\pi r^2 h$ for r $(r > 0)$ $r = \sqrt{\frac{3V}{\pi h}}$ or $r = \frac{\sqrt{3V\pi h}}{\pi h}$

68. $V = \frac{1}{3}s^2 h$ for s $(s > 0)$ $s = \sqrt{\frac{3V}{h}}$ or $s = \frac{\sqrt{3Vh}}{h}$

69. A corner shelf is to be made from a triangular piece of plywood, as shown in the diagram. Find the distance x that the shelf will extend along the walls. Assume that the walls are at right angles. Round the answer to a tenth of a foot.
The shelf extends 4.2 ft.

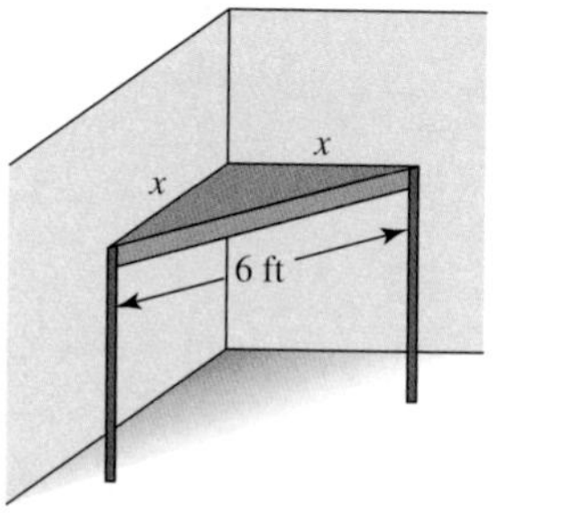

70. The volume $V(x)$ (in cubic inches) of a box with a square bottom and a height of 4 in. is given by $V(x) = 4x^2$, where x is the length (in inches) of the sides of the bottom of the box.

a. If the volume of the box is 289 in.^{3}, find the dimensions of the box. 8.5 in. by 8.5 in. by 4 in.

b. Are there two possible answers to part (a)? Why or why not?
One answer only. A length cannot be represented by a negative number.

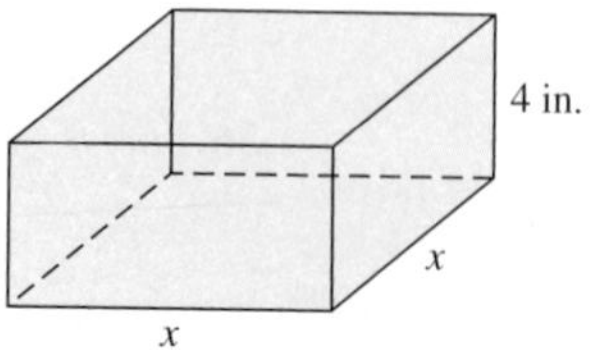

71. A square has an area of 50 in.^{2} What are the lengths of the sides? (Round to one decimal place.)
The sides are 7.1 in.

72. The amount of money A in an account with an interest rate r compounded annually is given by

$$A = P(1 + r)^t$$

where P is the initial principal and t is the number of years the money is invested.

a. If a \$10,000 investment grows to \$11,664 after 2 yr, find the interest rate. 8%

b. If a \$6000 investment grows to \$7392.60 after 2 yr, find the interest rate. 11%

c. Jamal wants to invest \$5000. He wants the money to grow to at least \$6500 in 2 yr to cover the cost of his son's first year at college. What interest rate does Jamal need for his investment to grow to \$6500 in 2 yr? Round to the nearest hundredth of a percent. 14.02%

73. A textbook company has discovered that the profit for selling its books is given by

$$P(x) = -\frac{1}{8}x^2 + 5x$$

where x is the number of textbooks produced (in thousands) and $P(x)$ is the corresponding profit (in thousands of dollars).

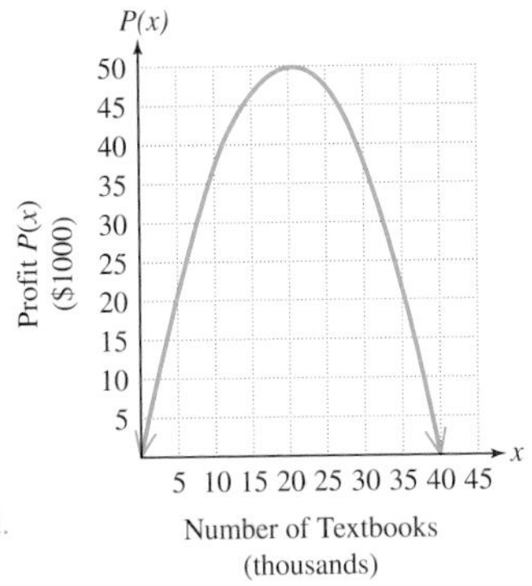

a. Approximate the number of books required to make a profit of \$20,000. [*Hint:* Let $P(x) = 20$. Then complete the square to solve for x.] Round to one decimal place. 4.5 thousand textbooks or 35.5 thousand textbooks

b. Why are there two answers to part (a)? Profit increases to a point as more books are produced. Beyond that point, the market is "flooded," and profit decreases. There are two points at which the profit is \$20,000. Producing 4.5 thousand books makes the same profit using fewer resources as producing 35.5 thousand books.

74. If we ignore air resistance, the distance $d(t)$ (in feet) that an object travels in free fall can be approximated by $d(t) = 16t^2$, where t is the time in seconds after the object was dropped.

a. If the CN Tower in Toronto is 1815 ft high, how long will it take an object to fall from the top of the building? Round to one decimal place. 10.7 sec

b. If the Renaissance Tower in Dallas is 886 ft high, how long will it take an object to fall from the top of the building? Round to one decimal place. 7.4 sec

© Songquan Deng/Shutterstock RF

© Digital Vision RF

Section 11.2 Quadratic Formula

Concepts

1. Derivation of the Quadratic Formula
2. Solving Quadratic Equations by Using the Quadratic Formula
3. Using the Quadratic Formula in Applications
4. Discriminant
5. Mixed Review: Methods to Solve a Quadratic Equation

1. Derivation of the Quadratic Formula

If we solve a quadratic equation in standard form $ax^2 + bx + c = 0$, $a > 0$, by completing the square and using the square root property, the result is a formula that gives the solutions for x in terms of a, b, and c.

$$ax^2 + bx + c = 0 \ (a \neq 0)$$ Begin with a quadratic equation in standard form.

$$\frac{ax^2}{a} + \frac{bx}{a} + \frac{c}{a} = \frac{0}{a}$$ Divide by the leading coefficient.

$$x^2 + \frac{b}{a}x + \frac{c}{a} = 0$$

$$x^2 + \frac{b}{a}x = -\frac{c}{a}$$ Isolate the terms containing x.

Instructor Note: Consider solving a quadratic equation with numerical coefficients such as $2x^2 + 3x + 5 = 0$ first. Then show the students the same steps using a, b, and c as coefficients.

$$x^2 + \frac{b}{a}x + \left(\frac{1}{2}\cdot\frac{b}{a}\right)^2 = \left(\frac{1}{2}\cdot\frac{b}{a}\right)^2 - \frac{c}{a}$$ Add the square of $\frac{1}{2}$ the linear term coefficient to both sides of the equation.

$$\left(x + \frac{b}{2a}\right)^2 = \frac{b^2}{4a^2} - \frac{c}{a}$$ Factor the left side as a perfect square.

$$\left(x + \frac{b}{2a}\right)^2 = \frac{b^2 - 4ac}{4a^2}$$ Combine fractions on the right side by getting a common denominator.

$$x + \frac{b}{2a} = \pm\sqrt{\frac{b^2 - 4ac}{4a^2}}$$ Apply the square root property.

$$x + \frac{b}{2a} = \frac{\pm\sqrt{b^2 - 4ac}}{2a}$$ Simplify the denominator.

$$x = -\frac{b}{2a} \pm \frac{\sqrt{b^2 - 4ac}}{2a}$$ Subtract $\frac{b}{2a}$ from both sides.

$$= \frac{-b \pm \sqrt{b^2 - 4ac}}{2a}$$ Combine fractions.

The solutions to the equation $ax^2 + bx + c = 0$ in terms of the coefficients a, b, and c are given by the **quadratic formula**.

The Quadratic Formula

For a quadratic equation of the form $ax^2 + bx + c = 0$ $(a \neq 0)$ the solutions are

$$x = \frac{-b \pm \sqrt{b^2 - 4ac}}{2a}$$

TIP: When applying the quadratic formula, note that a, b, and c are constants. The variable is x.

The quadratic formula gives us another technique to solve a quadratic equation. This method will work regardless of whether the equation is factorable or not factorable.

2. Solving Quadratic Equations by Using the Quadratic Formula

Example 1 **Solving a Quadratic Equation by Using the Quadratic Formula**

Classroom Example: p. 801, Exercise 16

Solve the quadratic equation by using the quadratic formula. $2x^2 - 3x = 5$

Solution:

$2x^2 - 3x = 5$

$2x^2 - 3x - 5 = 0$ Write the equation in the form $ax^2 + bx + c = 0$.

$a = 2, \quad b = -3, \quad c = -5$ Identify a, b, and c.

$x = \dfrac{-b \pm \sqrt{b^2 - 4ac}}{2a}$ Apply the quadratic formula.

$= \dfrac{-(-3) \pm \sqrt{(-3)^2 - 4(2)(-5)}}{2(2)}$ Substitute $a = 2$, $b = -3$, and $c = -5$.

$= \dfrac{3 \pm \sqrt{9 + 40}}{4}$ Simplify.

$= \dfrac{3 \pm \sqrt{49}}{4}$

$= \dfrac{3 \pm 7}{4}$

$\rightarrow x = \dfrac{3 + 7}{4} = \dfrac{10}{4} = \dfrac{5}{2}$

$\rightarrow x = \dfrac{3 - 7}{4} = \dfrac{-4}{4} = -1$

The solution set is $\left\{\frac{5}{2}, -1\right\}$. Both solutions check in the original equation.

Avoiding Mistakes

- The term, $-b$, represents the *opposite* of b.
- Remember to write the *entire* numerator over $2a$.

Skill Practice Solve the equation by using the quadratic formula.

1. $6x^2 - 5x = 4$

Example 2 **Solving a Quadratic Equation by Using the Quadratic Formula**

Classroom Example: p. 801, Exercise 22

Solve the quadratic equation by using the quadratic formula. $-x(x - 6) = 11$

Solution:

$-x(x - 6) = 11$

$-x^2 + 6x - 11 = 0$ Write the equation in the form $ax^2 + bx + c = 0$.

$-1(-x^2 + 6x - 11) = -1(0)$ If the leading coefficient of the quadratic polynomial is negative, we suggest multiplying both sides of the equation by -1. Although this is not mandatory, it is generally easier to simplify the quadratic formula when the value of a is positive.

$x^2 - 6x + 11 = 0$

Answer

1. $\left\{-\frac{1}{2}, \frac{4}{3}\right\}$

$a = 1, b = -6, \text{ and } c = 11$ — Identify a, b, and c.

$x = \dfrac{-b \pm \sqrt{b^2 - 4ac}}{2a}$ — Apply the quadratic formula.

$= \dfrac{-(-6) \pm \sqrt{(-6)^2 - 4(1)(11)}}{2(1)}$ — Substitute $a = 1, b = -6$, and $c = 11$.

$= \dfrac{6 \pm \sqrt{36 - 44}}{2}$ — Simplify.

$= \dfrac{6 \pm \sqrt{-8}}{2}$

$= \dfrac{6 \pm 2i\sqrt{2}}{2}$ — Simplify the radical.

$= \dfrac{2(3 \pm i\sqrt{2})}{2}$ — Factor the numerator.

$= \dfrac{\cancel{2}(3 \pm i\sqrt{2})}{\cancel{2}}$ — Simplify the fraction to lowest terms.

$= 3 \pm i\sqrt{2}$ → $x = 3 + i\sqrt{2}$, $x = 3 - i\sqrt{2}$ — The solutions are imaginary numbers.

The solution set is $\{3 \pm i\sqrt{2}\}$.

Avoiding Mistakes

When identifying a, b, and c, use the coefficients only, not the variable. For example, the value of b is -6 not $-6x$.

Avoiding Mistakes

Always simplify the radical completely before trying to reduce the fraction to lowest terms.

Skill Practice Solve the equation by using the quadratic formula.

2. $-y(y + 4) = 12$

3. Using the Quadratic Formula in Applications

Classroom Example: p. 801, Exercise 42

Example 3 Using the Quadratic Formula in an Application

A delivery truck travels south from Hartselle, Alabama, to Birmingham, Alabama, along Interstate 65. The truck then heads east to Atlanta, Georgia, along Interstate 20. The distance from Birmingham to Atlanta is 8 mi less than twice the distance from Hartselle to Birmingham. If the straight-line distance from Hartselle to Atlanta is 165 mi, find the distance from Hartselle to Birmingham and from Birmingham to Atlanta. (Round the answers to the nearest mile.)

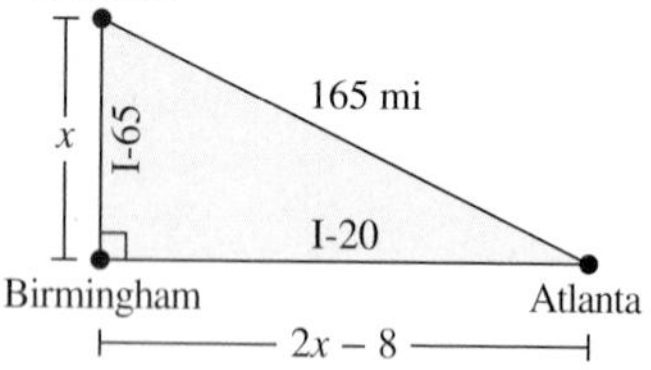

Figure 11-1

Solution:

The motorist travels due south and then due east. Therefore, the three cities form the vertices of a right triangle (Figure 11-1).

Let x represent the distance between Hartselle and Birmingham.

Then $2x - 8$ represents the distance between Birmingham and Atlanta.

Use the Pythagorean theorem to establish a relationship among the three sides of the triangle.

Answer

2. $\{-2 \pm 2i\sqrt{2}\}$

$$(x)^2 + (2x - 8)^2 = (165)^2$$

$$x^2 + 4x^2 - 32x + 64 = 27{,}225$$

$$5x^2 - 32x - 27{,}161 = 0$$ Write the equation in the form $ax^2 + bx + c = 0$.

$a = 5 \quad b = -32 \quad c = -27{,}161$ Identify a, b, and c.

$$x = \frac{-(-32) \pm \sqrt{(-32)^2 - 4(5)(-27{,}161)}}{2(5)}$$ Apply the quadratic formula.

$$= \frac{32 \pm \sqrt{1024 + 543{,}220}}{10}$$ Simplify.

$$= \frac{32 \pm \sqrt{544{,}244}}{10}$$

$$x = \frac{32 + \sqrt{544{,}244}}{10} \approx 76.97$$

$$x = \frac{32 - \sqrt{544{,}244}}{10} \approx -70.57$$

We reject the negative solution because distance cannot be negative. Rounding to the nearest whole unit, we have $x = 77$. Therefore, $2x - 8 = 2(77) - 8 = 146$.

The distance between Hartselle and Birmingham is 77 mi, and the distance between Birmingham and Atlanta is 146 mi.

Skill Practice

3. Steve and Tammy leave a campground, hiking on two different trails. Steve heads south and Tammy heads east. By lunchtime they are 9 mi apart. Steve walked 3 mi more than twice as many miles as Tammy. Find the distance each person hiked. (Round to the nearest tenth of a mile.)

Example 4 Analyzing a Quadratic Function

Classroom Example: p. 802, Exercise 48

A model rocket is launched straight upward from the side of a 144-ft cliff (Figure 11-2). The initial velocity is 112 ft/sec. The height of the rocket $h(t)$ is given by

$$h(t) = -16t^2 + 112t + 144$$

where $h(t)$ is measured in feet and t is the time in seconds after launch. Find the time(s) at which the rocket is 208 ft above the ground.

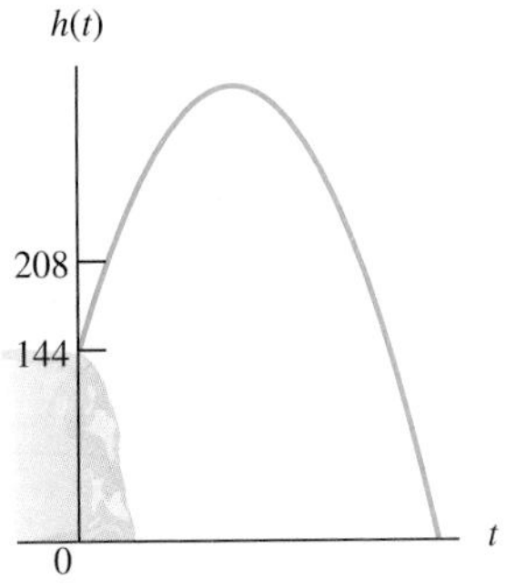

Figure 11-2

Solution:

$$h(t) = -16t^2 + 112t + 144$$

$$208 = -16t^2 + 112t + 144$$ Substitute 208 for $h(t)$.

$$16t^2 - 112t + 64 = 0$$ Write the equation in the form $at^2 + bt + c = 0$.

$$\frac{16t^2}{16} - \frac{112t}{16} + \frac{64}{16} = \frac{0}{16}$$ Divide by 16. This makes the coefficients smaller, and it is less cumbersome to solve.

$$t^2 - 7t + 4 = 0$$ The equation is not factorable. Apply the quadratic formula.

Answer

3. Tammy hiked 2.8 mi, and Steve hiked 8.6 mi.

$$t = \frac{-(-7) \pm \sqrt{(-7)^2 - 4(1)(4)}}{2(1)}$$ Let $a = 1$, $b = -7$, and $c = 4$.

$$= \frac{7 \pm \sqrt{33}}{2}$$

$$t = \frac{7 + \sqrt{33}}{2} \approx 6.37$$

$$t = \frac{7 - \sqrt{33}}{2} \approx 0.63$$

The rocket will reach a height of 208 ft after approximately 0.63 sec (on the way up) and after 6.37 sec (on the way down).

Skill Practice

4. A rocket is launched from the top of a 96-ft building with an initial velocity of 64 ft/sec. The height $h(t)$ of the rocket is given by $h(t) = -16t^2 + 64t + 96$. Find the time it takes for the rocket to hit the ground. [*Hint:* $h(t) = 0$ when the object hits the ground.]

4. Discriminant

The radicand within the quadratic formula is the expression $b^2 - 4ac$. This is called the **discriminant**. The discriminant can be used to determine the number of solutions to a quadratic equation as well as whether the solutions are rational, irrational, or imaginary numbers.

Instructor Note: You can sketch a graph to show that we cannot have one real solution and one imaginary solution to a quadratic equation with real coefficients.

Using the Discriminant to Determine the Number and Type of Solutions to a Quadratic Equation

Consider the equation $ax^2 + bx + c = 0$, where a, b, and c are rational numbers and $a \neq 0$. The expression $b^2 - 4ac$ is called the *discriminant*. Furthermore,

- If $b^2 - 4ac > 0$, then there will be two real solutions.
  - **a.** If $b^2 - 4ac$ is a perfect square, the solutions will be rational numbers.
  - **b.** If $b^2 - 4ac$ is not a perfect square, the solutions will be irrational numbers.
- If $b^2 - 4ac < 0$, then there will be two imaginary solutions.
- If $b^2 - 4ac = 0$, then there will be one rational solution.

Classroom Examples: p. 802, Exercises 50, 52, 54, and 56

Example 5 Using the Discriminant

Use the discriminant to determine the type and number of solutions for each equation.

a. $2x^2 - 5x + 9 = 0$ **b.** $3x^2 = -x + 2$

c. $-2x(2x - 3) = -1$ **d.** $3.6x^2 = -1.2x - 0.1$

Solution:

For each equation, first write the equation in standard form $ax^2 + bx + c = 0$. Then determine the discriminant.

Equation	Discriminant	Solution Type and Number
a. $2x^2 - 5x + 9 = 0$	$b^2 - 4ac$ $= (-5)^2 - 4(2)(9)$ $= 25 - 72$ $= -47$	Because $-47 < 0$, there will be two imaginary solutions.

Answer

4. $2 + \sqrt{10} \approx 5.16$ sec

b. $3x^2 = -x + 2$

$3x^2 + x - 2 = 0$	$b^2 - 4ac$ $= (1)^2 - 4(3)(-2)$ $= 1 - (-24)$ $= 25$	$25 > 0$ and 25 is a perfect square. There will be two rational solutions.

c. $-2x(2x - 3) = -1$

$-4x^2 + 6x = -1$

$-4x^2 + 6x + 1 = 0$	$b^2 - 4ac$ $= (6)^2 - 4(-4)(1)$ $= 36 - (-16)$ $= 52$	$52 > 0$, but 52 is *not* a perfect square. There will be two irrational solutions.

d. $3.6x^2 = -1.2x - 0.1$

$3.6x^2 + 1.2x + 0.1 = 0$	$b^2 - 4ac$ $= (1.2)^2 - 4(3.6)(0.1)$ $= 1.44 - 1.44$ $= 0$	Because the discriminant equals 0, there will be only one rational solution.

Skill Practice Use the discriminant to determine the type and number of solutions for the equation.

5. $3y^2 + y + 3 = 0$

6. $4t^2 = 6t - 2$

7. $3t(t + 1) = 9$

8. $\frac{2}{3}x^2 - \frac{2}{3}x + \frac{1}{6} = 0$

With the discriminant we can determine the number of real-valued solutions to the equation $ax^2 + bx + c = 0$, and thus the number of x-intercepts to the graph of $f(x) = ax^2 + bx + c$. The following illustrations show the graphical interpretation of the three cases of the discriminant.

$f(x) = x^2 - 4x + 3$

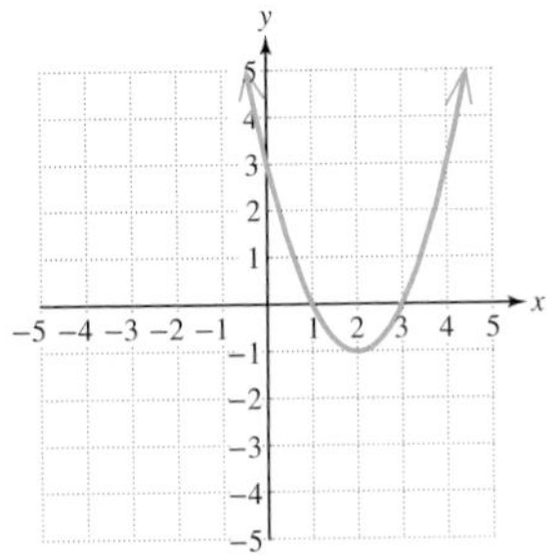

Use $x^2 - 4x + 3 = 0$ to find the value of the discriminant.

$$b^2 - 4ac = (-4)^2 - 4(1)(3) = 4$$

Since the discriminant is positive, there are two real solutions to the quadratic equation. Therefore, there are two x-intercepts to the corresponding quadratic function, (1, 0) and (3, 0).

$f(x) = x^2 - x + 1$

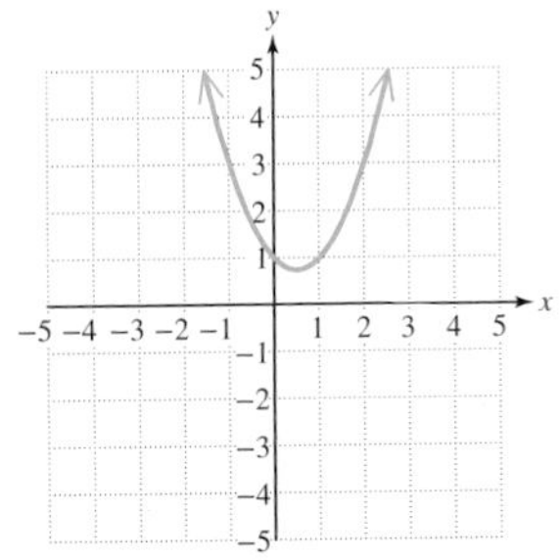

Use $x^2 - x + 1 = 0$ to find the value of the discriminant.

$$b^2 - 4ac = (-1)^2 - 4(1)(1) = -3$$

Since the discriminant is negative, there are no real solutions to the quadratic equation. Therefore, there are no x-intercepts to the corresponding quadratic function.

Answers

5. −35; two imaginary solutions
6. 4; two rational solutions
7. 117; two irrational solutions
8. 0; one rational solution

$f(x) = x^2 - 2x + 1$

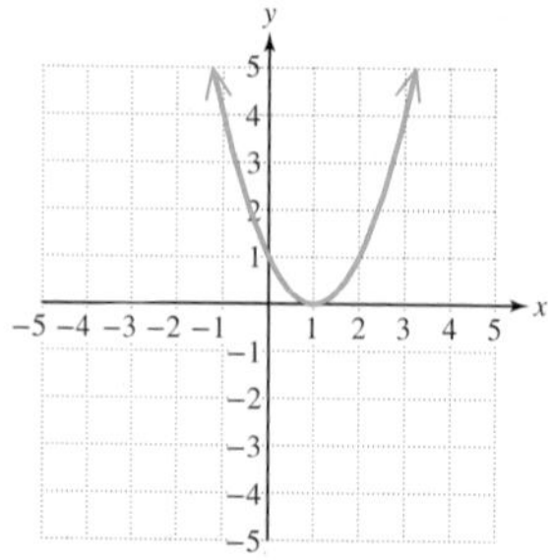

Use $x^2 - 2x + 1 = 0$ to find the value of the discriminant.

$$\begin{aligned} b^2 - 4ac &= (-2)^2 - 4(1)(1) \\ &= 0 \end{aligned}$$

Since the discriminant is zero, there is one real solution to the quadratic equation. Therefore, there is one x-intercept to the corresponding quadratic function, (1, 0).

Classroom Example: p. 802, Exercise 64

Example 6 Finding x- and y-Intercepts of a Quadratic Function

Given $f(x) = x^2 - 3x + 1$

a. Find the discriminant and use it to determine if there are any x-intercepts.

b. Find the x-intercept(s), if they exist.

c. Find the y-intercept.

Solution:

a. $a = 1, b = -3$, and $c = 1$.

The discriminant is $b^2 - 4ac = (-3)^2 - 4(1)(1)$
$$\begin{aligned} &= 9 - 4 \\ &= 5 \end{aligned}$$

Since $5 > 0$, there are two x-intercepts.

TIP: Recall that an x-intercept is a point $(a, 0)$ where the graph of a function intersects the x-axis. A y-intercept is a point $(0, b)$ where the graph intersects the y-axis.

b. The x-intercepts are given by the real solutions to the equation $f(x) = 0$. In this case, we have

$f(x) = x^2 - 3x + 1 = 0$

$x^2 - 3x + 1 = 0$ The equation is in the form $ax^2 + bx + c = 0$.

$x = \dfrac{-(-3) \pm \sqrt{(-3)^2 - (4)(1)(1)}}{2(1)}$ Apply the quadratic formula.

$= \dfrac{3 \pm \sqrt{5}}{2}$ → $x = \dfrac{3 + \sqrt{5}}{2} \approx 2.6$ and $x = \dfrac{3 - \sqrt{5}}{2} \approx 0.4$

The solutions are $\dfrac{3 + \sqrt{5}}{2}$ and $\dfrac{3 - \sqrt{5}}{2}$. Therefore, the x-intercepts are $\left(\dfrac{3 + \sqrt{5}}{2}, 0\right)$ and $\left(\dfrac{3 - \sqrt{5}}{2}, 0\right)$.

c. To find the y-intercept, evaluate $f(0)$.

$f(0) = (0)^2 - 3(0) + 1 = 1$

The y-intercept is located at (0, 1).

The parabola is shown in the graph with the x- and y-intercepts labeled.

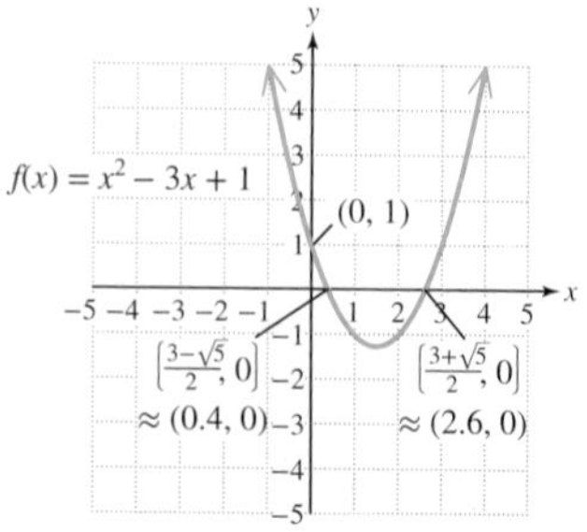

Skill Practice Given $f(x) = x^2 + 5x + 2$,

9. Find the discriminant and use it to determine if there are any x-intercepts.

10. Find the x- and y-intercepts.

Answers

9. Discriminant: 17; there are two x-intercepts.

10. x-intercepts: $\left(\dfrac{-5 + \sqrt{17}}{2}, 0\right)$, $\left(\dfrac{-5 - \sqrt{17}}{2}, 0\right)$

y-intercept: (0, 2)

Example 7 **Finding x- and y-Intercepts of a Quadratic Function**

Classroom Example: p. 802, Exercise 66

Given $f(x) = x^2 + x + 2$

a. Find the discriminant and use it to determine if there are any x-intercepts.

b. Find the x-intercept(s), if they exist.

c. Find the y-intercept.

Solution:

a. $a = 1, b = 1$, and $c = 2$.

The discriminant is $b^2 - 4ac = (1)^2 - 4(1)(2)$

$= 1 - 8$

$= -7$

Since $-7 < 0$, there are no x-intercepts.

b. There are no x-intercepts.

c. $f(0) = (0)^2 + (0) + 2$

$= 2$

The y-intercept is located at $(0, 2)$.

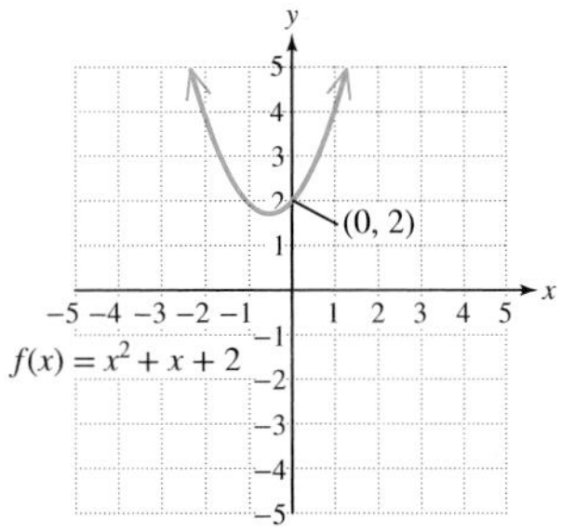

The parabola is shown. *Note:* The graph does not intersect the x-axis.

Skill Practice Given $f(x) = 2x^2 - 3x + 5$,

11. Find the discriminant and use it to determine if there are any x-intercepts.

12. Find the y-intercept.

5. Mixed Review: Methods to Solve a Quadratic Equation

Three methods have been presented to solve quadratic equations.

Methods to Solve a Quadratic Equation

Factor and use the zero product rule. • This method works well if you can factor the equation easily.	Example: $x^2 + 8x + 15 = 0$ factors as $(x + 3)(x + 5) = 0$
Use the square root property. Complete the square if necessary. This method is particularly good if • the equation is of the form $ax^2 + c = 0$ or • the equation is of the form $x^2 + bx + c = 0$, where b is even.	Examples: $4x^2 + 9 = 0$ $x^2 + 10x - 3 = 0$
Quadratic Formula • This method works in all cases—just be sure to write the equation in the form $ax^2 + bx + c = 0$ before applying the formula.	Example: $7x^2 - 3x + 11 = 0$

Answers

11. Discriminant: −31; there are no x-intercepts.

12. (0, 5)

Before solving a quadratic equation, take a minute to analyze it first. Each problem must be evaluated individually before choosing the most efficient method to find its solutions.

Classroom Example: p. 803, Exercise 72

Example 8 Solving a Quadratic Equation by Using Any Method

Solve the equation by using any method. $(x+3)^2 + x^2 - 9x = 8$

Solution:

$$(x+3)^2 + x^2 - 9x = 8$$

$$x^2 + 6x + 9 + x^2 - 9x - 8 = 0$$ Clear parentheses and write the equation in the form $ax^2 + bx + c = 0$.

$$2x^2 - 3x + 1 = 0$$ This equation is factorable.

$$(2x-1)(x-1) = 0$$ Factor.

$$2x - 1 = 0 \quad \text{or} \quad x - 1 = 0$$ Apply the zero product rule.

$$x = \tfrac{1}{2} \quad \text{or} \quad x = 1$$ Solve for x.

The solution set is $\{\frac{1}{2}, 1\}$.

This equation could have been solved by using any of the three methods, but factoring was the most efficient method.

Skill Practice Solve using any method.

13. $2t(t-1) + t^2 = 5$

Classroom Example: p. 803, Exercise 74

Example 9 Solving a Quadratic Equation by Using Any Method

Solve the equation by using any method. $x^2 + 5 = -2x$

Solution:

$$x^2 + 2x + 5 = 0$$ The equation does not factor.

$$x^2 + 2x = -5$$ Because $a = 1$ and b is even, we can easily complete the square.

$$x^2 + 2x + 1 = -5 + 1$$ Add $\left[\frac{1}{2}(2)\right]^2 = 1^2 = 1$ to both sides.

$$(x+1)^2 = -4$$

$$x + 1 = \pm\sqrt{-4}$$ Apply the square root property.

$$x = -1 \pm 2i$$ Solve for x.

The solution set is $\{-1 \pm 2i\}$.

This equation could also have been solved by using the quadratic formula.

Skill Practice Solve using any method.

14. $x^2 - 4x = -7$

Answers

13. $\left\{-1, \frac{5}{3}\right\}$

14. $\{2 \pm i\sqrt{3}\}$

Example 10 Solving a Quadratic Equation by Using Any Method

Classroom Example: p. 803, Exercise 82

Solve the equation by using any method. $\frac{1}{4}x^2 - \frac{1}{2}x + \frac{1}{3} = 0$

Solution:

$12 \cdot \left(\frac{1}{4}x^2 - \frac{1}{2}x + \frac{1}{3}\right) = 12 \cdot (0)$ Clear fractions.

$3x^2 - 6x + 4 = 0$ The equation is in the form $ax^2 + bx + c = 0$. The left-hand side does not factor.

$a = 3, b = -6$, and $c = 4$

$x = \frac{-(-6) \pm \sqrt{(-6)^2 - 4(3)(4)}}{2(3)}$ Apply the quadratic formula.

$= \frac{6 \pm \sqrt{-12}}{6}$ Simplify.

$= \frac{6 \pm 2i\sqrt{3}}{6}$ Simplify the radical.

$= \frac{\overset{1}{\cancel{2}}(3 \pm i\sqrt{3})}{\underset{3}{\cancel{6}}}$ Factor and simplify.

$= \frac{3 \pm i\sqrt{3}}{3}$

$= \frac{3}{3} \pm \frac{\sqrt{3}}{3}i$ Write in the form $a \pm bi$.

$= 1 \pm \frac{\sqrt{3}}{3}i$ Simplify.

The solution set is $\left\{1 \pm \frac{\sqrt{3}}{3}i\right\}$.

Skill Practice Solve using any method.

15. $\frac{1}{5}x^2 - \frac{4}{5}x + \frac{1}{2} = 0$

Answer

15. $\left\{\frac{4 \pm \sqrt{6}}{2}\right\}$

Classroom Example: p. 803, Exercise 86

Example 11 **Solving a Quadratic Equation by Using Any Method**

Solve the equation by using any method. $9p^2 - 11 = 0$

Solution:

$9p^2 - 11 = 0$ Because $b = 0$, use the square root property.

$9p^2 = 11$ Isolate the variable term.

$p^2 = \frac{11}{9}$ The equation is in the form $x^2 = k$.

$p = \pm\sqrt{\frac{11}{9}}$ Apply the square root property.

$p = \pm\frac{\sqrt{11}}{3}$ Simplify the radical.

The solution set is $\left\{\pm\frac{\sqrt{11}}{3}\right\}$.

Skill Practice Solve using any method.

16. $4y^2 - 13 = 0$

Answer

16. $\left\{\pm\frac{\sqrt{13}}{2}\right\}$

Section 11.2 Practice Exercises

For additional exercises, see Classroom Activities 11.2A–11.2D in the *Student's Resource Manual* at www.mhhe.com/moh.

Vocabulary and Key Concepts

1. **a.** For the equation $ax^2 + bx + c = 0$ $(a \neq 0)$, the ___quadratic___ formula gives the solutions as $x =$ ___$\frac{-b \pm \sqrt{b^2 - 4ac}}{2a}$___.

   b. To apply the quadratic formula, a quadratic equation must be written in the form ___$ax^2 + bx + c = 0$___ where $a \neq 0$.

   c. To apply the quadratic formula to solve the equation $8x^2 - 42x - 27 = 0$, the value of a is ___8___, the value of b is ___−42___, and the value of c is ___−27___.

   d. To apply the quadratic formula to solve the equation $3x^2 - 7x - 4 = 0$, the value of $-b$ is ___7___ and the value of the radicand is ___97___.

   e. The radicand within the quadratic formula is ___$b^2 - 4ac$___ and is called the ___discriminant___.

   f. If the discriminant is negative, then the solutions to a quadratic equation will be (real/imaginary) numbers. imaginary

   g. If the discriminant is positive, then the solutions to a quadratic equation will be (real/imaginary) numbers. real

   h. Given a quadratic function $f(x) = ax^2 + bx + c = 0$, the function will have no x-intercepts if the discriminant is (less than, greater than, equal to) zero. less than

Review Exercises

2. Use substitution to determine if $x = -3 + \sqrt{5}$ is a solution to $x^2 + 6x + 4 = 0$. Yes

For Exercises 3–6, simplify the expression.

3. $\frac{16 - \sqrt{320}}{4}$ $4 - 2\sqrt{5}$

4. $\frac{18 + \sqrt{180}}{3}$ $6 + 2\sqrt{5}$

5. $\frac{14 - \sqrt{-147}}{7}$ $2 - i\sqrt{3}$

6. $\frac{10 - \sqrt{-175}}{5}$ $2 - i\sqrt{7}$

Concept 2: Solving Quadratic Equations by Using the Quadratic Formula

For Exercises 7–8, determine whether the equation is linear or quadratic.

7. $2(x-5)+x^2=3x(x-4)-2x^2$ linear

8. $5x(x+3)-9=4x^2-3(x+1)$ quadratic

For Exercises 9–34, solve the equation by using the quadratic formula. Write imaginary solutions in the form $a+bi$. **(See Examples 1–2.)**

9. $x^2+11x-12=0$ $\{-12, 1\}$

10. $5x^2-14x-3=0$ $\left\{-\frac{1}{5}, 3\right\}$

11. $9y^2-2y+5=0$ $\left\{\frac{1}{9}\pm\frac{2\sqrt{11}}{9}i\right\}$

12. $2t^2+3t-7=0$ $\left\{\frac{-3\pm\sqrt{65}}{4}\right\}$

13. $12p^2-4p+5=0$ $\left\{\frac{1}{6}\pm\frac{\sqrt{14}}{6}i\right\}$

14. $-5n^2+4n-6=0$ $\left\{\frac{2}{5}\pm\frac{\sqrt{26}}{5}i\right\}$

15. $-z^2=-2z-35$ $\{7, -5\}$

16. $12x^2-5x=2$ $\left\{\frac{2}{3}, -\frac{1}{4}\right\}$

17. $y^2+3y=8$ $\left\{\frac{-3\pm\sqrt{41}}{2}\right\}$

18. $k^2+4=6k$ $\{3\pm\sqrt{5}\}$

19. $25x^2-20x+4=0$ $\left\{\frac{2}{5}\right\}$

20. $9y^2=-12y-4$ $\left\{-\frac{2}{3}\right\}$

21. $w(w-6)=-14$ $\{3\pm i\sqrt{5}\}$

22. $m(m+6)=-11$ $\{-3\pm i\sqrt{2}\}$

23. $(x+2)(x-3)=1$ $\left\{\frac{1\pm\sqrt{29}}{2}\right\}$

24. $3y(y+1)-7y(y+2)=6$ $\left\{-\frac{3}{4}, -2\right\}$

25. $-4a^2-2a+3=0$ $\left\{\frac{-1\pm\sqrt{13}}{4}\right\}$

26. $-2m^2-5m+3=0$ $\left\{-3, \frac{1}{2}\right\}$

27. $\frac{1}{2}y^2+\frac{2}{3}=-\frac{2}{3}y$ $\left\{-\frac{2}{3}\pm\frac{2\sqrt{2}}{3}i\right\}$ (*Hint:* Clear fractions first.)

28. $\frac{2}{3}p^2-\frac{1}{6}p+\frac{1}{2}=0$ $\left\{\frac{1}{8}\pm\frac{\sqrt{47}}{8}i\right\}$

29. $\frac{1}{5}h^2+h+\frac{3}{5}=0$ $\left\{\frac{-5\pm\sqrt{13}}{2}\right\}$

30. $\frac{1}{4}w^2+\frac{7}{4}w+1=0$ $\left\{\frac{-7\pm\sqrt{33}}{2}\right\}$

31. $0.01x^2+0.06x+0.08=0$ (*Hint:* Clear decimals first.) $\{-2, -4\}$

32. $0.5y^2-0.7y+0.2=0$ $\left\{\frac{2}{5}, 1\right\}$

33. $0.3t^2+0.7t-0.5=0$ $\left\{\frac{-7\pm\sqrt{109}}{6}\right\}$

34. $0.01x^2+0.04x-0.07=0$ $\{-2\pm\sqrt{11}\}$

For Exercises 35–38, factor the expression. Then use the zero product rule and the quadratic formula to solve the equation. There should be three solutions to each equation. Write imaginary solutions in the form $a+bi$.

35. a. Factor. x^3-27 $(x-3)(x^2+3x+9)$

b. Solve. $x^3-27=0$ $\left\{3, -\frac{3}{2}\pm\frac{3\sqrt{3}}{2}i\right\}$

36. a. Factor. $64x^3+1$ $(4x+1)(16x^2-4x+1)$

b. Solve. $64x^3+1=0$ $\left\{-\frac{1}{4}, \frac{1}{8}\pm\frac{\sqrt{3}}{8}i\right\}$

37. a. Factor. $3x^3-6x^2+6x$ $3x(x^2-2x+2)$

b. Solve. $3x^3-6x^2+6x=0$ $\{0, 1\pm i\}$

38. a. Factor. $5x^3+5x^2+10x$ $5x(x^2+x+2)$

b. Solve. $5x^3+5x^2+10x=0$ $\left\{0, -\frac{1}{2}\pm\frac{\sqrt{7}}{2}i\right\}$

Concept 3: Using the Quadratic Formula in Applications

39. The volume of a cube is 27 ft^3. Find the lengths of the sides. The length of each side is 3 ft.

40. The volume of a rectangular box is 64 ft^3. If the width is 3 times longer than the height, and the length is 9 times longer than the height, find the dimensions of the box. The dimensions are $1\frac{1}{3}$ ft by 4 ft by 12 ft.

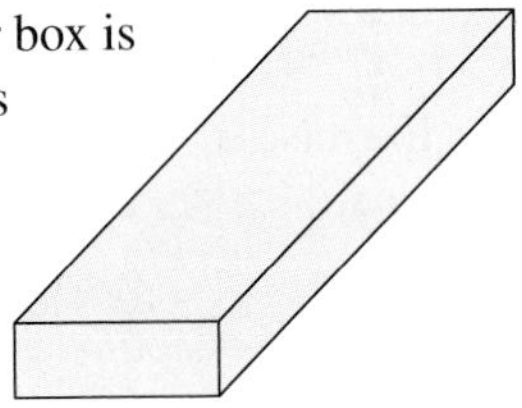

41. The hypotenuse of a right triangle measures 4 in. One leg of the triangle is 2 in. longer than the other leg. Find the lengths of the legs of the triangle. Round to one decimal place. **(See Example 3.)** The legs are approximately 1.6 in. and 3.6 in.

42. The length of one leg of a right triangle is 1 cm more than twice the length of the other leg. The hypotenuse measures 6 cm. Find the lengths of the legs. Round to one decimal place. The legs are approximately 2.3 cm and 5.6 cm.

43. The hypotenuse of a right triangle is 10.2 m long. One leg is 2.1 m shorter than the other leg. Find the lengths of the legs. Round to one decimal place. The legs are approximately 8.2 m and 6.1 m.

44. The hypotenuse of a right triangle is 17 ft long. One leg is 3.4 ft longer than the other leg. Find the lengths of the legs. The legs are approximately 10.2 ft and 13.6 ft.

45. The fatality rate (in fatalities per 100 million vehicle miles driven) can be approximated for drivers x years old according to the function, $F(x) = 0.0036x^2 - 0.35x + 9.2$. (*Source:* U.S. Department of Transportation)

a. Approximate the fatality rate for drivers 16 yr old. Approximately 4.5 fatalities per 100 million miles driven

b. Approximate the fatality rate for drivers 40 yr old. Approximately 1 fatality per 100 million miles driven

c. Approximate the fatality rate for drivers 80 yr old. Approximately 4.2 fatalities per 100 million miles driven

d. For what age(s) is the fatality rate approximately 2.5? For drivers 26 yr old and 71 yr old

46. The braking distance (in feet) of a car going v mph is given by

$$d(v) = \frac{v^2}{20} + v \qquad v \geq 0$$

a. Find the speed for a braking distance of 150 ft. Round to the nearest mile per hour. 46 mph

b. Find the speed for a braking distance of 100 ft. Round to the nearest mile per hour. 36 mph

47. Mitch throws a baseball straight up in the air from a cliff that is 48 ft high. The initial velocity is 48 ft/sec. The height (in feet) of the object after t sec is given by $h(t) = -16t^2 + 48t + 48$. Find the time at which the height of the object is 64 ft. **(See Example 4.)** The times are $\frac{3+\sqrt{5}}{2}$ sec ≈ 2.62 sec or $\frac{3-\sqrt{5}}{2}$ sec ≈ 0.38 sec.

48. An astronaut on the moon throws a rock into the air from the deck of a spacecraft that is 8 m high. The initial velocity of the rock is 2.4 m/sec. The height (in meters) of the rock after t sec is given by $h(t) = -0.8t^2 + 2.4t + 8$. Find the time at which the height of the rock is 6 m. The rock is 6 m high after $\frac{3+\sqrt{19}}{2}$ sec ≈ 3.68 sec.

Concept 4: Discriminant

For Exercises 49–56,

a. Write the equation in the form $ax^2 + bx + c = 0$, $a > 0$.

b. Find the value of the discriminant.

c. Use the discriminant to determine the number and type of solutions. Choose from imaginary, rational, and irrational. **(See Example 5.)**

49. $x^2 + 2x = -1$ a. $x^2 + 2x + 1 = 0$ b. 0 c. 1 rational solution

50. $12y - 9 = 4y^2$ a. $4y^2 - 12y + 9 = 0$ b. 0 c. 1 rational solution

51. $19m^2 = 8m$ a. $19m^2 - 8m + 0 = 0$ b. 64 c. 2 rational solutions

52. $2n - 5n^2 = 0$ a. $5n^2 - 2n + 0 = 0$ b. 4 c. 2 rational solutions

53. $5p^2 - 21 = 0$ a. $5p^2 + 0p - 21 = 0$ b. 420 c. 2 irrational solutions

54. $3k^2 = 7$ a. $3k^2 + 0k - 7 = 0$ b. 84 c. 2 irrational solutions

55. $4n(n-2) - 5n(n-1) = 4$ a. $n^2 + 3n + 4 = 0$ b. -7 c. 2 imaginary solutions

56. $(2x+1)(x-3) = -9$ a. $2x^2 - 5x + 6 = 0$ b. -23 c. 2 imaginary solutions

For Exercises 57–62, determine the discriminant. Then use the discriminant to determine the number of x-intercepts for the function.

57. $f(x) = x^2 - 6x + 5$ Discriminant: 16; two x-intercepts

58. $g(x) = -x^2 - 4x - 3$ Discriminant: 4; two x-intercepts

59. $h(x) = 4x^2 + 12x + 9$ Discriminant: 0; one x-intercept

60. $k(x) = 25x^2 - 10x + 1$ Discriminant: 0; one x-intercept

61. $p(x) = 2x^2 + 3x + 6$ Discriminant: -39; no x-intercepts

62. $m(x) = 3x^2 + 4x + 7$ Discriminant: -68; no x-intercepts

For Exercises 63–68, find the x- and y-intercepts of the quadratic function. **(See Examples 6–7.)**

63. $f(x) = x^2 - 5x + 3$ x-intercepts: $\left(\frac{5+\sqrt{13}}{2}, 0\right), \left(\frac{5-\sqrt{13}}{2}, 0\right)$; y-intercept: (0, 3)

64. $g(x) = 2x^2 + 7x + 2$ x-intercepts: $\left(\frac{-7-\sqrt{33}}{4}, 0\right), \left(\frac{-7+\sqrt{33}}{4}, 0\right)$; y-intercept: (0, 2)

65. $g(x) = -x^2 + x - 1$ x-intercepts: none; y-intercept: (0, −1)

66. $f(x) = 2x^2 + x + 5$ x-intercepts: none; y-intercept: (0, 5)

67. $p(x) = 2x^2 + 5x - 2$ x-intercepts: $\left(\frac{-5-\sqrt{41}}{4}, 0\right), \left(\frac{-5+\sqrt{41}}{4}, 0\right)$; y-intercept: (0, −2)

68. $h(x) = 3x^2 + 2x - 2$ x-intercepts: $\left(\frac{-1-\sqrt{7}}{3}, 0\right), \left(\frac{-1+\sqrt{7}}{3}, 0\right)$; y-intercept: (0, −2)

Concept 5: Mixed Review: Methods to Solve a Quadratic Equation

For Exercises 69–86, solve the quadratic equation by using any method. Write imaginary solutions in the form $a + bi$.
(See Examples 8–11.)

69. $a^2 + 2a + 10 = 0$ $\{-1 \pm 3i\}$

70. $4z^2 + 7z = 0$ $\left\{0, -\frac{7}{4}\right\}$

71. $(x - 2)^2 + 2x^2 - 13x = 10$ $\left\{-\frac{1}{3}, 6\right\}$

72. $(x - 3)^2 + 3x^2 - 5x = 12$ $\left\{-\frac{1}{4}, 3\right\}$

73. $4y^2 - 20y + 43 = 0$ $\left\{\frac{5}{2} \pm \frac{3\sqrt{2}}{2}i\right\}$

74. $k^2 + 18 = 4k$ $\{2 \pm i\sqrt{14}\}$

75. $\left(x + \frac{1}{2}\right)^2 + 4 = 0$ $\left\{-\frac{1}{2} \pm 2i\right\}$

76. $(2y + 3)^2 = 9$ $\{0, -3\}$

77. $2y(y - 3) = -1$ $\left\{\frac{3 \pm \sqrt{7}}{2}\right\}$

78. $w(w - 5) = 4$ $\left\{\frac{5 \pm \sqrt{41}}{2}\right\}$

79. $(2t + 5)(t - 1) = (t - 3)(t + 8)$ $\{1 \pm 3i\sqrt{2}\}$

80. $(b - 1)(b + 4) = (3b + 2)(b + 1)$ $\left\{-\frac{1}{2} \pm \frac{\sqrt{11}}{2}i\right\}$

81. $\frac{1}{8}x^2 - \frac{1}{2}x + \frac{1}{4} = 0$ $\{2 \pm \sqrt{2}\}$

82. $\frac{1}{6}x^2 - \frac{1}{2}x + \frac{1}{4} = 0$ $\left\{\frac{3 \pm \sqrt{3}}{2}\right\}$

83. $32z^2 - 20z - 3 = 0$ $\left\{-\frac{1}{8}, \frac{3}{4}\right\}$

84. $8k^2 - 14k + 3 = 0$ $\left\{\frac{3}{2}, \frac{1}{4}\right\}$

85. $4p^2 - 21 = 0$ $\left\{\pm\frac{\sqrt{21}}{2}\right\}$

86. $5h^2 - 120 = 0$ $\{\pm 2\sqrt{6}\}$

Sometimes students shy away from completing the square and using the square root property to solve a quadratic equation. However, sometimes this process leads to a simple solution. For Exercises 87–88, solve the equations two ways.

a. Solve the equation by completing the square and applying the square root property.

b. Solve the equation by applying the quadratic formula.

c. Which technique was easier for you?

87. $x^2 + 6x = 5$
a. $\{-3 \pm \sqrt{14}\}$
b. $\{-3 \pm \sqrt{14}\}$
c. Answers will vary.

88. $x^2 - 10x = -27$
a. $\{5 \pm i\sqrt{2}\}$
b. $\{5 \pm i\sqrt{2}\}$
c. Answers will vary.

Graphing Calculator Exercises

89. Graph $Y_1 = x^3 - 27$. Compare the x-intercepts with the solutions to the equation $x^3 - 27 = 0$ found in Exercise 35.

90. Graph $Y_1 = 64x^3 + 1$. Compare the x-intercepts with the solutions to the equation $64x^3 + 1 = 0$ found in Exercise 36.

91. Graph $Y_1 = 3x^3 - 6x^2 + 6x$. Compare the x-intercepts with the solutions to the equation $3x^3 - 6x^2 + 6x = 0$ found in Exercise 37.

92. Graph $Y_1 = 5x^3 + 5x^2 + 10x$. Compare the x-intercepts with the solutions to the equation $5x^3 + 5x^2 + 10x = 0$ found in Exercise 38.

Section 11.3 Equations in Quadratic Form

Concepts

1. Solving Equations by Using Substitution
2. Solving Equations Reducible to a Quadratic

1. Solving Equations by Using Substitution

We have learned to solve a variety of different types of equations, including linear, radical, rational, and polynomial equations. Sometimes, however, it is necessary to use a quadratic equation as a tool to solve other types of equations.

In Example 1, we will solve the equation $(2x^2 - 5)^2 - 16(2x^2 - 5) + 39 = 0$. Notice that the terms in the equation are written in descending order by degree. Furthermore, the first two terms have the same base, $2x^2 - 5$, and the exponent on the first term is exactly double the exponent on the second term. The third term is a constant. An equation in this pattern is called **quadratic in form**.

exponent is double third term is constant

$$(2x^2 - 5)^2 - 16(2x^2 - 5)^1 + 39 = 0.$$

To solve this equation we will use substitution as demonstrated in Example 1.

Classroom Example: p. 808, Exercise 12

Example 1 Solving an Equation in Quadratic Form

Solve the equation. $(2x^2 - 5)^2 - 16(2x^2 - 5) + 39 = 0$

Solution:

$(2x^2 - 5)^2 - 16(2x^2 - 5) + 39 = 0$ Substitute $u = (2x^2 - 5)$. Once the substitution is made, the equation becomes quadratic in the variable u.

$u^2 - 16u + 39 = 0$ The equation is in the form $au^2 + bu + c = 0$.

$(u - 13)(u - 3) = 0$ Factor.

$u = 13$ or $u = 3$ Apply the zero product rule.

Reverse substitute.

$2x^2 - 5 = 13$ or $2x^2 - 5 = 3$ Reverse substitute.

$2x^2 = 18$ or $2x^2 = 8$

$x^2 = 9$ or $x^2 = 4$ Write the equations in the form $x^2 = k$.

$x = \pm\sqrt{9}$ or $x = \pm\sqrt{4}$ Apply the square root property.

$= \pm 3$ or $= \pm 2$

The solution set is $\{3, -3, 2, -2\}$. All solutions check in the original equation.

Avoiding Mistakes

When using substitution, it is critical to reverse substitute to solve the equation in terms of the original variable.

Skill Practice Solve the equation.

1. $(3t^2 - 10)^2 + 5(3t^2 - 10) - 14 = 0$

Answer

1. $\{1, -1, 2, -2\}$

For an equation written in descending order, notice that u was set equal to the variable factor on the middle term. This is generally the case.

Example 2 Solving an Equation in Quadratic Form

Classroom Example: p. 808, Exercise 16

Solve the equation. $p^{2/3} - 2p^{1/3} = 8$

Solution:

$$p^{2/3} - 2p^{1/3} = 8$$

$$p^{2/3} - 2p^{1/3} - 8 = 0$$ Set the equation equal to zero.

$$(p^{1/3})^2 - 2(p^{1/3})^1 - 8 = 0$$ Make the substitution $u = p^{1/3}$.

Substitute $u = p^{1/3}$.

$$u^2 - 2u - 8 = 0$$ Then the equation is in the form $au^2 + bu + c = 0$.

$$(u - 4)(u + 2) = 0$$ Factor.

$$u = 4 \quad \text{or} \quad u = -2$$ Apply the zero product rule.

Reverse substitute.

$$p^{1/3} = 4 \quad \text{or} \quad p^{1/3} = -2$$

$$\sqrt[3]{p} = 4 \quad \text{or} \quad \sqrt[3]{p} = -2$$ The equations are radical equations.

$$(\sqrt[3]{p})^3 = (4)^3 \quad \text{or} \quad (\sqrt[3]{p})^3 = (-2)^3$$ Cube both sides.

$$p = 64 \quad \text{or} \quad p = -8$$

The solution set is $\{64, -8\}$. All solutions check in the original equation.

Skill Practice Solve the equation.

2. $y^{2/3} - y^{1/3} = 12$

Example 3 Solving an Equation in Quadratic Form

Classroom Example: p. 808, Exercise 20

Solve the equation. $x - \sqrt{x} - 12 = 0$

Solution:

The equation can be solved by first isolating the radical and then squaring both sides (this is left as an exercise—see Exercise 25). However, this equation is also quadratic in form. By writing $\sqrt{x}$ as $x^{1/2}$, we see that the exponent on the first term is exactly double the exponent on the middle term.

$$x^1 - x^{1/2} - 12 = 0$$

$$(x^{1/2})^2 - (x^{1/2})^1 - 12 = 0$$ Let $u = x^{1/2}$.

$$u^2 - u - 12 = 0$$

$$(u - 4)(u + 3) = 0$$ Factor.

$$u = 4 \quad \text{or} \quad u = -3$$ Solve for u.

$$x^{1/2} = 4 \quad \text{or} \quad x^{1/2} = -3$$ Reverse substitute.

Answer

2. $\{64, -27\}$

Avoiding Mistakes

Recall that when each side of an equation is raised to an even power, we must check the potential solutions.

$\sqrt{x} = 4$ or $\cancel{\sqrt{x} = -3}$	Solve each equation for x. Recall that the principal square root of a number cannot be negative.
$x = 16$	
The solution set is $\{16\}$.	The value 16 checks in the original equation.

Skill Practice Solve the equation.

3. $z - \sqrt{z} - 2 = 0$

2. Solving Equations Reducible to a Quadratic

Some equations are reducible to a quadratic equation. In Example 4, we solve a polynomial equation by factoring. The resulting factors are quadratic.

Classroom Example: p. 808, Exercise 26

Example 4 Solving a Polynomial Equation

Solve the equation. $4x^4 + 7x^2 - 2 = 0$

Solution:

$4x^4 + 7x^2 - 2 = 0$	This is a polynomial equation.
$(4x^2 - 1)(x^2 + 2) = 0$	Factor.
$4x^2 - 1 = 0$ or $x^2 + 2 = 0$	Set each factor equal to zero. Notice that the two equations are quadratic. Each can be solved by the square root property.
$x^2 = \frac{1}{4}$ or $x^2 = -2$	
$x = \pm\sqrt{\frac{1}{4}}$ or $x = \pm\sqrt{-2}$	Apply the square root property.
$x = \pm\frac{1}{2}$ or $x = \pm i\sqrt{2}$	Simplify the radicals.

The solution set is $\left\{\frac{1}{2}, -\frac{1}{2}, i\sqrt{2}, -i\sqrt{2}\right\}$.

Skill Practice Solve the equation.

4. $9x^4 + 35x^2 - 4 = 0$

Classroom Example: p. 808, Exercise 34

Example 5 Solving a Rational Equation

Solve the equation. $\frac{3y}{y+2} - \frac{2}{y-1} = 1$

Solution:

$\frac{3y}{y+2} - \frac{2}{y-1} = 1$ This is a rational equation. The LCD is $(y+2)(y-1)$. Also note that the restrictions on y are $y \neq -2$ and $y \neq 1$.

$\left(\frac{3y}{y+2} - \frac{2}{y-1}\right) \cdot (y+2)(y-1) = 1 \cdot (y+2)(y-1)$ Multiply both sides by the LCD.

$\frac{3y}{\cancel{y+2}} \cdot \cancel{(y+2)}(y-1) - \frac{2}{\cancel{y-1}} \cdot (y+2)\cancel{(y-1)} = 1 \cdot (y+2)(y-1)$

Answers

3. {4} (The value 1 does not check.)

4. $\left\{\pm\frac{1}{3}, \pm 2i\right\}$

$3y(y-1) - 2(y+2) = (y+2)(y-1)$ Clear fractions.

$3y^2 - 3y - 2y - 4 = y^2 - y + 2y - 2$ Apply the distributive property.

$3y^2 - 5y - 4 = y^2 + y - 2$ The equation is quadratic.

$2y^2 - 6y - 2 = 0$ Write the equation in descending order.

$\frac{2y^2}{2} - \frac{6y}{2} - \frac{2}{2} = \frac{0}{2}$

$y^2 - 3y - 1 = 0$

Each coefficient in the equation is divisible by 2. Therefore, if we divide both sides by 2, the coefficients in the equation are smaller. This will make it easier to apply the quadratic formula.

$y = \frac{-(-3) \pm \sqrt{(-3)^2 - 4(1)(-1)}}{2(1)}$ Apply the quadratic formula.

$= \frac{3 \pm \sqrt{9+4}}{2}$

$= \frac{3 \pm \sqrt{13}}{2}$ → $y = \frac{3+\sqrt{13}}{2}$, $y = \frac{3-\sqrt{13}}{2}$

The solution set is $\left\{\frac{3+\sqrt{13}}{2}, \frac{3-\sqrt{13}}{2}\right\}$.

Skill Practice Solve the equation.

5. $\frac{t}{2t-1} - \frac{1}{t+4} = 1$

Answer

5. $\left\{\frac{-5 \pm 3\sqrt{5}}{2}\right\}$

Section 11.3 Practice Exercises

For additional exercises, see Classroom Activities 11.3A–11.3B in the *Student's Resource Manual* at www.mhhe.com/moh.

Vocabulary and Key Concepts

1. a. An equation that can be written in the form $au^2 + bu + c = 0$ where u represents an algebraic expression is said to be in ___quadratic___ form.

   b. To use the method of substitution to solve the equation $(3x-1)^2 + 2(3x-1) - 8 = 0$, let $u =$ ___$3x - 1$___.

   c. To use the method of substitution to solve the equation $p^{2/3} - 2p^{1/3} - 15 = 0$, let $u =$ ___$p^{1/3}$___.

Review Exercises

For Exercises 2–7, solve the quadratic equations.

2. $16 = (2x-3)^2$ $\left\{\frac{7}{2}, -\frac{1}{2}\right\}$

3. $\left(x - \frac{3}{2}\right)^2 = \frac{7}{4}$ $\left\{\frac{3}{2} \pm \frac{\sqrt{7}}{2}\right\}$

4. $n(n-6) = -13$ $\{3 \pm 2i\}$

5. $x(x+8) = -16$ $\{-4\}$

6. $6k^2 + 7k = 6$ $\left\{\frac{-7 \pm \sqrt{193}}{12}\right\}$

7. $2x^2 - 8x - 44 = 0$ $\{2 \pm \sqrt{26}\}$

Concept 1: Solving Equations by Using Substitution

8. a. Solve the quadratic equation by factoring. $u^2 - 2u - 24 = 0$ $\{6, -4\}$

   b. Solve the equation by using substitution. $(x-5)^2 - 2(x-5) - 24 = 0$ $\{11, 1\}$

9. a. Solve the quadratic equation by factoring. $u^2 + 10u + 24 = 0$ $\{-4, -6\}$

b. Solve the equation by using substitution. $(y^2 + 5y)^2 + 10(y^2 + 5y) + 24 = 0$ $\{-4, -1, -2, -3\}$

10. a. Solve the quadratic equation by factoring. $u^2 - 2u - 35 = 0$ $\{7, -5\}$

b. Solve the equation by using substitution. $(w^2 - 6w)^2 - 2(w^2 - 6w) - 35 = 0$ $\{7, -1, 5, 1\}$

For Exercises 11–24, solve the equation by using substitution. **(See Examples 1–3.)**

11. $(x^2 - 2x)^2 + 2(x^2 - 2x) = 3$ $\{1 \pm i\sqrt{2}, 1 \pm \sqrt{2}\}$

12. $(x^2 + x)^2 - 8(x^2 + x) = -12$ $\{-2, 1, -3, 2\}$

13. $(y^2 - 4y)^2 - (y^2 - 4y) = 20$ $\{5, -1, 2\}$

14. $(w^2 - 2w)^2 - 11(w^2 - 2w) = -24$ $\{4, -2, 3, -1\}$

15. $m^{2/3} - m^{1/3} - 6 = 0$ $\{27, -8\}$

16. $2n^{2/3} + 7n^{1/3} - 15 = 0$ $\left\{\frac{27}{8}, -125\right\}$

17. $2t^{2/5} + 7t^{1/5} + 3 = 0$ $\left\{-\frac{1}{32}, -243\right\}$

18. $p^{2/5} + p^{1/5} - 2 = 0$ $\{-32, 1\}$

19. $y + 6\sqrt{y} = 16$ $\{4\}$ (The value 64 does not check.)

20. $p - 8\sqrt{p} = -15$ $\{25, 9\}$

21. $2x + 3\sqrt{x} - 2 = 0$ $\left\{\frac{1}{4}\right\}$ (The value 4 does not check.)

22. $3t + 5\sqrt{t} - 2 = 0$ $\left\{\frac{1}{9}\right\}$ (The value 4 does not check.)

23. $16\left(\frac{x+6}{4}\right)^2 + 8\left(\frac{x+6}{4}\right) + 1 = 0$ $\{-7\}$

24. $9\left(\frac{x+3}{2}\right)^2 - 6\left(\frac{x+3}{2}\right) + 1 = 0$ $\left\{-\frac{7}{3}\right\}$

25. In Example 3, we solved the equation $x - \sqrt{x} - 12 = 0$ by using substitution. Now solve this equation by first isolating the radical and then squaring both sides. Don't forget to check the potential solutions in the original equation. Do you obtain the same solution as in Example 3? $\{16\}$; yes

Concept 2: Solving Equations Reducible to a Quadratic

For Exercises 26–36, solve the equations. **(See Examples 4–5.)**

26. $t^4 + t^2 - 12 = 0$ $\{\pm\sqrt{3}, \pm 2i\}$

27. $w^4 + 4w^2 - 45 = 0$ $\{\pm 3i, \pm\sqrt{5}\}$

28. $x^2(9x^2 + 7) = 2$ $\left\{\pm\frac{\sqrt{2}}{3}, \pm i\right\}$

29. $y^2(4y^2 + 17) = 15$ $\left\{\pm\frac{\sqrt{3}}{2}, \pm i\sqrt{5}\right\}$

30. $\frac{y}{10} - 1 = -\frac{12}{5y}$ $\{4, 6\}$

31. $1 + \frac{5}{x} = -\frac{3}{x^2}$ $\left\{\frac{-5 \pm \sqrt{13}}{2}\right\}$

32. $\frac{x+5}{x} + \frac{x}{2} = \frac{x+19}{4x}$ $\left\{-1, -\frac{1}{2}\right\}$

33. $\frac{3x}{x+1} - \frac{2}{x-3} = 1$ $\left\{\frac{9 \pm \sqrt{73}}{4}\right\}$

34. $\frac{2t}{t-3} - \frac{1}{t+4} = 1$ $\{-3 \pm i\sqrt{6}\}$

35. $\frac{x}{2x-1} = \frac{1}{x-2}$ $\{2 \pm \sqrt{3}\}$

36. $\frac{z}{3z+2} = \frac{2}{z+1}$ $\left\{\frac{5 \pm \sqrt{41}}{2}\right\}$

Mixed Exercises

For Exercises 37–60, solve the equations.

37. $x^4 - 16 = 0$ $\{\pm 2, \pm 2i\}$

38. $t^4 - 625 = 0$ $\{\pm 5, \pm 5i\}$

39. $(4x + 5)^2 + 3(4x + 5) + 2 = 0$ $\left\{-\frac{7}{4}, -\frac{3}{2}\right\}$

40. $2(5x + 3)^2 - (5x + 3) - 28 = 0$ $\left\{-\frac{13}{10}, \frac{1}{5}\right\}$

41. $4m^4 - 9m^2 + 2 = 0$ $\left\{\frac{1}{2}, -\frac{1}{2}, \sqrt{2}, -\sqrt{2}\right\}$

42. $x^4 - 7x^2 + 12 = 0$ $\{2, -2, \sqrt{3}, -\sqrt{3}\}$

43. $x^6 - 9x^3 + 8 = 0$ $\left\{2, 1, -1 \pm i\sqrt{3}, -\frac{1}{2} \pm \frac{\sqrt{3}}{2}i\right\}$

44. $x^6 - 26x^3 - 27 = 0$ $\left\{3, -1, -\frac{3}{2} \pm \frac{3\sqrt{3}}{2}i, \frac{1}{2} \pm \frac{\sqrt{3}}{2}i\right\}$

45. $\sqrt{x^2 + 20} = 3\sqrt{x}$ $\{5, 4\}$

46. $\sqrt{x^2 + 60} = 4\sqrt{x}$ $\{6, 10\}$

47. $\sqrt{4t + 1} = t + 1$ $\{0, 2\}$

48. $\sqrt{t + 10} = t + 4$ $\{-1\}$ (The value -6 does not check.)

Writing | Translating Expression | Geometry | Scientific Calculator | Video

49. $2\left(\frac{t-4}{3}\right)^2 - \left(\frac{t-4}{3}\right) - 3 = 0$ $\left\{1, \frac{17}{2}\right\}$

50. $\left(\frac{x+1}{5}\right)^2 - 3\left(\frac{x+1}{5}\right) - 10 = 0$ $\{24, -11\}$

51. $x^{2/3} + x^{1/3} = 20$ $\{64, -125\}$

52. $x^{2/5} - 3x^{1/5} = -2$ $\{32, 1\}$

53. $m^4 + 2m^2 - 8 = 0$ $\{\pm\sqrt{2}, \pm 2i\}$

54. $2c^4 + c^2 - 1 = 0$ $\left\{\pm\frac{\sqrt{2}}{2}, \pm i\right\}$

55. $a^3 + 16a - a^2 - 16 = 0$ $\{\pm 4i, 1\}$
(*Hint:* Factor by grouping first.)

56. $b^3 + 9b - b^2 - 9 = 0$ $\{\pm 3i, 1\}$

57. $x^3 + 5x - 4x^2 - 20 = 0$ $\{4, \pm i\sqrt{5}\}$

58. $y^3 + 8y - 3y^2 - 24 = 0$ $\{3, \pm 2i\sqrt{2}\}$

59. $\left(\frac{2}{x-3}\right)^2 + 8\left(\frac{2}{x-3}\right) + 12 = 0$ $\left\{\frac{8}{3}, 2\right\}$

60. $\left(\frac{5}{x+1}\right)^2 - 6\left(\frac{5}{x+1}\right) - 16 = 0$ $\left\{-\frac{7}{2}, -\frac{3}{8}\right\}$

Graphing Calculator Exercises

61. **a.** Solve the equation $x^4 + 4x^2 + 4 = 0$. $\{\pm i\sqrt{2}\}$

b. How many solutions are real and how many solutions are imaginary? Two imaginary solutions; no real solutions

c. How many x-intercepts do you anticipate for the function defined by $y = x^4 + 4x^2 + 4$? No x-intercepts

d. Graph $Y_1 = x^4 + 4x^2 + 4$ on a standard viewing window.

62. **a.** Solve the equation $x^4 - 2x^2 + 1 = 0$. $\{1, -1\}$

b. How many solutions are real and how many solutions are imaginary? Two real solutions; no imaginary solutions

c. How many x-intercepts do you anticipate for the function defined by $y = x^4 - 2x^2 + 1$? Two x-intercepts

d. Graph $Y_1 = x^4 - 2x^2 + 1$ on a standard viewing window.

63. **a.** Solve the equation $x^4 - x^3 - 6x^2 = 0$. $\{0, 3, -2\}$

b. How many solutions are real and how many solutions are imaginary? Three real solutions; no imaginary solutions

c. How many x-intercepts do you anticipate for the function defined by $y = x^4 - x^3 - 6x^2$? Three x-intercepts

d. Graph $Y_1 = x^4 - x^3 - 6x^2$ on a standard viewing window.

64. **a.** Solve the equation $x^4 - 10x^2 + 9 = 0$. $\{\pm 1, \pm 3\}$

b. How many solutions are real and how many solutions are imaginary? Four real solutions; no imaginary solutions

c. How many x-intercepts do you anticipate for the function defined by $y = x^4 - 10x^2 + 9$? Four x-intercepts

d. Graph $Y_1 = x^4 - 10x^2 + 9$ on a standard viewing window.

Problem Recognition Exercises

Quadratic and Quadratic Type Equations

For Exercises 1–4, solve each equation by

a. Completing the square and applying the square root property.

b. Using the quadratic formula.

1. $x^2 + 10x + 3 = 0$ $\{-5 \pm \sqrt{22}\}$

2. $v^2 - 16v + 5 = 0$ $\{8 \pm \sqrt{59}\}$

3. $3t^2 + t + 4 = 0$ $\left\{-\frac{1}{6} \pm \frac{\sqrt{47}}{6}i\right\}$

4. $4y^2 + 3y + 5 = 0$ $\left\{-\frac{3}{8} \pm \frac{\sqrt{71}}{8}i\right\}$

In Exercises 5–24, we have presented all types of equations that you have learned up to this point. For each equation,

a. First determine the type of equation that is presented. Choose from: linear equation, quadratic equation, quadratic in form, rational equation, or radical equation.

b. Solve the equation by using a suitable method.

5. $t^2 + 5t - 14 = 0$ a. Quadratic b. $\{2, -7\}$

6. $a^2 - 9a + 20 = 0$ a. Quadratic b. $\{4, 5\}$

7. $a^4 - 10a^2 + 9 = 0$ a. Quadratic form b. $\{-3, -1, 1, 3\}$

8. $x^4 - 3x^2 - 4 = 0$ a. Quadratic form b. $\{2, -2, i, -i\}$

9. $x - 3x^{1/2} - 4 = 0$ a. Quadratic form (or radical) b. $\{16\}$ (The value 1 does not check.)

10. $x^2 - 9x - 2 = 0$ a. Quadratic b. $\left\{\frac{9 \pm \sqrt{89}}{2}\right\}$

11. $8b(b + 1) + 2(3b - 4) = 4b(2b + 3)$ a. Linear b. $\{4\}$

12. $6x(x + 1) - 3(x + 4) = 3x(2x + 5)$ a. Linear b. $\{-1\}$

13. $5a(a + 6) = 10(3a - 1)$ a. Quadratic b. $\{\pm i\sqrt{2}\}$

14. $4x(x + 3) = 6(2x - 4)$ a. Quadratic b. $\{\pm i\sqrt{6}\}$

15. $\frac{t}{t + 5} + \frac{3}{t - 4} = \frac{17}{t^2 + t - 20}$ a. Rational b. $\{2, -1\}$

16. $\frac{v}{v + 4} + \frac{12}{v^2 + 7v + 12} = \frac{5}{v + 3}$ a. Rational b. $\{-2, 4\}$

17. $c^2 - 20c - 1 = 0$ a. Quadratic b. $\{10 \pm \sqrt{101}\}$

18. $d^2 + 18d + 4 = 0$ a. Quadratic b. $\{-9 \pm \sqrt{77}\}$

19. $2u(u - 3) = 4(2 - u)$ a. Quadratic b. $\left\{\frac{1 \pm \sqrt{17}}{2}\right\}$

20. $3y(y + 2) = 9(y + 1)$ a. Quadratic b. $\left\{\frac{1 \pm \sqrt{13}}{2}\right\}$

21. $\sqrt{2b + 3} = b$ a. Radical b. $\{3\}$ (The value -1 does not check.)

22. $\sqrt{5t + 6} = t$ a. Radical b. $\{6\}$ (The value -1 does not check.)

23. $x^{2/3} + 2x^{1/3} - 15 = 0$ a. Quadratic form (or radical) b. $\{-125, 27\}$

24. $y^{2/3} + 5y^{1/3} + 4 = 0$ a. Quadratic form (or radical) b. $\{-64, -1\}$

Section 11.4 Graphs of Quadratic Functions

Concepts

1. **Quadratic Functions of the Form $f(x) = x^2 + k$**
2. **Quadratic Functions of the Form $f(x) = (x - h)^2$**
3. **Quadratic Functions of the Form $f(x) = ax^2$**
4. **Quadratic Functions of the Form $f(x) = a(x - h)^2 + k$**

A quadratic function is defined as a function of the form $f(x) = ax^2 + bx + c$ $(a \neq 0)$. The graph of a quadratic function is a **parabola**. In this section, we will learn how to graph parabolas.

A parabola opens upward if $a > 0$ (Figure 11-3) and opens downward if $a < 0$ (Figure 11-4). If a parabola opens upward, the **vertex** is the lowest point on the graph. If a parabola opens downward, the **vertex** is the highest point on the graph. The **axis of symmetry** is the vertical line that passes through the vertex.

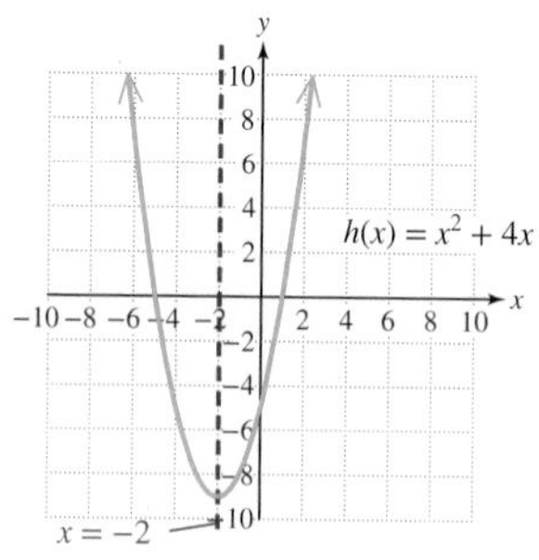

Figure 11-3

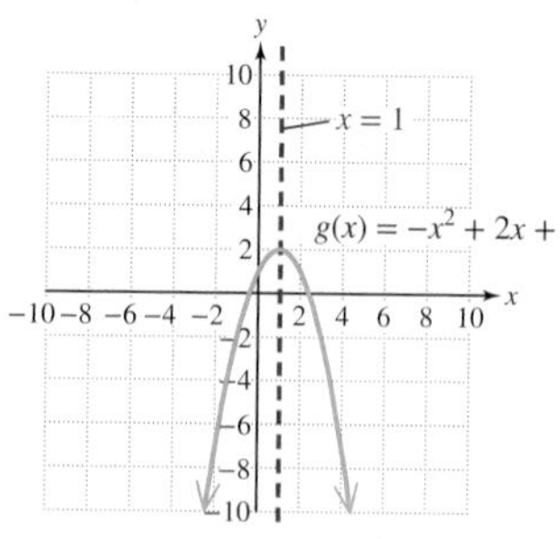

Figure 11-4

1. Quadratic Functions of the Form $f(x) = x^2 + k$

One technique for graphing a function is to plot a sufficient number of points on the graph until the general shape and defining characteristics can be determined. Then sketch a curve through the points.

Example 1 **Graphing Quadratic Functions of the Form $f(x) = x^2 + k$**

Classroom Example: p. 819, Exercise 12

Graph the functions f, g, and h on the same coordinate system.

$$f(x) = x^2 \qquad g(x) = x^2 + 1 \qquad h(x) = x^2 - 2$$

Solution:

Several function values for f, g, and h are shown in Table 11-1 for selected values of x. The corresponding graphs are pictured in Figure 11-5.

Table 11-1

x	$f(x) = x^2$	$g(x) = x^2 + 1$	$h(x) = x^2 - 2$
−3	9	10	7
−2	4	5	2
−1	1	2	−1
0	0	1	−2
1	1	2	−1
2	4	5	2
3	9	10	7

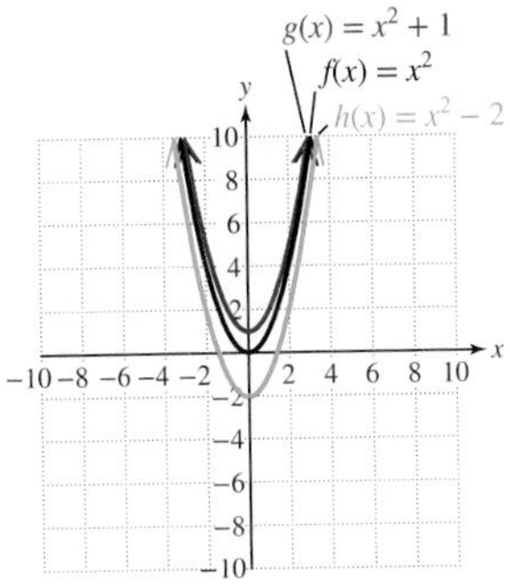

Figure 11-5

Skill Practice Refer to the graph of $f(x) = x^2 + k$ to determine the value of k.

1.

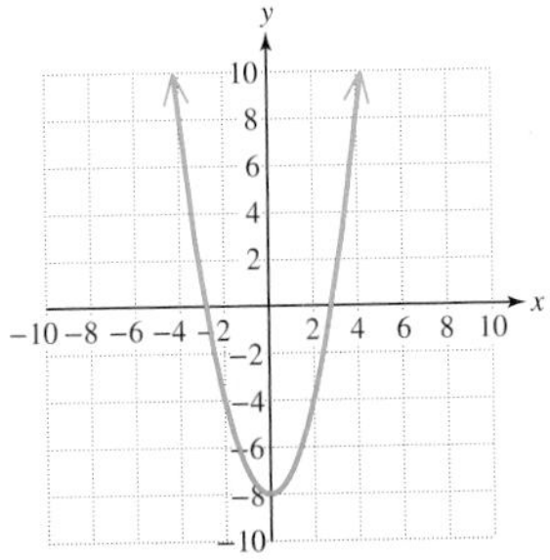

Notice that the graphs of $g(x) = x^2 + 1$ and $h(x) = x^2 - 2$ take on the same shape as $f(x) = x^2$. However, the y values of g are 1 greater than the y values of f. Hence, the graph of $g(x) = x^2 + 1$ is the same as the graph of $f(x) = x^2$ shifted *up* 1 unit. Likewise the y-values of h are 2 less than those of f. The graph of $h(x) = x^2 - 2$ is the same as the graph of $f(x) = x^2$ shifted *down* 2 units.

A function of the type $f(x) = x^2 + k$ represents a vertical shift of the graph of $f(x) = x^2$. The functions in Example 1 illustrate the following properties of quadratic functions of the form $f(x) = x^2 + k$.

Answer

1. $k = -8$

Graphs of $f(x) = x^2 + k$

A function of the type $f(x) = x^2 + k$ represents a vertical shift of the graph of $f(x) = x^2$.

- If $k > 0$, then the graph of $f(x) = x^2 + k$ is the same as the graph of $f(x) = x^2$ shifted *up* k units.
- If $k < 0$, then the graph of $f(x) = x^2 + k$ is the same as the graph of $f(x) = x^2$ shifted *down* $|k|$ units.

Calculator Connections

Topic: Investigating Vertical Shifts of a Function

Try experimenting with a graphing calculator by graphing functions of the form $y = x^2 + k$ for several values of k.

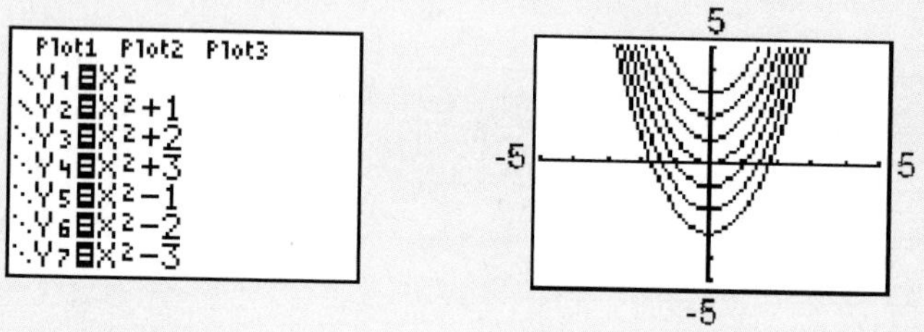

Classroom Example: p. 819, Exercise 14

Example 2 **Graphing Quadratic Functions of the Form $f(x) = x^2 + k$**

Sketch the functions defined by

a. $m(x) = x^2 - 4$ **b.** $n(x) = x^2 + \frac{7}{2}$

TIP: For more accuracy in the graph, plot one or two points near the vertex and use the symmetry of the curve to find additional points on the graph.

Solution:

a. $m(x) = x^2 - 4$

$m(x) = x^2 + (-4)$

Because $k = -4$ (negative), the graph is obtained by shifting the graph of $f(x) = x^2$ down $|-4|$ units (Figure 11-6).

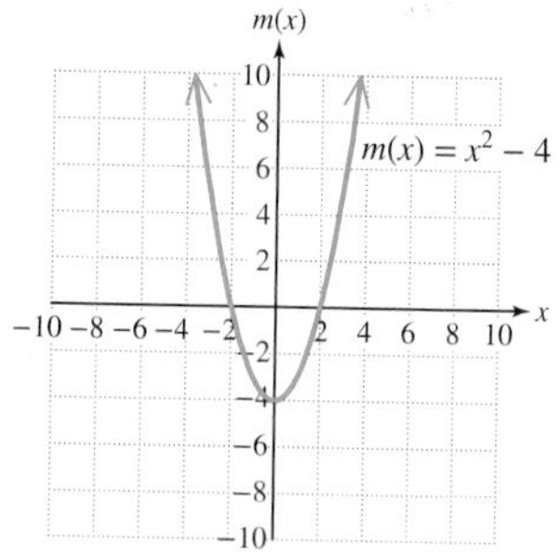

Figure 11-6

b. $n(x) = x^2 + \frac{7}{2}$

Because $k = \frac{7}{2}$ (positive), the graph is obtained by shifting the graph of $f(x) = x^2$ up $\frac{7}{2}$ units (Figure 11-7).

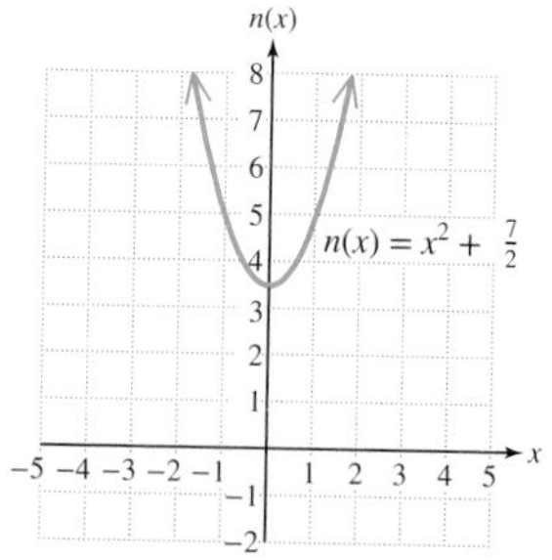

Figure 11-7

Skill Practice

2. Graph the functions f, g, and h on the same coordinate system.
$f(x) = x^2$ $g(x) = x^2 + 3$ $h(x) = x^2 - 5$

Answer

2.

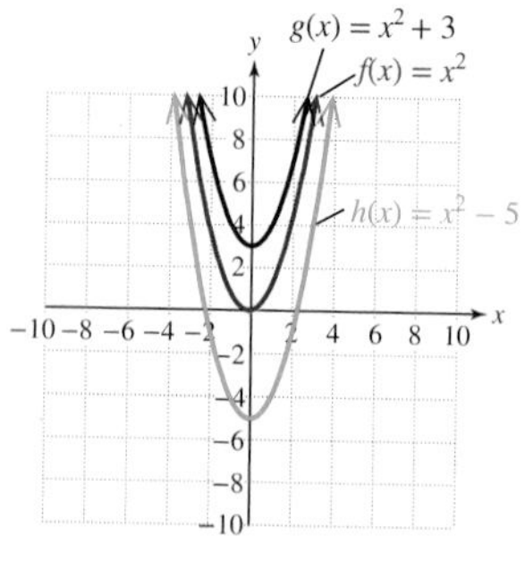

2. Quadratic Functions of the Form $f(x) = (x - h)^2$

The graph of $f(x) = x^2 + k$ represents a vertical shift (up or down) of the graph of $f(x) = x^2$. Example 3 shows that functions of the form $f(x) = (x - h)^2$ represent a horizontal shift (left or right) of the graph of $f(x) = x^2$.

Example 3 **Graphing Quadratic Functions of the Form $f(x) = (x - h)^2$**

Classroom Example: p. 820, Exercise 20

Graph the functions f, g, and h on the same coordinate system.

$$f(x) = x^2 \qquad g(x) = (x + 1)^2 \qquad h(x) = (x - 2)^2$$

Solution:

Several function values for f, g, and h are shown in Table 11-2 for selected values of x. The corresponding graphs are pictured in Figure 11-8.

Table 11-2

x	$f(x) = x^2$	$g(x) = (x + 1)^2$	$h(x) = (x - 2)^2$
−4	16	9	36
−3	9	4	25
−2	4	1	16
−1	1	0	9
0	0	1	4
1	1	4	1
2	4	9	0
3	9	16	1
4	16	25	4
5	25	36	9

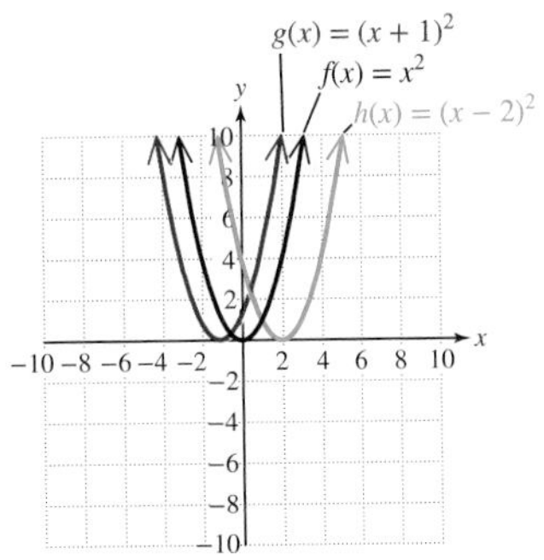

Figure 11-8

Skill Practice Refer to the graph of $f(x) = (x - h)^2$ to determine the value of h.

3.

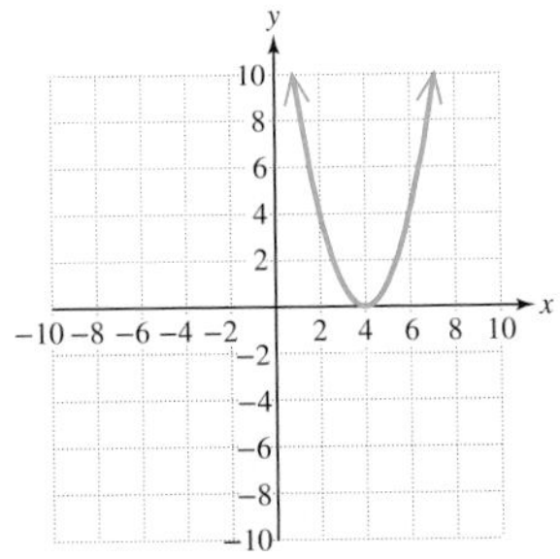

Example 3 illustrates the following properties of quadratic functions of the form $f(x) = (x - h)^2$.

Answer

3. $h = 4$

Graphs of $f(x) = (x - h)^2$

A function of the type $f(x) = (x - h)^2$ represents a horizontal shift of the graph of $f(x) = x^2$.

If $h > 0$, then the graph of $f(x) = (x - h)^2$ is the same as the graph of $f(x) = x^2$ shifted h units to the *right*.

If $h < 0$, then the graph of $f(x) = (x - h)^2$ is the same as the graph of $f(x) = x^2$ shifted $|h|$ units to the *left*.

From Example 3 we have

$h(x) = (x - 2)^2$ and $g(x) = (x + 1)^2$

$g(x) = [x - (-1)]^2$

$h(x)$: $y = x^2$ shifted 2 units to the right

$g(x)$: $y = x^2$ shifted $|-1|$ unit to the left

Classroom Example: p. 820, Exercise 26

Example 4 Graphing Functions of the Form $f(x) = (x - h)^2$

Sketch the functions p and q.

a. $p(x) = (x - 7)^2$ **b.** $q(x) = (x + 1.6)^2$

Solution:

a. $p(x) = (x - 7)^2$

Because $h = 7 > 0$, shift the graph of $f(x) = x^2$ to the *right* 7 units (Figure 11-9).

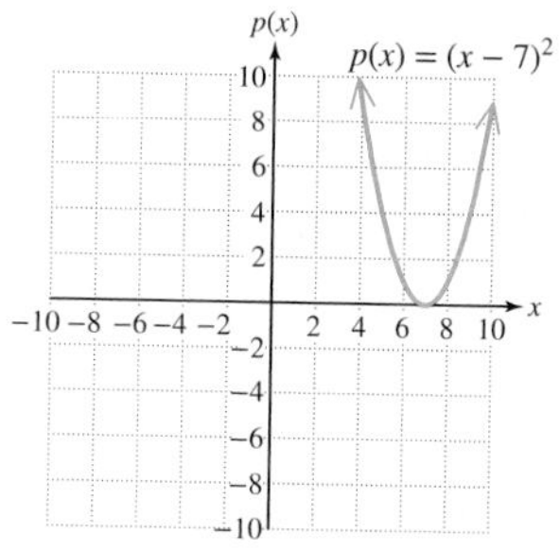

Figure 11-9

b. $q(x) = (x + 1.6)^2$

$q(x) = [x - (-1.6)]^2$

Because $h = -1.6 < 0$, shift the graph of $f(x) = x^2$ to the *left* 1.6 units (Figure 11-10).

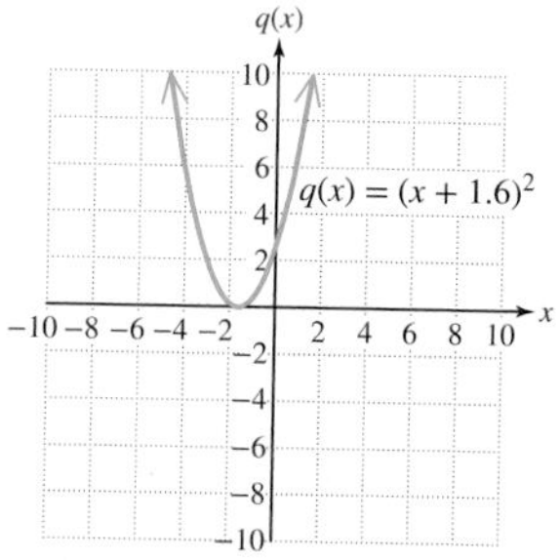

Figure 11-10

Answer

4.

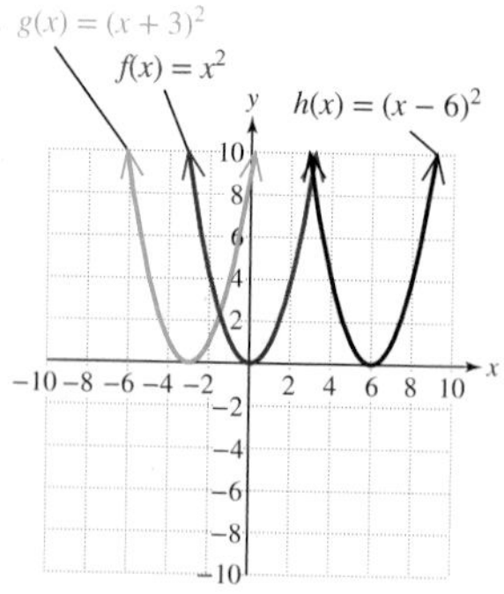

Skill Practice

4. Graph the functions f, g, and h on the same coordinate system.

$f(x) = x^2$

$g(x) = (x + 3)^2$

$h(x) = (x - 6)^2$

3. Quadratic Functions of the Form $f(x) = ax^2$

Examples 5 and 6 investigate functions of the form $f(x) = ax^2 \quad (a \neq 0)$.

Example 5 Graphing Functions of the Form $f(x) = ax^2$

Classroom Example: p. 820, Exercise 32

Graph the functions f, g, and h on the same coordinate system.

$$f(x) = x^2 \qquad g(x) = 2x^2 \qquad h(x) = \frac{1}{2}x^2$$

Solution:

Several function values for f, g, and h are shown in Table 11-3 for selected values of x. The corresponding graphs are pictured in Figure 11-11.

Table 11-3

x	$f(x) = x^2$	$g(x) = 2x^2$	$h(x) = \frac{1}{2}x^2$
−3	9	18	$\frac{9}{2}$
−2	4	8	2
−1	1	2	$\frac{1}{2}$
0	0	0	0
1	1	2	$\frac{1}{2}$
2	4	8	2
3	9	18	$\frac{9}{2}$

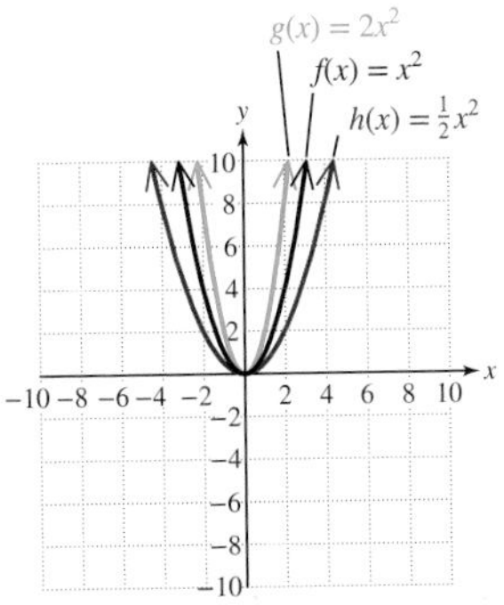

Figure 11-11

Skill Practice

5. Graph the functions f, g, and h on the same coordinate system.

$f(x) = x^2$

$g(x) = 3x^2$

$h(x) = \frac{1}{3}x^2$

In Example 5, the function values defined by $g(x) = 2x^2$ are twice those of $f(x) = x^2$. The graph of $g(x) = 2x^2$ is the same as the graph of $f(x) = x^2$ *stretched vertically* by a factor of 2 (the graph appears narrower than $f(x) = x^2$).

In Example 5, the function values defined by $h(x) = \frac{1}{2}x^2$ are one-half those of $f(x) = x^2$. The graph of $h(x) = \frac{1}{2}x^2$ is the same as the graph of $f(x) = x^2$ *shrunk vertically* by a factor of $\frac{1}{2}$ (the graph appears wider than $f(x) = x^2$).

Example 6 Graphing Functions of the Form $f(x) = ax^2$

Graph the functions f, g, and h on the same coordinate system.

$$f(x) = -x^2 \qquad g(x) = -3x^2 \qquad h(x) = -\frac{1}{3}x^2$$

Answers

5.

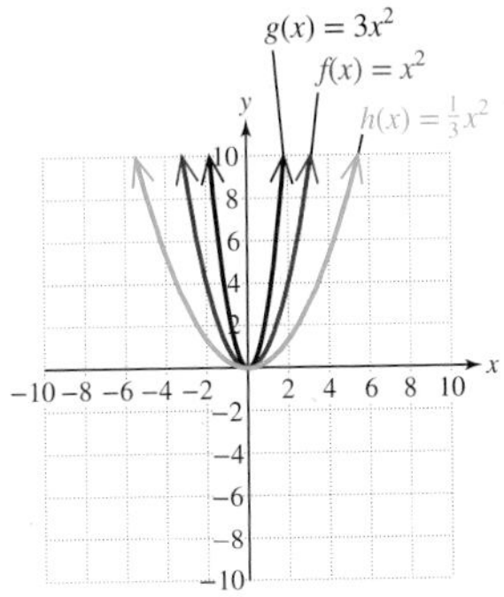

Classroom Example: p. 821, Exercise 34

Solution:

Several function values for f, g, and h are shown in Table 11-4 for selected values of x. The corresponding graphs are pictured in Figure 11-12.

Table 11-4

x	$f(x) = -x^2$	$g(x) = -3x^2$	$h(x) = -\frac{1}{3}x^2$
−3	−9	−27	−3
−2	−4	−12	$-\frac{4}{3}$
−1	−1	−3	$-\frac{1}{3}$
0	0	0	0
1	−1	−3	$-\frac{1}{3}$
2	−4	−12	$-\frac{4}{3}$
3	−9	−27	−3

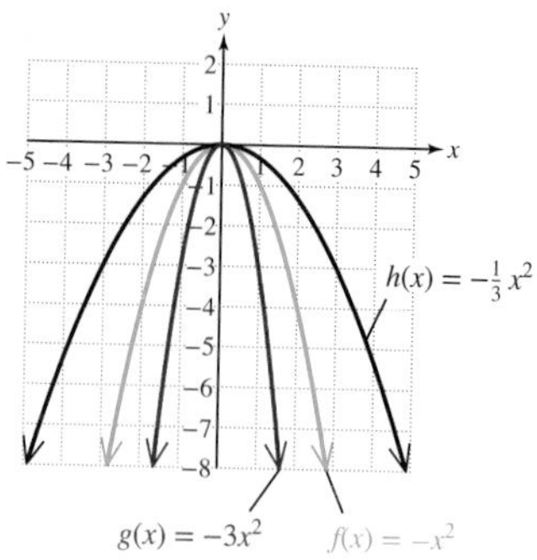

Figure 11-12

Skill Practice

6. Graph the functions f, g, and h on the same coordinate system.

$f(x) = -x^2 \qquad g(x) = -2x^2 \qquad h(x) = -\dfrac{1}{2}x^2$

Example 6 illustrates that if the coefficient of the squared term is negative, the parabola opens downward. The graph of $g(x) = -3x^2$ is the same as the graph of $f(x) = -x^2$ with a *vertical stretch* by a factor of $|-3|$. The graph of $h(x) = -\frac{1}{3}x^2$ is the same as the graph of $f(x) = -x^2$ with a *vertical shrink* by a factor of $|-\frac{1}{3}|$.

Graphs of $f(x) = ax^2$

1. If $a > 0$, the parabola opens upward. Furthermore,
- If $0 < a < 1$, then the graph of $f(x) = ax^2$ is the same as the graph of $f(x) = x^2$ with a *vertical shrink* by a factor of a.
- If $a > 1$, then the graph of $f(x) = ax^2$ is the same as the graph of $f(x) = x^2$ with a *vertical stretch* by a factor of a.

2. If $a < 0$, the parabola opens downward. Furthermore,
- If $0 < |a| < 1$, then the graph of $f(x) = ax^2$ is the same as the graph of $f(x) = -x^2$ with a *vertical shrink* by a factor of $|a|$.
- If $|a| > 1$, then the graph of $f(x) = ax^2$ is the same as the graph of $f(x) = -x^2$ with a *vertical stretch* by a factor of $|a|$.

Answer

6.

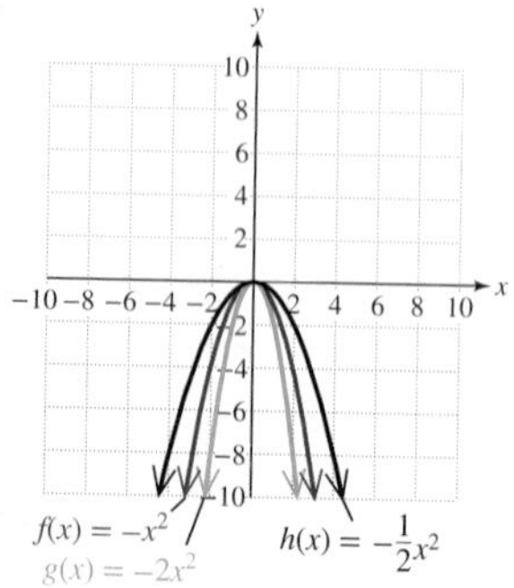

4. Quadratic Functions of the Form $f(x) = a(x - h)^2 + k$

We can summarize our findings from Examples 1–6 by graphing functions of the form $f(x) = a(x - h)^2 + k \quad (a \neq 0)$.

The graph of $f(x) = x^2$ has its vertex at the origin (0, 0). The graph of $f(x) = a(x - h)^2 + k$ is the same as the graph of $f(x) = x^2$ shifted to the right or left h units and shifted up or down k units. Therefore, the vertex is shifted from (0, 0) to (h, k). The axis of symmetry is the vertical line through the vertex. Therefore, the axis of symmetry must be the line $x = h$.

Graphs of $f(x) = a(x - h)^2 + k$

1. The vertex is (h, k).
2. The axis of symmetry is the line $x = h$.
3. If $a > 0$, the parabola opens upward, and k is the **minimum value** of the function.
4. If $a < 0$, the parabola opens downward, and k is the **maximum value** of the function.

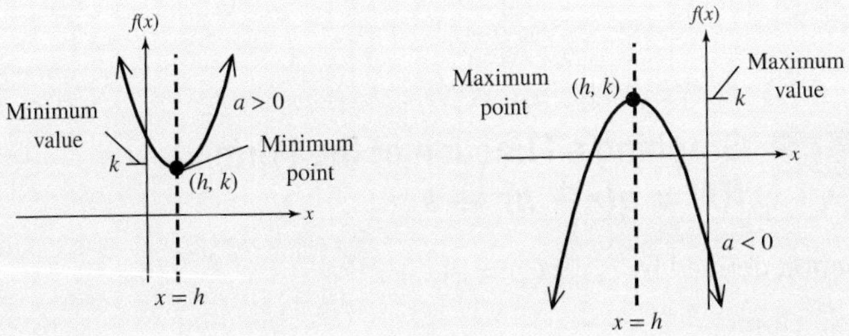

Example 7 Graphing a Function of the Form $f(x) = a(x - h)^2 + k$

Given the function defined by $f(x) = 2(x - 3)^2 + 4$

a. Identify the vertex.
b. Sketch the function.
c. Identify the axis of symmetry.
d. Identify the maximum or minimum value of the function.
e. Use the graph to determine the domain and range of f in interval notation.

Classroom Example: p. 822, Exercise 62

Solution:

a. The function is in the form $f(x) = a(x - h)^2 + k$, where $a = 2$, $h = 3$, and $k = 4$. Therefore, the vertex is $(3, 4)$.

b. The graph of f is the same as the graph of $f(x) = x^2$ shifted to the right 3 units, shifted up 4 units, and stretched vertically by a factor of 2 (Figure 11-13).

c. The axis of symmetry is the line $x = 3$.

d. Because $a > 0$, the function opens upward. Therefore, the minimum function value is 4. Notice that the minimum value is the minimum y-value on the graph.

e. The domain is all real numbers:$(-\infty, \infty)$. The vertex is the lowest point on the parabola, and its y-coordinate is 4. Therefore, the range is $[4, \infty)$.

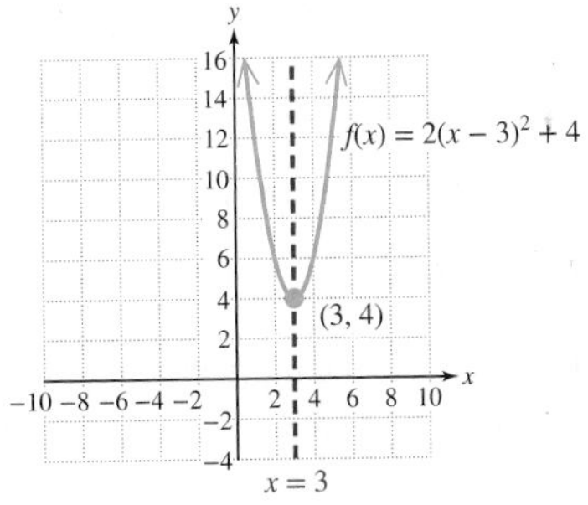

Figure 11-13

TIP: We can find additional points to the right or left of the vertex and use the symmetry of the parabola to refine the sketch of the curve.

x	$f(x)$
4	6
5	12

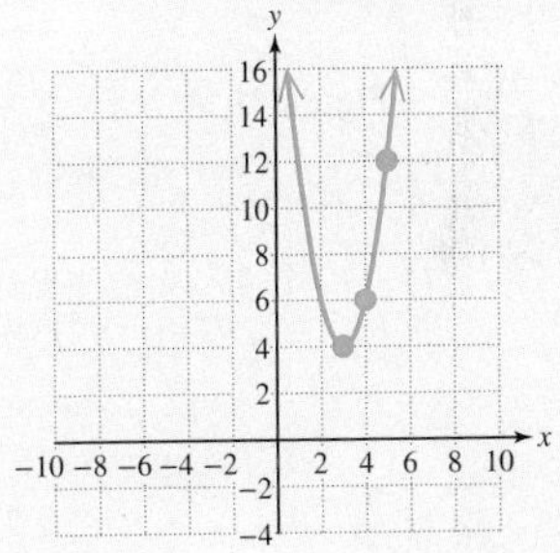

Skill Practice

7. Given the function defined by $g(x) = 3(x + 1)^2 - 3$
   a. Identify the vertex.
   b. Sketch the graph.
   c. Identify the axis of symmetry.
   d. Identify the maximum or minimum value of the function.
   e. Determine the domain and range in interval notation.

Answers

7. a. Vertex: $(-1, -3)$
   b.

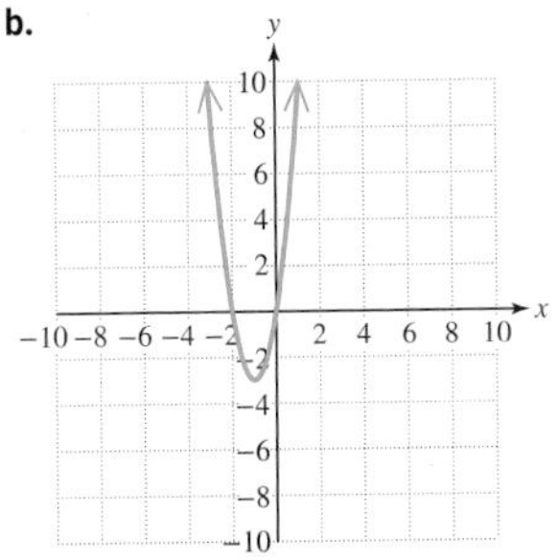

   c. Axis of symmetry: $x = -1$
   d. Minimum value: -3
   e. Domain: $(-\infty, \infty)$; range: $[-3, \infty)$

Calculator Connections

Topic: Using the Maximum and Minimum Features

Some graphing calculators have *Minimum* and *Maximum* features that enable the user to approximate the minimum and maximum values of a function.

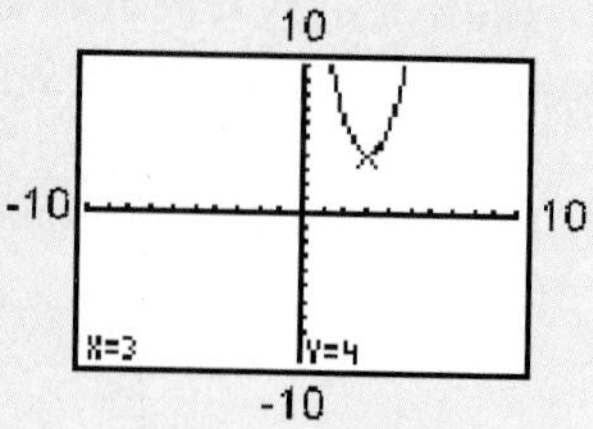

Classroom Example: p. 822, Exercise 60

Example 8 Graphing a Function of the Form $f(x) = a(x - h)^2 + k$

Given the function defined by $g(x) = -(x + 2)^2 - \frac{7}{4}$

a. Identify the vertex.

b. Sketch the function.

c. Identify the axis of symmetry.

d. Identify the maximum or minimum value of the function.

e. Use the graph to determine the domain and range of f in interval notation.

Solution:

a. $g(x) = -(x + 2)^2 - \frac{7}{4}$

$$= -1[x - (-2)]^2 + \left(-\frac{7}{4}\right)$$

The function is in the form $g(x) = a(x - h)^2 + k$, where $a = -1$, $h = -2$, and $k = -\frac{7}{4}$. Therefore, the vertex is $(-2, -\frac{7}{4})$.

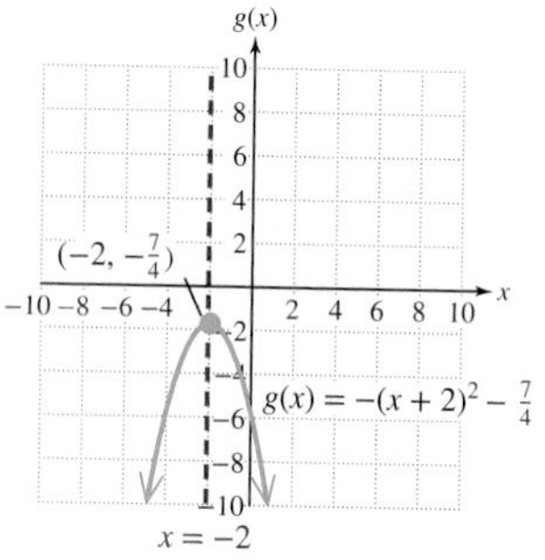

Figure 11-14

b. The graph of g is the same as the graph of $f(x) = x^2$ shifted to the left 2 units, shifted down $\frac{7}{4}$ units, and opening downward (Figure 11-14).

c. The axis of symmetry is the line $x = -2$.

d. The parabola opens downward, so the maximum function value is $-\frac{7}{4}$.

e. The domain is all real numbers: $(-\infty, \infty)$.

The vertex is the highest point on the parabola, and its y-coordinate is $-\frac{7}{4}$. Therefore, the range is $(-\infty, -\frac{7}{4}]$.

Skill Practice

8. Given the function defined by $h(x) = -\frac{1}{2}(x - 4)^2 + 2$

a. Identify the vertex.

b. Sketch the graph.

c. Identify the axis of symmetry.

d. Identify the maximum or minimum value of the function.

e. Determine the domain and range in interval notation.

Answers

8. a. Vertex: (4, 2)

b.

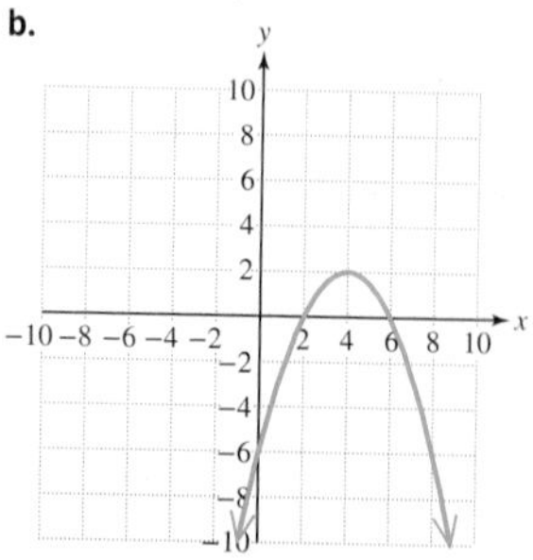

c. Axis of symmetry: $x = 4$

d. Maximum value: 2

e. Domain: $(-\infty, \infty)$; range: $(-\infty, 2]$

Section 11.4 Practice Exercises

For additional exercises, see Classroom Activities 11.4A–11.4D in the *Student's Resource Manual* at www.mhhe.com/moh.

Vocabulary and Key Concepts

1. a. The graph of a quadratic function, $f(x) = ax^2 + bx + c$, is a __parabola__.

b. The parabola defined by $f(x) = ax^2 + bx + c$ $(a \neq 0)$ will open upward if a __>__ 0 and will open downward if a __<__ 0.

c. If a parabola opens upward, the vertex is the (highest/lowest) point on the graph. If a parabola opens downward, the vertex is the (highest/lowest) point on the graph. lowest; highest

d. Given $f(x) = a(x - h)^2 + k$ $(a \neq 0)$, the vertex of the parabola is given by the ordered pair __(h, k)__. If the parabola opens __upward__, the value of k is the minimum value of the function. If the parabola opens __downward__, the value of k is the maximum value of the function.

e. Given $f(x) = a(x - h)^2 + k$ $(a \neq 0)$, the axis of symmetry of the parabola is the vertical line that passes through the __vertex__. An equation of the axis of symmetry is __$x = h$__.

Review Exercises

For Exercises 2–8, solve the equations.

2. $x^2 + x - 5 = 0$ $\left\{\frac{-1 \pm \sqrt{21}}{2}\right\}$

3. $(y - 3)^2 = -4$ $\{3 \pm 2i\}$

4. $\sqrt{2a + 2} = a + 1$ $\{1, -1\}$

5. $5t(t - 2) = -3$ $\left\{\frac{5 \pm \sqrt{10}}{5}\right\}$

6. $2z^2 - 3z - 9 = 0$ $\left\{-\frac{3}{2}, 3\right\}$

7. $x^{2/3} + 5x^{1/3} + 6 = 0$ $\{-27, -8\}$

8. $m^2(m^2 + 6) = 27$ $\{\pm\sqrt{3}, \pm 3i\}$

Concept 1: Quadratic Functions of the Form $f(x) = x^2 + k$

9. Describe how the value of k affects the graph of a function defined by $f(x) = x^2 + k$.
The value of k shifts the graph of $f(x) = x^2$ vertically.

For Exercises 10–17, graph the functions. **(See Examples 1–2.)**

10. $g(x) = x^2 + 1$

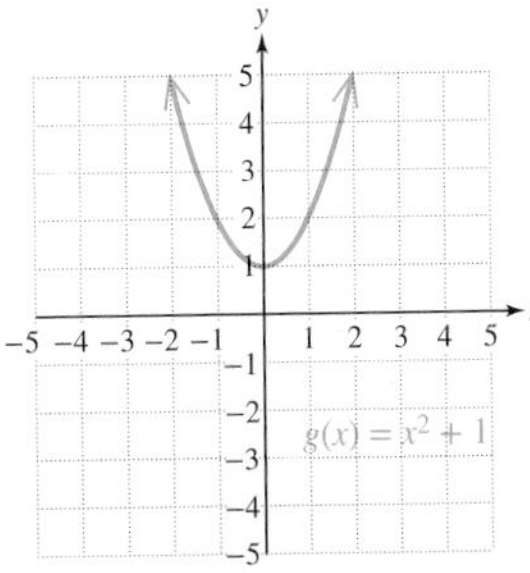

11. $f(x) = x^2 + 2$

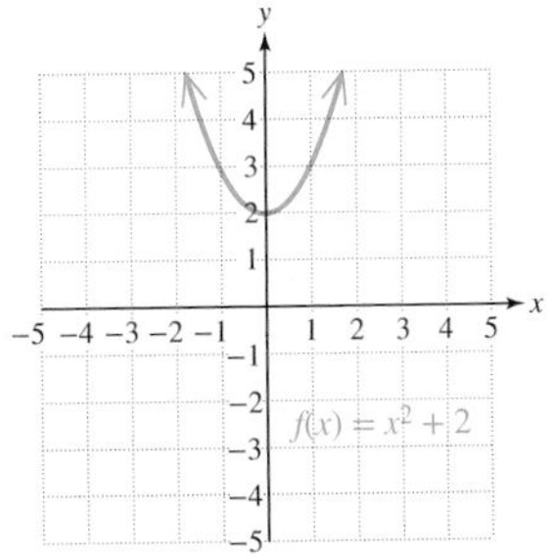

12. $p(x) = x^2 - 3$

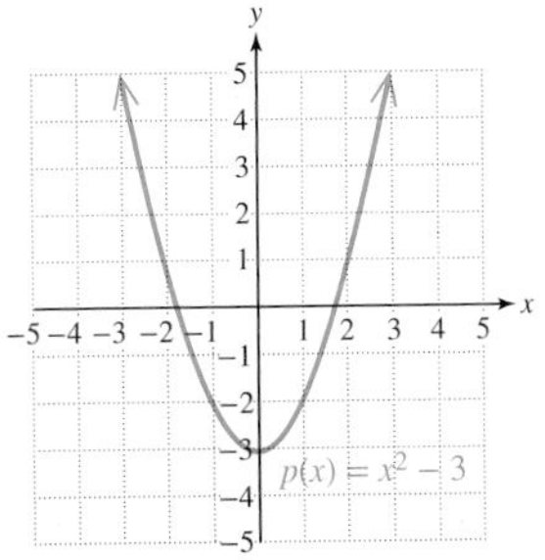

13. $q(x) = x^2 - 4$

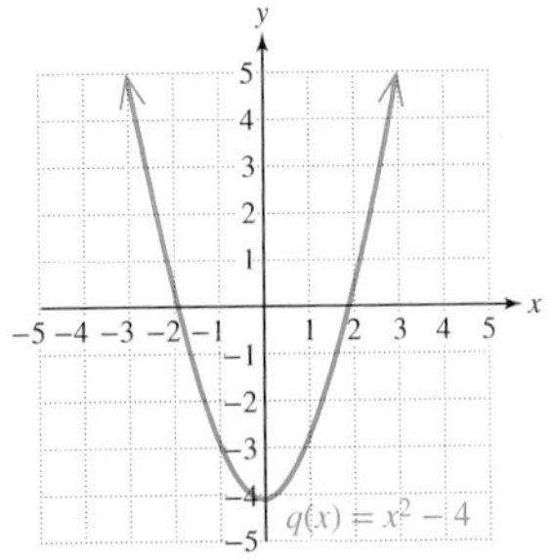

14. $T(x) = x^2 + \frac{3}{4}$

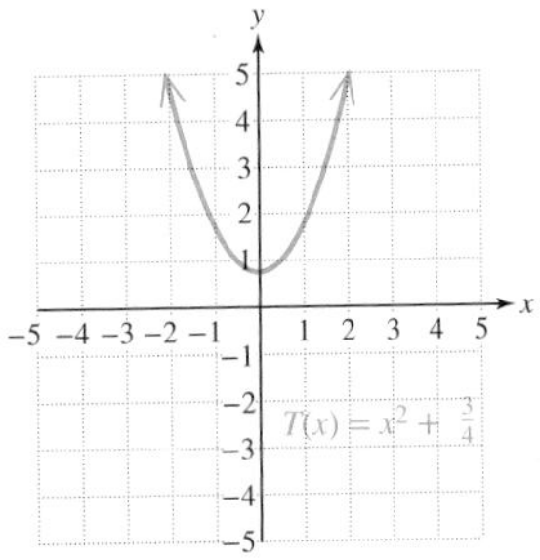

15. $S(x) = x^2 + \frac{3}{2}$

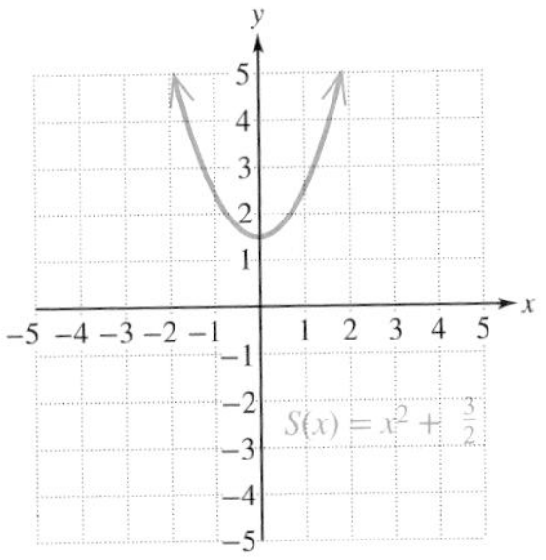

16. $M(x) = x^2 - \frac{5}{4}$

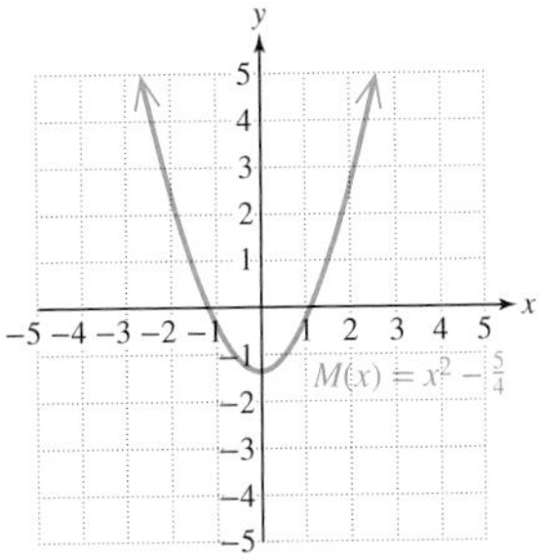

17. $n(x) = x^2 - \frac{1}{3}$

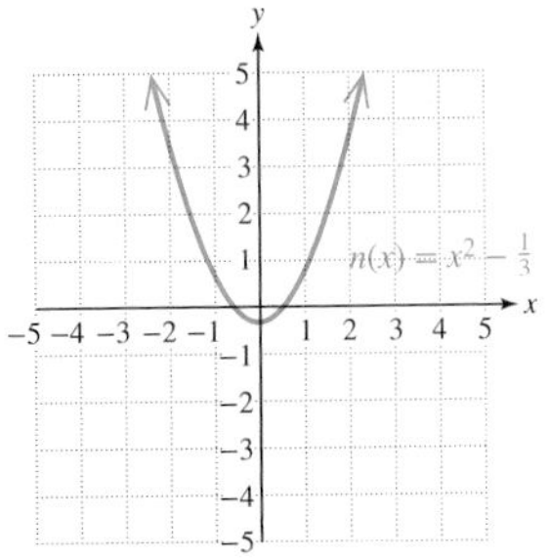

Writing Translating Expression Geometry Scientific Calculator Video

Concept 2: Quadratic Functions of the Form $f(x) = (x - h)^2$

18. Describe how the value of h affects the graph of a function defined by $f(x) = (x - h)^2$.
The value of h shifts the graph of $f(x) = x^2$ horizontally.

For Exercises 19–26, graph the functions. **(See Examples 3–4.)**

19. $r(x) = (x + 1)^2$

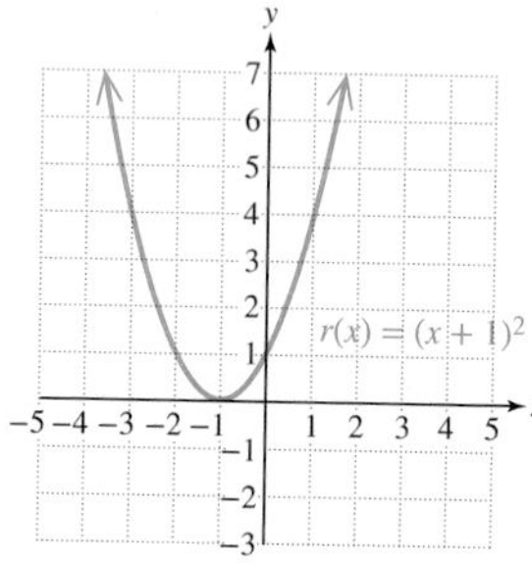

20. $h(x) = (x + 2)^2$

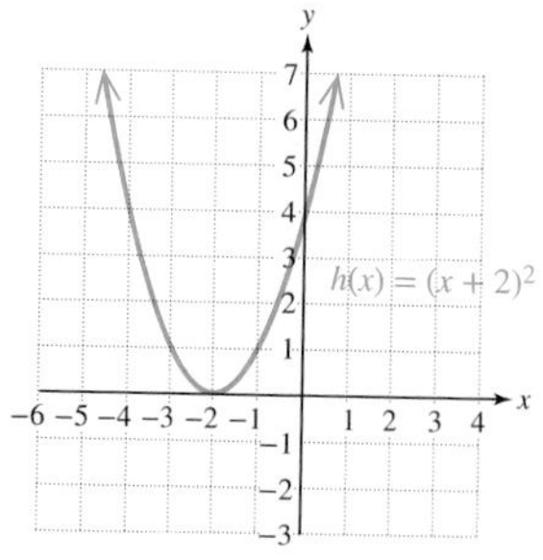

21. $k(x) = (x - 3)^2$

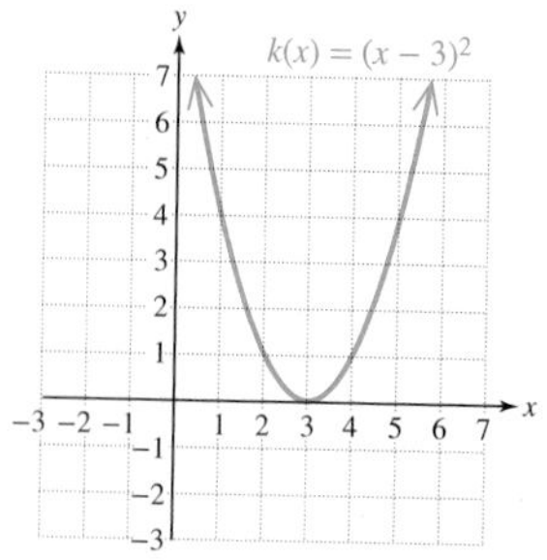

22. $L(x) = (x - 4)^2$

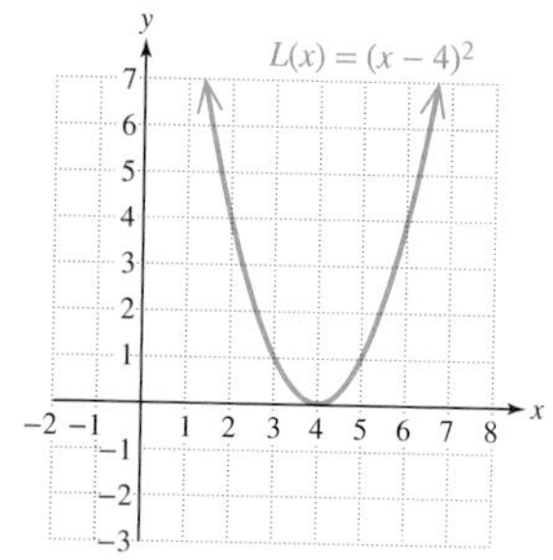

23. $A(x) = \left(x + \frac{3}{4}\right)^2$

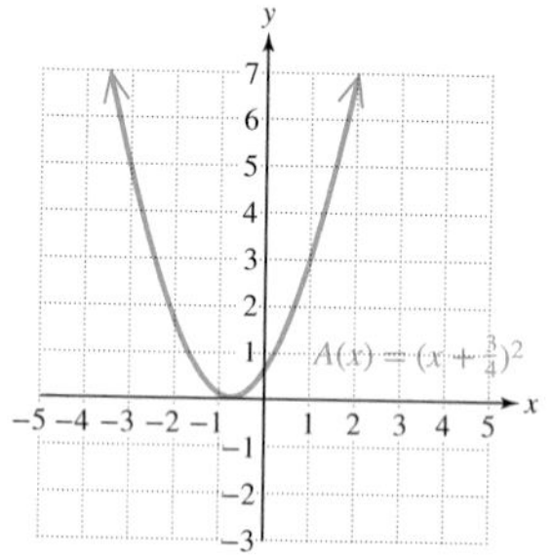

24. $r(x) = \left(x + \frac{3}{2}\right)^2$

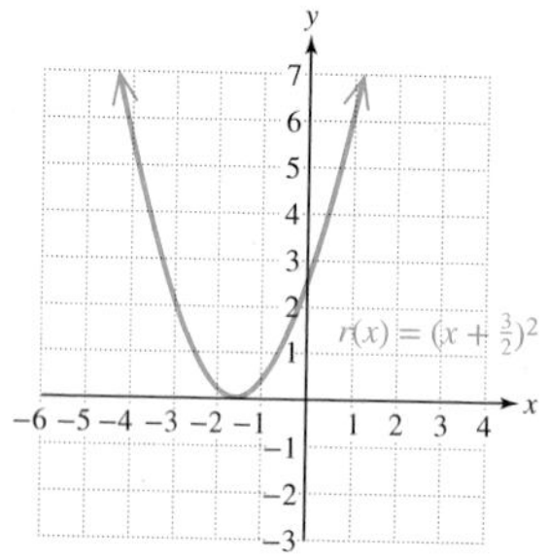

25. $W(x) = (x - 1.25)^2$

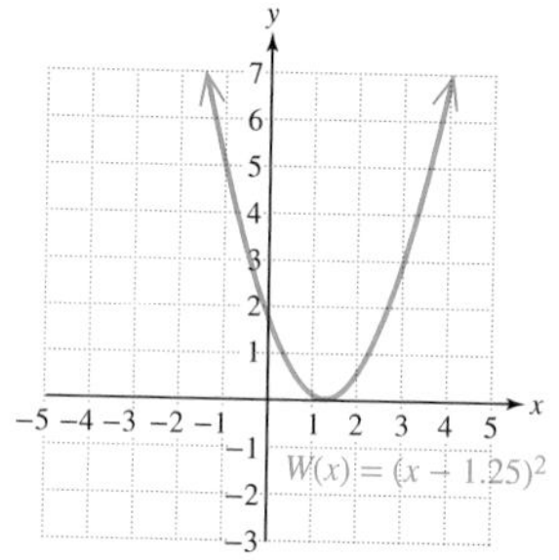

26. $V(x) = (x - 2.5)^2$

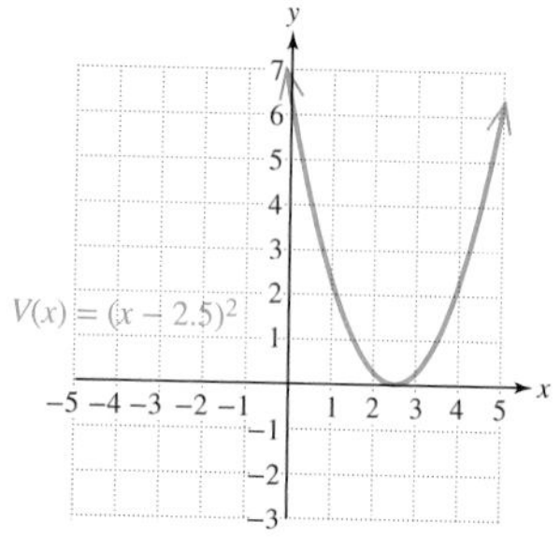

Concept 3: Quadratic Functions of the Form $f(x) = ax^2$

27. Describe how the value of a affects the graph of a function defined by $f(x) = ax^2$, where $a \neq 0$.
The value of a vertically stretches or shrinks the graph of $f(x) = x^2$.

28. How do you determine whether the graph of a function defined by $h(x) = ax^2 + bx + c$ $(a \neq 0)$ opens upward or downward? If $a > 0$, the parabola opens upward; if $a < 0$, the parabola opens downward.

For Exercises 29–36, graph the functions. **(See Examples 5–6.)**

29. $f(x) = 4x^2$

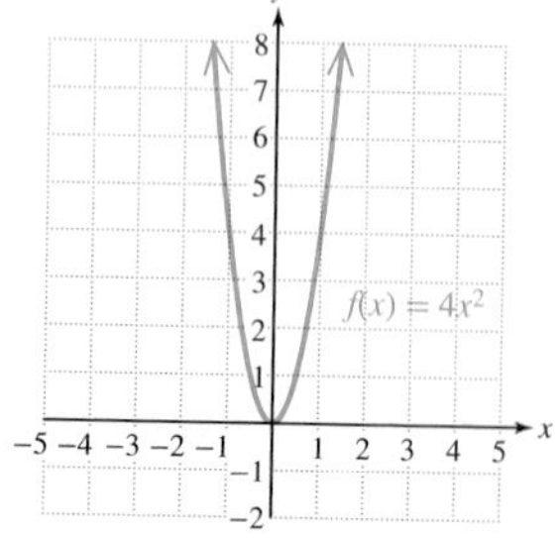

30. $g(x) = 3x^2$

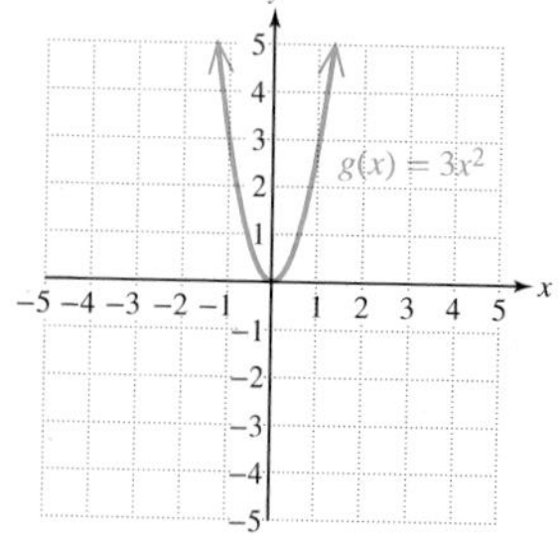

31. $h(x) = \frac{1}{4}x^2$

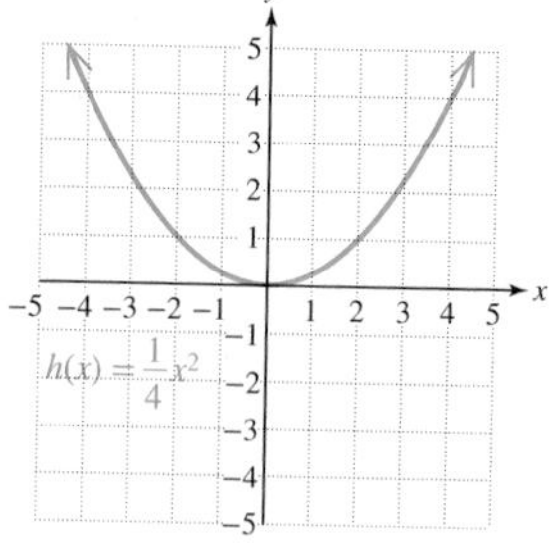

32. $f(x) = \frac{1}{5}x^2$

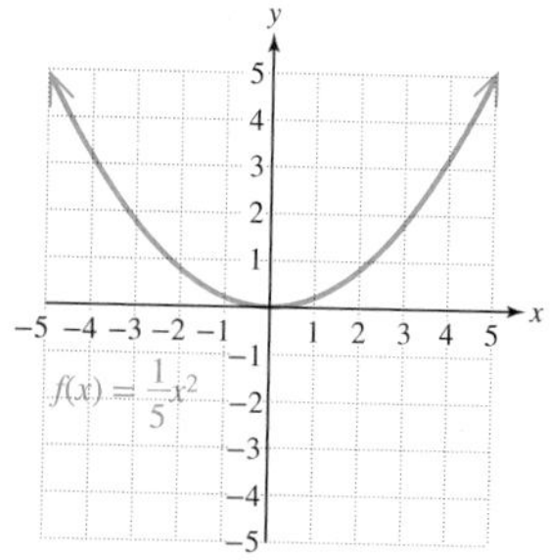

33. $c(x) = -x^2$

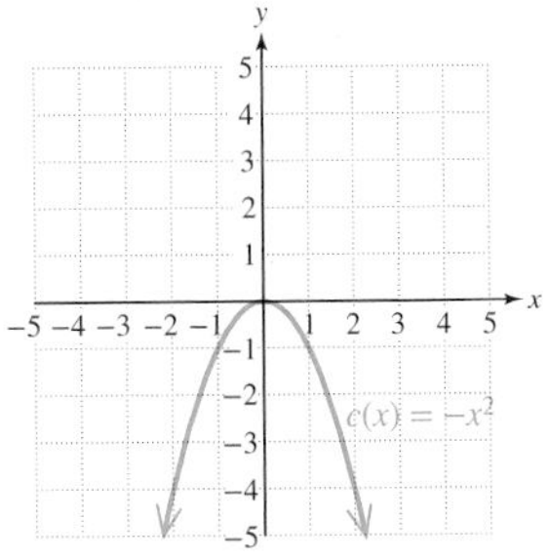

34. $g(x) = -4x^2$

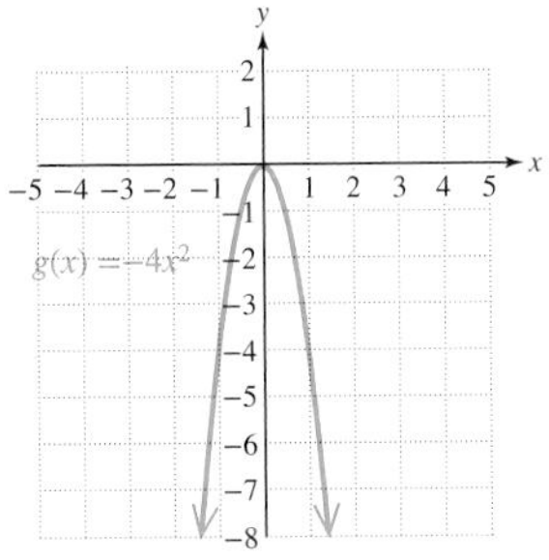

35. $v(x) = -\frac{1}{5}x^2$

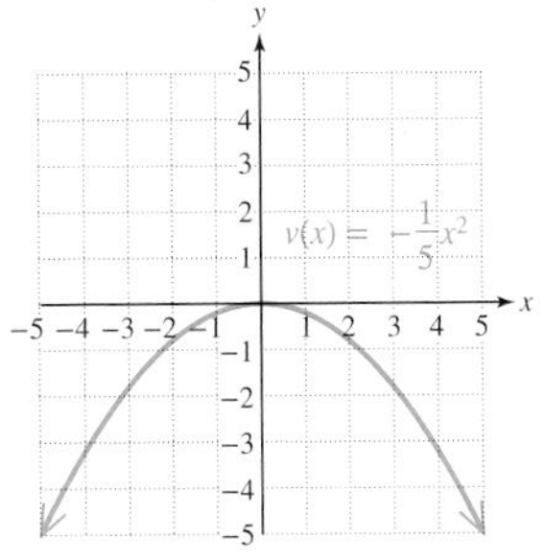

36. $f(x) = -\frac{1}{4}x^2$

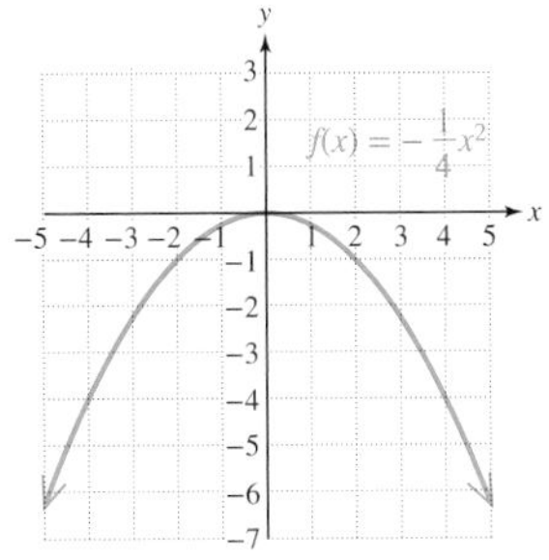

Concept 4: Quadratic Functions of the Form $f(x) = a(x - h)^2 + k$

For Exercises 37–44, match the function with its graph.

37. $f(x) = -\frac{1}{4}x^2$ d

38. $g(x) = (x + 3)^2$ c

39. $k(x) = (x - 3)^2$ g

40. $h(x) = \frac{1}{4}x^2$ h

41. $t(x) = x^2 + 2$ a

42. $m(x) = x^2 - 4$ f

43. $p(x) = (x + 1)^2 - 3$ e

44. $n(x) = -(x - 2)^2 + 3$ b

a.

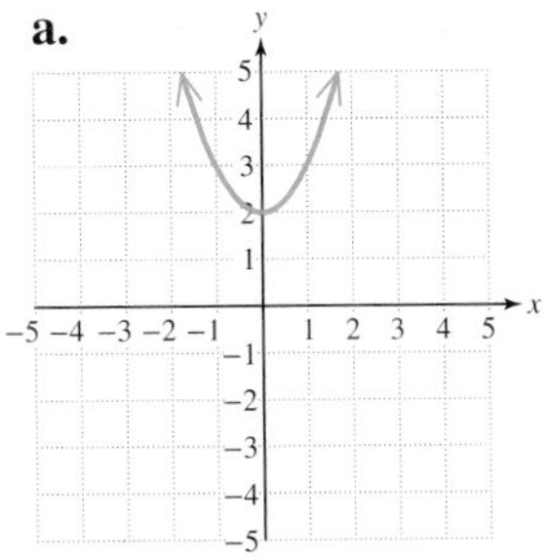

b.

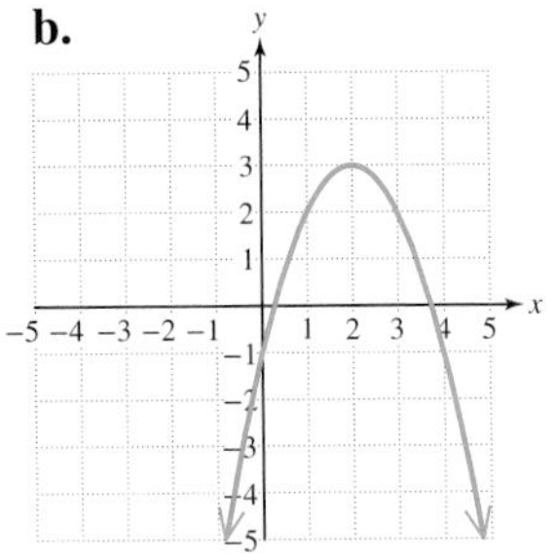

c.

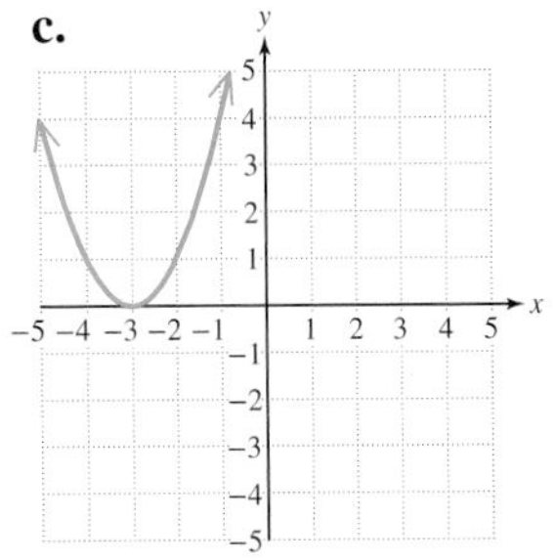

d.

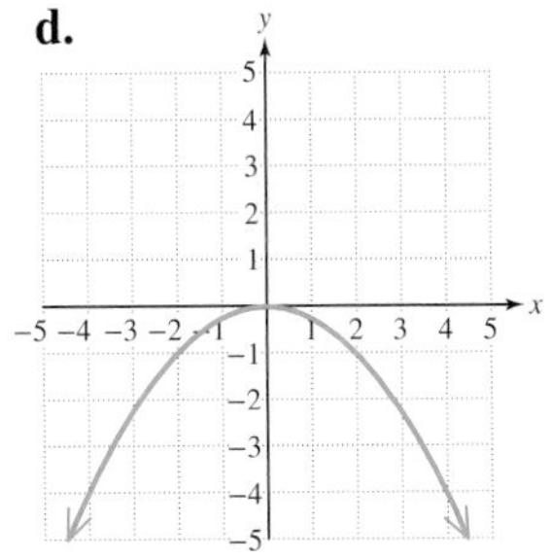

e.

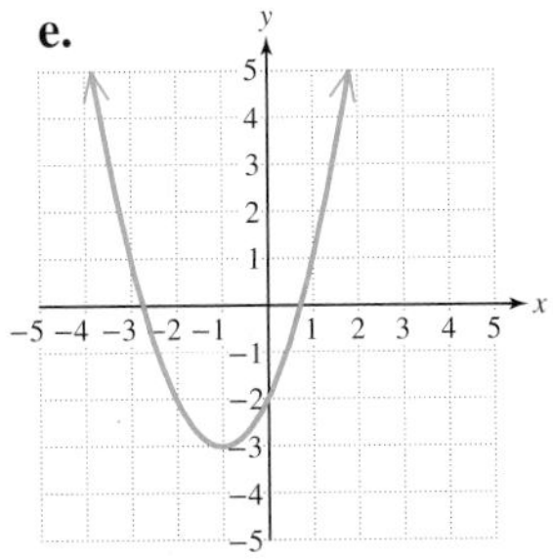

f.

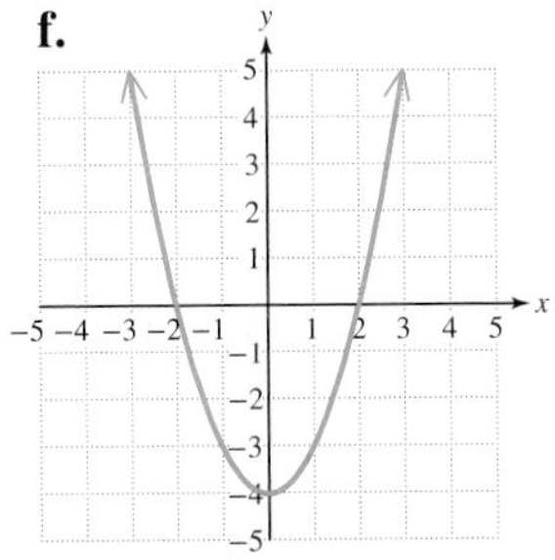

g.

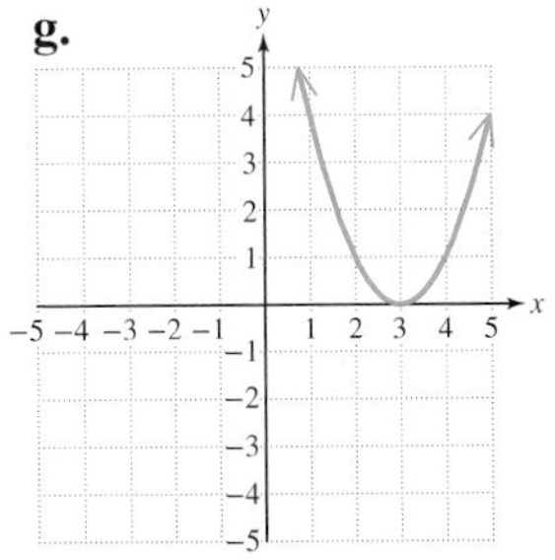

h.

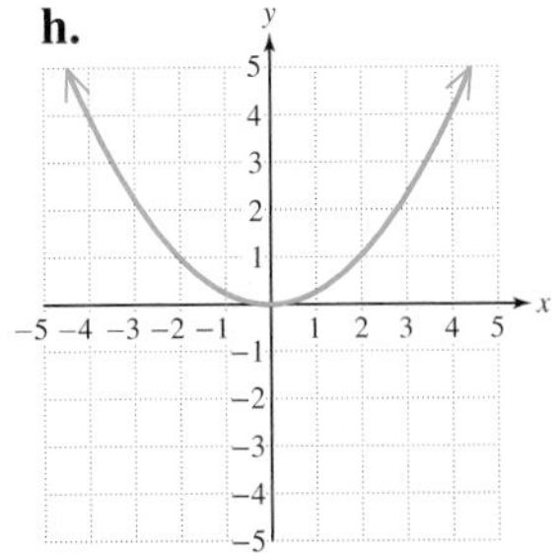

For Exercises 45–64, graph the parabola and the axis of symmetry. Label the coordinates of the vertex, and write the equation of the axis of symmetry. Use the graph to write the domain and range in interval notation. **(See Examples 7–8.)**

45. $f(x) = (x - 3)^2 + 2$

Domain: $(-\infty, \infty)$; range: $[2, \infty)$

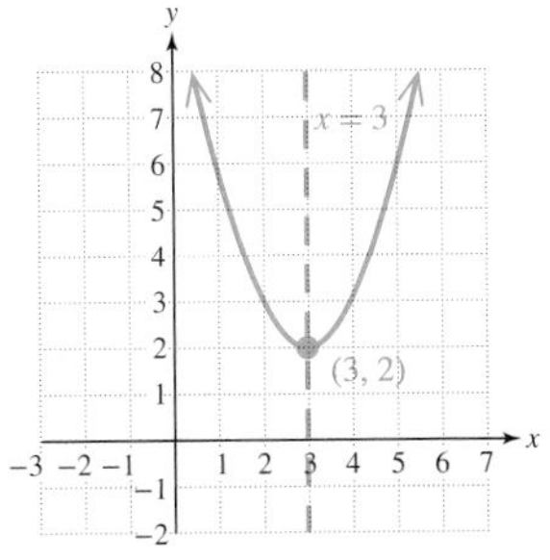

46. $f(x) = (x - 2)^2 + 3$

Domain: $(-\infty, \infty)$; range: $[3, \infty)$

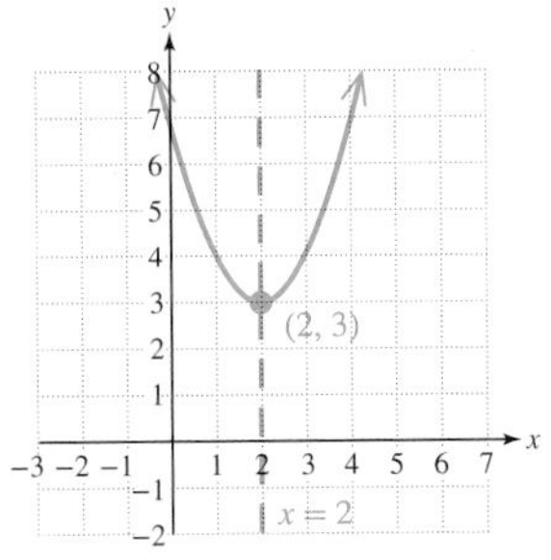

47. $f(x) = (x + 1)^2 - 3$

Domain: $(-\infty, \infty)$; range: $[-3, \infty)$

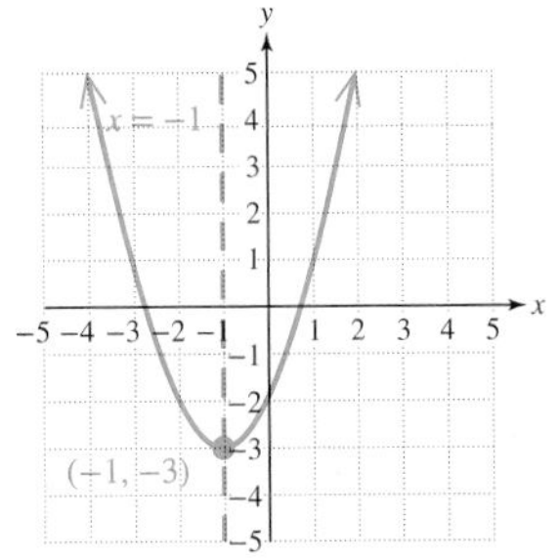

48. $f(x) = (x + 3)^2 - 1$

Domain: $(-\infty, \infty)$; range: $[-1, \infty)$

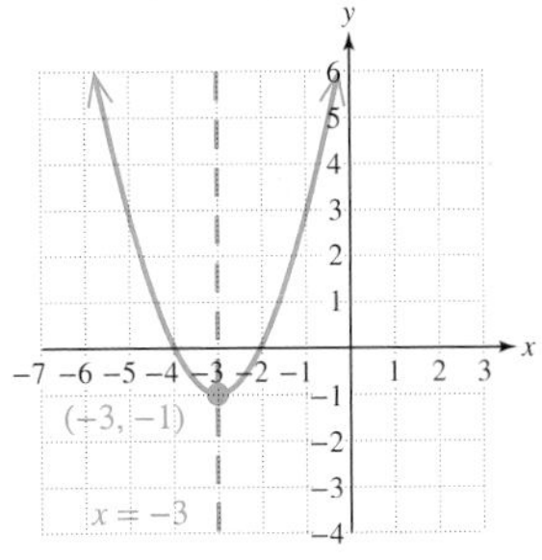

49. $f(x) = -(x-4)^2 - 2$
Domain: $(-\infty, \infty)$; range: $(-\infty, -2]$

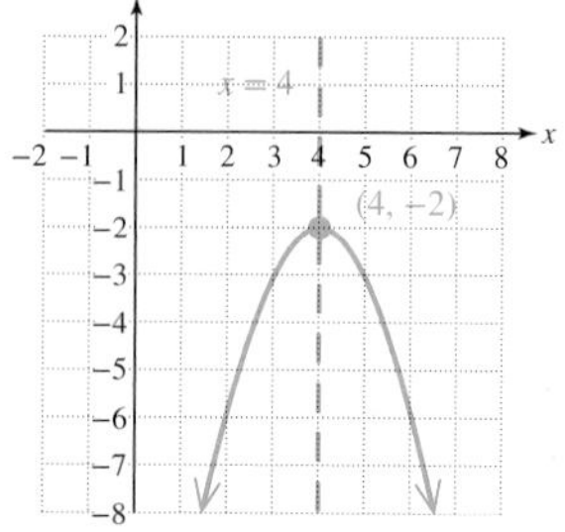

50. $f(x) = -(x-2)^2 - 4$
Domain: $(-\infty, \infty)$; range: $(-\infty, -4]$

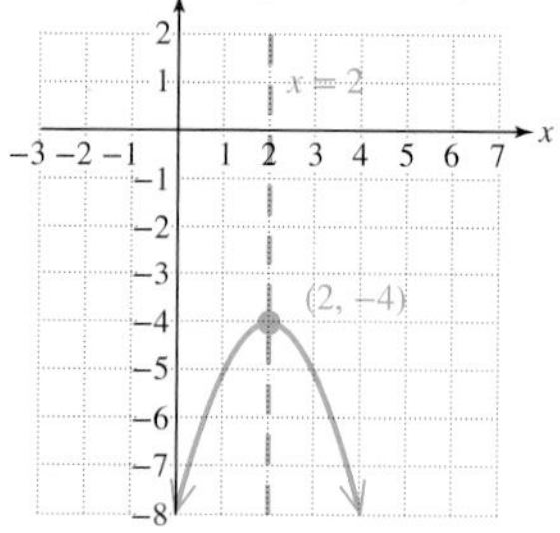

51. $f(x) = -(x+3)^2 + 3$
Domain: $(-\infty, \infty)$; range: $(-\infty, 3]$

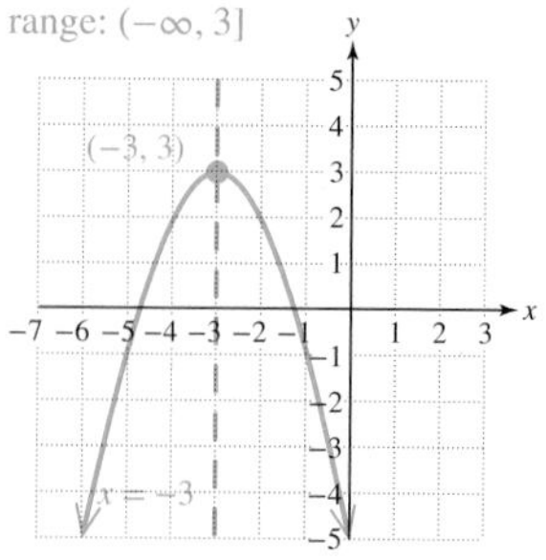

52. $f(x) = -(x+2)^2 + 2$
Domain: $(-\infty, \infty)$; range: $(-\infty, 2]$

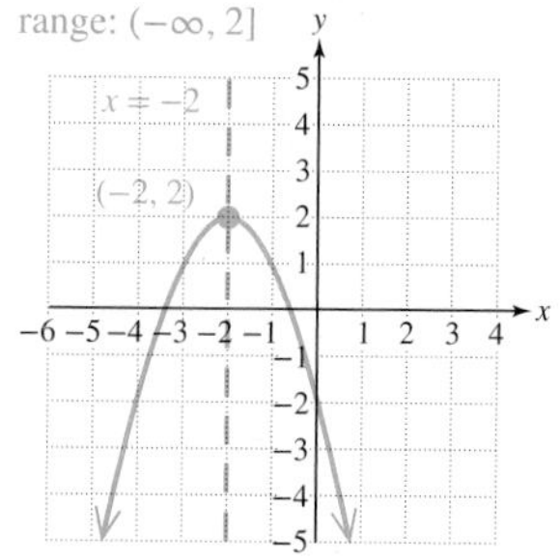

53. $f(x) = (x+1)^2 + 1$
Domain: $(-\infty, \infty)$; range: $[1, \infty)$

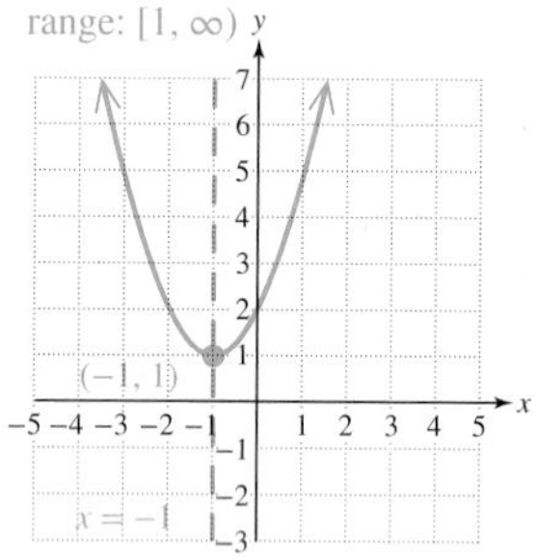

54. $f(x) = (x-4)^2 - 4$
Domain: $(-\infty, \infty)$; range: $[-4, \infty)$

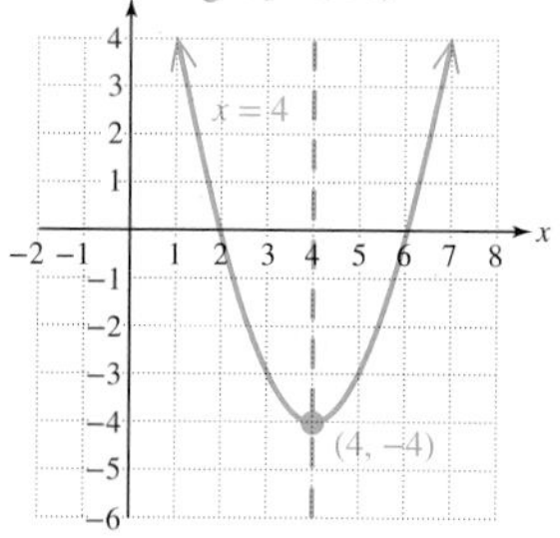

55. $f(x) = 3(x-1)^2$
Domain: $(-\infty, \infty)$; range: $[0, \infty)$

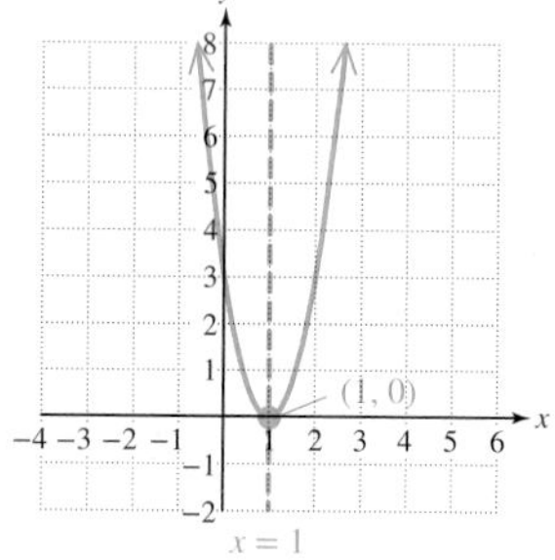

56. $f(x) = -3(x-1)^2$
Domain: $(-\infty, \infty)$; range: $(-\infty, 0]$

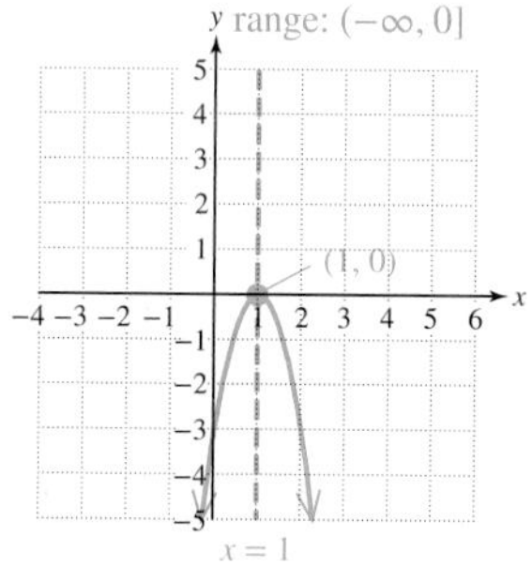

57. $f(x) = -4x^2 + 3$
Domain: $(-\infty, \infty)$; range: $(-\infty, 3]$

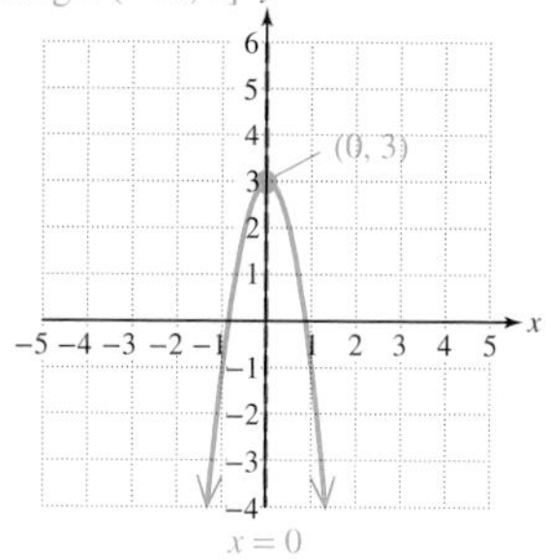

58. $f(x) = 4x^2 + 3$
Domain: $(-\infty, \infty)$; range: $[3, \infty)$

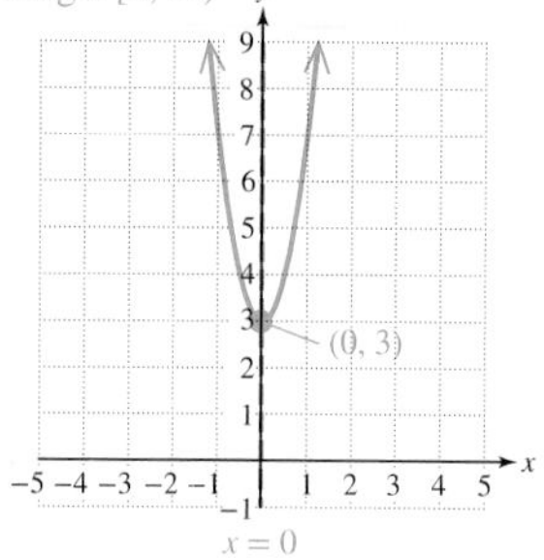

59. $f(x) = 2(x+3)^2 - 1$
Domain: $(-\infty, \infty)$; range: $[-1, \infty)$

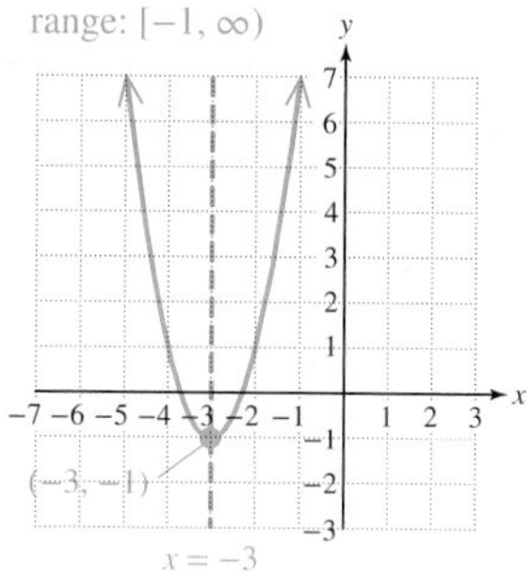

60. $f(x) = -2(x+3)^2 - 1$
Domain: $(-\infty, \infty)$; range: $(-\infty, -1]$

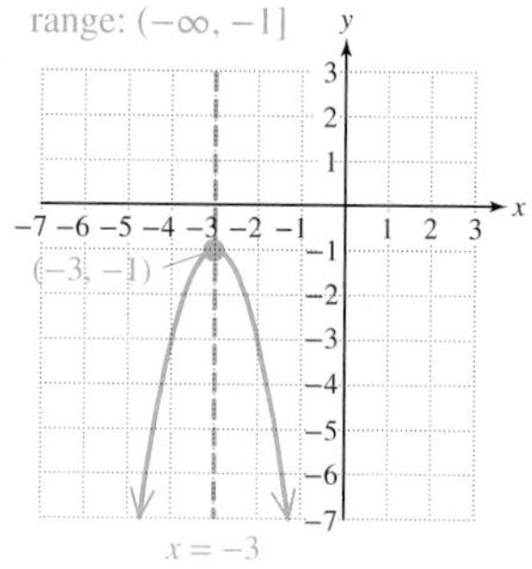

61. $f(x) = -\frac{1}{4}(x-1)^2 + 2$
Domain: $(-\infty, \infty)$; range: $(-\infty, 2]$

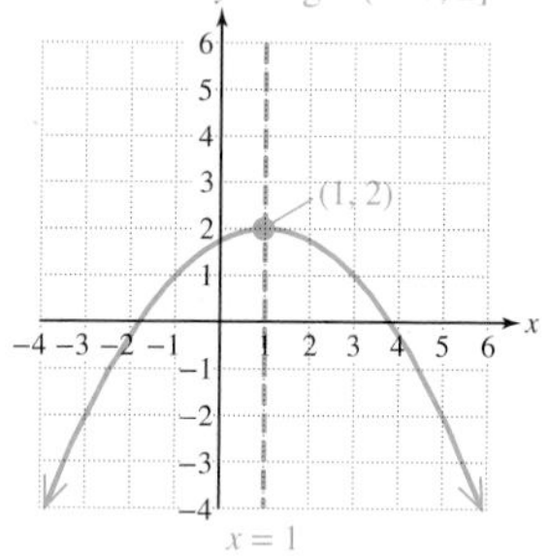

62. $f(x) = \frac{1}{4}(x-1)^2 + 2$
Domain: $(-\infty, \infty)$; range: $[2, \infty)$

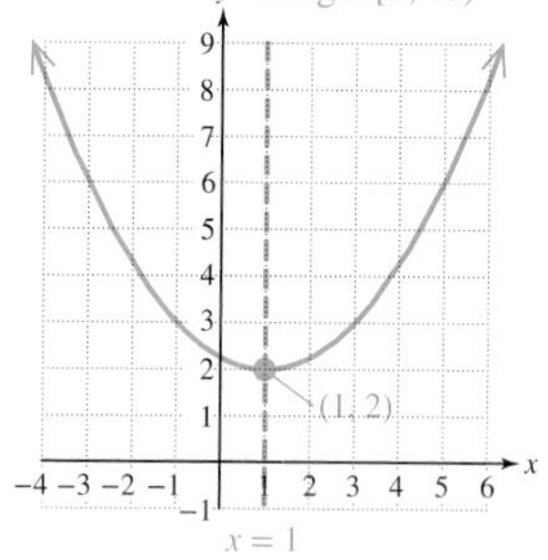

63. $f(x) = \frac{1}{3}(x-2)^2 + 1$
Domain: $(-\infty, \infty)$; range: $[1, \infty)$

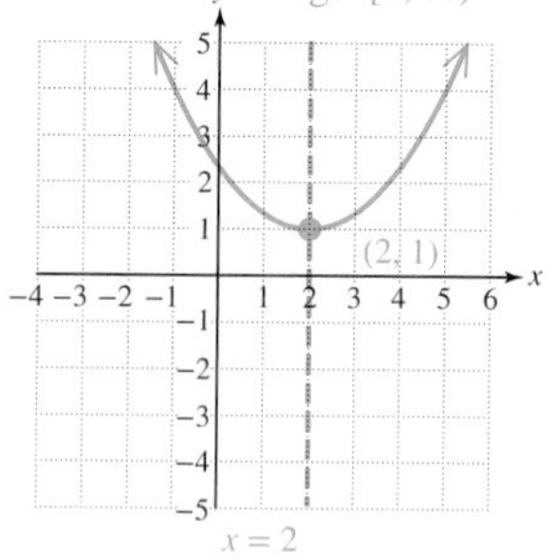

64. $f(x) = -\frac{1}{3}(x-2)^2 + 1$
Domain: $(-\infty, \infty)$; range: $(-\infty, 1]$

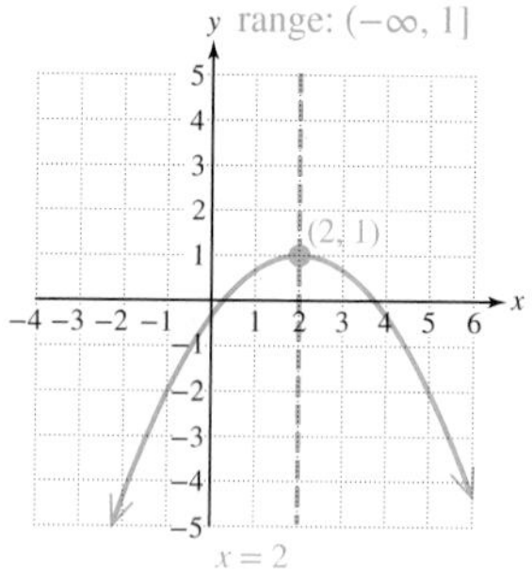

65. Compare the graphs of the following equations to the graph of $y = x^2$.

a. $y = x^2 + 3$
$y = x^2 + 3$ is $y = x^2$ shifted up 3 units.

b. $y = (x+3)^2$
$y = (x+3)^2$ is $y = x^2$ shifted left 3 units.

c. $y = 3x^2$ $y = 3x^2$ is $y = x^2$ with a vertical stretch.

66. Compare the graphs of the following equations to the graph of $y = x^2$.

a. $y = (x-2)^2$
$y = (x-2)^2$ is $y = x^2$ shifted right 2 units.

b. $y = 2x^2$
$y = 2x^2$ is $y = x^2$ with a vertical stretch.

c. $y = x^2 - 2$ $y = x^2 - 2$ is $y = x^2$ shifted down 2 units.

For Exercises 67–78, write the coordinates of the vertex and determine if the vertex is a maximum point or a minimum point. Then write the maximum or minimum value.

67. $f(x) = 4(x - 6)^2 - 9$
Vertex $(6, -9)$; minimum point; minimum value: -9

68. $g(x) = 3(x - 4)^2 - 7$
Vertex $(4, -7)$; minimum point; minimum value: -7

69. $p(x) = -\frac{2}{5}(x - 2)^2 + 5$
Vertex $(2, 5)$; maximum point; maximum value: 5

70. $h(x) = -\frac{3}{7}(x - 5)^2 + 10$
Vertex $(5, 10)$; maximum point; maximum value: 10

71. $k(x) = \frac{1}{2}(x + 8)^2$
Vertex $(-8, 0)$; minimum point; minimum value: 0

72. $m(x) = \frac{2}{9}(x + 11)^2$
Vertex $(-11, 0)$; minimum point; minimum value: 0

73. $n(x) = -6x^2 + \frac{21}{4}$
Vertex $\left(0, \frac{21}{4}\right)$; maximum point; maximum value: $\frac{21}{4}$

74. $q(x) = -4x^2 + \frac{1}{6}$
Vertex $\left(0, \frac{1}{6}\right)$; maximum point; maximum value: $\frac{1}{6}$

75. $A(x) = 2(x - 7)^2 - \frac{3}{2}$
Vertex $\left(7, -\frac{3}{2}\right)$; minimum point; minimum value: $-\frac{3}{2}$

76. $B(x) = 5(x - 3)^2 - \frac{1}{4}$
Vertex $\left(3, -\frac{1}{4}\right)$; minimum point; minimum value: $-\frac{1}{4}$

77. $F(x) = 7x^2$
Vertex $(0, 0)$; minimum point; minimum value: 0

78. $G(x) = -7x^2$
Vertex $(0, 0)$; maximum point; maximum value: 0

79. True or false: The function defined by $g(x) = -5x^2$ has a maximum value but no minimum value. True

80. True or false: The function defined by $f(x) = 2(x - 5)^2$ has a maximum value but no minimum value. False

81. True or false: If the vertex $(-2, 8)$ represents a minimum point, then the minimum value is -2. False

82. True or false: If the vertex $(-2, 8)$ represents a maximum point, then the maximum value is 8. True

Expanding Your Skills

83. A suspension bridge is 120 ft long. Its supporting cable hangs in a shape that resembles a parabola. The function defined by $H(x) = \frac{1}{90}(x - 60)^2 + 30$ (where $0 \le x \le 120$) approximates the height $H(x)$ (in feet) of the supporting cable a distance of x ft from the end of the bridge (see figure).

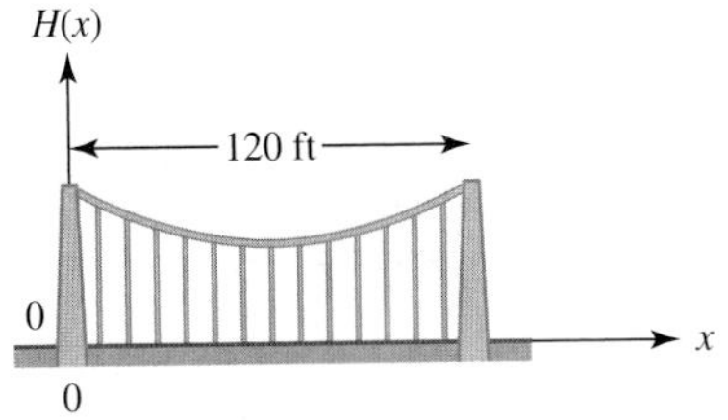

a. What is the location of the vertex of the parabolic cable? (60, 30)

b. What is the minimum height of the cable? 30 ft

c. How high are the towers at either end of the supporting cable? 70 ft

84. A 50-m bridge over a crevasse is supported by a parabolic arch. The function defined by $f(x) = -0.16(x - 25)^2 + 100$ (where $0 \le x \le 50$) approximates the height $f(x)$ (in feet) of the supporting arch x meters from the end of the bridge (see figure).

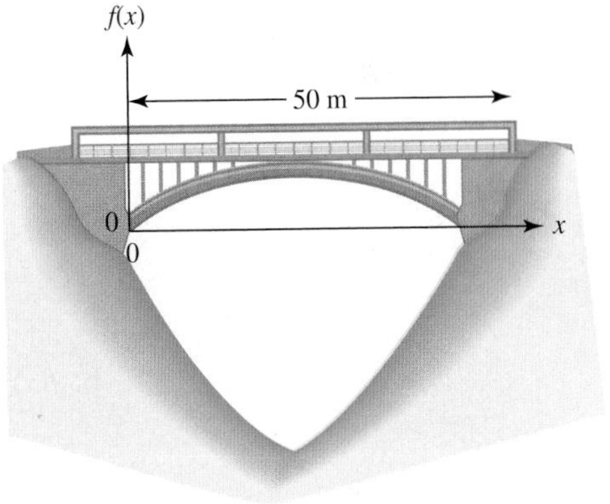

a. What is the location of the vertex of the arch? (25, 100)

b. What is the maximum height of the arch (relative to the origin)? 100 m

85. The staging platform for a fireworks display is 6 ft above ground, and the mortars leave the platform at 96 ft/sec. The height of the mortars $h(t)$ (in feet) can be modeled by $h(t) = -16(t - 3)^2 + 150$, where t is the time in seconds after launch.

a. If the fuses are set for 3 sec after launch, at what height will the fireworks explode?
The fireworks will explode at a height of 150 ft.

b. Will the fireworks explode at their maximum height? Explain.
Yes, because the ordered pair (3, 150) is the vertex.

Section 11.5 Vertex of a Parabola: Applications and Modeling

Concepts

1. Writing a Quadratic Function in the Form $f(x) = a(x - h)^2 + k$
2. Vertex Formula
3. Determining the Vertex and Intercepts of a Quadratic Function
4. Applications and Modeling of Quadratic Functions

Classroom Example: p. 831, Exercise 18

1. Writing a Quadratic Function in the Form $f(x) = a(x - h)^2 + k$

The graph of a quadratic function is a parabola, and if the function is written in the form $f(x) = a(x - h)^2 + k$ $(a \neq 0)$, then the vertex is (h, k). A quadratic function can be written in the form $f(x) = a(x - h)^2 + k$ $(a \neq 0)$ by completing the square. The process is similar to the steps to solve a quadratic equation by completing the square. However, in this context working with a function, we will perform all algebraic manipulations on the right side of the equation.

Example 1 Writing a Quadratic Function in the Form $f(x) = a(x - h)^2 + k \quad (a \neq 0)$

Given $f(x) = x^2 + 8x + 13$

a. Write the function in the form $f(x) = a(x - h)^2 + k$.

b. Identify the vertex, axis of symmetry, and minimum function value.

Solution:

a. $f(x) = x^2 + 8x + 13$

$= 1(x^2 + 8x) + 13$ Rather than dividing by the leading coefficient on both sides, we will factor out the leading coefficient from the variable terms on the right-hand side.

$= 1(x^2 + 8x \quad) + 13$ Next, complete the square on the expression within the parentheses: $\left[\frac{1}{2}(8)\right]^2 = 16$.

Avoiding Mistakes

Do not factor out the leading coefficient from the constant term.

$= 1(x^2 + 8x + 16 - 16) + 13$ Rather than add 16 to both sides of the function, we *add and subtract* 16 within the parentheses on the right-hand side. This has the effect of adding 0 to the right-hand side.

$= 1(x^2 + 8x + 16) - 16 + 13$ Use the associative property of addition to regroup terms and isolate the perfect square trinomial within the parentheses.

$= (x + 4)^2 - 3$ Factor and simplify.

b. $f(x) = (x + 4)^2 - 3$

The vertex is $(-4, -3)$.

The axis of symmetry is $x = -4$.

Because $a > 0$, the parabola opens upward.

The minimum value is -3 (Figure 11-15).

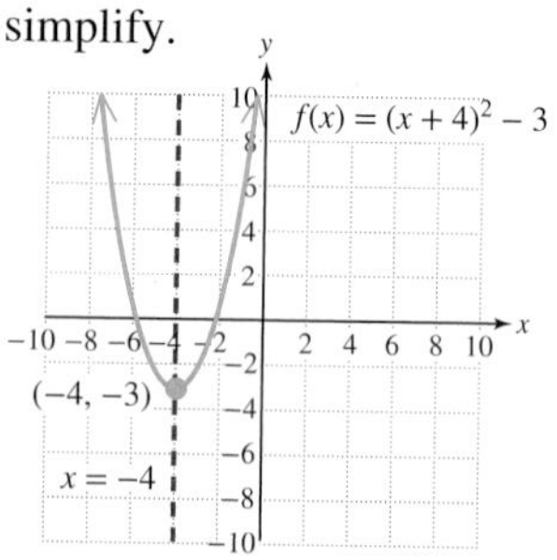

Figure 11-15

Skill Practice

1. Given: $f(x) = x^2 + 8x - 1$
   a. Write the function in the form $f(x) = a(x - h)^2 + k$.
   b. Identify the vertex, axis of symmetry, and minimum value of the function.

Answers

1. **a.** $f(x) = (x + 4)^2 - 17$
   b. Vertex: $(-4, -17)$; axis of symmetry: $x = -4$; minimum value: -17

Example 2 Analyzing a Quadratic Function

Given $f(x) = -2x^2 + 12x - 16$

a. Write the function in the form $f(x) = a(x - h)^2 + k$.

b. Find the vertex, axis of symmetry, and maximum function value.

c. Find the x- and y-intercepts.

d. Sketch the graph of the function.

Classroom Example: p. 831, Exercise 22

Solution:

a. $f(x) = -2x^2 + 12x - 16$ — To find the vertex, write the function in the form $f(x) = a(x - h)^2 + k$.

$= -2(x^2 - 6x \quad) - 16$ — If the leading coefficient is not 1, factor the coefficient from the variable terms.

$= -2(x^2 - 6x + 9 - 9) - 16$ — Add and subtract the quantity $[\frac{1}{2}(-6)]^2 = 9$ within the parentheses.

$= -2(x^2 - 6x + 9) + (-2)(-9) - 16$ — To remove the term -9 from the parentheses, we must first apply the distributive property. When -9 is removed from the parentheses, it carries with it a factor of -2.

$= -2(x - 3)^2 + 18 - 16$ — Factor and simplify.

$= -2(x - 3)^2 + 2$

b. $f(x) = -2(x - 3)^2 + 2$

The vertex is (3, 2). The axis of symmetry is $x = 3$. Because $a < 0$, the parabola opens downward and the maximum value is 2.

c. The y-intercept is given by $f(0) = -2(0)^2 + 12(0) - 16 = -16$.

The y-intercept is $(0, -16)$.

To find the x-intercept(s), find the real solutions to the equation $f(x) = 0$.

TIP: In Example 2(c), we could have used the form of the equation found in part (a) to find the intercepts.

$f(x) = -2x^2 + 12x - 16$

$0 = -2x^2 + 12x - 16$ — Substitute $f(x) = 0$.

$0 = -2(x^2 - 6x + 8)$ — Factor.

$0 = -2(x - 4)(x - 2)$

$x = 4 \quad \text{or} \quad x = 2$

The x-intercepts are (4, 0) and (2, 0).

d. Using the information from parts (a)–(c), sketch the graph (Figure 11-16).

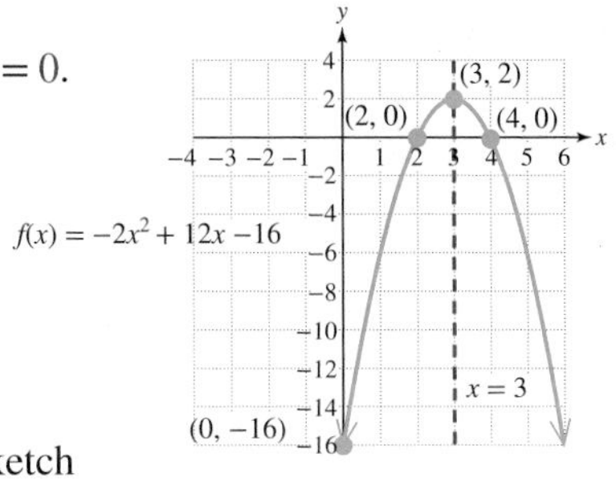

Figure 11-16

Instructor Note: Show students that when a quadratic function has two x-intercepts, the x-coordinate of the vertex is located halfway between the two x-intercepts.

Skill Practice

2. Given $g(x) = -x^2 + 6x - 5$
   a. Write the function in the form $g(x) = a(x - h)^2 + k$.
   b. Identify the vertex, axis of symmetry, and maximum value of the function.
   c. Determine the x- and y-intercepts.
   d. Graph the function.

2. Vertex Formula

Completing the square and writing a quadratic function in the form $f(x) = a(x - h)^2 + k$ $(a \neq 0)$ is one method to find the vertex of a parabola. Another method is to use the vertex formula. The **vertex formula** can be derived by completing the square on $f(x) = ax^2 + bx + c$ $(a \neq 0)$.

$$f(x) = ax^2 + bx + c \quad (a \neq 0)$$

$$= a\left(x^2 + \frac{b}{a}x \qquad\qquad \right) + c$$
Factor a from the variable terms.

$$= a\left(x^2 + \frac{b}{a}x + \frac{b^2}{4a^2} - \frac{b^2}{4a^2}\right) + c$$
Add and subtract $\left[\frac{1}{2}(b/a)\right]^2 = b^2/(4a^2)$ within the parentheses.

$$= a\left(x^2 + \frac{b}{a}x + \frac{b^2}{4a^2}\right) + (a)\left(-\frac{b^2}{4a^2}\right) + c$$
Apply the distributive property and remove the term $-b^2/(4a^2)$ from the parentheses.

$$= a\left(x + \frac{b}{2a}\right)^2 - \frac{b^2}{4a} + c$$
Factor the trinomial and simplify.

$$= a\left(x + \frac{b}{2a}\right)^2 + c - \frac{b^2}{4a}$$
Apply the commutative property of addition to reverse the last two terms.

$$= a\left(x + \frac{b}{2a}\right)^2 + \frac{4ac}{4a} - \frac{b^2}{4a}$$
Obtain a common denominator.

$$= a\left(x + \frac{b}{2a}\right)^2 + \frac{4ac - b^2}{4a}$$

$$= a\left[x - \left(-\frac{b}{2a}\right)\right]^2 + \frac{4ac - b^2}{4a}$$

$$f(x) = a(x \quad - \quad h)^2 \quad + \quad k$$

The function is in the form $f(x) = a(x - h)^2 + k$, where

$$h = \frac{-b}{2a} \quad \text{and} \quad k = \frac{4ac - b^2}{4a}$$

Therefore, the vertex is $\left(\dfrac{-b}{2a}, \dfrac{4ac - b^2}{4a}\right)$.

Although the y-coordinate of the vertex is given by $\dfrac{4ac - b^2}{4a}$, it is usually easier to determine the x-coordinate of the vertex first and then find y by evaluating the function at $x = -b/(2a)$.

Instructor Note: It can be interesting to let students know that calculus also provides a technique to find the vertex of the parabola.

Answers

2. a. $g(x) = -(x - 3)^2 + 4$
   b. Vertex: (3, 4); axis of symmetry: $x = 3$; maximum value: 4
   c. x-intercepts: (5, 0) and (1, 0); y-intercept: (0, −5)
   d.

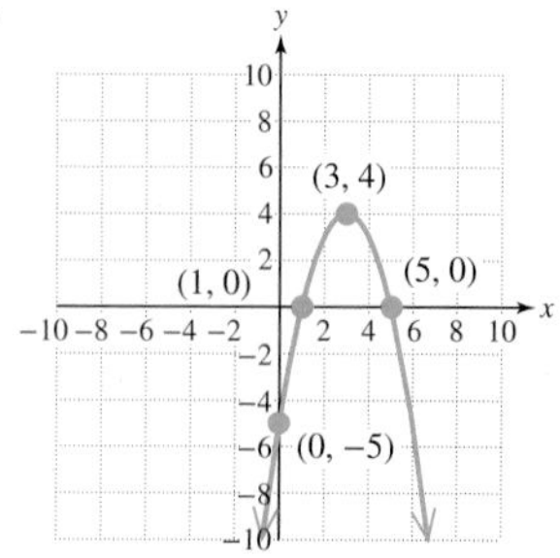

The Vertex Formula

For $f(x) = ax^2 + bx + c$ $(a \neq 0)$, the vertex is given by

$$\left(\frac{-b}{2a}, \frac{4ac - b^2}{4a}\right) \quad \text{or} \quad \left(\frac{-b}{2a}, f\left(\frac{-b}{2a}\right)\right)$$

3. Determining the Vertex and Intercepts of a Quadratic Function

Example 3 Determining the Vertex and Intercepts of a Quadratic Function

Classroom Example: p. 832, Exercise 46

Given: $h(x) = x^2 - 2x + 5$

a. Use the vertex formula to find the vertex.

b. Find the x- and y-intercepts.

c. Sketch the function.

Solution:

a. $h(x) = x^2 - 2x + 5$

$a = 1 \quad b = -2 \quad c = 5$ Identify a, b, and c.

The x-coordinate of the vertex is $\dfrac{-b}{2a} = \dfrac{-(-2)}{2(1)} = 1$.

The y-coordinate of the vertex is $h(1) = (1)^2 - 2(1) + 5 = 4$.

The vertex is $(1, 4)$.

b. The y-intercept is given by $h(0) = (0)^2 - 2(0) + 5 = 5$.

The y-intercept is $(0, 5)$.

To find the x-intercept(s), find the real solutions to the equation $h(x) = 0$.

$h(x) = x^2 - 2x + 5$

$0 = x^2 - 2x + 5$ This quadratic equation is not factorable. Apply the quadratic formula: $a = 1$, $b = -2$, $c = 5$

$$x = \frac{-(-2) \pm \sqrt{(-2)^2 - 4(1)(5)}}{2(1)}$$

$$= \frac{2 \pm \sqrt{4 - 20}}{2(1)}$$

$$= \frac{2 \pm \sqrt{-16}}{2}$$

$$= \frac{2 \pm 4i}{2}$$

$$= 1 \pm 2i$$

The solutions to the equation $h(x) = 0$ are not real numbers. Therefore, there are no x-intercepts.

c.

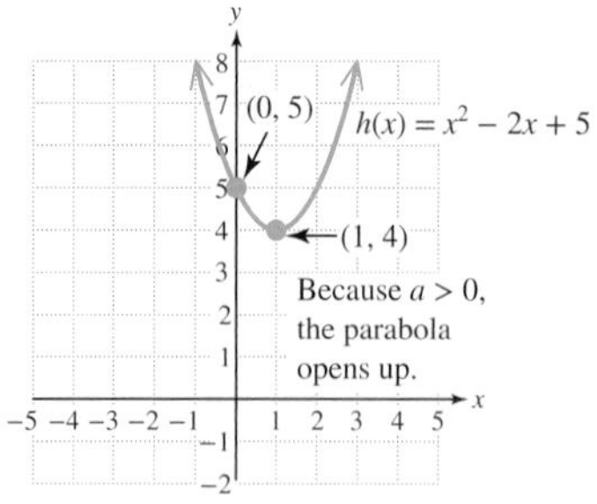

Figure 11-17

> **TIP:** The location of the vertex and the direction that the parabola opens can be used to determine whether the function has any *x*-intercepts.
> Given $h(x) = x^2 - 2x + 5$, the vertex (1, 4) is above the *x*-axis. Furthermore, because $a > 0$, the parabola opens upward. Therefore, it is not possible for the graph to cross the *x*-axis (Figure 11-17).

Skill Practice

3. Given: $f(x) = x^2 + 4x + 6$

a. Use the vertex formula to find the vertex of the parabola.

b. Determine the *x*- and *y*-intercepts.

c. Sketch the graph.

4. Applications and Modeling of Quadratic Functions

Classroom Example: p. 832, Exercise 54

Example 4 Applying a Quadratic Function

The crew from Extravaganza Entertainment launches fireworks at an angle of 60° from the horizontal. The height of one particular type of display can be approximated by

$$h(t) = -16t^2 + 128\sqrt{3}t$$

where $h(t)$ is measured in feet and t is measured in seconds.

a. How long will it take the fireworks to reach their maximum height? Round to the nearest second.

b. Find the maximum height. Round to the nearest foot.

© Royalty Free/Corbis RF

Solution:

$h(t) = -16t^2 + 128\sqrt{3}t$ — This parabola opens downward; therefore, the maximum height of the fireworks will occur at the vertex of the parabola.

$a = -16 \quad b = 128\sqrt{3} \quad c = 0$ — Identify *a*, *b*, and *c*, and apply the vertex formula.

The *x*-coordinate of the vertex is

$$\frac{-b}{2a} = \frac{-128\sqrt{3}}{2(-16)} = \frac{-128\sqrt{3}}{-32} \approx 6.9$$

Answers

3. a. Vertex: (−2, 2)

b. *x*-intercepts: none; *y*-intercept: (0, 6)

c.

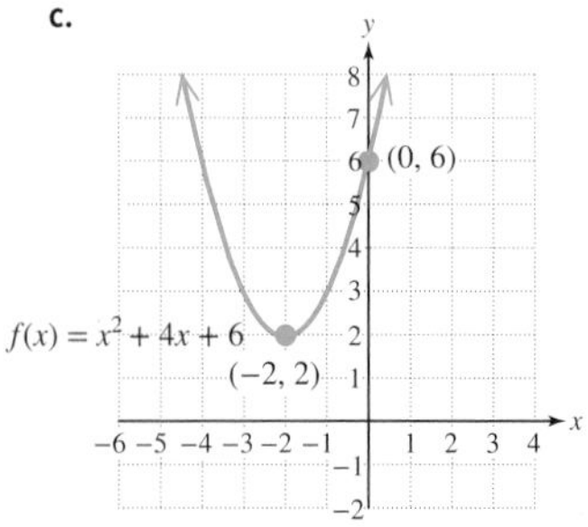

The y-coordinate of the vertex is approximately

$$h(6.9) = -16(6.9)^2 + 128\sqrt{3}(6.9) \approx 768$$

The vertex is (6.9, 768).

a. The fireworks will reach their maximum height in 6.9 sec.

b. The maximum height is 768 ft.

Skill Practice

4. An object is launched into the air with an initial velocity of 48 ft/sec from the top of a building 288 ft high. The height $h(t)$ of the object after t seconds is given by

$$h(t) = -16t^2 + 48t + 288$$

a. Find the time it takes for the object to reach its maximum height.

b. Find the maximum height.

In Example 5 we will learn how to write a quadratic model of a parabola given three points by using a system of equations and the standard form of a parabola: $y = ax^2 + bx + c$.

This process involves substituting the x- and y-coordinates of the three given points into the quadratic model. Then we solve the resulting system of three equations.

Example 5 Writing a Quadratic Model

Classroom Example: p. 833, Exercise 60

Write an equation of a parabola that passes through the points $(1, -1)$, $(-1, -5)$, and $(2, 4)$.

Solution:

Substitute $(1, -1)$ into the equation

$y = ax^2 + bx + c \longrightarrow$ $(-1) = a(1)^2 + b(1) + c$

$-1 = a + b + c$

$a + b + c = -1$

Substitute $(-1, -5)$ into the equation

$y = ax^2 + bx + c \longrightarrow$ $(-5) = a(-1)^2 + b(-1) + c$

$-5 = a - b + c$

$a - b + c = -5$

Substitute $(2, 4)$ into the equation

$y = ax^2 + bx + c \longrightarrow$ $(4) = a(2)^2 + b(2) + c$

$4 = 4a + 2b + c$

$4a + 2b + c = 4$

Solve the system:

$\boxed{A}$ $a + b + c = -1$

$\boxed{B}$ $a - b + c = -5$

$\boxed{C}$ $4a + 2b + c = 4$

Answers

4. a. 1.5 sec **b.** 324 ft

Notice that the c variables all have a coefficient of 1. Therefore, we choose to eliminate the c variable.

$$\boxed{A}\quad a + b + c = -1 \longrightarrow \quad a + b + c = -1$$
$$\boxed{B}\quad a - b + c = -5 \xrightarrow{\text{Multiply by } -1.} \quad -a + b - c = 5$$
$$2b = 4$$
$$b = 2 \quad \boxed{D}$$

$$\boxed{B}\quad a - b + c = -5 \longrightarrow \quad a - b + c = -5$$
$$\boxed{C}\quad 4a + 2b + c = 4 \xrightarrow{\text{Multiply by } -1.} \quad -4a - 2b - c = -4$$
$$-3a - 3b = -9 \quad \boxed{E}$$

Substitute b with 2 in equation $\boxed{E}$: $-3a - 3(2) = -9$

$$-3a - 6 = -9$$
$$-3a = -3$$
$$a = 1$$

Substitute a and b in equation $\boxed{A}$ to solve for c: $(1) + (2) + c = -1$

$$3 + c = -1$$
$$c = -4$$

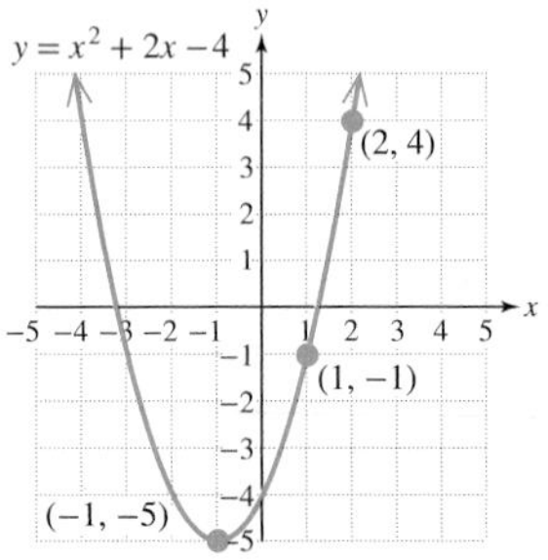

Figure 11-18

Substitute $a = 1$, $b = 2$, and $c = -4$ in the standard form of the parabola for the final answer.

$$y = ax^2 + bx + c$$
$$y = (1)x^2 + (2)x + (-4) \longrightarrow y = x^2 + 2x - 4$$

A graph of $y = x^2 + 2x - 4$ is shown in Figure 11-18. Notice that the graph of the function passes through the points $(1, -1)$, $(-1, -5)$, and $(2, 4)$.

Skill Practice

5. Write an equation of the parabola that passes through the points $(1, 1)$, $(-2, 1)$, and $(3, -9)$.

Answer

5. $a = -1$, $b = -1$, $c = 3$; $y = -x^2 - x + 3$

Section 11.5 Practice Exercises

For additional exercises, see Classroom Activities 11.5A–11.5C in the *Student's Resource Manual* at www.mhhe.com/moh.

Vocabulary and Key Concepts

1. **a.** Given $f(x) = ax^2 + bx + c$ $(a \neq 0)$, the vertex formula gives the x-coordinate of the vertex as ______. The y-coordinate can be found by evaluating the function at $x =$ ______. $\frac{-b}{2a}$; $\frac{-b}{2a}$

   b. Answer true or false. A parabola may have no x-intercepts. True

   c. Answer true or false. A parabola may have one x-intercept. True

   d. Answer true or false. A parabola may have two x-intercepts. True

   e. Answer true or false. A parabola may have three x-intercepts. False

Review Exercises

2. How does the graph of $f(x) = -2x^2$ compare with the graph of $y = x^2$?

   The graph of f is the graph of $y = x^2$ but opening downward and stretched vertically by a factor of 2.

3. How does the graph of $p(x) = \frac{1}{4}x^2$ compare with the graph of $y = x^2$?

   The graph of p is the graph of $y = x^2$ shrunk vertically by a factor of $\frac{1}{4}$.

4. How does the graph of $Q(x) = x^2 - \frac{8}{3}$ compare with the graph of $y = x^2$?

   The graph of Q is the graph of $y = x^2$ shifted down $\frac{8}{3}$ units.

5. How does the graph of $r(x) = x^2 + 7$ compare with the graph of $y = x^2$?
The graph of r is the graph of $y = x^2$ shifted up 7 units.

6. How does the graph of $s(x) = (x - 4)^2$ compare with the graph of $y = x^2$?
The graph of s is the graph of $y = x^2$ shifted to the right 4 units.

7. How does the graph of $t(x) = (x + 10)^2$ compare with the graph of $y = x^2$?
The graph of t is the graph of $y = x^2$ shifted to the left 10 units.

8. Find the coordinates of the vertex of the parabola defined by $g(x) = 2(x + 3)^2 - 4$. $(-3, -4)$

For Exercises 9–16, find the value of n to complete the square. Factor the resulting trinomial.

9. $x^2 - 8x + n$ $16; (x - 4)^2$

10. $x^2 + 4x + n$ $4; (x + 2)^2$

11. $y^2 + 7y + n$ $\frac{49}{4}; \left(y + \frac{7}{2}\right)^2$

12. $a^2 - a + n$ $\frac{1}{4}; \left(a - \frac{1}{2}\right)^2$

13. $b^2 + \frac{2}{9}b + n$ $\frac{1}{81}; \left(b + \frac{1}{9}\right)^2$

14. $m^2 - \frac{2}{7}m + n$ $\frac{1}{49}; \left(m - \frac{1}{7}\right)^2$

15. $t^2 - \frac{1}{3}t + n$ $\frac{1}{36}; \left(t - \frac{1}{6}\right)^2$

16. $p^2 + \frac{1}{4}p + n$ $\frac{1}{64}; \left(p + \frac{1}{8}\right)^2$

Concept 1: Writing a Quadratic Function in the Form $f(x) = a(x - h)^2 + k$

For Exercises 17–28, write the function in the form $f(x) = a(x - h)^2 + k$ by completing the square. Then identify the vertex. **(See Examples 1–2.)**

17. $g(x) = x^2 - 8x + 5$ $g(x) = (x - 4)^2 - 11; (4, -11)$

18. $h(x) = x^2 + 4x + 5$ $h(x) = (x + 2)^2 + 1; (-2, 1)$

19. $n(x) = 2x^2 + 12x + 13$ $n(x) = 2(x + 3)^2 - 5; (-3, -5)$

20. $f(x) = 4x^2 + 16x + 19$ $f(x) = 4(x + 2)^2 + 3; (-2, 3)$

21. $p(x) = -3x^2 + 6x - 5$ $p(x) = -3(x - 1)^2 - 2; (1, -2)$

22. $q(x) = -2x^2 + 12x - 11$ $q(x) = -2(x - 3)^2 + 7; (3, 7)$

23. $k(x) = x^2 + 7x - 10$ $k(x) = \left(x + \frac{7}{2}\right)^2 - \frac{89}{4}; \left(-\frac{7}{2}, -\frac{89}{4}\right)$

24. $m(x) = x^2 - x - 8$ $m(x) = \left(x - \frac{1}{2}\right)^2 - \frac{33}{4}; \left(\frac{1}{2}, -\frac{33}{4}\right)$

25. $F(x) = 5x^2 + 10x + 1$ $F(x) = 5(x + 1)^2 - 4; (-1, -4)$

26. $G(x) = 4x^2 + 4x - 7$ $G(x) = 4\left(x + \frac{1}{2}\right)^2 - 8; \left(-\frac{1}{2}, -8\right)$

27. $P(x) = -2x^2 + x$ $P(x) = -2\left(x - \frac{1}{4}\right)^2 + \frac{1}{8}; \left(\frac{1}{4}, \frac{1}{8}\right)$

28. $Q(x) = -3x^2 + 12x$ $Q(x) = -3(x - 2)^2 + 12; (2, 12)$

Concept 2: Vertex Formula

For Exercises 29–40, find the vertex by using the vertex formula. **(See Example 3.)**

29. $Q(x) = x^2 - 4x + 7$ $(2, 3)$

30. $T(x) = x^2 - 8x + 17$ $(4, 1)$

31. $r(x) = -3x^2 - 6x - 5$ $(-1, -2)$

32. $s(x) = -2x^2 - 12x - 19$ $(-3, -1)$

33. $N(x) = x^2 + 8x + 1$ $(-4, -15)$

34. $M(x) = x^2 + 6x - 5$ $(-3, -14)$

35. $m(x) = \frac{1}{2}x^2 + x + \frac{5}{2}$ $(-1, 2)$

36. $n(x) = \frac{1}{2}x^2 + 2x + 3$ $(-2, 1)$

37. $k(x) = -x^2 + 2x + 2$ $(1, 3)$

38. $h(x) = -x^2 + 4x - 3$ $(2, 1)$

39. $A(x) = -\frac{1}{3}x^2 + x$ $\left(\frac{3}{2}, \frac{3}{4}\right)$

40. $B(x) = -\frac{2}{3}x^2 - 2x$ $\left(-\frac{3}{2}, \frac{3}{2}\right)$

For Exercises 41–44, find the vertex two ways:

a. by completing the square and writing in the form $f(x) = a(x - h)^2 + k$.

b. by using the vertex formula.

41. $p(x) = x^2 + 8x + 1$ $(-4, -15)$

42. $F(x) = x^2 + 4x - 2$ $(-2, -6)$

43. $f(x) = 2x^2 + 4x + 6$ $(-1, 4)$

44. $g(x) = 3x^2 + 12x + 9$ $(-2, -3)$

Concept 3: Determining the Vertex and Intercepts of a Quadratic Function

For Exercises 45–52

a. Find the vertex.

b. Find the y-intercept.

c. Find the x-intercept(s), if they exist.

d. Use this information to graph the function. **(See Examples 2–3.)**

45. $f(x) = x^2 + 2x - 3$
a. $(-1, -4)$ b. $(0, -3)$
c. $(1, 0), (-3, 0)$
d.

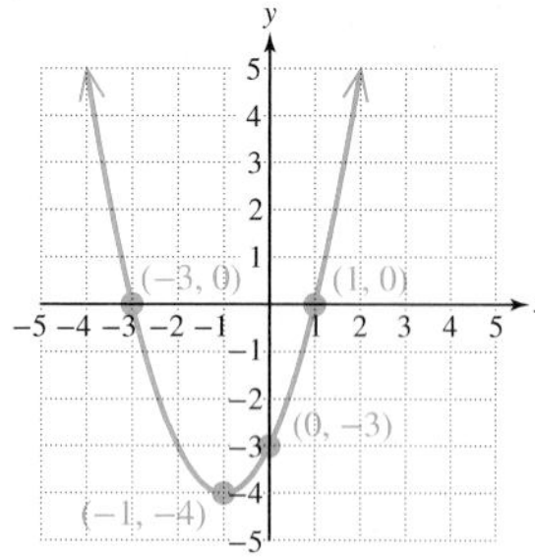

46. $f(x) = x^2 + 4x + 3$
a. $(-2, -1)$ b. $(0, 3)$
c. $(-1, 0), (-3, 0)$
d.

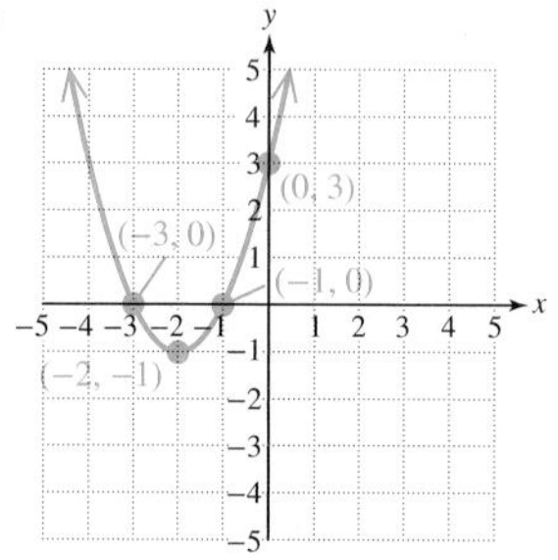

47. $f(x) = 2x^2 - 2x + 4$
a. $\left(\frac{1}{2}, \frac{7}{2}\right)$ b. $(0, 4)$
c. No x-intercepts
d.

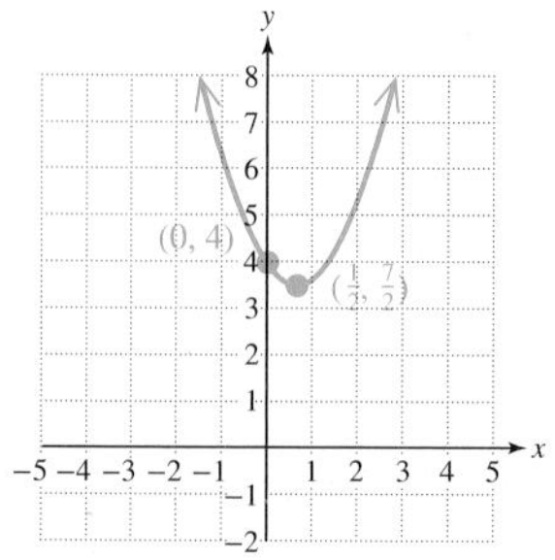

48. $f(x) = 2x^2 - 12x + 19$
a. $(3, 1)$ b. $(0, 19)$
c. No x-intercepts
d.

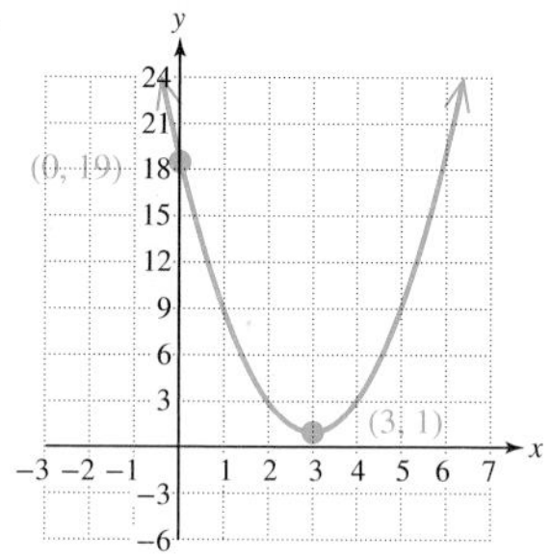

49. $f(x) = -x^2 + 3x - \dfrac{9}{4}$
a. $\left(\frac{3}{2}, 0\right)$ b. $\left(0, -\frac{9}{4}\right)$ c. $\left(\frac{3}{2}, 0\right)$
d.

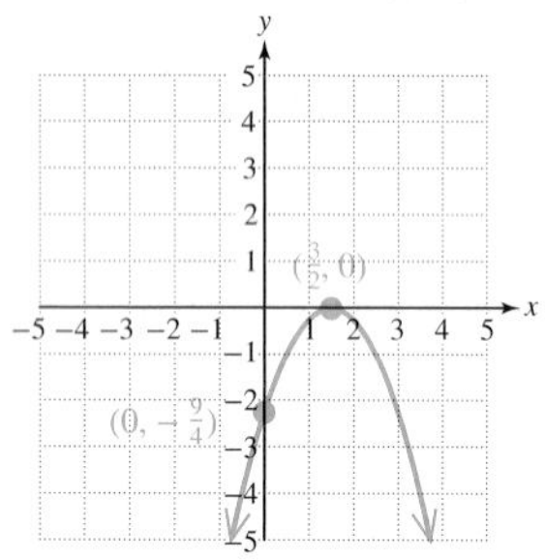

50. $f(x) = -x^2 - \dfrac{3}{2}x - \dfrac{9}{16}$
a. $\left(-\frac{3}{4}, 0\right)$ b. $\left(0, -\frac{9}{16}\right)$ c. $\left(-\frac{3}{4}, 0\right)$
d.

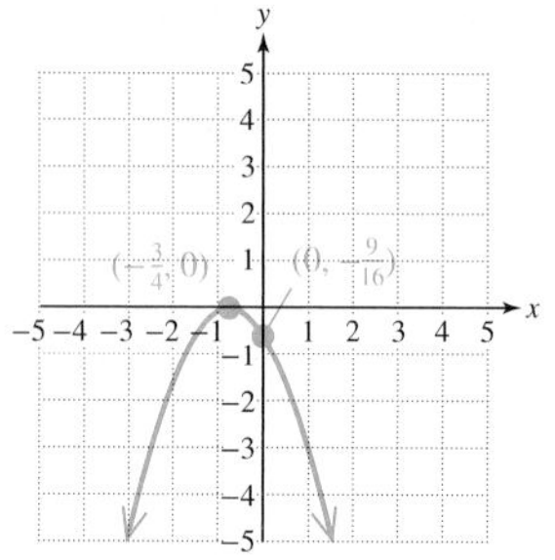

51. $f(x) = -x^2 - 2x + 3$
a. $(-1, 4)$ b. $(0, 3)$
c. $(1, 0), (-3, 0)$
d.

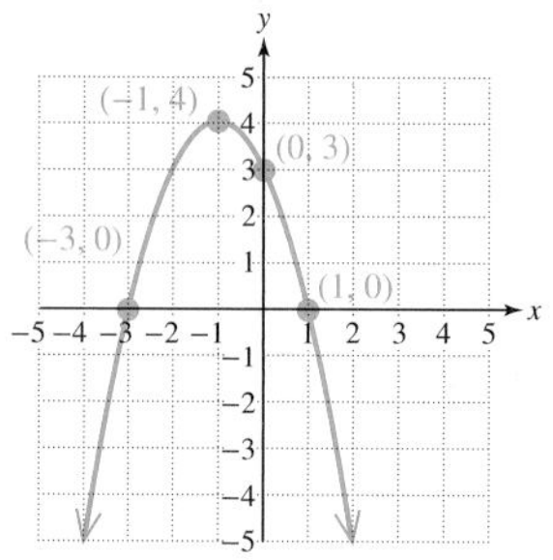

52. $f(x) = -x^2 - 4x$
a. $(-2, 4)$ b. $(0, 0)$
c. $(0, 0), (-4, 0)$
d.

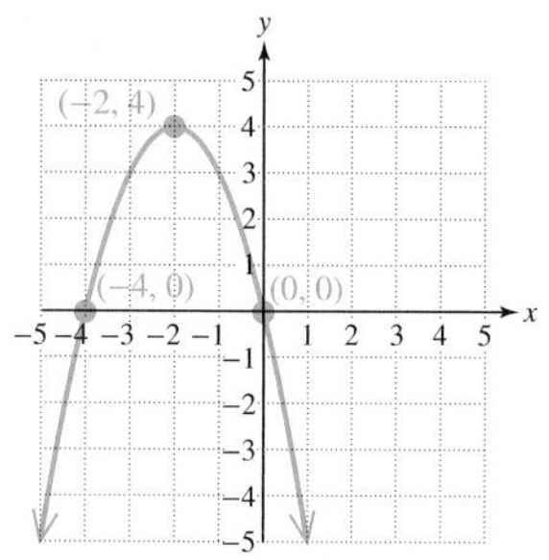

Concept 4: Applications and Modeling of Quadratic Functions

53. A set of fireworks mortar shells is launched from the staging platform at 100 ft/sec from an initial height of 8 ft above the ground. The height of the fireworks, $h(t)$, can be modeled by

$$h(t) = -16t^2 + 100t + 8,\ \text{where } t \text{ is the time in seconds after launch.}$$ **(See Example 4.)**

a. What is the maximum height that the shells can reach before exploding? 164.25 ft

b. For how many seconds after launch would the fuses need to be set so that the mortar shells would in fact explode at the maximum height? 3.125 sec

54. A baseball player throws a ball, and the height of the ball (in feet) can be approximated by

$$y(x) = -0.011x^2 + 0.577x + 5$$

where x is the horizontal position of the ball measured in feet from the origin.

a. For what value of x will the ball reach its highest point? Round to the nearest foot. 26 ft

b. What is the maximum height of the ball? Round to the nearest tenth of a foot. 12.6 ft

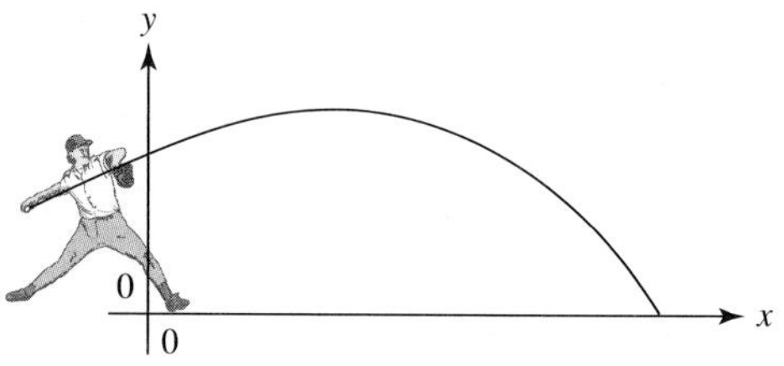

55. Gas mileage depends in part on the speed of the car. The gas mileage of a subcompact car is given by $m(x) = -0.04x^2 + 3.6x - 49$, where $20 \le x \le 70$ represents the speed in miles per hour and $m(x)$ is given in miles per gallon.

a. At what speed will the car get the maximum gas mileage? 45 mph

b. What is the maximum gas mileage? 32 mpg

56. Gas mileage depends in part on the speed of the car. The gas mileage of a luxury car is given by $L(x) = -0.015x^2 + 1.44x - 21$, where $25 \le x \le 70$ represents the speed in miles per hour and $L(x)$ is given in miles per gallon.

a. At what speed will the car get the maximum gas mileage? 48 mph

b. What is the maximum gas mileage? Round to the nearest whole unit. 14 mpg

57. The *Clostridium tetani* bacterium is cultured to produce tetanus toxin used in an inactive form for the tetanus vaccine. The amount of toxin produced per batch increases with time and then becomes unstable. The amount of toxin $b(t)$ (in grams) as a function of time t (in hours) can be approximated by:

$$b(t) = -\frac{1}{1152}t^2 + \frac{1}{12}t$$

a. How many hours will it take to produce the maximum yield? 48 hr

b. What is the maximum yield? 2 g

58. The bacterium *Pseudomonas aeruginosa* is cultured with an initial population of 10^4 active organisms. The population of active bacteria increases up to a point, and then due to a limited food supply and an increase of waste products, the population of living organisms decreases. Over the first 48 hr, the population $P(t)$ can be approximated by:

$$P(t) = -1718.75t^2 + 82{,}500t + 10{,}000$$

$$\text{where } 0 \le t \le 48$$

a. Find the time required for the population to reach its maximum value. 24 hr

b. What is the maximum population? 1,000,000 organisms

For Exercises 59–64, use the standard form of a parabola given by $y = ax^2 + bx + c$ to write an equation of a parabola that passes through the given points. **(See Example 5.)**

59. $(0, 4)$, $(1, 0)$ and $(-1, -10)$ — $a = -9, b = 5, c = 4$; $y = -9x^2 + 5x + 4$

60. $(0, 3)$, $(3, 0)$, $(-1, 8)$ — $a = 1, b = -4, c = 3$; $y = x^2 - 4x + 3$

61. $(2, 1)$, $(-2, 5)$, and $(1, -4)$ — $a = 2, b = -1, c = -5$; $y = 2x^2 - x - 5$

62. $(1, 2)$, $(-1, -6)$, and $(2, -3)$ — $a = -3, b = 4, c = 1$; $y = -3x^2 + 4x + 1$

63. $(2, -4)$, $(1, 1)$, and $(-1, -7)$ — $a = -3, b = 4, c = 0$; $y = -3x^2 + 4x$

64. $(1, 4)$, $(-1, 6)$, and $(2, 18)$ — $a = 5, b = -1, c = 0$; $y = 5x^2 - x$

Expanding Your Skills

65. A farmer wants to fence a rectangular corral adjacent to the side of a barn; however, she has only 200 ft of fencing and wants to enclose the largest possible area. See the figure.

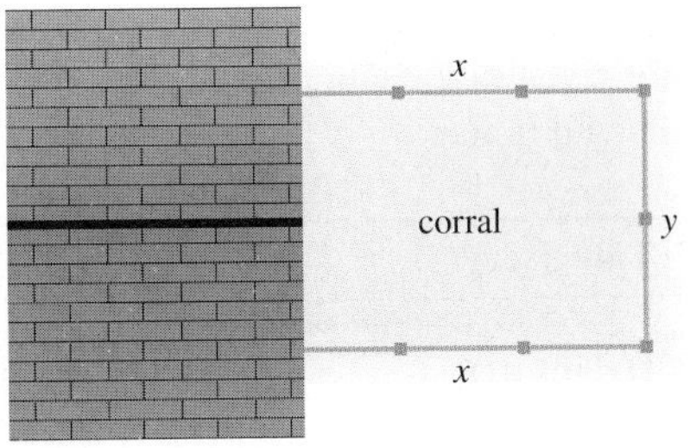

a. If x represents the length of the corral and y represents the width, explain why the dimensions of the corral are subject to the constraint $2x + y = 200$. The sum of the sides must equal the total amount of fencing.

b. The area of the corral is given by $A = xy$. Use the constraint equation from part (a) to express A as a function of x, where $0 < x < 100$. $A = x(200 - 2x)$

c. Use the function from part (b) to find the dimensions of the corral that will yield the maximum area. [*Hint:* Find the vertex of the function from part (b).] 50 ft by 100 ft

66. A veterinarian wants to construct two equal-sized pens of maximum area out of 240 ft of fencing. See the figure.

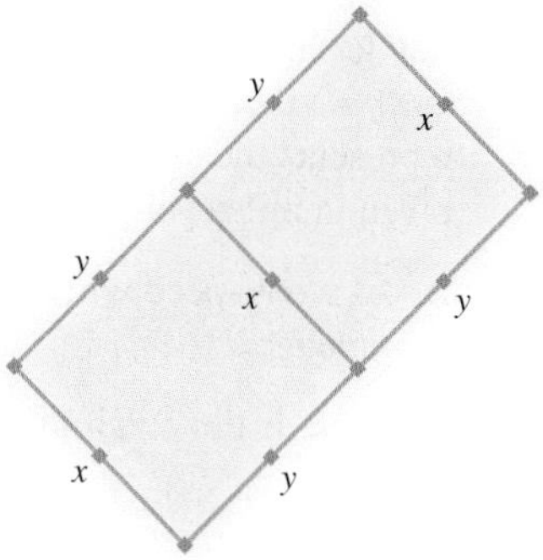

a. If x represents the length of each pen and y represents the width of each pen, explain why the dimensions of the pens are subject to the constraint $3x + 4y = 240$.
The sum of the sides must equal the total amount of fencing.

b. The area of each individual pen is given by $A = xy$. Use the constraint equation from part (a) to express A as a function of x, where $0 < x < 80$. $A = x\left(60 - \frac{3}{4}x\right)$

c. Use the function from part (b) to find the dimensions of an individual pen that will yield the maximum area. [*Hint:* Find the vertex of the function from part (b).] 30 ft by 40 ft

Graphing Calculator Exercises

For Exercises 67–72, graph the functions in Exercises 45–50 on a graphing calculator. Use the *Max* or *Min* feature to approximate the vertex.

67. $Y_1 = x^2 + 2x - 3$ (Exercise 45)

68. $Y_1 = x^2 + 4x + 3$ (Exercise 46)

69. $Y_1 = 2x^2 - 2x + 4$ (Exercise 47)

70. $Y_1 = 2x^2 - 12x + 19$ (Exercise 48)

71. $Y_1 = -x^2 + 3x - \frac{9}{4}$ (Exercise 49)

72. $Y_1 = -x^2 - \frac{3}{2}x - \frac{9}{16}$ (Exercise 50)

Group Activity

Creating a Quadratic Model of the Form $y = a(x - h)^2 + k$

Estimated time: 20 minutes

Group Size: 3

In an earlier group activity, we modeled the path of a softball that was thrown from right field to third base. The data points are given in the table. The values of t represent the time in seconds after the ball was released, and y represents the height of the ball in feet.

Time (sec) t	0	0.2	0.4	0.6	0.8	1.0	1.2	1.4	1.6	1.8	2.0
Height (ft) y	5	11	16	19	21	22	21	19	16	12	6

1. Graph the points defined by (t, y) in the table.

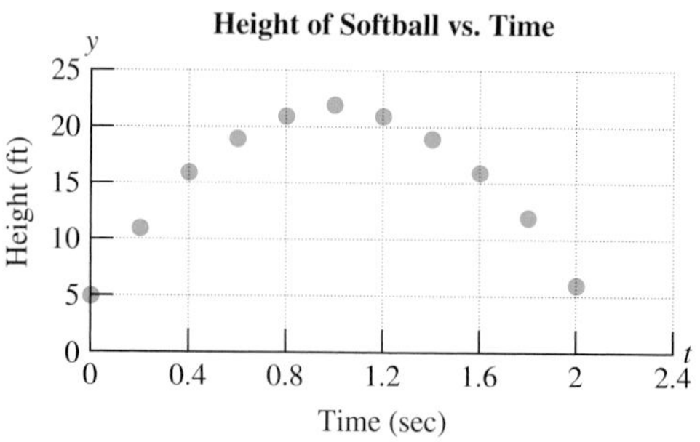

2. Select a point that you think best represents the vertex of the parabola. Label this point (h, k).

$(h, k) =$ (1, 22)

3. Substitute the values of h and k into the formula $y = a(t - h)^2 + k$, and write the equation here.

$y = a(t - \underline{\quad 1 \quad})^2 + \underline{\quad 22 \quad}$

4. Choose a different point (t, y) from the graph. Substitute these values into the equation in step 3 and then solve for a.
Answers will vary based on the choices for (h, k) and (t, y). However, a should be close to -16.

5. Substitute the values of h, k, and a that you found in steps 2 and 4 into the equation $y = a(t - h)^2 + k$.
Answers will vary, but should be close to $y = -16(t - 1)^2 + 22$.

6. Use the function found in step 5 to approximate the height of the ball after 0.7 sec.
Answers should be close to 20.56 ft.

7. Use the function found in step 5 to approximate the height of the ball after 1.8 sec. How well does this value match the observed value of 12 ft?
Answers will vary, but should be close to the observed value of 12 ft.

Chapter 11 Summary

Section 11.1 Square Root Property and Completing the Square

Key Concepts

The **square root property** states that

If $x^2 = k$ then $x = \pm\sqrt{k}$

Follow these steps to solve a quadratic equation in the form $ax^2 + bx + c = 0$ $(a \neq 0)$ by completing the square and applying the square root property:

1. Divide both sides by a to make the leading coefficient 1.
2. Isolate the variable terms on one side of the equation.
3. Complete the square: Add the square of one-half the linear term coefficient to both sides of the equation. Then factor the resulting perfect square trinomial.
4. Apply the square root property and solve for x.

Examples

Example 1

$$(x - 5)^2 = -13$$

$$x - 5 = \pm\sqrt{-13} \quad \text{(square root property)}$$

$$x = 5 \pm i\sqrt{13}$$

The solution set is $\{5 \pm i\sqrt{13}\}$.

Example 2

$$2x^2 - 12x - 16 = 0$$

$$\frac{2x^2}{2} - \frac{12x}{2} - \frac{16}{2} = \frac{0}{2}$$

$$x^2 - 6x - 8 = 0$$

$$x^2 - 6x = 8$$

$$x^2 - 6x + 9 = 8 + 9 \qquad \textit{Note: } [\tfrac{1}{2}(-6)]^2 = 9$$

$$(x - 3)^2 = 17$$

$$x - 3 = \pm\sqrt{17}$$

$$x = 3 \pm \sqrt{17}$$

The solution set is $\{3 \pm \sqrt{17}\}$.

Section 11.2 Quadratic Formula

Key Concepts

The solutions to a quadratic equation $ax^2 + bx + c = 0$ $(a \neq 0)$ are given by the **quadratic formula**

$$x = \frac{-b \pm \sqrt{b^2 - 4ac}}{2a}$$

The **discriminant** of a quadratic equation $ax^2 + bx + c = 0$ is $b^2 - 4ac$. If a, b, and c are rational numbers, then

1. If $b^2 - 4ac > 0$, then there will be two real solutions. Moreover,
   a. If $b^2 - 4ac$ is a perfect square, the solutions will be rational numbers.
   b. If $b^2 - 4ac$ is not a perfect square, the solutions will be irrational numbers.
2. If $b^2 - 4ac < 0$, then there will be two imaginary solutions.
3. If $b^2 - 4ac = 0$, then there will be one rational solution.

Three methods to solve a quadratic equation are

1. Factoring and applying the zero product rule.
2. Completing the square and applying the square root property.
3. Using the quadratic formula.

Example

Example 1

$$3x^2 - 2x + 4 = 0$$

$a = 3 \qquad b = -2 \qquad c = 4$

$$x = \frac{-(-2) \pm \sqrt{(-2)^2 - 4(3)(4)}}{2(3)}$$

$$= \frac{2 \pm \sqrt{4 - 48}}{6}$$

$$= \frac{2 \pm \sqrt{-44}}{6}$$

The discriminant is -44. Therefore, there will be two imaginary solutions.

$$= \frac{2 \pm 2i\sqrt{11}}{6}$$

$$= \frac{\overset{1}{\cancel{2}}(1 \pm i\sqrt{11})}{\underset{3}{\cancel{6}}}$$

$$= \frac{1 \pm i\sqrt{11}}{3}$$

$$= \frac{1}{3} \pm \frac{\sqrt{11}}{3}i$$

The solution set is $\left\{\frac{1}{3} \pm \frac{\sqrt{11}}{3}i\right\}$.

Section 11.3 Equations in Quadratic Form

Key Concepts

Substitution can be used to solve equations that are in quadratic form.

Example

Example 1

$x^{2/3} - x^{1/3} - 12 = 0 \qquad$ Let $u = x^{1/3}$.

$u^2 - u - 12 = 0$

$(u - 4)(u + 3) = 0$

$u = 4 \quad$ or $\quad u = -3$

$x^{1/3} = 4 \quad$ or $\quad x^{1/3} = -3$

$x = 64 \quad$ or $\quad x = -27 \qquad$ Cube both sides.

The solution set is $\{64, -27\}$.

Section 11.4 Graphs of Quadratic Functions

Key Concepts

A quadratic function of the form $f(x) = x^2 + k$ shifts the graph of $f(x) = x^2$ up k units if $k > 0$ and down $|k|$ units if $k < 0$.

A quadratic function of the form $f(x) = (x - h)^2$ shifts the graph of $f(x) = x^2$ to the right h units if $h > 0$ and to the left $|h|$ units if $h < 0$.

The graph of a quadratic function of the form $f(x) = ax^2$ is a parabola that opens upward when $a > 0$ and opens downward when $a < 0$. If $|a| > 1$, the graph of $f(x) = x^2$ is stretched vertically by a factor of $|a|$. If $0 < |a| < 1$, the graph of $f(x) = x^2$ is shrunk vertically by a factor of $|a|$.

A quadratic function of the form $f(x) = a(x - h)^2 + k$ has vertex (h, k). If $a > 0$, the vertex represents the minimum point. If $a < 0$, the vertex represents the maximum point.

Examples

Example 1

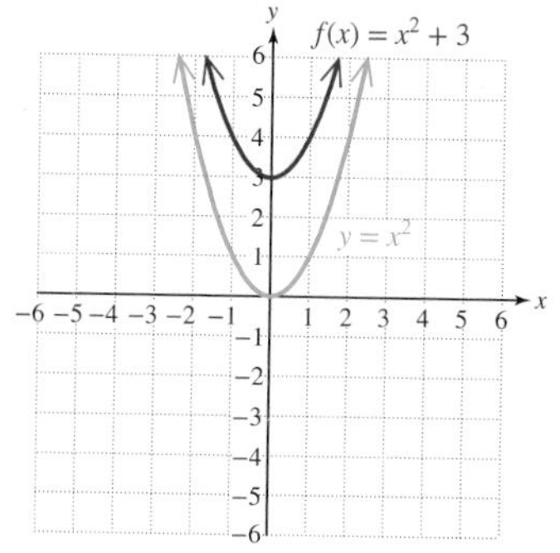

Example 2

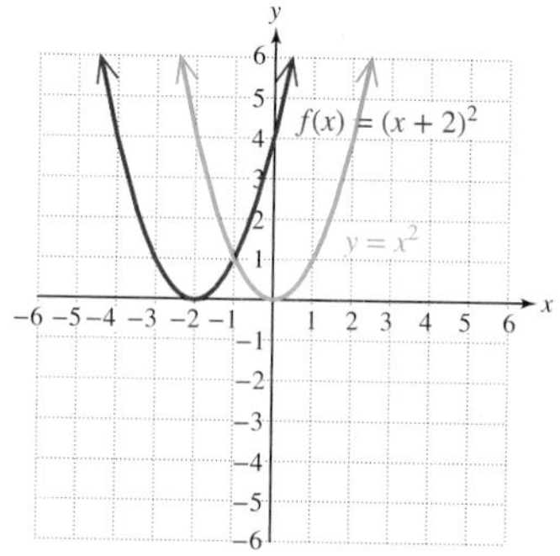

Example 3

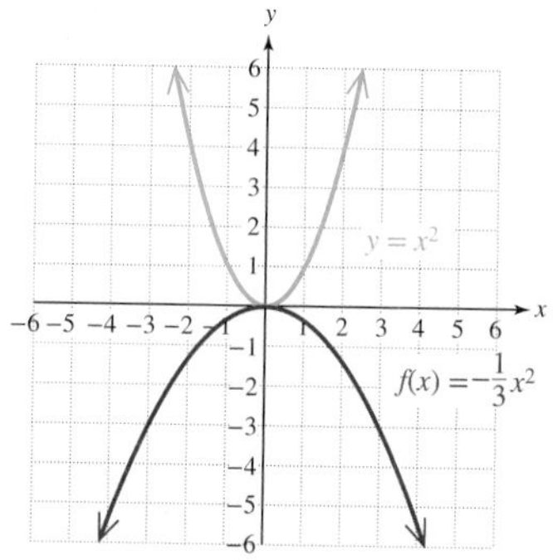

Example 4

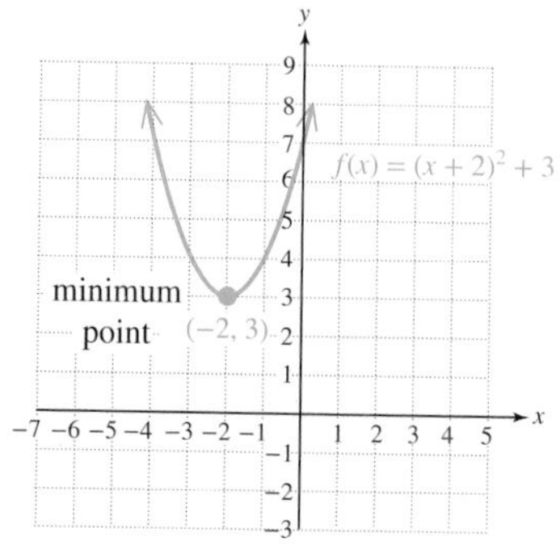

Section 11.5 Vertex of a Parabola: Applications and Modeling

Key Concepts

Completing the square is a technique used to write a quadratic function $f(x) = ax^2 + bx + c$ $(a \neq 0)$ in the form $f(x) = a(x - h)^2 + k$ for the purpose of identifying the vertex (h, k).

Examples

Example 1

$$
\begin{aligned}
f(x) &= 3x^2 + 6x + 11\\
&= 3(x^2 + 2x \qquad\quad) + 11\\
&= 3(x^2 + 2x + 1 - 1) + 11\\
&= 3(x^2 + 2x + 1) - 3 + 11\\
&= 3(x + 1)^2 + 8\\
&= 3[x - (-1)]^2 + 8
\end{aligned}
$$

The vertex is $(-1, 8)$. Because $a = 3 > 0$, the parabola opens upward and the vertex $(-1, 8)$ is a minimum point.

The **vertex formula** finds the vertex of a quadratic function $f(x) = ax^2 + bx + c$ $(a \neq 0)$.

The vertex is

$$\left(\frac{-b}{2a}, \frac{4ac - b^2}{4a}\right) \quad \text{or} \quad \left(\frac{-b}{2a}, f\left(\frac{-b}{2a}\right)\right)$$

Example 2

$f(x) = 3x^2 + 6x + 11$

$a = 3 \qquad b = 6 \qquad c = 11$

$$x = \frac{-6}{2(3)} = -1$$

$f(-1) = 3(-1)^2 + 6(-1) + 11 = 8$

The vertex is $(-1, 8)$.

Chapter 11 Review Exercises

Section 11.1

For Exercises 1–8, solve the equations by using the square root property.

1. $x^2 = 5$ $\{\pm\sqrt{5}\}$

2. $2y^2 = -8$ $\{\pm 2i\}$

3. $a^2 = 81$ $\{\pm 9\}$

4. $3b^2 = -19$ $\left\{\pm\frac{\sqrt{57}}{3}i\right\}$

5. $(x-2)^2 = 72$ $\{2 \pm 6\sqrt{2}\}$

6. $(2x-5)^2 = -9$ $\left\{\frac{5}{2} \pm \frac{3}{2}i\right\}$

7. $(3y-1)^2 = 3$ $\left\{\frac{1 \pm \sqrt{3}}{3}\right\}$

8. $3(m-4)^2 = 15$ $\{4 \pm \sqrt{5}\}$

9. The length of each side of an equilateral triangle is 10 in. Find the exact height of the triangle. Then round to the nearest tenth of an inch.

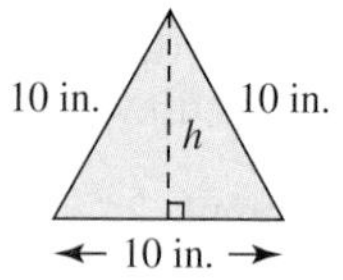

$5\sqrt{3}$ in. ≈ 87 in.

10. Use the square root property to find the length of the sides of a square whose area is 81 in^2. 9 in.

11. Use the square root property to find the exact length of the sides of a square whose area is 150 in^2. Then round to the nearest tenth of an inch.
$5\sqrt{6}$ in. ≈ 12.2 in.

For Exercises 12–15, find the value of n so that the expression is a perfect square trinomial. Then factor the trinomial.

12. $x^2 + 16x + n$ $n = 64; (x+8)^2$

13. $x^2 - 9x + n$ $n = \frac{81}{4}; \left(x - \frac{9}{2}\right)^2$

14. $y^2 + \frac{1}{2}y + n$ $n = \frac{1}{16}; \left(y + \frac{1}{4}\right)^2$

15. $z^2 - \frac{2}{5}z + n$ $n = \frac{1}{25}; \left(z - \frac{1}{5}\right)^2$

For Exercises 16–21, solve the equation by completing the square and applying the square root property.

16. $w^2 + 4w + 13 = 0$ $\{-2 \pm 3i\}$

17. $4y^2 - 8y - 20 = 0$ $\{1 \pm \sqrt{6}\}$

18. $2x^2 = 12x + 6$ $\{3 \pm 2\sqrt{3}\}$

19. $-t^2 + 8t - 25 = 0$ $\{4 \pm 3i\}$

20. $3x^2 + 2x = 1$ $\left\{\frac{1}{3}, -1\right\}$

21. $b^2 + \frac{7}{2}b = 2$ $\left\{\frac{1}{2}, -4\right\}$

22. Solve for r. $V = \pi r^2 h$ $(r > 0)$ $r = \sqrt{\frac{V}{\pi h}}$ or $r = \frac{\sqrt{V\pi h}}{\pi h}$

23. Solve for s. $A = 6s^2$ $(s > 0)$ $s = \sqrt{\frac{A}{6}}$ or $s = \frac{\sqrt{6A}}{6}$

Section 11.2

24. Describe the type and number of solutions to a quadratic equation whose discriminant is less than zero.
There will be two imaginary solutions.

For Exercises 25–30, determine the type (rational, irrational, or imaginary) and number of solutions for the equations by using the discriminant.

25. $x^2 - 5x = -6$ Two rational solutions

26. $2y^2 = -3y$ Two rational solutions

27. $z^2 + 23 = 17z$ Two irrational solutions

28. $a^2 + a + 1 = 0$ Two imaginary solutions

29. $10b + 1 = -25b^2$ One rational solution

30. $3x^2 + 15 = 0$ Two imaginary solutions

For Exercises 31–38, solve the equations by using the quadratic formula.

31. $y^2 - 4y + 1 = 0$ $\{2 \pm \sqrt{3}\}$

32. $m^2 - 5m + 25 = 0$ $\left\{\frac{5}{2} \pm \frac{5\sqrt{3}}{2}i\right\}$

33. $6a(a-1) = 10 + a$ $\left\{2, -\frac{5}{6}\right\}$

34. $3x(x-3) = x - 8$ $\left\{2, \frac{4}{3}\right\}$

35. $b^2 - \frac{4}{25} = \frac{3}{5}b$ $\left\{\frac{4}{5}, -\frac{1}{5}\right\}$

36. $k^2 + 0.4k = 0.05$ $\left\{\frac{1}{10}, -\frac{1}{2}\right\}$

37. $-32 + 4x - x^2 = 0$ $\{2 \pm 2i\sqrt{7}\}$

38. $8y - y^2 = 10$ $\{4 \pm \sqrt{6}\}$

For Exercises 39–42, solve using any method.

39. $3x^2 - 4x = 6$ $\left\{\frac{2 \pm \sqrt{22}}{3}\right\}$

40. $\frac{w}{8} - \frac{2}{w} = \frac{3}{4}$ $\{8, -2\}$

41. $y^2 + 14y = -46$ $\{-7 \pm \sqrt{3}\}$

42. $(a+1)^2 = 11$ $\{-1 \pm \sqrt{11}\}$

43. The landing distance that a certain plane will travel on a runway is determined by the initial landing speed at the instant the plane touches down. The function D relates landing distance in feet to initial landing speed s:

$$D(s) = \frac{1}{10}s^2 - 3s + 22 \text{ for } s \geq 50$$

where s is in feet per second.

a. Find the landing distance for a plane traveling 150 ft/sec at touchdown. 1822 ft

b. If the landing speed is too fast, the pilot may run out of runway. If the speed is too slow, the plane may stall. Find the maximum initial landing speed of a plane for a runway that is 1000 ft long. Round to one decimal place. 115 ft/sec

44. The recent population of Kenya (in thousands) can be approximated by $P(t) = 4.62t^2 + 564.6t + 13{,}128$ where t is the number of years since 1974.

a. If this trend continues, predict the number of people in Kenya for the year 2025. $\approx 53{,}939$ thousand

b. In what year after 1974 will the population of Kenya reach 50 million? (*Hint:* 50 million equals 50,000 thousand.) 2021

45. A custom-built kitchen island is in the shape of a rectangle. The length is 1 ft more than twice the width. If the area is 22.32 ft^2, determine the dimensions of the island. Round the length and width to the nearest tenth of a foot.
The dimensions are approximately 3.1 ft by 7.2 ft.

© Photodisc/Getty Images RF

46. Lincoln, Nebraska, Kansas City, Missouri, and Omaha, Nebraska, form the vertices of a right triangle. The distance between Lincoln and Kansas City is 10 mi more than 3 times the distance between Lincoln and Omaha. If the distance from Omaha and Kansas City is 167 mi, find the distance between Lincoln and Omaha. Round to the nearest mile.
The distance between Lincoln and Omaha is approximately 50 mi.

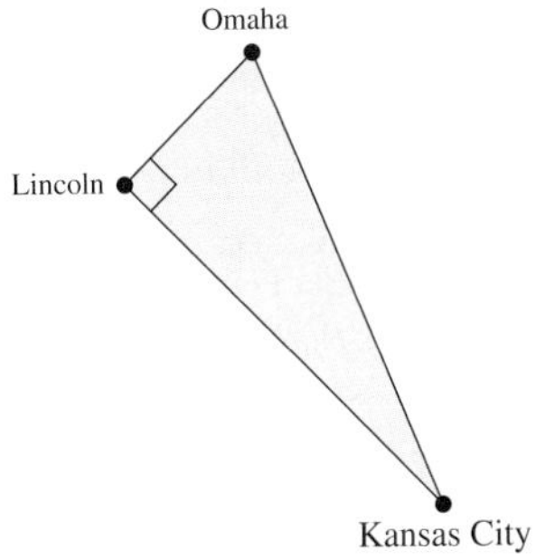

Section 11.3

For Exercises 47–56, solve the equations.

47. $x - 4\sqrt{x} - 21 = 0$ $\{49\}$ (The value 9 does not check.)

48. $n - 6\sqrt{n} + 8 = 0$ $\{4, 16\}$

49. $y^4 - 11y^2 + 18 = 0$ $\{\pm 3, \pm\sqrt{2}\}$

50. $2m^4 - m^2 - 3 = 0$ $\left\{\pm\frac{\sqrt{6}}{2}, \pm i\right\}$

51. $t^{2/5} + t^{1/5} - 6 = 0$ $\{-243, 32\}$

52. $p^{2/5} - 3p^{1/5} + 2 = 0$ $\{32, 1\}$

53. $\dfrac{2t}{t+1} + \dfrac{-3}{t-2} = 1$ $\{3 \pm \sqrt{10}\}$

54. $\dfrac{1}{m-2} - \dfrac{m}{m+3} = 2$ $\left\{\dfrac{1 \pm \sqrt{181}}{6}\right\}$

55. $(x^2 + 5)^2 + 2(x^2 + 5) - 8 = 0$ $\{\pm 3i, \pm i\sqrt{3}\}$

56. $(x^2 - 3)^2 - 5(x^2 - 3) + 4 = 0$ $\{\pm\sqrt{7}, \pm 2\}$

Section 11.4

For Exercises 57–64, graph the function and write the domain and range in interval notation.

57. $g(x) = x^2 - 5$

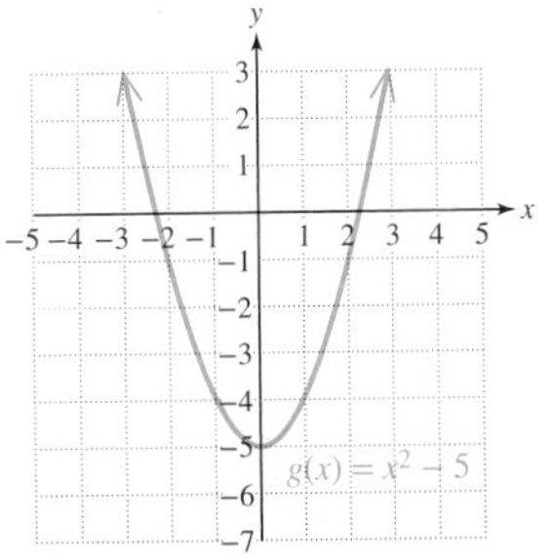

Domain: $(-\infty, \infty)$; range: $[-5, \infty)$

58. $f(x) = x^2 + 3$

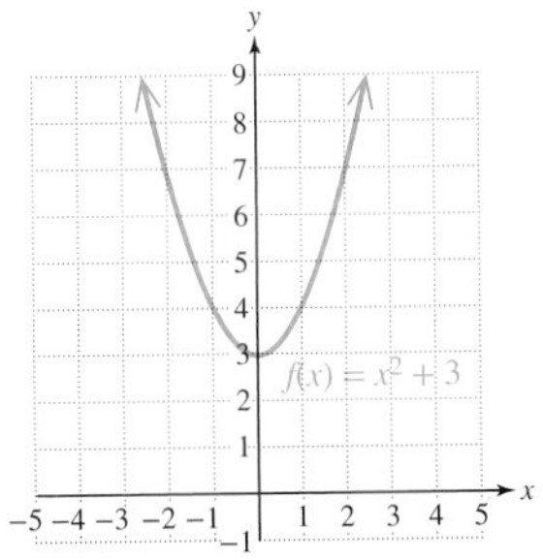

Domain: $(-\infty, \infty)$; range: $[3, \infty)$

59. $h(x) = (x - 5)^2$

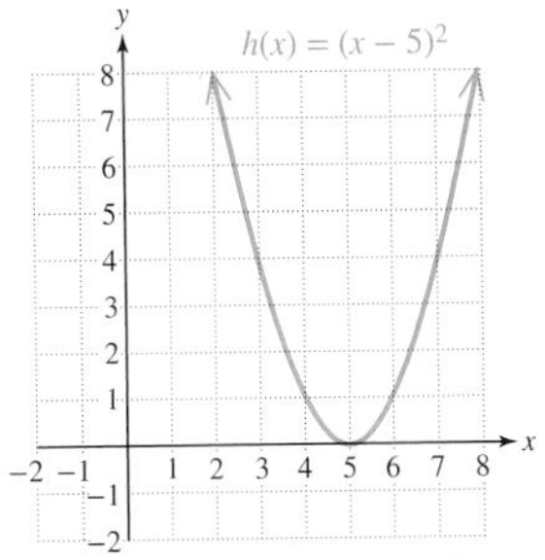

Domain: $(-\infty, \infty)$; range: $[0, \infty)$

60. $k(x) = (x + 3)^2$

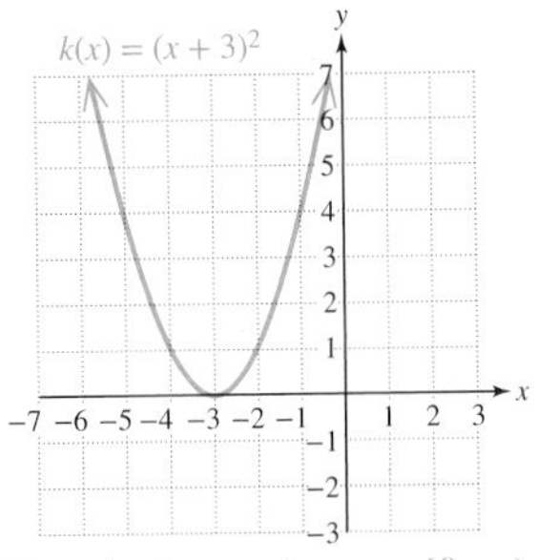

Domain: $(-\infty, \infty)$; range: $[0, \infty)$

61. $m(x) = -2x^2$

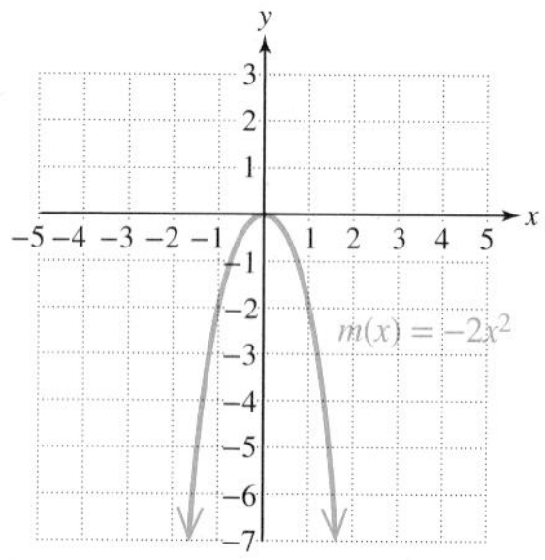

Domain: $(-\infty, \infty)$; range: $(-\infty, 0]$

62. $n(x) = -4x^2$

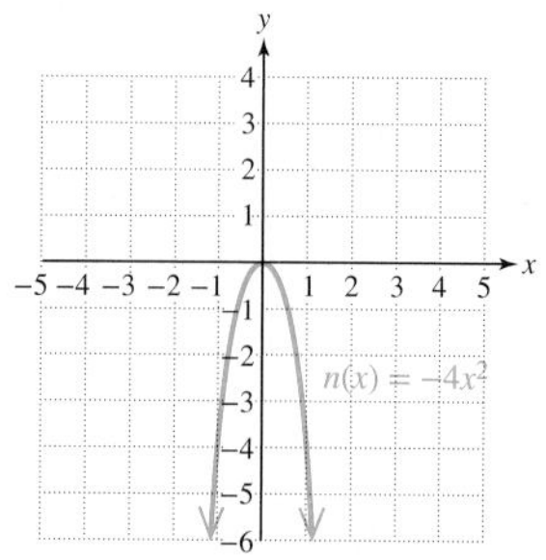

Domain: $(-\infty, \infty)$; range: $(-\infty, 0]$

63. $p(x) = -2(x - 5)^2 - 5$

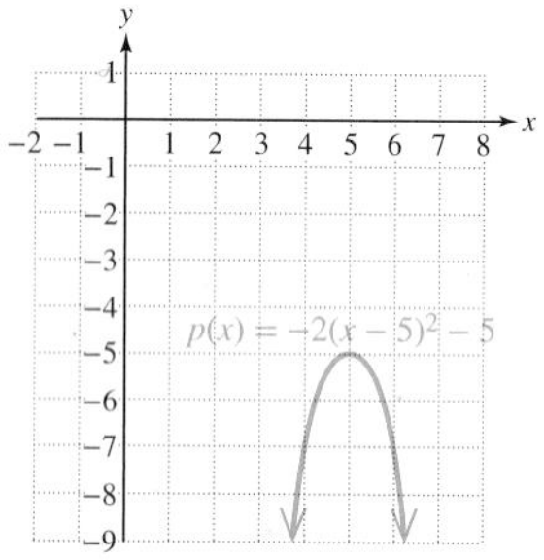

Domain: $(-\infty, \infty)$; range: $(-\infty, -5]$

64. $q(x) = -4(x + 3)^2 + 3$

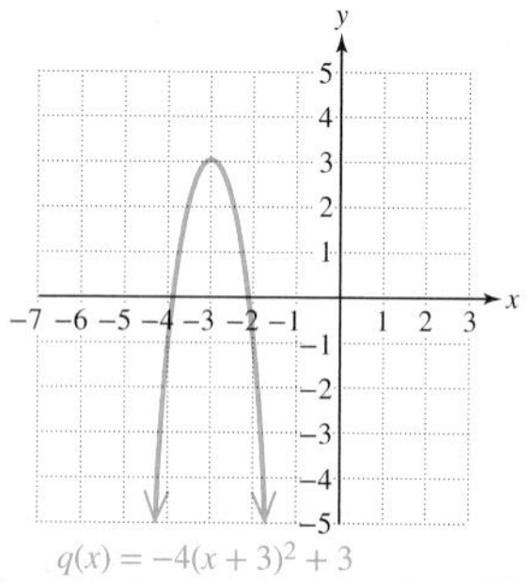

Domain: $(-\infty, \infty)$; range: $(-\infty, 3]$

For Exercises 65–66, write the coordinates of the vertex of the parabola and determine if the vertex is a maximum point or a minimum point. Then write the maximum or the minimum value.

65. $t(x) = \frac{1}{3}(x - 4)^2 + \frac{5}{3}$ $\left(4, \frac{5}{3}\right)$ is the minimum point. The minimum value is $\frac{5}{3}$.

66. $s(x) = -\frac{5}{7}(x - 1)^2 - \frac{1}{7}$ $\left(1, -\frac{1}{7}\right)$ is the maximum point. The maximum value is $-\frac{1}{7}$.

For Exercises 67–68, write the equation of the axis of symmetry of the parabola.

67. $a(x) = -\frac{3}{2}\left(x + \frac{2}{11}\right)^2 - \frac{4}{13}$ $x = -\frac{2}{11}$

68. $w(x) = -\frac{4}{3}\left(x - \frac{3}{16}\right)^2 + \frac{2}{9}$ $x = \frac{3}{16}$

Section 11.5

For Exercises 69–72, write the function in the form $f(x) = a(x - h)^2 + k$ by completing the square. Then write the coordinates of the vertex.

69. $z(x) = x^2 - 6x + 7$
$z(x) = (x - 3)^2 - 2$; $(3, -2)$

70. $b(x) = x^2 - 4x - 44$
$b(x) = (x - 2)^2 - 48$; $(2, -48)$

71. $p(x) = -5x^2 - 10x - 13$
$p(x) = -5(x + 1)^2 - 8$; $(-1, -8)$

72. $q(x) = -3x^2 - 24x - 54$
$q(x) = -3(x + 4)^2 - 6$; $(-4, -6)$

For Exercises 73–76, find the coordinates of the vertex of each parabola by using the vertex formula.

73. $f(x) = -2x^2 + 4x - 17$ $(1, -15)$

74. $g(x) = -4x^2 - 8x + 3$ $(-1, 7)$

75. $m(x) = 3x^2 - 3x + 11$ $\left(\frac{1}{2}, \frac{41}{4}\right)$

76. $n(x) = 3x^2 + 2x - 7$ $\left(-\frac{1}{3}, -\frac{22}{3}\right)$

77. For the quadratic equation $y = \frac{3}{4}x^2 - 3x$,

a. Write the coordinates of the vertex. $(2, -3)$

b. Find the x- and y-intercepts. $(0, 0)$, $(4, 0)$

c. Use this information to sketch a graph of the parabola.

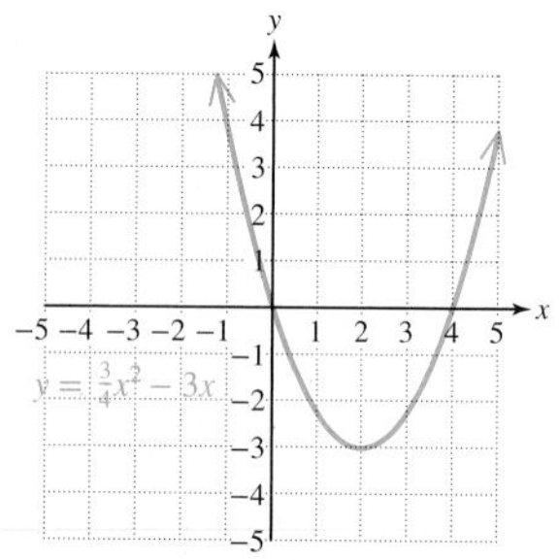

78. For the quadratic equation $y = -(x + 2)^2 + 4$,

a. Write the coordinates of the vertex. $(-2, 4)$

b. Find the x- and y-intercepts. $(0, 0)$, $(-4, 0)$

c. Use this information to sketch a graph of the parabola.

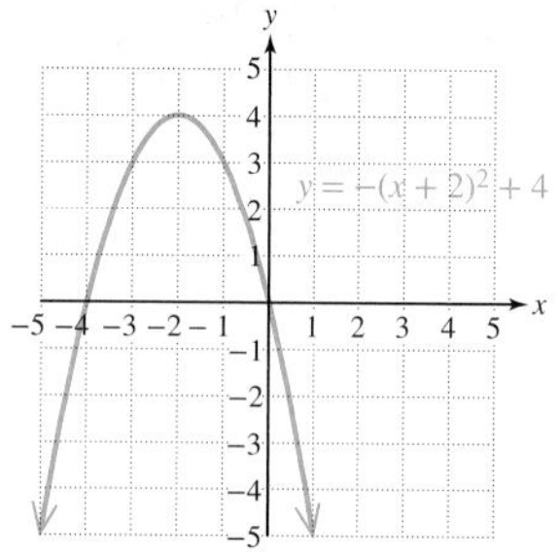

79. The height $h(t)$ (in feet) of a projectile fired vertically into the air from the ground is given by the equation $h(t) = -16t^2 + 96t$, where t represents the number of seconds after launch.

a. How long will it take the projectile to reach its maximum height? 3 sec

b. What is the maximum height? 144 ft

80. The weekly profit, $P(x)$ (in dollars), for a catering service is given by $P(x) = -0.053x^2 + 15.9x + 7.5$. In this context, x is the number of meals prepared.

a. Find the number of meals that should be prepared to obtain the maximum profit. 150 meals

b. What is the maximum profit? \$1200

81. Write an equation of a parabola that passes through the points $(-3, -4)$, $(-2, -5)$, and $(1, 4)$.
$a = 1, b = 4, c = -1; y = x^2 + 4x - 1$

82. Write an equation of a parabola that passes through the points $(4, 18)$, $(-2, 12)$, and $(-1, 8)$.
$a = 1, b = -1, c = 6; y = x^2 - x + 6$

Chapter 11 Test

For Exercises 1–3, solve the equation by using the square root property.

1. $(x + 3)^2 = 25$ $\{2, -8\}$

2. $(p - 2)^2 = 12$ $\{2 \pm 2\sqrt{3}\}$

3. $(m + 1)^2 = -1$ $\{-1 \pm i\}$

4. Find the value of n so that the expression is a perfect square trinomial. Then factor the trinomial $d^2 + 11d + n$. $n = \frac{121}{4}; \left(d + \frac{11}{2}\right)^2$

For Exercises 5–6, solve the equation by completing the square and applying the square root property.

5. $2x^2 + 12x - 36 = 0$ $\{-3 \pm 3\sqrt{3}\}$

6. $2x^2 = 3x - 7$ $\left\{\frac{3}{4} \pm \frac{\sqrt{47}}{4}i\right\}$

For Exercises 7–8,

a. Write the equation in standard form $ax^2 + bx + c = 0$.

b. Identify a, b, and c.

c. Find the discriminant.

d. Determine the number and type (rational, irrational, or imaginary) of solutions.

7. $x^2 - 3x = -12$
a. $x^2 - 3x + 12 = 0$
b. $a = 1, b = -3, c = 12$
c. -39
d. Two imaginary solutions

8. $y(y - 2) = -1$
a. $y^2 - 2y + 1 = 0$
b. $a = 1, b = -2, c = 1$
c. 0
d. One rational solution

For Exercises 9–10, solve the equation by using the quadratic formula.

9. $3x^2 - 4x + 1 = 0$ $\left\{1, \frac{1}{3}\right\}$

10. $x(x + 6) = -11 - x$ $\left\{\frac{-7 \pm \sqrt{5}}{2}\right\}$

11. The base of a triangle is 3 ft less than twice the height. The area of the triangle is 14 ft^2. Find the base and the height. Round the answers to the nearest tenth of a foot.
The height is approximately 4.6 ft and the base is 6.2 ft.

12. A circular garden has an area of approximately 450 ft^2. Find the radius. Round the answer to the nearest tenth of a foot.
The radius is approximately 12.0 ft.

For Exercises 13–21, solve the equation.

13. $x - \sqrt{x} - 6 = 0$
$\{9\}$ (The value 4 does not check.)

14. $y^{2/3} + 2y^{1/3} = 8$
$\{8, -64\}$

15. $(3y - 8)^2 - 13(3y - 8) + 30 = 0$ $\left\{\frac{11}{3}, 6\right\}$

16. $p^4 - 15p^2 = -54$
$\{\pm\sqrt{6}, \pm 3\}$

17. $3 = \frac{y}{2} - \frac{1}{y + 1}$
$\left\{\frac{5 \pm \sqrt{57}}{2}\right\}$

18. $2x^2 - 9x = 5$
$\left\{5, -\frac{1}{2}\right\}$

19. $x^2 - 8x + 1 = 0$
$\{4 \pm \sqrt{15}\}$

20. $(x + 7)^2 = -24$
$\{-7 \pm 2i\sqrt{6}\}$

21. $x(x - 12) = -13$
$\{6 \pm \sqrt{23}\}$

22. Find the vertex of $y = x^2 - 6x - 8$ two ways,

a. By completing the square.

b. By using the vertex formula. The vertex is $(3, -17)$.

For Exercises 23–25, graph the function. Use the graph to write the domain and range in interval notation.

23. $h(x) = x^2 - 4$

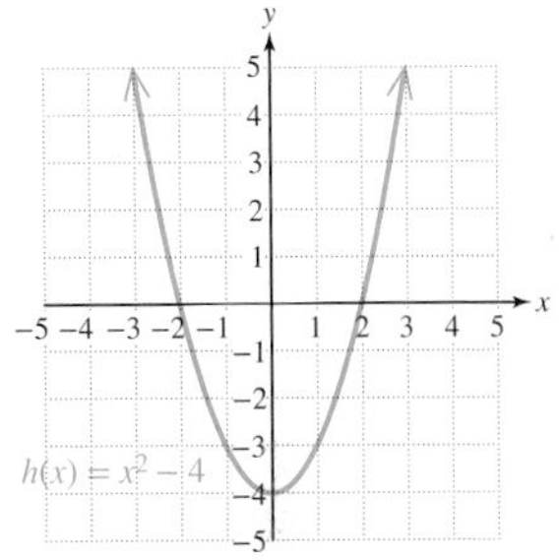

Domain: $(-\infty, \infty)$; range: $[-4, \infty)$

24. $f(x) = -(x - 4)^2$

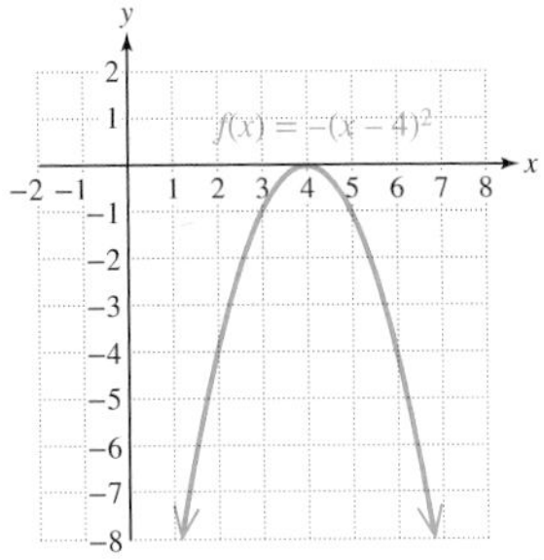

Domain: $(-\infty, \infty)$; range: $(-\infty, 0]$

25. $g(x) = \frac{1}{2}(x + 2)^2 - 3$

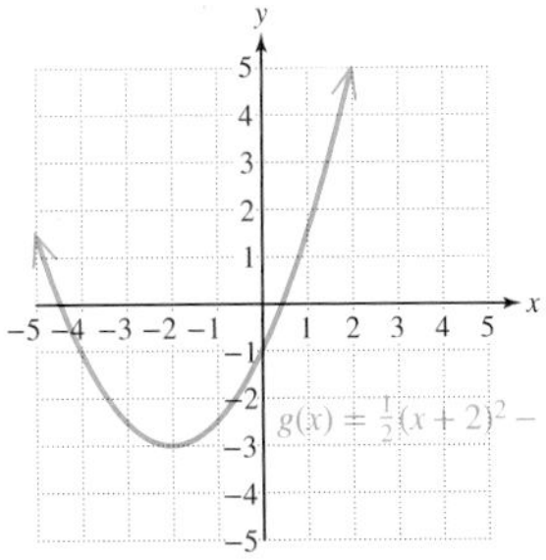

Domain: $(-\infty, \infty)$; range: $[-3, \infty)$

26. A child launches a toy rocket from the ground. The height of the rocket can be determined by its horizontal distance from the launch pad x by

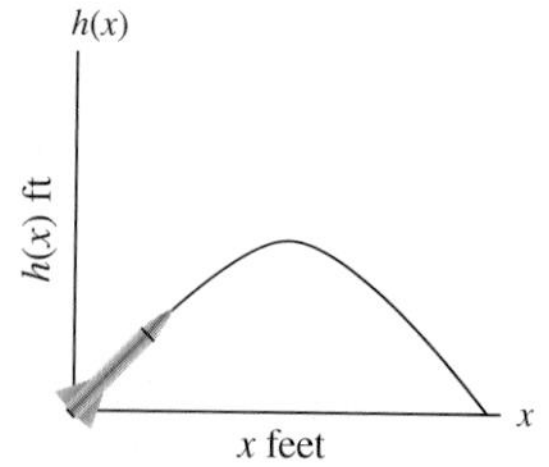

$$h(x) = -\frac{x^2}{256} + x$$

where x and $h(x)$ are in feet. How many feet from the launch pad will the rocket hit the ground?
The rocket will hit the ground 256 ft away.

27. The recent population of India (in millions) can be approximated by $P(t) = 0.135t^2 + 12.6t + 600$, where $t = 0$ corresponds to the year 1974.

a. Use the function to estimate the number of people in India in the year 2014. 1320 million

b. Approximate the year in which the population of India reached 1 billion (1000 million). (Round to the nearest year.) 1999

28. Explain the relationship between the graphs of $y = x^2$ and $y = x^2 - 2$. The graph of $y = x^2 - 2$ is the graph of $y = x^2$ shifted down 2 units.

29. Explain the relationship between the graphs of $y = x^2$ and $y = (x + 3)^2$. The graph of $y = (x + 3)^2$ is the graph of $y = x^2$ shifted 3 units to the left.

30. Explain the relationship between the graphs of $y = 4x^2$ and $y = -4x^2$. The graph of $y = -4x^2$ is the graph of $y = 4x^2$ opening downward instead of upward.

31. Given the function defined by

$$f(x) = -(x - 4)^2 + 2$$

a. Identify the vertex of the parabola. (4, 2)

b. Does this parabola open upward or downward? Downward

c. Does the vertex represent the maximum or minimum point of the function? Maximum point

d. What is the maximum or minimum value of the function f? The maximum value is 2.

e. Write an equation for the axis of symmetry. $x = 4$

32. For the function defined by $g(x) = 2x^2 - 20x + 51$, find the vertex by using two methods.

a. Complete the square to write $g(x)$ in the form $g(x) = a(x - h)^2 + k$. Identify the vertex. $g(x) = 2(x - 5)^2 + 1$; (5, 1)

b. Use the vertex formula to find the vertex. (5, 1)

33. Given $f(x) = x^2 + 4x - 12$

a. Write the equation for the function in the form $f(x) = a(x - h)^2 + k$. $f(x) = (x + 2)^2 - 16$

b. Determine the vertex. Vertex: $(-2, -16)$

c. Find the x- and y-intercepts. x-intercepts: $(-6, 0)$ and $(2, 0)$; y-intercept: $(0, -12)$

d. Determine the maximum or minimum value. The minimum value is -16.

e. Write an equation for the axis of symmetry. $x = -2$

34. A farmer has 400 ft of fencing with which to enclose a rectangular field. The field is situated such that one of its sides is adjacent to a river and requires no fencing. The area of the field (in square feet) can be modeled by

$$A(x) = -\frac{x^2}{2} + 200x$$

where x is the length of the side parallel to the river (measured in feet).

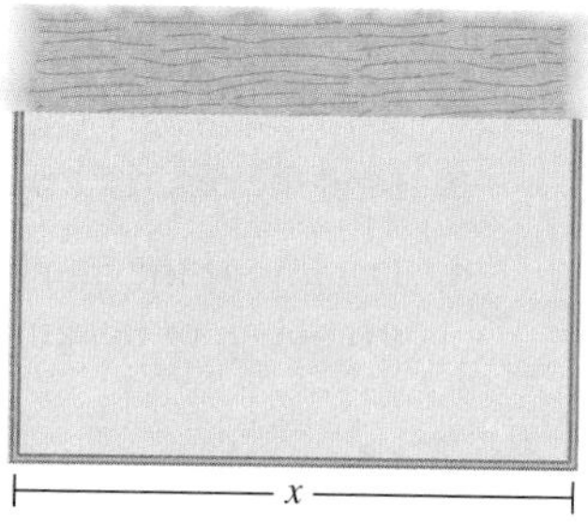

a. Determine the value of x that maximizes the area of the field. 200 ft

b. Determine the maximum area that can be enclosed. 20,000 ft^2

Chapters 1–11 Cumulative Review Exercises

1. Given $A = \{2, 4, 6, 8, 10\}$ and $B = \{2, 8, 12, 16\}$

a. Find $A \cup B$. $\{2, 4, 6, 8, 10, 12, 16\}$

b. Find $A \cap B$. $\{2, 8\}$

2. Perform the indicated operations and simplify.

$$(2x^2 - 5) - (x + 3)(5x - 2)$$

$-3x^2 - 13x + 1$

3. Simplify completely. $4^0 - \left(\frac{1}{2}\right)^{-3} - 81^{1/2}$ -16

4. Perform the indicated operation. Write the answer in scientific notation. 1.8×10^{10}

$$(3 \times 10^{12})(6 \times 10^{-3})$$

5. **a.** Factor completely. $x^3 + 2x^2 - 9x - 18$
$(x+2)(x+3)(x-3)$

b. Divide by using long division. Identify the quotient and remainder.

$$(x^3 + 2x^2 - 9x - 18) \div (x - 3)$$

Quotient: $x^2 + 5x + 6$; remainder: 0

6. Multiply. $(\sqrt{x} - \sqrt{2})(\sqrt{x} + \sqrt{2})$ $x - 2$

7. Simplify. $\dfrac{4}{\sqrt{2x}}$ $\dfrac{2\sqrt{2x}}{x}$

8. Jacques invests a total of \$10,000 in two mutual funds. After 1 yr, one fund produced 12% growth, and the other lost 3%. Find the amount invested in each fund if the total investment grew by \$900.
\$8000 in 12% account; \$2000 in 3% account

9. Solve the system of equations. $\{(8, 7)\}$

$$\frac{1}{9}x - \frac{1}{3}y = -\frac{13}{9}$$

$$x - \frac{1}{2}y = \frac{9}{2}$$

10. An object is fired straight up into the air from an initial height of 384 ft with an initial velocity of 160 ft/sec. The height in feet is given by

$$h(t) = -16t^2 + 160t + 384$$

where t is the time in seconds after launch.

a. Find the height of the object after 3 sec.
720 ft

b. Find the height of the object after 7 sec.
720 ft

c. Find the time required for the object to hit the ground. 12 sec

11. Solve. $(x - 3)^2 + 16 = 0$ $\{3 \pm 4i\}$

12. Solve. $2x^2 + 5x - 1 = 0$ $\left\{\dfrac{-5 \pm \sqrt{33}}{4}\right\}$

13. Find the value of n so that the expression is a perfect square trinomial. Then factor the trinomial $x^2 + 10x + n$. $n = 25$; $(x+5)^2$

14. Factor completely. $2x^3 + 250$
$2(x+5)(x^2 - 5x + 25)$

15. Graph the equation. $3x - 5y = 10$

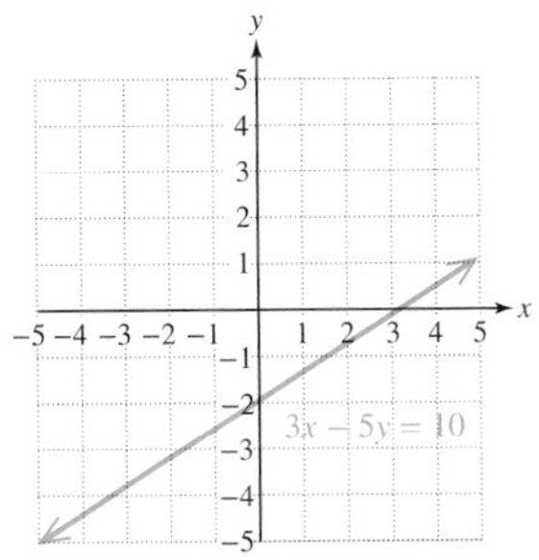

16. **a.** Find the x-intercepts of the function defined by $g(x) = 2x^2 - 9x + 10$. $\left(\frac{5}{2}, 0\right)$, $(2, 0)$

b. What is the y-intercept? $(0, 10)$

17. Explain why this relation is *not* a function.
The domain element 3 has more than one corresponding range element.

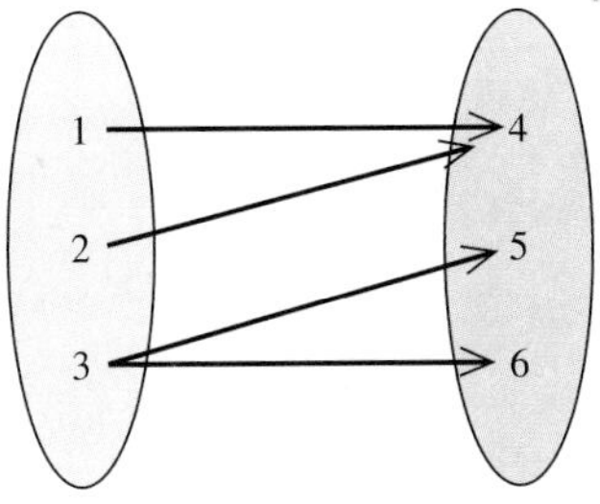

18. Graph the function defined by $f(x) = \dfrac{1}{x}$.

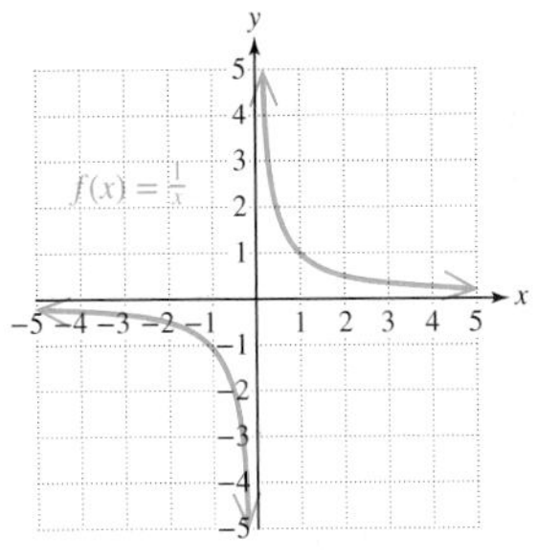

19. The quantity y varies directly as x and inversely as z. If $y = 15$ when $x = 50$ and $z = 10$, find y when $x = 65$ and $z = 5$. $y = 39$

20. The yearly number of flights (including passenger flights and cargo flights) at a large airport can be approximated by $F(x) = 300{,}000 + 0.008x$, where x is the number of passengers.

a. Is this function linear, quadratic, constant, or other? Linear

b. Find the y-intercept and interpret its meaning in the context of this problem. $(0, 300{,}000)$. If there are no passengers, the airport runs 300,000 flights per year. (These flights are cargo flights only.)

c. What is the slope of the function and what does the slope mean in the context of this problem?
$m = 0.008$ or $m = \frac{8}{1000}$. There are eight additional flights per 1000 passengers.

21. Let $m(x) = \sqrt{x + 4}$ and $n(x) = x^2 + 2$. Find

a. The domain of m
$[-4, \infty)$

b. The domain of n
$(-\infty, \infty)$

22. Consider the graph of $y = f(x)$. Find

a. The domain $(-\infty, 2]$ **b.** The range $(-\infty, 4]$

c. $f(1)$ 4 **d.** $f(0)$ 3

e. For what value(s) of x is $f(x) = 0$? $x = -1$

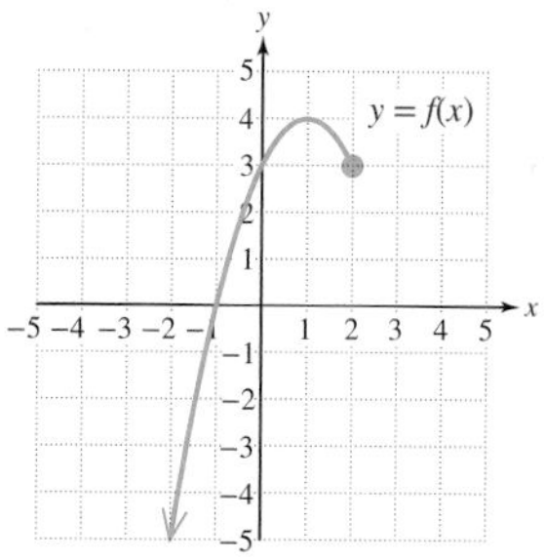

23. Solve. $\sqrt{8x+5} = \sqrt{2x} + 2$ $\left\{\frac{1}{18}, \frac{1}{2}\right\}$

24. Solve for f. $\frac{1}{p} + \frac{1}{q} = \frac{1}{f}$ $f = \frac{pq}{p+q}$

25. Solve. $\frac{15}{t^2 - 2t - 8} = \frac{1}{t-4} + \frac{2}{t+2}$ $\{7\}$

26. Simplify. $\dfrac{y - \dfrac{4}{y-3}}{y-4}$ $\frac{y+1}{y-3}$

27. Given the function defined by $f(x) = 2(x-3)^2 + 1$

a. Write the coordinates of the vertex. $(3, 1)$

b. Does the graph of the function open upward or downward? Upward

c. Write the coordinates of the y-intercept. $(0, 19)$

d. Find the x-intercepts, if possible. No x-intercept

e. Sketch the function.

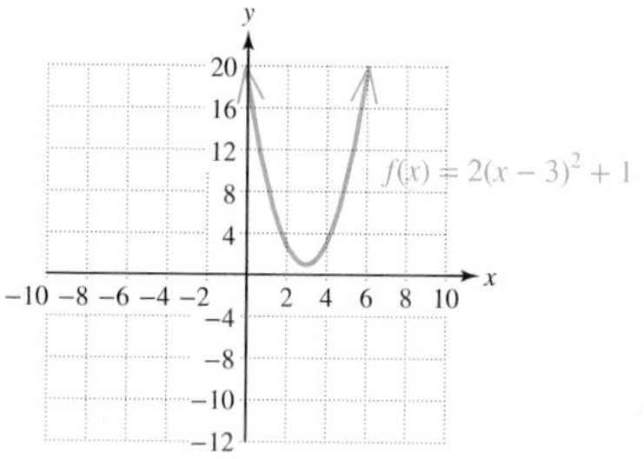

28. Find the vertex of the parabola. Vertex: $(8, -62)$

$$f(x) = x^2 - 16x + 2$$

Exponential and Logarithmic Functions and Applications

12

CHAPTER OUTLINE

Mathematics and Population Growth

Over short periods of time, human population growth is proportional to the number of humans in the population at a given time. That is, the more people in a population, the faster the population will grow. For example, a country with 10 million people will typically have a greater yearly increase in population than a country with only 1 million people. However, other variables such as food supply, mortality rates, birth control, and immigration also affect population growth.

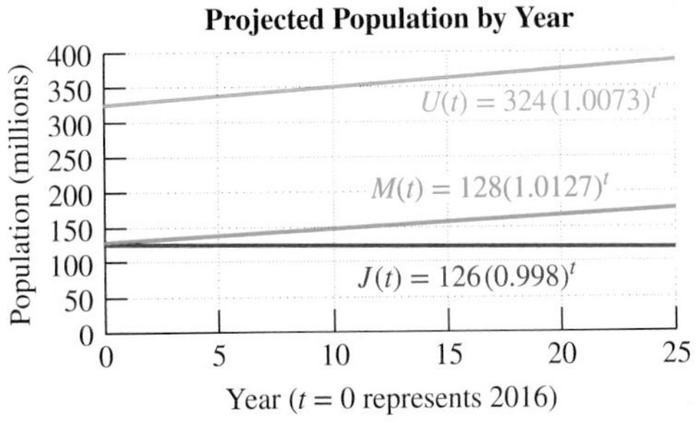

The graph shows the projected population growth for the United States, Mexico, and Japan based on growth rates of 0.73%, 1.27%, and −0.2%, respectively. Since Japan has a negative growth rate, its population is *decreasing*.

The functions *U*, *M*, and *J* that describe the population values versus time are called **exponential functions**. Exponential functions are characterized by having a constant base and variable exponent. In this chapter, we study exponential functions and their inverses, **logarithmic functions**. These functions have far-reaching applications including the study of population growth, the growth of investments, and radioactive decay.

Section 12.1 Inverse Functions

Concepts

1. Introduction to Inverse Functions
2. Definition of a One-to-One Function
3. Definition of the Inverse of a Function
4. Finding an Equation of the Inverse of a Function

Avoiding Mistakes

f^{-1} denotes the inverse of a function. The −1 does not represent an exponent.

1. Introduction to Inverse Functions

A function is a set of ordered pairs (x, y) such that for every element x in the domain, there corresponds exactly one element y in the range. For example, the function f relates the weight of a package of deli meat x to its cost y.

$$f = \{(1, 4), (2.5, 10), (4, 16)\}$$

That is, 1 lb of meat sells for \$4, 2.5 lb sells for \$10, and 4 lb sells for \$16. Now suppose we create a new function in which the values of x and y are interchanged. The new function, called the **inverse of *f***, denoted f^{-1}, relates the price of meat x to its weight y.

$$f^{-1} = \{(4, 1), (10, 2.5), (16, 4)\}$$

Notice that interchanging the x and y values has the following outcome. The domain of f is the same as the range of f^{-1}, and the range of f is the domain of f^{-1}.

2. Definition of a One-to-One Function

A necessary condition for a function f to have an inverse function is that no two ordered pairs in f have different x-coordinates and the same y-coordinate. A function that satisfies this condition is called a **one-to-one function**. The function relating the weight of a package of meat to its price is a one-to-one function. However, consider the function g defined by

$$g = \{(1, 4), (2, 3), (-2, 4)\}$$

same y

different x

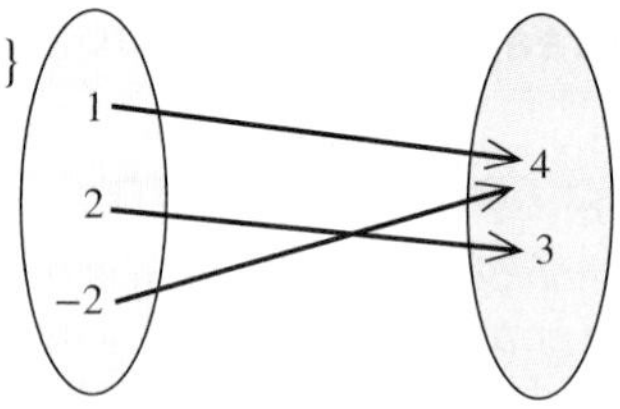

Not a one-to-one function because two different x values map to the same y value.

This function is not one-to-one because the range element 4 has two different x-coordinates, 1 and −2. Interchanging the x- and y-values produces a relation that violates the definition of a function.

$$\{(4, 1), (3, 2), (4, -2)\}$$

same x

different y

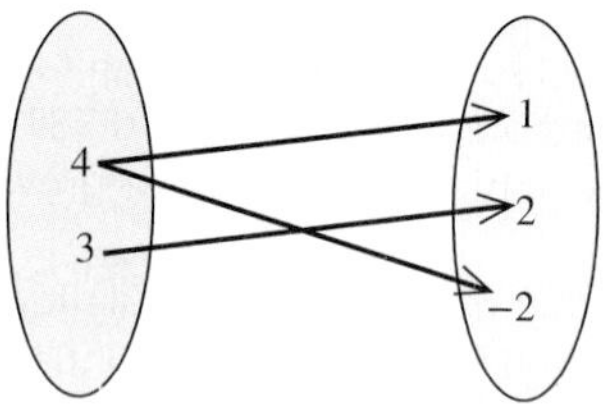

This relation is not a function because for $x = 4$, there are two different y-values.

We have already learned that the vertical line test can be used to visually determine if a graph represents a function. Similarly, we use a **horizontal line test** to determine whether a function is one-to-one.

Using the Horizontal Line Test

Consider a function defined by a set of points (x, y) in a rectangular coordinate system. Then y is a *one-to-one* function of x if no horizontal line intersects the graph in more than one point.

To understand the horizontal line test, consider the functions f and g.

$f = \{(1, 4), (2.5, 10), (4, 16)\}$ $\qquad$ $g = \{(1, 4), (2, 3), (-2, 4)\}$

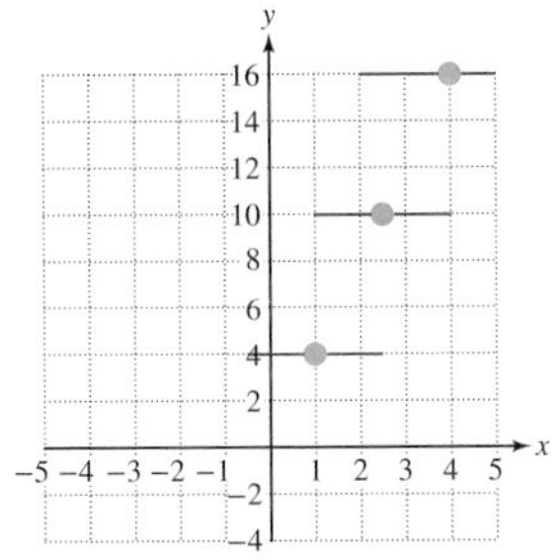

This function is one-to-one. No horizontal line intersects more than once.

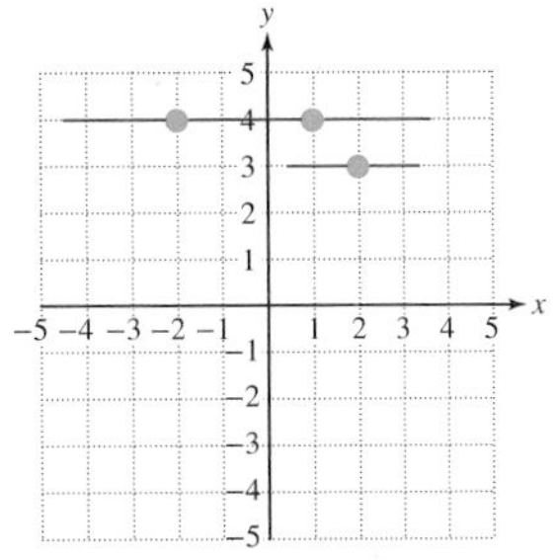

This function is *not* one-to-one. A horizontal line intersects more than once.

Example 1 Identifying a One-to-One Function

Classroom Examples: p. 855, Exercises 18 and 20

For each function, determine if the function is one-to-one.

a.

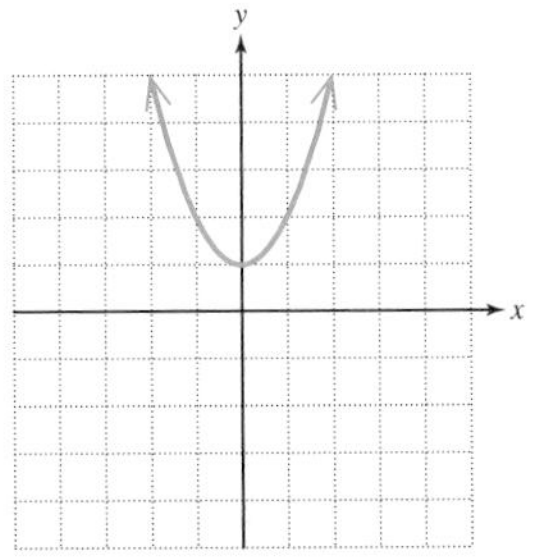

b.

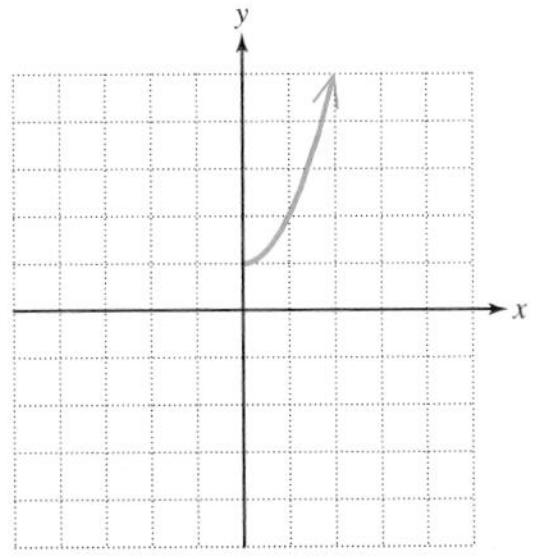

Solution:

a. Function is not one-to-one. A horizontal line intersects in more than one point.

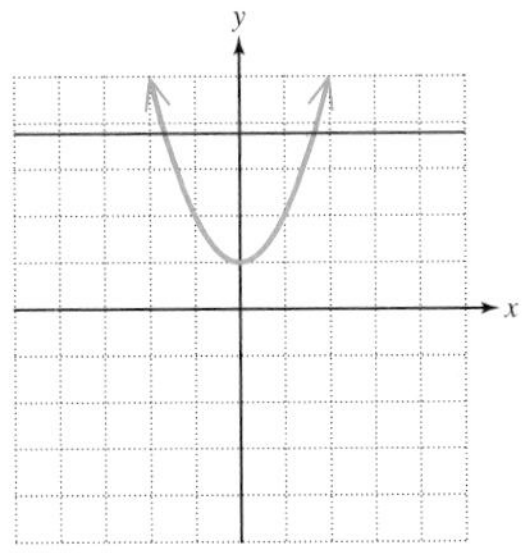

b. Function is one-to-one. No horizontal line intersects more than once.

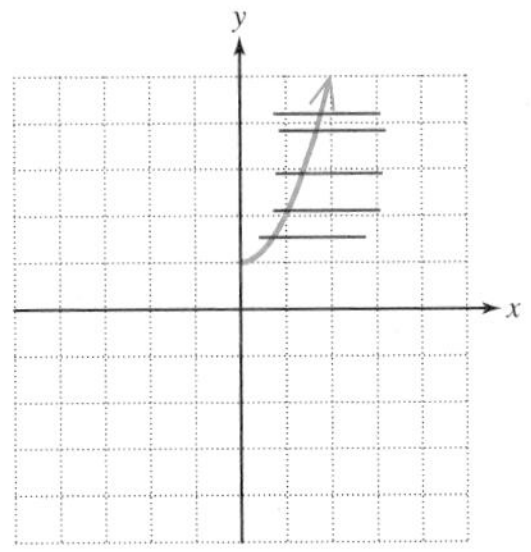

Skill Practice For each function determine if the function is one-to-one.

1.

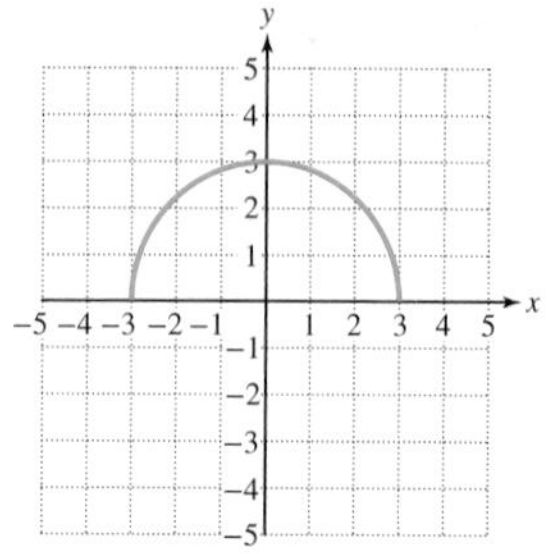

2.

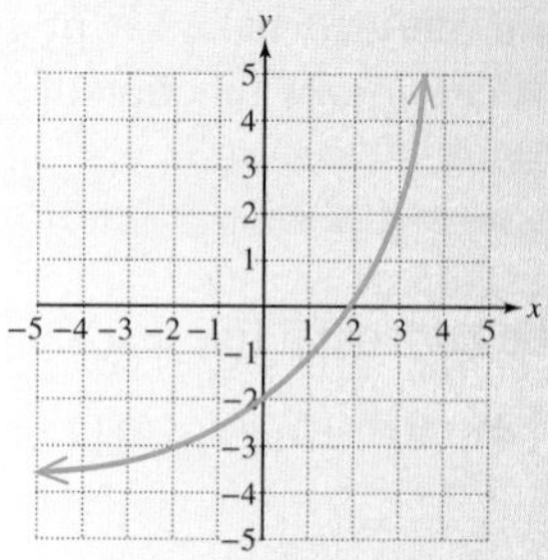

3. Definition of the Inverse of a Function

All one-to-one functions have an inverse function.

Definition of an Inverse Function

If f is a one-to-one function represented by ordered pairs of the form (x, y), then the inverse function, denoted by f^{-1}, is the set of ordered pairs given by (y, x).

Because the values of x and y are interchanged between a function f and its inverse f^{-1}, we have the following important relationship (Figure 12-1).

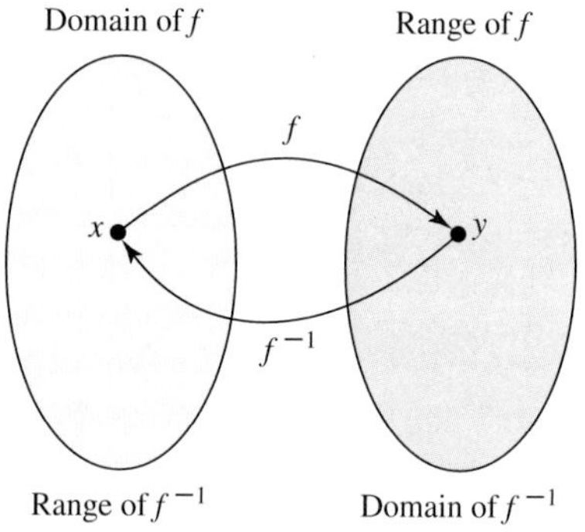

Figure 12-1

From Figure 12-1, we see that the operations performed by f are reversed by f^{-1}. This observation leads to the following important property.

Inverse Function Property

If f is a one-to-one function, then g is the inverse of f if and only if

$$(f \circ g)(x) = x \qquad \text{for all } x \text{ in the domain of } g$$

and

$$(g \circ f)(x) = x \qquad \text{for all } x \text{ in the domain of } f.$$

Answers

1. Not one-to-one
2. One-to-one

Example 2 **Composing a Function with Its Inverse**

Classroom Example: p. 855, Exercise 24

Show that the functions are inverses.

$$f(x) = 5x + 4 \qquad g(x) = \frac{x - 4}{5}$$

Solution:

To show that the functions f and g are inverses, confirm that $(f \circ g)(x) = x$ and $(g \circ f)(x) = x$.

$$\begin{aligned}(f \circ g)(x) &= f(g(x)) \\ &= f\left(\frac{x-4}{5}\right) \\ &= 5\left(\frac{x-4}{5}\right) + 4 \\ &= x - 4 + 4 \\ &= x \checkmark\end{aligned} \qquad \begin{aligned}(g \circ f)(x) &= g(f(x)) \\ &= g(5x+4) \\ &= \frac{(5x+4)-4}{5} \\ &= \frac{5x}{5} \\ &= x \checkmark\end{aligned}$$

Skill Practice Show that the functions are inverses.

3. $f(x) = 3x - 2$ and $g(x) = \dfrac{x + 2}{3}$

4. Finding an Equation of the Inverse of a Function

For a one-to-one function defined by $y = f(x)$, the inverse is a function $y = f^{-1}(x)$ that performs the inverse operations in the reverse order. For example, the function defined by $f(x) = 2x + 1$ multiplies x by 2 and then adds 1. Therefore, the inverse function must *subtract* 1 from x and *divide* by 2. We have

$$f^{-1}(x) = \frac{x - 1}{2}$$ The expression $f^{-1}(x)$ is read as "f inverse of x."

To facilitate the process of finding an equation of the inverse of a one-to-one function, we offer the following steps.

Finding an Equation of an Inverse of a Function

For a one-to-one function defined by $y = f(x)$, the equation of the inverse can be found as follows:

Step 1 Replace $f(x)$ by y.
Step 2 Interchange x and y.
Step 3 Solve for y.
Step 4 Replace y by $f^{-1}(x)$.

Answer

3. $(f \circ g)(x) = f(g(x)) = 3\left(\frac{x+2}{3}\right) - 2 = x$
$(g \circ f)(x) = g(f(x)) = \frac{3x - 2 + 2}{3} = x$

Classroom Example: p. 856, Exercise 30

Example 3 Finding an Equation of the Inverse of a Function

Find the inverse. $f(x) = 2x + 1$

Solution:

Avoiding Mistakes

It is important to check that a function is one-to-one before finding the inverse function.

Foremost, we know the graph of f is a nonvertical line. Therefore, $f(x) = 2x + 1$ defines a one-to-one function. To find the inverse we have

$y = 2x + 1$	**Step 1:**	Replace $f(x)$ by y.
$x = 2y + 1$	**Step 2:**	Interchange x and y.
$x - 1 = 2y$	**Step 3:**	Solve for y. Subtract 1 from both sides.
$\frac{x-1}{2} = y$		Divide both sides by 2.
$f^{-1}(x) = \frac{x-1}{2}$	**Step 4:**	Replace y by $f^{-1}(x)$.

Skill Practice Find the inverse.

4. $f(x) = 4x + 6$

In Example 3, we can verify that $f(x) = 2x + 1$ and $f^{-1}(x) = \frac{x-1}{2}$ are inverses by using function composition.

$$(f \circ f^{-1})(x) = f(f^{-1}(x)) = 2\left(\frac{x-1}{2}\right) + 1 = x \quad ✓ \quad \text{and}$$

$$(f^{-1} \circ f)(x) = f^{-1}(f(x)) = \frac{(2x+1) - 1}{2} = x \quad ✓$$

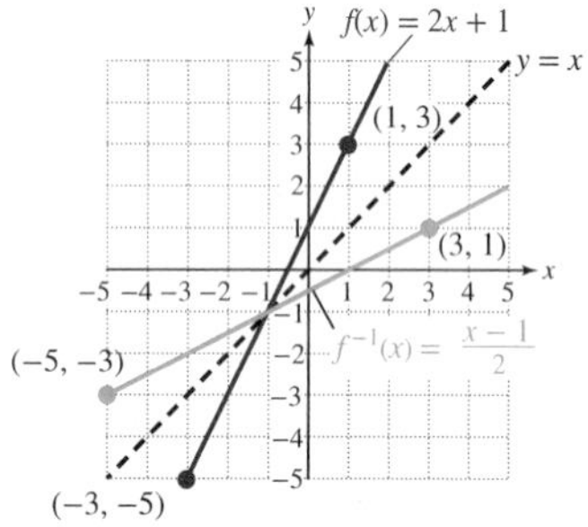

Figure 12-2

The key step in determining the equation of the inverse of a function is to interchange x and y. By so doing, a point (a, b) on f corresponds to a point (b, a) on f^{-1}. For this reason, the graphs of f and f^{-1} are symmetric with respect to the line $y = x$ (Figure 12-2). Notice that the point $(-3, -5)$ of the function f corresponds to the point $(-5, -3)$ of f^{-1}. Likewise, $(1, 3)$ of f corresponds to $(3, 1)$ of f^{-1}.

Classroom Example: p. 856, Exercise 38

Example 4 Finding an Equation of the Inverse of a Function

Find the inverse of the one-to-one function. $g(x) = \sqrt[3]{5x} - 4$

Solution:

$y = \sqrt[3]{5x} - 4$	**Step 1:**	Replace $g(x)$ by y.
$x = \sqrt[3]{5y} - 4$	**Step 2:**	Interchange x and y.
$x + 4 = \sqrt[3]{5y}$	**Step 3:**	Solve for y. Add 4 to both sides.
$(x + 4)^3 = (\sqrt[3]{5y})^3$		To eliminate the cube root, cube both sides.
$(x + 4)^3 = 5y$		Simplify the right side.
$\frac{(x+4)^3}{5} = y$		Divide both sides by 5.
$g^{-1}(x) = \frac{(x+4)^3}{5}$	**Step 4:**	Replace y by $g^{-1}(x)$.

Answer

4. $f^{-1}(x) = \frac{x-6}{4}$

Skill Practice Find the inverse.

5. $h(x) = \sqrt[3]{2x - 1}$

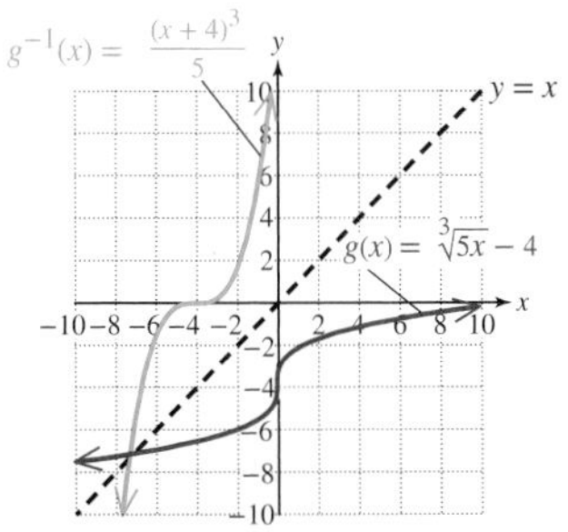

Figure 12-3

The graphs of g and g^{-1} from Example 4 are shown in Figure 12-3. Once again we see that the graphs of a function and its inverse are symmetric with respect to the line $y = x$.

For a function that is not one-to-one, sometimes we can restrict its domain to create a new function that is one-to-one. This is demonstrated in Example 5.

Example 5 Finding the Equation of an Inverse of a Function with a Restricted Domain

Classroom Example: p. 856, Exercise 42

Given the function defined by $m(x) = x^2 + 4$ for $x \geq 0$, find an equation defining m^{-1}.

Solution:

We know that $y = x^2 + 4$ is a parabola with vertex at (0, 4) (Figure 12-4). The graph represents a function that is not one-to-one. However, with the restriction on the domain $x \geq 0$, the graph of $m(x) = x^2 + 4$, $x \geq 0$, consists of only the "right" branch of the parabola (Figure 12-5). This *is* a one-to-one function.

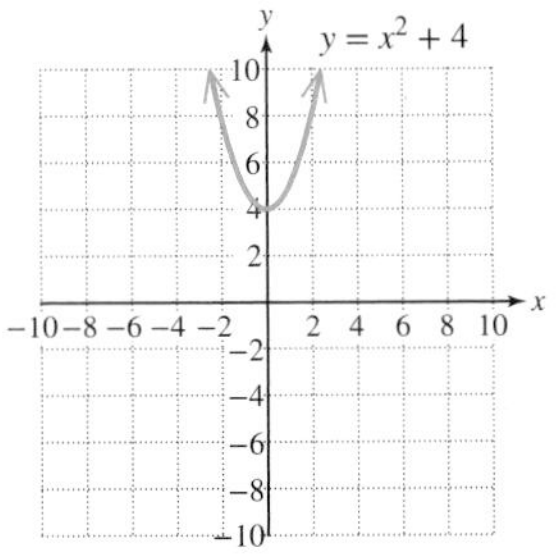

Figure 12-4

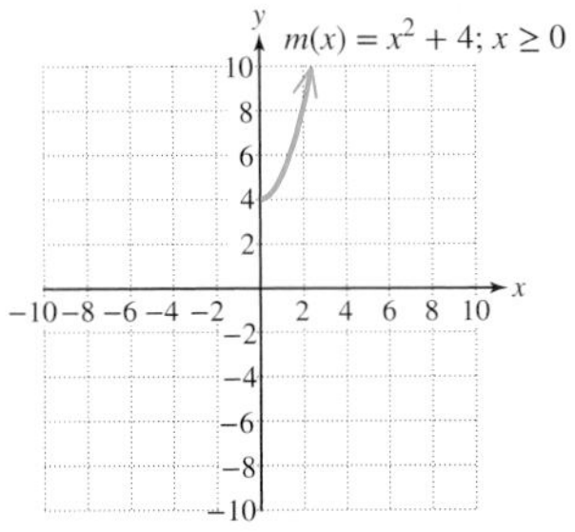

Figure 12-5

To find the inverse, we have

$y = x^2 + 4$	$x \geq 0$	**Step 1:**	Replace $m(x)$ by y.
$x = y^2 + 4$	$y \geq 0$	**Step 2:**	Interchange x and y. Notice that the restriction $x \geq 0$ becomes $y \geq 0$.
$x - 4 = y^2$	$y \geq 0$	**Step 3:**	Solve for y. Subtract 4 from both sides.
$\sqrt{x - 4} = y$	$y \geq 0$		Apply the square root property. Notice that we obtain the *positive* square root of $x - 4$ because of the restriction $y \geq 0$.
$m^{-1}(x) = \sqrt{x - 4}$		**Step 4:**	Replace y by $m^{-1}(x)$. Notice that the domain of m^{-1} has the same values as the range of m.

Figure 12-6 shows the graphs of m and m^{-1}.

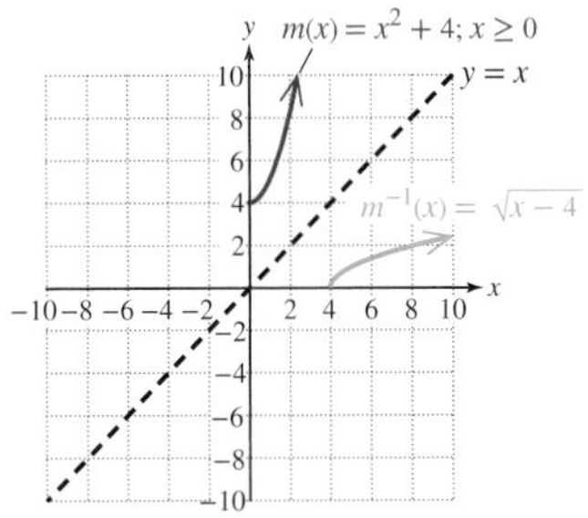

Figure 12-6

Skill Practice Find the inverse.

6. $g(x) = x^2 - 2 \quad x \geq 0$

Answers

5. $h^{-1}(x) = \dfrac{x^3 + 1}{2}$

6. $g^{-1}(x) = \sqrt{x + 2}$

Section 12.1 Practice Exercises

For additional exercises, see Classroom Activities 12.1A–12.1C in the *Student's Resource Manual* at www.mhhe.com/moh.

Vocabulary and Key Concepts

1. **a.** Given the function $f = \{(1, 2), (2, 3), (3, 4)\}$, write the set of ordered pairs representing f^{-1}. $\{(2, 1), (3, 2), (4, 3)\}$

   b. A necessary condition for a function f to be a ______-______-______ function is that no two ordered pairs in f have different x-coordinates and the same ______-coordinate. one-to-one; y

   c. The function $f = \{(1, 5), (-2, 3), (-4, 2), (2, 5)\}$ (is/is not) a one-to-one function. is not

   d. A function defined by $y = f(x)$ (is/is not) a one-to-one function if no horizontal line intersects the graph of f in more than one point. is

   e. The graph of a function and its inverse are symmetric with respect to the line ___$y = x$___.

   f. Let f be a one-to-one function and let g be the inverse of f. Then $(f \circ g)(x) =$ ___x___ and $(g \circ f)(x) =$ ___x___.

   g. The notation ___f^{-1}___ is often used to represent the inverse of a function f and not the reciprocal of f.

   h. If (a, b) is a point on the graph of a one-to-one function f, then the corresponding ordered pair ___(b, a)___ is a point on the graph of f^{-1}.

Review Exercises

2. Write the domain and range of the relation $\{(3, 4), (5, -2), (6, 1), (3, 0)\}$.
   Domain: $\{3, 5, 6\}$; range: $\{4, -2, 1, 0\}$

For Exercises 3–8, determine if the relation is a function by using the vertical line test.

3.

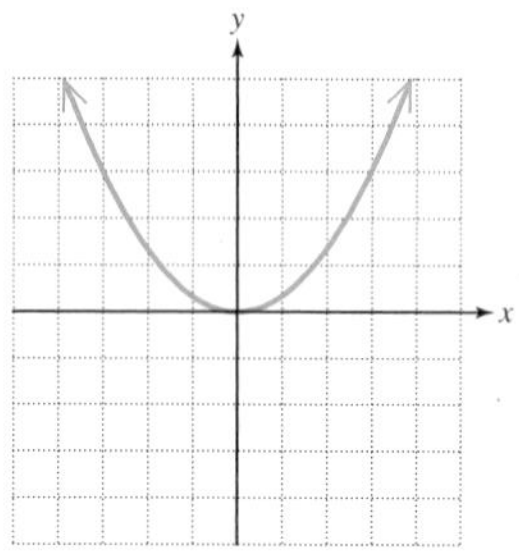

Yes

4.

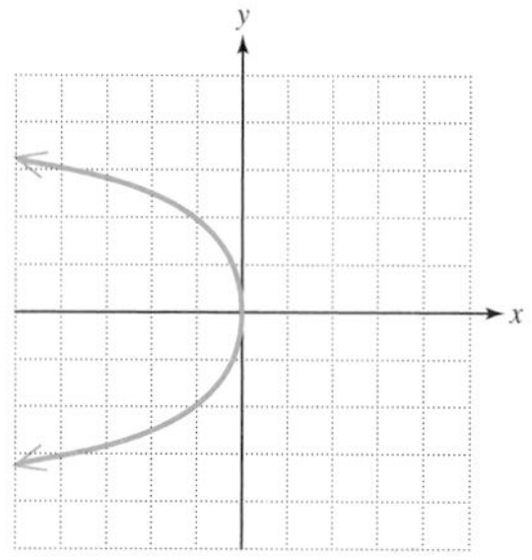

No

5.

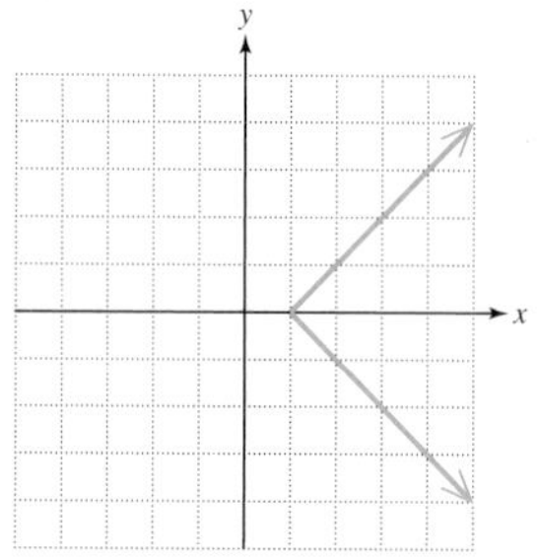

No

6.

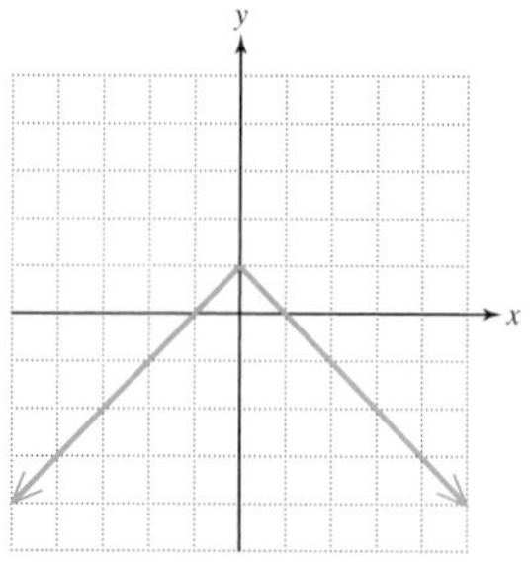

Yes

7.

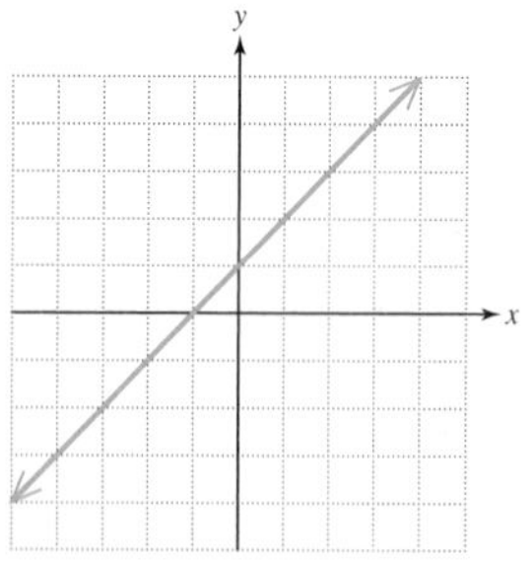

Yes

8.

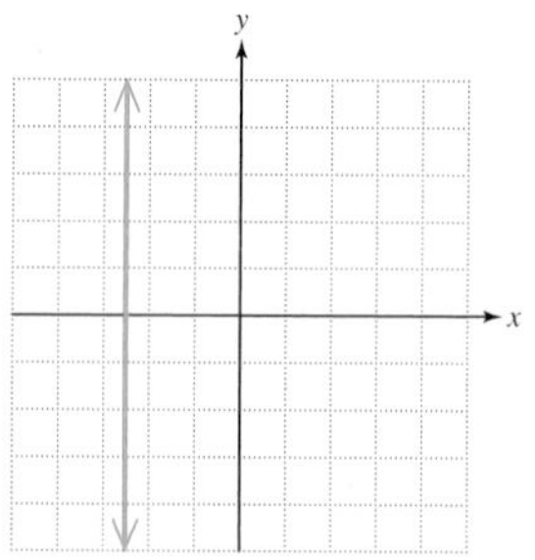

No

Concept 1: Introduction to Inverse Functions

For Exercises 9–12, write the inverse function for each function.

9. $g = \{(3, 5), (8, 1), (-3, 9), (0, 2)\}$
   $g^{-1} = \{(5, 3), (1, 8), (9, -3), (2, 0)\}$

10. $f = \{(-6, 2), (-9, 0), (-2, -1), (3, 4)\}$
    $f^{-1} = \{(2, -6), (0, -9), (-1, -2), (4, 3)\}$

11. $r = \{(a, 3), (b, 6), (c, 9)\}$
    $r^{-1} = \{(3, a), (6, b), (9, c)\}$

12. $s = \{(-1, x), (-2, y), (-3, z)\}$
    $s^{-1} = \{(x, -1), (y, -2), (z, -3)\}$

Concept 2: Definition of a One-to-One Function

13. The table relates a state x to the number of representatives in the House of Representatives y for a recent year. Does this relation define a one-to-one function? If so, write a function defining the inverse as a set of ordered pairs.
The function is not one-to-one.

State x	Number of Representatives y
Colorado	7
California	53
Texas	32
Louisiana	7
Pennsylvania	19

14. The table relates a city x to its average January temperature y. Does this relation define a one-to-one function? If so, write a function defining the inverse as a set of ordered pairs. The function is not one-to-one.

City x	Temperature y (°C)
Gainesville, Florida	13.6
Keene, New Hampshire	−6.0
Wooster, Ohio	−4.0
Rock Springs, Wyoming	−6.0
Lafayette, Louisiana	10.9

For Exercises 15–20, determine if the function is one-to-one by using the horizontal line test. **(See Example 1.)**

15.

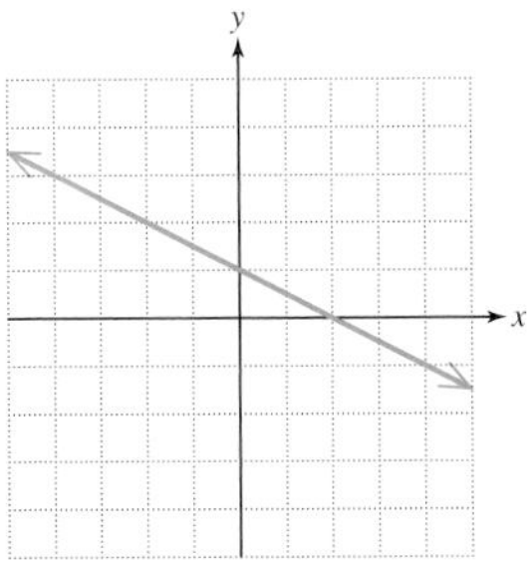

Yes

16.

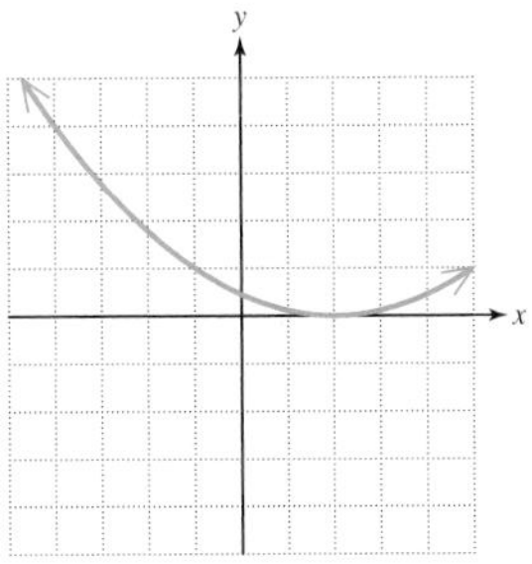

No

17.

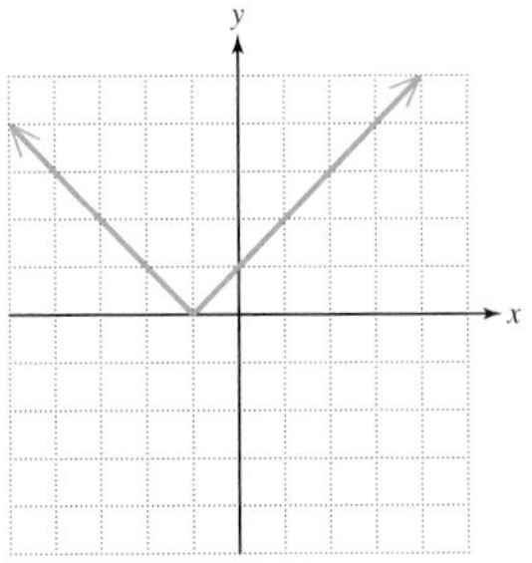

No

18.

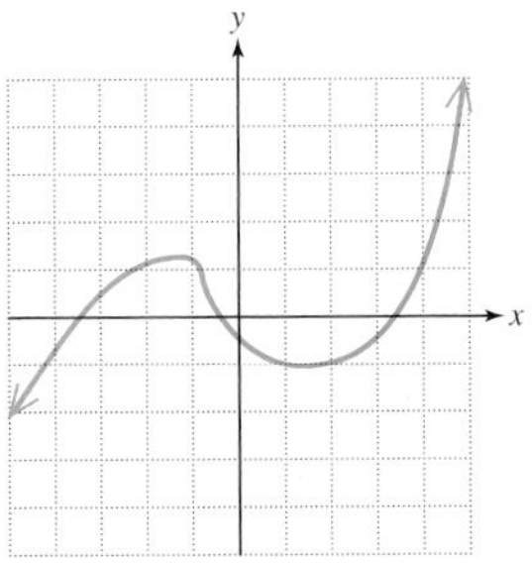

No

19.

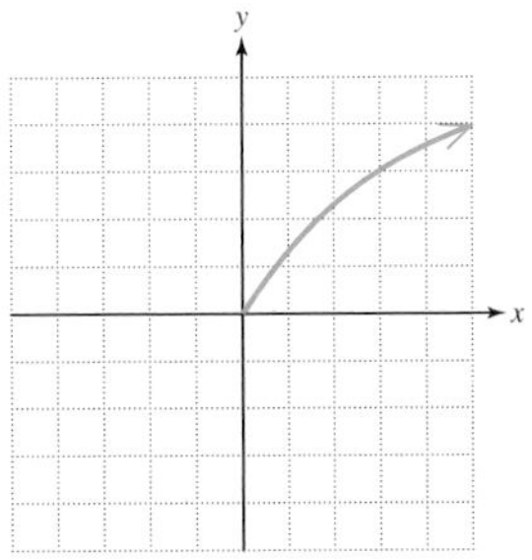

Yes

20.

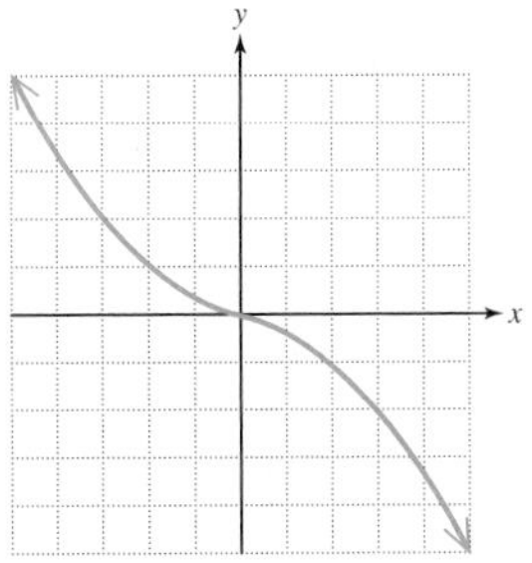

Yes

Concept 3: Definition of the Inverse of a Function

For Exercises 21–26, verify that f and g are inverse functions by showing that

a. $(f \circ g)(x) = x$ **b.** $(g \circ f)(x) = x$ **(See Example 2.)**

21. $f(x) = 6x + 1$ and $g(x) = \dfrac{x-1}{6}$
a. $(f \circ g)(x) = 6\left(\dfrac{x-1}{6}\right) + 1 = x$ b. $(g \circ f)(x) = \dfrac{(6x+1)-1}{6} = x$

22. $f(x) = 5x - 2$ and $g(x) = \dfrac{x+2}{5}$
a. $(f \circ g)(x) = 5\left(\dfrac{x+2}{5}\right) - 2 = x$ b. $(g \circ f)(x) = \dfrac{(5x-2)+2}{5} = x$

23. $f(x) = \dfrac{\sqrt[3]{x}}{2}$ and $g(x) = 8x^3$
a. $(f \circ g)(x) = \dfrac{\sqrt[3]{8x^3}}{2} = x$ b. $(g \circ f)(x) = 8\left(\dfrac{\sqrt[3]{x}}{2}\right)^3 = x$

24. $f(x) = \dfrac{\sqrt[3]{x}}{3}$ and $g(x) = 27x^3$
a. $(f \circ g)(x) = \dfrac{\sqrt[3]{27x^3}}{3} = x$ b. $(g \circ f)(x) = 27\left(\dfrac{\sqrt[3]{x}}{3}\right)^3 = x$

25. $f(x) = x^2 + 1, x \geq 0$, and $g(x) = \sqrt{x-1}, x \geq 1$
a. $(f \circ g)(x) = (\sqrt{x-1})^2 + 1 = x$
b. $(g \circ f)(x) = \sqrt{(x^2+1)-1} = x$

26. $f(x) = x^2 - 3, x \geq 0$, and $g(x) = \sqrt{x+3}, x \geq -3$
a. $(f \circ g)(x) = (\sqrt{x+3})^2 - 3 = x$
b. $(g \circ f)(x) = \sqrt{(x^2-3)+3} = x$

Concept 4: Finding an Equation of the Inverse of a Function

For Exercises 27–42, write an equation of the inverse for each one-to-one function as defined. **(See Examples 3–5.)**

27. $h(x) = x + 4$ $h^{-1}(x) = x - 4$

28. $k(x) = x - 3$ $k^{-1}(x) = x + 3$

29. $m(x) = \frac{1}{3}x - 2$ $m^{-1}(x) = 3(x + 2)$

30. $n(x) = 4x + 2$ $n^{-1}(x) = \frac{x - 2}{4}$

31. $p(x) = -x + 10$ $p^{-1}(x) = -x + 10$

32. $q(x) = -x - \frac{2}{3}$ $q^{-1}(x) = -x - \frac{2}{3}$

33. $n(x) = \frac{3x + 2}{5}$ $n^{-1}(x) = \frac{5x - 2}{3}$

34. $p(x) = \frac{2x - 7}{4}$ $p^{-1}(x) = \frac{4x + 7}{2}$

35. $h(x) = \frac{4x - 1}{3}$ $h^{-1}(x) = \frac{3x + 1}{4}$

36. $f(x) = \frac{6x + 3}{2}$ $f^{-1}(x) = \frac{2x - 3}{6}$

37. $f(x) = x^3 + 1$ $f^{-1}(x) = \sqrt[3]{x - 1}$

38. $g(x) = \sqrt[3]{x} + 2$ $g^{-1}(x) = (x - 2)^3$

39. $g(x) = \sqrt[3]{2x - 1}$ $g^{-1}(x) = \frac{x^3 + 1}{2}$

40. $f(x) = x^3 - 4$ $f^{-1}(x) = \sqrt[3]{x + 4}$

41. $g(x) = x^2 + 9 \quad x \ge 0$ $g^{-1}(x) = \sqrt{x - 9}$

42. $m(x) = x^2 - 1 \quad x \ge 0$ $m^{-1}(x) = \sqrt{x + 1}$

43. The function defined by $f(x) = 0.3048x$ converts a length of x feet into $f(x)$ meters.

a. Find the equivalent length in meters for a 4-ft board and a 50-ft wire. 1.2192 m, 15.24 m

b. Find an equation defining $y = f^{-1}(x)$. $f^{-1}(x) = \frac{x}{0.3048}$

c. Use the inverse function from part (b) to find the equivalent length in feet for a 1500-m race in track and field. Round to the nearest tenth of a foot. 4921.3 ft

44. The function defined by $s(x) = 1.47x$ converts a speed of x mph to $s(x)$ ft/sec.

a. Find the equivalent speed in feet per second for a car traveling 60 mph. 88.2 ft/sec

b. Find an equation defining $y = s^{-1}(x)$. $s^{-1}(x) = \frac{x}{1.47}$

c. Use the inverse function from part (b) to find the equivalent speed in miles per hour for a train traveling 132 ft/sec. Round to the nearest tenth. 89.8 mph

For Exercises 45–51, answer true or false.

45. The function defined by $y = 2$ has an inverse function defined by $x = 2$. False

46. The domain of any one-to-one function is the same as the domain of its inverse. False

47. All linear functions with a nonzero slope have an inverse function. True

48. The function defined by $g(x) = |x|$ is one-to-one. False

49. The function defined by $k(x) = x^2$ is one-to-one. False

50. The function defined by $h(x) = |x|$ for $x \ge 0$ is one-to-one. True

51. The function defined by $L(x) = x^2$ for $x \ge 0$ is one-to-one. True

52. Explain how the domain and range of a one-to-one function and its inverse are related. The domain of a one-to-one function is the same as the range of its inverse. The range of a one-to-one function is the same as the domain of its inverse.

53. If $(0, b)$ is the y-intercept of a one-to-one function, what is the x-intercept of its inverse? $(b, 0)$

54. If $(a, 0)$ is the x-intercept of a one-to-one function, what is the y-intercept of its inverse? $(0, a)$

55. a. Find the domain and range of the function defined by $f(x) = \sqrt{x - 1}$. Domain: $[1, \infty)$, range: $[0, \infty)$

b. Find the domain and range of the function defined by $f^{-1}(x) = x^2 + 1, x \ge 0$. Domain: $[0, \infty)$, range: $[1, \infty)$

56. a. Find the domain and range of the function defined by $g(x) = x^2 - 4, x \le 0$. Domain: $(-\infty, 0]$, range: $[-4, \infty)$

b. Find the domain and range of the function defined by $g^{-1}(x) = -\sqrt{x + 4}$. Domain: $[-4, \infty)$, range: $(-\infty, 0]$

For Exercises 57–60, the graph of $y = f(x)$ is given.

a. State the domain of f. **b.** State the range of f.

c. State the domain of f^{-1}. **d.** State the range of f^{-1}.

e. Graph the function defined by $y = f^{-1}(x)$. The line $y = x$ is provided for your reference.

57.

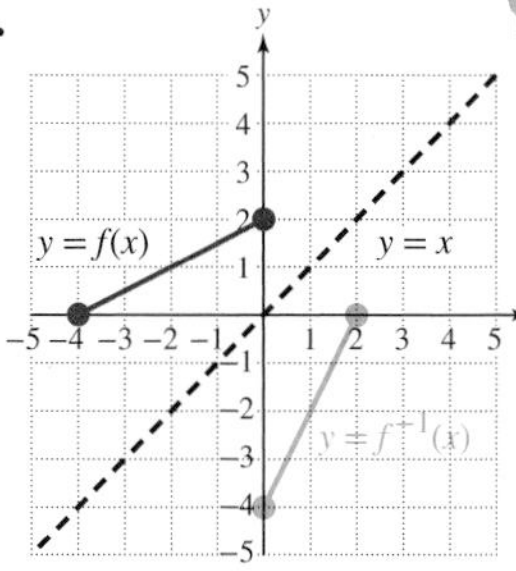

a. $[-4, 0]$ b. $[0, 2]$
c. $[0, 2]$ d. $[-4, 0]$

58.

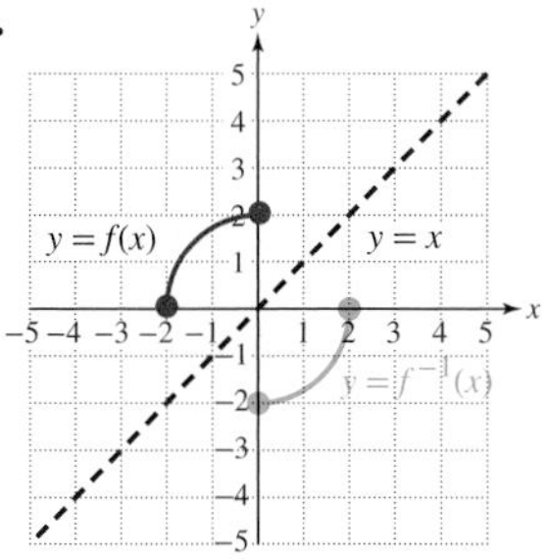

a. $[-2, 0]$ b. $[0, 2]$
c. $[0, 2]$ d. $[-2, 0]$

59.

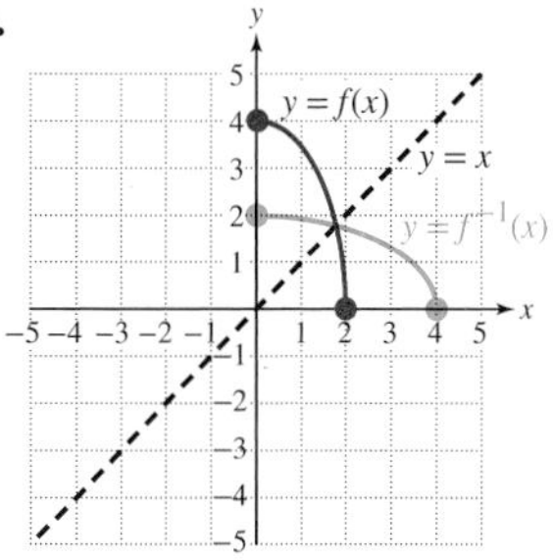

a. $[0, 2]$ b. $[0, 4]$
c. $[0, 4]$ d. $[0, 2]$

60.

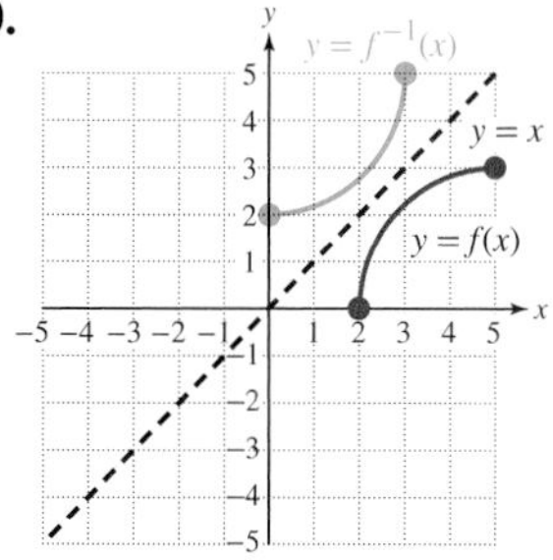

a. $[2, 5]$ b. $[0, 3]$
c. $[0, 3]$ d. $[2, 5]$

Expanding Your Skills

For Exercises 61–70, write an equation of the inverse of the one-to-one function.

61. $q(x) = \sqrt{x + 4}$ $q^{-1}(x) = x^2 - 4,\quad x \geq 0$

62. $v(x) = \sqrt{x + 16}$ $v^{-1}(x) = x^2 - 16,\quad x \geq 0$

63. $z(x) = -\sqrt{x + 4}$ $z^{-1}(x) = x^2 - 4,\quad x \leq 0$

64. $u(x) = -\sqrt{x + 16}$ $u^{-1}(x) = x^2 - 16,\quad x \leq 0$

65. $f(x) = \dfrac{x - 1}{x + 1}$ $f^{-1}(x) = \dfrac{x + 1}{1 - x}$

66. $p(x) = \dfrac{3 - x}{x + 3}$ $p^{-1}(x) = \dfrac{3 - 3x}{x + 1}$

67. $t(x) = \dfrac{2}{x - 1}$ $t^{-1}(x) = \dfrac{x + 2}{x}$

68. $w(x) = \dfrac{4}{x + 2}$ $w^{-1}(x) = \dfrac{4 - 2x}{x}$

69. $n(x) = x^2 + 9 \quad x \leq 0$ $n^{-1}(x) = -\sqrt{x - 9}$

70. $g(x) = x^2 - 1 \quad x \leq 0$ $g^{-1}(x) = -\sqrt{x + 1}$

Graphing Calculator Exercises

For Exercises 71–74, use a graphing calculator to graph each function on the standard viewing window. Use the graph of the function to determine if the function is one-to-one on the interval $-10 \leq x \leq 10$. If the function is one-to-one, find its inverse and graph both functions on the standard viewing window.

71. $f(x) = \sqrt[3]{x + 5}$ $f^{-1}(x) = x^3 - 5$

72. $k(x) = x^3 - 4$ $k^{-1}(x) = \sqrt[3]{x + 4}$

73. $g(x) = 0.5x^3 - 2$ $g^{-1}(x) = \sqrt[3]{2x + 4}$

74. $m(x) = 3x - 4$ $m^{-1}(x) = \dfrac{x + 4}{3}$

Exponential Functions

Section 12.2

1. Definition of an Exponential Function

Concepts

1. Definition of an Exponential Function
2. Approximating Exponential Expressions with a Calculator
3. Graphs of Exponential Functions
4. Applications of Exponential Functions

We have already learned to recognize several categories of functions, including constant, linear, rational, and quadratic functions. In this section and the next, we will define two new types of functions called exponential and logarithmic functions.

To introduce the concept of an exponential function, consider the following salary plans for a new job. Plan A pays \$1 million for a month's work. Plan B starts with 2¢ on the first day, and every day thereafter the salary is doubled.

At first glance, the million-dollar plan appears to be more favorable. Look, however, at Table 12-1, which shows the daily payments for 30 days under plan B.

Table 12-1

Day	Payment	Day	Payment	Day	Payment
1	2¢	11	\$20.48	21	\$20,971.52
2	4¢	12	\$40.96	22	\$41,943.04
3	8¢	13	\$81.92	23	\$83,886.08
4	16¢	14	\$163.84	24	\$167,772.16
5	32¢	15	\$327.68	25	\$335,544.32
6	64¢	16	\$655.36	26	\$671,088.64
7	\$1.28	17	\$1310.72	27	\$1,342,177.28
8	\$2.56	18	\$2621.44	28	\$2,684,354.56
9	\$5.12	19	\$5242.88	29	\$5,368,709.12
10	\$10.24	20	\$10,485.76	30	\$10,737,418.24

Notice that the salary on the 30th day for plan B is over \$10 million. Taking the sum of the payments, we see the total salary for the 30-day period is \$21,474,836.46.

The daily salary for plan B can be represented by the function $y = 2^x$, where x is the number of days on the job and y is the salary (in cents) for that day. An interesting feature of this function is that for every positive 1-unit change in x, the y-value doubles. The function $y = 2^x$ is called an exponential function.

Definition of an Exponential Function

Let b be any real number such that $b > 0$ and $b \neq 1$. Then for any real number x, a function of the form $f(x) = b^x$ is called an **exponential function**.

Instructor Note: Ask students: Is it possible to create a relation $y = b^x$ where b is negative? Why or why not?

An exponential function is recognized as a function with a constant base and exponent, x. Notice that the base of an exponential function must be a positive real number not equal to 1.

2. Approximating Exponential Expressions with a Calculator

Up to this point, we have evaluated exponential expressions with integer exponents and rational exponents, for example, $4^3 = 64$ and $4^{1/2} = \sqrt{4} = 2$. However, how do we evaluate an exponential expression with an irrational exponent such as 4^{π}? In such a case, the exponent is a nonterminating and nonrepeating decimal. The value of 4^{π} can be thought of as the limiting value of a sequence of approximations using rational exponents:

$$4^{3.14} \approx 77.7084726$$
$$4^{3.141} \approx 77.81627412$$
$$4^{3.1415} \approx 77.87023095$$
$$\vdots$$
$$4^{\pi} \approx 77.88023365$$

An exponential expression can be evaluated at all rational numbers and at all irrational numbers. Therefore, the domain of an exponential function is all real numbers.

Example 1 **Approximating Exponential Expressions with a Calculator**

Classroom Example: p. 864, Exercise 18

Approximate the expressions. Round the answers to four decimal places.

a. $8^{\sqrt{3}}$ **b.** $5^{-\sqrt{17}}$ **c.** $\sqrt{10}^{\sqrt{2}}$

Solution:

Calculator Connections

Topic: Investigating Exponential Expressions

On a calculator, use the [^], [y^x], or [x^y] key to approximate an expression with an irrational exponent.

a. $8^{\sqrt{3}} \approx 36.6604$ **b.** $5^{-\sqrt{17}} \approx 0.0013$

c. $\sqrt{10}^{\sqrt{2}} \approx 5.0946$

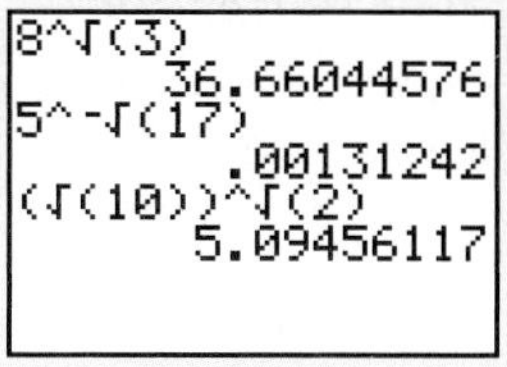

Skill Practice Approximate the value of the expressions. Round the answers to four decimal places.

1. 9^{π} **2.** $15^{\sqrt{5}}$ **3.** $\sqrt{7}^{\sqrt{3}}$

3. Graphs of Exponential Functions

The functions defined by $f(x) = 2^x$, $g(x) = \left(\frac{1}{2}\right)^x$, $h(x) = 3^x$, and $k(x) = 5^x$ are all examples of exponential functions. Example 2 illustrates the two general shapes of exponential functions.

Example 2 **Graphing Exponential Functions**

Classroom Examples: p. 865, Exercises 36 and 38

Graph the functions f and g.

a. $f(x) = 2^x$ **b.** $g(x) = \left(\frac{1}{2}\right)^x$

Solution:

Table 12-2 shows several function values for $f(x)$ and $g(x)$ for both positive and negative values of x. The graphs are shown in Figure 12-7.

Table 12-2

x	$f(x) = 2^x$	$g(x) = \left(\frac{1}{2}\right)^x$
−4	$\frac{1}{16}$	16
−3	$\frac{1}{8}$	8
−2	$\frac{1}{4}$	4
−1	$\frac{1}{2}$	2
0	1	1
1	2	$\frac{1}{2}$
2	4	$\frac{1}{4}$
3	8	$\frac{1}{8}$
4	16	$\frac{1}{16}$

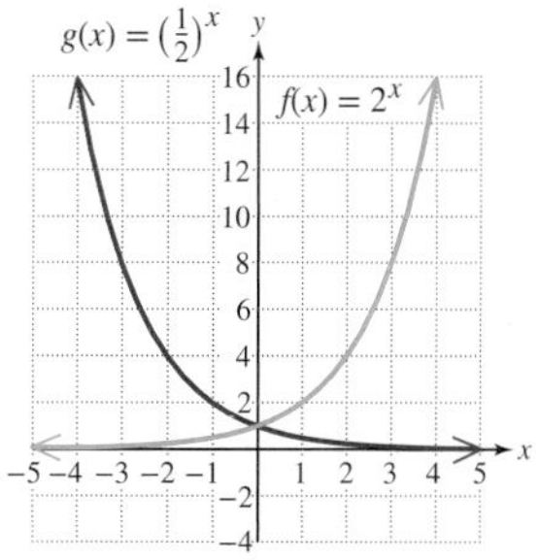

Figure 12-7

Answers

1. 995.0416 **2.** 426.4028
3. 5.3936

Skill Practice Graph the functions f and g on the same grid.

4. $f(x) = 3^x$ **5.** $g(x) = \left(\frac{1}{3}\right)^x$

The graphs in Figure 12-7 illustrate several important features of exponential functions.

Graphs of $f(x) = b^x$

The graph of an exponential function defined by $f(x) = b^x$ ($b > 0$ and $b \neq 1$) has the following properties.

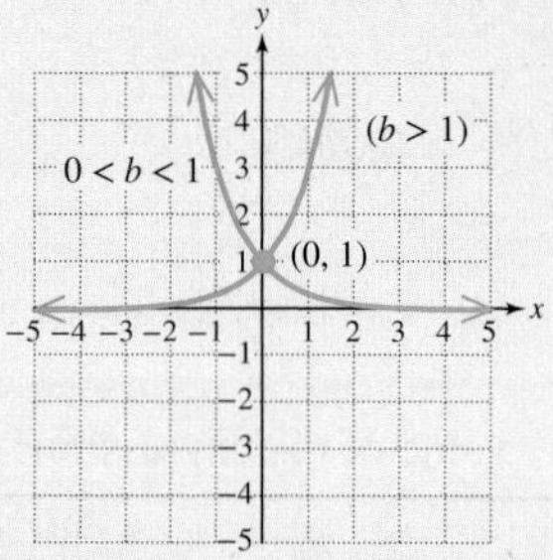

1. If $b > 1$, f is an *increasing* exponential function, sometimes called an **exponential growth function**.

   If $0 < b < 1$, f is a *decreasing* exponential function, sometimes called an **exponential decay function**.
2. The domain is the set of all real numbers, $(-\infty, \infty)$.
3. The range is $(0, \infty)$.
4. The line $y = 0$ (x-axis) is a horizontal asymptote.
5. The function passes through the point $(0, 1)$ because $f(0) = b^0 = 1$.

These properties indicate that the graph of an exponential function is an increasing function if the base is greater than 1. Furthermore, the base affects the rate of increase. Consider the graphs of $f(x) = 2^x$, $h(x) = 3^x$, and $k(x) = 5^x$ (Figure 12-8). For every positive 1-unit change in x, $f(x) = 2^x$ increases by 2 times, $h(x) = 3^x$ increases by 3 times, and $k(x) = 5^x$ increases by 5 times (Table 12-3).

Table 12-3

x	$f(x) = 2^x$	$h(x) = 3^x$	$k(x) = 5^x$
-3	$\frac{1}{8}$	$\frac{1}{27}$	$\frac{1}{125}$
-2	$\frac{1}{4}$	$\frac{1}{9}$	$\frac{1}{25}$
-1	$\frac{1}{2}$	$\frac{1}{3}$	$\frac{1}{5}$
0	1	1	1
1	2	3	5
2	4	9	25
3	8	27	125

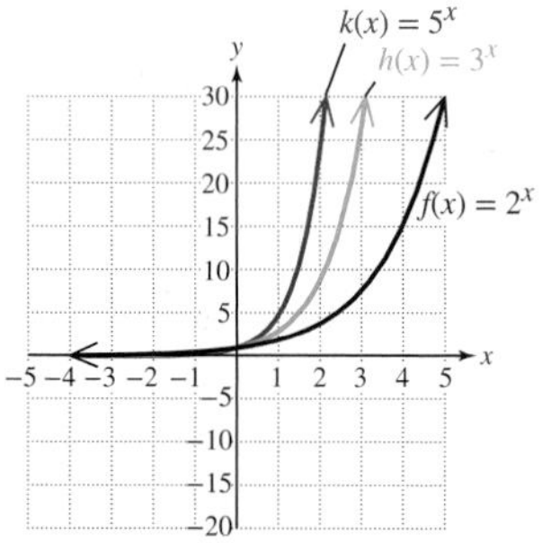

Figure 12-8

Answers

4–5.

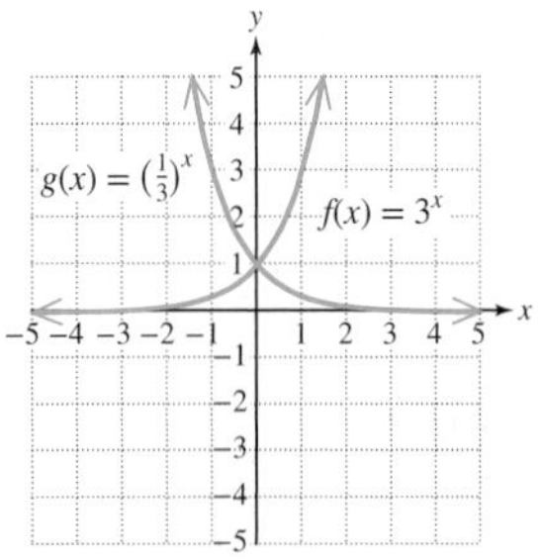

The graph of an exponential function is a *decreasing function* if the base is between 0 and 1. Consider the graphs of $g(x) = (\frac{1}{2})^x$, $m(x) = (\frac{1}{3})^x$, and $n(x) = (\frac{1}{5})^x$ (Table 12-4 and Figure 12-9).

Table 12-4

x	$g(x) = (\frac{1}{2})^x$	$m(x) = (\frac{1}{3})^x$	$n(x) = (\frac{1}{5})^x$
−3	8	27	125
−2	4	9	25
−1	2	3	5
0	1	1	1
1	$\frac{1}{2}$	$\frac{1}{3}$	$\frac{1}{5}$
2	$\frac{1}{4}$	$\frac{1}{9}$	$\frac{1}{25}$
3	$\frac{1}{8}$	$\frac{1}{27}$	$\frac{1}{125}$

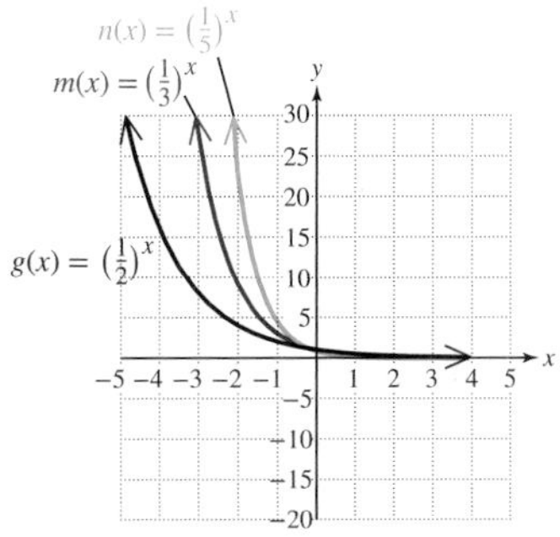

Figure 12-9

4. Applications of Exponential Functions

Exponential growth and decay can be found in a variety of real-world phenomena; for example,

- Short-term population growth can often be modeled by an exponential function.
- The growth of an investment under compound interest increases exponentially.
- The mass of a radioactive substance decreases exponentially with time.
- The temperature of a cup of coffee decreases exponentially as it approaches room temperature.

A substance that undergoes radioactive decay is said to be radioactive. The *half-life* of a radioactive substance is the amount of time it takes for one-half of the original amount of the substance to change into something else. That is, after each half-life the amount of the original substance decreases by one-half.

In 1898, Marie Curie discovered the highly radioactive element radium. She shared the 1903 Nobel Prize in physics for her research on radioactivity and was awarded the 1911 Nobel Prize in chemistry for her discovery of radium and polonium. Radium 226 (an isotope of radium) has a half-life of 1620 years and decays into radon 222 (a radioactive gas).

Marie and Pierre Curie

Example 3 Applying an Exponential Decay Function

Classroom Example: p. 865, Exercise 44

In a sample originally composed of 1 g of radium 226, the amount of radium 226 present after t years is given by

$$A(t) = \left(\frac{1}{2}\right)^{t/1620}$$

where $A(t)$ is the amount of radium in grams and t is the time in years.

a. How much radium 226 will be present after 1620 yr?

b. How much radium 226 will be present after 3240 yr?

c. How much radium 226 will be present after 4860 yr?

Solution:

$$A(t) = \left(\frac{1}{2}\right)^{t/1620}$$

a. $A(1620) = \left(\frac{1}{2}\right)^{1620/1620}$ Substitute $t = 1620$.

$$= \left(\frac{1}{2}\right)^{1}$$

$$= 0.5$$

After 1620 yr (1 half-life), 0.5 g remains.

b. $A(3240) = \left(\frac{1}{2}\right)^{3240/1620}$ Substitute $t = 3240$.

$$= \left(\frac{1}{2}\right)^{2}$$

$$= 0.25$$

After 3240 yr (2 half-lives), the amount of the original substance is reduced by one-half, 2 times. Thus, 0.25 g remains.

c. $A(4860) = \left(\frac{1}{2}\right)^{4860/1620}$ Substitute $t = 4860$.

$$= \left(\frac{1}{2}\right)^{3}$$

$$= 0.125$$

After 4860 yr (3 half-lives), the amount of the original substance is reduced by one-half, 3 times. Thus, 0.125 g remains.

Skill Practice Cesium 137 is a radioactive metal with a short half-life of 30 years. In a sample originally composed of 1 g of cesium 137, the amount, $A(t)$ (in grams), of cesium 137 present after t years is given by

$$A(t) = \left(\frac{1}{2}\right)^{t/30}$$

6. How much cesium 137 will be present after 30 years?

7. How much cesium 137 will be present after 90 years?

Exponential functions are often used to model population growth. Suppose the initial value of a population at some time $t = 0$ is P_0. If the annual rate of increase of a population is r, then after t years, the population $P(t)$ is given by

$$P(t) = P_0(1 + r)^t$$

Answers

6. 0.5 g

7. 0.125 g

Example 4 Applying an Exponential Growth Function

Classroom Example: p. 866, Exercise 48

The population of the Bahamas in 2008 was estimated at 321,000 with an annual rate of increase of 1.39%.

a. Find a mathematical model that relates the population of the Bahamas as a function of the number of years since 2008.

b. If the annual rate of increase remains the same, use this model to estimate the population of the Bahamas in the year 2016. Round to the nearest thousand.

Solution:

a. The initial population is $P_0 = 321{,}000$, and the rate of increase is 1.39%.

$P(t) = P_0(1 + r)^t$ Substitute $P_0 = 321{,}000$ and $r = 0.0139$.

$= 321{,}000(1 + 0.0139)^t$

$= 321{,}000(1.0139)^t$ Here $t = 0$ corresponds to the year 2008.

b. Because the initial population ($t = 0$) corresponds to the year 2008, we use $t = 8$ to find the population in the year 2016.

$P(8) = 321{,}000(1.0139)^8$

$\approx 358{,}000$ The population in the year 2016 was approximately 358,000.

Skill Practice The population of Colorado in 2000 was approximately 3,700,000 with an annual rate of increase of 2%.

8. Find a mathematical model that relates the population of Colorado as a function of the number of years since 2000.

9. Use this model to estimate the population of Colorado in 2016. Round to the nearest thousand.

Answers

8. $P(t) = 3{,}700{,}000(1.02)^t$

9. Approximately 5,079,000

Section 12.2 Practice Exercises

For additional exercises, see Classroom Activities 12.2A–12.2B in the *Student's Resource Manual* at www.mhhe.com/moh.

Vocabulary and Key Concepts

1. **a.** Given a real number b, where $b > 0$ and $b \neq 1$, then a function of the form $f(x) =$ ___ b^x ___ is called an exponential function.

   b. The function defined by $f(x) = x^4$ (is/is not) an exponential function, whereas the function defined by $f(x) = 4^x$ (is/is not) an exponential function. is not; is

   c. The graph of $f(x) = \left(\frac{7}{2}\right)^x$ is (increasing/decreasing) over its domain. increasing

   d. The graph of $f(x) = \left(\frac{2}{7}\right)^x$ is (increasing/decreasing) over its domain. decreasing

   e. In interval notation, the domain of an exponential function $f(x) = b^x$ is ___ $(-\infty, \infty)$ ___ and the range is ___ $(0, \infty)$ ___.

   f. All exponential functions $f(x) = b^x$ pass through the point ___ $(0, 1)$ ___.

   g. The horizontal asymptote of an exponential function $f(x) = b^x$ is the line ___ $y = 0$ ___.

   h. The function defined by $f(x) = 1^x$ (is/is not) an exponential function. is not

Review Exercises

For Exercises 2–7, find the functions, using f and g as given. $f(x) = 2x^2 + x + 2$ $g(x) = 3x - 1$

2. $(f + g)(x)$ $2x^2 + 4x + 1$

3. $(g - f)(x)$ $-2x^2 + 2x - 3$

4. $(f \cdot g)(x)$ $6x^3 + x^2 + 5x - 2$

5. $\left(\frac{g}{f}\right)(x)$ $\frac{3x - 1}{2x^2 + x + 2}$

6. $(f \circ g)(x)$ $18x^2 - 9x + 3$

7. $(g \circ f)(x)$ $6x^2 + 3x + 5$

8. Find the inverse. $\{(2, 3), (0, 0), (-8, 4), (10, 12)\}$ $\{(3, 2), (0, 0), (4, -8), (12, 10)\}$

For Exercises 9–16, evaluate the expression without the use of a calculator.

9. 5^2 25

10. 2^{-3} $\frac{1}{8}$

11. 10^{-3} $\frac{1}{1000}$

12. 3^4 81

13. $36^{1/2}$ 6

14. $27^{1/3}$ 3

15. $16^{3/4}$ 8

16. $8^{2/3}$ 4

Concept 2: Approximating Exponential Expressions with a Calculator

For Exercises 17–24, evaluate the expression by using a calculator. Round to four decimal places. **(See Example 1.)**

17. $5^{1.1}$ 5.8731

18. $2^{\sqrt{3}}$ 3.3220

19. 10^{π} 1385.4557

20. $3^{4.8}$ 195.0662

21. $36^{-\sqrt{2}}$ 0.0063

22. $27^{-0.5126}$ 0.1846

23. $16^{-0.04}$ 0.8950

24. $8^{-0.61}$ 0.2813

25. Solve for x.

a. $3^x = 9$ $x = 2$

b. $3^x = 27$ $x = 3$

c. Between what two consecutive integers must the solution to $3^x = 11$ lie? Between 2 and 3

26. Solve for x.

a. $5^x = 125$ $x = 3$

b. $5^x = 625$ $x = 4$

c. Between what two consecutive integers must the solution to $5^x = 130$ lie? Between 3 and 4

27. Solve for x.

a. $2^x = 16$ $x = 4$

b. $2^x = 32$ $x = 5$

c. Between what two consecutive integers must the solution to $2^x = 30$ lie? Between 4 and 5

28. Solve for x.

a. $4^x = 16$ $x = 2$

b. $4^x = 64$ $x = 3$

c. Between what two consecutive integers must the solution to $4^x = 20$ lie? Between 2 and 3

29. For $f(x) = (\frac{1}{5})^x$ find $f(0), f(1), f(2), f(-1)$, and $f(-2)$. $f(0) = 1, f(1) = \frac{1}{5}, f(2) = \frac{1}{25}, f(-1) = 5, f(-2) = 25$

30. For $g(x) = (\frac{2}{3})^x$ find $g(0)$, $g(1)$, $g(2)$, $g(-1)$, and $g(-2)$. $g(0) = 1, g(1) = \frac{2}{3}, g(2) = \frac{4}{9}, g(-1) = \frac{3}{2}, g(-2) = \frac{9}{4}$

31. For $h(x) = 3^x$ use a calculator to find $h(0)$, $h(1)$, $h(-1)$, $h(\sqrt{2})$, and $h(\pi)$. Round to two decimal places if necessary.
$h(0) = 1, h(1) = 3, h(-1) = \frac{1}{3}, h(\sqrt{2}) \approx 4.73, h(\pi) \approx 31.54$

32. For $k(x) = 5^x$ use a calculator to find $k(0)$, $k(1)$, $k(-1)$, $k(\pi)$, and $k(\sqrt{2})$. Round to two decimal places if necessary.
$k(0) = 1, k(1) = 5, k(-1) = \frac{1}{5}, k(\pi) \approx 156.99, k(\sqrt{2}) \approx 9.74$

Concept 3: Graphs of Exponential Functions

33. How do you determine whether the graph of $f(x) = b^x$ $(b > 0, b \neq 1)$ is increasing or decreasing?
If $b > 1$, the graph is increasing. If $0 < b < 1$, the graph is decreasing.

34. For $f(x) = b^x$ $(b > 0, b \neq 1)$, find $f(0)$. $f(0) = b^0 = 1$

Graph the functions defined in Exercises 35–42. Plot at least three points for each function. **(See Example 2.)**

35. $f(x) = 4^x$

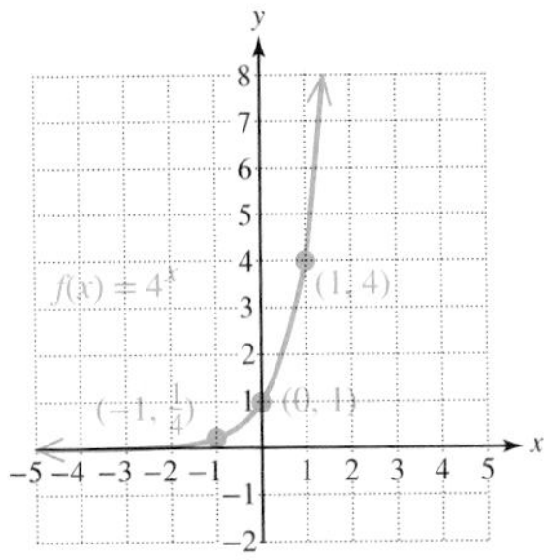

36. $g(x) = 6^x$

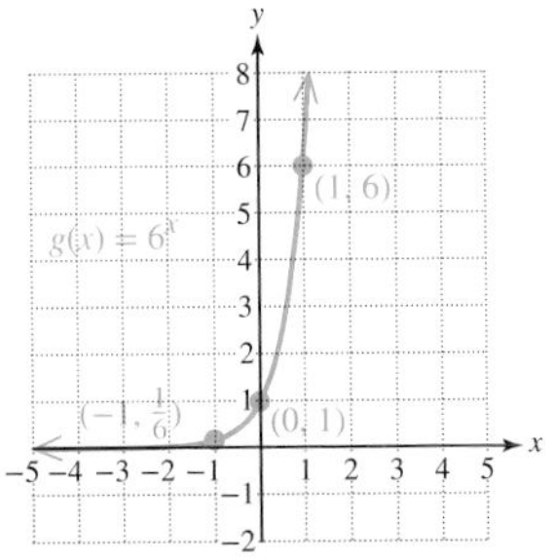

37. $m(x) = \left(\frac{1}{8}\right)^x$

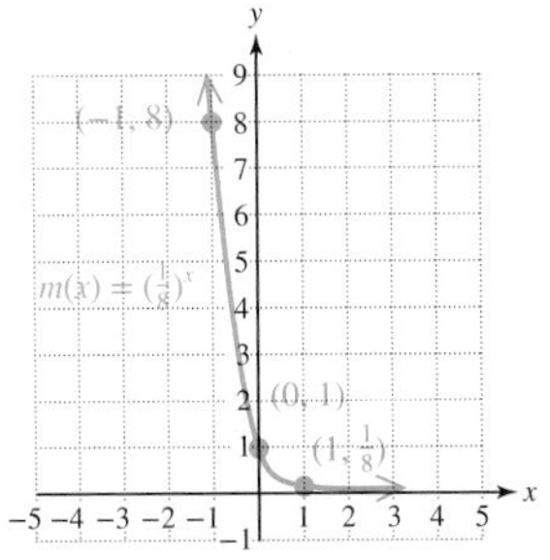

38. $n(x) = \left(\frac{1}{3}\right)^x$

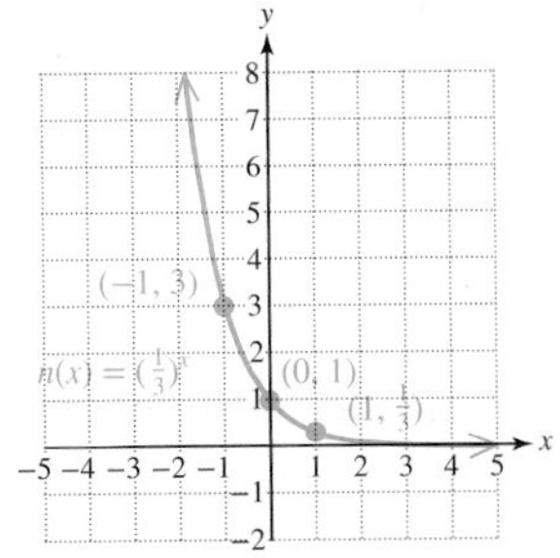

39. $h(x) = 2^{x+1}$

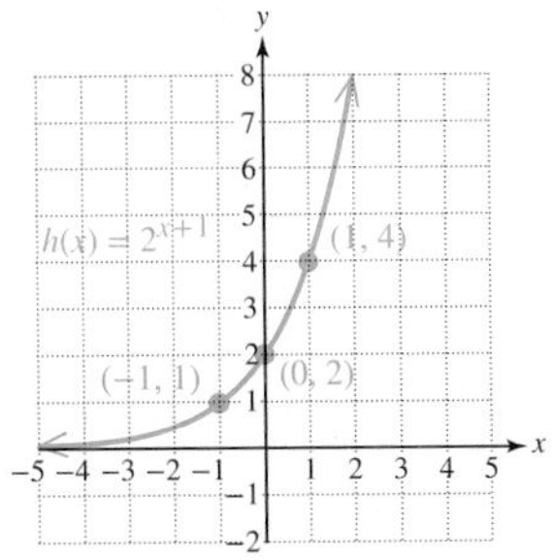

40. $k(x) = 5^{x-1}$

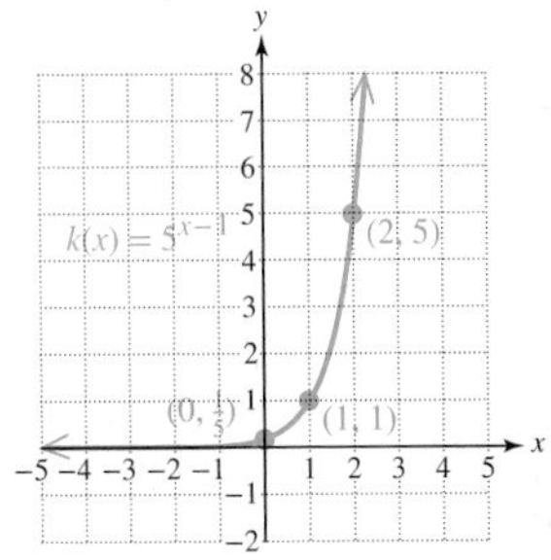

41. $g(x) = 5^{-x}$

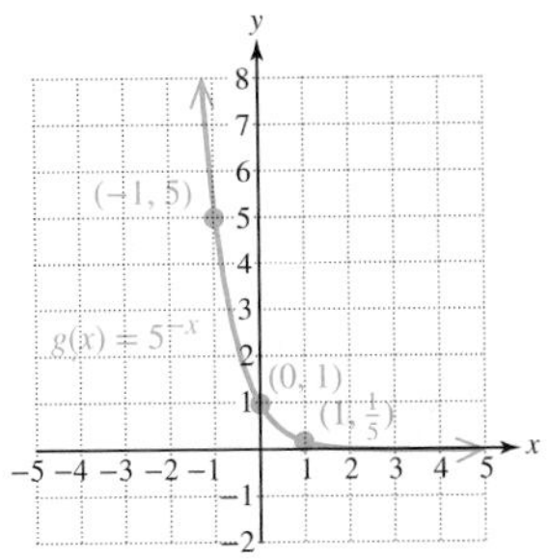

42. $f(x) = 2^{-x}$

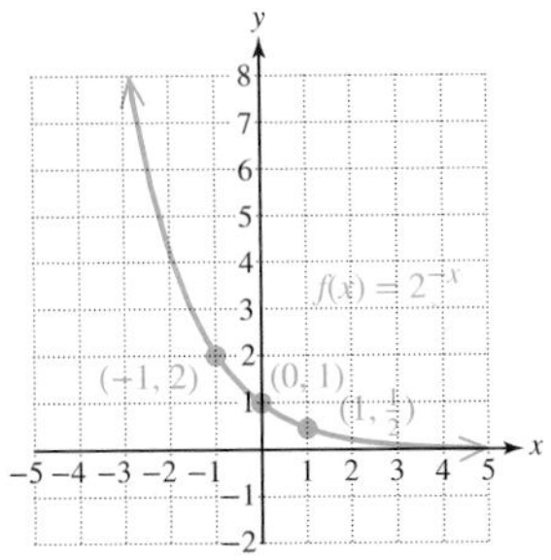

Concept 4: Applications of Exponential Functions

43. The half-life of the element radon (Rn 86) is 3.8 days. In a sample originally containing 1 g of radon, the amount left after t days is given by $A(t) = (0.5)^{t/3.8}$. (Round to two decimal places, if necessary.) **(See Example 3.)**

a. How much radon will be present after 7.6 days? 0.25 g

b. How much radon will be present after 10 days? ≈ 0.16 g

44. Nobelium, an element discovered in 1958, has a half-life of 10 min under certain conditions. In a sample containing 1 g of nobelium, the amount left after t min is given by $A(t) = (0.5)^{t/10}$. (Round to three decimal places.)

a. How much nobelium is left after 5 min? ≈ 0.707 g

b. How much nobelium is left after 1 hr? ≈ 0.016 g

45. Once an antibiotic is introduced to treat a bacterial infection, the number of bacteria decreases exponentially. For example, beginning with 1 million bacteria, the amount present t days from the time penicillin is introduced is given by $A(t) = 1{,}000{,}000(2)^{-t/5}$. Rounding to the nearest thousand, determine how many bacteria are present after

a. 2 days 758,000 **b.** 1 week 379,000 **c.** 2 weeks 144,000

46. Once an antibiotic is introduced to treat a bacterial infection, the number of bacteria decreases exponentially. For example, beginning with 1 million bacteria, the amount present t days from the time streptomycin is introduced is given by $A(t) = 1{,}000{,}000(2)^{-t/10}$. Rounding to the nearest thousand, determine how many bacteria are present after

a. 5 days 707,000 **b.** 1 week 616,000 **c.** 2 weeks 379,000

47. The population of Bangladesh was 153,000,000 in 2009 with an annual growth rate of 1.25%. **(See Example 4.)**

a. Find a mathematical model that relates the population of Bangladesh as a function of the number of years after 2009. $P(t) = 153{,}000{,}000(1.0125)^t$

b. If the annual rate of increase remains the same, use this model to predict the population of Bangladesh in the year 2050. Round to the nearest million. $P(41) \approx 255{,}000{,}000$

48. The population of Fiji was 908,000 in 2009 with an annual growth rate of 0.07%.

a. Find a mathematical model that relates the population of Fiji as a function of the number of years after 2009. $P(t) = 908{,}000(1.0007)^t$

b. If the annual rate of increase remains the same, use this model to predict the population of Fiji in the year 2050. Round to the nearest thousand. $P(41) \approx 934{,}000$

49. Suppose \$1000 is initially invested in an account and the value of the account grows exponentially. If the investment doubles in 7 yr, then the amount in the account t years after the initial investment is given by $A(t)$.

$$A(t) = 1000(2)^{t/7}$$

a. Find the amount in the account after 5 yr. \$1640.67

b. Find the amount in the account after 10 yr. \$2691.80

c. Find $A(0)$ and $A(7)$ and interpret the answers in the context of this problem. $A(0) = 1000$. The initial amount of the investment is \$1000. $A(7) = 2000$. The amount of the investment doubles in 7 yr.

50. Suppose \$1500 is initially invested in an account and the value of the account grows exponentially. If the investment doubles in 8 yr, then the amount in the account t years after the initial investment is given by $A(t)$.

$$A(t) = 1500(2)^{t/8}$$

a. Find the amount in the account after 5 yr. \$2313.32

b. Find the amount in the account after 10 yr. \$3567.62

c. Find $A(0)$ and $A(8)$ and interpret the answers in the context of this problem. $A(0) = 1500$. The initial amount of the investment is \$1500. $A(8) = 3000$. The amount of the investment doubles in 8 yr.

Graphing Calculator Exercises

For Exercises 51–58, graph the functions on your calculator to support your solutions to the indicated exercises.

51. $f(x) = 4^x$ (see Exercise 35)

52. $g(x) = 6^x$ (see Exercise 36)

53. $m(x) = (\frac{1}{8})^x$ (see Exercise 37)

54. $n(x) = (\frac{1}{3})^x$ (see Exercise 38)

55. $h(x) = 2^{x+1}$ (see Exercise 39)

56. $k(x) = 5^{x-1}$ (see Exercise 40)

57. $g(x) = 5^{-x}$ (see Exercise 41)

58. $f(x) = 2^{-x}$ (see Exercise 42)

Logarithmic Functions

Section 12.3

Concepts

1. Definition of a Logarithmic Function
2. Evaluating Logarithmic Expressions
3. The Common Logarithmic Function
4. Graphs of Logarithmic Functions
5. Applications of the Common Logarithmic Function

1. Definition of a Logarithmic Function

Consider the following equations in which the variable is located in the exponent of an expression. In some cases the solution can be found by inspection because the constant on the right-hand side of the equation is a perfect power of the base.

Equation		Solution
$5^x = 5$	$\longrightarrow$	$x = 1$
$5^x = 20$	$\longrightarrow$	$x = ?$
$5^x = 25$	$\longrightarrow$	$x = 2$
$5^x = 60$	$\longrightarrow$	$x = ?$
$5^x = 125$	$\longrightarrow$	$x = 3$

The equation $5^x = 20$ cannot be solved by inspection. However, we might suspect that x is between 1 and 2. Similarly, the solution to the equation $5^x = 60$ is between 2 and 3. To solve an exponential equation for an unknown exponent, we must use a new type of function called a logarithmic function.

Instructor Note: Emphasize to students that, like the notation $f(x)$, we are not multiplying log times x. We read $\log_b x$ as log, base b, of x.

Definition of a Logarithmic Function

If x and b are positive real numbers such that $b \neq 1$, then $y = \log_b x$ is called the **logarithmic function** with base b and

$$y = \log_b x \qquad \text{is equivalent to} \qquad b^y = x$$

Note: In the expression $y = \log_b x$, y is called the **logarithm**, b is called the **base**, and x is called the **argument**.

The expression $y = \log_b x$ is equivalent to $b^y = x$ and indicates that *the logarithm y is the exponent to which b must be raised to obtain x*. The expression $y = \log_b x$ is called the logarithmic form of the equation, and the expression $b^y = x$ is called the exponential form of the equation.

The definition of a logarithmic function suggests a close relationship with an exponential function of the same base. In fact, a logarithmic function is the inverse of the corresponding exponential function. For example, the following steps find the inverse of the exponential function defined by $f(x) = b^x$.

$f(x) = b^x$	
$y = b^x$	Replace $f(x)$ by y.
$x = b^y$	Interchange x and y.
$y = \log_b x$	Solve for y using the definition of a logarithmic function.
$f^{-1}(x) = \log_b x$	Replace y by $f^{-1}(x)$.

The concept of a logarithm is new and unfamiliar. Therefore, it is often advantageous to rewrite a logarithm in its exponential form.

Example 1 Converting from Logarithmic Form to Exponential Form

Classroom Examples: p. 876, Exercises 14 and 16

Rewrite the logarithmic equations in exponential form.

a. $\log_2 32 = 5$ **b.** $\log_{10}\left(\frac{1}{1000}\right) = -3$ **c.** $\log_5 1 = 0$

Solution:

	Logarithmic Form		**Exponential Form**
a.	$\log_2 32 = 5$	$\Leftrightarrow$	$2^5 = 32$
b.	$\log_{10}\left(\frac{1}{1000}\right) = -3$	$\Leftrightarrow$	$10^{-3} = \frac{1}{1000}$
c.	$\log_5 1 = 0$	$\Leftrightarrow$	$5^0 = 1$

Skill Practice Rewrite the logarithmic equations in exponential form.

1. $\log_3 9 = 2$ **2.** $\log_{10}\left(\frac{1}{100}\right) = -2$ **3.** $\log_8 1 = 0$

2. Evaluating Logarithmic Expressions

Classroom Examples: p. 876, Exercises 36 and 46

Example 2 Evaluating Logarithmic Expressions

Evaluate the logarithmic expressions.

a. $\log_8 64$ **b.** $\log_5\left(\frac{1}{125}\right)$ **c.** $\log_{1/2}\left(\frac{1}{8}\right)$

Solution:

a. $\log_8 64$ is the exponent to which 8 must be raised to obtain 64.

$y = \log_8 64$ Let y represent the value of the logarithm.

$8^y = 64$ Rewrite the expression in exponential form.

$8^y = 8^2$

$y = 2$ Therefore, $\log_8 64 = 2$.

b. $\log_5\left(\frac{1}{125}\right)$ is the exponent to which 5 must be raised to obtain $\frac{1}{125}$.

$y = \log_5\left(\frac{1}{125}\right)$ Let y represent the value of the logarithm.

$5^y = \frac{1}{125}$ Rewrite the expression in exponential form.

$5^y = \frac{1}{5^3} = 5^{-3}$

$y = -3$ Therefore, $\log_5\left(\frac{1}{125}\right) = -3$.

c. $\log_{1/2}\left(\frac{1}{8}\right)$ is the exponent to which $\frac{1}{2}$ must be raised to obtain $\frac{1}{8}$.

$y = \log_{1/2}\left(\frac{1}{8}\right)$ Let y represent the value of the logarithm.

$\left(\frac{1}{2}\right)^y = \frac{1}{8}$ Rewrite the expression in exponential form.

$\left(\frac{1}{2}\right)^y = \left(\frac{1}{2}\right)^3$

$y = 3$ Therefore, $\log_{1/2}\left(\frac{1}{8}\right) = 3$.

Skill Practice Evaluate the logarithmic expressions.

4. $\log_{10} 1000$ **5.** $\log_4\left(\frac{1}{16}\right)$ **6.** $\log_{1/3} 3$

Answers

1. $3^2 = 9$ **2.** $10^{-2} = \frac{1}{100}$
3. $8^0 = 1$ **4.** 3
5. -2 **6.** -1

Example 3 Evaluating Logarithmic Expressions

Classroom Examples: p. 876, Exercises 48 and 50

Evaluate the logarithmic expressions.

a. $\log_b b$ **b.** $\log_c c^7$ **c.** $\log_3 \sqrt[4]{3}$

Solution:

a. $\log_b b$ is the exponent to which b must be raised to obtain b.

$y = \log_b b$	Let y represent the value of the logarithm.
$b^y = b$	Rewrite the expression in exponential form.
$y = 1$	Therefore, $\log_b b = 1$.

b. $\log_c c^7$ is the exponent to which c must be raised to obtain c^7.

$y = \log_c c^7$	Let y represent the value of the logarithm.
$c^y = c^7$	Rewrite the expression in exponential form.
$y = 7$	Therefore, $\log_c c^7 = 7$.

c. $\log_3 \sqrt[4]{3} = \log_3 3^{1/4}$ is the exponent to which 3 must be raised to obtain $3^{1/4}$.

$y = \log_3 3^{1/4}$	Let y represent the value of the logarithm.
$3^y = 3^{1/4}$	Rewrite the expression in exponential form.
$y = \dfrac{1}{4}$	Therefore, $\log_3 \sqrt[4]{3} = \frac{1}{4}$.

Skill Practice Evaluate the logarithmic expressions.

7. $\log_x x$ **8.** $\log_b b^{10}$ **9.** $\log_5 \sqrt[3]{5}$

3. The Common Logarithmic Function

The logarithmic function with base 10 is called the **common logarithmic function** and is denoted by $y = \log x$. Notice that the base is not explicitly written but is understood to be 10. That is, $y = \log_{10} x$ is written simply as $y = \log x$.

Example 4 Evaluating Common Logarithms

Classroom Examples: p. 876, Exercises 52 and 56

Evaluate the logarithmic expressions.

a. $\log 100{,}000$ **b.** $\log 0.01$

Solution:

a. $\log 100{,}000$ is the exponent to which 10 must be raised to obtain 100,000.

$y = \log 100{,}000$	Let y represent the value of the logarithm.
$10^y = 100{,}000$	Rewrite the expression in exponential form.
$10^y = 10^5$	
$y = 5$	Therefore, $\log 100{,}000 = 5$.

Answers

7. 1 **8.** 10 **9.** $\frac{1}{3}$

b. log 0.01 is the exponent to which 10 must be raised to obtain 0.01 or $\frac{1}{100}$.

$y = \log 0.01$	Let y represent the value of the logarithm.
$10^y = 0.01$	Rewrite the expression in exponential form.
$10^y = 10^{-2}$	Note that $0.01 = \frac{1}{100}$ or 10^{-2}.
$y = -2$	Therefore, $\log 0.01 = -2$.

Skill Practice Evaluate the logarithmic expressions.

10. log 1,000,000 **11.** log 0.0001

On most calculators the LOG key is used to compute logarithms with base 10. This is demonstrated in Example 5.

Classroom Examples: p. 877, Exercises 60 and 68

Example 5 Evaluating Common Logarithms on a Calculator

Evaluate the common logarithms. Round the answers to four decimal places.

a. log 420 **b.** $\log(8.2 \times 10^9)$ **c.** log 0.0002

Solution:

a. $\log 420 \approx 2.6232$

b. $\log(8.2 \times 10^9) \approx 9.9138$

c. $\log 0.0002 \approx -3.6990$

Calculator Connections

Topic: Evaluating Common Logarithms

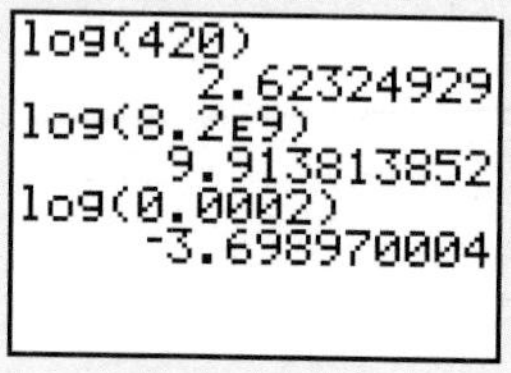

Skill Practice Evaluate the common logarithms. Round answers to four decimal places.

12. log 1200 **13.** $\log(6.3 \times 10^5)$ **14.** log 0.00025

TIP: On a scientific calculator, you may need to enter the logarithm and argument in reverse order. For example: 420 log.

4. Graphs of Logarithmic Functions

Recall that $f(x) = \log_b x$ is the inverse of $g(x) = b^x$. Therefore, the graph of $y = f(x)$ is symmetric to the graph of $y = g(x)$ about the line $y = x$, as shown in Figures 12-10 and 12-11.

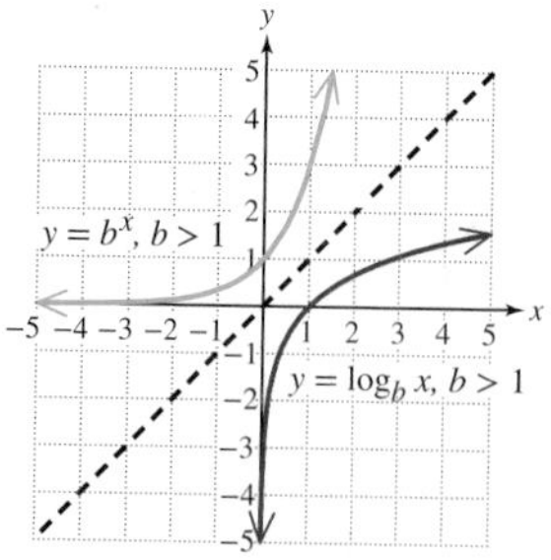

Figure 12-10

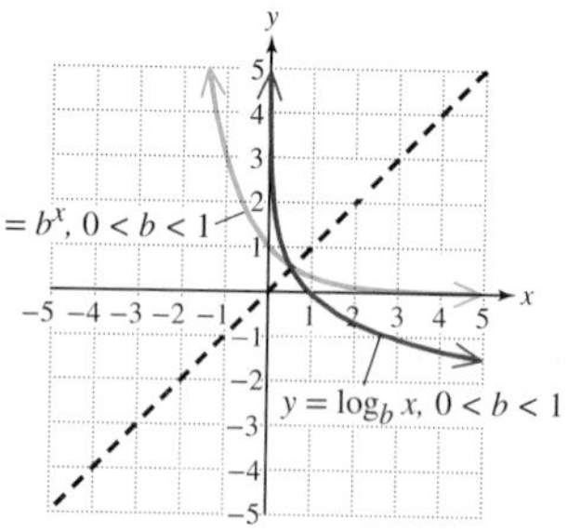

Figure 12-11

From Figures 12-10 and 12-11, we see that the range of $y = b^x$ is the set of positive real numbers. As expected, the domain of its inverse, the logarithmic function $y = \log_b x$, is also the set of positive real numbers. Therefore, the **domain of the logarithmic function** $y = \log_b x$ **is the set of positive real numbers.**

Answers

10. 6 **11.** −4
12. ≈ 3.0792 **13.** ≈ 5.7993
14. ≈ −3.6021

Example 6 Graphing Logarithmic Functions

Classroom Examples: pp. 877–878, Exercises 76 and 78

Graph the logarithmic functions.

a. $y = \log_2 x$ **b.** $y = \log_{1/4} x$

Solution:

A logarithmic function is the inverse of an exponential function with the same base. For this reason, we can reverse the coordinates of the ordered pairs on an exponential function to obtain ordered pairs on the related logarithmic function. For example, to graph the function $y = \log_2 x$ reverse the coordinates of the ordered pairs from its inverse function, $y = 2^x$.

a. Exponential function

x	$y = 2^x$
−3	$\frac{1}{8}$
−2	$\frac{1}{4}$
−1	$\frac{1}{2}$
0	1
1	2
2	4
3	8

Logarithmic function

x	$y = \log_2 x$
$\frac{1}{8}$	−3
$\frac{1}{4}$	−2
$\frac{1}{2}$	−1
1	0
2	1
4	2
8	3

Reverse the order.

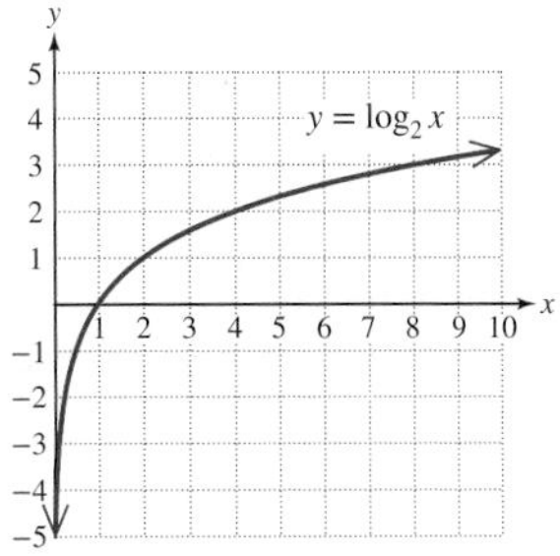

Figure 12-12

The graph of $y = \log_2 x$ is shown in Figure 12-12.

b. Exponential function

x	$y = (\frac{1}{4})^x$
−3	64
−2	16
−1	4
0	1
1	$\frac{1}{4}$
2	$\frac{1}{16}$
3	$\frac{1}{64}$

Logarithmic function

x	$y = \log_{1/4} x$
64	−3
16	−2
4	−1
1	0
$\frac{1}{4}$	1
$\frac{1}{16}$	2
$\frac{1}{64}$	3

Reverse the order.

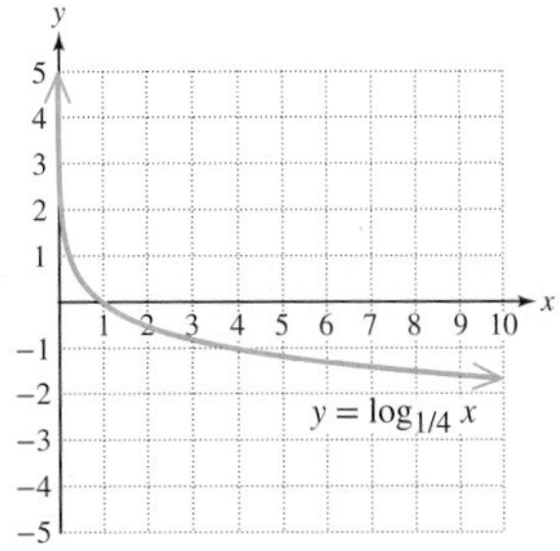

Figure 12-13

The graph of $y = \log_{1/4} x$ is shown in Figure 12-13.

Skill Practice Graph.

15. $y = \log_3 x$ **16.** $y = \log_{1/2} x$

Answers

15–16.

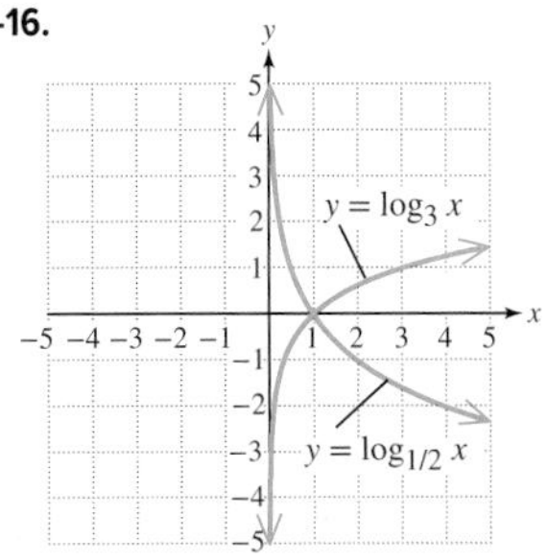

The general shape and important features of exponential and logarithmic functions are summarized as follows.

Graphs of Exponential and Logarithmic Functions

Exponential Functions

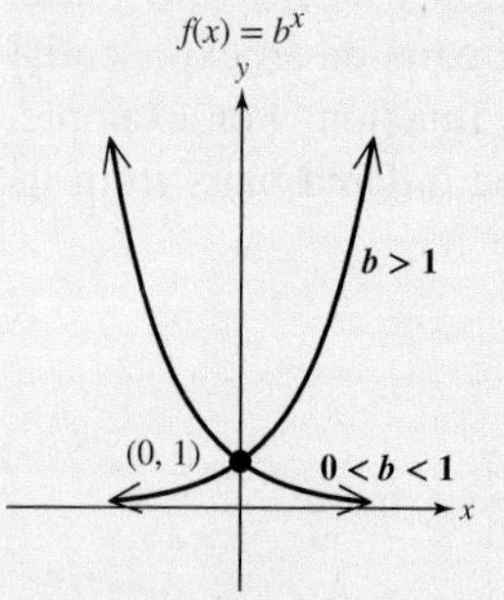

Domain: $(-\infty, \infty)$
Range: $(0, \infty)$
Horizontal asymptote: $y = 0$
Passes through (0, 1)
If $b > 1$, the function is increasing.
If $0 < b < 1$, the function is decreasing.

Logarithmic Functions

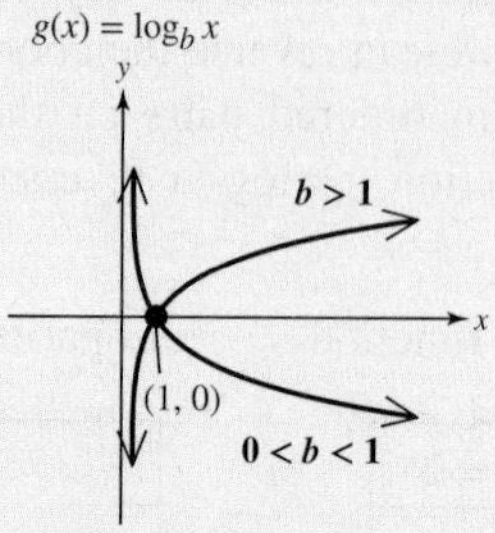

Domain: $(0, \infty)$
Range: $(-\infty, \infty)$
Vertical asymptote: $x = 0$
Passes through (1, 0)
If $b > 1$, the function is increasing.
If $0 < b < 1$, the function is decreasing.

Notice that the roles of x and y are interchanged for the functions $y = b^x$ and $b^y = x$. Therefore, it is not surprising that the domain and range are reversed between exponential and logarithmic functions. Moreover, an exponential function passes through (0, 1), whereas a logarithmic function passes through (1, 0). An exponential function has a horizontal asymptote at $y = 0$, whereas a logarithmic function has a vertical asymptote at $x = 0$.

When graphing a logarithmic equation, it is helpful to know its domain.

Classroom Examples: p. 878, Exercises 82 and 84

Example 7 Identifying the Domain of a Logarithmic Function

Find the domain of each function.

a. $f(x) = \log(4 - x)$ **b.** $g(x) = \log(2x + 6)$

Solution:

The domain of the function $y = \log_b x$ is the set of all positive real numbers. That is, the argument x must be greater than zero: $x > 0$.

a. $f(x) = \log(4 - x)$	The argument is $4 - x$.
$4 - x > 0$	The argument of the logarithm must be greater than zero.
$-x > -4$	Solve for x.
$x < 4$	Divide by -1 and reverse the inequality sign.

The domain is $(-\infty, 4)$.

b. $g(x) = \log(2x + 6)$ — The argument is $2x + 6$.

$2x + 6 > 0$ — The argument of the logarithm must be greater than zero.

$2x > -6$

$x > -3$

The domain is $(-3, \infty)$.

Skill Practice Find the domain of each function.

17. $f(x) = \log_3(x + 7)$ **18.** $g(x) = \log(4 - 8x)$

Calculator Connections

Topic: Graphing Common Logarithmic Functions

The graphs of $Y_1 = \log(4 - x)$ and $Y_2 = \log(2x + 6)$ are shown here and can be used to confirm the solutions to Example 7. Notice that each function has a vertical asymptote at the value of x where the argument equals zero.

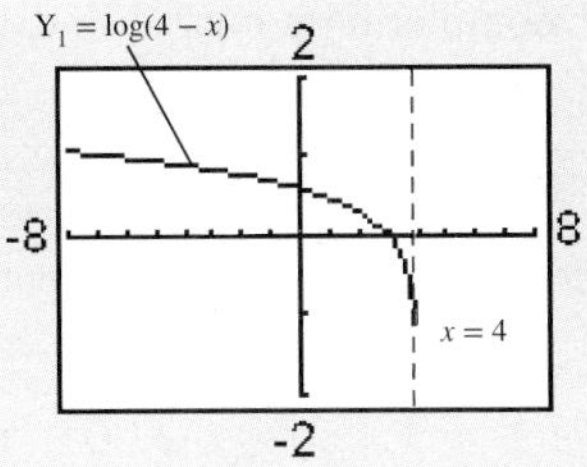

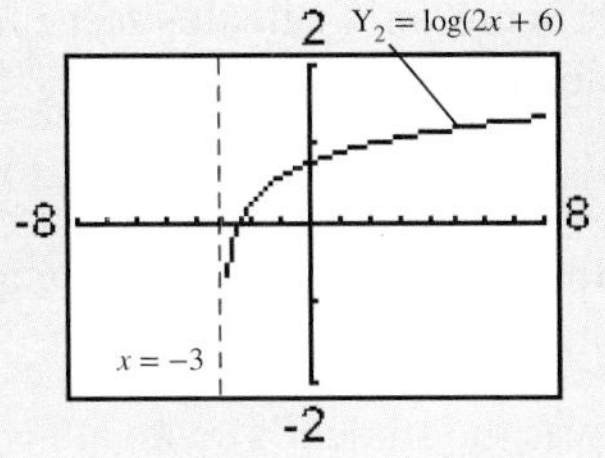

5. Applications of the Common Logarithmic Function

Example 8 Applying a Common Logarithm to Compute pH

Classroom Example: p. 878, Exercise 92

The pH (hydrogen potential) of a solution is defined as

$$\text{pH} = -\log[\text{H}^+]$$

where $[\text{H}^+]$ represents the concentration of hydrogen ions in moles per liter (mol/L). The pH scale ranges from 0 to 14. The midpoint of this range, 7, represents a neutral solution. Values below 7 are progressively more acidic, and values above 7 are progressively more alkaline. Based on the equation $\text{pH} = -\log[\text{H}^+]$, a 1-unit change in pH means a 10-fold change in hydrogen ion concentration.

a. Normal rain has a pH of 5.6. However, in some areas of the northeastern United States the rainwater is more acidic. What is the pH of a rain sample for which the concentration of hydrogen ions is 0.0002 mol/L?

b. Find the pH of household ammonia if the concentration of hydrogen ions is 1.0×10^{-11} mol/L.

Solution:

a. $\text{pH} = -\log[\text{H}^+]$

$= -\log(0.0002)$ — Substitute $[\text{H}^+] = 0.0002$.

≈ 3.7 — The pH of the rain sample is 3.7. (To compare this value with a familiar substance, note that the pH of orange juice is roughly 3.5.)

Answers

17. Domain: $(-7, \infty)$

18. Domain: $\left(-\infty, \frac{1}{2}\right)$

b. $\text{pH} = -\log\,[\text{H}^+]$

$= -\log\,(1.0 \times 10^{-11})$ Substitute $[\text{H}^+] = 1.0 \times 10^{-11}$.

$= -\log\,(10^{-11})$

$= -(-11)$

$= 11$ The pH of household ammonia is 11.

Skill Practice

19. A new all-natural shampoo on the market claims its hydrogen ion concentration is 5.88×10^{-7} mol/L. Use the formula $\text{pH} = -\log\,[\text{H}^+]$ to calculate the pH level of the shampoo.

Classroom Example: p. 879, Exercise 94

Example 9 **Applying a Logarithmic Function to a Memory Model**

One method of measuring a student's retention of material after taking a course is to retest the student at specified time intervals after the course has been completed. A student's score on a calculus test t months after completing a course in calculus is approximated by

$$S(t) = 85 - 25\log\,(t + 1)$$

where t is the time in months after completing the course and $S(t)$ is the student's score as a percent.

a. What was the student's score at $t = 0$?

b. What was the student's score after 2 months?

c. What was the student's score after 1 yr?

Solution:

a. $S(t) = 85 - 25\log\,(t + 1)$

$S(0) = 85 - 25\log\,(0 + 1)$ Substitute $t = 0$.

$= 85 - 25\log 1$ $\log 1 = 0$ because $10^0 = 1$.

$= 85 - 25(0)$

$= 85 - 0$

$= 85$ The student's score at the time the course was completed was 85%.

b. $S(t) = 85 - 25\log\,(t + 1)$

$S(2) = 85 - 25\log\,(2 + 1)$

$= 85 - 25\log 3$ Use a calculator to approximate log 3.

≈ 73.1 The student's score dropped to 73.1%.

c. $S(t) = 85 - 25\log\,(t + 1)$

$S(12) = 85 - 25\log\,(12 + 1)$

$= 85 - 25\log 13$ Use a calculator to approximate log 13.

≈ 57.2 The student's score dropped to 57.2%.

Answer

19. $\text{pH} \approx 6.23$

Skill Practice The memory model for a student's score on a statistics test t months after completion of the course in statistics is approximated by

$$S(t) = 92 - 28 \log (t + 1)$$

20. What was the student's score at the time the course was completed ($t = 0$)?
21. What was her score after 1 month?
22. What was the score after 2 months?

Answers
20. 92 **21.** 83.6 **22.** 78.6

Section 12.3 Practice Exercises

For additional exercises, see Classroom Activities 12.3A–12.3C in the *Student's Resource Manual* at www.mhhe.com/moh.

Vocabulary and Key Concepts

1. a. The function defined by $y = \log_b x$ is called the ____logarithmic____ function with base ____b____. The values of x and b are positive, and $b \neq 1$.

b. Given $y = \log_b x$, we call y the ____logarithm____, we call b the ____base____, and we call x the ____argument____.

c. In interval notation, the domain of $y = \log_b x$ is ____$(0, \infty)$____ and the range is ____$(-\infty, \infty)$____.

d. A logarithmic function base b is the inverse of the ____exponential____ function base b.

e. The logarithmic function base 10 is called the ____common____ logarithmic function and is denoted by $y = \log x$.

f. The graph of a logarithmic function is (increasing/decreasing) if the base $b > 1$, whereas the graph is (increasing/decreasing) if the base is between 0 and 1. increasing; decreasing

g. Which values of x are *not* in the domain of $y = \log (x - 4)$? $x = 2, x = 3, x = 4, x = 5, x = 6$ 2, 3, and 4

h. The graphs of a logarithmic function base b and an exponential function base b are symmetric with respect to the line ____$y = x$____.

Review Exercises

2. For which graph of $y = b^x$ is $0 < b < 1$? ii

3. For which graph of $y = b^x$ is $b > 1$? i

i.

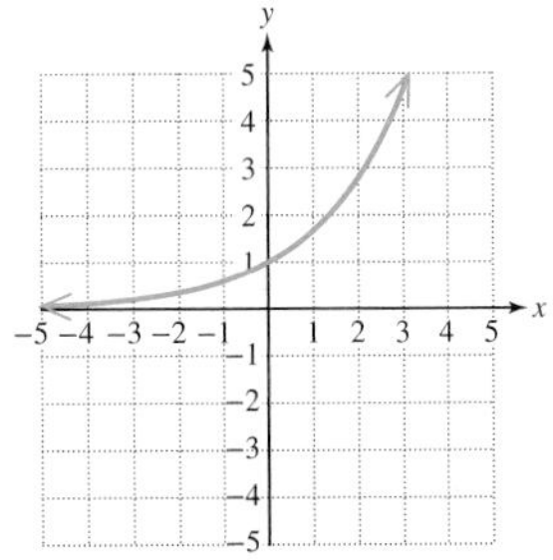

ii.

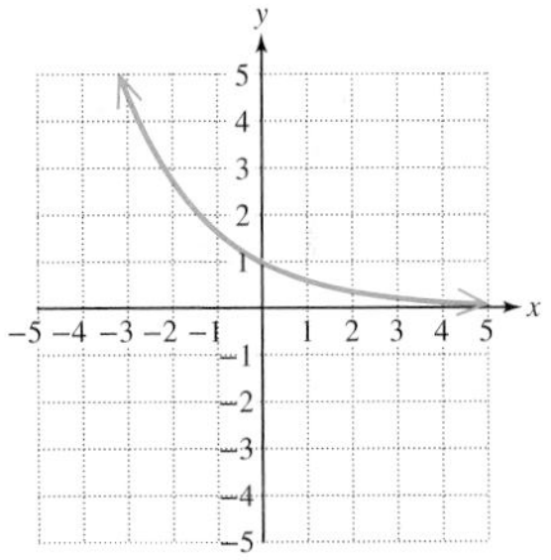

4. Let $f(x) = 6^x$. $f(-2) = \frac{1}{36}, f(-1) = \frac{1}{6}, f(0) = 1, f(1) = 6, f(2) = 36$

a. Find $f(-2), f(-1), f(0), f(1)$, and $f(2)$.

b. Graph $y = f(x)$.

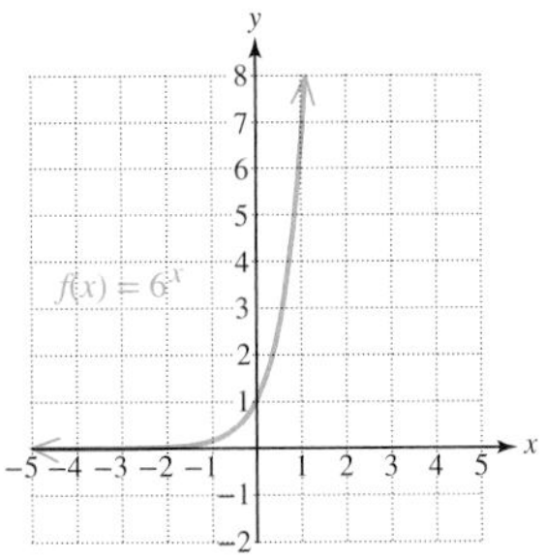

5. Let $s(x) = \left(\frac{2}{5}\right)^x$. $s(-2) = \frac{25}{4}, s(-1) = \frac{5}{2}, s(0) = 1, s(1) = \frac{2}{5}, s(2) = \frac{4}{25}$

a. Find $s(-2)$, $s(-1)$, $s(0)$, $s(1)$, and $s(2)$.

b. Graph $y = s(x)$.

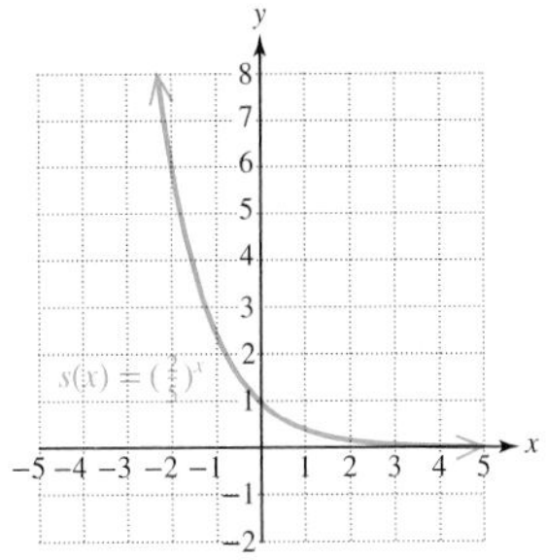

6. Let $r(x) = \left(\frac{3}{4}\right)^x$. Find $r(-2)$, $r(-1)$, $r(0)$, $r(1)$, and $r(2)$.
$r(-2) = \frac{16}{9}$, $r(-1) = \frac{4}{3}$, $r(0) = 1$, $r(1) = \frac{3}{4}$, $r(2) = \frac{9}{16}$

7. Let $g(x) = 3^x$. Find $g(-2)$, $g(-1)$, $g(0)$, $g(1)$, and $g(2)$.
$g(-2) = \frac{1}{9}$, $g(-1) = \frac{1}{3}$, $g(0) = 1$, $g(1) = 3$, $g(2) = 9$

Concept 1: Definition of a Logarithmic Function

8. For the equation $y = \log_b x$, identify the base, the argument, and the logarithm.
The base is b, x is the argument, y is the logarithm.

9. Rewrite the equation in exponential form. $y = \log_b x$ $b^y = x$

10. Write the equation in logarithmic form. $b^y = x$ $\log_b x = y$

For Exercises 11–22, write the equation in exponential form. **(See Example 1.)**

11. $\log_5 625 = 4$ $5^4 = 625$

12. $\log_{125} 25 = \frac{2}{3}$ $125^{2/3} = 25$

13. $\log_{10} (0.0001) = -4$ $10^{-4} = 0.0001$

14. $\log_{25}\left(\frac{1}{5}\right) = -\frac{1}{2}$ $25^{-1/2} = \frac{1}{5}$

15. $\log_6 36 = 2$ $6^2 = 36$

16. $\log_2 128 = 7$ $2^7 = 128$

17. $\log_b 15 = x$ $b^x = 15$

18. $\log_b 82 = y$ $b^y = 82$

19. $\log_3 5 = x$ $3^x = 5$

20. $\log_2 7 = x$ $2^x = 7$

21. $\log_{1/4} x = 10$ $\left(\frac{1}{4}\right)^{10} = x$

22. $\log_{1/2} x = 6$ $\left(\frac{1}{2}\right)^6 = x$

For Exercises 23–34, write the equation in logarithmic form.

23. $3^x = 81$ $\log_3 81 = x$

24. $10^3 = 1000$ $\log_{10} 1000 = 3$

25. $5^2 = 25$ $\log_5 25 = 2$

26. $8^{1/3} = 2$ $\log_8 2 = \frac{1}{3}$

27. $7^{-1} = \frac{1}{7}$ $\log_7\left(\frac{1}{7}\right) = -1$

28. $8^{-2} = \frac{1}{64}$ $\log_8\left(\frac{1}{64}\right) = -2$

29. $b^x = y$ $\log_b y = x$

30. $b^y = x$ $\log_b x = y$

31. $e^x = y$ $\log_e y = x$

32. $e^y = x$ $\log_e x = y$

33. $\left(\frac{1}{3}\right)^{-2} = 9$ $\log_{1/3} 9 = -2$

34. $\left(\frac{5}{2}\right)^{-1} = \frac{2}{5}$ $\log_{5/2}\left(\frac{2}{5}\right) = -1$

Concept 2: Evaluating Logarithmic Expressions

For Exercises 35–50, evaluate the logarithm without the use of a calculator. **(See Examples 2–3.)**

35. $\log_7 49$ 2

36. $\log_3 81$ 4

37. $\log_{10} 0.1$ −1

38. $\log_2\left(\frac{1}{16}\right)$ −4

39. $\log_{16} 4$ $\frac{1}{2}$

40. $\log_8 2$ $\frac{1}{3}$

41. $\log_{7/2} 1$ 0

42. $\log_{1/2} 2$ −1

43. $\log_3 3^5$ 5

44. $\log_9 9^3$ 3

45. $\log_{10} 10$ 1

46. $\log_7 1$ 0

47. $\log_a a^3$ 3

48. $\log_r r^4$ 4

49. $\log_x \sqrt{x}$ $\frac{1}{2}$

50. $\log_y \sqrt[3]{y}$ $\frac{1}{3}$

Concept 3: The Common Logarithmic Function

For Exercises 51–58, evaluate the common logarithm without the use of a calculator. **(See Example 4.)**

51. log 10 1

52. log 100 2

53. log 1000 3

54. log 10,000 4

55. $\log (1.0 \times 10^6)$ 6

56. log 0.1 −1

57. log 0.01 −2

58. log 0.001 −3

For Exercises 59–70, use a calculator to approximate the logarithms. Round to four decimal places. **(See Example 5.)**

59. $\log 6$ 0.7782

60. $\log 18$ 1.2553

61. $\log \pi$ 0.4971

62. $\log\left(\frac{1}{8}\right)$ −0.9031

63. $\log\left(\frac{1}{32}\right)$ −1.5051

64. $\log \sqrt{5}$ 0.3495

65. $\log 0.0054$ −2.2676

66. $\log 0.0000062$ −5.2076

67. $\log (3.4 \times 10^5)$ 5.5315

68. $\log (4.78 \times 10^9)$ 9.6794

69. $\log (3.8 \times 10^{-8})$ −7.4202

70. $\log (2.77 \times 10^{-4})$ −3.5575

71. Given: $\log 10 = 1$ and $\log 100 = 2$

a. Estimate $\log 93$. Slightly less than 2

b. Estimate $\log 12$. Slightly more than 1

c. Evaluate the logarithms in parts (a) and (b) on a calculator and compare to your estimates. $\log 93 \approx 1.9685$, $\log 12 \approx 1.0792$

72. Given: $\log\left(\frac{1}{10}\right) = -1$ and $\log 1 = 0$

a. Estimate $\log\left(\frac{9}{10}\right)$. Slightly less than 0

b. Estimate $\log\left(\frac{1}{5}\right)$. Slightly more than −1

c. Evaluate the logarithms in parts (a) and (b) on a calculator and compare to your estimates. $\log\left(\frac{9}{10}\right) \approx -0.0458$, $\log\left(\frac{1}{5}\right) \approx -0.6990$

Concept 4: Graphs of Logarithmic Functions

73. Let $f(x) = \log_4 x$. $f\left(\frac{1}{64}\right) = -3$, $f\left(\frac{1}{16}\right) = -2$, $f\left(\frac{1}{4}\right) = -1$,

a. Find the values of $f\left(\frac{1}{64}\right)$, $f\left(\frac{1}{16}\right)$, $f\left(\frac{1}{4}\right)$, $f(1)$, $f(4)$, $f(16)$, and $f(64)$. $f(1) = 0$, $f(4) = 1$, $f(16) = 2$, $f(64) = 3$

b. Graph $y = f(x)$. **(See Example 6.)**

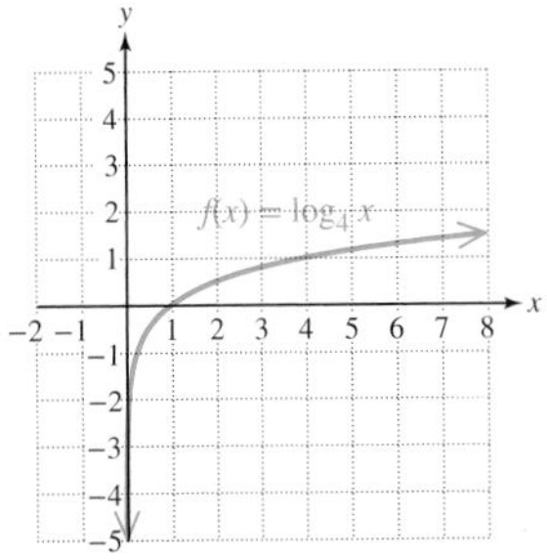

74. Let $g(x) = \log_2 x$. $g\left(\frac{1}{8}\right) = -3$, $g\left(\frac{1}{4}\right) = -2$, $g\left(\frac{1}{2}\right) = -1$,

a. Find the values of $g\left(\frac{1}{8}\right)$, $g\left(\frac{1}{4}\right)$, $g\left(\frac{1}{2}\right)$, $g(1)$, $g(2)$, $g(4)$, and $g(8)$. $g(1) = 0$, $g(2) = 1$, $g(4) = 2$, $g(8) = 3$

b. Graph $y = g(x)$.

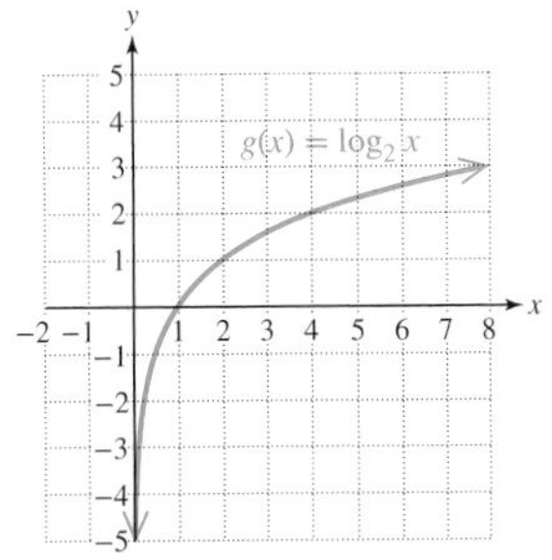

Graph the logarithmic functions in Exercises 75–78 by writing the function in exponential form and making a table of points. **(See Example 6.)**

75. $y = \log_3 x$ $3^y = x$

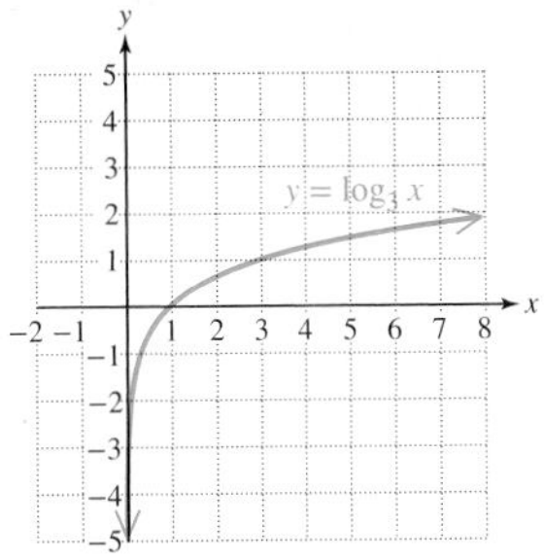

x	y
$\frac{1}{9}$	−2
$\frac{1}{3}$	−1
1	0
3	1
9	2

76. $y = \log_5 x$ $5^y = x$

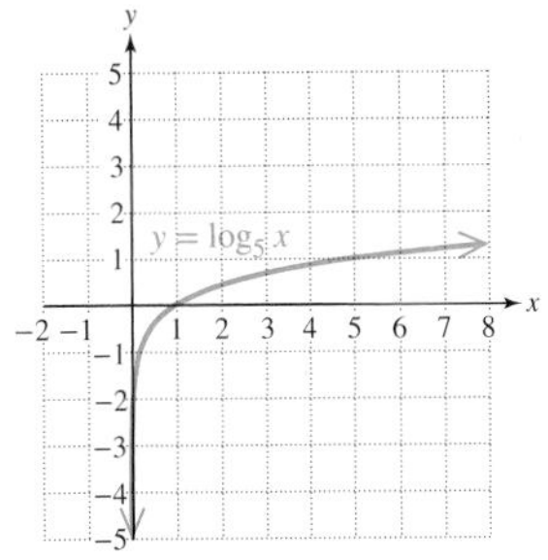

x	y
$\frac{1}{25}$	−2
$\frac{1}{5}$	−1
1	0
5	1
25	2

77. $y = \log_{1/2} x$ **(See Example 6.)** $\left(\frac{1}{2}\right)^y = x$

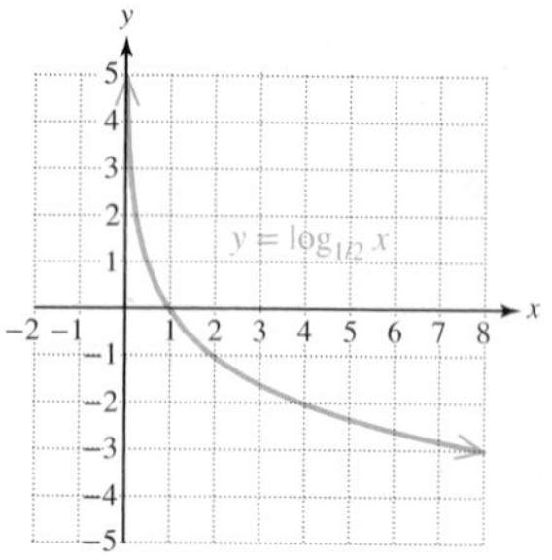

x	y
4	−2
2	−1
1	0
$\frac{1}{2}$	1
$\frac{1}{4}$	2

78. $y = \log_{1/3} x$ $\left(\frac{1}{3}\right)^y = x$

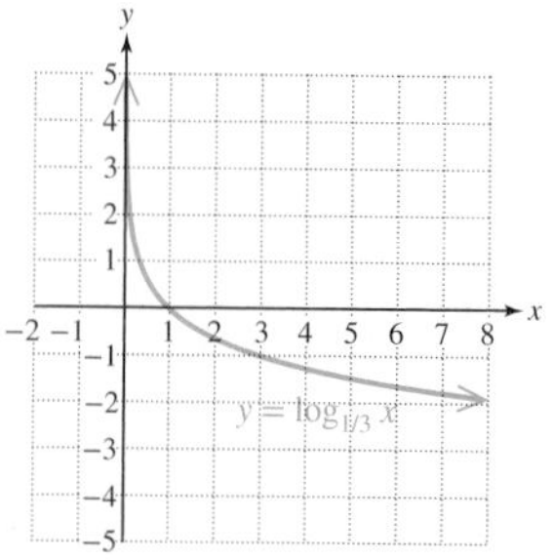

x	y
9	−2
3	−1
1	0
$\frac{1}{3}$	1
$\frac{1}{9}$	2

For Exercises 79–90, find the domain of the function and express the domain in interval notation. **(See Example 7.)**

79. $y = \log_7 (x - 5)$ $(5, \infty)$

80. $y = \log (x - 4)$ $(4, \infty)$

81. $g(x) = \log (2 - x)$ $(-\infty, 2)$

82. $f(x) = \log (1 - x)$ $(-\infty, 1)$

83. $y = \log (3x - 1)$ $\left(\frac{1}{3}, \infty\right)$

84. $y = \log_3 (2x + 1)$ $\left(-\frac{1}{2}, \infty\right)$

85. $y = \log_3 (x + 1.2)$ $(-1.2, \infty)$

86. $y = \log \left(x - \frac{1}{2}\right)$ $\left(\frac{1}{2}, \infty\right)$

87. $k(x) = \log (4 - 2x)$ $(-\infty, 2)$

88. $h(x) = \log (6 - 2x)$ $(-\infty, 3)$

89. $y = \log x^2$ $(-\infty, 0) \cup (0, \infty)$

90. $y = \log (x^2 + 1)$ $(-\infty, \infty)$

Concept 5: Applications of the Common Logarithmic Function

For Exercises 91–92, use the formula $\text{pH} = -\log [H^+]$, where $[H^+]$ represents the concentration of hydrogen ions in moles per liter. Round to two decimal places. **(See Example 8.)**

91. Normally, the level of hydrogen ions in the blood is approximately 4.47×10^{-8} mol/L. Find the pH level of blood. ≈ 7.35

92. The normal pH level for streams and rivers is between 6.5 and 8.5. A high level of bacteria in a particular stream caused environmentalists to test the water. The level of hydrogen ions was found to be 0.006 mol/L. What is the pH level of the stream? ≈ 2.22

93. A graduate student in education is doing research to compare the effectiveness of two different teaching techniques designed to teach vocabulary to sixth-graders. The first group of students (group 1) was taught with method I, in which the students worked individually to complete the assignments in a workbook. The second group (group 2) was taught with method II, in which the students worked cooperatively in groups of four to complete the assignments in the same workbook.

None of the students knew any of the vocabulary words before the study began. After completing the assignments in the workbook, the students were then tested on the vocabulary at 1-month intervals to assess how much material they had retained over time. The students' average score t months after completing the assignments are given by the following functions:

© Getty Images RF

Method I: $S_1(t) = 91 - 30 \log(t + 1)$, where t is the time in months and $S_1(t)$ is the average score of students in group 1.

Method II: $S_2(t) = 88 - 15 \log(t + 1)$, where t is the time in months and $S_2(t)$ is the average score of students in group 2.

a. Complete the table to find the average scores for each group of students after the indicated number of months. Round to one decimal place. **(See Example 9.)**

t (months)	0	1	2	6	12	24
$S_1(t)$	91	82.0	76.7	65.6	57.6	49.1
$S_2(t)$	88	83.5	80.8	75.3	71.3	67.0

b. Based on the table of values, what were the average scores for each group immediately after completion of the assigned material ($t = 0$)? Group 1: 91; Group 2: 88

c. Based on the table of values, which teaching method helped students retain the material better for a long time? Method II

94. Generally, the more money a company spends on advertising, the higher the sales. Let a represent the amount of money spent on advertising (in \$100s). Then the amount of money in sales $S(a)$ (in \$1000s) is given by

$$S(a) = 10 + 20 \log(a + 1) \text{ where } a \geq 0$$

$S(11) = 31.6$. If the company spends \$1100 on advertising, \$31,600 is returned in sales. $S(21) = 36.8$. If the company spends \$2100 on advertising, \$36,800 is returned in sales. $S(31) = 40.1$. If the company spends \$3100 on advertising, \$40,100 is returned in sales.

a. The value of $S(1) \approx 16.0$ means that if \$100 is spent on advertising, \$16,000 is returned in sales. Find the values of $S(11)$, $S(21)$, and $S(31)$. Round to one decimal place. Interpret the meaning of each function value in the context of this problem.

b. The graph of $y = S(a)$ is shown here. Use the graph and your answers from part (a) to explain why the money spent in advertising becomes less "efficient" as it is used in larger amounts. Although more money spent on advertising increases sales, the rate of increase in sales decreases.

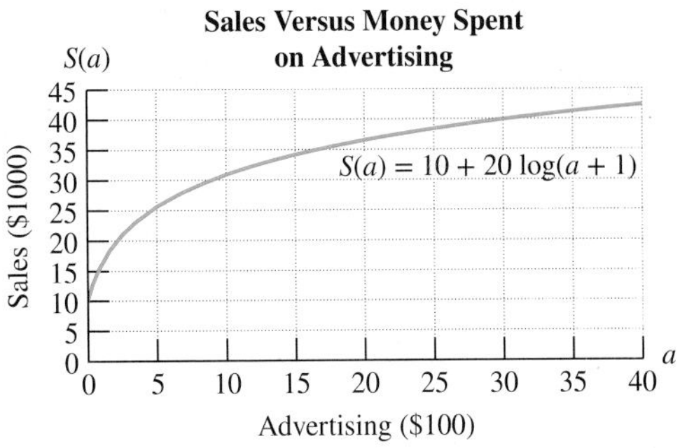

Graphing Calculator Exercises

For Exercises 95–100, graph the function on an appropriate viewing window. From the graph, identify the domain of the function and the location of the vertical asymptote.

95. $y = \log(x + 6)$
Domain: $(-6, \infty)$; asymptote: $x = -6$

96. $y = \log(2x + 4)$
Domain: $(-2, \infty)$; asymptote: $x = -2$

97. $y = \log(0.5x - 1)$
Domain: $(2, \infty)$; asymptote: $x = 2$

98. $y = \log(x + 8)$
Domain: $(-8, \infty)$; asymptote: $x = -8$

99. $y = \log(2 - x)$
Domain: $(-\infty, 2)$; asymptote: $x = 2$

100. $y = \log(3 - x)$
Domain: $(-\infty, 3)$; asymptote: $x = 3$

Problem Recognition Exercises

Identifying Graphs of Functions

Match the function with the appropriate graph. Do not use a calculator.

1. $g(x) = 3^x$ e
2. $f(x) = \log x$ l
3. $h(x) = x^2$ j
4. $k(x) = -2x - 3$ g
5. $L(x) = |x|$ c
6. $m(x) = \sqrt{x}$ a
7. $B(x) = 3$ k
8. $A(x) = -x^2$ b
9. $n(x) = \sqrt[3]{x}$ i
10. $p(x) = x^3$ h
11. $q(x) = \dfrac{1}{x}$ f
12. $r(x) = x$ d

a.

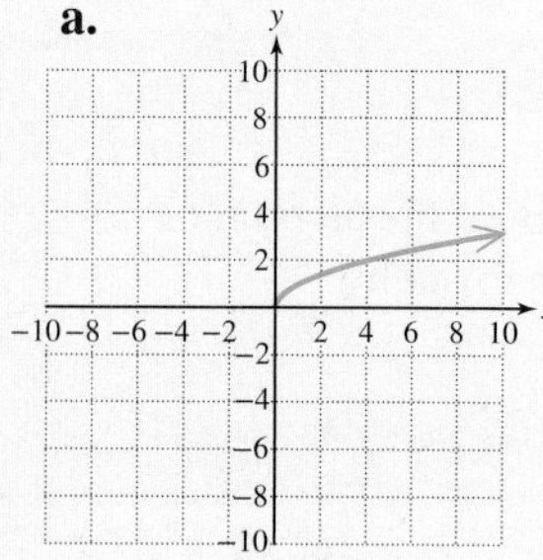

b.

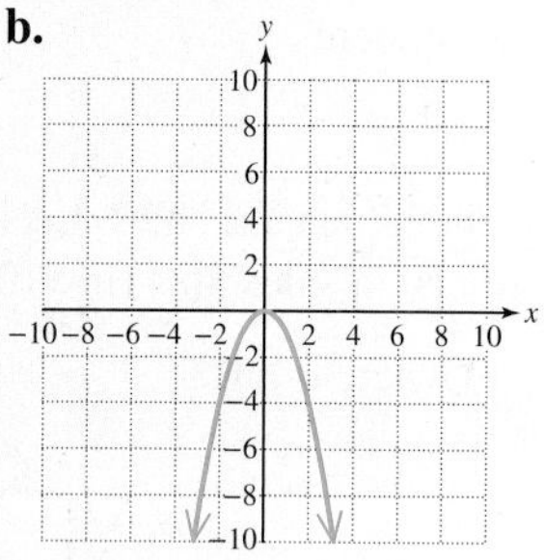

c.

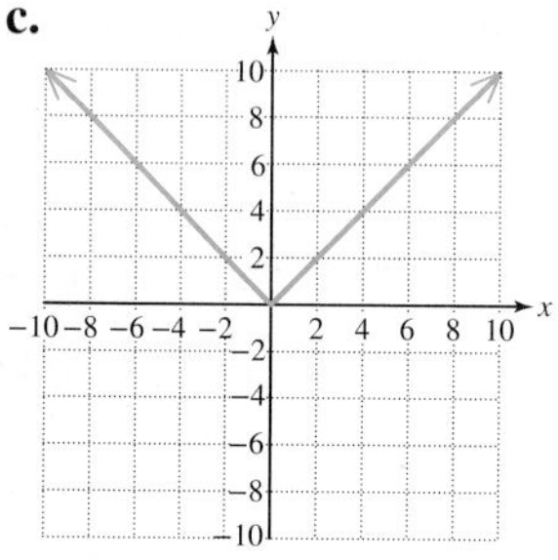

d.

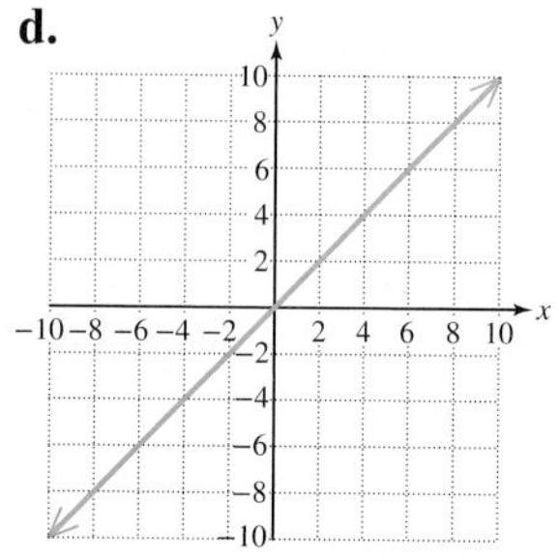

e.

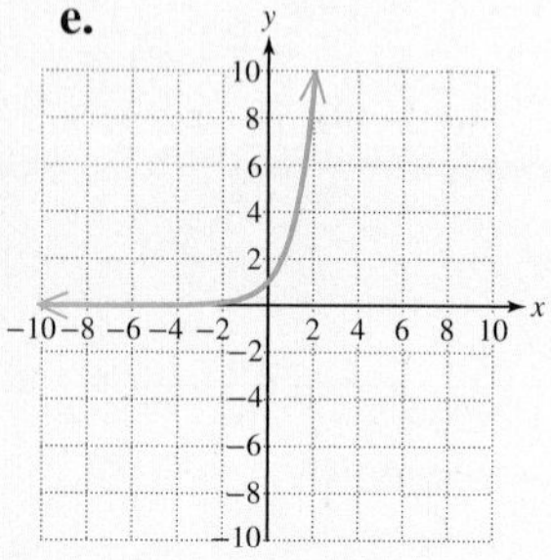

f.

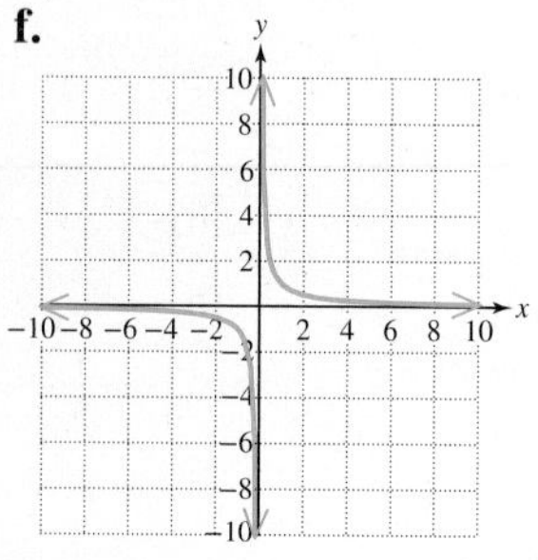

g.

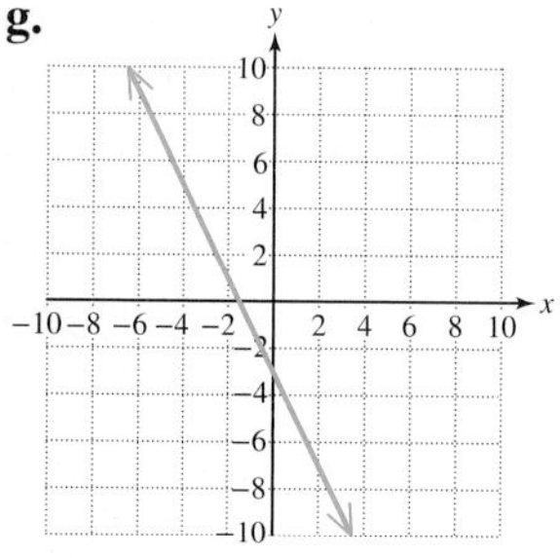

h.

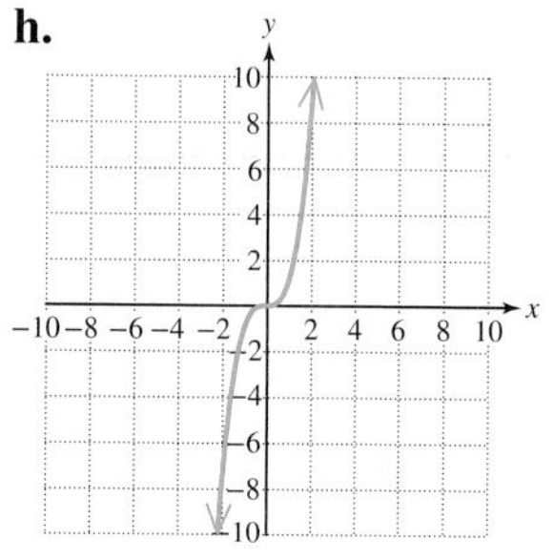

i.

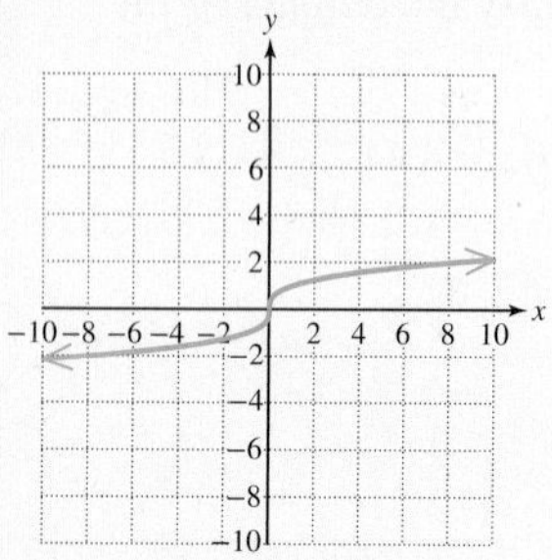

j.

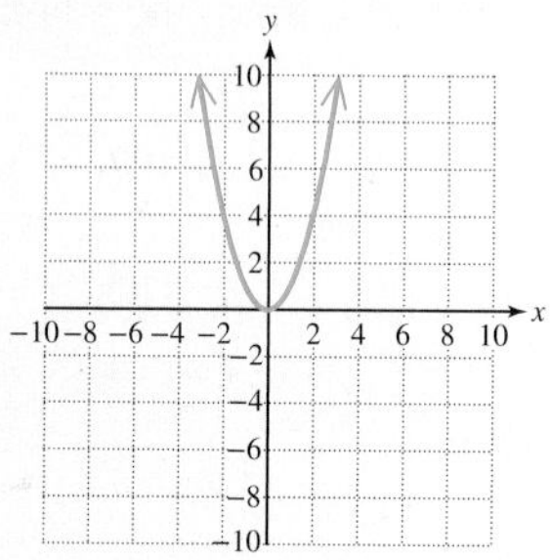

k.

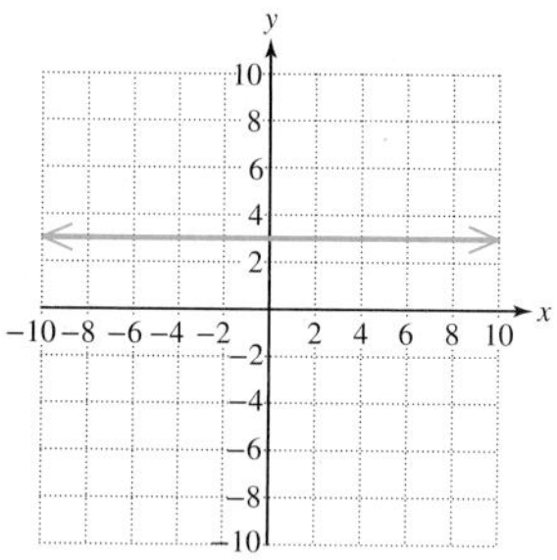

l.

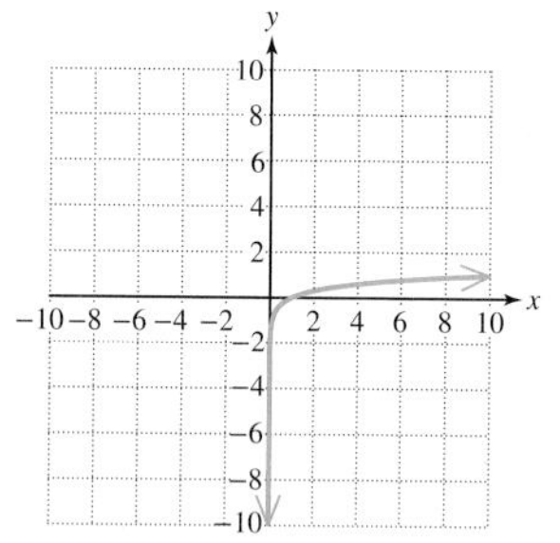

Properties of Logarithms

Section 12.4

Concepts

1. Properties of Logarithms
2. Expanded Logarithmic Expressions
3. Single Logarithmic Expressions

1. Properties of Logarithms

You have already been exposed to certain properties of logarithms that follow directly from the definition. Recall

$y = \log_b x$ is equivalent to $b^y = x$ for $x > 0$, $b > 0$, and $b \neq 1$

The following properties follow directly from the definition.

Property	Explanation
1. $\log_b 1 = 0$	Exponential form: $b^0 = 1$
2. $\log_b b = 1$	Exponential form: $b^1 = b$
3. $\log_b b^p = p$	Exponential form: $b^p = b^p$
4. $b^{\log_b x} = x$	Logarithmic form: $\log_b x = \log_b x$

Example 1 Applying the Properties of Logarithms to Simplify Expressions

Classroom Examples: p. 887, Exercises 22 and 24

Use the properties of logarithms to simplify the expressions. Assume that all variable expressions within the logarithms represent positive real numbers.

a. $\log_8 8 + \log_8 1$ **b.** $10^{\log(x+2)}$ **c.** $\log_{1/2}\left(\frac{1}{2}\right)^x$

Solution:

a. $\log_8 8 + \log_8 1 = 1 + 0 = 1$ Properties 2 and 1

b. $10^{\log(x+2)} = x + 2$ Property 4

c. $\log_{1/2}\left(\frac{1}{2}\right)^x = x$ Property 3

Skill Practice Use the properties of logarithms to simplify the expressions.

1. $\log_5 1 + \log_5 5$ **2.** $15^{\log_{15} 7}$ **3.** $\log_{1/3}\left(\frac{1}{3}\right)^c$

Three additional properties are useful when simplifying logarithmic expressions. The first is the product property for logarithms.

Product Property of Logarithms

Let b, x, and y be positive real numbers where $b \neq 1$. Then

$$\log_b(xy) = \log_b x + \log_b y$$

The logarithm of a product equals the sum of the logarithms of the factors.

Answers

1. 1 **2.** 7 **3.** c

Proof:

Let $M = \log_b x$, which implies $b^M = x$.

Let $N = \log_b y$, which implies $b^N = y$.

Then $xy = b^M b^N = b^{M+N}$.

Writing the expression $xy = b^{M+N}$ in logarithmic form, we have,

$$\log_b (xy) = M + N$$

$$\log_b (xy) = \log_b x + \log_b y \checkmark$$

To demonstrate the product property for logarithms, simplify the following expressions by using the order of operations.

$$\log_3 (3 \cdot 9) \stackrel{?}{=} \log_3 3 + \log_3 9$$

$$\log_3 27 \stackrel{?}{=} 1 + 2$$

$$3 \stackrel{?}{=} 3 \checkmark \text{ True}$$

Quotient Property of Logarithms

Let b, x, and y be positive real numbers where $b \neq 1$. Then

$$\log_b \left(\frac{x}{y}\right) = \log_b x - \log_b y$$

The logarithm of a quotient equals the difference of the logarithms of the numerator and denominator.

Instructor Note: Students should be reminded that when simplifying factors within a logarithmic expression, they cannot "cancel" with factors outside the expression. For example:

$$\frac{\log_b m}{m} \neq \frac{\log_b \cancel{m}}{\cancel{m}}$$

The proof of the quotient property for logarithms is similar to the proof of the product property and is omitted here. To demonstrate the quotient property for logarithms, simplify the following expressions by using the order of operations.

$$\log \left(\frac{1{,}000{,}000}{100}\right) \stackrel{?}{=} \log (1{,}000{,}000) - \log (100)$$

$$\log (10{,}000) \stackrel{?}{=} 6 - 2$$

$$4 \stackrel{?}{=} 4 \checkmark \text{ True}$$

Power Property of Logarithms

Let b and x be positive real numbers where $b \neq 1$. Let p be any real number. Then

$$\log_b x^p = p \log_b x$$

To demonstrate the power property for logarithms, simplify the following expressions by using the order of operations.

$$\log_4 4^2 \stackrel{?}{=} 2 \log_4 4$$

$$2 \stackrel{?}{=} 2 \cdot 1$$

$$2 \stackrel{?}{=} 2 \checkmark \text{ True}$$

The properties of logarithms are summarized in the box.

Summary of the Properties of Logarithms

Let b, x, and y be positive real numbers where $b \neq 1$, and let p be a real number. Then the following properties of logarithms are true.

1. $\log_b 1 = 0$	**5.** $\log_b (xy) = \log_b x + \log_b y$	**Product property for logarithms**
2. $\log_b b = 1$	**6.** $\log_b \left(\frac{x}{y}\right) = \log_b x - \log_b y$	**Quotient property for logarithms**
3. $\log_b b^p = p$	**7.** $\log_b x^p = p \log_b x$	**Power property for logarithms**
4. $b^{\log_b x} = x$		

2. Expanded Logarithmic Expressions

In many applications, it is advantageous to expand a logarithm into a sum or difference of simpler logarithms.

Example 2 Writing a Logarithmic Expression in Expanded Form

Classroom Example: p. 888, Exercise 52

Write the expression as the sum or difference of logarithms of x, y, and z. Assume all variables represent positive real numbers.

$$\log_3 \left(\frac{xy^3}{z^2}\right)$$

Solution:

$\log_3 \left(\frac{xy^3}{z^2}\right)$

$= \log_3 (xy^3) - \log_3 z^2$	Quotient property for logarithms (property 6)
$= [\log_3 x + \log_3 y^3] - \log_3 z^2$	Product property for logarithms (property 5)
$= \log_3 x + 3 \log_3 y - 2 \log_3 z$	Power property for logarithms (property 7)

Skill Practice Write the expression as the sum or difference of logarithms of a, b, and c. Assume all variables represent positive real numbers.

4. $\log_5 \left(\frac{a^2b^3}{c}\right)$

Example 3 Writing a Logarithmic Expression in Expanded Form

Classroom Example: p. 888, Exercise 56

Write the expression as the sum or difference of logarithms of x and y. Assume all variables represent positive real numbers.

$$\log \left(\frac{\sqrt{x+y}}{10}\right)$$

Answer

4. $2 \log_5 a + 3 \log_5 b - \log_5 c$

Solution:

$\log\left(\dfrac{\sqrt{x+y}}{10}\right)$

$= \log(\sqrt{x+y}) - \log 10$ Quotient property for logarithms (property 6)

$= \log(x+y)^{1/2} - 1$ Write $\sqrt{x+y}$ as $(x+y)^{1/2}$ and simplify $\log 10 = 1$.

$= \dfrac{1}{2}\log(x+y) - 1$ Power property for logarithms (property 7)

Skill Practice Write the expression as the sum or difference of logarithms of a and b. Assume $a > b$.

5. $\log\dfrac{(a-b)^2}{\sqrt{10}}$

Classroom Example: p. 888, Exercise 58

Example 4 Writing a Logarithmic Expression in Expanded Form

Write the expression as the sum or difference of logarithms of x, y, and z. Assume all variables represent positive real numbers.

$$\log_b \sqrt[5]{\frac{x^4}{yz^3}}$$

Solution:

Instructor Note: For Example 4, some students may simplify using the rules of exponents first.
$\log_b\left(\dfrac{x^{4/5}}{y^{1/5}z^{3/5}}\right)$

$\log_b \sqrt[5]{\dfrac{x^4}{yz^3}}$

$= \log_b\left(\dfrac{x^4}{yz^3}\right)^{1/5}$ Write $\sqrt[5]{\dfrac{x^4}{yz^3}}$ as $\left(\dfrac{x^4}{yz^3}\right)^{1/5}$.

$= \dfrac{1}{5}\log_b\left(\dfrac{x^4}{yz^3}\right)$ Power property for logarithms (property 7)

$= \dfrac{1}{5}[\log_b x^4 - \log_b(yz^3)]$ Quotient property for logarithms (property 6)

$= \dfrac{1}{5}[\log_b x^4 - (\log_b y + \log_b z^3)]$ Product property for logarithms (property 5)

$= \dfrac{1}{5}[\log_b x^4 - \log_b y - \log_b z^3]$ Distributive property

$= \dfrac{1}{5}[4\log_b x - \log_b y - 3\log_b z]$ Power property for logarithms (property 7)

or $\dfrac{4}{5}\log_b x - \dfrac{1}{5}\log_b y - \dfrac{3}{5}\log_b z$

Skill Practice Write the expression as the sum or difference of logarithms of a, b, and c. Assume all variables represent positive real numbers.

6. $\log_3 \sqrt[4]{\dfrac{a}{bc^5}}$

Answers

5. $2\log(a-b) - \dfrac{1}{2}$

6. $\dfrac{1}{4}\log_3 a - \dfrac{1}{4}\log_3 b - \dfrac{5}{4}\log_3 c$

3. Single Logarithmic Expressions

In some applications, it is necessary to write a sum or difference of logarithms as a single logarithm.

Example 5 **Writing a Sum or Difference of Logarithms as a Single Logarithm**

Classroom Example: p. 888, Exercise 64

Rewrite the expression as a single logarithm, and simplify the result, if possible.

$$\log_2 560 - \log_2 7 - \log_2 5$$

Solution:

$\log_2 560 - \log_2 7 - \log_2 5$

$= \log_2 560 - (\log_2 7 + \log_2 5)$	Factor out -1 from the last two terms.
$= \log_2 560 - \log_2 (7 \cdot 5)$	Product property for logarithms (property 5)
$= \log_2\left(\dfrac{560}{7 \cdot 5}\right)$	Quotient property for logarithms (property 6)
$= \log_2 16$	Simplify inside parentheses.
$= \log_2 2^4$	Write 16 in base 2. That is, $16 = 2^4$.
$= 4$	Property 3

Skill Practice Write the expression as a single logarithm, and simplify the result, if possible.

7. $\log_3 54 + \log_3 10 - \log_3 20$

Example 6 **Writing a Sum or Difference of Logarithms as a Single Logarithm**

Classroom Example: p. 888, Exercise 70

Rewrite the expression as a single logarithm, and simplify the result, if possible. Assume all variable expressions within the logarithms represent positive real numbers.

$$2 \log x - \frac{1}{2} \log y + 3 \log z$$

Solution:

$2 \log x - \dfrac{1}{2} \log y + 3 \log z$

$= \log x^2 - \log y^{1/2} + \log z^3$	Power property for logarithms (property 7)
$= \log x^2 + \log z^3 - \log y^{1/2}$	Group terms with positive coefficients.
$= \log (x^2z^3) - \log y^{1/2}$	Product property for logarithms (property 5)
$= \log\left(\dfrac{x^2z^3}{y^{1/2}}\right)$ or $\log\left(\dfrac{x^2z^3}{\sqrt{y}}\right)$	Quotient property for logarithms (property 6)

Skill Practice Write the expression as a single logarithm, and simplify, if possible.

8. $3 \log x + \dfrac{1}{3} \log y - 2 \log z$

Answers

7. 3 **8.** $\log\left(\dfrac{x^3\sqrt[3]{y}}{z^2}\right)$

It is important to note that the properties of logarithms may be used to write a single logarithm as a sum or difference of logarithms. Furthermore, the properties may be used to write a sum or difference of logarithms as a single logarithm. In either case, these operations may change the domain.

For example, consider the function $y = \log_b x^2$. Using the power property for logarithms, we have $y = 2 \log_b x$. Consider the domain of each function:

$y = \log_b x^2$ Domain: $(-\infty, 0) \cup (0, \infty)$

$y = 2 \log_b x$ Domain: $(0, \infty)$

These two functions are equivalent only for values of x in the intersection of the two domains, that is, for $(0, \infty)$.

Section 12.4 Practice Exercises

For additional exercises, see Classroom Activities 12.4A–12.4B in the *Student's Resource Manual* at www.mhhe.com/moh.

Vocabulary and Key Concepts

1. a. Fill in the blanks to complete the basic properties of logarithms.
$\log_b b =$ ___1___, $\log_b 1 =$ ___0___, $\log_b b^x =$ ___x___, and $b^{\log_b x} =$ ___x___.

   b. If b, x, and y are positive real numbers and $b \neq 1$, then $\log_b(xy) =$ ______ and $\log_b\left(\frac{x}{y}\right) =$ ______.
$\log_b x + \log_b y$; $\log_b x - \log_b y$

   c. If b and x are positive real numbers and $b \neq 1$, then for any real number p, $\log_b x^p$ can be written as ___$p \log_b x$___.

   d. Determine if the statement is true or false: $\log_b(xy) = (\log_b x)(\log_b y)$
Use the expression $\log_2 (4 \cdot 8)$ to help you answer. False

   e. Determine if the statement is true or false: $\log_b\left(\frac{x}{y}\right) = \frac{\log_b x}{\log_b y}$
Use the expression $\log_3\left(\frac{27}{9}\right)$ to help you answer. False

   f. Determine if the statement is true or false: $\log_b(x)^p = (\log_b x)^p$
Use the expression $\log(1000)^2$ to help you answer. False

Review Exercises

For Exercises 2–5, find the values of the logarithmic and exponential expressions without using a calculator.

2. 8^{-2} $\frac{1}{64}$
3. $\log 10{,}000$ 4
4. $\log_2 32$ 5
5. 6^{-1} $\frac{1}{6}$

For Exercises 6–9, approximate the values of the logarithmic and exponential expressions by using a calculator. Round to four decimal places.

6. $(\sqrt{2})^{\pi}$ 2.9707
7. $\log 8$ 0.9031
8. $\log 27$ 1.4314
9. $\pi^{\sqrt{2}}$ 5.0475

For Exercises 10–13, match the function with the appropriate graph.

10. $f(x) = 4^x$ d

11. $q(x) = \left(\frac{1}{5}\right)^x$ a

12. $h(x) = \log_5 x$ b

13. $k(x) = \log_{1/3} x$ c

a.

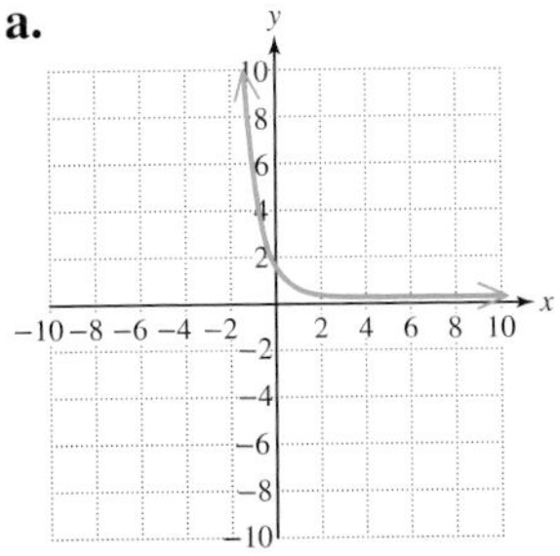

b.

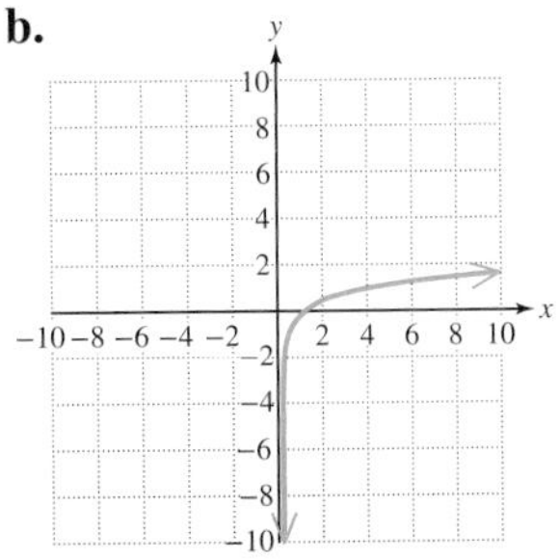

c.

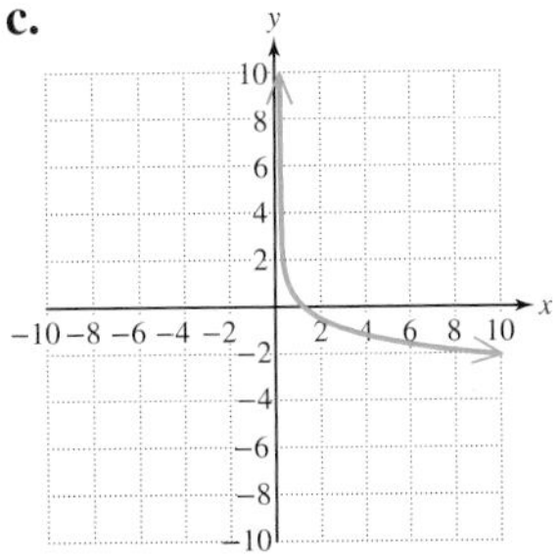

d.

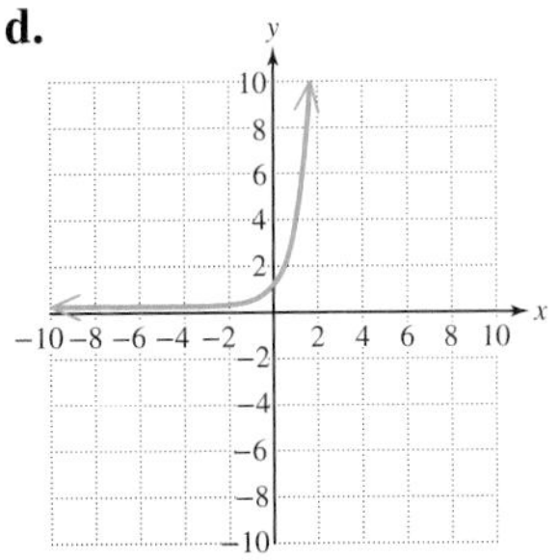

Concept 1: Properties of Logarithms

14. Select the values that are equivalent to $\log_5 5^2$. a, b, c

a. $\log_5 25$

b. $2 \log_5 5$

c. $\log_5 5 + \log_5 5$

15. Select the values that are equivalent to $\log_2 2^3$. a, b, c

a. $3 \log_2 2$

b. $\log_2 8$

c. 3

16. Select the values that are equivalent to $\log 10^4$. a, b, c

a. 4

b. $4 \log 10$

c. $\log 10{,}000$

For Exercises 17–40, evaluate each expression. **(See Example 1.)**

17. $\log_3 3$ 1

18. $\log 10$ 1

19. $\log_5 5^4$ 4

20. $\log_4 4^5$ 5

21. $6^{\log_6 11}$ 11

22. $7^{\log_7 2}$ 2

23. $\log 10^3$ 3

24. $\log_6 6^3$ 3

25. $\log_3 1$ 0

26. $\log_8 1$ 0

27. $10^{\log 9}$ 9

28. $8^{\log_8 5}$ 5

29. $\log_{1/2} 1$ 0

30. $\log_{1/3}\left(\frac{1}{3}\right)$ 1

31. $\log_2 1 + \log_2 2^3$ 3

32. $\log 10^4 + \log 10$ 5

33. $\log_4 4 + \log_2 1$ 1

34. $\log_7 7 + \log_4 4^2$ 3

35. $\log_{1/4}\left(\frac{1}{4}\right)^{2x}$ $2x$

36. $\log_{2/3}\left(\frac{2}{3}\right)^p$ p

37. $\log_a a^4$ 4

38. $\log_y y^2$ 2

39. $\log 10^2 - \log_3 3^2$ 0

40. $\log_6 6^4 - \log 10^4$ 0

41. Compare the expressions by approximating their values on a calculator. Which two expressions are equivalent?

a. $\log(3 \cdot 5)$ **b.** $\log 3 \cdot \log 5$ **c.** $\log 3 + \log 5$ Expressions a and c are equivalent.

42. Compare the expressions by approximating their values on a calculator. Which two expressions are equivalent?
Expressions a and c are equivalent.

a. $\log\left(\frac{6}{5}\right)$ **b.** $\frac{\log 6}{\log 5}$ **c.** $\log 6 - \log 5$

43. Compare the expressions by approximating their values on a calculator. Which two expressions are equivalent?
Expressions a and c are equivalent.

a. $\log 20^2$ **b.** $[\log 20]^2$ **c.** $2 \log 20$

44. Compare the expressions by approximating their values on a calculator. Which two expressions are equivalent?
Expressions a and b are equivalent.

a. $\log \sqrt{4}$ **b.** $\frac{1}{2} \log 4$ **c.** $\sqrt{\log 4}$

Concept 2: Expanded Logarithmic Expressions

For Exercises 45–62, expand into sums and/or differences of logarithms. Assume all variables represent positive real numbers. **(See Examples 2–4.)**

45. $\log_3\left(\frac{x}{5}\right)$ $\log_3 x - \log_3 5$

46. $\log_2\left(\frac{y}{z}\right)$ $\log_2 y - \log_2 z$

47. $\log (2x)$ $\log 2 + \log x$

48. $\log_6 (xyz)$ $\log_6 x + \log_6 y + \log_6 z$

49. $\log_5 x^4$ $4 \log_5 x$

50. $\log_7 z^{1/3}$ $\frac{1}{3}\log_7 z$

51. $\log_4\left(\frac{ab}{c}\right)$ $\log_4 a + \log_4 b - \log_4 c$

52. $\log_2\left(\frac{x}{yz}\right)$ $\log_2 x - \log_2 y - \log_2 z$

53. $\log_b\left(\frac{\sqrt{xy}}{z^3 w}\right)$ $\frac{1}{2}\log_b x + \log_b y - 3\log_b z - \log_b w$

54. $\log\left(\frac{a\sqrt[3]{b}}{cd^2}\right)$ $\log a + \frac{1}{3}\log b - \log c - 2\log d$

55. $\log_2\left(\frac{x+1}{y^2\sqrt{z}}\right)$ $\log_2 (x+1) - 2\log_2 y - \frac{1}{2}\log_2 z$

56. $\log\left(\frac{a+1}{b\sqrt[3]{c}}\right)$ $\log (a+1) - \log b - \frac{1}{3}\log c$

57. $\log\left(\sqrt[3]{\frac{ab^2}{c}}\right)$ $\frac{1}{3}\log a + \frac{2}{3}\log b - \frac{1}{3}\log c$

58. $\log_5\left(\sqrt[4]{\frac{w^3 z}{x^2}}\right)$ $\frac{3}{4}\log_5 w + \frac{1}{4}\log_5 z - \frac{1}{2}\log_5 x$

59. $\log\left(\frac{1}{w^5}\right)$ $-5\log w$

60. $\log_3\left(\frac{1}{z^4}\right)$ $-4\log_3 z$

61. $\log_b\left(\frac{\sqrt{a}}{b^3 c}\right)$ $\frac{1}{2}\log_b a - 3 - \log_b c$

62. $\log_x\left(\frac{x}{y\sqrt{z}}\right)$ $1 - \log_x y - \frac{1}{2}\log_x z$

Concept 3: Single Logarithmic Expressions

For Exercises 63–78, write the expressions as a single logarithm and simplify if possible. Assume all variable expressions represent positive real numbers. **(See Examples 5–6.)**

63. $\log_3 270 - \log_3 2 - \log_3 5$ 3

64. $\log_5 8 + \log_5 50 - \log_5 16$ 2

65. $\log_7 98 - \log_7 2$ 2

66. $\log_6 24 - \log_6 4$ 1

67. $2\log_3 x - 3\log_3 y + \log_3 z$ $\log_3\left(\frac{x^2 z}{y^3}\right)$

68. $\log C + \log A + \log B + \log I + \log N$ $\log (CABIN)$

69. $2\log_3 a - \frac{1}{4}\log_3 b + \log_3 c$ $\log_3\left(\frac{a^2 c}{\sqrt[4]{b}}\right)$

70. $\log_5 a - \frac{1}{2}\log_5 b - 3\log_5 c$ $\log_5\left(\frac{a}{\sqrt{b}c^3}\right)$

71. $\log_b x - 3\log_b x + 4\log_b x$ $\log_b x^2$

72. $2\log_3 z + \log_3 z - \frac{1}{2}\log_3 z$ $\log_3 z^{5/2}$

73. $5\log_8 a - \log_8 1 + \log_8 8$ $\log_8 (8a^5)$ or $\log_8 a^5 + 1$

74. $\log_2 2 + 2\log_2 b - \log_2 1$ $\log_2 (2b^2)$ or $1 + \log_2 b^2$

75. $2\log (x+6) + \frac{1}{3}\log y - 5\log z$ $\log\left[\frac{(x+6)^2\sqrt[3]{y}}{z^5}\right]$

76. $\frac{1}{4}\log (a+1) - 2\log b - 4\log c$ $\log\left(\frac{\sqrt[4]{a+1}}{b^2 c^4}\right)$

77. $\log_b (x+1) - \log_b (x^2-1)$ $\log_b\left(\frac{1}{x-1}\right)$

78. $\log_x (p^2-4) - \log_x (p-2)$ $\log_x (p+2)$

Expanding Your Skills

For Exercises 79–90, find the values of the logarithms given that $\log_b 2 \approx 0.693$, $\log_b 3 \approx 1.099$, and $\log_b 5 \approx 1.609$.

79. $\log_b 6$ 1.792

80. $\log_b 4$ 1.386

81. $\log_b 12$ 2.485

82. $\log_b 25$ 3.218

83. $\log_b 81$ 4.396

84. $\log_b 30$ 3.401

85. $\log_b\left(\frac{5}{2}\right)$ 0.916

86. $\log_b\left(\frac{25}{3}\right)$ 2.119

87. $\log_b 10^6$ 13.812

88. $\log_b 15^3$ 8.124

89. $\log_b 5^{10}$ 16.09

90. $\log_b 2^{12}$ 8.316

91. The intensity of sound waves is measured in decibels and is calculated by the formula

$$B = 10 \log\left(\frac{I}{I_0}\right)$$

where I_0 is the minimum detectable decibel level.

a. Expand this formula by using the properties of logarithms. $B = 10 \log I - 10 \log I_0$

b. Let $I_0 = 10^{-16}$ W/cm^2 and simplify. $10 \log I + 160$

92. The Richter scale is used to measure the intensity of an earthquake and is calculated by the formula

$$R = \log\left(\frac{I}{I_0}\right)$$

where I_0 is the minimum level detectable by a seismograph.

a. Expand this formula by using the properties of logarithms. $R = \log I - \log I_0$

b. Let $I_0 = 1$ and simplify. $\log I$

Graphing Calculator Exercises

93. **a.** Graph $Y_1 = \log x^2$ and state its domain. Domain: $(-\infty, 0) \cup (0, \infty)$

b. Graph $Y_2 = 2 \log x$ and state its domain. Domain: $(0, \infty)$

c. For what values of x are the expressions $\log x^2$ and $2 \log x$ equivalent?
They are equivalent for all x in the intersection of their domains, $(0, \infty)$.

94. **a.** Graph $Y_1 = \log (x - 1)^2$ and state its domain. Domain: $(-\infty, 1) \cup (1, \infty)$

b. Graph $Y_2 = 2 \log (x - 1)$ and state its domain. Domain: $(1, \infty)$

c. For what values of x are the expressions $\log (x - 1)^2$ and $2 \log (x - 1)$ equivalent?
They are equivalent for all x in the intersection of their domains, $(1, \infty)$.

The Irrational Number e and Change of Base

Section 12.5

Concepts

1. The Irrational Number e
2. Computing Compound Interest
3. The Natural Logarithmic Function
4. Change-of-Base Formula
5. Applications of the Natural Logarithmic Function

1. The Irrational Number e

The exponential function base 10 is particularly easy to work with because integral powers of 10 represent different place positions in the base-10 numbering system. In this section, we introduce another important exponential function whose base is an irrational number called e.

Consider the expression $(1 + \frac{1}{x})^x$. The value of the expression for increasingly large values of x approaches a constant (Table 12-5).

Table 12-5

x	$\left(1 + \frac{1}{x}\right)^x$
100	2.70481382942
1000	2.71692393224
10,000	2.71814592683
100,000	2.71826823717
1,000,000	2.71828046932
1,000,000,000	2.71828182710

As x approaches infinity, the expression $(1 + \frac{1}{x})^x$ approaches a constant value that we call $\boldsymbol{e}$. From Table 12-5, this value is approximately 2.718281828.

$$e \approx 2.718281828$$

The value of e is an irrational number (a nonterminating, nonrepeating decimal) and like the number π, it is a universal constant.

Classroom Example: p. 897, Exercise 8

Example 1 Graphing $f(x) = e^x$

Graph the function defined by $f(x) = e^x$.

Solution:

Because the base of the function is greater than 1 ($e \approx 2.718281828$), the graph is an increasing exponential function. We can use a calculator to evaluate $f(x) = e^x$ at several values of x.

TIP: On a scientific calculator, you may need to enter the base and exponent of an exponential expression in reverse order. For example, enter e^2 as:

2 [2nd] [LN]

Calculator Connections

Topic: Evaluating Exponential Expressions Base e

Practice using your calculator by evaluating e^x for $x = 1$, $x = 2$, and $x = -1$.

```
e^(1)
          2.718281828
e^(2)
          7.389056099
e^(-1)
          .3678794412
```

If you are using your calculator correctly, your answers should match those found in Table 12-6. Values are rounded to three decimal places. The corresponding graph of $f(x) = e^x$ is shown in Figure 12-14.

Table 12-6

x	$f(x) = e^x$
−3	0.050
−2	0.135
−1	0.368
0	1.000
1	2.718
2	7.389
3	20.086

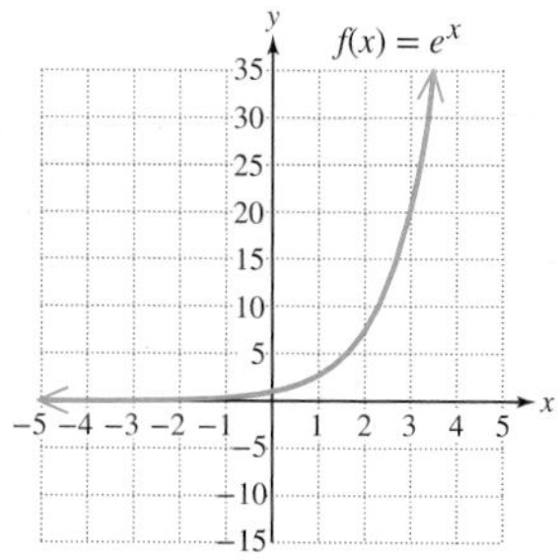

Figure 12-14

Skill Practice

1. Graph $f(x) = e^x + 1$.

2. Computing Compound Interest

One particularly interesting application of exponential functions is in computing compound interest.

1. If the number of compounding periods per year is finite, then the amount $A(t)$ in an account is given by

$$A(t) = P\left(1 + \frac{r}{n}\right)^{nt}$$

where P is the initial principal, r is the annual interest rate, n is the number of times compounded per year, and t is the time in years that the money is invested.

Answer

1.

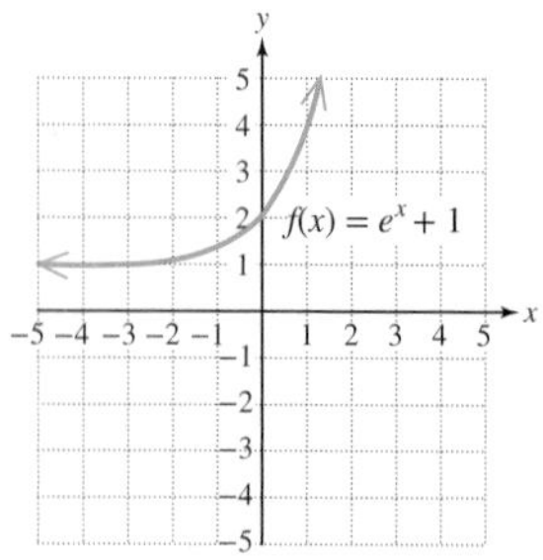

2. If the number of compound periods per year is infinite, then interest is said to be **compounded continuously**. In such a case, the amount $A(t)$ in the account is given by

$$A(t) = Pe^{rt}$$

where P is the initial principal, r is the annual interest rate, and t is the time in years that the money is invested.

Example 2 Computing the Balance on an Account

Classroom Example: p. 898, Exercise 14

Suppose \$5000 is invested in an account earning 6.5% interest. Find the balance in the account after 10 yr under the following compounding options.

a. Compounded annually **b.** Compounded quarterly

c. Compounded monthly **d.** Compounded daily

e. Compounded continuously

Solution:

Compounding Option	n Value	Formula	Result
Annually	$n = 1$	$A(10) = 5000\left(1 + \frac{0.065}{1}\right)^{(1)(10)}$	\$9385.69
Quarterly	$n = 4$	$A(10) = 5000\left(1 + \frac{0.065}{4}\right)^{(4)(10)}$	\$9527.79
Monthly	$n = 12$	$A(10) = 5000\left(1 + \frac{0.065}{12}\right)^{(12)(10)}$	\$9560.92
Daily	$n = 365$	$A(10) = 5000\left(1 + \frac{0.065}{365}\right)^{(365)(10)}$	\$9577.15
Continuously	Not applicable	$A(10) = 5000e^{(0.065)(10)}$	\$9577.70

Notice that there is a \$191.46 difference in the account balance between annual compounding and daily compounding. However, the difference between compounding daily and compounding continuously is small, \$0.55. As n gets infinitely large, the function defined by

$$A(t) = P\left(1 + \frac{r}{n}\right)^{nt} \qquad \text{converges to } A(t) = Pe^{rt}$$

Skill Practice

2. Suppose \$1000 is invested at 5%. Find the balance after 8 yr under the following options.
   a. Compounded annually **b.** Compounded quarterly
   c. Compounded monthly **d.** Compounded daily
   e. Compounded continuously

3. The Natural Logarithmic Function

Recall that the common logarithmic function $y = \log x$ has a base of 10. Another important logarithmic function is called the **natural logarithmic function**. The natural logarithmic function has a base of e and is written as $y = \ln x$. That is,

$$y = \ln x = \log_e x$$

Answer

2. a. \$1477.46 b. \$1488.13
c. \$1490.59 d. \$1491.78
e. \$1491.82

Classroom Example: p. 899, Exercise 18

TIP: On a scientific calculator, you may need to enter a logarithm and argument in reverse order. For example, enter ln 2 as

2 LN

Example 3 Graphing $y = \ln x$

Graph $y = \ln x$.

Solution:

Because the base of the function $y = \ln x$ is e and $e > 1$, the graph is an increasing logarithmic function. We can use a calculator to find specific points on the graph of $y = \ln x$ by pressing the LN key.

Practice using your calculator by evaluating $\ln x$ for the following values of x. If you are using your calculator correctly, your answers should match those found in Table 12-7. Values are rounded to three decimal places. The corresponding graph of $y = \ln x$ is shown in Figure 12-15.

Table 12-7

x	$\ln x$
0.25	−1.386
0.5	−0.693
1	0.000
2	0.693
3	1.099
4	1.386
5	1.609
6	1.792
7	1.946

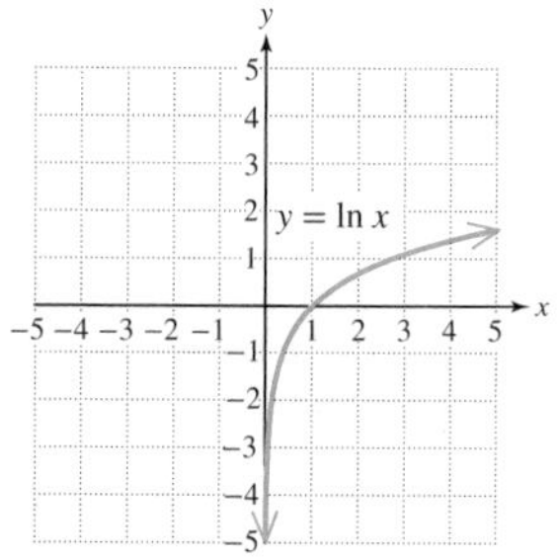

Figure 12-15

Calculator Connections

Topic: Evaluating Natural Logarithms

```
ln(1)
                0
ln(2)
      .6931471806
ln(3)
      1.098612289
```

Skill Practice

3. Graph $y = \ln x + 1$.

The properties of logarithms learned earlier in this chapter are also true for natural logarithms.

Instructor Note: Show that the natural logarithmic function $f(x) = \ln x$ is the inverse of the function $g(x) = e^x$, by composing $f \circ g$ and $g \circ f$.

Properties of the Natural Logarithmic Function

Let x and y be positive real numbers, and let p be a real number. Then the following properties are true.

1. $\ln 1 = 0$
2. $\ln e = 1$
3. $\ln e^p = p$
4. $e^{\ln x} = x$
5. $\ln (xy) = \ln x + \ln y$ **Product property for logarithms**
6. $\ln\left(\frac{x}{y}\right) = \ln x - \ln y$ **Quotient property for logarithms**
7. $\ln x^p = p \ln x$ **Power property for logarithms**

Answer

3.

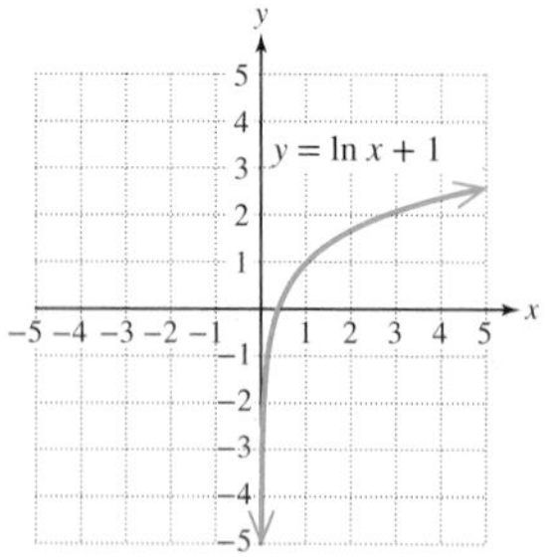

Example 4 **Simplifying Expressions with Natural Logarithms**

Classroom Examples: p. 899, Exercises 24 and 26

Simplify the expressions. Assume that all variable expressions within the logarithms represent positive real numbers.

a. $\ln e$ **b.** $\ln 1$ **c.** $\ln (e^{x+1})$ **d.** $e^{\ln(x+1)}$

Solution:

a. $\ln e = 1$ Property 2

b. $\ln 1 = 0$ Property 1

c. $\ln (e^{x+1}) = x + 1$ Property 3

d. $e^{\ln(x+1)} = x + 1$ Property 4

Skill Practice Simplify.

4. $\ln e^2$ **5.** $-3 \ln 1$ **6.** $\ln e^{(x+y)}$ **7.** $e^{\ln(3x)}$

Example 5 **Writing a Sum or Difference of Natural Logarithms as a Single Logarithm**

Classroom Example: p. 900, Exercise 38

Write the expression as a single logarithm. Assume that all variable expressions within the logarithms represent positive real numbers.

$$\ln x - \frac{1}{3} \ln y - \ln z$$

Solution:

$\ln x - \frac{1}{3} \ln y - \ln z$

$= \ln x - \ln y^{1/3} - \ln z$ Power property for logarithms (property 7)

$= \ln x - (\ln y^{1/3} + \ln z)$ Factor out -1 from the last two terms.

$= \ln x - \ln (y^{1/3} \cdot z)$ Product property for logarithms (property 5)

$= \ln \left(\frac{x}{y^{1/3}z}\right)$ Quotient property for logarithms (property 6)

$= \ln \left(\frac{x}{\sqrt[3]{y}\, z}\right)$ Write the rational exponent as a radical.

Skill Practice Write as a single logarithm.

8. $\frac{1}{4} \ln a - \ln b + \ln c$

Answers

4. 2 **5.** 0 **6.** $x + y$

7. $3x$ **8.** $\ln \left(\frac{\sqrt[4]{a}\, c}{b}\right)$

Classroom Example: p. 900, Exercise 44

Example 6 Writing a Logarithmic Expression in Expanded Form

Write the expression as a sum or difference of logarithms of x and y. Assume all variable expressions within the logarithm represent positive real numbers.

$$\ln\left(\frac{e}{x^2\sqrt{y}}\right)$$

Solution:

$$\ln\left(\frac{e}{x^2\sqrt{y}}\right)$$

$= \ln e - \ln(x^2\sqrt{y})$	Quotient property for logarithms (property 6)
$= \ln e - (\ln x^2 + \ln\sqrt{y})$	Product property for logarithms (property 5)
$= 1 - \ln x^2 - \ln y^{1/2}$	Distributive property. Also simplify $\ln e = 1$ (property 2).
$= 1 - 2\ln x - \frac{1}{2}\ln y$	Power property for logarithms (property 7)

Skill Practice Write as a sum or difference of logarithms of x and y.

9. $\ln\left(\frac{x^3\sqrt{y}}{e^2}\right)$

4. Change-of-Base Formula

A calculator can be used to approximate the value of a logarithm with a base of 10 or a base of e by using the LOG key or the LN key, respectively. However, to use a calculator to evaluate a logarithmic expression with a base other than 10 or e, we must use the **change-of-base formula**.

Change-of-Base Formula

Let a and b be positive real numbers such that $a \neq 1$ and $b \neq 1$. Then for any positive real number x,

$$\log_b x = \frac{\log_a x}{\log_a b}$$

Proof:

Let $M = \log_b x$, which implies that $b^M = x$.

Take the logarithm, base a, on both sides: $\log_a b^M = \log_a x$

Apply the power property for logarithms: $M \cdot \log_a b = \log_a x$

Divide both sides by $\log_a b$: $\frac{M \cdot \log_a b}{\log_a b} = \frac{\log_a x}{\log_a b}$

$$M = \frac{\log_a x}{\log_a b}$$

Because $M = \log_b x$, we have $\log_b x = \frac{\log_a x}{\log_a b}$ ✓

Answer

9. $3\ln x + \frac{1}{2}\ln y - 2$

The change-of-base formula converts a logarithm of one base to a ratio of logarithms of a different base. For the sake of using a calculator, we often apply the change-of-base formula with base 10 or base e.

Example 7 Using the Change-of-Base Formula

Classroom Example: p. 900, Exercise 50

a. Use the change-of-base formula to evaluate $\log_4 80$ by using base 10. (Round to three decimal places.)

b. Use the change-of-base formula to evaluate $\log_4 80$ by using base e. (Round to three decimal places.)

Solution:

a. $\log_4 80 = \dfrac{\log_{10} 80}{\log_{10} 4} = \dfrac{\log 80}{\log 4} \approx \dfrac{1.903089987}{0.6020599913} \approx 3.161$

b. $\log_4 80 = \dfrac{\log_e 80}{\log_e 4} = \dfrac{\ln 80}{\ln 4} \approx \dfrac{4.382026635}{1.386294361} \approx 3.161$

To check the result, we see that $4^{3.161} \approx 80$.

Skill Practice

10. Use the change-of-base formula to evaluate $\log_5 95$ by using base 10. Round to three decimal places.

11. Use the change-of-base formula to evaluate $\log_5 95$ by using base e. Round to three decimal places.

Calculator Connections

Topic: Applying the Change-of-Base Formula

Use the change-of-base formula to evaluate $\log_4 80$.

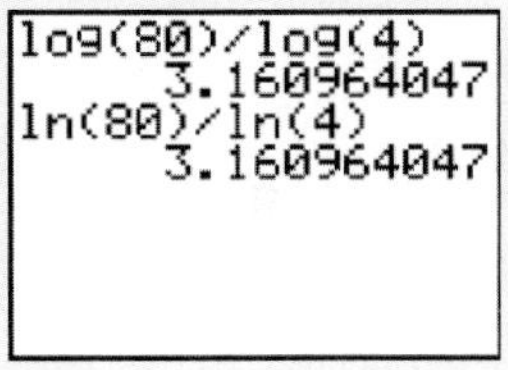

Calculator Connections

Topic: Using the Change-of-Base Formula to Graph Logarithmic Functions

The change-of-base formula can be used to graph logarithmic functions with bases other than 10 or e. For example, to graph $Y_1 = \log_2 x$, we can enter the function as either

$$Y_1 = (\log x)/(\log 2) \quad \text{or} \quad Y_1 = (\ln x)/(\ln 2)$$

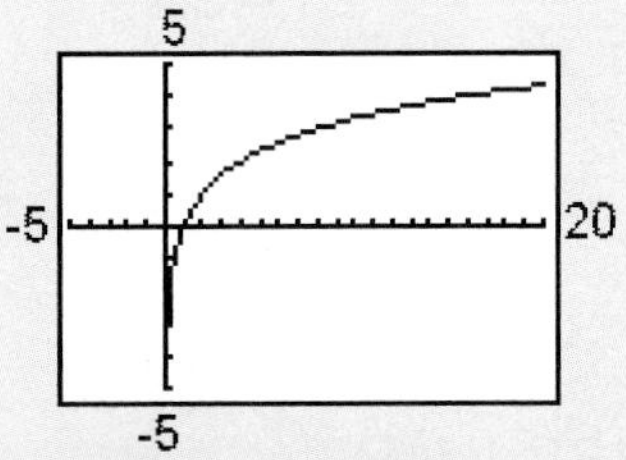

5. Applications of the Natural Logarithmic Function

Plant and animal tissue contains both carbon 12 and carbon 14. Carbon 12 is a stable form of carbon, whereas carbon 14 is a radioactive isotope with a half-life of approximately 5730 years. While a plant or animal is living, it takes in carbon from the atmosphere either through photosynthesis or through its food. The ratio of carbon 14 to carbon 12 in a living organism is constant and is the same as the ratio found in the atmosphere.

Answers

10. 2.829 **11.** 2.829

When a plant or animal dies, it no longer ingests carbon from the atmosphere. The amount of stable carbon 12 remains unchanged from the time of death, but the carbon 14 begins to decay. Because the rate of decay is constant, a tissue sample can be dated by comparing the percent of carbon 14 still present to the percentage of carbon 14 assumed to be in its original living state.

The age of a tissue sample is a function of the percent of carbon 14 still present in the organism according to the following model:

$$A(p) = \frac{\ln p}{-0.000121}$$

where $A(p)$ is the age in years and p is the percentage (in decimal form) of carbon 14 still present.

Classroom Example: p. 901, Exercise 62

Example 8 Applying the Natural Logarithmic Function to Radioactive Decay

Using the formula

$$A(p) = \frac{\ln p}{-0.000121}$$

a. Find the age of a bone that has 72% of its initial carbon 14.

b. Find the age of the Iceman, a body uncovered in the mountains of northern Italy in 1991. Samples of his hair revealed that 52.7% of the original carbon 14 was present after his death.

Solution:

a. $A(p) = \frac{\ln p}{-0.000121}$

$A(0.72) = \frac{\ln 0.72}{-0.000121}$ Substitute 0.72 for p.

≈ 2715 years

b. $A(p) = \frac{\ln p}{-0.000121}$

$A(0.527) = \frac{\ln 0.527}{-0.000121}$ Substitute 0.527 for p.

≈ 5300 years The body of the Iceman is approximately 5300 yr old.

Skill Practice

12. Use the formula

$$A(p) = \frac{\ln p}{-0.000121}$$

(where $A(p)$ is the age in years and p is the percent of carbon 14 still present) to determine the age of a human skull that has 90% of its initial carbon 14.

Answer

12. ≈ 871 yr

Section 12.5 Practice Exercises

For additional exercises, see Classroom Activities 12.5A–12.5E in the *Student's Resource Manual* at www.mhhe.com/moh.

Vocabulary and Key Concepts

1. a. As x becomes increasingly large, the value of $(1 + \frac{1}{x})^x$ approaches ___e___ ≈ 2.71828.

b. The function $f(x) = e^x$ is the exponential function base ___e___.

c. The logarithmic function base e is called the ___natural___ logarithmic function and is denoted by $y =$ ___$\ln x$___.

d. If x is a positive real number, then $\ln 1 =$ ___0___, $\ln e =$ ___1___, $\ln e^p =$ ___p___, and $e^{\ln x} =$ ___x___.

e. If x and y are positive real numbers, then $\ln(xy) =$ ___$\ln x + \ln y$___ and $\ln\left(\frac{x}{y}\right) =$ ___$\ln x - \ln y$___.

f. If x is a positive real number, then for any real number p, $\ln x^p$ can be written as ___$p \ln x$___.

g. The change-of-base formula states that $\log_b x = \frac{\log_a x}{\square}$, where a is a positive real number and $a \neq 1$.
$\log_a b$

Review Exercises

For Exercises 2–3, write the expression as a single logarithm. Assume that all variables represent positive real numbers.

2. $\log_5 x + 3 \log_5 y - \log_5 z$ $\quad \log_5\left(\frac{xy^3}{z}\right)$

3. $\log_3 a - 5 \log_3 c + \frac{1}{2} \log_3 d$ $\quad \log_3\left(\frac{a\sqrt{d}}{c^5}\right)$

For Exercises 4–5, write the expression as the sum or difference of logarithms of x, y, and z. Assume that all variables represent positive real numbers.

4. $\log\left(\frac{\sqrt{x}}{yz^4}\right)$ $\quad \frac{1}{2}\log x - \log y - 4 \log z$

5. $\log_6 \sqrt[4]{\frac{xy^2}{z^3}}$ $\quad \frac{1}{4}\log_6 x + \frac{1}{2}\log_6 y - \frac{3}{4}\log_6 z$

Concept 1: The Irrational Number *e*

6. From memory, write a decimal approximation of the number e, correct to three decimal places. 2.718

For Exercises 7–10, graph the equation by completing the table and plotting points. Identify the domain. Round to two decimal places when necessary. **(See Example 1.)**

7. $y = e^{x+1}$

x	y
−4	0.05
−3	0.14
−2	0.37
−1	1
0	2.72
1	7.39

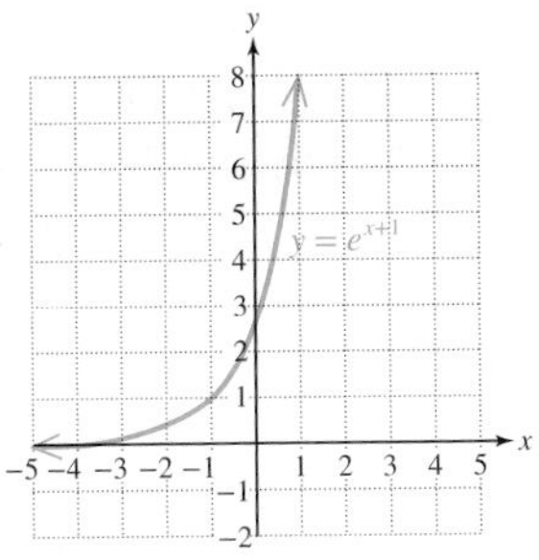

Domain: $(-\infty, \infty)$

8. $y = e^{x+2}$

x	y
−5	0.05
−4	0.14
−3	0.37
−2	1
−1	2.72
0	7.39

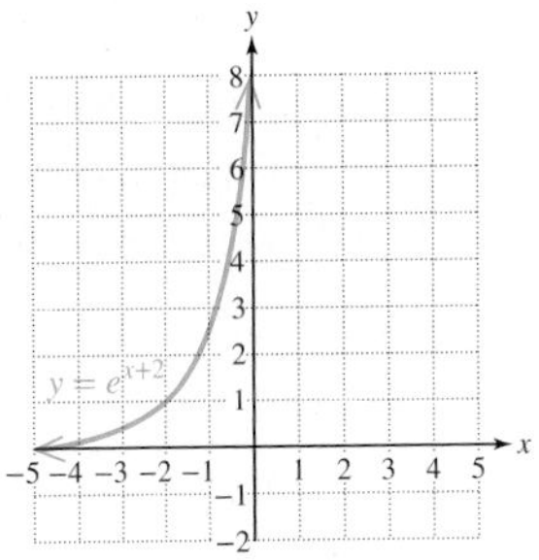

Domain: $(-\infty, \infty)$

Writing Translating Expression Geometry Scientific Calculator Video

9. $y = e^x + 2$

x	y
−2	2.14
−1	2.37
0	3
1	4.72
2	9.39
3	22.09

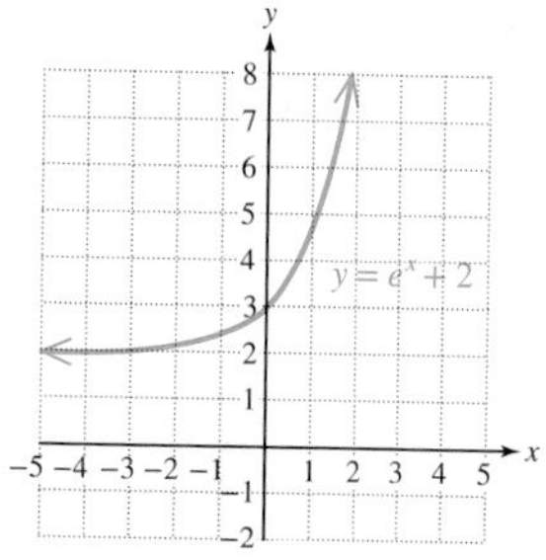

Domain: $(-\infty, \infty)$

10. $y = e^x - 1$

x	y
−4	−0.98
−3	−0.95
−2	−0.86
−1	−0.63
0	0
1	1.72

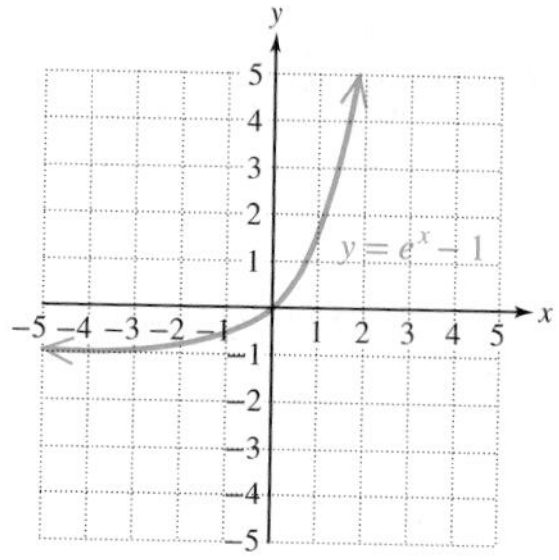

Domain: $(-\infty, \infty)$

Concept 2: Computing Compound Interest

For Exercises 11–16, suppose that P dollars in principal is invested at an annual interest rate r. For interest compounded n times per year, the amount $A(t)$ in the account after t years is given by $A(t) = P\left(1 + \frac{r}{n}\right)^{nt}$. If interest is compounded continuously, the amount is given by $A(t) = Pe^{rt}$.

11. Suppose an investor deposits \$10,000 in an account for 5 yr for which the interest is compounded monthly. Find the total amount of money in the account for the following interest rates. Compare your answers and comment on the effect of interest rate on an investment. **(See Example 2.)**

a. $r = 4.0\%$ \$12,209.97
b. $r = 6.0\%$ \$13,488.50
c. $r = 8.0\%$ \$14,898.46
d. $r = 9.5\%$ \$16,050.09

An investment grows more rapidly at higher interest rates.

12. Suppose an investor deposits \$5000 in an account for 8 yr for which the interest is compounded quarterly. Find the total amount of money in the account for the following interest rates. Compare your answers and comment on the effect of interest rate on an investment.

a. $r = 4.5\%$ \$7152.26
b. $r = 5.5\%$ \$7740.30
c. $r = 7.0\%$ \$8711.07
d. $r = 9.0\%$ \$10,190.52

An investment grows more rapidly at higher interest rates.

13. Suppose an investor deposits \$8000 in an account for 10 yr at 4.5% interest. Find the total amount of money in the account for the following compounding options. Compare your answers. How does the number of compound periods per year affect the total investment?

Animation

a. Compounded annually \$12,423.76
b. Compounded quarterly \$12,515.01
c. Compounded monthly \$12,535.94
d. Compounded daily \$12,546.15
e. Compounded continuously \$12,546.50

More money is earned at a greater number of compounding periods per year.

14. Suppose an investor deposits \$15,000 in an account for 8 yr at 5.0% interest. Find the total amount of money in the account for the following compounding options. Compare your answers. How does the number of compound periods per year affect the total investment?

a. Compounded annually \$22,161.83
b. Compounded quarterly \$22,321.96
c. Compounded monthly \$22,358.78
d. Compounded daily \$22,376.76
e. Compounded continuously \$22,377.37

More money is earned at a greater number of compounding periods per year.

15. Suppose an investor deposits \$5000 in an account earning 6.5% interest compounded continuously. Find the total amount in the account for the following time periods. How does the length of time affect the amount of interest earned?

a. 5 yr \$6920.15
b. 10 yr \$9577.70
c. 15 yr \$13,255.84
d. 20 yr \$18,346.48
e. 30 yr \$35,143.44

More money is earned over a longer period of time.

16. Suppose an investor deposits \$10,000 in an account earning 6.0% interest compounded continuously. Find the total amount in the account for the following time periods. How does the length of time affect the amount of interest earned?

a. 5 yr \$13,498.59 **b.** 10 yr \$18,221.19 **c.** 15 yr \$24,596.03 **d.** 20 yr \$33,201.17 **e.** 30 yr \$60,496.47

More money is earned over a longer period of time.

Concept 3: The Natural Logarithmic Function

For Exercises 17–20, graph the equation by completing the table and plotting the points. Identify the domain. Round to two decimal places when necessary. **(See Example 3.)**

17. $y = \ln(x - 2)$

x	y
2.25	−1.39
2.50	−0.69
2.75	−0.29
3	0
4	0.69
5	1.10
6	1.39

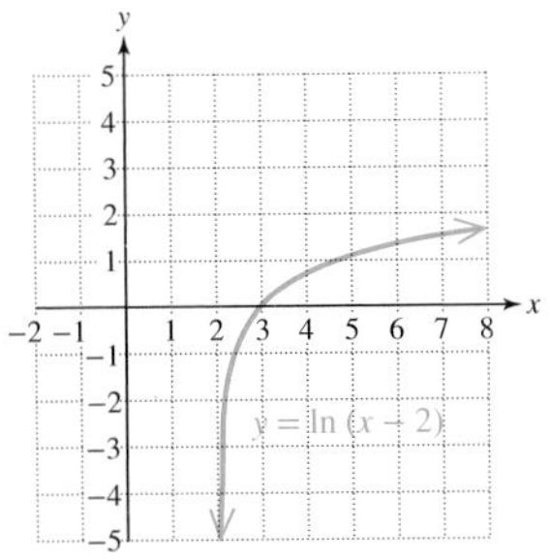

Domain: $(2, \infty)$

18. $y = \ln(x - 1)$

x	y
1.25	−1.39
1.50	−0.69
1.75	−0.29
2	0
3	0.69
4	1.10
5	1.39

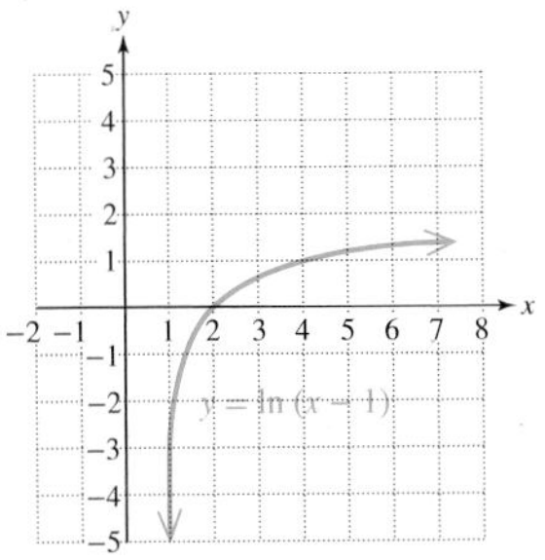

Domain: $(1, \infty)$

19. $y = \ln x - 1$

x	y
0.25	−2.39
0.5	−1.69
0.75	−1.29
1	−1.00
2	−0.31
3	0.10
4	0.39

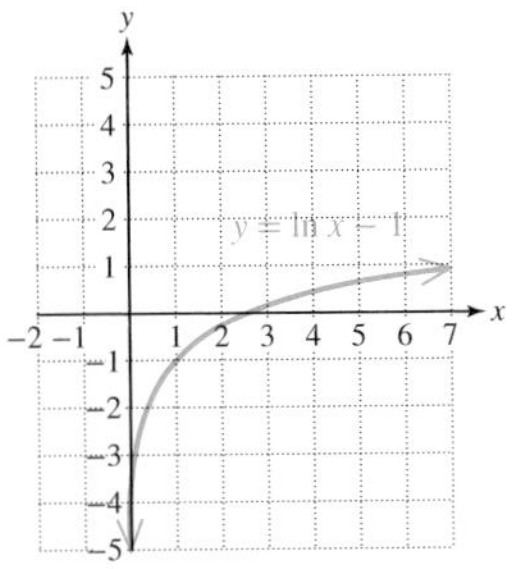

Domain: $(0, \infty)$

20. $y = \ln x + 2$

x	y
0.25	0.61
0.5	1.31
0.75	1.71
1	2.00
2	2.69
3	3.10
4	3.39

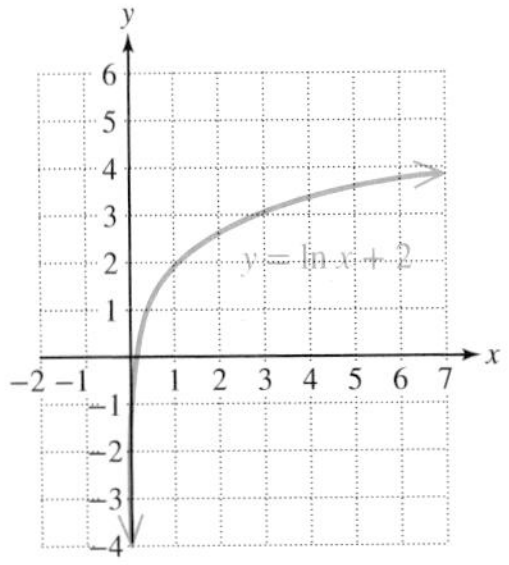

Domain: $(0, \infty)$

21. a. Graph $f(x) = 10^x$ and $g(x) = \log x$.

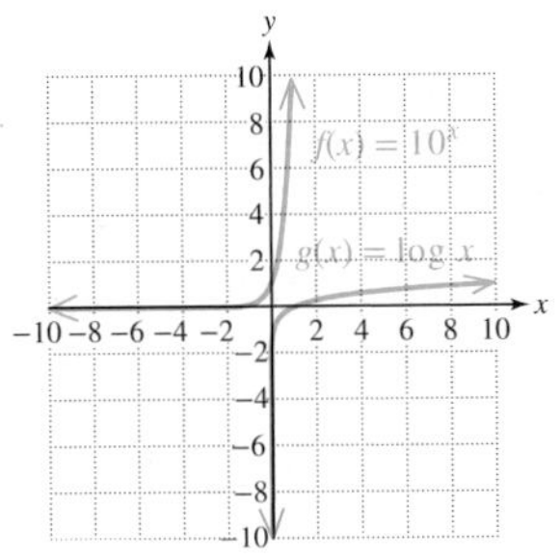

b. Identify the domain and range of f.
Domain: $(-\infty, \infty)$; range: $(0, \infty)$

c. Identify the domain and range of g.
Domain: $(0, \infty)$; range: $(-\infty, \infty)$

22. a. Graph $f(x) = e^x$ and $g(x) = \ln x$.

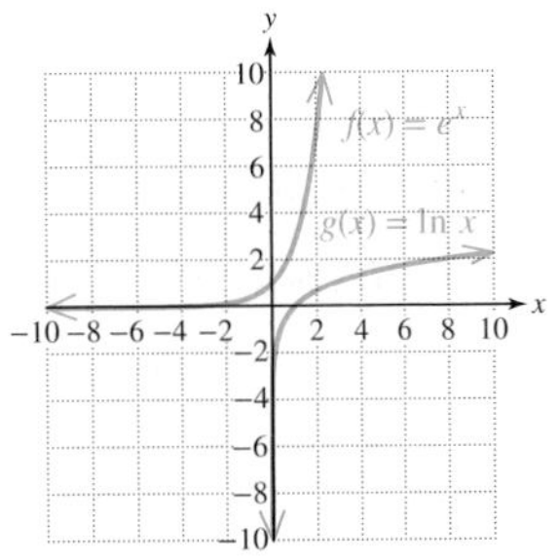

b. Identify the domain and range of f.
Domain: $(-\infty, \infty)$; range: $(0, \infty)$

c. Identify the domain and range of g.
Domain: $(0, \infty)$; range: $(-\infty, \infty)$

For Exercises 23–30, simplify the expressions. Assume all variables represent positive real numbers. **(See Example 4.)**

23. $\ln e$ 1 **24.** $\ln e^2$ 2 **25.** $\ln 1$ 0 **26.** $e^{\ln x}$ x

27. $\ln e^{-6}$ −6 **28.** $\ln e^{(5-3x)}$ $5 - 3x$ **29.** $e^{\ln(2x+3)}$ $2x + 3$ **30.** $e^{\ln 4}$ 4

For Exercises 31–38, write the expression as a single logarithm. Assume all variables represent positive real numbers. **(See Example 5.)**

31. $6 \ln p + \frac{1}{3} \ln q$ $\ln(p^6 \sqrt[3]{q})$

32. $2 \ln w + \ln z$ $\ln(w^2 z)$

33. $\frac{1}{2}(\ln x - 3 \ln y)$ $\ln\sqrt{\frac{x}{y^3}}$

34. $\frac{1}{3}(4 \ln a - \ln b)$ $\ln\sqrt[3]{\frac{a^4}{b}}$

35. $2 \ln a - \ln b - \frac{1}{3} \ln c$ $\ln\left(\frac{a^2}{b\sqrt[3]{c}}\right)$

36. $-\ln x + 3 \ln y - \ln z$ $\ln\left(\frac{y^3}{xz}\right)$

37. $4 \ln x - 3 \ln y - \ln z$ $\ln\left(\frac{x^4}{y^3 z}\right)$

38. $\frac{1}{2} \ln c + \ln a - 2 \ln b$ $\ln\left(\frac{\sqrt{c} \cdot a}{b^2}\right)$

For Exercises 39–46, write the expression as a sum and/or difference of ln *a*, ln *b*, and ln *c*. Assume all variables represent positive real numbers. **(See Example 6.)**

39. $\ln\left(\frac{a}{b}\right)^2$ $2 \ln a - 2 \ln b$

40. $\ln\sqrt[3]{\frac{a}{b}}$ $\frac{1}{3} \ln a - \frac{1}{3} \ln b$

41. $\ln(b^2 \cdot e)$ $2 \ln b + 1$

42. $\ln(\sqrt{c} \cdot e)$ $\frac{1}{2} \ln c + 1$

43. $\ln\left(\frac{a^4\sqrt{b}}{c}\right)$ $4 \ln a + \frac{1}{2} \ln b - \ln c$

44. $\ln\left(\frac{\sqrt{ab}}{c^3}\right)$ $\frac{1}{2} \ln a + \frac{1}{2} \ln b - 3 \ln c$

45. $\ln\left(\frac{ab}{c^2}\right)^{1/5}$ $\frac{1}{5} \ln a + \frac{1}{5} \ln b - \frac{2}{5} \ln c$

46. $\ln\sqrt{2ab}$ $\frac{1}{2} \ln 2 + \frac{1}{2} \ln a + \frac{1}{2} \ln b$

Concept 4: Change-of-Base Formula

47. a. Evaluate $\log_6 200$ by computing $\frac{\log 200}{\log 6}$ to four decimal places. 2.9570

b. Evaluate $\log_6 200$ by computing $\frac{\ln 200}{\ln 6}$ to four decimal places. 2.9570

c. How do your answers to parts (a) and (b) compare? They are the same.

48. a. Evaluate $\log_8 120$ by computing $\frac{\log 120}{\log 8}$ to four decimal places. 2.3023

b. Evaluate $\log_8 120$ by computing $\frac{\ln 120}{\ln 8}$ to four decimal places. 2.3023

c. How do your answers to parts (a) and (b) compare? They are the same.

For Exercises 49–60, use the change-of-base formula to approximate the logarithms to four decimal places. Check your answers by using the exponential key on your calculator. **(See Example 7.)**

49. $\log_2 7$ 2.8074

50. $\log_3 5$ 1.4650

51. $\log_8 24$ 1.5283

52. $\log_4 17$ 2.0437

53. $\log_8 0.012$ −2.1269

54. $\log_7 0.251$ −0.7104

55. $\log_9 1$ 0

56. $\log_2\left(\frac{1}{5}\right)$ −2.3219

57. $\log_4\left(\frac{1}{100}\right)$ −3.3219

58. $\log_5 0.0025$ −3.7227

59. $\log_7 0.0006$ −3.8124

60. $\log_2 0.24$ −2.0589

Concept 5: Applications of the Natural Logarithmic Function

Under continuous compounding, the amount of time t in years required for an investment to double is a function of the annual interest rate r according to the formula:

$$t = \frac{\ln 2}{r}$$

Use the formula for Exercises 61–63. **(See Example 8.)**

61. **a.** If you invest \$5000, how long will it take the investment to reach \$10,000 if the interest rate is 4.5%? Round to one decimal place. 15.4 yr

b. If you invest \$5000, how long will it take the investment to reach \$10,000 if the interest rate is 10%? Round to one decimal place. 6.9 yr

c. Using the doubling time found in part (b), how long would it take a \$5000 investment to reach \$20,000 if the interest rate is 10%? 13.8 yr

62. **a.** If you invest \$3000, how long will it take the investment to reach \$6000 if the interest rate is 5.5%? Round to one decimal place. 12.6 yr

b. If you invest \$3000, how long will it take the investment to reach \$6000 if the interest rate is 8%? Round to one decimal place. 8.7 yr

c. Using the doubling time found in part (b), how long would it take a \$3000 investment to reach \$12,000 if the interest rate is 8%? 17.4 yr

63. **a.** If you invest \$4000, how long will it take the investment to reach \$8000 if the interest rate is 3.5%? Round to one decimal place. 19.8 yr

b. If you invest \$4000, how long will it take the investment to reach \$8000 if the interest rate is 5%? Round to one decimal place. 13.9 yr

c. Using the doubling time found in part (b), how long would it take a \$4000 investment to reach \$16,000 if the interest rate is 5%? 27.8 yr

64. On August 31, 1854, an epidemic of cholera was discovered in London, England, resulting from a contaminated community water pump at Broad Street. By the end of September more than 600 citizens who drank water from the pump had died.

The cumulative number of deaths from cholera in the 1854 London epidemic can be approximated by

$$D(t) = 91 + 160 \ln (t + 1)$$

where t is the number of days after the start of the epidemic ($t = 0$ corresponds to September 1, 1854).

a. Approximate the total number of deaths as of September 1 ($t = 0$). 91 deaths

b. Approximate the total number of deaths as of September 5, September 10, and September 20.
Sept. 5: 349 deaths; Sept. 10: 459 deaths; Sept. 20: 570 deaths

Graphing Calculator Exercises

65. **a.** Graph the function defined by $f(x) = \log_3 x$ by graphing $Y_1 = \dfrac{\log x}{\log 3}$.

b. Graph the function defined by $f(x) = \log_3 x$ by graphing $Y_2 = \dfrac{\ln x}{\ln 3}$.

c. Does it appear that $Y_1 = Y_2$ on the standard viewing window?
They appear to be the same.

66. **a.** Graph the function defined by $f(x) = \log_7 x$ by graphing $Y_1 = \frac{\log x}{\log 7}$.

b. Graph the function defined by $f(x) = \log_7 x$ by graphing $Y_2 = \frac{\ln x}{\ln 7}$.

c. Does it appear that $Y_1 = Y_2$ on the standard viewing window?
They appear to be the same.

For Exercises 67–69, graph the functions on a graphing calculator.

67. Graph $s(x) = \log_{1/2} x$

68. Graph $y = e^{x-2}$

69. Graph $y = e^{x-1}$

Problem Recognition Exercises

Logarithmic and Exponential Forms

Fill out the table by writing the exponential expressions in logarithmic form, and the logarithmic expressions in exponential form. Use the fact that:

$$y = \log_b x \quad \text{is equivalent to} \quad b^y = x$$

	Exponential Form	Logarithmic Form
1.	$2^5 = 32$	$\log_2 32 = 5$
2.	$3^4 = 81$	$\log_3 81 = 4$
3.	$z^y = x$	$\log_z x = y$
4.	$b^c = a$	$\log_b a = c$
5.	$10^3 = 1000$	$\log 1000 = 3$
6.	$10^1 = 10$	$\log 10 = 1$
7.	$e^a = b$	$\ln b = a$
8.	$e^q = p$	$\ln p = q$
9.	$(\frac{1}{2})^2 = \frac{1}{4}$	$\log_{1/2} (\frac{1}{4}) = 2$
10.	$(\frac{1}{3})^{-2} = 9$	$\log_{1/3} 9 = -2$
11.	$10^{-2} = 0.01$	$\log 0.01 = -2$
12.	$10^x = 4$	$\log 4 = x$
13.	$e^0 = 1$	$\ln 1 = 0$
14.	$e^1 = e$	$\ln e = 1$
15.	$25^{1/2} = 5$	$\log_{25} 5 = \frac{1}{2}$
16.	$16^{1/4} = 2$	$\log_{16} 2 = \frac{1}{4}$
17.	$e^t = s$	$\ln s = t$
18.	$e^r = w$	$\ln w = r$
19.	$15^{-2} = \frac{1}{225}$	$\log_{15} (\frac{1}{225}) = -2$
20.	$3^{-1} = p$	$\log_3 p = -1$

Logarithmic and Exponential Equations and Applications

Section 12.6

Concepts

1. Solving Logarithmic Equations

Equations containing one or more logarithms are called **logarithmic equations**. For example, the following are logarithmic equations.

$$\log_3(2x+5) = 1 \qquad \text{and} \qquad \log_4 x = 1 - \log_4(x-3)$$

To solve equations involving logarithms of first degree, we use the following guidelines.

Solving Logarithmic Equations

Step 1 Isolate the logarithms on one side of the equation.

Step 2 Write a sum or difference of logarithms as a single logarithm.

Step 3 Rewrite the equation in step 2 in exponential form.

Step 4 Solve the resulting equation from step 3.

Step 5 Check all solutions to verify that they are within the domain of the logarithmic expressions in the original equation.

Example 1 Solving a Logarithmic Equation

Classroom Example: p. 912, Exercise 22

Solve the equation. $\log_3(2x+5) = 1$

Solution:

$\log_3(2x+5) = 1$ This equation has a single logarithm isolated on the left-hand side.

$2x + 5 = 3^1$ Write the logarithm in its equivalent exponential form.

$2x + 5 = 3$ Solve the resulting equation.

$2x = -2$

$x = -1$ Check: $x = -1$

$\log_3(2x+5) = 1$

$\log_3[2(-1)+5] \stackrel{?}{=} 1$

$\log_3(3) \stackrel{?}{=} 1$ ✓

The solution set is $\{-1\}$.

Skill Practice Solve the equation.

1. $\log_6(5x-4) = 2$

Answer

1. $\{8\}$

Classroom Example: p. 912, Exercise 30

Example 2 Solving a Logarithmic Equation

Solve the equation. $\log_4 x = 1 - \log_4 (x - 3)$

Solution:

Instructor Note: It is very important that students realize that there is a possibility of extraneous solutions for logarithmic equations.

$\log_4 x = 1 - \log_4 (x - 3)$	
$\log_4 x + \log_4 (x - 3) = 1$	Isolate the logarithms on one side of the equation.
$\log_4 [x(x - 3)] = 1$	Write as a single logarithm.
$\log_4 (x^2 - 3x) = 1$	Simplify inside the parentheses.
$x^2 - 3x = 4^1$	Write the equation in exponential form.
$x^2 - 3x - 4 = 0$	The resulting equation is quadratic.
$(x - 4)(x + 1) = 0$	Factor.
$x = 4$ or $x = -1$	Apply the zero product rule.

Notice that -1 is *not* a solution because $\log_4 x$ is not defined at $x = -1$. However, $x = 4$ *is* defined in both expressions $\log_4 x$ and $\log_4 (x - 3)$. We can substitute $x = 4$ into the original equation to show that it checks.

Check: $x = 4$

$$\log_4 x = 1 - \log_4 (x - 3)$$
$$\log_4 4 \stackrel{?}{=} 1 - \log_4 (4 - 3)$$
$$1 \stackrel{?}{=} 1 - \log_4 1$$
$$1 \stackrel{?}{=} 1 - 0 \checkmark \text{ True}$$

The solution set is $\{4\}$. (The value -1 does not check.)

Skill Practice Solve the equation.

2. $\log_3 (x - 8) = 2 - \log_3 x$

Classroom Example: p. 912, Exercise 14

Example 3 Solving a Logarithmic Equation

Solve the equation. $\log (x + 300) = 3.7$

Solution:

$\log (x + 300) = 3.7$	The equation has a single logarithm that is already isolated.
$10^{3.7} = x + 300$	Write the equation in exponential form.
$10^{3.7} - 300 = x$	Solve for x.
$x = 10^{3.7} - 300$	
≈ 4711.87	

Answer

2. {9} (The value −1 does not check.)

Check: $x = 10^{3.7} - 300$ — Check the exact value of x in the original equation.

$$\log(x + 300) = 3.7$$
$$\log[(10^{3.7} - 300) + 300] \stackrel{?}{=} 3.7$$
$$\log(10^{3.7} - 300 + 300) \stackrel{?}{=} 3.7$$
$$\log 10^{3.7} \stackrel{?}{=} 3.7$$

Property 3 of logarithms: $\log_b b^p = p$

$$3.7 \stackrel{?}{=} 3.7 \checkmark \text{ True}$$

The solution $10^{3.7} - 300$ checks.

The solution set is $\{10^{3.7} - 300\}$.

Skill Practice Solve the equation.

3. $\log(p + 6) = 1.3$

The following property is another useful tool to solve a logarithmic equation. This is demonstrated in Example 4.

Equivalence of Logarithmic Expressions

Let x, y, and b represent real numbers such that $x > 0$, $y > 0$, $b > 0$, and $b \neq 1$. Then

$$\log_b x = \log_b y \quad \text{implies} \quad x = y$$

The equivalence property of logarithmic expressions indicates that if two logarithms of the same base are equal, then their arguments are equal.

Example 4 Solving a Logarithmic Equation

Classroom Example: p. 912, Exercise 34

Solve the equation.

$$\ln(x + 2) + \ln(x - 1) = \ln(9x - 17)$$

Solution:

$$\ln(x + 2) + \ln(x - 1) = \ln(9x - 17)$$

$$\ln[(x + 2)(x - 1)] = \ln(9x - 17)$$ Write the logarithms on the left-hand side as a single logarithm.

$$\ln(x^2 + x - 2) = \ln(9x - 17)$$ Simplify.

$$x^2 + x - 2 = 9x - 17$$ Use the equivalence property of logarithms. That is, equate the arguments of each log.

$$x^2 - 8x + 15 = 0$$ Solve the resulting quadratic equation.

$$(x - 5)(x - 3) = 0$$

$$x = 5 \quad \text{or} \quad x = 3$$

Answer

3. $\{10^{1.3} - 6\}$

The solutions 5 and 3 are both within the domain of the logarithmic functions in the original equation. Both solutions check.

The solution set is $\{5, 3\}$.

Skill Practice Solve the equation.

4. $\ln(t - 3) + \ln(t - 1) = \ln(2t - 5)$

2. Solving Exponential Equations

An equation with one or more exponential expressions is called an **exponential equation**. The following property is often useful in solving exponential equations.

Equivalence of Exponential Expressions

Let x, y, and b be real numbers such that $b > 0$ and $b \neq 1$. Then

$$b^x = b^y \quad \text{implies} \quad x = y$$

The equivalence property of exponential expressions indicates that if two exponential expressions of the same base are equal, then their exponents must be equal.

Classroom Example: p. 912, Exercise 46

Example 5 Solving an Exponential Equation

Solve the equation. $4^{2x-9} = 64$

Solution:

$4^{2x-9} = 64$

$4^{2x-9} = 4^3$ Write both sides with a common base.

$2x - 9 = 3$ If $b^x = b^y$, then $x = y$.

$2x = 12$ Solve for x.

$x = 6$

To check, substitute $x = 6$ into the original equation.

$$4^{2(6)-9} \stackrel{?}{=} 64$$

$$4^{12-9} \stackrel{?}{=} 64$$

$$4^3 \stackrel{?}{=} 64 \checkmark \text{ True}$$

The solution set is $\{6\}$.

Skill Practice Solve the equation.

5. $2^{3x+1} = 8$

Answers

4. $\{4\}$ (The value 2 does not check.)

5. $\left\{\frac{2}{3}\right\}$

Example 6 Solving an Exponential Equation

Classroom Example: p. 912, Exercise 50

Solve the equation. $(2^x)^{x+3} = \frac{1}{4}$

Solution:

$(2^x)^{x+3} = \frac{1}{4}$

$2^{x^2+3x} = 2^{-2}$ — Apply the multiplication property of exponents. Write both sides of the equation with a common base.

$x^2 + 3x = -2$ — If $b^x = b^y$, then $x = y$.

$x^2 + 3x + 2 = 0$ — The resulting equation is quadratic.

$(x + 2)(x + 1) = 0$ — Solve for x.

$x = -2$ or $x = -1$ — Both solutions check.

The solution set is $\{-2, -1\}$.

Skill Practice Solve the equation.

6. $(3^x)^{x-5} = \frac{1}{81}$

Example 7 Solving an Exponential Equation

Classroom Example: p. 912, Exercise 56

Solve the equation. $4^x = 25$

Solution:

Because 25 cannot be written as a recognizable power of 4, we cannot easily use the property that if $b^x = b^y$, then $x = y$. Instead, we can take a logarithm of any base on both sides of the equation. Then by applying the power property of logarithms, the unknown exponent can be written as a factor.

$4^x = 25$

$\log 4^x = \log 25$ — Take the common logarithm of both sides.

$x \log 4 = \log 25$ — Apply the power property of logarithms to express the exponent as a factor. This is now a linear equation in x.

$\frac{x \log 4}{\log 4} = \frac{\log 25}{\log 4}$ — Solve for x.

$x = \frac{\log 25}{\log 4}$ or approximately 2.322.

The solution set is $\left\{\frac{\log 25}{\log 4}\right\}$ or equivalently $\left\{\frac{\ln 25}{\ln 4}\right\}$.

Skill Practice Solve the equation.

7. $5^x = 32$

Calculator Connections

Topic: Analyzing an Exponential Equation Graphically

Graph $Y_1 = 4^x$ and $Y_2 = 25$. An *Intersect* feature can be used to find the x-coordinate where $Y_1 = Y_2$.

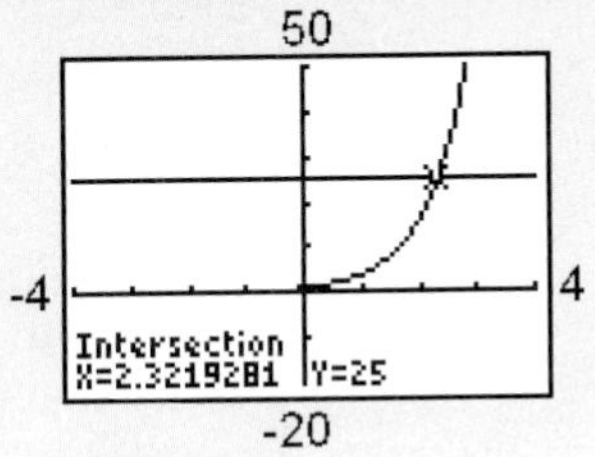

Answers

6. $\{1, 4\}$

7. $\left\{\frac{\log 32}{\log 5}\right\}$ or $\left\{\frac{\ln 32}{\ln 5}\right\}$

TIP: The equation from Example 7 is written in the form b^x = constant. In this special case, we also have the option of rewriting the equation in its corresponding logarithmic form to solve for x.

$$4^x = 25$$
$$x = \log_4 25$$
$$= \frac{\ln 25}{\ln 4} \quad \text{(Change-of-base formula)}$$

Solving Exponential Equations

Step 1 Isolate one of the exponential expressions in the equation.

Step 2 Take a logarithm on both sides of the equation. (The natural logarithmic function or the common logarithmic function is often used so that the final answer can be approximated with a calculator.)

Step 3 Use the power property of logarithms (property 7) to write exponents as factors. Recall: $\log_b x^p = p \log_b x$.

Step 4 Solve the resulting equation from step 3.

Classroom Example: p. 912, Exercise 62

Example 8 Solving an Exponential Equation by Taking a Logarithm on Both Sides

Solve the equation. $e^{-3.6x} - 2 = 7.74$

Solution:

$$e^{-3.6x} - 2 = 7.74$$

$$e^{-3.6x} = 9.74$$ Add 2 to both sides to isolate the exponential expression.

$$\ln e^{-3.6x} = \ln 9.74$$ The exponential expression has a base of e, so it is convenient to take the natural logarithm of both sides.

$$(-3.6x) \ln e = \ln 9.74$$ Use the power property of logarithms.

$$-3.6x = \ln 9.74$$ Simplify (recall that $\ln e = 1$).

$$x = \frac{\ln 9.74}{-3.6} \approx -0.632$$ Divide both sides by −3.6.

The solution set is $\left\{-\frac{\ln 9.74}{3.6}\right\}$.

Skill Practice Solve the equation.

8. $e^{-0.2t} + 1 = 8.52$

Answer

8. $\left\{\frac{\ln 7.52}{-0.2}\right\}$

Example 9 **Solving an Exponential Equation by Taking a Logarithm on Both Sides**

Classroom Example: p. 912, Exercise 66

Solve the equation. $2^{x+3} = 7^x$

Solution:

$2^{x+3} = 7^x$

$\ln 2^{(x+3)} = \ln 7^x$ Take the natural logarithm of both sides.

$(x + 3) \ln 2 = x \ln 7$ Use the power property of logarithms.

$x (\ln 2) + 3 (\ln 2) = x \ln 7$ Apply the distributive property.

$x (\ln 2) - x (\ln 7) = -3 \ln 2$ Collect x-terms on one side.

$x(\ln 2 - \ln 7) = -3 \ln 2$ Factor out x.

$\frac{x(\ln 2 - \ln 7)}{(\ln 2 - \ln 7)} = \frac{-3 \ln 2}{\ln 2 - \ln 7}$ Solve for x.

$x = \frac{-3 \ln 2}{\ln 2 - \ln 7} \approx 1.66$

The solution set is $\left\{-\frac{3 \ln 2}{\ln 2 - \ln 7}\right\}$.

TIP: The exponential equation $2^{x+3} = 7^x$ could have been solved by taking a logarithm of *any* base on both sides of the equation.

TIP: Using the properties of logarithms, we can write the solution to Example 9 in other forms, such as:

$x = -\frac{\ln 8}{\ln 2 - \ln 7}$ and

$x = \frac{\ln 8}{\ln 3.5}$

Skill Practice Solve the equation.

9. $3^x = 8^{x+2}$

3. Applications

Example 10 **Applying an Exponential Function to World Population**

Classroom Example: p. 913, Exercise 76

The population of the world was estimated to have reached 6.5 billion in April 2006. The population growth rate for the world is estimated to be 1.4%. (*Source:* U.S. Census Bureau) The function defined by

$$P(t) = 6.5(1.014)^t$$

represents the world population $P(t)$ in billions as a function of the number of years after April 2006 ($t = 0$ represents April 2006).

a. Use the function to estimate the world population in April 2010.

b. Use the function to predict the amount of time after April 2006 required for the world population to reach 13 billion if this trend continues.

Solution:

a. $P(t) = 6.5(1.014)^t$

$P(4) = 6.5(1.014)^4$ The year 2010 corresponds to $t = 4$.

≈ 6.87 In 2010, the world's population was approximately 6.87 billion.

Answer

9. $\left\{\frac{2 \ln 8}{\ln 3 - \ln 8}\right\}$

b.

$$P(t) = 6.5(1.014)^t$$

$$13 = 6.5(1.014)^t$$ Substitute $P(t) = 13$ and solve for t.

$$\frac{13}{6.5} = \frac{6.5(1.014)^t}{6.5}$$ Isolate the exponential expression on one side of the equation.

$$2 = 1.014^t$$

$$\ln 2 = \ln 1.014^t$$ Take the natural logarithm of both sides.

$$\ln 2 = t \ln 1.014$$ Use the power property of logarithms.

$$\frac{\ln 2}{\ln 1.014} = \frac{t \ln 1.014}{\ln 1.014}$$ Solve for t.

$$t = \frac{\ln 2}{\ln 1.014} \approx 50$$ The population will reach 13 billion (double the April 2006 value) approximately 50 yr after 2006.

Note: It has taken thousands of years for the world's population to reach 6.5 billion. However, with a growth rate of 1.4%, it will take only 50 years to gain an additional 6.5 billion, if this trend continues.

Skill Practice Use the population function from Example 10.

10. Predict the world population in April 2020.

11. Predict the year in which the world population will reach 9 billion.

On Friday, April 25, 1986, a nuclear accident occurred at the Chernobyl nuclear reactor, resulting in radioactive contaminates being released into the atmosphere. The most hazardous isotopes released in this accident were ^{137}Cs (cesium 137), ^{131}I (iodine 131), and ^{90}Sr (strontium 90). People living close to Chernobyl (in Ukraine) were at risk of radiation exposure from inhalation, from absorption through the skin, and from food contamination. Years after the incident, scientists have seen an increase in the incidence of thyroid disease among children living in the contaminated areas. Because iodine is readily absorbed in the thyroid gland, scientists suspect that radiation from iodine 131 is the cause.

Classroom Example: p. 914, Exercise 84

Example 11 Applying an Exponential Equation to Radioactive Decay

The half-life of radioactive iodine, ^{131}I, is 8.04 days. If 10 g of iodine 131 is initially present, then the amount $A(t)$ (in grams) of radioactive iodine still present after t days is approximated by

$$A(t) = 10e^{-0.0862t}$$

where t is the time in days.

a. Use the model to approximate the amount of ^{131}I still present after 2 weeks. Round to the nearest 0.1 g.

b. How long will it take for the amount of ^{131}I to decay to 0.5 g? Round to the nearest 0.1 day.

Answers

10. Approximately 7.9 billion

11. The year 2029

Solution:

a. $A(t) = 10e^{-0.0862t}$

$A(14) = 10e^{-0.0862(14)}$ — Substitute $t = 14$ (2 weeks).

≈ 3.0 g — There was 3.0 g still present after 2 weeks.

b. $A(t) = 10e^{-0.0862t}$

$0.5 = 10e^{-0.0862t}$ — Substitute $A = 0.5$.

$\frac{0.5}{10} = \frac{10e^{-0.0862t}}{10}$ — Isolate the exponential expression.

$0.05 = e^{-0.0862t}$

$\ln 0.05 = \ln e^{-0.0862t}$ — Take the natural logarithm of both sides.

$\ln 0.05 = -0.0862t$ — The resulting equation is linear.

$\frac{\ln 0.05}{-0.0862} = \frac{-0.0862t}{-0.0862}$ — Solve for t.

$t = \frac{\ln 0.05}{-0.0862} \approx 34.8$ days — It will take 34.8 days for 10 g of ^{131}I to decay to 0.5 g.

Skill Practice Radioactive strontium 90 (^{90}Sr) has a half-life of 28 yr. If 100 g of strontium 90 is initially present, the amount left after t years is approximated by

$$A(t) = 100e^{-0.0248t}$$

12. Find the amount of ^{90}Sr present after 85 yr.
13. How long will it take for the amount of ^{90}Sr to decay to 40 g?

Answers
12. 12.1 g **13.** 36.9 years

Section 12.6 Practice Exercises

For additional exercises, see Classroom Activities 12.6A–12.6C in the *Student's Resource Manual* at www.mhhe.com/moh.

Vocabulary and Key Concepts

1. **a.** The equivalence property of logarithmic expressions states that if $\log_b x = \log_b y$, then ___$x = y$___.
   b. The equivalence property of exponential expressions states that if $b^x = b^y$, then ___$x = y$___.

Review Exercises

For Exercises 2–6, write the expression as a single logarithm. Assume all variables represent positive real numbers.

2. $\log_b (x - 1) + \log_b (x + 2)$ $\log_b [(x-1)(x+2)]$

3. $\log_b x + \log_b (2x + 3)$ $\log_b [x(2x+3)]$

4. $\log_b x - \log_b (1 - x)$ $\log_b\left(\frac{x}{1-x}\right)$

5. $\log_b (x + 2) - \log_b (3x - 5)$ $\log_b\left(\frac{x+2}{3x-5}\right)$

6. $2 \log_b x - \log_b (x + 1)$ $\log_b\left(\frac{x^2}{x+1}\right)$

Concept 1: Solving Logarithmic Equations

For Exercises 7–38, solve the logarithmic equation. **(See Examples 1–4.)**

7. $\log_3 x = 2$ $\{9\}$

8. $\log_4 x = 9$ $\{4^9\}$

9. $\log p = 42$ $\{10^{42}\}$

10. $\log q = \frac{1}{2}$ $\{\sqrt{10}\}$

11. $\ln x = 0.08$ $\{e^{0.08}\}$

12. $\ln x = 19$ $\{e^{19}\}$

13. $\log (x + 40) = -9.2$ $\{10^{-9.2} - 40\}$

14. $\log (z - 3) = -6.7$ $\{10^{-6.7} + 3\}$

15. $\log_x 25 = 2$ $(x > 0)$ $\{5\}$

16. $\log_x 100 = 2$ $(x > 0)$ $\{10\}$

17. $\log_b 10{,}000 = 4$ $(b > 0)$ $\{10\}$

18. $\log_b e^3 = 3$ $(b > 0)$ $\{e\}$

19. $\log_y 5 = \frac{1}{2}$ $(y > 0)$ $\{25\}$

20. $\log_b 8 = \frac{1}{2}$ $(b > 0)$ $\{64\}$

21. $\log_4 (c + 5) = 3$ $\{59\}$

22. $\log_5 (a - 4) = 2$ $\{29\}$

23. $\log_5 (4y + 1) = 1$ $\{1\}$

24. $\log_6 (5t - 2) = 1$ $\left\{\frac{8}{5}\right\}$

25. $\ln (1 - x) = 0$ $\{0\}$

26. $\log_4 (2 - x) = 1$ $\{-2\}$

27. $\log_3 8 - \log_3 (x + 5) = 2$ $\left\{-\frac{37}{9}\right\}$

28. $\log_2 (x + 3) - \log_2 (x + 2) = 1$ $\{-1\}$

29. $\log_2 (h - 1) + \log_2 (h + 1) = 3$ $\{3\}$ (The value -3 does not check.)

30. $\log_3 k + \log_3 (2k + 3) = 2$ $\left\{\frac{3}{2}\right\}$ (The value -3 does not check.)

31. $\log (x + 2) = \log (3x - 6)$ $\{4\}$

32. $\log x = \log (1 - x)$ $\left\{\frac{1}{2}\right\}$

33. $\ln x - \ln (4x - 9) = 0$ $\{3\}$

34. $\ln (x + 5) - \ln x = \ln (4x)$ $\left\{\frac{5}{4}\right\}$ (The value -1 does not check.)

35. $\log_5 (3t + 2) - \log_5 t = \log_5 4$ $\{2\}$

36. $\log (6y - 7) + \log y = \log 5$ $\left\{\frac{5}{3}\right\}$ (The value $-\frac{1}{2}$ does not check.)

37. $\log (4m) = \log 2 + \log (m - 3)$ $\{\ \}$ (The value -3 does not check.)

38. $\log (-h) + \log 3 = \log (2h - 15)$ $\{\ \}$ (The value 3 does not check.)

Concept 2: Solving Exponential Equations

For Exercises 39–54, solve the exponential equation by using the property that $b^x = b^y$ implies $x = y$, for $b > 0$ and $b \neq 1$. **(See Examples 5–6.)**

39. $5^x = 625$ $\{4\}$

40. $3^x = 81$ $\{4\}$

41. $2^{-x} = 64$ $\{-6\}$

42. $6^{-x} = 216$ $\{-3\}$

43. $36^x = 6$ $\left\{\frac{1}{2}\right\}$

44. $343^x = 7$ $\left\{\frac{1}{3}\right\}$

45. $4^{2x-1} = 64$ $\{2\}$

46. $5^{3x-1} = 125$ $\left\{\frac{4}{3}\right\}$

47. $81^{3x-4} = \frac{1}{243}$ $\left\{\frac{11}{12}\right\}$

48. $4^{2x-7} = \frac{1}{128}$ $\left\{\frac{7}{4}\right\}$

49. $\left(\frac{2}{3}\right)^{-x+4} = \frac{8}{27}$ $\{1\}$

50. $\left(\frac{1}{4}\right)^{3x+2} = \frac{1}{64}$ $\left\{\frac{1}{3}\right\}$

51. $16^{-x+1} = 8^{5x}$ $\left\{\frac{4}{19}\right\}$

52. $27^{(1/3)x} = \left(\frac{1}{9}\right)^{2x-1}$ $\left\{\frac{2}{5}\right\}$

53. $(4^x)^{x+1} = 16$ $\{-2, 1\}$

54. $(3^x)^{x+2} = \frac{1}{3}$ $\{-1\}$

For Exercises 55–74, solve the exponential equation by taking a logarithm of both sides. **(See Examples 7–9.)**

55. $8^a = 21$ $\left\{\frac{\ln 21}{\ln 8}\right\}$

56. $6^y = 39$ $\left\{\frac{\ln 39}{\ln 6}\right\}$

57. $e^x = 8.1254$ $\{\ln 8.1254\}$

58. $e^x = 0.3151$ $\{\ln 0.3151\}$

59. $10^t = 0.0138$ $\{\log 0.0138\}$

60. $10^p = 16.8125$ $\{\log 16.8125\}$

61. $e^{0.07h} - 6 = 9$ $\left\{\frac{\ln 15}{0.07}\right\}$

62. $e^{0.03k} + 7 = 11$ $\left\{\frac{\ln 4}{0.03}\right\}$

63. $e^{1.2t} = 3$ $\left\{\frac{\ln 3}{1.2}\right\}$

64. $e^{1.5t} = 7$ $\left\{\frac{\ln 7}{1.5}\right\}$

65. $3^{x+1} = 5^x$ $\left\{\frac{\ln 3}{\ln 5 - \ln 3}\right\}$

66. $2^{x-1} = 7^x$ $\left\{\frac{\ln 2}{\ln 2 - \ln 7}\right\}$

67. $2^{x+2} = 6^x$ $\left\{\frac{2 \ln 2}{\ln 6 - \ln 2}\right\}$

68. $5^{x-2} = 3^x$ $\left\{\frac{2 \ln 5}{\ln 5 - \ln 3}\right\}$

69. $32e^{0.04m} = 128$ $\left\{\frac{\ln 4}{0.04}\right\}$

70. $8e^{0.05n} = 160$ $\left\{\frac{\ln 20}{0.05}\right\}$

71. $6e^{x/3} = 125$ $\left\{3 \ln \left(\frac{125}{6}\right)\right\}$

72. $8e^{x/5} = 155$ $\left\{5 \ln \left(\frac{155}{8}\right)\right\}$

73. $5^{x-2} - 4 = 16$ $\left\{\frac{\ln 20}{\ln 5} + 2\right\}$

74. $2^{x+4} + 17 = 50$ $\left\{\frac{\ln 33}{\ln 2} - 4\right\}$

Concept 3: Applications

75. The population of China can be modeled by

$$P(t) = 1237(1.0095)^t$$

where $P(t)$ is in millions and t is the number of years since 1998. **(See Example 10.)**

a. Using this model, what was the population in the year 2002? $\approx$ 1285 million (or 1,285,000,000) people

b. Estimate the population in the year 2016. $\approx$ 1466.5 million (or 1,466,500,000) people

c. If this growth rate continues, in what year will the population reach 2 billion people (2 billion is 2000 million)? The year 2049 ($t \approx 50.8$)

76. The population of Delhi, India, can be modeled by

$$P(t) = 9817(1.031)^t$$

where $P(t)$ is in thousands and t is the number of years since 2001.

a. Using this model, estimate the population in the year 2018. 16,496 thousand (or 16,496,000) people

b. In what year did the population reach 15 million (15 million is 15,000 thousand)? The year 2015 ($t \approx 13.9$)

77. The growth of a certain bacteria in a culture is given by the model

$$A(t) = 500e^{0.0277t}$$

where $A(t)$ is the number of bacteria and t is time in minutes.

a. What is the initial number of bacteria? 500 bacteria

b. What is the population after 10 min? $\approx$ 660 bacteria

c. How long will it take for the population to double (that is, reach 1000)? $\approx$ 25 min

78. The population of the bacteria *Salmonella typhimurium* is given by the model

$$A(t) = 300e^{0.01733t}$$

where $A(t)$ is the number of bacteria and t is time in minutes.

a. What is the initial number of bacteria? 300 bacteria

b. What is the population after 10 min? $\approx$ 357 bacteria

c. How long will it take for the population to double? $\approx$ 40 min

79. Suppose \$5000 is invested at 7% interest compounded continuously. How long will it take for the investment to grow to \$10,000? Use the model $A(t) = Pe^{rt}$ and round to the nearest tenth of a year. It will take 9.9 yr for the investment to double.

80. Suppose \$2000 is invested at 10% interest compounded continuously. How long will it take for the investment to triple? Use the model $A(t) = Pe^{rt}$ and round to the nearest year. It will take 11 yr for the investment to triple.

81. Suppose that \$8000 is invested at 4.5% interest compounded monthly. How long will it take the investment to reach \$10,000? Use the model $A(t) = P\left(1 + \frac{r}{n}\right)^{nt}$ and round to the nearest year. 5 yr

82. Suppose that a couple invests \$30,000 in a bond fund that pays 6.5% interest compounded quarterly. How long will it take the investment to reach \$250,000? Use the model $A(t) = P\left(1 + \frac{r}{n}\right)^{nt}$ and round to the nearest year. 33 yr

83. Phosphorus 32 (^{32}P) has a half-life of approximately 14 days. If 10 g of ^{32}P is present initially, then the amount $A(t)$ (in grams) of phosphorus 32 still present after t days is given by $A(t) = 10(0.5)^{t/14}$. **(See Example 11.)**

a. Find the amount of phosphorus 32 still present after 5 days. Round to the nearest tenth of a gram. 7.8 g

b. Find the amount of time necessary for the amount of ^{32}P to decay to 4 g. Round to the nearest tenth of a day. 18.5 days

84. Polonium 210 (^{210}Po) has a half-life of approximately 138.6 days. If 4 g of ^{210}Po is present initially, then the amount $A(t)$ (in grams) of polonium 210 still present after t days is given by $A(t) = 4e^{-0.005t}$.

a. Find the amount of polonium 210 still present after 50 days. Round to the nearest tenth of a gram. 3.1 g

b. Find the amount of time necessary for the amount of ^{210}P to decay to 0.5 g. Round to the nearest tenth of a day. 415.9 days

The decibel level of sound can be found by the equation $D = 10 \log\left(\frac{I}{I_0}\right)$, where I is the intensity of the sound and I_0 is the intensity of the least audible sound that an average person can hear. Generally I_0 is found as 10^{-12} watt per square meter (W/m^2). Use this information to answer Exercises 85–86.

85. Given that heavy traffic has a decibel level of 89.3 and that $I_0 = 10^{-12}$, find the intensity of the sound of heavy traffic. The intensity of sound of heavy traffic is $10^{-3.07}$ W/m^2.

86. Given that normal conversation has a decibel level of 65 and $I_0 = 10^{-12}$, find the intensity of the sound of normal conversation. The intensity of sound of normal conversation is $10^{-5.5}$ W/m^2.

87. Suppose you save $10,000 from working an extra job. Rather than spending the money, you decide to save the money for retirement by investing in a mutual fund that averages 12% per year. How long will it take for this money to grow to $1,000,000? Use the model $A(t) = Pe^{rt}$ and round to the nearest tenth of a year. It will take 38.4 yr.

88. The model $A = Pe^{rt}$ is used to compute the total amount of money in an account after t years at an interest rate r, compounded continuously. The value P is the initial principal. Find the amount of time required for the investment to double as a function of the interest rate. (*Hint:* Substitute $A = 2P$ and solve for t.) $t = \frac{\ln 2}{r}$

Expanding Your Skills

89. The isotope of plutonium of mass 238 (written ^{238}Pu) is used to make thermoelectric power sources for spacecraft. The heat and electric power derived from such units have made the Voyager, Gallileo, and Cassini missions to the outer reaches of our solar system possible. The half-life of ^{238}Pu is 87.7 yr.

Suppose a space probe was launched in the year 2002 with 2.0 kg of ^{238}Pu. Then the amount of ^{238}Pu available to power the spacecraft decays over time according to

$$P(t) = 2e^{-0.0079t}$$

where $t \geq 0$ is the number of years since 2002 and $P(t)$ is the amount of plutonium still present (in kilograms).

a. Suppose the space probe is due to arrive at Pluto in the year 2045. How much plutonium will remain when the spacecraft reaches Pluto? Round to two decimal places. 1.42 kg

b. If 1.5 kg of ^{238}Pu is required to power the spacecraft's data transmitter, will there be enough power in the year 2045 for us to receive close-up images of Pluto? No

90. ^{99m}Tc is a radionuclide of technetium that is widely used in nuclear medicine. Although its half-life is only 6 hr, the isotope is continuously produced via the decay of its longer-lived parent ^{99}Mo (molybdenum 99) whose half-life is approximately 3 days. The ^{99}Mo generators (or "cows") are sold to hospitals in which the ^{99m}Tc can be "milked" as needed over a period of a few weeks. Once separated from its parent, the ^{99m}Tc may be chemically incorporated into a variety of imaging agents, each of which is designed to be taken up by a specific target organ within the body. Special cameras, sensitive to the gamma rays emitted by the technetium, are then used to record a "picture" (similar in appearance to an X-ray film) of the selected organ.

Suppose a technician prepares a sample of ^{99m}Tc-pyrophosphate to image the heart of a patient suspected of having had a mild heart attack. If the injection contains 10 millicuries (mCi) of ^{99m}Tc at 1:00 P.M., then the amount of technetium still present is given by

$$T(t) = 10e^{-0.1155t}$$

where $t > 0$ represents the time in hours after 1:00 P.M. and $T(t)$ represents the amount of ^{99m}Tc (in millicuries) still present.

a. How many millicuries of ^{99m}Tc will remain at 4:20 P.M. when the image is recorded? Round to the nearest tenth of a millicurie. 6.8 mCi

b. How long will it take for the radioactive level of the ^{99m}Tc to reach 2 mCi? Round to the nearest tenth of an hour. 13.9 hr

For Exercises 91–94, solve the equations.

91. $(\log x)^2 - 2 \log x - 15 = 0$
(*Hint:* Let $u = \log x$.) $\{10^5, 10^{-3}\}$

92. $(\log_2 z)^2 - 3 \log_2 z - 4 = 0$ $\left\{16, \frac{1}{2}\right\}$

93. $(\log_3 w)^2 + 5 \log_3 w + 6 = 0$ $\left\{\frac{1}{27}, \frac{1}{9}\right\}$

94. $(\ln x)^2 - 2 \ln x = 0$ $\{1, e^2\}$

Graphing Calculator Exercises

95. Graph $Y_1 = 8^x$ and $Y_2 = 21$ on a window where $0 \le x \le 5$ and $0 \le y \le 40$. Use the graph and an *Intersect* feature to support your answer to Exercise 55.

96. Graph $Y_1 = 6^x$ and $Y_2 = 39$ on a window where $0 \le x \le 5$ and $0 \le y \le 50$. Use the graph and an *Intersect* feature to support your answer to Exercise 56.

Group Activity

Creating a Population Model

Materials: A computer with Internet access and a calculator

Estimated time: 15–20 minutes

Answers will vary.

Group Size: 3

1. Go to a website such as http://www.census.gov/ and determine the population of your state for the year 2000, and then for another year after that time. For example, the population of Florida in the year 2000 was approximately 16,050,000. Florida's population in 2006 was approximately 18,090,000.

2. Let the variable t represent the number of years since the year 2000. Therefore, $t = 0$ represents the year 2000, $t = 1$ represents the year 2001, and so on. Write your data from step 1 as ordered pairs. For example: (0, 16050000) and (6, 18090000). (__________, __________) (__________, __________)

3. Population growth can be modeled by an exponential function of the form:

$P(t) = P_0e^{kt}$ where P_0 is the initial population for $t = 0$

$P(t)$ is the population at time, t

k is the growth constant

Writing | Translating Expression | Geometry | Scientific Calculator | Video

Substitute the population for the year 2000 into the model for P_0, and write the function here:

$P(t) =$ ____________ e^{kt} [For example: $P(t) = 16{,}050{,}000e^{kt}$]

4. Substitute the population value and t value from the second ordered pair into the function for $P(t)$ and t, respectively. [For example: $18{,}090{,}000 = 16{,}050{,}000e^{k(6)}$]

5. Solve the equation from step 4 for the value of k. Round k to five decimal places.

6. Substitute the values of P_0 and k in the original model, $P(t) = P_0e^{kt}$, and write the function here:

   $P(t) =$ ____________

   You should now have a function that models the population of your state as a function of the time in years since 2000.

7. Using this function, estimate the population of your state in the year 2015.

8. Assuming that the population follows this trend, predict the population of your state in the year 2050.

Instructor Note: As a follow-up, you might ask students if the growth rate can continue indefinitely. You can ask students to predict the number of years it will take so that each person in your state will have only 1 m^2 of land area.

Chapter 12 Summary

Section 12.1 Inverse Functions

Key Concepts

Horizontal Line Test

Consider a function defined by a set of points (x, y) in a rectangular coordinate system. Then y is a one-to-one function of x if no horizontal line intersects the graph in more than one point.

Finding an Equation of the Inverse of a Function

For a one-to-one function defined by $y = f(x)$, the equation of the inverse can be found as follows:

1. Replace $f(x)$ by y.
2. Interchange x and y.
3. Solve for y.
4. Replace y by $f^{-1}(x)$.

The graphs defined by $y = f(x)$ and $y = f^{-1}(x)$ are symmetric with respect to the line $y = x$.

Definition of an Inverse Function

If f is a one-to-one function represented by ordered pairs of the form (x, y), then the inverse function, denoted f^{-1}, is the set of ordered pairs (y, x).

Inverse Function Property

If f is a one-to-one function, then g is the inverse of f if and only if $(f \circ g)(x) = x$ for all x in the domain of g, and $(g \circ f)(x) = x$ for all x in the domain of f.

Examples

Example 1

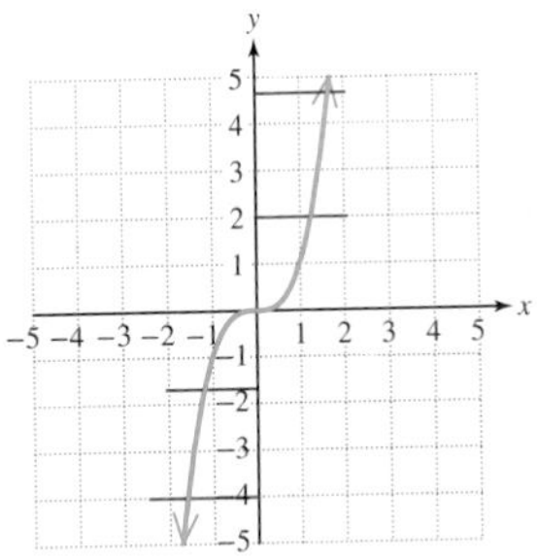

The function is one-to-one because it passes the horizontal line test.

Example 2

Find the inverse of the one-to-one function defined by $f(x) = 3 - x^3$.

1. $y = 3 - x^3$
2. $x = 3 - y^3$
3. $x - 3 = -y^3$
   $-x + 3 = y^3$
   $\sqrt[3]{-x + 3} = y$
4. $f^{-1}(x) = \sqrt[3]{-x + 3}$

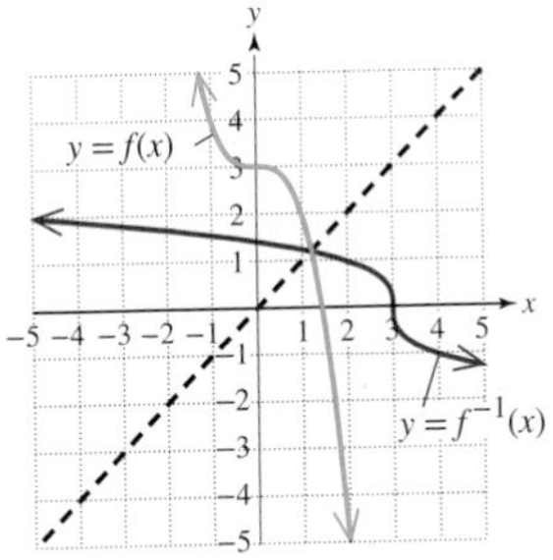

Example 3

Verify that the functions defined by $f(x) = x - 1$ and $g(x) = x + 1$ are inverses.

$(f \circ g)(x) = f(x + 1) = (x + 1) - 1 = x$

$(g \circ f)(x) = g(x - 1) = (x - 1) + 1 = x$

Section 12.2 Exponential Functions

Key Concepts

A function $f(x) = b^x$ $(b > 0, b \neq 1)$ is an **exponential function**.

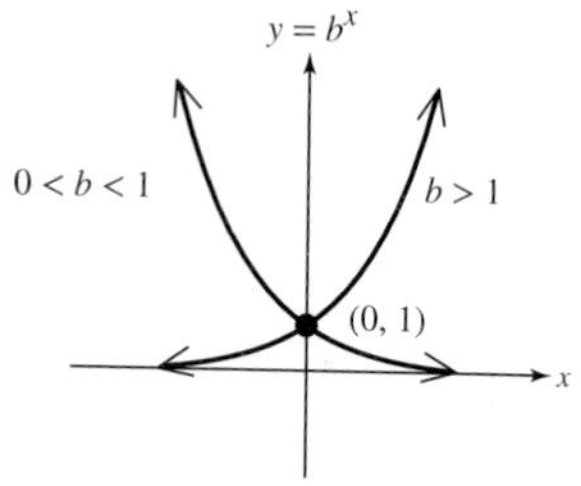

The domain is $(-\infty, \infty)$.

The range is $(0, \infty)$.

The line $y = 0$ (x-axis) is a horizontal asymptote.

The y-intercept is (0, 1).

Example

Example 1

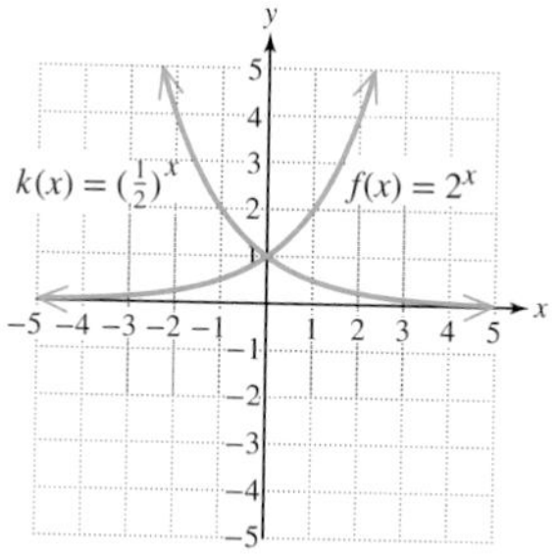

Section 12.3 Logarithmic Functions

Key Concepts

The function $y = \log_b x$ is a **logarithmic function**.

$y = \log_b x \Leftrightarrow b^y = x \quad (x > 0, b > 0, b \neq 1)$

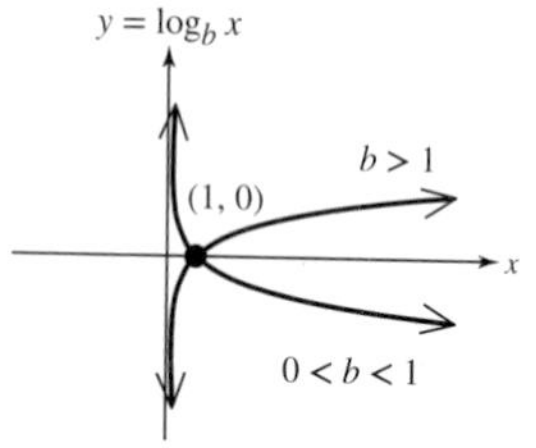

For $y = \log_b x$, the domain is $(0, \infty)$.

The range is $(-\infty, \infty)$.

The line $x = 0$ (y-axis) is a vertical asymptote.

The x-intercept is (1, 0).

The function $f(x) = \log x$ is the **common logarithmic function** (base 10).

Examples

Example 1

$\log_4 64 = 3$ because $4^3 = 64$

Example 2

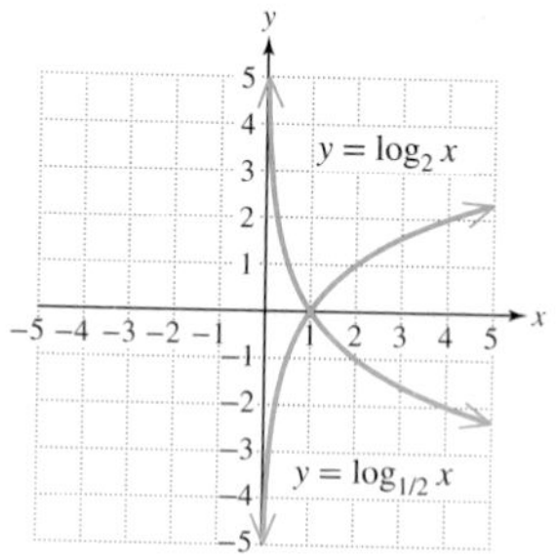

Example 3

$\log 10{,}000 = 4$ because $10^4 = 10{,}000$

Section 12.4 Properties of Logarithms

Key Concepts

Let b, x, and y be positive real numbers where $b \neq 1$, and let p be a real number. Then the following properties are true.

1. $\log_b 1 = 0$
2. $\log_b b = 1$
3. $\log_b b^p = p$
4. $b^{\log_b x} = x$
5. $\log_b (xy) = \log_b x + \log_b y$
6. $\log_b \left(\frac{x}{y}\right) = \log_b x - \log_b y$
7. $\log_b x^p = p \log_b x$

Examples

Example 1

1. $\log_5 1 = 0$
2. $\log_6 6 = 1$
3. $\log_4 4^7 = 7$
4. $2^{\log_2 5} = 5$
5. $\log (5x) = \log 5 + \log x$
6. $\log_7 \left(\frac{z}{10}\right) = \log_7 z - \log_7 10$
7. $\log x^5 = 5 \log x$

The **properties of logarithms** can be used to write multiple logarithms as a single logarithm.

Example 2

$$\log x - \frac{1}{2}\log y - 3 \log z$$
$$= \log x - \log y^{1/2} - \log z^3$$
$$= \log x - (\log y^{1/2} + \log z^3)$$
$$= \log x - \log (\sqrt{y}z^3)$$
$$= \log\left(\frac{x}{\sqrt{y}z^3}\right)$$

The **properties of logarithms** can be used to write a single logarithm as a sum or difference of logarithms.

Example 3

$$\log \sqrt[3]{\frac{x}{y^2}}$$
$$= \log \left(\frac{x}{y^2}\right)^{1/3}$$
$$= \frac{1}{3}\log \left(\frac{x}{y^2}\right)$$
$$= \frac{1}{3}(\log x - \log y^2)$$
$$= \frac{1}{3}(\log x - 2 \log y)$$
$$= \frac{1}{3}\log x - \frac{2}{3}\log y$$

Section 12.5 The Irrational Number e and Change of Base

Key Concepts

The function $y = e^x$ is the exponential function with base e.

The **natural logarithm function** $y = \ln x$ is the logarithm function with base e.

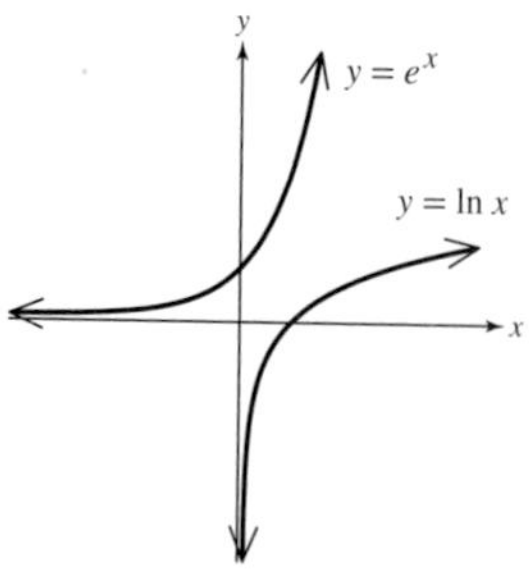

Change-of-Base Formula

$$\log_b x = \frac{\log_a x}{\log_a b} \qquad a > 0, a \neq 1, b > 0, b \neq 1$$

Examples

Example 1

Use a calculator to approximate the value of the expressions.

$e^{7.5} \approx 1808.0424$

$e^{-\pi} \approx 0.0432$

$\ln 107 \approx 4.6728$

$\ln\left(\frac{1}{\sqrt{2}}\right) \approx -0.3466$

Example 2

$$\log_3 59 = \frac{\log 59}{\log 3} \approx 3.7115$$

Section 12.6 Logarithmic and Exponential Equations and Applications

Key Concepts

Guidelines to Solve Logarithmic Equations

1. Isolate the logarithms on one side of the equation.
2. Write a sum or difference of logarithms as a single logarithm.
3. Rewrite the equation in step 2 in exponential form.
4. Solve the resulting equation from step 3.
5. Check all solutions to verify that they are within the domain of the logarithmic expressions in the equation.

Equivalence Property of Logarithmic Expressions

If two logarithms with the same base are equal, then their arguments are equal. That is,

If $\log_b x = \log_b y$, then $x = y$.

Example 2

$\ln(x - 4) + \ln(3) = \ln(2x + 3)$

$\ln[3(x - 4)] = \ln(2x + 3)$

$\ln(3x - 12) = \ln(2x + 3)$

$3x - 12 = 2x + 3$ Arguments are equal.

$x = 15$ The solution checks.

The solution set is $\{15\}$.

Examples

Example 1

$\log(3x - 1) + 1 = \log(2x + 1)$

Step 1: $\log(3x - 1) - \log(2x + 1) = -1$

Step 2: $\log\left(\frac{3x - 1}{2x + 1}\right) = -1$

Step 3: $10^{-1} = \frac{3x - 1}{2x + 1}$

Step 4: $\frac{1}{10} = \frac{3x - 1}{2x + 1}$

$2x + 1 = 10(3x - 1)$

$2x + 1 = 30x - 10$

$-28x = -11$

$x = \frac{11}{28}$ The solution checks.

Step 5: The solution set is $\left\{\frac{11}{28}\right\}$.

Equivalence Property of Exponential Expressions

If two exponential expressions with the same base are equal, then their exponents are equal. That is,

If $b^x = b^y$, then $x = y$.

Example 3

$5^{2x} = 125$

$5^{2x} = 5^3$ implies that $2x = 3$

$x = \dfrac{3}{2}$

The solution set is $\left\{\dfrac{3}{2}\right\}$.

Guidelines to Solve Exponential Equations

1. Isolate one of the exponential expressions in the equation.
2. Take a logarithm of both sides of the equation.
3. Use the power property of logarithms to write exponents as factors.
4. Solve the resulting equation from step 3.

Example 4

$4^{x+1} - 2 = 1055$

Step 1: $4^{x+1} = 1057$

Step 2: $\ln 4^{x+1} = \ln 1057$

Step 3: $(x + 1)\ln 4 = \ln 1057$

Step 4: $x + 1 = \dfrac{\ln 1057}{\ln 4}$

$x = \dfrac{\ln 1057}{\ln 4} - 1 \approx 4.023$

The solution set is $\left\{\dfrac{\ln 1057}{\ln 4} - 1\right\}$.

Chapter 12 Review Exercises

Section 12.1

For Exercises 1–2, determine if the function is one-to-one by using the horizontal line test.

1. No

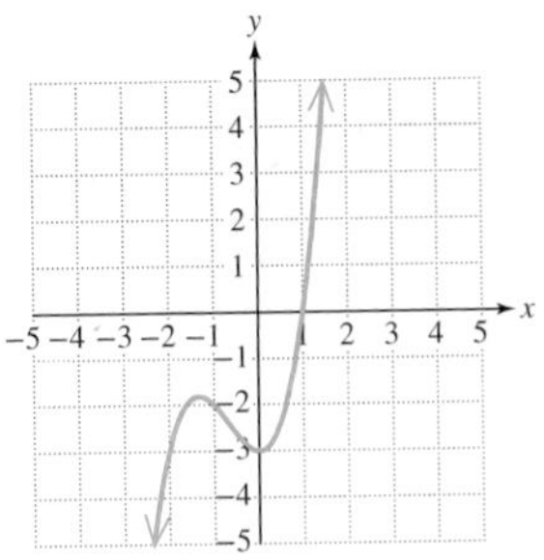

2. Yes

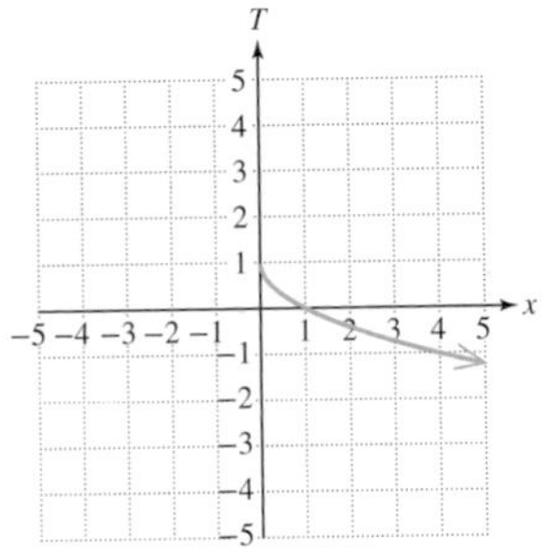

For Exercises 3–7, write the inverse for each one-to-one function.

3. $\{(3, 5), (2, 9), (0, -1), (4, 1)\}$

$\{(5, 3), (9, 2), (-1, 0), (1, 4)\}$

4. $q(x) = \dfrac{3}{4}x - 2$

$q^{-1}(x) = \dfrac{4}{3}(x + 2)$

5. $g(x) = \sqrt[5]{x} + 3$

$g^{-1}(x) = (x - 3)^5$

6. $f(x) = (x - 1)^3$

$f^{-1}(x) = \sqrt[3]{x} + 1$

7. $n(x) = \dfrac{4}{x - 2}$ $\quad n^{-1}(x) = \dfrac{2x + 4}{x}$

8. Verify that the functions defined by $f(x) = 5x - 2$ and $g(x) = \frac{1}{5}x + \frac{2}{5}$ are inverses by showing that $(f \circ g)(x) = x$ and $(g \circ f)(x) = x$.

$(f \circ g)(x) = 5\left(\dfrac{1}{5}x + \dfrac{2}{5}\right) - 2 = x + 2 - 2 = x$

$(g \circ f)(x) = \dfrac{1}{5}(5x - 2) + \dfrac{2}{5} = x - \dfrac{2}{5} + \dfrac{2}{5} = x$

9. Graph the functions q and q^{-1} from Exercise 23 on the same grid. What can you say about the relationship between these two graphs?

The graphs are symmetric about the line $y = x$.

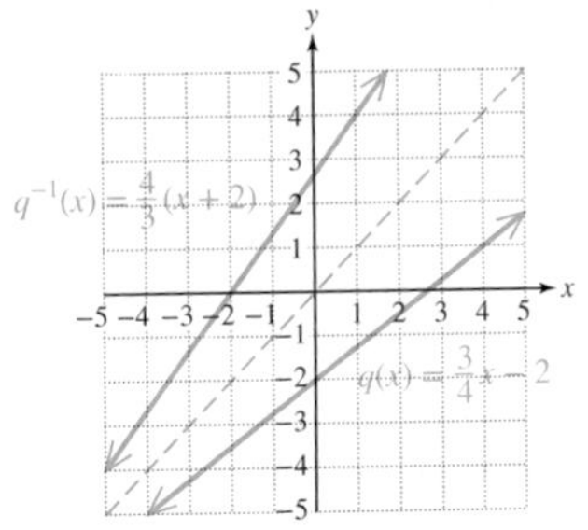

10. **a.** Find the domain and range of the function defined by $h(x) = \sqrt{x+1}$.
Domain: $[-1, \infty)$; range: $[0, \infty)$

b. Find the domain and range of the function defined by $k(x) = x^2 - 1, x \geq 0$.
Domain: $[0, \infty)$; range: $[-1, \infty)$

11. Determine the inverse of the function $p(x) = \sqrt{x} + 2$. $p^{-1}(x) = (x-2)^2, x \geq 2$

Section 12.2

For Exercises 12–19, evaluate the exponential expressions. Use a calculator and round to three decimal places, if necessary.

12. 4^5 1024

13. 6^{-2} $\frac{1}{36} \approx 0.028$

14. $8^{1/3}$ 2

15. $\left(\frac{1}{100}\right)^{-1/2}$ 10

16. 2^{π} 8.825

17. $5^{\sqrt{3}}$ 16.242

18. $(\sqrt{7})^{1/2}$ 1.627

19. $\left(\frac{3}{4}\right)^{4/3}$ 0.681

For Exercises 20–23, graph the functions.

20. $f(x) = 3^x$

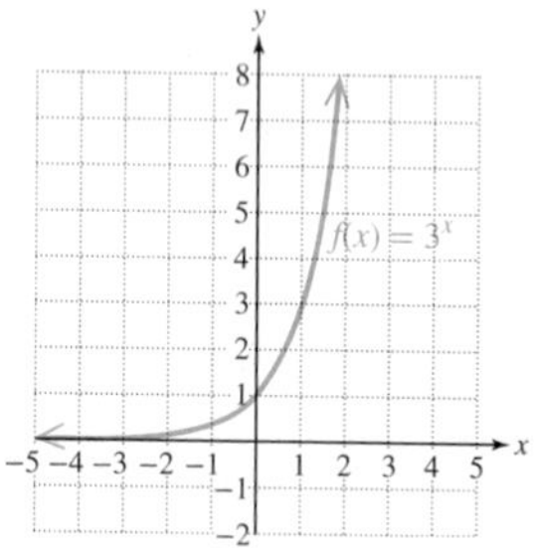

21. $g(x) = \left(\frac{1}{4}\right)^x$

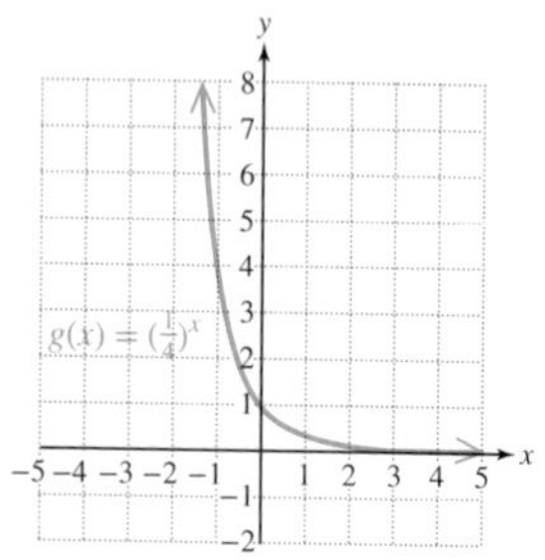

22. $h(x) = 5^{-x}$

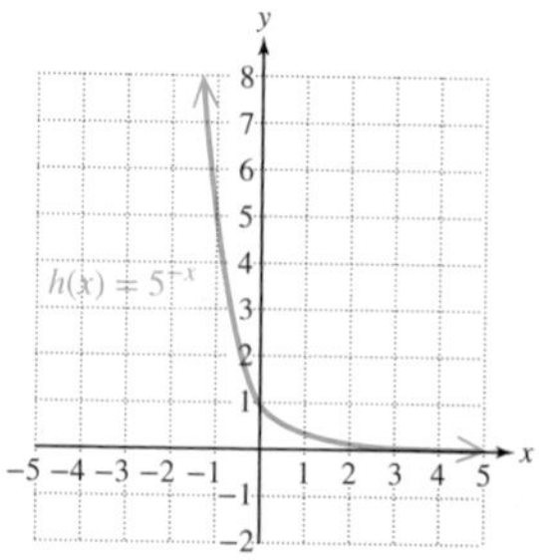

23. $k(x) = \left(\frac{2}{5}\right)^{-x}$

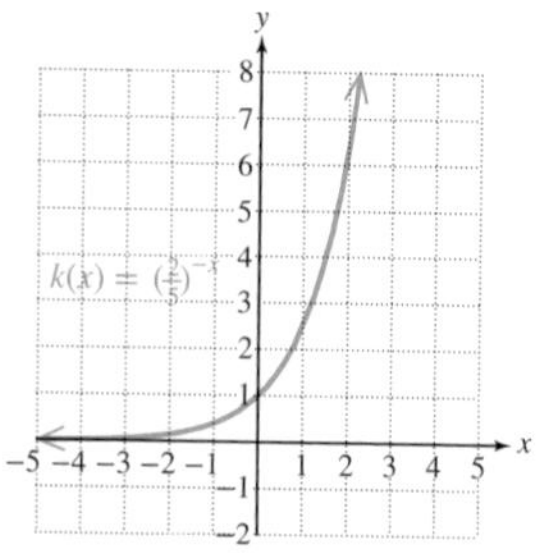

24. **a.** Does the graph of $y = b^x, b > 0, b \neq 1$, have a vertical or a horizontal asymptote?
Horizontal

b. Write an equation of the asymptote. $y = 0$

25. Background radiation is radiation that we are exposed to from naturally occurring sources including the soil, the foods we eat, and the Sun. Background radiation varies depending on where we live. A typical background radiation level is 150 millirems (mrem) per year. (A rem is a measure of energy produced from radiation.) Suppose a substance emits 30,000 mrem per year and has a half-life of 5 yr. The function defined by

$$A(t) = 30{,}000\left(\frac{1}{2}\right)^{t/5}$$

gives the radiation level (in millirems) of this substance after t years.

a. What is the radiation level after 5 yr?
15,000 mrem

b. What is the radiation level after 15 yr?
3750 mrem

c. Will the radiation level of this substance be below the background level of 150 mrem after 50 yr? Yes

Section 12.3

For Exercises 26–33, evaluate the logarithms without using a calculator.

26. $\log_3\left(\frac{1}{27}\right)$ -3

27. $\log_5 1$ 0

28. $\log_7 7$ 1

29. $\log_2 2^8$ 8

30. $\log_2 16$ 4

31. $\log_3 81$ 4

32. $\log 100{,}000$ 5

33. $\log_8\left(\frac{1}{8}\right)$ -1

For Exercises 34–35, graph the logarithmic functions.

34. $q(x) = \log_3 x$

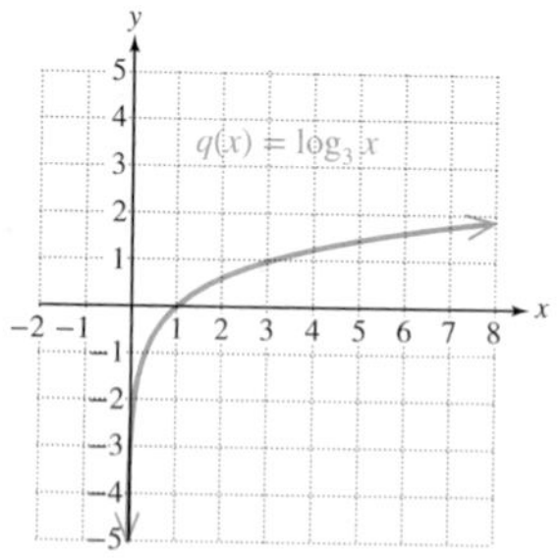

35. $r(x) = \log_{1/2} x$

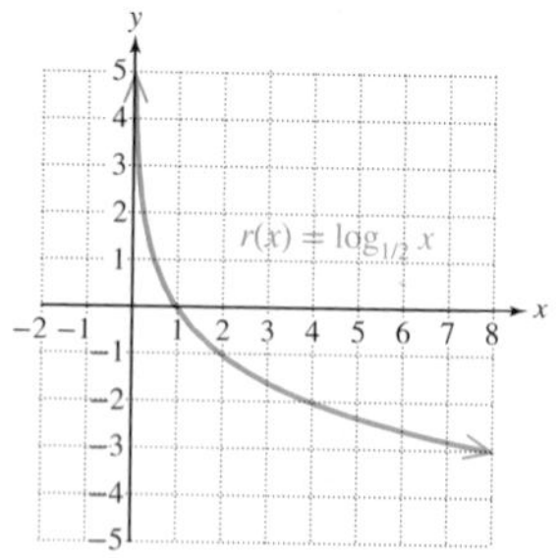

36. **a.** Does the graph of $y = \log_b x$ have a vertical or a horizontal asymptote? Vertical asymptote

b. Write an equation of the asymptote. $x = 0$

37. Acidity of a substance is measured by its pH. The pH can be calculated by the formula $pH = -\log [H^+]$, where $[H^+]$ is the hydrogen ion concentration.

a. What is the pH of a fruit with a hydrogen ion concentration of 0.00316 mol/L? Round to one decimal place. 2.5

b. What is the pH of an antacid tablet with $[H^+] = 3.16 \times 10^{-10}$? Round to one decimal place. 9.5

Section 12.4

For Exercises 38–41, evaluate the logarithms without using a calculator.

38. $\log_8 8$ 1

39. $\log_{11} 11^6$ 6

40. $\log_{1/2} 1$ 0

41. $12^{\log_{12} 7}$ 7

42. Complete the properties Assume x, y, and b are positive real numbers such that $b \neq 1$.

a. $\log_b (xy) =$ $\log_b x + \log_b y$

b. $\log_b x - \log_b y =$ $\log_b \left(\frac{x}{y}\right)$

c. $\log_b x^p =$ $p \log_b x$

For Exercises 43–46, write the logarithmic expressions as a single logarithm and simplify if possible.

43. $\frac{1}{4}(\log_b y - 4 \log_b z + 3 \log_b x)$ $\log_b \left(\frac{\sqrt[4]{x^3 y}}{z}\right)$

44. $\frac{1}{2}\log_3 a + \frac{1}{2}\log_3 b - 2 \log_3 c - 4 \log_3 d$ $\log_3 \left(\frac{\sqrt{ab}}{c^2 d^4}\right)$

45. $\log 540 - 3 \log 3 - 2 \log 2$ $\log 5$

46. $-\log_4 18 + \log_4 6 + \log_4 3 - \log_4 1$ 0

47. Which of the following is equivalent to $\frac{2 \log 7}{\log 7 + \log 6}$? b

a. $\frac{\log 7}{\log 6}$ **b.** $\frac{\log 49}{\log 42}$ **c.** $\log\left(\frac{7}{6}\right)$

48. Which of the following is equivalent to $\frac{\log 8^{-3}}{\log 2 + \log 4}$? a

a. -3 **b.** $-3 \log\left(\frac{4}{3}\right)$ **c.** $\frac{-3 \log 4}{\log 3}$

Section 12.5

For Exercises 49–56, use a calculator to approximate the expressions to four decimal places.

49. e^5 148.4132

50. $e^{\sqrt{7}}$ 14.0940

51. $32e^{0.008}$ 32.2570

52. $58e^{-0.0125}$ 57.2795

53. $\ln 6$ 1.7918

54. $\ln\left(\frac{1}{9}\right)$ −2.1972

55. $\log 22$ 1.3424

56. $\log e^3$ 1.3029

For Exercises 57–60, use the change-of-base formula to approximate the logarithms to four decimal places.

57. $\log_2 10$ 3.3219

58. $\log_9 80$ 1.9943

59. $\log_5 0.26$ −0.8370

60. $\log_4 0.0062$ −3.6668

61. An investor wants to deposit \$20,000 in an account for 10 yr at 5.25% interest. Compare the amount $A(t)$ she would have if her money were invested with the following different compounding options. Use

$$A(t) = P\left(1 + \frac{r}{n}\right)^{nt}$$

for interest compounded n times per year and $A(t) = Pe^{rt}$ for interest compounded continuously.

a. Compounded annually \$33,361.92

b. Compounded quarterly \$33,693.90

c. Compounded monthly \$33,770.48

d. Compounded continuously \$33,809.18

62. To measure a student's retention of material at the end of a course, researchers give the student a test on the material every month for 24 months after the course is over. The student's average score t months after completing the course is given by

$$S(t) = 75e^{-0.5t} + 20$$

where $S(t)$ is the test score.

a. Find $S(0)$ and interpret the result.
$S(0) = 95$; the student's score is 95 at the end of the course.

b. Find $S(6)$ and interpret the result.
$S(6) \approx 23.7$; the student's score is 23.7 after 6 months.

c. Find $S(12)$ and interpret the result.
$S(12) \approx 20.2$; the student's score is 20.2 after 1 yr.

For Exercises 63–70, identify the domain. Write the answer in interval notation.

63. $f(x) = e^x$ $(-\infty, \infty)$

64. $g(x) = e^{x+6}$ $(-\infty, \infty)$

65. $h(x) = e^{x-3}$ $(-\infty, \infty)$

66. $k(x) = \ln x$ $(0, \infty)$

67. $q(x) = \ln(x+5)$ $(-5, \infty)$

68. $p(x) = \ln(x-7)$ $(7, \infty)$

69. $r(x) = \ln(3x-4)$ $\left(\frac{4}{3}, \infty\right)$

70. $w(x) = \ln(5-x)$ $(-\infty, 5)$

Section 12.6

For Exercises 71–88, solve the equations.

71. $\log_5 x = 3$ $\{125\}$

72. $\log_7 x = -2$ $\left\{\frac{1}{49}\right\}$

73. $\log_6 y = 3$ $\{216\}$

74. $\log_3 y = \frac{1}{12}$ $\{3^{1/12}\}$

75. $\log(2w-1) = 3$ $\left\{\frac{1001}{2}\right\}$

76. $\log_2(3w+5) = 5$ $\{9\}$

77. $-1 + \log p = -\log(p-3)$
$\{5\}$ (The value -2 does not check.)

78. $\log_4(2+t) - 3 = \log_4(3-5t)$ $\left\{\frac{190}{321}\right\}$

79. $4^{3x+5} = 16$ $\{-1\}$

80. $5^{7x} = 625$ $\left\{\frac{4}{7}\right\}$

81. $4^a = 21$ $\left\{\frac{\ln 21}{\ln 4}\right\}$

82. $5^a = 18$ $\left\{\frac{\ln 18}{\ln 5}\right\}$

83. $e^{-x} = 0.1$
$\{-\ln 0.1\}$

84. $e^{-2x} = 0.06$
$\left\{-\frac{\ln 0.06}{2}\right\}$

85. $10^{2n} = 1512$
$\left\{\frac{\log 1512}{2}\right\}$

86. $10^{-3m} = \frac{1}{821}$ $\left\{\frac{\log 821}{3}\right\}$

87. $2^{x+3} = 7^x$ $\left\{\frac{3\ln 2}{\ln 7 - \ln 2}\right\}$

88. $14^{x-5} = 6^x$ $\left\{\frac{5\ln 14}{\ln 14 - \ln 6}\right\}$

89. Radioactive iodine (^{131}I) is used to treat patients with a hyperactive (overactive) thyroid. The halflife of radioactive iodine is 8.04 days. If a patient is given an initial dose of 2 μg, then the amount of iodine in the body after t days is approximated by

$$A(t) = 2e^{-0.0862t}$$

where t is the time in days and $A(t)$ is the amount (in micrograms) of ^{131}I remaining.

a. How much radioactive iodine is present after a week? Round to two decimal places. 1.09 μg

b. How much radioactive iodine is present after 30 days? Round to two decimal places. 0.15 μg

c. How long will it take for the level of radioactive iodine to reach 0.5 μg? 16.08 days

90. The growth of a certain bacteria in a culture is given by the model $A(t) = 150e^{0.007t}$, where $A(t)$ is the number of bacteria and t is time in minutes.

a. What is the initial number of bacteria?
150 bacteria

b. What is the population after $\frac{1}{2}$ hr?
$\approx$ 185 bacteria

c. How long will it take for the population to double? $\approx$ 99 min

91. The value of a car is depreciated with time according to

$$V(t) = 15{,}000e^{-0.15t}$$

where $V(t)$ is the value in dollars and t is the time in years after purchase.

a. Find $V(0)$ and interpret the result in the context of this problem.
$V(0) = 15{,}000$; the initial value of the car is \$15,000.

b. Find $V(10)$ and interpret the result in the context of this problem. Round to the nearest dollar.
$V(10) = 3347$; the value of the car after 10 yr is \$3347.

c. Find the time required for the value of the car to drop to \$5000. Round to the nearest tenth of a year. 7.3 yr

Chapter 12 Test

1. Explain how to determine graphically if a function is one-to-one. A function is one-to-one if it passes the horizontal line test.

2. Which of the functions is one-to-one? b

a.

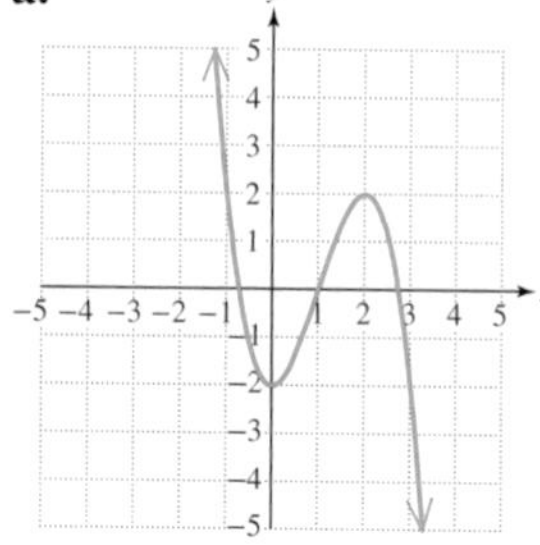

b.

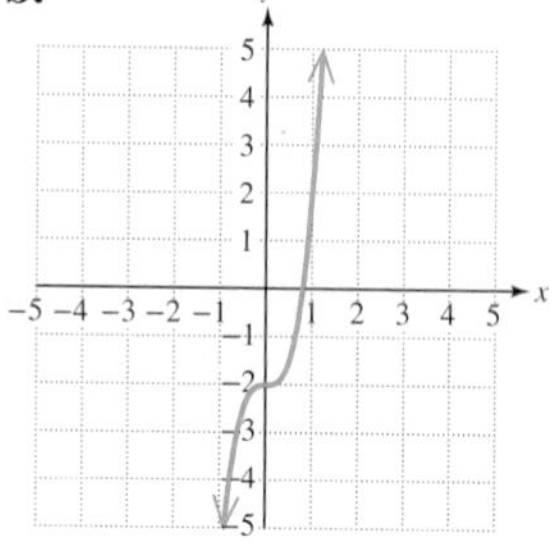

3. Write an equation of the inverse of the one-to-one function defined by $f(x) = \frac{1}{4}x + 3$.
$f^{-1}(x) = 4x - 12$

4. Write an equation of the inverse of the function defined by $g(x) = (x-1)^2, \quad x \geq 1$.
$g^{-1}(x) = \sqrt{x} + 1$

5. Given the graph of the function $y = p(x)$, graph its inverse $p^{-1}(x)$.

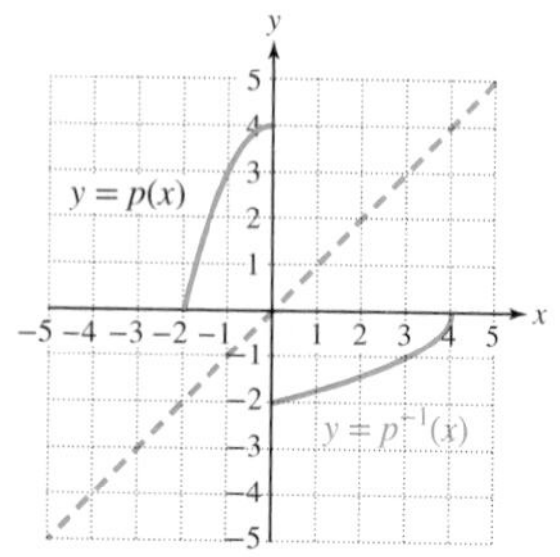

Writing | Translating Expression | Geometry | Scientific Calculator | Video

6. Use a calculator to approximate the expression to four decimal places.

a. $10^{2/3}$ 4.6416 **b.** $3^{\sqrt{10}}$ 32.2693 **c.** 8^{π} 687.2913

7. Graph $f(x) = 4^{x-1}$.

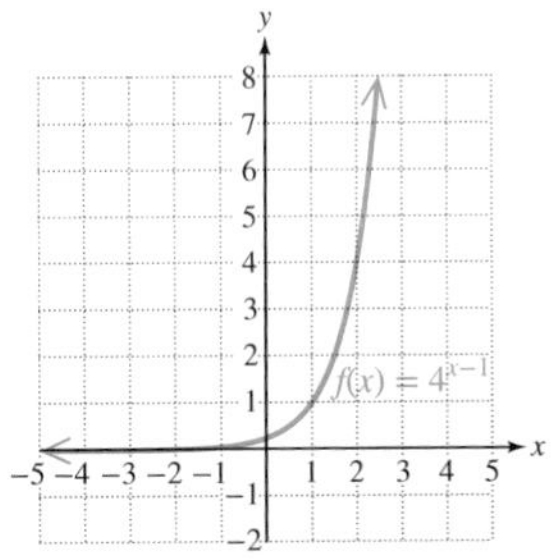

8. **a.** Write in logarithmic form. $16^{3/4} = 8$
$\log_{16} 8 = \frac{3}{4}$

b. Write in exponential form. $\log_x 31 = 5$
$x^5 = 31$

9. Graph $g(x) = \log_3 x$.

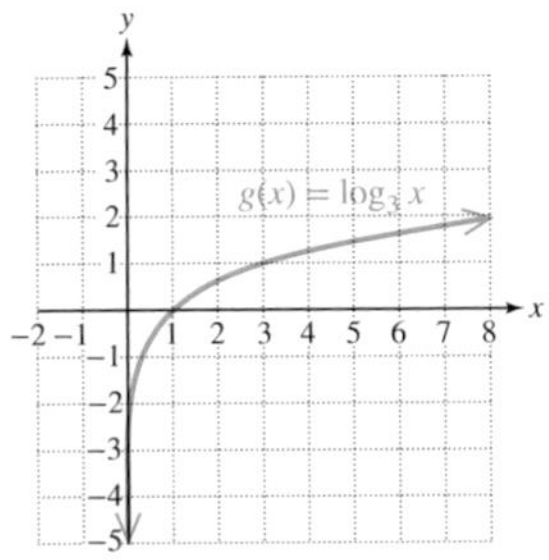

10. Complete the change-of-base formula: $\log_b n =$ ______ $\frac{\log_a n}{\log_a b}$

11. Use a calculator to approximate the expression to four decimal places.

a. $\log 21$ 1.3222 **b.** $\log_4 13$ 1.8502 **c.** $\log_{1/2} 6$ −2.5850

12. Using the properties of logarithms, expand and simplify. Assume all variables represent positive real numbers.

a. $-\log_3\left(\frac{3}{9x}\right)$ $1 + \log_3 x$ **b.** $\log\left(\frac{1}{10^5}\right)$ −5

13. Write as a single logarithm. Assume all variables represent positive real numbers.

a. $\frac{1}{2}\log_b x + 3\log_b y$ $\log_b(\sqrt{x}y^3)$ **b.** $\log a - 4\log a$ $\log\left(\frac{1}{a^3}\right)$ or $-\log a^3$

14. Use a calculator to approximate the expression to four decimal places, if necessary.

a. $e^{1/2}$ 1.6487 **b.** e^{-3} 0.0498

c. $\ln\left(\frac{1}{3}\right)$ −1.0986 **d.** $\ln e$ 1

15. Identify the graphs as $y = e^x$ or $y = \ln x$.

a. $y = \ln x$

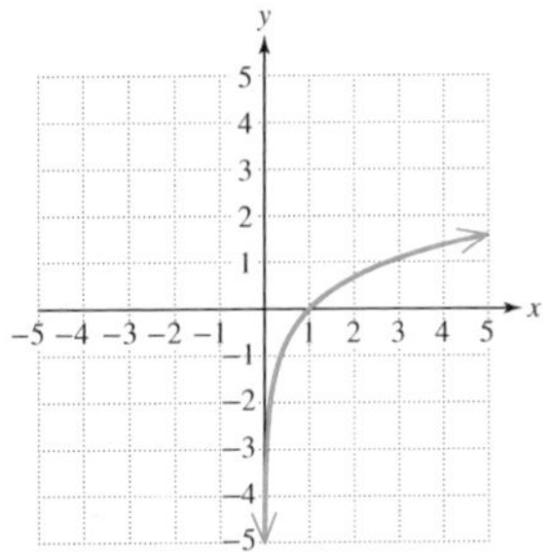

b. $y = e^x$

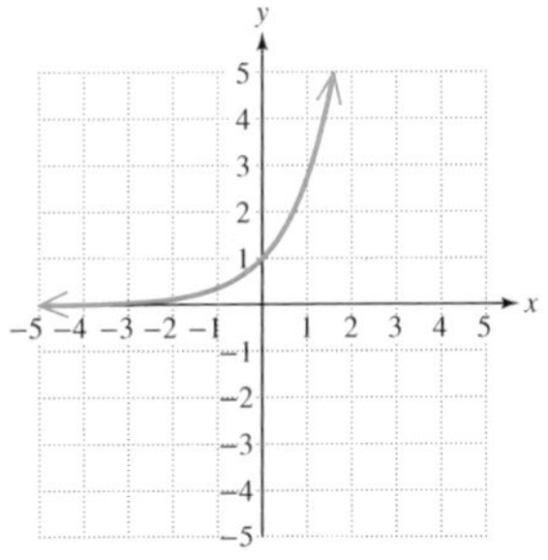

16. Researchers found that t months after taking a course, students remembered $p\%$ of the material according to

$$p(t) = 92 - 20\ln(t + 1)$$

where $0 \le t \le 24$ is the time in months.

a. Find $p(4)$ and interpret the results.
$p(4) \approx 59.8$; 59.8% of the material is retained after 4 months.

b. Find $p(12)$ and interpret the results.
$p(12) \approx 40.7$; 40.7% of the material is retained after 1 yr.

c. Find $p(0)$ and interpret the results.
$p(0) = 92$; 92% of the material is retained at the end of the course.

17. The population of New York City has a 2% growth rate and can be modeled by the function $P(t) = 8008(1.02)^t$, where $P(t)$ is in thousands and t is in years ($t = 0$ corresponds to the year 2000).

a. Using this model, estimate the population in the year 2010. 9762 thousand (or 9,762,000) people

b. In what year will the population reach 12 million (12 million is 12,000 thousand)?
The year 2020 ($t \approx 20.4$)

18. A certain bacterial culture grows according to

$$P(t) = \frac{1{,}500{,}000}{1 + 5000e^{-0.8t}}$$

where P is the population of the bacteria and t is the time in hours.

a. Find $P(0)$ and interpret the result. Round to the nearest whole number.
$P(0) = 300$; there are 300 bacteria initially.

b. How many bacteria will be present after 6 hr?
35,588 bacteria

c. How many bacteria will be present after 12 hr?
1,120,537 bacteria

d. How many bacteria will be present after 18 hr?
1,495,831 bacteria

For Exercises 19–26, solve the exponential and logarithmic equations.

19. $\log x + \log(x - 21) = 2$
{25} (The value −4 does not check.)

20. $\log_{1/2} x = -5$ {32}

21. $\ln(x + 7) = 2.4$
$\{e^{2.4} - 7\}$

22. $3^{x+4} = \frac{1}{27}$ {−7}

23. $4^x = 50$ $\left\{\frac{\ln 50}{\ln 4}\right\}$

24. $e^{2.4x} = 250$ $\left\{\frac{\ln 250}{2.4}\right\}$

25. $68 = 10 + 2^{x-3}$ $\left\{\frac{\ln 58}{\ln 2} + 3\right\}$

26. $4^{x+7} = 5^x$ $\left\{\frac{7 \ln 4}{\ln 5 - \ln 4}\right\}$

27. Atmospheric pressure P decreases exponentially with altitude x according to

$$P(x) = 760e^{-0.000122x}$$

where $P(x)$ is the pressure measured in millimeters of mercury (mm Hg) and x is the altitude measured in meters.

a. Find $P(2500)$ and interpret the result. Round to one decimal place. $P(2500) = 560.2$; at 2500 m the atmospheric pressure is 560.2 mm Hg.

b. Find the pressure at sea level. 760 mm Hg

c. Find the altitude at which the pressure is 633 mm Hg. 1498.8 m

28. Use the formula $A(t) = Pe^{rt}$ to compute the value of an investment under continuous compounding.

a. If \$2000 is invested at 7.5% compounded continuously, find the value of the investment after 5 yr. \$2909.98

b. How long will it take the investment to double? Round to two decimal places. 9.24 yr to double

Chapters 1–12 Cumulative Review Exercises

1. Simplify completely.

$$\frac{8 - 4 \cdot 2^2 + 15 \div 5}{|-3 + 7|} \qquad -\frac{5}{4}$$

2. Divide. $\dfrac{-8p^2 + 4p^3 + 6p^5}{8p^2}$ $\quad -1 + \frac{p}{2} + \frac{3p^3}{4}$

3. Divide. $(t^4 - 13t^2 + 36) \div (t - 2)$ Identify the quotient and remainder.
Quotient: $t^3 + 2t^2 - 9t - 18$; remainder: 0

4. Simplify. $\sqrt{x^2 - 6x + 9}$ $\quad |x - 3|$

5. Simplify. $\dfrac{4}{\sqrt[3]{40}}$ $\quad \frac{2\sqrt[3]{25}}{5}$

6. Find the length of the missing side. $2\sqrt{7}$ in.

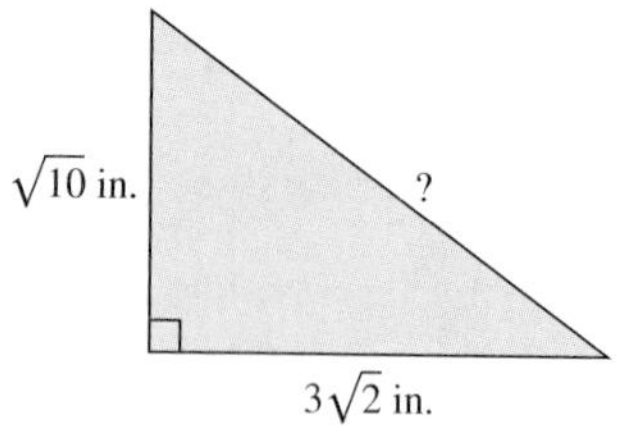

7. Simplify. Write the answer with positive exponents only.

$$\frac{2^{2/5}c^{-1/4}d^{1/5}}{2^{-8/5}c^{3/4}d^{1/10}} \qquad \frac{4d^{1/10}}{c}$$

8. Find the area of the rectangle. $(\sqrt{15} - \sqrt{6} + \sqrt{30} - 2\sqrt{3})$ m²

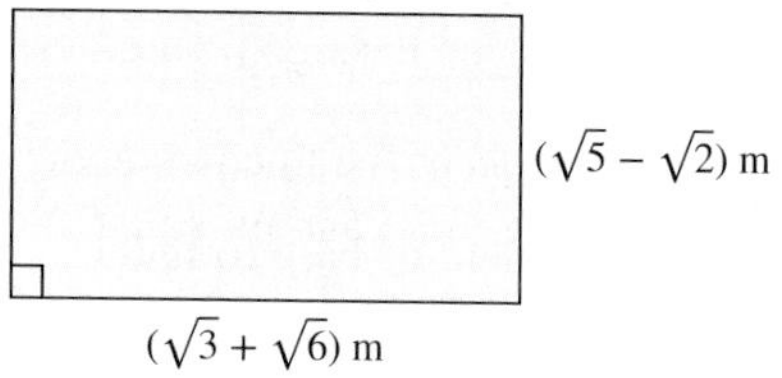

9. Perform the indicated operation.

$$\frac{4 - 3i}{2 + 5i} \qquad -\frac{7}{29} - \frac{26}{29}i$$

10. Solve. $2x(x - 7) = x - 18$ $\quad \left\{6, \frac{3}{2}\right\}$

11. How many liters of pure alcohol must be mixed with 8 L of 20% alcohol to bring the concentration up to 50% alcohol? 4.8 L

12. Bank robbers leave the scene of a crime and head north through winding mountain roads to their hideaway. Their average rate of speed is 40 mph. The police leave 6 min later in pursuit. If the police car averages 50 mph traveling the same route, how long will it take the police to catch the bank robbers? 24 min

13. Solve the system by using the Gauss-Jordan method. $\{(7, -1)\}$

$$5x + 10y = 25$$
$$-2x + 6y = -20$$

14. Solve. $-2[w - 3(w + 1)] = 4 - 7(w + 3)$ $\left\{-\frac{23}{11}\right\}$

15. Solve for x. $ax - c = bx + d$ $x = \frac{c + d}{a - b}$

16. Solve for t. $s = \frac{1}{2}gt^2 \quad t \geq 0$ $t = \frac{\sqrt{2sg}}{g}$

17. Solve. $3w(w - 2) = 6 + 2w$ $\left\{\frac{4 \pm \sqrt{34}}{3}\right\}$

18. Find the x-intercepts of the function defined by $f(x) = |x - 5| - 2$. $(7, 0), (3, 0)$

19. Let $f(t) = 6$, $g(t) = -5t$, and $h(t) = 2t^2$. Find

a. $(f \cdot g)(t)$ $-30t$ **b.** $(g \circ h)(t)$ $-10t^2$ **c.** $(h - g)(t)$ $2t^2 + 5t$

20. Solve. $|2q - 5| = |2q + 5|$ $\{0\}$

21. **a.** Find an equation of the line parallel to the y-axis and passing through the point (2, 6). $x = 2$

b. Find an equation of the line perpendicular to the y-axis and passing through the point (2, 6). $y = 6$

c. Find an equation of the line perpendicular to the line $2x + y = 4$ and passing through the point (2, 6). Write the answer in slope-intercept form. $y = \frac{1}{2}x + 5$

22. The smallest angle in a triangle measures one-half the largest angle. The smallest angle measures 20° less than the middle angle. Find the measures of all three angles. 40°, 80°, 60°

23. Solve the system. Infinitely many solutions; $\{(x, y) | -2x + y = -4\}$; dependent equations

$$\frac{1}{2}x - \frac{1}{4}y = 1$$
$$-2x + y = -4$$

24. Find the domain. $f(x) = \sqrt{2x - 1}$. $\left[\frac{1}{2}, \infty\right)$

25. Find $f^{-1}(x)$, given $f(x) = 5x - \frac{2}{3}$. $f^{-1}(x) = \frac{1}{5}x + \frac{2}{15}$

26. The volume of a gas varies directly as its temperature and inversely with pressure. At a temperature of 100 kelvins (K) and a pressure of 10 newtons per square meter (N/m^2), the gas occupies a volume of 30 m^3. Find the volume at a temperature of 200 K and pressure of 15 N/m^2. 40 m^3

27. Perform the indicated operations. $\frac{-x^2 + 5x - 25}{(2x + 1)(x - 2)}$

$$\frac{5x - 10}{x^2 - 4x + 4} \div \frac{5x^2 - 125}{25 - 5x} \cdot \frac{x^3 + 125}{10x + 5}$$

28. Perform the indicated operations. $1 + x$

$$\frac{x}{x - y} + \frac{y}{y - x} + x$$

29. Given the equation

$$\frac{2}{x - 4} = \frac{5}{x + 2}$$

a. Are there any restrictions on x for which the rational expressions are undefined? Yes; $x \neq 4$, $x \neq -2$

b. Solve the equation. $\{8\}$

c. Solve the related inequality. $(-\infty, -2) \cup (4, 8]$

$$\frac{2}{x - 4} \geq \frac{5}{x + 2}$$

Write the answer in interval notation.

30. Two more than 3 times the reciprocal of a number is $\frac{5}{4}$ less than the number. Find all such numbers. The numbers are $-\frac{3}{4}$, 4.

31. Solve. $\sqrt{-x} = x + 6$ $\{-4\}$ (The value -9 does not check.)

32. Solve the inequality $2|x - 3| + 1 > -7$. Write the answer in interval notation. $(-\infty, \infty)$

33. Four million *Escherichia coli (E. coli)* bacteria are present in a laboratory culture. An antibacterial agent is introduced and the population $P(t)$ of bacteria decreases by one-half every 6 hr according to

$$P(t) = 4{,}000{,}000\left(\frac{1}{2}\right)^{t/6} \quad t \geq 0$$

where t is the time in hours.

a. Find the population of bacteria after 6, 12, 18, 24, and 30 hr. $P(6) = 2{,}000{,}000$, $P(12) = 1{,}000{,}000$, $P(18) = 500{,}000$, $P(24) = 250{,}000$, $P(30) = 125{,}000$

b. Predict the time required for the population to decrease to 15,625 bacteria. 48 hr

34. Evaluate the expressions without a calculator.

a. $\log_7 49$ 2 **b.** $\log_4\left(\frac{1}{64}\right)$ -3

c. $\log 1{,}000{,}000$ 6 **d.** $\ln e^3$ 3

35. Use a calculator to approximate the expressions to four decimal places.

a. $\pi^{4.7}$ 217.0723 **b.** e^{π} 23.1407

c. $(\sqrt{2})^{-5}$ 0.1768 **d.** $\log 5362$ 3.7293

e. $\ln 0.67$ −0.4005 **f.** $\log_4 37$ 2.6047

36. Solve. $5^2 = 125^x$ $\left\{\frac{2}{3}\right\}$

37. Solve. $e^x = 100$ $\{\ln 100\}$

38. Solve. $\log_3(x+6) - 3 = -\log_3 x$
{3} (The value −9 does not check.)

39. Write the following expression as a single logarithm.

$$\frac{1}{2}\log z - 2\log x - 3\log y \quad \log\left(\frac{\sqrt{z}}{x^2y^3}\right)$$

40. Write the following expression as a sum or difference of logarithms

$$\ln\sqrt[3]{\frac{x^2}{y}} \quad \frac{2}{3}\ln x - \frac{1}{3}\ln y$$

Conic Sections

13

CHAPTER OUTLINE

Mathematics in Engineering

In this chapter, we will revisit our study of parabolas as well as two new curves called *ellipses* and *hyperbolas*. These curves are called **conic sections**. Conic sections and their three-dimensional counterparts have numerous applications in engineering. For example, the mirror in a reflecting telescope has cross sections in the shape of a parabola. This is important because the curved surface of the mirror focuses light to a common point called the **focus**. This targeted focusing of light enables astronomers to view an image from a distant star with better clarity.

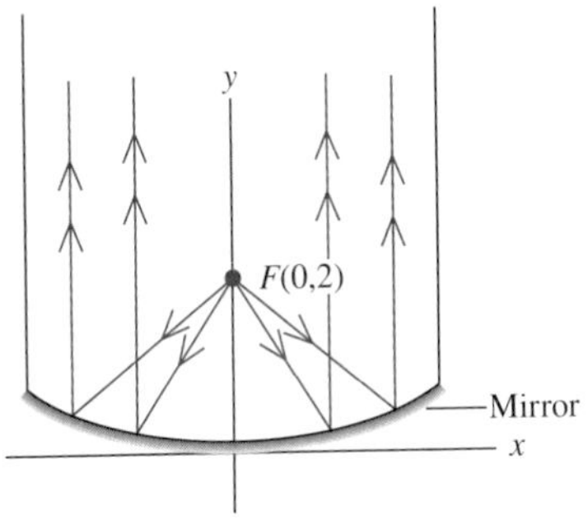

© Aaron Roeth Photography

The cooling towers for nuclear power plants have cross sections in the shape of a hyperbola. One advantage of a hyperbolic cooling tower is that air accelerates as it rises inside, toward the narrow portion of the tower. This provides for an efficient, nonturbulent flow. Then, above the narrow part, the tower flares out for efficient dispersal of warm air.

The ellipse is an oval-shaped curve that also has numerous applications such as in architectural design and for describing the orbits of planets. For example, the Roman Coliseum is an elliptical stone and concrete amphitheater in the center of Rome, built between 70 A.D. and 80 A.D. The Coliseum seated approximately 50,000 spectators and was used for gladiatorial contests among other things.

© Michael Evans/Life File/Getty Images RF

Section 13.1 Distance Formula, Midpoint Formula, and Circles

Concepts

1. Distance Formula
2. Circles
3. Writing an Equation of a Circle
4. The Midpoint Formula

1. Distance Formula

Suppose we are given two points (x_1, y_1) and (x_2, y_2) in a rectangular coordinate system. The distance between the two points can be found by using the Pythagorean theorem (Figure 13-1).

First draw a right triangle with the distance d as the hypotenuse. The length of the horizontal leg a is $|x_2 - x_1|$, and the length of the vertical leg b is $|y_2 - y_1|$. From the Pythagorean theorem we have

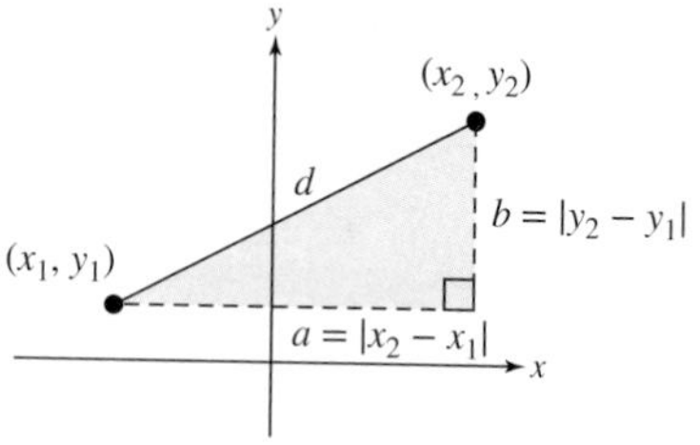

Figure 13-1

$$d^2 = a^2 + b^2$$
$$= |x_2 - x_1|^2 + |y_2 - y_1|^2$$
$$= (x_2 - x_1)^2 + (y_2 - y_1)^2$$
$$d = \pm\sqrt{(x_2 - x_1)^2 + (y_2 - y_1)^2}$$
$$= \sqrt{(x_2 - x_1)^2 + (y_2 - y_1)^2}$$

Because distance is positive, reject the negative value.

TIP: Squaring any real-valued quantity results in a nonnegative real number. Therefore, the absolute value bars can be dropped.

The Distance Formula

The distance d between the points (x_1, y_1) and (x_2, y_2) is

$$d = \sqrt{(x_2 - x_1)^2 + (y_2 - y_1)^2}$$

Classroom Example: p. 936, Exercise 2

Example 1 Finding the Distance Between Two Points

Find the distance between the points (−2, 3) and (4, −1) (Figure 13-2).

Solution:

(−2, 3) and (4, −1)
(x_1, y_1) (x_2, y_2) Label the points.

$$d = \sqrt{(x_2 - x_1)^2 + (y_2 - y_1)^2}$$
$$= \sqrt{[(4) - (-2)]^2 + [(-1) - (3)]^2}$$ Apply the distance formula.
$$= \sqrt{(6)^2 + (-4)^2}$$
$$= \sqrt{36 + 16}$$
$$= \sqrt{52}$$
$$= \sqrt{4 \cdot 13}$$
$$= 2\sqrt{13}$$

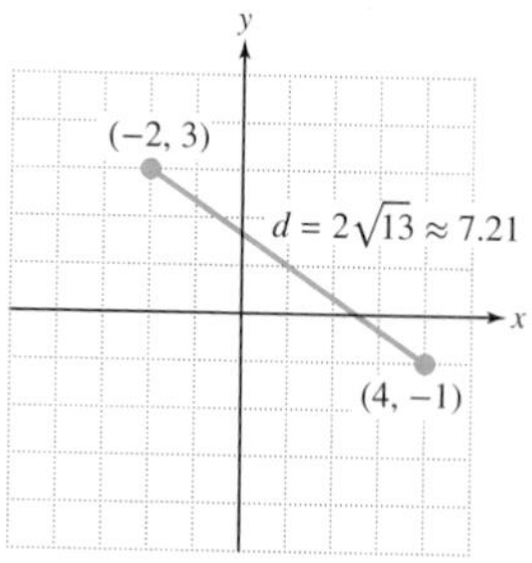

Figure 13-2

Skill Practice

1. Find the distance between the points (−4, −2) and (2, −5).

Answer

1. $3\sqrt{5}$

TIP: The order in which the points are labeled does not affect the result of the distance formula. For example, if the points in Example 1 had been labeled in reverse, the distance formula would still yield the same result:

$(-2, 3)$ and $(4, -1)$
(x_2, y_2) (x_1, y_1)

$$\begin{aligned} d &= \sqrt{(x_2 - x_1)^2 + (y_2 - y_1)^2} \\ &= \sqrt{[(-2) - (4)]^2 + [3 - (-1)]^2} \\ &= \sqrt{(-6)^2 + (4)^2} \\ &= \sqrt{36 + 16} \\ &= \sqrt{52} \\ &= 2\sqrt{13} \end{aligned}$$

2. Circles

A **circle** is defined as the set of all points in a plane that are equidistant from a fixed point called the **center**. The fixed distance from the center is called the **radius** and is denoted by r, where $r > 0$.

Suppose a circle is centered at the point (h, k) and has radius, r (Figure 13-3). The distance formula can be used to derive an equation of the circle.

Let (x, y) be any arbitrary point on the circle. Then, by definition, the distance between (h, k) and (x, y) must be r.

$$\sqrt{(x - h)^2 + (y - k)^2} = r$$

$$(x - h)^2 + (y - k)^2 = r^2 \qquad \text{Square both sides.}$$

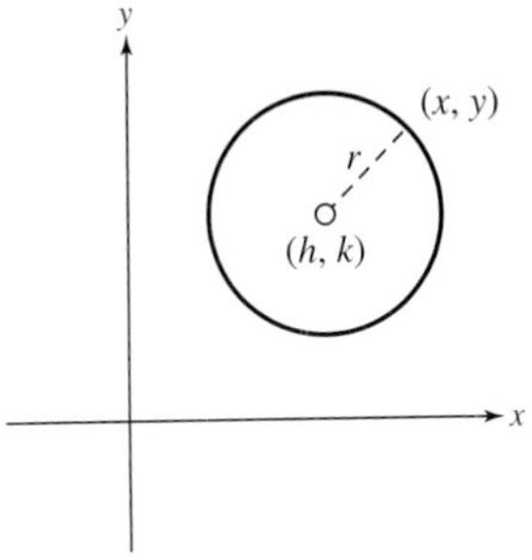

Figure 13-3

Standard Equation of a Circle

The **standard equation of a circle**, centered at (h, k) with radius r, is given by

$$(x - h)^2 + (y - k)^2 = r^2 \qquad \text{where } r > 0.$$

Note: If a circle is centered at the origin $(0, 0)$, then $h = 0$ and $k = 0$, and the equation simplifies to $x^2 + y^2 = r^2$.

Example 2 Graphing a Circle

Classroom Example: p. 936, Exercise 28

Find the center and radius of the circle. Then graph the circle.

$$(x - 3)^2 + (y + 4)^2 = 36$$

Solution:

$$(x - 3)^2 + (y + 4)^2 = 36$$

$$(x - 3)^2 + [y - (-4)]^2 = (6)^2$$

$$h = 3, k = -4, \text{ and } r = 6$$

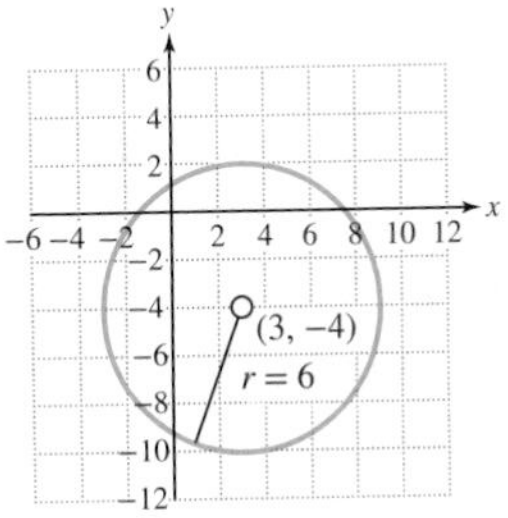

Figure 13-4

The equation is in standard form $(x - h)^2 + (y - k)^2 = r^2$. The center is $(3, -4)$, and the radius is $r = 6$. To graph the circle, first locate the center. From the center, mark points 6 units to the right, left, above, and below the center. Then sketch the circle through these four points (Figure 13-4).

Note that the center of the circle is not actually part of the circle. It is drawn as an open dot for reference.

Skill Practice Find the center and radius of the circle. Then graph the circle.

2. $(x + 1)^2 + (y - 2)^2 = 9$

Answer

2. Center: $(-1, 2)$; radius: 3

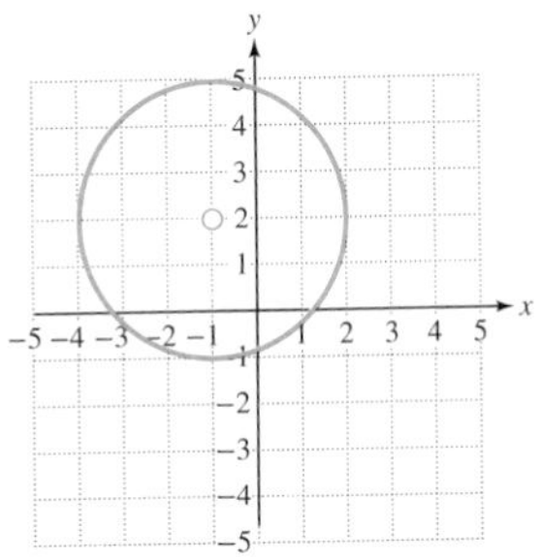

Calculator Connections

Topic: Graphing a Circle

Graphing calculators are designed to graph *functions*, in which y is written in terms of x. A circle is not a function. However, it can be graphed as the union of two functions—one representing the top semicircle and the other representing the bottom semicircle.

Solving for y in Example 2, we have

$$(x-3)^2 + (y+4)^2 = 36$$

$$(y+4)^2 = 36 - (x-3)^2$$

$$y + 4 = \pm\sqrt{36-(x-3)^2}$$

$$y = -4 \pm \sqrt{36-(x-3)^2}$$

Graph these functions as Y_1 and Y_2, using a square viewing window.

$$Y_1 = -4 + \sqrt{36-(x-3)^2}$$

$$Y_2 = -4 - \sqrt{36-(x-3)^2}$$

Instructor Note: Ask students why a circle is not a function.

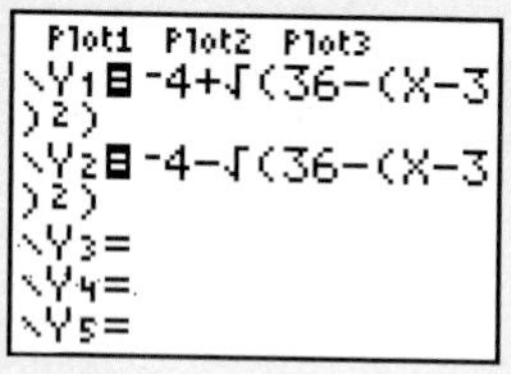

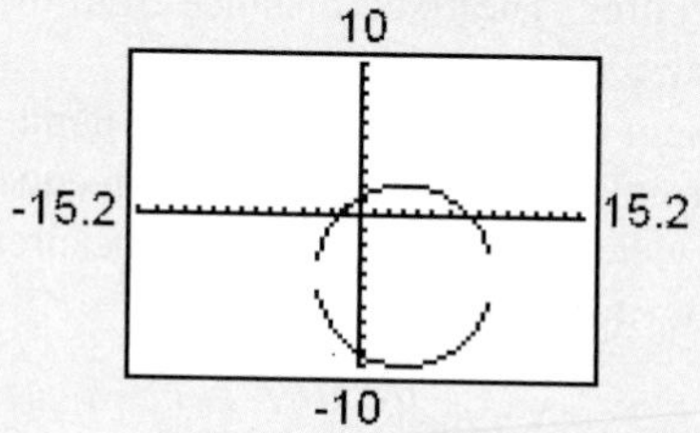

Notice that the image from the calculator does not show the upper and lower semicircles connecting at their endpoints, when in fact the semicircles should "hook up." This is due to the calculator's limited resolution.

Classroom Examples: p. 937, Exercises 36 and 38

Example 3 Graphing a Circle

Find the center and radius of each circle. Then graph the circle.

a. $x^2 + \left(y - \frac{10}{3}\right)^2 = \frac{25}{9}$ **b.** $x^2 + y^2 = 10$

Solution:

a. $x^2 + \left(y - \frac{10}{3}\right)^2 = \frac{25}{9}$

$$(x-0)^2 + \left(y - \frac{10}{3}\right)^2 = \left(\frac{5}{3}\right)^2$$

The equation is now in standard form $(x-h)^2 + (y-k)^2 = r^2$.

The center is $\left(0, \frac{10}{3}\right)$ and the radius is $\frac{5}{3}$ (Figure 13-5).

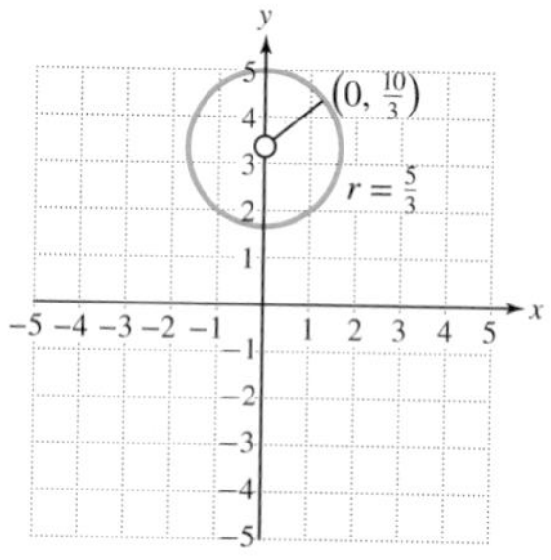

Figure 13-5

b. $x^2 + y^2 = 10$

$(x - 0)^2 + (y - 0)^2 = (\sqrt{10})^2$

$(x - h)^2 + (y - k)^2 = r^2$

The center is (0, 0) and the radius is $\sqrt{10} \approx 3.16$ (Figure 13-6).

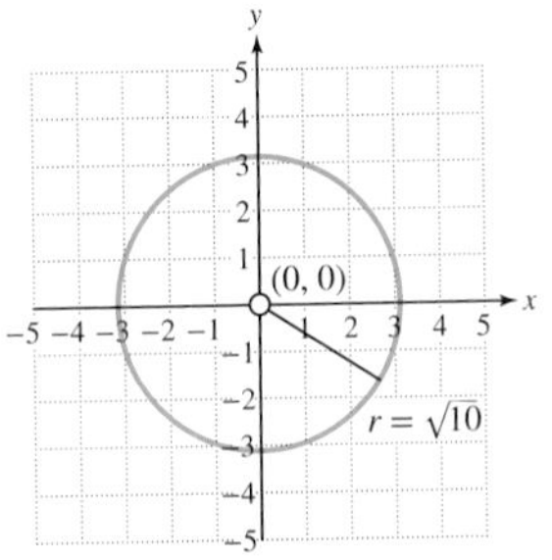

Figure 13-6

Skill Practice Find the center and radius of the circle. Then graph the circle.

3. $\left(x + \frac{7}{2}\right)^2 + y^2 = \frac{9}{4}$

Sometimes it is necessary to complete the square to write an equation of a circle in standard form.

Example 4 **Writing an Equation of a Circle in the Form $(x - h)^2 + (y - k)^2 = r^2$**

Classroom Example: p. 937, Exercise 40

Identify the center and radius of the circle given by the equation.

$$x^2 + y^2 + 2x - 16y + 61 = 0$$

Solution:

$x^2 + y^2 + 2x - 16y + 61 = 0$ — To identify the center and radius, write the equation in the form $(x - h)^2 + (y - k)^2 = r^2$.

$(x^2 + 2x \quad) + (y^2 - 16y \quad) = -61$ — Group the x terms and group the y terms. Move the constant to the right-hand side.

$(x^2 + 2x + 1) + (y^2 - 16y + 64) = -61 + 1 + 64$

- Complete the square on x. Add $\left[\frac{1}{2}(2)\right]^2 = 1$ to both sides of the equation.
- Complete the square on y. Add $\left[\frac{1}{2}(-16)\right]^2 = 64$ to both sides of the equation.

$(x + 1)^2 + (y - 8)^2 = 4$ — Factor and simplify.

$[x - (-1)]^2 + (y - 8)^2 = 2^2$ — Standard form: $(x - h)^2 + (y - k)^2 = r^2$

The center is $(-1, 8)$ and the radius is 2.

Skill Practice Identify the center and radius of the circle given by the equation.

4. $x^2 + y^2 - 10x + 4y - 7 = 0$

Answers

3. Center: $\left(-\frac{7}{2}, 0\right)$; radius: $\frac{3}{2}$

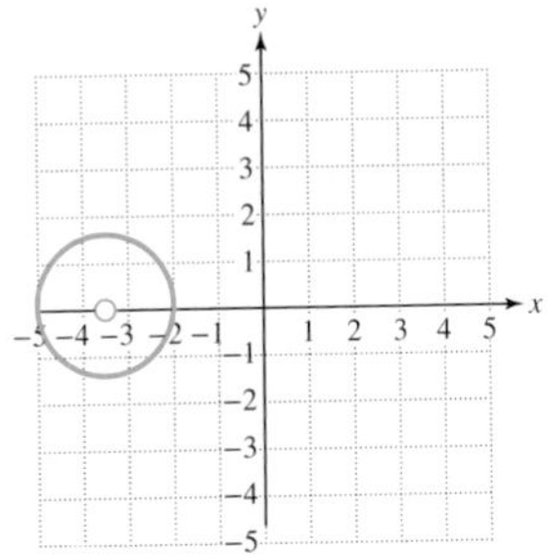

4. Center: $(5, -2)$; radius: 6

3. Writing an Equation of a Circle

Classroom Example: p. 938, Exercise 54

Example 5 Writing an Equation of a Circle

Write an equation of the circle shown in Figure 13-7.

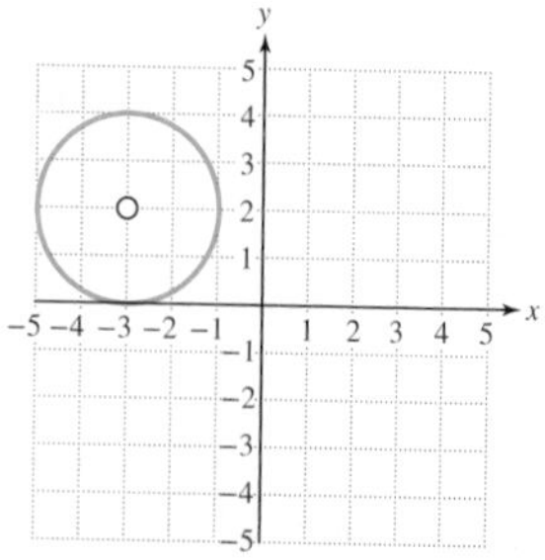

Figure 13-7

Solution:

The center is $(-3, 2)$; therefore, $h = -3$ and $k = 2$.
From the graph, $r = 2$.

$$(x - h)^2 + (y - k)^2 = r^2$$
$$[x - (-3)]^2 + (y - 2)^2 = (2)^2$$
$$(x + 3)^2 + (y - 2)^2 = 4$$

Avoiding Mistakes

Be sure that you *subtract* both coordinates of the center, when substituting the coordinates into the standard form of a circle.

Skill Practice

5. Write an equation for a circle whose center is $(6, -1)$ and whose radius is 8.

4. The Midpoint Formula

Consider two points in the coordinate plane and the line segment determined by the points. It is sometimes necessary to determine the point that is halfway between the endpoints of the segment. This point is called the *midpoint*.

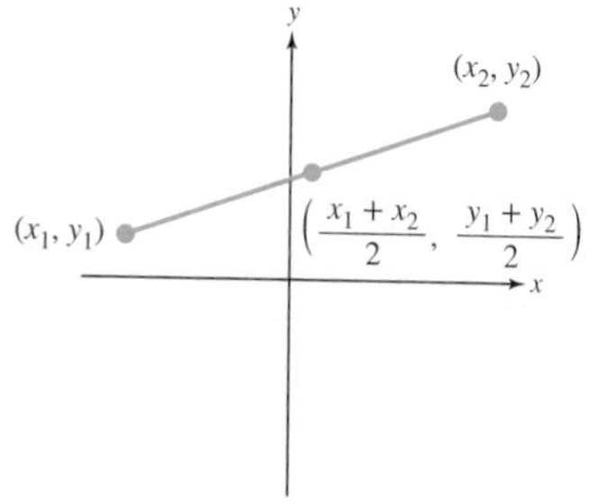

TIP: The midpoint of a line segment is found by taking the *average* of the *x*-coordinates and the *average* of the *y*-coordinates of the endpoints.

Midpoint Formula

Given two points (x_1, y_1) and (x_2, y_2), the midpoint of the line segment between the two points is given by

$$\textbf{Midpoint:} \quad \left(\frac{x_1 + x_2}{2}, \frac{y_1 + y_2}{2}\right)$$

Classroom Example: p. 939, Exercise 66

Example 6 Finding the Midpoint of a Segment

Find the midpoint of the line segment with the given endpoints.

a. $(-4, 6)$ and $(8, 1)$ **b.** $(-1.2, -3.1)$ and $(-6.6, 1.2)$

Solution:

a. $(-4, 6)$ and $(8, 1)$
(x_1, y_1) (x_2, y_2)

$\left(\frac{-4 + 8}{2}, \frac{6 + 1}{2}\right)$ Apply the midpoint formula: $\left(\frac{x_1 + x_2}{2}, \frac{y_1 + y_2}{2}\right)$

$\left(2, \frac{7}{2}\right)$ Simplify.

The midpoint of the segment is $(2, \frac{7}{2})$.

Avoiding Mistakes

Always remember that the midpoint of a line segment is a *point*. The answer should be an ordered pair, (x, y).

Answer

5. $(x - 6)^2 + (y + 1)^2 = 64$

b. $(-1.2, -3.1)$ and $(-6.6, 1.2)$
(x_1, y_1) (x_2, y_2)

$\left(\frac{-1.2 + (-6.6)}{2}, \frac{-3.1 + 1.2}{2}\right)$ Apply the midpoint formula.

$(-3.9, -0.95)$ Simplify.

Skill Practice Find the midpoint of the line segment with the given endpoints.

6. $(5, 6)$ and $(-10, 4)$ **7.** $(-2.6, -6.3)$ and $(1.2, 4.1)$

Example 7 Applying the Midpoint Formula

Classroom Example: p. 940, Exercise 76

Suppose that $(-2, 3)$ and $(4, 1)$ are endpoints of a diameter of a circle.

a. Find the center of the circle. **b.** Write an equation of the circle.

Solution:

a. Because the midpoint of a diameter of a circle is the center of the circle, apply the midpoint formula. See Figure 13-8.

$(-2, 3)$ and $(4, 1)$
(x_1, y_1) (x_2, y_2)

$\left(\frac{x_1 + x_2}{2}, \frac{y_1 + y_2}{2}\right)$

$\left(\frac{-2 + 4}{2}, \frac{3 + 1}{2}\right)$ Apply the midpoint formula.

$(1, 2)$ Simplify.

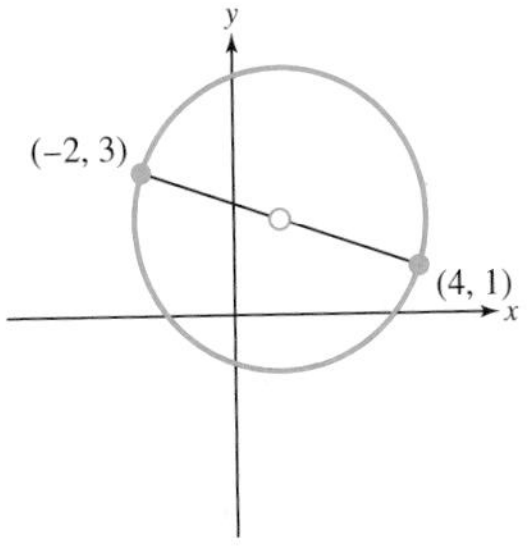

Figure 13-8

The center of the circle is $(1, 2)$.

b. The radius can be determined by finding the distance between the center and either endpoint of the diameter.

$(1, 2)$ and $(4, 1)$
(x_1, y_1) (x_2, y_2)

$d = \sqrt{(x_2 - x_1)^2 + (y_2 - y_1)^2}$ Apply the distance formula.

$d = \sqrt{(4 - 1)^2 + (1 - 2)^2}$ Substitute $(1, 2)$ and $(4, 1)$ for (x_1, y_1) and (x_2, y_2).

$= \sqrt{(3)^2 + (-1)^2}$ Simplify.

$= \sqrt{10}$

The circle is represented by $(x - 1)^2 + (y - 2)^2 = (\sqrt{10})^2$
or $(x - 1)^2 + (y - 2)^2 = 10$.

Skill Practice

8. Suppose that $(3, 2)$ and $(7, 10)$ are endpoints of a diameter of a circle.
   a. Find the center of the circle.
   b. Write an equation of the circle.

Answers

6. $\left(-\frac{5}{2}, 5\right)$ 7. $(-0.7, -1.1)$
8. a. $(5, 6)$
b. $(x - 5)^2 + (y - 6)^2 = 20$

Section 13.1 Practice Exercises

For additional exercises, see Classroom Activities 13.1A–13.1D in the *Student's Resource Manual* at www.mhhe.com/moh.

Vocabulary and Key Concepts

1. **a.** The distance between two distinct points (x_1, y_1) and (x_2, y_2) is given by $d =$ $\sqrt{(x_2 - x_1)^2 + (y_2 - y_1)^2}$.
   b. A circle is the set of all points equidistant from a fixed point called the center.
   c. The distance from the center of a circle to any point on the circle is called the radius and is often denoted by r.
   d. The standard equation of a circle with center (h, k) and radius r is given by $(x - h)^2 + (y - k)^2 = r^2$.
   e. The midpoint of the line segment with endpoints (x_1, y_1) and (x_2, y_2) is given by ______. $\left(\frac{x_1 + x_2}{2}, \frac{y_1 + y_2}{2}\right)$

Concept 1: Distance Formula

For Exercises 2–16, use the distance formula to find the distance between the two points. **(See Example 1.)**

2. $(-2, 7)$ and $(4, -5)$ $6\sqrt{5}$

3. $(1, 10)$ and $(-2, 4)$ $3\sqrt{5}$

4. $(0, 5)$ and $(-3, 8)$ $3\sqrt{2}$

5. $(6, 7)$ and $(3, 2)$ $\sqrt{34}$

6. $\left(\frac{2}{3}, \frac{1}{5}\right)$ and $\left(-\frac{5}{6}, \frac{3}{10}\right)$ $\frac{\sqrt{226}}{10}$

7. $\left(-\frac{1}{2}, \frac{5}{8}\right)$ and $\left(-\frac{3}{2}, \frac{1}{4}\right)$ $\frac{\sqrt{73}}{8}$

8. $(4, 13)$ and $(4, -6)$ 19

9. $(-2, 5)$ and $(-2, 9)$ 4

10. $(8, -6)$ and $(-2, -6)$ 10

11. $(7, 2)$ and $(15, 2)$ 8

12. $(-6, -2)$ and $(-3, -5)$ $3\sqrt{2}$

13. $(-1, -5)$ and $(-5, -9)$ $4\sqrt{2}$

14. $(3\sqrt{5}, 2\sqrt{7})$ and $(-\sqrt{5}, -3\sqrt{7})$ $\sqrt{255}$

15. $(4\sqrt{6}, -2\sqrt{2})$ and $(2\sqrt{6}, \sqrt{2})$ $\sqrt{42}$

16. $(6, 0)$ and $(0, -1)$ $\sqrt{37}$

17. Explain how to find the distance between 5 and -7 on the y-axis.
Subtract 5 and -7. This becomes $5 - (-7) = 12$.

18. Explain how to find the distance between 15 and -37 on the x-axis.
Subtract 15 and -37. This becomes $15 - (-37) = 52$.

19. Find the values of y such that the distance between the points $(4, 7)$ and $(-4, y)$ is 10 units.
$y = 13, y = 1$

20. Find the values of x such that the distance between the points $(-4, -2)$ and $(x, 3)$ is 13 units.
$x = 8, x = -16$

21. Find the values of x such that the distance between the points $(x, 2)$ and $(4, -1)$ is 5 units.
$x = 0, x = 8$

22. Find the values of y such that the distance between the points $(-5, 2)$ and $(3, y)$ is 10 units.
$y = 8, y = -4$

For Exercises 23–26, determine if the three points define the vertices of a right triangle.

23. $(-3, 2), (-2, -4)$, and $(3, 3)$ Yes

24. $(1, -2), (-2, 4)$, and $(7, 1)$ Yes

25. $(-3, -2), (4, -3)$, and $(1, 5)$ No

26. $(1, 4), (5, 3)$, and $(2, 0)$ No

Concept 2: Circles

For Exercises 27–47, identify the center and radius of the circle and then graph the circle. Complete the square, if necessary. **(See Examples 2–4.)**

27. $(x - 4)^2 + (y + 2)^2 = 9$

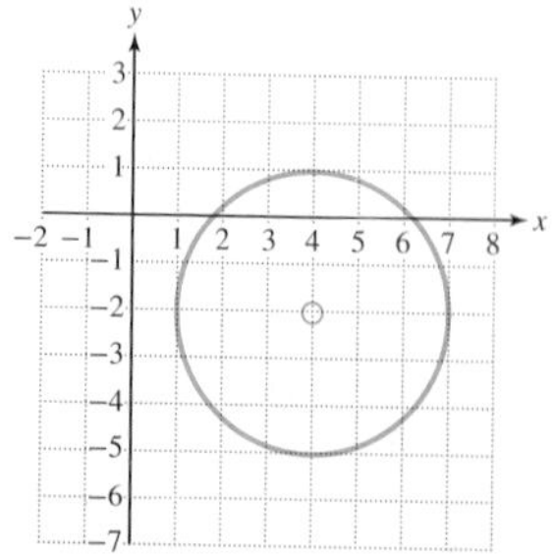

Center $(4, -2)$; $r = 3$

28. $(x - 3)^2 + (y + 1)^2 = 16$

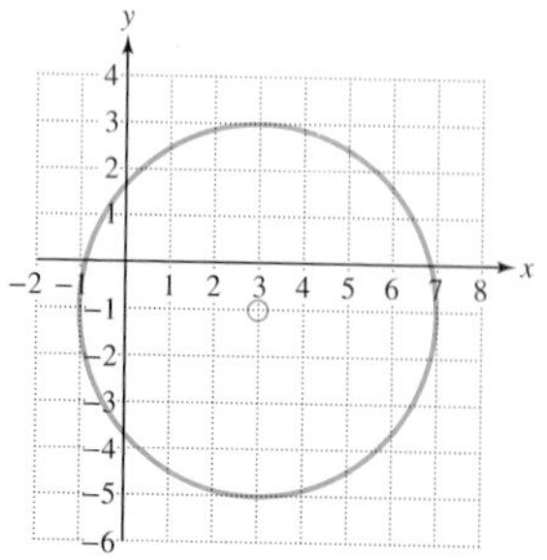

Center $(3, -1)$; $r = 4$

29. $(x + 1)^2 + (y + 1)^2 = 1$

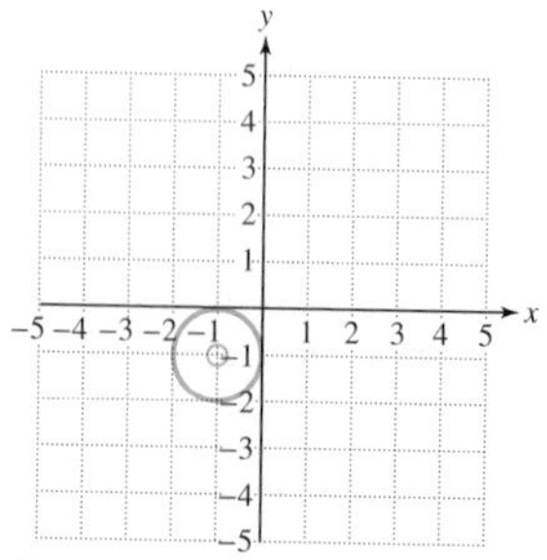

Center $(-1, -1)$; $r = 1$

30. $(x-4)^2+(y-4)^2=4$

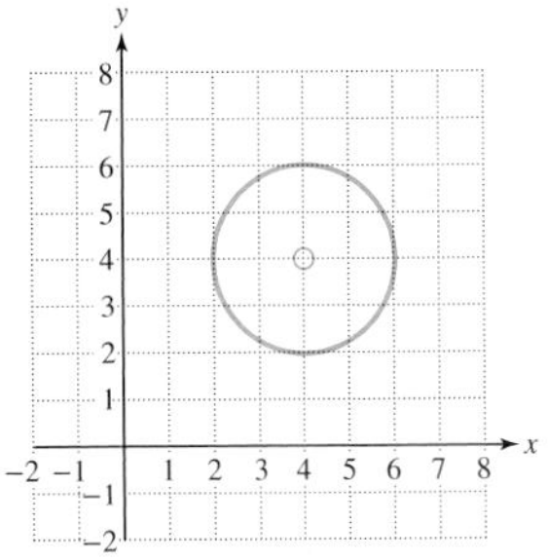

Center $(4, 4)$; $r = 2$

31. $x^2+(y-2)^2=4$

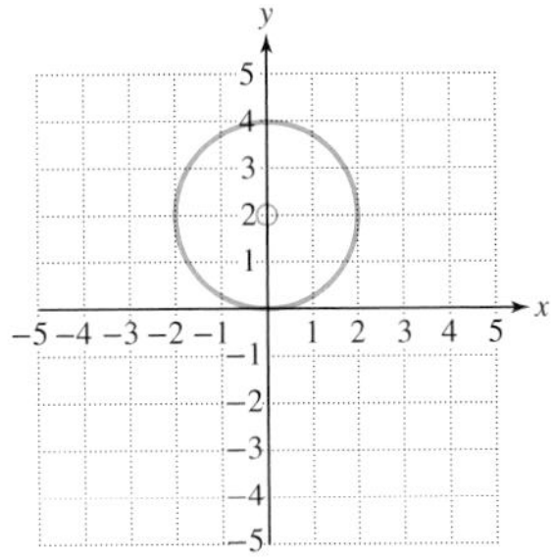

Center $(0, 2)$; $r = 2$

32. $(x+1)^2+y^2=1$

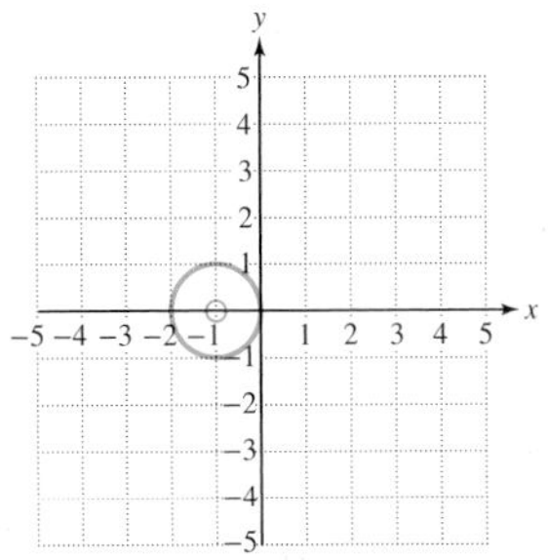

Center $(-1, 0)$; $r = 1$

33. $(x-3)^2+y^2=8$

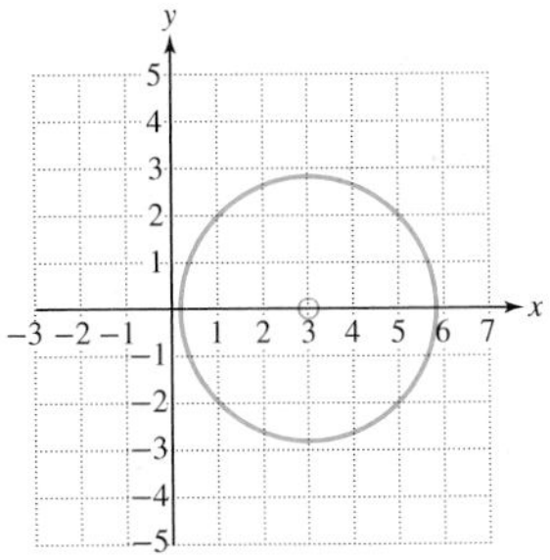

Center $(3, 0)$; $r = 2\sqrt{2}$

34. $x^2+(y+2)^2=20$

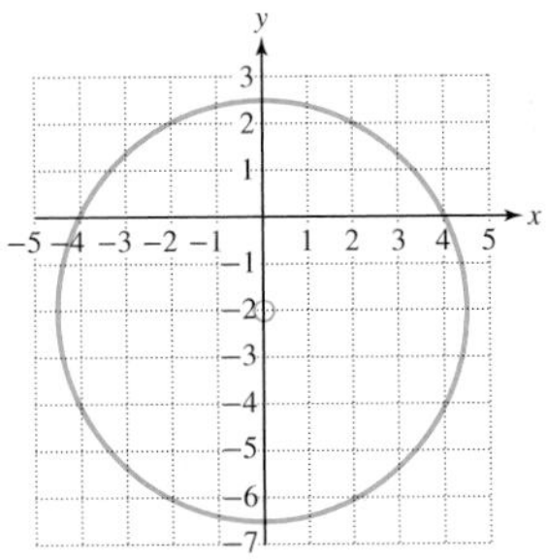

Center $(0, -2)$; $r = 2\sqrt{5}$

35. $x^2+y^2=6$

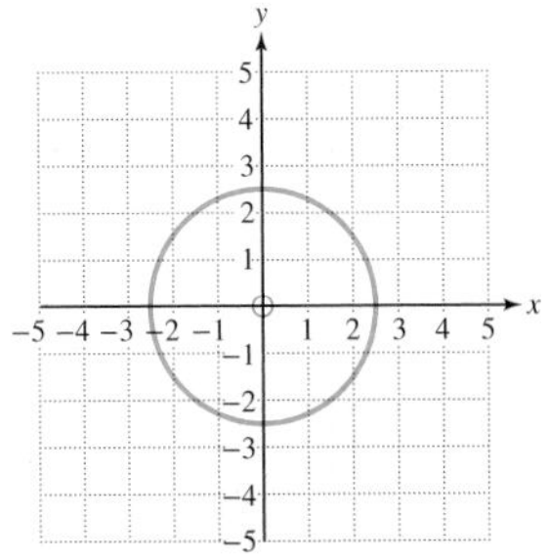

Center $(0, 0)$; $r = \sqrt{6}$

36. $x^2+y^2=15$

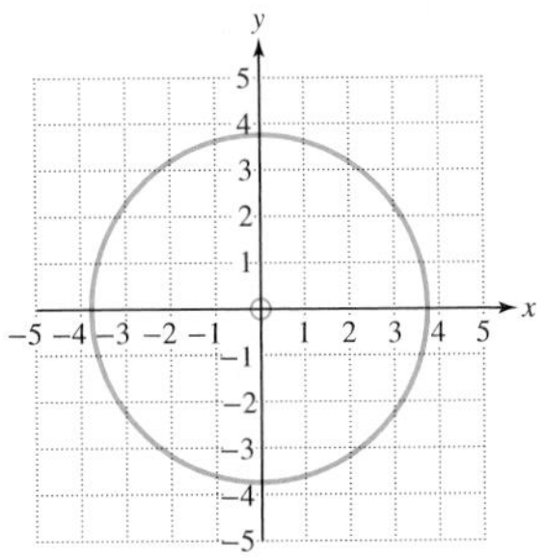

Center $(0, 0)$; $r = \sqrt{15}$

37. $\left(x+\frac{4}{5}\right)^2+y^2=\frac{64}{25}$

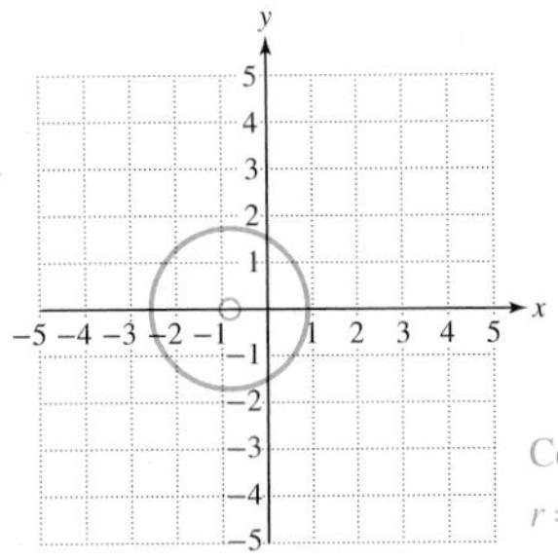

Center $\left(-\frac{4}{5}, 0\right)$; $r = \frac{8}{5}$

38. $x^2+\left(y-\frac{5}{2}\right)^2=\frac{9}{4}$

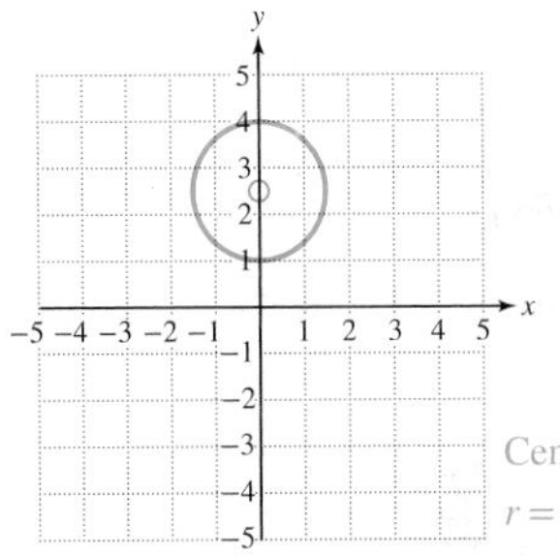

Center $\left(0, \frac{5}{2}\right)$; $r = \frac{3}{2}$

39. $x^2+y^2-2x-6y-26=0$

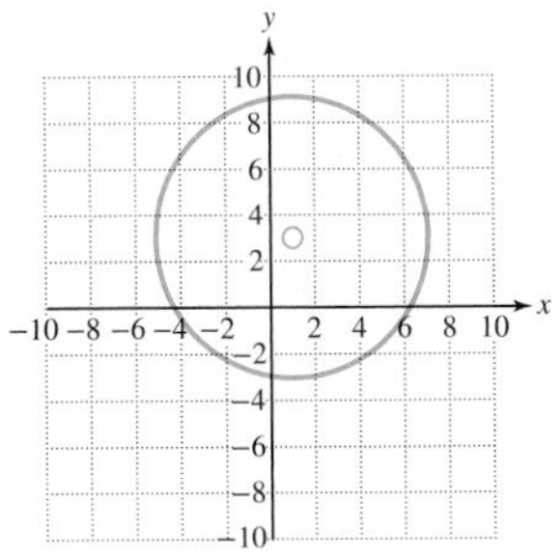

Center $(1, 3)$; $r = 6$

40. $x^2+y^2+4x-8y+16=0$

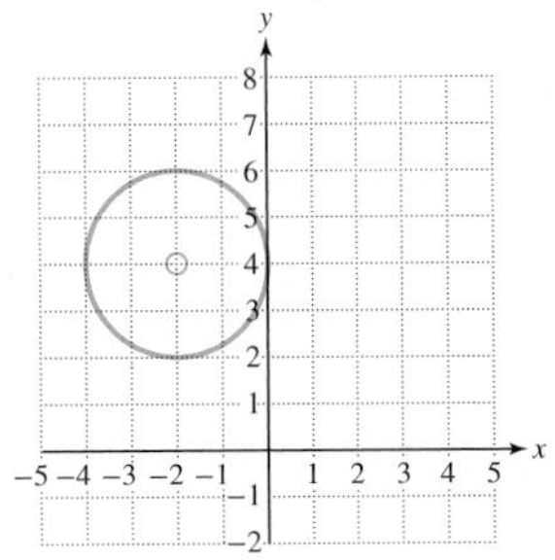

Center $(-2, 4)$; $r = 2$

41. $x^2+y^2-6y+5=0$

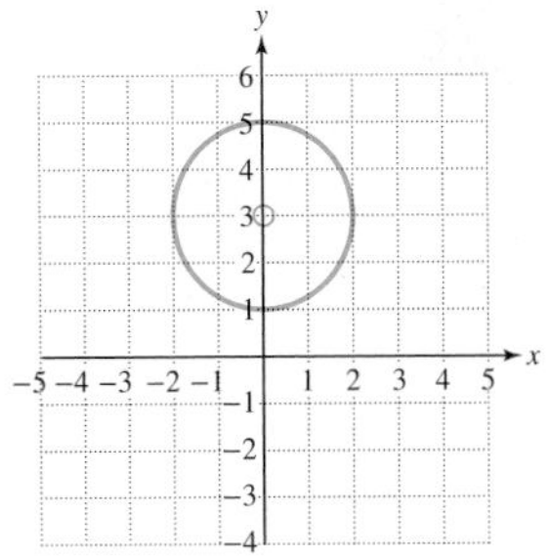

Center $(0, 3)$; $r = 2$

42. $x^2 + 2x + y^2 - 15 = 0$

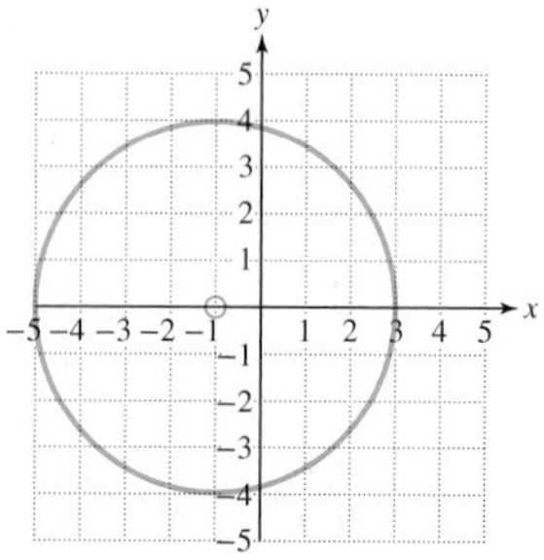

Center $(-1, 0)$; $r = 4$

43. $x^2 + y^2 + 6y + \frac{65}{9} = 0$

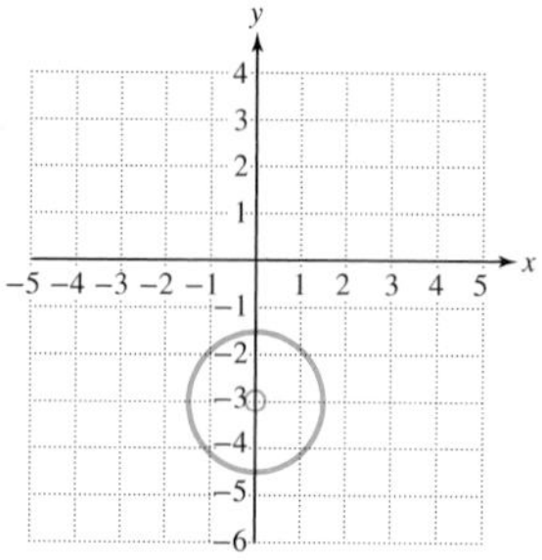

Center $(0, -3)$; $r = \frac{4}{3}$

44. $x^2 + y^2 - 12x + 12y + 71 = 0$

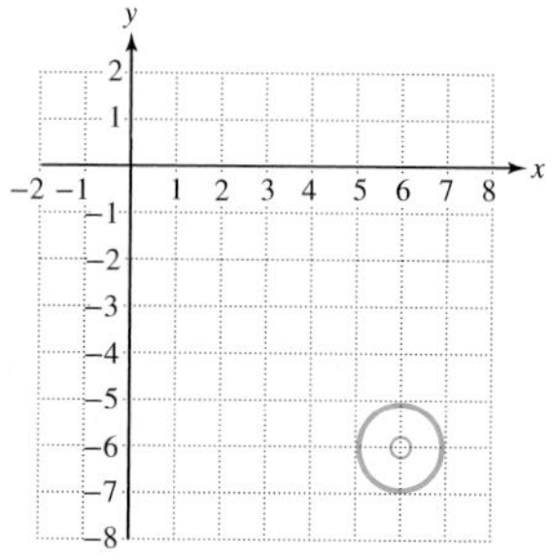

Center $(6, -6)$; $r = 1$

45. $x^2 + y^2 + 2x + 4y - 4 = 0$

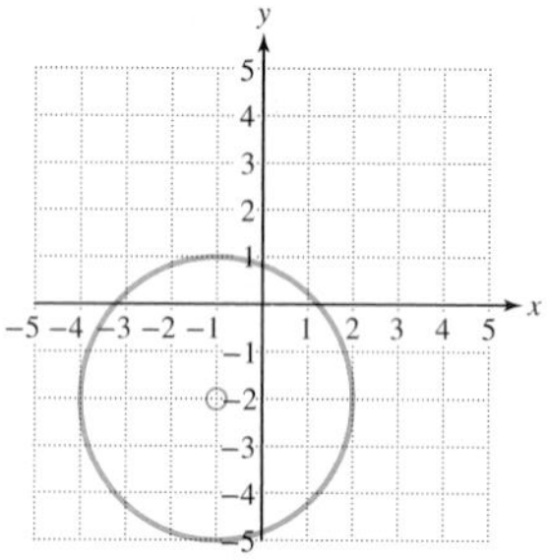

Center $(-1, -2)$; $r = 3$

46. $2x^2 + 2y^2 = 32$

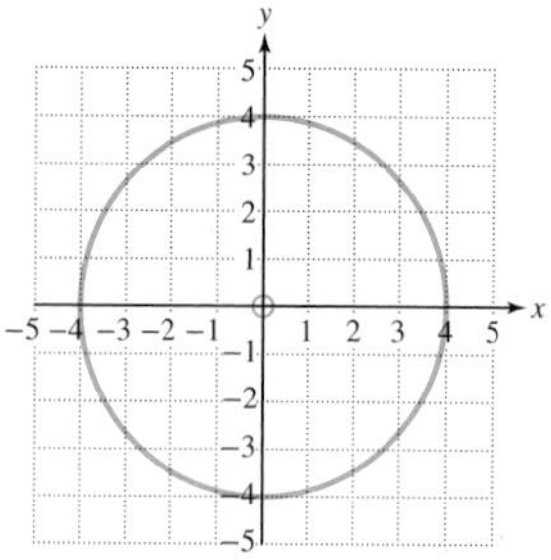

Center $(0, 0)$; $r = 4$

47. $3x^2 + 3y^2 = 3$

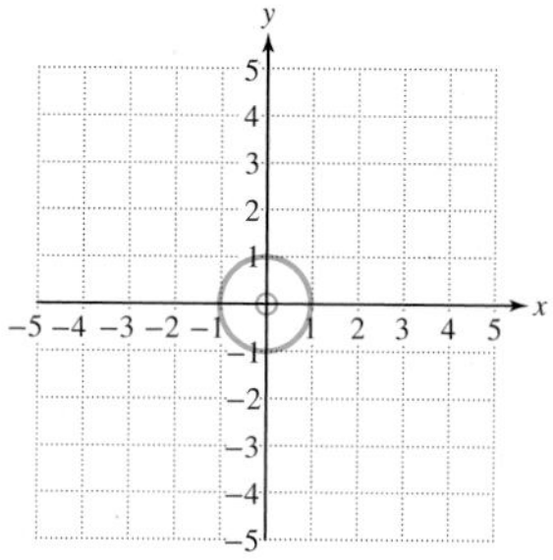

Center $(0, 0)$; $r = 1$

Concept 3: Writing an Equation of a Circle

48. If the diameter of a circle is 10 ft, what is the radius? 5 ft

For Exercises 49–54, write an equation that represents the graph of the circle. **(See Example 5.)**

49.

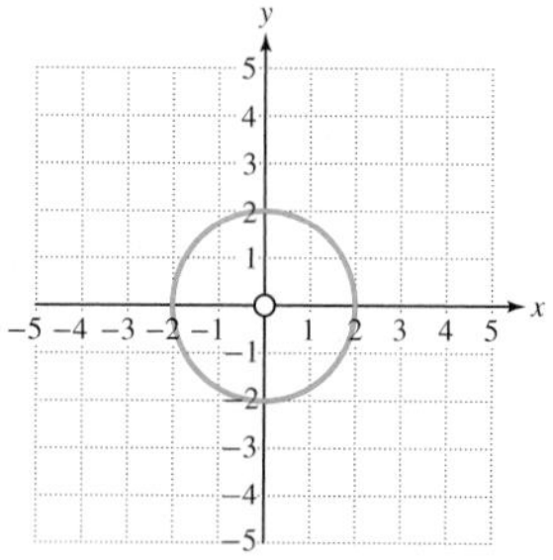

$x^2 + y^2 = 4$

50.

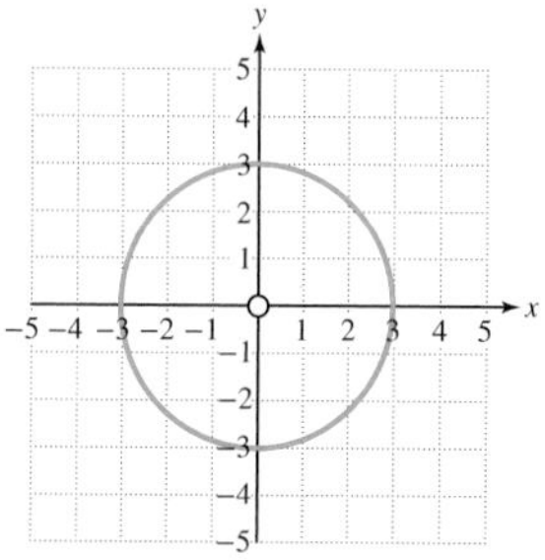

$x^2 + y^2 = 9$

51.

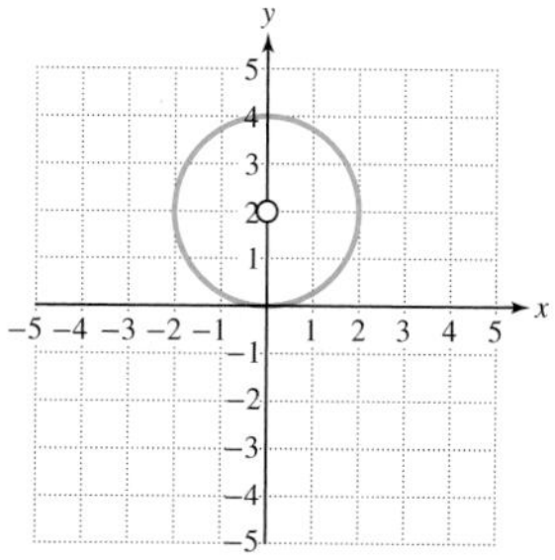

$x^2 + (y - 2)^2 = 4$

52.

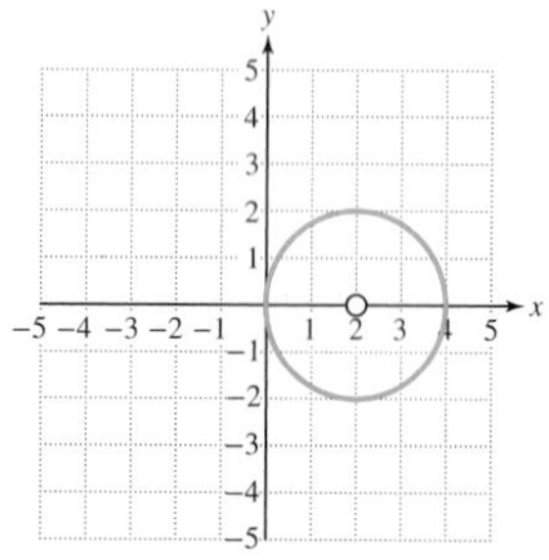

$(x - 2)^2 + y^2 = 4$

53.

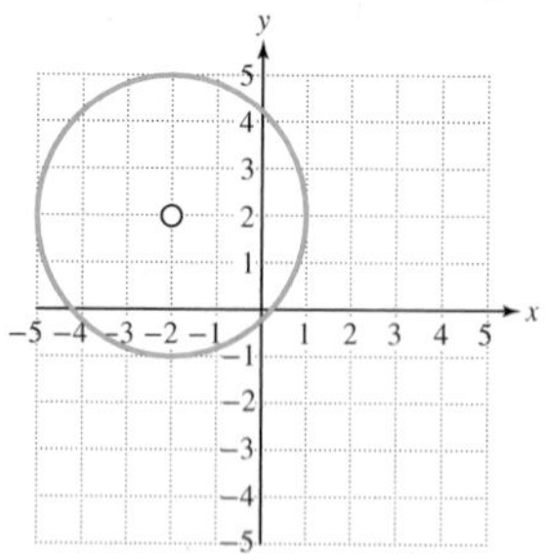

$(x + 2)^2 + (y - 2)^2 = 9$

54.

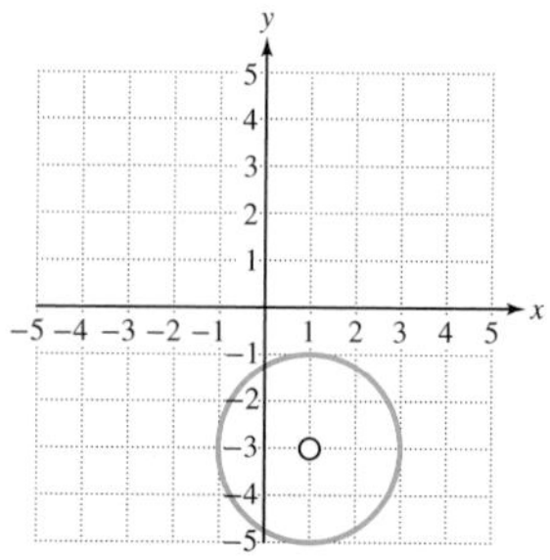

$(x - 1)^2 + (y + 3)^2 = 4$

55. Write an equation of a circle centered at the origin with a radius of 7.
$x^2 + y^2 = 49$

56. Write an equation of a circle centered at the origin with a radius of 12.
$x^2 + y^2 = 144$

57. Write an equation of a circle centered at $(-3, -4)$ with a diameter of 12.
$(x + 3)^2 + (y + 4)^2 = 36$

58. Write an equation of a circle centered at $(5, -1)$ with a diameter of 8. $(x - 5)^2 + (y + 1)^2 = 16$

59. A cell tower is a site where antennas, transmitters, and receivers are placed to create a cellular network. Suppose that a cell tower is located at a point $A(5, 3)$ on a map and its range is 1.5 mi. Write an equation that represents the boundary of the area that can receive a signal from the tower. Assume that all distances are in miles.
$(x - 5)^2 + (y - 3)^2 = 2.25$

60. A radar transmitter on a ship has a range of 20 nautical miles. If the ship is located at a point $(-28, 32)$ on a map, write an equation for the boundary of the area within the range of the ship's radar. Assume that all distances on the map are represented in nautical miles.
$(x + 28)^2 + (y - 32)^2 = 400$

Concept 4: The Midpoint Formula

For Exercises 61–64, find the midpoint of the line segment. Check your answers by plotting the midpoint on the graph.

61.

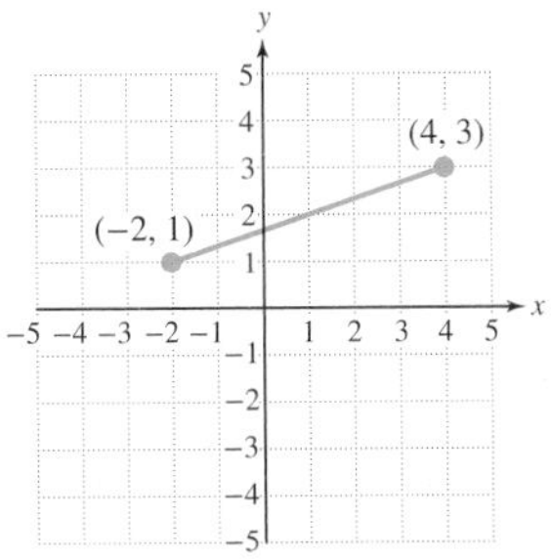

(1, 2)

62.

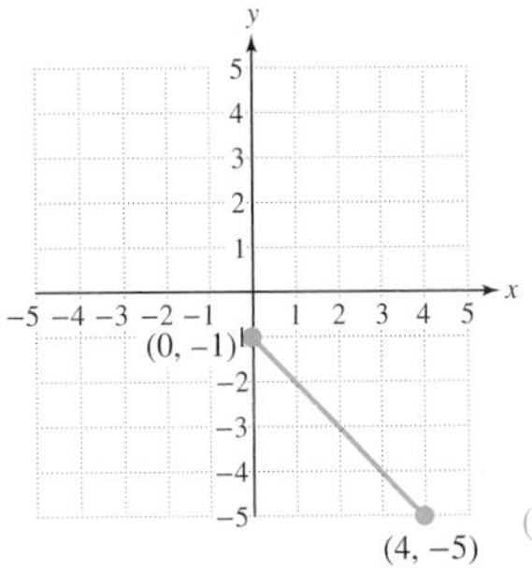

(2, −3)

63.

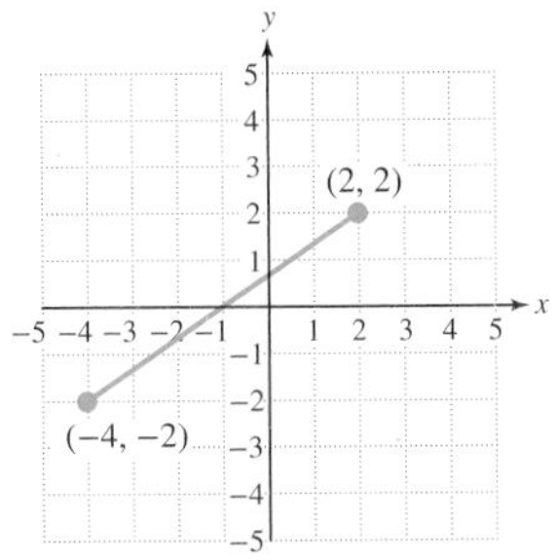

(−1, 0)

64.

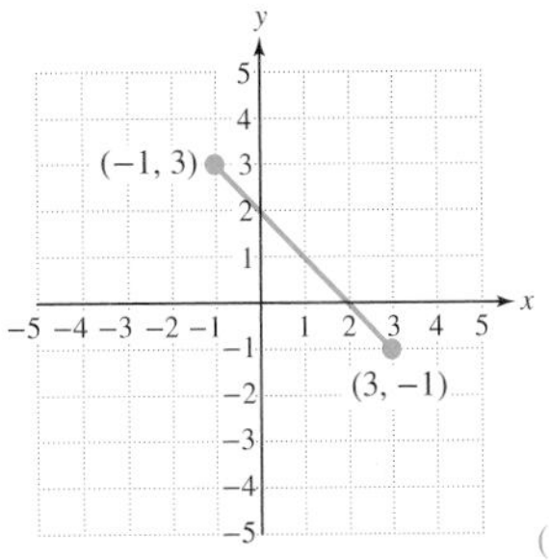

(1, 1)

For Exercises 65–72, find the midpoint of the line segment between the two given points. **(See Example 6.)**

65. $(4, 0)$ and $(-6, 12)$ $(-1, 6)$

66. $(-7, 2)$ and $(-3, -2)$ $(-5, 0)$

67. $(-3, 8)$ and $(3, -2)$ $(0, 3)$

68. $(0, 5)$ and $(4, -5)$ $(2, 0)$

69. $(5, 2)$ and $(-6, 1)$ $\left(-\frac{1}{2}, \frac{3}{2}\right)$

70. $(-9, 3)$ and $(0, -4)$ $\left(-\frac{9}{2}, -\frac{1}{2}\right)$

71. $(-2.4, -3.1)$ and $(1.6, 1.1)$
$(-0.4, -1)$

72. $(0.8, 5.3)$ and $(-4.2, 7.1)$
$(-1.7, 6.2)$

73. Two courier trucks leave the warehouse to make deliveries. One travels 20 mi north and 30 mi east. The other truck travels 5 mi south and 50 mi east. If the two drivers want to meet for lunch at a restaurant at a point halfway between them, where should they meet relative to the warehouse? (*Hint:* Label the warehouse as the origin, and find the coordinates of the restaurant. See the figure.)
$(40, 7\frac{1}{2})$; they should meet 40 mi east, $7\frac{1}{2}$ mi north of the warehouse.

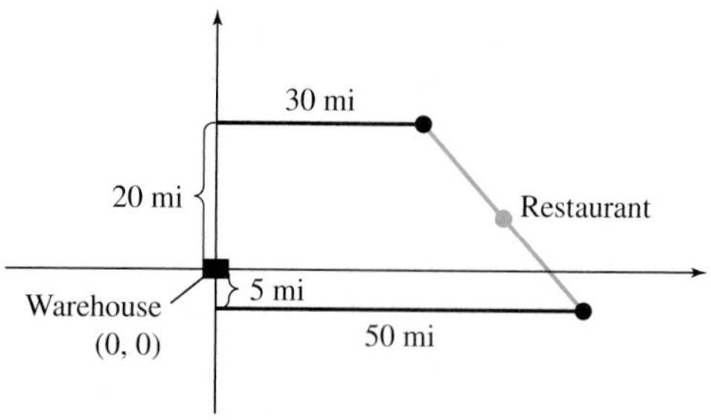

74. A map of a hiking area is drawn so that the Visitor Center is at the origin of a rectangular grid. Two hikers are located at positions $(-1, 1)$ and $(-3, -2)$ with respect to the Visitor Center where all units are in miles. A campground is located exactly halfway between the hikers. What are the coordinates of the campground? $\left(-2, -\frac{1}{2}\right)$

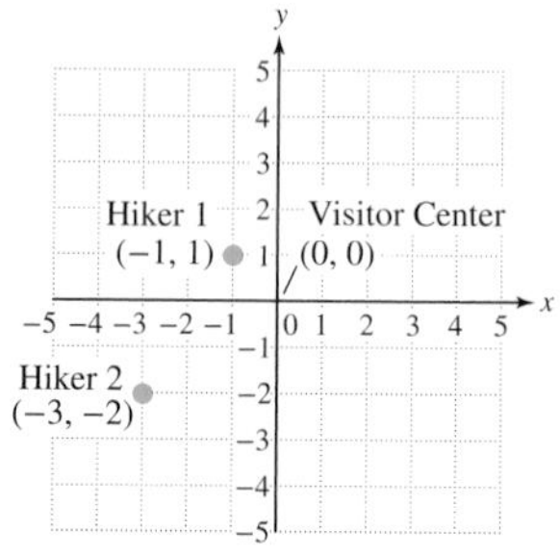

For Exercises 75–78, the two given points are endpoints of a diameter of a circle.

a. Find the center of the circle.

b. Write an equation of the circle. **(See Example 7.)**

75. $(-1, 2)$ and $(3, 4)$
a. $(1, 3)$
b. $(x - 1)^2 + (y - 3)^2 = 5$

76. $(-3, 3)$ and $(7, -1)$
a. $(2, 1)$
b. $(x - 2)^2 + (y - 1)^2 = 29$

77. $(-2, 3)$ and $(2, 3)$
a. $(0, 3)$
b. $x^2 + (y - 3)^2 = 4$

78. $(-1, 3)$ and $(-1, -3)$
a. $(-1, 0)$
b. $(x + 1)^2 + y^2 = 9$

Expanding Your Skills

79. Write an equation of a circle whose center is $(4, 4)$ and is tangent to the x- and y-axes. (*Hint:* Sketch the circle first.)
$(x - 4)^2 + (y - 4)^2 = 16$

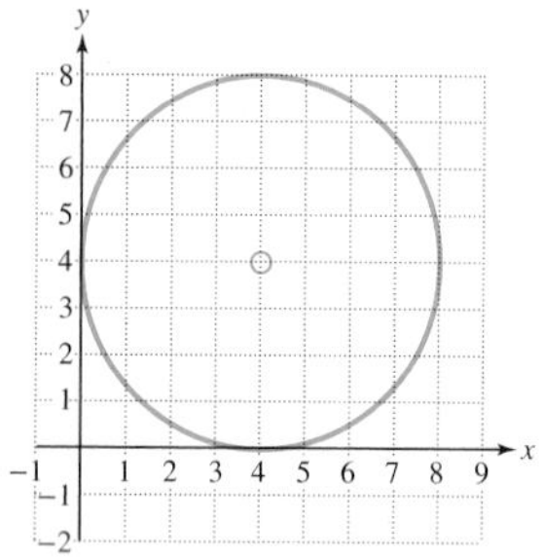

80. Write an equation of a circle whose center is $(-3, 3)$ and is tangent to the x- and y-axes. (*Hint:* Sketch the circle first.)
$(x + 3)^2 + (y - 3)^2 = 9$

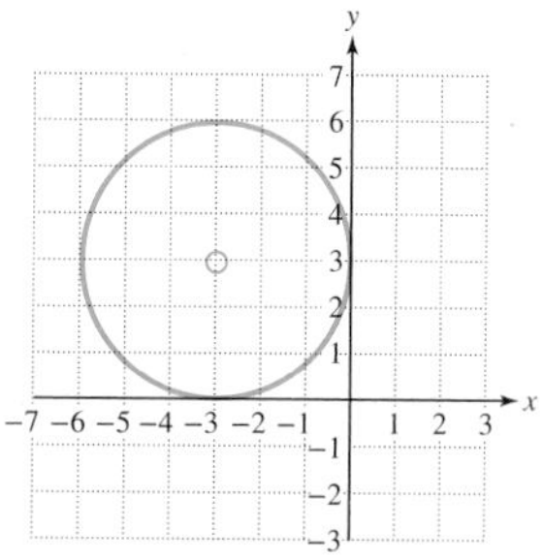

81. Write an equation of a circle whose center is $(1, 1)$ and that passes through the point $(-4, 3)$. $(x - 1)^2 + (y - 1)^2 = 29$

82. Write an equation of a circle whose center is $(-3, -1)$ and that passes through the point $(5, -2)$. $(x + 3)^2 + (y + 1)^2 = 65$

Graphing Calculator Exercises

For Exercises 83–88, graph the circle from the indicated exercise on a square viewing window, and approximate the center and the radius from the graph.

83. $(x - 4)^2 + (y + 2)^2 = 9$ (Exercise 27)

84. $(x - 3)^2 + (y + 1)^2 = 16$ (Exercise 28)

85. $x^2 + (y - 2)^2 = 4$ (Exercise 31)

86. $(x + 1)^2 + y^2 = 1$ (Exercise 32)

87. $x^2 + y^2 = 6$ (Exercise 35)

88. $x^2 + y^2 = 15$ (Exercise 36)

More on the Parabola

Section 13.2

Concepts

1. Introduction to Conic Sections
2. Parabola—Vertical Axis of Symmetry
3. Parabola—Horizontal Axis of Symmetry
4. Vertex Formula

Instructor Note: Three-dimensional models of the conic sections can really help students visualize these intersections more clearly.

1. Introduction to Conic Sections

The graph of a second-degree equation of the form $y = ax^2 + bx + c$ $(a \neq 0)$ is a parabola and the graph of $(x - h)^2 + (y - k)^2 = r^2$ is a circle. These and two other types of figures called ellipses and hyperbolas are called **conic sections**. Conic sections derive their names because each is the intersection of a plane and a double-napped cone.

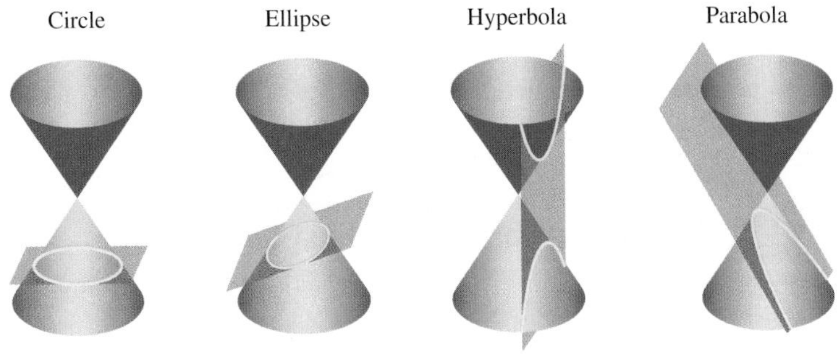

2. Parabola—Vertical Axis of Symmetry

A **parabola** is defined by a set of points in a plane that are equidistant from a fixed line (called the directrix) and a fixed point (called the focus) not on the directrix (Figure 13-9). Parabolas have numerous real-world applications. For example, a flashlight has a mirror with the cross section in the shape of a parabola. The bulb is located at the focus. The light hits the mirror and is reflected outward parallel to the sides of the cylinder. This forms a beam of light (Figure 13-10).

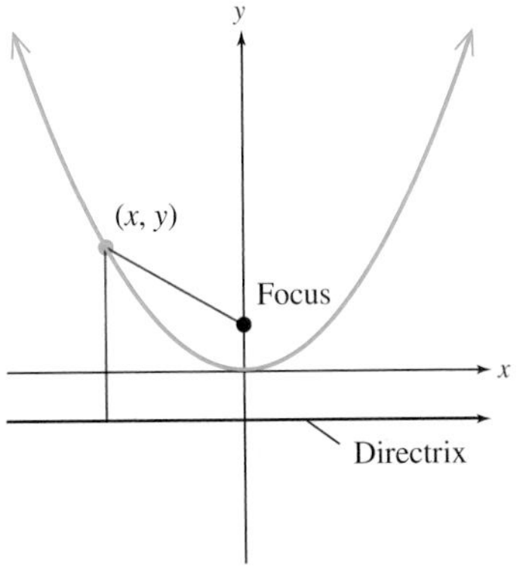

Figure 13-9

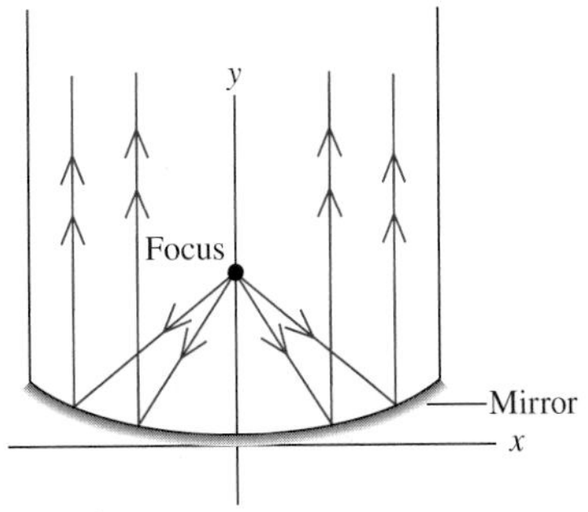

Figure 13-10

The graph of the solutions to the quadratic equation $y = ax^2 + bx + c$ is a parabola. Recall that the **vertex** is the highest or the lowest point of a parabola. The **axis of symmetry** of the parabola is a line that passes through the vertex and is perpendicular to the directrix (Figure 13-11).

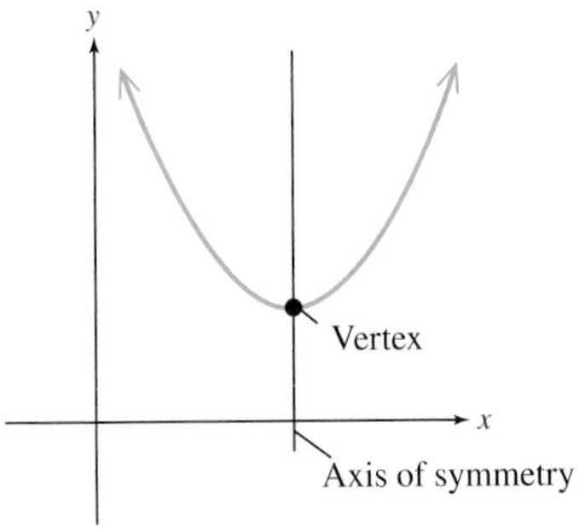

Figure 13-11

Standard Form of the Equation of a Parabola—Vertical Axis of Symmetry

The standard form of the equation of a parabola with vertex (h, k) and vertical axis of symmetry is

$$y = a(x - h)^2 + k \qquad \text{where } a \neq 0$$

If $a > 0$, the parabola opens upward; and if $a < 0$, the parabola opens downward.

The axis of symmetry is given by $x = h$.

It is sometimes necessary to complete the square to write an equation of a parabola in standard form.

Classroom Example: p. 948, Exercise 14

Example 1 Graphing a Parabola by First Completing the Square

Given the equation of the parabola $y = -2x^2 + 4x + 1$,

a. Write the equation in standard form $y = a(x - h)^2 + k$.

b. Identify the vertex and axis of symmetry. Determine if the parabola opens upward or downward.

c. Graph the parabola.

Solution:

a. Complete the square to write the equation in the form $y = a(x - h)^2 + k$.

$y = -2x^2 + 4x + 1$

$y = -2(x^2 - 2x) + 1$ Factor out -2 from the variable terms.

$y = -2(x^2 - 2x + 1 - 1) + 1$ Add and subtract the quantity $[\frac{1}{2}(-2)]^2 = 1$.

$y = -2(x^2 - 2x + 1) + (-2)(-1) + 1$ Remove the -1 term from within the parentheses by first applying the distributive property. When -1 is removed from the parentheses, it carries with it the factor of -2 from outside the parentheses.

$y = -2(x - 1)^2 + 2 + 1$

$y = -2(x - 1)^2 + 3$

The equation is in the form $y = a(x - h)^2 + k$ where $a = -2$, $h = 1$, and $k = 3$.

b. The vertex is $(1, 3)$. Because a is negative, the parabola opens downward. The axis of symmetry is $x = 1$.

c. To graph the parabola, we know that its orientation is downward because the leading term is negative. Furthermore, we know the vertex is (1, 3). To find other points on the parabola, select several values of x and solve for y. Recall that the y-intercept is found by substituting $x = 0$ and solving for y.

x	y	
1	3	← Vertex
0	1	← y-intercept
−1	−5	
2	1	
3	−5	

Choose x. Solve for y.

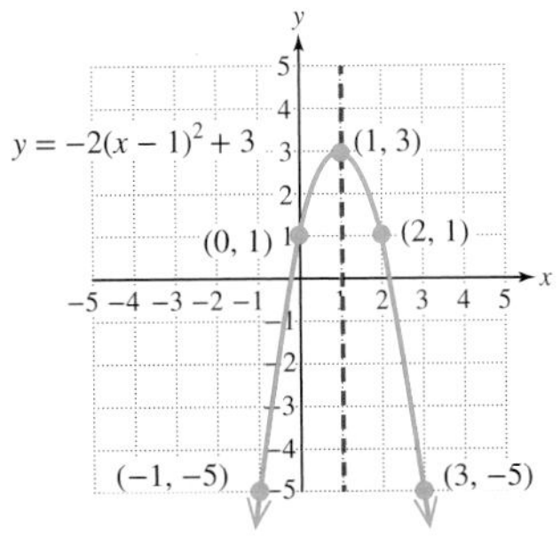

Notice that the points (2, 1) and (3, −5) are the mirror images of the points (0, 1) and (−1, −5) around the axis of symmetry, $x = 1$. For this reason, once we plot several points on one side of the axis of symmetry, the points on the other side automatically follow as a mirror image.

Skill Practice Given the equation of the parabola $y = 3x^2 + 6x + 4$,

1. Write the equation in standard form.
2. Identify the vertex and axis of symmetry.
3. Graph the parabola.

3. Parabola—Horizontal Axis of Symmetry

We have seen that the graph of a parabola $y = ax^2 + bx + c$ opens upward if $a > 0$ and downward if $a < 0$. A parabola can also open to the left or right. In such a case, the "roles" of x and y are essentially interchanged in the equation. Thus, the graph of $x = ay^2 + by + c$ opens to the right if $a > 0$ (Figure 13-12) and to the left if $a < 0$ (Figure 13-13).

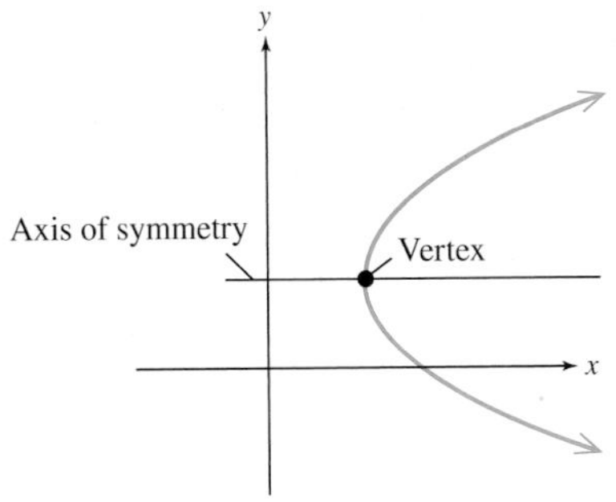

$x = ay^2 + by + c, a > 0$

Figure 13-12

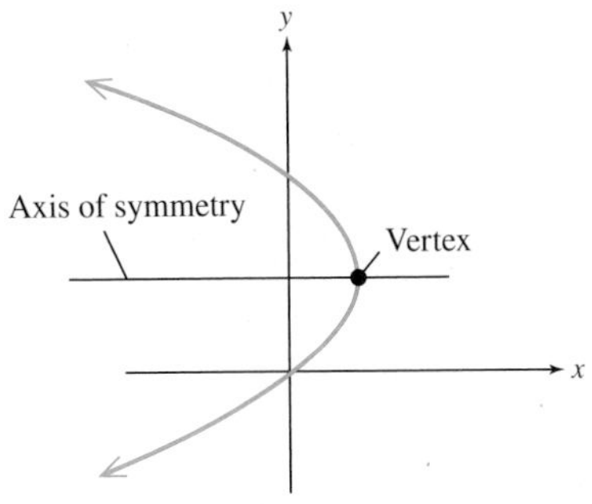

$x = ay^2 + by + c, a < 0$

Figure 13-13

Answers

1. $y = 3(x + 1)^2 + 1$
2. Vertex: (−1, 1); axis of symmetry: $x = -1$
3.

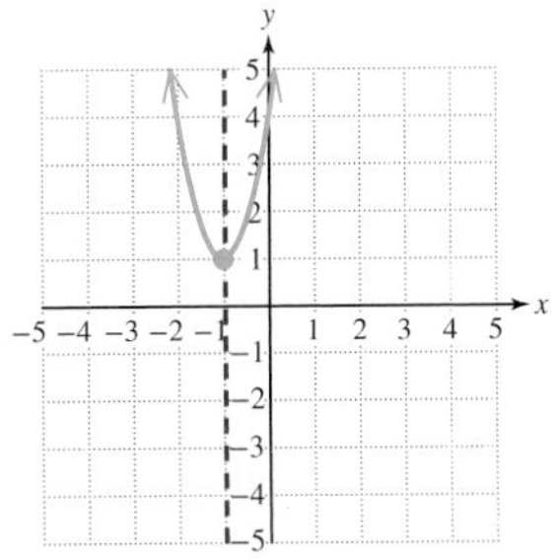

Instructor Note: Ask students whether $x = a(y - k)^2 + h$ defines y as a function of x.

Standard Form of the Equation of a Parabola—Horizontal Axis of Symmetry

The standard form of an equation of a parabola with vertex (h, k) and horizontal axis of symmetry is

$$x = a(y - k)^2 + h \qquad \text{where } a \neq 0$$

If $a > 0$, the parabola opens to the right and if $a < 0$, the parabola opens to the left.

The axis of symmetry is given by $y = k$.

Classroom Example: p. 949, Exercise 18

Example 2 Graphing a Parabola with a Horizontal Axis of Symmetry

Given the equation of the parabola $x = 4y^2$,

a. Determine the coordinates of the vertex and the equation of the axis of symmetry.

b. Use the value of a to determine if the parabola opens to the right or left.

c. Plot several points and graph the parabola.

Solution:

a. The equation can be written in the form $x = a(y - k)^2 + h$:

$$x = 4(y - 0)^2 + 0$$

Therefore, $h = 0$ and $k = 0$.

The vertex is $(0, 0)$. The axis of symmetry is $y = 0$ (the x-axis).

b. Because a is positive, the parabola opens to the right.

c. The vertex of the parabola is $(0, 0)$. To find other points on the graph, select values for y and solve for x.

TIP: For Example 2, the x-axis is the axis of symmetry. Therefore, once we find points on the parabola above the axis of symmetry, their mirror image will be points on the parabola below the axis of symmetry.

x	y	
0	0	← Vertex
4	1	
4	−1	
16	2	
16	−2	

Solve for x. Choose y.

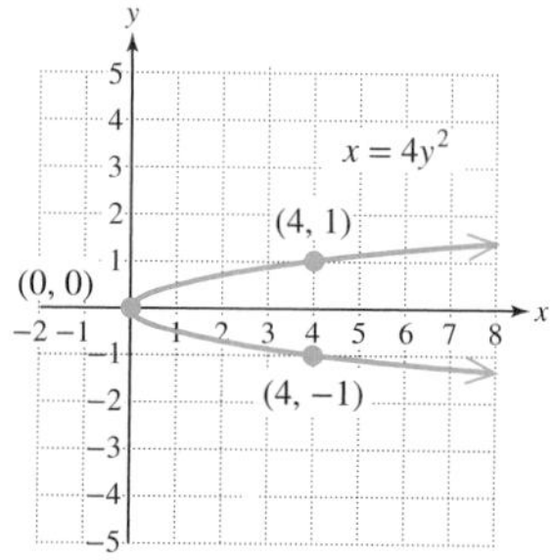

Skill Practice Given the equation $x = -y^2 + 1$,

4. Identify the vertex and the axis of symmetry.

5. Determine if the parabola opens to the right or to the left.

6. Graph the parabola.

Answers

4. Vertex: (1, 0); axis of symmetry: $y = 0$

5. Parabola opens left.

6.

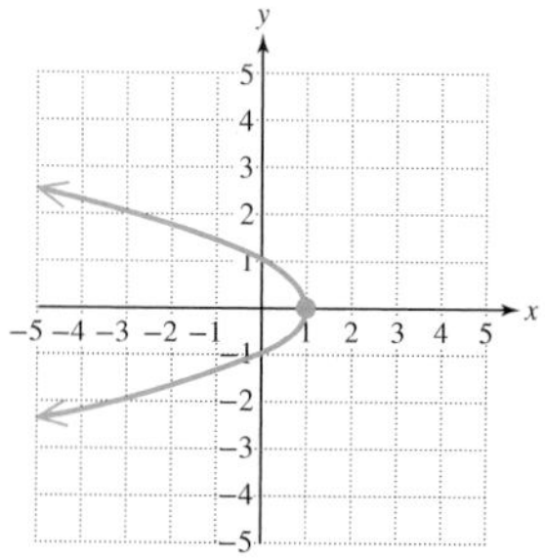

Calculator Connections

Topic: Graphing a Parabola Opening Left or Right

Graphing calculators are designed to graph functions, where y is written as a function of x. The parabola from Example 2 is not a function. It can be graphed, however, as the union of two functions, one representing the top branch and the other representing the bottom branch.

Solving for y in Example 2, we have:

$$x = 4y^2$$

$$y^2 = \frac{x}{4}$$

$$y = \pm\sqrt{\frac{x}{4}}$$

$$y = \pm\frac{\sqrt{x}}{2}$$

Graph these functions as Y_1 and Y_2.

$$Y_1 = \frac{\sqrt{x}}{2} \quad \text{and} \quad Y_2 = -\frac{\sqrt{x}}{2}$$

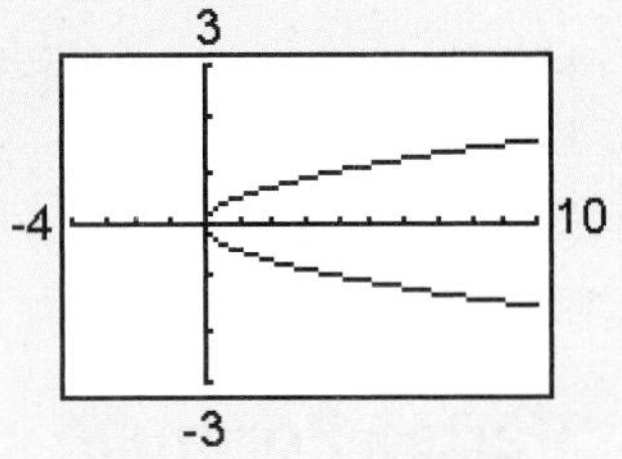

Example 3 Graphing a Parabola by First Completing the Square

Classroom Example: p. 949, Exercise 22

Given the equation of the parabola $x = -y^2 + 8y - 14$,

a. Write the equation in standard form $x = a(y - k)^2 + h$.

b. Identify the vertex and axis of symmetry. Determine if the parabola opens to the right or left.

c. Graph the parabola.

Solution:

a. Complete the square to write the equation in the form $x = a(y - k)^2 + h$.

$x = -y^2 + 8y - 14$

$x = -1(y^2 - 8y) - 14$ — Factor out -1 from the variable terms.

$x = -1(y^2 - 8y + 16 - 16) - 14$ — Add and subtract the quantity $[\frac{1}{2}(-8)]^2 = 16$.

$x = -1(y^2 - 8y + 16) + (-1)(-16) - 14$ — Remove the -16 term from within the parentheses by first applying the distributive property. When -16 is removed from the parentheses, it carries with it the factor of -1 from outside the parentheses.

$x = -1(y - 4)^2 + 16 - 14$

$x = -1(y - 4)^2 + 2$

The equation is in the form $x = a(y - k)^2 + h$, where $a = -1$, $h = 2$, and $k = 4$.

b. The vertex is (2, 4) Because a is negative, the parabola opens to the left. The axis of symmetry is $y = 4$.

c.

x	y
2	4
1	5
1	3
−2	6
−2	2

← Vertex (row 1)

Solve for x. (column x) Choose y. (column y)

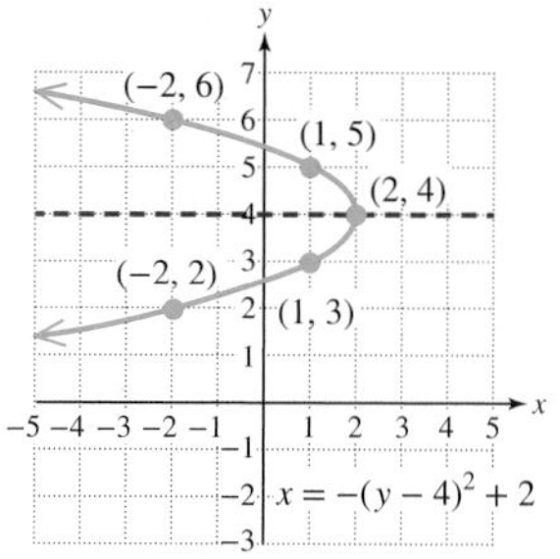

Skill Practice Given the equation of the parabola $x = y^2 + 4y + 7$,

7. Identify the vertex and axis of symmetry.

8. Determine if the parabola opens to the right or to the left.

9. Graph the parabola.

4. Vertex Formula

The vertex formula can also be used to find the vertex of a parabola.

Vertex Formula

For a parabola defined by $y = ax^2 + bx + c$,

- The x-coordinate of the vertex is given by $x = \frac{-b}{2a}$.
- The y-coordinate of the vertex is found by substituting this value for x into the original equation and solving for y.

For a parabola defined by $x = ay^2 + by + c$,

- The y-coordinate of the vertex is given by $y = \frac{-b}{2a}$.
- The x-coordinate of the vertex is found by substituting this value for y into the original equation and solving for x.

Classroom Example: p. 949, Exercise 28

Example 4 Finding the Vertex of a Parabola by Using the Vertex Formula

Find the vertex by using the vertex formula. $x = y^2 + 4y + 5$

Solution:

$x = y^2 + 4y + 5$ The parabola is in the form $x = ay^2 + by + c$.

$a = 1 \quad b = 4 \quad c = 5$ Identify a, b, and c.

The y-coordinate of the vertex is given by $y = \dfrac{-b}{2a} = \dfrac{-(4)}{2(1)} = -2$.

The x-coordinate of the vertex is found by substitution:

$$x = (-2)^2 + 4(-2) + 5 = 1$$

The vertex is $(1, -2)$.

Skill Practice Find the vertex by using the vertex formula.

10. $x = -4y^2 + 12y$

Answers

7. Vertex: $(3, -2)$; Axis of symmetry: $y = -2$

8. Parabola opens right.

9.

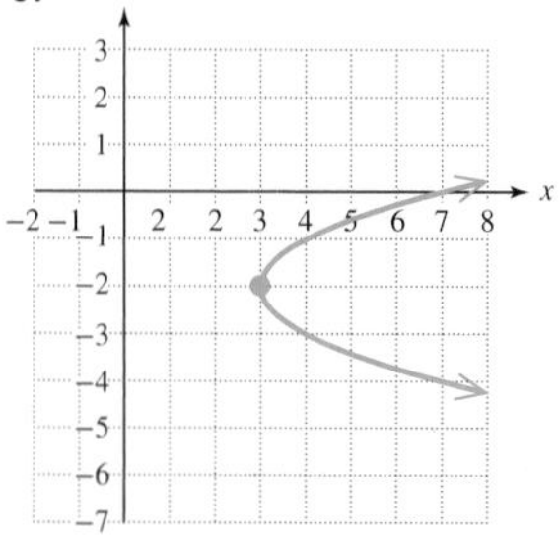

10. Vertex: $\left(9, \frac{3}{2}\right)$

Example 5 **Find the Vertex of a Parabola by Using the Vertex Formula**

Classroom Example: p. 949, Exercise 30

Find the vertex by using the vertex formula. $y = \frac{1}{2}x^2 - 3x + \frac{5}{2}$

Solution:

$y = \frac{1}{2}x^2 - 3x + \frac{5}{2}$ The parabola is in the form $y = ax^2 + bx + c$.

$a = \frac{1}{2} \quad b = -3 \quad c = \frac{5}{2}$ Identify a, b, and c.

The x-coordinate of the vertex is given by $x = \frac{-b}{2a} = \frac{-(-3)}{2\left(\frac{1}{2}\right)} = 3$.

The y-coordinate of the vertex is found by substitution.

$$\begin{aligned} y &= \frac{1}{2}(3)^2 - 3(3) + \frac{5}{2} \\ &= \frac{9}{2} - 9 + \frac{5}{2} \\ &= \frac{14}{2} - 9 \\ &= 7 - 9 \\ &= -2 \end{aligned}$$

The vertex is $(3, -2)$.

Skill Practice Find the vertex by using the vertex formula.

11. $y = \frac{3}{4}x^2 + 3x + 5$

Answer

11. $(-2, 2)$

Section 13.2 Practice Exercises

For additional exercises, see Classroom Activities 13.2A–13.2B in the *Student's Resource Manual* at www.mhhe.com/moh.

Vocabulary and Key Concepts

1. **a.** A circle, a parabola, an ellipse, and a hyperbola are curves that collectively are called __conic__ sections. These types of curves derive their names because each is the intersection of a __plane__ and a double-napped cone.

   b. A __parabola__ is defined by a set of points in a plane that are equidistant from a fixed line (called the __directrix__) and a fixed point (called the __focus__).

   c. Given a parabola defined by $y = a(x - h)^2 + k$ $(a \neq 0)$, the __vertex__ is (h, k) and is the highest or lowest point on the graph. The axis of __symmetry__ is the vertical line through the vertex whose equation is $x = h$.

   d. Given a parabola defined by $x = a(y - k)^2 + h$ $(a \neq 0)$, the axis of symmetry is the horizontal line whose equation is __$y = k$__.

Review Exercises

2. Determine the distance between the points $(1, 1)$ and $(2, -2)$. $\sqrt{10}$

3. Determine the distance from the origin to the point $(4, -3)$. 5

4. Determine the distance between the points $(11, 3)$ and $(5, 3)$. 6

For Exercises 5–6, identify the center and radius of the circle and then graph the circle.

5. $x^2 + (y + 1)^2 = 16$

Center $(0, -1)$; radius: 4

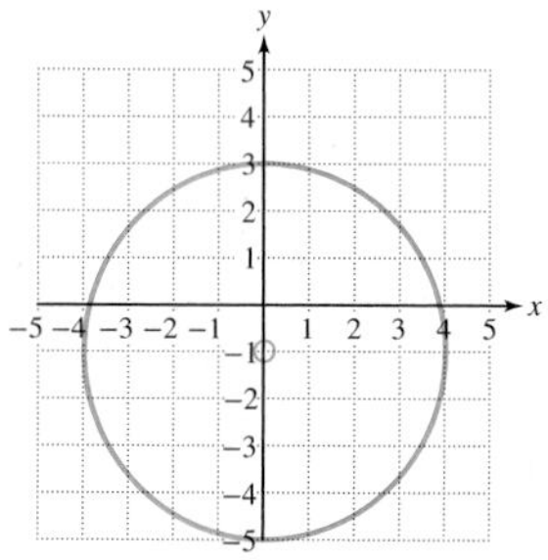

6. $(x - 3)^2 + y^2 = 4$

Center: $(3, 0)$; radius: 2

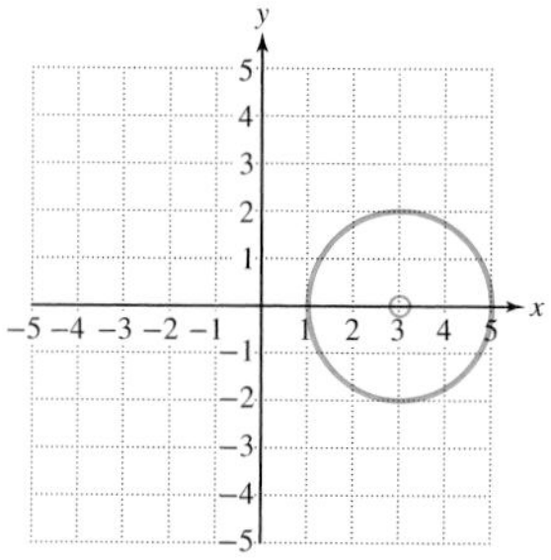

7. Find the midpoint of the line segment between the points $(7, -3)$ and $(4, 5)$.

$\left(\frac{11}{2}, 1\right)$

8. Find the midpoint of the line segment between the points $(-3, 0)$ and $(-1, 9)$.

$\left(-2, \frac{9}{2}\right)$

Concept 2: Parabola—Vertical Axis of Symmetry

For Exercises 9–16, use the equation of the parabola in standard form $y = a(x - h)^2 + k$ to determine the coordinates of the vertex and the equation of the axis of symmetry (complete the square if necessary). Then graph the parabola. **(See Example 1.)**

9. $y = (x + 2)^2 + 1$

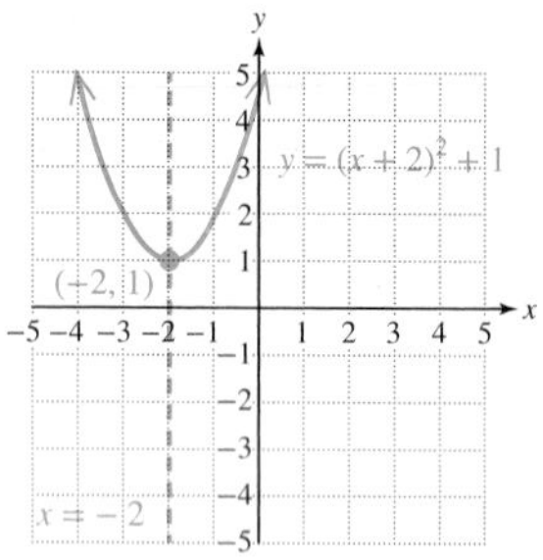

10. $y = (x - 1)^2 + 1$

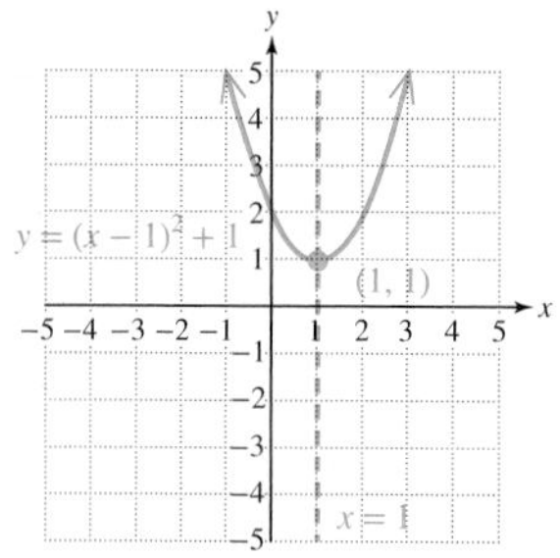

11. $y = x^2 - 4x + 3$

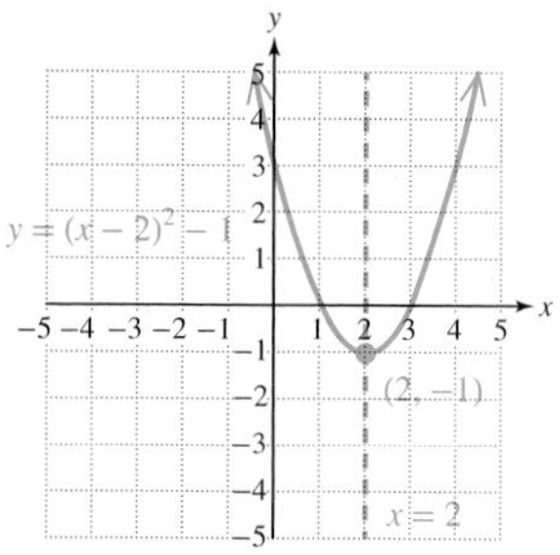

12. $y = x^2 + 6x + 5$

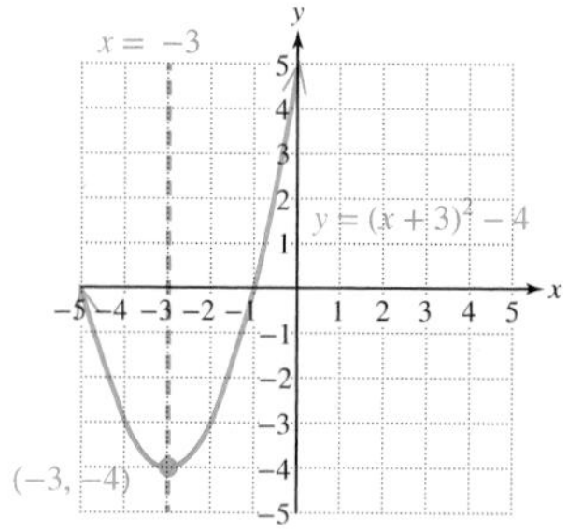

13. $y = -2x^2 + 8x$

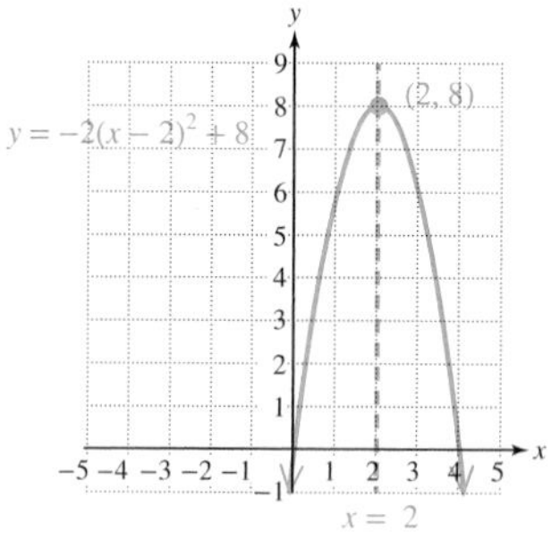

14. $y = -3x^2 - 6x$

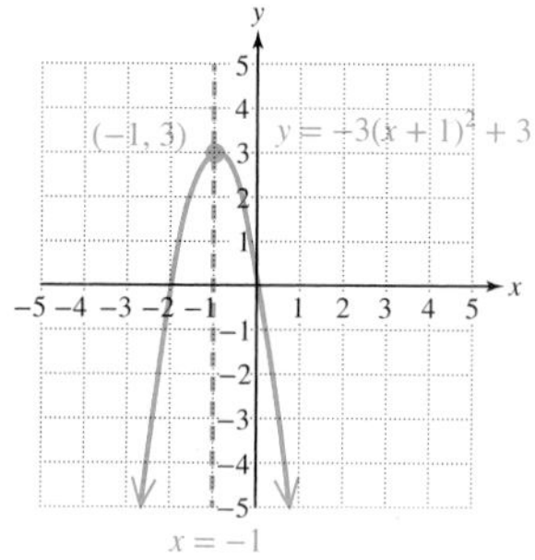

15. $y = -x^2 - 3x + 2$

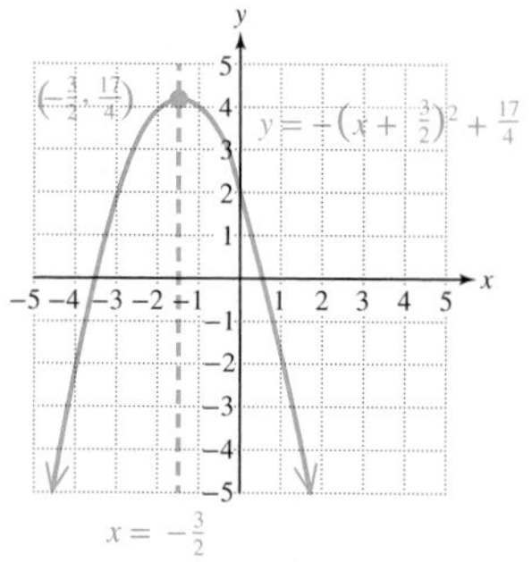

16. $y = -x^2 + x - 4$

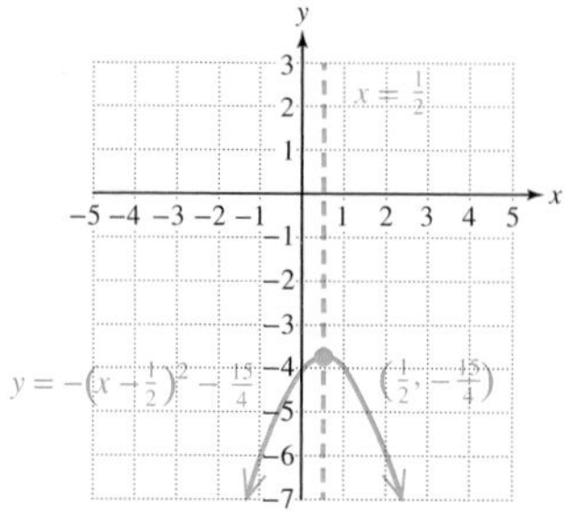

Concept 3: Parabola—Horizontal Axis of Symmetry

For Exercises 17–24, use the equation of the parabola in standard form $x = a(y - k)^2 + h$ to determine the coordinates of the vertex and the axis of symmetry (complete the square if necessary). Then graph the parabola. **(See Examples 2–3.)**

17. $x = y^2 - 3$

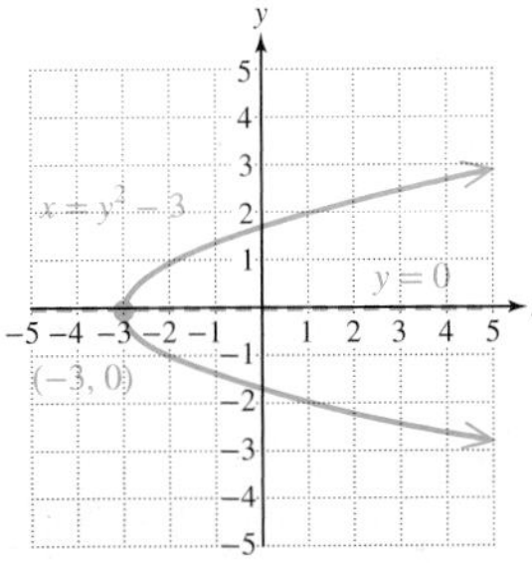

18. $x = y^2 + 1$

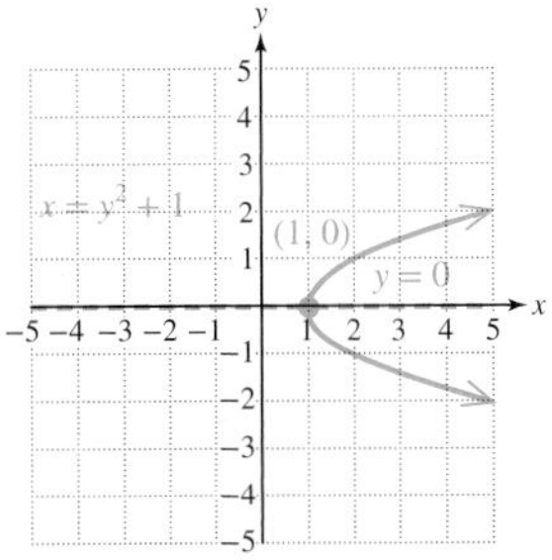

19. $x = -(y - 3)^2 - 3$

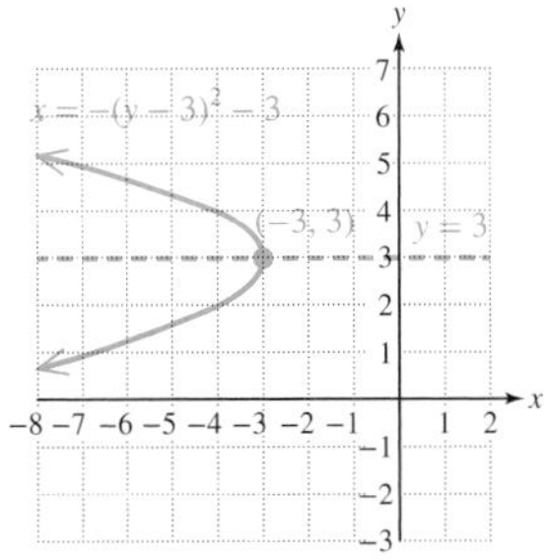

20. $x = -2(y + 2)^2 + 1$

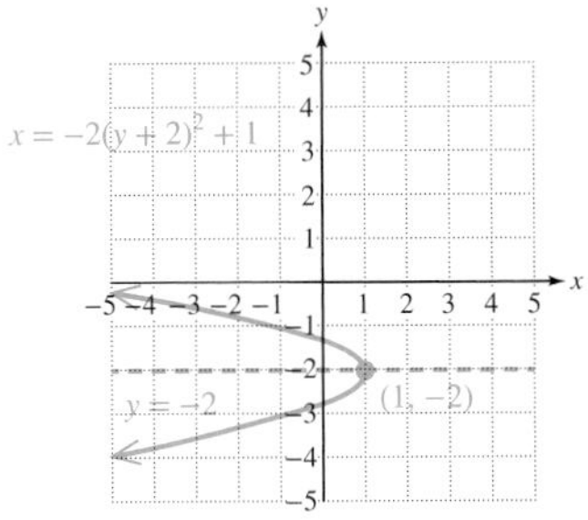

21. $x = -y^2 + 4y - 4$

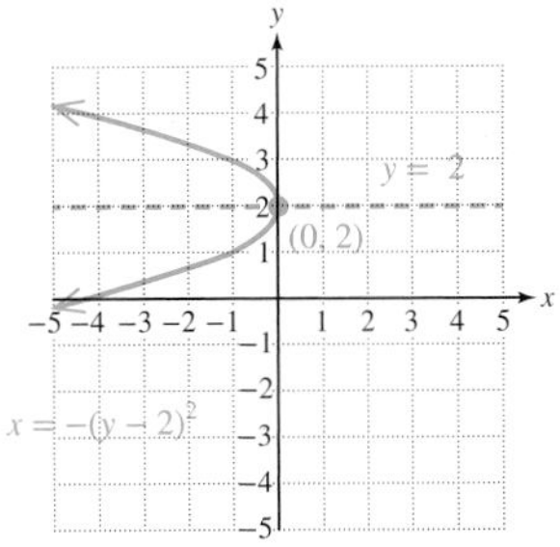

22. $x = -4y^2 - 4y - 2$

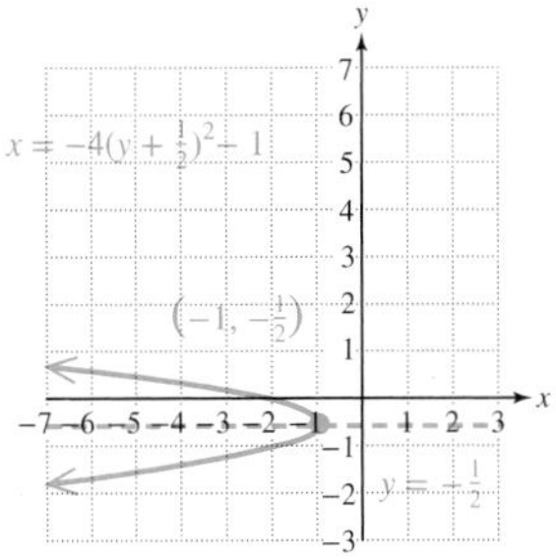

23. $x = y^2 - 2y + 2$

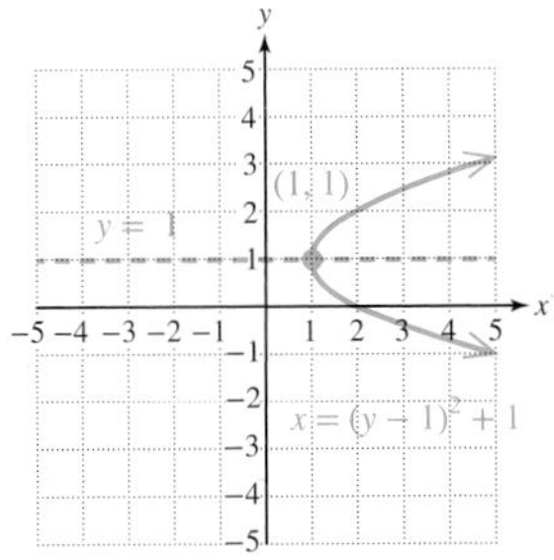

24. $x = y^2 + 4y + 1$

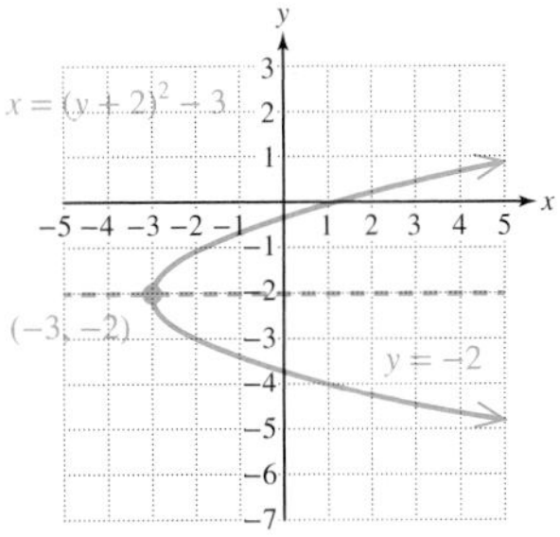

Concept 4: Vertex Formula

For Exercises 25–33, determine the vertex by using the vertex formula. **(See Examples 4–5.)**

25. $y = x^2 - 4x + 3$ $(2, -1)$

26. $y = x^2 + 6x - 2$ $(-3, -11)$

27. $x = y^2 + 2y + 6$ $(5, -1)$

28. $x = y^2 - 8y + 3$ $(-13, 4)$

29. $y = -\frac{1}{4}x^2 + x + \frac{3}{4}$ $\left(2, \frac{7}{4}\right)$

30. $y = -\frac{1}{2}x^2 - x + \frac{1}{2}$ $(-1, 1)$

31. $y = x^2 - 3x + 2$ $\left(\frac{3}{2}, -\frac{1}{4}\right)$

32. $x = -2y^2 + 16y + 1$ $(33, 4)$

33. $x = -3y^2 - 6y + 7$ $(10, -1)$

34. Ricardo has a satellite dish for his television. The cross sections of the satellite dish are parabolic in shape. A cross section through the vertex can be described by the equation

$$d(x) = \frac{2}{25}x^2 - \frac{2}{5}x$$

where $d(x)$ is the depth of the dish (in feet) at a distance of x ft from the edge of the dish. How deep is the satellite dish?
The satellite dish is $\frac{1}{2}$ ft deep.

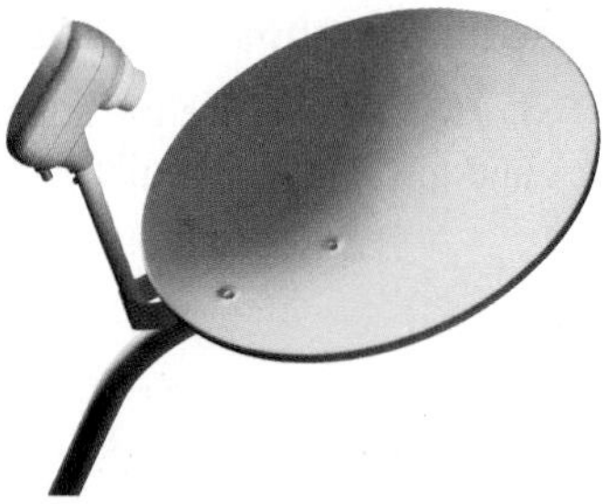
© Photodisc/Getty Images RF

35. Water from an outdoor fountain is projected outward from a jet on the side wall of the fountain. The water follows a parabolic path, and can be modeled by $h(x) = -x^2 + 10x - 3$. In this function, $h(x)$ represents the height of the water, x ft from the jet. Find the maximum height of the water.
The maximum height of the water is 22 ft.

© Royalty Free/Corbis RF

Mixed Exercises

36. Explain how to determine whether a parabola opens upward, downward, left, or right.
For a parabola whose equation is written in the form $y = a(x - h)^2 + k$, if $a > 0$, the parabola opens upward; if $a < 0$, the parabola opens downward. For a parabola written in the form $x = a(y - k)^2 + h$, if $a > 0$, the parabola opens right; if $a < 0$, the parabola opens left.

37. Explain how to determine whether a parabola has a vertical or horizontal axis of symmetry.
A parabola whose equation is in the form $y = a(x - h)^2 + k$ has a vertical axis of symmetry. A parabola whose equation is in the form $x = a(y - k)^2 + h$ has a horizontal axis of symmetry.

For Exercises 38–49, use the equation of the parabola first to determine whether the axis of symmetry is vertical or horizontal. Then determine if the parabola opens upward, downward, left, or right.

38. $y = (x - 2)^2 + 3$ Vertical axis of symmetry; opens upward

39. $y = (x - 4)^2 + 2$ Vertical axis of symmetry; opens upward

40. $y = -2(x + 1)^2 - 4$ Vertical axis of symmetry; opens downward

41. $y = -3(x + 2)^2 - 1$ Vertical axis of symmetry; opens downward

42. $x = y^2 + 4$ Horizontal axis of symmetry; opens right

43. $x = y^2 - 2$ Horizontal axis of symmetry; opens right

44. $x = -(y + 3)^2 + 2$ Horizontal axis of symmetry; opens left

45. $x = -2(y - 1)^2 - 3$ Horizontal axis of symmetry; opens left

46. $y = -2x^2 - 5$ Vertical axis of symmetry; opens downward

47. $y = -x^2 + 3$ Vertical axis of symmetry; opens downward

48. $x = 2y^2 + 3y - 2$ Horizontal axis of symmetry; opens right

49. $x = y^2 - 5y + 1$ Horizontal axis of symmetry; opens right

Section 13.3 The Ellipse and Hyperbola

Concepts

1. Standard Form of an Equation of an Ellipse
2. Standard Form of an Equation of a Hyperbola

1. Standard Form of an Equation of an Ellipse

In this section, we will study the two remaining conic sections: the ellipse and the hyperbola. An **ellipse** is the set of all points (x, y) such that the sum of the distances between (x, y) and two distinct points is a constant. The fixed points are called the foci (plural of *focus*) of the ellipse.

To visualize an ellipse, consider the following application. Suppose Sonya wants to cut an elliptical rug from a rectangular rug to avoid a stain made by the family dog. She places two tacks along the center horizontal line. Then she ties the ends of a slack piece of rope to each tack. With the rope pulled tight, she traces out a curve. This curve is an ellipse, and the tacks are located at the foci of the ellipse (Figure 13-14).

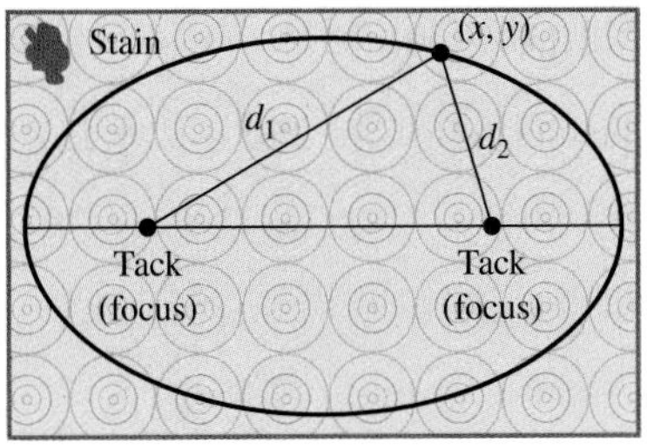

Figure 13-14

Instructor Note: Use the graph of an ellipse to explain why an ellipse is not a function.

We will first graph ellipses that are centered at the origin.

> **Standard Form of an Equation of an Ellipse Centered at the Origin**
>
> An ellipse with the center at the origin has the equation $\dfrac{x^2}{a^2} + \dfrac{y^2}{b^2} = 1$, where a and b are positive real numbers. In the standard form of the equation, the right side must equal 1.

To graph an ellipse centered at the origin, find the x- and y-intercepts.

To find the x-intercepts, let $y = 0$.

$$\frac{x^2}{a^2} + \frac{0}{b^2} = 1$$

$$\frac{x^2}{a^2} = 1$$

$$x^2 = a^2$$

$$x = \pm\sqrt{a^2}$$

$$x = \pm a$$

The x-intercepts are $(a, 0)$ and $(-a, 0)$. See Figure 13-15.

To find the y-intercepts, let $x = 0$.

$$\frac{0}{a^2} + \frac{y^2}{b^2} = 1$$

$$\frac{y^2}{b^2} = 1$$

$$y^2 = b^2$$

$$y = \pm\sqrt{b^2}$$

$$y = \pm b$$

The y-intercepts are $(0, b)$ and $(0, -b)$. See Figure 13-15.

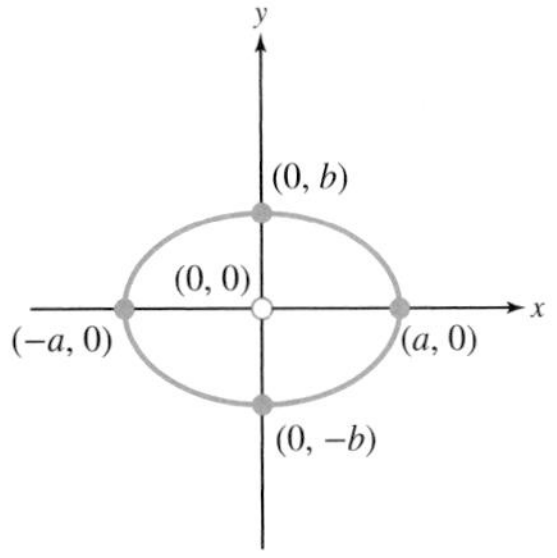

Figure 13-15

Example 1 **Graphing an Ellipse**

Graph the ellipse given by the equation. $\dfrac{x^2}{9} + \dfrac{y^2}{4} = 1$

Solution:

The equation can be written as $\dfrac{x^2}{3^2} + \dfrac{y^2}{2^2} = 1$.

The equation is in standard form $\dfrac{x^2}{a^2} + \dfrac{y^2}{b^2} = 1$, therefore, $a = 3$ and $b = 2$.

Graph the intercepts $(3, 0)$, $(-3, 0)$, $(0, 2)$, $(0, -2)$ and sketch the ellipse.

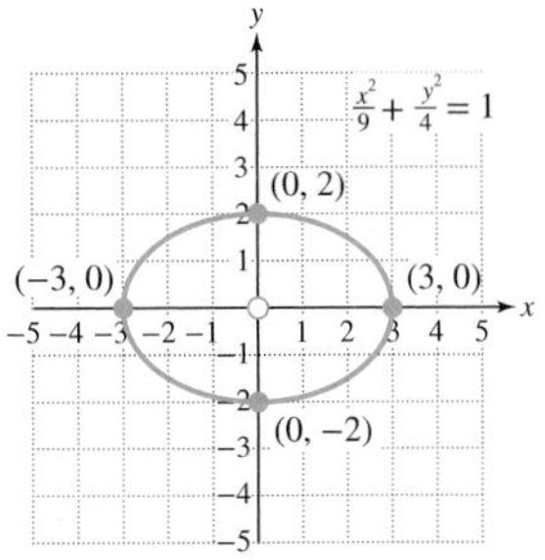

Classroom Example: p. 956, Exercise 12

Skill Practice

1. Graph the ellipse given by the equation. $\dfrac{x^2}{4} + \dfrac{y^2}{16} = 1$

Answer

1.

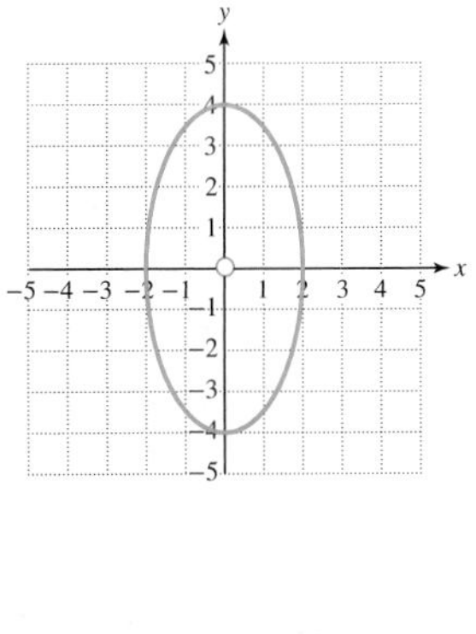

Classroom Example: p. 956, Exercise 14

Example 2 Graphing an Ellipse

Graph the ellipse given by the equation. $25x^2 + y^2 = 25$

Solution:

$25x^2 + y^2 = 25$ Divide both sides by 25.

$$\frac{25x^2}{25} + \frac{y^2}{25} = \frac{25}{25}$$

$$x^2 + \frac{y^2}{25} = 1$$

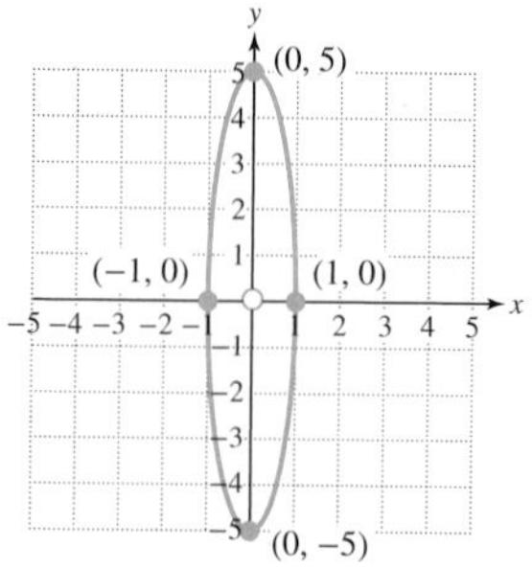

The equation can then be written as $\frac{x^2}{1^2} + \frac{y^2}{5^2} = 1$.

The equation is in standard form $\frac{x^2}{a^2} + \frac{y^2}{b^2} = 1$, therefore, $a = 1$ and $b = 5$.

Graph the intercepts (1, 0), (−1, 0), (0, 5), and (0, −5) and sketch the ellipse.

Skill Practice

2. Graph the ellipse given by the equation. $x^2 + 9y^2 = 9$

A circle is a special case of an ellipse where $a = b$. Therefore, it is not surprising that we graph an ellipse centered at the point (h, k) in much the same way we graph a circle.

Classroom Example: p. 956, Exercise 18

Example 3 Graphing an Ellipse Whose Center Is Not at the Origin

Graph the ellipse given by the equation. $\frac{(x-1)^2}{16} + \frac{(y+3)^2}{4} = 1$

Solution:

Just as we would find the center of a circle, we see that the center of the ellipse is (1, −3). Now we can use the values of a and b to help us plot four strategic points to define the curve.

The equation can be written as

$$\frac{(x-1)^2}{(4)^2} + \frac{(y+3)^2}{(2)^2} = 1$$

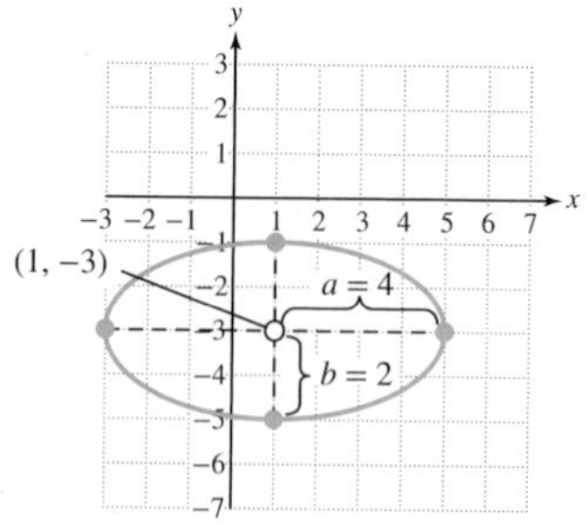

From this, we have $a = 4$ and $b = 2$. To sketch the curve, locate the center at (1, −3). Then move $a = 4$ units to the left and right of the center and plot two points. Similarly, move $b = 2$ units up and down from the center and plot two points.

Skill Practice

3. Graph the ellipse. $\frac{(x+1)^2}{4} + \frac{(y-4)^2}{9} = 1$

Answers

2.

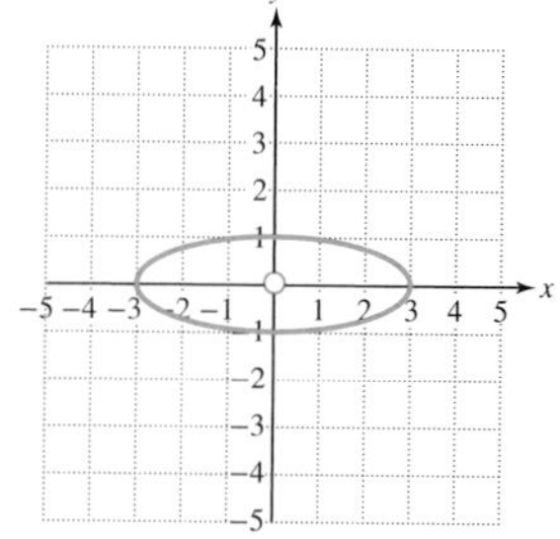

3.

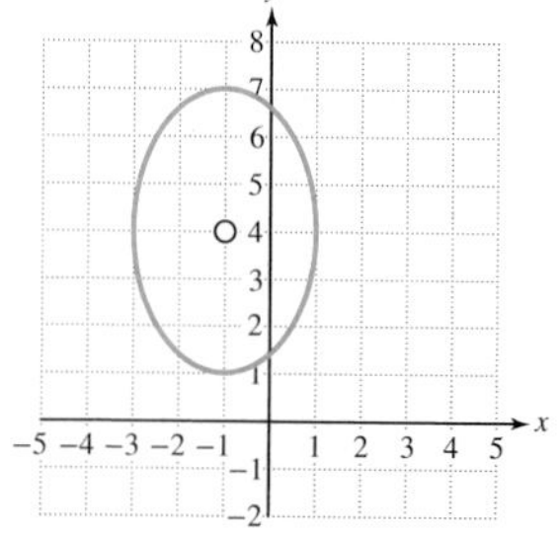

2. Standard Form of an Equation of a Hyperbola

A **hyperbola** is the set of all points (x, y) such that the absolute value of the *difference* of the distances between (x, y) and two distinct points is a constant. The fixed points are called the foci of the hyperbola. The graph of a hyperbola has two parts, called branches. A hyperbola has two vertices that lie on an axis of symmetry called the **transverse axis**. For the hyperbolas studied here, the transverse axis is either horizontal or vertical.

Instructor Note: Students may think that a hyperbola is two parabolas. Emphasize that they are not the same curves. The curvature on the branches of a hyperbola is different than that of a parabola.

Instructor Note: Ask students if either form of hyperbola would pass the vertical line test.

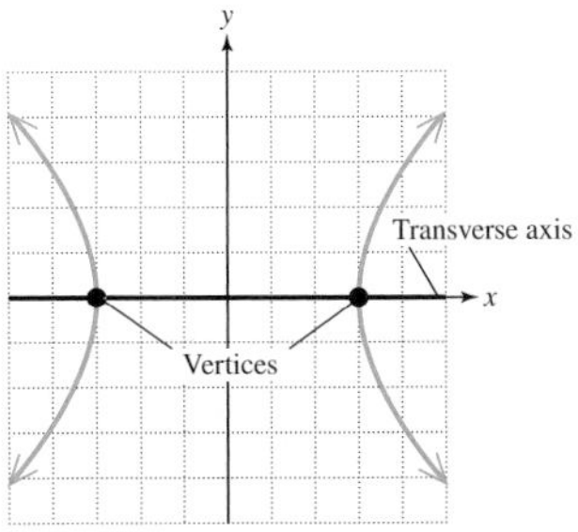

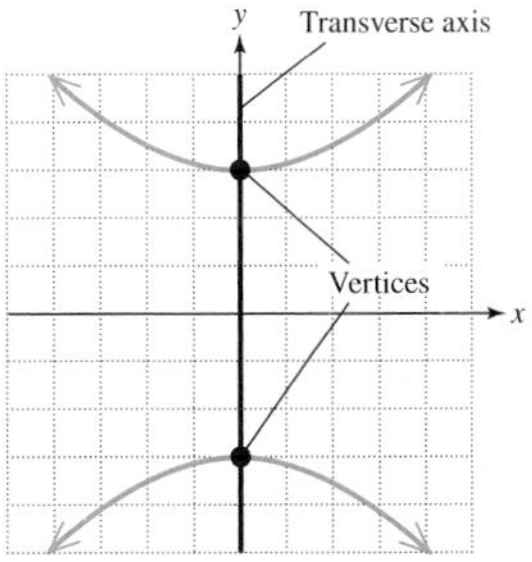

Standard Forms of an Equation of a Hyperbola with Center at the Origin

Let a and b represent positive real numbers.

Horizontal transverse axis:
The standard form of an equation of a hyperbola with a *horizontal transverse axis* and center at the origin is given by $\dfrac{x^2}{a^2} - \dfrac{y^2}{b^2} = 1$.

Note: The x term is positive. The branches of the hyperbola open left and right.

Vertical transverse axis:
The standard form of an equation of a hyperbola with a *vertical transverse axis* and center at the origin is given by $\dfrac{y^2}{b^2} - \dfrac{x^2}{a^2} = 1$.

Note: The y term is positive. The branches of the hyperbola open up and down.

In the standard forms of an equation of a hyperbola, the right side must equal 1.

To graph a hyperbola centered at the origin, first construct a reference rectangle. Draw this rectangle by using the points (a, b), $(-a, b)$, $(a, -b)$, and $(-a, -b)$. Asymptotes lie on the diagonals of the rectangle. The branches of the hyperbola are drawn to approach the asymptotes.

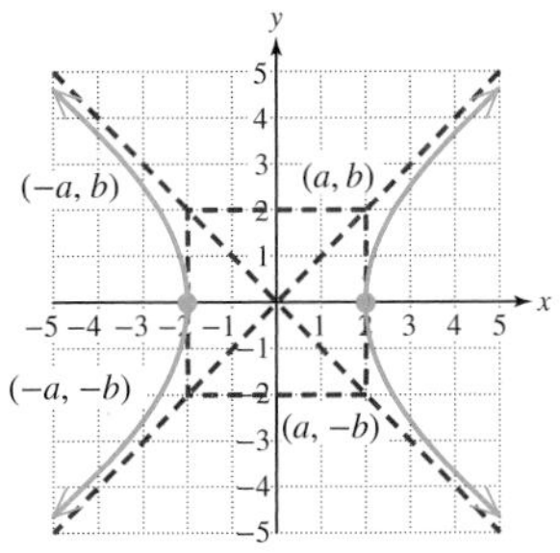

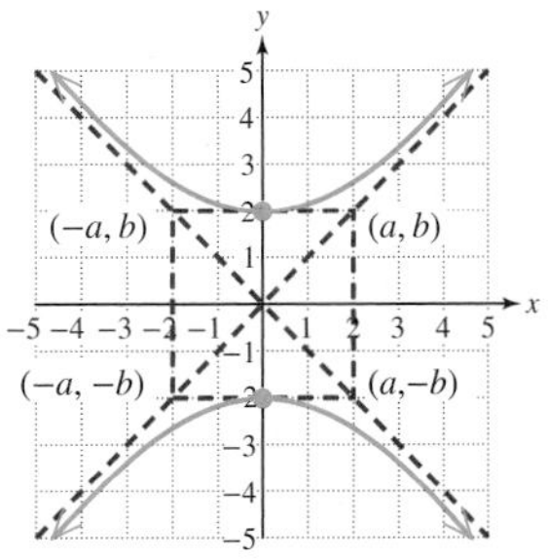

Classroom Example: p. 957, Exercise 34

Example 4 Graphing a Hyperbola

Graph the hyperbola given by the equation. $\dfrac{x^2}{36} - \dfrac{y^2}{9} = 1$

a. Determine whether the transverse axis is horizontal or vertical.

b. Draw the reference rectangle and asymptotes.

c. Graph the hyperbola and label the vertices.

Solution:

a. Since the x-term is positive, the transverse axis is horizontal.

b. The equation can be written $\dfrac{x^2}{6^2} - \dfrac{y^2}{3^2} = 1$; therefore, $a = 6$ and $b = 3$. Graph the reference rectangle from the points $(6, 3)$, $(6, -3)$, $(-6, 3)$, $(-6, -3)$.

c. The vertices are $(-6, 0)$ and $(6, 0)$.

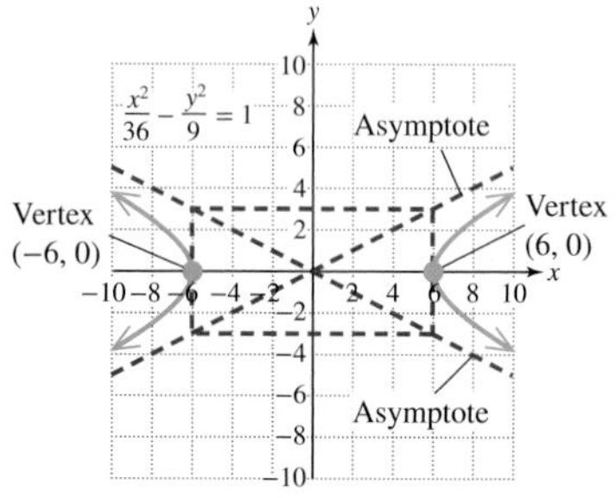

Skill Practice

4. Graph the hyperbola. $x^2 - \dfrac{y^2}{9} = 1$

Classroom Example: p. 958, Exercise 40

Example 5 Graphing a Hyperbola

Graph the hyperbola given by the equation. $y^2 - 4x^2 - 16 = 0$

a. Write the equation in standard form to determine whether the transverse axis is horizontal or vertical.

b. Draw the reference rectangle and asymptotes.

c. Graph the hyperbola and label the vertices.

Solution:

a. $y^2 - 4x^2 - 16 = 0$

$y^2 - 4x^2 = 16$ Isolate the constant term on the right.

$\dfrac{y^2}{16} - \dfrac{4x^2}{16} = \dfrac{16}{16}$ Divide by 16 to make the constant term 1.

$\dfrac{y^2}{16} - \dfrac{x^2}{4} = 1$

Since the y term is positive, the transverse axis is vertical.

b. The equation can be written $\dfrac{y^2}{4^2} - \dfrac{x^2}{2^2} = 1$; therefore, $a = 2$ and $b = 4$. Graph the reference rectangle from the points $(2, 4)$, $(2, -4)$, $(-2, 4)$, $(-2, -4)$.

c. The vertices are $(0, 4)$ and $(0, -4)$.

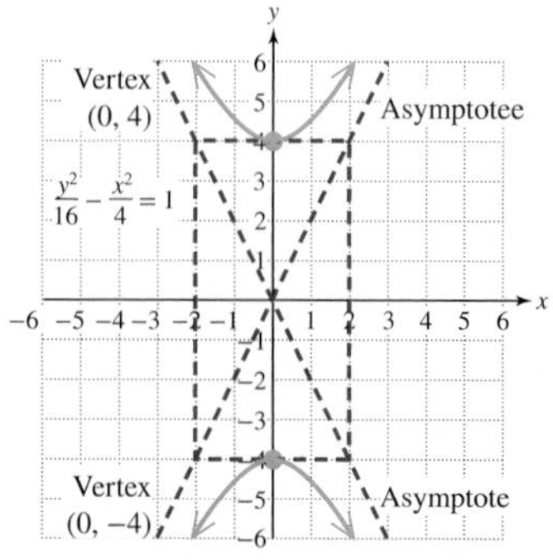

Skill Practice

5. Graph the hyperbola. $9y^2 - 4x^2 = 36$

Answers

4.

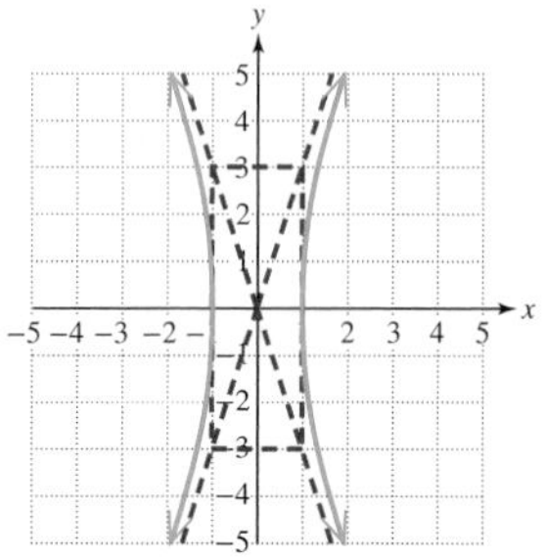

5.

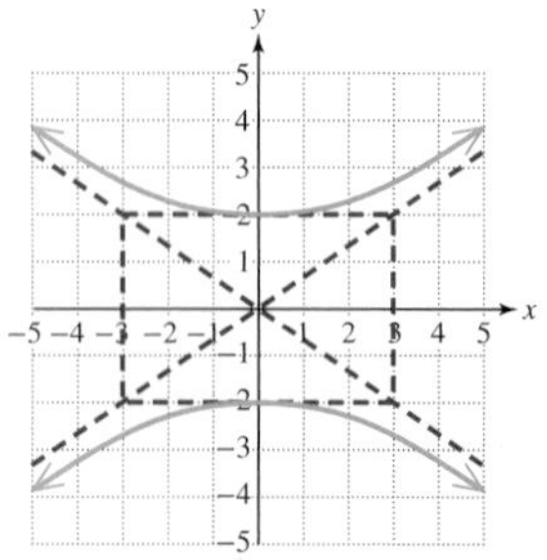

The following summarizes the steps for graphing ellipses and hyperbolas.

Graphing an Ellipse with Center at the Origin

1. Write the equation in standard form:
$$\frac{x^2}{a^2} + \frac{y^2}{b^2} = 1$$
2. Plot the intercepts.
x-intercepts: $(a, 0)$ and $(-a, 0)$
y-intercepts: $(0, b)$ and $(0, -b)$
3. Sketch the ellipse through the intercepts.

Graphing a Hyperbola with Center at the Origin

1. Write the equation in standard form:
   - Horizontal transverse axis:
   $$\frac{x^2}{a^2} - \frac{y^2}{b^2} = 1$$ Branches open left and right
   - Vertical transverse axis:
   $$\frac{y^2}{b^2} - \frac{x^2}{a^2} = 1$$ Branches open up and down
2. Draw the reference rectangle through the points (a, b), $(a, -b)$, $(-a, b)$, and $(-a, -b)$.
3. Draw the asymptotes.
4. Plot the vertices and sketch the hyperbola.

Section 13.3 Practice Exercises

For additional exercises, see Classroom Activities 13.3A–13.3D in the *Student's Resource Manual* at www.mhhe.com/moh.

Vocabulary and Key Concepts

1. **a.** A(n) ___ellipse___ is the set of all points (x, y) such that the sum of the distances between (x, y) and two distinct points (called ___foci___) is constant.

   b. The standard form of an equation of an ___ellipse___ with center at the origin is $\frac{x^2}{a^2} + \frac{y^2}{b^2} = 1$.

   c. A(n) ___hyperbola___ is the set of all points (x, y) such that the absolute value of the difference in distances between (x, y) and two distinct points (called ___foci___) is a constant.

   d. A hyperbola has two vertices that lie on an axis of symmetry called the ___transverse___ axis.

   e. The standard form of an equation of a hyperbola with a *horizontal* transverse axis and center at (0, 0), is given by ________. $\frac{x^2}{a^2} - \frac{y^2}{b^2} = 1$

   f. The standard form of an equation of a hyperbola with a *vertical* transverse axis and center at (0, 0), is given by ________. $\frac{y^2}{b^2} - \frac{x^2}{a^2} = 1$

Review Exercises

2. Write the standard form of a circle with center at (h, k) and radius, r. $(x - h)^2 + (y - k)^2 = r^2$

For Exercises 3–4, identify the center and radius of the circle.

3. $x^2 + y^2 - 16x + 12y = 0$ Center: (8, −6); radius: 10

4. $x^2 + y^2 + 4x + 4y - 1 = 0$ Center: (−2, −2); radius: 3

For Exercises 5–6, identify the vertex and the axis of symmetry.

5. $y = 3(x + 3)^2 - 1$ Vertex: (−3, −1); $x = -3$

6. $x = -\frac{1}{4}(y - 1)^2 - 6$ Vertex: (−6, 1); $y = 1$

7. Write an equation for a circle whose center has coordinates $\left(\frac{1}{2}, \frac{5}{2}\right)$ with radius equal to $\frac{1}{2}$. $\left(x - \frac{1}{2}\right)^2 + \left(y - \frac{5}{2}\right)^2 = \frac{1}{4}$

8. Write an equation for the circle centered at the origin and with radius equal to $\frac{1}{8}$. $x^2 + y^2 = \frac{1}{64}$

Concept 1: Standard Form of an Equation of an Ellipse

For Exercises 9–16, find the x- and y-intercepts and graph the ellipse. **(See Examples 1–2.)**

9. $\frac{x^2}{4} + \frac{y^2}{9} = 1$

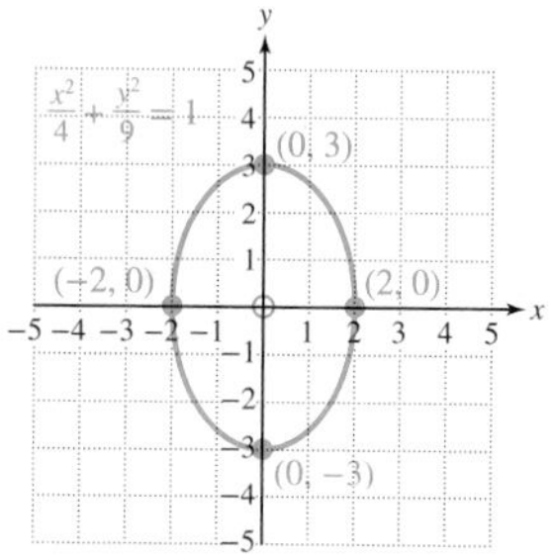

10. $\frac{x^2}{16} + \frac{y^2}{25} = 1$

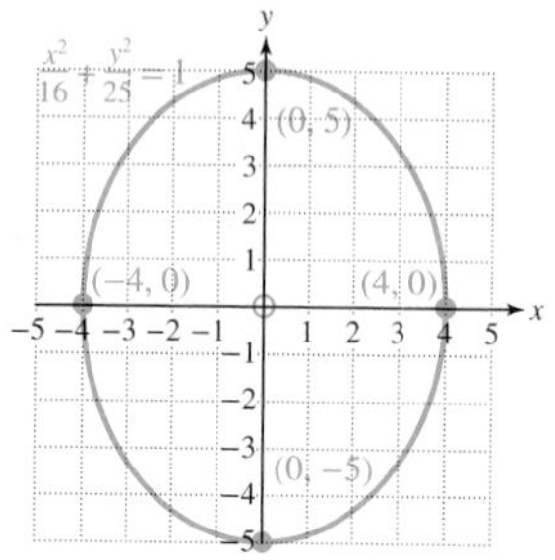

11. $\frac{x^2}{16} + \frac{y^2}{9} = 1$

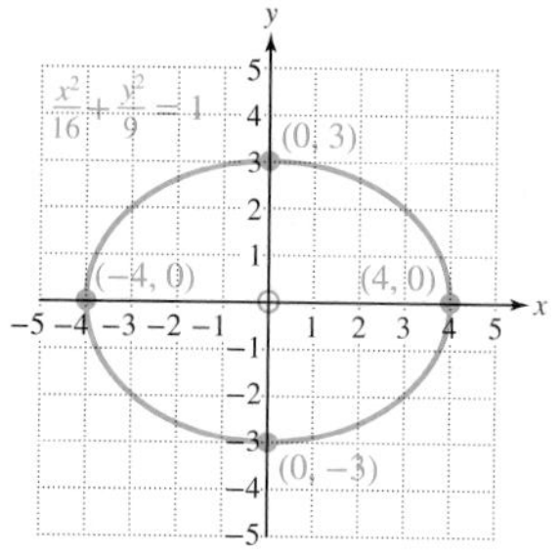

12. $\frac{x^2}{36} + \frac{y^2}{4} = 1$

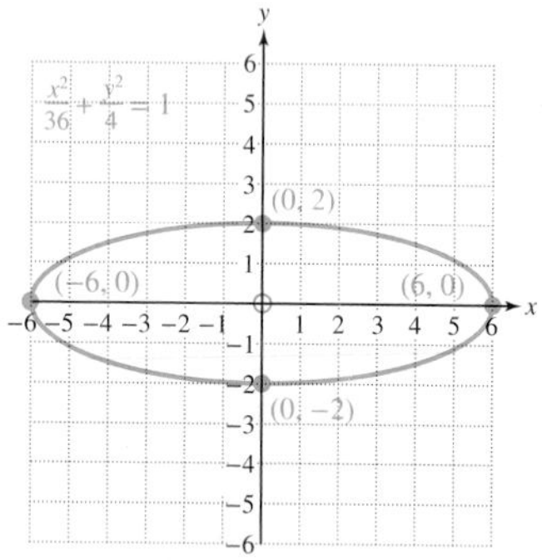

13. $4x^2 + y^2 = 4$

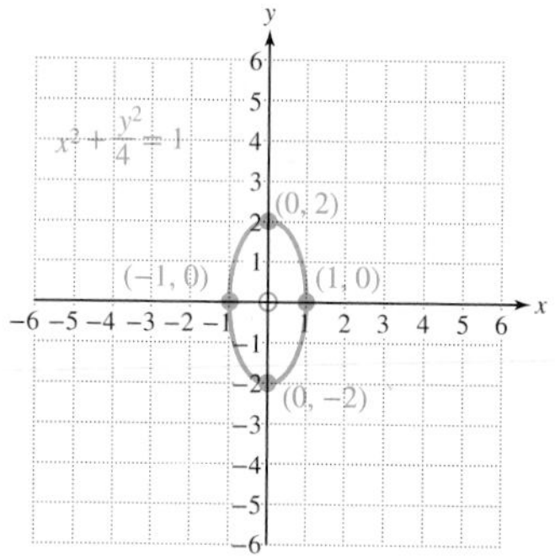

14. $9x^2 + y^2 = 36$

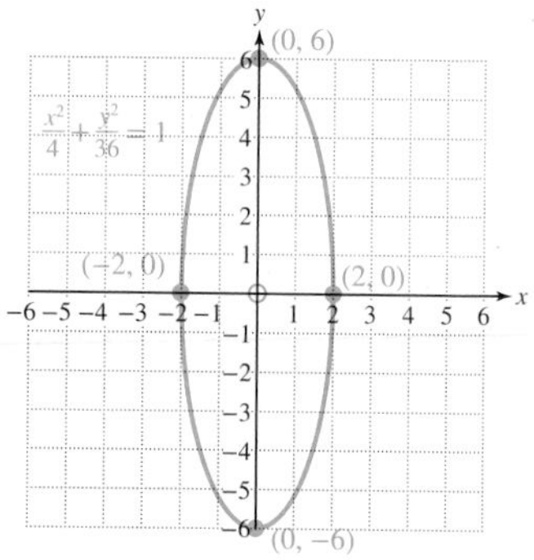

15. $x^2 + 25y^2 - 25 = 0$

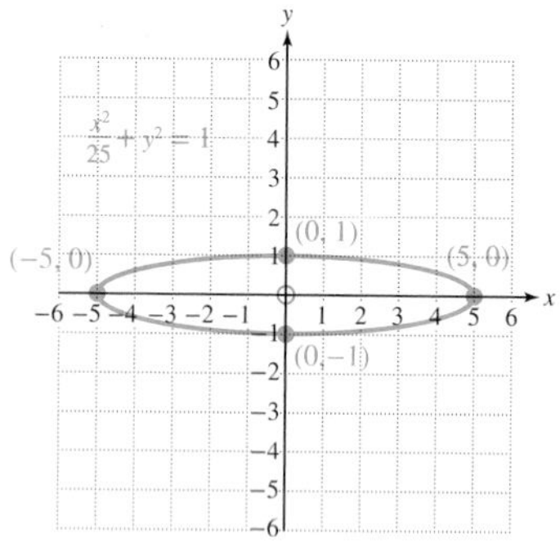

16. $4x^2 + 9y^2 = 144$

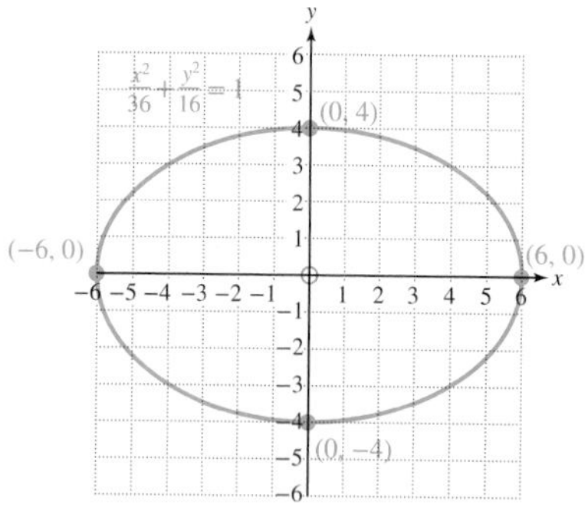

For Exercises 17–24, identify the center (h, k) of the ellipse. Then graph the ellipse. **(See Example 3.)**

17. $\frac{(x-4)^2}{4} + \frac{(y-5)^2}{9} = 1$

Center: (4, 5)

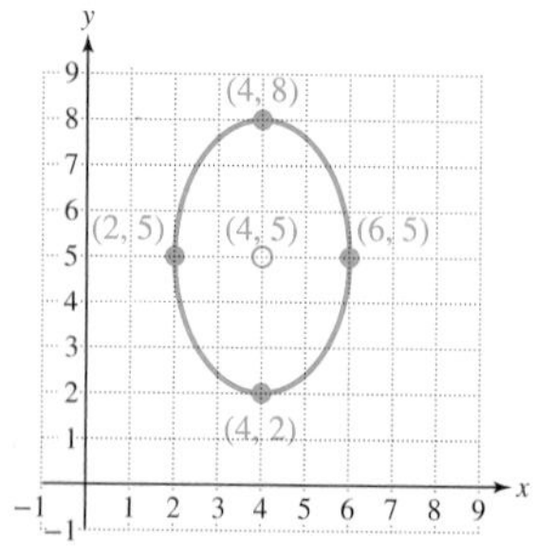

18. $\frac{(x+2)^2}{9} + \frac{(y-1)^2}{16} = 1$

Center: (−2, 1)

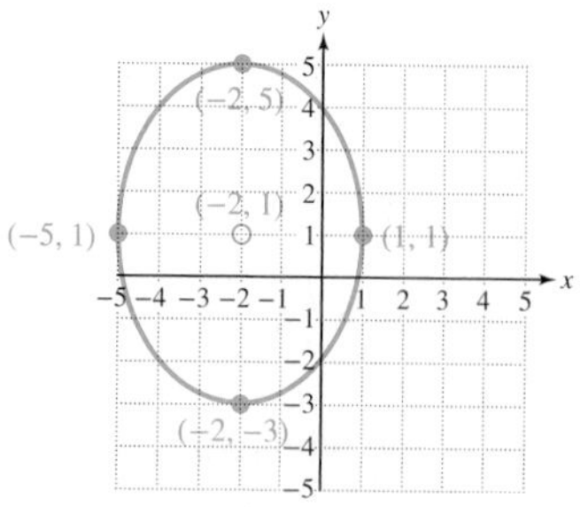

19. $\frac{(x+1)^2}{25} + \frac{(y-2)^2}{9} = 1$

Center: (−1, 2)

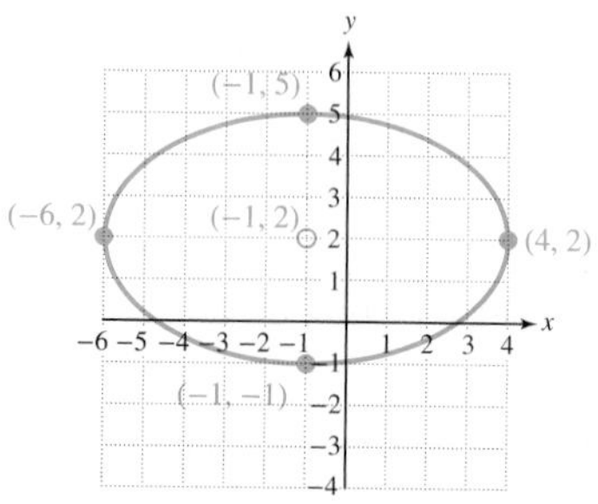

20. $\dfrac{(x-4)^2}{25} + \dfrac{(y+1)^2}{16} = 1$

Center: (4, −1)

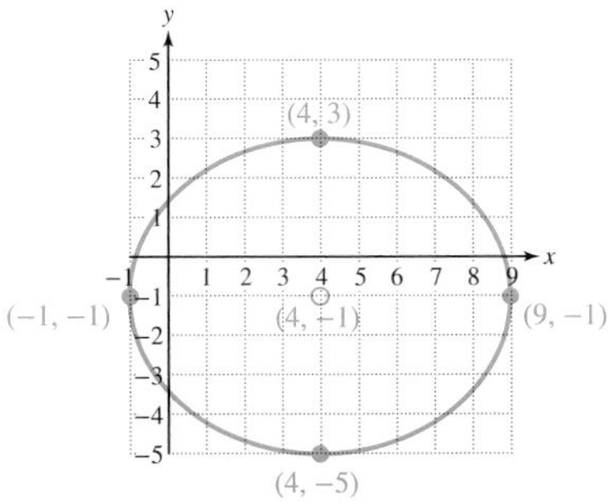

21. $\dfrac{(x-2)^2}{9} + (y+3)^2 = 1$

Center: (2, −3)

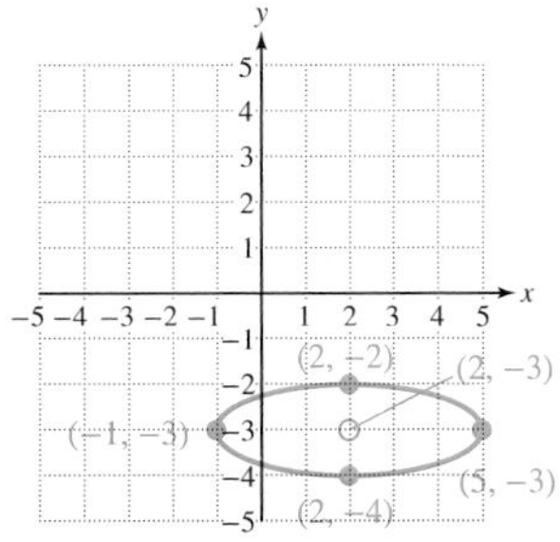

22. $(x-5)^2 + \dfrac{(y-3)^2}{4} = 1$

Center: (5, 3)

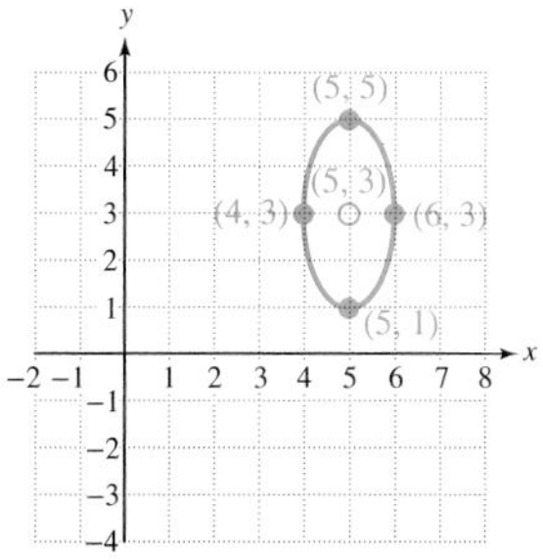

23. $\dfrac{x^2}{36} + \dfrac{(y-1)^2}{25} = 1$

Center: (0, 1)

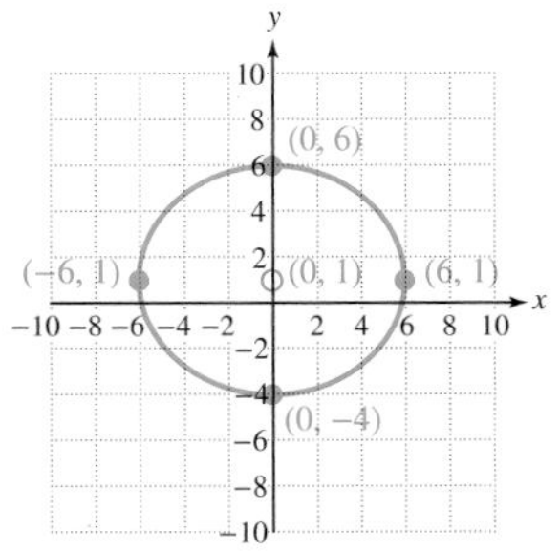

24. $\dfrac{(x+5)^2}{4} + \dfrac{y^2}{16} = 1$ Center: (−5, 0)

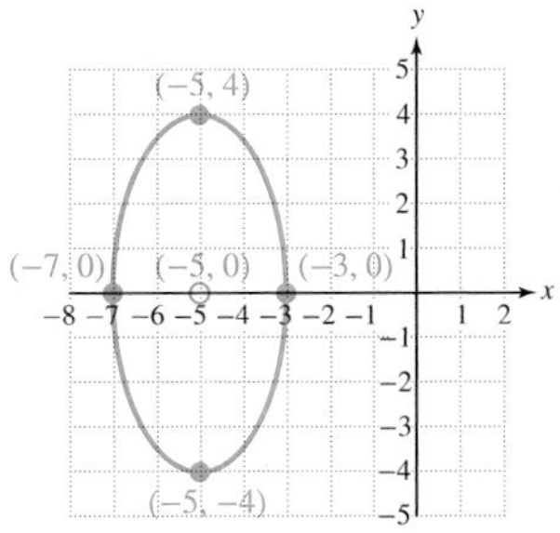

Concept 2: Standard Form of an Equation of a Hyperbola

For Exercises 25–32, determine whether the transverse axis is horizontal or vertical.

25. $\dfrac{y^2}{6} - \dfrac{x^2}{18} = 1$

Vertical

26. $\dfrac{y^2}{10} - \dfrac{x^2}{4} = 1$

Vertical

27. $\dfrac{x^2}{20} - \dfrac{y^2}{15} = 1$

Horizontal

28. $\dfrac{x^2}{12} - \dfrac{y^2}{9} = 1$

Horizontal

29. $x^2 - y^2 = 12$

Horizontal

30. $x^2 - y^2 = 15$

Horizontal

31. $x^2 - 3y^2 = -9$

Vertical

32. $2x^2 - y^2 = -10$

Vertical

For Exercises 33–40, use the equation in standard form to graph the hyperbola. Label the vertices of the hyperbola.
(See Examples 4–5.)

33. $\dfrac{x^2}{25} - \dfrac{y^2}{16} = 1$

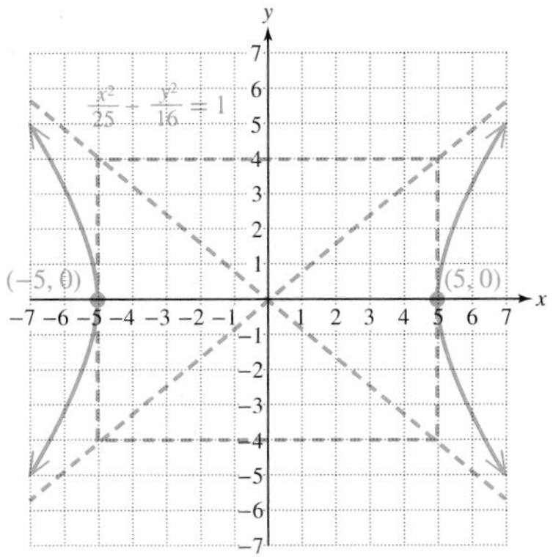

34. $\dfrac{x^2}{9} - \dfrac{y^2}{36} = 1$

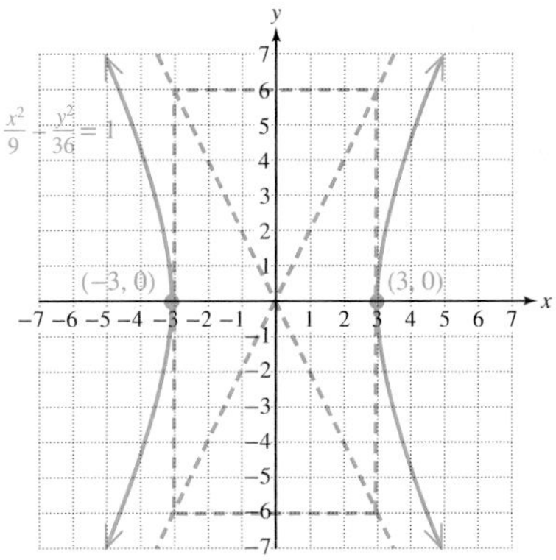

35. $\dfrac{y^2}{4} - \dfrac{x^2}{4} = 1$

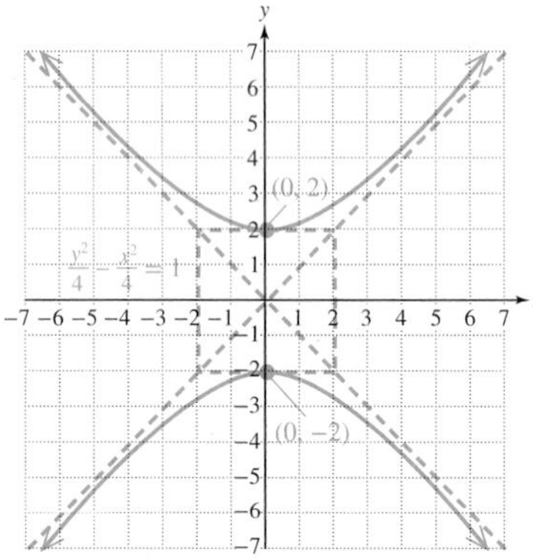

36. $\dfrac{y^2}{9} - \dfrac{x^2}{9} = 1$

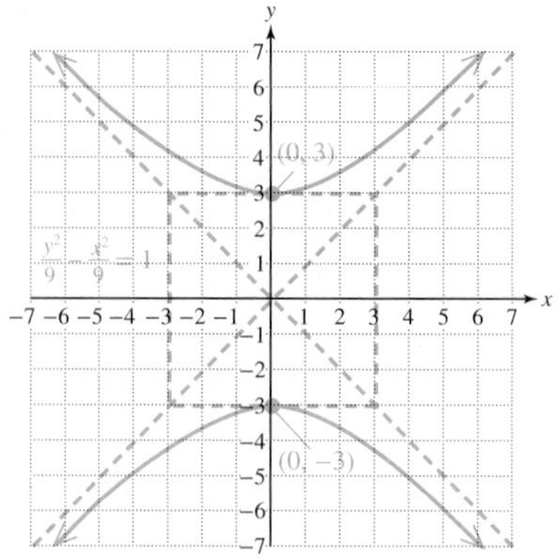

37. $36x^2 - y^2 = 36$

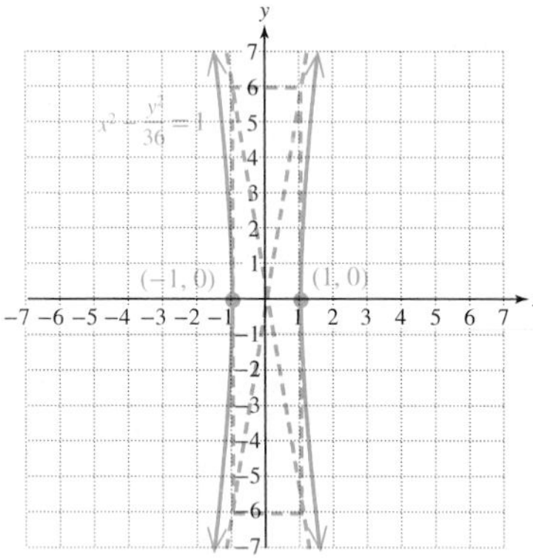

38. $x^2 - 25y^2 = 25$

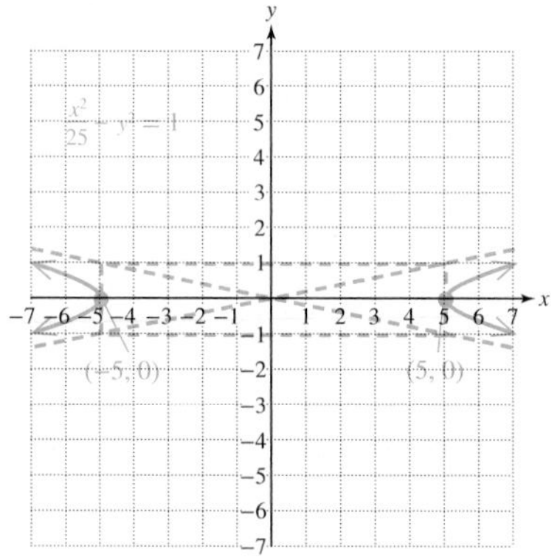

39. $y^2 - 4x^2 - 16 = 0$

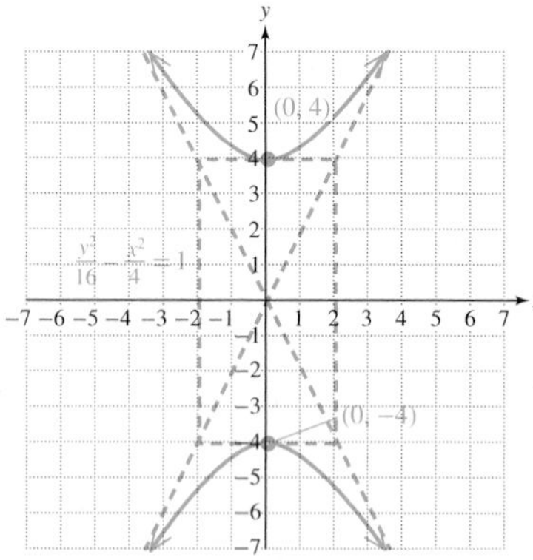

40. $y^2 - 4x^2 - 36 = 0$

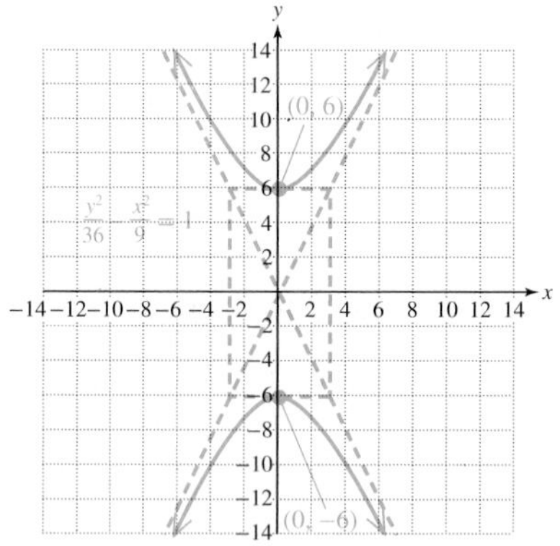

Mixed Exercises

For Exercises 41–52, determine if the equation represents an ellipse or a hyperbola.

41. $\dfrac{x^2}{6} - \dfrac{y^2}{10} = 1$
Hyperbola

42. $\dfrac{x^2}{14} + \dfrac{y^2}{2} = 1$
Ellipse

43. $\dfrac{y^2}{4} + \dfrac{x^2}{16} = 1$
Ellipse

44. $\dfrac{x^2}{5} + \dfrac{y^2}{10} = 1$
Ellipse

45. $4x^2 + y^2 = 16$
Ellipse

46. $-3x^2 - 4y^2 = -36$
Ellipse

47. $-y^2 + 2x^2 = -10$
Hyperbola

48. $x^2 - y^2 = -1$
Hyperbola

49. $5x^2 + y^2 - 10 = 0$
Ellipse

50. $5x^2 - 3y^2 = 15$
Hyperbola

51. $y^2 - 6x^2 = 6$
Hyperbola

52. $3x^2 + 5y^2 = 15$
Ellipse

Expanding Your Skills

53. An arch for a tunnel is in the shape of a semiellipse. The distance between vertices is 120 ft, and the height to the top of the arch is 50 ft. Find the height of the arch 10 ft from the center. Round to the nearest foot.
The height 10 ft from the center is approximately 49 ft.

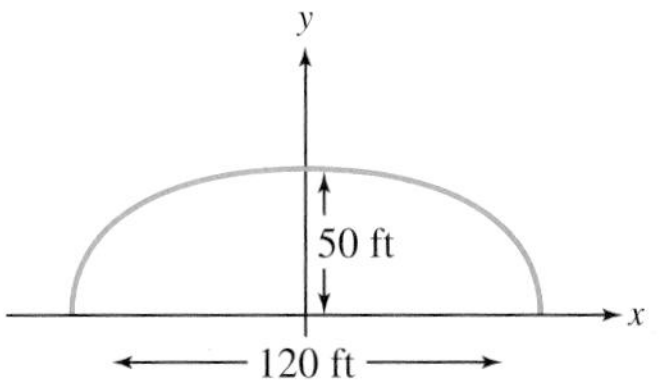

54. A bridge over a gorge is supported by an arch in the shape of a semiellipse. The length of the bridge is 400 ft, and the height is 100 ft. Find the height of the arch 50 ft from the center. Round to the nearest foot.
The height 50 ft from the center is approximately 97 ft.

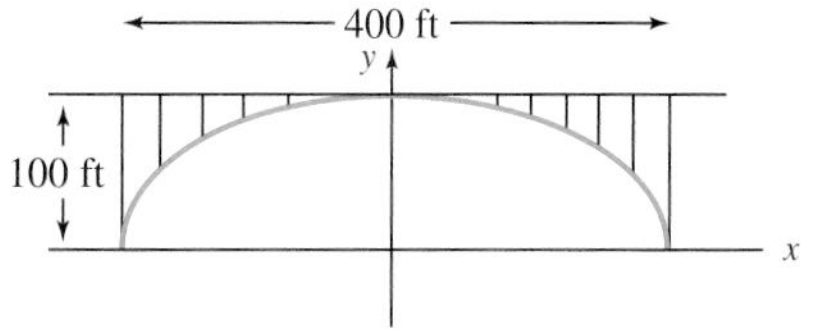

In Exercises 55–58, graph the hyperbola centered at (h, k) by following these guidelines. First locate the center. Then draw the reference rectangle relative to the center (h, k). Using the reference rectangle as a guide, sketch the hyperbola. Label the center and vertices.

55. $\dfrac{(x-1)^2}{9} - \dfrac{(y+2)^2}{4} = 1$

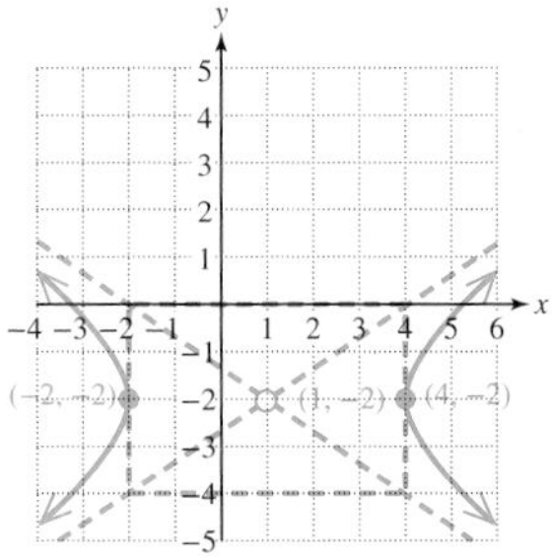

56. $\dfrac{(x+2)^2}{16} - \dfrac{(y-3)^2}{4} = 1$

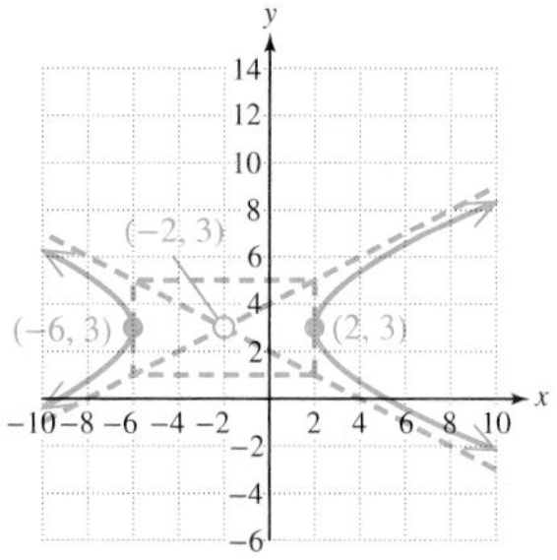

57. $\dfrac{(y-1)^2}{4} - (x+3)^2 = 1$

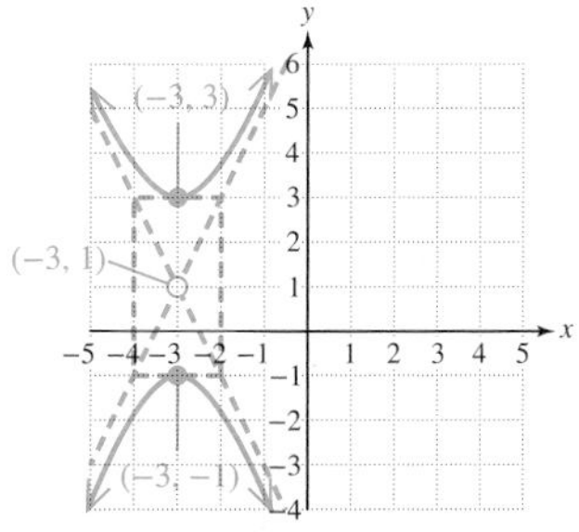

58. $(y+2)^2 - \dfrac{(x+3)^2}{4} = 1$

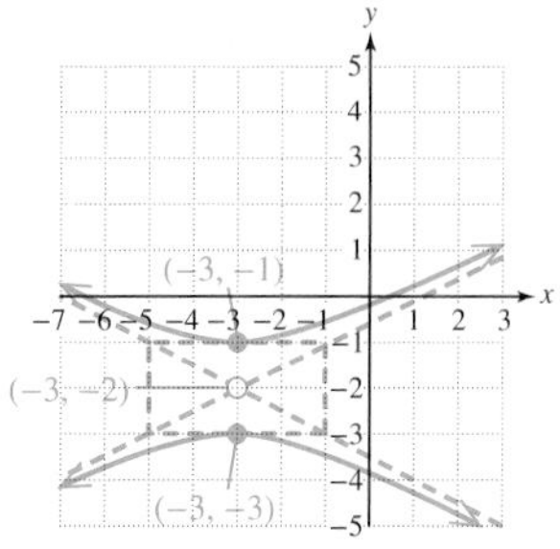

Problem Recognition Exercises

Formulas and Conic Sections

For Exercises 1–8, identify the formula.

1. $(x-h)^2 + (y-k)^2 = r^2$
Standard equation of a circle

2. $\dfrac{x^2}{a^2} + \dfrac{y^2}{b^2} = 1$
Ellipse centered at the origin

3. $\sqrt{(x_2-x_1)^2 + (y_2-y_1)^2}$
Distance between two points

4. $\left(\dfrac{x_1+x_2}{2}, \dfrac{y_1+y_2}{2}\right)$
Midpoint between two points

5. $y = a(x-h)^2 + k$
Parabola with vertical axis of symmetry

6. $\dfrac{x^2}{a^2} - \dfrac{y^2}{b^2} = 1$
Hyperbola with horizontal transverse axis

7. $\dfrac{y^2}{b^2} - \dfrac{x^2}{a^2} = 1$
Hyperbola with vertical transverse axis

8. $x = a(y-k)^2 + h$
Parabola with horizontal axis of symmetry

For Exercises 9–30, identify the equation as representing a circle, parabola, ellipse, hyperbola, or none of these.

9. $y = -2(x - 3)^2 + 4$ Parabola

10. $\frac{x^2}{4} - \frac{y^2}{1} = 1$ Hyperbola

11. $(x + 3)^2 + (y + 2)^2 = 4$ Circle

12. $(x - 2)^2 + (y - 4)^2 = 9$ Circle

13. $\frac{x^2}{9} - \frac{y^2}{9} = 1$ Hyperbola

14. $\frac{x^2}{9} + \frac{y^2}{16} = 1$ Ellipse

15. $\frac{x^2}{16} + \frac{y^2}{4} = 0$ None of these

16. $x^2 + y^2 - 2x + 4y - 4 = 0$ Circle

17. $y = \frac{1}{2}(x + 2)^2 - 3$ Parabola

18. $\frac{x^2}{4} - \frac{y^2}{2} = 1$ Hyperbola

19. $x = (y + 2)^2 - 4$ Parabola

20. $x^2 + y^2 + 6x + 8 = 0$ Circle

21. $(x - 1)^2 + (y + 1)^2 = 0$ None of these

22. $x = -(y - 2)^2 - 1$ Parabola

23. $\frac{x^2}{25} + \frac{y^2}{4} = 1$ Ellipse

24. $x^2 + y^2 = 15$ Circle

25. $y = (x - 6)^2 + 4$ Parabola

26. $\frac{(x + 1)^2}{2} + \frac{(y + 1)^2}{5} = 1$ Ellipse

27. $\frac{y^2}{3} - \frac{x^2}{3} = 1$ Hyperbola

28. $3x^2 + 3y^2 = 1$ Circle

29. $\frac{x^2}{9} + \frac{y^2}{12} = 1$ Ellipse

30. $x = (y + 2)^2 - 5$ Parabola

Section 13.4 Nonlinear Systems of Equations in Two Variables

Concepts

1. Solving Nonlinear Systems of Equations by the Substitution Method
2. Solving Nonlinear Systems of Equations by the Addition Method

1. Solving Nonlinear Systems of Equations by the Substitution Method

Recall that a linear equation in two variables x and y is an equation that can be written in the form $Ax + By = C$, where A and B are not both zero. We have solved systems of linear equations in two variables by using the graphing method, the substitution method, and the addition method. In this section, we will solve *nonlinear* systems of equations by using the same methods. A **nonlinear system of equations** is a system in which at least one of the equations is nonlinear.

Graphing the equations in a nonlinear system helps to determine the number of solutions and to approximate the coordinates of the solutions. The substitution method is used most often to solve a nonlinear system of equations analytically.

Classroom Example: p. 965, Exercise 18

Example 1 Solving a Nonlinear System of Equations

Given the system $\quad x - 7y = -25$

$\quad x^2 + y^2 = 25$

a. Solve the system by graphing.

b. Solve the system by the substitution method.

Solution:

a. $x - 7y = -25$ is a line (the slope-intercept form is $y = \frac{1}{7}x + \frac{25}{7}$).

$x^2 + y^2 = 25$ is a circle centered at the origin with radius 5.

From Figure 13-16, we appear to have two solutions $(-4, 3)$ and $(3, 4)$.

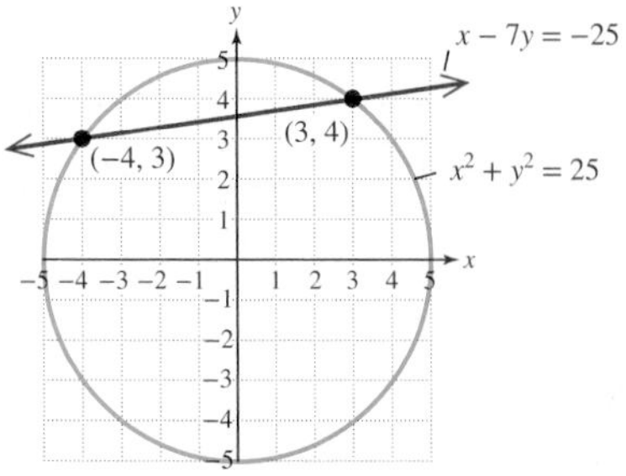

Figure 13-16

b. To use the substitution method, isolate one of the variables from one of the equations. We will solve for x in the first equation.

$$\boxed{A} \quad x - 7y = -25 \xrightarrow{\text{Solve for } x.} x = 7y - 25$$

$$\boxed{B} \quad x^2 + y^2 = 25$$

$\boxed{B}$ $(7y - 25)^2 + y^2 = 25$ — Substitute $(7y - 25)$ for x in the second equation.

$49y^2 - 350y + 625 + y^2 = 25$ — The resulting equation is quadratic in y.

$50y^2 - 350y + 600 = 0$ — Set the equation equal to zero.

$50(y^2 - 7y + 12) = 0$ — Factor.

$50(y - 3)(y - 4) = 0$

$y = 3 \quad \text{or} \quad y = 4$

For each value of y, find the corresponding x value from the equation $x = 7y - 25$.

$y = 3$: $x = 7(3) - 25 = -4$ — The solution point is $(-4, 3)$.

$y = 4$: $x = 7(4) - 25 = 3$ — The solution point is $(3, 4)$. (See Figure 13-16.)

The solution set is $\{(-4, 3), (3, 4)\}$.

Skill Practice Given the system

$$2x + y = 5$$
$$x^2 + y^2 = 50$$

1. Solve the system by graphing.
2. Solve the system by the substitution method.

Example 2 Solving a Nonlinear System by the Substitution Method

Classroom Example: p. 966, Exercise 24

Given the system

$$y = \sqrt{x}$$
$$x^2 + y^2 = 20$$

a. Sketch the graphs.

b. Solve the system by the substitution method.

Solution:

a. $y = \sqrt{x}$ is the basic square root function.

$x^2 + y^2 = 20$ is a circle centered at the origin with radius $\sqrt{20} \approx 4.5$.

From Figure 13-17, we see that there is one solution.

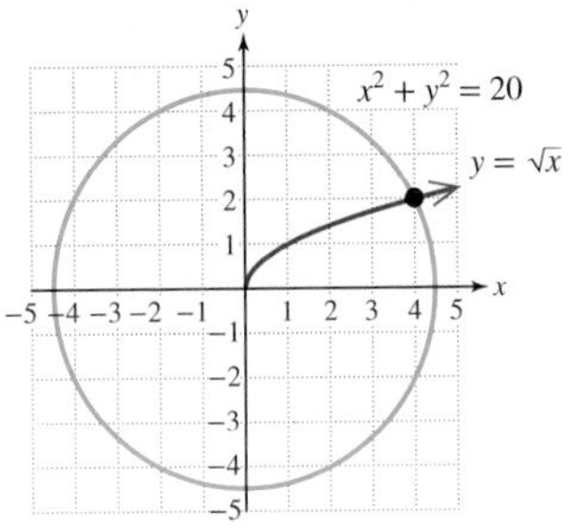

Figure 13-17

Answers

1.

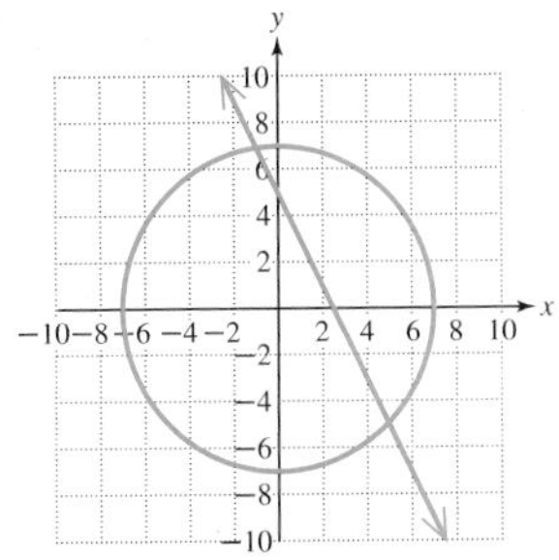

The solutions appear to be $(-1, 7)$ and $(5, -5)$.

2. $\{(-1, 7), (5, -5)\}$

b. To use the substitution method, we will substitute $y = \sqrt{x}$ into equation $\boxed{B}$.

$\boxed{A}$ $y = \sqrt{x}$ — Substitute $y = \sqrt{x}$ into the second equation.

$\boxed{B}$ $x^2 + y^2 = 20$

$\boxed{B}$ $x^2 + (\sqrt{x})^2 = 20$

$x^2 + x = 20$

$x^2 + x - 20 = 0$ — Set the second equation equal to zero.

$(x + 5)(x - 4) = 0$ — Factor.

~~$x = -5$~~ or $x = 4$ — Reject $x = -5$ because it is not in the domain of $y = \sqrt{x}$.

Substitute $x = 4$ into the equation $y = \sqrt{x}$.

If $x = 4$, then $y = \sqrt{4} = 2$. The solution set is $\{(4, 2)\}$.

Skill Practice Given the system

$$y = \sqrt{2x}$$
$$x^2 + y^2 = 8$$

3. Sketch the graphs.

4. Solve the system by using the substitution method.

Calculator Connections

Topic: Graphing a Nonlinear System of Equations

Graph the equations from Example 2 to confirm your solution to the system of equations. Use an *Intersect* feature to approximate the point of intersection. Recall that the circle must be entered into the calculator as two functions:

$$Y_1 = \sqrt{20 - x^2}$$
$$Y_2 = -\sqrt{20 - x^2}$$
$$Y_3 = \sqrt{x}$$

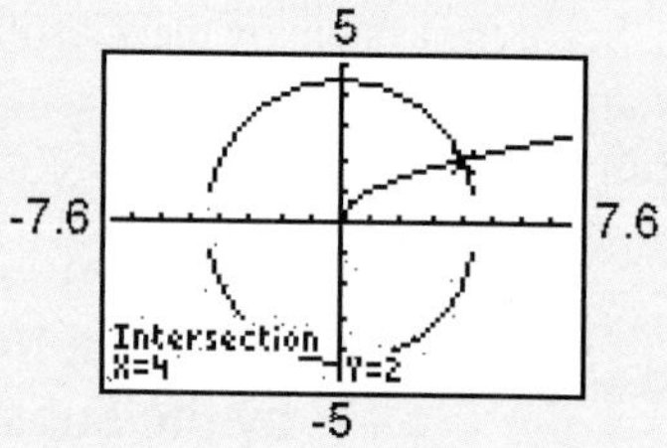

Classroom Example: p. 966, Exercise 26

Answers

3.

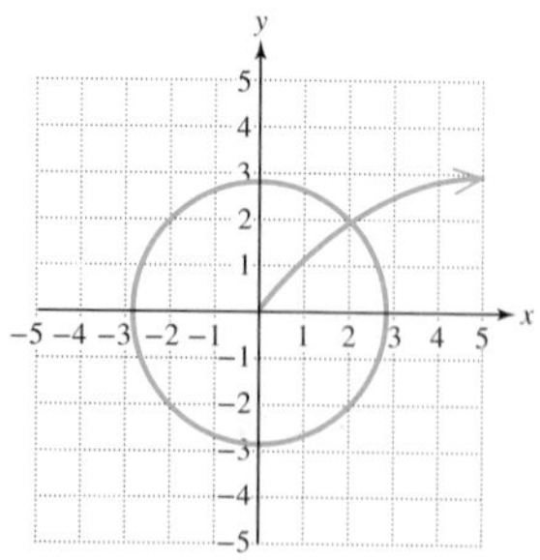

4. $\{(2, 2)\}$

Example 3 Solving a Nonlinear System by the Substitution Method

Solve the system by using the substitution method.

$$y = \sqrt[3]{x}$$
$$y = x$$

Solution:

$\boxed{A}$ $y = \sqrt[3]{x}$

$\boxed{B}$ $y = x$

$\sqrt[3]{x} = x$ — Because y is isolated in both equations, we can equate the expressions for y.

$(\sqrt[3]{x})^3 = (x)^3$ — To solve the radical equation, raise both sides to the third power.

$x = x^3$ This is a third-degree polynomial equation.

$0 = x^3 - x$ Set the equation equal to zero.

$0 = x(x^2 - 1)$ Factor out the GCF.

$0 = x(x + 1)(x - 1)$ Factor completely.

$x = 0$ or $x = -1$ or $x = 1$

For each value of x, find the corresponding y-value from either original equation. We will use equation [B]: $y = x$.

If $x = 0$, then $y = 0$. The solution point is $(0, 0)$.

If $x = -1$, then $y = -1$. The solution point is $(-1, -1)$.

If $x = 1$, then $y = 1$. The solution point is $(1, 1)$.

The solution set is $\{(0, 0), (-1, -1), (1, 1)\}$. See Figure 13-18.

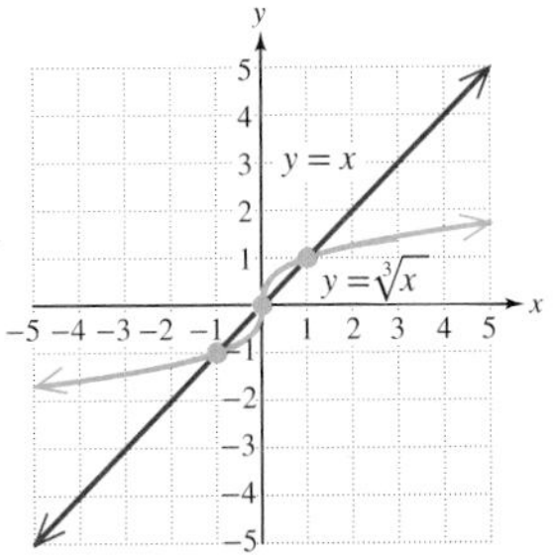

Figure 13-18

Skill Practice Solve the system by using the substitution method.

5. $y = \sqrt[3]{9x}$
$y = x$

2. Solving Nonlinear Systems of Equations by the Addition Method

The substitution method is used most often to solve a system of nonlinear equations. In some situations, however, the addition method offers an efficient means of finding a solution. Example 4 demonstrates that we can eliminate a variable from both equations provided the terms containing the corresponding variables are *like* terms.

Example 4 **Solving a Nonlinear System of Equations by the Addition Method**

Classroom Example: p. 966, Exercise 34

Solve the system. $2x^2 + y^2 = 17$
$x^2 + 2y^2 = 22$

Solution:

[A] $2x^2 + y^2 = 17$ Notice that the y^2 terms are *like* in each equation.

[B] $x^2 + 2y^2 = 22$ To eliminate the y^2 terms, multiply the first equation by −2.

[A] $2x^2 + y^2 = 17$ $\xrightarrow{\text{Multiply by } -2.}$ $-4x^2 - 2y^2 = -34$

[B] $x^2 + 2y^2 = 22$ $\longrightarrow$ $x^2 + 2y^2 = 22$

$-3x^2 = -12$ Eliminate the y^2 term.

$$\frac{-3x^2}{-3} = \frac{-12}{-3}$$

$x^2 = 4$

$x = \pm 2$ Use the square root property.

TIP: In Example 4, the x^2 terms are also *like* in both equations. We could have eliminated the x^2 terms by multiplying equation [B] by −2.

Answer

5. $\{(0, 0), (3, 3), (-3, -3)\}$

Substitute each value of x into one of the original equations to solve for y. We will use equation $\boxed{A}$: $2x^2 + y^2 = 17$.

$x = 2$: $\boxed{A}$
$$2(2)^2 + y^2 = 17$$
$$8 + y^2 = 17$$
$$y^2 = 9$$
$$y = \pm 3$$
The solution points are (2, 3) and (2, −3).

$x = -2$: $\boxed{A}$
$$2(-2)^2 + y^2 = 17$$
$$8 + y^2 = 17$$
$$y^2 = 9$$
$$y = \pm 3$$
The solution points are (−2, 3) and (−2, −3).

The solution set is {(2, 3), (2, −3), (−2, 3), (−2, −3)}.

TIP: The two equations in Example 4 are ellipses but an exact graph is difficult to render by hand.

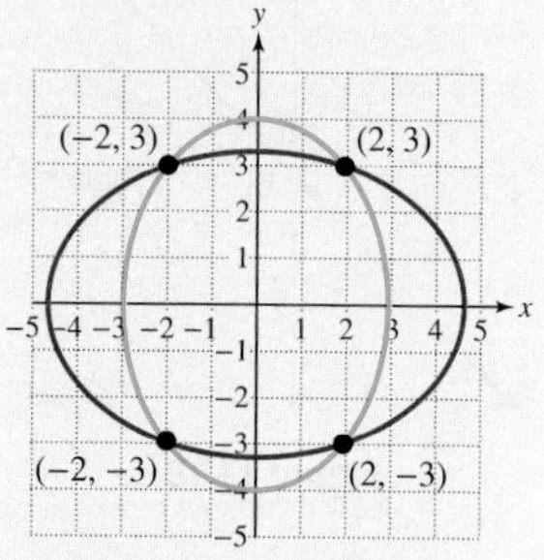

To check the solutions to the system, verify that each ordered pair satisfies both equations.

Skill Practice Solve the system by using the addition method.

6. $x^2 - y^2 = 24$
$3x^2 + y^2 = 76$

TIP: It is important to note that the addition method can be used only if two equations share a pair of *like* terms. The substitution method is effective in solving a wider range of systems of equations. The system in Example 4 could also have been solved by using substitution.

$\boxed{A}$ $2x^2 + y^2 = 17$ —Solve for y^2.→ $y^2 = 17 - 2x^2$

$\boxed{B}$ $x^2 + 2y^2 = 22$

$\boxed{B}$ $x^2 + 2(17 - 2x^2) = 22$

$$x^2 + 34 - 4x^2 = 22$$
$$-3x^2 = -12$$
$$x^2 = 4$$
$$x = \pm 2$$

$x = 2$: $y^2 = 17 - 2(2)^2$
$y^2 = 9$
$y = \pm 3$ The solutions are (2, 3) and (−2, −3).

$x = -2$: $y^2 = 17 - 2(-2)^2$
$y^2 = 9$
$y = \pm 3$ The solutions are (−2, 3) and (−2, −3).

Answer

6. {(5, 1), (5, −1), (−5, 1), (−5, −1)}

Section 13.4 Practice Exercises

Vocabulary and Key Concepts

For additional exercises, see Classroom Activities 13.4A–13.4B in the *Student's Resource Manual* at www.mhhe.com/moh.

1. a. A __nonlinear__ system of equations in two variables is a system in which at least one of the equations is nonlinear.

b. Graphically, the solution set to a nonlinear system of equations is the set of ordered pairs representing the points of __intersection__ of the graphs of the two equations.

Writing   Translating Expression   Geometry   Scientific Calculator   Video

Review Exercises

2. Write the distance formula between two points (x_1, y_1) and (x_2, y_2) from memory. $d = \sqrt{(x_2 - x_1)^2 + (y_2 - y_1)^2}$

3. Find the distance between the two points $(8, -1)$ and $(1, -8)$. $7\sqrt{2}$

4. Write an equation representing the set of all points 2 units from the point $(-1, 1)$. $(x + 1)^2 + (y - 1)^2 = 4$

5. Write an equation representing the set of all points 8 units from the point $(-5, 3)$. $(x + 5)^2 + (y - 3)^2 = 64$

6. Write the formula for the midpoint between the points (x_1, y_1) and (x_2, y_2). $\left(\frac{x_1 + x_2}{2}, \frac{y_1 + y_2}{2}\right)$

7. Find the midpoint of the line segment with the endpoints $(3, -9)$ and $(-4, 2)$. $\left(-\frac{1}{2}, -\frac{7}{2}\right)$

8. Find the midpoint of the line segment with the endpoints $(2.4, 1.8)$ and $(-1.6, -5.2)$. $(0.4, -1.7)$

Concept 1: Solving Nonlinear Systems of Equations by the Substitution Method

For Exercises 9–16, use sketches to explain.

9. How many points of intersection are possible between a line and a parabola? Zero, one, or two

10. How many points of intersection are possible between a line and a circle? Zero, one, or two

11. How many points of intersection are possible between two distinct circles? Zero, one, or two

12. How many points of intersection are possible between two distinct parabolas of the form $y = ax^2 + bx + c, a \neq 0$? Zero, one, or two

13. How many points of intersection are possible between a circle and a parabola? Zero, one, two, three, or four

14. How many points of intersection are possible between two distinct lines? Zero or one

15. How many points of intersection are possible between an ellipse and a hyperbola? Zero, one, two, three, or four

16. How many points of intersection are possible between an ellipse and a parabola? Zero, one, two, three, or four

For Exercises 17–22, sketch each system of equations. Then solve the system by the substitution method. **(See Example 1.)**

17. $y = x + 3$
$x^2 + y = 9$ $\{(-3, 0), (2, 5)\}$

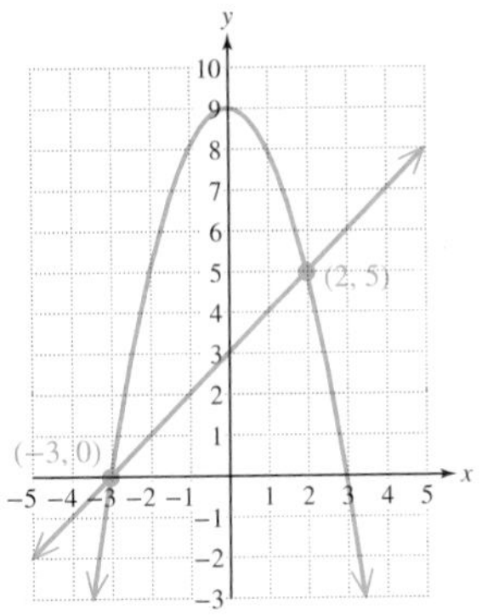

18. $y = x - 2$
$x^2 + y = 4$ $\{(-3, -5), (2, 0)\}$

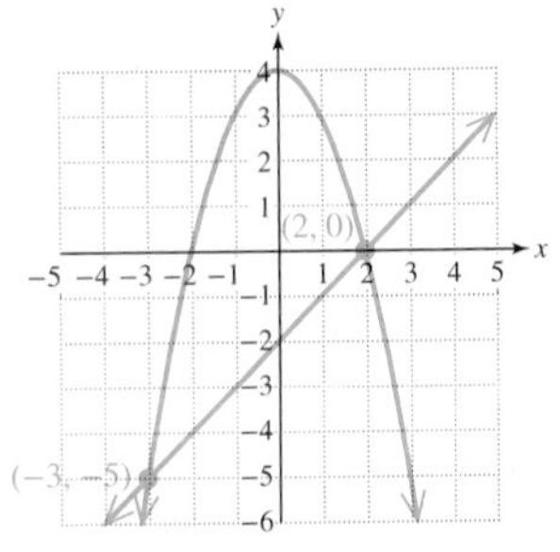

19. $x^2 + y^2 = 1$
$y = x + 1$ $\{(0, 1), (-1, 0)\}$

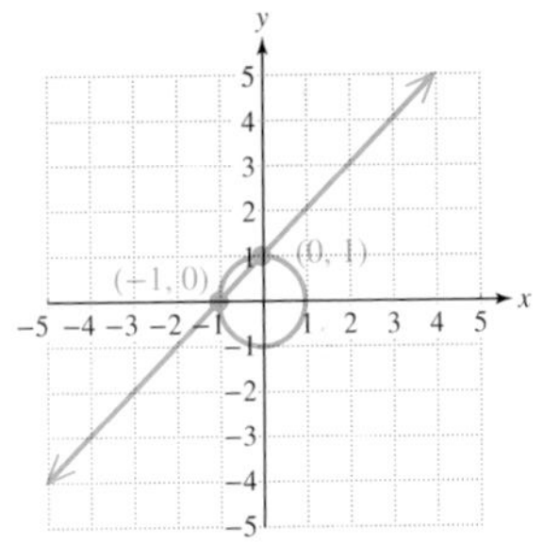

20. $x^2 + y^2 = 25$

$y = 2x$ $\{(\sqrt{5}, 2\sqrt{5}), (-\sqrt{5}, -2\sqrt{5})\}$

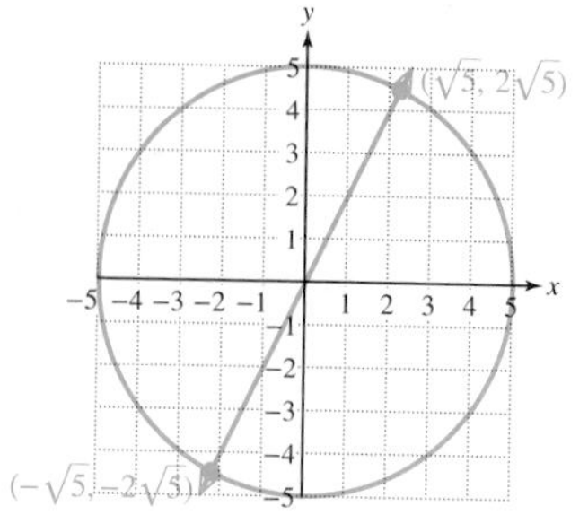

21. $x^2 + y^2 = 6$

$y = x^2$ $\{(\sqrt{2}, 2), (-\sqrt{2}, 2)\}$

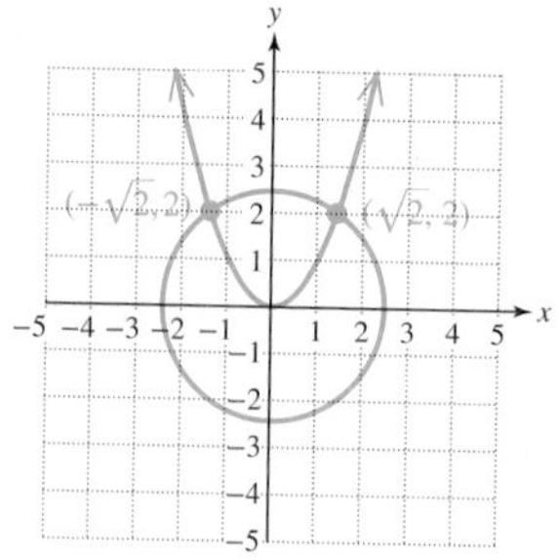

22. $x^2 + y^2 = 12$

$y = x^2$ $\{(\sqrt{3}, 3), (-\sqrt{3}, 3)\}$

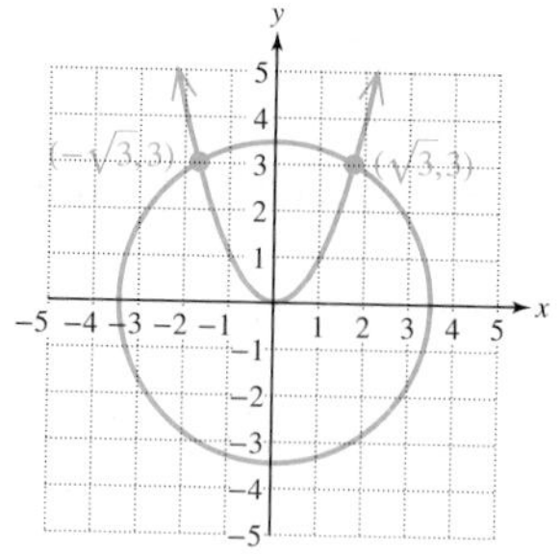

For Exercises 23–31, solve the system by the substitution method. **(See Examples 2–3.)**

23. $y = \sqrt{x}$

$2x^2 - y^2 = 1$ $\{(1, 1)\}$

24. $x^2 + y^2 = 30$

$y = \sqrt{x}$ $\{(5, \sqrt{5})\}$

25. $y = x^2$

$y = -\sqrt{x}$ $\{(0, 0)\}$

26. $y = -x^2$

$y = -\sqrt{x}$ $\{(0, 0), (1, -1)\}$

27. $y = x^2$

$y = (x - 3)^2$ $\left\{\left(\frac{3}{2}, \frac{9}{4}\right)\right\}$

28. $y = (x + 4)^2$

$y = x^2$ $\{(-2, 4)\}$

29. $y = x^2 + 6x$

$y = 4x$ $\{(0, 0), (-2, -8)\}$

30. $y = 3x^2 - 6x$

$y = 3x$ $\{(0, 0), (3, 9)\}$

31. $x^2 - 5x + y = 0$

$y = 3x + 1$ $\{(1, 4)\}$

Concept 2: Solving Nonlinear Systems of Equations by the Addition Method

For Exercises 32–48, solve the system of nonlinear equations by the addition method if appropriate. **(See Example 4.)**

32. $x^2 + y^2 = 13$

$x^2 - y^2 = 5$

$\{(3, 2), (3, -2), (-3, 2), (-3, -2)\}$

33. $4x^2 - y^2 = 4$

$4x^2 + y^2 = 4$ $\{(1, 0), (-1, 0)\}$

34. $9x^2 + 4y^2 = 36$

$x^2 + y^2 = 9$ $\{(0, 3), (0, -3)\}$

35. $x^2 + y^2 = 4$

$2x^2 + y^2 = 8$ $\{(2, 0), (-2, 0)\}$

36. $3x^2 + 4y^2 = 16$

$2x^2 - 3y^2 = 5$

$\{(2, 1), (-2, 1), (2, -1), (-2, -1)\}$

37. $2x^2 - 5y^2 = -2$

$3x^2 + 2y^2 = 35$

$\{(3, 2), (-3, 2), (3, -2), (-3, -2)\}$

38. $x^2 + y^2 = 169$

$12x - 5y = 0$ $\{(5, 12), (-5, -12)\}$

39. $x^2 + y^2 = 100$

$4y - 3x = 0$ $\{(8, 6), (-8, -6)\}$

40. $\dfrac{x^2}{4} + \dfrac{y^2}{9} = 1$

$x^2 + y^2 = 4$ $\{(2, 0), (-2, 0)\}$

41. $\dfrac{x^2}{16} + \dfrac{y^2}{4} = 1$

$x^2 + y^2 = 4$ $\{(0, -2), (0, 2)\}$

42. $\dfrac{x^2}{10} + \dfrac{y^2}{10} = 1$

$2x^2 + y^2 = 11$

$\{(1, 3), (1, -3), (-1, 3), (-1, -3)\}$

43. $2y = -x + 2$

$x^2 + 4y^2 = 4$ $\{(2, 0), (0, 1)\}$

44. $2y = -3x - 6$

$9x^2 + 4y^2 = 36$ $\{(-2, 0), (0, -3)\}$

45. $x^2 - xy = -4$

$2x^2 - xy = 12$ $\{(4, 5), (-4, -5)\}$

46. $x^2 - xy = 3$

$2x^2 + xy = 6$ $\{(\sqrt{3}, 0), (-\sqrt{3}, 0)\}$

47. $3x^2 + 2xy = 4$

$x^2 - xy = 3$

$\left\{\left(-\sqrt{2}, \frac{\sqrt{2}}{2}\right), \left(\sqrt{2}, -\frac{\sqrt{2}}{2}\right)\right\}$

48. $x^2 - 3xy = 8$

$x^2 + xy = 4$ $\left\{\left(-\sqrt{5}, \frac{\sqrt{5}}{5}\right), \left(\sqrt{5}, -\frac{\sqrt{5}}{5}\right)\right\}$

Expanding Your Skills

49. The sum of two numbers is 7. The sum of the squares of the numbers is 25. Find the numbers.
The numbers are 3 and 4.

50. The sum of the squares of two numbers is 100. The sum of the numbers is 2. Find the numbers.
The numbers are −6 and 8.

51. The sum of the squares of two numbers is 32. The difference of the squares of the numbers is 18. Find the numbers. The numbers are 5 and $\sqrt{7}$, −5 and $\sqrt{7}$, 5 and $-\sqrt{7}$, or −5 and $-\sqrt{7}$.

52. The sum of the squares of two numbers is 24. The difference of the squares of the numbers is 8. Find the numbers. The numbers are 4 and $2\sqrt{2}$, −4 and $2\sqrt{2}$, 4 and $-2\sqrt{2}$, or −4 and $-2\sqrt{2}$.

Graphing Calculator Exercises

For Exercises 53–56, use the *Intersect* feature to approximate the solutions to the system.

53. $y = x + 3$ (Exercise 17)
$x^2 + y = 9$

54. $y = x - 2$ (Exercise 18)
$x^2 + y = 4$

55. $y = x^2$ (Exercise 25)
$y = -\sqrt{x}$

56. $y = -x^2$ (Exercise 26)
$y = -\sqrt{x}$

For Exercises 57–58, graph the system on a square viewing window. What can be said about the solution to the system?

57. $x^2 + y^2 = 4$
$y = x^2 + 3$ { }

58. $x^2 + y^2 = 16$
$y = -x^2 - 5$ { }

Nonlinear Inequalities and Systems of Inequalities in Two Variables

Section 13.5

Concepts

1. Nonlinear Inequalities in Two Variables
2. Systems of Nonlinear Inequalities in Two Variables

1. Nonlinear Inequalities in Two Variables

In our earlier study of linear inequalities in two variables, we used the test point method to graph the solution set. For example, to graph the solution set to $y \le 2x + 1$, first graph the related equation $y = 2x + 1$. This is the line shown in Figure 13-19. Then using test points, we see that points on and below the line make up the solution set to the inequality.

Test Point Above: (−2, 2)

$y \le 2x + 1$

$2 \overset{?}{\le} 2(-2) + 1$

$2 \overset{?}{\le} -3$ False

Test Point Below: (0, 0)

$y \le 2x + 1$

$0 \overset{?}{\le} 2(0) + 1$

$0 \overset{?}{\le} 1$ ✓True

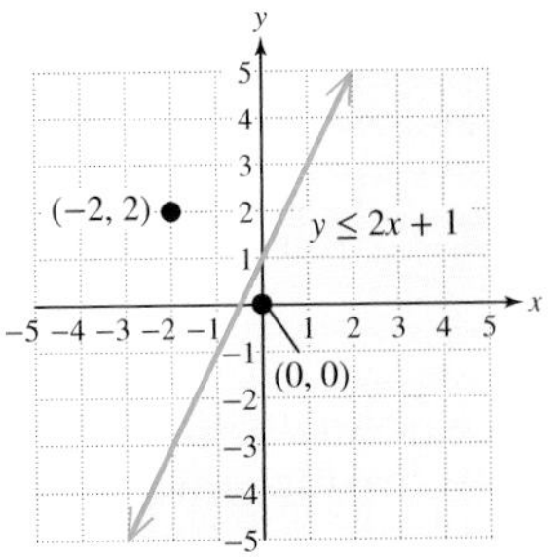

Figure 13-19

Classroom Example: p. 973, Exercise 28

Avoiding Mistakes

The first step in solving an inequality in two variables is to graph the related equation.

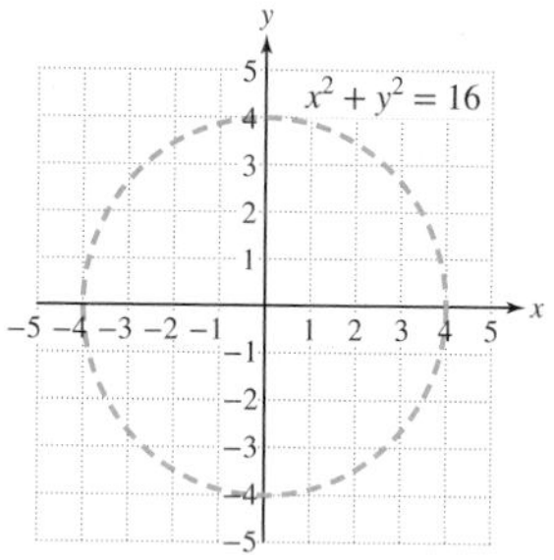

Figure 13-20

Example 1 Graphing a Nonlinear Inequality in Two Variables

Graph the solution set of the inequality $x^2 + y^2 < 16$.

Solution:

The related equation $x^2 + y^2 = 16$ is a circle of radius 4, centered at the origin. Graph the related equation by using a dashed curve because the points satisfying the equation $x^2 + y^2 = 16$ are not part of the solution to the strict inequality $x^2 + y^2 < 16$. See Figure 13-20.

Notice that the dashed curve separates the *xy*-plane into two regions, one "inside" the circle, the other "outside" the circle. Select a test point from each region and test the point in the original inequality.

Test Point "Inside": (0, 0)	**Test Point "Outside": (4, 4)**
$x^2 + y^2 < 16$	$x^2 + y^2 < 16$
$(0)^2 + (0)^2 \overset{?}{<} 16$	$(4)^2 + (4)^2 \overset{?}{<} 16$
$0 \overset{?}{<} 16$ True	$32 \overset{?}{<} 16$ False

The inequality $x^2 + y^2 < 16$ is true at the test point (0, 0). Therefore, the solution set is the region "inside" the circle. See Figure 13-21.

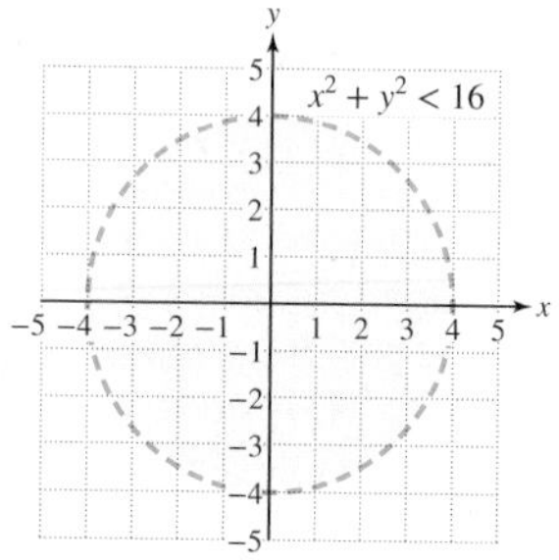

Figure 13-21

Skill Practice

1. Graph the solution set of the inequality. $x^2 + y^2 \geq 9$

Classroom Example: p. 973, Exercise 32

Example 2 Graphing a Nonlinear Inequality in Two Variables

Graph the solution set of the inequality $9y^2 \geq 36 + 4x^2$.

Solution:

First graph the related equation $9y^2 = 36 + 4x^2$. Notice that the equation can be written in the standard form of a hyperbola.

$$9y^2 = 36 + 4x^2$$

$$9y^2 - 4x^2 = 36 \qquad \text{Subtract } 4x^2 \text{ from both sides.}$$

$$\frac{9y^2}{36} - \frac{4x^2}{36} = \frac{36}{36} \qquad \text{Divide both sides by 36.}$$

$$\frac{y^2}{4} - \frac{x^2}{9} = 1$$

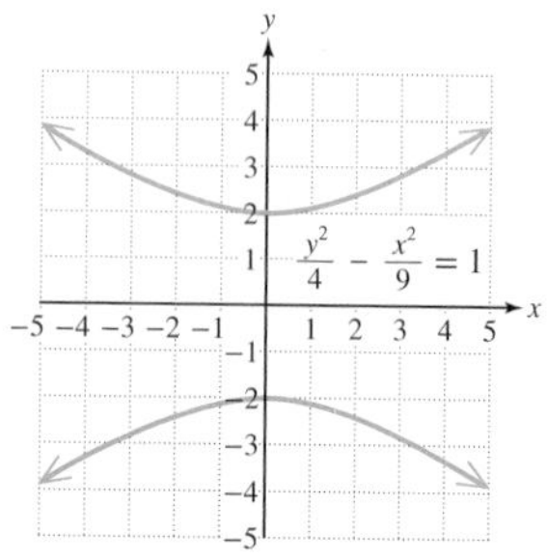

Figure 13-22

Graph the hyperbola as a solid curve, because the original inequality includes equality. See Figure 13-22.

Answer

1.

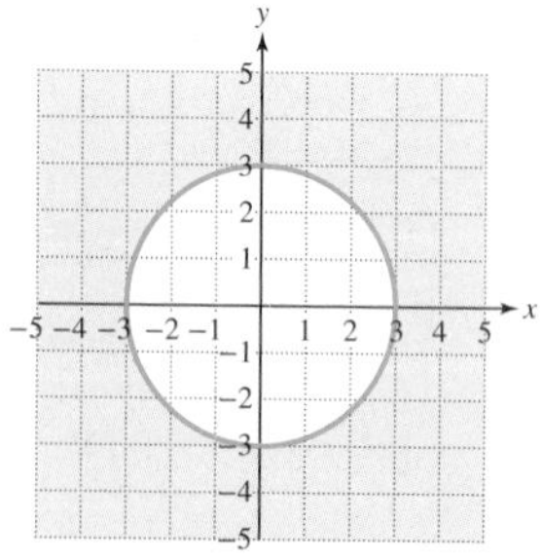

The hyperbola divides the xy-plane into three regions: a region above the upper branch, a region between the branches, and a region below the lower branch. Select a test point from each region.

$$9y^2 \geq 36 + 4x^2$$

Test: (0, 3)	**Test: (0, 0)**	**Test: (0, −3)**
$9(3)^2 \overset{?}{\geq} 36 + 4(0)^2$	$9(0)^2 \overset{?}{\geq} 36 + 4(0)^2$	$9(-3)^2 \overset{?}{\geq} 36 + 4(0)^2$
$81 \overset{?}{\geq} 36$ True	$0 \overset{?}{\geq} 36$ False	$81 \overset{?}{\geq} 36$ True

Shade the regions above the top branch and below the bottom branch of the hyperbola. See Figure 13-23.

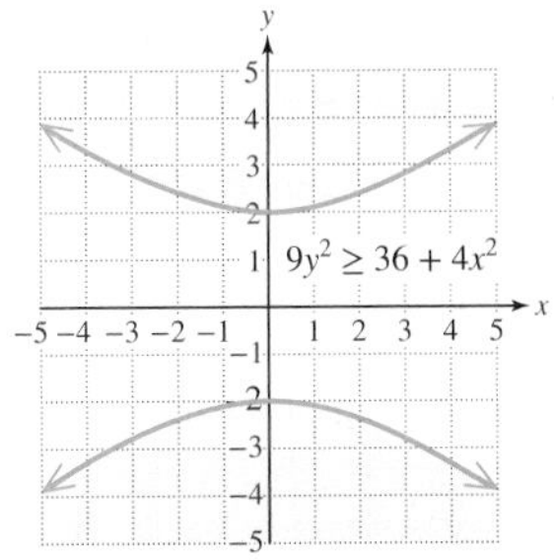

Figure 13-23

Skill Practice

2. Graph the solution set of the inequality. $9x^2 < 144 - 16y^2$

2. Systems of Nonlinear Inequalities in Two Variables

The solution set for a system of nonlinear equations in two variables is a set of ordered pairs that satisfy both equations simultaneously. We will now solve systems of nonlinear inequalities in two variables. Similarly, the solution set is the set of all ordered pairs that simultaneously satisfy each inequality. To solve a system of inequalities, we will graph the solution to each individual inequality and then take the intersection of the solution sets.

Example 3 Graphing a System of Nonlinear Inequalities in Two Variables

Classroom Example: p. 974, Exercise 40

Graph the solution set.

$$y > \frac{1}{3}x^2$$
$$y < -x^2 + 2$$

Solution:

The solution to $y > \frac{1}{3}x^2$ is the set of points above the parabola $y = \frac{1}{3}x^2$. See Figure 13-24. The solution to $y < -x^2 + 2$ is the set of points below the parabola $y = -x^2 + 2$. See Figure 13-25.

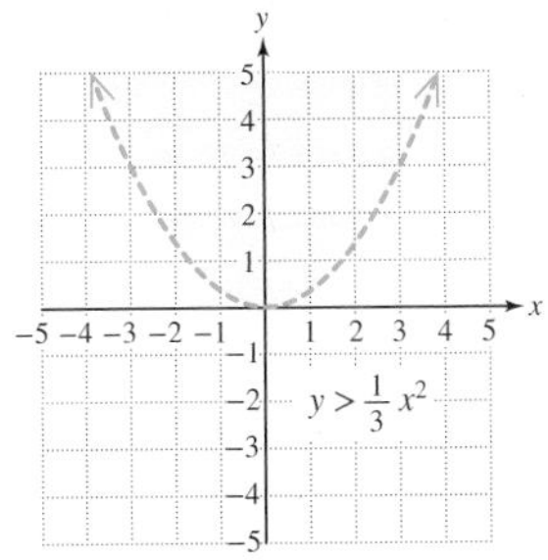

Figure 13-24

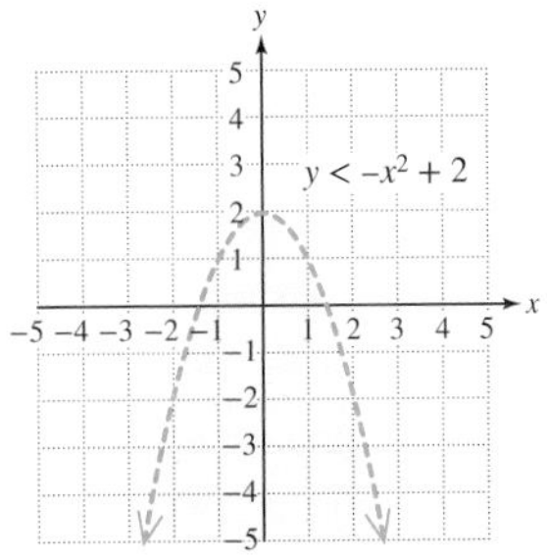

Figure 13-25

Answer

2.

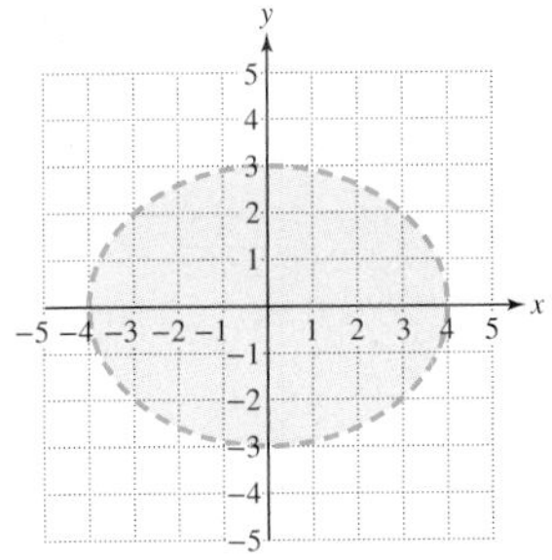

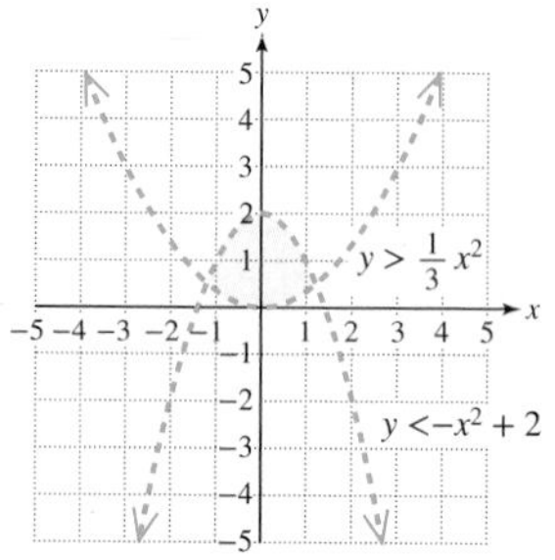

Figure 13-26

The solution to the system of inequalities is the intersection of the solution sets of the individual inequalities. See Figure 13-26.

Skill Practice

3. Graph the solution set. $\frac{x^2}{4} + \frac{y^2}{9} < 1$

$x > y^2$

Classroom Example: p. 975, Exercise 48

Example 4 Graphing a System of Nonlinear Inequalities in Two Variables

Graph the solution set. $y > e^x$

$y < -x^2 + 4$

Solution:

The solution to $y > e^x$ is the set of points above the curve $y = e^x$. See Figure 13-27. The solution to $y < -x^2 + 4$ is the set of points below the parabola $y = -x^2 + 4$. See Figure 13-28.

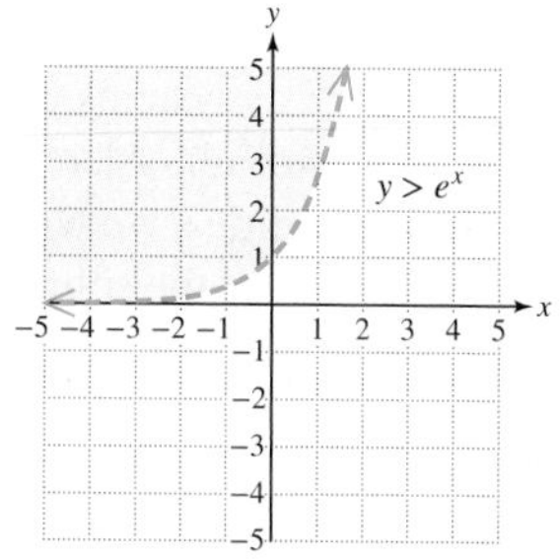

Figure 13-27

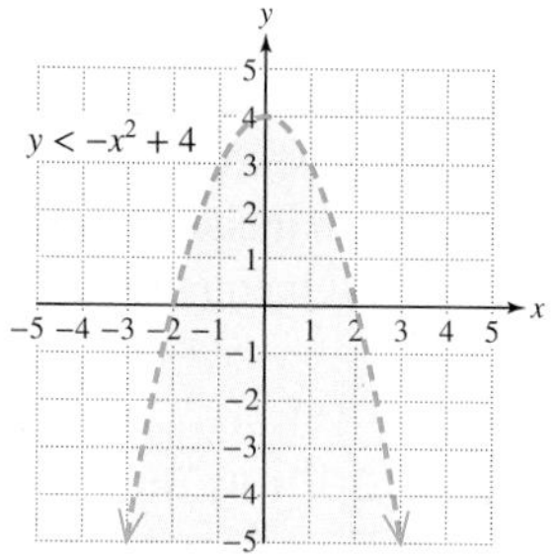

Figure 13-28

The solution to the system of inequalities is the intersection of the solution sets of the individual inequalities. See Figure 13-29.

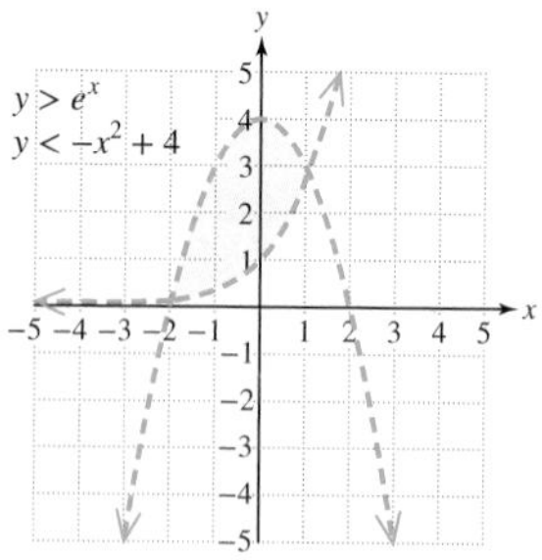

Figure 13-29

Skill Practice

4. Graph the solution set. $y > \frac{1}{2}x^2$

$x > y^2$

Answers

3.

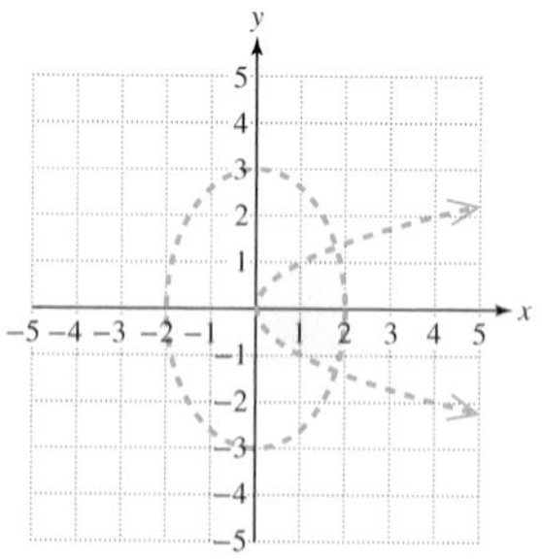

4.

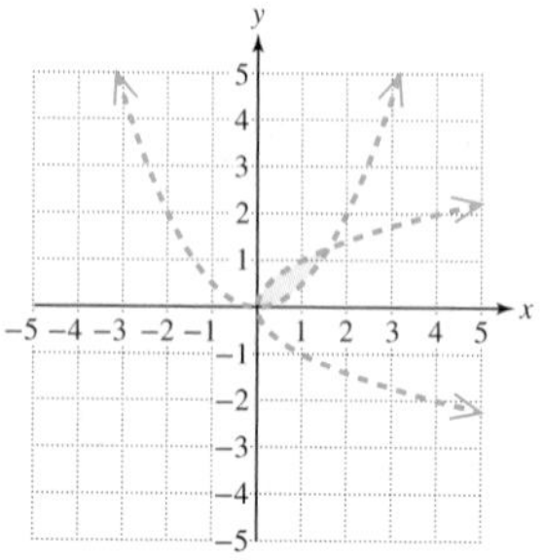

Section 13.5 Practice Exercises

For additional exercises, see Classroom Activities 13.5A–13.5B in the *Student's Resource Manual* at www.mhhe.com/moh.

Review Exercises

For Exercises 1–12, match the equation with its graph.

1. $y = \left(\frac{1}{3}\right)^x$ k
2. $y = 4x - 1$ g
3. $y = -4x^2$ e
4. $y = e^x$ h
5. $y = x^3$ i
6. $\frac{x^2}{4} + \frac{y^2}{9} = 1$ f
7. $\frac{x^2}{4} - \frac{y^2}{9} = 1$ j
8. $y = \frac{1}{x}$ c
9. $y = \log_2(x)$ a
10. $y = \sqrt{x}$ b
11. $(x + 2)^2 + (y - 1)^2 = 4$ d
12. $x = -y^2$ l

a.
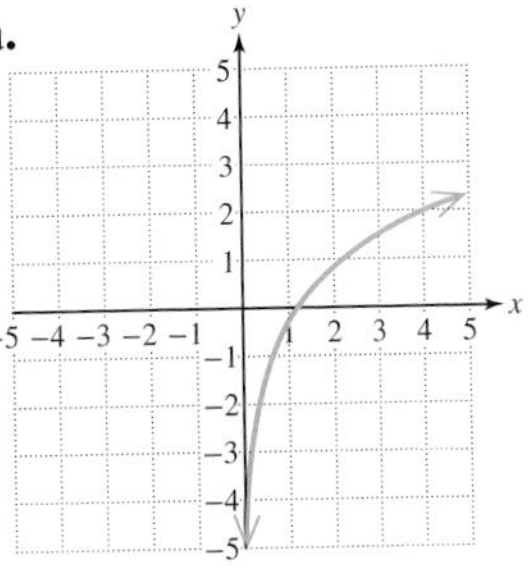

b.
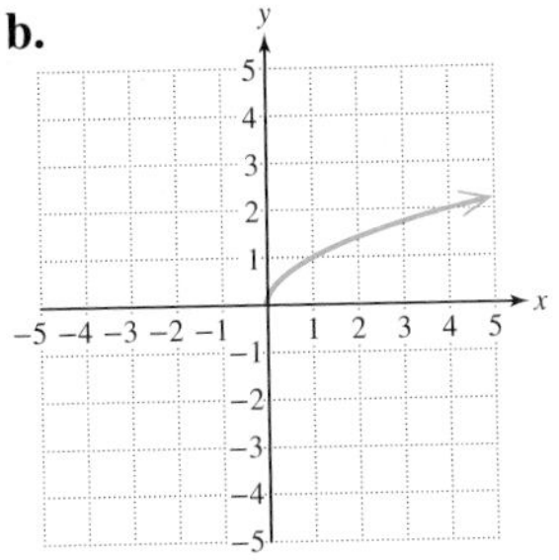

c.
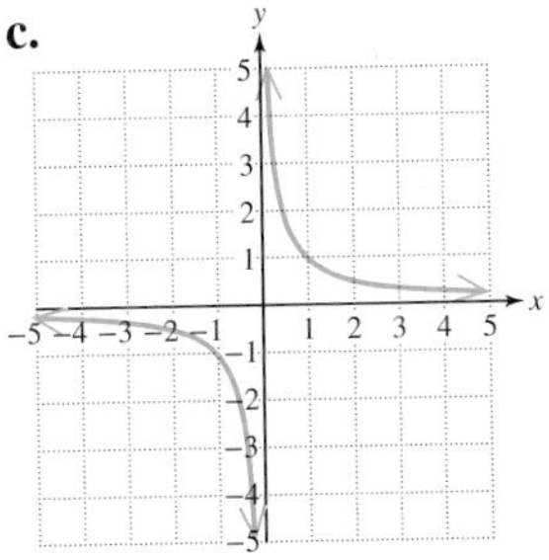

d.
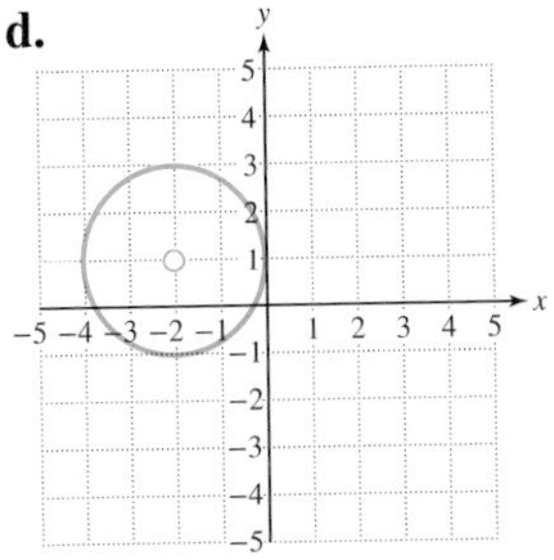

e.
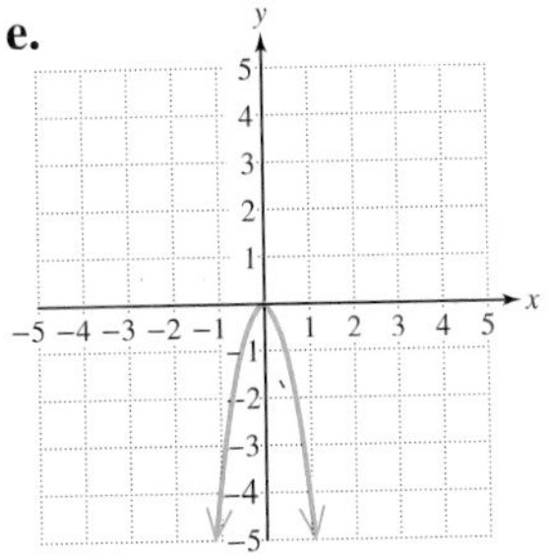

f.
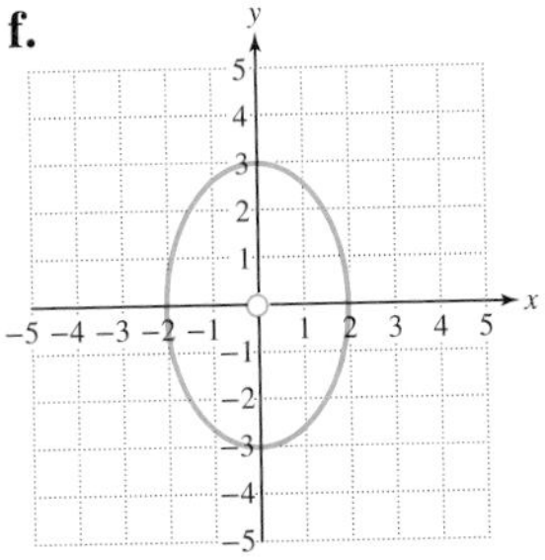

g.
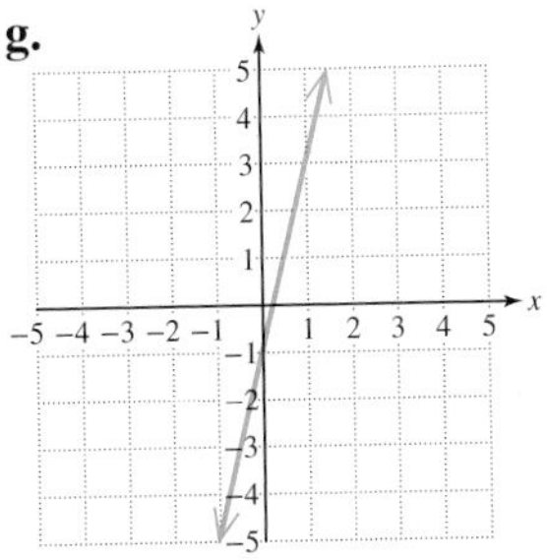

h.
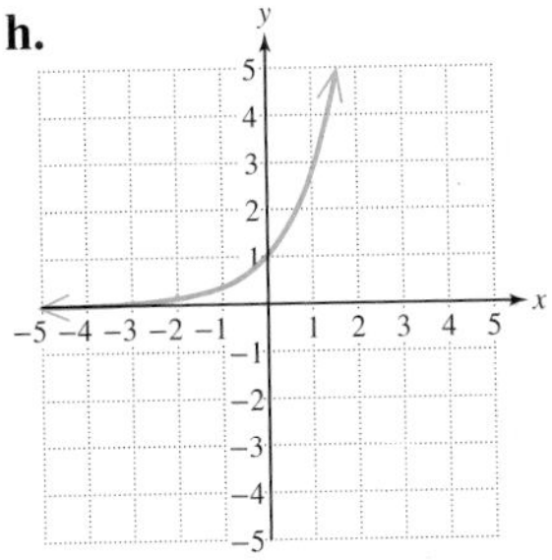

i.
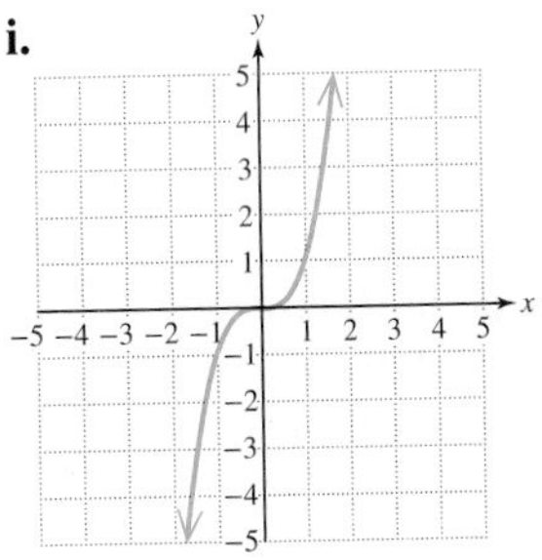

j.
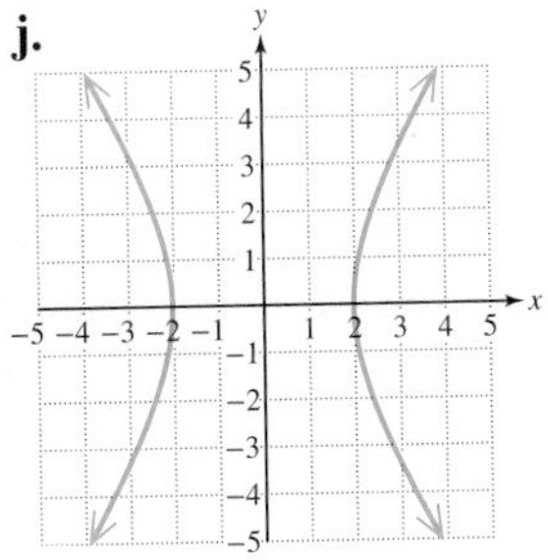

k.
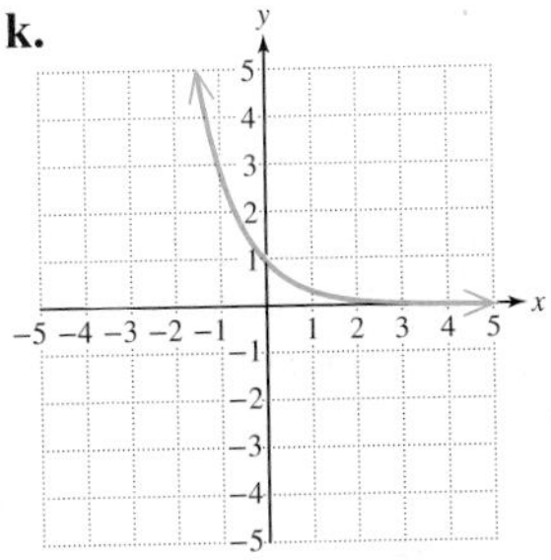

l.
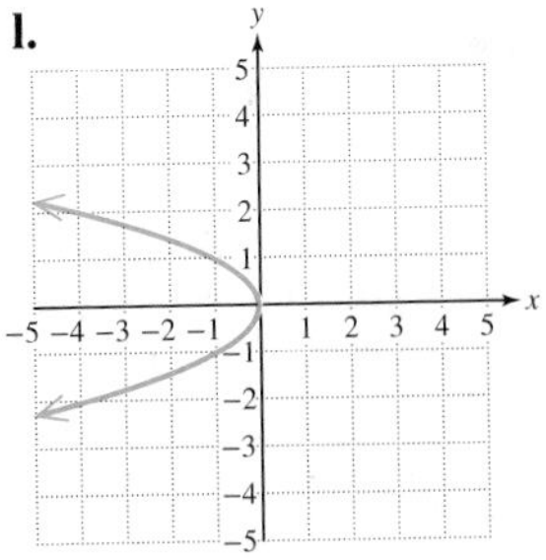

Concept 1: Nonlinear Inequalities in Two Variables

13. True or false: The point (2, 3) satisfies the inequality $-x^2 + y^3 > 1$. True

14. True or false: The point (4, −2) satisfies the inequality $4x^2 - 2x + 1 + y^2 < 3$. False

15. True or false: The point (5, 4) satisfies the system of inequalities. False

$$\frac{x^2}{36} + \frac{y^2}{25} < 1$$

$$x^2 + y^2 \geq 4$$

16. True or false: The point (1, −2) satisfies the system of inequalities. True

$$y < x^2$$

$$y > x^2 - 4$$

17. **a.** Graph the solution set for $x^2 + y^2 \leq 9$.

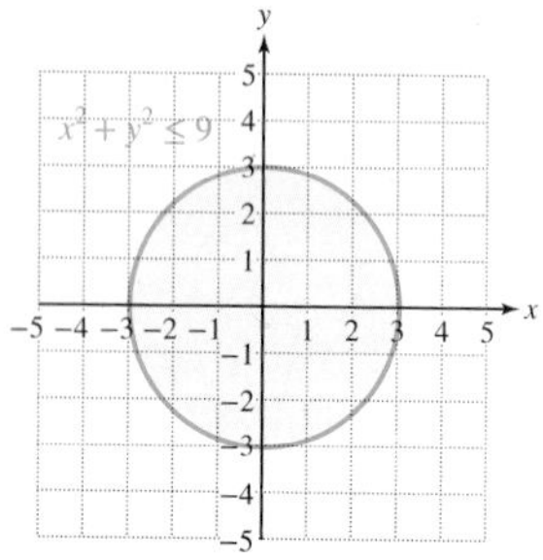

b. Describe the solution set for the inequality $x^2 + y^2 \geq 9$.

The set of points on and "outside" the circle $x^2 + y^2 = 9$

c. Describe the solution set for the equation $x^2 + y^2 = 9$

The set of points on the circle $x^2 + y^2 = 9$

18. **a.** Graph the solution set for $\frac{x^2}{4} + \frac{y^2}{9} \geq 1$.

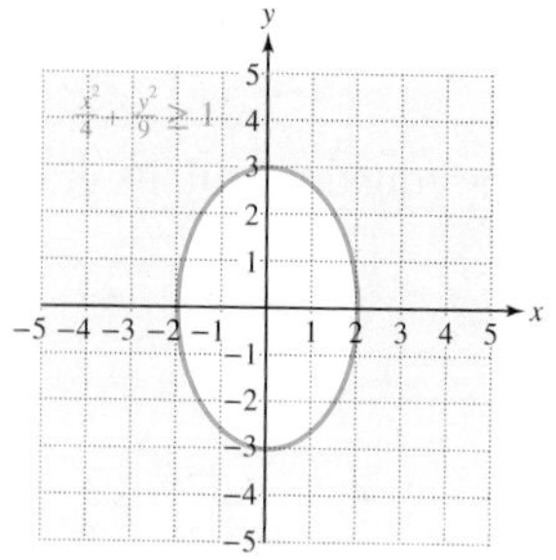

b. Describe the solution set for the inequality $\frac{x^2}{4} + \frac{y^2}{9} \leq 1$.

The set of points on and "inside" the ellipse $\frac{x^2}{4} + \frac{y^2}{9} = 1$

c. Describe the solution set for the equation $\frac{x^2}{4} + \frac{y^2}{9} = 1$

The set of points on the ellipse $\frac{x^2}{4} + \frac{y^2}{9} = 1$

19. **a.** Graph the solution set for $y \geq x^2 + 1$.

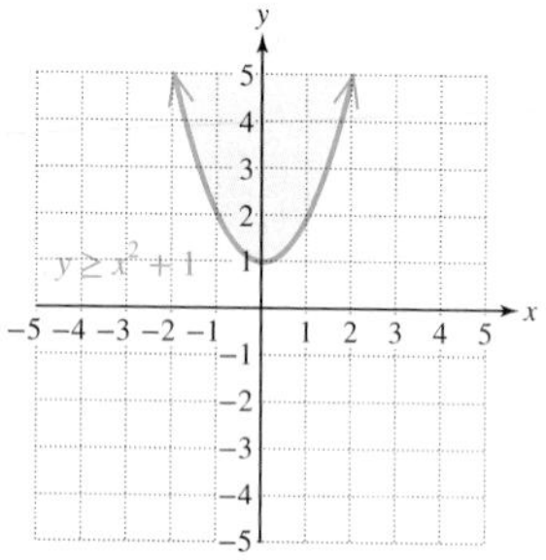

b. How would the solution change for the strict inequality $y > x^2 + 1$? The parabola $y = x^2 + 1$ would be drawn as a dashed curve.

20. **a.** Graph the solution set for $\frac{x^2}{4} - \frac{y^2}{9} \leq 1$.

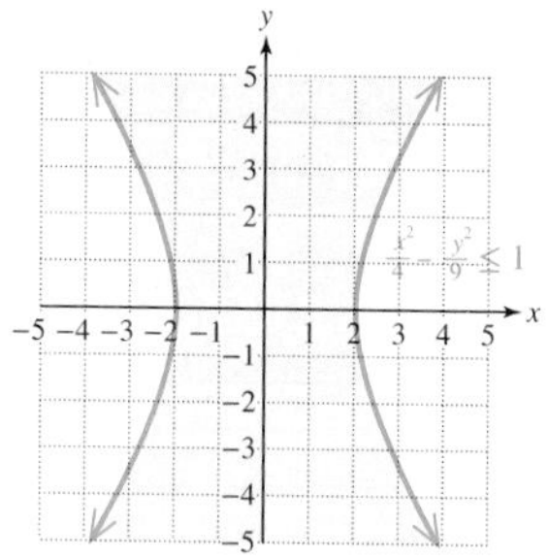

b. How would the solution change for the strict inequality $\frac{x^2}{4} - \frac{y^2}{9} < 1$. The hyperbola $\frac{x^2}{4} - \frac{y^2}{9} = 1$ would be drawn as a dashed curve.

21. A weak earthquake occurred in northern California roughly 4 mi south and 3 mi east of Sunol, California. The quake could be felt 25 mi away. Suppose the origin of a map is placed at the center of Sunol with the positive x-axis pointing east and the positive y-axis pointing north. Find an inequality that describes the points on the map for which the earthquake could be felt.

$(x - 3)^2 + (y + 4)^2 \leq 625$

22. A coordinate system is placed at the center of a town with the positive x-axis pointing east, and the positive y-axis pointing north. A cell tower is located 2 mi west and 4 mi north of the center of town. If the tower has a 30-mi range, write an inequality that represents the points on the map serviced by this tower.

$(x + 2)^2 + (y - 4)^2 \leq 900$

For Exercises 23–37, graph the solution set. **(See Examples 1–2.)**

23. $2x + y \geq 1$

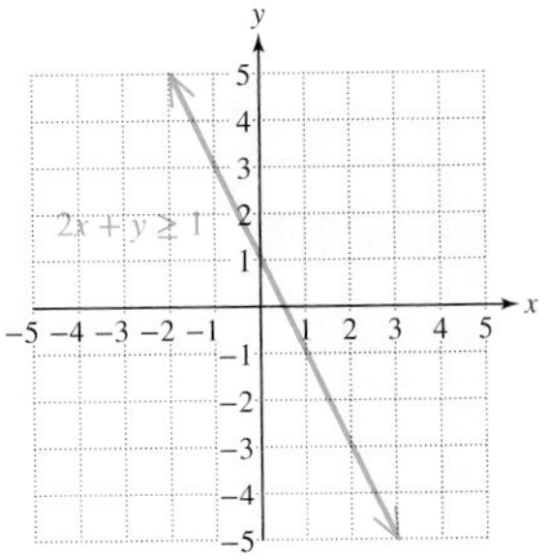

24. $3x + 2y \geq 6$

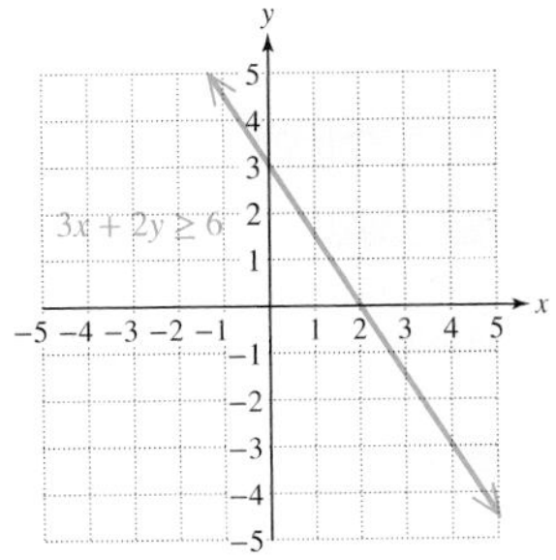

25. $x \leq y^2$

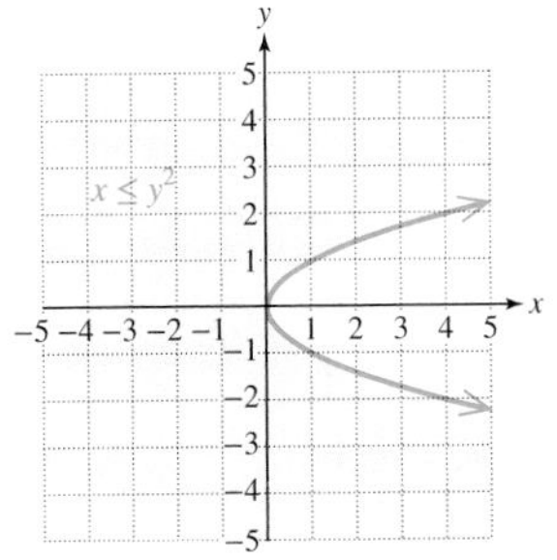

26. $y \leq -x^2$

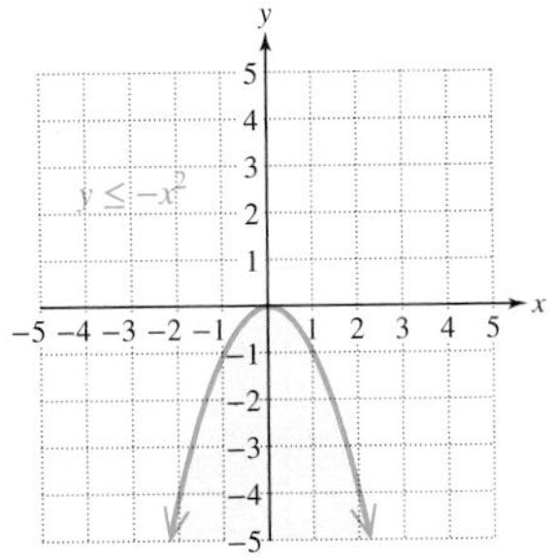

27. $(x - 1)^2 + (y + 2)^2 > 9$

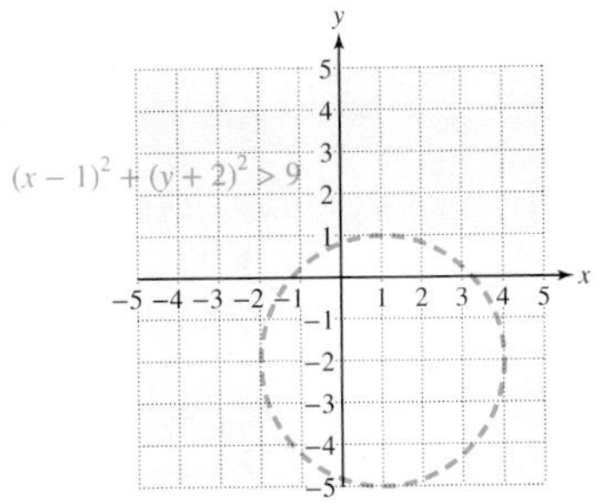

28. $(x + 1)^2 + (y - 4)^2 > 1$

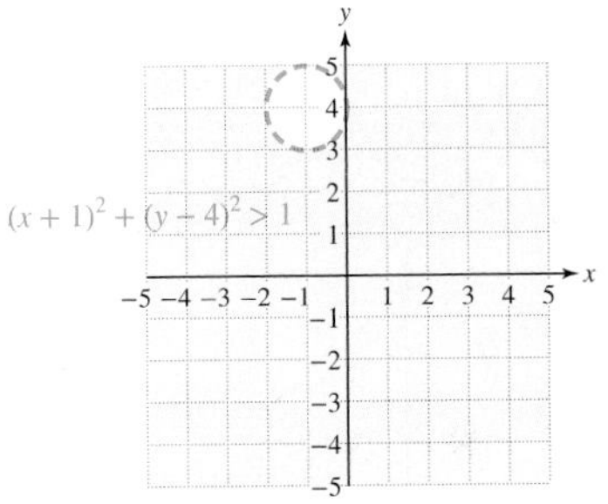

29. $x + y^2 \geq 4$

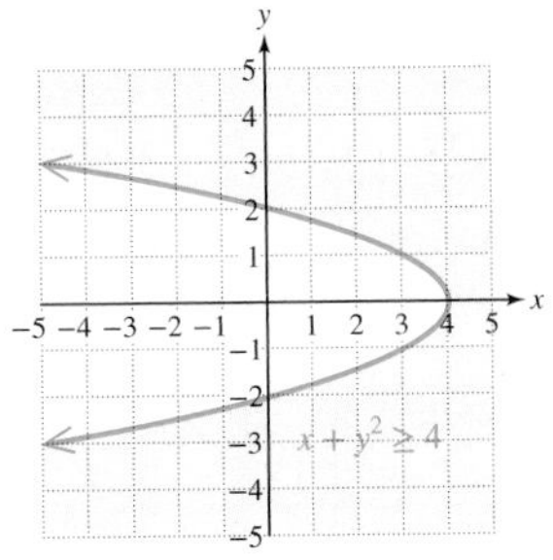

30. $x^2 + 2x + y - 1 \leq 0$

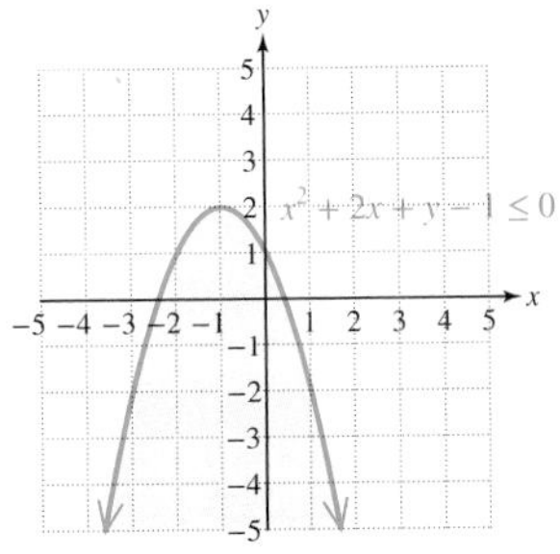

31. $9x^2 - y^2 > 9$

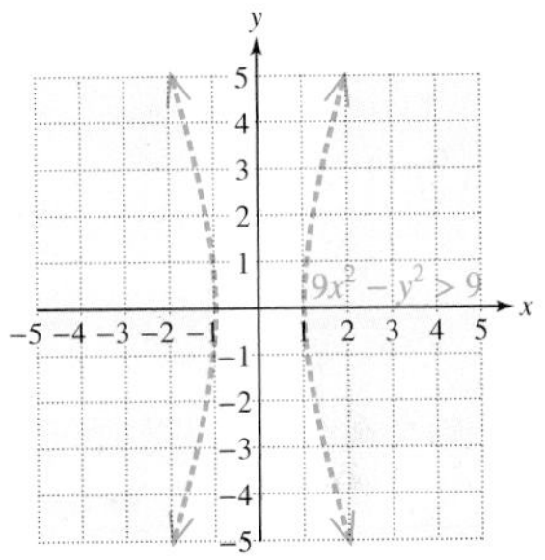

32. $y^2 - 4x^2 \leq 4$

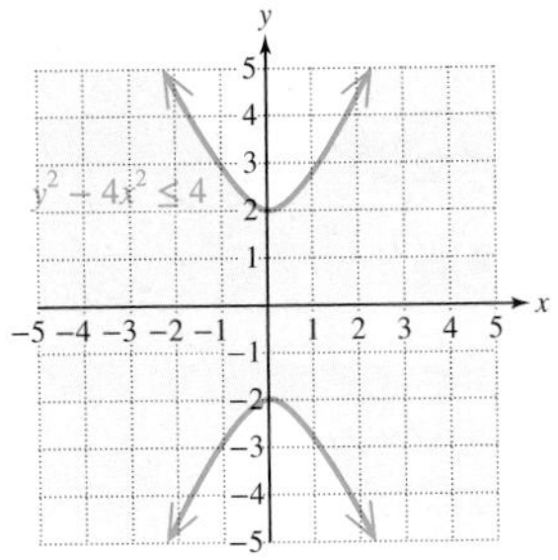

33. $x^2 + 16y^2 \leq 16$

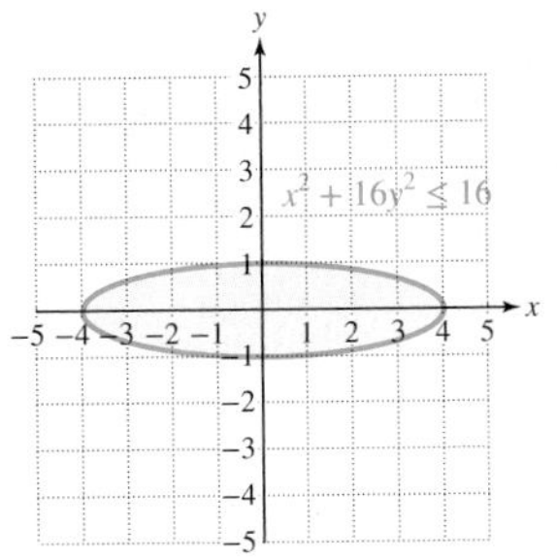

34. $4x^2 + y^2 \leq 4$

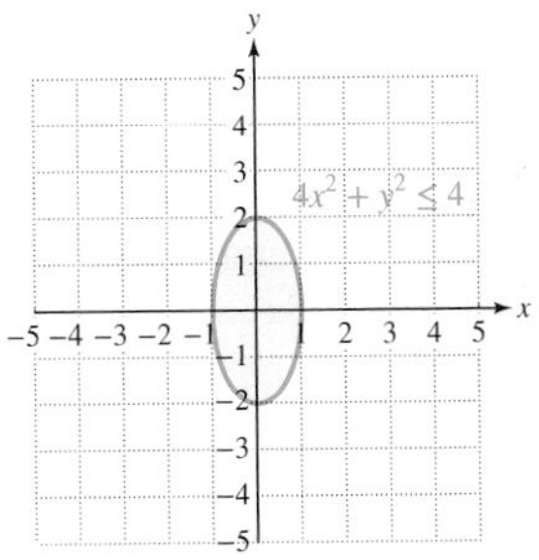

35. $y \le \ln x$

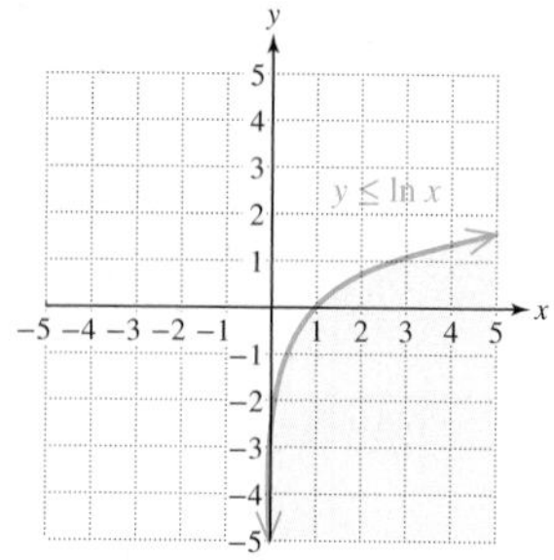

36. $y \le \log x$

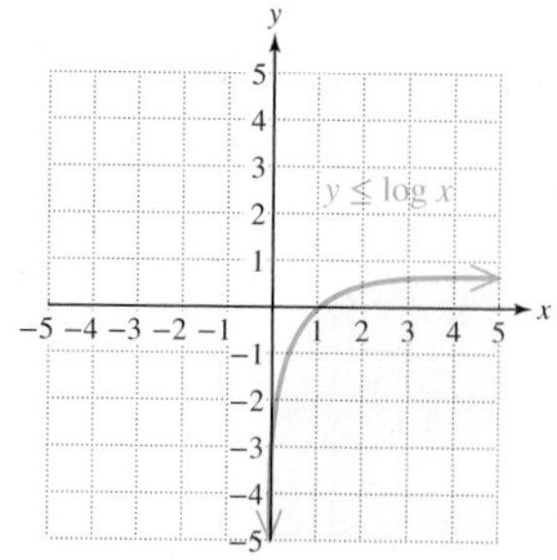

37. $y > 5^x$

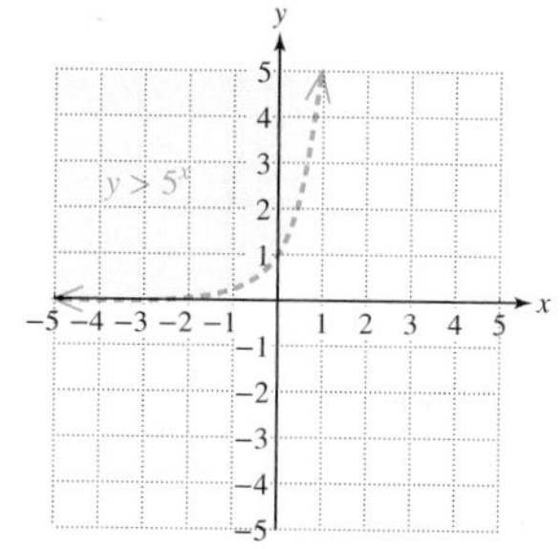

Concept 2: Systems of Nonlinear Inequalities in Two Variables

For Exercises 38–51, graph the solution set to the system of inequalities. **(See Examples 3–4.)**

38. $y < \sqrt{x}$

$x > 1$

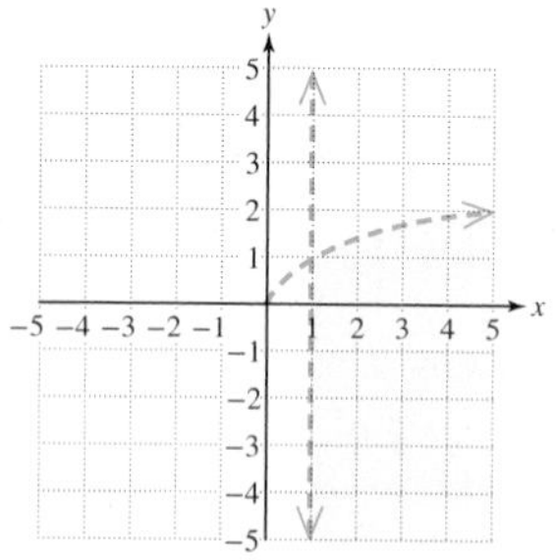

39. $y \ge \sqrt{x}$

$x \ge 0$

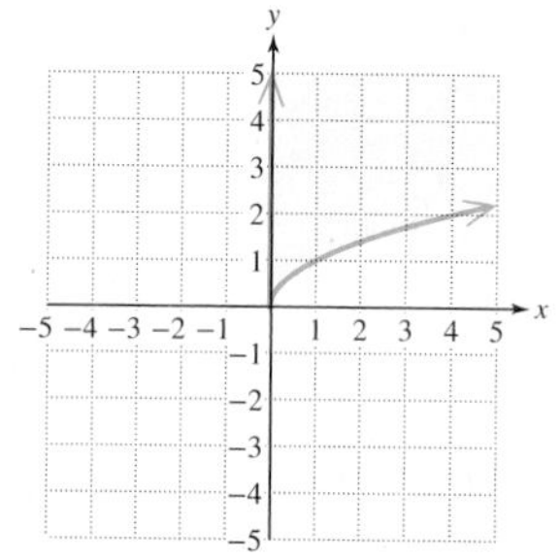

40. $\dfrac{x^2}{36} + \dfrac{y^2}{25} < 1$

$x^2 + y^2 \ge 4$

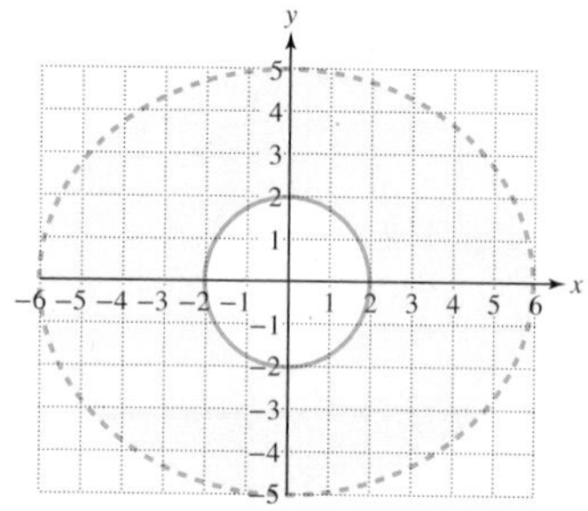

41. $x^2 - y^2 \ge 1$

$x \le 0$

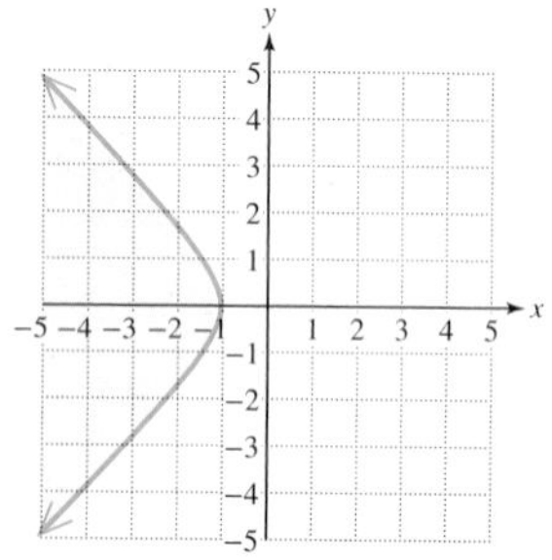

42. $y < x^2$

$y > x^2 - 4$

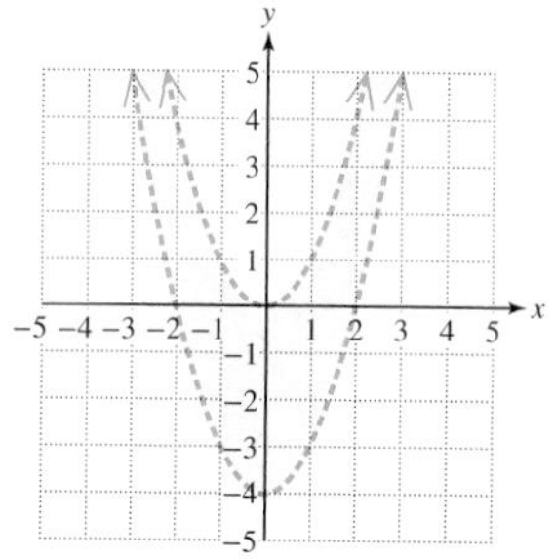

43. $y^2 - x^2 \ge 1$

$y \ge 0$

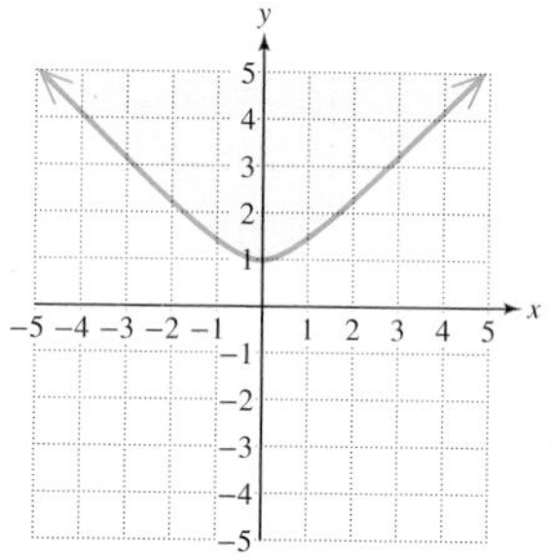

44. $y < \dfrac{1}{x}$

$y > 0$

$y < x$

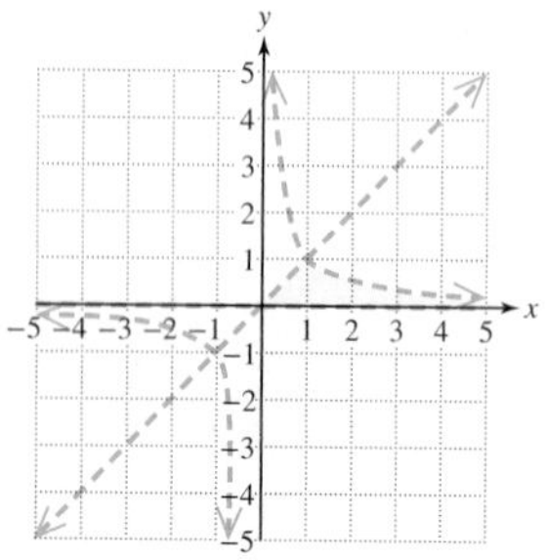

45. $y > x^3$

$y < 8$

$x > 0$

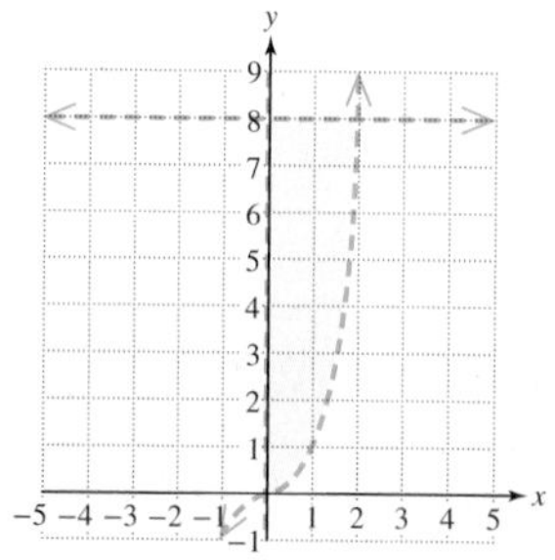

46. $x^2 + y^2 \ge 25$

$x^2 + y^2 \le 9$

{ }

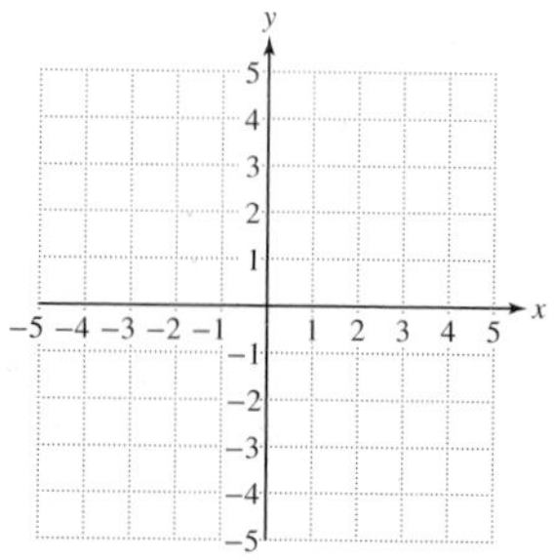

47. $\dfrac{x^2}{4} + \dfrac{y^2}{25} \geq 1$

$x^2 + \dfrac{y^2}{4} \leq 1$

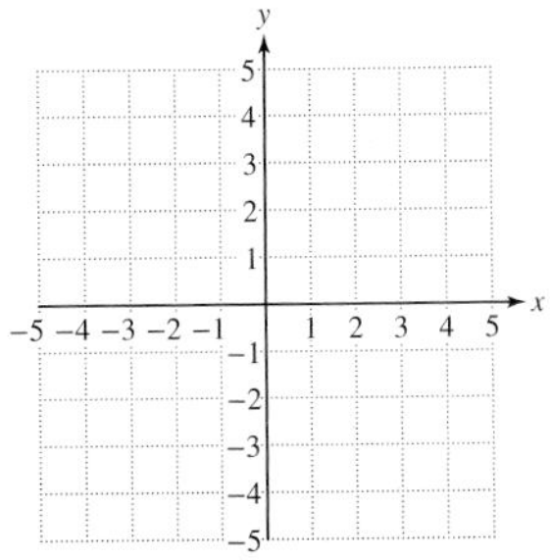

48. $x < -(y-1)^2 + 3$

$x + y > 2$

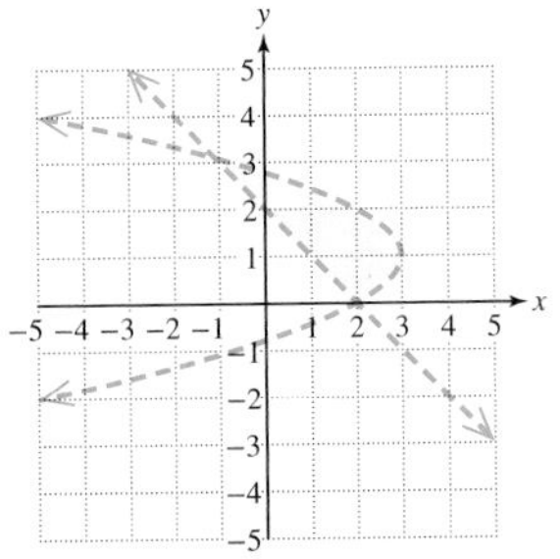

49. $x > (y-2)^2 + 1$

$x - y < 1$

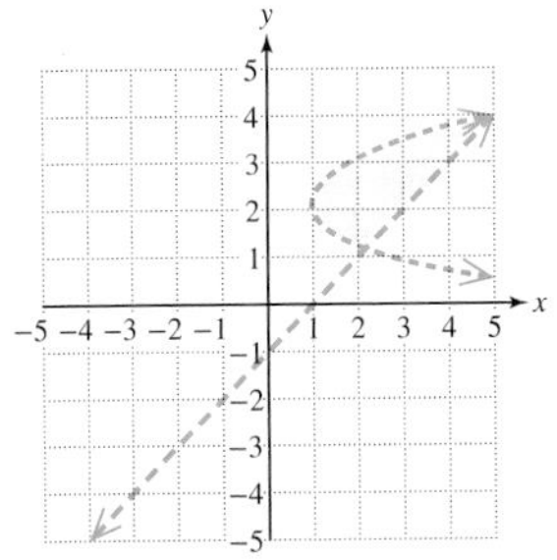

50. $x^2 + y^2 < 25$

$y < \dfrac{4}{3}x$

$y > -\dfrac{4}{3}x$

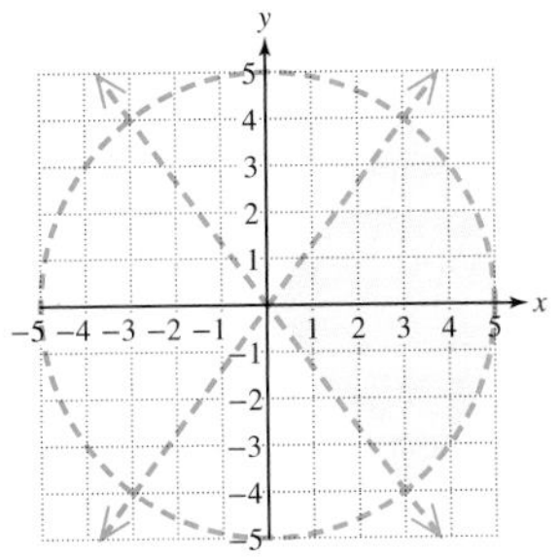

51. $y < e^x$

$y > 1$

$x < 2$

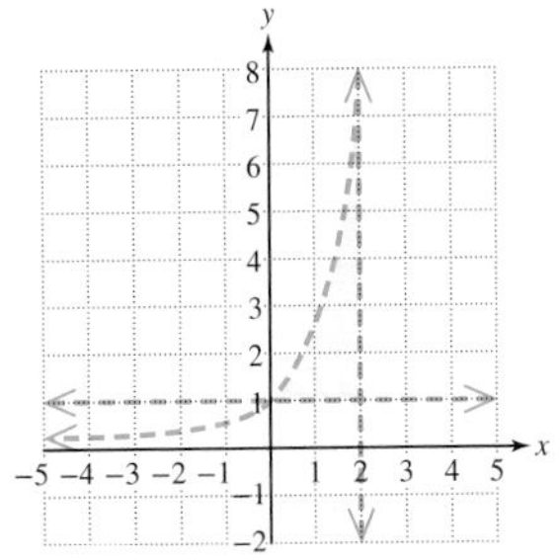

Expanding Your Skills

For Exercises 52–55, graph the compound inequalities.

52. $x^2 + y^2 \leq 36$ or $x + y \geq 0$

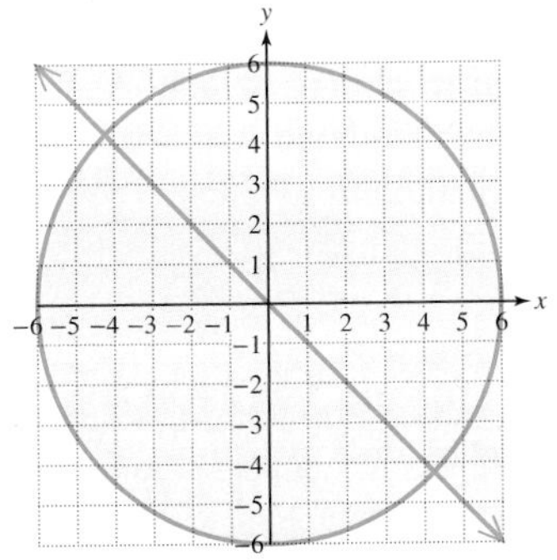

53. $y \leq -x^2 + 4$ or $y \geq x^2 - 4$

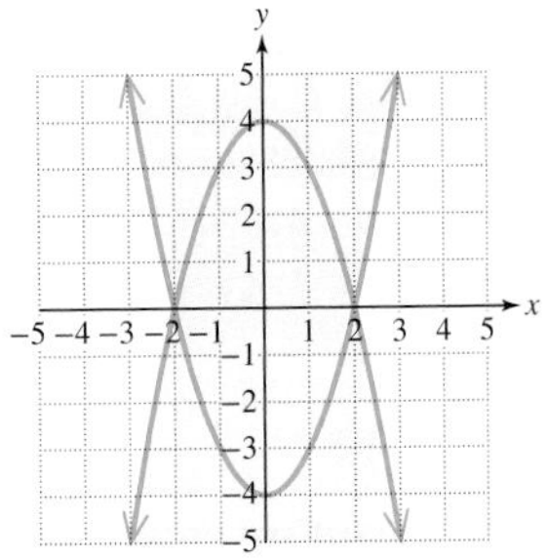

54. $y + 1 \geq x^2$ or $y + 1 \leq -x^2$

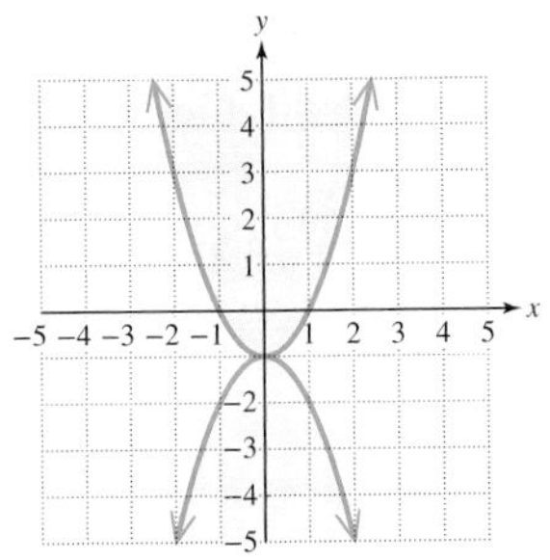

55. $(x+2)^2 + (y+3)^2 \leq 4$ or $x \geq y^2$

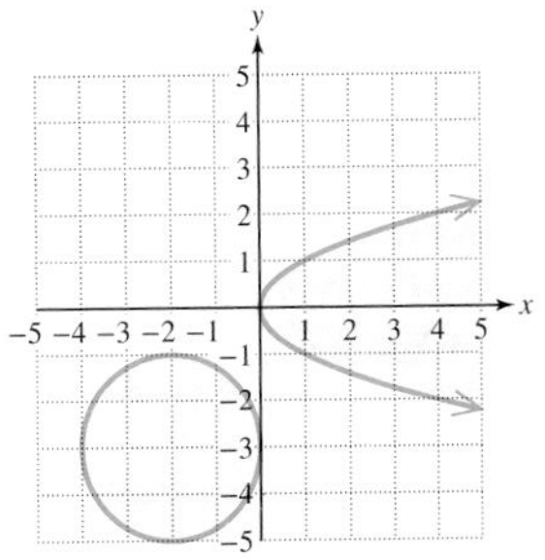

Group Activity

Investigating the Graphs of Conic Sections on a Calculator

Materials: Graphing calculator

Estimated time: 15 minutes

Group Size: 3

1. a. Given $x^2 + y^2 = 25$, use analytical methods to determine the x- and y-intercepts.

x-intercepts: (−5, 0), (5, 0) y-intercepts: (0, −5), (0, 5)

b. Solve the equation for y: $x^2 + y^2 = 25$. (*Hint:* When taking the square root of both sides of the equation, don't forget the ±.)

$Y_1 =$ $Y_1 = \sqrt{25 - x^2}$

$Y_2 =$ $Y_2 = -\sqrt{25 - x^2}$

c. Graph the two functions from part (b) on a graphing calculator. Use a window defined by $-7.6 \le x \le 7.6$ and $-5 \le y \le 5$.

d. Does it look like the functions graphed on the calculator intersect with the x-axis? Why do the x-intercepts not show up in the graph? If you relied solely on your calculator to find the x-intercepts, do you think that you would always get reliable results? No, the calculator has limited resolution.

2. a. Given $(x + 1)^2 - \frac{y^2}{9} = 1$, use analytical methods to find the x- and y-intercepts.

x-intercepts: (−2, 0), (0, 0) y-intercepts: (0, 0)

b. Solve the equation for y. $(x + 1)^2 - \frac{y^2}{9} = 1$

$Y_1 =$ $Y_1 = \sqrt{9(x+1)^2 - 9}$

$Y_2 =$ $Y_2 = -\sqrt{9(x+1)^2 - 9}$

c. Graph the two functions from part (b) on a graphing calculator. Use a window defined by $-7.6 \le x \le 7.6$ and $-5 \le y \le 5$.

d. Does it look like the functions graphed on the calculator intersect with the x-axis? Why do the x-intercepts not show up in the graph? If you relied solely on your calculator to find the x-intercepts, do you think that you would always get reliable results? No, the calculator has limited resolution.

3. Solve the equation for y and graph the functions on a graphing calculator. Use a window defined by $-7.6 \le x \le 7.6$ and $-5 \le y \le 5$.

a. $\frac{x^2}{4} + \frac{y^2}{16} = 1$ $Y_1 =$ $Y_1 = \sqrt{16 - 4x^2}$

$Y_2 =$ $Y_2 = -\sqrt{16 - 4x^2}$

b. Determine the x- and y-intercepts for the equation $\frac{x^2}{4} + \frac{y^2}{16} = 1$.

x-intercepts: (−2, 0), (2, 0) y-intercepts: (0, −4), (0, 4)

Chapter 13 Summary

Section 13.1 Distance Formula, Midpoint Formula, and Circles

Key Concepts

The distance between two points (x_1, y_1) and (x_2, y_2) is

$$d = \sqrt{(x_2 - x_1)^2 + (y_2 - y_1)^2}$$

The standard equation of a **circle** with center (h, k) and radius r is

$$(x - h)^2 + (y - k)^2 = r^2$$

The midpoint between two points is found by using the formula:

$$\left(\frac{x_1 + x_2}{2}, \frac{y_1 + y_2}{2}\right)$$

Examples

Example 1

Find the distance between two points.
$(5, -2)$ and $(-1, -6)$

$$\begin{aligned} d &= \sqrt{(-1 - 5)^2 + [-6 - (-2)]^2} \\ &= \sqrt{(-6)^2 + (-4)^2} \\ &= \sqrt{36 + 16} \\ &= \sqrt{52} = 2\sqrt{13} \end{aligned}$$

Example 2

Find the center and radius of the circle.

$$x^2 + y^2 - 8x + 6y = 0$$
$$(x^2 - 8x + 16) + (y^2 + 6y + 9) = 16 + 9$$
$$(x - 4)^2 + (y + 3)^2 = 25$$

The center is $(4, -3)$ and the radius is 5.

Example 3

Find the midpoint between $(-3, 1)$ and $(5, 7)$.

$$\left(\frac{-3 + 5}{2}, \frac{1 + 7}{2}\right) = (1, 4)$$

Section 13.2 More on the Parabola

Key Concepts

A **parabola** is the set of points in a plane that are equidistant from a fixed line (called the directrix) and a fixed point (called the focus) not on the directrix.

The standard form of an equation of a parabola with **vertex** (h, k) and vertical **axis of symmetry** is

$$y = a(x - h)^2 + k \qquad \text{where } a \neq 0$$

- The equation of the axis of symmetry is $x = h$.
- If $a > 0$, the parabola opens upward.
- If $a < 0$, the parabola opens downward.

The standard form of an equation of a parabola with vertex (h, k) and horizontal axis of symmetry is

$$x = a(y - k)^2 + h \qquad \text{where } a \neq 0$$

- The equation of the axis of symmetry is $y = k$.
- If $a > 0$, the parabola opens to the right.
- If $a < 0$, the parabola opens to the left.

Examples

Example 1

Given the parabola $y = (x - 2)^2 + 1$,

The vertex is $(2, 1)$.

The axis of symmetry is $x = 2$.

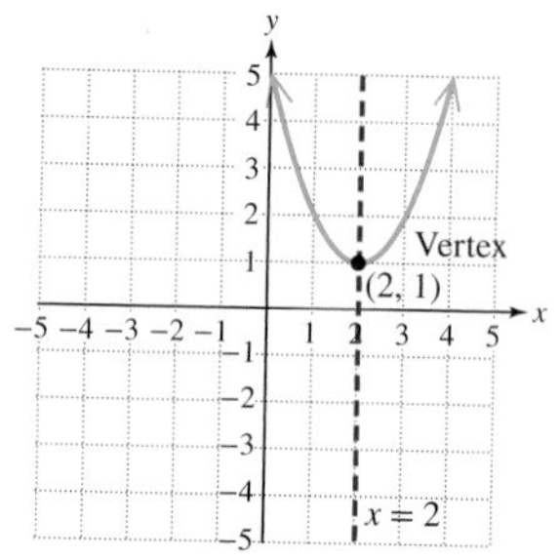

Example 2

Given the parabola $x = -\frac{1}{4}y^2 + 1$, determine the coordinates of the vertex and the equation of the axis of symmetry.

$$x = -\frac{1}{4}(y - 0)^2 + 1$$

The vertex is $(1, 0)$.

The axis of symmetry is $y = 0$.

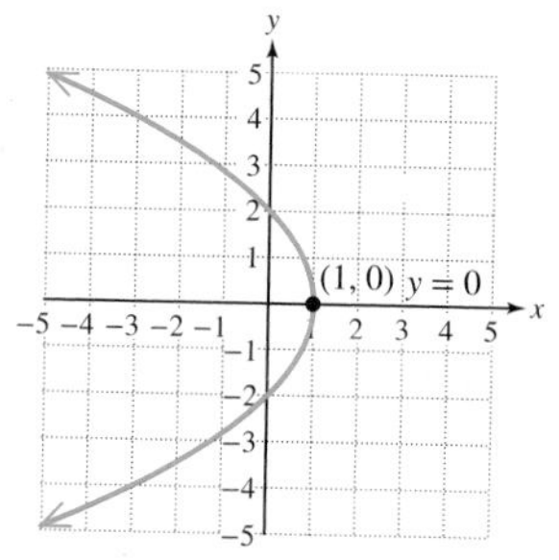

Section 13.3 The Ellipse and Hyperbola

Key Concepts

An **ellipse** is the set of all points (x, y) such that the sum of the distances between (x, y) and two distinct points (called foci) is constant.

Standard Form of an Ellipse with Center at the Origin

An ellipse with the center at the origin has the equation

$$\frac{x^2}{a^2} + \frac{y^2}{b^2} = 1$$

where a and b are positive real numbers.

For an ellipse centered at the origin, the x-intercepts are given by $(a, 0)$ and $(-a, 0)$, and the y-intercepts are given by $(0, b)$ and $(0, -b)$.

A **hyperbola** is the set of all points (x, y) such that the absolute value of the difference of the distances between (x, y) and two distinct points is a constant. The fixed points are called the foci of the hyperbola.

Standard Forms of an Equation of a Hyperbola

Let a and b represent positive real numbers.

Horizontal Transverse Axis. The standard form of an equation of a hyperbola with a horizontal transverse axis and center at the origin is given by

$$\frac{x^2}{a^2} - \frac{y^2}{b^2} = 1$$

Vertical Transverse Axis. The standard form of an equation of a hyperbola with a vertical transverse axis and center at the origin is given by

$$\frac{y^2}{b^2} - \frac{x^2}{a^2} = 1$$

Examples

Example 1

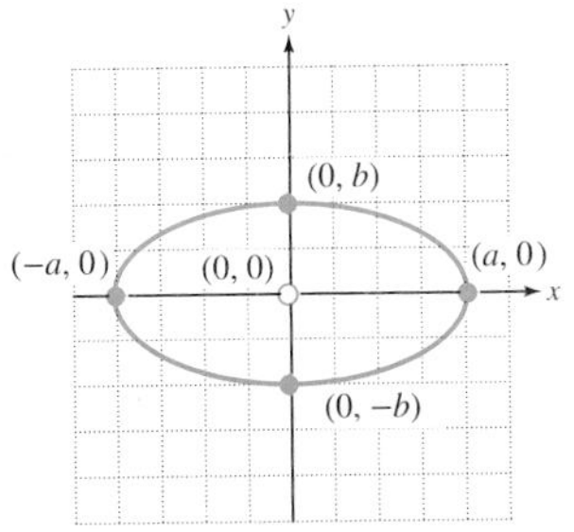

Example 2

$$\frac{x^2}{25} + \frac{y^2}{9} = 1$$

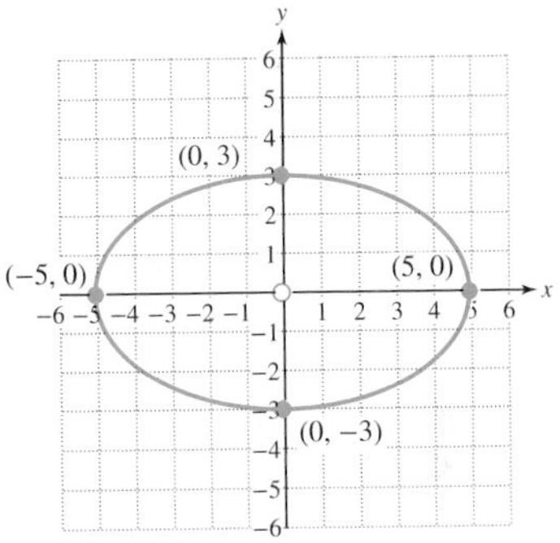

Example 3

$$\frac{x^2}{4} - \frac{y^2}{16} = 1$$

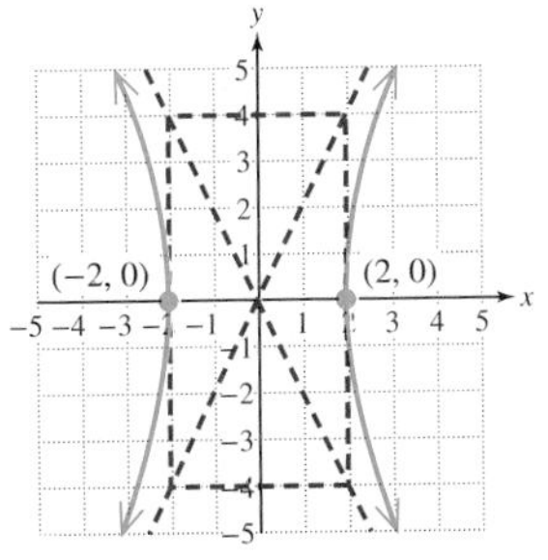

Example 4

$$\frac{y^2}{4} - \frac{x^2}{16} = 1$$

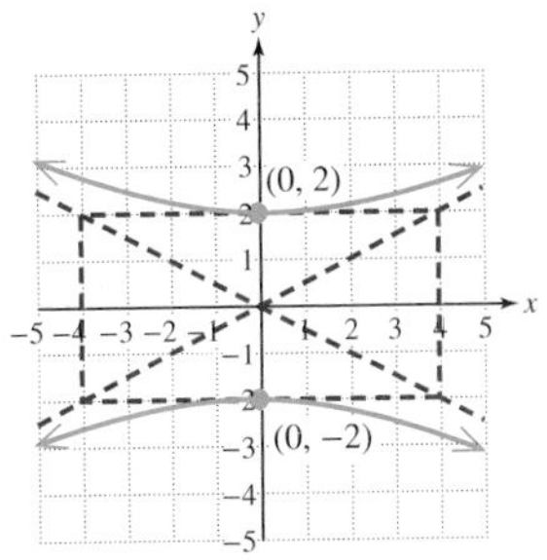

Section 13.4 Nonlinear Systems of Equations in Two Variables

Key Concepts

A **nonlinear system of equations** can be solved by graphing or by the substitution method.

$2x^2 + y^2 = 15$

$x^2 - y = 0$

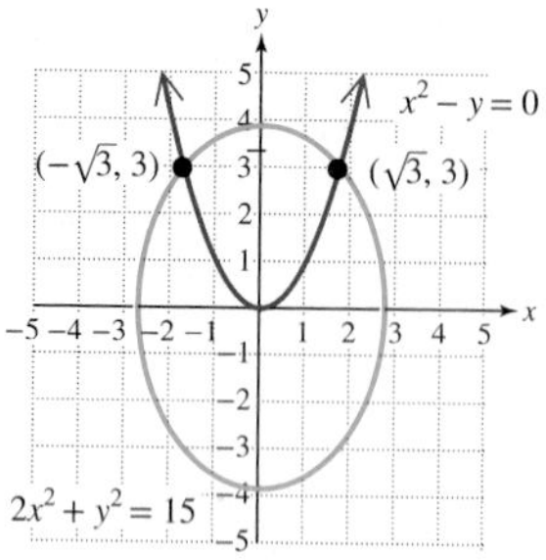

Examples

Example 1

A $2x^2 + y^2 = 15$

B $x^2 - y = 0$ Solve for y. $y = x^2$

A $2x^2 + (x^2)^2 = 15$ Substitute in first equation.

$2x^2 + x^4 = 15$

$x^4 + 2x^2 - 15 = 0$

$(x^2 + 5)(x^2 - 3) = 0$

$x^2 + 5 = 0$ or $x^2 - 3 = 0$

~~$x^2 = -5$~~ or $x^2 = 3$

$x = \pm\sqrt{3}$

If $x = \sqrt{3}$ then $y = (\sqrt{3})^2 = 3$.

If $x = -\sqrt{3}$ then $y = (-\sqrt{3})^2 = 3$.

Points of intersection are $(\sqrt{3}, 3)$ and $(-\sqrt{3}, 3)$.

The solution set is $\{(\sqrt{3}, 3), (-\sqrt{3}, 3)\}$.

Section 13.5 Nonlinear Inequalities and Systems of Inequalities in Two Variables

Key Concepts

Graph a nonlinear inequality by using the test point method. That is, graph the related equation. Then choose test points in each region to determine where the inequality is true.

Graph a system of nonlinear inequalities by finding the intersection of the solution sets. That is, graph the solution set for each individual inequality, then take the intersection.

Examples

Example 1

$y \geq x^2$

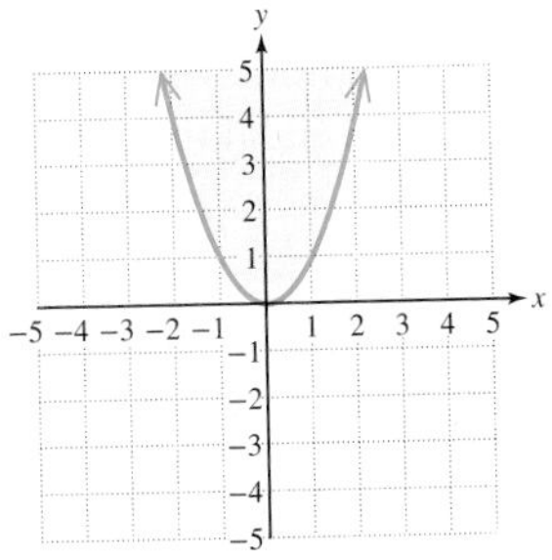

Example 2

$x^2 + y^2 < 4$

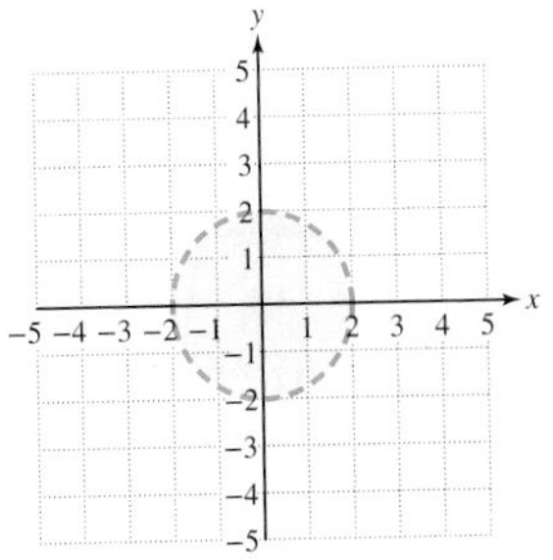

Example 3

$x \geq 0, \quad y > x^2, \quad \text{and} \quad x^2 + y^2 < 4$

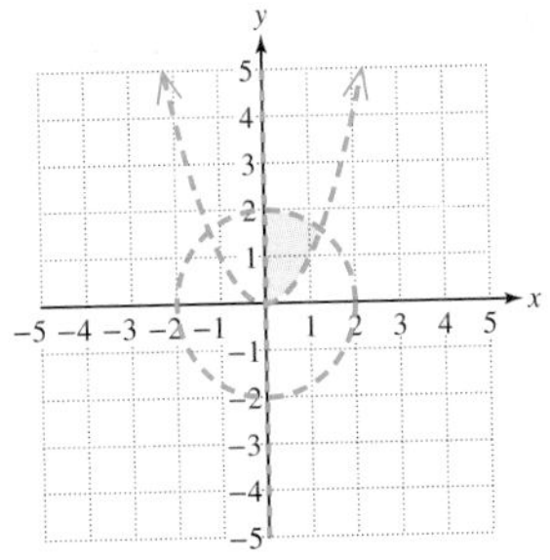

Chapter 13 Review Exercises

Section 13.1

For Exercises 1–2, find the distance between the two points by using the distance formula.

1. $(-6, 3)$ and $(0, 1)$
$2\sqrt{10}$

2. $(4, 13)$ and $(-1, 5)$
$\sqrt{89}$

3. Find x such that $(x, 5)$ is 5 units from $(2, 9)$.
$x = 5$ or $x = -1$

4. Find x such that $(-3, 4)$ is 3 units from $(x, 1)$.
$x = -3$

For Exercises 5–8, find the center and the radius of the circle.

5. $(x - 12)^2 + (y - 3)^2 = 16$ Center $(12, 3)$; $r = 4$

6. $(x + 7)^2 + (y - 5)^2 = 81$ Center $(-7, 5)$; $r = 9$

7. $(x + 3)^2 + (y + 8)^2 = 20$ Center $(-3, -8)$; $r = 2\sqrt{5}$

8. $(x - 1)^2 + (y + 6)^2 = 32$ Center $(1, -6)$; $r = 4\sqrt{2}$

9. A stained glass window is in the shape of a circle with a 16-in. diameter. Find an equation of the circle relative to the origin for each of the following graphs.

a.

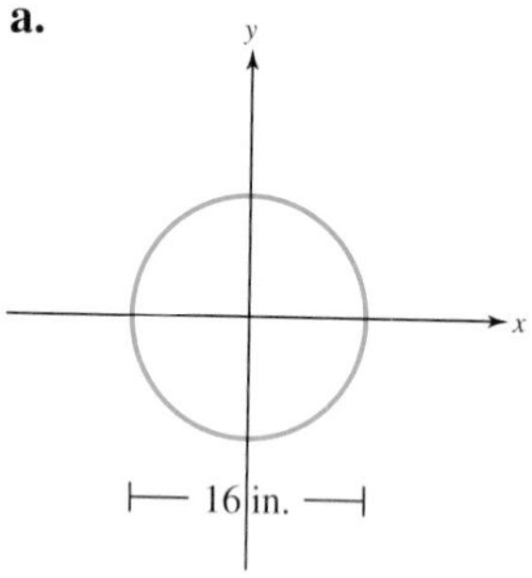

$x^2 + y^2 = 64$

b.

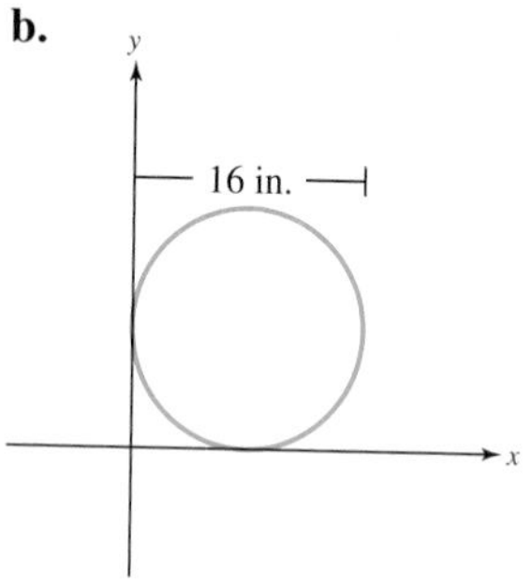

$(x - 8)^2 + (y - 8)^2 = 64$

For Exercises 10–13, write the equation of the circle in standard form by completing the square.

10. $x^2 + y^2 + 12x - 10y + 51 = 0$
$(x + 6)^2 + (y - 5)^2 = 10$

11. $x^2 + y^2 + 4x + 16y + 60 = 0$
$(x + 2)^2 + (y + 8)^2 = 8$

12. $x^2 + y^2 - x - 4y + \frac{1}{4} = 0$
$\left(x - \frac{1}{2}\right)^2 + (y - 2)^2 = 4$

13. $x^2 + y^2 - 6x - \frac{2}{3}y + \frac{1}{9} = 0$
$(x - 3)^2 + \left(y - \frac{1}{3}\right)^2 = 9$

14. Write an equation of a circle with center at the origin and a diameter of 7 m.
$x^2 + y^2 = \frac{49}{4}$

15. Write an equation of a circle with center $(0, 2)$ and radius 3 m.
$x^2 + (y - 2)^2 = 9$

For Exercises 16–17, find the midpoint of the segment with the given endpoints.

16. $(-3, 1)$ and $(-5, -5)$
$(-4, -2)$

17. $(0, 9)$ and $(-2, 7)$
$(-1, 8)$

Section 13.2

For Exercises 18–21, determine whether the axis of symmetry is vertical or horizontal and if the parabola opens upward, downward, left, or right.

18. $y = -2(x - 3)^2 + 2$
Vertical axis of symmetry; parabola opens downward

19. $x = 3(y - 9)^2 + 1$
Horizontal axis of symmetry; parabola opens right

20. $x = -(y + 4)^2 - 8$
Horizontal axis of symmetry; parabola opens left

21. $y = (x + 3)^2 - 10$
Vertical axis of symmetry; parabola opens upward

For Exercises 22–25, determine the coordinates of the vertex and the equation of the axis of symmetry. Then use this information to graph the parabola.

22. $x = -(y - 1)^2$

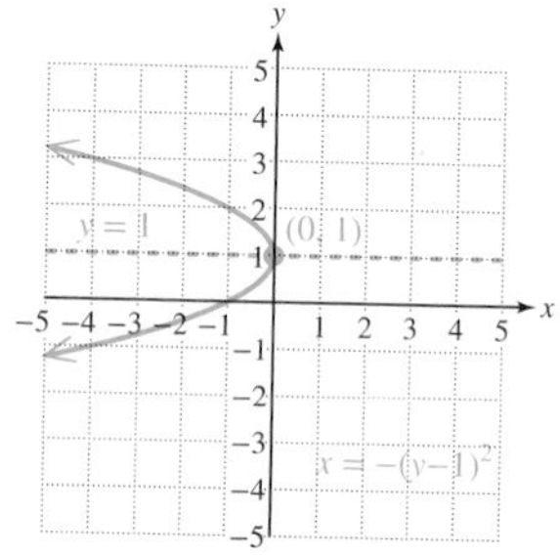

23. $y = (x + 2)^2$

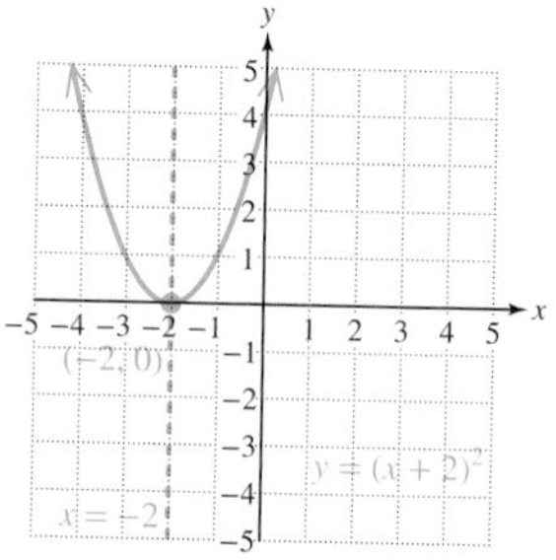

24. $y = -\frac{1}{4}x^2$

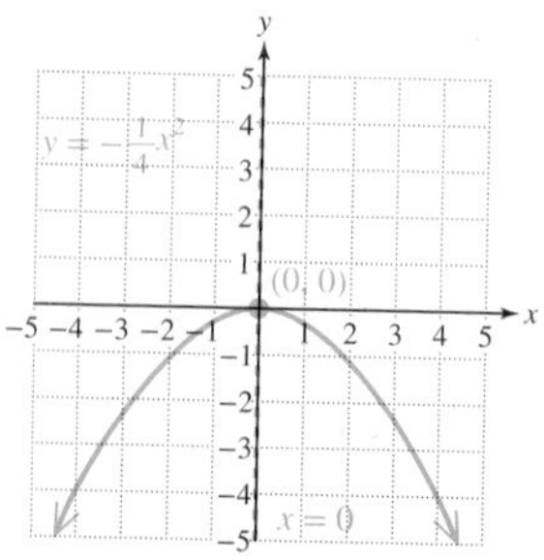

25. $x = 2y^2 - 1$

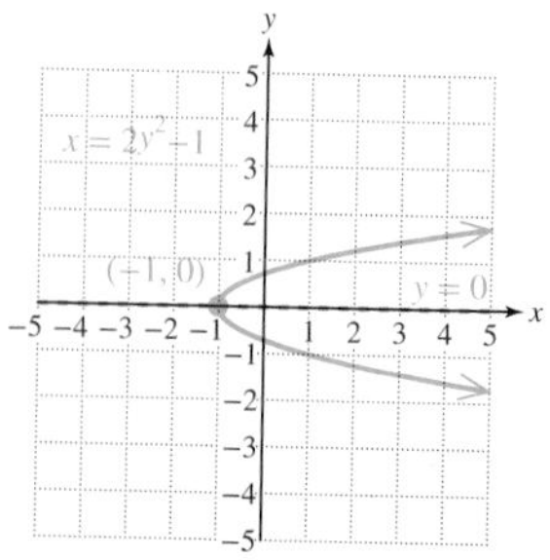

For Exercises 26–29, write the equation in standard form $y = a(x - h)^2 + k$ or $x = a(y - k)^2 + h$. Then identify the vertex and axis of symmetry.

26. $y = x^2 - 6x + 5$ $y = (x - 3)^2 - 4$; vertex: $(3, -4)$; axis of symmetry: $x = 3$

27. $x = y^2 + 4y + 2$ $x = (y + 2)^2 - 2$; vertex: $(-2, -2)$; axis of symmetry: $y = -2$

28. $x = -4y^2 + 4y$ $x = -4\left(y - \frac{1}{2}\right)^2 + 1$; vertex: $\left(1, \frac{1}{2}\right)$; axis of symmetry: $y = \frac{1}{2}$

29. $y = -2x^2 - 2x$

$y = -2\left(x + \frac{1}{2}\right)^2 + \frac{1}{2}$; vertex: $\left(-\frac{1}{2}, \frac{1}{2}\right)$; axis of symmetry: $x = -\frac{1}{2}$

Section 13.3

For Exercises 30–31, identify the *x*- and *y*-intercepts. Then graph the ellipse.

30. $\frac{x^2}{9} + \frac{y^2}{25} = 1$

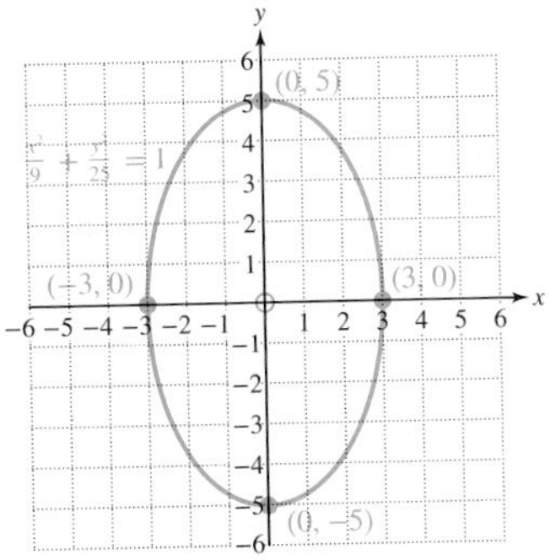

31. $x^2 + 4y^2 = 36$

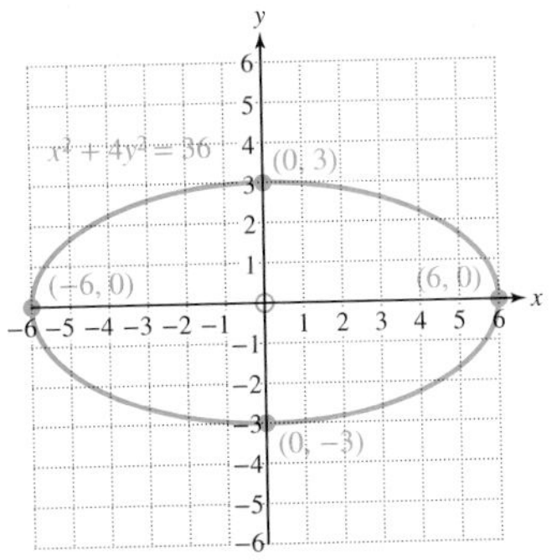

For Exercises 32–33, identify the center of the ellipse and graph the ellipse.

32. $\frac{(x - 5)^2}{4} + \frac{(y + 3)^2}{16} = 1$ Center: $(5, -3)$

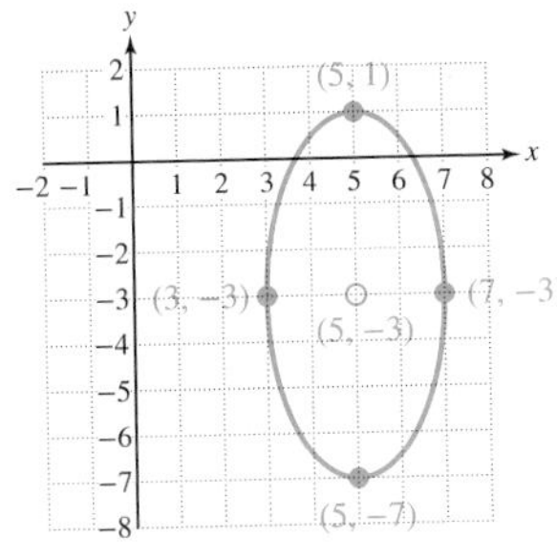

33. $\frac{x^2}{25} + \frac{(y - 2)^2}{9} = 1$ Center: $(0, 2)$

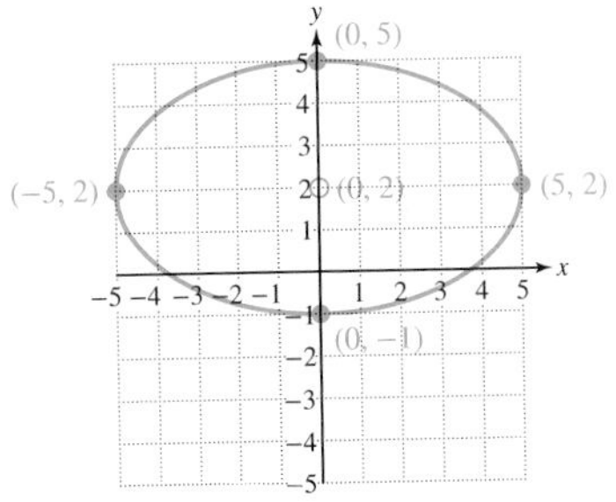

For Exercises 34–37, determine whether the transverse axis of the hyperbola is horizontal or vertical.

34. $\frac{x^2}{12} - \frac{y^2}{16} = 1$ Horizontal

35. $\frac{y^2}{9} - \frac{x^2}{9} = 1$ Vertical

36. $y^2 - 8x^2 = 16$ Vertical

37. $3x^2 - y^2 = 18$ Horizontal

For Exercises 38–39, graph the hyperbola by first drawing the reference rectangle and the asymptotes. Label the vertices.

38. $\frac{x^2}{4} - y^2 = 1$

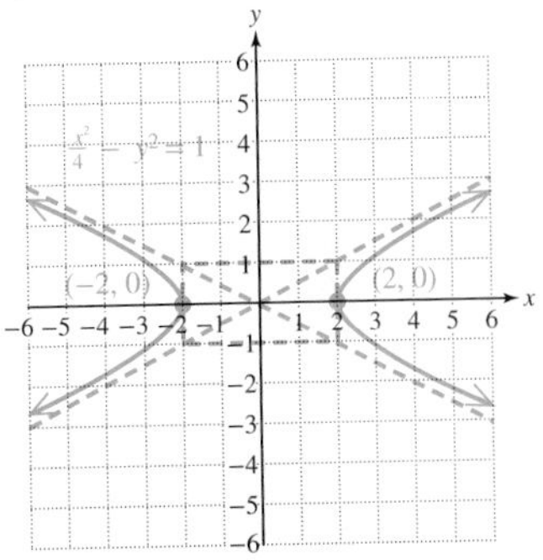

39. $y^2 - x^2 = 16$

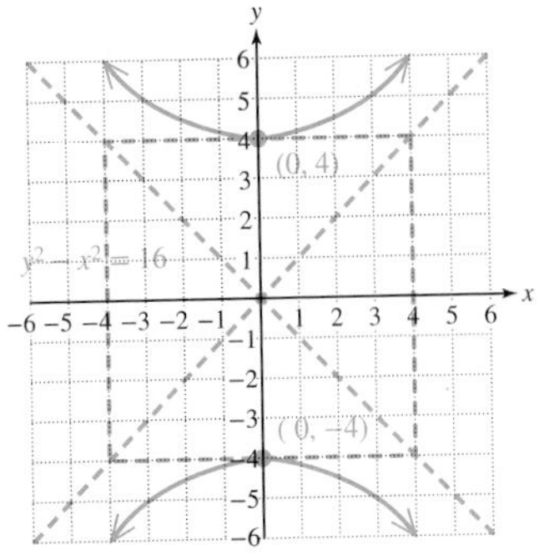

For Exercises 40–43, identify the equations as representing an ellipse or a hyperbola.

40. $\dfrac{x^2}{4} - \dfrac{y^2}{9} = 1$ Hyperbola

41. $\dfrac{x^2}{16} + \dfrac{y^2}{9} = 1$ Ellipse

42. $\dfrac{x^2}{4} + \dfrac{y^2}{1} = 1$ Ellipse

43. $\dfrac{y^2}{1} - \dfrac{x^2}{16} = 1$ Hyperbola

Section 13.4

For Exercises 44–47,

a. Identify each equation as representing a line, a parabola, a circle, an ellipse, or a hyperbola.

b. Graph both equations on the same coordinate system.

c. Solve the system analytically and verify the answers from the graph.

44. $3x + 2y = 10$

$y = x^2 - 5$

a. Line and parabola

b.

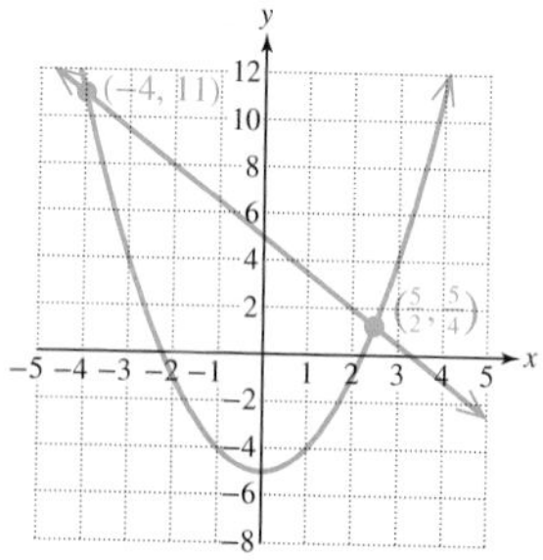

c. $\left\{\left(\frac{5}{2}, \frac{5}{4}\right), (-4, 11)\right\}$

45. $4x + 2y = 10$

$y = x^2 - 10$

a. Line and parabola

b.

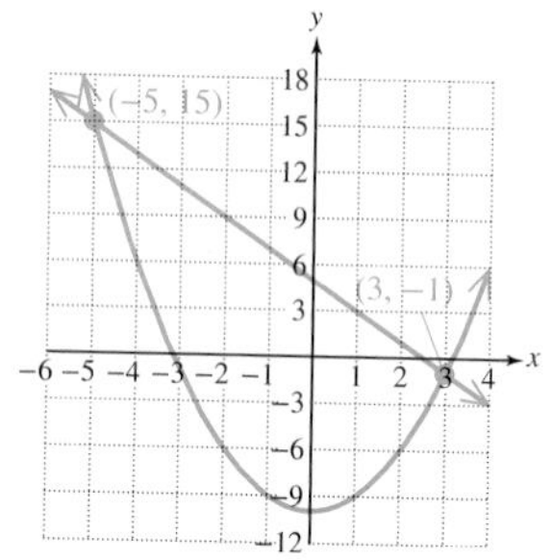

c. $\{(-5, 15), (3, -1)\}$

46. $x^2 + y^2 = 9$

$2x + y = 3$

a. Circle and line.

b.

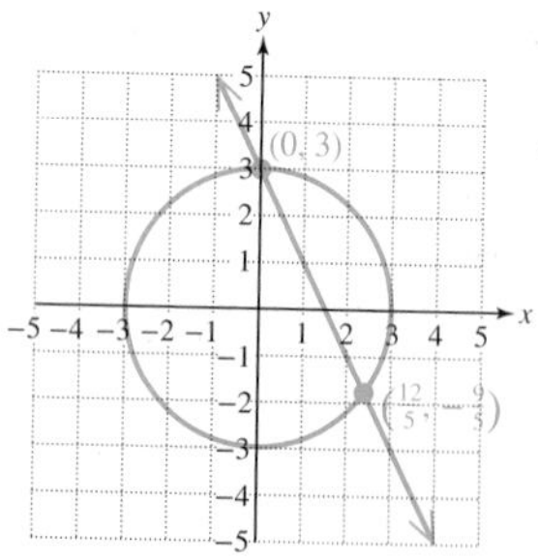

c. $\left\{(0, 3), \left(\frac{12}{5}, -\frac{9}{5}\right)\right\}$

47. $x^2 + y^2 = 16$

$x - 2y = 8$

a. Circle and line

b.

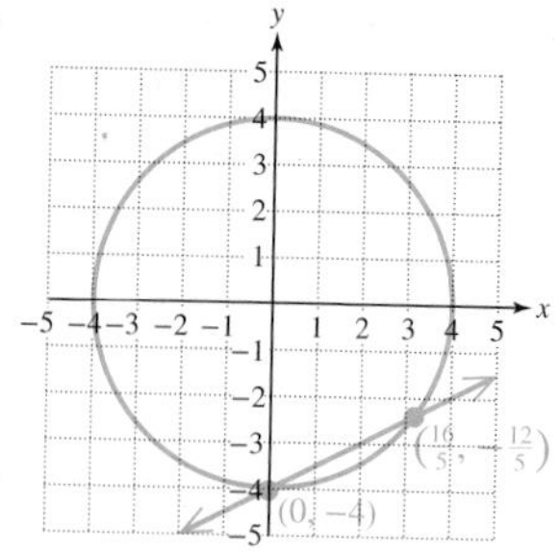

c. $\left\{(0, -4), \left(\frac{16}{5}, -\frac{12}{5}\right)\right\}$

For Exercises 48–53, solve the system of nonlinear equations by using either the substitution method or the addition method.

48. $x^2 + 2y^2 = 8$

$2x - y = 2$

$\left\{(0, -2), \left(\frac{16}{9}, \frac{14}{9}\right)\right\}$

49. $x^2 + 4y^2 = 29$

$x - y = -4$

$\left\{\left(-\frac{7}{5}, \frac{13}{5}\right), (-5, -1)\right\}$

50. $x - y = 4$

$y^2 = 2x$

$\{(8, 4), (2, -2)\}$

51. $y = x^2$

$6x^2 - y^2 = 8$

$\{(2, 4), (-2, 4), (\sqrt{2}, 2), (-\sqrt{2}, 2)\}$

52. $x^2 + y^2 = 10$

$x^2 + 9y^2 = 18$

$\{(3, 1), (3, -1), (-3, 1), (-3, -1)\}$

53. $x^2 + y^2 = 61$

$x^2 - y^2 = 11$

$\{(6, 5), (-6, 5), (6, -5), (-6, -5)\}$

Section 13.5

For Exercises 54–59, graph the solution set to the inequality.

54. $\dfrac{x^2}{16} + \dfrac{y^2}{81} < 1$

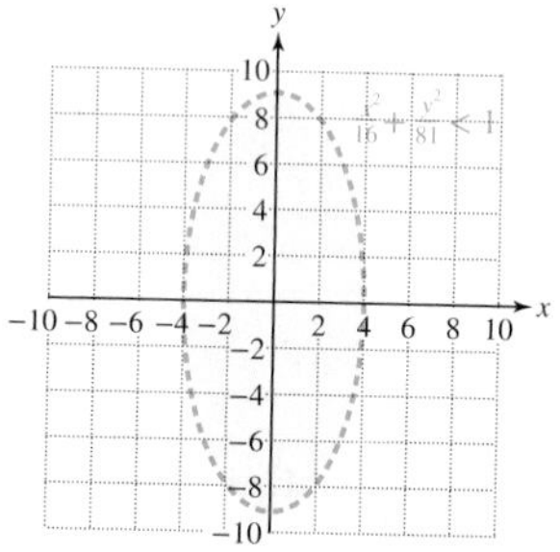

55. $\dfrac{x^2}{25} + \dfrac{y^2}{4} > 1$

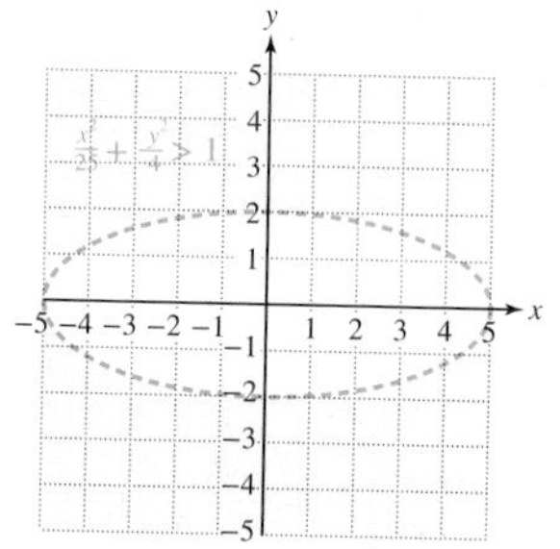

56. $(x - 3)^2 + (y + 1)^2 \geq 9$

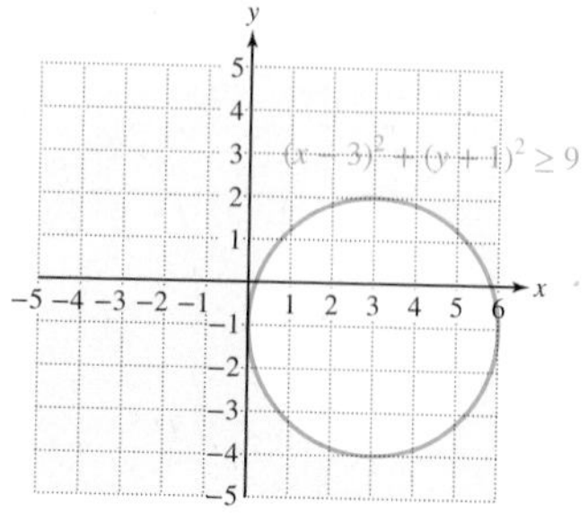

57. $(x + 2)^2 + (y + 1)^2 \leq 4$

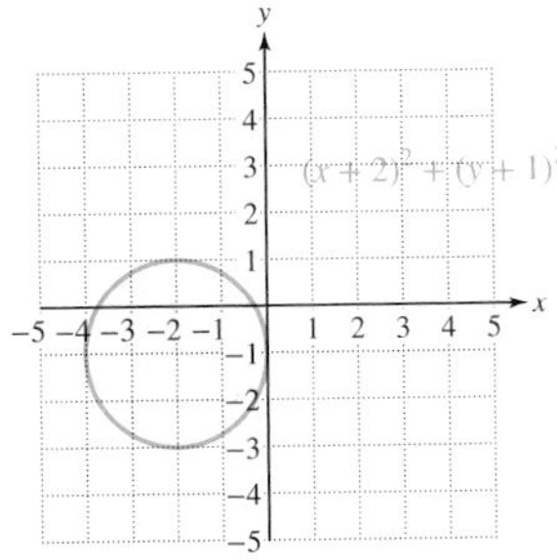

58. $y > (x - 1)^2$

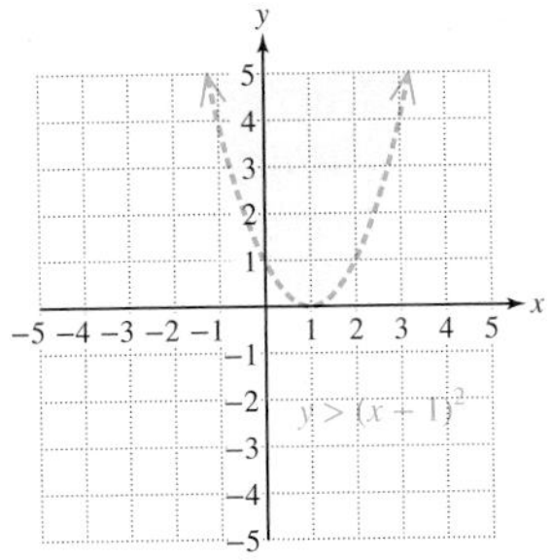

59. $x^2 - \dfrac{y^2}{4} \leq 1$

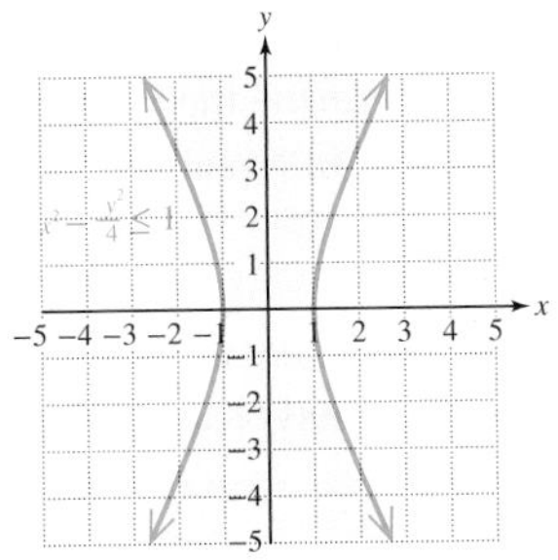

For Exercises 60–61, graph the solution set to the system of nonlinear inequalities.

60. $y > 2^x$

$x^2 + y^2 < 4$

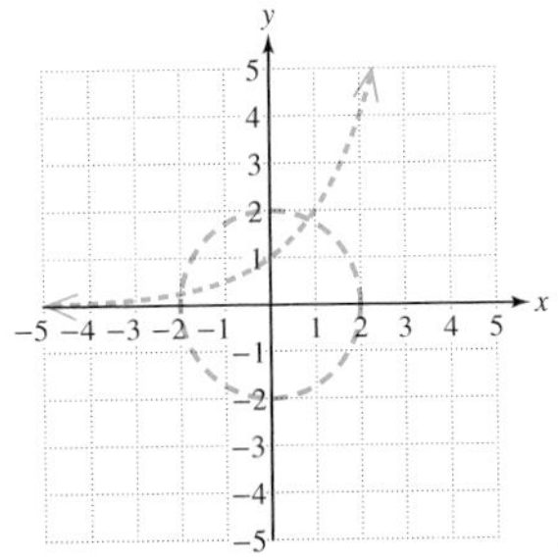

61. $y < x^2$

$x^2 + y^2 < 9$

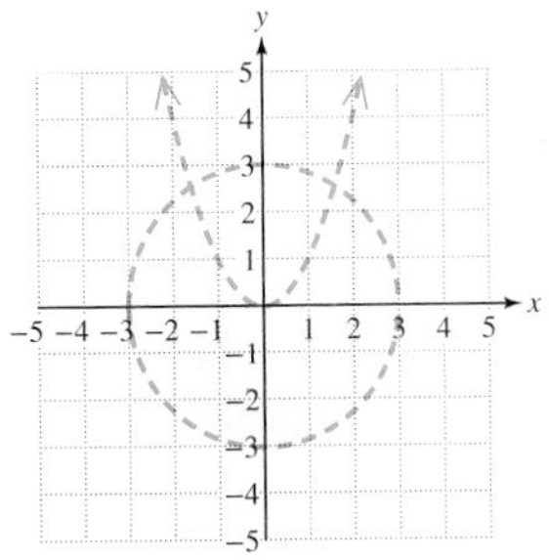

Chapter 13 Test

1. Use the distance formula to find the distance between the two points $(-5, 2)$ and $(-1, 6)$.
   $4\sqrt{2}$

2. Determine the center and radius of the circle.

$$\left(x - \frac{5}{6}\right)^2 + \left(y + \frac{1}{3}\right)^2 = \frac{25}{49}$$

   Center $\left(\frac{5}{6}, -\frac{1}{3}\right)$; $r = \frac{5}{7}$

3. Determine the center and radius of the circle.
   Center $(0, 2)$; $r = 3$

$$x^2 + y^2 - 4y - 5 = 0$$

4. Let $(0, 4)$ be the center of a circle that passes through the point $(-2, 5)$.

   a. What is the radius of the circle? $\sqrt{5}$

   b. Write the equation of the circle in standard form. $x^2 + (y - 4)^2 = 5$

5. Find the center of the circle that has a diameter with endpoints $(7.3, -1.2)$ and $(0.3, 5.1)$.
   The center is the midpoint $(3.8, 1.95)$.

6. Determine the vertex and the equation of the axis of symmetry. Then graph the parabola.

$$x = -(y - 2)^2 + 3$$

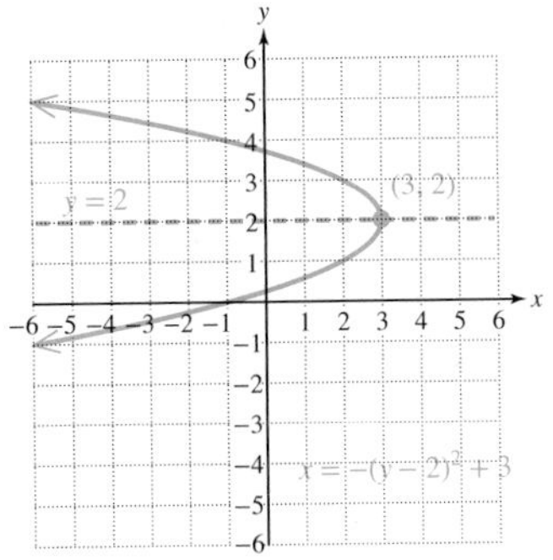

7. Write the equation in standard form $y = a(x - h)^2 + k$, and graph the parabola.

$y = x^2 + 4x + 5$

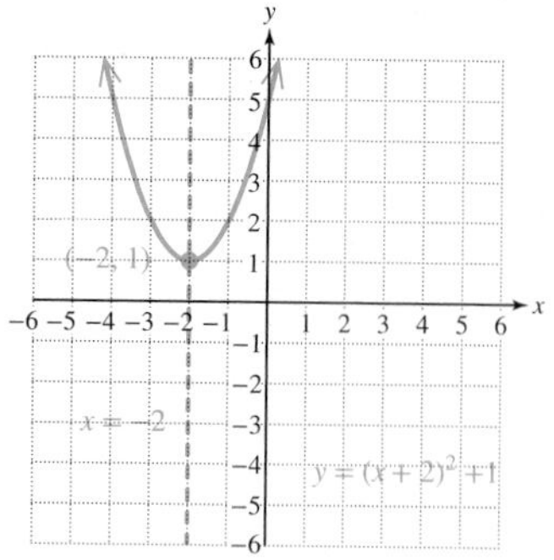

8. Graph the ellipse.

$$\frac{x^2}{16} + \frac{y^2}{49} = 1$$

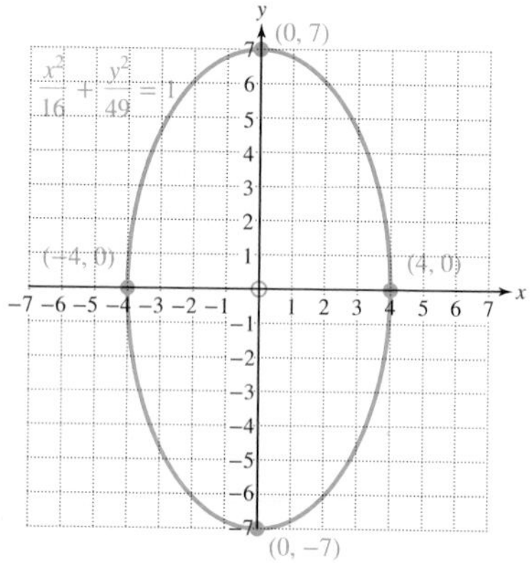

9. Graph the ellipse.

$$\frac{(x + 4)^2}{25} + (y - 3)^2 = 1$$

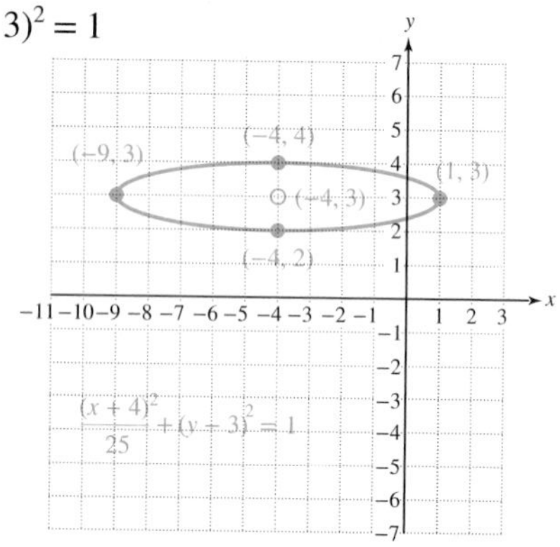

10. Graph the hyperbola.

$$y^2 - \frac{x^2}{4} = 1$$

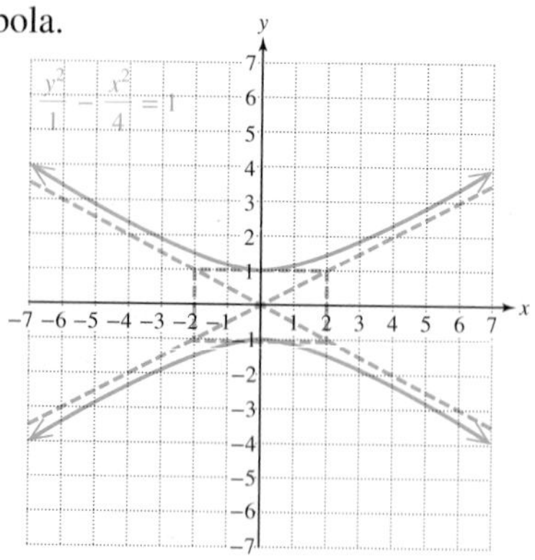

For Exercises 11–12, solve the system and identify the correct graph.

11. $16x^2 + 9y^2 = 144$

$4x - 3y = -12$

$\{(-3, 0), (0, 4)\}$; graph b

12. $x^2 + 4y^2 = 4$

$4x - 3y = -12$

{ }; graph a

a.

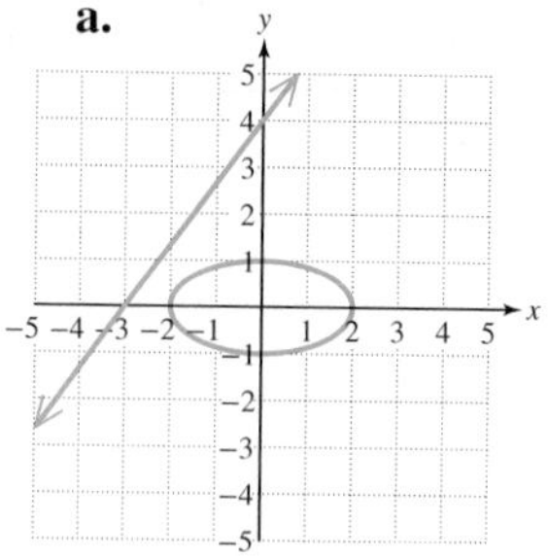

b.

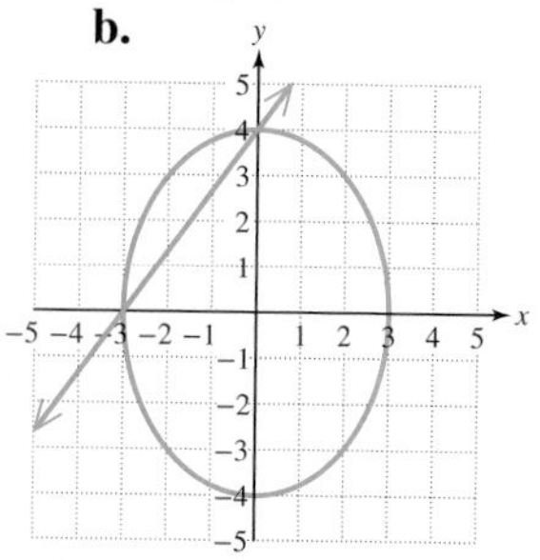

13. Describe the circumstances in which a nonlinear system of equations can be solved by using the addition method. The addition method can be used if the equations have corresponding *like* terms.

14. Solve the system by using either the substitution method or the addition method. $\{(2, 0), (-2, 0)\}$

$$25x^2 + 4y^2 = 100$$

$$25x^2 - 4y^2 = 100$$

For Exercises 15–18, graph the solution set.

15. $x \leq y^2 + 1$

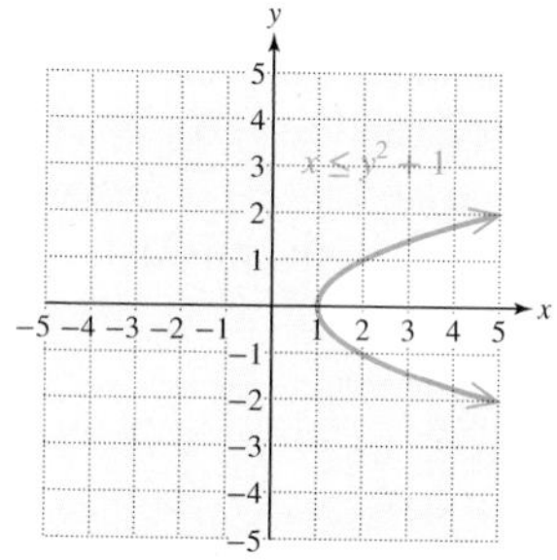

16. $y \geq -\frac{1}{3}x + 1$

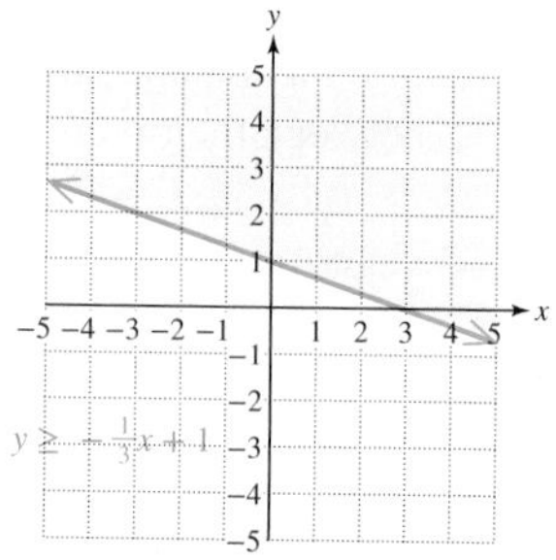

17. $x < y^2 + 1$

$y > -\frac{1}{3}x + 1$

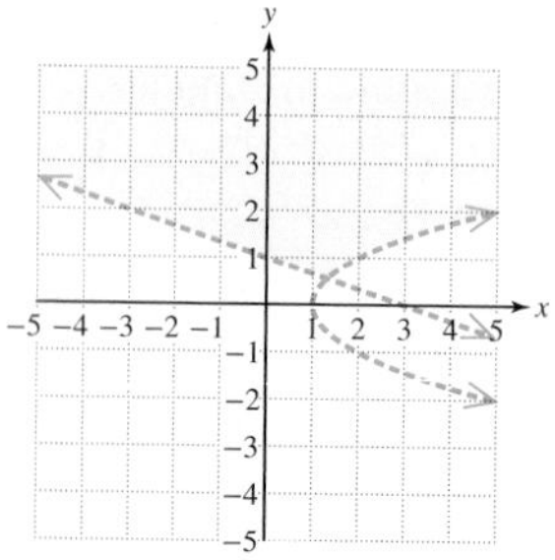

18. $y < \sqrt{x}$

$y > x - 2$

$x > 0$

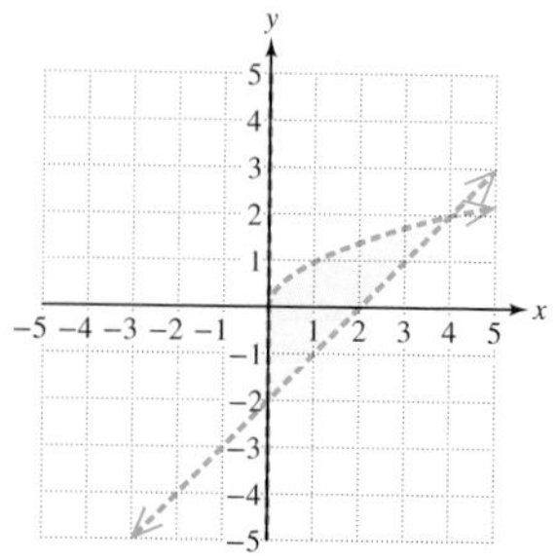

Chapters 1–13 Cumulative Review Exercises

1. Solve. $5(2y - 1) = 2y - 4 + 8y - 1$
$\{x \mid x \text{ is a real number}\}$

2. Solve the inequality. Graph the solution and write the solution in interval notation.

$$4(x - 1) + 2 > 3x + 8 - 2x$$

$\left(\frac{10}{3}, \infty\right)$

3. The product of two integers is 150. If one integer is 5 less than twice the other, find the integers.
The integers are 10 and 15.

4. For $5y - 3x - 15 = 0$,

a. Find the x- and y-intercepts.
$(-5, 0), (0, 3)$

b. Find the slope. $m = \frac{3}{5}$

c. Graph the line.

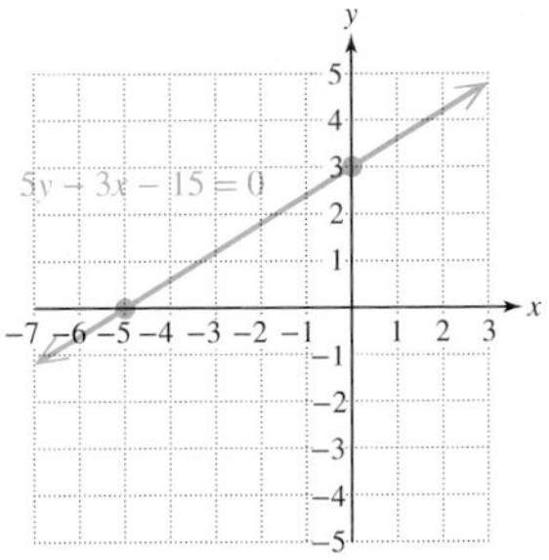

5. Find the slope and y-intercept of $3x - 4y = 6$.
slope: $\frac{3}{4}$; y-intercept: $\left(0, -\frac{3}{2}\right)$

6. A collection of dimes and quarters has a total value of \$2.45. If there are 17 coins, how many of each type are there? There are 12 dimes and 5 quarters.

7. Solve the system. $\{(2, -3, 1)\}$

$$\begin{aligned} x + y \quad\;\; &= -1 \\ 2x \quad\; - z &= 3 \\ y + 2z &= -1 \end{aligned}$$

8. Solve the system. $\left\{\left(\frac{5}{2}, \frac{3}{2}\right)\right\}$

$$4x - 2y = 7$$
$$-3x + 5y = 0$$

9. Solve by using the Gauss-Jordan method. $\{(6, 3)\}$

$$3x - 4y = 6$$
$$x + 2y = 12$$

10. For $f(x) = 3x - x^2 - 12$, find the function values $f(0), f(-1), f(2)$, and $f(4)$.
$f(0) = -12; f(-1) = -16; f(2) = -10; f(4) = -16$

11. Solve the inequality. $x^2 + 6x < -8$ $(-4, -2)$

12. The quantity z varies jointly as y and as the square of x. If z is 80 when x is 5 and y is 2, find z when $x = 2$ and $y = 5$. $z = 32$

13. For $f(x) = \sqrt{x + 1}$ and $g(x) = x^2 + 6$, find $(g \circ f)(x)$. $(g \circ f)(x) = x + 7; x \geq -1$

14. a. Find the value of the expression $x^3 + x^2 + x + 1$ for $x = -2$. -5

b. Factor the expression $x^3 + x^2 + x + 1$ and find the value when x is -2. $(x + 1)(x^2 + 1); -5$

c. Compare the values for parts (a) and (b).
They are the same.

15. Factor completely. $x^2 - y^2 - 6x - 6y$
$(x + y)(x - y - 6)$

16. Multiply. $(x - 4)(x^2 + 2x + 1)$ $x^3 - 2x^2 - 7x - 4$

17. Solve. $2x(x - 7) = x - 18$ $\left\{6, \frac{3}{2}\right\}$

18. Simplify. $\dfrac{3a^2 - a - 2}{3a^2 + 8a + 4}$ $\dfrac{a - 1}{a + 2}$

19. Subtract. $\dfrac{2}{x + 3} - \dfrac{x}{x - 2}$ $\dfrac{-x^2 - x - 4}{(x + 3)(x - 2)}$

20. Solve. $\dfrac{2}{x + 3} - \dfrac{x}{x - 2} = \dfrac{-4}{x^2 + x - 6}$ $\{0, -1\}$

21. Solve the radical equations.

a. $\sqrt{2x - 5} = -3$ $\{\ \}$

b. $\sqrt[3]{2x - 5} = -3$ $\{-11\}$

For Exercises 22–23, perform the indicated operations with complex numbers.

22. $6i(4 + 5i)$ $-30 + 24i$

23. $\dfrac{3}{4 - 5i}$ $\dfrac{12}{41} + \dfrac{15}{41}i$

24. Find the length of the missing side. $2\sqrt{7}$ m

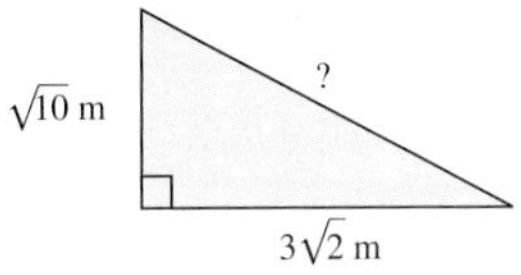

25. An automobile starts from rest and accelerates at a constant rate for 10 sec. The distance, $d(t)$, in feet traveled by the car is given by

$$d(t) = 4.4t^2$$

where $0 \le t \le 10$ is the time in seconds.

a. How far has the car traveled after 2, 3, and 4 sec, respectively? 17.6 ft; 39.6 ft; 70.4 ft

b. How long will it take for the car to travel 281.6 ft? 8 sec

26. Solve the equation $125w^3 + 1 = 0$ by factoring and using the quadratic formula. (*Hint:* You will find one real solution and two imaginary solutions.) $\left\{-\frac{1}{5}, \frac{1}{10} \pm \frac{\sqrt{3}}{10}i\right\}$

27. Solve. $\dfrac{x}{x+2} - \dfrac{3}{x-1} = \dfrac{1}{x^2+x-2}$ $\{2 \pm \sqrt{11}\}$

28. Find the coordinates of the vertex of the parabola defined by $f(x) = x^2 + 10x - 11$ by completing the square. $(-5, -36)$

29. Graph the quadratic function defined by $g(x) = -x^2 - 2x + 3$.

a. Label the x-intercepts. $(-3, 0), (1, 0)$

b. Label the y-intercept. $(0, 3)$

c. Label the vertex. $(-1, 4)$

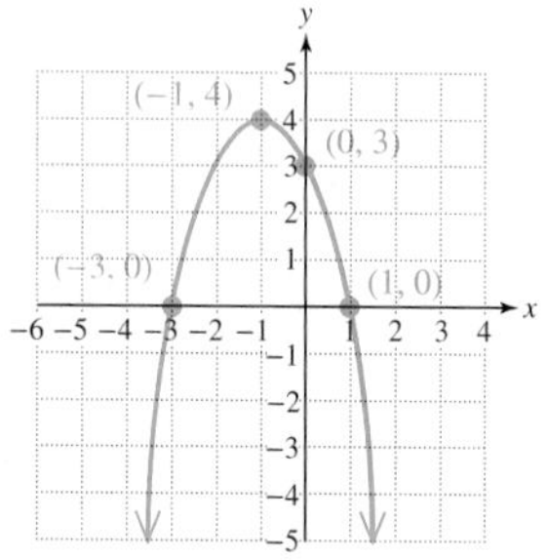

30. Solve the inequality and write the answer in interval notation. $(-1, 19)$

$$|x - 9| - 3 < 7$$

31. Solve the inequality. $|2x - 5| \ge 4$ $\left(-\infty, \frac{1}{2}\right] \cup \left[\frac{9}{2}, \infty\right)$

32. Write the expression in logarithmic form. $8^{5/3} = 32$ $\log_8 32 = \frac{5}{3}$

33. Solve. $5^2 = 125^x$ $\left\{\frac{2}{3}\right\}$

34. For $h(x) = x^3 - 1$, find $h^{-1}(x)$. $h^{-1}(x) = \sqrt[3]{x+1}$

35. Write an equation representing the set of all points 4 units from the point (0, 5). $x^2 + (y - 5)^2 = 16$

36. Graph the ellipse. $\dfrac{x^2}{4} + \dfrac{y^2}{25} = 1$

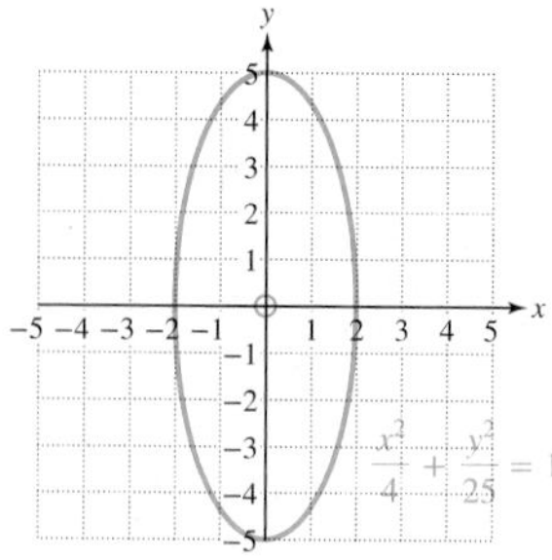

37. Determine the center of the circle, given the endpoints of a diameter. $\left(-\frac{1}{2}, 0\right)$

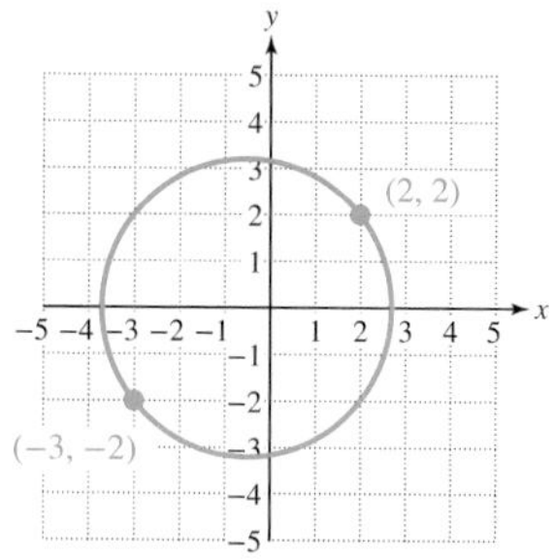

38. Solve the system of nonlinear equations. $\{(0, -4)\}$

$$x^2 + y^2 = 16$$
$$y = -x^2 - 4$$

39. Graph the solution set.

$$y^2 - x^2 < 1$$

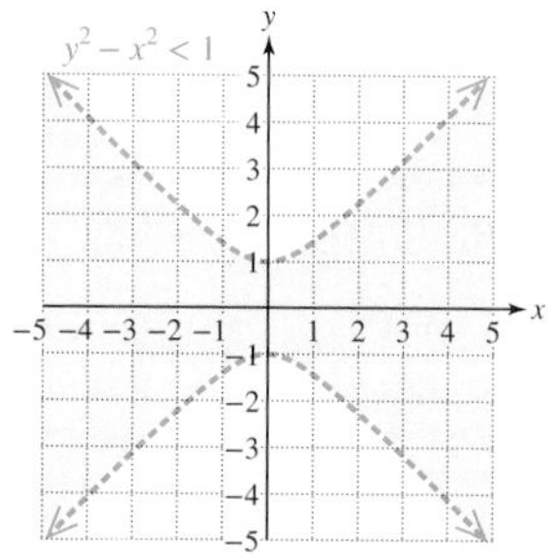

40. Graph the solution set to this system.

$$y > \left(\frac{1}{2}\right)^x$$
$$x < 0$$

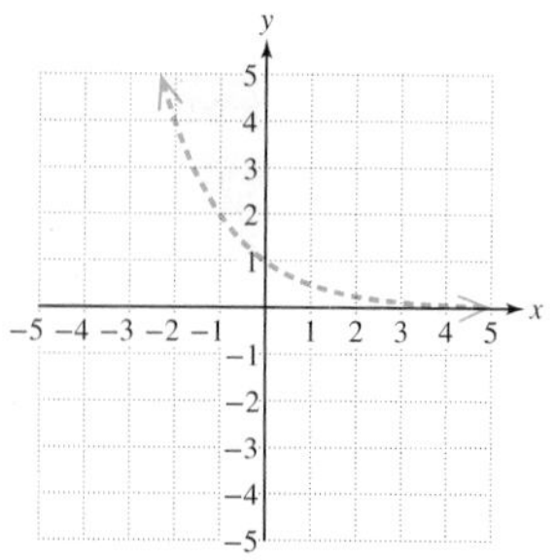

Binomial Expansions, Sequences, and Series

14

CHAPTER OUTLINE

Mathematics in Business

In this chapter we present applications involving sequences and series. A **sequence** is a function whose domain is the set of positive integers. While infinitely many sequences can be defined, two specific categories are presented here: **arithmetic** and **geometric sequences**. An arithmetic sequence is a progression of numbers that increase or decrease by a fixed amount, whereas the numbers in a geometric sequence increase or decrease by a fixed ratio. A **series** is a sum of the terms in a sequence.

To illustrate the difference between an arithmetic and a geometric sequence, suppose that you have two different job offers. The first pays $60,000 per year with a $2000 raise at the start of each new year. The second pays $58,000 with a 4% raise at the start of each new year. The salaries for each job for each year can be written as the terms of a sequence. For example, the terms of the sequence of salaries for Job 1 are $60,000, 62,000, 64,000, and so on.

Year	Job 1	Job 2		Total Job 1	Total Job 2
1	$60,000	$58,000		$60,000	$58,000
2	$62,000	$60,320		$122,000	$118,320
3	$64,000	$62,733		$186,000	$181,053
4	$66,000	$65,242		$252,000	$246,295
5	$68,000	$67,852		$320,000	$314,147
6	$70,000	$70,566		$390,000	$384,713
7	$72,000	$73,389		$462,000	$458,101
8	$74,000	$76,324		$536,000	$534,425
9	$76,000	$79,377		$612,000	$613,802
10	$78,000	$82,552		$690,000	$696,354

Notice that the yearly salary for Job 1 is initially more, but the salary increases by a fixed amount each year. The initial salary for Job 2 is less, but it grows exponentially and eventually overtakes the salary for Job 1. The sum of the salaries for the first 6 years can be added directly from the given data, or can be computed using formulas presented in this chapter. The total income over 6 years for Job 1 is $390,000, and the total income for Job 2 over 6 years is $384,713. However, because the yearly salary for Job 2 grows at a faster rate, by year 9 the cumulative income for Job 2 will be greater. The total income for Job 2 for the first 9 years will be $613,802, whereas for Job 1, the total income will be $612,000.

Our study of sequences and series in this chapter will help you learn to analyze numerical patterns and to make informed financial decisions.

Section 14.1 Binomial Expansions

Concepts

1. Binomial Expansions and Pascal's Triangle
2. Factorial Notation
3. The Binomial Theorem

1. Binomial Expansions and Pascal's Triangle

In this section, we will learn how to raise binomials to positive integer powers. First recall the formula to square a binomial.

$$(a+b)^2 = a^2 + 2ab + b^2$$

The expression $a^2 + 2ab + b^2$ is called the **binomial expansion** of $(a+b)^2$. To expand $(a+b)^3$, we can find the product $(a+b)(a+b)^2$.

$$\begin{aligned}(a+b)(a+b)^2 &= (a+b)(a^2+2ab+b^2)\\ &= a^3 + 2a^2b + ab^2 + a^2b + 2ab^2 + b^3\\ &= a^3 + 3a^2b + 3ab^2 + b^3\end{aligned}$$

Similarly, to expand $(a+b)^4$, we can multiply $(a+b)$ by $(a+b)^3$. Using this method, we can expand several powers of $(a+b)$ to find the following pattern:

$$\begin{aligned}(a+b)^0 &= 1\\ (a+b)^1 &= a+b\\ (a+b)^2 &= a^2+2ab+b^2\\ (a+b)^3 &= a^3+3a^2b+3ab^2+b^3\\ (a+b)^4 &= a^4+4a^3b+6a^2b^2+4ab^3+b^4\\ (a+b)^5 &= a^5+5a^4b+10a^3b^2+10a^2b^3+5ab^4+b^5\end{aligned}$$

Notice that the exponents on a decrease from left to right, while the exponents on b increase from left to right. Also observe that for each term, the sum of the exponents is equal to the exponent to which $(a+b)$ is raised. Finally, notice that the number of terms in the expansion is exactly 1 more than the power to which $(a+b)$ is raised. For example, the expansion of $(a+b)^4$ has five terms, and the expansion of $(a+b)^5$ has six terms.

With these guidelines in mind, we know that $(a+b)^6$ will contain seven terms involving

$$a^6 \quad a^5b \quad a^4b^2 \quad a^3b^3 \quad a^2b^4 \quad ab^5 \quad b^6$$

We can complete the expansion of $(a+b)^6$ if we can determine the correct coefficients of each term.

If we write the coefficients for several expansions of $(a+b)^n$, where $n \geq 0$, we have a triangular array of numbers.

$(a+b)^0 = 1$	1
$(a+b)^1 = 1a + 1b$	1 1
$(a+b)^2 = 1a^2 + 2ab + 1b^2$	1 2 1
$(a+b)^3 = 1a^3 + 3a^2b + 3ab^2 + 1b^3$	1 3 3 1
$(a+b)^4 = 1a^4 + 4a^3b + 6a^2b^2 + 4ab^3 + 1b^4$	1 4 6 4 1
$(a+b)^5 = 1a^5 + 5a^4b + 10a^3b^2 + 10a^2b^3 + 5ab^4 + 1b^5$	1 5 10 10 5 1

Each row begins and ends with a 1, and each entry in between is the sum of the two entries from the line above. For example, in row six, $5 = 1 + 4$, $10 = 4 + 6$, and so on. This triangular array of coefficients for a binomial expansion is called **Pascal's triangle**, named after French mathematician Blaise Pascal (1623–1662).

$$
\begin{array}{c}
1 \\
1 \quad 1 \\
1 \quad 2 \quad 1 \\
1 \quad 3 \quad 3 \quad 1 \\
1 \quad 4 \quad 6 \quad 4 \quad 1 \\
1 \quad 5 \quad 10 \quad 10 \quad 5 \quad 1 \\
1 \quad 6 \quad 15 \quad 20 \quad 15 \quad 6 \quad 1
\end{array}
$$

By using the pattern shown in Pascal's triangle, the coefficients corresponding to $(a + b)^6$ would be 1, 6, 15, 20, 15, 6, 1. By inserting the coefficients, the sum becomes

$$(a + b)^6 = 1a^6 + 6a^5b + 15a^4b^2 + 20a^3b^3 + 15a^2b^4 + 6ab^5 + 1b^6$$

2. Factorial Notation

Although Pascal's triangle provides an easy method to find the coefficients of $(a + b)^n$, it is impractical for large values of n. A more efficient method to find the coefficients of a binomial expansion involves **factorial notation**.

Definition of n!

Let n be a positive integer. Then $n!$ (read as "n factorial") is defined as the product of integers from 1 through n. That is,

$$n! = n(n - 1)(n - 2) \cdots (2)(1)$$

Note: We define $0! = 1$.

Example 1 Evaluating Factorial Notation

Classroom Example: p. 996, Exercise 16

Evaluate the expressions.

a. $4!$ **b.** $10!$ **c.** $0!$

Solution:

a. $4! = 4 \cdot 3 \cdot 2 \cdot 1 = 24$

b. $10! = 10 \cdot 9 \cdot 8 \cdot 7 \cdot 6 \cdot 5 \cdot 4 \cdot 3 \cdot 2 \cdot 1 = 3{,}628{,}800$

c. $0! = 1$ by definition

Skill Practice Evaluate the expressions.

1. $3!$ **2.** $8!$ **3.** $1!$

Calculator Connections

Topic: Evaluating Expressions with Factorial Notation

Most calculators have a [!] function. Try evaluating the expressions from Example 1 on a calculator:

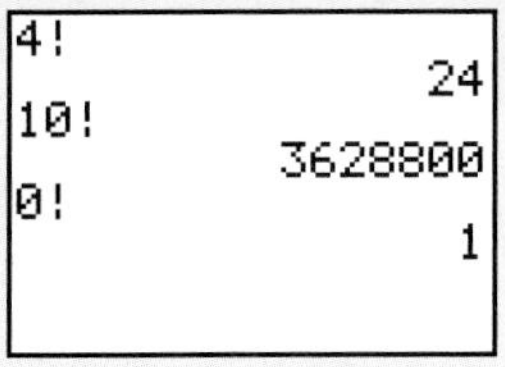

Answers

1. 6 **2.** 40,320 **3.** 1

Sometimes factorial notation is used with other operations such as multiplication and division.

Classroom Example: p. 996, Exercise 30

Calculator Connections

Topic: Multiplying and Dividing Factorial Expressions

To evaluate the expressions from Example 2 on a calculator, use parentheses around the factors in the denominator.

```
4!/(4!*0!)
                1
4!/(3!*1!)
                4
4!/(2!*2!)
                6
```

Example 2 Evaluating Expressions with Factorials

Evaluate the expressions.

a. $\dfrac{4!}{4!\cdot 0!}$ **b.** $\dfrac{4!}{3!\cdot 1!}$ **c.** $\dfrac{4!}{2!\cdot 2!}$ **d.** $\dfrac{4!}{1!\cdot 3!}$ **e.** $\dfrac{4!}{0!\cdot 4!}$

Solution:

a. $\dfrac{4!}{4!\cdot 0!}=\dfrac{\cancel{4!}}{\cancel{4!}\cdot 1}=1$

b. $\dfrac{4!}{3!\cdot 1!}=\dfrac{4\cdot \cancel{3!}}{\cancel{3!}\cdot 1}=4$ Note that $4! = 4\cdot(3\cdot 2\cdot 1) = 4\cdot 3!$

c. $\dfrac{4!}{2!\cdot 2!}=\dfrac{4\cdot 3\cdot \cancel{2!}}{\cancel{2!}\cdot 2\cdot 1}=\dfrac{12}{2}=6$

d. $\dfrac{4!}{1!\cdot 3!}=\dfrac{4\cdot \cancel{3!}}{1\cdot \cancel{3!}}=4$

e. $\dfrac{4!}{0!\cdot 4!}=\dfrac{\cancel{4!}}{1\cdot \cancel{4!}}=1$

Skill Practice Evaluate.

4. $\dfrac{5!}{5!\cdot 0!}$ **5.** $\dfrac{5!}{4!\cdot 1!}$ **6.** $\dfrac{5!}{3!\cdot 2!}$

3. The Binomial Theorem

Notice from Example 2 that the values of

$$\frac{4!}{4!\cdot 0!}\quad \frac{4!}{3!\cdot 1!}\quad \frac{4!}{2!\cdot 2!}\quad \frac{4!}{1!\cdot 3!}\quad \text{and}\quad \frac{4!}{0!\cdot 4!}$$

correspond to the values 1, 4, 6, 4, 1, which are the coefficients for the expansion of $(a+b)^4$. Generalizing this pattern, we see the coefficients for the terms in the expansion of $(a+b)^n$ are given by

$$\frac{n!}{r!\cdot(n-r)!}$$

where r corresponds to the exponent on the factor of a and $(n-r)$ corresponds to the exponent on the factor of b. Using this formula for the coefficients in a binomial expansion results in the **binomial theorem**.

Answers

4. 1 **5.** 5 **6.** 10

The Binomial Theorem

For any positive integer n,

$$(a+b)^n = \frac{n!}{n!\cdot 0!}a^n + \frac{n!}{(n-1)!\cdot 1!}a^{(n-1)}b + \frac{n!}{(n-2)!\cdot 2!}a^{(n-2)}b^2 + \cdots + \frac{n!}{0!\cdot n!}b^n$$

Example 3 Applying the Binomial Theorem

Classroom Example: p. 996, Exercise 34

Write out the first three terms of the expansion of $(a+b)^{10}$.

Solution:

The first three terms of $(a+b)^{10}$ are

$$\frac{10!}{10!\cdot 0!}a^{10} + \frac{10!}{9!\cdot 1!}a^9b + \frac{10!}{8!\cdot 2!}a^8b^2$$

$$= \frac{\cancel{10!}}{\cancel{10!}\cdot 1}a^{10} + \frac{10\cdot\cancel{9!}}{\cancel{9!}\cdot 1!}a^9b + \frac{10\cdot 9\cdot\cancel{8!}}{\cancel{8!}\cdot 2\cdot 1}a^8b^2$$

$$= a^{10} + 10a^9b + 45a^8b^2$$

TIP: When applying the binomial theorem, exponents on a and b must add up to n.

Skill Practice

7. Write out the first three terms of $(x+y)^5$.

Example 4 Applying the Binomial Theorem

Classroom Example: p. 996, Exercise 44

Use the binomial theorem to expand $(2m+7)^3$.

Solution:

This expression is of the form $(a+b)^3$, where $a = 2m$ and $b = 7$. Applying the binomial theorem we have

$$(a+b)^3 = \frac{3!}{3!\cdot 0!}a^3 + \frac{3!}{2!\cdot 1!}a^2b + \frac{3!}{1!\cdot 2!}ab^2 + \frac{3!}{0!\cdot 3!}b^3$$

$$= \frac{3!}{3!\cdot 0!}(2m)^3 + \frac{3!}{2!\cdot 1!}(2m)^2(7) + \frac{3!}{1!\cdot 2!}(2m)(7)^2 + \frac{3!}{0!\cdot 3!}(7)^3$$

$$= 1\cdot(8m^3) + 3\cdot(4m^2)(7) + 3\cdot(2m)(49) + 1\cdot(343)$$

$$= 8m^3 + 84m^2 + 294m + 343$$

TIP: The values of $\frac{n!}{r!\cdot(n-r)!}$ can also be found by using Pascal's triangle.

1

1 1

1 2 1

1 3 3 1

Skill Practice

8. Use the binomial theorem to expand $(3y+4)^3$.

Answers

7. $x^5 + 5x^4y + 10x^3y^2$
8. $27y^3 + 108y^2 + 144y + 64$

Classroom Example: p. 996, Exercise 46

TIP: The values of $\dfrac{n!}{r! \cdot (n-r)!}$ can also be found by using Pascal's triangle.

1
1 1
1 2 1
1 3 3 1
1 4 6 4 1

Example 5 Applying the Binomial Theorem

Use the binomial theorem to expand $(3x^2 - 5y)^4$.

Solution:

Write $(3x^2 - 5y)^4$ as $[(3x^2) + (-5y)]^4$. In this case, the expressions $3x^2$ and $-5y$ may be substituted for a and b in the expansion of $(a + b)^4$.

$$(a+b)^4 = \frac{4!}{4! \cdot 0!}a^4 + \frac{4!}{3! \cdot 1!}a^3b + \frac{4!}{2! \cdot 2!}a^2b^2 + \frac{4!}{1! \cdot 3!}ab^3 + \frac{4!}{0! \cdot 4!}b^4$$

$$= \frac{4!}{4! \cdot 0!}(3x^2)^4 + \frac{4!}{3! \cdot 1!}(3x^2)^3(-5y) + \frac{4!}{2! \cdot 2!}(3x^2)^2(-5y)^2$$

$$+ \frac{4!}{1! \cdot 3!}(3x^2)(-5y)^3 + \frac{4!}{0! \cdot 4!}(-5y)^4$$

$$= 1 \cdot (81x^8) + 4 \cdot (27x^6)(-5y) + 6 \cdot (9x^4)(25y^2) + 4 \cdot (3x^2)(-125y^3) + 1 \cdot (625y^4)$$

$$= 81x^8 - 540x^6y + 1350x^4y^2 - 1500x^2y^3 + 625y^4$$

Skill Practice

9. Use the binomial theorem to expand $(2a - 3b^2)^4$.

The binomial theorem may also be used to find a specific term in a binomial expansion.

Classroom Example: p. 996, Exercise 52

Example 6 Finding a Specific Term in a Binomial Expansion

Find the fourth term of the expansion $(a + b)^{13}$.

Solution:

There are 14 terms in the expansion of $(a + b)^{13}$. The first term will have variable factors $a^{13}b^0$. The second term will have variable factors $a^{12}b^1$. The third term will have $a^{11}b^2$, and the fourth term will have $a^{10}b^3$. Hence, the fourth term is

$$\frac{13!}{10! \cdot 3!}a^{10}b^3 = 286a^{10}b^3$$

Skill Practice

10. Find the fourth term of $(x + y)^8$.

From Example 6, we see that for the kth term in the expansion $(a + b)^n$, where k is an integer greater than zero, the variable factors are $a^{n-(k-1)}$ and b^{k-1}. Therefore, to find the kth term of $(a + b)^n$, we can make the following generalization.

Finding a Specific Term in a Binomial Expansion

Let n and k be positive integers such that $k \le n$. Then the kth term in the expansion of $(a + b)^n$ is given by

$$\frac{n!}{[n-(k-1)]! \cdot (k-1)!} \cdot a^{n-(k-1)} \cdot b^{k-1}$$

Answers

9. $16a^4 - 96a^3b^2 + 216a^2b^4 - 216ab^6 + 81b^8$
10. $56x^5y^3$

Example 7 Finding a Specific Term in a Binomial Expansion

Classroom Example: p. 996, Exercise 54

Find the sixth term of $(p^3 + 2w)^8$.

Solution:

Apply the formula.

$$\frac{n!}{[n-(k-1)]! \cdot (k-1)!} \cdot a^{n-(k-1)} \cdot b^{k-1} \quad \text{with } n = 8, k = 6, a = p^3, \text{ and } b = 2w$$

$$\frac{8!}{[8-(6-1)]! \cdot (6-1)!} \cdot (p^3)^{8-(6-1)} \cdot (2w)^{6-1}$$

$$= \frac{8!}{(3)! \cdot (5)!} \cdot (p^3)^3 \cdot (2w)^5$$

$$= 56 \cdot (p^9) \cdot (32w^5)$$

$$= 1792p^9w^5$$

Skill Practice

11. Find the fifth term of $(t - m^2)^8$.

Answer

11. $70t^4m^8$

Section 14.1 Practice Exercises

For additional exercises, see Classroom Activities 14.1A–14.1C in the *Student's Resource Manual* at www.mhhe.com/moh.

Vocabulary and Key Concepts

1. **a.** The expanded form of $(a + b)^2 =$ $a^2 + 2ab + b^2$. The expanded form of $(a + b)^3 =$ $a^3 + 3a^2b + 3ab^2 + b^3$. These are both called binomial expansions.

   b. Given a positive integer n, the value of $n!$ is $n(n-1)(n-2)\cdots(2)(1)$. Furthermore, $n!$ is read as "n factorial."

   c. $3! =$ 6, $2! =$ 2, $1! =$ 1, and $0! =$ 1.

   d. The binomial theorem states that for any positive integer n,

   $$(a+b)^n = \frac{n!}{n! \cdot 0!}a^n + \frac{n!}{(n-1)! \cdot 1!}a^{(n-1)}b + \frac{n!}{(n-2)! \cdot 2!}a^{(n-2)}b^2 + \cdots + \frac{n!}{0! \cdot n!}b^n.$$

   e. The coefficients of the binomial expansion of $(a + b)^n$ can also be found by using Pascal's triangle.

Concept 1: Binomial Expansions and Pascal's Triangle

For Exercises 2–7, expand the binomials. Use Pascal's triangle to find the coefficients.

2. $(x + y)^4$ $x^4 + 4x^3y + 6x^2y^2 + 4xy^3 + y^4$
3. $(a + b)^3$ $a^3 + 3a^2b + 3ab^2 + b^3$
4. $(4 + p)^3$ $64 + 48p + 12p^2 + p^3$
5. $(1 + g)^4$ $1 + 4g + 6g^2 + 4g^3 + g^4$
6. $(a^2 + b)^6$ $a^{12} + 6a^{10}b + 15a^8b^2 + 20a^6b^3 + 15a^4b^4 + 6a^2b^5 + b^6$
7. $(p + q^2)^7$ $p^7 + 7p^6q^2 + 21p^5q^4 + 35p^4q^6 + 35p^3q^8 + 21p^2q^{10} + 7pq^{12} + q^{14}$

For Exercises 8–13, rewrite each binomial of the form $(a - b)^n$ as $[a + (-b)]^n$. Then expand the binomials. Use Pascal's triangle to find the coefficients.

8. $(t - 2)^5$ $t^5 - 10t^4 + 40t^3 - 80t^2 + 80t - 32$
9. $(s - t)^5$ $s^5 - 5s^4t + 10s^3t^2 - 10s^2t^3 + 5st^4 - t^5$
10. $(p^2 - w)^3$ $p^6 - 3p^4w + 3p^2w^2 - w^3$
11. $(5 - u^3)^4$ $625 - 500u^3 + 150u^6 - 20u^9 + u^{12}$
12. $(a - b^2)^4$ $a^4 - 4a^3b^2 + 6a^2b^4 - 4ab^6 + b^8$
13. $(x^2 - 4)^3$ $x^6 - 12x^4 + 48x^2 - 64$

14. For $a > 0$ and $b > 0$, what happens to the signs of the terms when expanding the binomial $(a - b)^n$ compared with $(a + b)^n$?
The signs alternate on the terms of the expression $(a - b)^n$. The signs for the expression $(a + b)^n$ are all positive.

Concept 2: Factorial Notation

For Exercises 15–18, evaluate the expression. **(See Example 1.)**

15. $5!$ 120

16. $3!$ 6

17. $0!$ 1

18. $1!$ 1

19. True or false: $0! \neq 1!$ False

20. True or false: $n!$ is defined for negative integers. False

21. True or false: $n! = n$ for $n = 1$ and 2. True

22. Show that $9! = 9 \cdot 8!$
$9! = 9 \cdot (8 \cdot 7 \cdot 6 \cdot 5 \cdot 4 \cdot 3 \cdot 2 \cdot 1) = 9 \cdot 8!$

23. Show that $6! = 6 \cdot 5!$
$6! = 6 \cdot (5 \cdot 4 \cdot 3 \cdot 2 \cdot 1) = 6 \cdot 5!$

24. Show that $8! = 8 \cdot 7!$
$8! = 8 \cdot (7 \cdot 6 \cdot 5 \cdot 4 \cdot 3 \cdot 2 \cdot 1) = 8 \cdot 7!$

For Exercises 25–32, evaluate the expression. **(See Example 2.)**

25. $\dfrac{8!}{4!}$ 1680

26. $\dfrac{7!}{5!}$ 42

27. $\dfrac{3!}{0!}$ 6

28. $\dfrac{4!}{0!}$ 24

29. $\dfrac{8!}{3! \cdot 5!}$ 56

30. $\dfrac{6!}{2! \cdot 4!}$ 15

31. $\dfrac{4!}{0! \cdot 4!}$ 1

32. $\dfrac{6!}{0! \cdot 6!}$ 1

Concept 3: The Binomial Theorem

For Exercises 33–36, find the first three terms of the expansion. **(See Example 3.)**

33. $(m + n)^{11}$
$m^{11} + 11m^{10}n + 55m^9n^2$

34. $(p + q)^9$
$p^9 + 9p^8q + 36p^7q^2$

35. $(u^2 - v)^{12}$
$u^{24} - 12u^{22}v + 66u^{20}v^2$

36. $(r - s^2)^8$
$r^8 - 8r^7s^2 + 28r^6s^4$

37. How many terms are in the expansion of $(a + b)^8$? 9 terms

38. How many terms are in the expansion of $(x + y)^{13}$? 14 terms

For Exercises 39–50, use the binomial theorem to expand the binomials. **(See Examples 4–5.)**

39. $(s + t)^6$
$s^6 + 6s^5t + 15s^4t^2 + 20s^3t^3 + 15s^2t^4 + 6st^5 + t^6$

40. $(h + k)^4$
$h^4 + 4h^3k + 6h^2k^2 + 4hk^3 + k^4$

41. $(b - 3)^3$
$b^3 - 9b^2 + 27b - 27$

42. $(c - 2)^5$
$c^5 - 10c^4 + 40c^3 - 80c^2 + 80c - 32$

43. $(2x + y)^4$
$16x^4 + 32x^3y + 24x^2y^2 + 8xy^3 + y^4$

44. $(p + 3q)^3$
$p^3 + 9p^2q + 27pq^2 + 27q^3$

45. $(c^2 - d)^7$
$c^{14} - 7c^{12}d + 21c^{10}d^2 - 35c^8d^3 + 35c^6d^4 - 21c^4d^5 + 7c^2d^6 - d^7$

46. $(u - v^3)^6$
$u^6 - 6u^5v^3 + 15u^4v^6 - 20u^3v^9 + 15u^2v^{12} - 6uv^{15} + v^{18}$

47. $\left(\dfrac{a}{2} - b\right)^5$
$\frac{1}{32}a^5 - \frac{5}{16}a^4b + \frac{5}{4}a^3b^2 - \frac{5}{2}a^2b^3 + \frac{5}{2}ab^4 - b^5$

48. $\left(\dfrac{s}{3} + t\right)^5$
$\frac{1}{243}s^5 + \frac{5}{81}s^4t + \frac{10}{27}s^3t^2 + \frac{10}{9}s^2t^3 + \frac{5}{3}st^4 + t^5$

49. $(x + 4y)^4$
$x^4 + 16x^3y + 96x^2y^2 + 256xy^3 + 256y^4$

50. $(3y - w)^3$
$27y^3 - 27y^2w + 9yw^2 - w^3$

For Exercises 51–56, find the indicated term of the binomial expansion. **(See Examples 6–7.)**

51. $(m - n)^{11}$; sixth term
$-462m^6n^5$

52. $(p - q)^9$; fourth term
$-84p^6q^3$

53. $(u^2 - v)^{12}$; fifth term
$495u^{16}v^4$

54. $(2r - s^2)^8$; sixth term
$-448r^3s^{10}$

55. $(5f + g)^9$; 10th term
g^9

56. $(4m + n)^{10}$; 11th term
n^{10}

Section 14.2 Sequences and Series

Concepts

1. Finite and Infinite Sequences
2. Series

1. Finite and Infinite Sequences

In day-to-day life, we think of a sequence as a set of items with some order or pattern. In mathematics, a sequence is a list of terms that correspond to the set of positive integers.

For example, suppose Justine is allowed to choose between two salary plans. Plan A offers \$48,000 as a starting salary with a 5% raise each year. Plan B offers

\$50,000 with a \$2000 raise each year. Then the following sequences represent the salaries for each plan for the first 5 yr.

Plan A:	\$48,000	\$50,400	\$52,920	\$55,566	\$58,344.30
Plan B:	\$50,000	\$52,000	\$54,000	\$56,000	\$58,000

By studying sequences we can see that Plan A yields a better salary if Justine plans to stay in the job for at least 5 yr.

These sequences are called *finite sequences* because they have a finite number of terms. The sequence 1, 4, 9, 16, 25, . . . is called an *infinite sequence* because it continues indefinitely.

Because the terms in a sequence are related to the set of positive integers, we give a formal definition of finite and infinite sequences, using the language of functions.

Definition of Finite and Infinite Sequences

An **infinite sequence** is a function whose domain is the set of positive integers.
A **finite sequence** is a function whose domain is the set of the first n positive integers.

For any positive integer n, the value of the sequence is denoted by a_n (read as "a sub n"). The values $a_1, a_2, a_3, \ldots$ are called the **terms of the sequence**. The expression a_n defines the **nth term** (or general term) **of the sequence**.

Example 1 Listing the Terms of a Sequence

Classroom Example: p. 1003, Exercise 8

List the terms of the following sequences.

a. $a_n = 3n^2 - 4, \quad 1 \le n \le 4$ **b.** $a_n = 3 \cdot 2^n$

Solution:

a. The domain is restricted to the first four positive integers, indicating that the sequence is finite.

n	a_n
1	$3(1)^2 - 4 = -1$
2	$3(2)^2 - 4 = 8$
3	$3(3)^2 - 4 = 23$
4	$3(4)^2 - 4 = 44$

The sequence is $-1, 8, 23, 44$.

b. The sequence $a_n = 3 \cdot 2^n$ has no restrictions on its domain; therefore, it is an infinite sequence.

n	a_n
1	$3 \cdot 2^1 = 6$
2	$3 \cdot 2^2 = 12$
3	$3 \cdot 2^3 = 24$
4	$3 \cdot 2^4 = 48$

. . .

The sequence is 6, 12, 24, 48, . . .

Skill Practice List the terms of the sequences.

1. $a_n = n^3 - 2, \quad 1 \le n \le 3$ **2.** $a_n = \left(\frac{2}{3}\right)^n$

Answers

1. $-1, 6, 25$ **2.** $\frac{2}{3}, \frac{4}{9}, \frac{8}{27}, \ldots$

Calculator Connections

Topic: Displaying Terms of a Sequence

If the *n*th term of a sequence is known, a seq(function on a graphing utility can display a list of terms. Finding the first four terms of the sequence from Example 1(b) is outlined here: $a_n = 3 \cdot 2^n$.

- Select the MODE key and highlight SEQ.
- Then access the seq(function from the LIST menu and enter the parameters as prompted.
- Paste the seq(command on the home screen and select ENTER.

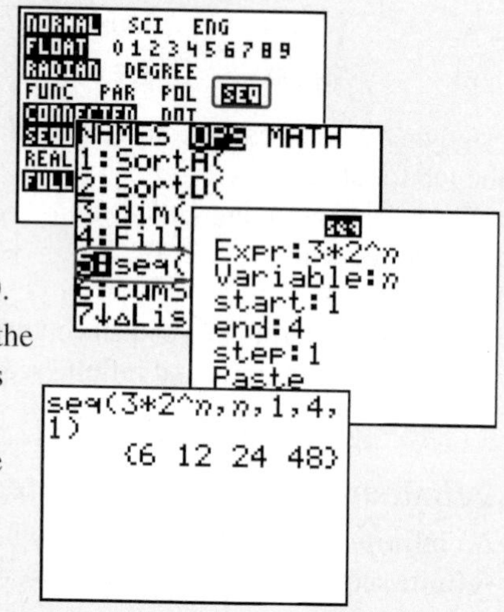

Sometimes the terms of a sequence may have alternating signs. Such a sequence is called an **alternating sequence**.

Classroom Example: p. 1003, Exercise 14

Example 2 Listing the Terms of an Alternating Sequence

List the first four terms of each alternating sequence.

a. $a_n = (-1)^n \cdot \dfrac{1}{n}$ **b.** $a_n = (-1)^{n+1} \cdot \left(\dfrac{2}{3}\right)^n$

Solution:

a.

n	a_n
1	$(-1)^1 \cdot \frac{1}{1} = -1$
2	$(-1)^2 \cdot \frac{1}{2} = \frac{1}{2}$
3	$(-1)^3 \cdot \frac{1}{3} = -\frac{1}{3}$
4	$(-1)^4 \cdot \frac{1}{4} = \frac{1}{4}$

The first four terms are $-1, \frac{1}{2}, -\frac{1}{3}, \frac{1}{4}$.

TIP: Notice that the factor $(-1)^n$ makes the even-numbered terms positive and the odd-numbered terms negative.

b.

n	a_n
1	$(-1)^{1+1} \cdot \left(\frac{2}{3}\right)^1 = (-1)^2 \cdot \left(\frac{2}{3}\right) = \frac{2}{3}$
2	$(-1)^{2+1} \cdot \left(\frac{2}{3}\right)^2 = (-1)^3 \cdot \left(\frac{4}{9}\right) = -\frac{4}{9}$
3	$(-1)^{3+1} \cdot \left(\frac{2}{3}\right)^3 = (-1)^4 \cdot \left(\frac{8}{27}\right) = \frac{8}{27}$
4	$(-1)^{4+1} \cdot \left(\frac{2}{3}\right)^4 = (-1)^5 \cdot \left(\frac{16}{81}\right) = -\frac{16}{81}$

The first four terms are $\frac{2}{3}, -\frac{4}{9}, \frac{8}{27}, -\frac{16}{81}$.

TIP: Notice that the factor $(-1)^{n+1}$ makes the odd-numbered terms positive and the even-numbered terms negative.

Skill Practice List the first four terms of each alternating sequence.

3. $a_n = (-1)^n\left(\frac{1}{2}\right)^n$ **4.** $a_n = (-1)^{n+1}\left(\frac{2}{n}\right)$

In Examples 1 and 2, we were given the formula for the nth term of a sequence and asked to list several terms of the sequence. We now consider the reverse process. Given several terms of the sequence, we will find a formula for the nth term. To do so, look for a pattern that establishes each term as a function of the term number.

Example 3 Finding the nth Term of a Sequence

Classroom Examples: p. 1003, Exercises 24 and 30

Find a formula for the nth term of the sequence.

a. $\frac{1}{2}, \frac{2}{3}, \frac{3}{4}, \frac{4}{5}, \ldots$ **b.** $-2, 4, -6, 8, -10, \ldots$ **c.** $\frac{1}{2}, \frac{1}{4}, \frac{1}{8}, \frac{1}{16}, \ldots$

Solution:

a. For each term in the sequence, the numerator is equal to the term number, and the denominator is equal to 1 more than the term number. Therefore, the nth term may be given by

$$a_n = \frac{n}{n+1}$$

b. The odd-numbered terms are negative, and the even-numbered terms are positive. The factor $(-1)^n$ will produce the required alternation of signs. The numbers 2, 4, 6, 8, 10, . . . are equal to 2(1), 2(2), 2(3), 2(4), 2(5), ... Therefore, the nth term may be given by

$$a_n = (-1)^n \cdot 2n$$

c. The denominators are consecutive powers of 2. The sequence can be written as

$$\frac{1}{2^1}, \frac{1}{2^2}, \frac{1}{2^3}, \frac{1}{2^4}, \ldots$$

Therefore, the nth term may be given by

$$a_n = \frac{1}{2^n}$$

Skill Practice Find a formula for the nth term of the sequence.

5. $\frac{1}{3}, \frac{1}{9}, \frac{1}{27}, \frac{1}{81}, \ldots$ **6.** $-1, 4, -9, 16, -25, \ldots$ **7.** $\frac{3}{2}, \frac{4}{3}, \frac{5}{4}, \frac{6}{5}, \frac{7}{6}, \ldots$

Answers

3. $-\frac{1}{2}, \frac{1}{4}, -\frac{1}{8}, \frac{1}{16}$

4. $2, -1, \frac{2}{3}, -\frac{1}{2}$

5. $a_n = \frac{1}{3^n}$ **6.** $a_n = (-1)^n n^2$

7. $a_n = \frac{n+2}{n+1}$

TIP: The first few terms of a sequence are not sufficient to define the sequence uniquely. For example, consider the sequence

$$\frac{1}{2}, \frac{1}{4}, \frac{1}{8}, \ldots$$

The following formulas both produce the first three terms, but differ at the fourth term:

$$a_n = \frac{1}{2^n} \quad \text{and} \quad b_n = \frac{1}{n^2 - n + 2}$$

$$a_4 = \frac{1}{16} \quad \text{whereas} \quad b_4 = \frac{1}{14}$$

To define a sequence uniquely, the nth term must be provided.

Classroom Example: p. 1003, Exercise 36

Example 4 Using a Sequence in an Application

A child drops a ball from a height of 4 ft. With each bounce, the ball rebounds to 50% of its height. Write a sequence whose terms represent the heights from which the ball falls (begin with the initial height from which the ball was dropped).

Solution:

The ball first drops 4 ft and then rebounds to a new height of $0.50(4 \text{ ft}) = 2$ ft. Similarly, it falls from 2 ft and rebounds $0.50(2 \text{ ft}) = 1$ ft. Repeating this process, we have

$$4, 2, 1, \frac{1}{2}, \frac{1}{4}, \frac{1}{8}, \ldots$$

The nth term can be represented by $a_n = 4 \cdot (0.50)^{n-1}$.

Skill Practice

8. The first swing of a pendulum measures 30°. If each swing that follows is 25% less, list the first three terms of this sequence.

2. Series

In many mathematical applications it is important to find the sum of the terms of a sequence. For example, suppose that the yearly interest earned in an account over a 4-yr period is given by the sequence

$$\$250, \quad \$265, \quad \$278.25, \quad \$292.16$$

The sum of the terms gives the total interest earned

$$\$250 + \$265 + \$278.25 + \$292.16 = \$1085.41$$

By adding the terms of a sequence, we obtain a series.

Definition of a Series

The indicated sum of the terms of a sequence is called a **series**.

Answer

8. 30°, 22.5°, 16.875°

As with a sequence, a series may be a finite or an infinite sum of terms.

A convenient notation used to denote the sum of a set of terms is called **summation notation**, or sigma notation. The Greek letter Σ (sigma) is used to indicate sums. For example, the sum of the first four terms of the sequence defined by $a_n = n^3$ are denoted by

$$\sum_{n=1}^{4} n^3$$

This is read as "the sum from n equals 1 to 4 of n^3" and is simplified as

$$\sum_{n=1}^{4} n^3 = (1)^3 + (2)^3 + (3)^3 + (4)^3$$
$$= 1 + 8 + 27 + 64$$
$$= 100$$

In this example, the letter n is called the **index of summation**. Many times, the letters i, j, and k are also used for the index of summation.

Calculator Connections

Topic: Finding the Sum of a Finite Sequence of Terms

The sum of a finite series may be found on a graphing calculator if the nth term of the corresponding sequence is known. The calculator takes the sum of a sequence by using the Sum and Seq functions.

```
sum(seq(n^3,n,1,
4,1))
                100
```

Example 5 Finding a Sum from Summation Notation

Find the sum. $\sum_{i=1}^{4} 2^i$

Solution:

$$\sum_{i=1}^{4} 2^i = 2^1 + 2^2 + 2^3 + 2^4$$
$$= 2 + 4 + 8 + 16$$
$$= 30$$

Classroom Example: p. 1004, Exercise 42

Skill Practice Find the sum.

9. $\sum_{i=1}^{4} i(i + 4)$

Example 6 Finding a Sum from Summation Notation

Find the sum. $\sum_{i=1}^{3} (-1)^{i+1} \cdot (3i + 4)$

Solution:

$$\sum_{i=1}^{3} (-1)^{i+1} \cdot (3i + 4) = (-1)^{1+1} \cdot [3(1) + 4] + (-1)^{2+1} \cdot [3(2) + 4] + (-1)^{3+1} \cdot [3(3) + 4]$$
$$= (-1)^2 \cdot (7) + (-1)^3 \cdot (10) + (-1)^4 \cdot (13)$$
$$= 7 - 10 + 13$$
$$= 10$$

Classroom Example: p. 1004, Exercise 46

Avoiding Mistakes

The letter i is used as a variable for the index of summation. In this context, it does not represent an imaginary number.

Skill Practice Find the sum.

10. $\sum_{i=1}^{4} (-1)^i(4i - 3)$

Answers

9. 70 **10.** 8

Classroom Example: p. 1004, Exercise 62

Example 7 **Converting to Summation Notation**

Write the series in summation notation.

a. $\frac{2}{3}+\frac{4}{9}+\frac{8}{27}+\frac{16}{81}$ Use n as the index of summation.

b. $1-\frac{1}{2}+\frac{1}{3}-\frac{1}{4}+\frac{1}{5}-\frac{1}{6}$ Use j as the index of summation.

Solution:

a. The sum can be written as

$$\left(\frac{2}{3}\right)^1+\left(\frac{2}{3}\right)^2+\left(\frac{2}{3}\right)^3+\left(\frac{2}{3}\right)^4$$

Taking n from 1 to 4, we have

$$\sum_{n=1}^{4}\left(\frac{2}{3}\right)^n$$

b. The even-numbered terms are negative. The factor $(-1)^{j+1}$ is negative for even values of j. Therefore, the series can be written as

$$\sum_{j=1}^{6}(-1)^{j+1}\cdot\frac{1}{j}$$

Answers

11. $\sum_{i=1}^{4}\frac{1}{4^i}$

12. $\sum_{i=1}^{5}(-1)^{i+1}\frac{1}{2i}$

Skill Practice Write the series in summation notation.

11. $\frac{1}{4}+\frac{1}{16}+\frac{1}{64}+\frac{1}{256}$ **12.** $\frac{1}{2}-\frac{1}{4}+\frac{1}{6}-\frac{1}{8}+\frac{1}{10}$

Section 14.2 Practice Exercises

For additional exercises, see Classroom Activities 14.2A–14.2C in the *Student's Resource Manual* at www.mhhe.com/moh.

Vocabulary and Key Concepts

1. **a.** A(n) (finite/infinite) sequence is a function whose domain is the set of positive integers. A(n) (finite/infinite) sequence is a function whose domain is the set of the first n positive integers. infinite; finite

b. Given a sequence, the values a_1, a_2, a_3, and so on are called the ____terms____ of the sequence. The expression a_n defines the ____nth____ term (or general term) of the sequence.

c. In an ____alternating____ sequence, consecutive terms alternate in sign.

d. A sum of a sequence is called a ____series____.

e. To represent a sum of terms, ____summation____ notation is often used and is represented by the Greek letter Σ.

f. Given the sum $\sum_{n=1}^{5}n^2$, the letter n is called the ____________ of summation. In expanded form, this series is $(1)^2+(2)^2+$ ____________ $=55$. index; $(3)^2+(4)^2+(5)^2$

Review Exercises

For Exercises 2–4, evaluate the expression.

2. $9!$ 362,880 **3.** $\frac{8!}{2!\cdot 6!}$ 28 **4.** $\frac{7!}{7!\cdot 0!}$ 1

For Exercises 5–6, expand the binomial.

5. $(2x + z)^4$ $16x^4 + 32x^3z + 24x^2z^2 + 8xz^3 + z^4$

6. $(4m - 3t)^3$ $64m^3 - 144m^2t + 108mt^2 - 27t^3$

Concept 1: Finite and Infinite Sequences

For Exercises 7–18, list the terms of each sequence. **(See Examples 1–2.)**

7. $a_n = 3n + 1, \quad 1 \le n \le 5$ 4, 7, 10, 13, 16

8. $a_n = -2n + 3, \quad 1 \le n \le 5$ 1, −1, −3, −5, −7

9. $a_n = \sqrt{n + 2}, \quad 1 \le n \le 4$ $\sqrt{3}, 2, \sqrt{5}, \sqrt{6}$

10. $a_n = \sqrt{n - 1}, \quad 1 \le n \le 4$ $0, 1, \sqrt{2}, \sqrt{3}$

11. $a_n = (-1)^n \dfrac{n + 1}{n + 2}, \quad 1 \le n \le 4$ $-\frac{2}{3}, \frac{3}{4}, -\frac{4}{5}, \frac{5}{6}$

12. $a_n = (-1)^n \dfrac{n - 1}{n + 2}, \quad 1 \le n \le 4$ $0, \frac{1}{4}, -\frac{2}{5}, \frac{1}{2}$

13. $a_n = (-1)^{n+1}(n^2 - 1), \quad 1 \le n \le 3$ 0, −3, 8

14. $a_n = (-1)^{n+1}(n^2), \quad 1 \le n \le 3$ 1, −4, 9

15. $a_n = n^2 - n, \quad 1 \le n \le 6$ 0, 2, 6, 12, 20, 30

16. $a_n = n(n^2 - 1), \quad 1 \le n \le 6$ 0, 6, 24, 60, 120, 210

17. $a_n = (-1)^n 3^n, \quad 1 \le n \le 4$ −3, 9, −27, 81

18. $a_n = (-1)^n n, \quad 1 \le n \le 4$ −1, 2, −3, 4

19. If the nth term of a sequence is $a_n = (-1)^n \cdot n^2$, which terms are positive and which are negative? When n is odd, the term is negative. When n is even, the term is positive.

20. If the nth term of a sequence is $a_n = (-1)^{n-1} \cdot \frac{1}{n}$, which terms are positive and which are negative? When n is odd, the term is positive. When n is even, the term is negative.

For Exercises 21–32, find a formula for the nth term of the sequence. Answers may vary. **(See Example 3.)**

21. 2, 4, 6, 8, . . . $a_n = 2n$

22. 3, 6, 9, 12, . . . $a_n = 3n$

23. 1, 3, 5, 7, . . . $a_n = 2n - 1$

24. 3, 5, 7, 9, . . . $a_n = 2n + 1$

25. $1, \frac{1}{4}, \frac{1}{9}, \frac{1}{16}, \ldots$ $a_n = \frac{1}{n^2}$

26. $\frac{1}{2}, \frac{2}{3}, \frac{3}{4}, \frac{4}{5}, \ldots$ $a_n = \frac{n}{n+1}$

27. 1, −1, 1, −1, . . . $a_n = (-1)^{n+1}$

28. −1, 1 −1, 1, . . . $a_n = (-1)^n$

29. −2, 4, −8, 16, . . . $a_n = (-1)^n 2^n$

30. 3, −9, 27, −81, . . . $a_n = (-1)^{n+1} 3^n$

31. $\frac{3}{5}, \frac{3}{25}, \frac{3}{125}, \frac{3}{625}, \ldots$ $a_n = \frac{3}{5^n}$

32. $\frac{1}{4}, \frac{1}{16}, \frac{1}{64}, \frac{1}{256}, \ldots$ $a_n = \frac{1}{4^n}$

33. Edmond borrowed \$500. To pay off the loan, he agreed to pay 2% of the balance plus \$50 each month. Write a sequence representing the amount Edmond will pay each month for the next 4 months. Round each term to the nearest cent. \$60, \$58.80, \$57.62, \$56.47

34. Janice deposited \$1000 in an account that pays 3% interest compounded annually. Write a sequence representing the amount Janice receives in interest each year for the first 4 yr. Round each term to the nearest cent. \$30.00, \$30.90, \$31.83, \$32.78

35. A certain bacteria culture doubles its size each day. If there are 25,000 bacteria on the first day, write a sequence representing the population each day for the first week (7 days). **(See Example 4.)**
25,000; 50,000; 100,000; 200,000; 400,000; 800,000; 1,600,000

36. A radioactive chemical decays by one-half of its amount each week. If there is 16 g of the chemical in week 1, write a sequence representing the amount present each week for 2 months (8 weeks).
$16, 8, 4, 2, 1, \frac{1}{2}, \frac{1}{4}, \frac{1}{8}$ (grams)

Concept 2: Series

37. What is the difference between a sequence and a series?
A sequence is an ordered list of terms. A series is the sum of the terms of a sequence.

38. **a.** Identify the index of summation for the series. $\displaystyle\sum_{k=1}^{7} (k^2 + 1)$ k

b. How many terms does this series have? 7

For Exercises 39–54, find the sums. **(See Examples 5–6.)**

39. $\sum_{i=1}^{4}(3i)^2$ 90

40. $\sum_{i=1}^{4}(2i^2)$ 60

41. $\sum_{j=0}^{4}\left(\frac{1}{2}\right)^j$ $\frac{31}{16}$

42. $\sum_{j=0}^{4}\left(\frac{1}{3}\right)^j$ $\frac{121}{81}$

43. $\sum_{i=1}^{6}5$ 30

44. $\sum_{i=1}^{7}3$ 21

45. $\sum_{j=1}^{4}(-1)^j(5j)$ 10

46. $\sum_{j=1}^{4}(-1)^j(4j)$ 8

47. $\sum_{i=1}^{4}\frac{i+1}{i}$ $\frac{73}{12}$

48. $\sum_{i=2}^{5}\frac{i-1}{i}$ $\frac{163}{60}$

49. $\sum_{j=1}^{3}(j+1)(j+2)$ 38

50. $\sum_{j=1}^{3}j(j+2)$ 26

51. $\sum_{k=1}^{7}(-1)^k$ -1

52. $\sum_{k=0}^{5}(-1)^{k+1}$ 0

53. $\sum_{k=1}^{5}k^2$ 55

54. $\sum_{k=1}^{5}2^k$ 62

For Exercises 55–66,write the series in summation notation. **(See Example 7.)**

55. $1+2+3+4+5+6$ $\sum_{n=1}^{6}n$

56. $1-2+3-4+5-6$ $\sum_{n=1}^{6}(-1)^{n+1}n$

57. $4+4+4+4+4$ $\sum_{i=1}^{5}4$

58. $8+8+8+8+8$ $\sum_{i=1}^{5}8$

59. $4+8+12+16+20$ $\sum_{j=1}^{5}4j$

60. $3+6+9+12+15$ $\sum_{j=1}^{5}3j$

61. $\frac{1}{3}-\frac{1}{9}+\frac{1}{27}-\frac{1}{81}$ $\sum_{k=1}^{4}(-1)^{k+1}\frac{1}{3^k}$

62. $\frac{1}{2}-\frac{1}{4}+\frac{1}{8}-\frac{1}{16}$ $\sum_{k=1}^{4}(-1)^{k+1}\frac{1}{2^k}$

63. $\frac{5}{11}+\frac{6}{22}+\frac{7}{33}+\frac{8}{44}+\frac{9}{55}+\frac{10}{66}$ $\sum_{i=1}^{6}\frac{i+4}{11i}$

64. $-\frac{5}{7}-\frac{10}{8}-\frac{15}{9}-\frac{20}{10}-\frac{25}{11}-\frac{30}{12}-\frac{35}{13}$ $\sum_{i=1}^{7}-\frac{5i}{i+6}$

65. $x+x^2+x^3+x^4+x^5$ $\sum_{n=1}^{5}x^n$

66. $y^2+y^4+y^6+y^8+y^{10}$ $\sum_{n=1}^{5}y^{2n}$

Expanding Your Skills

Some sequences are defined by a recursive formula, which defines each term of a sequence in terms of one or more of its preceding terms. For example, if $a_1 = 5$ and $a_n = 2a_{n-1} + 1$ for $n > 1$, then the terms of the sequence are 5, 11, 23, 47, ... In this case, each term after the first is one more than twice the term before it.

For Exercises 67–70, list the first five terms of the sequence.

67. $a_1 = -3,\ a_n = a_{n-1} + 5$ for $n > 1$
$-3, 2, 7, 12, 17$

68. $a_1 = 10,\ a_n = a_{n-1} - 3$ for $n > 1$
$10, 7, 4, 1, -2$

69. $a_1 = 5,\ a_n = 4a_{n-1} + 1$ for $n > 1$
5, 21, 85, 341, 1365

70. $a_1 = -2,\ a_n = -3a_{n-1} + 4$ for $n > 1$
$-2, 10, -26, 82, -242$

71. A famous sequence in mathematics is called the Fibonacci sequence, named after the Italian mathematician Leonardo Fibonacci of the thirteenth century. The Fibonacci sequence is defined by

$$a_1 = 1$$

$$a_2 = 1$$

$$a_n = a_{n-1} + a_{n-2} \quad \text{for } n > 2$$

This definition implies that beginning with the third term, each term is the sum of the preceding two terms. Write out the first 10 terms of the Fibonacci sequence. 1, 1, 2, 3, 5, 8, 13, 21, 34, 55

Arithmetic Sequences and Series

Section 14.3

Concepts

1. Arithmetic Sequences
2. Arithmetic Series

1. Arithmetic Sequences

In this section, we present a special type of sequence called an arithmetic sequence, and then we will study its related sum called an arithmetic series. The sequence 4, 7, 10, 13, 16, . . . is an example of an arithmetic sequence. Note the characteristic that each successive term after the first is a fixed value more than the previous term (in this case the terms differ by 3).

Definition of an Arithmetic Sequence

An **arithmetic sequence** is a sequence in which the difference between consecutive terms is constant.

The fixed difference between a term and its predecessor is called the **common difference** and is denoted by the letter d. That is,

$$d = a_{n+1} - a_n$$

Furthermore, if a_1 is the first term, then

$a_1 = a_1 + 0d$

$a_2 = a_1 + 1d$ is the second term,

$a_3 = a_1 + 2d$ is the third term,

$a_4 = a_1 + 3d$ is the fourth term, and so on.

. . .

In general, $a_n = a_1 + (n - 1)d$.

nth Term of an Arithmetic Sequence

The nth term of an arithmetic sequence is given by

$$a_n = a_1 + (n - 1)d$$

where a_1 is the first term of the sequence and d is the common difference.

Example 1 Writing the nth Term of an Arithmetic Sequence

Classroom Example: p. 1010, Exercise 26

Write the nth term of the sequence. 9, 2, −5, −12, . . .

Solution:

9, 2, −5, −12, . . .

(differences: −7 −7 −7)

The common difference can be found by subtracting a term from its predecessor: $2 - 9 = -7$

TIP: Notice that the terms of an arithmetic sequence increase or decrease linearly. In Example 1, the terms decrease by 7 for each subsequent term. This is similar to a line with a slope of −7.

With $a_1 = 9$ and $d = -7$, we have

$$\begin{aligned} a_n &= 9 + (n - 1)(-7) \\ &= 9 - 7n + 7 \\ &= -7n + 16 \end{aligned}$$

Skill Practice Write the nth term of the sequence.

1. $-3, -1, 1, 3, 5, \ldots$

In Example 1, the common difference between terms is -7. Accordingly, each term of the sequence *decreases* by 7.

The formula $a_n = a_1 + (n - 1)d$ contains four variables: a_n, a_1, n, and d. Consequently, if we know the value of three of the four variables, we can solve for the fourth.

Classroom Example: p. 1010, Exercise 40

Example 2 Finding a Specified Term of an Arithmetic Sequence

Find the ninth term of the arithmetic sequence in which $a_1 = -4$ and $a_{22} = 164$.

Solution:

To find the value of the ninth term a_9, we need to determine the value of d. To find d, substitute $a_1 = -4$, $n = 22$, and $a_{22} = 164$ into the formula $a_n = a_1 + (n - 1)d$.

$$\begin{aligned} a_n &= a_1 + (n - 1)d \\ 164 &= -4 + (22 - 1)d \\ 164 &= -4 + 21d \\ 168 &= 21d \\ d &= 8 \end{aligned}$$

Therefore, $a_n = -4 + (n - 1)(8)$

$$\begin{aligned} a_9 &= -4 + (9 - 1)(8) \\ &= -4 + (8)(8) \\ &= 60 \end{aligned}$$

Instructor Note: Consider showing your students the similarity between an arithmetic sequence and a linear equation in two variables. The term number, n, behaves as the independent variable, x. The common difference, d, behaves as the slope, m.

Skill Practice

2. Find the tenth term of the arithmetic sequence in which $a_1 = 14$ and $a_{15} = -28$. (*Hint:* First find d.)

Classroom Example: p. 1010, Exercise 42

Example 3 Finding the Number of Terms in an Arithmetic Sequence

Find the number of terms of the sequence $7, 3, -1, -5, \ldots, -113$.

Answers

1. $2n - 5$ **2.** $d = -3, a_{10} = -13$

Solution:

To find the number of terms n, we can substitute $a_1 = 7$, $d = -4$, and $a_n = -113$ into the formula for the nth term.

$$\begin{aligned} a_n &= a_1 + (n - 1)d \\ -113 &= 7 + (n - 1)(-4) \\ -113 &= 7 - 4n + 4 \\ -113 &= 11 - 4n \\ -124 &= -4n \\ n &= 31 \end{aligned}$$

Skill Practice Find the number of terms of the sequence.

3. $-15, -11, -7, -3, \ldots, 81$

2. Arithmetic Series

The indicated sum of an arithmetic sequence is called an **arithmetic series**. For example, the series

$$3 + 7 + 11 + 15 + 19 + 23$$

is an arithmetic series because the common difference between terms is constant (4). Adding the terms in a lengthy sum is cumbersome, so we offer the following "shortcut," which is developed here. Let S represent the sum of the terms in the series.

$$\begin{aligned} S &= 3 + 7 + 11 + 15 + 19 + 23 && \text{Add the terms in ascending order.} \\ S &= 23 + 19 + 15 + 11 + 7 + 3 && \text{Add the terms in descending order.} \\ \hline 2S &= 26 + 26 + 26 + 26 + 26 + 26 && \text{Adding the two series produces six terms of 26.} \\ 2S &= 6 \cdot 26 \\ S &= \frac{6 \cdot 26}{2} \\ &= 78 \end{aligned}$$

By adding the terms in ascending and descending order, we double the sum but create a pattern that is easily added. This is true in general. To find the sum, S_n, of the first n terms of the arithmetic series $a_1 + a_2 + a_3 + \cdots + a_n$, we have

$$\begin{aligned} S_n &= a_1 + (a_1 + d) + (a_1 + 2d) + \cdots + a_n && \text{Ascending order} \\ S_n &= a_n + (a_n - d) + (a_n - 2d) + \cdots + a_1 && \text{Descending order} \\ \hline 2S_n &= (a_1 + a_n) + (a_1 + a_n) + (a_1 + a_n) + \cdots + (a_1 + a_n) \\ 2S_n &= n(a_1 + a_n) \\ S_n &= \frac{n}{2}(a_1 + a_n) \end{aligned}$$

Answer

3. 25

Sum of an Arithmetic Series

The sum S_n of the first n terms of an arithmetic series is given by

$$S_n = \frac{n}{2}(a_1 + a_n)$$

where a_1 is the first term of the series and a_n is the nth term of the series.

Classroom Example: p. 1010, Exercise 56

Avoiding Mistakes

When we apply the sum formula $S_n = \frac{n}{2}(a_1 + a_n)$ to find the sum $\sum_{i=1}^{n} a_n$, the index of summation i must begin at 1.

Example 4 Finding the Sum of an Arithmetic Series

Find the sum of the series. $\sum_{i=1}^{25} (2i + 3)$

Solution:

In this series, $n = 25$. Furthermore, $a_1 = 2(1) + 3 = 5$ and $a_{25} = 2(25) + 3 = 53$. Therefore,

$$S_{25} = \frac{25}{2}(5 + 53) \qquad \text{Apply the formula } S_n = \frac{n}{2}(a_1 + a_n).$$

$$= \frac{25}{2}(58) \qquad \text{Simplify.}$$

$$= 725$$

Skill Practice Find the sum of the series.

4. $\sum_{i=1}^{20} (3i - 2)$

Classroom Example: p. 1010, Exercise 64

Example 5 Finding the Sum of an Arithmetic Series

Find the sum of the series.

$$-3 + (-5) + (-7) + \cdots + (-127)$$

Solution:

For this series, $a_1 = -3$ and $a_n = -127$. However, to determine the sum, we also need to find the value of n. The difference between the second term and its predecessor is $-5 - (-3) = -2$. Thus, $d = -2$. We have

$$-127 = -3 + (n - 1)(-2) \qquad \text{Apply the formula } a_n = a_1 + (n - 1)d.$$

$$-127 = -3 - 2n + 2 \qquad \text{Apply the distributive property.}$$

$$-127 = -1 - 2n \qquad \text{Combine } like \text{ terms.}$$

$$-126 = -2n \qquad \text{Solve for } n.$$

$$n = 63$$

Using $n = 63$, $a_1 = -3$, and $a_{63} = -127$, we have

$$S_n = \frac{n}{2}(a_1 + a_n) = \frac{63}{2}[-3 + (-127)] = \frac{63}{2}(-130) = -4095$$

Skill Practice Find the sum of the series.

5. $8 + 3 + (-2) + \cdots + (-137)$

Answers

4. 590 5. −1935

Section 14.3 Practice Exercises

For additional exercises, see Classroom Activities 14.3A–14.3B in the *Student's Resource Manual* at www.mhhe.com/moh.

Vocabulary and Key Concepts

1. a. An ___arithmetic___ sequence is a sequence in which the difference between consecutive terms is constant.

   b. The common ___difference___ between a term and its predecessor in an arithmetic sequence is often denoted by the letter d.

   c. The nth term of an arithmetic sequence is given by $a_n =$ ___$a_1 + (n-1)d$___, where a_n is the nth term, a_1 is the first term, n is the number of terms, and ___d___ is the common difference between terms.

   d. An indicated sum of an arithmetic sequence is called an arithmetic ___series___.

   e. The sum S_n of the first n terms of an arithmetic series is given by $S_n =$ ___$\frac{n}{2}(a_1 + a_n)$___, where a_1 is the first term and a_n is the nth term.

Review Exercises

2. Write the first four terms of the sequence. $c_n = \dfrac{n^2}{n+1}$ $\quad \frac{1}{2}, \frac{4}{3}, \frac{9}{4}, \frac{16}{5}$

3. Write the first four terms of the sequence. $d_n = (-1)^n$ $\quad -1, 1, -1, 1$

4. Find the sum. $\displaystyle\sum_{n=1}^{10} (-1)^{n+1}$ $\quad 0$

5. Find the sum. $\displaystyle\sum_{n=1}^{5} (1 - 4n)$ $\quad -55$

Concept 1: Arithmetic Sequences

6. Explain how to determine if a sequence is arithmetic. A sequence is arithmetic if the difference between any term and the preceding term is constant.

For Exercises 7–12, the first term of an arithmetic sequence is given along with its common difference. Write the first five terms of the sequence.

7. $a_1 = 3, d = 8$ $\quad 3, 11, 19, 27, 35$

8. $a_1 = -5, d = 2$ $\quad -5, -3, -1, 1, 3$

9. $a_1 = 80, d = -20$ $\quad 80, 60, 40, 20, 0$

10. $a_1 = -4, d = -5$ $\quad -4, -9, -14, -19, -24$

11. $a_1 = 3, d = \dfrac{3}{4}$ $\quad 3, \frac{15}{4}, \frac{9}{2}, \frac{21}{4}, 6$

12. $a_1 = 1, d = \dfrac{2}{3}$ $\quad 1, \frac{5}{3}, \frac{7}{3}, 3, \frac{11}{3}$

For Exercises 13–18, find the common difference d for each arithmetic sequence.

13. $1, 3, 5, 7, 9, \ldots$ $\quad 2$

14. $2, 8, 14, 20, 26, \ldots$ $\quad 6$

15. $6, 3, 0, -3, -6, \ldots$ $\quad -3$

16. $8, 3, -2, -7, -12, \ldots$ $\quad -5$

17. $-7, -9, -11, -13, -15, \ldots$ $\quad -2$

18. $-15, -11, -7, -3, 1, \ldots$ $\quad 4$

For Exercises 19–24, write the first five terms of the arithmetic sequence.

19. $a_1 = 3, d = 5$ $\quad 3, 8, 13, 18, 23$

20. $a_1 = -3, d = 2$ $\quad -3, -1, 1, 3, 5$

21. $a_1 = 2, d = \dfrac{1}{2}$ $\quad 2, \frac{5}{2}, 3, \frac{7}{2}, 4$

22. $a_1 = 0, d = \dfrac{1}{3}$ $\quad 0, \frac{1}{3}, \frac{2}{3}, 1, \frac{4}{3}$

23. $a_1 = 2, d = -4$ $\quad 2, -2, -6, -10, -14$

24. $a_1 = 10, d = -6$ $\quad 10, 4, -2, -8, -14$

For Exercises 25–33, write the nth term of the sequence. **(See Example 1.)**

25. $0, 5, 10, 15, 20, \ldots$
$a_n = -5 + 5n$

26. $7, 12, 17, 22, 27, \ldots$
$a_n = 2 + 5n$

27. $-2, -4, -6, -8, -10, \ldots$
$a_n = -2n$

28. $1, -3, -7, -11, -15, \ldots$
$a_n = 5 - 4n$

29. $2, \frac{5}{2}, 3, \frac{7}{2}, 4, \ldots$ $a_n = \frac{3}{2} + \frac{1}{2}n$

30. $1, \frac{4}{3}, \frac{5}{3}, 2, \frac{7}{3}, \ldots$ $a_n = \frac{2}{3} + \frac{1}{3}n$

31. $21, 17, 13, 9, 5, \ldots$
$a_n = 25 - 4n$

32. $9, 6, 3, 0, -3, \ldots$
$a_n = 12 - 3n$

33. $-8, -2, 4, 10, 16, \ldots$
$a_n = -14 + 6n$

For Exercises 34–41, find the indicated term of each arithmetic sequence. **(See Example 2.)**

34. Find the eighth term given $a_1 = -6$ and $d = -3$.
$a_8 = -27$

35. Find the sixth term given $a_1 = -3$ and $d = 4$.
$a_6 = 17$

36. Find the 12th term given $a_1 = -8$ and $d = -2$.
$a_{12} = -30$

37. Find the ninth term given $a_1 = -1$ and $d = 6$.
$a_9 = 47$

38. Find the tenth term given $a_1 = 1$ and $a_7 = 31$
$a_{10} = 46$

39. Find the seventh term given $a_1 = 0$ and $a_{10} = -45$.
$a_7 = -30$

40. Find the sixth term given $a_1 = 3$ and $a_{13} = 39$.
$a_6 = 18$

41. Find the 11th term given $a_1 = 12$ and $a_6 = -18$.
$a_{11} = -48$

For Exercises 42–49, find the number of terms, n, of each arithmetic sequence. **(See Example 3.)**

42. $2, 0, -2, \ldots, -56$
30

43. $8, 13, 18, \ldots, 98$
19

44. $1, -3, -7, \ldots, -67$
18

45. $1, 5, 9, \ldots, 85$
22

46. $1, \frac{3}{4}, \frac{1}{2}, \ldots, -4$ 21

47. $2, \frac{5}{2}, 3, \ldots, 13$ 23

48. $-\frac{5}{3}, -1, -\frac{1}{3}, \ldots, \frac{37}{3}$ 22

49. $\frac{13}{3}, \frac{19}{3}, \frac{25}{3}, \ldots, \frac{73}{3}$ 11

50. If the third and fourth terms of an arithmetic sequence are 18 and 21, what are the first and second terms? $a_1 = 12, a_2 = 15$

51. If the third and fourth terms of an arithmetic sequence are -8 and -11, what are the first and second terms? $a_1 = -2, a_2 = -5$

Concept 2: Arithmetic Series

52. Explain the difference between an arithmetic sequence and an arithmetic series.
An arithmetic sequence is an ordered list of terms in which the difference between a term and its predecessor is constant. An arithmetic series is the sum of the terms in such a sequence.

For Exercises 53–66, find the sum of the arithmetic series. **(See Examples 4–5.)**

53. $\sum_{i=1}^{20} (3i + 2)$ 670

54. $\sum_{i=1}^{15} (2i - 3)$ 195

55. $\sum_{i=1}^{20} (i + 4)$ 290

56. $\sum_{i=1}^{25} (i - 3)$ 250

57. $\sum_{j=1}^{10} (4 - j)$ −15

58. $\sum_{j=1}^{10} (6 - j)$ 5

59. $\sum_{j=1}^{15} \left(\frac{2}{3}j + 1\right)$ 95

60. $\sum_{j=1}^{15} \left(\frac{1}{2}j - 2\right)$ 30

61. $4 + 8 + 12 + \cdots + 84$ 924

62. $4 + 9 + 14 + \cdots + 49$ 265

63. $6 + 8 + 10 + \cdots + 34$ 300

64. $-4 + (-3) + (-2) + \cdots + 12$ 68

65. $-3 + (-7) + (-11) + \cdots + (-39)$ −210

66. $2 + 5 + 8 + \cdots + 53$ 495

67. Find the sum of the first 100 positive integers.
5050

68. Find the sum of the first 50 positive even integers.
2550

69. The seating in a certain theater is arranged so that there are 30 seats in row 1, 32 in row 2, 34 in row 3, and so on. If there are 20 rows, how many total seats are there? What is the total revenue if the average ticket price is \$15 per seat and the theater is sold out?
980 seats; \$14,700

70. A triangular array of dominoes has one domino in the first row, two dominoes in the second row, three dominoes in the third row, and so on. If there are 15 rows, how many dominoes are in the array? 120 dominoes

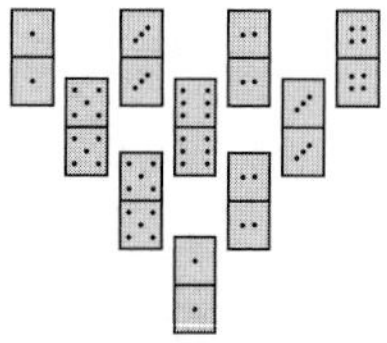

Geometric Sequences and Series

Section 14.4

Concepts

1. Geometric Sequences
2. Geometric Series

1. Geometric Sequences

The sequence 2, 4, 8, 16, 32, . . . is not an arithmetic sequence because the difference between terms is not constant. However, a different pattern exists. Notice that each term after the first is 2 times the preceding term. This sequence is called a geometric sequence.

Definition of a Geometric Sequence

A **geometric sequence** is a sequence in which the ratio between each term and its predecessor is constant.

The constant quotient of a term and its predecessor is called the **common ratio** and is denoted by r. The common ratio is found by dividing a term by the preceding term. That is,

$$r = \frac{a_{n+1}}{a_n}$$

For the sequence 2, 4, 8, 16, 32, . . . we have $r = \frac{4}{2} = \frac{8}{4} = \frac{16}{8} = \frac{32}{16} = 2$.

If a_1 denotes the first term of a geometric sequence, then

$a_2 = a_1 r$ is the second term,

$a_3 = a_1 r^2$ is the third term,

$a_4 = a_1 r^3$ is the fourth term, and so on.

. . .

This pattern gives $a_n = a_1 r^{n-1}$.

***n*th Term of a Geometric Sequence**

The nth term of a geometric sequence is given by

$$a_n = a_1 r^{n-1}$$

where a_1 is the first term and r is the common ratio.

Example 1 Finding the *n*th Term of a Geometric Sequence

Classroom Example: p. 1017, Exercise 26

Find the nth term of the sequence. **a.** $-1, 4, -16, 64, \ldots$ **b.** $12, 8, \frac{16}{3}, \frac{32}{9}, \ldots$

Solution:

a. The common ratio is found by dividing any term (after the first) by its predecessor.

$$r = \frac{4}{-1} = -4$$

With $r = -4$ and $a_1 = -1$, we have $a_n = -1(-4)^{n-1}$.

b. The common ratio is $r = \frac{8}{12} = \frac{2}{3}$. With $a_1 = 12$ and $r = \frac{2}{3}$, we have

$$a_n = 12\left(\frac{2}{3}\right)^{n-1}$$

Skill Practice Find the nth term of the geometric sequence.

1. 6, 12, 24, 48, . . . **2.** $6, 2, \frac{2}{3}, \frac{2}{9}, \ldots$

The formula $a_n = a_1r^{n-1}$ contains the variables a_n, a_1, n, and r. If we know the value of three of the four variables, we can find the fourth.

Classroom Example: p. 1017, Exercise 32

Example 2 Finding a Specified Term of a Geometric Sequence

Given $a_n = 6\left(\frac{1}{2}\right)^{n-1}$, find a_5.

Solution:

$$a_n = 6\left(\frac{1}{2}\right)^{n-1}$$

$$a_5 = 6\left(\frac{1}{2}\right)^{5-1} = 6\left(\frac{1}{2}\right)^{4} = 6\left(\frac{1}{16}\right) = \frac{3}{8}$$

Skill Practice

3. Given $a_n = 3(-2)^{n-1}$, find a_6.

Classroom Example: p. 1017, Exercise 38

Example 3 Finding a Specified Term of a Geometric Sequence

Find the first term of the geometric sequence where $a_5 = -162$ and $r = 3$.

Solution:

$-162 = a_1(3)^{5-1}$	Substitute $a_5 = -162$, $n = 5$, and $r = 3$ into the formula $a_n = a_1r^{n-1}$.
$-162 = a_1(3)^4$	Simplify and solve for a_1.
$-162 = a_1(81)$	
$a_1 = -2$	

Skill Practice

4. Find the first term of the geometric sequence where $a_4 = \frac{25}{32}$ and $r = \frac{1}{4}$.

2. Geometric Series

The indicated sum of a geometric sequence is called a **geometric series**. For example,

$$1 + 3 + 9 + 27 + 81 + 243$$

is a geometric series. To find the sum, consider the following procedure. Let S represent the sum

$$S = 1 + 3 + 9 + 27 + 81 + 243$$

Answers

1. $a_n = 6(2)^{n-1}$ **2.** $a_n = 6\left(\frac{1}{3}\right)^{n-1}$

3. -96 **4.** 50

Now multiply S by the common ratio, which in this case is 3.

$$3S = 3 + 9 + 27 + 81 + 243 + 729$$

Then

$$\begin{aligned}3S - S &= (3 + 9 + 27 + 81 + 243 + 729) - (1 + 3 + 9 + 27 + 81 + 243)\\ 2S &= 3 + 9 + 27 + 81 + 243 + 729 - 1 - 3 - 9 - 27 - 81 - 243\\ 2S &= 729 - 1 \qquad \text{The terms in red form a sum of zero.}\\ 2S &= 728\\ S &= 364\end{aligned}$$

A similar procedure can be used to find the sum S_n of the first n terms of any geometric series. Subtract rS_n from S_n.

$$\begin{aligned}S_n &= a_1 \quad + a_1r \quad + a_1r^2 \quad + \cdots + a_1r^{n-1}\\ rS_n &= a_1r \quad + a_1r^2 \quad + a_1r^3 \quad + \cdots + a_1r^n\end{aligned}$$

$$S_n - rS_n = (a_1 - a_1r) + (a_1r - a_1r^2) + (a_1r^2 - a_1r^3) + \cdots + (a_1r^{n-1} - a_1r^n)$$

$$\begin{aligned}S_n - rS_n &= a_1 - a_1r^n \qquad \text{The terms in red form a sum of zero.}\\ S_n(1 - r) &= a_1(1 - r^n) \qquad \text{Factor each side of the equation.}\\ S_n &= \frac{a_1(1 - r^n)}{1 - r} \qquad \text{Divide by } (1 - r).\end{aligned}$$

Sum of a Geometric Series

The sum, S_n, of the first n terms of a geometric series $\sum_{i=1}^{n} a_1r^{i-1}$ is given by

$$S_n = \frac{a_1(1 - r^n)}{1 - r}$$

where a_1 is the first term of the series, r is the common ratio, and $r \neq 1$.

Example 4 Finding the Sum of a Geometric Series

Classroom Example: p. 1017, Exercise 48

Find the sum of the series. $\sum_{i=1}^{6} 4\left(\frac{1}{2}\right)^{i-1}$

Solution:

By expanding the terms of this series, we see that the series is geometric.

$$\sum_{i=1}^{6} 4\left(\frac{1}{2}\right)^{i-1} = 4 + 2 + 1 + \frac{1}{2} + \frac{1}{4} + \frac{1}{8}$$

We have: $a_1 = 4$, $r = \frac{1}{2}$, and $n = 6$,

$$S_n = \frac{a_1(1 - r^n)}{1 - r} = \frac{4[1 - (\frac{1}{2})^6]}{1 - \frac{1}{2}} = \frac{4(1 - \frac{1}{64})}{\frac{1}{2}} = 8\left(\frac{63}{64}\right) = \frac{63}{8}$$

Skill Practice Find the sum of the geometric series.

5. $\frac{1}{9} + \frac{1}{3} + 1 + 3 + 9 + 27$

Answer

5. $\frac{364}{9}$

Classroom Example: p. 1017, Exercise 54

Example 5 Finding the Sum of a Geometric Series

Find the sum of the series $5 + 10 + 20 + \cdots + 5120$.

Solution:

The common ratio is 2 and $a_1 = 5$. The nth term of the sequence can be written as $a_n = 5(2)^{n-1}$. To find the value of n, substitute 5120 for a_n.

$$5120 = 5(2)^{n-1}$$

$$\frac{5120}{5} = \frac{5(2)^{n-1}}{5} \qquad \text{Divide both sides by 5.}$$

$$1024 = 2^{n-1} \qquad \text{To solve the exponential equation, write each side as a power of 2.}$$

$$2^{10} = 2^{n-1}$$

$$10 = n - 1 \qquad \text{Recall that if } b^x = b^y \text{, then } x = y.$$

$$n = 11$$

With $a_1 = 5$, $r = 2$, and $n = 11$, we have

$$S_n = \frac{a_1(1 - r^n)}{1 - r} = \frac{5(1 - 2^{11})}{1 - 2} = \frac{5(1 - 2048)}{-1} = \frac{5(-2047)}{-1} = 10{,}235$$

Skill Practice Find the sum of the geometric series.

6. $3 + 6 + 12 + \cdots + 768$

Consider a geometric series where $|r| < 1$. For increasing values of n, r^n decreases. For example,

$$\left(\frac{1}{2}\right)^5 = 0.03125 \qquad \left(\frac{1}{2}\right)^{10} \approx 0.00097656 \qquad \left(\frac{1}{2}\right)^{15} \approx 0.00003052$$

For $|r| < 1$, r^n approaches 0 as n gets larger and larger. As n approaches infinity, the sum

$$S = \frac{a_1(1 - r^n)}{1 - r} \quad \text{approaches} \quad \frac{a_1(1 - 0)}{1 - r} = \frac{a_1}{1 - r}$$

Sum of an Infinite Geometric Series

Given an infinite geometric series $a_1 + a_1r + a_1r^2 + \cdots$, with $|r| < 1$, the sum S of all terms in the series is given by

$$S = \frac{a_1}{1 - r}$$

Note: If $|r| \geq 1$, then the sum does not exist.

Classroom Example: p. 1018, Exercise 62

Example 6 Finding the Sum of an Infinite Geometric Series

Find the sum of the series. $\displaystyle\sum_{i=1}^{\infty} \left(\frac{1}{3}\right)^{i-1}$

Solution:

In this example, the upper limit of summation is ∞. This indicates that we have an infinite series where the pattern for the sum of terms continues indefinitely.

$$\sum_{i=1}^{\infty} \left(\frac{1}{3}\right)^{i-1} = 1 + \frac{1}{3} + \frac{1}{9} + \frac{1}{27} + \frac{1}{81} + \cdots$$

Answer

6. 1533

The series is geometric with $a_1 = 1$ and $r = \frac{1}{3}$. Because $|r| = |\frac{1}{3}| < 1$, we have

$$S = \frac{a_1}{1 - r} = \frac{1}{1 - \frac{1}{3}} = \frac{1}{\frac{2}{3}} = \frac{3}{2}$$

The sum is $\frac{3}{2}$.

Skill Practice Find the sum of the series.

7. $\sum_{i=1}^{\infty} 4\left(\frac{3}{4}\right)^{i-1}$

Example 7 Using a Geometric Series in a Physics Application

Classroom Example: p. 1018, Exercise 66

A child drops a ball from a height of 4 ft. With each bounce, the ball rebounds to 50% of its original height. Determine the total distance traveled by the ball.

Solution:

The heights (in ft) from which the ball drops are given by the sequence

$$4, 2, 1, \frac{1}{2}, \frac{1}{4}, \ldots$$

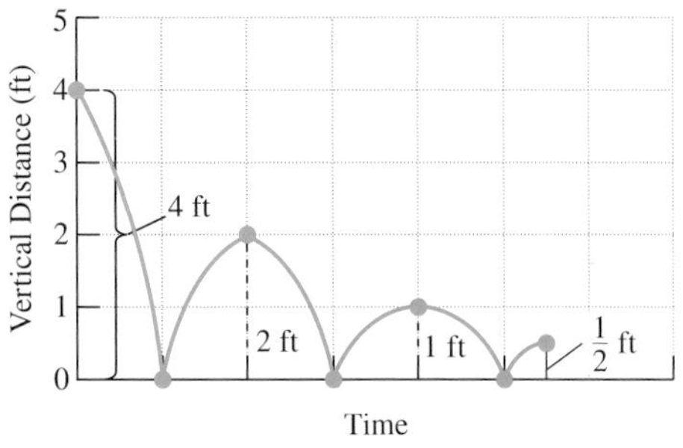

After the ball falls from its initial height of 4 ft, the distance traveled for every bounce thereafter is doubled (the ball travels up and down). Therefore, the total distance traveled is given by the series

$$4 + 2 \cdot 2 + 2 \cdot 1 + 2 \cdot \frac{1}{2} + 2 \cdot \frac{1}{4} + \cdots$$

or equivalently

$$4 + 4 + 2 + 1 + \frac{1}{2} + \cdots$$

The series $4 + 2 + 1 + \frac{1}{2} + \cdots$ is an infinite geometric series with $a_1 = 4$ and $r = \frac{1}{2}$.

Initial height from which the ball was dropped → 4; Infinite geometric series → $4 + 2 + 1 + \frac{1}{2} + \cdots$

$$4 \quad + \quad \overbrace{4 + 2 + 1 + \frac{1}{2} + \cdots}$$

$$= 4 + \frac{4}{1 - \frac{1}{2}}$$

$$= 4 + \frac{4}{\frac{1}{2}}$$

$$= 4 + 8 = 12$$

The ball traveled a total of 12 ft.

Skill Practice

8. A child drops a ball from a height of 3 ft. With each bounce, the ball rebounds to $\frac{1}{3}$ of its original height. Determine the total distance traveled by the ball.

Answers

7. 16 **8.** 6 ft

Section 14.4 Practice Exercises

For additional exercises, see Classroom Activities 14.4A–14.4C in the *Student's Resource Manual* at www.mhhe.com/moh.

Vocabulary and Key Concepts

1. a. A ___geometric___ sequence is a sequence in which the ratio between each term and its predecessor is constant.
   b. The common ___ratio___ between a term and its predecessor in a geometric sequence is often denoted by r.
   c. The nth term of a geometric sequence is given by $a_n =$ ___a_1r^{n-1}___, where a_n is the nth term in the sequence, a_1 is the first term, and r is the common ratio.
   d. The sum S_n of the first n terms of a geometric series $\sum_{i=1}^{n} a_1 r^{i-1}$ is given by $S_n =$ ___$\frac{a_1(1-r^n)}{1-r}$___, where a_1 is the first term and r is the common ratio.
   e. Given an infinite geometric series $a_1 + a_2r + a_1r^2 + \cdots$ with $|r| < 1$, the sum of all terms in the sequence is given by $S =$ ______. If $|r| \geq$ ______, then the sum does not exist. $\frac{a_1}{1-r}$; 1

Review Exercises

2. Determine the common difference. $7, 1, -5, -11, \ldots$ -6

3. Write an expression for the nth term of the sequence. $-4, 0, 4, 8, 12, \ldots$ $a_n = 4n - 8$

4. Find the sum of the series. $\sum_{i=1}^{6} (3i^2 - 4)$ 249

5. Find the fifth term of the arithmetic sequence with $a_1 = -15$ and $d = 10$. 25

Concept 1: Geometric Sequences

6. Explain how to determine if a sequence is geometric. A sequence is geometric if the ratio between each term and the preceding term is constant.

For Exercises 7–12, the first term of a geometric sequence is given along with the common ratio. Write the first four terms of the sequence.

7. $a_1 = 1; r = 10$ 1, 10, 100, 1000
8. $a_1 = 2; r = 5$ 2, 10, 50, 250
9. $a_1 = 64; r = \frac{1}{2}$ 64, 32, 16, 8
10. $a_1 = 3; r = \frac{2}{3}$ $3, 2, \frac{4}{3}, \frac{8}{9}$
11. $a_1 = 8; r = -\frac{1}{4}$ $8, -2, \frac{1}{2}, -\frac{1}{8}$
12. $a_1 = 9; r = -\frac{1}{3}$ $9, -3, 1, -\frac{1}{3}$

For Exercises 13–18, determine the common ratio, r, for the geometric sequence.

13. $5, 10, 20, 40, \ldots$ 2
14. $-2, -1, -\frac{1}{2}, -\frac{1}{4}, \ldots$ $\frac{1}{2}$
15. $8, -2, \frac{1}{2}, -\frac{1}{8}, \ldots$ $-\frac{1}{4}$
16. $4, -12, 36, -108, \ldots$ -3
17. $3, -6, 12, -24, \ldots$ -2
18. $1, 4, 16, 64, \ldots$ 4

For Exercises 19–24, write the first five terms of the geometric sequence.

19. $a_1 = -3, r = -2$ $-3, 6, -12, 24, -48$
20. $a_1 = -4, r = -1$ $-4, 4, -4, 4, -4$
21. $a_1 = 6, r = \frac{1}{2}$ $6, 3, \frac{3}{2}, \frac{3}{4}, \frac{3}{8}$
22. $a_1 = 8, r = \frac{1}{4}$ $8, 2, \frac{1}{2}, \frac{1}{8}, \frac{1}{32}$
23. $a_1 = -1, r = 6$ $-1, -6, -36, -216, -1296$
24. $a_1 = 2, r = -3$ $2, -6, 18, -54, 162$

For Exercises 25–30, find the nth term of each geometric sequence. **(See Example 1.)**

25. 3, 12, 48, 192, . . . $a_n = 3(4)^{n-1}$

26. 2, 6, 18, 54, . . . $a_n = 2(3)^{n-1}$

27. −5, 15, −45, 135, . . . $a_n = -5(-3)^{n-1}$

28. −6, 12, −24, 48, . . . $a_n = -6(-2)^{n-1}$

29. $\frac{1}{2}$, 2, 8, 32, . . . $a_n = \frac{1}{2}(4)^{n-1}$

30. $\frac{16}{3}$, 4, 3, $\frac{9}{4}$, . . . $a_n = \frac{16}{3}\left(\frac{3}{4}\right)^{n-1}$

For Exercises 31–40, find the indicated term of each geometric sequence. **(See Examples 2–3.)**

31. Given $a_n = 2(\frac{1}{2})^{n-1}$, find a_8. $\frac{1}{64}$

32. Given $a_n = -3(\frac{1}{2})^{n-1}$, find a_8. $-\frac{3}{128}$

33. Given $a_n = 4(-\frac{3}{2})^{n-1}$, find a_6. $-\frac{243}{8}$

34. Given $a_n = 6(-\frac{1}{3})^{n-1}$, find a_6. $-\frac{2}{81}$

35. Given $a_n = -3(2)^{n-1}$, find a_5. −48

36. Given $a_n = 5(3)^{n-1}$, find a_4. 135

37. Given $a_5 = -\frac{16}{9}$ and $r = -\frac{2}{3}$, find a_1. −9

38. Given $a_6 = \frac{5}{16}$ and $r = -\frac{1}{2}$, find a_1. −10

39. Given $a_7 = 8$ and $r = 2$, find a_1. $\frac{1}{8}$

40. Given $a_6 = 27$ and $r = 3$, find a_1. $\frac{1}{9}$

41. If the second and third terms of a geometric sequence are 16 and 64, what is the first term? 4

42. If the second and third terms of a geometric sequence are $\frac{1}{3}$ and $\frac{1}{9}$, what is the first term? 1

Concept 2: Geometric Series

43. Explain the difference between a geometric sequence and a geometric series. A geometric sequence is an ordered list of numbers in which the ratio between each term and its predecessor is constant. A geometric series is the sum of the terms of such a sequence.

44. a. Write the series in expanded form. $\sum_{i=1}^{5} 4(2)^{i-1}$ $4 + 8 + 16 + 32 + 64$

b. Find the sum. $\sum_{i=1}^{5} 4(2)^{i-1}$ 124

45. a. Write the series in expanded form. $\sum_{i=1}^{4} 3(4)^{i-1}$ $3 + 12 + 48 + 192$

b. Find the sum. $\sum_{i=1}^{4} 3(4)^{i-1}$ 255

46. a. Write the series in expanded form. $\sum_{i=1}^{4} 6\left(\frac{1}{2}\right)^{i-1}$ $6 + 3 + \frac{3}{2} + \frac{3}{4}$

b. Find the sum. $\sum_{i=1}^{4} 6\left(\frac{1}{2}\right)^{i-1}$ $\frac{45}{4}$ or $11\frac{1}{4}$

For Exercises 47–56, find the sum of the geometric series. **(See Examples 4–5.)**

47. $10 + 2 + \frac{2}{5} + \frac{2}{25} + \frac{2}{125}$ $\frac{1562}{125}$

48. $1 + 3 + 9 + 27 + 81 + 243$ 364

49. $-2 + 1 + \left(-\frac{1}{2}\right) + \frac{1}{4} + \left(-\frac{1}{8}\right)$ $-\frac{11}{8}$

50. $\frac{1}{4} + (-1) + 4 + (-16) + 64$ $\frac{205}{4}$

51. $12 + 16 + \frac{64}{3} + \frac{256}{9} + \frac{1024}{27}$ $\frac{3124}{27}$

52. $9 + 6 + 4 + \frac{8}{3} + \frac{16}{9}$ $\frac{211}{9}$

53. $1 + \frac{2}{3} + \frac{4}{9} + \cdots + \frac{32}{243}$ $\frac{665}{243}$

54. $\frac{8}{3} + 2 + \frac{3}{2} + \cdots + \frac{243}{512}$ $\frac{14{,}197}{1536}$

55. $-4 + 8 + (-16) + \cdots + (-256)$ −172

56. $-\frac{7}{3} + 7 + (-21) + \cdots + 5103$ $\frac{11{,}480}{3}$

57. A deposit of \$1000 is made in an account that earns 5% interest compounded annually. The balance in the account after n years is given by

$$a_n = 1000(1.05)^n \quad \text{for } n \geq 1$$

a. List the first four terms of the sequence. Round to the nearest cent. \$1050.00, \$1102.50, \$1157.63, \$1215.51

b. Find the balance after 10 yr, 20 yr, and 40 yr by computing a_{10}, a_{20}, and a_{40}. Round to the nearest cent.
$a_{10} = \$1628.89$; $a_{20} = \$2653.30$; $a_{40} = \$7039.99$

58. A home purchased for \$125,000 increases by 4% of its value each year. The value of the home after n years is given by

$$a_n = 125{,}000(1.04)^n \quad \text{for } n \geq 1$$

a. List the first four terms of the sequence. Round to the nearest dollar.
\$130,000, \$135,200, \$140,608, \$146,232

b. Find the value of the home after 5 yr, 10 yr, and 20 yr by computing a_5, a_{10}, and a_{20}. Round to the nearest dollar.
$a_5 = \$152{,}082$; $a_{10} = \$185{,}031$; $a_{20} = \$273{,}890$

For Exercises 59–64, first find the common ratio r. Then determine the sum of the infinite series, if it exists. **(See Example 6.)**

59. $1 + \frac{1}{6} + \frac{1}{36} + \frac{1}{216} + \cdots$ $r = \frac{1}{6}$; sum is $\frac{6}{5}$

60. $-2 + \left(-\frac{1}{2}\right) + \left(-\frac{1}{8}\right) + \left(-\frac{1}{32}\right) + \cdots$ $r = \frac{1}{4}$; sum is $-\frac{8}{3}$

61. $\sum_{i=1}^{\infty} \left(-\frac{1}{4}\right)^{i-1}$ $r = -\frac{1}{4}$; sum is $\frac{4}{5}$

62. $\sum_{i=1}^{\infty} \left(-\frac{1}{5}\right)^{i-1}$ $r = -\frac{1}{5}$; sum is $\frac{5}{6}$

63. $\frac{2}{3} + (-1) + \frac{3}{2} + \left(-\frac{9}{4}\right) + \cdots$ $r = -\frac{3}{2}$; sum does not exist

64. $3 + 5 + \frac{25}{3} + \frac{125}{9} + \cdots$ $r = \frac{5}{3}$; sum does not exist

65. Suppose \$200 million is spent by tourists at a certain resort town. Further suppose that 75% of the revenue is respent in the community and then respent over and over, each time at a rate of 75%. The series

$$200 + 200(0.75) + 200(0.75)^2 + 200(0.75)^3 + \cdots$$

gives the total amount spent (and respent) in the community. Find the sum of the infinite series. **(See Example 7.)**
The sum is \$800 million.

66. A bungee jumper jumps off a platform and stretches the cord 80 ft before rebounding upward. Each successive bounce stretches the cord 60% of its previous length. The total vertical distance traveled is given by

$$80 + 2(0.60)(80) + 2(0.60)^2(80) + 2(0.60)^3(80) + \cdots$$

After the first term, the series is an infinite geometric series. Compute the total vertical distance traveled.
The total vertical distance traveled is 320 ft.

67. A ball drops from a height of 4 ft. With each bounce, the ball rebounds to $\frac{3}{4}$ of its height. The total vertical distance traveled is given by

$$4 + 2\left(\frac{3}{4}\right)(4) + 2\left(\frac{3}{4}\right)^2(4) + 2\left(\frac{3}{4}\right)^3(4) + \cdots$$

After the first term, the series is an infinite geometric series. Compute the total vertical distance traveled.
The total vertical distance traveled is 28 ft.

68. The repeating decimal number $0.\overline{2}$ can be written as an infinite geometric series by

$$\frac{2}{10}+\frac{2}{100}+\frac{2}{1000}+\cdots$$

a. What is a_1? $\frac{2}{10}$ **b.** What is r? $\frac{1}{10}$ **c.** Find the sum of the series. $\frac{2}{9}$

69. The repeating decimal number $0.\overline{7}$ can be written as an infinite geometric series by

$$\frac{7}{10}+\frac{7}{100}+\frac{7}{1000}+\cdots$$

a. What is a_1? $\frac{7}{10}$ **b.** What is r? $\frac{1}{10}$ **c.** Find the sum of the series. $\frac{7}{9}$

Expanding Your Skills

70. The yearly salary for Job A is \$40,000 initially with an annual raise of \$3000 per year. The yearly salary for Job B is \$38,000 initially with an annual raise of 6% per year.

a. Find the total earnings for Job A over 20 yr. Is this an arithmetic or geometric series? \$1,370,000; arithmetic

b. For Job B, what is the amount of the raise after 1 yr? \$2280

c. Find the total earnings for Job B over 20 yr. Round to the nearest dollar. Is this an arithmetic or geometric series? \$1,397,852; geometric

d. What is the difference in total salary earned over 20 yr between Job A and Job B? \$27,852

71. a. Brook has a job that pays \$48,000 the first year. She receives a 4% raise each year. Find the sum of her yearly salaries over a 20-yr period. Round to the nearest dollar. \$1,429,348

b. Chamille has a job that pays \$48,000 the first year. She receives a 4.5% raise each year. Find the sum of her yearly salaries over a 20-yr period. Round to the nearest dollar. \$1,505,828

c. Chamille's raise each year was 0.5% higher than Brook's raise. How much more total income did Chamille receive than Brook over 20 yr? \$76,480

Problem Recognition Exercises

Identifying Arithmetic and Geometric Sequences

For Exercises 1–18, determine if the sequence is arithmetic, geometric, or neither. If the sequence is arithmetic, find d. If the sequence is geometric, find r.

1. $5, -\frac{5}{2}, \frac{5}{4}, -\frac{5}{8}, \ldots$ Geometric, $r=-\frac{1}{2}$

2. $\frac{1}{2}, 1, \frac{3}{2}, 2, \frac{5}{2}, \ldots$ Arithmetic, $d=\frac{1}{2}$

3. $-2, -4, -8, -16, -32, \ldots$ Geometric, $r=2$

4. $-2, -4, -7, -11, -16, \ldots$ Neither

5. $-\frac{1}{3}, \frac{1}{3}, 1, \frac{5}{3}, \ldots$ Arithmetic, $d=\frac{2}{3}$

6. $1, -\frac{3}{2}, \frac{9}{4}, -\frac{27}{8}, \ldots$ Geometric, $r=-\frac{3}{2}$

7. $2, 6, 11, 17, 24, \ldots$ Neither

8. $2, -2, 2, -2, 2, \ldots$ Geometric, $r=-1$

9. $-2, -4, -6, -8, -10, \ldots$ Arithmetic, $d=-2$

10. $1, 3, 1, 3, 1, \ldots$ Neither

11. $0, 1, 0, 1, 0, 1, \ldots$ Neither

12. $2, 6, 10, 14, 18, 22, \ldots$ Arithmetic, $d=4$

13. $\frac{1}{4}\pi, \frac{1}{2}\pi, \frac{3}{4}\pi, \pi, \frac{5}{4}\pi, \cdots$ Arithmetic; $d=\frac{1}{4}\pi$

14. $-1, 1, -1, 1, -1, \ldots$ Geometric, $r=-1$

15. $1, 4, 9, 16, 25, \ldots$ Neither

16. $\frac{1}{3}e, \frac{2}{3}e, e, \frac{4}{3}e, \frac{5}{3}e, \cdots$ Arithmetic; $d=\frac{1}{3}e$

17. $\frac{\pi}{2}, \frac{\pi}{3}, \frac{\pi}{4}, \frac{\pi}{5}, \frac{\pi}{6}, \cdots$ Neither

18. $2, 6, 18, 54, 162, \ldots$ Geometric, $r=3$

Group Activity

Investigating Mean and Standard Deviation

Materials: A computer with Internet access and a calculator

Estimated time: 15–20 minutes

Group Size: 2

To study the characteristics of a population, statisticians often use a sample or part of the population. A sample of data values is smaller and less cumbersome than data from the entire population. Furthermore, if the sample is taken randomly, the sample is generally a good representation of the population as a whole.

Once a collection of data is obtained, statisticians may compute the mean and standard deviation of the sample. The mean is the average of the data values. The standard deviation is a measure of variability and is based on finding the deviation between the given data values and the mean.

The formulas to compute sample mean (denoted by $\bar{x}$) and sample standard deviation (denoted by s) are as follows. In each case, the sample size is n, and the individual data values are denoted by $x_1, x_2, x_3, \ldots, x_n$. Notice that sometimes the summations are given without the index of summation. This is common practice in statistics. The index of summation is understood to be from 1 to n.

$$\bar{x} = \frac{\sum_{i=1}^{n} x_i}{n}$$

- Take the sum of the data values $(x_1 + x_2 + x_3 + \cdots + x_n)$ and divide by n.

$$s = \sqrt{\frac{n \cdot \Sigma(x^2) - (\Sigma x)^2}{n(n-1)}}$$

- For the first term in the numerator, square each value of x first, then take the sum and multiply by the sample size, n.
- For the second term in the numerator, add the values of x first and then square the result.

1. The following data represent a sample of eight breakfast cereals and the corresponding number of calories for a 1-cup serving. Find the mean number of calories. Round to one decimal place.

   160 120 140 240 180 210 380 320 $\bar{x} = 218.8$ calories

2. Use the data from Question 1 to compute the standard deviation. Use the given chart to help you organize the calculations. Round to one decimal place. $s = 90.8$ calories

Brand	x	x^2
1	160	
2	120	
3	140	
4	240	
5	180	
6	210	
7	380	
8	320	
Sum:		

3. Select two cities in different parts of the country that have roughly the same latitude (same distance north from the equator) such as Phoenix, Arizona, and Charleston, South Carolina. Visit a website that gives the average monthly temperatures for each city for a 1-yr period. Record the data here. Answers will vary.

	Jan.	Feb.	Mar.	Apr.	May	June	July	Aug.	Sept.	Oct.	Nov.	Dec.
City 1 temp.												
City 2 temp.												

4. Compute the mean and standard deviation for the average monthly temperature for each city.
Answers will vary.

5. Based on the mean and standard deviation, what conclusions can you make about the differences between the monthly temperatures of each city? Answers will vary. For example, one might expect Phoenix to have a greater standard deviation than Charleston. There is more variability in temperatures in a desert climate than on the coast.

Chapter 14 Summary

Section 14.1 Binomial Expansions

Key Concepts

For a whole number, n, the expression $\boldsymbol{n!}$ (read as "n factorial") is defined as the product of integers from 1 to n, for $n \geq 1$.

$n! = n(n-1)(n-2)\ldots(2)(1)$

$0! = 1$ by definition

For a positive integer, n, the expression $(a+b)^n$ can be expanded using the **binomial theorem**:

$$(a+b)^n = \frac{n!}{n!\cdot 0!}a^n + \frac{n!}{(n-1)!\cdot 1!}a^{(n-1)}b + \frac{n!}{(n-2)!\cdot 2!}a^{(n-2)}b^2 + \cdots + \frac{n!}{0!\cdot n!}b^n$$

The coefficients of the expansion may also be found by using **Pascal's triangle**.

```
            1
         1     1
      1     2     1
   1     3     3     1
1     4     6     4     1
```

Let n and k be positive integers such that $k \leq n$. Then the kth term in the expansion of $(a+b)^n$ is

$$\frac{n!}{[n-(k-1)]!\cdot(k-1)!}\cdot a^{n-(k-1)}\cdot b^{k-1}$$

Examples

Example 1

$6! = (6)(5)(4)(3)(2)(1) = 720$

Example 2

$$\frac{7!}{2!\cdot 5!} = \frac{7\cdot \overset{3}{\cancel{6}}\cdot \cancel{5\cdot 4\cdot 3\cdot 2\cdot 1}}{(2\cdot 1)(\cancel{5\cdot 4\cdot 3\cdot 2\cdot 1})} = 21$$

Example 3

$(2x-4y)^4 = [2x+(-4y)]^4$

$$= \frac{4!}{4!\cdot 0!}(2x)^4 + \frac{4!}{3!\cdot 1!}(2x)^3(-4y) + \frac{4!}{2!\cdot 2!}(2x)^2(-4y)^2 + \frac{4!}{1!\cdot 3!}(2x)(-4y)^3 + \frac{4!}{0!\cdot 4!}(-4y)^4$$

$$= 1(2x)^4 + 4(2x)^3(-4y) + 6(2x)^2(-4y)^2 + 4(2x)(-4y)^3 + 1(-4y)^4$$

$$= 16x^4 - 128x^3y + 384x^2y^2 - 512xy^3 + 256y^4$$

Example 4

The third term of $(3x+y^2)^7$ is

$$\frac{7!}{[7-(3-1)]!\cdot(3-1)!}\cdot(3x)^{7-(3-1)}\cdot(y^2)^{3-1}$$

$$= \frac{7!}{5!\cdot 2!}(3x)^5(y^2)^2$$

$$= 5103x^5y^4$$

Section 14.2 Sequences and Series

Key Concepts

An **infinite sequence** is a function whose domain is the set of positive integers.

A **finite sequence** is a function whose domain is the set of the first n positive integers.

The expression $\boldsymbol{a_n}$ defines the nth term (or general term) of a sequence.

A **series** is the sum of a sequence.

Examples

Example 1

$a_n = 8 - 3n$

$= 5, 2, -1, -4, -7, -10, \ldots$

Example 2

$a_n = (-1)^n \dfrac{n}{n+1}$ for $1 \le n \le 5$

$= -\dfrac{1}{2}, \dfrac{2}{3}, -\dfrac{3}{4}, \dfrac{4}{5}, -\dfrac{5}{6}$

Example 3

$\sum_{i=1}^{4} 5i = 5 + 10 + 15 + 20 = 50$

Section 14.3 Arithmetic Sequences and Series

Key Concepts

An **arithmetic sequence** is a sequence in which the **common difference,** d, between two consecutive terms is a constant.

The nth term of an arithmetic sequence is given by

$$a_n = a_1 + (n - 1)\, d$$

This formula has four variables, a_n, a_1, n, and d. Sometimes it is necessary to solve for one or more of the variables before the nth term can be identified.

Examples

Example 1

Write the nth term of the sequence:
10, 8, 6, 4, . . .

$a_1 = 10$ (the first term)

$d = -2$ (the common difference)

$a_n = 10 + (n - 1) \cdot (-2)$

$a_n = -2n + 12$

Example 2

Find the 12th term of the arithmetic sequence in which $a_1 = -6$ and $a_{20} = 51$.

$a_n = a_1 + (n - 1)d$ Find d first.

$51 = -6 + (20 - 1)d$ Substitute known values for a_1 and a_{20}.

$57 = 19d$

$3 = d$

$a_n = -6 + (n - 1) \cdot 3 \longrightarrow a_{12} = -6 + (12 - 1) \cdot 3$

$a_{12} = 27$

The sum of an arithmetic sequence is an **arithmetic series**. The sum of the first n terms of an arithmetic series is given by

$$S_n = \frac{n}{2}(a_1 + a_n)$$

Example 3

Find the sum. $\sum_{i=1}^{50}(3i - 1)$

$n = 50, a_1 = 2, a_{50} = 149$

$$S_n = \frac{n}{2}(a_1 + a_n) = \frac{50}{2}(2 + 149)$$

$$= 3775$$

Section 14.4 Geometric Sequences and Series

Key Concepts

A **geometric sequence** is a sequence in which the ratio between each term and its predecessor is constant. This constant is called the **common ratio**, ***r***.

The nth term of a geometric sequence is given by

$$a_n = a_1 r^{n-1}$$

The sum of a geometric sequence is called a **geometric series**. The sum of the first n terms of a geometric series is given by

$$S_n = \frac{a_1(1 - r^n)}{1 - r}$$

The sum of an infinite geometric series is given by

$$S_n = \frac{a_1}{1 - r} \quad \text{provided } |r| < 1$$

Examples

Example 1

Find the common ratio: $\frac{8}{5}, \frac{6}{5}, \frac{9}{10}, \frac{27}{40}, \ldots$

$$r = \frac{6}{5} \div \frac{8}{5} = \frac{6}{5} \cdot \frac{5}{8} = \frac{30}{40} = \frac{3}{4}$$

Example 2

Find the fourth term.

$$a_n = 3\left(\frac{2}{3}\right)^{n-1} \longrightarrow a_4 = 3\left(\frac{2}{3}\right)^{4-1} = 3\left(\frac{2}{3}\right)^3 = \frac{8}{9}$$

Example 3

Find the sum. $48 + 24 + 12 + 6 + 3 + \frac{3}{2}$

$a_1 = 48, r = \frac{1}{2}, n = 6$

$$S_n = \frac{a_1(1 - r^n)}{1 - r} = \frac{48\left[1 - \left(\frac{1}{2}\right)^6\right]}{1 - \frac{1}{2}} = \frac{189}{2}$$

Example 4

Find the sum of the series: $4 - 2 + 1 - \frac{1}{2} + \cdots$

$a_1 = 4$ and the common ratio is $-2 \div 4 = -\frac{1}{2}$.

Since $\left|-\frac{1}{2}\right| < 1$,

$$S_n = \frac{a_1}{1 - r} = \frac{4}{1 - \left(-\frac{1}{2}\right)} = \frac{4}{\frac{3}{2}} = \frac{8}{3}$$

Chapter 14 Review Exercises

Section 14.1

For Exercises 1–4, simplify the expression.

1. $8!$ 40,320 **2.** $5!$ 120 **3.** $\dfrac{12!}{10! \cdot 2!}$ 66 **4.** $\dfrac{9!}{6! \cdot 3!}$ 84

For Exercises 5–6, expand the binomial.

5. $(x^2 + 4)^5$ $x^{10} + 20x^8 + 160x^6 + 640x^4 + 1280x^2 + 1024$

6. $(c - 3d)^4$ $c^4 - 12c^3d + 54c^2d^2 - 108cd^3 + 81d^4$

7. Find the first three terms of the binomial expansion. $(a - 2b)^{11}$ $a^{11} - 22a^{10}b + 220a^9b^2$

8. Find the fourth term of the binomial expansion. $(x^2 + 3y)^8$ $1512x^{10}y^3$

9. Find the eighth term of the binomial expansion. $(5x - y^3)^{10}$ $-15{,}000x^3y^{21}$

10. Find the middle term of the binomial expansion. $(a + 2b)^6$ $160a^3b^3$

Section 14.2

For Exercises 11–14, write the terms of the sequence.

11. $a_n = -3n + 4;\ 1 \le n \le 5$ $1, -2, -5, -8, -11$

12. $a_n = -2n^3;\ 1 \le n \le 3$ $-2, -16, -54$

13. $a_n = (-1)^{n+1} \cdot \dfrac{n}{n+2};\ 1 \le n \le 4$ $\frac{1}{3}, -\frac{1}{2}, \frac{3}{5}, -\frac{2}{3}$

14. $a_n = \left(-\dfrac{2}{3}\right)^n;\ 1 \le n \le 4$ $-\frac{2}{3}, \frac{4}{9}, -\frac{8}{27}, \frac{16}{81}$

For Exercises 15–16, write a formula for the nth term of the sequence.

15. $\dfrac{1}{2}, \dfrac{2}{3}, \dfrac{3}{4}, \dfrac{4}{5}, \ldots$ $a_n = \frac{n}{n+1}$

16. $-\dfrac{3}{2}, \dfrac{3}{4}, -\dfrac{3}{8}, \dfrac{3}{16}, \ldots$ $a_n = (-1)^n \cdot \frac{3}{2^n}$

17. What is the index of summation for the series?

$$\sum_{k=1}^{7} (2n + 3)$$ k

18. How many terms are in the series? $\displaystyle\sum_{j=1}^{5} j^3$ 5

For Exercises 19–20, find the sum of the series.

19. $\displaystyle\sum_{i=1}^{7} 5(-1)^{i-1}$ 5 **20.** $\displaystyle\sum_{n=1}^{5} (-2)^n$ -22

21. Write the sum in summation notation.

$$\frac{4}{1} + \frac{5}{2} + \frac{6}{3} + \frac{7}{4} + \frac{8}{5} + \frac{9}{6} + \frac{10}{7}$$ $\sum_{i=1}^{7} \frac{i+3}{i}$

22. Study the figures and the corresponding expression for the area of each region. Write the nth term of a sequence representing the area of a region with base n.
$a_n = n^2 + \left(\frac{n}{2}\right)h$

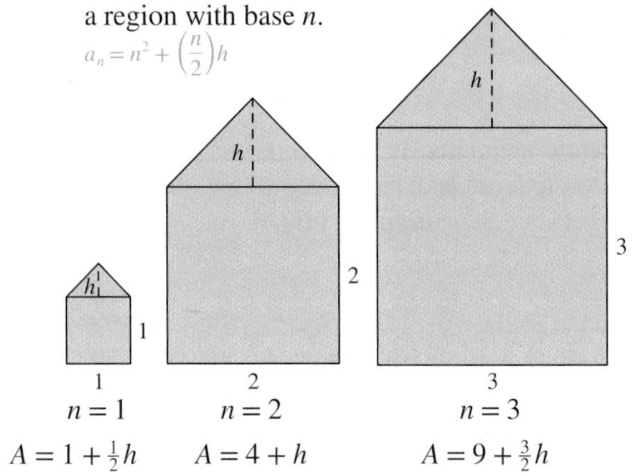

Section 14.3

For Exercises 23–24, write the first five terms of the arithmetic sequence.

23. $a_1 = -12,\ d = 1.5$ $-12, -10.5, -9, -7.5, -6$

24. $a_1 = \dfrac{2}{3},\ d = \dfrac{1}{3}$ $\frac{2}{3}, 1, \frac{4}{3}, \frac{5}{3}, 2$

For Exercises 25–26, write an expression for the nth term of the sequence.

25. $1, 11, 21, 31, \ldots$ $a_n = 10n - 9$

26. $6, -8, -22, -36, \ldots$ $a_n = -14n + 20$

For Exercises 27–28, find the indicated term of the arithmetic sequence.

27. $a_n = \dfrac{1}{2} + (n - 1) \cdot \dfrac{1}{4}$; 17th term $a_{17} = \frac{9}{2}$

28. $a_1 = -11,\ d = -6$; 25th term $a_{25} = -155$

For Exercises 29–30, find the number of terms.

29. $3, 8, 13, 18, \ldots, 118$ 24 terms

30. $4, 1, -2, -5, \ldots, -50$ 19 terms

Writing Translating Expression Geometry Scientific Calculator Video

31. Find the common difference for an arithmetic sequence, given $a_1 = -40$ and $a_{19} = 140$. $d = 10$

32. Write an expression for the nth term of the arithmetic sequence, 14, 9, 4, −1, −6,....
$a_n = -5n + 19$

For Exercises 33–36, find the sum of the arithmetic series.

33. $\sum_{k=1}^{40}(5 - k)$ -620

34. $\sum_{i=1}^{20}(0.25i + 2)$ 92.5

35. $-6 + (-4) + (-2) + \cdots + 34$ 294

36. $4 + 5 + 6 + \cdots + 109$ 5989

Section 14.4

For Exercises 37–38, find the common ratio.

37. 5, 15, 45, 135, . . . $r = 3$

38. 2, 2.4, 2.88, 3.456 $r = 1.2$

For Exercises 39–40, write the first four terms of the geometric series.

39. $a_1 = -1$ and $r = -\frac{1}{4}$ $-1, \frac{1}{4}, -\frac{1}{16}, \frac{1}{64}$

40. $a_n = 10(2)^{n-1}$ 10, 20, 40, 80

For Exercises 41–42, write an expression for the nth term of the geometric series.

41. −4, −8, −16, −32, ... $a_n = -4(2)^{n-1}$

42. $6, -2, \frac{2}{3}, -\frac{2}{9}, \ldots$ $a_n = 6\left(-\frac{1}{3}\right)^{n-1}$

43. Given $a_n = 4\left(\frac{2}{3}\right)^{n-1}$, find a_6. $a_6 = \frac{128}{243}$

44. Given $a_n = 10(3)^{n-1}$, find a_4. $a_4 = 270$

45. Given $a_7 = \frac{1}{16}$ and $r = \frac{1}{2}$, find a_1. $a_1 = 4$

46. Given $a_5 = 81$ and $r = 3$, find a_1. $a_1 = 1$

47. Find the sum of the series. $\sum_{n=1}^{8} 5(2)^{n-1}$ 1275

48. Find the sum of the series.
$\frac{1}{3} + (-1) + 3 + (-9) + \cdots + (-81)$ $-\frac{182}{3}$

49. Find the sum of the series.
$6 + 4 + \frac{8}{3} + \frac{16}{9} + \cdots$ 18

50. Find the sum of the series.
$10 + 2 + \frac{2}{5} + \frac{2}{25} + \cdots$ $\frac{25}{2}$

51. An investment of \$10,000 is originally invested in a mutual fund. After 10 yr, the yearly return averaged approximately 7%. The balance on the account is given by $b_n = 10{,}000(1.07)^n$.

a. Find the first three terms of the sequence.
\$10,700, \$11,449, \$12,250.43

b. Interpret the value of b_3.
The account is worth \$12,250.43 after 3 yr.

c. Find the amount in the account after 10 yr.
\$19,671.51

Chapter 14 Test

For Exercises 1–2, simplify.

1. 0! 1

2. $\frac{10!}{6! \cdot 4!}$ 210

3. Write the expansion of $(a + b)^4$. Use Pascal's triangle to determine the coefficients of the expansion. $a^4 + 4a^3b + 6a^2b^2 + 4ab^3 + b^4$

4. Expand. $(3y - 2x^2)^4$
$81y^4 - 216y^3x^2 + 216y^2x^4 - 96yx^6 + 16x^8$

5. Find the sixth term. $(a - c^3)^8$ $-56a^3c^{15}$

6. Write the terms of the sequence.
$a_n = -\frac{3}{n+2}$; $1 \le n \le 4$ $-1, -\frac{3}{4}, -\frac{3}{5}, -\frac{1}{2}$

7. Find the sum. $\sum_{i=1}^{5}(i^2 + 2)$ 65

8. a. An 8-in. tomato seedling is planted on Sunday. Each day, it grows an average of 1.5 in. Write five terms representing the height of the plant each day, beginning with Sunday. 8, 9.5, 11, 12.5, 14

b. Write the nth term of the sequence.
$a_n = 1.5n + 6.5$

9. Write the series in summation notation.
$x^3 + x^6 + x^9 + x^{12}$ $\sum_{n=1}^{4} x^{3n}$

10. Find the common difference. $3, \frac{13}{4}, \frac{7}{2}, \frac{15}{4}, \ldots$
$d = \frac{1}{4}$

11. Find the common ratio. $9, 3, 1, \frac{1}{3}, \ldots$ $r = \frac{1}{3}$

12. Given an arithmetic sequence with $a_1 = -15$ and $d = -3$,

a. Write the first four terms of the sequence.
$-15, -18, -21, -24$

b. Write an expression for the nth term of the sequence. $a_n = -3n - 12$

c. Find the 40th term of the sequence. $a_{40} = -132$

13. Given a geometric sequence with $a_1 = 4$ and $r = -2$,

a. Write the first four terms of the sequence.
$4, -8, 16, -32$

b. Write an expression for the nth term of the sequence. $a_n = 4(-2)^{n-1}$

c. Find the 10th term of the sequence. $a_{10} = -2048$

14. Write an expression for the nth term of the sequence. $\frac{3}{5}, \frac{3}{10}, \frac{3}{20}, \frac{3}{40}, \ldots$ $a_n = \frac{3}{5} \cdot \left(\frac{1}{2}\right)^{n-1}$

15. Write an expression for the nth term of the sequence. $20, 18, 16, 14, \ldots$ $a_n = -2n + 22$

16. Find the number of terms in the sequence.
$3, 10, 17, 24, \ldots, 213$ 31 terms

17. Find the number of terms in the sequence.
$1, \frac{2}{3}, \frac{4}{9}, \ldots, \frac{64}{729}$ 7 terms

18. Find the sum of the arithmetic series.
$\sum_{i=1}^{100} (8 + 2i)$ 10,900

19. Find the sum of the geometric series.
$\sum_{n=1}^{10} 8\left(\frac{1}{2}\right)^{n-1}$ $\frac{1023}{64}$

20. Find the sum of the infinite geometric series.
$4 + 2 + 1 + \frac{1}{2} + \cdots$ 8

21. Given a geometric series with $a_6 = 9$ and $r = 3$, find a_1. $a_1 = \frac{1}{27}$

22. Find the 18th term of the arithmetic sequence in which $a_1 = -66$ and $a_{40} = -378$. $a_{18} = -202$

23. Suppose a student smokes one pack of cigarettes per day at a cost of \$5.50 per pack.

a. If the student quits smoking and puts the \$5.50 saved per day in a jar, how much money will the student have saved at the end of 1 yr? \$2007.50

b. If the student takes the first year's savings from part (a) and invests the money in a bond fund paying 4% annual interest, how much will this money be worth 1 yr later? \$2087.80

c. Suppose that the student reinvests the principal and interest each year so that the money is compounded annually. The student will have:

End of year 1: \$2007.50

End of year 2: (2007.50)(1.04) = \$2087.80

End of year 3: $(2007.50)(1.04)^2$ = \$2171.31

The sequence $a_n = \$2007.50(1.04)^{n-1}$ represents the value of the investment at the end of n years. Find the value of the investment after 30 yr. (Round to two decimal places.) \$6260.69

d. Now suppose that the student saves \$2007.50 per year each year for 30 yr. Further suppose that the student invests each year's saving at 4% interest compounded annually. The following series represents the total savings plus interest over 30 yr. Find the sum. \$112,590.51

$$\sum_{n=1}^{30} 2007.5(1.04)^{n-1}$$

Chapters 1–14 Cumulative Review Exercises

For Exercises 1–8, simplify the expressions.

1. $(2x-3)(x-4)-(x-5)^2$ x^2-x-13

2. $\dfrac{5a^2b^{-3}}{25a^{-4}b}\cdot\left(\dfrac{10c^0}{b^3}\right)^2$ $\dfrac{20a^6}{b^{10}}$

3. $64^{-2/3}$ $\dfrac{1}{16}$

4. $\dfrac{5}{\sqrt{10}}$ $\dfrac{\sqrt{10}}{2}$

5. $\dfrac{2c^2-3c-20}{2c^2-32}$ $\dfrac{2c+5}{2(c+4)}$

6. $\dfrac{x^{-1}-y^{-1}}{y^{-2}-x^{-2}}$ $-\dfrac{xy}{x+y}$

7. $\log_3 81$ 4

8. $\sqrt[3]{54x^5y^{12}z^2}$ $3xy^4\sqrt[3]{2x^2z^2}$

For Exercises 9–12, perform the indicated operations.

9. $\dfrac{a^3+64}{16-a^2}\div\dfrac{a^3-4a^2+16a}{a^2-3a-4}$ $-\dfrac{a+1}{a}$

10. $\dfrac{1}{x^2-7x+10}+\dfrac{1}{x^2+8x-20}$ $\dfrac{2x+5}{(x-5)(x-2)(x+10)}$

11. $\sqrt{50x^5}+4x\sqrt{2x^3}-x^2\sqrt{8x}$ $7x^2\sqrt{2x}$

12. $(\sqrt{x}+3\sqrt{y})(\sqrt{x}-3\sqrt{y})$ $x-9y$

13. Divide using long division or synthetic division.

$\dfrac{2x^4-x^3+5x-7}{x-2}$ $2x^3+3x^2+6x+17+\dfrac{27}{x-2}$

For Exercises 14–17, factor completely.

14. $6a^2-17a-14$ $(2a-7)(3a+2)$

15. $75c^3-12c$ $3c(5c-2)(5c+2)$

16. $27x^3+64y^6$ $(3x+4y^2)(9x^2-12xy^2+16y^4)$

17. $w^3+9w^2-4w-36$ $(w+9)(w-2)(w+2)$

For Exercises 18–25, solve the equation.

18. $\dfrac{1}{2}t-\dfrac{3}{5}=\dfrac{1}{10}t+1$ $\{4\}$

19. $\dfrac{9}{x-4}+\dfrac{3}{x+2}=\dfrac{6}{x^2-2x-8}$ $\{0\}$

20. $\sqrt[3]{4x+3}-9=-7$ $\left\{\dfrac{5}{4}\right\}$

21. $(5y-2)^2+7=4$ $\left\{\dfrac{2}{5}\pm\dfrac{\sqrt{3}}{5}i\right\}$

22. $c^4-17c^2+16=0$ $\{4,-4,1,-1\}$

23. $|x+5|=|3x-2|$ $\left\{\dfrac{7}{2},-\dfrac{3}{4}\right\}$

24. $5^{2x+1}=125$ $\{1\}$

25. $\log x+\log(x+3)=1$ $\{2\}$ (The value -5 does not check.)

26. Write the expression as a single logarithm.

$\ln x-5\ln y+\dfrac{1}{2}\ln z$ $\ln\left(\dfrac{x\sqrt{z}}{y^5}\right)$

27. Use a calculator to approximate the value of the expression. Round to four decimal places.

$\log_7 895$ 3.4929

For Exercises 28–32, solve the inequality. Write the answer in interval notation if possible.

28. $2x-4<6$ and $-3x\le 6$ $[-2,5)$

29. $3x(x+5)(x-1)\ge 0$ $[-5,0]\cup[1,\infty)$

30. $x^2-10x\le -25$ $\{5\}$

31. $\dfrac{3}{x+4}\le 1$ $(-\infty,-4)\cup[-1,\infty)$

32. $|2x-4|+5>7$ $(-\infty,1)\cup(3,\infty)$

For Exercises 33–35, graph the equation.

33. $3x-2y=6$

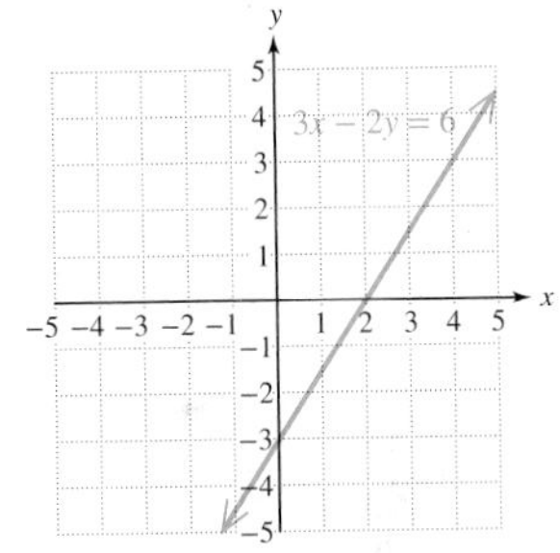

34. $(x-2)^2+y^2=9$

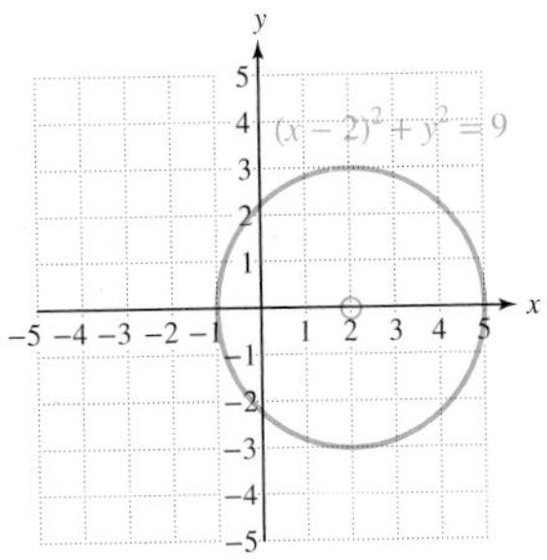

35. $y=2^x$

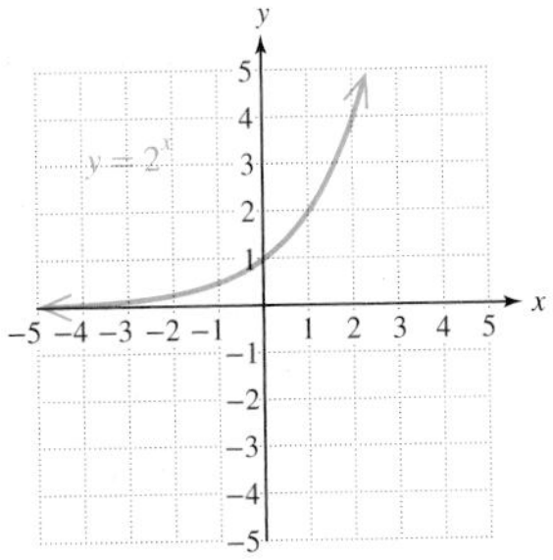

36. Graph the solution set. $\frac{x^2}{9}+\frac{y^2}{25}\le 1$

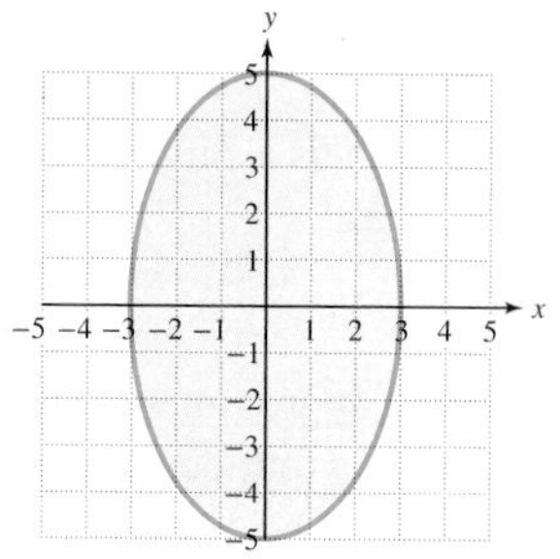

37. Given $f(x)=x^2+6x+5$,

a. Determine the x-intercepts. $(-1, 0), (-5, 0)$

b. Determine the y-intercept. $(0, 5)$

c. Determine the vertex of the parabola. $(-3, -4)$

38. Determine the slope and y-intercept of the line defined by $4x+y=6$.
slope -4; y-intercept $(0, 6)$

39. Write an equation of the line passing through the point $(4, -2)$ and perpendicular to the line defined by $x-5y=2$. $y=-5x+18$

40. Refer to the graph of $y=f(x)$.

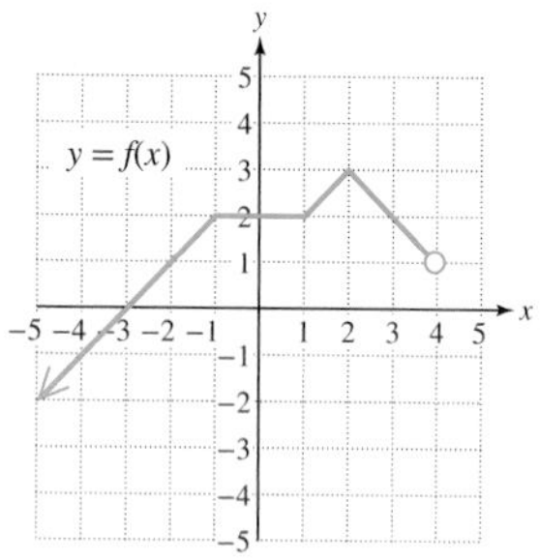

a. Find $f(-1)$. 2

b. Find $f(4)$.
undefined

c. For what value(s) of x is $f(x)=3$?
$x=2$

d. Write the domain in interval notation.
$(-\infty, 4)$

e. Write the range in interval notation.
$(-\infty, 3]$

41. Given $f(x)=\sqrt{5-x}$ write the domain of f. $(-\infty, 5]$

For Exercises 42–43, solve the system.

42. $x=1-2y$ $\{(3, -1)\}$
$7y=3x-16$

43. $x \quad + 2z = 7$ $\{(1,2,3)\}$
$2x+4y \quad = 10$
$-3y+5z=9$

44. Given the points $(9, -4)$ and $(3, 0)$,

a. Find the distance between the points. $2\sqrt{13}$

b. Find the midpoint of the line segment between the two points. $(6, -2)$

45. Given $A=\frac{1}{2}(b_1+b_2)h$, solve for b_1. $b_1=\frac{2A-hb_2}{h}$

46. The time $t(n)$ (in minutes) required for a rat to run through a maze depends on the number of trials n that the rat has practiced. Find $t(9)$ and interpret its meaning in the context of this problem.

$$t(n)=\frac{3n+15}{n+1} \quad \text{for } n\ge 1$$

$t(9)=4.2$; This means that it will take the rat 4.2 min if the rat has practiced 9 times.

47. The speed of a car varies inversely as the time to travel a fixed distance. A car traveling the speed limit of 60 mph travels between two points in 10 sec. How fast is a car moving if it takes only 8 sec to cover the same distance?
The car is moving 75 mph.

48. Two angles are supplementary. One angle measures 9° more than twice the other angle. Find the measures of the angles.
The angles are 57° and 123°.

49. Chemique invests \$3000 less in an account earning 5% simple interest than she does in an account earning 6.5% simple interest. At the end of 1 yr, she earns a total of \$770 in interest. Find the amount invested in each account.
She invested \$8000 at 6.5% and \$5000 at 5%.

50. Against the wind, a plane can travel 4950 mi in 11 hr. On the return trip flying with the same wind, the plane can fly the same distance in 9 hr. Find the wind speed and the speed of the plane in still air.
The plane travels 500 mph in still air. The wind speed is 50 mph.

Additional Topics Appendix

Additional Factoring

Section A.1

Concepts

1. Factoring by Using Substitution
2. Factoring 1 Term with 3 Terms
3. Additional Factoring Strategies

1. Factoring by Using Substitution

The trinomial $u^2 + 4u - 21$ has a leading coefficient 1 and factors as $(u + 7)(u - 3)$. Now compare the following polynomials to $u^2 + 4u - 21$. In each case, the variable expressions in the first and second terms are the same. Furthermore, the coefficients are 1, 4, and −21. By letting the single variable u represent the variable expression in parentheses, the polynomial is a quadratic trinomial in u.

Polynomial	Substitution	New form
$u^2 + 4u - 21$		
$(a + b)^2 + 4(a + b) - 21$ ⟶	Let $u = a + b$ ⟶	$u^2 + 4u - 21$
$(y - 3)^2 + 4(y - 3) - 21$ ⟶	Let $u = y - 3$ ⟶	$u^2 + 4u - 21$

With an appropriate substitution, the polynomials are easier to factor.

Example 1 Factoring by Using Substitution

Classroom Example: p. A-4, Exercise 6

Factor completely. $(a + b)^2 + 4(a + b) - 21$

Solution:

$(a + b)^2 + 4(a + b) - 21$ — The polynomial is a quadratic trinomial with variable $(a + b)$.

$= u^2 + 4u - 21$ — Let $u = a + b$.

$= (u + 7)(u - 3)$ — Factor the trinomial.

$= [(a + b) + 7][(a + b) - 3]$ — Back substitute.

$= (a + b + 7)(a + b - 3)$ — Simplify.

Skill Practice Factor completely.

1. $(w - 6)^2 - 3(w - 6) - 10$

In Examples 2 and 3, we use substitution to factor a difference of squares and a sum of cubes.

Answer

1. $(w - 11)(w - 4)$

Classroom Example: p. A-4, Exercise 12

Example 2 **Factoring by Using Substitution**

Factor completely. $9(4x-1)^2-25$

Solution:

$9(4x-1)^2-25$	The polynomial is a difference of squares.
$=9u^2-25$	Let $u=4x-1$.
$=(3u-5)(3u+5)$	Factor as $a^2-b^2=(a-b)(a+b)$.
$=[3(4x-1)-5][3(4x-1)+5]$	Back substitute.
$=(12x-3-5)(12x-3+5)$	Apply the distributive property and simplify.
$=(12x-8)(12x+2)$	The remaining factors each have a common factor.
$=4(3x-2)2(6x+1)$	Factor out 4 from the first binomial and 2 from the second binomial.
$=8(3x-2)(6x+1)$	Simplify.

Skill Practice Factor completely.

2. $(2x+1)^2-9$

Classroom Example: p. A-5, Exercise 18

Example 3 **Factoring by Using Substitution**

Factor completely. $(x+1)^3+8$

Solution:

$(x+1)^3+8$	The polynomial is a sum of cubes.
$=u^3+8$	Let $u=x+1$.
$=(u+2)(u^2-2u+4)$	Factor as $a^3+b^3=(a+b)(a^2-ab+b^2)$.
$=[(x+1)+2][(x+1)^2-2(x+1)+4]$	Back substitute.
$=(x+3)[(x^2+2x+1)-2x-2+4]$	Apply the distributive property.
$=(x+3)(x^2+3)$	Simplify.

Skill Practice Factor completely.

3. $(y+3)^3+64$

2. Factoring 1 Term with 3 Terms

When confronted with a 4-term polynomial, sometimes the standard method of grouping does not apply. For example, consider the polynomial x^2-y^2-6y-9. Notice that grouping 2 terms with 2 terms does not result in common binomial factors.

$$x^2-y^2 \mid -6y-9$$

$$=1\underbrace{(x^2-y^2)}-3\underbrace{(2x-3)}$$

Binomial factors do not match.

Answers

2. $4(x-1)(x+2)$
3. $(y+7)(y^2+2y+13)$

However, if a factor of -1 is removed from the last three terms, the last three terms result in a perfect square trinomial. This is called grouping 1 term with 3 terms.

Example 4 **Factoring by Grouping 1 Term with 3 Terms**

Classroom Example: p. A-5, Exercise 24

Factor completely. $x^2 - y^2 - 6y - 9$

Solution:

This polynomial has 4 terms. However, the standard grouping method does not work even if we try rearranging terms.

$x^2 - y^2 - 6y - 9$ — We might try grouping one term with three terms. The reason is that after factoring out -1 from the last three terms we have a perfect square trinomial.

$= x^2 - 1(y^2 + 6y + 9)$

$= x^2 - (y + 3)^2$ ← difference of squares — The resulting expression is a difference of squares.

$= x^2 - u^2$ — The difference of squares can be factored by using substitution. Let $u = y + 3$.

$= (x + u)(x - u)$ — Factor.

$= [x + (y + 3)][x - (y + 3)]$ — Back substitute.

$= (x + y + 3)(x - y - 3)$ — Simplify.

Skill Practice Factor completely.

4. $n^2 - m^2 - 8m - 16$

The difference of squares $(x)^2 - (y + 3)^2$ can also be factored without using a substitution.

$$\begin{aligned}&(x)^2 - (y + 3)^2\\&= [x + (y + 3)][x - (y + 3)]\\&= (x + y + 3)(x - y - 3)\end{aligned}$$

3. Additional Factoring Strategies

Thus far, we have learned how to factor polynomials that fit the following patterns.

- Difference of squares
- Difference of cubes
- Sum of cubes
- Perfect square trinomials
- Nonperfect square trinomials
- Grouping 2 terms by 2 terms
- Grouping 3 terms by 1 term

Answer

4. $(n + m + 4)(n - m - 4)$

Many polynomials do not fit any of these patterns, and many polynomials do not factor using these techniques. However, sometimes a combination of patterns exists and we can find the factored form. In Example 5, the polynomial has 6 terms. We might try grouping 3 terms with 3 terms or 4 terms with 2 terms, or even 2 terms, 2 terms and 2 terms. In any case, we should expect to try a variety of approaches before a workable strategy is identified.

Classroom Example: p. A-5, Exercise 34

Example 5 **Factoring a Polynomial**

Factor completely. $2ac + 2a - bc - b - c - 1$

Solution:

$2ac + 2a - bc - b - c - 1$ — The polynomial has 6 terms. After considerable trial and error, we might try grouping the first 2 terms, the second 2 terms, and the last 2 terms.

$= 2ac + 2a \,|\, -bc - b \,|\, -c - 1$

$= 2a(c + 1) - b(c + 1) - 1(c + 1)$ — Factor out the GCF from each pair of terms.

$= (c + 1)(2a - b - 1)$ — Factor out the common factor of $c + 1$.

Skill Practice Factor completely.

5. $xy + 2y + 3xz + 6z - x - 2$

Answer

5. $(x + 2)(y + 3z - 1)$

Section A.1 Practice Exercises

Vocabulary and Key Concepts

For additional exercises, see Classroom Activities A.1A–A.1B in the *Student's Resource Manual* at www.mhhe.com/moh

1. Given the expression $(3x - 2)^2 - (3x - 2) - 12$, what substitution could be used for u to make this a simpler quadratic trinomial in terms of u? Let $u = 3x - 2$.
2. Given the expression $49(p - 3)^2 - 36$, what substitution could be used for u to make this a simpler difference of squares in terms of u? Let $u = p - 3$.
3. What would be the first step to factor $x^2 - 4x + 4 - y^2$ by grouping 3 terms with 1 term?
   Factor the first three terms as $(x - 2)^2$.
4. What would be the first two steps to factor $9a^2 - 4b^2 - 20b - 25$ by grouping 1 term with 3 terms?
   Factor out -1 from the last three terms. Then factor the trinomial in parentheses as $(2b + 5)^2$.

Concept 1: Factoring by Using Substitution

For Exercises 5–20, factor completely. **(See Examples 1–3.)**

5. $(4t - 1)^2 + 3(4t - 1) - 4$
   $2(4t + 3)(2t - 1)$
6. $(2p + 5)^2 - 4(2p + 5) - 12$
   $(2p - 1)(2p + 7)$
7. $2(w - 2)^2 - 5(w - 2) - 3$
   $(2w - 3)(w - 5)$
8. $3(y + 4)^2 + 11(y + 4) - 4$
   $(3y + 11)(y + 8)$
9. $25(x + 4)^2 - y^2$
   $(5x + 20 - y)(5x + 20 + y)$
10. $36(y - 5)^2 - z^2$
    $(6y - 30 - z)(6y - 30 + z)$
11. $9(5a - 3)^2 - 4$
    $(15a - 7)(15a - 11)$
12. $25(3b + 7)^2 - 16$
    $3(15b + 31)(5b + 13)$
13. $(t - 2)^2 - (2t + 1)^2$
    $-1(t + 3)(3t - 1)$
14. $(w + 3)^2 - (3w - 5)^2$
    $-4(w - 4)(2w - 1)$
15. $(a + b)^3 + c^3$
    $(a + b + c)(a^2 + 2ab + b^2 - ac - bc + c^2)$
16. $(x + 4)^3 - y^3$
    $(x + 4 - y)(x^2 + 8x + 16 + xy + 4y + y^2)$

17. $27c^3 - (d + 2)^3$
$(3c - d - 2)(9c^2 + 3cd + 6c + d^2 + 4d + 4)$

18. $125v^3 + (w - 1)^3$
$(5v + w - 1)(25v^2 - 5vw + 5v + w^2 - 2w + 1)$

19. $4x^2 + 28x(2y + 1) + 49(2y + 1)^2$
$(2x + 14y + 7)^2$

20. $9a^2 - 12a(b + 1) + 4(b + 1)^2$
$(3a - 2b - 2)^2$

Concept 2: Factoring 1 Term with 3 Terms

For Exercises 21–28, factor completely. **(See Example 4.)**

21. $x^2 - 10x + 25 - y^2$
$(x - 5 - y)(x - 5 + y)$

22. $m^2 - 22m + 121 - n^2$
$(m - 11 - n)(m - 11 + n)$

23. $a^2 - x^2 - 18xy - 81y^2$
$(a - x - 9y)(a + x + 9y)$

24. $c^2 - a^2 + 16ab - 64b^2$
$(c - a + 8b)(c + a - 8b)$

25. $25a^2 + 20ab + 4b^2 - 100c^2$
$(5a + 2b - 10c)(5a + 2b + 10c)$

26. $36x^2 + 60xy + 25y^2 - 121z^2$
$(6x + 5y - 11z)(6x + 5y + 11z)$

27. $64w^2 - 9t^2 + 24tp - 16p^2$
$(8w - 3t + 4p)(8w + 3t - 4p)$

28. $49k^2 - 25m^2 + 30mn - 9n^2$
$(7k - 5m + 3n)(7k + 5m - 3n)$

Concept 3: Additional Strategies and Mixed Exercises

For Exercises 29–68, factor completely. **(See Examples 1–5.)**

29. $x^2 - 4y^2 - x - 2y$
$(x + 2y)(x - 2y - 1)$

30. $9v^2 - w^2 - 3v + w$
$(3v - w)(3v + w - 1)$

31. $w^7 + 8w^4 - w^3 - 8$
$(w + 2)(w^2 - 2w + 4)(w^2 + 1)(w - 1)(w + 1)$

32. $t^5 - 125t^2 - 4t^3 + 500$
$(t - 5)(t^2 + 5t + 25)(t - 2)(t + 2)$

33. $xy - 4x + 2yz - 8z - 2y + 8$
$(y - 4)(x + 2z - 2)$

34. $ax + 4a + 2bx + 8b - cx - 4c$
$(x + 4)(a + 2b - c)$

35. $x^2 + xy - 2y^2 + x - y$
$(x - y)(x + 2y + 1)$

36. $a^2 + 2ab - 3b^2 - b + a$
$(a - b)(a + 3b + 1)$

37. $n^6 - 63n^3 - 64$
$(n - 4)(n^2 + 4n + 16)(n + 1)(n^2 - n + 1)$

38. $m^6 + 7m^3 - 8$
$(m + 2)(m^2 - 2m + 4)(m - 1)(m^2 + m + 1)$

39. $(a + b)^2 - 6(a + b)(c - d) + 9(c - d)^2$
$(a + b - 3c + 3d)^2$

40. $(x + 1)^2 - 4(x + 1)(x - 2) + 4(x - 2)^2$
$(-x + 5)^2$ or $(x - 5)^2$

41. $4x^4 - 10x^3 - 36x^2 + 90x$
$2x(2x - 5)(x + 3)(x - 3)$

42. $15x^4 - 5x^3 - 60x^2 + 20x$
$5x(3x - 1)(x + 2)(x - 2)$

43. $a^2 + 2ab + b^2 - a - b$
$(a + b)(a + b - 1)$

44. $v^2 + 6vw + 9w^2 - v - 3w$
$(v + 3w)(v + 3w - 1)$

45. $x^2(x + y) - y^2(x + y)$
$(x - y)(x + y)^2$

46. $u^2(u - v) - v^2(u - v)$
$(u - v)^2(u + v)$

47. $(a + 3)^4 + 6(a + 3)^3$
$(a + 3)^3(a + 9)$

48. $(4 - b)^4 - 2(4 - b)^3$
$(4 - b)^3(2 - b)$

49. $24(3x + 5)^3 - 30(3x + 5)^2$
$18(3x + 5)^2(4x + 5)$

50. $10(2y + 3)^2 + 15(2y + 3)$
$5(2y + 3)(4y + 9)$

51. $\frac{1}{100}x^2 + \frac{1}{35}x + \frac{1}{49}$ $\quad\left(\frac{1}{10}x + \frac{1}{7}\right)^2$

52. $\frac{1}{25}a^2 + \frac{1}{15}a + \frac{1}{36}$ $\quad\left(\frac{1}{5}a + \frac{1}{6}\right)^2$

53. $(5x^2 - 1)^2 - 4(5x^2 - 1) - 5$
$5x^2(5x^2 - 6)$

54. $(x^3 + 4)^2 - 10(x^3 + 4) + 24$
$x^3(x^3 - 2)$

55. $16p^4 - q^4$
$(4p^2 + q^2)(2p - q)(2p + q)$

56. $s^4t^4 - 81$
$(s^2t^2 + 9)(st - 3)(st + 3)$

57. $y^3 + \frac{1}{64}$ $\quad\left(y + \frac{1}{4}\right)\left(y^2 - \frac{1}{4}y + \frac{1}{16}\right)$

58. $z^3 + \frac{1}{125}$ $\quad\left(z + \frac{1}{5}\right)\left(z^2 - \frac{1}{5}z + \frac{1}{25}\right)$

59. $6a^3 + a^2b - 6ab^2 - b^3$
$(a + b)(a - b)(6a + b)$

60. $4p^3 + 12p^2q - pq^2 - 3q^3$
$(2p - q)(2p + q)(p + 3q)$

61. $\frac{1}{9}t^2 + \frac{1}{6}t + \frac{1}{16}$ $\quad\left(\frac{1}{3}t + \frac{1}{4}\right)^2$

62. $\frac{1}{25}y^2 + \frac{1}{5}y + \frac{1}{4}$ $\quad\left(\frac{1}{5}y + \frac{1}{2}\right)^2$

63. $6ax + 2bx - by - 3ay$
$(3a + b)(2x - y)$

64. $5pq - 4q - 12 + 15p$
$(q + 3)(5p - 4)$

65. $x^8 - 1$
$(x^4 + 1)(x^2 + 1)(x + 1)(x - 1)$

66. $y^8 - 256$
$(y^4 + 16)(y^2 + 4)(y + 2)(y - 2)$

67. $25c^2 - 9d^2 + 5c - 3d$
$(5c - 3d)(5c + 3d + 1)$

68. $5wx^3 + 5wy^3 - 2zx^3 - 2zy^3$
$(x + y)(x^2 - xy + y^2)(5w - 2z)$

Section A.2 Mean, Median, and Mode

Concepts

1. Mean
2. Median
3. Mode
4. Weighted Mean

1. Mean

When given a list of numerical data, it is often desirable to obtain a single number that represents the central value of the data. In this section, we discuss three such values called the mean, median, and mode.

Instructor Note: Ask students to compute the mean of their quiz scores or test scores for this class, as a warm-up exercise.

Definition of a Mean

The **mean** (or average) of a set of numbers is the sum of the values divided by the number of values. We can write this as a formula.

$$\text{Mean} = \frac{\text{sum of the values}}{\text{number of values}}$$

Classroom Example: p. A-11, Exercise 10

Example 1 Finding the Mean of a Data Set

A small business employs five workers. Their yearly salaries are

\$42,000 \$36,000 \$45,000 \$35,000 \$38,000

a. Find the mean yearly salary for the five employees.

b. Suppose the owner of the business makes \$218,000 per year. Find the mean salary for all six individuals (that is, include the owner's salary).

Solution:

a. Mean salary of five employees

$$= \frac{42{,}000 + 36{,}000 + 45{,}000 + 35{,}000 + 38{,}000}{5}$$

$$= \frac{196{,}000}{5} \quad \text{Add the data values.}$$

$$= 39{,}200 \quad \text{Divide.}$$

The mean salary for employees is \$39,200.

Avoiding Mistakes

When computing a mean remember to add the data first before dividing.

b. Mean of all six individuals

$$= \frac{42{,}000 + 36{,}000 + 45{,}000 + 35{,}000 + 38{,}000 + 218{,}000}{6}$$

$$= \frac{414{,}000}{6}$$

$$= 69{,}000$$

The mean salary with the owner's salary included is \$69,000.

Skill Practice Housing prices for five homes in one neighborhood are given.

$108,000 $149,000 $164,000 $118,000 $144,000

1. Find the mean of these five prices.
2. Suppose a new home is built in the neighborhood for $1.3 million ($1,300,000). Find the mean price of all six homes.

2. Median

In Example 1, you may have noticed that the mean salary was greatly affected by the unusually high value of $218,000. For this reason, you may want to use a different measure of "center" called the median. The median is the "middle" number in an ordered list of numbers.

Finding the Median

To compute the **median** of a list of numbers, first arrange the numbers in order from least to greatest.

- If the number of data values in the list is *odd,* then the median is the middle number in the list.
- If the number of data values is *even,* there is no single middle number. Therefore, the median is the mean (average) of the two middle numbers in the list.

Example 2 Finding the Median of a Data Set

Classroom Examples: p. A-12, Exercises 16 and 18

Consider the salaries of the five workers from Example 1.

$42,000 $36,000 $45,000 $35,000 $38,000

a. Find the median salary for the five workers.

b. Find the median salary including the owner's salary of $218,000.

Solution:

a. 35,000 36,000 38,000 42,000 45,000 Arrange the data in order.

Because there are five data values (an *odd* number), the median is the middle number.

The median is $38,000.

b. Now consider the scores of all six individuals (including the owner). Arrange the data in order.

35,000 36,000 38,000 42,000 45,000 218,000

$$\frac{38{,}000 + 42{,}000}{2}$$ There are six data values (an *even* number). The median is the average of the two middle numbers.

$$= \frac{80{,}000}{2}$$ Add the two middle numbers.

$$= 40{,}000$$ Divide.

The median of all six salaries is $40,000.

Answers

1. $136,600 2. $330,500

Skill Practice Housing prices for five homes in one neighborhood are given.

$108,000 $149,000 $164,000 $118,000 $144,000

3. Find the median price of these five houses.
4. Suppose a new home is built in the neighborhood for $1,300,000. Find the median price of all six homes. Compare this price with the mean in Skill Practice Exercise 2.

In Examples 1 and 2, the mean of all six salaries is $69,000, whereas the median is $40,000. These examples show that the median is a better representation for a central value when the data list has an unusually high (or low) value.

Classroom Example: p. A-13, Exercise 24

Example 3 Determining the Median of a Data Set

The average monthly temperatures (in °C) for the South Pole are given in the table. Find the median temperature. (*Source:* NOAA)

Jan.	Feb.	March	April	May	June	July	Aug.	Sept.	Oct.	Nov.	Dec.
−2.9	−9.5	−19.2	−20.7	−21.7	−23.0	−25.7	−26.1	−24.6	−18.9	−9.7	−3.4

Solution:

First arrange the numbers in order from least to greatest.

−26.1 −25.7 −24.6 −23.0 −21.7 −20.7 −19.2 −18.9 −9.7 −9.5 −3.4 −2.9

$$\text{Median} = \frac{-20.7 + (-19.2)}{2} = -19.95$$

TIP: Note that the median may not be one of the original data values.

There are 12 data values (an *even* number). Therefore, the median is the average of the two middle numbers. The median temperature at the South Pole is −19.95°C.

Skill Practice The gain or loss for a stock is given for an 8-day period. Find the median gain or loss.

5. −2.4 −2.0 1.25 0.6 −1.8 −0.4 0.6 −0.9

3. Mode

A third representative value for a list of data is called the mode.

Definition of a Mode

The **mode** of a set of data is the value or values that occur most often.

- If two values occur most often we say the data are bimodal.
- If more than two values occur most often, we say there is no mode.

Answers

3. $144,000 4. $146,500
5. −0.65

Example 4 Finding the Mode of a Data Set

Classroom Example: p. A-13, Exercise 28

The student-to-teacher ratio is given for elementary schools for ten selected states. For example, California has a student-to-teacher ratio of 20.6. This means that there are approximately 20.6 students per teacher in California elementary schools. (*Source:* National Center for Education Statistics)

ME	ND	WI	NH	RI	IL	IN	MS	CA	UT
12.5	13.4	14.1	14.5	14.8	16.1	16.1	16.1	20.6	21.9

Find the mode of the student-to-teacher ratio for these states.

Solution:

The data value 16.1 appears most often. Therefore, the mode is 16.1 students per teacher.

Skill Practice The monthly rainfall amounts (in inches) for Houston, Texas, are given. Find the mode. (*Source:* NOAA)

6.

4.5	3.0	3.2	3.5	5.1	6.8
4.3	4.5	5.6	5.3	4.5	3.8

Example 5 Finding the Mode of a Data Set

Classroom Example: p. A-13, Exercise 32

Find the mode of the list of average monthly temperatures for Albany, New York. Values are in °F.

Jan.	Feb.	March	April	May	June	July	Aug.	Sept.	Oct.	Nov.	Dec.
22	25	35	47	58	66	71	69	61	49	39	26

Solution:

No data value occurs most often. There is no mode for this set of data.

Skill Practice

7. Find the mode of the weights in pounds of babies born one day at Brackenridge Hospital in Austin, Texas.

7.2 8.1 6.9 9.3 8.3 7.7 7.9 6.4 7.5

Example 6 Finding the Mode of a Data Set

Classroom Example: p. A-13, Exercise 36

The grades for a quiz in college algebra are as follows. The scores are out of a possible 10 points.

9	4	6	9	9	8	2	1	4	9
5	10	10	5	7	7	9	8	7	3
9	7	10	7	10	1	7	4	5	6

Answers

6. 4.5 in. **7.** There is no mode.

Solution:

Sometimes arranging the data in order makes it easier to find the repeated values.

1	1	2	3	4	4	4	5	5	5
6	6	7	7	7	7	7	7	8	8
9	9	9	9	9	9	10	10	10	10

The score of 7 occurs 6 times. The score of 9 occurs 6 times. There are two modes, 7 and 9, because these scores both occur more than any other score. We say that these data are *bimodal.*

TIP: To remember the difference between median and mode, think of the *median* of a highway that goes down the *middle*. Think of the word *mode* as sounding similar to the word *most.*

Skill Practice

8. The ages of children participating in an after-school sports program are given. Find the mode(s).

13	15	17	15	14	15	16	16
15	16	12	13	15	14	16	15
15	16	16	13	16	13	14	18

4. Weighted Mean

Sometimes data values in a list appear multiple times. In such a case, we can compute a weighted mean. In Example 7, we demonstrate how to use a weighted mean to compute a grade point average (GPA). To compute GPA, each grade is assigned a numerical value. For example, an "A" is worth 4 points, a "B" is worth 3 points, and so on. Then each grade for a course is "weighted" by the number of credit-hours that the course is worth.

Classroom Example: p. A-14, Exercise 44

Example 7 Using a Weighted Mean to Compute GPA

At a certain college, the grades A–F are assigned numerical values as follows.

$A = 4.0$ $B+ = 3.5$ $B = 3.0$ $C+ = 2.5$

$C = 2.0$ $D+ = 1.5$ $D = 1.0$ $F = 0.0$

Elmer takes the following classes with the grades as shown. Determine Elmer's GPA.

Course	Grade	Number of Credit-Hours
Prealgebra	A = 4 pts	3
Study Skills	C = 2 pts	1
First Aid	B+ = 3.5 pts	2
English I	D = 1.0 pt	4

Solution:

The data in the table can be visualized as follows.

4 pts	4 pts	4 pts	2 pts	3.5 pts	3.5 pts	1 pt	1 pt	1 pt	1 pt
A	A	A	C	B+	B+	D	D	D	D
3 of these			1 of these	2 of these		4 of these			

Answer

8. There are two modes, 15 and 16.

The number of grade points earned for each course is the product of the grade for the course and the number of credit-hours for the course. For example:

Grade points for Prealgebra: (4 pts)(3 credit-hours) = 12 points

Course	Grade	Number of Credit-Hours (Weights)	Product Number of Grade Points
Prealgebra	A = 4 pts	3	(4 pts)(3 credit-hours) = 12 pts
Study Skills	C = 2 pts	1	(2 pts)(1 credit-hour) = 2 pts
First Aid	B+ = 3.5 pts	2	(3.5 pts)(2 credit-hours) = 7 pts
English I	D = 1.0 pt	4	(1 pt)(4 credit-hours) = 4 pts
		Total hours: 10	Total grade points: 25 pts

To determine GPA, we will add the number of grade points earned for each course and then divide by the total number of credit-hours taken.

$$\text{Mean} = \frac{25}{10} = 2.5 \qquad \text{Elmer's GPA for this term is 2.5.}$$

Skill Practice

9. Clyde received the following grades for the semester. Use the numerical values assigned to grades from Example 7 to find Clyde's GPA.

Course	Grade	Credit-Hours
Math	B+	4
Science	C	3
Speech	A	3

In Example 7, notice that the value of each grade is "weighted" by the number of credit-hours. The grade of "A" for Prealgebra is weighted three times. The grade of "C" for the study skills course is weighted one time. The grade that hurt Elmer's GPA was the "D" in English. Not only did he receive a low grade, but the course was weighted heavily (4 credit-hours). In Exercise 47, we recompute Elmer's GPA with a "B" in English to see how this grade affects his GPA.

Answer
9. 3.2

Section A.2 Practice Exercises

For additional exercises, see Classroom Activities A.2A–A.2B in the *Student's Resource Manual* at www.mhhe.com/moh.

Concept 1: Mean

For Exercises 1–7, find the mean of each set of numbers. **(See Example 1.)**

1. 93, 96, 88, 72, 91 88

2. 4, 6, 5, 10, 4, 5, 8 6

3. 3, 8, 5, 7, 4, 2, 7, 4 5

4. 0, 5, 7, 4, 7, 2, 4, 3 4

5. 7, 6, 5, 10, 8, 4, 8, 6, 0 6

6. −10, −13, −18, −20, −15 −15.2

7. −22, −14, −12, −16, −15 −15.8

8. Compute the mean of your test scores for this class up to this point. Answers will vary.

9. The flight times in hours for six flights between New York and Los Angeles are given. Find the mean flight time. Round to the nearest tenth of an hour. 5.8 hr

5.5, 6.0, 5.8, 5.8, 6.0, 5.6

10. A nurse takes the temperature of a patient every 10 min and records the temperatures as follows: 98°F, 98.4°F, 98.9°F, 100.1°F, and 99.2°F. Find the patient's mean temperature. 98.92°F

11. The number of Calories for six different chicken sandwiches and chicken salads is given in the table.

Chicken Sandwiches	Salads with Chicken
360	310
370	325
380	350
400	390
400	440
470	500

a. What is the mean number of Calories for a chicken sandwich? Round to the nearest whole unit. 397 Cal

b. What is the mean number of Calories for a salad with chicken? Round to the nearest whole unit. 386 Cal

c. What is the difference in the means? There is only an 11-Cal difference in the means.

12. The heights of the players from two NBA teams are given in the table. All heights are in inches.

Philadelphia 76ers' Height (in.)	Milwaukee Bucks' Height (in.)
83	70
83	83
72	82
79	72
77	82
84	85
75	75
76	75
82	78
79	77

a. Find the mean height for the players on the Philadelphia 76ers. 79 in.

b. Find the mean height for the players on the Milwaukee Bucks. 77.9 in.

c. What is the difference in the mean heights? The mean height for the 76ers is slightly higher by 1.1 in.

13. Zach received the following scores for his first four tests: 98%, 80%, 78%, 90%.

a. Find Zach's mean test score. 86.5%

b. Zach got a 59% on his fifth test. Find the mean of all five tests. 81%

c. How did the low score of 59% affect the overall mean of five tests? The low score of 59% decreased Zach's average by 5.5%.

14. The prices of four steam irons are \$50, \$30, \$25, and \$45.

a. Find the mean of these prices. \$37.50

b. An iron that costs \$140 is added to the list. What is the mean of all five irons? \$58.00

c. How does the expensive iron affect the mean? By including the iron for \$140, the mean increased by \$20.50.

Concept 2: Median

For Exercises 15–20, find the median for each set of numbers. **(See Examples 2–3.)**

15. 16, 14, 22, 13, 20, 19, 17
17

16. 32, 35, 22, 36, 30, 31, 38
32

17. 109, 118, 111, 110, 123, 100
110.5

18. 134, 132, 120, 135, 140, 118
133

19. −58, −55, −50, −40, −40, −55
−52.5

20. −82, −90, −99, −82, −88, −87
−87.5

21. The infant mortality rates for five countries are given in the table. Find the median.
3.93 deaths per 1000

Country	Infant Mortality Rate (Deaths per 1000)
Sweden	3.93
Japan	4.10
Finland	3.82
Andorra	4.09
Singapore	3.87

22. The snowfall amounts for 5 winter months in Burlington, Vermont, are given in the table. Find the median. 16.8 in.

Month	Snowfall (in.)
November	6.6
December	18.1
January	18.8
February	16.8
March	12.4

23. Jonas Slackman played 8 golf tournaments, each with 72-holes of golf. His scores for the tournaments are given. Find the median score.

$-3, -5, 1, 4, -8, 2, 8, -1$ 0

24. Andrew Strauss recorded the daily low temperature (in °C) at his home in Virginia for 8 days in January. Find the median temperature.

$5, 6, -5, 1, -4, -11, -8, -5$ −4.5°C

25. The number of passengers (in millions) on 9 leading airlines for a recent year is listed. Find the median number of passengers. (*Source:* International Airline Transport Association)

48.3, 42.4, 91.6, 86.8, 46.5, 71.2, 45.4, 56.4, 51.7
51.7 million passengers

26. For a recent year the number of albums sold (in millions) is listed for the 10 best sellers. Find the median number of albums sold.

2.7, 3.0, 4.8, 7.4, 3.4, 2.6, 3.0, 3.0, 3.9, 3.2
3.1 million albums

Concept 3: Mode

For Exercises 27–32, find the mode(s) for each set of numbers. **(See Examples 4–5.)**

27. 4, 5, 3, 8, 4, 9, 4, 2, 1, 4 4

28. 12, 14, 13, 17, 19, 18, 19, 17, 17 17

29. $-28, -21, -24, -23, -24, -30, -21$
−21 and −24

30. $-45, -42, -40, -41, -49, -49, -42$
−42 and −49

31. 90, 89, 91, 77, 88 No mode

32. 132, 253, 553, 255, 552, 234 No mode

33. The table gives the monthly precipitation for Portland, Oregon for selected months. Find the mode. 3.66 in.

Month	Rainfall (in.)
January	4.88
February	3.66
March	3.66
April	2.72
May	2.48
June	1.69

34. The table gives the number of hazardous waste sites for selected states. Find the mode. 39

State	Number of Sites
Florida	51
New Jersey	112
Michigan	67
Wisconsin	39
California	96
Pennsylvania	94
Illinois	39
New York	90

35. The unemployment rates for nine countries are given. Find the mode. **(See Example 6.)**

6.3%, 7.0%, 5.8%, 9.1%, 5.2%, 8.8%, 8.4%, 5.8%, 5.2% 5.2% and 5.8%

36. The list gives the number of children who were absent from class for an 11-day period. Find the mode.

4, 1, 6, 2, 4, 4, 4, 2, 2, 3, 2 2 children and 4 children

Mixed Exercises

37. Six test scores for Jonathan's history class are listed. Find the mean and median. Round to the nearest tenth if necessary. Does the mean or median give a better overall score for Jonathan's performance?

92%, 98%, 43%, 98%, 97%, 85%
Mean: 85.5%; median: 94.5%; The median gives Jonathan a better overall score.

38. Nora's math test results are listed. Find the mean and median. Round to the nearest tenth if necessary. Does the mean or median give a better overall score for Nora's performance?

52%, 85%, 89%, 90%, 83%, 89%
Mean: 81.3%; median: 87%; The median gives Nora a better overall score.

39. Listed below are monthly costs for seven health insurance companies for a self-employed person, 55 years of age, and in good health. Find the mean, median, and mode (if one exists). Round to the nearest dollar. (*Source:* eHealth Insurance Company, 2007)

\$312, \$225, \$221, \$256, \$308, \$280, \$147

Mean: \$250; median: \$256; mode: There is no mode.

40. The salaries for seven Associate Professors at a large university are listed. Find the mean, median, and mode (if one exists). Round to the nearest dollar.

\$104,000, \$107,000, \$67,750, \$82,500,

\$73,500, \$88,300, \$104,000

Mean: \$89,579; median: \$88,300; mode: \$104,000

41. The prices of 10 single-family, three-bedroom homes for sale in Santa Rosa, California, are listed for a recent year. Find the mean, median, and mode (if one exists).

\$850,000, \$835,000, \$839,000, \$829,000,

\$850,000, \$850,000, \$850,000, \$847,000,

\$1,850,000, \$825,000

Mean: \$942,500; median: \$848,500; mode: \$850,000

42. The prices of 10 single-family, three-bedroom homes for sale in Boston, Massachusetts, are listed for a recent year. Find the mean, median, and mode (if one exists).

\$300,000, \$2,495,000, \$2,120,000, \$220,000,

\$194,000, \$391,000, \$315,000, \$330,000,

\$435,000, \$250,000

Mean: \$705,000; median: \$322,500; mode: There is no mode.

Concept 4: Weighted Mean

For Exercises 43–46, use the following numerical values assigned to grades to compute GPA. Round each GPA to the hundredths place. **(See Example 7.)**

A = 4.0	B+ = 3.5	B = 3.0	C+ = 2.5
C = 2.0	D+ = 1.5	D = 1.0	F = 0.0

43. Compute the GPA for the following grades. Round to the nearest hundredth. 2.38

Course	Grade	Number of Credit-Hours (Weights)
Intermediate Algebra	B	4
Theater	C	1
Music Appreciation	A	3
World History	D	5

44. Compute the GPA for the following grades. Round to the nearest hundredth. 3.59

Course	Grade	Number of Credit-Hours (Weights)
General Psychology	B+	3
Beginning Algebra	A	4
Student Success	A	1
Freshman English	B	3

45. Compute the GPA for the following grades. Round to the nearest hundredth. 2.77

Course	Grade	Number of Credit-Hours (Weights)
Business Calculus	B+	3
Biology	C	4
Library Research	F	1
American Literature	A	3

46. Compute the GPA for the following grades. Round to the nearest hundredth. 2.73

Course	Grade	Number of Credit-Hours (Weights)
University Physics	C+	5
Calculus I	A	4
Computer Programming	D	3
Swimming	A	1

47. Refer to the table given in Example 7. Replace the grade of "D" in English I with a grade of "B" and compute the GPA. How did Elmer's GPA differ with a better grade in the 4-hour English class?

3.3; Elmer's GPA improved from 2.5 to 3.3.

Expanding Your Skills

48. There are 20 students enrolled in a 12th-grade math class. The graph displays the number of students by age. First complete the table, and then find the mean.

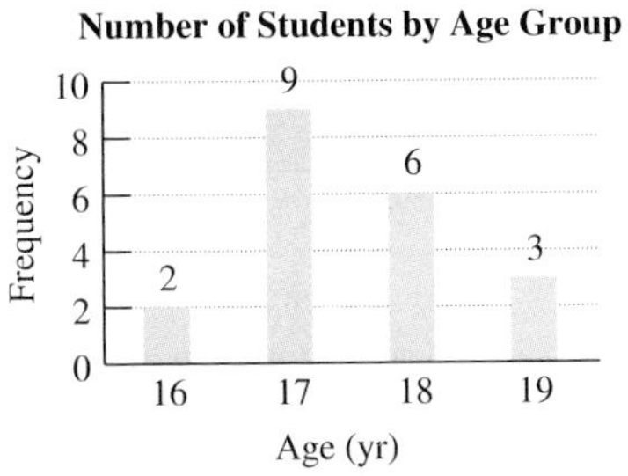

Age (yr)	Number of Students	Product
16	2	32
17	9	153
18	6	108
19	3	57
Total:	20	350

The mean age is 17.5 years.

49. A survey was made in a neighborhood of 37 houses. The graph represents the number of residents who live in each house. Complete the table and determine the mean number of residents per house.

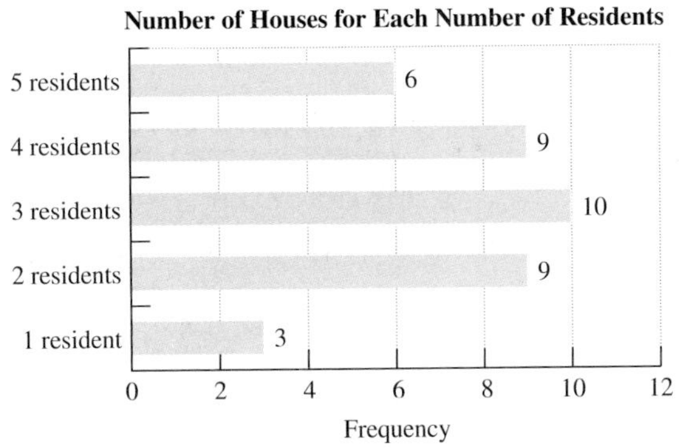

Number of Residents in Each House	Number of Houses	Product
1	3	3
2	9	18
3	10	30
4	9	36
5	6	30
Total:	37	117

The mean number of residents is approximately 3.2.

Introduction to Geometry

Section A.3

Concepts

1. Perimeter
2. Area
3. Volume
4. Angles
5. Triangles

1. Perimeter

In this section, we present several facts and formulas that may be used throughout the text in applications of geometry. One of the most important uses of geometry involves the measurement of objects of various shapes. We begin with an introduction to perimeter, area, and volume for several common shapes and objects.

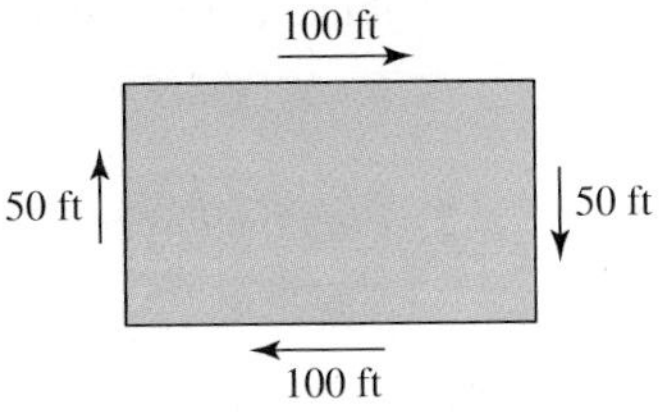

Perimeter = 300 ft

Figure A-1

Perimeter is defined as the distance around a figure. If we were to put up a fence around a field, the perimeter would determine the amount of fencing. For example, in Figure A-1 the distance around the field is 300 ft. For a polygon (a closed figure constructed from line segments), the perimeter is the sum of the lengths of the sides. For a circle, the distance around the outside is called the circumference.

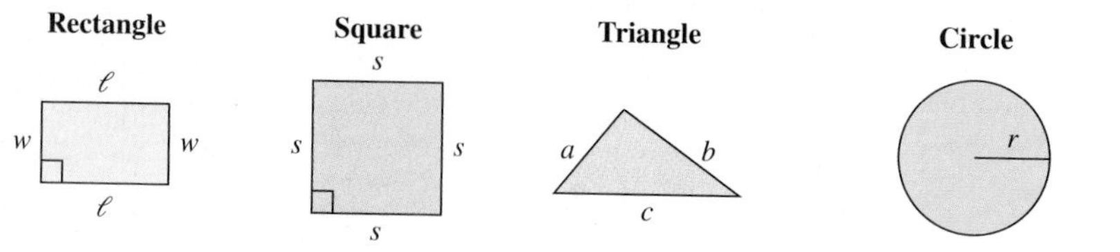

$P = 2\ell + 2w$ | $P = 4s$ | $P = a + b + c$ | Circumference: $C = 2\pi r$

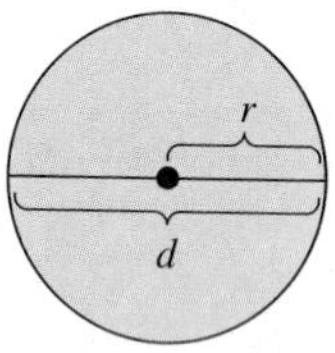

$d = 2r$

For a circle, r represents the length of a radius—the distance from the center to any point on the circle. The length of a diameter, d, of a circle is twice that of a radius. Thus, $d = 2r$. The number π is a constant equal to the circumference of a circle divided by the length of a diameter. That is, $\pi = \frac{C}{d}$. The value of π is often approximated by 3.14 or $\frac{22}{7}$.

Classroom Examples: p. A-25, Exercises 4 and 10

Example 1 Finding Perimeter and Circumference

Find the perimeter or circumference as indicated. Use 3.14 for π.

a. Perimeter of the rectangle

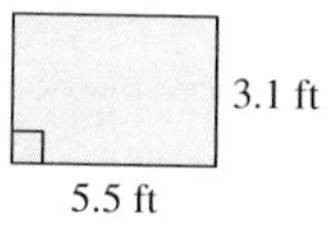

b. Circumference of the circle

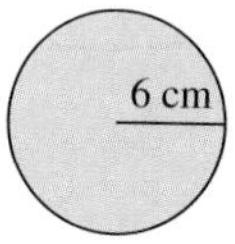

Solution:

a. $P = 2\ell + 2w$

$= 2(5.5 \text{ ft}) + 2(3.1 \text{ ft})$ Substitute $\ell = 5.5$ ft and $w = 3.1$ ft.

$= 11 \text{ ft} + 6.2 \text{ ft}$

$= 17.2 \text{ ft}$ The perimeter is 17.2 ft.

b. $C = 2\pi r$

$\approx 2(3.14)(6 \text{ cm})$ Substitute 3.14 for π and $r = 6$ cm.

$= 6.28(6 \text{ cm})$

$= 37.68 \text{ cm}$ The circumference is 37.68 cm.

TIP: If a calculator is used to find the circumference of a circle, use the π key to get a more accurate answer.

Skill Practice

1. Find the perimeter of the square.

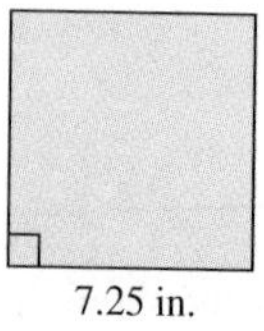

2. Find the circumference. Use 3.14 for π.

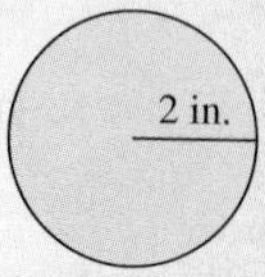

Answers

1. 29 in. **2.** 12.56 in.

2. Area

The area of a geometric figure is the number of square units that can be enclosed within the figure. In applications, we would find the area of a region if we were laying carpet or putting down sod for a lawn. For example, the rectangle shown in Figure A-2 encloses 6 square inches (6 in.^{2}).

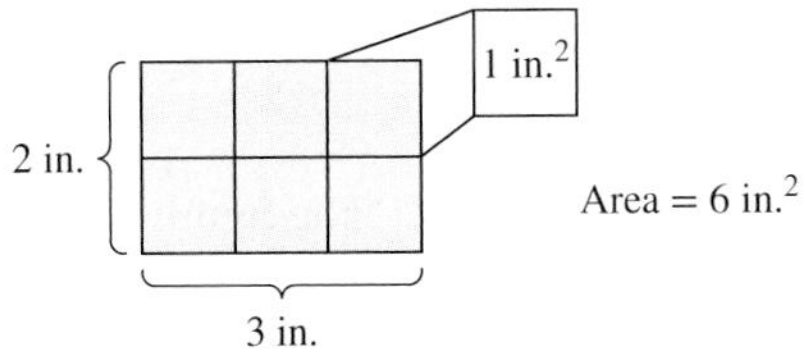

Figure A-2

The formulas used to compute the area for several common geometric shapes are given here:

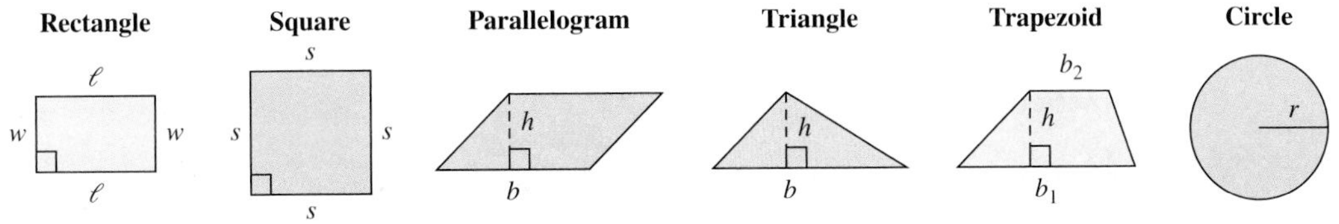

Rectangle	Square	Parallelogram	Triangle	Trapezoid	Circle
$A = \ell w$	$A = s^2$	$A = bh$	$A = \frac{1}{2}bh$	$A = \frac{1}{2}(b_1 + b_2)h$	$A = \pi r^2$

Example 2 **Finding Area**

Find the area.

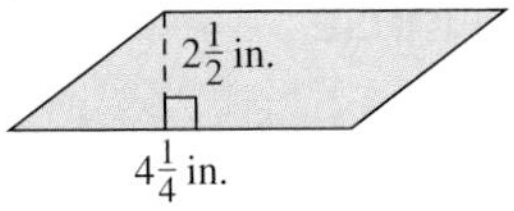

Solution:

$A = bh$ — The figure is a parallelogram.

$= (4\frac{1}{4} \text{ in.})(2\frac{1}{2} \text{ in.})$ — Substitute $b = 4\frac{1}{4}$ in. and $h = 2\frac{1}{2}$ in.

$$= \left(\frac{17}{4} \text{ in.}\right)\left(\frac{5}{2} \text{ in.}\right)$$

$$= \frac{85}{8} \text{ in.}^2 \text{ or } 10\tfrac{5}{8} \text{ in.}^2$$

Skill Practice Find the area.

3.

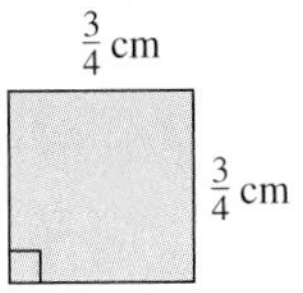

Classroom Example: p. A-25, Exercise 18

TIP: The units of area are given in square units such as square inches (in.^{2}), square feet (ft^2), square yards (yd^2), square centimeters (cm^2), and so on.

Answer

3. $\frac{9}{16}$ cm^2

Classroom Example: p. A-26, Exercise 24

Example 3 Finding Area

Find the area.

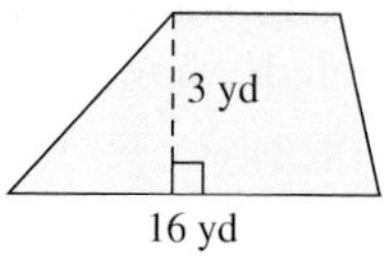

Solution:

$A = \frac{1}{2}(b_1 + b_2)h$ The figure is a trapezoid.

$= \frac{1}{2}(16 \text{ yd} + 10 \text{ yd})(3 \text{ yd})$ Substitute $b_1 = 16$ yd, $b_2 = 10$ yd, and $h = 3$ yd.

$= \frac{1}{2}(26 \text{ yd})(3 \text{ yd})$

$= (13 \text{ yd})(3 \text{ yd})$

$= 39 \text{ yd}^2$ The area is 39 yd^2.

Skill Practice Find the area.

4.

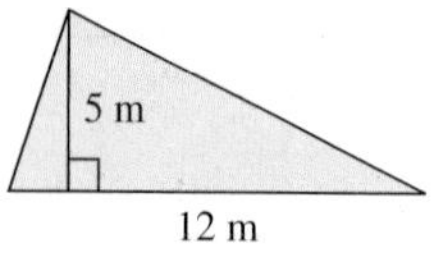

Classroom Example: p. A-26, Exercise 22

Example 4 Finding the Area of a Circle

Find the area of a circular fountain if the diameter is 50 ft. Use 3.14 for π.

Solution:

$A = \pi r^2$ We need the radius, which is $\frac{1}{2}$ the diameter. $r = \frac{1}{2}(50) = 25$ ft

$\approx (3.14)(25 \text{ ft})^2$ Substitute 3.14 for π and $r = 25$ ft.

$= (3.14)(625 \text{ ft}^2)$

$= 1962.5 \text{ ft}^2$ The area of the fountain is 1962.5 ft^2.

Skill Practice Find the area of the circular region. Use 3.14 for π.

5.

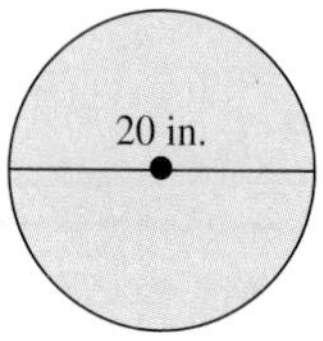

Answers

4. 30 m^2 **5.** 314 in.^2

3. Volume

The volume of a solid is the number of cubic units that can be enclosed within a solid. The solid shown in Figure A-3 contains 18 cubic inches (18 in.^{3}). In applications, volume might refer to the amount of water in a swimming pool.

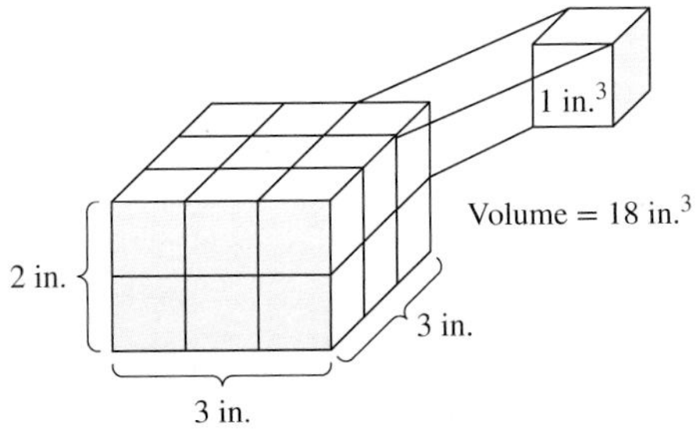

Figure A-3

The formulas used to compute the volume of several common solids are given here:

Rectangular Solid	Cube	Right Circular Cylinder
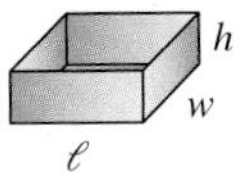	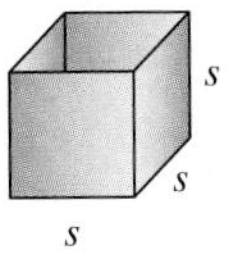	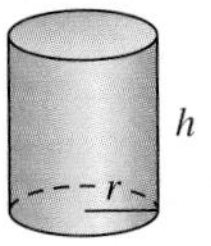
$V = \ell wh$	$V = s^3$	$V = \pi r^2 h$

TIP: Notice that the volume formulas for the three figures just shown are given by the product of the area of the base and the height of the figure:

$V = \ell wh$	$V = s \cdot s \cdot s$	$V = \pi r^2 h$
↑ Area of Rectangular Base	↑ Area of Square Base	↑ Area of Circular Base

Two additional geometric solids often used in geometry are the right circular cone and the sphere.

Right Circular Cone	Sphere
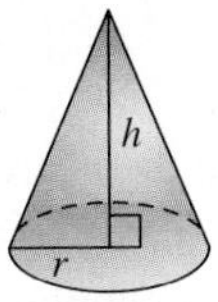	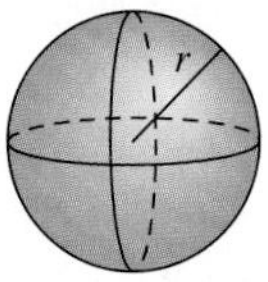
$V = \frac{1}{3}\pi r^2 h$	$V = \frac{4}{3}\pi r^3$

Example 5 **Finding Volume**

Find the volume.

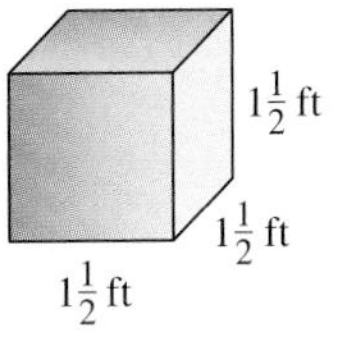

Classroom Example: p. A-26, Exercise 32

Animation

Solution:

$V = s^3$ The object is a cube.

$= (1\frac{1}{2}\text{ ft})^3$ Substitute $s = 1\frac{1}{2}$ ft.

$= \left(\frac{3}{2}\text{ ft}\right)^3$

$= \left(\frac{3}{2}\text{ ft}\right)\left(\frac{3}{2}\text{ ft}\right)\left(\frac{3}{2}\text{ ft}\right)$

$= \frac{27}{8}\text{ ft}^3$, or $3\frac{3}{8}\text{ ft}^3$

TIP: The units of volume are cubic units such as cubic inches (in.^{3}), cubic feet (ft^3), cubic yards (yd^3), cubic centimeters (cm^3), and so on.

Skill Practice Find the volume.

6.

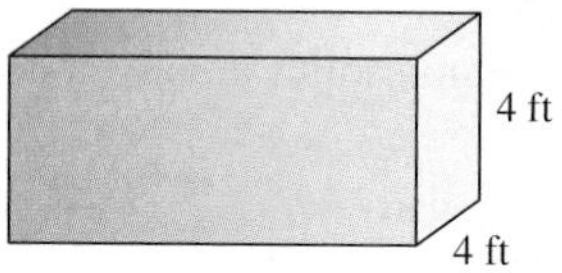

Classroom Example: p. A-26, Exercise 36

Example 6 Finding Volume

Find the volume. Round to the nearest whole unit.

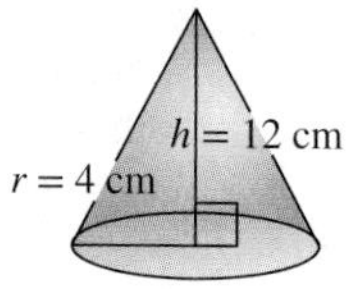

Solution:

$V = \frac{1}{3}\pi r^2 h$ The object is a right circular cone.

$\approx \frac{1}{3}(3.14)(4\text{ cm})^2(12\text{ cm})$ Substitute 3.14 for π, $r = 4$ cm, and $h = 12$ cm.

$= \frac{1}{3}(3.14)(16\text{ cm}^2)(12\text{ cm})$

$= 200.96\text{ cm}^3$

$\approx 201\text{ cm}^3$ Round to the nearest whole unit.

Skill Practice Find the volume. Use 3.14 for π. Round to the nearest whole unit.

7.

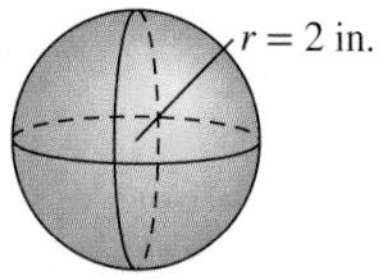

Answers

6. 128 ft^3 **7.** 33 in.^{3}

Example 7 **Finding Volume in an Application**

Classroom Example: p. A-27, Exercise 52

An underground gas tank is in the shape of a right circular cylinder. Find the volume of the tank. Use 3.14 for π.

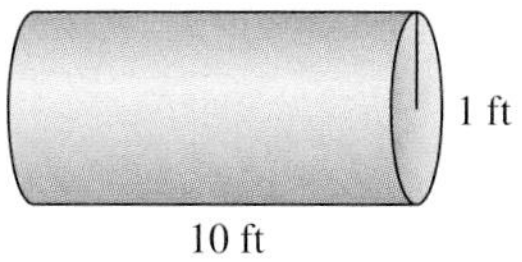

Solution:

$V = \pi r^2 h$

$\approx (3.14)(1 \text{ ft})^2(10 \text{ ft})$ — Substitute 3.14 for π, $r = 1$ ft, and $h = 10$ ft.

$= (3.14)(1 \text{ ft}^2)(10 \text{ ft})$

$= 31.4 \text{ ft}^3$ — The tank holds 31.4 ft^3 of gasoline.

Skill Practice

8. Find the volume of soda in the can. Use 3.14 for π. Round to the nearest whole unit.

4. Angles

Applications involving angles and their measure come up often in the study of algebra, trigonometry, calculus, and applied sciences. The most common unit to measure an angle is the degree (°). Several angles and their corresponding degree measure are shown in Figure A-4.

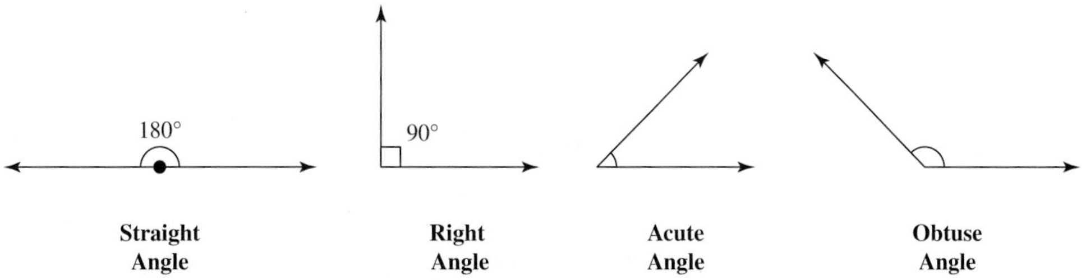

Figure A-4

- An angle that measures 90° is a **right angle** (right angles are often marked with a square or corner symbol, □).
- An angle that measures 180° is called a **straight angle**.
- An angle that measures between 0° and 90° is called an **acute angle**.
- An angle that measures between 90° and 180° is called an **obtuse angle**.
- Two angles with the same measure are **congruent angles**.

The measure of an angle will be denoted by the symbol m written in front of the angle. Therefore, the measure of $\angle A$ is denoted $m(\angle A)$.

Answer

8. 339 cm^3

- Two angles are **complementary** if the sum of their measures is 90°.

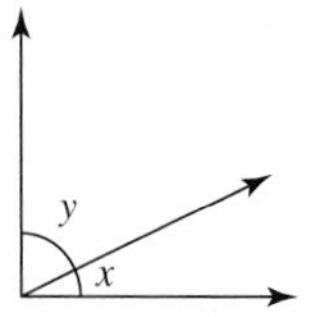

$m(\angle x) + m(\angle y) = 90°$

- Two angles are **supplementary** if the sum of their measures is 180°.

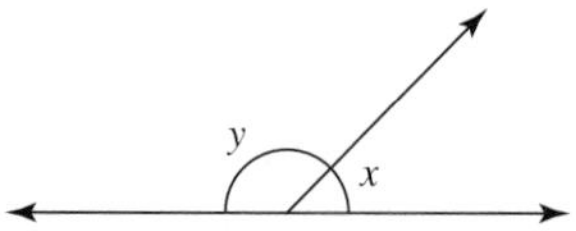

$m(\angle x) + m(\angle y) = 180°$

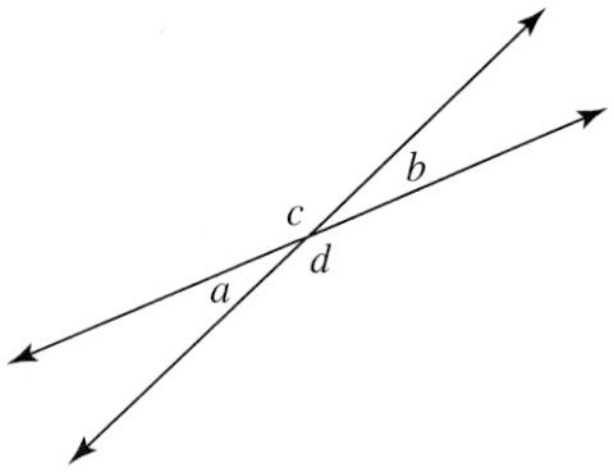

Figure A-5

When two lines intersect, four angles are formed (Figure A-5). In Figure A-5, $\angle a$ and $\angle b$ are a pair of vertical angles. Another set of vertical angles is the pair $\angle c$ and $\angle d$. An important property of vertical angles is that the measures of two vertical angles are *equal*. In the figure, $m(\angle a) = m(\angle b)$ and $m(\angle c) = m(\angle d)$.

Parallel lines are lines that lie in the same plane and do not intersect. In Figure A-6, the lines L_1 and L_2 are parallel lines. If a line intersects two parallel lines, the line forms eight angles with the parallel lines.

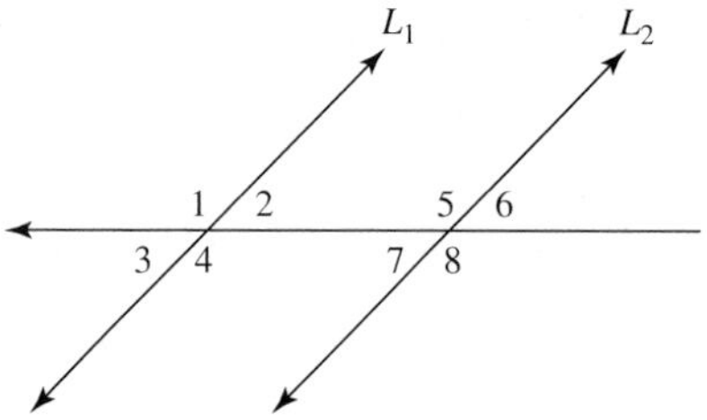

Figure A-6

The measures of angles 1–8 in Figure A-6 have the following special properties.

L_1 and L_2 are Parallel	Name of Angles	Property
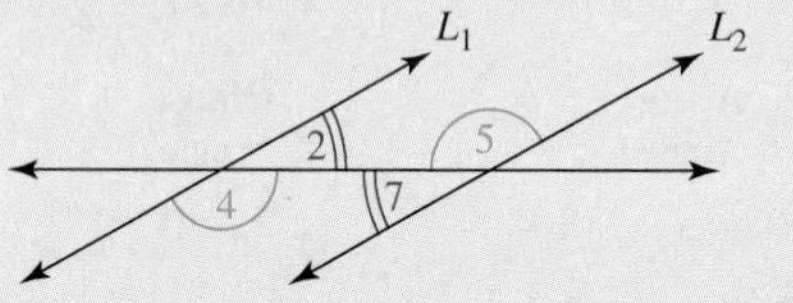	The following pairs of angles are called alternate interior angles: $\angle 2$ and $\angle 7$ $\angle 4$ and $\angle 5$	Alternate interior angles are equal in measure. $m(\angle 2) = m(\angle 7)$ $m(\angle 4) = m(\angle 5)$
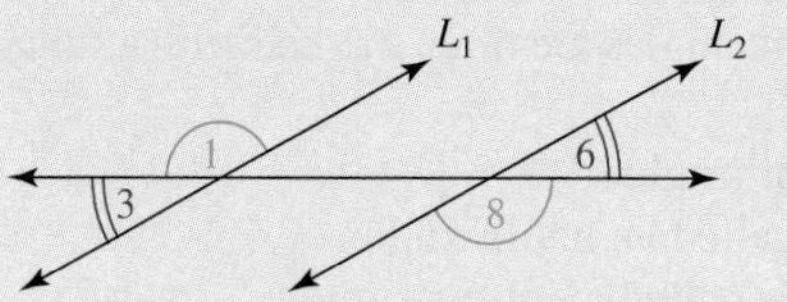	The following pairs of angles are called alternate exterior angles: $\angle 1$ and $\angle 8$ $\angle 3$ and $\angle 6$	Alternate exterior angles are equal in measure. $m(\angle 1) = m(\angle 8)$ $m(\angle 3) = m(\angle 6)$
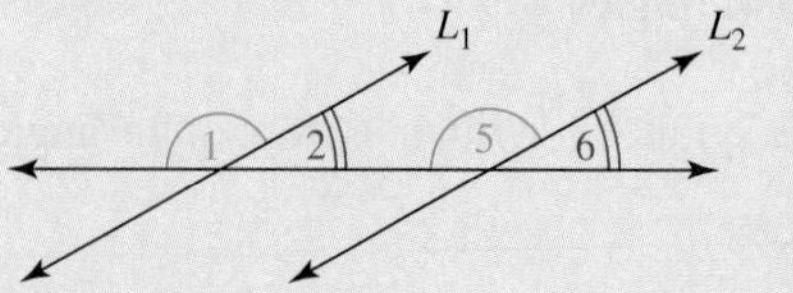 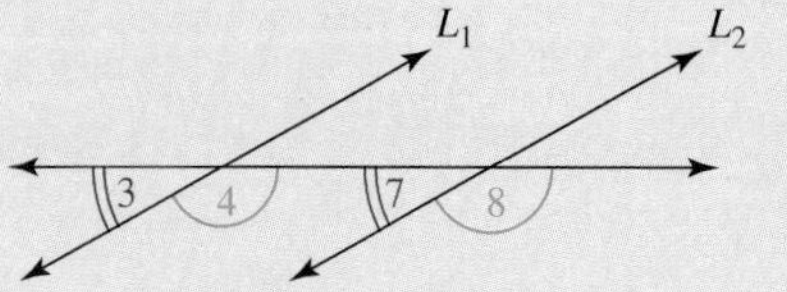	The following pairs of angles are called corresponding angles: $\angle 1$ and $\angle 5$ $\angle 2$ and $\angle 6$ $\angle 3$ and $\angle 7$ $\angle 4$ and $\angle 8$	Corresponding angles are equal in measure. $m(\angle 1) = m(\angle 5)$ $m(\angle 2) = m(\angle 6)$ $m(\angle 3) = m(\angle 7)$ $m(\angle 4) = m(\angle 8)$

Example 8 Finding the Measures of Angles in a Diagram

Classroom Examples: p. A-29, Exercises 76 and 78

Find the measure of each angle and explain how the angle is related to the given angle of 70°.

a. $\angle a$ **b.** $\angle b$

c. $\angle c$ **d.** $\angle d$

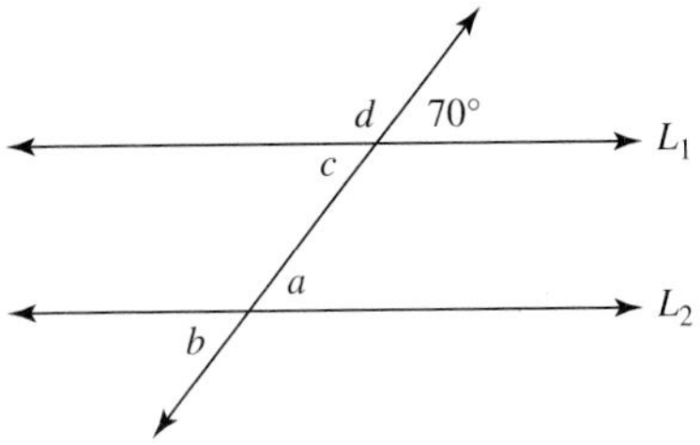

Solution:

a. $m(\angle a) = 70°$ — $\angle a$ is a corresponding angle to the given angle of 70°.

b. $m(\angle b) = 70°$ — $\angle b$ and the given angle of 70° are alternate exterior angles.

c. $m(\angle c) = 70°$ — $\angle c$ and the given angle of 70° are vertical angles.

d. $m(\angle d) = 110°$ — $\angle d$ is the supplement of the given angle of 70°.

Skill Practice Refer to the figure. Assume that lines L_1 and L_2 are parallel.

9. Given that $m(\angle 3) = 23°$, find $m(\angle 2)$, $m(\angle 4)$, $m(\angle 7)$, and $m(\angle 8)$.

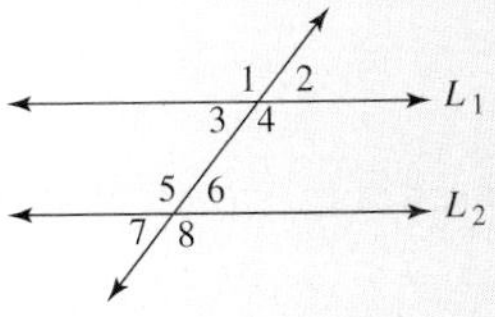

5. Triangles

Triangles are categorized by the measures of the angles (Figure A-7) and by the number of equal sides or angles (Figure A-8).

- An **acute triangle** is a triangle in which all three angles are acute.
- A **right triangle** is a triangle in which one angle is a right angle.
- An **obtuse triangle** is a triangle in which one angle is obtuse.

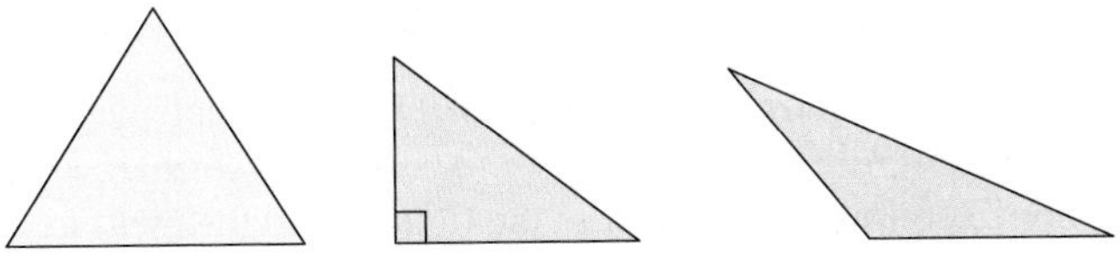

Acute Triangle **Right Triangle** **Obtuse Triangle**

Figure A-7

- An **equilateral triangle** is a triangle in which all three sides (and all three angles) are equal in measure.
- An **isosceles triangle** is a triangle in which two sides are equal in measure (the angles opposite the equal sides are also equal in measure).
- A **scalene triangle** is a triangle in which no sides (or angles) are equal in measure.

Answer

9. $m(\angle 2) = 23°$; $m(\angle 4) = 157°$; $m(\angle 7) = 23°$; $m(\angle 8) = 157°$

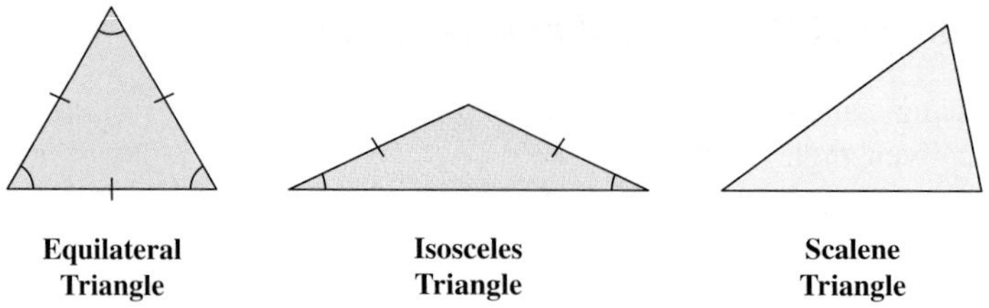

Figure A-8

The following important property is true for all triangles.

Animation

Sum of the Angles in a Triangle

The sum of the measures of the angles of a triangle is 180°.

Classroom Example: p. A-30, Exercise 98

Example 9 Finding the Measures of Angles in a Diagram

Find the measure of each angle in the figure.

a. $\angle a$

b. $\angle b$

c. $\angle c$

d. $\angle d$

e. $\angle e$

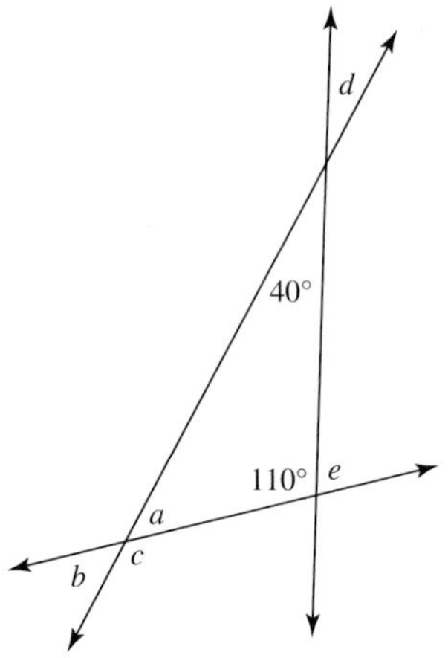

Solution:

a. $m(\angle a) = 30°$	The sum of the angles in a triangle is 180°.
b. $m(\angle b) = 30°$	$\angle a$ and $\angle b$ are vertical angles and have equal measures.
c. $m(\angle c) = 150°$	$\angle c$ and $\angle a$ are supplementary angles ($\angle c$ and $\angle b$ are also supplementary).
d. $m(\angle d) = 40°$	$\angle d$ and the given angle of 40° are vertical angles.
e. $m(\angle e) = 70°$	$\angle e$ and the given angle of 110° are supplementary angles.

Skill Practice For Exercises 10–14, refer to the figure. Find the measure of the indicated angle.

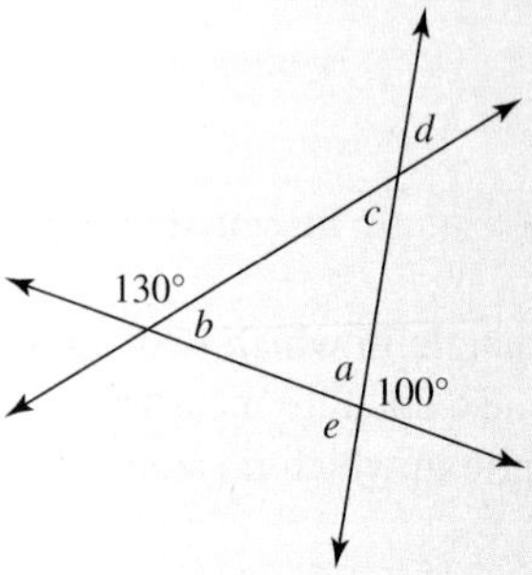

10. $\angle a$ **11.** $\angle b$ **12.** $\angle c$ **13.** $\angle d$ **14.** $\angle e$

Answers

10. 80° **11.** 50° **12.** 50°
13. 50° **14.** 100°

Section A.3 Practice Exercises

For additional exercises, see Classroom Activities A.3A–A.3C in the *Student's Resource Manual* at www.mhhe.com/moh.

Concept 1: Perimeter

1. Would you measure area or perimeter to determine the amount of decorative fence needed to enclose a garden? Perimeter

2. Identify which of the following units could be measures of perimeter. b, e, i

a. Square inches ($in.^2$)	**b.** Meters (m)	**c.** Cubic feet (ft^3)
d. Cubic meters (m^3)	**e.** Miles (mi)	**f.** Square centimeters (cm^2)
g. Square yards (yd^2)	**h.** Cubic inches ($in.^3$)	**i.** Kilometers (km)

For Exercises 3–10, find the perimeter or circumference of each figure. Use 3.14 for π. **(See Example 1.)**

3. 32 m

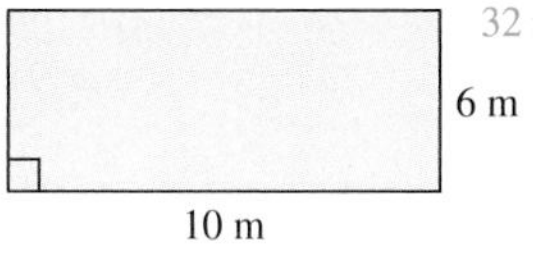

4. 108 cm

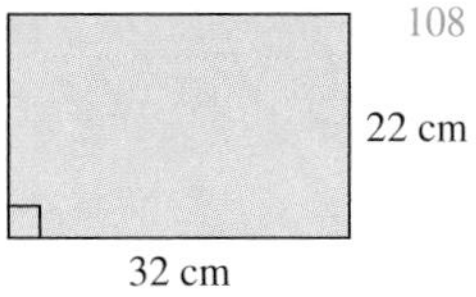

5. 17.2 mi

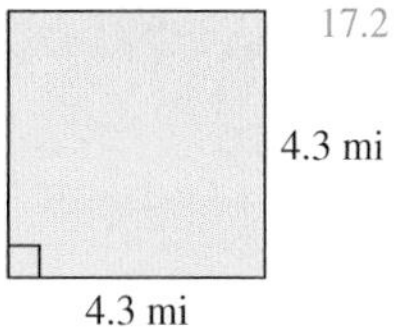

6. 1 ft

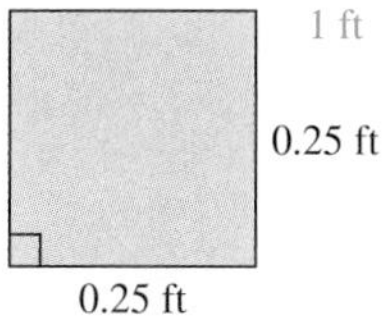

7.

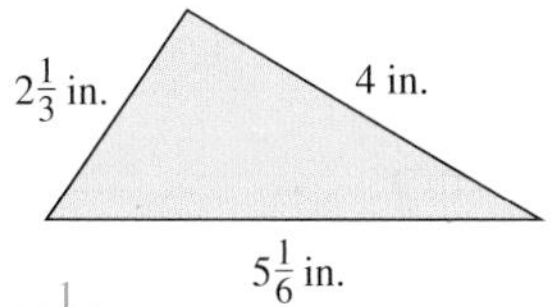

$11\frac{1}{2}$ in.

8.

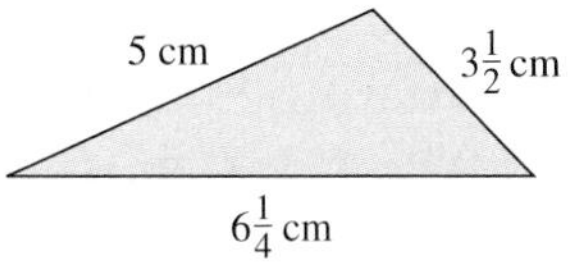

$14\frac{3}{4}$ cm

9.

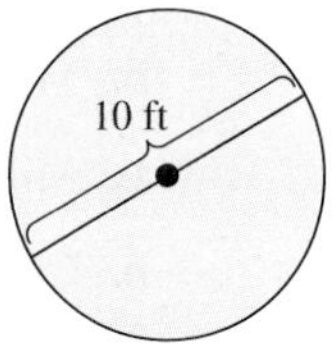

31.4 ft

10.

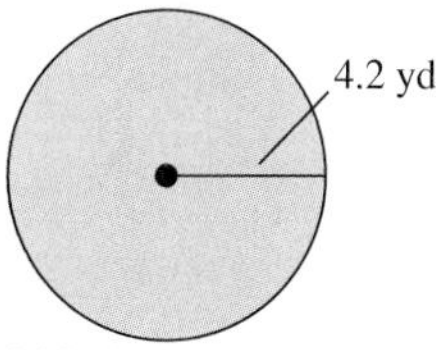

26.376 yd

Concept 2: Area

11. Identify which of the following units could be measures of area. a, f, g

a. Square inches ($in.^2$)	**b.** Meters (m)	**c.** Cubic feet (ft^3)
d. Cubic meters (m^3)	**e.** Miles (mi)	**f.** Square centimeters (cm^2)
g. Square yards (yd^2)	**h.** Cubic inches ($in.^3$)	**i.** Kilometers (km)

12. Would you measure area or perimeter to determine the amount of carpeting needed for a room? Area

For Exercises 13–26, find the area. Use 3.14 for π. **(See Examples 2–4.)**

13. 33 cm^2

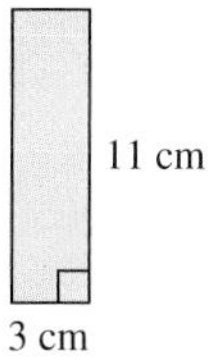

14. 40 ft^2

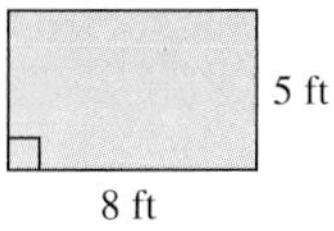

15. 16.81 m^2

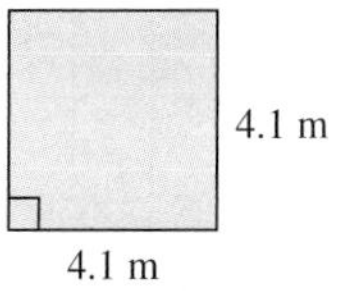

16. 37.21 $in.^2$

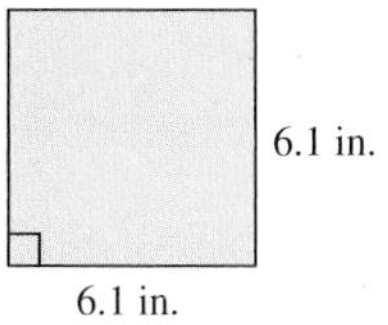

17. 84 $in.^2$

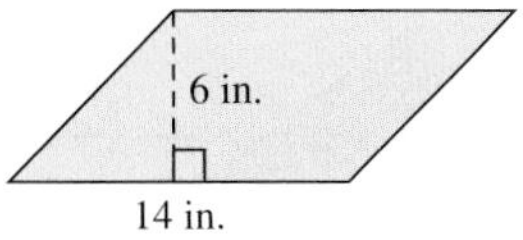

18. 0.0004 m^2

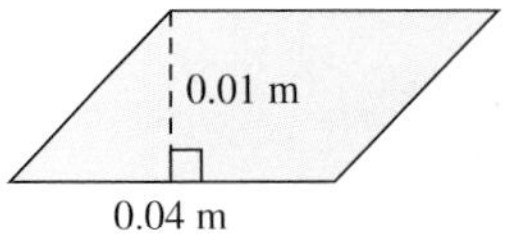

19. 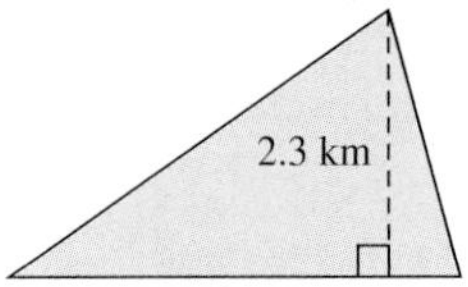

10.12 km^2

20. 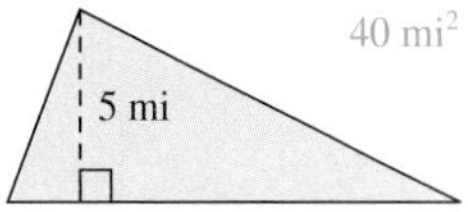

40 mi^2

21. 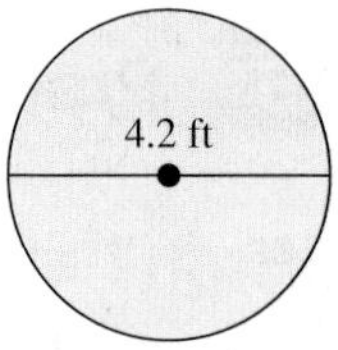

13.8474 ft^2

22. 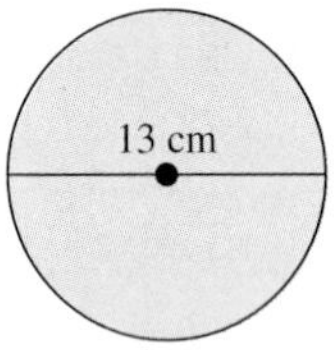

132.665 cm^2

23. 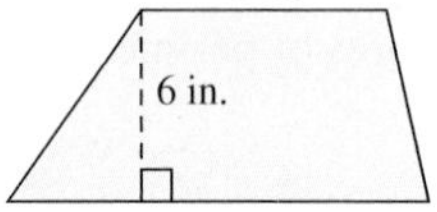

66 in.^{2}

24. 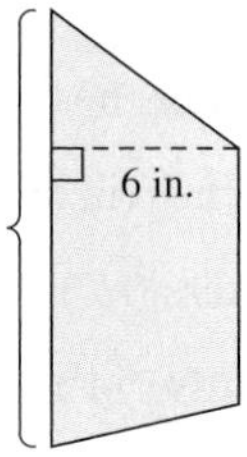

66 in.^{2}

25. 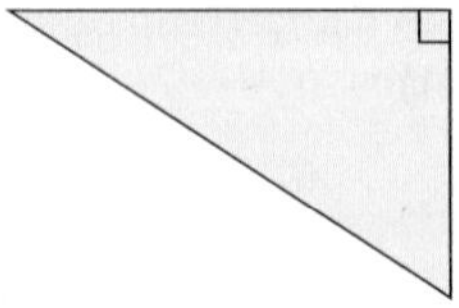

31.5 ft^2

26. 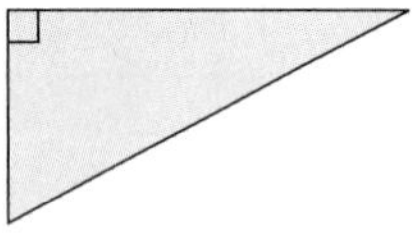

6 km^2

Concept 3: Volume

27. Identify which of the following units could be measures of volume. c, d, h

a. Square inches (in.^{2}) **b.** Meters (m) **c.** Cubic feet (ft^3)

d. Cubic meters (m^3) **e.** Miles (mi) **f.** Square centimeters (cm^2)

g. Square yards (yd^2) **h.** Cubic inches (in.^{3}) **i.** Kilometers (km)

28. Would you measure perimeter, area, or volume to determine the amount of water needed to fill a swimming pool? Volume

For Exercises 29–36, find the volume of each figure. Use 3.14 for π. **(See Examples 5–7.)**

29. 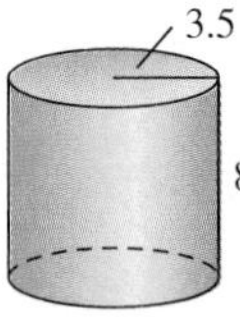

307.72 cm^3

30. 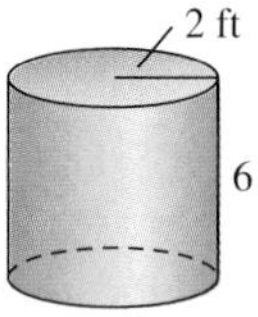

75.36 ft^3

31. 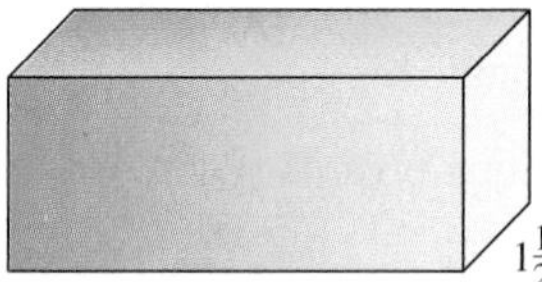

39 in.^{3}

32. 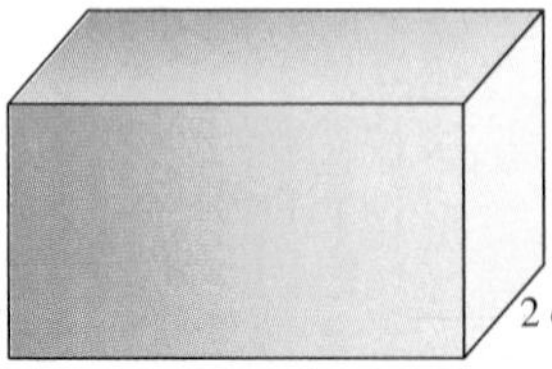

$24\frac{7}{16}$ cm^3

33. 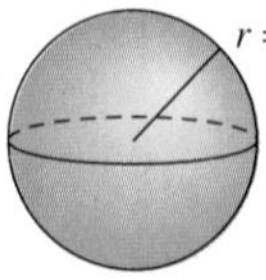

113.04 cm^3

34. 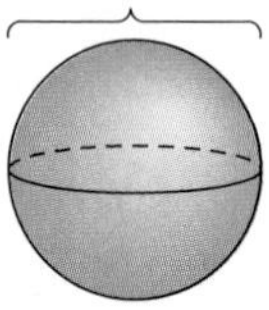

904.32 ft^3

35. 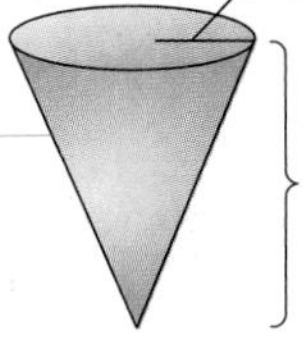

1695.6 cm^3

36. 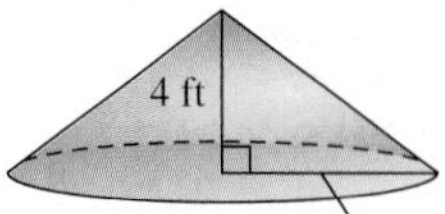

150.72 ft^3

37. A florist sells balloons and needs to know how much helium to order. Each balloon is approximately spherical with a radius of 9 in. How much helium is needed to fill one balloon? Use 3.14 for π. 3052.08 in.^{3}

38. Find the volume of a spherical ball whose radius is 2 in. Use 3.14 for π. Round to the nearest whole unit. 33 in.^{3}

39. Find the volume of a snow cone in the shape of a right circular cone whose radius is 3 cm and whose height is 12 cm. Use 3.14 for π. 113.04 cm^3

40. A landscaping supply company has a pile of gravel in the shape of a right circular cone whose radius is 10 yd and whose height is 18 yd. Find the volume of the gravel. Use 3.14 for π. 1884 yd^3

Mixed Exercises: Perimeter, Area, and Volume

41. A wall measuring 20 ft by 8 ft can be painted for $40.

a. What is the price per square foot? $0.25/ft^2

b. At this rate, how much would it cost to paint the remaining three walls that measure 20 ft by 8 ft, 16 ft by 8 ft, and 16 ft by 8 ft? $104

42. Suppose it costs $336 to carpet a 16 ft by 12 ft room.

a. What is the price per square foot? $1.75/ft^2

b. At this rate, how much would it cost to carpet a room that is 20 ft by 32 ft? $1120

43. If you were to purchase wood to frame a photograph, would you measure the perimeter or area of the photograph? Perimeter

44. If you were to purchase sod (grass) for your front yard, would you measure the perimeter or area of the yard? Area

45. How much fencing is needed to enclose a triangularly shaped garden whose sides measure 12 ft, 22 ft, and 20 ft? 54 ft

46. A regulation soccer field is 100 yd long by 60 yd wide. Find the perimeter of the field. 320 yd

47. a. An American football field is 360 ft long by 160 ft wide. What is the area of the field? 57,600 ft^2

b. How many pieces of sod, each 1 ft wide and 3 ft long, are needed to sod an entire field? (*Hint:* First find the area of a piece of sod.) 19,200 pieces

48. The Transamerica Pyramid in San Francisco is a tower with triangular sides (excluding the "wings"). Each side measures 145 ft wide with a height of 853 ft. What is the area of each side? 61,842.5 ft^2

© R. Morley/PhotoLink/Getty Images RF

49. a. Find the area of a circular pizza that is 8 in. in diameter (the radius is 4 in.). Use 3.14 for π. 50.24 in.^{2}

b. Find the area of a circular pizza that is 12 in. in diameter (the radius is 6 in.). 113.04 in.^{2}

c. Assume that the 8-in. diameter and 12-in. diameter pizzas are both the same thickness. Which would provide more pizza, two 8-in. pizzas or one 12-in. pizza? One 12-in. pizza

50. a. Find the area of a rectangular pizza that is 12 in. by 8 in. 96 in.^{2}

b. Find the area of a circular pizza that has a 16-in. diameter. Use 3.14 for π. 200.96 in.^{2}

c. Assume that the two pizzas have the same thickness. Which would provide more pizza? Two rectangular pizzas or one circular pizza? One circular pizza

51. Find the volume of a soup can in the shape of a right circular cylinder if its radius is 3.2 cm and its height is 9 cm. Use 3.14 for π. 289.3824 cm^3

52. Find the volume of a coffee mug whose radius is 2.5 in. and whose height is 6 in. Use 3.14 for π. 117.75 in.^{3}

Concept 4: Angles

For Exercises 53–58, answer true or false. If an answer is false, explain why.

53. The sum of the measures of two right angles equals the measure of a straight angle. True

54. Two right angles are complementary. False; they are supplementary.

55. Two right angles are supplementary. True

56. Two acute angles cannot be supplementary. True

57. Two obtuse angles cannot be supplementary. True

58. An obtuse angle and an acute angle can be supplementary. True

59. If possible, find two acute angles that are supplementary. Not possible

60. If possible, find two acute angles that are complementary. Answers may vary. For example: 30°, 60°

61. If possible, find an obtuse angle and an acute angle that are supplementary. Answers may vary. For example: 100°, 80°

62. If possible, find two obtuse angles that are supplementary. Not possible

63. What angle is its own complement? 45°

64. What angle is its own supplement? 90°

65. Refer to the figure.

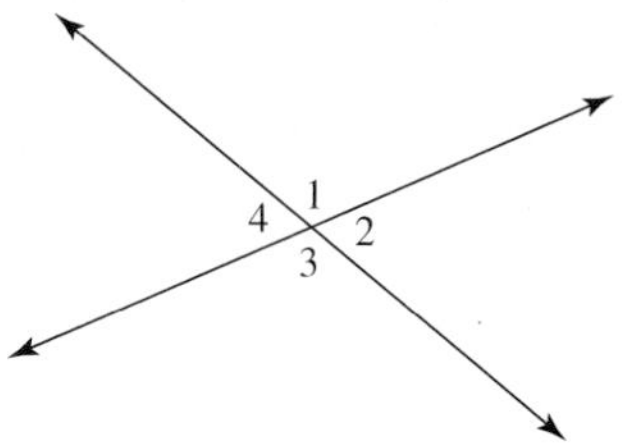

a. State all the pairs of vertical angles. ∠1 and ∠3, ∠2 and ∠4

b. State all the pairs of supplementary angles. ∠1 and ∠2, ∠2 and ∠3, ∠3 and ∠4, ∠1 and ∠4

c. If the measure of ∠4 is 80°, find the measures of ∠1, ∠2, and ∠3. $m(\angle 1) = 100°$, $m(\angle 2) = 80°$, $m(\angle 3) = 100°$

66. Refer to the figure.

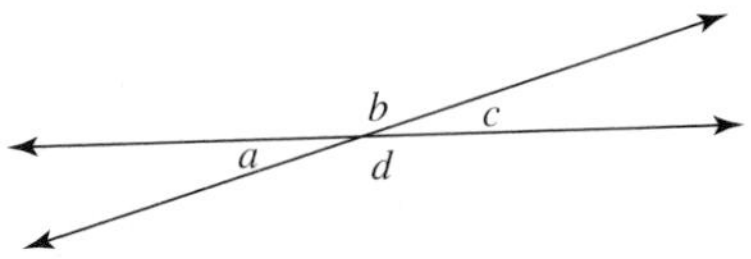

a. State all the pairs of vertical angles. ∠*b* and ∠*d*, ∠*a* and ∠*c*

b. State all the pairs of supplementary angles. ∠*a* and ∠*b*, ∠*b* and ∠*c*, ∠*c* and ∠*d*, ∠*a* and ∠*d*

c. If the measure of ∠*a* is 25°, find the measures of ∠*b*, ∠*c*, and ∠*d*. $m(\angle b) = 155°$, $m(\angle c) = 25°$, $m(\angle d) = 155°$

For Exercises 67–70, the measure of an angle is given. Find the measure of its complement.

67. 33° 57° **68.** 87° 3° **69.** 12° 78° **70.** 45° 45°

For Exercises 71–74, the measure of an angle is given. Find the measure of its supplement.

71. 33° 147° **72.** 87° 93° **73.** 122° 58° **74.** 90° 90°

For Exercises 75–82, refer to the figure. Assume that L_1 and L_2 are parallel lines. **(See Example 8.)**

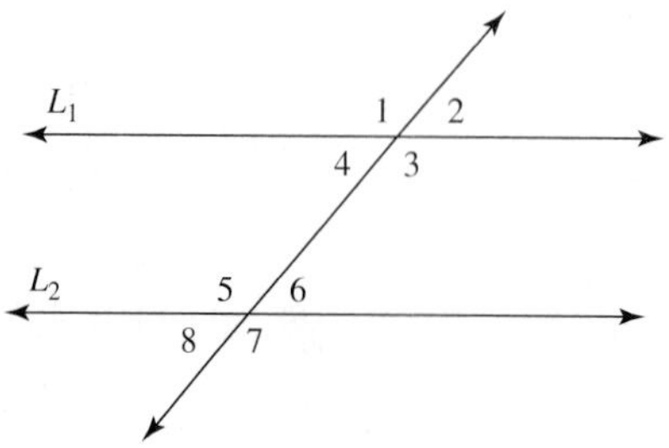

75. $m(\angle 5) = m(\angle \underline{\quad 7 \quad})$ Reason: Vertical angles have equal measures.

76. $m(\angle 5) = m(\angle \underline{\quad 3 \quad})$ Reason: Alternate interior angles have equal measures.

77. $m(\angle 5) = m(\angle \underline{\quad 1 \quad})$ Reason: Corresponding angles have equal measures.

78. $m(\angle 7) = m(\angle \underline{\quad 3 \quad})$ Reason: Corresponding angles have equal measures.

79. $m(\angle 7) = m(\angle \underline{\quad 1 \quad})$ Reason: Alternate exterior angles have equal measures.

80. $m(\angle 7) = m(\angle \underline{\quad 5 \quad})$ Reason: Vertical angles have equal measures.

81. $m(\angle 3) = m(\angle \underline{\quad 5 \quad})$ Reason: Alternate interior angles have equal measures.

82. $m(\angle 3) = m(\angle \underline{\quad 1 \quad})$ Reason: Vertical angles have equal measures.

83. Find the measures of angles a–g in the figure. Assume that L_1 and L_2 are parallel.
$m(\angle a) = 45°$, $m(\angle b) = 135°$, $m(\angle c) = 45°$, $m(\angle d) = 135°$, $m(\angle e) = 45°$, $m(\angle f) = 135°$, $m(\angle g) = 45°$

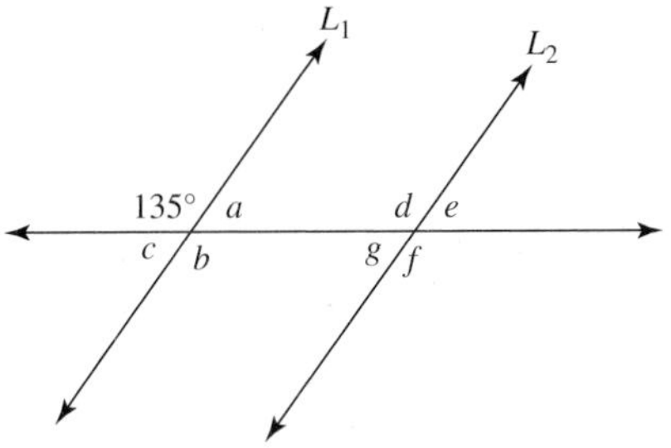

84. Find the measures of angles a–g in the figure. Assume that L_1 and L_2 are parallel.
$m(\angle a) = 65°$, $m(\angle b) = 115°$, $m(\angle c) = 115°$, $m(\angle d) = 65°$, $m(\angle e) = 115°$, $m(\angle f) = 115°$, $m(\angle g) = 65°$

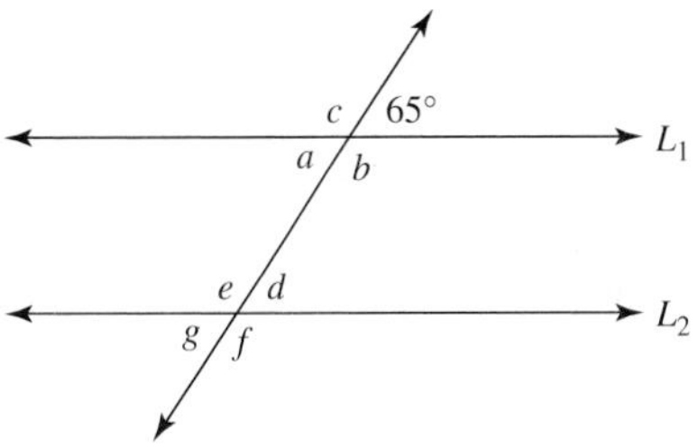

Concept 5: Triangles

For Exercises 85–88, identify the triangle as equilateral, isosceles, or scalene.

85.

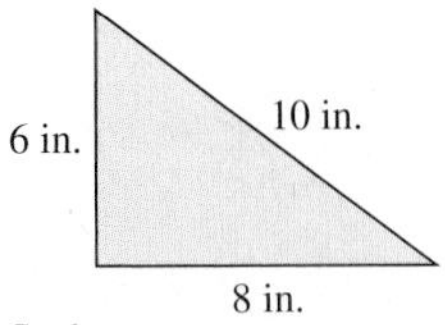

Scalene

86.

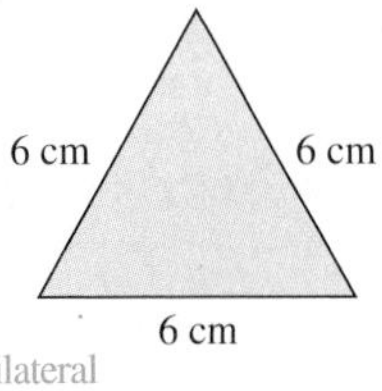

Equilateral

87.

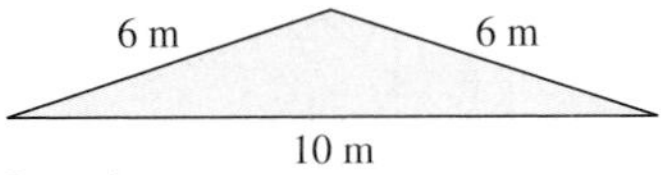

Isosceles

88.

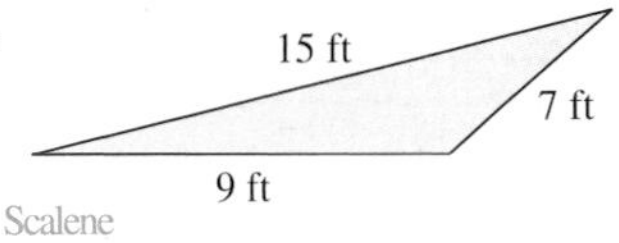

Scalene

89. True or False? If a triangle is equilateral, then it is not scalene. True

90. True or False? If a triangle is isosceles, then it is also scalene. False; an isosceles triangle has two sides that are the same length. A scalene triangle has three sides of different length.

91. Can a triangle be both a right triangle and an obtuse triangle? Explain. No, a 90° angle plus an angle greater than 90° would make the sum of the angles greater than 180°.

92. Can a triangle be both a right triangle and an isosceles triangle? Explain.
Yes, the sides forming the right angle can be equal.

For Exercises 93–96, find the measure of each missing angle.

93. 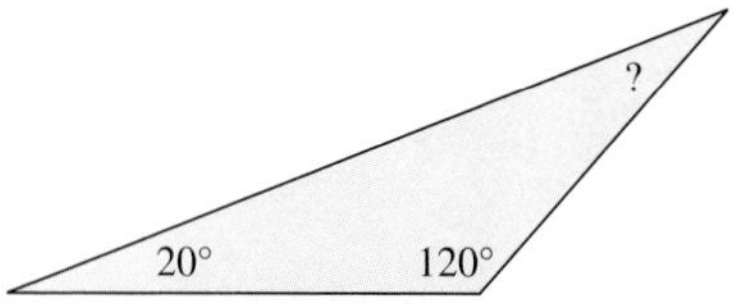

40°

94. 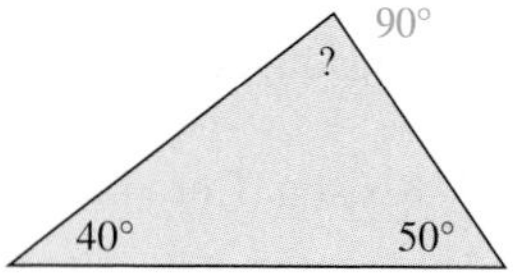

90°

95. 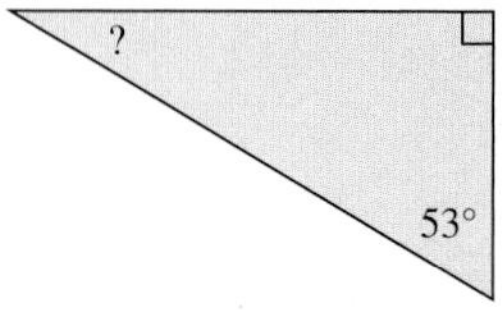

37°

96. 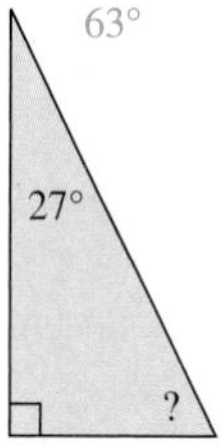

63°

97. Refer to the figure. Find the measures of angles a–j. **(See Example 9.)** $m(\angle a) = 80°$, $m(\angle b) = 80°$, $m(\angle c) = 100°$, $m(\angle d) = 100°$, $m(\angle e) = 65°$, $m(\angle f) = 115°$, $m(\angle g) = 115°$, $m(\angle h) = 35°$, $m(\angle i) = 145°$, $m(\angle j) = 145°$

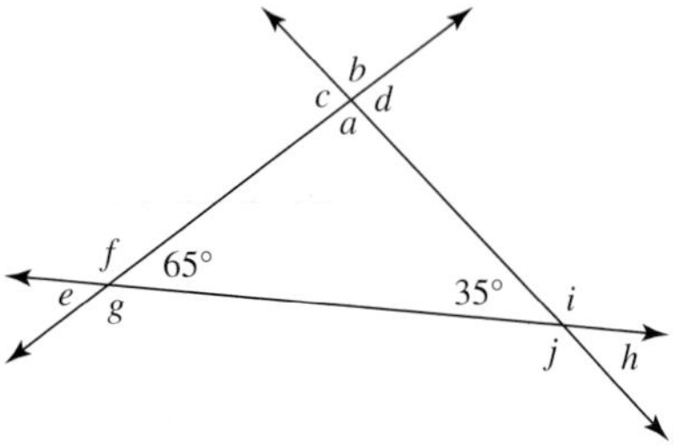

98. Refer to the figure. Find the measures of angles a–j.
$m(\angle a) = 120°$, $m(\angle b) = 60°$, $m(\angle c) = 60°$, $m(\angle d) = 40°$, $m(\angle e) = 40°$, $m(\angle f) = 140°$, $m(\angle g) = 140°$, $m(\angle h) = 160°$, $m(\angle i) = 20°$, $m(\angle j) = 160°$

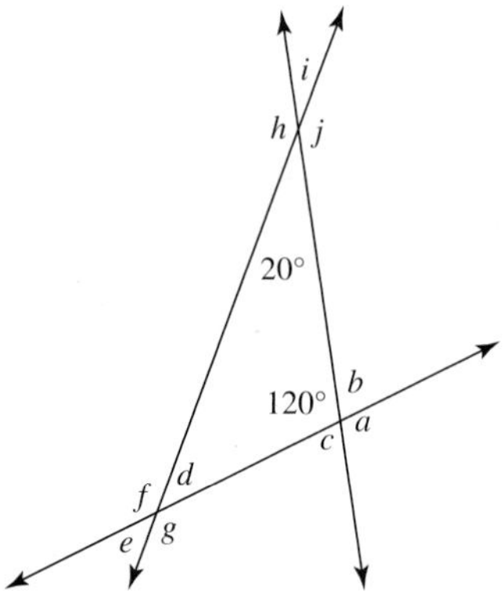

99. Refer to the figure. Find the measures of angles a–k. Assume that L_1 and L_2 are parallel.
$m(\angle a) = 70°$, $m(\angle b) = 65°$, $m(\angle c) = 65°$, $m(\angle d) = 110°$, $m(\angle e) = 70°$, $m(\angle f) = 110°$, $m(\angle g) = 115°$, $m(\angle h) = 115°$, $m(\angle i) = 65°$, $m(\angle j) = 70°$, $m(\angle k) = 65°$

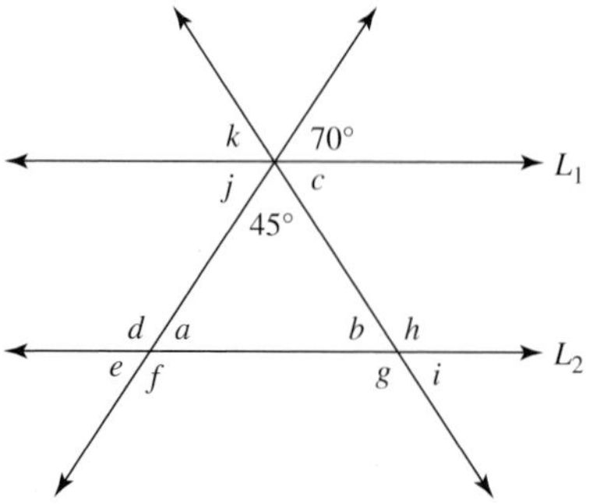

100. Refer to the figure. Find the measures of angles a–k. Assume that L_1 and L_2 are parallel.
$m(\angle a) = 75°$, $m(\angle b) = 65°$, $m(\angle c) = 40°$, $m(\angle d) = 65°$, $m(\angle e) = 65°$, $m(\angle f) = 40°$, $m(\angle g) = 40°$, $m(\angle h) = 140°$, $m(\angle i) = 140°$, $m(\angle j) = 115°$, $m(\angle k) = 115°$

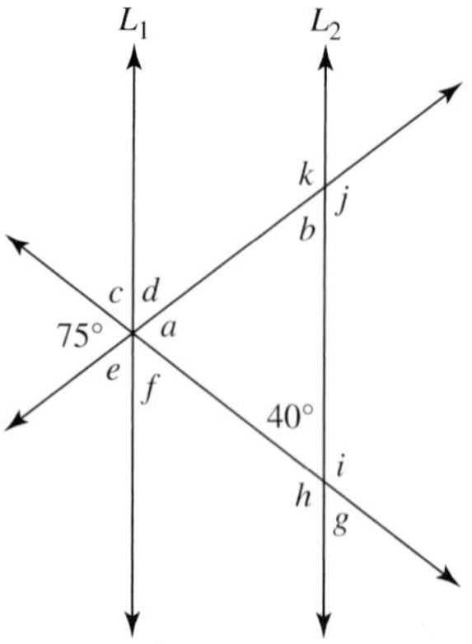

Expanding Your Skills

For Exercises 101–102, find the perimeter.

101.

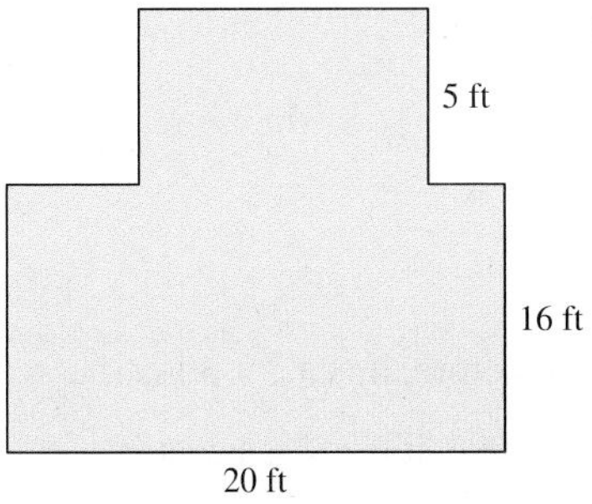

82 ft

102.

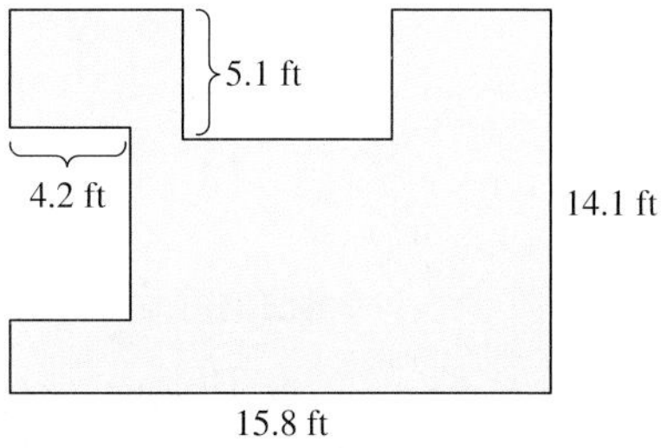

78.4 ft

For Exercises 103–106, find the area of the shaded region. Use 3.14 for π.

103.

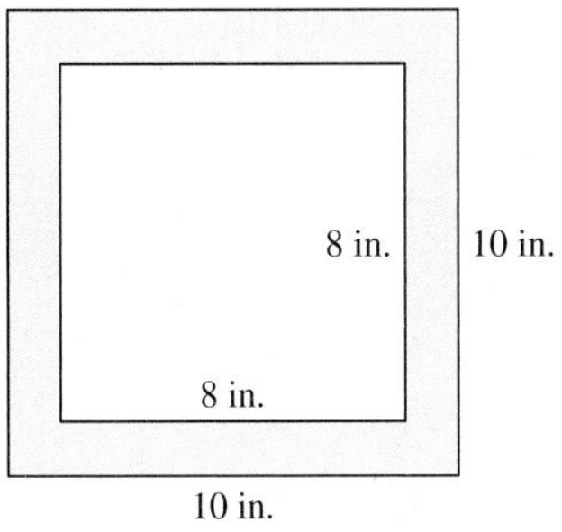

36 in.^{2}

104.

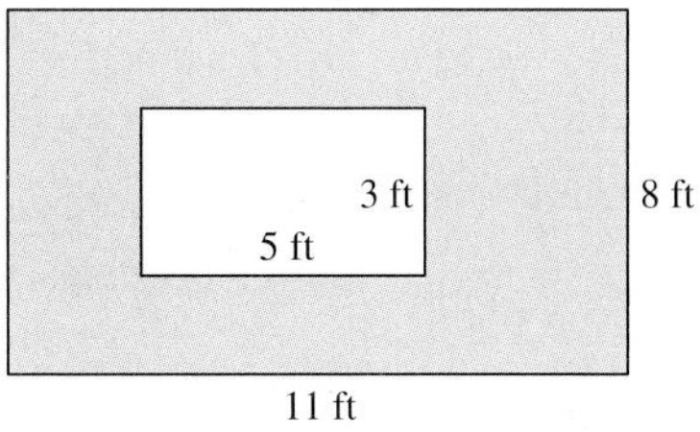

73 ft^2

105.

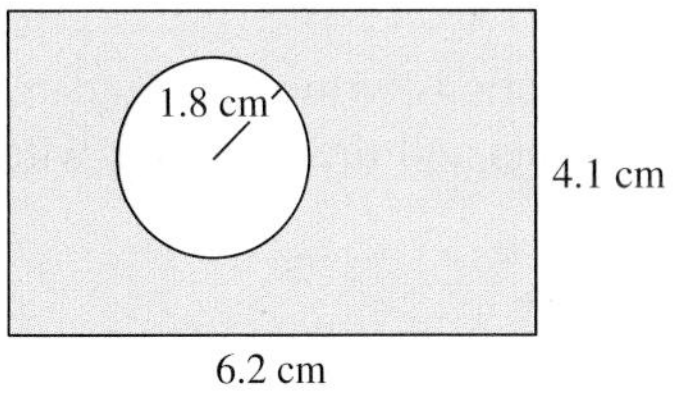

15.2464 cm^2

106.

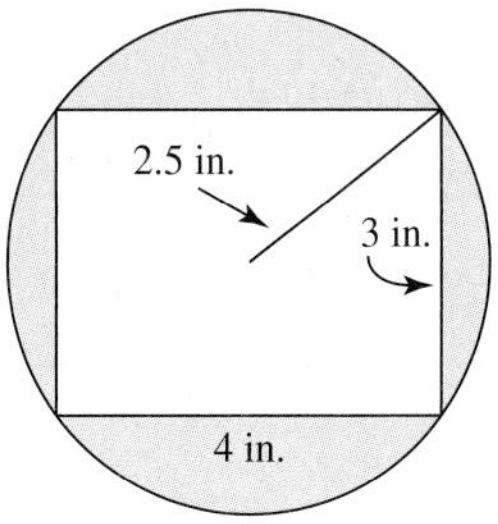

7.625 in.^{2}

Solving Systems of Linear Equations by Using Matrices

Section A.4

Concepts

1. Introduction to Matrices
2. Solving Systems of Linear Equations by Using the Gauss-Jordan Method

1. Introduction to Matrices

We have already learned how to solve systems of linear equations by using the substitution method and the addition method. We now present a third method called the Gauss-Jordan method that uses matrices to solve a linear system.

A **matrix** is a rectangular array of numbers (the plural of *matrix* is *matrices*). The rows of a matrix are read horizontally, and the columns of a matrix are read vertically. Every number or entry within a matrix is called an element of the matrix.

The **order of a matrix** is determined by the number of rows and number of columns. A matrix with m rows and n columns is an $m \times n$ (read as "m by n") matrix. Notice that with the order of a matrix, the number of rows is given first, followed by the number of columns.

Classroom Examples: p. A-38, Exercises 6, 10, and 14

Example 1 Determining the Order of a Matrix

Determine the order of each matrix.

a. $\begin{bmatrix} 2 & -4 & 1 \\ 5 & \pi & \sqrt{7} \end{bmatrix}$ **b.** $\begin{bmatrix} 1.9 \\ 0 \\ 7.2 \\ -6.1 \end{bmatrix}$ **c.** $\begin{bmatrix} 1 & 0 & 0 \\ 0 & 1 & 0 \\ 0 & 0 & 1 \end{bmatrix}$ **d.** $[a \quad b \quad c]$

Solution:

a. This matrix has two rows and three columns. Therefore, it is a 2×3 matrix.

b. This matrix has four rows and one column. Therefore, it is a 4×1 matrix. A matrix with one column is called a **column matrix**.

Instructor Note: "Row" and "column" may not be familiar to some students. They need to understand that rows are horizontal and columns are vertical.

c. This matrix has three rows and three columns. Therefore, it is a 3×3 matrix. A matrix with the same number of rows and columns is called a **square matrix**.

d. This matrix has one row and three columns. Therefore, it is a 1×3 matrix. A matrix with one row is called a **row matrix**.

Skill Practice Determine the order of the matrix.

1. $\begin{bmatrix} -5 & 2 \\ 1 & 3 \\ 8 & 9 \end{bmatrix}$ **2.** $[4 \quad -8]$ **3.** $\begin{bmatrix} 5 \\ 10 \\ 15 \end{bmatrix}$ **4.** $\begin{bmatrix} 2 & -0.5 \\ -1 & 6 \end{bmatrix}$

A matrix can be used to represent a system of linear equations written in standard form. To do so, we extract the coefficients of the variable terms and the constants within the equation. For example, consider the system

$$\begin{aligned} 2x - y &= 5 \\ x + 2y &= -5 \end{aligned}$$

The matrix **A** is called the **coefficient matrix**.

$$\mathbf{A} = \begin{bmatrix} 2 & -1 \\ 1 & 2 \end{bmatrix}$$

If we extract both the coefficients and the constants from the equations, we can construct the **augmented matrix** of the system:

$$\left[\begin{array}{cc|c} 2 & -1 & 5 \\ 1 & 2 & -5 \end{array}\right]$$

A vertical bar is inserted into an augmented matrix to designate the position of the equal signs.

Classroom Example: p. A-38, Exercise 18

Example 2 Writing an Augmented Matrix for a System of Linear Equations

Write the augmented matrix for each linear system.

a. $\begin{aligned} -3x - 4y &= 3 \\ 2x + 4y &= 2 \end{aligned}$ **b.** $\begin{aligned} 2x \qquad - 3z &= 14 \\ 2y + z &= 2 \\ x + y \qquad &= 4 \end{aligned}$

Answers

1. 3×2 2. 1×2
3. 3×1 4. 2×2

Solution:

a. $\left[\begin{array}{cc|c} -3 & -4 & 3 \\ 2 & 4 & 2 \end{array}\right]$ **b.** $\left[\begin{array}{ccc|c} 2 & 0 & -3 & 14 \\ 0 & 2 & 1 & 2 \\ 1 & 1 & 0 & 4 \end{array}\right]$

TIP: Notice that zeros are inserted to denote the coefficient of each missing term.

Instructor Note: Discuss the difference between a "0" coefficient and a "1" as a coefficient.

Skill Practice Write the augmented matrix for each system.

5. $-x + y = 4$
$2x - y = 1$

6. $2x - y + z = 14$
$-3x + 4y = 8$
$x - y + 5z = 0$

Example 3 **Writing a Linear System from an Augmented Matrix**

Classroom Examples: p. A-39, Exercises 20 and 22

Write a system of linear equations represented by each augmented matrix. Use x, y, and z as the variables.

a. $\left[\begin{array}{cc|c} 2 & -5 & -8 \\ 4 & 1 & 6 \end{array}\right]$ **b.** $\left[\begin{array}{ccc|c} 2 & -1 & 3 & 14 \\ 1 & 1 & -2 & -5 \\ 3 & 1 & -1 & 2 \end{array}\right]$ **c.** $\left[\begin{array}{ccc|c} 1 & 0 & 0 & 4 \\ 0 & 1 & 0 & -1 \\ 0 & 0 & 1 & 0 \end{array}\right]$

Solution:

a. $2x - 5y = -8$
$4x + y = 6$

b. $2x - y + 3z = 14$
$x + y - 2z = -5$
$3x + y - z = 2$

c. $x + 0y + 0z = 4$
$0x + y + 0z = -1$
$0x + 0y + z = 0$

or

$x = 4$
$y = -1$
$z = 0$

Skill Practice Write a system of linear equations represented by each augmented matrix. Use x, y, and z as the variables.

7. $\left[\begin{array}{cc|c} 2 & 3 & 5 \\ -1 & 8 & 1 \end{array}\right]$ **8.** $\left[\begin{array}{ccc|c} -3 & 2 & 1 & 4 \\ 14 & 1 & 0 & 20 \\ -8 & 3 & 5 & 6 \end{array}\right]$ **9.** $\left[\begin{array}{ccc|c} 1 & 0 & 0 & -8 \\ 0 & 1 & 0 & 2 \\ 0 & 0 & 1 & 15 \end{array}\right]$

2. Solving Systems of Linear Equations by Using the Gauss-Jordan Method

We know that interchanging two equations results in an equivalent system of linear equations. Interchanging two rows in an augmented matrix results in an equivalent augmented matrix. Similarly, because each row in an augmented matrix represents a linear equation, we can perform the following elementary row operations that result in an equivalent augmented matrix.

Elementary Row Operations

The following *elementary row operations* performed on an augmented matrix produce an equivalent augmented matrix:

- Interchange two rows.
- Multiply every element in a row by a nonzero real number.
- Add a multiple of one row to another row.

Answers

5. $\left[\begin{array}{cc|c} -1 & 1 & 4 \\ 2 & -1 & 1 \end{array}\right]$

6. $\left[\begin{array}{ccc|c} 2 & -1 & 1 & 14 \\ -3 & 4 & 0 & 8 \\ 1 & -1 & 5 & 0 \end{array}\right]$

7. $2x + 3y = 5$
$-x + 8y = 1$

8. $-3x + 2y + z = 4$
$14x + y = 20$
$-8x + 3y + 5z = 6$

9. $x = -8, y = 2, z = 15$

When we are solving a system of linear equations by any method, the goal is to write a series of simpler but equivalent systems of equations until the solution is obvious. The *Gauss-Jordan method* uses a series of elementary row operations performed on the augmented matrix to produce a simpler augmented matrix. In particular, we want to produce an augmented matrix that has 1's along the diagonal of the matrix of coefficients and 0's for the remaining entries in the matrix of coefficients. A matrix written in this way is said to be written in **reduced row echelon form**. For example, the augmented matrix from Example 3(c) is written in reduced row echelon form.

$$\left[\begin{array}{ccc|c} 1 & 0 & 0 & 4 \\ 0 & 1 & 0 & -1 \\ 0 & 0 & 1 & 0 \end{array}\right]$$

The solution to the corresponding system of equations is easily recognized as $x = 4$, $y = -1$, and $z = 0$.

Similarly, matrix **B** represents a solution of $x = a$ and $y = b$ to a system of two linear equations.

$$\mathbf{B} = \left[\begin{array}{cc|c} 1 & 0 & a \\ 0 & 1 & b \end{array}\right]$$

Classroom Example: p. A-40, Exercise 42

Example 4 Solving a System by Using the Gauss-Jordan Method

Solve by using the Gauss-Jordan method.

$$2x - y = 5$$
$$x + 2y = -5$$

Solution:

$$\left[\begin{array}{cc|c} 2 & -1 & 5 \\ 1 & 2 & -5 \end{array}\right]$$ Set up the augmented matrix.

$\xrightarrow{R_1 \Leftrightarrow R_2}$ $\left[\begin{array}{cc|c} 1 & 2 & -5 \\ 2 & -1 & 5 \end{array}\right]$ Switch row 1 and row 2 to get a 1 in the upper left position.

$\xrightarrow{-2R_1 + R_2 \Rightarrow R_2}$ $\left[\begin{array}{cc|c} 1 & 2 & -5 \\ 0 & -5 & 15 \end{array}\right]$ Multiply row 1 by -2 and add the result to row 2. This produces an entry of 0 below the upper left position.

$\xrightarrow{-\frac{1}{5}R_2 \Rightarrow R_2}$ $\left[\begin{array}{cc|c} 1 & 2 & -5 \\ 0 & 1 & -3 \end{array}\right]$ Multiply row 2 by $-\frac{1}{5}$ to produce a 1 along the diagonal in the second row.

$\xrightarrow{-2R_2 + R_1 \Rightarrow R_1}$ $\left[\begin{array}{cc|c} 1 & 0 & 1 \\ 0 & 1 & -3 \end{array}\right]$ Multiply row 2 by -2 and add the result to row 1. This produces a 0 in the first row, second column.

$$\mathbf{C} = \left[\begin{array}{cc|c} 1 & 0 & 1 \\ 0 & 1 & -3 \end{array}\right]$$

The matrix **C** is in reduced row echelon form. From the augmented matrix, we have $x = 1$ and $y = -3$. The solution set is $\{(1, -3)\}$.

Skill Practice

10. Solve by using the Gauss-Jordan method.

$$\begin{aligned} x - 2y &= -21 \\ 2x + y &= -2 \end{aligned}$$

The order in which we manipulate the elements of an augmented matrix to produce reduced row echelon form was demonstrated in Example 4. In general, the order is as follows.

- First produce a 1 in the first row, first column. Then use the first row to obtain 0's in the first column below this element.
- Next, if possible, produce a 1 in the second row, second column. Use the second row to obtain 0's above and below this element.
- Next, if possible, produce a 1 in the third row, third column. Use the third row to obtain 0's above and below this element.
- The process continues until reduced row echelon form is obtained.

Example 5 **Solving a System by Using the Gauss-Jordan Method**

Classroom Example: p. A-40, Exercise 56

Solve by using the Gauss-Jordan method.

$$\begin{aligned} x &= -y + 5 \\ -2x + 2z &= y - 10 \\ 3x + 6y + 7z &= 14 \end{aligned}$$

Solution:

First write each equation in the system in standard form.

$$\begin{aligned} x &= -y + 5 &\longrightarrow\quad x + y &= 5 \\ -2x + 2z &= y - 10 &\longrightarrow\quad -2x - y + 2z &= -10 \\ 3x + 6y + 7z &= 14 &\longrightarrow\quad 3x + 6y + 7z &= 14 \end{aligned}$$

$$\left[\begin{array}{rrr|r} 1 & 1 & 0 & 5 \\ -2 & -1 & 2 & -10 \\ 3 & 6 & 7 & 14 \end{array}\right]$$ Set up the augmented matrix.

$$\begin{array}{l} 2R_1 + R_2 \Rightarrow R_2 \longrightarrow \\ -3R_1 + R_3 \Rightarrow R_3 \longrightarrow \end{array} \left[\begin{array}{rrr|r} 1 & 1 & 0 & 5 \\ 0 & 1 & 2 & 0 \\ 0 & 3 & 7 & -1 \end{array}\right]$$ Multiply row 1 by 2 and add the result to row 2. Multiply row 1 by −3 and add the result to row 3.

$$\begin{array}{l} -1R_2 + R_1 \Rightarrow R_1 \longrightarrow \\ -3R_2 + R_3 \Rightarrow R_3 \longrightarrow \end{array} \left[\begin{array}{rrr|r} 1 & 0 & -2 & 5 \\ 0 & 1 & 2 & 0 \\ 0 & 0 & 1 & -1 \end{array}\right]$$ Multiply row 2 by −1 and add the result to row 1. Multiply row 2 by −3 and add the result to row 3.

Answer

10. $\{(-5, 8)\}$

$$\begin{array}{l} 2R_3 + R_1 \Rightarrow R_1 \longrightarrow \\ -2R_3 + R_2 \Rightarrow R_2 \longrightarrow \end{array} \left[\begin{array}{ccc|c} 1 & 0 & 0 & 3 \\ 0 & 1 & 0 & 2 \\ 0 & 0 & 1 & -1 \end{array}\right]$$

Multiply row 3 by 2 and add the result to row 1.
Multiply row 3 by −2 and add the result to row 2.

From the reduced row echelon form of the matrix, we have $x = 3$, $y = 2$, and $z = -1$. The solution set is $\{(3, 2, -1)\}$.

Skill Practice Solve by using the Gauss-Jordan method.

11. $x + y + z = 2$

$x - y + z = 4$

$x + 4y + 2z = 1$

It is particularly easy to recognize a system of dependent equations or an inconsistent system of equations from the reduced row echelon form of an augmented matrix. This is demonstrated in Examples 6 and 7.

Classroom Example: p. A-40, Exercise 46

Example 6 Solving a System of Dependent Equations by Using the Gauss-Jordan Method

Solve by using the Gauss-Jordan method.

$$x - 3y = 4$$

$$\frac{1}{2}x - \frac{3}{2}y = 2$$

Solution:

$$\left[\begin{array}{cc|c} 1 & -3 & 4 \\ \frac{1}{2} & -\frac{3}{2} & 2 \end{array}\right]$$

Set up the augmented matrix.

$$-\tfrac{1}{2}R_1 + R_2 \Rightarrow R_2 \longrightarrow \left[\begin{array}{cc|c} 1 & -3 & 4 \\ 0 & 0 & 0 \end{array}\right]$$

Multiply row 1 by $-\frac{1}{2}$ and add the result to row 2.

The second row of the augmented matrix represents the equation $0 = 0$. The equations are dependent. The solution set is $\{(x, y) \mid x - 3y = 4\}$.

Skill Practice Solve by using the Gauss-Jordan method.

12. $4x - 6y = 16$

$6x - 9y = 24$

Answers

11. $\{(1, -1, 2)\}$

12. Infinitely many solutions; $\{(x, y) \mid 4x - 6y = 16\}$; dependent equations

Example 7

Solving an Inconsistent System by Using the Gauss-Jordan Method

Classroom Example: p. A-40, Exercise 52

Solve by using the Gauss-Jordan method.

$$x + 3y = 2$$
$$-3x - 9y = 1$$

Solution:

$$\left[\begin{array}{cc|c} 1 & 3 & 2 \\ -3 & -9 & 1 \end{array}\right]$$ Set up the augmented matrix.

$$\xrightarrow{3R_1 + R_2 \Rightarrow R_2} \left[\begin{array}{cc|c} 1 & 3 & 2 \\ 0 & 0 & 7 \end{array}\right]$$ Multiply row 1 by 3 and add the result to row 2.

The second row of the augmented matrix represents the contradiction $0 = 7$. The system is inconsistent. There is no solution, { }.

Skill Practice Solve by using the Gauss-Jordan method.

13. $6x + 10y = 1$

$15x + 25y = 3$

Calculator Connections

Topic: Entering a Matrix into a Calculator

Many graphing calculators have a matrix editor in which the user defines the order of the matrix and then enters the elements of the matrix. For example, consider the system of equations and the related 2×3 augmented matrix.

$$2x - 3y = -13 \qquad \mathbf{A} = \left[\begin{array}{cc|c} 2 & -3 & -13 \\ 3 & 1 & 8 \end{array}\right]$$
$$3x + y = 8$$

Matrix **A** is entered as shown.

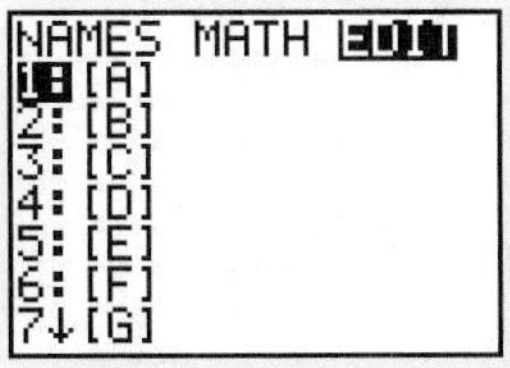

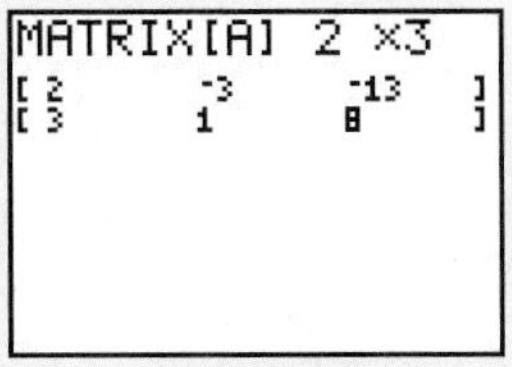

Once an augmented matrix has been entered into a graphing calculator, a *rref* function can be used to transform the matrix into reduced row echelon form.

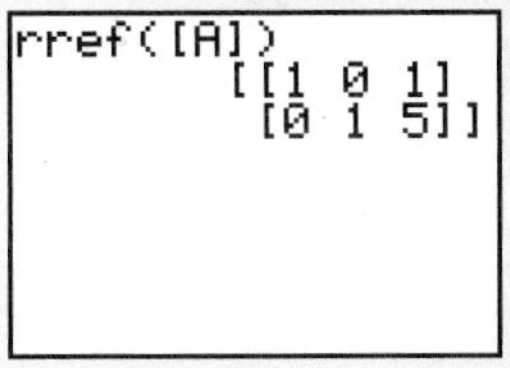

The solution set to the system is {(1, 5)}.

Answer

13. No solution; { }; inconsistent system

Section A.4 Practice Exercises

For additional exercises, see Classroom Activities A.4A–A.4D in the *Student's Resource Manual* at www.mhhe.com/moh.

Vocabulary and Key Concepts

1. a. A __matrix__ is a rectangular array of numbers. The order of a matrix is $m \times n$ where m is the number of __rows__ and n is the number of __columns__.

b. A matrix that has exactly one column is called a __column__ matrix. A matrix that has exactly __one__ row is called a row matrix, and a matrix with the same number of rows and columns is called a __square__ matrix.

c. Given the system of equations shown, matrix **A** is called the __coefficient__ matrix. The matrix **B** is called the __augmented__ matrix.

$$\begin{aligned} 3x - 2y &= 6 \\ 4x + 5y &= 9 \end{aligned} \qquad \mathbf{A} = \begin{bmatrix} 3 & -2 \\ 4 & 5 \end{bmatrix} \qquad \mathbf{B} = \left[\begin{array}{cc|c} 3 & -2 & 6 \\ 4 & 5 & 9 \end{array}\right]$$

d. The matrix **A** is said to be written in reduced __row echelon__ form.

$$\mathbf{A} = \left[\begin{array}{cc|c} 1 & 0 & 8 \\ 0 & 1 & 2 \end{array}\right]$$

Review Exercises

2. How much 50% acid solution should be mixed with pure acid to obtain 20 L of a mixture that is 70% acid?
Mix 12 L of the 50% mixture with 8 L of pure acid.

For Exercises 3–5, solve the system by using any method.

3. $\begin{aligned} x - 6y &= 9 \\ x + 2y &= 13 \end{aligned}$ $\left\{\left(12, \frac{1}{2}\right)\right\}$

4. $\begin{aligned} x + y - z &= 8 \\ x - 2y + z &= 3 \\ x + 3y + 2z &= 7 \end{aligned}$ $\{(6, 1, -1)\}$

5. $\begin{aligned} 2x - y + z &= -4 \\ -x + y + 3z &= -7 \\ x + 3y - 4z &= 22 \end{aligned}$ $\{(1, 3, -3)\}$

Concept 1: Introduction to Matrices

For Exercises 6–14, (**a**) determine the order of each matrix and (**b**) determine if the matrix is a row matrix, a column matrix, a square matrix, or none of these. **(See Example 1.)**

6. $\begin{bmatrix} 4 \\ 5 \\ -3 \\ 0 \end{bmatrix}$ a. 4×1 b. column matrix

7. $\begin{bmatrix} 5 \\ -1 \\ 2 \end{bmatrix}$ a. 3×1 b. column matrix

8. $\begin{bmatrix} -9 & 4 & 3 \\ -1 & -8 & 4 \\ 5 & 8 & 7 \end{bmatrix}$ a. 3×3 b. square matrix

9. $\begin{bmatrix} 3 & -9 \\ -1 & -3 \end{bmatrix}$ a. 2×2 b. square matrix

10. $\begin{bmatrix} 4 & -7 \end{bmatrix}$ a. 1×2 b. row matrix

11. $\begin{bmatrix} 0 & -8 & 11 & 5 \end{bmatrix}$ a. 1×4 b. row matrix

12. $\begin{bmatrix} 5 & -8.1 & 4.2 & 0 \\ 4.3 & -9 & 18 & 3 \end{bmatrix}$ a. 2×4 b. none of these

13. $\begin{bmatrix} \frac{1}{3} & \frac{3}{4} & 6 \\ -2 & 1 & -\frac{7}{8} \end{bmatrix}$ a. 2×3 b. none of these

14. $\begin{bmatrix} 5 & 1 \\ -1 & 2 \\ 0 & 7 \end{bmatrix}$ a. 3×2 b. none of these

For Exercises 15–18, set up the augmented matrix. **(See Example 2.)**

15. $\begin{aligned} x - 2y &= -1 \\ 2x + y &= -7 \end{aligned}$ $\left[\begin{array}{cc|c} 1 & -2 & -1 \\ 2 & 1 & -7 \end{array}\right]$

16. $\begin{aligned} x - 3y &= 3 \\ 2x - 5y &= 4 \end{aligned}$ $\left[\begin{array}{cc|c} 1 & -3 & 3 \\ 2 & -5 & 4 \end{array}\right]$

17. $\begin{aligned} x - 2y &= 5 - z \\ 2x + 6y + 3z &= -2 \\ 3x - y - 2z &= 1 \end{aligned}$ $\left[\begin{array}{ccc|c} 1 & -2 & 1 & 5 \\ 2 & 6 & 3 & -2 \\ 3 & -1 & -2 & 1 \end{array}\right]$

18. $\begin{aligned} 5x - 17 &= -2z \\ 8x + 6z &= 26 + y \\ 8x + 3y - 12z &= 24 \end{aligned}$ $\left[\begin{array}{ccc|c} 5 & 0 & 2 & 17 \\ 8 & -1 & 6 & 26 \\ 8 & 3 & -12 & 24 \end{array}\right]$

Writing · Translating Expression · Geometry · Scientific Calculator · Video

For Exercises 19–22, write a system of linear equations represented by the augmented matrix. Use x, y, and z as the variables. **(See Example 3.)**

19. $\left[\begin{array}{cc|c} 4 & 3 & 6 \\ 12 & 5 & -6 \end{array}\right]$ $4x + 3y = 6$; $12x + 5y = -6$

20. $\left[\begin{array}{cc|c} -2 & 5 & -15 \\ -7 & 15 & -45 \end{array}\right]$ $-2x + 5y = -15$; $-7x + 15y = -45$

21. $\left[\begin{array}{ccc|c} 1 & 0 & 0 & 4 \\ 0 & 1 & 0 & -1 \\ 0 & 0 & 1 & 7 \end{array}\right]$ $x = 4, y = -1, z = 7$

22. $\left[\begin{array}{ccc|c} 1 & 0 & 0 & 0.5 \\ 0 & 1 & 0 & 6.1 \\ 0 & 0 & 1 & 3.9 \end{array}\right]$ $x = 0.5, y = 6.1, z = 3.9$

Concept 2: Solving Systems of Linear Equations by Using the Gauss-Jordan Method

23. Given the matrix **E**

$$\mathbf{E} = \left[\begin{array}{cc|c} 3 & -2 & 8 \\ 9 & -1 & 7 \end{array}\right]$$

a. What is the element in the second row and third column? 7

b. What is the element in the first row and second column? −2

24. Given the matrix **F**

$$\mathbf{F} = \left[\begin{array}{cc|c} 1 & 8 & 0 \\ 12 & -13 & -2 \end{array}\right]$$

a. What is the element in the second row and second column? −13

b. What is the element in the first row and third column? 0

25. Given the matrix **Z**

$$\mathbf{Z} = \left[\begin{array}{cc|c} 2 & 1 & 11 \\ 2 & -1 & 1 \end{array}\right] \quad \left[\begin{array}{cc|c} 1 & \frac{1}{2} & \frac{11}{2} \\ 2 & -1 & 1 \end{array}\right]$$

write the matrix obtained by multiplying the elements in the first row by $\frac{1}{2}$.

26. Given the matrix **J**

$$\mathbf{J} = \left[\begin{array}{cc|c} 1 & 1 & 7 \\ 0 & 3 & -6 \end{array}\right] \quad \left[\begin{array}{cc|c} 1 & 1 & 7 \\ 0 & 1 & -2 \end{array}\right]$$

write the matrix obtained by multiplying the elements in the second row by $\frac{1}{3}$.

27. Given the matrix **K**

$$\mathbf{K} = \left[\begin{array}{cc|c} 5 & 2 & 1 \\ 1 & -4 & 3 \end{array}\right] \quad \left[\begin{array}{cc|c} 1 & -4 & 3 \\ 5 & 2 & 1 \end{array}\right]$$

write the matrix obtained by interchanging rows 1 and 2.

28. Given the matrix **L**

$$\mathbf{L} = \left[\begin{array}{cc|c} 9 & 6 & 13 \\ -7 & 2 & 19 \end{array}\right] \quad \left[\begin{array}{cc|c} -7 & 2 & 19 \\ 9 & 6 & 13 \end{array}\right]$$

write the matrix obtained by interchanging rows 1 and 2.

29. Given the matrix **M**

$$\mathbf{M} = \left[\begin{array}{cc|c} 1 & 5 & 2 \\ -3 & -4 & -1 \end{array}\right] \quad \left[\begin{array}{cc|c} 1 & 5 & 2 \\ 0 & 11 & 5 \end{array}\right]$$

write the matrix obtained by multiplying the first row by 3 and adding the result to row 2.

30. Given the matrix **N**

$$\mathbf{N} = \left[\begin{array}{cc|c} 1 & 3 & -5 \\ -2 & 2 & 12 \end{array}\right] \quad \left[\begin{array}{cc|c} 1 & 3 & -5 \\ 0 & 8 & 2 \end{array}\right]$$

write the matrix obtained by multiplying the first row by 2 and adding the result to row 2.

31. Given the matrix **R**

$$\mathbf{R} = \left[\begin{array}{ccc|c} 1 & 3 & 0 & -1 \\ 4 & 1 & -5 & 6 \\ -2 & 0 & -3 & 10 \end{array}\right] \quad \left[\begin{array}{ccc|c} 1 & 3 & 0 & -1 \\ 0 & -11 & -5 & 10 \\ -2 & 0 & -3 & 10 \end{array}\right]$$

a. Write the matrix obtained by multiplying the first row by −4 and adding the result to row 2.

b. Using the matrix obtained from part (a), write the matrix obtained by multiplying the first row by 2 and adding the result to row 3.

$$\left[\begin{array}{ccc|c} 1 & 3 & 0 & -1 \\ 0 & -11 & -5 & 10 \\ 0 & 6 & -3 & 8 \end{array}\right]$$

32. Given the matrix **S**

$$\mathbf{S} = \left[\begin{array}{ccc|c} 1 & 2 & 0 & 10 \\ 5 & 1 & -4 & 3 \\ -3 & 4 & 5 & 2 \end{array}\right] \quad \left[\begin{array}{ccc|c} 1 & 2 & 0 & 10 \\ 0 & -9 & -4 & -47 \\ -3 & 4 & 5 & 2 \end{array}\right]$$

a. Write the matrix obtained by multiplying the first row by −5 and adding the result to row 2.

b. Using the matrix obtained from part (a), write the matrix obtained by multiplying the first row by 3 and adding the result to row 3.

$$\left[\begin{array}{ccc|c} 1 & 2 & 0 & 10 \\ 0 & -9 & -4 & -47 \\ 0 & 10 & 5 & 32 \end{array}\right]$$

For Exercises 33–36, use the augmented matrices **A**, **B**, **C**, and **D** to answer true or false.

$$\mathbf{A} = \left[\begin{array}{cc|c} 6 & -4 & 2 \\ 5 & -2 & 7 \end{array}\right] \quad \mathbf{B} = \left[\begin{array}{cc|c} 5 & -2 & 7 \\ 6 & -4 & 2 \end{array}\right] \quad \mathbf{C} = \left[\begin{array}{cc|c} 1 & -\frac{2}{3} & \frac{1}{3} \\ 5 & -2 & 7 \end{array}\right] \quad \mathbf{D} = \left[\begin{array}{cc|c} 5 & -2 & 7 \\ -12 & 8 & -4 \end{array}\right]$$

33. The matrix **A** is a 2×3 matrix.
True

34. Matrix **B** is equivalent to matrix **A**.
True

35. Matrix **A** is equivalent to matrix **C**.
True

36. Matrix **B** is equivalent to matrix **D**.
True

37. What does the notation $R_2 \Leftrightarrow R_1$ mean when one is performing the Gauss-Jordan method?
Interchange rows 1 and 2.

38. What does the notation $2R_3 \Rightarrow R_3$ mean when one is performing the Gauss-Jordan method?
Multiply row 3 by 2. Replace row 3 with the result.

39. What does the notation $-3R_1 + R_2 \Rightarrow R_2$ mean when one is performing the Gauss-Jordan method?
Multiply row 1 by −3 and add to row 2. Replace row 2 with the result.

40. What does the notation $4R_2 + R_3 \Rightarrow R_3$ mean when one is performing the Gauss-Jordan method?
Multiply row 2 by 4 and add to row 3. Replace row 3 with the result.

For Exercises 41–56, solve the system by using the Gauss-Jordan method. For systems that do not have one unique solution, also state the number of solutions and whether the system is inconsistent or the equations are dependent. **(See Example 4–7.)**

41. $x - 2y = -1$
$2x + y = -7$
$\{(-3, -1)\}$

42. $x - 3y = 3$
$2x - 5y = 4$
$\{(-3, -2)\}$

43. $x + 3y = 6$
$-4x - 9y = 3$
$\{(-21, 9)\}$

44. $2x - 3y = -2$
$x + 2y = 13$
$\{(5, 4)\}$

45. $x + 3y = 3$
$4x + 12y = 12$
Infinitely many solutions; $\{(x, y) \mid x + 3y = 3\}$; dependent equations

46. $2x + 5y = 1$
$-4x - 10y = -2$
Infinitely many solutions; $\{(x, y) \mid 2x + 5y = 1\}$; dependent equations

47. $x - y = 4$
$2x + y = 5$
$\{(3, -1)\}$

48. $2x - y = 0$
$x + y = 3$
$\{(1, 2)\}$

49. $x + 3y = -1$
$-3x - 6y = 12$
$\{(-10, 3)\}$

50. $x + y = 4$
$2x - 4y = -4$
$\{(2, 2)\}$

51. $3x + y = -4$
$-6x - 2y = 3$
No solution; { }; inconsistent system

52. $2x + y = 4$
$6x + 3y = -1$
No solution; { }; inconsistent system

53. $x + y + z = 6$
$x - y + z = 2$
$x + y - z = 0$
$\{(1, 2, 3)\}$

54. $2x - 3y - 2z = 11$
$x + 3y + 8z = 1$
$3x - y + 14z = -2$
$\{(7, 2, -\frac{3}{2})\}$

55. $x - 2y = 5 - z$
$2x + 6y + 3z = -10$
$3x - y - 2z = 5$
$\{(1, -2, 0)\}$

56. $5x = 10z + 15$
$x - y + 6z = 23$
$x + 3y - 12z = 13$
$\{(13, 20, 5)\}$

Graphing Calculator Exercises

For Exercises 57–62, use the matrix features on a graphing calculator to express each augmented matrix in reduced row echelon form. Compare your results to the solution you obtained in the indicated exercise.

57. $\left[\begin{array}{cc|c} 1 & -2 & -1 \\ 2 & 1 & -7 \end{array}\right]$
Compare with Exercise 41.

58. $\left[\begin{array}{cc|c} 1 & -3 & 3 \\ 2 & -5 & 4 \end{array}\right]$
Compare with Exercise 42.

59. $\left[\begin{array}{cc|c} 1 & 3 & 6 \\ -4 & -9 & 3 \end{array}\right]$
Compare with Exercise 43.

60. $\left[\begin{array}{cc|c} 2 & -3 & -2 \\ 1 & 2 & 13 \end{array}\right]$
Compare with Exercise 44.

61. $\left[\begin{array}{ccc|c} 1 & 1 & 1 & 6 \\ 1 & -1 & 1 & 2 \\ 1 & 1 & -1 & 0 \end{array}\right]$
Compare with Exercise 53.

62. $\left[\begin{array}{ccc|c} 2 & -3 & -2 & 11 \\ 1 & 3 & 8 & 1 \\ 3 & -1 & 14 & -2 \end{array}\right]$
Compare with Exercise 54.

Determinants and Cramer's Rule

Section A.5

Concepts

1. Introduction to Determinants
2. Determinant of a 3 × 3 Matrix
3. Cramer's Rule

1. Introduction to Determinants

Associated with every square matrix is a real number called the **determinant** of the matrix. The determinant of a square matrix **A**, denoted det **A**, is written by enclosing the elements of the matrix within two vertical bars. For example,

$$\text{If} \quad \mathbf{A} = \begin{bmatrix} 2 & -1 \\ 6 & 0 \end{bmatrix} \quad \text{then} \quad \det \mathbf{A} = \begin{vmatrix} 2 & -1 \\ 6 & 0 \end{vmatrix}$$

$$\text{If} \quad \mathbf{B} = \begin{bmatrix} 0 & -5 & 1 \\ 4 & 0 & \frac{1}{2} \\ -2 & 10 & 1 \end{bmatrix} \quad \text{then} \quad \det \mathbf{B} = \begin{vmatrix} 0 & -5 & 1 \\ 4 & 0 & \frac{1}{2} \\ -2 & 10 & 1 \end{vmatrix}$$

Determinants have many applications in mathematics, including solving systems of linear equations, finding the area of a triangle, determining whether three points are collinear, and finding an equation of a line between two points.

The determinant of a 2×2 matrix is defined as follows.

Definition of a Determinant of a 2 × 2 Matrix

The determinant of the matrix $\begin{bmatrix} a & b \\ c & d \end{bmatrix}$ is the real number $ad - bc$. It is written as

$$\begin{vmatrix} a & b \\ c & d \end{vmatrix} = ad - bc$$

Example 1 Evaluating a 2 × 2 Determinant

Classroom Example: p. A-49, Exercise 2

Evaluate the determinants.

a. $\begin{vmatrix} 6 & -2 \\ 5 & \frac{1}{3} \end{vmatrix}$ **b.** $\begin{vmatrix} 2 & -11 \\ 0 & 0 \end{vmatrix}$

Solution:

a. $\begin{vmatrix} 6 & -2 \\ 5 & \frac{1}{3} \end{vmatrix}$ For this determinant, $a = 6$, $b = -2$, $c = 5$, and $d = \frac{1}{3}$.

$$\begin{aligned} ad - bc &= (6)\left(\frac{1}{3}\right) - (-2)(5) \\ &= 2 + 10 \\ &= 12 \end{aligned}$$

b. $\begin{vmatrix} 2 & -11 \\ 0 & 0 \end{vmatrix}$ For this determinant, $a = 2$, $b = -11$, $c = 0$, $d = 0$.

$$\begin{aligned} ad - bc &= (2)(0) - (-11)(0) \\ &= 0 - 0 \\ &= 0 \end{aligned}$$

TIP: Example 1(b) illustrates that the value of a determinant having a row of all zeros is 0. The same is true for a determinant having a column of all zeros.

Skill Practice Evaluate the determinants.

1. $\begin{vmatrix} 2 & 8 \\ -1 & 5 \end{vmatrix}$ **2.** $\begin{vmatrix} -6 & 0 \\ 4 & 0 \end{vmatrix}$

Answers

1. 18 **2.** 0

2. Determinant of a 3 × 3 Matrix

To find the determinant of a 3 × 3 matrix, we first need to define the **minor** of an element of the matrix. For any element of a 3 × 3 matrix, the minor of that element is the determinant of the 2 × 2 matrix obtained by deleting the row and column in which the element resides. For example, consider the matrix

$$\begin{bmatrix} 5 & -1 & 6 \\ 0 & -7 & 1 \\ 4 & 2 & 6 \end{bmatrix}$$

The minor of the element 5 is found by deleting the first row and first column and then evaluating the determinant of the remaining 2 × 2 matrix:

$$\begin{bmatrix} 5 & -1 & 6 \\ 0 & -7 & 1 \\ 4 & 2 & 6 \end{bmatrix} \quad \text{Now evaluate the determinant:} \quad \begin{vmatrix} -7 & 1 \\ 2 & 6 \end{vmatrix} = (-7)(6) - (1)(2)$$

$$= -44$$

For this matrix, the minor for the element 5 is −44.

To find the minor of the element −7, delete the second row and second column, and then evaluate the determinant of the remaining 2 × 2 matrix.

$$\begin{bmatrix} 5 & -1 & 6 \\ 0 & -7 & 1 \\ 4 & 2 & 6 \end{bmatrix} \quad \text{Now evaluate the determinant:} \quad \begin{vmatrix} 5 & 6 \\ 4 & 6 \end{vmatrix} = (5)(6) - (6)(4) = 6$$

For this matrix, the minor for the element −7 is 6.

Classroom Example: p. A-49, Exercise 8

Example 2 Determining the Minor for Elements in a 3 × 3 Matrix

Find the minor for each element in the first column of the matrix.

$$\begin{bmatrix} 3 & 4 & -1 \\ 2 & -4 & 5 \\ 0 & 1 & -6 \end{bmatrix}$$

Solution:

For 3: $\begin{bmatrix} 3 & 4 & -1 \\ 2 & -4 & 5 \\ 0 & 1 & -6 \end{bmatrix}$ The minor is: $\begin{vmatrix} -4 & 5 \\ 1 & -6 \end{vmatrix} = (-4)(-6) - (5)(1) = 19$

For 2: $\begin{bmatrix} 3 & 4 & -1 \\ 2 & -4 & 5 \\ 0 & 1 & -6 \end{bmatrix}$ The minor is: $\begin{vmatrix} 4 & -1 \\ 1 & -6 \end{vmatrix} = (4)(-6) - (-1)(1) = -23$

For 0: $\begin{bmatrix} 3 & 4 & -1 \\ 2 & -4 & 5 \\ 0 & 1 & -6 \end{bmatrix}$ The minor is: $\begin{vmatrix} 4 & -1 \\ -4 & 5 \end{vmatrix} = (4)(5) - (-1)(-4) = 16$

Skill Practice Find the minor for the element 3.

3. $\begin{bmatrix} -1 & 8 & -6 \\ \frac{1}{2} & 3 & 2 \\ 5 & 7 & 4 \end{bmatrix}$

Answer

3. $\begin{vmatrix} -1 & -6 \\ 5 & 4 \end{vmatrix} = 26$

The determinant of a 3×3 matrix is defined as follows.

Definition of a Determinant of a 3 × 3 Matrix

$$\begin{vmatrix} a_1 & b_1 & c_1 \\ a_2 & b_2 & c_2 \\ a_3 & b_3 & c_3 \end{vmatrix} = a_1 \cdot \begin{vmatrix} b_2 & c_2 \\ b_3 & c_3 \end{vmatrix} - a_2 \cdot \begin{vmatrix} b_1 & c_1 \\ b_3 & c_3 \end{vmatrix} + a_3 \cdot \begin{vmatrix} b_1 & c_1 \\ b_2 & c_2 \end{vmatrix}$$

From this definition, we see that the determinant of a 3×3 matrix can be written as

$$a_1 \cdot (\text{minor of } a_1) - a_2 \cdot (\text{minor of } a_2) + a_3 \cdot (\text{minor of } a_3)$$

Evaluating determinants in this way is called *expanding minors.*

Example 3 Evaluating a 3 × 3 Determinant

Classroom Example: p. A-50, Exercise 20

Evaluate the determinant. $\begin{vmatrix} 2 & 4 & 2 \\ 1 & -3 & 0 \\ -5 & 5 & -1 \end{vmatrix}$

Solution:

$$\begin{vmatrix} 2 & 4 & 2 \\ 1 & -3 & 0 \\ -5 & 5 & -1 \end{vmatrix} = 2 \cdot \begin{vmatrix} -3 & 0 \\ 5 & -1 \end{vmatrix} - (1) \cdot \begin{vmatrix} 4 & 2 \\ 5 & -1 \end{vmatrix} + (-5) \cdot \begin{vmatrix} 4 & 2 \\ -3 & 0 \end{vmatrix}$$

$$= 2[(-3)(-1) - (0)(5)] - 1[(4)(-1) - (2)(5)] - 5[(4)(0) - (2)(-3)]$$

$$= 2(3) - 1(-14) - 5(6)$$

$$= 6 + 14 - 30$$

$$= -10$$

Skill Practice Evaluate the determinant.

4. $\begin{vmatrix} -2 & 4 & 9 \\ 5 & -1 & 2 \\ 1 & 1 & 6 \end{vmatrix}$

Although we defined the determinant of a matrix by expanding the minors of the elements in the first column, *any row or column can be used*. However, we must choose the correct sign to apply to each term in the expansion. The following array of signs is helpful.

$$\begin{matrix} + & - & + \\ - & + & - \\ + & - & + \end{matrix}$$

The signs alternate for each row and column, beginning with + in the first row, first column.

TIP: There is another method to determine the signs for each term of the expansion. For the a_{ij} element, multiply the term by $(-1)^{i+j}$.

Answer

4. −42

Classroom Example: p. A-50, Exercise 18

Example 4 Evaluating a 3 × 3 Determinant

Evaluate the determinant by expanding minors about the elements in the second row.

$$\begin{vmatrix} 2 & 4 & 2 \\ 1 & -3 & 0 \\ -5 & 5 & -1 \end{vmatrix}$$

Solution:

Signs obtained from the array of signs

$$\begin{vmatrix} 2 & 4 & 2 \\ 1 & -3 & 0 \\ -5 & 5 & -1 \end{vmatrix} = -(1)\cdot\begin{vmatrix} 4 & 2 \\ 5 & -1 \end{vmatrix} + (-3)\cdot\begin{vmatrix} 2 & 2 \\ -5 & -1 \end{vmatrix} - (0)\cdot\begin{vmatrix} 2 & 4 \\ -5 & 5 \end{vmatrix}$$

$$= -1[(4)(-1) - (2)(5)] - 3[(2)(-1) - (2)(-5)] - 0$$

$$= -1(-14) - 3(8)$$

$$= 14 - 24$$

$$= -10$$

Notice that the value of the determinant is the same as the result obtained in Example 3.

Skill Practice Evaluate the determinant.

5. $\begin{vmatrix} 4 & -1 & 2 \\ 3 & 6 & -8 \\ 0 & \frac{1}{2} & 5 \end{vmatrix}$

Calculator Connections

Topic: Evaluating a Determinant

The determinant of a matrix can be evaluated on a graphing calculator. First use the matrix editor to enter the elements of the matrix. Then use a *det* function to evaluate the determinant. The determinant from Examples 3 and 4 is evaluated below.

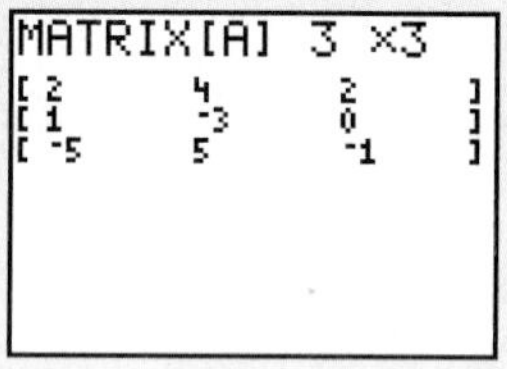

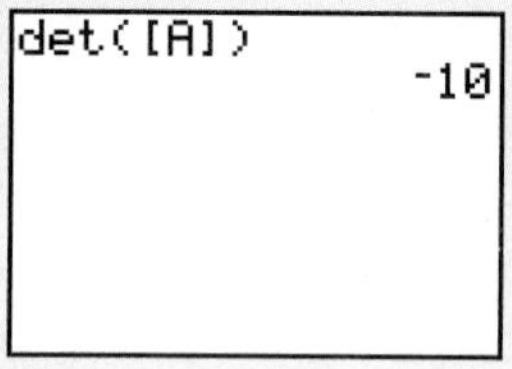

In Example 4, the third term in the expansion of minors was zero because the element 0 when multiplied by its minor is zero. To simplify the arithmetic in evaluating a determinant of a 3 × 3 matrix, expand about the row or column that has the most 0 elements.

Answer

5. 154

3. Cramer's Rule

In this section, we will learn another method to solve a system of linear equations. This method is called **Cramer's rule**.

Cramer's Rule for a 2 × 2 System of Linear Equations

The solution to the system
$$a_1x + b_1y = c_1$$
$$a_2x + b_2y = c_2$$

is given by $x = \dfrac{\mathbf{D}_x}{\mathbf{D}}$ and $y = \dfrac{\mathbf{D}_y}{\mathbf{D}}$

where $\mathbf{D} = \begin{vmatrix} a_1 & b_1 \\ a_2 & b_2 \end{vmatrix}$ (and $\mathbf{D} \neq 0$) $\quad \mathbf{D}_x = \begin{vmatrix} c_1 & b_1 \\ c_2 & b_2 \end{vmatrix} \quad \mathbf{D}_y = \begin{vmatrix} a_1 & c_1 \\ a_2 & c_2 \end{vmatrix}$

Example 5 Using Cramer's Rule to Solve a 2 × 2 System of Linear Equations

Classroom Example: p. A-50, Exercise 36

Solve the system by using Cramer's rule.
$$3x - 5y = 11$$
$$-x + 3y = -5$$

Solution:

For this system: $a_1 = 3 \quad b_1 = -5 \quad c_1 = 11$

$a_2 = -1 \quad b_2 = 3 \quad c_2 = -5$

$$\mathbf{D} = \begin{vmatrix} 3 & -5 \\ -1 & 3 \end{vmatrix} = (3)(3) - (-5)(-1) = 9 - 5 = 4$$

$$\mathbf{D}_x = \begin{vmatrix} 11 & -5 \\ -5 & 3 \end{vmatrix} = (11)(3) - (-5)(-5) = 33 - 25 = 8$$

$$\mathbf{D}_y = \begin{vmatrix} 3 & 11 \\ -1 & -5 \end{vmatrix} = (3)(-5) - (11)(-1) = -15 + 11 = -4$$

Therefore, $x = \dfrac{\mathbf{D}_x}{\mathbf{D}} = \dfrac{8}{4} = 2 \qquad y = \dfrac{\mathbf{D}_y}{\mathbf{D}} = \dfrac{-4}{4} = -1$

Check the ordered pair (2, −1) in both original equations.

Check: $3x - 5y = 11 \longrightarrow 3(2) - 5(-1) \stackrel{?}{=} 11$ ✓

$-x + 3y = -5 \longrightarrow -(2) + 3(-1) \stackrel{?}{=} -5$ ✓

The solution set is $\{(2, -1)\}$.

Skill Practice Solve using Cramer's rule.

6. $2x + y = 5$
$-x - 3y = 5$

Answer

6. $\{(4, -3)\}$

TIP: Here are some memory tips to help you remember Cramer's rule to solve:

$a_1x + b_1y = c_1$

$a_2x + b_2y = c_2$

1. The determinant **D** is the determinant of the coefficients of x and y.

Coefficients of x-terms, y-terms

$$\mathbf{D} = \begin{vmatrix} a_1 & b_1 \\ a_2 & b_2 \end{vmatrix}$$

2. The determinant $\mathbf{D}_x$ has the column of x-term coefficients replaced by c_1 and c_2.

x-coefficients replaced by c_1 and c_2

$$\mathbf{D}_x = \begin{vmatrix} c_1 & b_1 \\ c_2 & b_2 \end{vmatrix}$$

3. The determinant $\mathbf{D}_y$ has the column of y-term coefficients replaced by c_1 and c_2.

y-coefficients replaced by c_1 and c_2

$$\mathbf{D}_y = \begin{vmatrix} a_1 & c_1 \\ a_2 & c_2 \end{vmatrix}$$

It is important to note that the linear equations must be written in standard form to apply Cramer's rule.

Classroom Example: p. A-51, Exercise 38

Example 6 Using Cramer's Rule to Solve a 2 × 2 System of Linear Equations

Solve the system by using Cramer's rule.

$$-16y = -40x - 7$$
$$40y = 24x + 27$$

Solution:

$-16y = -40x - 7 \longrightarrow 40x - 16y = -7$

$40y = 24x + 27 \longrightarrow -24x + 40y = 27$

Rewrite each equation in standard form.

For this system: $a_1 = 40$, $b_1 = -16$, $c_1 = -7$

$a_2 = -24$, $b_2 = 40$, $c_2 = 27$

$$\mathbf{D} = \begin{vmatrix} 40 & -16 \\ -24 & 40 \end{vmatrix} = (40)(40) - (-16)(-24) = 1216$$

$$\mathbf{D}_x = \begin{vmatrix} -7 & -16 \\ 27 & 40 \end{vmatrix} = (-7)(40) - (-16)(27) = 152$$

$$\mathbf{D}_y = \begin{vmatrix} 40 & -7 \\ -24 & 27 \end{vmatrix} = (40)(27) - (-7)(-24) = 912$$

Therefore, $x = \dfrac{\mathbf{D}_x}{\mathbf{D}} = \dfrac{152}{1216} = \dfrac{1}{8}$ $y = \dfrac{\mathbf{D}_y}{\mathbf{D}} = \dfrac{912}{1216} = \dfrac{3}{4}$

The ordered pair $\left(\frac{1}{8}, \frac{3}{4}\right)$ checks in both original equations.

The solution set is $\left\{\left(\frac{1}{8}, \frac{3}{4}\right)\right\}$.

Skill Practice Solve by using Cramer's rule.

7. $9x = 12y - 8$
   $30y = -18x - 7$

Answer

7. $\left\{\left(-\frac{2}{3}, \frac{1}{6}\right)\right\}$

Cramer's rule can be used to solve a 3×3 system of linear equations by using a similar pattern of determinants.

Cramer's Rule for a 3×3 System of Linear Equations

The solution to the system

$$a_1x + b_1y + c_1z = d_1$$
$$a_2x + b_2y + c_2z = d_2$$
$$a_3x + b_3y + c_3z = d_3$$

is given by $x = \dfrac{\mathbf{D}_x}{\mathbf{D}}$ $\quad y = \dfrac{\mathbf{D}_y}{\mathbf{D}}$ $\quad$ and $\quad z = \dfrac{\mathbf{D}_z}{\mathbf{D}}$

Where $\mathbf{D} = \begin{vmatrix} a_1 & b_1 & c_1 \\ a_2 & b_2 & c_2 \\ a_3 & b_3 & c_3 \end{vmatrix}$ (and $\mathbf{D} \neq 0$) $\quad \mathbf{D}_x = \begin{vmatrix} d_1 & b_1 & c_1 \\ d_2 & b_2 & c_2 \\ d_3 & b_3 & c_3 \end{vmatrix}$

$\mathbf{D}_y = \begin{vmatrix} a_1 & d_1 & c_1 \\ a_2 & d_2 & c_2 \\ a_3 & d_3 & c_3 \end{vmatrix}$ $\quad \mathbf{D}_z = \begin{vmatrix} a_1 & b_1 & d_1 \\ a_2 & b_2 & d_2 \\ a_3 & b_3 & d_3 \end{vmatrix}$

Example 7 Using Cramer's Rule to Solve a 3×3 System of Linear Equations

Classroom Example: p. A-51, Exercise 44

Solve the system by using Cramer's rule.

$$2x - 3y + 5z = 11$$
$$-5x + 7y - 2z = -6$$
$$9x - 2y + 3z = 4$$

Solution:

$$\mathbf{D} = \begin{vmatrix} 2 & -3 & 5 \\ -5 & 7 & -2 \\ 9 & -2 & 3 \end{vmatrix} = 2 \cdot \begin{vmatrix} 7 & -2 \\ -2 & 3 \end{vmatrix} - (-5) \cdot \begin{vmatrix} -3 & 5 \\ -2 & 3 \end{vmatrix} + 9 \cdot \begin{vmatrix} -3 & 5 \\ 7 & -2 \end{vmatrix}$$
$$= 2(17) + 5(1) + 9(-29)$$
$$= -222$$

TIP: In Example 7, we expanded the determinants about the first column.

$$\mathbf{D}_x = \begin{vmatrix} 11 & -3 & 5 \\ -6 & 7 & -2 \\ 4 & -2 & 3 \end{vmatrix} = 11 \cdot \begin{vmatrix} 7 & -2 \\ -2 & 3 \end{vmatrix} - (-6) \cdot \begin{vmatrix} -3 & 5 \\ -2 & 3 \end{vmatrix} + 4 \cdot \begin{vmatrix} -3 & 5 \\ 7 & -2 \end{vmatrix}$$
$$= 11(17) + 6(1) + 4(-29)$$
$$= 77$$

$$\mathbf{D}_y = \begin{vmatrix} 2 & 11 & 5 \\ -5 & -6 & -2 \\ 9 & 4 & 3 \end{vmatrix} = 2 \cdot \begin{vmatrix} -6 & -2 \\ 4 & 3 \end{vmatrix} - (-5) \cdot \begin{vmatrix} 11 & 5 \\ 4 & 3 \end{vmatrix} + 9 \cdot \begin{vmatrix} 11 & 5 \\ -6 & -2 \end{vmatrix}$$
$$= 2(-10) + 5(13) + 9(8)$$
$$= 117$$

$$\mathbf{D}_z = \begin{vmatrix} 2 & -3 & 11 \\ -5 & 7 & -6 \\ 9 & -2 & 4 \end{vmatrix} = 2 \cdot \begin{vmatrix} 7 & -6 \\ -2 & 4 \end{vmatrix} - (-5) \cdot \begin{vmatrix} -3 & 11 \\ -2 & 4 \end{vmatrix} + 9 \cdot \begin{vmatrix} -3 & 11 \\ 7 & -6 \end{vmatrix}$$

$$= 2(16) + 5(10) + 9(-59)$$

$$= -449$$

$$x = \frac{\mathbf{D}_x}{\mathbf{D}} = \frac{77}{-222} = -\frac{77}{222}$$

$$y = \frac{\mathbf{D}_y}{\mathbf{D}} = \frac{117}{-222} = -\frac{39}{74}$$

$$z = \frac{\mathbf{D}_z}{\mathbf{D}} = \frac{-449}{-222} = \frac{449}{222}$$

The solution $\left(-\frac{77}{222}, -\frac{39}{74}, \frac{449}{222}\right)$ checks in each of the original equations.

The solution set is $\left\{\left(-\frac{77}{222}, -\frac{39}{74}, \frac{449}{222}\right)\right\}$.

Skill Practice Solve by using Cramer's rule.

8. $x + 3y - 3z = -14$
$x - 4y + z = 2$
$x + y + 2z = 6$

Cramer's rule may seem cumbersome for solving a 3×3 system of linear equations. However, it provides convenient formulas that can be programmed into a computer or calculator to solve for x, y, and z. Cramer's rule can also be extended to solve a 4×4 system of linear equations, a 5×5 system of linear equations, and in general an $n \times n$ system of linear equations.

It is important to remember that Cramer's rule does not apply if $\mathbf{D} = 0$. In such a case, either the equations are dependent or the system is inconsistent, and another method may be needed to analyze the system.

Classroom Example: p. A-51, Exercise 54

Example 8 Analyzing a Dependent System of Equations

Solve the system. Use Cramer's rule if possible.

$$2x - 3y = 6$$
$$-6x + 9y = -18$$

TIP: When Cramer's rule does not apply, that is, when $\mathbf{D} = 0$, you may also use the substitution method or the Gauss-Jordan method to get a solution.

Solution:

$$\mathbf{D} = \begin{vmatrix} 2 & -3 \\ -6 & 9 \end{vmatrix} = (2)(9) - (-3)(-6) = 18 - 18 = 0$$

Because $\mathbf{D} = 0$, Cramer's rule does not apply. Using the addition method to solve the system, we have

$$2x - 3y = 6 \xrightarrow{\text{Multiply by 3.}} 6x - 9y = 18$$
$$-6x + 9y = -18 \longrightarrow \underline{-6x + 9y = -18}$$
$$0 = 0 \quad \text{The equations are dependent.}$$

The solution set is $\{(x, y) \mid 2x - 3y = 6\}$.

Answer

8. $\{(-2, 0, 4)\}$

Skill Practice Solve. Use Cramer's rule if possible.

9. $x - 6y = 2$
$2x - 12y = -2$

TIP: In a 2×2 system of equations, if $\mathbf{D} = 0$, then the equations are dependent or the system is inconsistent.

- If $\mathbf{D} = 0$ and both $\mathbf{D}_x = 0$ and $\mathbf{D}_y = 0$, then the equations are dependent and the system has infinitely many solutions.
- If $\mathbf{D} = 0$ and either $\mathbf{D}_x \neq 0$ or $\mathbf{D}_y \neq 0$, then the system is inconsistent and has no solution.

Answer

9. { }; inconsistent system

Section A.5 Practice Exercises

For additional exercises, see Classroom Activities A.5A–A.5D in the *Student's Resource Manual* at www.mhhe.com/moh.

Vocabulary and Key Concepts

1. a. Given the matrix $\mathbf{A} = \begin{bmatrix} a & b \\ c & d \end{bmatrix}$, the __________ of **A** is denoted det **A** and is written as $\begin{vmatrix} a & b \\ c & d \end{vmatrix}$. The value of det **A** is the real number equal to __________. determinant; $ad - bc$

b. Given a 3×3 matrix, the __________ of an element in the matrix is the determinant of the 2×2 matrix formed by deleting the row and column in which the element resides. minor

c. Complete the expression on the right to represent the value of the 3×3 determinant shown here.

$$\begin{vmatrix} a_1 & b_1 & c_1 \\ a_2 & b_2 & c_2 \\ a_3 & b_3 & c_3 \end{vmatrix} = a_1\begin{vmatrix} b_2 & c_2 \\ b_3 & c_3 \end{vmatrix} - \square\begin{vmatrix} b_1 & c_1 \\ b_3 & c_3 \end{vmatrix} + a_3\begin{vmatrix} \square & \square \\ \square & \square \end{vmatrix}$$

a_2; $\begin{vmatrix} b_1 & c_1 \\ b_2 & c_2 \end{vmatrix}$

Concept 1: Introduction to Determinants

For Exercises 2–7, evaluate the determinant of the 2×2 matrix. **(See Example 1.)**

2. $\begin{vmatrix} -3 & 1 \\ 5 & 2 \end{vmatrix}$ −11

3. $\begin{vmatrix} 5 & 6 \\ 4 & 8 \end{vmatrix}$ 16

4. $\begin{vmatrix} -2 & 2 \\ -3 & -5 \end{vmatrix}$ 16

5. $\begin{vmatrix} 5 & -1 \\ 1 & 0 \end{vmatrix}$ 1

6. $\begin{vmatrix} \frac{1}{2} & 3 \\ -2 & 4 \end{vmatrix}$ 8

7. $\begin{vmatrix} -3 & \frac{1}{4} \\ 8 & -2 \end{vmatrix}$ 4

Concept 2: Determinant of a 3 × 3 Matrix

For Exercises 8–11, evaluate the minor corresponding to the given element from matrix **A**. **(See Example 2.)**

$$\mathbf{A} = \begin{bmatrix} 4 & -1 & 8 \\ 2 & 6 & 0 \\ -7 & 5 & 3 \end{bmatrix}$$

8. 4 18

9. −1 6

10. 2 −43

11. 3 26

For Exercises 12–15, evaluate the minor corresponding to the given element from matrix **B**.

$$\mathbf{B} = \begin{bmatrix} -2 & 6 & 0 \\ 4 & -2 & 1 \\ 5 & 9 & -1 \end{bmatrix}$$

12. 6 -9 **13.** 5 6 **14.** 1 -48 **15.** 0 46

16. Construct the sign array for a 3×3 matrix. $\begin{bmatrix} + & - & + \\ - & + & - \\ + & - & + \end{bmatrix}$

17. Evaluate the determinant of matrix **B**, using expansion by minors. **(See Exercises 3–4.)**

$$\mathbf{B} = \begin{bmatrix} 0 & 1 & 2 \\ 3 & -1 & 2 \\ 3 & 2 & -2 \end{bmatrix}$$

a. About the first column 30

b. About the second row 30

18. Evaluate the determinant of matrix **C**, using expansion by minors.

$$\mathbf{C} = \begin{bmatrix} 4 & 1 & 3 \\ 2 & -2 & 1 \\ 3 & 1 & 2 \end{bmatrix}$$

a. About the first row 3

b. About the second column 3

19. When evaluating the determinant of a 3×3 matrix, explain the advantage of being able to choose any row or column about which to expand minors. Choosing the row or column with the most zero elements simplifies the arithmetic when evaluating a determinant.

For Exercises 20–25, evaluate the determinant. **(See Examples 3–4.)**

20. $\begin{vmatrix} 8 & 2 & -4 \\ 4 & 0 & 2 \\ 3 & 0 & -1 \end{vmatrix}$ 20

21. $\begin{vmatrix} 5 & 2 & 1 \\ 3 & -6 & 0 \\ -2 & 8 & 0 \end{vmatrix}$ 12

22. $\begin{vmatrix} -2 & 1 & 3 \\ 1 & 4 & 4 \\ 1 & 0 & 2 \end{vmatrix}$ -26

23. $\begin{vmatrix} 3 & 2 & 1 \\ 1 & -1 & 2 \\ 1 & 0 & 4 \end{vmatrix}$ -15

24. $\begin{vmatrix} -5 & 4 & 2 \\ 0 & 0 & 0 \\ 3 & -1 & 5 \end{vmatrix}$ 0

25. $\begin{vmatrix} 0 & 5 & -8 \\ 0 & -4 & 1 \\ 0 & 3 & 6 \end{vmatrix}$ 0

For Exercises 26–31, evaluate the determinant.

26. $\begin{vmatrix} x & 3 \\ y & -2 \end{vmatrix}$ $-2x - 3y$

27. $\begin{vmatrix} a & 2 \\ b & 8 \end{vmatrix}$ $8a - 2b$

28. $\begin{vmatrix} a & 5 & -1 \\ b & -3 & 0 \\ c & 3 & 4 \end{vmatrix}$ $-12a - 23b - 3c$

29. $\begin{vmatrix} x & 0 & 3 \\ y & -2 & 6 \\ z & -1 & 1 \end{vmatrix}$ $4x - 3y + 6z$

30. $\begin{vmatrix} p & 0 & q \\ r & 0 & s \\ t & 0 & u \end{vmatrix}$ 0

31. $\begin{vmatrix} f & e & 0 \\ d & c & 0 \\ b & a & 0 \end{vmatrix}$ 0

Concept 3: Cramer's Rule

For Exercises 32–34, evaluate the determinants represented by $\mathbf{D}$, $\mathbf{D}_x$, and $\mathbf{D}_y$.

32. $x - 4y = 2$
$3x + 2y = 1$
$\mathbf{D} = 14$; $\mathbf{D}_x = 8$; $\mathbf{D}_y = -5$

33. $4x + 6y = 9$
$-2x + y = 12$
$\mathbf{D} = 16$; $\mathbf{D}_x = -63$; $\mathbf{D}_y = 66$

34. $-3x + 8y = -10$
$5x + 5y = -13$
$\mathbf{D} = -55$; $\mathbf{D}_x = 54$; $\mathbf{D}_y = 89$

For Exercises 35–40, solve the system by using Cramer's rule. **(See Examples 5–6.)**

35. $2x + y = 3$
$x - 4y = 6$ $\{(2, -1)\}$

36. $2x - y = -1$
$3x + y = 6$ $\{(1, 3)\}$

37. $4y = x - 8$
$3x = -7y + 5$ $\{(4, -1)\}$

38. $7x - 4 = -3y$; $5x = 4y + 9$ $\{(1, -1)\}$

39. $4x - 3y = 5$; $2x + 5y = 7$ $\left\{\left(\frac{23}{13}, \frac{9}{13}\right)\right\}$

40. $2x + 3y = 4$; $6x - 12y = -5$ $\left\{\left(\frac{11}{14}, \frac{17}{21}\right)\right\}$

For Exercises 41–46, solve for the indicated variable by using Cramer's rule. **(See Example 7.)**

41. $2x - y + 3z = 9$; $x + 4y + 4z = 5$; $3x + 2y + 2z = 5$ for x $x = 1$

42. $x + 2y + 3z = 8$; $2x - 3y + z = 5$; $3x - 4y + 2z = 9$ for y $y = -2$

43. $3x - 2y + 2z = 5$; $6x + 3y - 4z = -1$; $3x - y + 2z = 4$ for z $z = \frac{1}{2}$

44. $4x + 4y - 3z = 3$; $8x + 2y + 3y = 0$; $4x - 4y + 6z = -3$ for x $x = \frac{1}{4}$

45. $5x + 6z = 5$; $-2x + y = -6$; $3y - z = 3$ for y $y = \frac{16}{41}$

46. $8x + y = 1$; $7y + z = 0$; $x - 3z = -2$ for y $y = -\frac{17}{167}$

47. When does Cramer's rule not apply in solving a system of equations? Cramer's rule does not apply when the determinant $\mathbf{D} = 0$.

48. How can a system be solved if Cramer's rule does not apply? The addition method, substitution method, or Gauss-Jordan method can be used if Cramer's rule fails.

For Exercises 49–58, solve the system by using Cramer's rule, if possible. Otherwise, use another method. If a system does not have a unique solution, determine the number of solutions and whether the system is inconsistent or the equations are dependent. **(See Example 8.)**

49. $4x - 2y = 3$; $-2x + y = 1$ No solution; { }; inconsistent system

50. $6x - 6y = 5$; $x - y = 8$ No solution; { }; inconsistent system

51. $4x + y = 0$; $x - 7y = 0$ $\{(0, 0)\}$

52. $-3x - 2y = 0$; $-x + 5y = 0$ $\{(0, 0)\}$

53. $x + 5y = 3$; $2x + 10y = 6$ Infinitely many solutions; $\{(x, y) \mid x + 5y = 3\}$; dependent equations

54. $-2x - 10y = -4$; $x + 5y = 2$ Infinitely many solutions; $\{(x, y) \mid x + 5y = 2\}$; dependent equations

55. $x = 3$; $-x + 3y = 3$; $y + 2z = 4$ $\{(3, 2, 1)\}$

56. $4x + z = 7$; $y = 2$; $x + z = 4$ $\{(1, 2, 3)\}$

57. $x + y + 8z = 3$; $2x + y + 11z = 4$; $x + 3z = 0$ No solution; { }; inconsistent system

58. $-8x + y + z = 6$; $2x - y + z = 3$; $3x - z = 0$ No solution; { }; inconsistent system

Expanding Your Skills

For Exercises 59–62, solve the equation.

59. $\begin{vmatrix} 6 & x \\ 2 & -4 \end{vmatrix} = 14$ $x = -19$

60. $\begin{vmatrix} y & -2 \\ 8 & 7 \end{vmatrix} = 30$ $y = 2$

61. $\begin{vmatrix} 3 & 1 & 0 \\ 0 & 4 & -2 \\ 1 & 0 & w \end{vmatrix} = 10$ $w = 1$

62. $\begin{vmatrix} -1 & 0 & 2 \\ 4 & t & 0 \\ 0 & -5 & 3 \end{vmatrix} = -4$ $t = -12$

For Exercises 63–64, evaluate the determinant by using expansion by minors about the first column.

63. $\begin{vmatrix} 1 & 0 & 3 & 0 \\ 0 & 1 & 2 & 4 \\ -2 & 0 & 0 & 1 \\ 4 & -1 & -2 & 0 \end{vmatrix}$ 36

64. $\begin{vmatrix} 5 & 2 & 0 & 0 \\ 0 & 4 & -1 & 1 \\ -1 & 0 & 3 & 0 \\ 0 & -2 & 1 & 0 \end{vmatrix}$ 32

For Exercises 65–66, refer to the following system of four variables.

$$\begin{aligned} x + y + z + w &= 0 \\ 2x \qquad - z + w &= 5 \\ 2x + y \qquad - w &= 0 \\ y + z \qquad &= -1 \end{aligned}$$

65. **a.** Evaluate the determinant **D**. 2

b. Evaluate the determinant $\mathbf{D}_x$. −2

c. Solve for x by computing $\frac{\mathbf{D}_x}{\mathbf{D}}$. $x = -1$

66. **a.** Evaluate the determinant $\mathbf{D}_y$. 8

b. Solve for y by computing $\frac{\mathbf{D}_y}{\mathbf{D}}$. $y = 4$

67. Two angles are complementary. The measure of one angle is $\frac{5}{7}$ the measure of the other. Find the measures of the two angles. The measures are 37.5° and 52.5°.

68. Two angles are supplementary. The measure of the larger angle is 61° more than $\frac{3}{4}$ the measure of the smaller angle. Find the measures of the angles. The measures are 112° and 68°.

69. A theater charges $80 per ticket for seats in section A, $50 per ticket for seats in section B, and $30 per ticket for seats in section C. For one performance, 3000 tickets were sold for a total of $165,000 in revenue. If the total number of tickets in sections A and C is equal to the number of tickets sold in section B, how many tickets in each section were sold? 900 tickets in section A, 1500 tickets in section B, and 600 tickets in section C were sold.

70. The measure of the largest angle in a triangle is 80° larger than the sum of the measures of the other two angles. The measure of the smallest angle is 22° less than the measure of the middle angle. Find the measure of each angle. The angles are 130°, 36°, and 14°.

71. Suppose 1000 people were surveyed in southern California, and 445 said that they worked-out at least three times a week. If $\frac{1}{2}$ of the women and $\frac{3}{8}$ of the men said that they worked-out at least three times a week, how many men and how many women were in the survey? There were 560 women and 440 men in the survey.

72. During a 1-hr television program, there were 22 commercials. Some commercials were 15 sec long and some were 30 sec long. Find the number of 15-sec commercials and the number of 30-sec commercials if the total playing time for commercials was 9.5 min. There were six 15-sec commercials and sixteen 30-sec commercials.

Student Answer Appendix

Chapter 1

Section 1.1 Practice Exercises, pp. 17–21

1. a. product **b.** factors **c.** numerator; b **d.** lowest **e.** 1; 4 **f.** reciprocals **g.** multiple **h.** least
3. Numerator: 2; denominator: 3; proper
5. Numerator: 5; denominator: 2; improper
7. Numerator: 4; denominator: 4; improper
9. Numerator: 5; denominator: 1; improper
11. $\frac{3}{4}$ **13.** $\frac{4}{3}$ **15.** $\frac{1}{6}$ **17.** $\frac{2}{2}$ **19.** $\frac{5}{2}$ or $2\frac{1}{2}$ **21.** $\frac{6}{2}$ or 3
23. The set of whole numbers includes the number 0 and the set of natural numbers does not.
25. For example: $\frac{2}{4}$ **27.** Prime **29.** Composite
31. Composite **33.** Prime **35.** $2 \times 2 \times 3 \times 3$
37. $2 \times 3 \times 7$ **39.** $2 \times 5 \times 11$ **41.** $3 \times 3 \times 3 \times 5$
43. $\frac{1}{5}$ **45.** $\frac{8}{3}$ or $2\frac{2}{3}$ **47.** $\frac{7}{8}$ **49.** $\frac{3}{4}$ **51.** $\frac{5}{8}$ **53.** $\frac{4}{3}$ or $1\frac{1}{3}$
55. False: When adding or subtracting fractions, it is necessary to have a common denominator.
57. $\frac{4}{3}$ or $1\frac{1}{3}$ **59.** $\frac{2}{3}$ **61.** $\frac{9}{2}$ or $4\frac{1}{2}$ **63.** $\frac{3}{5}$ **65.** $\frac{5}{3}$ or $1\frac{2}{3}$
67. $\frac{90}{13}$ or $6\frac{12}{13}$ **69.** \$704 **71.** 35 students **73.** 8 pieces
75. 8 jars **77.** $\frac{3}{7}$ **79.** $\frac{1}{2}$ **81.** 30 **83.** 40 **85.** $\frac{7}{8}$
87. $\frac{43}{40}$ or $1\frac{3}{40}$ **89.** $\frac{3}{26}$ **91.** $\frac{29}{36}$ **93.** $\frac{6}{5}$ or $1\frac{1}{5}$ **95.** $\frac{35}{48}$
97. $\frac{7}{24}$ **99.** $\frac{51}{28}$ or $1\frac{23}{28}$ **101.** $\frac{11}{12}$ cup sugar **103.** $\frac{7}{50}$ in.
105. $\frac{46}{5}$ or $9\frac{1}{5}$ **107.** $\frac{1}{6}$ **109.** $\frac{11}{54}$ **111.** $\frac{7}{2}$ or $3\frac{1}{2}$
113. $\frac{13}{8}$ or $1\frac{5}{8}$ **115.** $\frac{59}{12}$ or $4\frac{11}{12}$ **117.** $\frac{1}{8}$ **119.** $8\frac{19}{24}$ in.
121. $1\frac{7}{12}$ hr **123.** $2\frac{1}{4}$ lb **125.** 25 in.

Section 1.2 Calculator Connections, pp. 30–31

1. ≈ 3.464101615 **2.** ≈ 9.949874371
3. ≈ 12.56637061 **4.** ≈ 1.772453851

Section 1.2 Practice Exercises, pp. 31–34

1. a. variable **b.** constants **c.** set **d.** inequalities **e.** a is less than b **f.** c is greater than or equal to d **g.** 5 is not equal to 6 **h.** opposites **i.** $|a|$; 0 **3.** $8\frac{1}{4}$ or $\frac{33}{4}$ **5.** 15 **7.** 3
9. 4 **11.** 5.3 **13.** $\frac{1}{80}$ **15. a.** \$3.87 **b.** \$10.32 **c.** \$12.90 **17. a.** 375 calories **b.** 630 calories **c.** 270 calories
19.

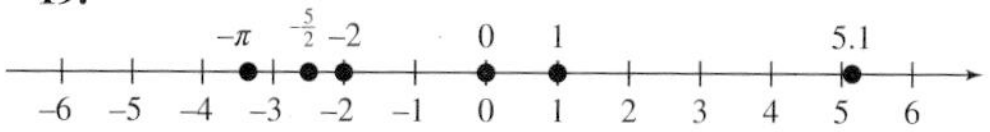

21. a; rational **23.** b; rational **25.** a; rational
27. c; irrational **29.** a; rational **31.** a; rational
33. b; rational **35.** c; irrational **37.** For example: $\pi, -\sqrt{2}, \sqrt{3}$
39. For example: $-4, -1, 0$ **41.** For example: $-\frac{3}{4}, \frac{1}{2}, 0.206$
43. $-\frac{3}{2}, -4, 0.\overline{6}, 0, 1$ **45.** 1 **47.** $-4, 0, 1$ **49. a.** $>$ **b.** $>$ **c.** $<$ **d.** $>$ **51.** -18 **53.** 6.1 **55.** $\frac{5}{8}$ **57.** $-\frac{7}{3}$
59. 3 **61.** $-\frac{7}{3}$ **63.** 8 **65.** -72.1 **67.** 2 **69.** 1.5
71. -1.5 **73.** $\frac{3}{2}$ **75.** -10 **77.** $-\frac{1}{2}$
79. False, $|n|$ is never negative. **81.** True **83.** False
85. True **87.** False **89.** False **91.** False
93. True **95.** True **97.** False **99.** True
101. True **103.** True **105.** For all $a < 0$

Section 1.3 Calculator Connections, pp. 41–42

1. 2 **2.** 91 **3.** 84 **4.** 12 **5.** 49 **6.** 18

1–3.

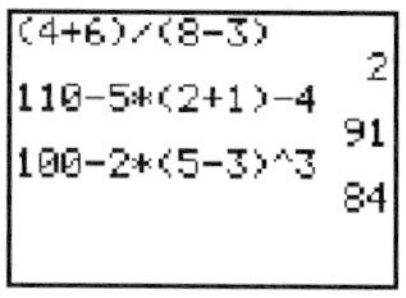

4–6.

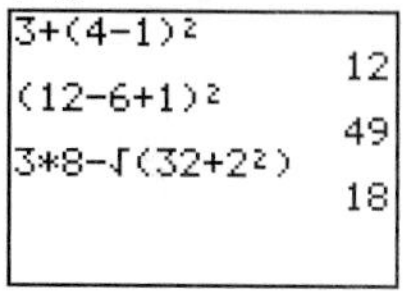

7. 4 **8.** 27 **9.** 0.5

7–9.

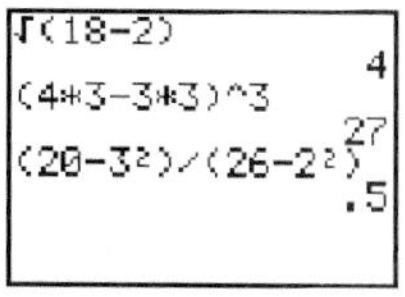

Section 1.3 Practice Exercises, pp. 42–45

1. a. quotient; product; sum; difference **b.** base; exponent; power **c.** 8^2 **d.** p^4 **e.** radical; square **f.** order of operations
3. 56 **5.** -19 **7.** $\left(\frac{1}{6}\right)^4$ **9.** a^3b^2 **11.** $(5c)^5$
13. a. x **b.** Yes, 1 **15.** $x \cdot x \cdot x$ **17.** $2b \cdot 2b \cdot 2b$
19. $10 \cdot y \cdot y \cdot y \cdot y \cdot y$ **21.** $2 \cdot w \cdot z \cdot z$ **23.** 36 **25.** $\frac{1}{49}$
27. 0.008 **29.** 64 **31.** 9 **33.** 2 **35.** 12 **37.** 4
39. $\frac{1}{3}$ **41.** $\frac{5}{9}$ **43.** 20 **45.** 60 **47.** 8 **49.** 78 **51.** 0
53. $\frac{7}{6}$ **55.** 45 **57.** 16 **59.** 15 **61.** 19 **63.** 75 **65.** 3
67. 39 **69.** 26 **71.** $\frac{5}{12}$ **73.** $\frac{5}{2}$ **75. a.** 0.12 **b.** Yes. $0.12 < 0.20$ **77.** 57,600 ft^2 **79.** 21 ft^2 **81.** $3x$
83. $\frac{x}{7}$ or $x \div 7$ **85.** $2 - a$ **87.** $2y + x$ **89.** $4(x + 12)$
91. $3 - Q$ **93.** $2y^3$; 16 **95.** $|z - 8|$; 2 **97.** $5\sqrt{x}$; 10
99. $yz - x$; 16 **101.** 1 **103.** $\frac{1}{4}$
105. a. $36 \div 4 \cdot 3 = 9 \cdot 3 = 27$ Division must be performed before multiplication.
b. $36 - 4 + 3 = 32 + 3 = 35$ Subtraction must be performed before addition.

107. This is acceptable, provided division and multiplication are performed in order from left to right, and subtraction and addition are performed in order from left to right.

Section 1.4 Practice Exercises, pp. 51–53

1. a. negative **b.** b **3.** > **5.** > **7.** > **9.** −6 **11.** 3 **13.** 3 **15.** −3 **17.** −17 **19.** 7 **21.** −19 **23.** −23 **25.** −5 **27.** −3 **29.** 0 **31.** 0 **33.** −5 **35.** −3 **37.** 0 **39.** −23 **41.** −6 **43.** −3 **45.** 21.3 **47.** $-\frac{3}{14}$ **49.** $-\frac{1}{6}$ **51.** $-\frac{15}{16}$ **53.** $\frac{1}{20}$ **55.** −2.4 or $-\frac{12}{5}$ **57.** $\frac{1}{4}$ or 0.25 **59.** 0 **61.** $-\frac{7}{8}$ **63.** −1 **65.** $\frac{11}{9}$ **67.** −23.08 **69.** −0.002117 **71.** To add two numbers with different signs, subtract the smaller absolute value from the larger absolute value and apply the sign of the number with the larger absolute value. **73.** −1 **75.** 10 **77.** 5 **79.** 1 **81.** −6 + (−10); −16 **83.** −3 + 8; 5 **85.** −21 + 17; −4 **87.** 3(−14 + 20); 18 **89.** [−7 + (−2)] + 5; −4 **91.** −5 + 13 + (−11); −3°F **93.** −8 + 1 + 2 + (−5) = −10; Amara lost 10 lb. **95. a.** 52.23 + (−52.95) **b.** Yes **97.** −6; She was 6 below par.

Section 1.5 Calculator Connections, p. 59

1. −13 **2.** −2 **3.** 711

1–3.

```
-8+(-5)
                -13
4+(-5)+(-1)
                 -2
627-(-84)
                711
```

4. −0.18 **5.** −17.7 **6.** −990 **7.** −17 **8.** 38

4–6.

```
-0.06-0.12
                -.18
-3.2+(-14.5)
               -17.7
-472+(-518)
                -990
```

7–8.

```
-12-9+4
                 -17
209-108+(-63)
                  38
```

Section 1.5 Practice Exercises, pp. 59–62

1. a. $-b$ **b.** positive **3.** x^2 **5.** $-b + 2$ **7.** 9 **9.** −3 **11.** −12 **13.** 4 **15.** −2 **17.** 8 **19.** −8 **21.** 2 **23.** 6 **25.** 40 **27.** −40 **29.** 0 **31.** −20 **33.** −24 **35.** 25 **37.** −5 **39.** $-\frac{3}{2}$ **41.** $\frac{41}{24}$ **43.** $\frac{2}{5}$ **45.** $-\frac{2}{3}$ **47.** 9.2 **49.** −5.72 **51.** −10 **53.** −14 **55.** −20 **57.** −173.188 **59.** 3.243 **61.** 6 − (−7); 13 **63.** 3 − 18; −15 **65.** −5 − (−11); 6 **67.** −1 − (−13); 12 **69.** −32 − 20; −52 **71.** 200 + 400 + 600 + 800 − 1000; $1000 **73.** 152°F **75.** 19,881 m **77.** 13 **79.** −9 **81.** 5 **83.** −25 **85.** −2 **87.** $-\frac{11}{30}$ **89.** $-\frac{29}{9}$ **91.** −2 **93.** −11 **95.** 2 **97.** −7 **99.** 5 **101.** 5 **103.** 3

Chapter 1 Problem Recognition Exercises, p. 62

1. Add their absolute values and apply a negative sign.
2. Subtract the smaller absolute value from the larger absolute value. Apply the sign of the number with the larger absolute value.
3. a. 6 **b.** −6 **c.** −22 **d.** 22 **e.** −22 **4. a.** −2 **b.** −8 **c.** −8 **d.** −2 **e.** 8 **5. a.** 0 **b.** 0 **c.** 50 **d.** 0 **e.** −50 **6. a.** $-\frac{1}{6}$ **b.** $\frac{1}{6}$ **c.** $-\frac{7}{6}$ **d.** $\frac{7}{6}$ **e.** $-\frac{7}{6}$ **7. a.** −3.6 **b.** 10.6 **c.** 3.6 **d.** 3.6 **e.** −10.6 **8. a.** 4 **b.** −4 **c.** 6 **d.** 6 **9. a.** −270 **b.** −110 **c.** −90 **d.** −270 **10. a.** 402 **b.** −108 **c.** 484 **d.** 24

Section 1.6 Calculator Connections, pp. 69–70

1. −30 **2.** −2 **3.** 625 **4.** 625 **5.** −625 **6.** −5.76

1–3.

```
-6(5)
                 -30
-5.2/2.6
                  -2
(-5)(-5)(-5)(-5)
                 625
```

4–6.

```
(-5)^4
                 625
-5^4
                -625
-2.4²
               -5.76
```

7. 5.76 **8.** −1 **9.** 4 **10.** −36

7–8.

```
(-2.4)²
                5.76
(-1)(-1)(-1)
                  -1
```

9–10.

```
-8.4/-2.1
                   4
90/(-5)(2)
                 -36
```

Section 1.6 Practice Exercises, pp. 70–74

1. a. $\frac{1}{a}$ **b.** 0 **c.** 0 **d.** undefined **e.** positive **f.** negative **g.** 1; $-\frac{3}{2}$ **h.** All of these **3.** True **5.** False **7.** −56 **9.** 143 **11.** −12.76 **13.** $\frac{3}{4}$ **15.** 36 **17.** −36 **19.** $-\frac{27}{125}$ **21.** 0.0016 **23.** −6 **25.** $\frac{15}{17}$ **27.** 1 **29.** $-\frac{1}{5}$ **31.** (−2)(−7) = 14 **33.** −5 · 0 = 0 **35.** No number multiplied by zero equals 6. **37.** (−6)(4) = −24 **39.** 6 **41.** −6 **43.** −8 **45.** 8 **47.** 0 **49.** Undefined **51.** 0 **53.** 0 **55.** $-\frac{3}{2}$ **57.** $\frac{3}{10}$ **59.** −2 **61.** −7.912 **63.** 0.092 **65.** −6 **67.** 2.1 **69.** 9 **71.** −9 **73.** $-\frac{64}{27}$ **75.** 340 **77.** $\frac{14}{9}$ **79.** −30 **81.** 96 **83.** 2 **85.** −1 **87.** $-\frac{4}{33}$ **89.** $-\frac{4}{7}$ **91.** −24 **93.** $-\frac{1}{20}$ **95.** −23 **97.** 12 **99.** $\frac{9}{7}$ **101.** Undefined **103.** −48 **105.** −6 **107.** −1 **109.** 7 **111.** −4 **113.** −40 **115.** $\frac{7}{2}$ **117.** No. The first expression is equivalent to 10 ÷ (5x). The second is 10 ÷ 5 · x. **119.** −3.75(0.3); −1.125 **121.** $\frac{16}{5} \div \left(-\frac{8}{9}\right); -\frac{18}{5}$ **123.** −0.4 + 6(−0.42); −2.92 **125.** $-\frac{1}{4} - 6\left(-\frac{1}{3}\right); \frac{7}{4}$ **127.** 3(−2) + 3 = −3; loss of $3 **129.** 2(5) + 3(−3) = 1; Lorne was one sale above quota for the week. **131.** $\frac{12 + (-15) + 4 + (-9) + 3}{5} = -1$; The average loss was 1 oz. **133. a.** −10 **b.** 24 **c.** In part (a), we subtract; in part (b), we multiply.

Chapter 1 Problem Recognition Exercises, p. 74

1. a. −4 **b.** 32 **c.** −12 **d.** 2 **2. a.** 10 **b.** 14 **c.** −24 **d.** −6 **3. a.** −27 **b.** −324 **c.** −4 **d.** −45 **4. a.** 30 **b.** 24 **c.** −81 **d.** −9 **5. a.** 50 **b.** −15 **c.** $\frac{1}{2}$ **d.** 5 **6. a.** −5 **b.** −24 **c.** −16 **d.** −80 **7. a.** 64 **b.** 12 **c.** $\frac{1}{4}$ **d.** −20 **8. a.** −7 **b.** −24 **c.** −63 **d.** −18 **9. a.** −400 **b.** 85 **c.** −16 **d.** 75 **10. a.** 7 **b.** 294 **c.** $\frac{2}{3}$ **d.** −35 **11. a.** 8 **b.** 4 **c.** 4 **d.** 8 **12. a.** −16 **b.** 2 **c.** −2 **d.** 16

Section 1.7 Practice Exercises, pp. 84–87

1. a. constant **b.** coefficient **c.** 1; 1 **d.** like **3.** 7 **5.** 18 **7.** $-\frac{27}{5}$ or -5.4 **9.** 0 **11.** $\frac{1}{3}$ **13.** $\frac{11}{15}$ **15.** $-8+5$ **17.** $x+8$ **19.** 4(5) **21.** $-12x$ **23.** $x+(-3)$; $-3+x$ **25.** $4p+(-9)$; $-9+4p$ **27.** $x+(4+9)$; $x+13$ **29.** $(-5\cdot 3)x$; $-15x$ **31.** $\left(\frac{6}{11}\cdot\frac{11}{6}\right)x$; x **33.** $\left(-4\cdot -\frac{1}{4}\right)t$; t **35.** $(-8+2)+y$; $-6+y$ **37.** $(-5\cdot 2)x$; $-10x$ **39.** Reciprocal **41.** 0 **43.** $30x+6$ **45.** $-2a-16$ **47.** $15c-3d$ **49.** $-7y+14$ **51.** $-\frac{2}{3}x+4$ **53.** $\frac{1}{3}m-1$ **55.** $-2p-10$ **57.** $6w+10z-16$ **59.** $4x+8y-4z$ **61.** $6w-x+3y$ **63.** $6+2x$ **65.** $24z$ **67.** $-14x$ **69.** $-4-4x$ **71.** b **73.** i **75.** g **77.** d **79.** h

81.

Term	Coefficient
$2x$	2
$-y$	−1
$18xy$	18
5	5

83.

Term	Coefficient
$-x$	−1
$8y$	8
$-9x^2y$	−9
−3	−3

85. The variable factors are different. **87.** The variables are the same and raised to the same power. **89.** For example: $5y$, $-2x$, 6 **91.** $-6p$ **93.** $-6y^2$ **95.** $7x^3y-4$ **97.** $3t-\frac{7}{5}$ **99.** $-6x+22$ **101.** $4w$ **103.** $-3x+17$ **105.** $10t-44w$ **107.** $-18u$ **109.** $-2t+7$ **111.** $51a-27$ **113.** −6 **115.** $4q-\frac{1}{3}$ **117.** $6n$ **119.** $2x+18$ **121.** $2.2c-0.32$ **123.** $-2x-34$ **125.** $9z-35$ **127.** Equivalent **129.** Not equivalent. The terms are not *like* terms and cannot be combined. **131.** Not equivalent; subtraction is not commutative. **133.** Equivalent **135. a.** 55 **b.** 210

Chapter 1 Review Exercises, pp. 94–96

1. Improper **2.** Proper **3.** Improper **4.** Improper **5.** $2\times 2\times 2\times 2\times 7$ **6.** $\frac{6}{5}$ **7.** $\frac{35}{36}$ **8.** $\frac{13}{16}$ **9.** $\frac{2}{7}$ **10.** $\frac{6}{5}$ or $1\frac{1}{5}$ **11.** 3 **12.** $\frac{17}{10}$ or $1\frac{7}{10}$ **13.** 357 million km^2 **14. a.** 7, 1 **b.** 7, −4, 0, 1 **c.** 7, 0, 1 **d.** 7, $\frac{1}{3}$, −4, 0, $-0.\overline{2}$, 1 **e.** $-\sqrt{3}$, π **f.** 7, $\frac{1}{3}$, −4, 0, $-\sqrt{3}$, $-0.\overline{2}$, π, 1 **15.** $\frac{1}{2}$ **16.** 6 **17.** $\sqrt{7}$ **18.** 0 **19.** False **20.** False **21.** True **22.** True **23.** True **24.** True **25.** False **26.** True **27.** True **28.** 0 **29.** 60 **30.** 3 **31.** 4 **32.** $x\cdot\frac{2}{3}$ or $\frac{2}{3}x$ **33.** $\frac{7}{y}$ or $7\div y$ **34.** $2+3b$ **35.** $a-5$ **36.** $5k+2$ **37.** $13z-7$ **38.** 216 **39.** 225 **40.** 6 **41.** $\frac{1}{10}$ **42.** $\frac{1}{16}$ **43.** $\frac{27}{8}$ **44.** 13 **45.** 11 **46.** 7 **47.** 10 **48.** 2 **49.** 4 **50.** 15 **51.** −17 **52.** $\frac{11}{63}$ **53.** $-\frac{5}{22}$ **54.** $-\frac{14}{15}$ **55.** $-\frac{27}{10}$ **56.** −2.15 **57.** −4.28 **58.** 3 **59.** 8 **60.** 4 **61.** When a and b are both negative or when a and b have different signs and the number with the larger absolute value is negative. **62.** No. He is still overdrawn by \$8. **63.** −12 **64.** 33 **65.** −1 **66.** −17 **67.** $-\frac{29}{18}$ **68.** $-\frac{19}{24}$ **69.** −1.2 **70.** −4.25 **71.** −10.2 **72.** 12.09 **73.** $\frac{10}{3}$ **74.** $-\frac{17}{20}$ **75.** −1 **76.** If $a < b$ **77.** $-7-(-18)$; 11 **78.** $-6-41$; −47 **79.** $7-13$; −6 **80.** $[20-(-7)]-5$; 22 **81.** $[6+(-12)]-21$; −27 **82.** 175°F **83.** −170 **84.** −91 **85.** −2 **86.** 3 **87.** $-\frac{1}{6}$ **88.** $-\frac{8}{11}$ **89.** 0 **90.** Undefined **91.** 0 **92.** 2.25 **93.** $-\frac{3}{2}$ **94.** $\frac{1}{4}$ **95.** −30 **96.** 450 **97.** $\frac{1}{4}$ **98.** $-\frac{1}{7}$ **99.** −2 **100.** $\frac{18}{7}$ **101.** 17 **102.** 6 **103.** $-\frac{7}{120}$ **104.** 4.4 **105.** $-\frac{1}{3}$ **106.** −1 **107.** −2 **108.** 11 **109.** 36 **110.** −6 **111.** 70.6 **112.** True **113.** False, any nonzero real number raised to an even power is positive. **114.** True **115.** True **116.** False, the product of two negative numbers is positive. **117.** True **118.** True **119.** For example: $2+3=3+2$ **120.** For example: $(2+3)+4=2+(3+4)$ **121.** For example: $5+(-5)=0$ **122.** For example: $7+0=7$ **123.** For example: $5\cdot 2=2\cdot 5$ **124.** For example: $(8\cdot 2)10=8(2\cdot 10)$ **125.** For example: $3\cdot\frac{1}{3}=1$ **126.** For example: $8\cdot 1=8$ **127.** $5x-2y=5x+(-2y)$, then use the commutative property of addition. **128.** $3a-9y=3a+(-9y)$, then use the commutative property of addition. **129.** $3y$, $10x$, -12, xy **130.** 3, 10, −12, 1 **131.** $8a-b-10$ **132.** $-7p-11q+16$ **133.** $-8z-18$ **134.** $20w-40y+5$ **135.** $p-2w$ **136.** $-h+14m$ **137.** $-14q-1$ **138.** $-5.7b+2.4$ **139.** $4x+24$ **140.** $50y+105$

Chapter 1 Test, pp. 96–97

1. $\frac{15}{4}$ **2.** $\frac{3}{2}$ **3.** $3\frac{1}{16}$ **4.** $2\frac{3}{8}$ **5.** Rational, all repeating decimals are rational numbers. **6. a.** $(4x)(4x)(4x)$ **b.** $4\cdot x\cdot x\cdot x$

7. 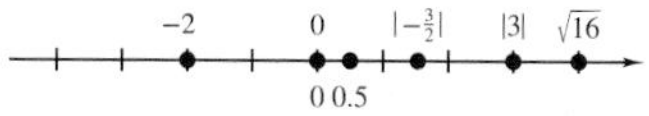

8. a. False **b.** True **c.** True **d.** True **9. a.** Commutative property of multiplication **b.** Identity property of addition **c.** Associative property of addition **d.** Inverse property of multiplication **e.** Associative property of multiplication **10. a.** Twice the difference of a and b **b.** b subtracted from twice a **11.** $\frac{\sqrt{c}}{d^2}$ or $\sqrt{c}\div d^2$ **12.** $12-(-4)$; 16 **13.** $6-8$; −2 **14.** $\frac{10}{-12}$; $-\frac{5}{6}$ **15.** $-\frac{7}{8}$ **16.** −12 **17.** 28 **18.** −12 **19.** −32 **20.** 96 **21.** 0 **22.** Undefined **23.** 6 **24.** 4.66 **25.** −28 **26.** $\frac{2}{3}$ **27.** $\frac{1}{3}$ **28.** 9 **29.** −8 **30.** The difference is 9.5°C. **31. a.** $5+2+(-10)+4$ **b.** He gained 1 yd. **32.** $-6k-8$ **33.** $-12x+2y-4$ **34.** $-4p-23$ **35.** $-12m-24p+21$ **36.** $4p-\frac{4}{3}$ **37.** 5 **38.** 18 **39.** −6 **40.** −32

Chapter 2

Section 2.1 Practice Exercises, pp. 109–111

1. a. equation **b.** solution **c.** linear **d.** solution set **3.** Expression **5.** Equation **7.** Substitute the value into the equation and determine if the right-hand side is equal to the left-hand side. **9.** No **11.** Yes **13.** Yes **15.** $\{-1\}$ **17.** $\{20\}$ **19.** $\{-17\}$ **21.** $\{-16\}$ **23.** $\{0\}$ **25.** $\{1.3\}$ **27.** $\left\{\frac{11}{2}\right\}$ or $\left\{5\frac{1}{2}\right\}$ **29.** $\{-2\}$ **31.** $\{-2.13\}$ **33.** $\{-3.2675\}$ **35.** $\{9\}$ **37.** $\{-4\}$ **39.** $\{0\}$ **41.** $\{-15\}$ **43.** $\left\{-\frac{4}{5}\right\}$ **45.** $\{-10\}$ **47.** $\{4\}$ **49.** $\{41\}$ **51.** $\{-127\}$ **53.** $\{-2.6\}$ **55.** $-8 + x = 42$; The number is 50. **57.** $x - (-6) = 18$; The number is 12. **59.** $x \cdot 7 = -63$ or $7x = -63$; The number is -9. **61.** $x - 3.2 = 2.1$; The number is 5.3. **63.** $\frac{x}{12} = \frac{1}{3}$; The number is 4. **65.** $x + \frac{5}{8} = \frac{13}{8}$; The number is 1. **67. a.** $\{10\}$ **b.** $\left\{-\frac{1}{9}\right\}$ **69. a.** $\{-12\}$ **b.** $\left\{\frac{22}{3}\right\}$ **71.** $\{-36\}$ **73.** $\{16\}$ **75.** $\{2\}$ **77.** $\left\{-\frac{7}{4}\right\}$ **79.** $\{11\}$ **81.** $\{-36\}$ **83.** $\left\{\frac{7}{2}\right\}$ **85.** $\{4\}$ **87.** $\{3.6\}$ **89.** $\{0.4084\}$ **91.** Yes **93.** No **95.** Yes **97.** Yes **99.** For example: $y + 9 = 15$ **101.** For example: $2p = -8$ **103.** For example: $5a + 5 = 5$ **105.** $\{-1\}$ **107.** $\{7\}$

Section 2.2 Practice Exercises, pp. 118–120

1. a. conditional **b.** contradiction **c.** empty or null **d.** identity **3.** $4w + 8$ **5.** $6y - 22$ **7.** $\{19\}$ **9.** $\{-3\}$ **11.** $\{-5\}$ **13.** $\{2\}$ **15.** $\{6\}$ **17.** $\left\{\frac{5}{2}\right\}$ **19.** $\{-42\}$ **21.** $\left\{-\frac{3}{4}\right\}$ **23.** $\{5\}$ **25.** $\{-4\}$ **27.** $\{-26\}$ **29.** $\{10\}$ **31.** $\{-8\}$ **33.** $\left\{-\frac{7}{3}\right\}$ **35.** $\{0\}$ **37.** $\{-3\}$ **39.** $\{-2\}$ **41.** $\left\{\frac{9}{2}\right\}$ **43.** $\left\{-\frac{1}{3}\right\}$ **45.** $\{10\}$ **47.** $\{-6\}$ **49.** $\{0\}$ **51.** $\{-2\}$ **53.** $\left\{-\frac{25}{4}\right\}$ **55.** $\left\{\frac{10}{3}\right\}$ **57.** $\{-0.25\}$ **59.** $\{\ \}$; contradiction **61.** $\{-15\}$; conditional equation **63.** The set of real numbers; identity **65.** One solution **67.** Infinitely many solutions **69.** $\{7\}$ **71.** $\left\{\frac{1}{2}\right\}$ **73.** $\{0\}$ **75.** The set of real numbers **77.** $\{-46\}$ **79.** $\{2\}$ **81.** $\left\{\frac{13}{2}\right\}$ **83.** $\{-5\}$ **85.** $\{\ \}$ **87.** $\{2.205\}$ **89.** $\{10\}$ **91.** $\{-1\}$ **93.** $a = 15$ **95.** $a = 4$ **97.** For example: $5x + 2 = 2 + 5x$

Section 2.3 Practice Exercises, pp. 126–127

1. a. clearing fractions **b.** clearing decimals **3.** $\{-2\}$ **5.** $\{-5\}$ **7.** $\{\ \}$ **9.** 18, 36 **11.** 100; 1000; 10,000 **13.** 30, 60 **15.** $\{4\}$ **17.** $\{-12\}$ **19.** $\left\{-\frac{15}{4}\right\}$ **21.** $\{8\}$ **23.** $\{3\}$ **25.** $\{15\}$ **27.** $\{\ \}$ **29.** The set of real numbers **31.** $\{5\}$ **33.** $\{2\}$ **35.** $\{-15\}$ **37.** $\{6\}$ **39.** $\{107\}$ **41.** The set of real numbers **43.** $\{67\}$ **45.** $\{90\}$ **47.** $\{4\}$ **49.** $\{4\}$ **51.** $\{\ \}$ **53.** $\{-0.25\}$ **55.** $\{-6\}$ **57.** $\left\{\frac{8}{3}\right\}$ or $\left\{2\frac{2}{3}\right\}$ **59.** $\{-11\}$ **61.** $\left\{\frac{1}{10}\right\}$ **63.** $\{-2\}$ **65.** $\{-1\}$ **67.** $\{2\}$

Chapter 2 Problem Recognition Exercises, p. 128

1. Expression; $-4b + 18$ **2.** Expression; $20p - 30$ **3.** Equation; $\{-8\}$ **4.** Equation; $\{-14\}$ **5.** Equation; $\left\{\frac{1}{3}\right\}$ **6.** Equation; $\left\{-\frac{4}{3}\right\}$ **7.** Expression; $6z - 23$ **8.** Expression; $-x - 9$ **9.** Equation; $\left\{\frac{7}{9}\right\}$ **10.** Equation; $\left\{-\frac{13}{10}\right\}$ **11.** Equation; $\{20\}$ **12.** Equation; $\{-3\}$ **13.** Equation; $\left\{\frac{1}{2}\right\}$ **14.** Equation; $\{-6\}$ **15.** Expression; $\frac{5}{8}x + \frac{7}{4}$ **16.** Expression; $-26t + 18$ **17.** Equation; $\{\ \}$ **18.** Equation; $\{\ \}$ **19.** Equation; $\left\{\frac{23}{12}\right\}$ **20.** Equation; $\left\{\frac{5}{8}\right\}$ **21.** Equation; The set of real numbers **22.** Equation; The set of real numbers **23.** Equation; $\left\{\frac{1}{2}\right\}$ **24.** Equation; $\{0\}$ **25.** Expression; 0 **26.** Expression; -1 **27.** Expression; $2a + 13$ **28.** Expression; $8q + 3$ **29.** Equation; $\{10\}$ **30.** Equation; $\left\{-\frac{1}{20}\right\}$ **31.** Expression; $-\frac{1}{6}y + \frac{1}{3}$ **32.** Expression; $\frac{7}{10}x + \frac{2}{5}$

Section 2.4 Practice Exercises, pp. 135–138

1. a. consecutive **b.** even **c.** odd **d.** 1 **e.** 2 **f.** 2 **3.** $x - 5{,}682{,}080$ **5.** $10x$ **7.** $3x - 20$ **9.** The number is -4. **11.** The number is -3. **13.** The number is 5. **15.** The number is -5. **17.** The number is 3. **19. a.** $x + 1, x + 2$ **b.** $x - 1, x - 2$ **21.** The integers are -34 and -33. **23.** The integers are 13 and 15. **25.** The sides are 14 in., 15 in., 16 in., 17 in., and 18 in. **27.** The integers are -54, -52, and -50. **29.** The integers are 13, 15, and 17. **31.** The lengths of the pieces are 33 cm and 53 cm. **33.** Karen's music library has 23 playlists and Claran's library has 35 playlists. **35.** There were 201 Republicans and 232 Democrats. **37.** There were 190 passenger cars and 230 SUVs sold. **39.** The Congo River is 4370 km long, and the Nile River is 6825 km. **41.** The area of Africa is 30,065,000 km^2. The area of Asia is 44,579,000 km^2. **43.** They walked 12.3 mi on the first day and 8.2 mi on the second. **45.** The pieces are 9 in., 17 in., and 22 in. **47.** The integers are 42, 43, and 44. **49.** The winner earned \$14 million and the runner-up earned \$5 million. **51.** The number is 11. **53.** The page numbers are 470 and 471. **55.** The number is 10. **57.** The deepest point in the Arctic Ocean is 5122 m. **59.** The number is $\frac{7}{16}$. **61.** The number is 2.5.

Section 2.5 Practice Exercises, pp. 143–146

1. a. simple **b.** 100 **3.** The numbers are 21 and 22. **5.** 12.5% **7.** 85% **9.** 0.75 **11.** 1050.8 **13.** 885 **15.** 2200 **17.** Molly will have to pay \$106.99. **19.** Approximately 231,000 cases **21.** 2% **23.** Javon's taxable income was \$84,000. **25.** Aidan would earn \$9 more in the CD. **27.** Bob borrowed \$1200. **29.** The rate is 6%. **31.** Perry needs to invest \$3302. **33. a.** \$7.44 **b.** \$54.56 **35.** The original price was \$470.59. **37.** The discount rate is 12%. **39.** The original dosage was 15 cc. **41.** The tax rate is 5%. **43.** The original cost was \$11.58 per pack. **45.** The original price was \$210,000. **47.** Alina made \$4600 that month. **49.** Diane sold \$645 over \$200 worth of merchandise.

Section 2.6 Calculator Connections, p. 152

1. 140.056 **2.** 31.831 **3.** 1.273 **4.** 0.455

1–2.

```
880/(2π)
           140.0563499
1600/(π*(4)²)
           31.83098862
```

3–4.

```
20/(5π)
           1.273239545
10/(7π)
           .4547284088
```

Section 2.6 Practice Exercises, pp. 152–156

1. $\{-5\}$ **3.** $\{0\}$ **5.** $\{-2\}$ **7.** $\{\ \}$ **9.** $a = P - b - c$

11. $y = x + z$ **13.** $q = p - 250$ **15.** $b = \dfrac{A}{h}$

17. $t = \dfrac{PV}{nr}$ **19.** $x = 5 + y$ **21.** $y = -3x - 19$

23. $y = \dfrac{-2x+6}{3}$ or $y = -\dfrac{2}{3}x + 2$

25. $x = \dfrac{y+9}{-2}$ or $x = -\dfrac{1}{2}y - \dfrac{9}{2}$

27. $y = \dfrac{-4x+12}{-3}$ or $y = \dfrac{4}{3}x - 4$

29. $y = \dfrac{-ax+c}{b}$ or $y = -\dfrac{a}{b}x + \dfrac{c}{b}$

31. $t = \dfrac{A-P}{Pr}$ or $t = \dfrac{A}{Pr} - \dfrac{1}{r}$

33. $c = \dfrac{a-2b}{2}$ or $c = \dfrac{a}{2} - b$ **35.** $y = 2Q - x$

37. $a = MS$ **39.** $R = \dfrac{P}{I^2}$

41. The length is 7 ft and the width is 5 ft.
43. The length is 120 yd and the width is 30 yd.
45. The length is 195 m and the width is 100 m.
47. The sides are 22 m, 22 m, and 27 m.
49. "Adjacent supplementary angles form a straight angle." The words *Supplementary* and *Straight* both begin with the same letter.
51. The angles are 23.5° and 66.5°.
53. The angles are 34.8° and 145.2°.
55. $x = 20$; the vertical angles measure 37°.
57. The measures of the angles are 30°, 60°, and 90°.
59. The measures of the angles are 42°, 54°, and 84°.
61. $x = 17$; the measures of the angles are 34° and 56°.

63. a. $A = lw$ **b.** $w = \dfrac{A}{l}$ **c.** The width is 29.5 ft.

65. a. $P = 2l + 2w$ **b.** $l = \dfrac{P-2w}{2}$ **c.** The length is 103 m.

67. a. $C = 2\pi r$ **b.** $r = \dfrac{C}{2\pi}$ **c.** The radius is approximately 140 ft.

69. a. 415.48 m^2 **b.** 10,386.89 m^3

Section 2.7 Practice Exercises, pp. 161–165

1. a. $x = \dfrac{c+by}{a}$ **3.** $y = \dfrac{18-7x}{x}$ **5.** $\{4\}$

7. $200 - t$ **9.** $100 - x$ **11.** $3000 - y$
13. 53 tickets were sold at \$3 and 28 tickets were sold at \$2.
15. There were 17 songs purchased at \$1.29 and 8 songs purchased at \$1.49.
17. Amber bought 21 books at \$6.99 and 11 books at \$9.99. **19.** $x + 7$
21. $d + 2000$ **23.** Mix 500 gal of 5% ethanol fuel mixture.
25. The pharmacist needs to use 21 mL of the 1% saline solution.
27. The contractor needs to mix 6.75 oz of 50% acid solution.
29. a. 300 mi **b.** $5x$ **c.** $5(x + 12)$ or $5x + 60$ **31.** She walks 4 mph to the lake. **33.** Bryan hiked 6 mi up the canyon.
35. The plane travels 600 mph in still air. **37.** The slower car travels 48 mph and the faster car travels 52 mph. **39.** The speeds of the vehicles are 40 mph and 50 mph. **41.** Sarah walks 3.5 mph and Jeanette runs 7 mph. **43. a.** 2 lb **b.** $0.10x$ **c.** $0.10(x + 3) = 0.10x + 0.30$ **45.** Mix 10 lb of coffee sold at \$12 per pound and 40 lb of coffee sold at \$8 per pound. **47.** The boats will meet in $\frac{3}{4}$ hr (45 min). **49.** Sam purchased 16 packages of wax and 5 bottles of sunscreen. **51.** 2.5 quarts of 85% chlorine solution
53. 20 L of water must be added. **55.** The Japanese bullet train travels 300 km/hr and the Acela Express travels 240 km/hr.

Section 2.8 Practice Exercises, pp. 176–180

1. a. linear inequality **b.** inequality **c.** set-builder; interval

3. $\{-3\}$ **5.** 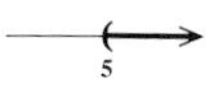

7. 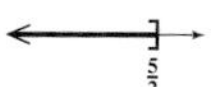

9. 

11. 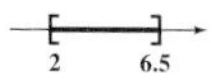

13. 

15. 

Set-Builder Notation	Graph	Interval Notation
17. $\{x \mid x \geq 6\}$		$[6, \infty)$
19. $\{x \mid x \leq 2.1\}$	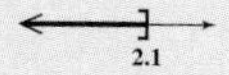	$(-\infty, 2.1]$
21. $\{x \mid -2 < x \leq 7\}$		$(-2, 7]$

Set-Builder Notation	Graph	Interval Notation
23. $\left\{x \,\middle|\, x > \dfrac{3}{4}\right\}$		$\left(\dfrac{3}{4}, \infty\right)$
25. $\{x \mid -1 < x < 8\}$		$(-1, 8)$
27. $\{x \mid x \leq -14\}$	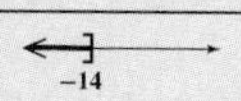	$(-\infty, -14]$

Set-Builder Notation	Graph	Interval Notation
29. $\{x \mid x \geq 18\}$		$[18, \infty)$
31. $\{x \mid x < -0.6\}$	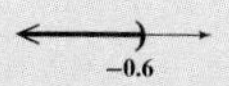	$(-\infty, -0.6)$
33. $\{x \mid -3.5 \leq x < 7.1\}$		$[-3.5, 7.1)$

35. a. $\{3\}$
b. $\{x \mid x > 3\}$; $(3, \infty)$

37. a. $\{13\}$
b. $\{p \mid p \leq 13\}$; $(-\infty, 13]$
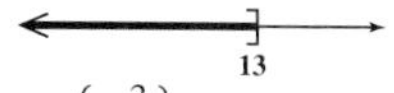

39. a. $\{-3\}$
b. $\{c \mid c < -3\}$; $(-\infty, -3)$

41. a. $\left\{-\dfrac{3}{2}\right\}$
b. $\left\{z \,\middle|\, z \geq -\dfrac{3}{2}\right\}$; $\left[-\dfrac{3}{2}, \infty\right)$

43. $(-1, 4]$

45. $(-3, 5)$

47. $[2, 6]$

49. a. $\{x \mid x \leq 1\}$ **b.** $(-\infty, 1]$
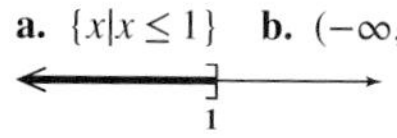

51. a. $\{q \mid q > 10\}$
b. $(10, \infty)$

53. a. $\{x \mid x > 3\}$
b. $(3, \infty)$

55. a. $\{c \mid c > 2\}$
b. $(2, \infty)$

57. a. $\{c \mid c < -2\}$
b. $(-\infty, -2)$
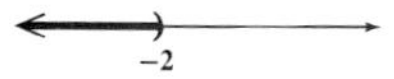

59. a. $\{h \mid h \geq 14\}$
b. $[14, \infty)$

61. a. $\{x \mid x \geq -24\}$
b. $[-24, \infty)$

63. a. $\{p \mid -3 \leq p < 3\}$
b. $[-3, 3)$
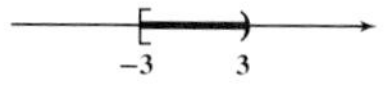

65. a. $\left\{h \,\middle|\, 0 < h < \dfrac{5}{2}\right\}$
b. $\left(0, \dfrac{5}{2}\right)$

67. a. $\{x \mid 10 < x < 12\}$
b. $(10, 12)$

69. a. $\{x \mid -8 \leq x < 24\}$
b. $[-8, 24)$

71. a. $\{y|y > -9\}$
b. $(-9, \infty)$

73. a. $\left\{x \middle| x \geq -\frac{15}{2}\right\}$
b. $\left[-\frac{15}{2}, \infty\right)$

75. a. $\{x|x < -3\}$
b. $(-\infty, -3)$

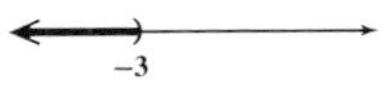

77. a. $\left\{b \middle| b \geq -\frac{1}{3}\right\}$
b. $\left[-\frac{1}{3}, \infty\right)$

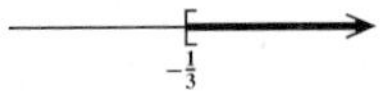

79. a. $\{n|n > -3\}$
b. $(-3, \infty)$

81. a. $\{x|x < 7\}$
b. $(-\infty, 7)$

83. a. $\{x|x \leq -5\}$
b. $(-\infty, -5]$

85. a. $\{z|z \leq -2\}$
b. $(-\infty, -2]$

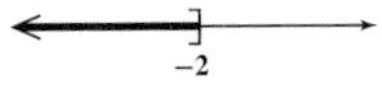

87. a. $\left\{a \middle| a > -\frac{2}{3}\right\}$
b. $\left(-\frac{2}{3}, \infty\right)$

89. a. $\left\{p \middle| p \leq \frac{15}{4}\right\}$
b. $\left(-\infty, \frac{15}{4}\right]$

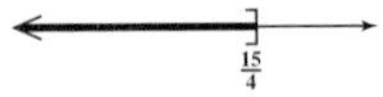

91. a. $\{y|y < -9\}$
b. $(-\infty, -9)$

93. a. $\{a|a > -3\}$
b. $(-3, \infty)$

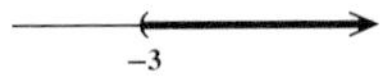

95. a. $\{x|x \leq 0\}$ **b.** $(-\infty, 0]$

97. No **99.** Yes **101.** $L \geq 10$ **103.** $w > 75$
105. $t \leq 72$ **107.** $L \geq 8$ **109.** $2 < h < 5$
111. More than 10.2 in. of rain is needed. **113.** Trevor needs at least 86 to get a B in the course. **115. a.** $1539
b. 200 birdhouses cost $1440. It is cheaper to purchase 200 birdhouses because the discount is greater. **117.** Company A is better if more than 400 flyers are printed. **119.** Madison needs to babysit a minimum of 39.5 hr.

Chapter 2 Review Exercises, pp. 187–190

1. a. Equation **b.** Expression **c.** Equation **d.** Equation
2. A linear equation can be written in the form $ax + b = c, a \neq 0$.
3. a. No **b.** Yes **c.** No **d.** Yes **4. a.** No **b.** Yes
5. $\{-8\}$ **6.** $\{15\}$ **7.** $\left\{\frac{21}{4}\right\}$ **8.** $\{70\}$ **9.** $\left\{-\frac{21}{5}\right\}$
10. $\{-60\}$ **11.** $\left\{-\frac{10}{7}\right\}$ **12.** $\{27\}$ **13.** The number is 60.
14. The number is $\frac{7}{24}$. **15.** The number is -8.
16. The number is -2. **17.** $\{1\}$ **18.** $\left\{-\frac{3}{5}\right\}$ **19.** $\{2\}$
20. $\{-6\}$ **21.** $\{-3\}$ **22.** $\{18\}$ **23.** $\left\{\frac{3}{4}\right\}$ **24.** $\{-3\}$
25. $\{0\}$ **26.** $\left\{\frac{1}{8}\right\}$ **27.** $\{2\}$ **28.** $\{6\}$ **29.** A contradiction has no solution and an identity is true for all real numbers.
30. Identity **31.** Conditional equation **32.** Contradiction
33. Identity **34.** Contradiction **35.** Conditional equation
36. $\{6\}$ **37.** $\{22\}$ **38.** $\{13\}$ **39.** $\{-27\}$ **40.** $\{-10\}$
41. $\{-7\}$ **42.** $\left\{\frac{5}{3}\right\}$ **43.** $\left\{-\frac{9}{4}\right\}$ **44.** $\{2.5\}$ **45.** $\{-4\}$
46. $\{-4.2\}$ **47.** $\{2.5\}$ **48.** $\{-312\}$ **49.** $\{200\}$ **50.** $\{\ \}$
51. $\{\ \}$ **52.** The set of real numbers **53.** The set of real numbers **54.** The number is 30. **55.** The number is 11.
56. The number is -7. **57.** The number is -10.
58. The integers are 66, 68, and 70. **59.** The integers are 27, 28, and 29. **60.** The sides are 25 in., 26 in., and 27 in.
61. The sides are 36 cm, 37 cm, 38 cm, 39 cm, and 40 cm.
62. In 1975 the minimum salary was $16,000.
63. Indiana has 6.2 million people and Kentucky has 4.1 million.
64. 23.8 **65.** 28.8 **66.** 12.5% **67.** 95% **68.** 160
69. 1750 **70.** The dinner was $40 before tax and tip.
71. a. $840 **b.** $3840 **72.** He invested $12,000.
73. The novel originally cost $29.50. **74.** $K = C + 273$
75. $C = K - 273$ **76.** $s = \frac{P}{4}$ **77.** $s = \frac{P}{3}$
78. $x = \frac{y - b}{m}$ **79.** $x = \frac{c - a}{b}$ **80.** $y = \frac{-2x - 2}{5}$
81. $b = \frac{Q - 4a}{4}$ or $b = \frac{Q}{4} - a$ **82.** The height is 7 m.
83. a. $h = \frac{3V}{\pi r^2}$ **b.** The height is 5.1 in. **84.** The angles are 22°, 78°, and 80°. **85.** The angles are 50° and 40°.
86. The length is 5 ft and the width is 4 ft. **87.** $x = 20$. The angle measure is 65°. **88.** The measure of angle y is 53°.
89. The truck travels 45 km/hr in bad weather and 60 km/hr in good weather. **90.** Gus rides 15 mph and Winston rides 18 mph.
91. The cars will be 327.6 mi apart after 2.8 hr (2 hr and 48 min).
92. They meet in 2.25 hr (2 hr and 15 min). **93.** 2 lb of 24% fat content beef is needed. **94.** 20 lb of the 40% solder should be used.
95. $(-2, \infty)$

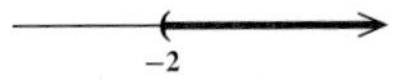

96. $\left(-\infty, \frac{1}{2}\right]$

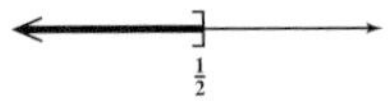

97. $(-1, 4]$

98. a. $637 **b.** 300 plants cost $1410, and 295 plants cost $1416. 295 plants cost more.
99. $\{c|c < 17\}$; $(-\infty, 17)$

100. $\left\{w \middle| w > -\frac{1}{3}\right\}$; $\left(-\frac{1}{3}, \infty\right)$

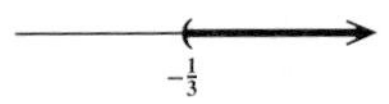

101. $\{x|x \leq -6\}$; $(-\infty, -6]$

102. $\left\{y \middle| y \leq -\frac{14}{5}\right\}$; $\left(-\infty, -\frac{14}{5}\right]$

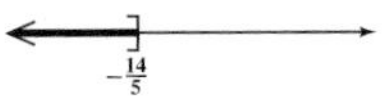

103. $\{a|a \geq 49\}$; $[49, \infty)$

104. $\{t|t < 34.5\}$; $(-\infty, 34.5)$

105. $\{k|k > 18\}$; $(18, \infty)$

106. $\left\{h \middle| h \leq \frac{5}{2}\right\}$; $\left(-\infty, \frac{5}{2}\right]$

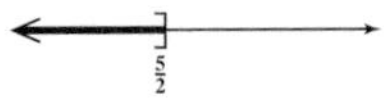

107. $\{x|x < -1\}$; $(-\infty, -1)$

108. $\{b|-3 < b \leq 7\}$; $(-3, 7]$

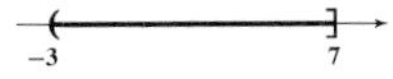

109. $\{z|-6 \leq z \leq 5\}$; $[-6, 5]$

110. More than 2.5 in. is required.
111. Collette can have at most 18 wings.

Chapter 2 Test, pp. 190–191

1. b, d **2. a.** $5x + 7$ **b.** $\{9\}$ **3.** $\left\{\frac{7}{3}\right\}$ **4.** $\{\ \}$
5. $\{-16\}$ **6.** $\left\{\frac{13}{4}\right\}$ **7.** $\{12\}$ **8.** $\left\{\frac{20}{21}\right\}$ **9.** $\left\{-\frac{16}{9}\right\}$
10. $\{15\}$ **11.** The set of real numbers **12.** $\{-3\}$
13. $\{-47\}$ **14.** $y = -3x - 4$ **15.** $r = \frac{C}{2\pi}$ **16.** 90
17. a. $(-\infty, 0)$

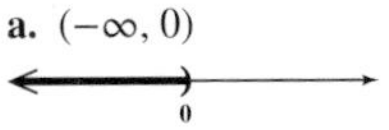

b. $[-2, 5)$

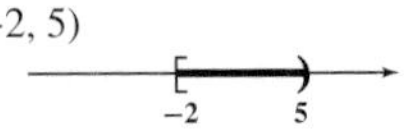

18. $\{x|x > -2\}$; $(-2, \infty)$

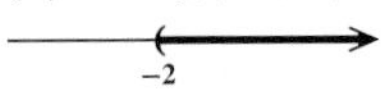

19. $\{x|x \leq -4\}$; $(-\infty, -4]$

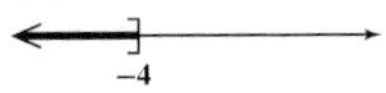

20. $\left\{y \,\middle|\, y > -\frac{3}{2}\right\}$; $\left(-\frac{3}{2}, \infty\right)$ 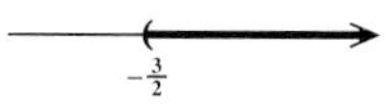

21. $\{p|-5 \le p \le 1\}$; $[-5, 1]$

22. The cost was \$82.00. **23.** Clarita originally borrowed \$5000. **24.** The numbers are 18 and 13. **25.** One family travels 55 mph and the other travels 50 mph. **26.** More than 26.5 in. is required. **27.** The sides are 61 in., 62 in., 63 in., 64 in., and 65 in. **28.** Matthew needs 30 lb of macadamia nuts. **29.** Each basketball ticket was \$36.32, and each hockey ticket was \$40.64. **30.** The measures of the angles are 32° and 58°. **31.** The field is 110 m long and 75 m wide. **32.** $y = 30$; The measures of the angles are 30°, 39°, and 111°.

Chapters 1–2 Cumulative Review Exercises, pp. 191–192

1. $\frac{1}{2}$ **2.** -7 **3.** $-\frac{5}{12}$ **4.** 16 **5.** 4 **6.** $\sqrt{5^2 - 9}$; 4 **7.** $-14 + 12$; -2 **8.** $-7x^2y$, $4xy$, -6 **9.** $9x + 13$ **10.** $\{4\}$ **11.** $\{-7.2\}$ **12.** The set of real numbers **13.** $\{-8\}$ **14.** $\left\{-\frac{4}{7}\right\}$ **15.** $\{-80\}$ **16.** The numbers are 77 and 79. **17.** The cost before tax was \$350.00. **18.** The height is $\frac{41}{6}$ cm or $6\frac{5}{6}$ cm. **19.** $\{x|x > -2\}$; $(-2, \infty)$ **20.** $\{x|-1 \le x \le 9\}$; $[-1, 9]$

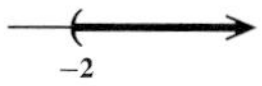

Chapter 3

Section 3.1 Practice Exercises, pp. 198–203

1. a. x; y-axis **b.** ordered **c.** origin; (0, 0) **d.** quadrants **e.** negative **f.** III **3. a.** Month 10 **b.** 30 **c.** Between months 3 and 5 and between months 10 and 12 **d.** Months 8 and 9 **e.** Month 3 **f.** 80 **5. a.** On day 1 the price per share was \$89.25. **b.** \$1.75 **c.** $-\$2.75$

7.

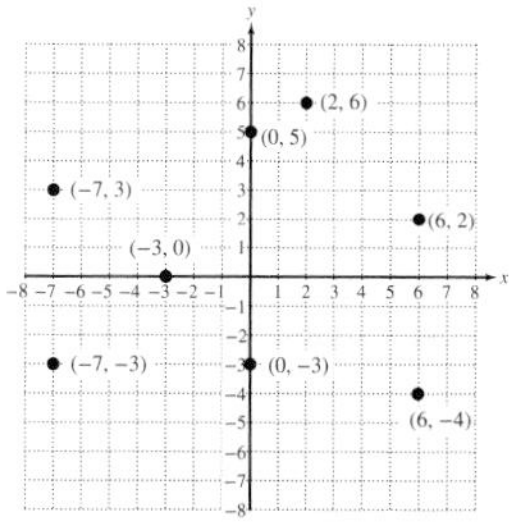

9.

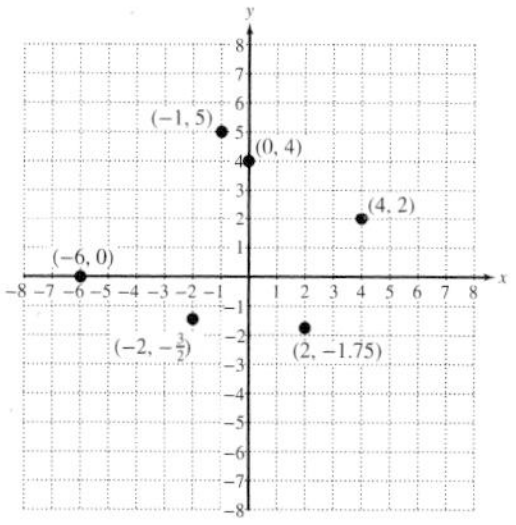

11. IV **13.** II **15.** III **17.** I **19.** $(0, -5)$ lies on the y-axis. **21.** $(\frac{7}{8}, 0)$ is located on the x-axis. **23.** $A(-4, 2)$, $B(\frac{1}{2}, 4)$, $C(3, -4)$, $D(-3, -4)$, $E(0, -3)$, $F(5, 0)$ **25. a.** $A(400, 200)$, $B(200, -150)$, $C(-300, -200)$, $D(-300, 250)$, $E(0, 450)$ **b.** 450 m **27. a.** (250, 225), (175, 193), (315, 330), (220, 209), (450, 570), (400, 480), (190, 185); the ordered pair (250, 225) means that 250 people produce \$225 in popcorn sales.

b.

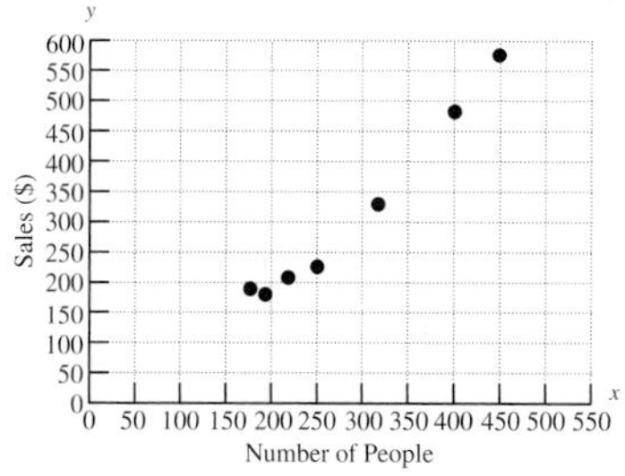

29. a. (1, −10.2), (2, −9.0), (3, −2.5), (4, 5.7), (5, 13.0), (6, 18.3), (7, 20.9), (8, 19.6), (9, 14.8), (10, 8.7), (11, 2.0), (12, −6.9)

b.

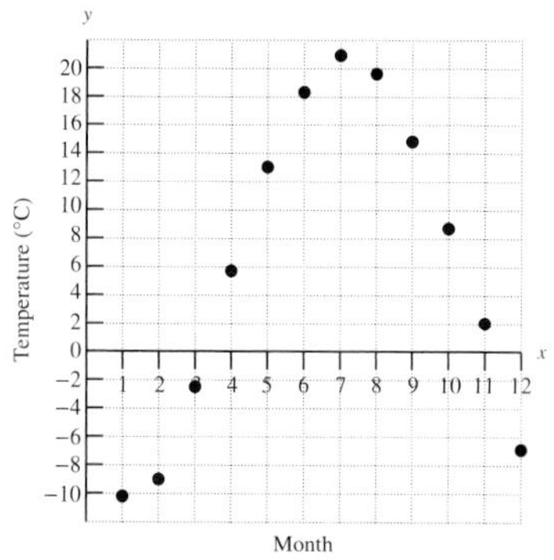

31. a.

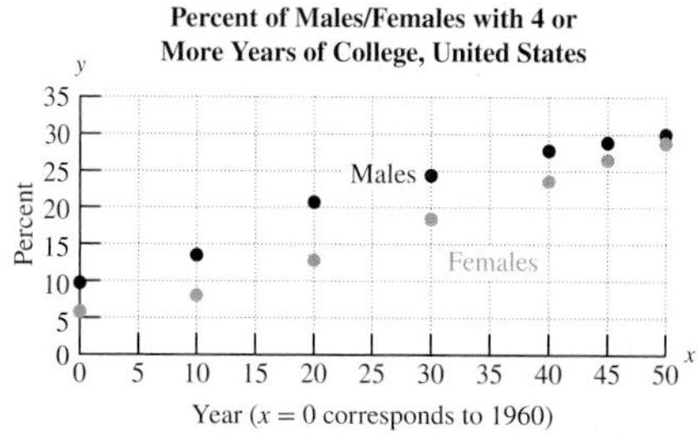

b. Increasing **c.** Increasing

Section 3.2 Calculator Connections, pp. 211–212

1.

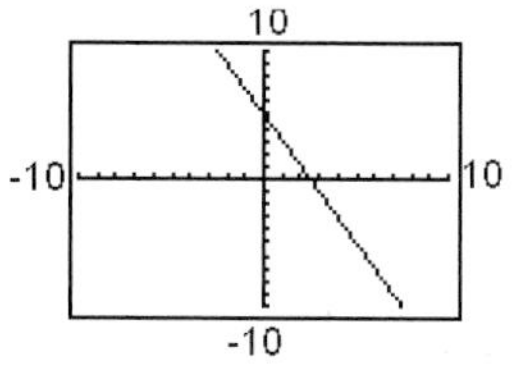

2.

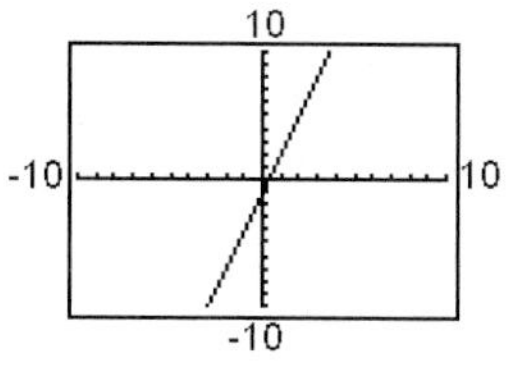

3.

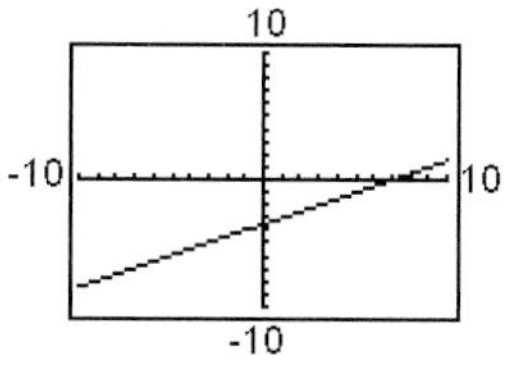

4.

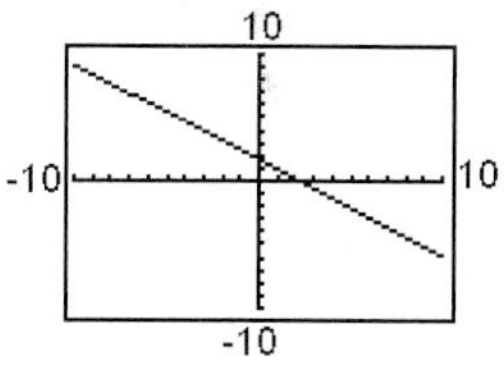

5.

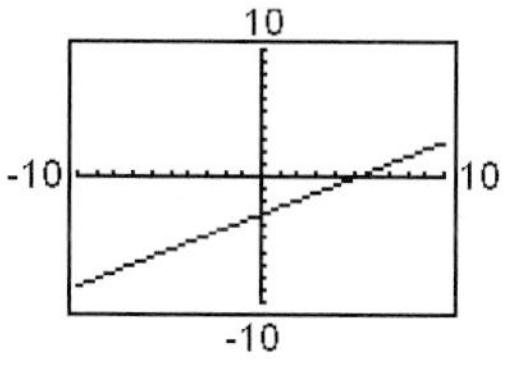

6.

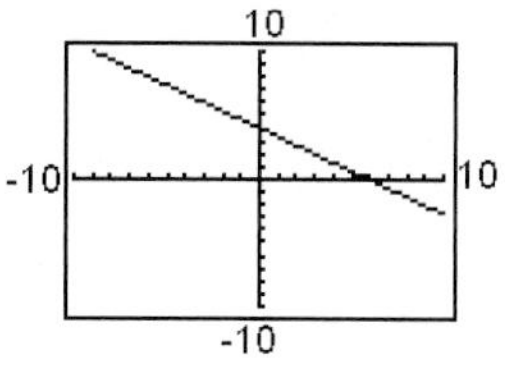

7.

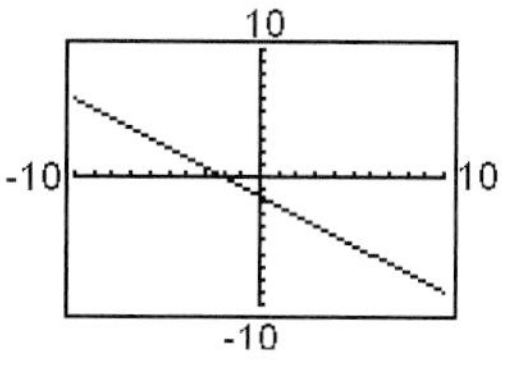

8.

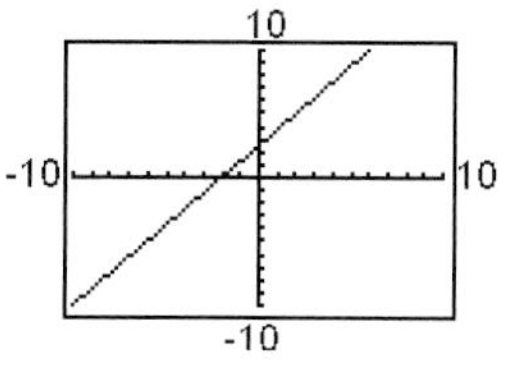

9.

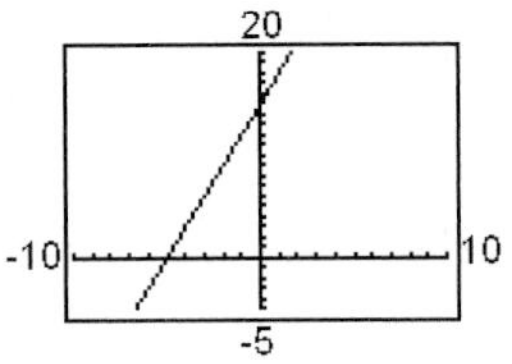

10.

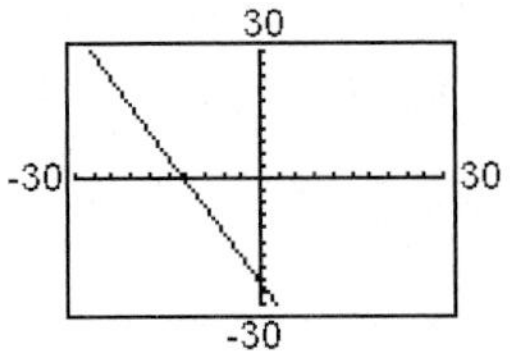

11.

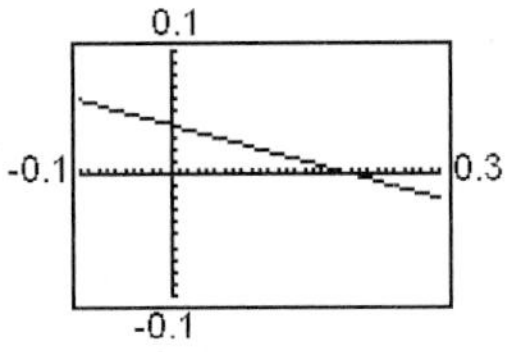

12.

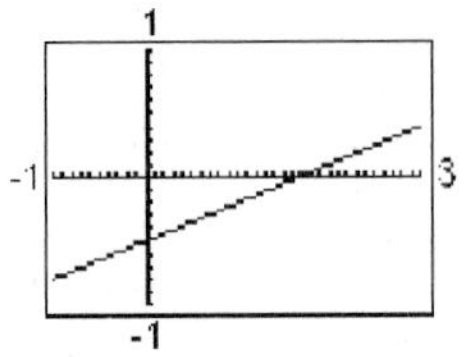

Section 3.2 Practice Exercises, pp. 212–218

1. a. $Ax + By = C$ **b.** x-intercept **c.** y-intercept **d.** vertical **e.** horizontal **3.** $(-2, -2)$; quadrant III

5. $(-5, 0)$; x-axis **7.** $(-3, 2)$; quadrant II **9.** Yes

11. Yes **13.** No **15.** No **17.** Yes

19.

x	y
1	−3
−2	0
−3	1
−4	2

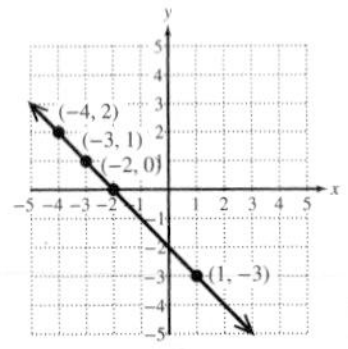

21.

x	y
−2	3
−1	0
−4	9

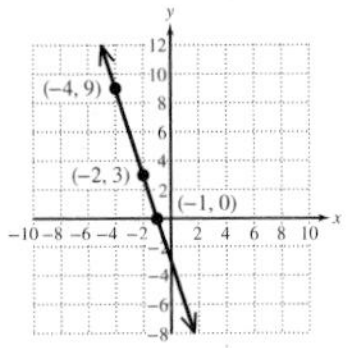

23.

x	y
0	4
2	0
3	−2

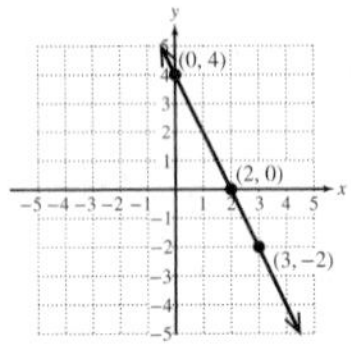

25.

x	y
0	−2
5	−5
10	−8

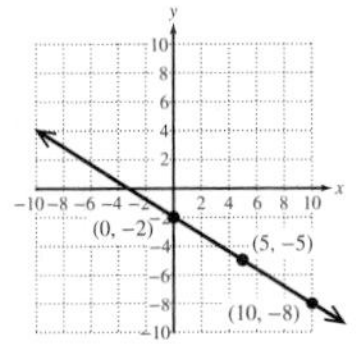

27.

x	y
0	−2
−3	−2
5	−2

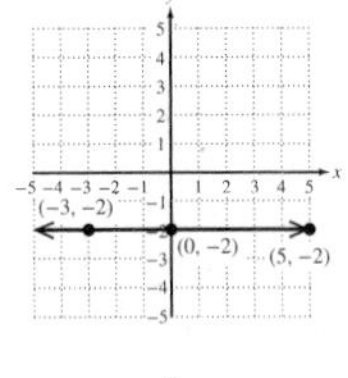

29.

x	y
3/2	−1
3/2	2
3/2	−3

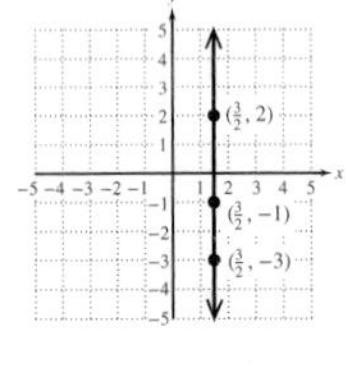

31.

x	y
0	4.6
1	3.4
2	2.2

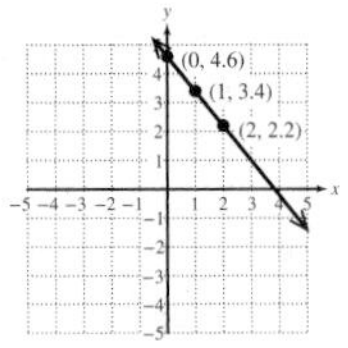

33.

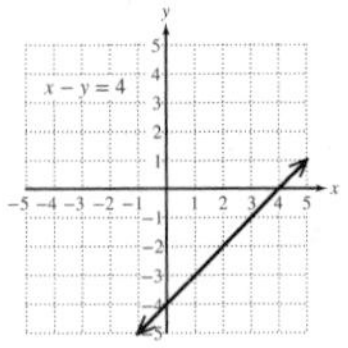

35.

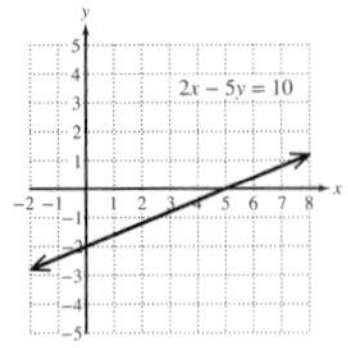

37.

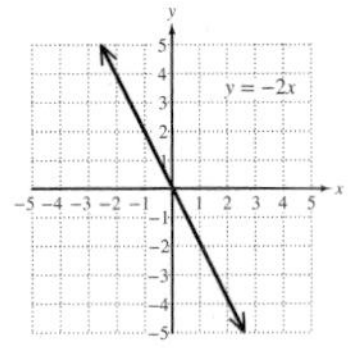

39.

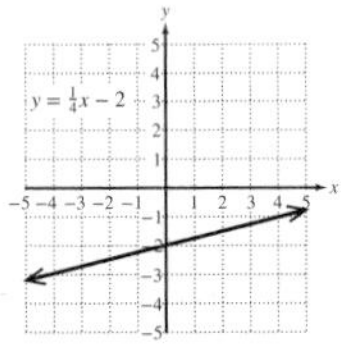

41.

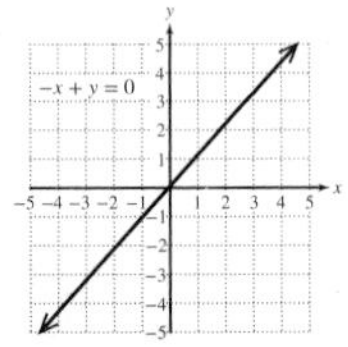

43.

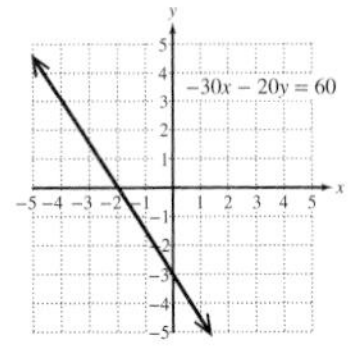

45. y-axis **47.** x-intercept: $(-1, 0)$; y-intercept: $(0, -3)$

49. x-intercept: $(-4, 0)$; y-intercept: $(0, 1)$

51. x-intercept: $\left(-\frac{9}{4}, 0\right)$; y-intercept: $(0, 3)$

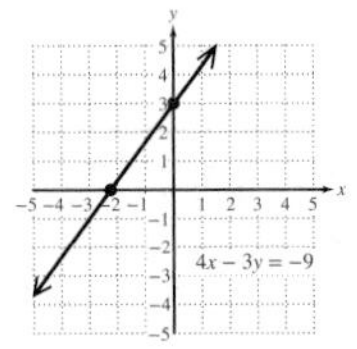

53. x-intercept: $\left(\frac{8}{3}, 0\right)$; y-intercept: $(0, 2)$

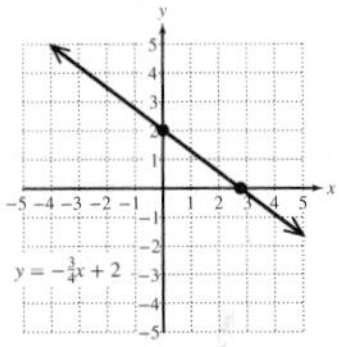

55. x-intercept: $(-4, 0)$; y-intercept: $(0, 8)$

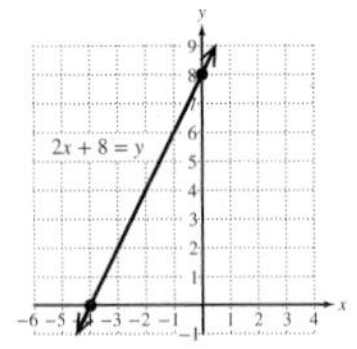

57. x-intercept: $(0, 0)$; y-intercept: $(0, 0)$

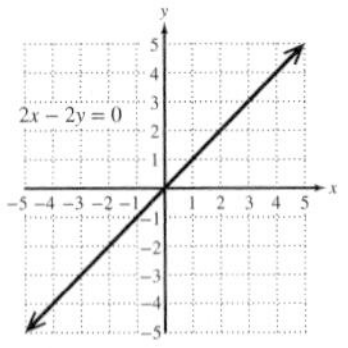

59. x-intercept: $(10, 0)$; y-intercept: $(0, 5)$

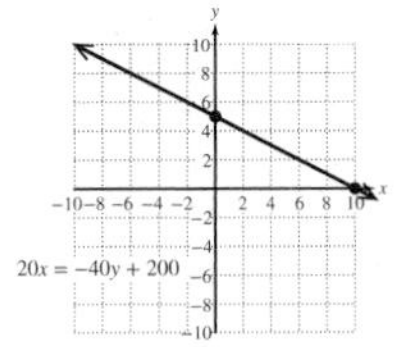

61. x-intercept: $(0, 0)$; y-intercept: $(0, 0)$

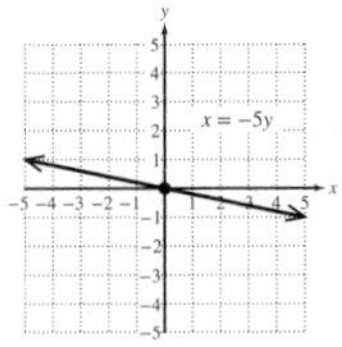

63. True

65. True

67. a. Horizontal line

c. no x-intercept; y-intercept: $(0, -1)$

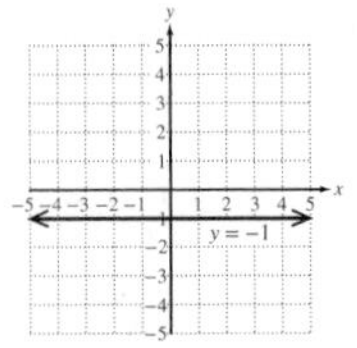

69. a. Vertical line

c. x-intercept: $(4, 0)$; no y-intercept

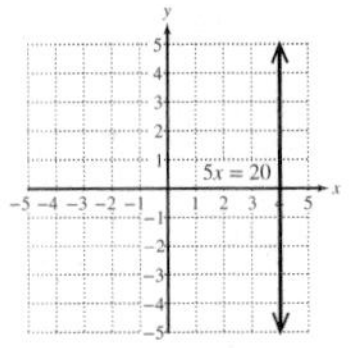

71. **a.** Horizontal line **c.** no x-intercept; y-intercept: (0, 3)

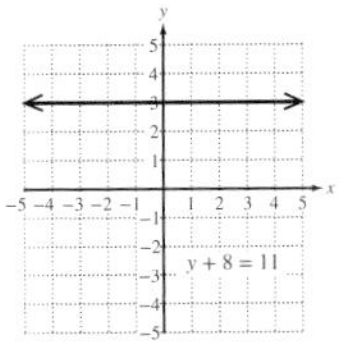

73. **a.** Vertical line **c.** All points on the y-axis are y-intercepts; x-intercept: (0, 0)

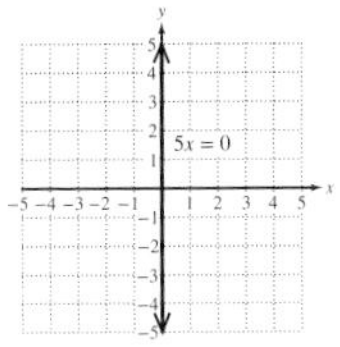

75. A horizontal line may not have an x-intercept. A vertical line may not have a y-intercept. **77.** a, b, d **79.** **a.** $y = 11{,}190$ **b.** $x = 3$ **c.** (1, 11190) One year after purchase the value of the car is \$11,190. (3, 9140) Three years after purchase the value of the car is \$9140.

Section 3.3 Practice Exercises, pp. 225–231

1. **a.** slope; $\dfrac{y_2 - y_1}{x_2 - x_1}$ **b.** parallel **c.** right **d.** -1 **e.** undefined; horizontal

3. x-intercept: (6, 0); y-intercept: (0, −2)

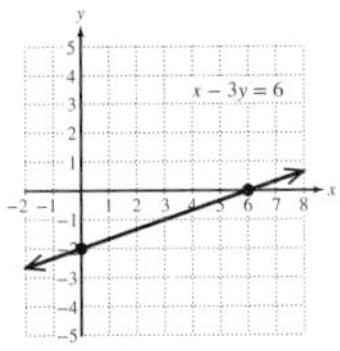

5. x-intercept: none; y-intercept: $\left(0, \dfrac{3}{2}\right)$

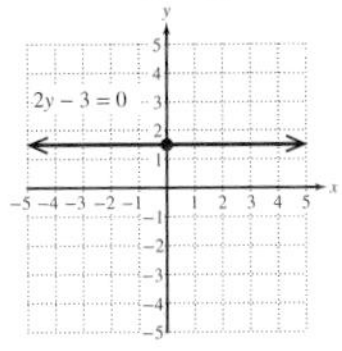

7. $m = \dfrac{1}{3}$ **9.** $m = \dfrac{6}{11}$ **11.** undefined **13.** positive

15. Negative **17.** Zero **19.** Undefined **21.** Positive

23. Negative **25.** $m = \dfrac{1}{2}$ **27.** $m = -3$ **29.** $m = 0$

31. The slope is undefined. **33.** $\dfrac{1}{3}$ **35.** -3 **37.** $\dfrac{3}{5}$

39. Zero **41.** Undefined **43.** $\dfrac{28}{5}$ **45.** $-\dfrac{7}{8}$

47. -0.45 or $-\dfrac{9}{20}$ **49.** -0.15 or $-\dfrac{3}{20}$ **51.** **a.** -2 **b.** $\dfrac{1}{2}$

53. **a.** 0 **b.** undefined **55.** **a.** $\dfrac{4}{5}$ **b.** $-\dfrac{5}{4}$ **57.** Perpendicular

59. Parallel **61.** Neither **63.** l_1: $m = 2$, l_2: $m = 2$; parallel

65. l_1: $m = 5$, l_2: $m = -\dfrac{1}{5}$; perpendicular

67. l_1: $m = \dfrac{1}{4}$, l_2: $m = 4$; neither **69.** The average rate of change is −\$160 per year. **71.** **a.** $m = 47$ **b.** The number of male prisoners increased at a rate of 47 thousand per year during this time period. **73.** **a.** 1 mi **b.** 2 mi **c.** 3 mi **d.** $m = 0.2$; The distance between a lightning strike and an observer increases by 0.2 mi for every additional second between seeing lightning and hearing thunder.

75. $m = \dfrac{3}{4}$ **77.** $m = 0$

79. For example: (4, −4) and (−2, 0)

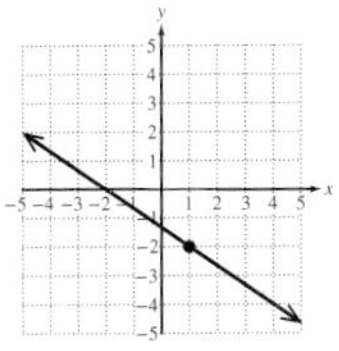

81. For example: (3, 5) and (1, −1)

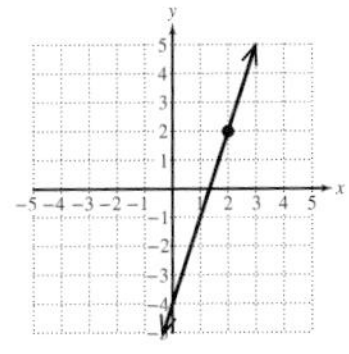

83. For example: (−3, 1) and (−3, 4)

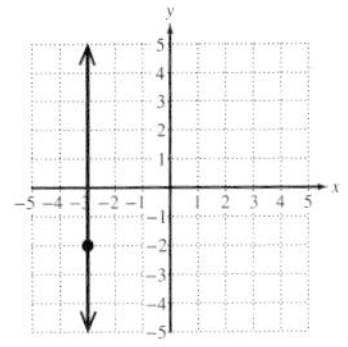

85.

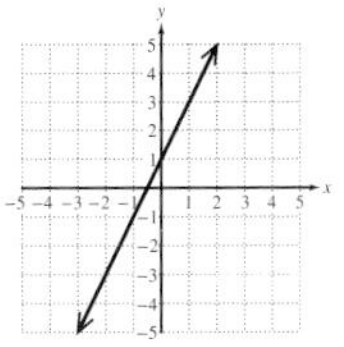

87.

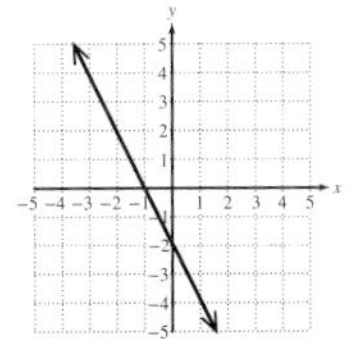

89.

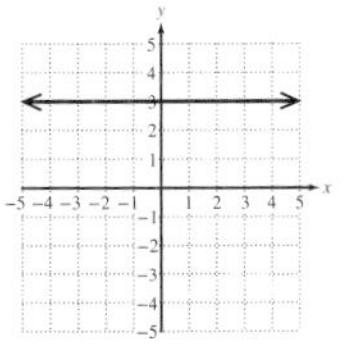

91. $\dfrac{3m - 3n}{2b}$ or $\dfrac{-3m + 3n}{-2b}$ **93.** $\left(\dfrac{c}{a}, 0\right)$

95. For example: (7, 1)

Section 3.4 Calculator Connections, p. 237

1. Perpendicular

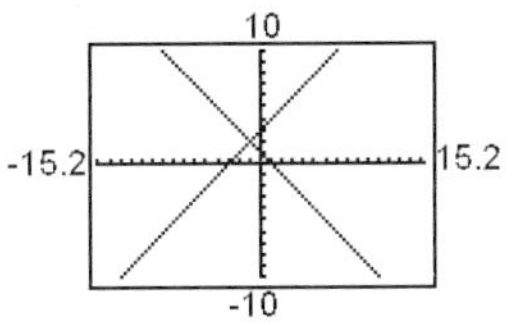

2. Parallel

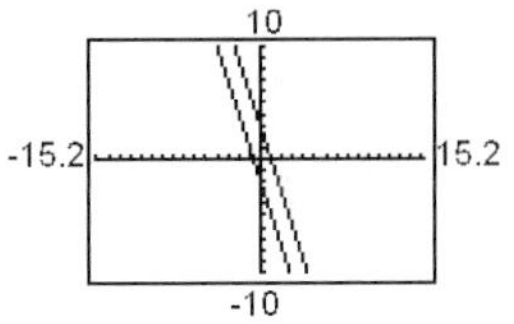

3. Neither

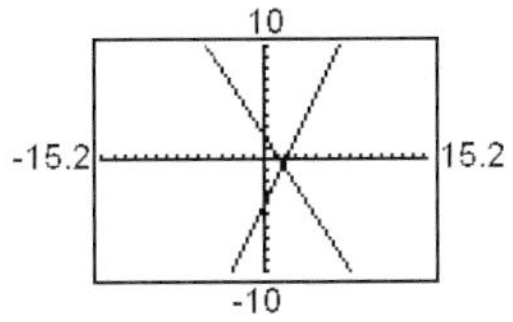

4. The lines may appear parallel; however, they are not parallel because the slopes are different. **5.** The lines may appear to coincide on a graph; however, they are not the same line because the y-intercepts are different. **6.** The line may appear to be horizontal, but it is not. The slope is 0.001 rather than 0.

Section 3.4 Practice Exercises, pp. 238–242

1. **a.** $y = mx + b$ **b.** standard **3.** x-intercept: (10, 0); y-intercept: (0, −2) **5.** x-intercept: none; y-intercept: (0, −3)

7. x-intercept: (0, 0); y-intercept: (0, 0) **9.** x-intercept: (4, 0); y-intercept: none **11.** $m = -2$; y-intercept: (0, 3) **13.** $m = 1$; y-intercept: (0, −2) **15.** $m = -1$; y-intercept: (0, 0)

17. $m = \dfrac{3}{4}$; y-intercept: (0, −1) **19.** $m = \dfrac{2}{5}$; y-intercept: $\left(0, -\dfrac{4}{5}\right)$ **21.** $m = 3$; y-intercept: (0, −5)

23. $m = -1$; y-intercept: (0, 6) **25.** Undefined slope; no y-intercept **27.** $m = 0$; y-intercept: $\left(0, -\dfrac{1}{4}\right)$

29. $m = \dfrac{2}{3}$; y-intercept: (0, 0)

31.

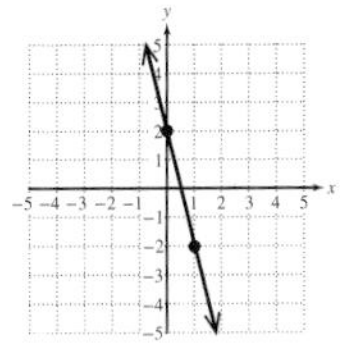

33.

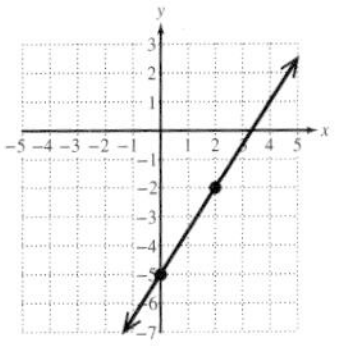

35. b **37.** e **39.** c

41. $y = -2x + 9$

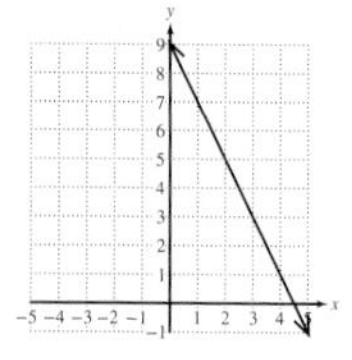

43. $y = \frac{1}{2}x - 3$

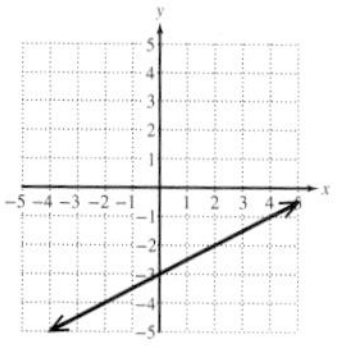

45. $y = -\frac{1}{2}x + \frac{3}{2}$

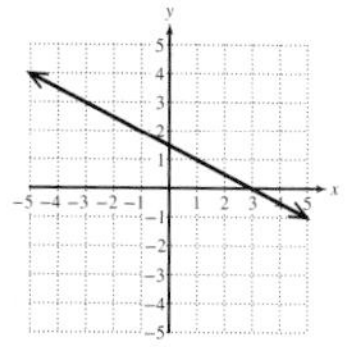

47. $y = -x$

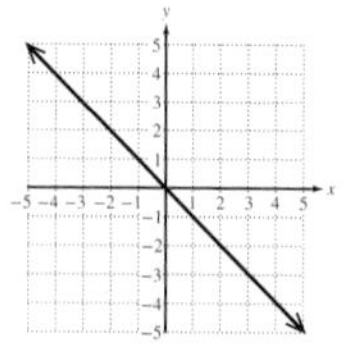

49. $y = \frac{4}{5}x$

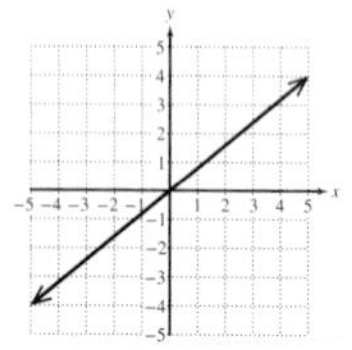

51. $y = -\frac{2}{3}$

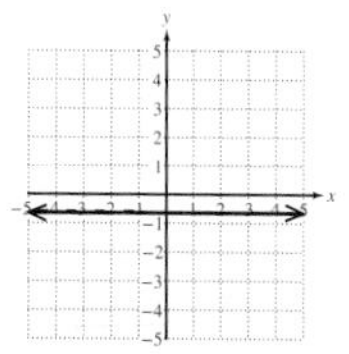

53. Perpendicular **55.** Neither **57.** Parallel
59. Perpendicular **61.** Parallel **63.** Perpendicular
65. Neither **67.** Parallel **69.** $y = -\frac{1}{3}x + 2$
71. $y = 10x - 19$ **73.** $y = 6x - 8$ **75.** $y = \frac{1}{2}x - 3$
77. $y = -11$ **79.** $y = 5x$ **81.** $y = -2x + 3$
83. $y = -\frac{1}{3}x + 2$ **85.** $y = 4x - 1$ **87. a.** $m = 1203$; The slope represents the rate of increase in the number of cases of Lyme disease per year. **b.** (0, 10006); In the year 1993 there were 10,006 cases reported. **c.** 30,457 cases **d.** $x = 27$; the year 2020
89. $y = -\frac{A}{B}x + \frac{C}{B}$; the slope is $-\frac{A}{B}$.
91. $m = -\frac{6}{7}$ **93.** $m = \frac{11}{8}$

Chapter 3 Problem Recognition Exercises, p. 242

1. a, c, d **2.** b, f, h **3.** a **4.** f **5.** b, f **6.** c
7. c, d **8.** f **9.** e **10.** g **11.** b **12.** h
13. g **14.** e **15.** c **16.** b, h **17.** e **18.** e
19. b, f, h **20.** c, d

Section 3.5 Practice Exercises, pp. 247–251

1. a. $Ax + By = C$ **b.** horizontal **c.** vertical **d.** slope; y-intercept **e.** $y - y_1 = m(x - x_1)$

3.

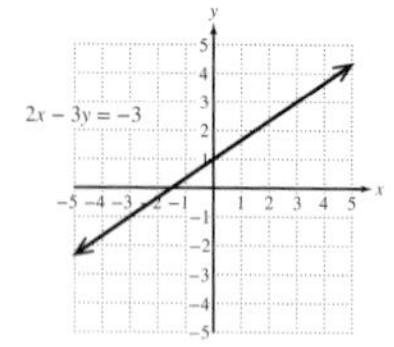

5.

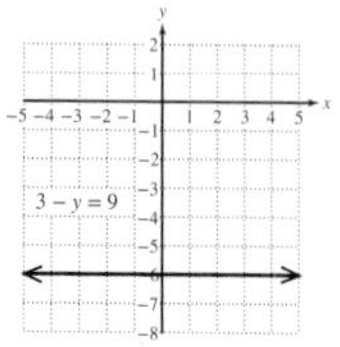

7. 9 **9.** 0 **11.** $y = 3x + 7$ or $3x - y = -7$
13. $y = -4x - 14$ or $4x + y = -14$ **15.** $y = -\frac{1}{2}x - \frac{1}{2}$ or $x + 2y = -1$ **17.** $y = 2x - 2$ or $2x - y = 2$
19. $y = -x - 4$ or $x + y = -4$
21. $y = -0.2x - 2.86$ or $20x + 100y = -286$
23. $y = -2x + 1$ **25.** $y = 2x + 4$ **27.** $y = \frac{1}{2}x - 1$
29. $y = 4x + 13$ or $4x - y = -13$
31. $y = -\frac{3}{2}x + 6$ or $3x + 2y = 12$
33. $y = -2x - 8$ or $2x + y = -8$ **35.** $y = -\frac{1}{5}x - 6$ or $x + 5y = -30$ **37.** iv **39.** vi **41.** iii **43.** $y = 1$
45. $x = 2$ **47.** $y = 2$ **49.** $y = \frac{1}{4}x + 8$ or $x - 4y = -32$
51. $y = 3x - 8$ or $3x - y = 8$ **53.** $y = 4.5x - 25.6$ or $45x - 10y = 256$ **55.** $x = -6$ **57.** $y = -2$
59. $x = -4$ **61.** $y = 2x - 4$ **63.** $y = -\frac{1}{2}x + 1$

Section 3.6 Calculator Connections, p. 255

1. 13.3

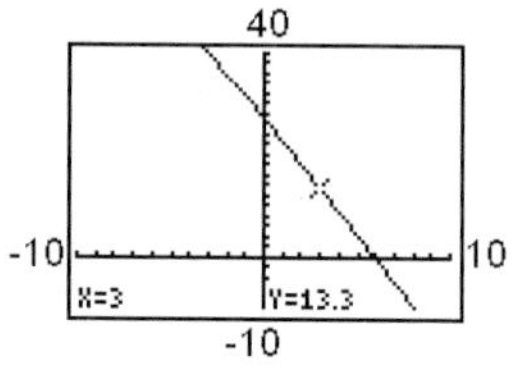

2. −42.3

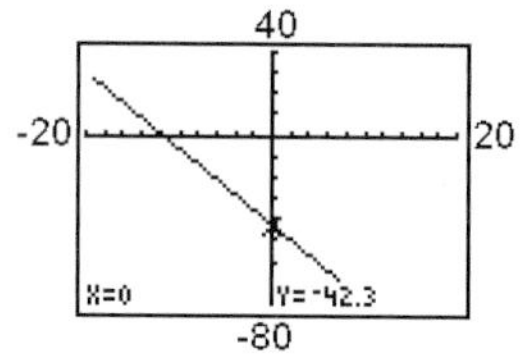

3. 345

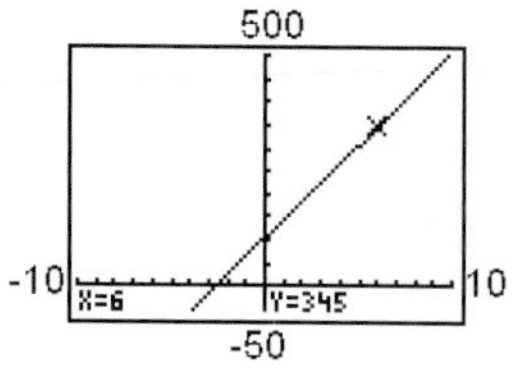

4. 95

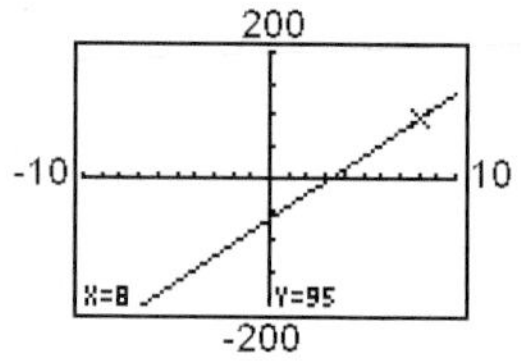

Section 3.6 Practice Exercises, pp. 255–259

1. $m = -\frac{5}{2}$ **3.** x-intercept: (6, 0); y-intercept: (0, 5)
5. x-intercept: (−2, 0); y-intercept: (0, −4) **7.** x-intercept: none; y-intercept: (0, −9) **9. a.** \$3.00 **b.** \$7.90 **c.** The y-intercept is (0, 1.6). This indicates that the minimum wage was \$1.60 per hour in the year 1970. **d.** The slope is 0.14. This indicates that the minimum wage has risen approximately \$0.14 per year during this period.
11. a. $m = \frac{2}{7}$ **b.** $m = \frac{4}{7}$ **c.** $m = \frac{2}{7}$ means that Grindel's weight increased at a rate of 2 oz in 7 days. $m = \frac{4}{7}$ means that Frisco's weight increased at a rate of 4 oz in 7 days. **d.** Frisco gained weight more rapidly. **13. a.** \$106.95 **b.** \$201.95 **c.** (0, 11.95). For 0 kilowatt-hours used, the cost consists of only the fixed monthly tax of \$11.95. **d.** $m = 0.095$. The cost increases by \$0.095 for each kilowatt-hour used. **15. a.** $m = -1.0$ **b.** $y = -1.0x + 1051$ **c.** The minimum pressure was approximately 921 mb.
17. a. $m = 21.5$ **b.** The slope means that the consumption of wind energy in the United States increased by 21.5 trillion Btu per year. **c.** $y = 21.5x + 57$ **d.** 272 trillion Btu **19. a.** $y = 0.10x + 5000$ **b.** \$6130 **21. a.** $y = 90x + 105$ **b.** \$1185.00
23. a. $y = 0.8x + 100$ **b.** \$260.00

Chapter 3 Review Exercises, pp. 265–269

1.

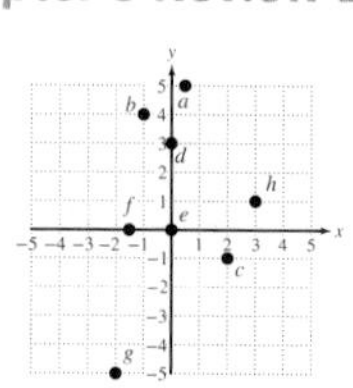

2. $A(4, -3)$; $B(-3, -2)$; $C(\frac{5}{2}, 5)$; $D(-4, 1)$; $E(-\frac{1}{2}, 0)$; $F(0, -5)$

3. III **4.** II **5.** IV **6.** I **7.** IV **8.** III **9.** x-axis **10.** y-axis **11. a.** On day 1, the price was \$26.25. **b.** Day 2 **c.** \$2.25 **12. a.** In 2003 (8 years after 1995), there was only one space shuttle launch. (This was the year that the Columbia and its crew were lost.)

b.

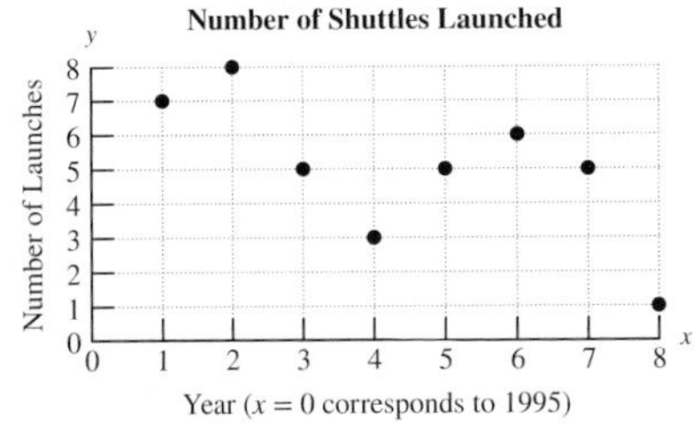

13. No **14.** No **15.** Yes **16.** Yes

17.

x	y
2	1
3	4
1	−2

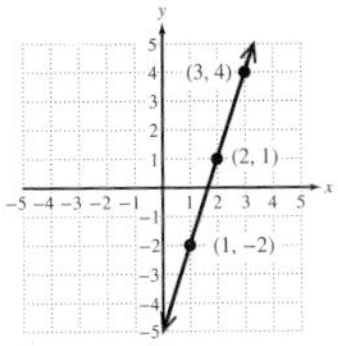

18.

x	y
0	2
−2	7/3
−6	3

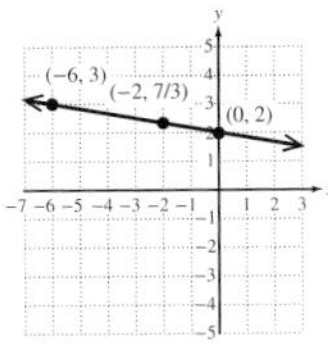

19.

x	y
0	−1
3	1
−6	−5

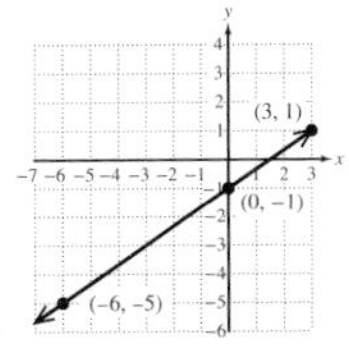

20.

x	y
0	−3
−3	3
1	−5

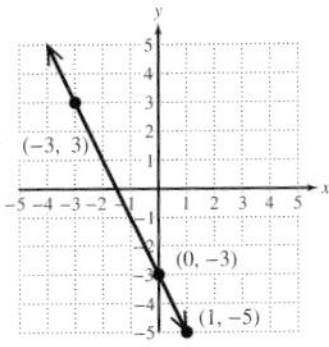

21.

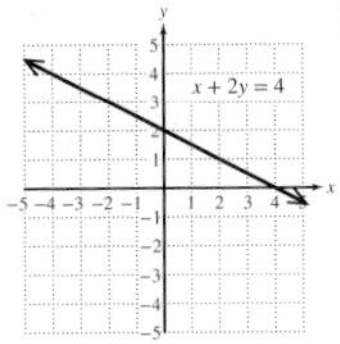

22.

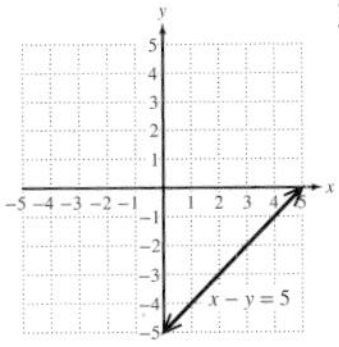

23.

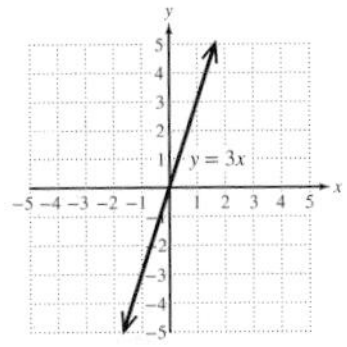

24.

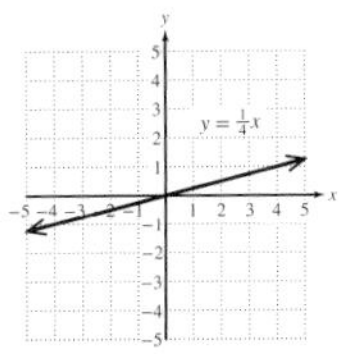

25. Vertical

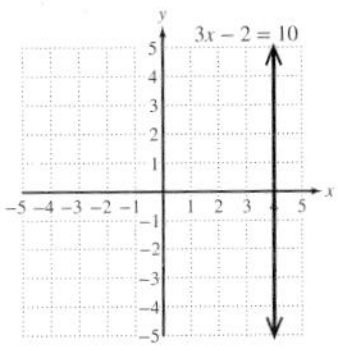

26. Vertical

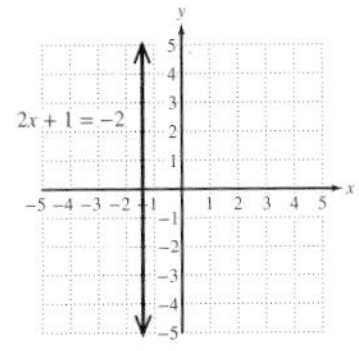

27. Horizontal

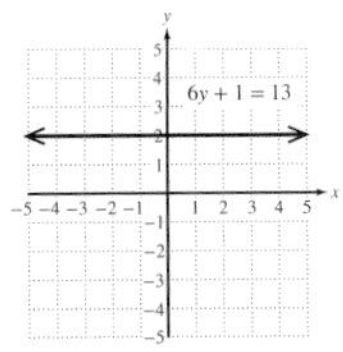

28. Horizontal

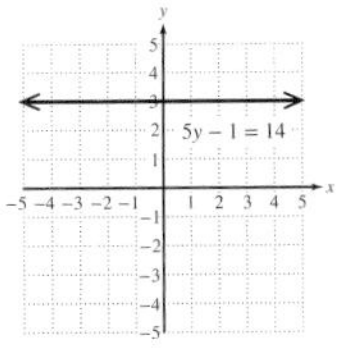

29. x-intercept: $(-3, 0)$; y-intercept: $\left(0, \frac{3}{2}\right)$

30. x-intercept: $(3, 0)$; y-intercept: $(0, 6)$ **31.** x-intercept: $(0, 0)$; y-intercept: $(0, 0)$ **32.** x-intercept: $(0, 0)$; y-intercept: $(0, 0)$ **33.** x-intercept: none; y-intercept: $(0, -4)$ **34.** x-intercept: none; y-intercept: $(0, 2)$ **35.** x-intercept: $\left(-\frac{5}{2}, 0\right)$; y-intercept: none **36.** x-intercept: $\left(\frac{1}{3}, 0\right)$; y-intercept: none **37.** $m = \frac{12}{5}$

38. -2 **39.** $-\frac{2}{3}$ **40.** 8 **41.** Undefined **42.** 0

43. a. -5 **b.** $\frac{1}{5}$ **44. a.** 0 **b.** Undefined

45. $m_1 = \frac{2}{3}$; $m_2 = \frac{2}{3}$; parallel **46.** $m_1 = 8$; $m_2 = 8$; parallel

47. $m_1 = -\frac{5}{12}$; $m_2 = \frac{12}{5}$; perpendicular **48.** m_1 is undefined; $m_2 = 0$; perpendicular **49. a.** $m = 35$ **b.** The number of kilowatt-hours increased at a rate of 35 kilowatt-hours per day.

50. a. $m = -994$ **b.** The number of new cars sold in Maryland decreased at a rate of 994 cars per year.

51. $y = \frac{5}{2}x - 5$; $m = \frac{5}{2}$; y-intercept: $(0, -5)$

52. $y = -\frac{3}{4}x + 3$; $m = -\frac{3}{4}$; y-intercept: $(0, 3)$

53. $y = \frac{1}{3}x$; $m = \frac{1}{3}$; y-intercept: $(0, 0)$ **54.** $y = \frac{12}{5}$; $m = 0$; y-intercept: $\left(0, \frac{12}{5}\right)$ **55.** $y = -\frac{5}{2}$; $m = 0$; y-intercept: $\left(0, -\frac{5}{2}\right)$

56. $y = x$; $m = 1$; y-intercept: $(0, 0)$ **57.** Neither **58.** Perpendicular **59.** Parallel **60.** Parallel

61. Perpendicular **62.** Neither **63.** $y = -\frac{4}{3}x - 1$ or $4x + 3y = -3$ **64.** $y = 5x$ or $5x - y = 0$ **65.** $y = -\frac{4}{3}x - 6$ or $4x + 3y = -18$ **66.** $y = 5x - 3$ or $5x - y = 3$

67. For example: $y = 3x + 2$ **68.** For example: $5x + 2y = -4$

69. $m = \frac{y_2 - y_1}{x_2 - x_1}$ **70.** $y - y_1 = m(x - x_1)$

71. For example: $x = 6$ **72.** For example: $y = -5$

73. $y = -6x + 2$ or $6x + y = 2$ **74.** $y = \frac{2}{3}x + \frac{5}{3}$ or $2x - 3y = -5$ **75.** $y = \frac{1}{4}x - 4$ or $x - 4y = 16$ **76.** $y = -5$

77. $y = \frac{6}{5}x + 6$ or $6x - 5y = -30$ **78.** $y = 4x + 31$ or $4x - y = -31$ **79. a.** 47.8 in. **b.** The slope is 2.4 and indicates that the average height for girls increases at a rate of 2.4 in. per year.

80. a. $m = 137$ **b.** The number of prescriptions increased by 137 million per year during this time period. **c.** $y = 137x + 2825$ **d.** 4880 million **81. a.** $y = 20x + 55$ **b.** \$235

82. a. $y = 8x + 700$ **b.** \$1340

Chapter 3 Test, pp. 269–271

1. a. II **b.** IV **c.** III **2.** 0 **3.** 0

4. a. (4, 14) After 4 days the bamboo plant is 14 in. tall. (8, 28), (12, 42), (16, 56), (20, 70)

b.

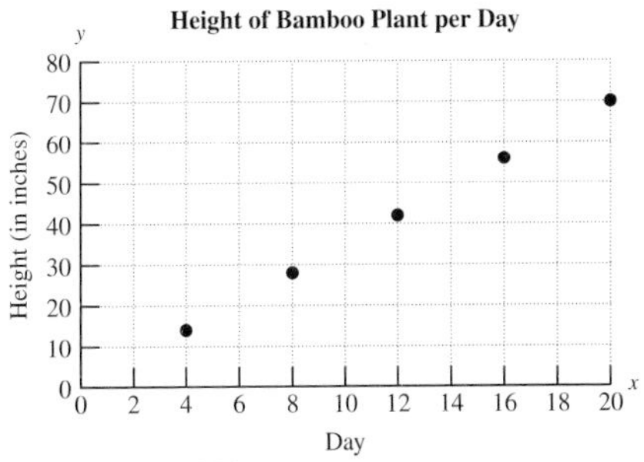

c. Approximately 35 in.

5. a. No **b.** Yes **c.** Yes **d.** Yes

6.

x	y
0	−2
4	−1
6	$-\frac{1}{2}$

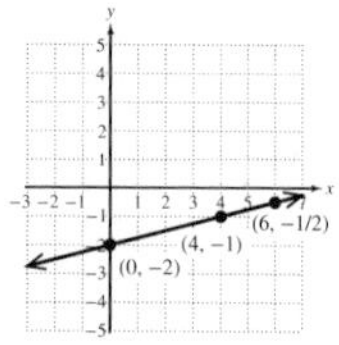

7.

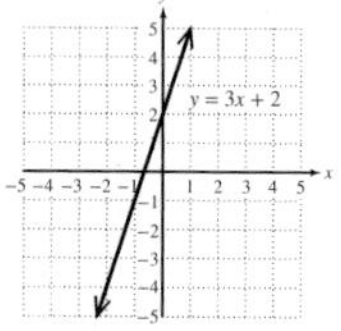

8.

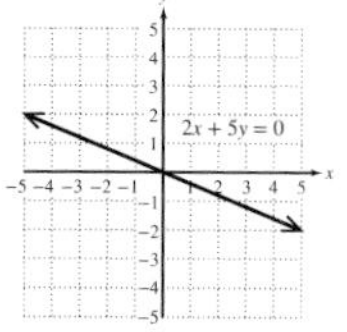

9.

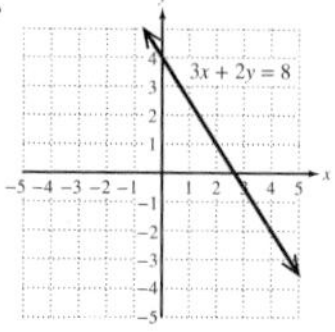

10.

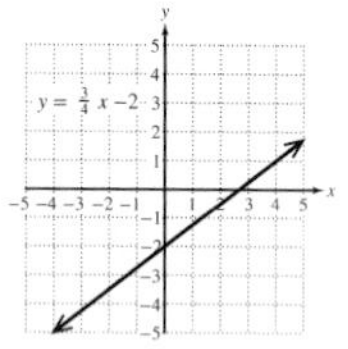

11. Horizontal

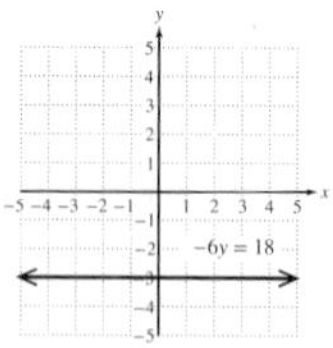

12. Vertical

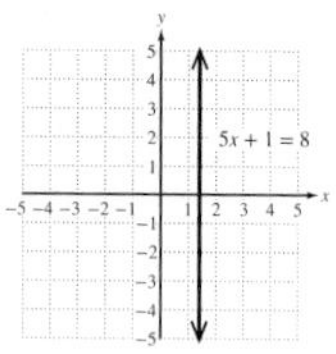

13. x-intercept: $\left(-\frac{3}{2}, 0\right)$; y-intercept: (0, 2) **14.** x-intercept: (0, 0); y-intercept: (0, 0) **15.** x-intercept: (4, 0); y-intercept: none **16.** x-intercept: none; y-intercept: (0, 3) **17.** $\frac{2}{5}$ **18. a.** $\frac{1}{3}$ **b.** $\frac{4}{3}$ **19. a.** $-\frac{1}{4}$ **b.** 4 **20. a.** Undefined **b.** 0 **21. a.** $m = 0.6$ **b.** The cost of renting a truck increases at a rate of $0.60 per mile. **22.** Parallel **23.** Perpendicular **24.** $y = -\frac{1}{3}x + 1$ or $x + 3y = 3$ **25.** $y = -\frac{7}{2}x + 15$ or $7x + 2y = 30$ **26.** $y = \frac{1}{4}x + \frac{1}{2}$ or $x - 4y = -2$ **27.** $y = 3x + 8$ or $3x - y = -8$ **28.** $y = -6$ **29.** $y = -x - 3$ or $x + y = -3$ **30. a.** $y = 1.5x + 10$ **b.** $25 **31. a.** $m = 20$; The slope indicates that there is an increase of 20 thousand medical doctors per year. **b.** $y = 20x + 414$ **c.** 1114 thousand or, equivalently, 1,114,000

Chapters 1–3 Cumulative Review Exercises, pp. 271–272

1. a. Rational **b.** Rational **c.** Irrational **d.** Rational **2. a.** $\frac{2}{3}; \frac{2}{3}$ **b.** −5.3; 5.3 **3.** 69 **4.** −13 **5.** 18 **6.** $\frac{3}{4} \div \left(-\frac{7}{8}\right); -\frac{6}{7}$ **7.** (−2.1)(−6); 12.6 **8.** The associative property of addition **9.** {4} **10.** {5} **11.** $\left\{-\frac{9}{2}\right\}$ **12.** {−2} **13.** 9241 mi^2 **14.** $a = \frac{c-b}{3}$

15.

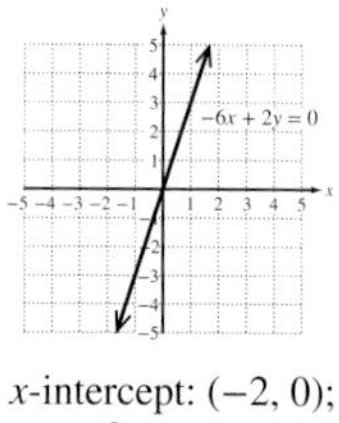

16. x-intercept: (−2, 0); y-intercept: (0, 1) **17.** $y = -\frac{3}{2}x - 6$; slope: $-\frac{3}{2}$; y-intercept: (0, −6) **18.** $2x + 3 = 5$ can be written as $x = 1$, which represents a vertical line. A vertical line of the form $x = k\ (k \neq 0)$ has an x-intercept of $(k, 0)$ and no y-intercept. **19.** $y = -3x + 1$ or $3x + y = 1$ **20.** $y = \frac{2}{3}x + 6$ or $2x - 3y = -18$

Chapter 4

Section 4.1 Calculator Connections, pp. 278–279

1. {(2, 1)}

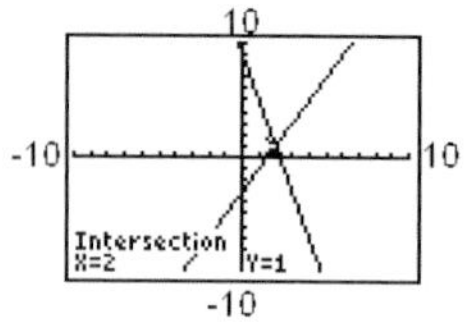

2. {(6, −1)}

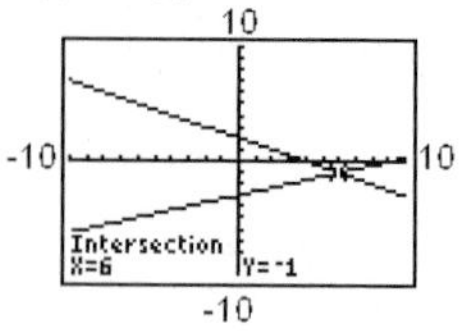

3. {(3, 1)}

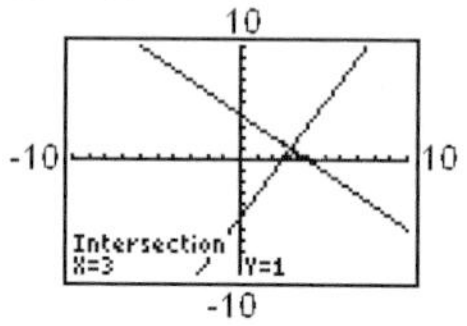

4. {(−2, 0)}

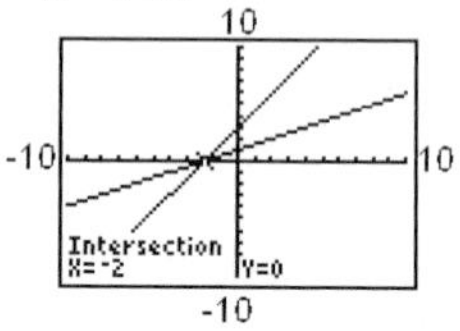

5. { }

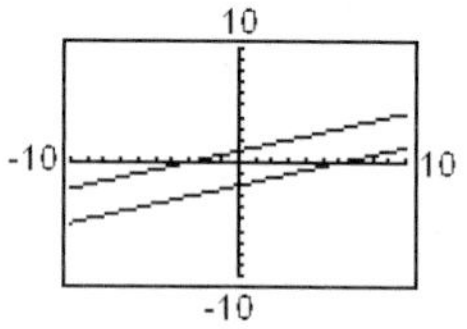

6. $\left\{(x, y) \middle| y = -\frac{1}{4}x + 2\right\}$

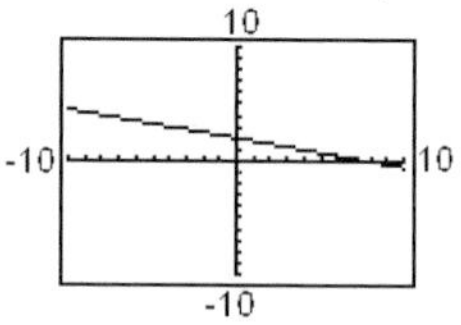

Section 4.1 Practice Exercises, pp. 279–284

1. a. system **b.** solution **c.** intersect **d.** consistent **e.** { } **f.** dependent **g.** independent **3.** Yes **5.** No **7.** Yes **9.** No **11.** b **13.** d

15. a.

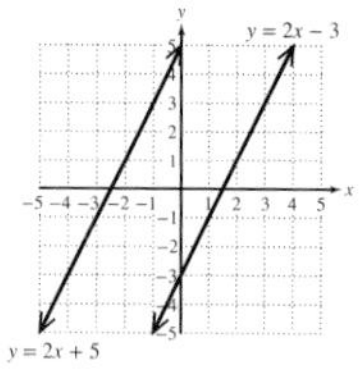

b.

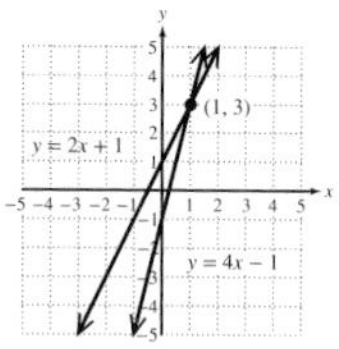

c.

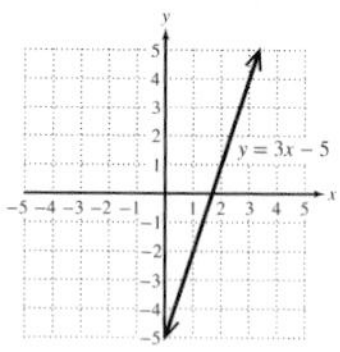

17. c **19.** a **21.** a **23.** b **25.** c

27. {(3, 1)}

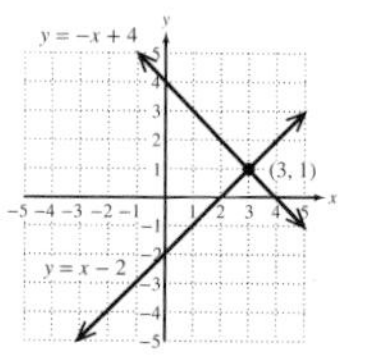

29. {(1, −2)}

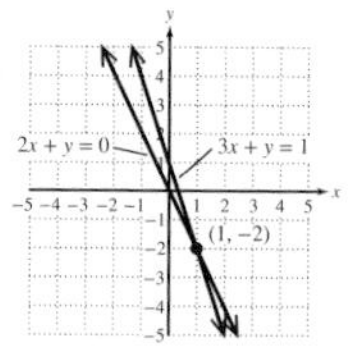

31. {(1, 4)}

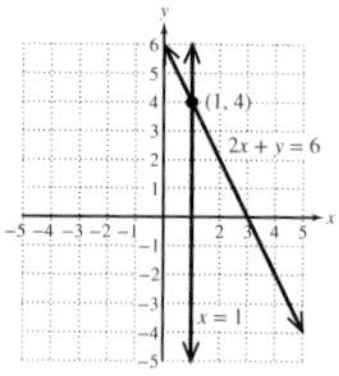

33. No solution; { }; inconsistent system

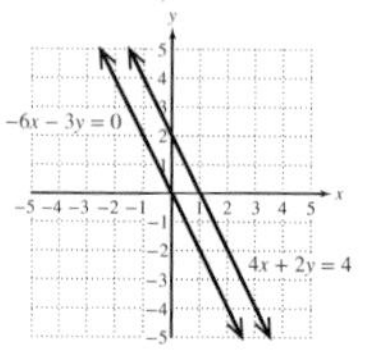

35. Infinitely many solutions; $\{(x, y) \mid -2x + y = 3\}$; dependent equations

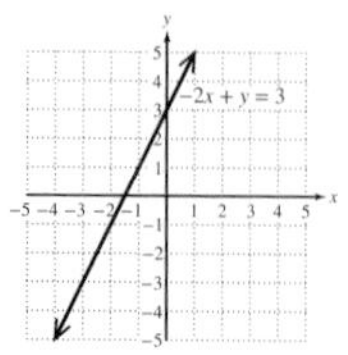

37. {(−3, 6)}

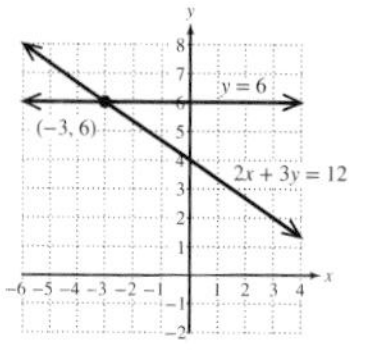

39. {(2, −2)}

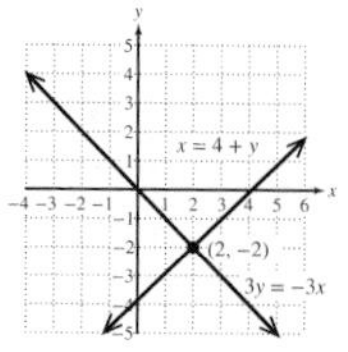

41. No solution; { }; inconsistent system

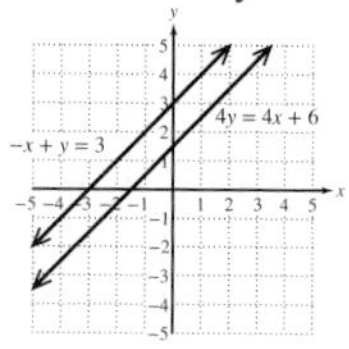

43. $\{(4, 2)\}$ **45.** $\{(1, 2)\}$

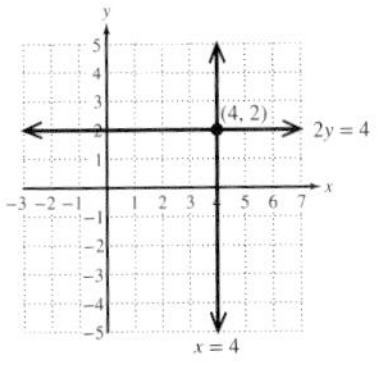

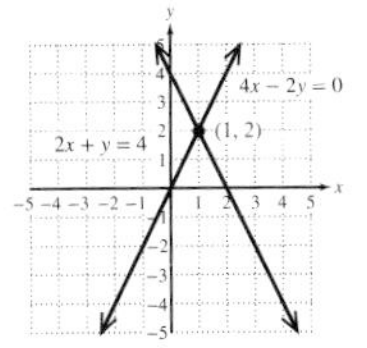

47. Infinitely many solutions; $\{(x, y) \mid y = 0.5x + 2\}$; dependent equations **49.** $\{(-3, -1)\}$

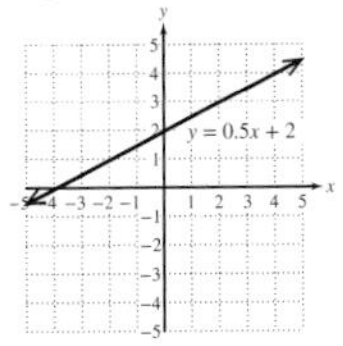

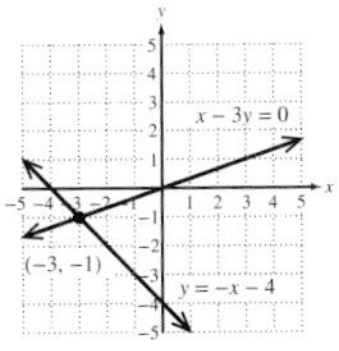

51. The same cost occurs when \$2500 of merchandise is purchased. **53.** The point of intersection is below the x-axis and cannot have a positive y-coordinate. **55.** For example: $4x + y = 9$; $-2x - y = -5$ **57.** For example: $2x + 2y = 1$

Section 4.2 Practice Exercises, pp. 292–294

1. $y = 2x - 4$; $y = 2x - 4$; coinciding lines

3. $y = -\frac{2}{3}x + 2$; $y = x - 5$; intersecting lines

5. $y = 4x - 4$; $y = 4x - 13$; parallel lines **7.** $\{(3, -6)\}$

9. $\{(0, 4)\}$ **11. a.** y in the second equation is easiest to isolate because its coefficient is 1. **b.** $\{(1, 5)\}$ **13.** $\{(5, 2)\}$ **15.** $\{(10, 5)\}$

17. $\left\{\left(\frac{1}{2}, 3\right)\right\}$ **19.** $\{(5, 3)\}$ **21.** $\{(1, 0)\}$ **23.** $\{(1, 4)\}$

25. No solution; { }; inconsistent system **27.** Infinitely many solutions; $\{(x, y) \mid 2x - 6y = -2\}$; dependent equations **29.** $\{(5, -7)\}$

31. $\left\{\left(-5, \frac{3}{2}\right)\right\}$ **33.** $\{(2, -5)\}$ **35.** $\{(-4, 6)\}$ **37.** $\{(0, 2)\}$

39. Infinitely many solutions; $\{(x, y) \mid y = 0.25x + 1\}$; dependent equations **41.** $\{(1, 1)\}$ **43.** No solution; { }; inconsistent system

45. $\{(-1, 5)\}$ **47.** $\{(-6, -4)\}$ **49.** The numbers are 48 and 58. **51.** The numbers are 13 and 39. **53.** The angles are 165° and 15°. **55.** The angles are 70° and 20°. **57.** The angles are 42° and 48°. **59.** For example: (0, 3), (1, 5), (−1, 1)

Section 4.3 Practice Exercises, pp. 301–303

1. No **3.** No **5.** Yes **7. a.** True **b.** False, multiply the second equation by 5. **9. a.** x would be easier. **b.** $\{(0, -3)\}$

11. $\{(4, -1)\}$ **13.** $\{(4, 3)\}$ **15.** $\{(2, 3)\}$ **17.** $\{(1, -4)\}$

19. $\{(1, -1)\}$ **21.** $\{(-4, -6)\}$ **23.** $\left\{\left(\frac{7}{9}, \frac{5}{9}\right)\right\}$

25. The system will have no solution. The lines are parallel.

27. There are infinitely many solutions. The lines coincide.

29. The system will have one solution. The lines intersect at a point whose x-coordinate is 0. **31.** No solution; { }; inconsistent system

33. Infinitely many solutions; $\{(x, y) \mid x + 2y = 2\}$; dependent equations **35.** $\{(1, 4)\}$ **37.** $\{(-1, -2)\}$ **39.** $\{(2, 1)\}$

41. No solution; { }; inconsistent system **43.** $\{(2, 3)\}$ **45.** $\{(3.5, 2.5)\}$

47. $\left\{\left(\frac{1}{3}, 2\right)\right\}$ **49.** $\{(-2, 5)\}$ **51.** $\left\{\left(-\frac{1}{2}, 1\right)\right\}$ **53.** $\{(0, 3)\}$

55. { } **57.** $\{(1, 4)\}$ **59.** $\{(4, 0)\}$ **61.** Infinitely many solutions; $\{(a, b) \mid 9a - 2b = 8\}$ **63.** $\left\{\left(\frac{7}{16}, -\frac{7}{8}\right)\right\}$

65. The numbers are 17 and 19. **67.** The numbers are −1 and 3. **69.** The angles are 46° and 134°. **71.** $\{(1, 3)\}$ **73.** One line within the system of equations would have to "bend" for the system to have exactly two points of intersection. This is not possible.

75. $A = -5$, $B = 2$

Chapter 4 Problem Recognition Exercises, p. 304

1. Infinitely many solutions. The equations represent the same line. **2.** No solution. The equations represent parallel lines.

3. One solution. The equations represent intersecting lines.

4. One solution. The equations represent intersecting lines.

5. No solution. The equations represent parallel lines.

6. Infinitely many solutions. The equations represent the same line.

7. The y variable will easily be eliminated by adding the equations. The solution set is $\{(-3, 1)\}$. **8.** The x variable will easily be eliminated by multiplying the second equation by 2 and then adding the equations. The solution set is $\{(3, 4)\}$. **9.** Because the variable x is already isolated in the first equation, the expression $-3y + 4$ can be easily substituted for x in the second equation. The solution set is $\{(-2, 2)\}$. **10.** Because the variable y is already isolated in the second equation, the expression $x - 8$ can be easily substituted for y in the first equation. The solution set is $\{(8, 0)\}$. **11.** $\{(5, 0)\}$

12. $\{(1, -7)\}$ **13.** $\{(4, -5)\}$ **14.** $\{(2, 3)\}$ **15.** $\{(2, 0)\}$

16. $\{(8, 10)\}$ **17.** $\left\{\left(2, -\frac{5}{7}\right)\right\}$ **18.** $\left\{\left(-\frac{14}{3}, -4\right)\right\}$

19. No solution; { }; inconsistent system **20.** No solution; { }; inconsistent system

21. $\{(-1, 0)\}$ **22.** $\{(5, 0)\}$ **23.** Infinitely many solutions; $\{(x, y) \mid y = 2x - 14\}$; dependent equations **24.** Infinitely many solutions; $\{(x, y) \mid x = 5y - 9\}$; dependent equations

25. $\{(2200, 1000)\}$ **26.** $\{(3300, 1200)\}$ **27.** $\{(5, -7)\}$

28. $\{(2, -1)\}$ **29.** $\left\{\left(\frac{2}{3}, \frac{1}{2}\right)\right\}$ **30.** $\left\{\left(\frac{1}{4}, -\frac{3}{2}\right)\right\}$

Section 4.4 Practice Exercises, pp. 310–314

1. $\{(-1, 4)\}$ **3.** $\left\{\left(\frac{5}{2}, 1\right)\right\}$ **5.** The numbers are 4 and 16.

7. The angles are 80° and 10°. **9.** A video game costs \$21.50 and a DVD costs \$15.00. **11.** Technology stock costs \$16 per share, and the mutual fund costs \$11 per share. **13.** Mylee bought thirty-five 47-cent stamps and fifteen 34-cent stamps. **15.** Shanelle invested \$3500 in the 10% account and \$6500 in the 7% account.

17. \$9000 was borrowed at 6%, and \$3000 was borrowed at 9%.

19. Invest \$12,000 in the bond fund and \$18,000 in the stock fund.

21. 15 gal of the 50% mixture should be mixed with 10 gal of the 40% mixture. **23.** 12 gal of the 45% disinfectant solution should be mixed with 8 gal of the 30% disinfectant solution.

25. She should mix 20 mL of the 13% solution with 30 mL of the 18% solution. **27.** Chad needs 1 L of pure antifreeze and 5 L of the 40% solution. **29.** The speed of the boat in still water is 6 mph, and the speed of the current is 2 mph. **31.** The speed of the plane in still air is 300 mph, and the wind is 20 mph. **33.** The speed of the plane in still air is 525 mph and the speed of the wind is 75 mph. **35.** There are 17 dimes and 22 nickels. **37.** 2 qt of water should be mixed. **39. a.** 835 free throws and 1597 field goals **b.** 4029 points **c.** Approximately 50 points per game

41. The speed of the plane in still air is 160 mph, and the wind is 40 mph. **43.** \$15,000 was invested in the 5.5% account, and \$45,000 was invested in the 6.5% account. **45.** 12 lb of candy should be mixed with 8 lb of nuts. **47.** Dallas scored 30 points, and Buffalo scored 13 points. **49.** There were 300 women and 200 men in the survey.

Section 4.5 Practice Exercises, pp. 320–322

1. a. linear **b.** ordered triples **3.** { } **5.** The speeds are 65 mph and 58 mph. **7.** (4, 0, 2) is a solution.

9. (1, 1, 1) is a solution. **11.** $\{(1, -2, 4)\}$

13. $\{(-1, 2, 0)\}$ **15.** $\{(-2, -1, -3)\}$ **17.** $\{(1, -4, -2)\}$

19. $\{(1, 2, 3)\}$ **21.** $\{(-6, 1, 7)\}$ **23.** $\left\{\left(\frac{1}{2}, \frac{2}{3}, -\frac{5}{6}\right)\right\}$

25. $\left\{\left(\frac{1}{2}, 2, -\frac{1}{2}\right)\right\}$ **27.** $\{(6, -3, -2)\}$ **29.** $\{(0, 4, -4)\}$

31. $\{(1, 0, -1)\}$ **33.** $\{(-20, 8, 0)\}$

35. Dependent equations **37.** Inconsistent system

39. $\{(1, 3, 1)\}$ **41.** $\left\{\left(-\frac{1}{2}, \frac{1}{3}, \frac{1}{6}\right)\right\}$ **43.** Dependent equations **45.** $\{(1, 0, 1)\}$ **47.** $\{(0, 0, 0)\}$ **49.** Dependent equations

Section 4.6 Practice Exercises, pp. 325–327

1. $\{(-7, 0, 8)\}$ **3.** Inconsistent system **5.** 67°, 82°, 31° **7.** 25°, 56°, 99° **9.** 10 cm, 18 cm, 27 cm **11.** 11 in., 17 in., 26 in. **13.** The fiber supplement has 3 g; the oatmeal has 4 g; and the cereal has 1.5 g. **15.** Kyoki invested \$2000 in bonds, \$6000 in mutual funds, and \$2000 in the Treasury note. **17.** \$1500 at 5%, \$2000 at 5.5%, \$1000 at 4% **19.** He made six free throws, seven 2-point shots, and three 3-point shots. **21.** 24 oz peanuts, 8 oz pecans, 16 oz cashews **23.** 1500 seats in section A, 400 seats in section B, and 500 seats in section C were sold.

Chapter 4 Review Exercises, pp. 335–337

1. Yes **2.** No **3.** No **4.** Yes **5.** Intersecting lines (The lines have different slopes.) **6.** Intersecting lines (The lines have different slopes.) **7.** Parallel lines (The lines have the same slope but different y-intercepts.) **8.** Intersecting lines (The lines have different slopes.) **9.** Coinciding lines (The lines have the same slope and same y-intercept.) **10.** Intersecting lines (The lines have different slopes.)

11. $\{(0, -2)\}$

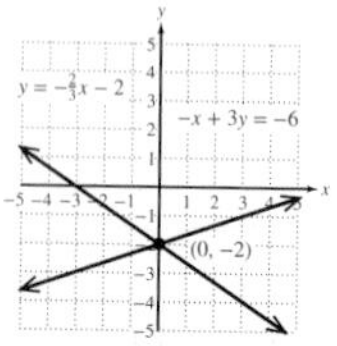

12. $\{(-2, 3)\}$

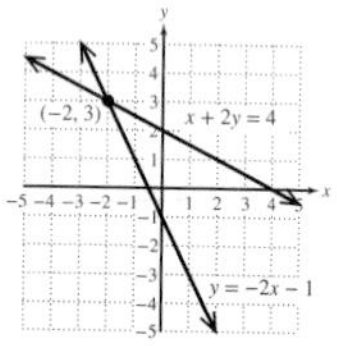

13. Infinitely many solutions; $\{(x, y) \mid 2x + y = 5\}$; dependent equations

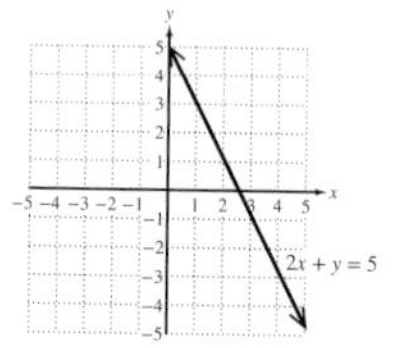

14. Infinitely many solutions; $\{(x, y) \mid -x + 5y = -5\}$; dependent equations

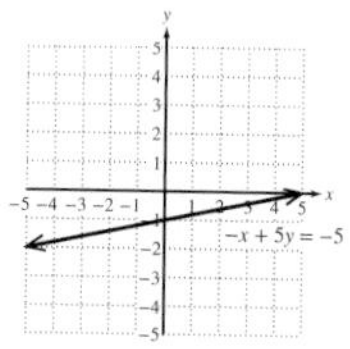

15. $\{(1, -1)\}$

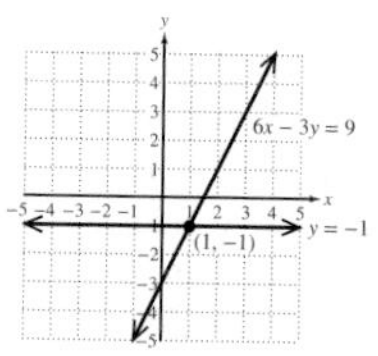

16. $\{(-1, 2)\}$

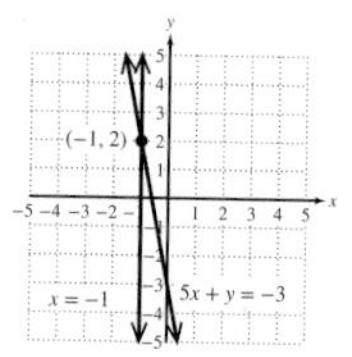

17. No solution; { }; inconsistent system

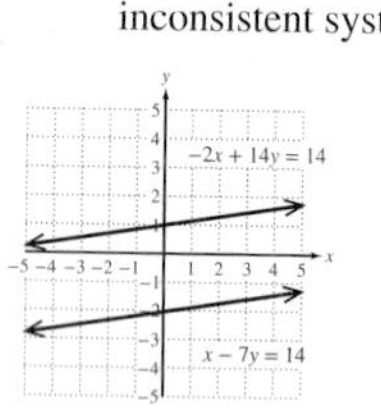

18. No solution; { }; inconsistent system

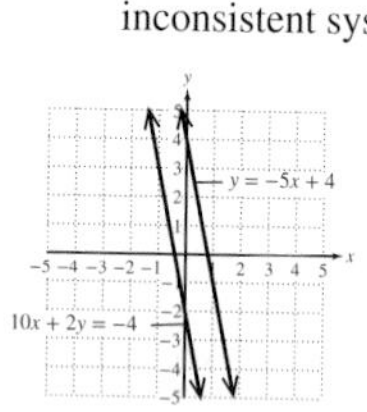

19. Using 39 minutes per month, the cost per month for each company is \$9.75. **20.** $\left\{\left(\frac{2}{3}, -2\right)\right\}$ **21.** $\{(-4, 1)\}$ **22.** { } **23.** Infinitely many solutions; $\{(x, y) \mid y = -2x + 2\}$ **24. a.** x in the first equation is easiest to isolate because its coefficient is 1. **b.** $\left\{\left(6, \frac{5}{2}\right)\right\}$ **25. a.** y in the second equation is easiest to isolate because its coefficient is 1. **b.** $\left\{\left(\frac{9}{2}, 3\right)\right\}$

26. $\{(5, -4)\}$ **27.** $\{(0, 4)\}$ **28.** Infinitely many solutions; $\{(x, y) \mid x - 3y = 9\}$ **29.** { } **30.** The numbers are 50 and 8. **31.** The angles are 41° and 49°. **32.** The angles are $115\frac{1}{3}$° and $64\frac{2}{3}$°. **33. b.** $\{(-1, 4)\}$ **34. b.** $\{(-3, -2)\}$ **35. b.** $\{(2, 2)\}$ **36.** $\{(2, -1)\}$ **37.** $\{(-6, 2)\}$ **38.** $\left\{\left(-\frac{1}{2}, \frac{1}{3}\right)\right\}$ **39.** $\left\{\left(\frac{1}{4}, -\frac{2}{5}\right)\right\}$ **40.** Infinitely many solutions; $\{(x, y) \mid -4x - 6y = -2\}$ **41.** { } **42.** $\{(-4, -2)\}$ **43.** $\{(1, 0)\}$ **44. a.** Use the substitution method because y is already isolated in the second equation. **b.** $\{(5, -3)\}$ **45. a.** Use the addition method. The substitution method would be cumbersome because isolating either variable from either equation would result in fractional coefficients. **b.** $\{(-2, -1)\}$

46. There were 8 adult tickets and 52 children's tickets sold.
47. He should invest \$75,000 at 12% and \$525,000 at 4%.
48. 20 gal of whole milk should be mixed with 40 gal of low fat milk.
49. The speed of the boat is 18 mph, and that of the current is 2 mph.
50. The plane's speed in still air is 320 mph. The wind speed is 30 mph. **51.** A hot dog costs \$4.50 and a drink costs \$3.50.
52. The score was 72 on the first round and 82 on the second round.
53. $\{(2, -1, 5)\}$ **54.** Inconsistent system
55. Dependent equations **56.** $\{(-1, -2, 2)\}$ **57.** $\{(1, -3, -2)\}$
58. $\{(-1, 4, 0)\}$ **59.** 5 ft, 12 ft, and 13 ft **60.** The pumps can drain 250, 300, and 400 gal/hr. **61.** She invested \$6000 in Fund A, \$4000 in Fund B, and \$2000 in Fund C. **62.** The angles are 13°, 39°, and 128°.

Chapter 4 Test, pp. 338–339

1. $y = -\frac{5}{2}x - 3$; $y = -\frac{5}{2}x + 3$; Parallel lines

2. $\{(3, 2)\}$

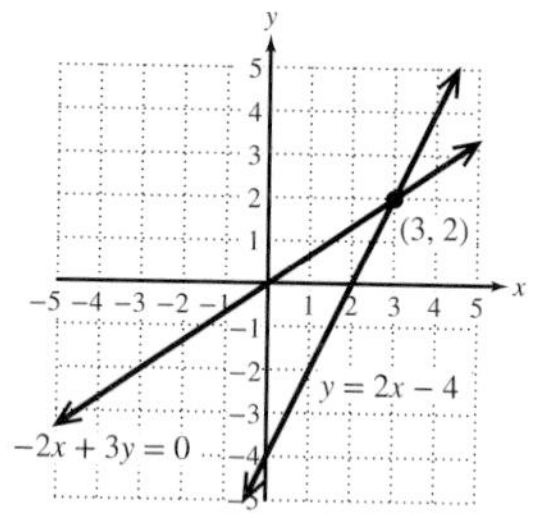

3. Infinitely many solutions; $\{(x, y) \mid 2x + 4y = 12\}$

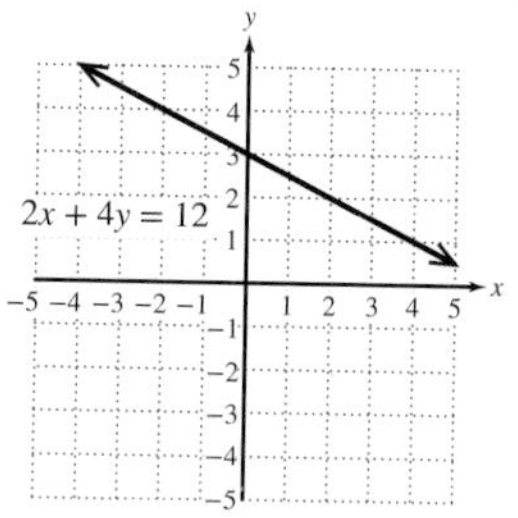

4. $\{(-2, 0)\}$ **5.** Swoopes scored 614 points and Jackson scored 597. **6.** $\left\{\left(2, -\frac{1}{3}\right)\right\}$ **7.** 12 mL of the 50% acid solution should be mixed with 24 mL of the 20% solution.
8. a. No solution **b.** Infinitely many solutions **c.** One solution
9. $\{(-5, 4)\}$ **10.** { } **11.** $\{(3, -5)\}$ **12.** $\{(-1, 2)\}$
13. Infinitely many solutions; $\{(x, y) \mid 10x + 2y = -8\}$
14. $\{(1, -2)\}$ **15.** CDs cost \$8 each and DVDs cost \$11 each.
16. a. \$18 was required. **b.** They used 24 quarters and 12 \$1 bills.
17. \$1200 was borrowed at 10%, and \$3800 was borrowed at 8%.
18. They would be the same cost for a distance of approximately 24 mi.
19. The plane travels 500 mph in still air, and the wind speed is 45 mph.
20. The cake has 340 calories, and the ice cream has 120 calories.
21. 60 mL of 10% solution and 40 mL of 25% solution
22. $\{(16, -37, 9)\}$ **23.** $\{(2, -2, 5)\}$ **24.** { }

25. The sides are 5 ft, 15 ft, and 23 ft **26.** \$5500 was invested in Fund A. \$4000 was invested in Fund B, and \$2000 was invested in Fund C. **27.** Joanne can process 142 orders, Kent can process 162 orders, and Geoff can process 200 orders.

Chapters 1–4 Cumulative Review Exercises, pp. 339–340

1. $\frac{11}{6}$ **2.** $\left\{-\frac{21}{2}\right\}$ **3.** { } **4.** $y = \frac{3}{2}x - 3$ **5.** $x = 5z + m$
6. $\left[\frac{3}{11}, \infty\right)$ 

7. The angles are 37°, 33°, and 110°. **8.** The rates of the hikers are 2 mph and 4 mph. **9.** Jesse Ventura received approximately 762,200 votes. **10.** 36% of the goal has been achieved.
11. The angles are 36.5° and 53.5°. **12.** Slope: $-\frac{5}{3}$; y-intercept: (0, −2)
13. a. $-\frac{2}{3}$ **b.** $\frac{3}{2}$ **14.** $y = -3x + 3$
15. c. {(0, 2)} **16.** {(0, 2)}

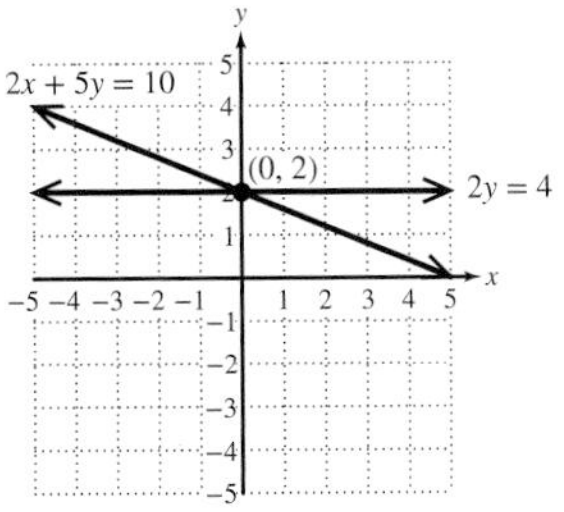

17. 20 gal of the 15% solution should be mixed with 40 gal of the 60% solution. **18.** x is 27°; y is 63° **19. a.** 1.4 **b.** Between 1920 and 1990, the winning speed in the Indianapolis 500 increased on average by 1.4 mph per year. **20.** {(1, 0, 4)}

Chapter 5

Section 5.1 Calculator Connections, p. 348

1.–3.

```
(1.06)^5
          1.338225578
(1.02)^40
          2.208039664
5000(1.06)^5
          6691.127888
```

4.–6.

```
2000(1.02)^40
          4416.079327
3000(1+.06)^2
               3370.8
1000(1+.05)^3
             1157.625
```

Section 5.1 Practice Exercises, pp. 349–351

1. a. exponent **b.** base; exponent **c.** 1 **d.** $I = Prt$ **e.** compound interest **3.** Base: x; exponent: 4 **5.** Base: 3; exponent: 5 **7.** Base: −1; exponent: 4 **9.** Base: 13; exponent: 1 **11.** Base: 10; exponent: 3 **13.** Base: t; exponent: 6 **15.** v **17.** 1 **19.** $(-6b)^2$ **21.** $-6b^2$ **23.** $(y + 2)^4$
25. $\frac{-2}{t^3}$ **27.** No; $-5^2 = -25$ and $(-5)^2 = 25$ **29.** Yes; −32
31. Yes; $\frac{1}{8}$ **33.** Yes; −16 **35.** 16 **37.** −1 **39.** $\frac{1}{9}$
41. $-\frac{4}{25}$ **43.** 48 **45.** 4 **47.** 9 **49.** 50 **51.** −100
53. 400 **55.** 1 **57.** 1 **59.** 1000 **61.** −800
63. a. $(x \cdot x \cdot x \cdot x)(x \cdot x \cdot x) = x^7$ **b.** $(5 \cdot 5 \cdot 5 \cdot 5)(5 \cdot 5 \cdot 5) = 5^7$
65. z^8 **67.** a^9 **69.** 4^{14} **71.** $\left(\frac{2}{3}\right)^4$ **73.** c^{14} **75.** x^{18}
77. a. $\frac{p \cdot p \cdot p \cdot p \cdot p \cdot p \cdot p \cdot p}{p \cdot p \cdot p} = p^5$
b. $\frac{8 \cdot 8 \cdot 8 \cdot 8 \cdot 8 \cdot 8 \cdot 8 \cdot 8}{8 \cdot 8 \cdot 8} = 8^5$ **79.** x^2 **81.** a^9 **83.** 7^7
85. 5^7 **87.** y **89.** h^4 **91.** 7^7 **93.** 10^9 **95.** $6x^7$
97. $40a^5b^5$ **99.** s^9t^{16} **101.** $-30v^8$ **103.** $16m^{20}n^{10}$
105. $2cd^4$ **107.** z^4 **109.** $\frac{25hjk^4}{12}$ **111.** $-8p^7q^9r^6$
113. $-3stu$ **115.** \$5724.50 **117.** \$4764.06 **119.** 201 in.^{2}
121. 268 in.^{3} **123.** x^{2n+1} **125.** p^{2m+3} **127.** z **129.** r^3

Section 5.2 Practice Exercises, pp. 355–356

1. 4^9 **3.** a^{20} **5.** d^9 **7.** 7^6 **9.** When multiplying expressions with the same base, add the exponents. When raising an expression with an exponent to a power, multiply the exponents.
11. 5^{12} **13.** 12^6 **15.** y^{14} **17.** w^{25} **19.** a^{36} **21.** y^{14}
23. They are both equal to 2^6. **25.** $4^{3^2} = 4^9$; $(4^3)^2 = 4^6$; the expression 4^{3^2} is greater than $(4^3)^2$. **27.** $25w^2$ **29.** $s^4r^4t^4$
31. $\frac{16}{r^4}$ **33.** $\frac{x^5}{y^5}$ **35.** $81a^4$ **37.** $-27a^3b^3c^3$ **39.** $-\frac{64}{x^3}$
41. $\frac{a^2}{b^2}$ **43.** $6^3u^6v^{12}$ or $216u^6v^{12}$ **45.** $5x^8y^4$ **47.** $-h^{28}$
49. m^{12} **51.** $\frac{4^5}{r^5s^{20}}$ or $\frac{1024}{r^5s^{20}}$ **53.** $\frac{3^5p^5}{q^{15}}$ or $\frac{243p^5}{q^{15}}$ **55.** y^{14}
57. x^{31} **59.** $200a^{14}b^9$ **61.** $16p^8q^{16}$ **63.** $-m^{35}n^{15}$
65. $25a^{18}b^6$ **67.** $\frac{4c^2d^6}{9}$ **69.** $\frac{c^{27}d^{31}}{2}$ **71.** $-\frac{27a^9b^3}{c^6}$
73. $16b^{26}$ **75.** x^{2m} **77.** $125a^{6n}$ **79.** $\frac{m^{2b}}{n^{3b}}$ **81.** $\frac{3^na^{3n}}{5^nb^{4n}}$

Section 5.3 Practice Exercises, pp. 364–366

1. a. 1 **b.** $\left(\frac{1}{b}\right)^n$ or $\frac{1}{b^n}$ **3.** c^9 **5.** y **7.** 3^6 or 729
9. $7^4w^{28}z^8$ or $2401w^{28}z^8$ **11. a.** 1 **b.** 1 **13.** 1 **15.** 1
17. −1 **19.** 1 **21.** 1 **23.** −7 **25. a.** $\frac{1}{t^5}$ **b.** $\frac{1}{t^5}$
27. $\frac{343}{8}$ **29.** 25 **31.** $\frac{1}{a^3}$ **33.** $\frac{1}{12}$ **35.** $\frac{1}{16b^2}$ **37.** $\frac{6}{x^2}$
39. $\frac{1}{64}$ **41.** $-\frac{3}{y^4}$ **43.** $-\frac{1}{t^3}$ **45.** a^5
47. $\frac{x^4}{x^{-6}} = x^{4-(-6)} = x^{10}$ **49.** $2a^{-3} = 2 \cdot \frac{1}{a^3} = \frac{2}{a^3}$ **51.** $\frac{1}{x^4}$
53. 1 **55.** y^4 **57.** $\frac{n^{27}}{m^{18}}$ **59.** $\frac{81k^{24}}{j^{20}}$ **61.** $\frac{1}{p^6}$ **63.** $\frac{1}{r^3}$
65. a^8 **67.** $\frac{1}{y^8}$ **69.** $\frac{1}{7^7}$ **71.** 1 **73.** $\frac{1}{a^4b^6}$ **75.** $\frac{1}{w^{21}}$
77. $\frac{1}{27}$ **79.** 1 **81.** $\frac{1}{64x^6}$ **83.** $-\frac{16y^4}{z^2}$ **85.** $-\frac{a^{12}}{6}$
87. $80c^{21}d^{24}$ **89.** $\frac{9y^2}{8x^5}$ **91.** $\frac{4d^{16}}{c^2}$ **93.** $\frac{9y^2}{2x}$ **95.** $\frac{9}{20}$
97. $\frac{9}{10}$ **99.** $\frac{5}{4}$ **101.** $\frac{10}{3}$ **103.** 2 **105.** −11

Chapter 5 Problem Recognition Exercises, p. 366

1. t^8 **2.** 2^8 or 256 **3.** y^5 **4.** p^6 **5.** r^4s^8 **6.** $a^3b^9c^6$
7. w^6 **8.** $\frac{1}{m^{16}}$ **9.** $\frac{x^4z^3}{y^7}$ **10.** $\frac{a^3c^8}{b^6}$ **11.** x^6 **12.** $\frac{1}{y^{10}}$
13. $\frac{1}{t^5}$ **14.** w^7 **15.** p^{15} **16.** p^{15} **17.** $\frac{1}{v^2}$ **18.** $c^{50}d^{40}$
19. 3 **20.** −4 **21.** $\frac{b^9}{2^{15}}$ **22.** $\frac{81}{y^6}$ **23.** $\frac{16y^4}{81x^4}$ **24.** $\frac{25d^6}{36c^2}$
25. $3a^7b^5$ **26.** $64x^7y^{11}$ **27.** $\frac{y^4}{x^8}$ **28.** $\frac{1}{a^{10}b^{10}}$ **29.** $\frac{1}{t^2}$ **30.** $\frac{1}{p^7}$
31. $\frac{8w^6x^9}{27}$ **32.** $\frac{25b^8}{16c^6}$ **33.** $\frac{q^3s}{r^2t^5}$ **34.** $\frac{m^2p^3q}{n^3}$ **35.** $\frac{1}{y^{13}}$
36. w^{10} **37.** $-\frac{1}{8a^{18}b^6}$ **38.** $\frac{4x^{18}}{9y^{10}}$ **39.** $\frac{k^8}{5h^6}$ **40.** $\frac{6n^{10}}{m^{12}}$

Section 5.4 Calculator Connections, p. 370

1.–2.

```
(5.2E6)*(4.6E-3)
                23920
(2.19E-8)*(7.84E
-4)
         1.71696E-11
```

3.–4.

```
(4.76E-5)/(2.38E
9)
                2E-14
(8.5E4)/(4.0E-1)
               212500
```

5.

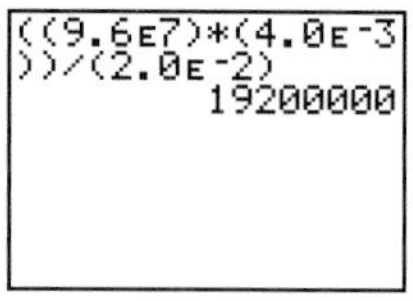

6.

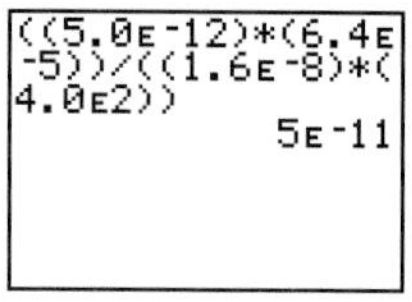

Section 5.4 Practice Exercises, pp. 371–373

1. scientific notation **3.** b^{13} **5.** 10^{13} **7.** $\frac{1}{y^5}$ **9.** $\frac{x^{20}}{y^{12}}$
11. w^4 **13.** 10^4 **15.** Move the decimal point between the 2 and 3 and multiply by 10^{-10}; 2.3×10^{-10}. **17.** 5×10^4
19. 2.08×10^5 **21.** 6.01×10^6 **23.** 8×10^{-6}
25. 1.25×10^{-4} **27.** 6.708×10^{-3} **29.** 1.7×10^{-24} g
31. $\$2.7 \times 10^{10}$ **33.** 6.8×10^7 gal; 1×10^2 miles
35. Move the decimal point nine places to the left; 0.000 000 0031.
37. 0.00005 **39.** 2800 **41.** 0.000603 **43.** 2,400,000
45. 0.019 **47.** 7032 **49.** 0.000 000 000 001 g
51. 1600 Cal and 2800 Cal **53.** 5×10^4 **55.** 3.6×10^{11}
57. 2.2×10^4 **59.** 2.25×10^{-13} **61.** 3.2×10^{14}
63. 2.432×10^{-10} **65.** 3×10^{13} **67.** 6×10^5 **69.** 1.38×10^1
71. 5×10^{-14} **73.** 3.75 in. **75.** $\$2.97 \times 10^{10}$
77. a. 6.5×10^7 **b.** 2.3725×10^{10} days **c.** 5.694×10^{11} hr **d.** 2.04984×10^{15} sec

Section 5.5 Practice Exercises, pp. 379–382

1. a. polynomial **b.** coefficient; degree **c.** 1 **d.** one **e.** binomial **f.** trinomial **g.** leading; leading coefficient **h.** greatest **i.** zero **3.** $\frac{45}{x^2}$ **5.** $\frac{2}{t^4}$ **7.** $\frac{1}{3^{12}}$ **9.** 4×10^{-2} is in scientific notation in which 10 is raised to the -2 power. 4^{-2} is not in scientific notation and 4 is being raised to the -2 power.
11. a. $-7x^5 + 7x^2 + 9x + 6$ **b.** -7 **c.** 5 **13.** Binomial; 75
15. Monomial; 54 **17.** Binomial; -12 **19.** Trinomial; 27
21. Monomial; -192 **23.** The exponents on the x-factors are different. **25.** $35x^2y$ **27.** $8b^5d^2 - 9d$ **29.** $4y^2 + y - 9$
31. $-x^3 + 5x^2 + 9x - 10$ **33.** $10.9y$ **35.** $4a - 8c$
37. $a - \frac{1}{2}b - 2$ **39.** $\frac{4}{3}z^2 - \frac{5}{3}$ **41.** $7.9t^3 - 3.4t^2 + 6t - 4.2$
43. $-4h + 5$ **45.** $2.3m^2 - 3.1m + 1.5$
47. $-3v^3 - 5v^2 - 10v - 22$ **49.** $-8a^3b^2$ **51.** $-53x^3$
53. $-5a - 3$ **55.** $16k + 9$ **57.** $2m^4 - 14m$
59. $3s^2 - 4st - 3t^2$ **61.** $-2r - 3s + 3t$ **63.** $\frac{3}{4}x + \frac{1}{3}y - \frac{3}{10}$
65. $-\frac{2}{3}h^2 + \frac{3}{5}h - \frac{5}{2}$ **67.** $2.4x^4 - 3.1x^2 - 4.4x - 7.9$
69. $4b^3 + 12b^2 - 5b - 12$ **71.** $-\frac{7}{2}x^2 + 5x - 11$
73. $4y^3 + 2y^2 + 2$ **75.** $3a^2 - 3a + 5$
77. $9ab^2 - 3ab + 16a^2b$ **79.** $4z^5 + z^4 + 9z^3 - 3z - 2$
81. $2x^4 + 11x^3 - 3x^2 + 8x - 4$ **83.** $-w^3 + 0.2w^2 + 3.7w - 0.7$
85. $-p^2q - 4pq^2 + 3pq$ **87.** 0 **89.** $-5ab + 6ab^2$
91. $11y^2 - 10y - 4$ **93.** For example: $x^3 + 6$
95. For example: $8x^5$ **97.** For example: $-6x^2 + 2x + 5$

Section 5.6 Practice Exercises, pp. 389–392

1. a. $5 - 2x$ **b.** squares; $a^2 - b^2$ **c.** perfect; $a^2 + 2ab + b^2$
3. $-2y^2$ **5.** $-8y^4$ **7.** $8uvw^2$ **9.** $7u^2v^2w^4$ **11.** $-12y$
13. $21p$ **15.** $12a^{14}b^8$ **17.** $-2c^{10}d^{12}$
19. $16p^2q^2 - 24p^2q + 40pq^2$ **21.** $-4k^3 + 52k^2 + 24k$
23. $-45p^3q - 15p^4q^3 + 30pq^2$ **25.** $y^2 + 19y + 90$
27. $m^2 - 14m + 24$ **29.** $12p^2 - 5p - 2$
31. $12w^2 - 32w + 16$ **33.** $p^2 - 14pw + 33w^2$
35. $12x^2 + 28x - 5$ **37.** $6a^2 - 21.5a + 18$
39. $9t^3 - 21t^2 + 3t - 7$ **41.** $9m^2 + 30mn + 24n^2$
43. $5s^3 + 8s^2 - 7s - 6$ **45.** $27w^3 - 8$
47. $p^4 + 5p^3 - 2p^2 - 21p + 5$ **49.** $6a^3 - 23a^2 + 38a - 45$
51. $8x^3 - 36x^2y + 54xy^2 - 27y^3$ **53.** $1.2x^2 + 7.6xy + 2.4y^2$
55. $y^2 - 36$ **57.** $9a^2 - 16b^2$ **59.** $81k^2 - 36$
61. $\frac{4}{9}t^2 - 9$ **63.** $u^6 - 25v^2$ **65.** $\frac{4}{9} - p^2$
67. $a^2 + 10a + 25$ **69.** $x^2 - 2xy + y^2$ **71.** $4c^2 + 20c + 25$
73. $9t^4 - 24st^2 + 16s^2$ **75.** $t^2 - 14t + 49$ **77.** $16q^2 + 24q + 9$
79. a. 36 **b.** 20 **c.** $(a + b)^2 \neq a^2 + b^2$ in general.
81. $4x^2 - 25$ **83.** $16p^2 + 40p + 25$
85. $27p^3 - 135p^2 + 225p - 125$ **87.** $15a^5 - 6a^2$
89. $49x^2 - y^2$ **91.** $25s^2 + 30st + 9t^2$ **93.** $21x^2 - 65xy + 24y^2$
95. $2t^2 + \frac{26}{3}t + 8$ **97.** $-30x^2 - 35x + 25$
99. $6a^3 + 11a^2 - 7a - 2$ **101.** $y^3 - 3y^2 - 6y - 20$
103. $\frac{1}{9}m^2 - \frac{2}{3}mn + n^2$ **105.** $42w^3 - 84w^2$ **107.** $16y^2 - 65.61$
109. $21c^4 + 4c^2 - 32$ **111.** $9.61x^2 + 27.9x + 20.25$
113. $k^3 - 12k^2 + 48k - 64$ **115.** $125x^3 + 225x^2 + 135x + 27$
117. $2y^4 + 3y^3 + 3y^2 + 5y + 3$ **119.** $6a^3 + 22a^2 - 40a$
121. $2x^3 - 13x^2 + 17x + 12$ **123.** $2x - 7$
125. $k = 10$ or -10 **127.** $k = 8$ or -8

Section 5.7 Practice Exercises, pp. 400–402

1. a. division; quotient; remainder **b.** Synthetic
3. a. $-4a - 11b$ **b.** $5a^2 - 49ab - 10b^2$
5. a. $7x^2 + 2$ **b.** $6x^4 - 5x^3 + x^2 - 2x$
7. For example: $(5y + 1)^2 = 25y^2 + 10y + 1$
9. $-4t^3 + t - 5$ **11.** $12 + 8y + 2y^2$
13. $x^2 + 3xy - y^2$ **15.** $2y^2 + 3y - 8$
17. $-\frac{1}{2}p^3 + p^2 - \frac{1}{3}p + \frac{1}{6}$ **19.** $a^2 + 5a + 1 - \frac{5}{a}$
21. $-3s^2t + 4s - \frac{5}{t^2}$ **23.** $8p^2q^6 - 9p^3q^5 - 11p - \frac{4}{p^2q}$
25. a. Divisor: $(x - 2)$; quotient: $(2x^2 - 3x - 1)$; remainder: (-3) **b.** Multiply the quotient and the divisor, then add the remainder. The result should equal the dividend.
27. $x + 7 + \frac{-9}{x + 4}$ **29.** $3y^2 + 2y + 2 + \frac{9}{y - 3}$
31. $-4a + 11$ **33.** $6y - 5$ **35.** $6x^2 + 4x + 5 + \frac{22}{3x - 2}$
37. $4a^2 - 2a + 1$ **39.** $x^2 - 2x + 2$ **41.** $x^2 + 2x + 5$
43. $x^2 - 1 + \frac{8}{x^2 - 2}$ **45.** $n^3 + 2n^2 + 4n + 8$
47. $3y^2 - 3 + \frac{2y + 6}{y^2 + 1}$
49. The divisor must be of the form $x - r$.
51. No. The divisor is not of the form $x - r$.
53. a. $x - 5$ **b.** $x^2 + 3x + 11$ **c.** 58
55. $x + 6$ **57.** $t - 4$ **59.** $5y + 10 + \frac{11}{y - 1}$
61. $3y^2 - 2y + 2 + \frac{-3}{y + 3}$ **63.** $x^2 - x - 2$
65. $a^4 + 2a^3 + 4a^2 + 8a + 16$ **67.** $x^2 + 6x + 36$
69. $4w^3 + 2w^2 + 6$ **71.** $-x^2 - 4x + 13 + \frac{-54}{x + 4}$
73. $2x - 1 + \frac{3}{x}$ **75.** $4y - 3 + \frac{4y + 5}{3y^2 - 2y + 5}$
77. $2x^2 + 3x - 1$ **79.** $2k^3 - 4k^2 + 1 - \frac{5}{k^4}$
81. $x + \frac{9}{5} + \frac{2}{x}$

Chapter 5 Problem Recognition Exercises, p. 403

1. a. $8x^2$ **b.** $12x^4$ **2. a.** $9y^3$ **b.** $8y^6$ **3. a.** $16x^2 + 8xy + y^2$ **b.** $16x^2y^2$ **4. a.** $4a^2 + 4ab + b^2$ **b.** $4a^2b^2$ **5. a.** $6x + 1$ **b.** $8x^2 + 8x - 6$ **6. a.** $6m^2 + m + 1$ **b.** $5m^4 + 5m^3 + m^2 + m$

7. a. $9z^2 + 12z + 4$ **b.** $9z^2 - 4$ **8. a.** $36y^2 - 84y + 49$ **b.** $36y^2 - 49$ **9. a.** $2x^3 - 8x^2 + 14x - 12$ **b.** $x^2 - 1$

10. a. $-3y^4 - 20y^2 - 32$ **b.** $4y^2 + 12$ **11. a.** $2x$ **b.** x^2

12. a. $4c$ **b.** $4c^2$ **13.** $49m^2n^2$ **14.** $64p^2q^2$ **15.** $-x^2 - 3x + 4$

16. $5m^2 - 4m + 1$ **17.** $-7m^2 - 16m$

18. $-4n^5 + n^4 + 6n^2 - 7n + 2$ **19.** $8x^2 + 16x + 34 + \dfrac{74}{x-2}$

20. $-4x^2 - 10x - 30 + \dfrac{-95}{x-3}$ **21.** $6x^3 + 5x^2y - 6xy^2 + y^3$

22. $6a^3 - a^2b + 5ab^2 + 2b^3$ **23.** $x^3 + y^6$ **24.** $m^6 + 1$

25. $4b$ **26.** $-12z$ **27.** $a^6 - 4b^2$ **28.** $y^6 - 36z^2$

29. $4p + 4 + \dfrac{-2}{2p-1}$ **30.** $2v - 7 + \dfrac{29}{2v+3}$ **31.** $4x^2y^2$

32. $-9pq$ **33.** $\dfrac{9}{49}x^2 - \dfrac{1}{4}$ **34.** $\dfrac{4}{25}y^2 - \dfrac{16}{9}$

35. $-\dfrac{11}{9}x^3 + \dfrac{5}{9}x^2 - \dfrac{1}{2}x - 4$ **36.** $-\dfrac{13}{10}y^2 - \dfrac{9}{10}y + \dfrac{4}{15}$

37. $1.3x^2 - 0.3x - 0.5$ **38.** $5w^3 - 4.1w^2 + 2.8w - 1.2$

39. $-6x^3y^6$ **40.** $50a^4b^6$

Chapter 5 Review Exercises, pp. 408–411

1. Base: 5; exponent: 3 **2.** Base: x; exponent: 4

3. Base: −2; exponent: 0 **4.** Base: y; exponent: 1

5. a. 36 **b.** 36 **c.** −36 **6. a.** 64 **b.** −64 **c.** −64

7. 5^{13} **8.** a^{11} **9.** x^9 **10.** 6^9 **11.** 10^3 **12.** y^6

13. b^8 **14.** 7^7 **15.** k **16.** 1 **17.** 2^8 **18.** q^6

19. Exponents are added only when multiplying factors with the same base. In such a case, the base does not change.

20. Exponents are subtracted only when dividing factors with the same base. In such a case, the base does not change. **21.** \$7146.10

22. \$22,050 **23.** 7^{12} **24.** c^{12} **25.** p^{18} **26.** 9^{28}

27. $\dfrac{a^2}{b^2}$ **28.** $\dfrac{1}{3^4}$ **29.** $\dfrac{5^2}{c^4d^{10}}$ **30.** $\dfrac{m^{10}}{4^5n^{30}}$ **31.** $2^4a^4b^8$

32. $x^{14}y^2$ **33.** $-\dfrac{3^3x^9}{5^3y^6z^3}$ **34.** $\dfrac{r^{15}}{s^{10}t^{30}}$ **35.** a^{11} **36.** 8^2

37. $4h^{14}$ **38.** $2p^{14}q^{13}$ **39.** $\dfrac{x^6y^2}{4}$ **40.** a^9b^6 **41.** 1

42. 1 **43.** −1 **44.** 1 **45.** 2 **46.** 1 **47.** $\dfrac{1}{z^5}$

48. $\dfrac{1}{10^4}$ **49.** $\dfrac{1}{36a^2}$ **50.** $\dfrac{6}{a^2}$ **51.** $\dfrac{17}{16}$ **52.** $\dfrac{10}{9}$

53. $\dfrac{1}{t^8}$ **54.** $\dfrac{1}{r}$ **55.** $\dfrac{2y^7}{x^6}$ **56.** $\dfrac{4a^6bc}{5}$ **57.** $\dfrac{n^{16}}{16m^8}$

58. $\dfrac{u^{15}}{27v^6}$ **59.** $\dfrac{k^{21}}{5}$ **60.** $\dfrac{h^9}{9}$ **61.** $\dfrac{1}{2}$ **62.** $\dfrac{5}{4}$

63. a. 9.74×10^7 **b.** 4.2×10^{-3} in. **64. a.** 0.000 000 0001 **b.** \$256,000 **65.** 9.43×10^5 **66.** 1.55×10^{10}

67. 2.5×10^8 **68.** 1.638×10^3 **69.** $\approx 9.5367 \times 10^{13}$. This number has too many digits to fit on most calculator displays.

70. $\approx 1.1529 \times 10^{-12}$. This number has too many digits to fit on most calculator displays. **71. a.** $\approx 5.84 \times 10^8$ mi **b.** $\approx 6.67 \times 10^4$ mph **72. a.** $\approx 2.26 \times 10^8$ mi **b.** $\approx 1.07 \times 10^5$ mph **73. a.** Trinomial **b.** 4 **c.** 7

74. a. Binomial **b.** 7 **c.** −5 **75.** $7x - 3$

76. $-y^2 - 14y - 2$ **77.** $14a^2 - 2a - 6$

78. $\dfrac{15}{2}x^3 + \dfrac{1}{4}x^2 + \dfrac{1}{2}x + 2$ **79.** $10w^4 + 2w^3 - 7w + 4$

80. $0.01b^5 + b^4 - 0.1b^3 + 0.3b + 0.33$ **81.** $-2x^2 - 9x - 6$

82. $-5x^2 - 9x - 12$ **83.** For example, $-5x^2 + 2x - 4$

84. For example, $6x^5 + 8$ **85.** $6w + 6$ **86.** $-75x^6y^4$

87. $18a^8b^4$ **88.** $15c^4 - 35c^2 + 25c$ **89.** $-2x^3 - 10x^2 + 6x$

90. $5k^2 + k - 4$ **91.** $20t^2 + 3t - 2$ **92.** $6q^2 + 47q - 8$

93. $2a^2 + 4a - 30$ **94.** $49a^2 + 7a + \dfrac{1}{4}$ **95.** $b^2 - 8b + 16$

96. $8p^3 - 27$ **97.** $-2w^3 - 5w^2 - 5w + 4$

98. $4x^3 - 8x^2 + 11x - 4$ **99.** $12a^3 + 11a^2 - 13a - 10$

100. $b^2 - 16$ **101.** $\dfrac{1}{9}r^8 - s^4$ **102.** $49z^4 - 84z^2 + 36$

103. $2h^5 + h^4 - h^3 + h^2 - h + 3$ **104.** $2x^2 + 3x - 20$

105. $4y^2 - 2y$ **106.** $2a^2b - a - 3b$ **107.** $-3x^2 + 2x - 1$

108. $-\dfrac{z^5w^3}{2} + \dfrac{3zw}{4} + \dfrac{1}{z}$ **109.** $x + 2$ **110.** $2t + 5$

111. $p - 3 + \dfrac{5}{2p+7}$ **112.** $a + 6 + \dfrac{-4}{5a-3}$

113. $b^2 + 5b + 25$ **114.** $z + 4$ **115.** $y^2 - 4y + 2 + \dfrac{9y-4}{y^2+3}$

116. $t^2 - 3t + 1 + \dfrac{-2t-6}{3t^2+t+1}$ **117.** $w^2 + w - 1$

Chapter 5 Test, pp. 411–412

1. $\dfrac{(3\cdot 3\cdot 3\cdot 3)\cdot(3\cdot 3\cdot 3)}{3\cdot 3\cdot 3\cdot 3\cdot 3\cdot 3} = 3$ **2.** 9^6 **3.** q^8 **4.** 1

5. $\dfrac{1}{c^3}$ **6.** $\dfrac{5}{4}$ **7.** $\dfrac{3}{2}$ **8.** $27a^6b^3$ **9.** $\dfrac{16x^4}{y^{12}}$ **10.** 14

11. $49s^{18}t$ **12.** $\dfrac{4}{b^{12}}$ **13.** $\dfrac{16a^{12}}{9b^6}$ **14. a.** 4.3×10^{10} **b.** 0.000 0056 **15.** 8.4×10^{-9} **16.** 7.5×10^6

17. a. 2.4192×10^8 m^3 **b.** 8.83008×10^{10} m^3

18. $5x^3 - 7x^2 + 4x + 11$ **a.** 3 **b.** 5

19. $5t^4 + 12t^3 + 7t - 19$ **20.** $24w^2 - 3w - 4$

21. $-10x^5 - 2x^4 + 30x^3$ **22.** $8a^2 - 10a + 3$

23. $4y^3 - 25y^2 + 37y - 15$ **24.** $4 - 9b^2$ **25.** $25z^2 - 60z + 36$

26. $15x^2 - x - 6$ **27.** $-4x^2 + 5x + 7$

28. $y^3 - 11y^2 + 32y - 12$ **29.** $15x^3 - 7x^2 - 2x + 1$

30. Perimeter: $12x - 2$; area: $5x^2 - 13x - 6$

31. $-3x^6 + \dfrac{x^4}{4} - 2x$ **32.** $-4a^2 + \dfrac{ab}{2} - 2$ **33.** $2y - 7$

34. $w^2 - 4w + 5 + \dfrac{-10}{2w+3}$ **35.** $3x^2 + x - 12 + \dfrac{15}{x^2+4}$

Chapters 1–5 Cumulative Review Exercises, pp. 412–413

1. $-\dfrac{35}{2}$ **2.** 4 **3.** $5^2 - \sqrt{4}$; 23 **4.** $\left\{\dfrac{28}{3}\right\}$

5. { } **6.** Quadrant III **7.** y-axis

8. The measures are 31°, 54°, 95°. **9. a.** 12 in. **b.** 19.5 in. **c.** 5.5 hr **10.** $\{(-3, 4)\}$

11. $[-5, \infty)$ 

12. $5x^2 - 9x - 15$ **13.** $-2y^2 - 13yz - 15z^2$

14. $16t^2 - 24t + 9$ **15.** $\dfrac{4}{25}a^2 - \dfrac{1}{9}$

16. $-4a^3b^2 + 2ab - 1$ **17.** $4m^2 + 8m + 11 + \dfrac{24}{m-2}$

18. $\dfrac{c^2}{16d^4}$ **19.** $\dfrac{2b^3}{a^2}$ **20.** 4.1×10^3

Chapter 6

Section 6.1 Practice Exercises, pp. 423–425

1. a. product **b.** prime **c.** greatest common factor **d.** prime **e.** greatest common factor (GCF) **f.** grouping **3.** 7 **5.** 6 **7.** y **9.** $4w^2z$ **11.** $2xy^4z^2$ **13.** $(x-y)$ **15. a.** $3x-6y$ **b.** $3(x-2y)$ **17.** $4(p+3)$ **19.** $5(c^2-2c+3)$ **21.** $x^3(x^2+1)$ **23.** $t(t^3-4+8t)$ **25.** $2ab(1+2a^2)$ **27.** $19x^2y(2-y^3)$ **29.** $6xy^5(x^2-3y^4z)$ **31.** The expression is prime because it is not factorable. **33.** $7pq^2(6p^2+2-p^3q^2)$ **35.** $t^2(t^3+2rt-3t^2+4r^2)$ **37. a.** $-2x(x^2+2x-4)$ **b.** $2x(-x^2-2x+4)$ **39.** $-1(8t^2+9t+2)$ **41.** $-15p^2(p+2)$ **43.** $-3mn(m^3n-2m+3n)$ **45.** $-1(7x+6y+2z)$ **47.** $(a+6)(13-4b)$ **49.** $(w^2-2)(8v+1)$ **51.** $7x(x+3)^2$ **53.** $(2a-b)(4a+3c)$ **55.** $(q+p)(3+r)$ **57.** $(2x+1)(3x+2)$ **59.** $(t+3)(2t-1)$ **61.** $(3y-1)(2y-3)$ **63.** $(b+1)(b^3-4)$ **65.** $(j^2+5)(3k+1)$ **67.** $(2x^6+1)(7w^6-1)$ **69.** $(y+x)(a+b)$ **71.** $(vw+1)(w-3)$ **73.** $5x(x^2+y^2)(3x+2y)$ **75.** $4b(a-b)(x-1)$ **77.** $6t(t-3)(s-t^2)$ **79.** $P=2(l+w)$ **81.** $S=2\pi r(r+h)$ **83.** $\frac{1}{7}(x^2+3x-5)$ **85.** $\frac{1}{4}(5w^2+3w+9)$ **87.** For example: $6x^2+9x$ **89.** For example: $16p^4q^2+8p^3q-4p^2q$

Section 6.2 Practice Exercises, pp. 430–432

1. a. positive **b.** different **c.** Both are correct. **d.** $3(x+6)(x+2)$ **3.** $3(t-5)(t-2)$ **5.** $(a+2b)(x-5)$ **7.** $(x+8)(x+2)$ **9.** $(z-9)(z-2)$ **11.** $(z-6)(z+3)$ **13.** $(p-8)(p+5)$ **15.** $(t+10)(t-4)$ **17.** Prime **19.** $(n+4)^2$ **21.** a **23.** c **25.** They are both correct because multiplication of polynomials is a commutative operation. **27.** The expressions are equal and both are correct. **29.** It should be written in descending order. **31.** $(x-15)(x+2)$ **33.** $(w-13)(w-5)$ **35.** $(t+18)(t+4)$ **37.** $3(x-12)(x+2)$ **39.** $8p(p-1)(p-4)$ **41.** $y^2z^2(y-6)(y-6)$ or $y^2z^2(y-6)^2$ **43.** $-(x-4)(x-6)$ **45.** $-5(a-3x)(a+2x)$ **47.** $-2(c+2)(c+1)$ **49.** $xy^3(x-4)(x-15)$ **51.** $12(p-7)(p-1)$ **53.** $-2(m-10)(m-1)$ **55.** $(c+5d)(c+d)$ **57.** $(a-2b)(a-7b)$ **59.** Prime **61.** $(q-7)(q+9)$ **63.** $(x+10)^2$ **65.** $(t+20)(t-2)$ **67.** The student forgot to factor out the GCF before factoring the trinomial further. The polynomial is not factored completely, because $(2x-4)$ has a common factor of 2. **69.** $x^2+9x-52$ **71. a.** $3x^2+9x-12$ **b.** $3(x+4)(x-1)$ **73.** $(x^2+1)(x^2+9)$ **75.** $(w^2+5)(w^2-3)$ **77.** 7, 5, −7, −5 **79.** For example: $c=-16$

Section 6.3 Practice Exercises, pp. 439–440

1. a. Both are correct. **b.** $2(3x-5)(x+1)$ **3.** $(n-1)(m-2)$ **5.** $6(a-7)(a+2)$ **7.** a **9.** b **11.** $(3n+1)(n+4)$ **13.** $(2y+1)(y-2)$ **15.** $(5x+1)(x-3)$ **17.** $(4c+1)(3c-2)$ **19.** $(10w-3)(w+4)$ **21.** $(3q+2)(2q-3)$ **23.** Prime **25.** $(5m+2)(5m-4)$ **27.** $(6y-5x)(y+4x)$ **29.** $2(m+4)(m-10)$ **31.** $y^3(2y+1)(y+6)$ **33.** $-(a+17)(a-2)$ **35.** $-10(4m+p)(2m-3p)$ **37.** $(x^2+1)(x^2+9)$ **39.** $(w^2+5)(w^2-3)$ **41.** $(2x^2+3)(x^2-5)$ **43.** $-2(z-9)(z-1)$ **45.** $(q-7)(q-6)$ **47.** $(2t+3)(3t-1)$ **49.** $(2m-5)^2$ **51.** Prime **53.** $(2x-5y)(3x-2y)$ **55.** $(4m+5n)(3m-n)$ **57.** $5(3r+2)(2r-1)$ **59.** Prime **61.** $(2t-5)(5t+1)$ **63.** $(7w-4)(2w+3)$ **65.** $(a-12)(a+2)$ **67.** $(x+5y)(x+4y)$ **69.** $(a+20b)(a+b)$ **71.** $(t-7)(t-3)$ **73.** $d(5d^2+3d-10)$ **75.** $4b(b-5)(b+4)$ **77.** $y^2(x-3)(x-10)$ **79.** $-2u(2u+5)(3u-2)$ **81.** $(2x^2+3)(4x^2+1)$ **83. a.** 36 ft **b.** $-4(4t+5)(t-2)$; Yes **85. a.** $(x-12)(x+2)$ **b.** $(x-6)(x-4)$ **87. a.** $(x-6)(x+1)$ **b.** $(x-2)(x-3)$

Section 6.4 Practice Exercises, pp. 446–447

1. a. Both are correct. **b.** $3(4x+3)(x-2)$ **3.** $(y+5)(8+9y)$ **5.** 12, 1 **7.** −8, −1 **9.** 5, −4 **11.** 9, −2 **13.** $(x+4)(3x+1)$ **15.** $(w-2)(4w-1)$ **17.** $(x+9)(x-2)$ **19.** $(m+3)(2m-1)$ **21.** $(4k+3)(2k-3)$ **23.** $(2k-5)^2$ **25.** Prime **27.** $(3z-5)(3z-2)$ **29.** $(6y-5z)(2y+3z)$ **31.** $2(7y+4)(y+3)$ **33.** $-(3w-5)(5w+1)$ **35.** $-4(x-y)(3x-2y)$ **37.** $6y(y+1)(3y+7)$ **39.** $(a^2+2)(a^2+3)$ **41.** $(3x^2-5)(2x^2+3)$ **43.** $(8p^2-3)(p^2+5)$ **45.** $(5p-1)(4p-3)$ **47.** $(3u-2v)(2u-5v)$ **49.** $(4a+5b)(3a-b)$ **51.** $(h+7k)(3h-2k)$ **53.** Prime **55.** $(2z-1)(8z-3)$ **57.** $(b-4)^2$ **59.** $-5(x-2)(x-3)$ **61.** $(t-3)(t+2)$ **63.** Prime **65.** $2(12x-1)(3x+1)$ **67.** $p(p+3)(p-9)$ **69.** $x(3x+7)(x+1)$ **71.** $2p(p-15)(p-4)$ **73.** $x^2(y+3)(y+11)$ **75.** $-(k+2)(k+5)$ **77.** $-3(n+6)(n-5)$ **79.** $(x^2-2)(x^2-5)$ **81.** No. $(2x+4)$ contains a common factor of 2. **83. a.** 128 customers **b.** $-2(x-18)(x-2)$; 128; Yes **85. a.** 42 **b.** $n(n+1)$; 42; Yes

Section 6.5 Practice Exercises, pp. 453–454

1. a. difference; $(a+b)(a-b)$ **b.** sum **c.** is not **d.** square **e.** $(a+b)^2$; $(a-b)^2$ **3.** $(3x-1)(2x-5)$ **5.** $5xy^5(3x-2y)$ **7.** $(x+b)(a-6)$ **9.** $(y+10)(y-4)$ **11.** x^2-25 **13.** $4p^2-9q^2$ **15.** $(x-6)(x+6)$ **17.** $3(w+10)(w-10)$ **19.** $(2a-11b)(2a+11b)$ **21.** $(7m-4n)(7m+4n)$ **23.** Prime **25.** $(y+2z)(y-2z)$ **27.** $(a-b^2)(a+b^2)$ **29.** $(5pq-1)(5pq+1)$ **31.** $\left(c-\frac{1}{5}\right)\left(c+\frac{1}{5}\right)$ **33.** $2(5-4t)(5+4t)$ **35.** $(x+4)(x-4)(x^2+16)$ **37.** $(2-z)(2+z)(4+z^2)$ **39.** $(x+5)(x+3)(x-3)$ **41.** $(c-1)(c+5)(c-5)$ **43.** $(x+3)(x-3)(2+y)$ **45.** $(y+3)(y-3)(x+2)(x-2)$ **47.** $9x^2+30x+25$ **49. a.** x^2+4x+4 is a perfect square trinomial. **b.** $x^2+4x+4=(x+2)^2$; $x^2+5x+4=(x+1)(x+4)$ **51.** $(x+9)^2$ **53.** $(5z-2)^2$ **55.** $(7a+3b)^2$ **57.** $(y-1)^2$ **59.** $5(4z+3w)^2$ **61.** $(3y+25)(3y+1)$ **63.** $2(a-5)^2$ **65.** Prime **67.** $(2x+y)^2$ **69.** $3x(x-1)^2$ **71.** $y(y-6)$ **73.** $(2p-5)(2p+7)$ **75.** $(-t+2)(t+6)$ or $-(t-2)(t+6)$ **77.** $(2a-5+10b)(2a-5-10b)$ **79. a.** a^2-b^2 **b.** $(a-b)(a+b)$

Section 6.6 Practice Exercises, pp. 459–460

1. a. sum; cubes **b.** difference; cubes **c.** $(a-b)(a^2+ab+b^2)$ **d.** $(a+b)(a^2-ab+b^2)$ **3.** $5(2-t)(2+t)$ **5.** $(t+u)(2+s)$ **7.** $(3v-4)(v+3)$ **9.** $-(c+5)^2$ **11.** x^3, 8, y^6, $27q^3$, w^{12}, r^3s^6 **13.** t^3, −1, 27, a^3b^6, 125, y^6 **15.** $(y-2)(y^2+2y+4)$ **17.** $(1-p)(1+p+p^2)$ **19.** $(w+4)(w^2-4w+16)$ **21.** $(x-10y)(x^2+10xy+100y^2)$ **23.** $(4t+1)(16t^2-4t+1)$ **25.** $(10a+3)(100a^2-30a+9)$ **27.** $\left(n-\frac{1}{2}\right)\left(n^2+\frac{1}{2}n+\frac{1}{4}\right)$ **29.** $(5x+2y)(25x^2-10xy+4y^2)$ **31.** $(x^2-2)(x^2+2)$ **33.** Prime **35.** $(t+4)(t^2-4t+16)$ **37.** Prime **39.** $4(b+3)(b^2-3b+9)$ **41.** $5(p-5)(p+5)$ **43.** $\left(\frac{1}{4}-2h\right)\left(\frac{1}{16}+\frac{1}{2}h+4h^2\right)$ **45.** $(x-2)(x+2)(x^2+4)$ **47.** $\left(\frac{2}{3}x-w\right)\left(\frac{2}{3}x+w\right)$ **49.** $(q-2)(q^2+2q+4)(q+2)(q^2-2q+4)$ **51.** $(x^3+4y)(x^6-4x^3y+16y^2)$ **53.** $(2x+3)(x-1)(x+1)$ **55.** $(2x-y)(2x+y)(4x^2+y^2)$ **57.** $(3y-2)(3y+2)(9y^2+4)$ **59.** $(a+b^2)(a^2-ab^2+b^4)$ **61.** $(x^2+y^2)(x-y)(x+y)$ **63.** $(k+4)(k-3)(k+3)$ **65.** $2(t-5)(t-1)(t+1)$ **67.** $\left(\frac{4}{5}p-\frac{1}{2}q\right)\left(\frac{16}{25}p^2+\frac{2}{5}pq+\frac{1}{4}q^2\right)$ **69.** $(a^4+b^4)(a^8-a^4b^4+b^8)$ **71. a.** The quotient is x^2+2x+4. **b.** $(x-2)(x^2+2x+4)$ **73.** $x^2+4x+16$ **75.** $2x+1$

Chapter 6 Problem Recognition Exercises, pp. 461–462

1. A prime polynomial cannot be factored further. **2.** Factor out the GCF. **3.** Look for a difference of squares: $a^2 - b^2$, a difference of cubes: $a^3 - b^3$, or a sum of cubes: $a^3 + b^3$. **4.** Grouping
5. a. Difference of squares **b.** $2(a - 9)(a + 9)$
6. a. Nonperfect square trinomial **b.** $(y + 3)(y + 1)$
7. a. None of these **b.** $6w(w - 1)$
8. a. Difference of squares **b.** $(2z + 3)(2z - 3)(4z^2 + 9)$
9. a. Nonperfect square trinomial **b.** $(3t + 1)(t + 4)$
10. a. Sum of cubes **b.** $5(r + 1)(r^2 - r + 1)$
11. a. Four terms-grouping **b.** $(3c + d)(a - b)$
12. a. Difference of cubes **b.** $(x - 5)(x^2 + 5x + 25)$
13. a. Sum of cubes **b.** $(y + 2)(y^2 - 2y + 4)$
14. a. Nonperfect square trinomial **b.** $(7p - 1)(p - 4)$
15. a. Nonperfect square trinomial **b.** $3(q - 4)(q + 1)$
16. a. Perfect square trinomial **b.** $-2(x - 2)^2$
17. a. None of these **b.** $6a(3a + 2)$
18. a. Difference of cubes **b.** $2(3 - y)(9 + 3y + y^2)$
19. a. Difference of squares **b.** $4(t - 5)(t + 5)$
20. a. Nonperfect square trinomial **b.** $(4t + 1)(t - 8)$
21. a. Nonperfect square trinomial **b.** $10(c^2 + c + 1)$
22. a. Four terms-grouping **b.** $(w - 5)(2x + 3y)$
23. a. Sum of cubes **b.** $(x + 0.1)(x^2 - 0.1x + 0.01)$
24. a. Difference of squares **b.** $(2q - 3)(2q + 3)$
25. a. Perfect square trinomial **b.** $(8 + k)^2$
26. a. Four terms-grouping **b.** $(t + 6)(s^2 + 5)$
27. a. Four terms-grouping **b.** $(x + 1)(2x - y)$
28. a. Sum of cubes **b.** $(w + y)(w^2 - wy + y^2)$
29. a. Difference of cubes **b.** $(a - c)(a^2 + ac + c^2)$
30. a. Nonperfect square trinomial **b.** Prime
31. a. Nonperfect square trinomial **b.** Prime
32. a. Perfect square trinomial **b.** $(a + 1)^2$
33. a. Perfect square trinomial **b.** $(b + 5)^2$
34. a. Nonperfect square trinomial **b.** $-(t + 8)(t - 4)$
35. a. Nonperfect square trinomial **b.** $-p(p + 4)(p + 1)$
36. a. Difference of squares **b.** $(xy - 7)(xy + 7)$
37. a. Nonperfect square trinomial **b.** $3(2x + 3)(x - 5)$
38. a. Nonperfect square trinomial **b.** $2(5y - 1)(2y - 1)$
39. a. None of these **b.** $abc^2(5ac - 7)$
40. a. Difference of squares **b.** $2(2a - 5)(2a + 5)$
41. a. Nonperfect square trinomial **b.** $(t + 9)(t - 7)$
42. a. Nonperfect square trinomial **b.** $(b + 10)(b - 8)$
43. a. Four terms-grouping **b.** $(b + y)(a - b)$
44. a. None of these **b.** $3x^2y^4(2x + y)$
45. a. Nonperfect square trinomial **b.** $(7u - 2v)(2u - v)$
46. a. Nonperfect square trinomial **b.** Prime
47. a. Nonperfect square trinomial **b.** $2(2q^2 - 4q - 3)$
48. a. Nonperfect square trinomial **b.** $3(3w^2 + w - 5)$
49. a. Sum of squares **b.** Prime
50. a. Perfect square trinomial **b.** $5(b - 3)^2$
51. a. Nonperfect square trinomial **b.** $(3r + 1)(2r + 3)$
52. a. Nonperfect square trinomial **b.** $(2s - 3)(2s + 5)$
53. a. Difference of squares **b.** $(2a - 1)(2a + 1)(4a^2 + 1)$
54. a. Four terms-grouping **b.** $(p + c)(p - 3)(p + 3)$
55. a. Perfect square trinomial **b.** $(9u - 5v)^2$
56. a. Sum of squares **b.** $4(x^2 + 4)$
57. a. Nonperfect square trinomial **b.** $(x - 6)(x + 1)$
58. a. Nonperfect square trinomial **b.** Prime
59. a. Four terms-grouping **b.** $2(x - 3y)(a + 2b)$
60. a. Nonperfect square trinomial **b.** $m(4m + 1)(2m - 3)$
61. a. Nonperfect square trinomial **b.** $x^2y(3x + 5)(7x + 2)$
62. a. Difference of squares **b.** $2(m^2 - 8)(m^2 + 8)$
63. a. Four terms-grouping **b.** $(4v - 3)(2u + 3)$
64. a. Four terms-grouping **b.** $(t - 5)(4t + s)$
65. a. Perfect square trinomial **b.** $3(2x - 1)^2$
66. a. Perfect square trinomial **b.** $(p + q)^2$
67. a. Nonperfect square trinomial **b.** $n(2n - 1)(3n + 4)$
68. a. Nonperfect square trinomial **b.** $k(2k - 1)(2k + 3)$
69. a. Difference of squares **b.** $(8 - y)(8 + y)$
70. a. Difference of squares **b.** $b(6 - b)(6 + b)$
71. a. Nonperfect square trinomial **b.** Prime
72. a. Nonperfect square trinomial **b.** $(y + 4)(y + 2)$
73. a. Nonperfect square trinomial **b.** $(c^2 - 10)(c^2 - 2)$

Section 6.7 Practice Exercises, pp. 467–469

1. a. quadratic **b.** 0; 0 **3.** $4(b - 5)(b - 6)$ **5.** $(3x - 2)(x + 4)$ **7.** $4(x^2 + 4y^2)$ **9.** Neither **11.** Quadratic **13.** Linear **15.** $\{-3, 1\}$ **17.** $\left\{\frac{7}{2}, -\frac{7}{2}\right\}$ **19.** $\{-5\}$ **21.** $\left\{0, \frac{1}{5}\right\}$ **23.** The polynomial must be factored completely. **25.** $\{5, -3\}$ **27.** $\{-12, 2\}$ **29.** $\left\{4, -\frac{1}{2}\right\}$ **31.** $\left\{\frac{2}{3}, -\frac{2}{3}\right\}$ **33.** $\{6, 8\}$ **35.** $\left\{0, -\frac{3}{2}, 4\right\}$ **37.** $\left\{-\frac{1}{3}, 3, -6\right\}$ **39.** $\left\{0, 4, -\frac{3}{2}\right\}$ **41.** $\left\{0, -\frac{9}{2}, 11\right\}$ **43.** $\{0, 4, -4\}$ **45.** $\{-6, 0\}$ **47.** $\left\{\frac{3}{4}, -\frac{3}{4}\right\}$ **49.** $\{0, -5, -2\}$ **51.** $\left\{-\frac{14}{3}\right\}$ **53.** $\{5, 3\}$ **55.** $\{0, -2\}$ **57.** $\{-3\}$ **59.** $\{-3, 1\}$ **61.** $\left\{\frac{3}{2}\right\}$ **63.** $\left\{0, \frac{1}{3}\right\}$ **65.** $\{0, 2\}$ **67.** $\{3, -2, 2\}$ **69.** $\{-5, 4\}$ **71.** $\{-5, -1\}$

Chapter 6 Problem Recognition Exercises, p. 469

1. a. $(x + 7)(x - 1)$ **b.** $\{-7, 1\}$ **2. a.** $(c + 6)(c + 2)$ **b.** $\{-6, -2\}$ **3. a.** $(2y + 1)(y + 3)$ **b.** $\left\{-\frac{1}{2}, -3\right\}$ **4. a.** $(3x - 5)(x - 1)$ **b.** $\left\{\frac{5}{3}, 1\right\}$ **5. a.** $\left\{\frac{4}{5}, -1\right\}$ **b.** $(5q - 4)(q + 1)$ **6. a.** $\left\{-\frac{1}{3}, \frac{3}{2}\right\}$ **b.** $(3a + 1)(2a - 3)$ **7. a.** $\{-8, 8\}$ **b.** $(a + 8)(a - 8)$ **8. a.** $\{-10, 10\}$ **b.** $(v + 10)(v - 10)$ **9. a.** $(2b + 9)(2b - 9)$ **b.** $\left\{-\frac{9}{2}, \frac{9}{2}\right\}$ **10. a.** $(6t + 7)(6t - 7)$ **b.** $\left\{-\frac{7}{6}, \frac{7}{6}\right\}$ **11. a.** $\left\{-\frac{3}{2}, -\frac{1}{2}\right\}$ **b.** $2(2x + 3)(2x + 1)$ **12. a.** $\left\{-\frac{4}{3}, -2\right\}$ **b.** $4(3y + 4)(y + 2)$ **13. a.** $x(x - 10)(x + 2)$ **b.** $\{0, 10, -2\}$ **14. a.** $k(k + 7)(k - 2)$ **b.** $\{0, -7, 2\}$ **15. a.** $\{-1, 3, -3\}$ **b.** $(b + 1)(b - 3)(b + 3)$ **16. a.** $\{8, -2, 2\}$ **b.** $(x - 8)(x + 2)(x - 2)$ **17.** $(s - 3)(2s + r)$ **18.** $(2t + 1)(3t + 5u)$ **19.** $\left\{-\frac{1}{2}, 0, \frac{1}{2}\right\}$ **20.** $\{-5, 0, 5\}$ **21.** $\{0, 1\}$ **22.** $\{-3, 0\}$ **23.** $\left\{\frac{1}{3}\right\}$ **24.** $\left\{-\frac{7}{12}\right\}$ **25.** $(2w + 3)(4w^2 - 6w + 9)$ **26.** $(10q - 1)(100q^2 + 10q + 1)$ **27.** $\left\{-\frac{7}{5}, 1\right\}$ **28.** $\left\{-6, -\frac{1}{4}\right\}$ **29.** $\left\{-\frac{2}{3}, -5\right\}$ **30.** $\left\{-1, -\frac{1}{2}\right\}$ **31.** $\{3\}$ **32.** $\{0\}$ **33.** $\{-4, 4\}$ **34.** $\left\{-\frac{2}{3}, \frac{2}{3}\right\}$ **35.** $\{1, 6\}$ **36.** $\{-2, -12\}$

Section 6.8 Practice Exercises, pp. 474–477

1. a. $x + 1$ **b.** $x + 2$ **c.** $x + 2$ **d.** LW **e.** $\frac{1}{2}bh$ **f.** $a^2 + b^2 = c^2$ **3.** $\left\{0, -\frac{2}{3}\right\}$ **5.** $\{6, -1\}$ **7.** $\left\{-\frac{5}{6}, 2\right\}$ **9.** The numbers are 7 and −7. **11.** The numbers are 10 and −4. **13.** The numbers are −9 and −7, or 7 and 9. **15.** The numbers are 5 and 6, or −6 and −5. **17.** The height of the painting is 11 ft and the width is 9 ft. **19. a.** The slab is 7 m by 4 m. **b.** The perimeter is 22 m. **21.** The base is 7 ft and the height is 4 ft.

23. The base is 5 cm and the height is 8 cm. **25.** The ball hits the ground in 3 sec.
27. The object is at ground level at 0 sec and 1.5 sec.
29.
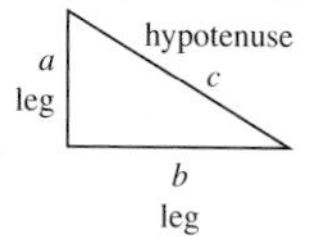

31. $c = 25$ cm **33.** $a = 15$ in.
35. The brace is 20 in. long. **37.** The kite is 19 yd high.
39. The bottom of the ladder is 8 ft from the house. The distance from the top of the ladder to the ground is 15 ft.
41. The hypotenuse is 10 m.

Chapter 6 Review Exercises, pp. 483–485

1. $3a^2b$ **2.** $x + 5$ **3.** $2c(3c - 5)$ **4.** $-2yz$ or $2yz$
5. $2x(3x + x^3 - 4)$ **6.** $11w^2y^3(w - 4y^2)$
7. $t(-t + 5)$ or $-t(t - 5)$ **8.** $u(-6u - 1)$ or $-u(6u + 1)$
9. $(b + 2)(3b - 7)$ **10.** $2(5x + 9)(1 + 4x)$
11. $(w + 2)(7w + b)$ **12.** $(b - 2)(b + y)$
13. $3(4y - 3)(5y - 1)$ **14.** $a(2 - a)(3 - b)$
15. $(x - 3)(x - 7)$ **16.** $(y - 8)(y - 11)$
17. $(z - 12)(z + 6)$ **18.** $(q - 13)(q + 3)$
19. $3w(p + 10)(p + 2)$ **20.** $2m^2(m + 8)(m + 5)$
21. $-(t - 8)(t - 2)$ **22.** $-(w - 4)(w + 5)$
23. $(a + b)(a + 11b)$ **24.** $(c - 6d)(c + 3d)$
25. Different **26.** Both negative **27.** Both positive
28. Different **29.** $(2y + 3)(y - 4)$ **30.** $(4w + 3)(w - 2)$
31. $(2z + 5)(5z + 2)$ **32.** $(4z - 3)(2z + 3)$ **33.** Prime
34. Prime **35.** $10(w - 9)(w + 3)$ **36.** $-3(y - 8)(y + 2)$
37. $(3c - 5d)^2$ **38.** $(x + 6)^2$ **39.** $(3g + 2h)(2g + h)$
40. $(6m - n)(2m - 5n)$ **41.** $(v^2 + 1)(v^2 - 3)$
42. $(x^2 + 5)(x^2 + 2)$ **43.** 5, −1 **44.** −3, −5
45. $(c - 2)(3c + 1)$ **46.** $(y + 3)(4y + 1)$ **47.** $(t + 12w)(t + w)$
48. $(4x^2 - 3)(x^2 + 5)$ **49.** $(w^2 + 5)(w^2 + 2)$
50. $(p - 3q)(p - 5q)$ **51.** $-2(4v + 3)(5v - 1)$
52. $10(4s - 5)(s + 2)$ **53.** $ab(a - 6b)(a - 4b)$
54. $2z^4(z + 7)(z - 3)$ **55.** Prime **56.** Prime **57.** $(7x + 10)^2$
58. $(3w - z)^2$ **59.** $(a - b)(a + b)$ **60.** Prime
61. $(a - 7)(a + 7)$ **62.** $(d - 8)(d + 8)$ **63.** $(10 - 9t)(10 + 9t)$
64. $(2 - 5k)(2 + 5k)$ **65.** Prime **66.** Prime **67.** $(y + 6)^2$
68. $(t + 8)^2$ **69.** $(3a - 2)^2$ **70.** $(5x - 4)^2$ **71.** $-3(v + 2)^2$
72. $-2(x - 5)^2$ **73.** $2(c^2 - 3)(c^2 + 3)$ **74.** $2(6x - y)(6x + y)$
75. $(p + 3)(p - 4)(p + 4)$ **76.** $(k - 2)(2 - k)(2 + k)$ or $-(k - 2)^2(2 + k)$ **77.** $(a + b)(a^2 - ab + b^2)$
78. $(a - b)(a^2 + ab + b^2)$ **79.** $(4 + a)(16 - 4a + a^2)$
80. $(5 - b)(25 + 5b + b^2)$ **81.** $(p^2 + 2)(p^4 - 2p^2 + 4)$
82. $\left(q^2 - \frac{1}{3}\right)\left(q^4 + \frac{1}{3}q^2 + \frac{1}{9}\right)$ **83.** $6(x - 2)(x^2 + 2x + 4)$
84. $7(y + 1)(y^2 - y + 1)$ **85.** $x(x - 6)(x + 6)$
86. $q(q - 4)(q^2 + 4q + 16)$ **87.** $4(2h^2 + 5)$ **88.** $m(m - 8)$
89. $(x + 4)(x + 1)(x - 1)$ **90.** $5q(p^2 - 2q)(p^2 + 2q)$
91. $n(2 + n)(4 - 2n + n^2)$ **92.** $14(m - 1)(m^2 + m + 1)$
93. $(x - 3)(2x + 1) = 0$ can be solved directly by the zero product rule because it is a product of factors set equal to zero.
94. $\left\{\frac{1}{4}, -\frac{2}{3}\right\}$ **95.** $\left\{9, \frac{1}{2}\right\}$ **96.** $\left\{0, -3, -\frac{2}{5}\right\}$
97. $\left\{0, 7, \frac{9}{4}\right\}$ **98.** $\left\{-\frac{5}{7}, 2\right\}$ **99.** $\left\{-\frac{1}{4}, 6\right\}$
100. $\{12, -12\}$ **101.** $\{5, -5\}$ **102.** $\left\{0, \frac{1}{5}\right\}$ **103.** $\{4, 2\}$
104. $\left\{-\frac{5}{6}\right\}$ **105.** $\left\{-\frac{2}{3}\right\}$ **106.** $\left\{\frac{2}{3}, 6\right\}$ **107.** $\left\{\frac{11}{2}, -12\right\}$
108. $\{0, 7, 2\}$ **109.** $\{0, 2, -2\}$ **110.** The height is 6 ft, and the base is 13 ft. **111.** The ball is at ground level at 0 and 1 sec.
112. The ramp is 13 ft long. **113.** The legs are 6 ft and 8 ft; the hypotenuse is 10 ft. **114.** The numbers are −8 and 8.
115. The numbers are 29 and 30, or −2 and −1.
116. The height is 4 m, and the base is 9 m.

Chapter 6 Test, p. 485

1. $3x(5x^3 - 1 + 2x^2)$ **2.** $(a - 5)(7 - a)$
3. $(6w - 1)(w - 7)$ **4.** $(13 - p)(13 + p)$
5. $(q - 8)^2$ **6.** $(2 + t)(4 - 2t + t^2)$ **7.** $(a + 4)(a + 8)$
8. $(x + 7)(x - 6)$ **9.** $(2y - 1)(y - 8)$ **10.** $(2z + 1)(3z + 8)$
11. $(3t - 10)(3t + 10)$ **12.** $(v + 9)(v - 9)$ **13.** $3(a + 6b)(a + 3b)$
14. $(c - 1)(c + 1)(c^2 + 1)$ **15.** $(y - 7)(x + 3)$ **16.** Prime
17. $-10(u - 2)(u - 1)$ **18.** $3(2t - 5)(2t + 5)$ **19.** $5(y - 5)^2$
20. $7q(3q + 2)$ **21.** $(2x + 1)(x - 2)(x + 2)$
22. $(y - 5)(y^2 + 5y + 25)$ **23.** $(mn - 9)(mn + 9)$
24. $16(a - 2b)(a + 2b)$ **25.** $(4x - 3y^2)(16x^2 + 12xy^2 + 9y^4)$
26. $3y(x - 4)(x + 2)$ **27.** $\left\{\frac{3}{2}, -5\right\}$ **28.** $\{0, 7\}$ **29.** $\{8, -2\}$
30. $\left\{\frac{1}{5}, -1\right\}$ **31.** $\{3, -3, -10\}$
32. The tennis court is 12 yd by 26 yd. **33.** The two integers are 5 and 7, or −5 and −7. **34.** The base is 12 in., and the height is 7 in.
35. The shorter leg is 5 ft. **36.** The stone hits the ground in 2 sec.

Chapters 1–6 Cumulative Review Exercises, p. 486

1. $\frac{7}{5}$ **2.** $\{-3\}$ **3.** $y = \frac{3}{2}x - 4$
4. There are 10 quarters and 7 dimes.
5. $[-4, \infty)$

6. a. Yes **b.** 1 **c.** $(0, 4)$ **d.** $(-4, 0)$ **e.**
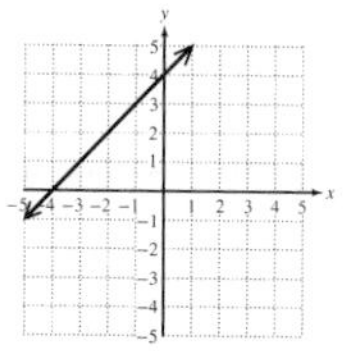
7. a. Vertical line **b.** Undefined **c.** $(5, 0)$ **d.** Does not exist
8. $y = 3x + 14$ **9.** $\{(5, 2)\}$ **10.** $-\frac{7}{2}y^2 - 5y - 14$
11. $8p^3 - 22p^2 + 13p + 3$ **12.** $4w^2 - 28w + 49$
13. $r^3 + 5r^2 + 15r + 40 + \frac{121}{r - 3}$ **14.** c^4 **15.** $\frac{a^4}{9b^2}$
16. 1.6×10^3 **17.** $(w - 2)(w + 2)(w^2 + 4)$
18. $(a + 5b)(2x - 3y)$ **19.** $(2x - 5)(2x + 1)$
20. $\left\{0, \frac{1}{2}, -5\right\}$

Chapter 7

Section 7.1 Practice Exercises, pp. 495–498

1. a. rational **b.** denominator; zero **c.** $\frac{p}{q}$ **d.** 1; −1 **3.** 0
5. $-\frac{1}{8}$ **7.** $-\frac{1}{2}$ **9.** Undefined **11. a.** $3\frac{1}{5}$ hr or 3.2 hr
b. $1\frac{3}{4}$ hr or 1.75 hr **13.** $k = -2$ **15.** $x = \frac{5}{2}, x = -8$
17. $m = -2, m = -3$ **19.** There are no restricted values.
21. There are no restricted values. **23.** $t = 0$
25. For example: $\frac{1}{x - 2}$ **27.** For example: $\frac{1}{(x + 3)(x - 7)}$
29. a. $\frac{2}{5}$ **b.** $\frac{2}{5}$ **31. a.** Undefined **b.** Undefined
33. a. $y = -2$ **b.** $\frac{1}{2}$ **35. a.** $t = -1$ **b.** $t - 1$
37. a. $w = 0, w = \frac{5}{3}$ **b.** $\frac{1}{3w - 5}$ **39. a.** $x = -\frac{2}{3}$ **b.** $\frac{3x - 2}{2}$
41. a. $a = -3, a = 2$ **b.** $\frac{a + 5}{a + 3}$ **43.** $\frac{b}{3}$ **45.** $-\frac{3xy}{z^2}$
47. $\frac{p - 3}{p + 4}$ **49.** $\frac{1}{4(m - 11)}$ **51.** $\frac{2x + 1}{4x^2}$ **53.** $\frac{1}{4a - 5}$
55. $\frac{x - 2}{3(y + 2)}$ **57.** $\frac{2}{x - 5}$ **59.** $a + 7$ **61.** Cannot simplify

63. $\frac{y+3}{2y-5}$ **65.** $\frac{5}{(q+1)(q-1)}$ **67.** $\frac{c-d}{2c+d}$ **69.** $5x+4$

71. $\frac{x+y}{x-4y}$ **73.** They are opposites. **75.** -1 **77.** -1

79. $-\frac{1}{2}$ **81.** Cannot simplify **83.** $\frac{5x-6}{5x+6}$ **85.** $-\frac{x+3}{4+x}$

87. $\frac{3x-2}{x+4}$ **89.** $-\frac{1}{2}$ **91.** $-\frac{w+2}{4}$ **93.** $\frac{3t^2}{2}$ **95.** $-\frac{2r-s}{s+2r}$

97. $-\frac{3}{2(x-y)}$ **99.** $\frac{1}{t(t-5)}$ **101.** $w-2$ **103.** $\frac{z+4}{z^2+4z+16}$

Section 7.2 Practice Exercises, pp. 503–505

1. $\frac{3}{10}$ **3.** 2 **5.** $\frac{5}{2}$ **7.** $\frac{15}{4}$ **9.** $\frac{3}{2x}$ **11.** $3xy^4$

13. $\frac{x-6}{8}$ **15.** $\frac{2}{y}$ **17.** $-\frac{5}{8}$ **19.** $-\frac{b+a}{a-b}$ **21.** $\frac{y+1}{5}$

23. $\frac{2(x+6)}{2x+1}$ **25.** 6 **27.** $\frac{m^6}{n^2}$ **29.** $\frac{10}{9}$ **31.** $\frac{6}{7}$

33. $-m(m+n)$ **35.** $\frac{3p+4q}{4(p+2q)}$ **37.** $\frac{p}{p-1}$ **39.** $\frac{w}{2w-1}$

41. $\frac{4r}{2r+3}$ **43.** $\frac{5}{6}$ **45.** $\frac{1}{4}$ **47.** $\frac{y+9}{y-6}$ **49.** 1

51. $\frac{3t+8}{t+2}$ **53.** $\frac{x+4}{x+1}$ **55.** $-\frac{w-3}{2}$ **57.** $\frac{k+6}{k+3}$ **59.** $\frac{2}{a}$

61. $2y(y+1)$ **63.** $x+y$ **65.** 2 **67.** $\frac{1}{a-2}$ **69.** $\frac{p+q}{2}$

Section 7.3 Practice Exercises, pp. 509–511

1. multiple; denominators **3.** $x=1, x=-1$; $\frac{3}{5(x-1)}$

5. $\frac{a+5}{a+7}$ **7.** $\frac{2}{3y}$ **9.** a, b, c, d **11.** x^5 is the greatest power of x that appears in any denominator. **13.** 45 **15.** 48 **17.** 63 **19.** $9x^2y^3$ **21.** w^2y **23.** $(p+3)(p-1)(p+2)$ **25.** $9t(t+1)^2$ **27.** $(y-2)(y+2)(y+3)$ **29.** $3-x$ or $x-3$ **31.** Because $(b-1)$ and $(1-b)$ are opposites, they differ by a factor of -1. **33.** $\frac{6}{5x^2}$; $\frac{5x}{5x^2}$ **35.** $\frac{24x}{30x^3}$; $\frac{5y}{30x^3}$

37. $\frac{10}{12a^2b}$; $\frac{a^3}{12a^2b}$ **39.** $\frac{6m-6}{(m+4)(m-1)}$; $\frac{3m+12}{(m+4)(m-1)}$

41. $\frac{6x+18}{(2x-5)(x+3)}$; $\frac{2x-5}{(2x-5)(x+3)}$

43. $\frac{6w+6}{(w+3)(w-8)(w+1)}$; $\frac{w^2+3w}{(w+3)(w-8)(w+1)}$

45. $\frac{6p^2+12p}{(p-2)(p+2)^2}$; $\frac{3p-6}{(p-2)(p+2)^2}$

47. $\frac{1}{a-4}$; $\frac{-a}{a-4}$ or $\frac{-1}{4-a}$; $\frac{a}{4-a}$

49. $\frac{8}{2(x-7)}$; $\frac{-y}{2(x-7)}$ or $\frac{-8}{2(7-x)}$; $\frac{y}{2(7-x)}$

51. $\frac{1}{a+b}$; $\frac{-6}{a+b}$ or $\frac{-1}{-a-b}$; $\frac{6}{-a-b}$

53. $\frac{-9}{24(3y+1)}$; $\frac{20}{24(3y+1)}$ **55.** $\frac{3z+12}{5z(z+4)}$; $\frac{5z}{5z(z+4)}$

57. $\frac{z^2+3z}{(z+2)(z+7)(z+3)}$; $\frac{-3z^2-6z}{(z+2)(z+7)(z+3)}$; $\frac{5z+35}{(z+2)(z+7)(z+3)}$

59. $\frac{3p+6}{(p-2)(p^2+2p+4)(p+2)}$; $\frac{p^3+2p^2+4p}{(p-2)(p^2+2p+4)(p+2)}$; $\frac{5p^3-20p}{(p-2)(p^2+2p+4)(p+2)}$

Section 7.4 Practice Exercises, pp. 518–520

1. a. $-\frac{1}{2}$, -2, 0, undefined, undefined **b.** $(x-5)(x-2)$; $x=5, x=2$ **c.** $\frac{x+1}{x-2}$ **3.** $\frac{2(2x-3)}{(x-3)(x-1)}$

5. $\frac{5}{4}$ **7.** $\frac{3}{8}$ **9.** 2 **11.** 5 **13.** $\frac{-2(t-2)}{t-8}$ **15.** $3x+7$

17. $m+5$ **19.** 2 **21.** $x-5$ **23.** $\frac{1}{r+1}$ **25.** $\frac{1}{y+7}$

27. $\frac{15x}{y}$ **29.** $\frac{5a+6}{4a}$ **31.** $\frac{2(6+x^2y)}{15xy^3}$ **33.** $\frac{2s-3t^2}{s^4t^3}$

35. $-\frac{2}{3}$ **37.** $\frac{19}{3(a+1)}$ **39.** $\frac{-3(k+4)}{(k-3)(k+3)}$ **41.** $\frac{a-4}{2a}$

43. $\frac{(x+6)(x-2)}{(x-4)(x+1)}$ **45.** $\frac{x(4x+9)}{(x+3)^2(x+2)}$

47. $\frac{5p-1}{3}$ or $\frac{-5p+1}{-3}$ **49.** $\frac{9}{x-3}$ or $\frac{-9}{3-x}$

51. $\frac{6n-1}{n-8}$ or $\frac{-6n+1}{8-n}$ **53.** $\frac{2(4x+5)}{x(x+2)}$ **55.** $\frac{3y}{2(2y+1)}$

57. $\frac{2(w-3)}{(w+3)(w-1)}$ **59.** $\frac{4a-13}{(a-3)(a-4)}$ **61.** $\frac{3x(x+7)}{(x+5)^2(x-1)}$

63. $\frac{-y(y+8)}{(2y+1)(y-1)(y-4)}$ **65.** $\frac{1}{2p+1}$ **67.** $\frac{-2mn+1}{(m+n)(m-n)}$

69. 0 **71.** $\frac{2(3x+7)}{(x+3)(x+2)}$ **73.** $\frac{1}{n}$ **75.** $\frac{5}{n+2}$

77. $n+\left(7\cdot\frac{1}{n}\right)$; $\frac{n^2+7}{n}$ **79.** $\frac{1}{n}-\frac{2}{n}$; $-\frac{1}{n}$

81. $\frac{-w^2}{(w+3)(w-3)(w^2-3w+9)}$ **83.** $\frac{p^2-2p+7}{(p+2)(p+3)(p-1)}$

85. $\frac{-m-21}{2(m+5)(m-2)}$ or $\frac{m+21}{2(m+5)(2-m)}$ **87.** $\frac{3k+5}{4k+7}$ **89.** $\frac{1}{a}$

Chapter 7 Problem Recognition Exercises, p. 521

1. $\frac{-2x+9}{3x+1}$ **2.** $\frac{1}{w-4}$ **3.** $\frac{y-5}{2y-3}$ **4.** $\frac{7}{(x+3)(2x-1)}$

5. $-\frac{1}{x}$ **6.** $\frac{1}{3}$ **7.** $\frac{c+3}{c}$ **8.** $\frac{x+3}{5}$ **9.** $\frac{a}{12b^4c}$

10. $\frac{2a-b}{a-b}$ **11.** $\frac{p-q}{5}$ **12.** 4 **13.** $\frac{10}{2x+1}$ **14.** $\frac{w+2z}{w+z}$

15. $\frac{3}{2x+5}$ **16.** $\frac{y+7}{x+a}$ **17.** $\frac{1}{2(a+3)}$

18. $\frac{2(3y+10)}{(y-6)(y+6)(y+2)}$ **19.** $(t+8)^2$ **20.** $6b+5$

Section 7.5 Practice Exercises, pp. 527–529

1. complex **3.** $\frac{1}{2a-3}$ **5.** $\frac{3(2k-5)}{5(k-2)}$ **7.** $\frac{7}{4y}$ **9.** $\frac{1}{2y}$

11. $\frac{24b}{a^3}$ **13.** $\frac{2r^5t^4}{s^6}$ **15.** $\frac{35}{2}$ **17.** $k+h$ **19.** $\frac{n+1}{2(n-3)}$

21. $\frac{2x+1}{4x+1}$ **23.** $m-7$ **25.** $\frac{2y(y-5)}{7y^2+10}$ **27.** $-\frac{a+8}{a-2}$ or $\frac{a+8}{2-a}$

29. $\frac{t-2}{t-4}$ **31.** $\frac{t+3}{t-5}$ **33.** $\frac{1}{2}$ **35.** $\frac{\frac{1}{2}+\frac{2}{3}}{5}$; $\frac{7}{30}$

37. $\frac{3}{\frac{2}{3}+\frac{3}{4}}$; $\frac{36}{17}$ **39. a.** $\frac{6}{5}\,\Omega$ **b.** $6\,\Omega$ **41.** $\frac{xy}{y+x}$ **43.** $\frac{y+4x}{2y}$

45. $\frac{1}{n^2+m^2}$ **47.** $\frac{2z-5}{3(z+3)}$ **49.** $-\frac{x+1}{x-1}$ or $\frac{x+1}{1-x}$ **51.** $\frac{3}{2}$

Section 7.6 Practice Exercises, pp. 537–539

1. a. linear; quadratic **b.** rational **c.** denominator **3.** $\frac{2}{4x-1}$

5. $5(h+1)$ **7.** $\frac{(x+4)(x-3)}{x^2}$ **9.** $\{3\}$ **11.** $\left\{\frac{5}{11}\right\}$

13. $\left\{\frac{1}{3}\right\}$ 15. a. $z=0$ b. $5z$ c. $\{5\}$ 17. $\left\{-\frac{200}{19}\right\}$

19. $\{-7\}$ 21. $\left\{\frac{47}{6}\right\}$ 23. $\{3, -1\}$ 25. $\{4\}$

27. $\{5\}$ (The value 0 does not check.) 29. $\{-5\}$

31. { } (The value 4 does not check.) 33. $\{4\}$ 35. $\{4, -3\}$

37. $\{-4\}$; (The value 1 does not check.) 39. { } (The value -4 does not check.) 41. $\{4\}$ (The value -6 does not check.)

43. $\{-25\}$ 45. $\{-2, 7\}$ 47. The number is 8.

49. The number is -26. 51. $m=\frac{FK}{a}$ 53. $E=\frac{IR}{K}$

55. $R=\frac{E-Ir}{I}$ or $R=\frac{E}{I}-r$

57. $B=\frac{2A-hb}{h}$ or $B=\frac{2A}{h}-b$ 59. $h=\frac{V}{r^2\pi}$

61. $t=\frac{b}{x-a}$ or $t=\frac{-b}{a-x}$ 63. $x=\frac{y}{1-yz}$ or $x=\frac{-y}{yz-1}$

65. $h=\frac{2A}{a+b}$ 67. $R=\frac{R_1R_2}{R_2+R_1}$

Chapter 7 Problem Recognition Exercises, p. 540

1. $\frac{y-2}{2y}$ 2. $\{6\}$ 3. $\{2\}$ 4. $\frac{3a-17}{a-5}$ 5. $\frac{4p+27}{18p^2}$

6. $\frac{b(b-5)}{(b-1)(b+1)}$ 7. $\{5\}$ 8. $\frac{2w+5}{(w+1)^2}$ 9. $\{7\}$ 10. $\{5\}$

11. $\frac{3x+14}{4(x+1)}$ 12. $\left\{\frac{11}{3}\right\}$ 13. $\left\{\frac{41}{10}\right\}$ 14. $\frac{7-3t}{t(t-5)}$

15. $\frac{8a+1}{2a-1}$ 16. $\{5\}$ (The value 2 does not check.)

17. $\{-1\}$ (The value 3 does not check.) 18. $\frac{11}{12k}$

19. $\frac{h+9}{(h-3)(h+3)}$ 20. $\{7\}$

Section 7.7 Practice Exercises, pp. 548–552

1. a. proportion b. proportional

3. Expression; $\frac{m^2+m+2}{(m-1)(m+3)}$ 5. Expression; $\frac{3}{10}$

7. Equation; $\{2\}$ 9. $\{95\}$ 11. $\{1\}$ 13. $\left\{\frac{40}{3}\right\}$ 15. $\{40\}$

17. $\{3\}$ 19. $\{-1\}$ 21. $\{1\}$ 23. a. $V_f=\frac{V_iT_f}{T_i}$ b. $T_f=\frac{T_iV_f}{V_i}$

25. Toni can drive 297 mi on 9 gal of gas. 27. Mix 14.82 mL of plant food. 29. 5 oz contains 12 g of carbohydrate.

31. The minimum length is 20 ft. 33. $x=4$ cm; $y=5$ cm

35. $x=3.75$ cm; $y=4.5$ cm 37. The height of the pole is 7 m.

39. The light post is 24 ft high. 41. The speed of the boat is 20 mph. 43. The plane flies 210 mph in still air. 45. He runs 8 mph and bikes 16 mph. 47. Floyd walks 4 mph and Rachel walks 2 mph. 49. Sergio rode 12 mph and walked 3 mph.

51. $5\frac{5}{11}$ $(5.\overline{45})$ min 53. $22\frac{2}{9}$ $(22.\overline{2})$ min 55. 48 hr

57. $3\frac{1}{3}$ $(3.\overline{3})$ days 59. There are 40 smokers and 140 nonsmokers.

61. There are 240 men and 200 women.

Chapter 7 Review Exercises pp. 558–560

1. a. $-\frac{2}{9}, -\frac{1}{10}, 0, -\frac{5}{6}$, undefined b. $t=-9$

2. a. $-\frac{1}{5}, -\frac{1}{2}$, undefined, $0, \frac{1}{7}$ b. $k=5$ 3. a, c, d

4. $x=\frac{5}{2}, x=3; \frac{1}{2x-5}$ 5. $h=-\frac{1}{3}, h=-7; \frac{1}{3h+1}$

6. $a=2, a=-2; \frac{4a-1}{a-2}$ 7. $w=4, w=-4; \frac{2w+3}{w-4}$

8. $z=4; -\frac{z}{2}$ 9. $k=0, k=5; -\frac{3}{2k}$ 10. $b=-3; \frac{b-1}{2}$

11. $m=-1; \frac{m-5}{3}$ 12. $n=-3; \frac{1}{n+3}$ 13. $p=-7; \frac{1}{p+7}$

14. y^2 15. $\frac{u^2}{2}$ 16. $v+2$ 17. $\frac{3}{2(x-5)}$ 18. $\frac{c(c+1)}{2(c+5)}$

19. $\frac{q-2}{4}$ 20. $-2t(t-5)$ 21. $4s(s-4)$ 22. $\frac{1}{7}$

23. $\frac{1}{n-2}$ 24. $-\frac{1}{6}$ 25. $\frac{1}{m+3}$ 26. $\frac{-1}{(x+3)(x+2)}$

27. $-\frac{2y-1}{y+1}$ 28. LCD $=(n+3)(n-3)(n+2)$

29. LCD $=(m+4)(m-4)(m+3)$ 30. $c-2$ or $2-c$

31. $3-x$ or $x-3$ 32. $\frac{4b}{10ab}; \frac{3a}{10ab}$ 33. $\frac{21y}{12xy}; \frac{22x}{12xy}$

34. $\frac{y}{x^2y^5}; \frac{3x}{x^2y^5}$ 35. $\frac{5c^2}{ab^3c^2}; \frac{3b^3}{ab^3c^2}$

36. $\frac{5p-20}{(p+2)(p-4)}; \frac{p^2+2p}{(p+2)(p-4)}$ 37. $\frac{6q+48}{q(q+8)}; \frac{q}{q(q+8)}$

38. 2 39. 2 40. $a+5$ 41. $x-7$

42. $\frac{-y-18}{(y-9)(y+9)}$ or $\frac{y+18}{(9-y)(y+9)}$ 43. $\frac{t^2+2t+3}{(2-t)(2+t)}$

44. $\frac{m+8}{3m(m+2)}$ 45. $\frac{3(r-4)}{2r(r+6)}$ 46. $\frac{p}{(p+4)(p+5)}$

47. $\frac{q}{(q+5)(q+4)}$ 48. $\frac{1}{2}$ 49. $\frac{1}{3}$ 50. $\frac{a-4}{a-2}$

51. $\frac{3(z+5)}{z(z-5)}$ 52. $\frac{w}{2}$ 53. $\frac{8}{y}$ 54. $y-x$ 55. $-(b+a)$

56. $-\frac{2p+7}{2p}$ 57. $-\frac{k+10}{k+4}$ 58. $\{-8\}$ 59. $\{-2\}$

60. $\{0\}$ 61. $\{2\}$ 62. $\{-2\}$ 63. $\{-1\}$ (The value 3 does not check.) 64. { } (The value 2 does not check.) 65. $\{-11, 1\}$

66. The number is 4. 67. $h=\frac{3V}{\pi r^2}$ 68. $b=\frac{2A}{h}$

69. $\left\{\frac{6}{5}\right\}$ 70. $\left\{\frac{96}{5}\right\}$ 71. It contains 10 g of fat.

72. Ed travels 60 mph, and Bud travels 70 mph.

73. Together the pumps would fill the pool in 16.8 min.

74. $x=11; b=26$

Chapter 7 Test, pp. 560–561

1. a. $x=2$ b. $-\frac{x+1}{6}$ 2. a. $a=6, a=-2, a=0$ b. $\frac{7}{a+2}$ 3. b, c, d 4. a. $15(x+3)$ b. $3x^2y^2$

5. $\frac{y+7}{3(y+3)(y+1)}$ 6. $-\frac{b+3}{5}$ 7. $\frac{1}{w+1}$ 8. $\frac{t+4}{t+2}$

9. $\frac{x(x+5)}{(x+4)(x-2)}$ 10. $\frac{2y+7}{y-6}$ or $\frac{-2y-7}{6-y}$ 11. $\frac{1}{m+4}$

12. $\left\{\frac{8}{5}\right\}$ 13. $\{2\}$ 14. $\{1\}$ 15. { } (The value 4 does not check.) 16. $\{-5\}$ (The value 2 does not check.)

17. $r=\frac{2A}{C}$ 18. $\{-8\}$ 19. $1\frac{1}{4}$ (1.25) cups of carrots

20. The speed of the current is 5 mph. 21. It would take the second printer 3 hr to do the job working alone.

22. $a=5.6; b=12$

Chapters 1–7 Cumulative Review Exercises, pp. 561–562

1. 32 2. 7 3. $\left\{\frac{10}{9}\right\}$

4.

Set-Builder Notation	Graph	Interval Notation
$\{x \mid x \geq -1\}$	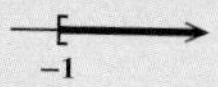	$[-1, \infty)$
$\{x \mid x < 5\}$	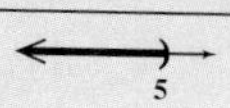	$(-\infty, 5)$

5. The width is 17 m and the length is 35 m. **6.** The base is 10 in. and the height is 8 in. **7.** $\frac{x^2yz^{17}}{2}$
8. a. $6x + 4$ **b.** $2x^2 + x - 3$ **9.** $(5x - 3)^2$
10. $(2c + 1)(5d - 3)$ **11.** $x = 5, x = -\frac{1}{2}$ **12.** $\{(1, -4)\}$
13. $\frac{1}{5(x+4)}$ **14.** -3 **15.** $\{1\}$ **16.** $\left\{-\frac{7}{2}\right\}$
17. a. x-intercept: $(-4, 0)$; y-intercept: $(0, 2)$ **b.** x-intercept: $(0, 0)$; y-intercept: $(0, 0)$
18. a. $m = -\frac{7}{5}$ **b.** $m = -\frac{2}{3}$ **c.** $m = 4$ **d.** $m = -\frac{1}{4}$
19. $y = 5x - 3$ **20.** One large popcorn costs \$4.50, and one drink costs \$3.00.

Chapter 8

Section 8.1 Practice Exercises, pp. 569–572

1. a. relation **b.** domain **c.** range
3. a. {(Northeast, 54.1), (Midwest, 65.6), (South, 110.7), (West, 70.7)} **b.** Domain: {Northeast, Midwest, South, West}; Range: {54.1, 65.6, 110.7, 70.7} **5. a.** {(USSR, 1961), (USA, 1962), (Poland, 1978), (Vietnam, 1980), (Cuba, 1980)} **b.** Domain: {USSR, USA, Poland, Vietnam, Cuba}; range: {1961, 1962, 1978, 1980}
7. a. {(A, 1), (A, 2), (B, 2), (C, 3), (D, 5), (E, 4)} **b.** Domain: {A, B, C, D, E}; range: {1, 2, 3, 4, 5}
9. a. {(6, A), (6, B), (6, C)} **b.** Domain: {6}; range: {A, B, C}
11. a. $\{(-4, 1), (0, 3), (1, -1), (3, 0)\}$ **b.** Domain: $\{-4, 0, 1, 3\}$; range: $\{-1, 0, 1, 3\}$
13. a. $\{(-4, 4), (1, 1), (2, 1), (3, 1), (4, -2)\}$ **b.** Domain: $\{-4, 1, 2, 3, 4\}$; range: $\{-2, 1, 4\}$
15. Domain: $[0, 4]$; range: $[-2, 2]$ **17.** Domain: $[-5, 3]$; range: $[-2.1, 2.8]$ **19.** Domain: $(-\infty, 2]$; range: $(-\infty, \infty)$
21. Domain: $(-\infty, \infty)$; range: $(-\infty, \infty)$ **23.** Domain: $\{-3\}$; range: $(-\infty, \infty)$ **25.** Domain: $(-\infty, 2)$; range: $[-1.3, \infty)$
27. Domain: $\{-3, -1, 1, 3\}$; range: $\{0, 1, 2, 3\}$
29. Domain: $[-4, 5)$; range: $\{-2, 1, 3\}$ **31. a.** 2.85 **b.** 9.33 **c.** Dec. **d.** Nov. **e.** 7.63 **f.** {Jan., Feb., Mar., Apr., May, June, July, Aug., Sept., Oct., Nov., Dec.}
33. a. 33.484 million or 33,484,000 **b.** The year 2015
35. a. For example: {(Julie, New York), (Peggy, Florida), (Stephen, Kansas), (Pat, New York)} **b.** Domain: {Julie, Peggy, Stephen, Pat}; range: {New York, Florida, Kansas}
37. $y = 2x - 1$ **39.** $y = x^2$

Section 8.2 Practice Exercises, pp. 580–584

1. a. function **b.** vertical **c.** $2x + 1$ **d.** x values **e.** y values **f.** denominator **g.** negative
3. a. $\{(-2, -4), (-1, -1), (0, 0), (1, -1), (2, -4)\}$ **b.** $\{-2, -1, 0, 1, 2\}$ **c.** $\{-4, -1, 0\}$ **5.** Function
7. Not a function **9.** Function **11.** Not a function
13. Function **15.** Not a function **17.** When x is 2, the function value y is 5. **19.** $(0, 2)$ **21.** -11 **23.** 1
25. 2 **27.** $6t - 2$ **29.** 7 **31.** 4 **33.** 4
35. $6x + 4$ **37.** $-4x^2 - 8x + 1$ **39.** $-\pi^2 + 4\pi + 1$
41. 7 **43.** $-6a - 2$ **45.** $|-c - 2|$ **47.** 1 **49.** 7
51. -18.8 **53.** -7 **55.** 2π **57.** -5 **59.** 4
61. a. 3 **b.** 1 **c.** 1 **d.** $x = -3$ **e.** $x = 0, x = 2$ **f.** $(-\infty, 3]$ **g.** $(-\infty, 5]$ **63. a.** 3 **b.** $H(4)$ is not defined because 4 is not in the domain of H. **c.** 4 **d.** $x = -3$ and $x = 2$ **e.** All x on the interval $[-2, 1]$ **f.** $[-4, 4)$ **g.** $[2, 5)$
65. a. -4 **b.** 0 **c.** -3 **d.** $x = -1$ **e.** There are no such values of x. **f.** $(-\infty, \infty)$ **g.** $(-\infty, -3] \cup (-2, \infty)$
67. $\{-3, -7, -\frac{3}{2}, 1.2\}$ **69.** $\{6, 0\}$
71. $x = -3$ and $x = 1.2$ **73.** $x = 6$ and $x = 1$ **75.** -3
77. The domain is the set of all real numbers for which the denominator is not zero. Set the denominator equal to zero, and solve the resulting equation. The solution(s) to the equation must be excluded from the domain. In this case, setting $x - 2 = 0$ indicates that $x = 2$ must be excluded from the domain. The domain is $(-\infty, 2) \cup (2, \infty)$. **79.** $(-\infty, -6) \cup (-6, \infty)$
81. $(-\infty, 0) \cup (0, \infty)$ **83.** $(-\infty, \infty)$ **85.** $[-7, \infty)$
87. $[3, \infty)$ **89.** $(-\infty, \frac{1}{2}]$ **91.** $(-\infty, \infty)$ **93.** $(-\infty, \infty)$
95. a. $h(1) = 64$ and $h(1.5) = 44$ **b.** $h(1) = 64$ means that after 1 sec, the height of the ball is 64 ft. $h(1.5) = 44$ means that after 1.5 sec, the height of the ball is 44 ft. **97. a.** $d(1) = 11.5$ and $d(1.5) = 17.25$ **b.** $d(1) = 11.5$ means that after 1 hr, the distance traveled is 11.5 mi. $d(1.5) = 17.25$ means that after 1.5 hr, the distance traveled is 17.25 mi. **99.** $f(x) = 2x + 3$
101. $f(x) = |x| - 10$ **103.** $(-2, \infty)$

Section 8.2 Graphing Calculator Exercises, p. 584

105.

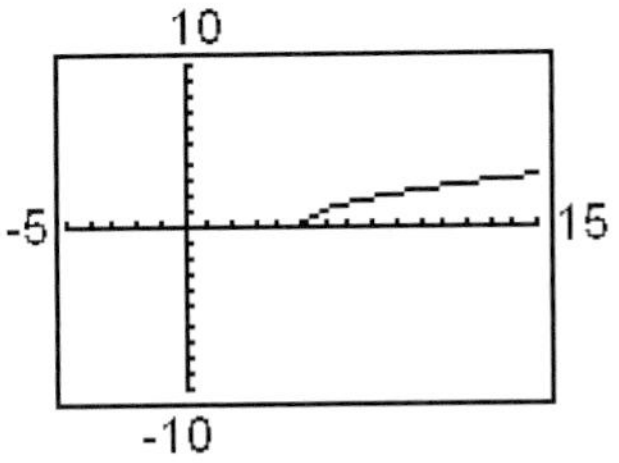

106.

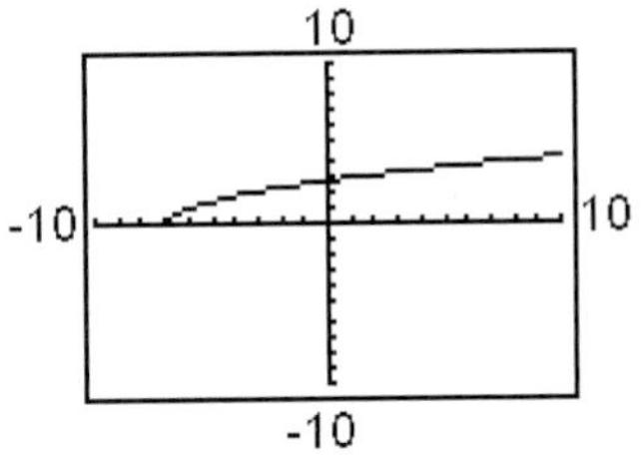

Section 8.3 Practice Exercises, pp. 592–596

1. a. linear **b.** constant **c.** quadratic **d.** parabola **e.** 0 **f.** y **3. a.** Yes **b.** $\{7, 2, -5\}$ **c.** $\{3\}$
5. $f(3) = 9$ means that 9 lb of force is required to stretch the spring 3 in. $f(10) = 30$ means that 30 lb of force is required to stretch the spring 10 in. **7.** horizontal
9. Domain $(-\infty, \infty)$; range $\{2\}$

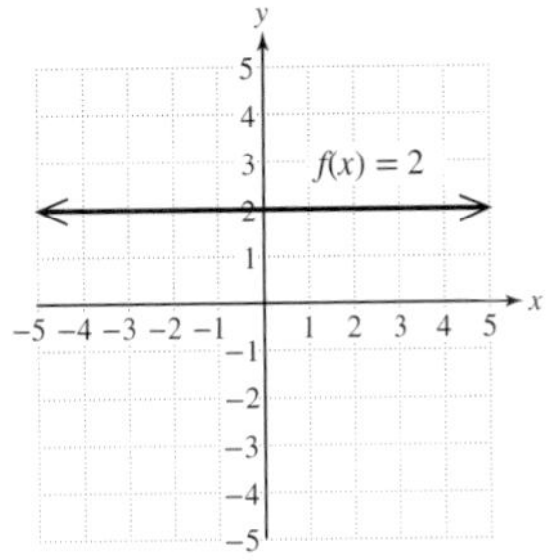

11.

x	$f(x)$	x	$f(x)$
-2	$-\frac{1}{2}$	$\frac{1}{4}$	4
-1	-1	$\frac{1}{2}$	2
$-\frac{1}{2}$	-2	1	1
$-\frac{1}{4}$	-4	2	$\frac{1}{2}$

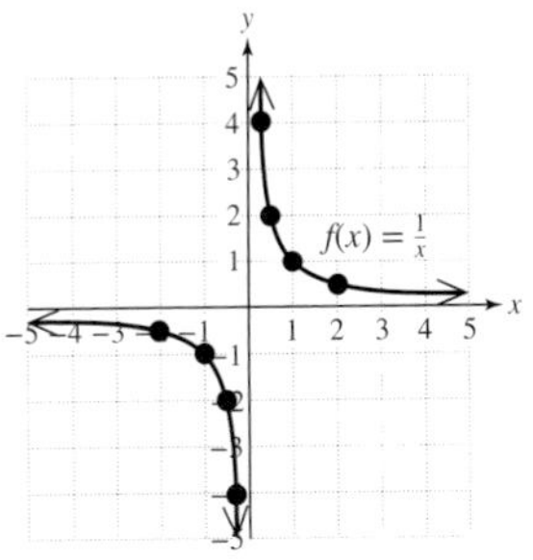

13.

x	$h(x)$
−2	−8
−1	−1
0	0
1	1
2	8

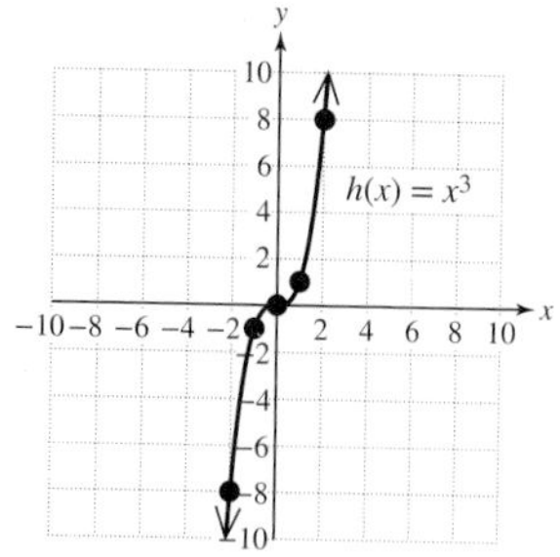

15.

x	$q(x)$
−2	4
−1	1
0	0
1	1
2	4

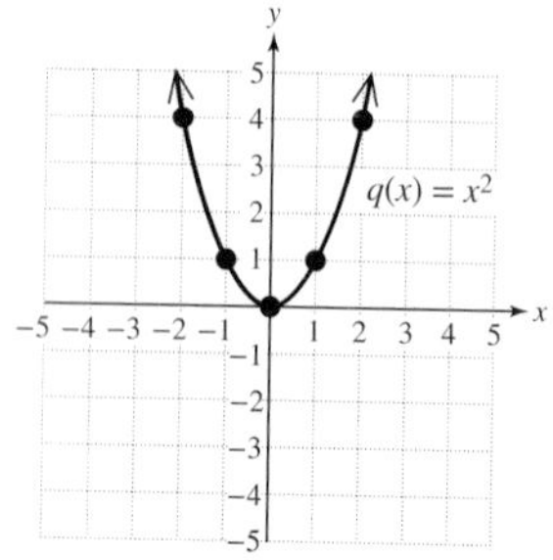

17. Quadratic **19.** Linear **21.** Constant
23. None of these **25.** Linear **27.** None of these
29. x-intercept: (2, 0); y-intercept: (0, −10)

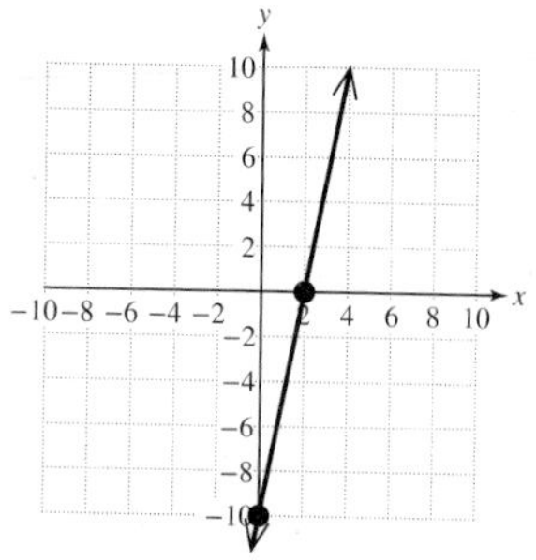

31. x-intercept: $\left(\frac{5}{6}, 0\right)$; y-intercept: (0, 5)

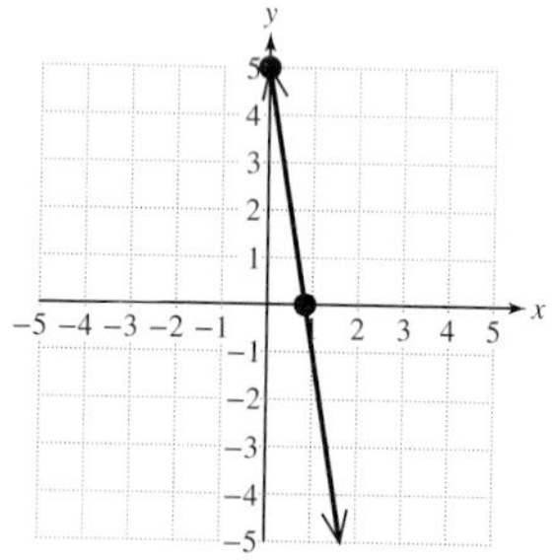

33. x-intercept: none; y-intercept: (0, 18)

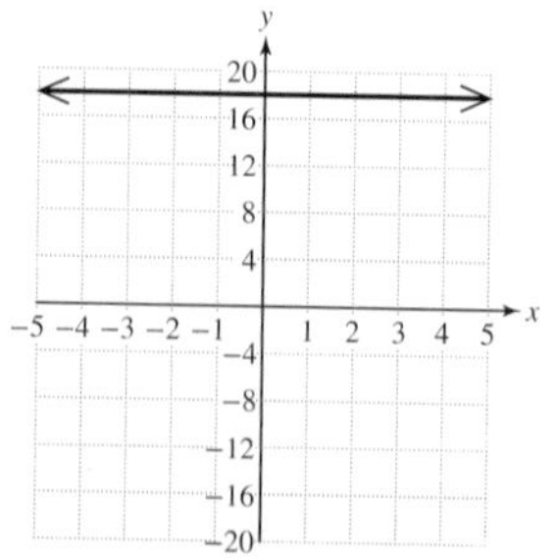

35. x-intercept: (−3, 0); y-intercept: (0, 2)

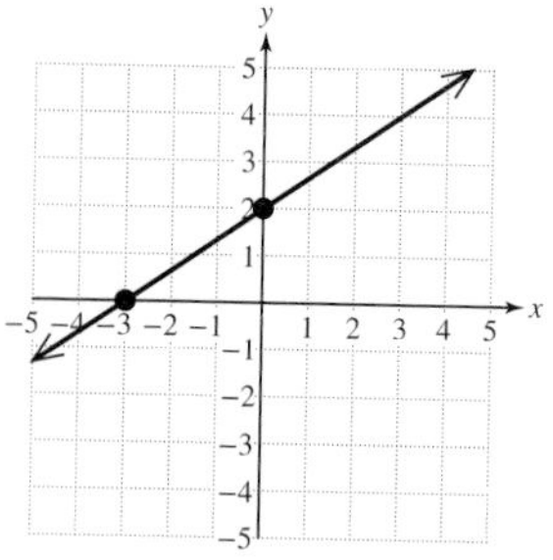

37. a. $x = -1$ **b.** $f(0) = 1$ **39. a.** $x = -2$ and $x = 2$ **b.** $f(0) = -2$ **41. a.** None **b.** $f(0) = 2$
43. a. $(-\infty, \infty)$ **b.** (0, 0) **c.** vi **45. a.** $(-\infty, \infty)$ **b.** (0, 1) **c.** viii **47. a.** $[-1, \infty)$ **b.** (0, 1) **c.** vii
49. a. $(-\infty, 3) \cup (3, \infty)$ **b.** $\left(0, -\frac{1}{3}\right)$ **c.** ii
51. a. $(-\infty, \infty)$ **b.** (0, 2) **c.** iv **53. a.** Linear
b. $G(90) = 82.5$. This means that if the student gets a 90% score on her final exam, then her overall course average is 82.5%.
c. $G(50) = 72.5$. This means that if the student gets a 50% score on her final exam, then her overall course average is 72.5%.
55. $f(x) = x^2 + 2$ **57.** $f(x) = 3$ **59.** $f(x) = \frac{1}{2}x - 2$

Section 8.3 Graphing Calculator Exercises, pp. 596–597

61.

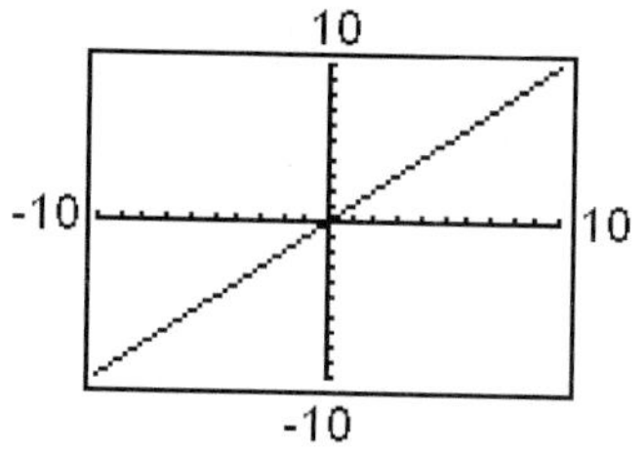

62.

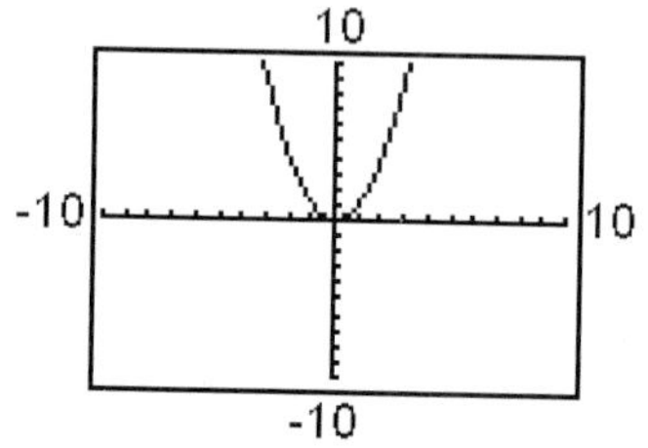

63.

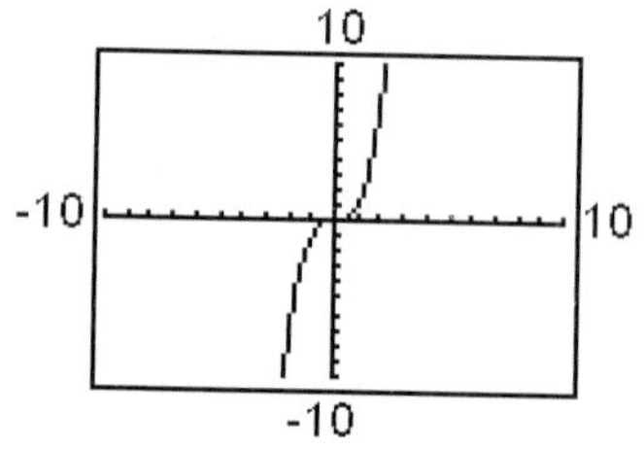

64.

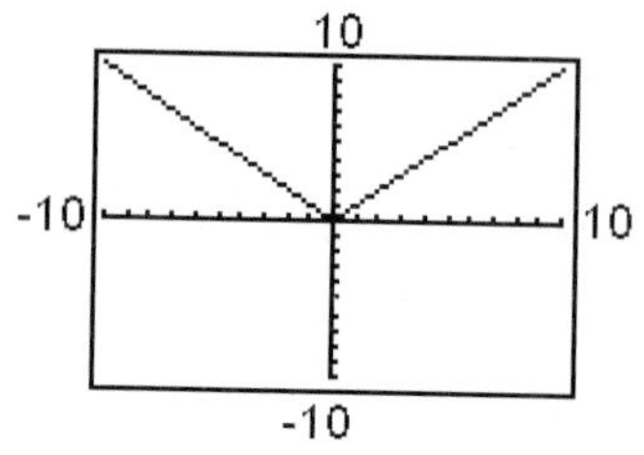

65.

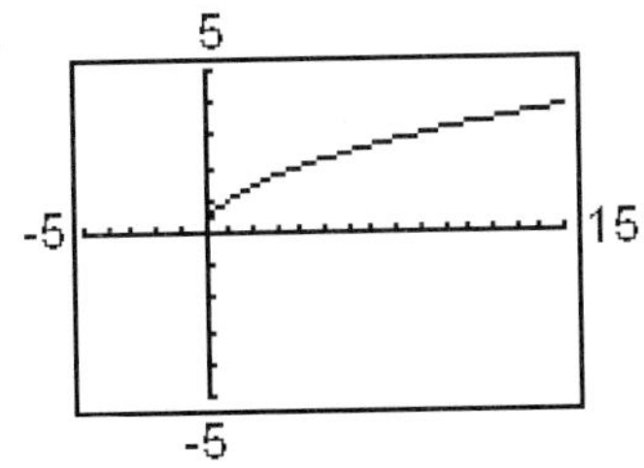

66.

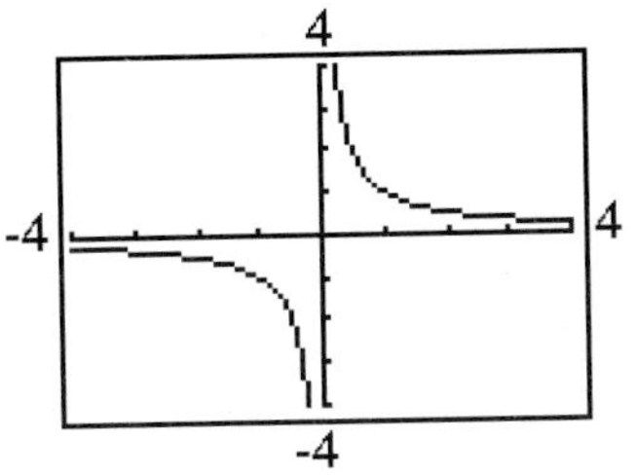

67. x-intercept: (8, 0); y-intercept: (0, 1) **68.** x-intercept: (−6, 0); y-intercept: (0, −3) **69.** x-intercept: (−5, 0); y-intercept: (0, 4) **70.** x-intercept: (2, 0); y-intercept: (0, −7)

Chapter 8 Problem Recognition Exercises, p. 597

1. a, c, d, f, g **2.** a, b, d, f, h **3.** 4 **4.** 2 **5.** $\{0, 1, \frac{1}{2}, -3, 2\}$ **6.** {4, 3, 6, 1, 10} **7.** [−2, 4] **8.** $[0, \infty)$ **9.** 0 **10.** $\left(\frac{9}{5}, 0\right)$ **11.** (0, −1), (0, 1) **12.** 1 **13.** c **14.** d **15.** 3

Section 8.4 Practice Exercises, pp. 602–604

1. a. $f(x)$; $g(x)$ **b.** $g(x)$; $g(x)$ **c.** $f(g(x))$
3. $(f + g)(x) = 2x^2 + 5x + 4$
5. $(g - f)(x) = 2x^2 + 3x - 4$
7. $(f \cdot h)(x) = x^3 + 4x^2 + x + 4$
9. $(g \cdot f)(x) = 2x^3 + 12x^2 + 16x$
11. $\left(\frac{h}{f}\right)(x) = \frac{x^2 + 1}{x + 4}, x \neq -4$
13. $\left(\frac{f}{g}\right)(x) = \frac{x + 4}{2x^2 + 4x}, x \neq 0, x \neq -2$
15. $(f \circ g)(x) = 2x^2 + 4x + 4$
17. $(g \circ f)(x) = 2x^2 + 20x + 48$ **19.** $(k \circ h)(x) = \frac{1}{x^2 + 1}$
21. $(k \circ g)(x) = \frac{1}{2x^2 + 4x}, x \neq 0, x \neq -2$ **23.** No
25. $(f \circ g)(x) = 25x^2 - 15x + 1$; $(g \circ f)(x) = 5x^2 - 15x + 5$
27. $(f \circ g)(x) = |x^3 - 1|$; $(g \circ f)(x) = |x|^3 - 1$
29. $(h \circ h)(x) = 25x - 24$ **31.** 0 **33.** −64 **35.** 2
37. 1 **39.** $\frac{1}{64}$ **41.** 0 **43.** Not a real number
45. $\frac{4}{9}$ **47.** −2 **49.** 2 **51.** 0 **53.** 1 **55.** 0
57. Undefined **59.** −1 **61.** 2 **63.** 2 **65.** −1
67. −2 **69.** 3 **71.** −6 **73.** −1 **75.** 4
77. 0 **79.** 2 **81. a.** $P(x) = 3.78x - 1$ **b.** $188
83. a. $F(t) = 0.2t + 6.4$; $F(t)$ represents the amount of child support (in billion dollars) not paid for year t. **b.** $F(4) = 7.2$ means that in year 4, $7.2 billion of child support was not paid.
85. a. $(D \circ r)(t) = 560t$; This function represents the total distance Joe travels as a function of time that he rides. **b.** 5600 ft

Section 8.5 Practice Exercises, pp. 610–613

1. a. kx **b.** $\frac{k}{x}$ **c.** kxw **3.** $x^2 - 4x + 4$ **5.** $x^2 - 2$
7. −1 **9.** Inversely **11.** $T = kq$ **13.** $b = \frac{k}{c}$
15. $Q = \frac{kx}{y}$ **17.** $c = kst$ **19.** $L = kw\sqrt{v}$ **21.** $x = \frac{ky^2}{z}$
23. $k = \frac{9}{2}$ **25.** $k = 512$ **27.** $k = 1.75$ **29.** $x = 70$
31. $b = 6$ **33.** $Z = 56$ **35.** $Q = 9$ **37.** $L = 9$
39. $B = \frac{15}{2}$ **41. a.** The heart weighs 0.92 lb. **b.** Answers will vary. **43. a.** 3.6 g **b.** 4.5 g **c.** 2.4 g **45. a.** $0.40 **b.** $0.30 **c.** $1.00 **47.** 355,000 tons **49.** 42.6 ft **51.** 300 W **53.** 18.5 A **55.** 20 lb **57.** $3500

Chapter 8 Review Exercises, pp. 618–621

1. Domain; $\left\{\frac{1}{3}, 6, \frac{1}{4}, 7\right\}$; range; $\left\{10, -\frac{1}{2}, 4, \frac{2}{5}\right\}$
2. Domain; {−3, −1, 0, 2, 3}; range; $\left\{-2, 0, 1, \frac{5}{2}\right\}$
3. Domain; [−3, 9]; range; [0, 60] **4.** Domain; [−4, 4]; range; [1, 3]

5.

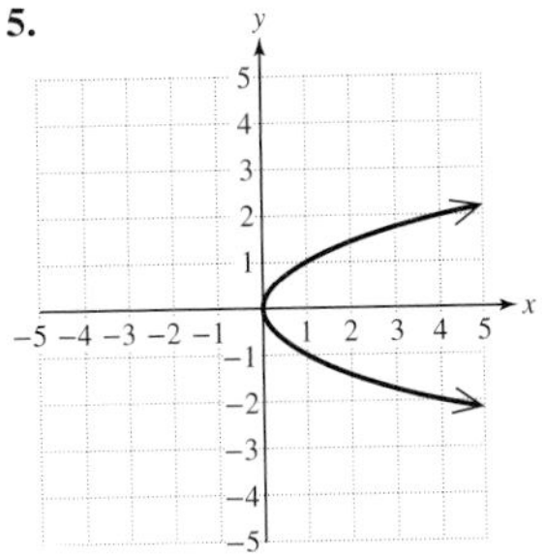

6.

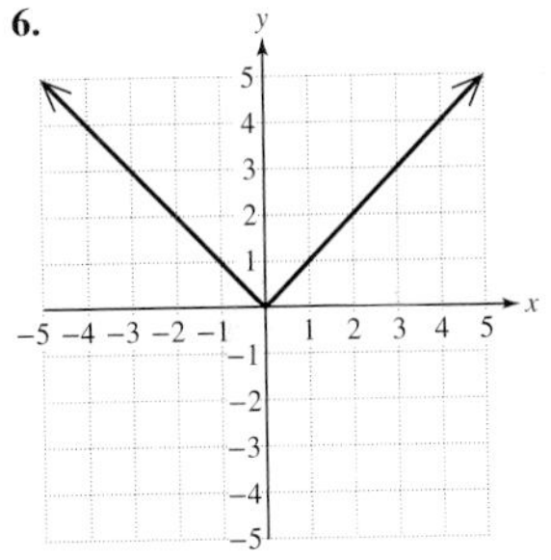

7. a. Not a function **b.** [1, 3] **c.** [−4, 4]
8. a. Function **b.** $(-\infty, \infty)$ **c.** $(-\infty, 0.35]$
9. a. Function **b.** {1, 2, 3, 4} **c.** {3}
10. a. Not a function **b.** {0, 4} **c.** {2, 3, 4, 5}
11. a. Not a function **b.** {4, 9} **c.** {2, −2, 3, −3}
12. a. Function **b.** {6, 7, 8, 9} **c.** {9, 10, 11, 12}
13. −4 **14.** 2 **15.** 2 **16.** $6t^2 - 4$ **17.** $6b^2 - 4$
18. $6\pi^2 - 4$ **19.** $6a^2 - 4$ **20.** 20 **21.** $(-\infty, \infty)$
22. $(-\infty, 11) \cup (11, \infty)$ **23.** $[8, \infty)$ **24.** $[-2, \infty)$
25. a. $150 **b.** $175 **c.** $200

26.

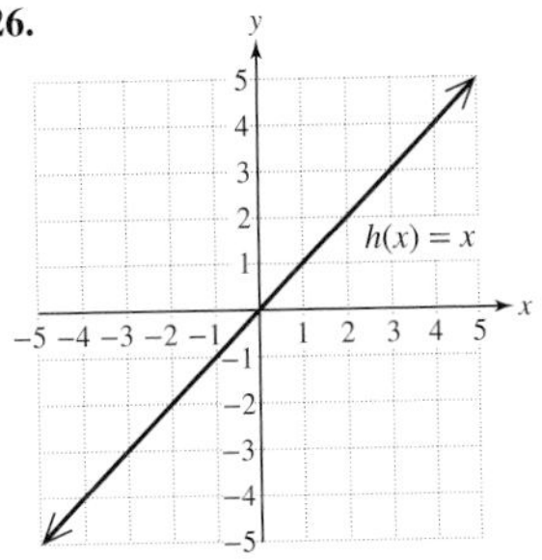

27.

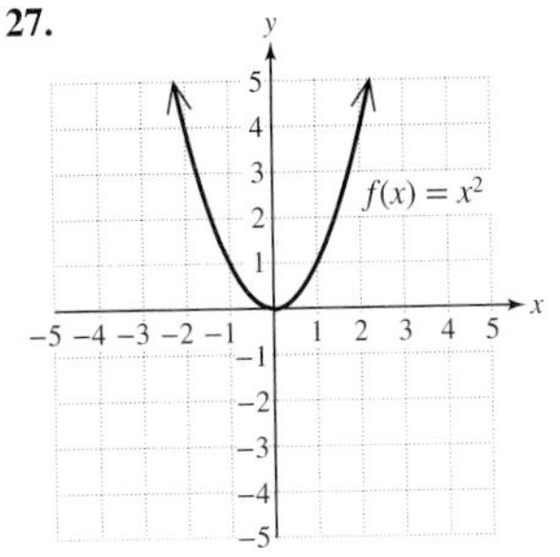

28.

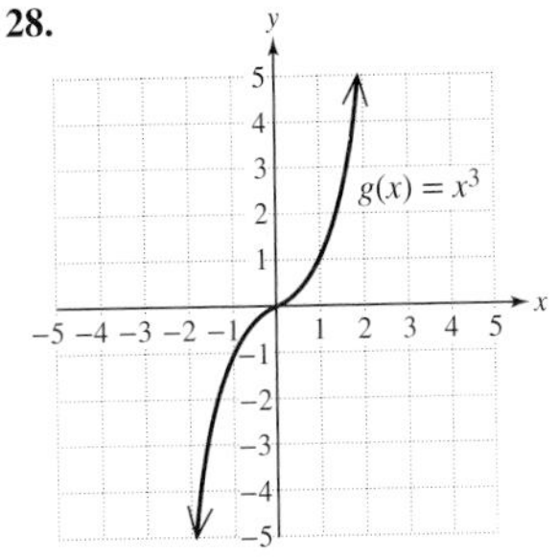

29.

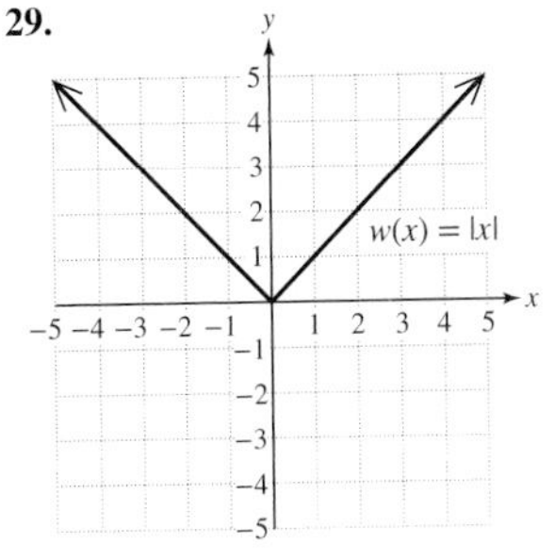

30.

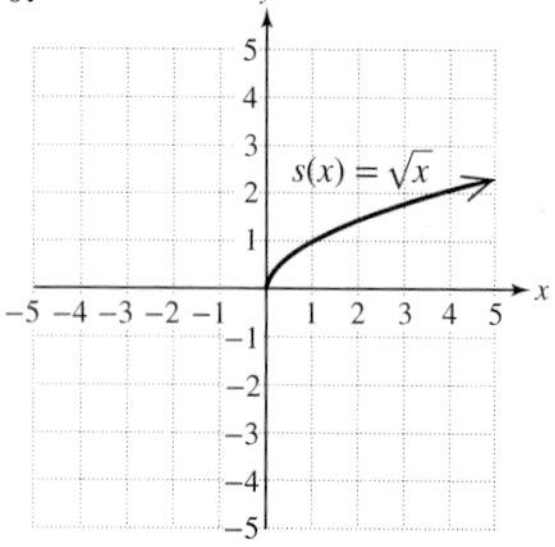

31.

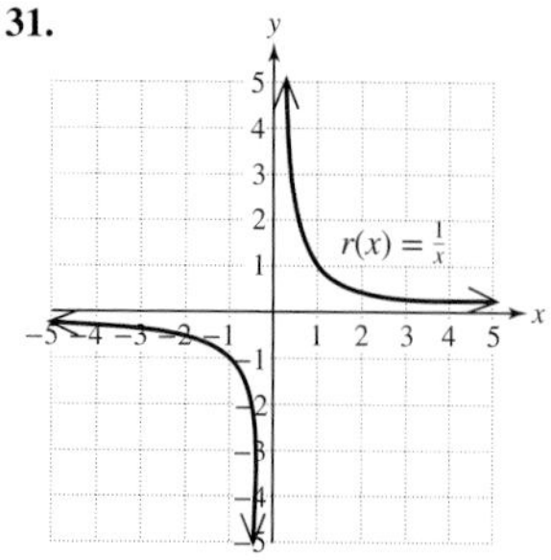

32.

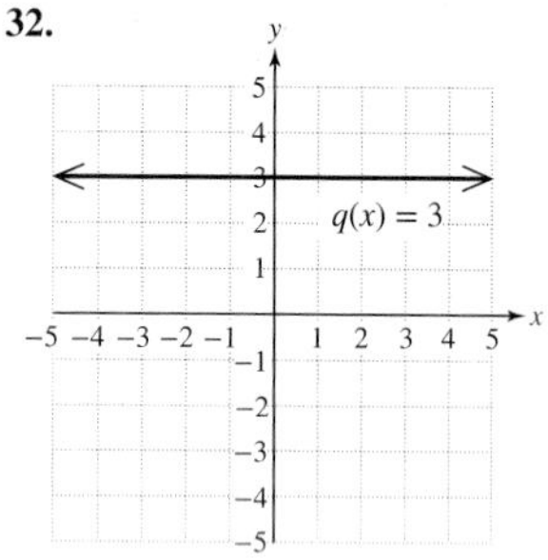

33.

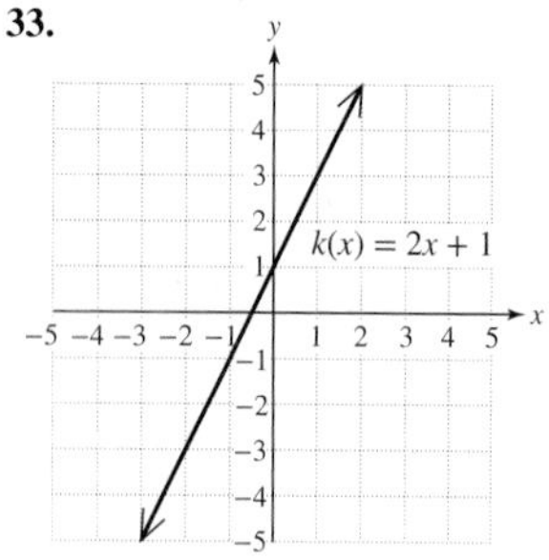

34. a. $s(4) = 4, s(-3) = 25, s(2) = 0, s(1) = 1, s(0) = 4$ **b.** $(-\infty, \infty)$ **35. a.** $r(2)$ is not a real number, $r(4) = 0, r(5) = 2, r(8) = 4$ **b.** $[4, \infty)$

36. a. $h(-3) = -\frac{1}{2}, h(0) = -1, h(2) = -3, h(5) = \frac{3}{2}$ **b.** $(-\infty, 3) \cup (3, \infty)$

37. a. $k(-5) = -2, k(-4) = -1, k(-3) = 0, k(2) = -5$ **b.** $(-\infty, \infty)$ **38.** x-intercept: $\left(\frac{7}{4}, 0\right)$; y-intercept: $(0, -7)$

39. x-intercept: $\left(\frac{9}{2}, 0\right)$; y-intercept: $(0, 9)$

40. a. $b(0) = 28.3$. In 2010 consumption was 28.3 gal of bottled water per capita. $b(5) = 36.5$. In 2015 consumption was 36.5 gal of bottled water per capita. **b.** $m = 1.64$. Consumption increased at a rate of 1.64 gal/year.

41. -1 **42.** 0 **43.** $x = 0$ and $x = 4$

44. There are no values of x for which $g(x) = 4$.

45. $(-4, \infty)$ **46.** $(-\infty, 1]$ **47.** $(f - g)(x) = 2x^3 + 9x - 7$

48. $(f + g)(x) = -2x^3 - 7x - 7$ **49.** $(f \cdot n)(x) = \frac{x - 7}{x - 2}, x \neq 2$

50. $(f \cdot m)(x) = x^3 - 7x^2$ **51.** $\left(\frac{f}{g}\right)(x) = \frac{x - 7}{-2x^3 - 8x}; x \neq 0$

52. $\left(\frac{g}{f}\right)(x) = \frac{-2x^3 - 8x}{x - 7}, x \neq 7$

53. $(m \circ f)(x) = (x - 7)^2$ or $x^2 - 14x + 49$

54. $(n \circ f)(x) = \frac{1}{x - 9}, x \neq 9$ **55.** 100 **56.** $\frac{1}{8}$

57. -167 **58.** -10 **59. a.** $(2x + 1)^2$ or $4x^2 + 4x + 1$

b. $2x^2 + 1$ **c.** No, $f \circ g \neq g \circ f$ **60.** $\frac{1}{4}$ **61.** -3

62. 0 **63.** -1 **64.** 4 **65.** 1 **66. a.** $F = kd$

b. $k = 3$ **c.** 12.6 lb **67.** $y = \frac{8}{3}$ **68.** $y = 12$ **69.** 48 km

Chapter 8 Test, pp. 621–622

1. a. Not a function **b.** $\{-3, -1, 1, 3\}$ **c.** $\{-2, -1, 1, 3\}$ **2. a.** Function **b.** $(-\infty, \infty)$ **c.** $(-\infty, 0]$ **3.** To find the x-intercept(s), solve for the real solutions of the equation $f(x) = 0$. To find the y-intercept, find $f(0)$.

4.

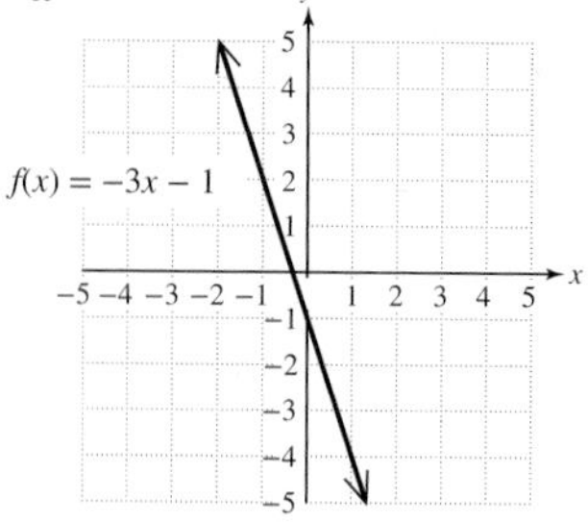

5.

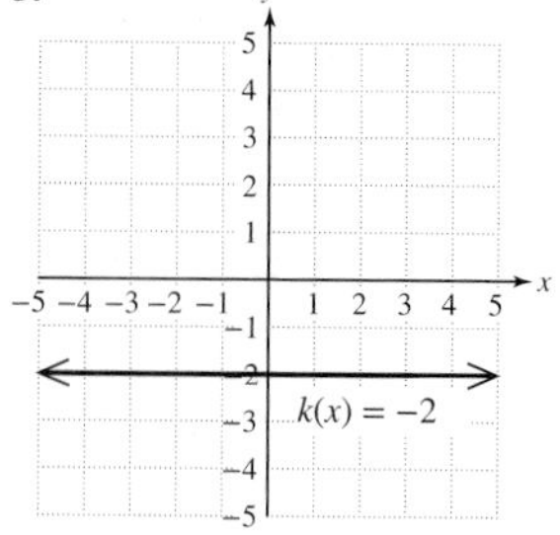

6.

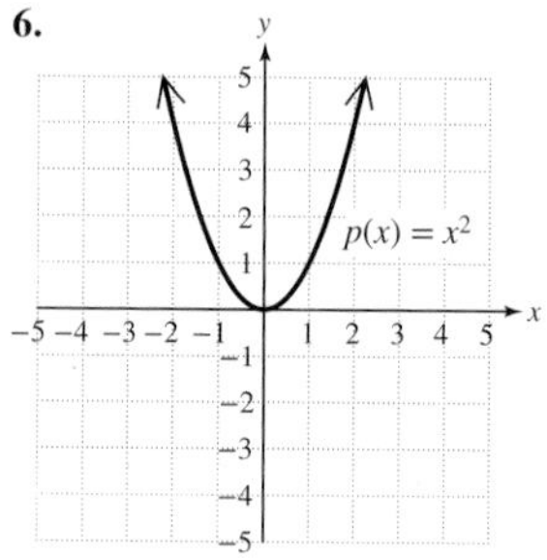

7.

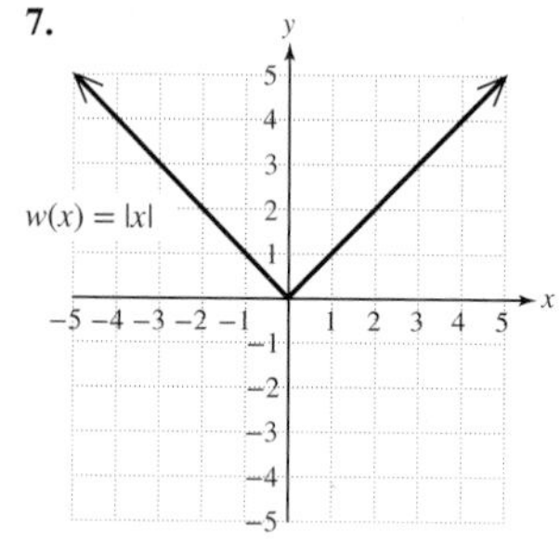

8. $(-\infty, -7) \cup (-7, \infty)$ **9.** $[-7, \infty)$ **10.** $(-\infty, \infty)$

11. a. $r(-2) = 9, r(0) = 1, r(3) = 4$ **b.** $(-\infty, \infty)$

12. $s(0) = 0.96$. At the beginning of the study (year 0) the per capita consumption was 0.96 c per day. $s(20) = 0.8$. In year 20, the per capita consumption was 0.8 c per day.

13. 1 **14.** 2 **15.** $(-1, 7]$ **16.** $[-1, 4)$

17. False **18.** $(6, 0)$ **19.** $x = 6$ **20.** All x in the interval $[1, 3]$ and $x = 5$ **21.** Quadratic **22.** Linear

23. Constant **24.** None of these

25. x-intercept: $(-12, 0)$; y-intercept: $(0, 9)$

26. $\left(\frac{f}{g}\right)(x) = \frac{x - 4}{x^2 + 2}$ **27.** $(h \cdot g)(x) = \frac{x^2 + 2}{x}, x \neq 0$

28. $(g \circ f)(x) = x^2 - 8x + 18$ **29.** $(h \circ f)(x) = \frac{1}{x - 4}, x \neq 4$

30. -48 **31.** $-\frac{3}{2}$ **32.** $\frac{1}{18}$ **33.** 18

34. $\left(\frac{g}{f}\right)(x) = \frac{x^2 + 2}{x - 4}, x \neq 4$ **35.** 8.25 mL

36. 200 drinks are sold.

Chapters 1–8 Cumulative Review Exercises, p. 623

1. -1 **2.** $21x - 62y + 12$ **3.** $\{-15\}$ **4.** $\{\ \}$

5. $[-3, \infty)$ **6.** x-intercept: $\left(\frac{10}{3}, 0\right)$ y-intercept: $(0, -2)$

7. $m = -\frac{1}{5}$ **8.** $m = \frac{5}{2}$ **9.** $\{(2, -1)\}$ **10.** $\{(-4, 0, 5)\}$

11. $\frac{9x^2}{y^6}$ **12.** $5x^2 - 8x + 7$ **13.** $-10x^3 + 47x^2 - 42x$

14. $(2x + 1)(x + 3)$ **15.** $5(x - 4)(x + 4)$ **16.** $\frac{x^2 + 5}{(x - 5)(x + 1)}$

17. $\frac{x + 2}{x^2}$ **18.** Domain: $\{2, -1, 9, -6\}$ Range: $\{4, 2, 8\}$

19. $(-\infty, 0) \cup (0, \infty)$ **20.** $(f \circ g)(x) = x^2 + 2x - 5$

Chapter 9

Section 9.1 Practice Exercises, pp. 634–638

1. a. union; $A \cup B$ **b.** intersection; $A \cap B$ **c.** intersection **d.** $a < x < b$ **e.** union **3.** $(-\infty, 2]$ **5.** $(-\infty, 15)$
7. a. $\{-3, -1\}$ **b.** $\{-4, -3, -2, -1, 0, 1, 3, 5\}$
9. $[-7, -4)$ **11.** $(-\infty, -4) \cup (2, \infty)$ **13.** { } **15.** $[-7, \infty)$
17. $[0, 5)$ **19.** $[-7, \infty)$ **21. a.** $[-1, 5)$ **b.** $(-2, \infty)$
23. a. $(-1, 3)$ **b.** $\left(-\frac{5}{2}, \frac{9}{2}\right)$ **25. a.** $(0, 2]$ **b.** $(-4, 5]$

27. $[-2, 3]$ 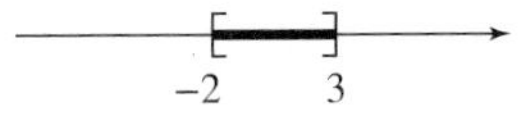

29. $(3, 6)$ 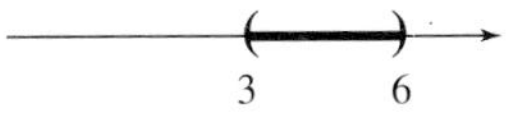

31. $(-\infty, 2]$ 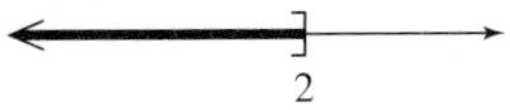

33. $[8, \infty)$ 

35. { } **37.** $-4 \le t$ and $t < \frac{3}{4}$ **39.** The statement $6 < x < 2$ is equivalent to $6 < x$ and $x < 2$. However, no real number is greater than 6 and also less than 2.
41. The statement $-5 > y > -2$ is equivalent to $-5 > y$ and $y > -2$. However, no real number is less than -5 and also greater than -2.

43. $\left[\frac{5}{2}, 7\right)$ 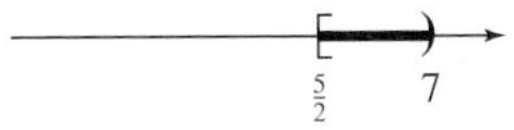

45. $(-6, 6]$ 

47. $(2, 8)$ 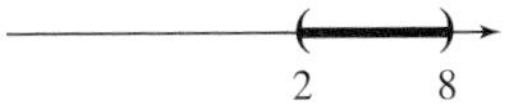

49. $\left[-\frac{10}{3}, -\frac{7}{3}\right]$ 

51. $\left[-\frac{1}{2}, \frac{3}{2}\right)$ 

53. $(-0.4, 0.2)$ 

55. $(-\infty, -2) \cup [2, \infty)$ 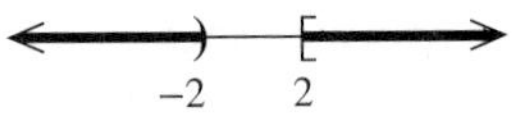

57. $(-\infty, 2]$ 

59. $[-6, \infty)$ 

61. $(-\infty, \infty)$ 

63. $(-\infty, -4] \cup (4.5, \infty)$ 

65. a. $(-10, 8)$ **b.** $(-\infty, \infty)$
67. a. $(-\infty, -8] \cup [1.3, \infty)$ **b.** { }
69. $\left(-\frac{11}{2}, \frac{7}{2}\right]$ **71.** $\left(-\frac{13}{2}, \infty\right)$ **73.** $(-\infty, 1) \cup (5, \infty)$
75. a. $4800 \le x \le 10{,}800$ **b.** $x < 4800$ or $x > 10{,}800$
77. a. $44\% < x < 48\%$ **b.** $x \le 44\%$ or $x \ge 48\%$
79. All real numbers between $-\frac{3}{2}$ and 6
81. All real numbers greater than 2 or less than -1
83. a. Amy would need 82% or better on her final exam. **b.** If Amy scores at least 32% and less than 82% on her final exam she will receive a "B" in the class.
85. $32° \le F \le 42.08°$

Section 9.2 Practice Exercises, pp. 645–648

1. a. quadratic **b.** solutions; undefined **c.** test point **d.** true **e.** rational **f.** zero
3. $(-\infty, -4) \cup \left(\frac{1}{3}, \infty\right)$ **5.** $\left[3, \frac{16}{5}\right]$ **7.** $[-1, 3]$
9. a. $(-\infty, -2) \cup (3, \infty)$ **b.** $(-2, 3)$ **c.** $[-2, 3]$ **d.** $(-\infty, -2] \cup [3, \infty)$ **11. a.** $(-2, 0) \cup (3, \infty)$ **b.** $(-\infty, -2) \cup (0, 3)$ **c.** $(-\infty, -2] \cup [0, 3]$ **d.** $[-2, 0] \cup [3, \infty)$ **13. a.** $\{4, -\frac{1}{2}\}$ **b.** $(-\infty, -\frac{1}{2}) \cup (4, \infty)$ **c.** $(-\frac{1}{2}, 4)$ **15. a.** $\{-10, 3\}$ **b.** $(-10, 3)$ **c.** $(-\infty, -10) \cup (3, \infty)$
17. a. $\left\{-\frac{1}{2}, 3\right\}$ **b.** $\left[-\frac{1}{2}, 3\right]$ **c.** $\left(-\infty, -\frac{1}{2}\right] \cup [3, \infty)$
19. $(1, 7)$ **21.** $(-\infty, -2) \cup (5, \infty)$ **23.** $[-5, 0]$ **25.** $[4, 8]$
27. $\left(-\infty, -\frac{1}{5}\right) \cup (1, \infty)$ **29.** $(-11, 11)$
31. $\left(-\infty, -\frac{1}{3}\right] \cup [3, \infty)$ **33.** $(-\infty, -3] \cup [0, 4]$
35. $(-2, -1) \cup (2, \infty)$ **37. a.** $(-1, 1]$ **b.** $(-\infty, -1) \cup [1, \infty)$ **c.** $(-\infty, -1) \cup (1, \infty)$ **d.** $(-1, 1)$
39. a. $(-\infty, -1) \cup (2, \infty)$ **b.** $(-1, 2)$ **c.** $[-1, 2)$ **d.** $(-\infty, -1] \cup (2, \infty)$ **41. a.** $\{7\}$ **b.** $(-\infty, 5) \cup (7, \infty)$ **c.** $(5, 7)$
43. a. $\{4\}$ **b.** $[4, 6)$ **c.** $(-\infty, 4] \cup (6, \infty)$ **45.** $(1, \infty)$
47. $(-\infty, -4) \cup (4, \infty)$ **49.** $\left(2, \frac{7}{2}\right)$ **51.** $(5, 7]$
53. $(-\infty, 0) \cup \left[\frac{1}{2}, \infty\right)$ **55.** $(0, \infty)$ **57.** Quadratic; $[-4, 4]$
59. Quadratic; $(-\infty, -\frac{4}{5}) \cup (0, \infty)$ **61.** Linear; $(-\frac{5}{2}, \infty)$
63. Rational; $(-\infty, -1)$ **65.** Polynomial (degree > 2); $(0, 5) \cup (5, \infty)$ **67.** Polynomial (degree > 2); $(2, \infty)$
69. Polynomial (degree > 2); $(-\infty, 5]$ **71.** Quadratic; $(-2, 2)$
73. Rational; $(-\infty, -2] \cup (5, \infty)$ **75.** Linear; $(-\infty, 5]$
77. $(-\infty, \infty)$ **79.** { } **81.** $\{0\}$ **83.** { } **85.** { }
87. $(-\infty, \infty)$ **89.** $(-\infty, -11) \cup (-11, \infty)$ **91.** $\{\frac{3}{2}\}$

Section 9.2 Graphing Calculator Exercises, p. 648

93. $(-\infty, 0) \cup (2, \infty)$

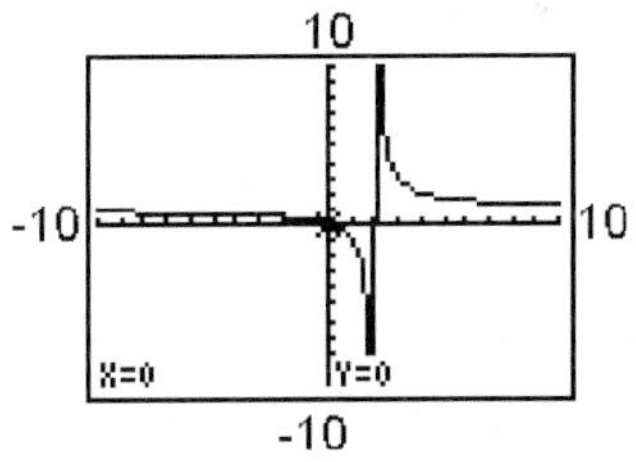

94. $(0, 2)$

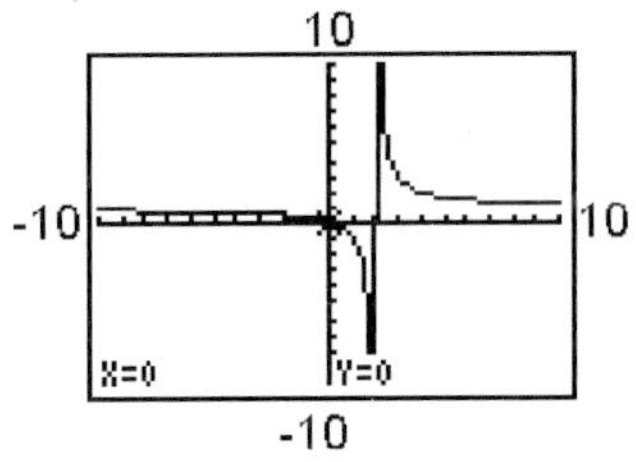

95. $(-1, 1)$

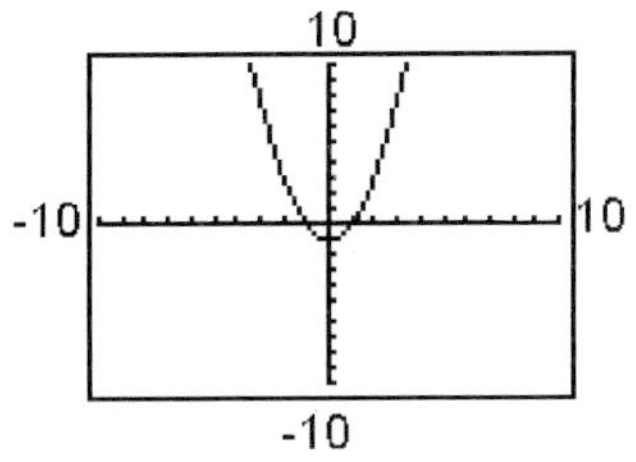

96. $(-\infty, -1) \cup (1, \infty)$

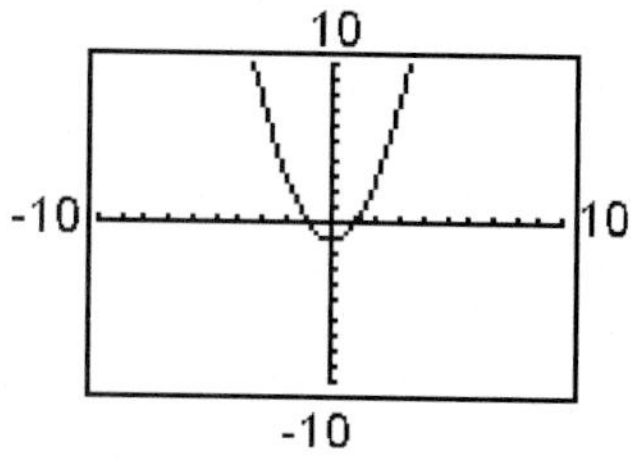

97. $\{-5\}$

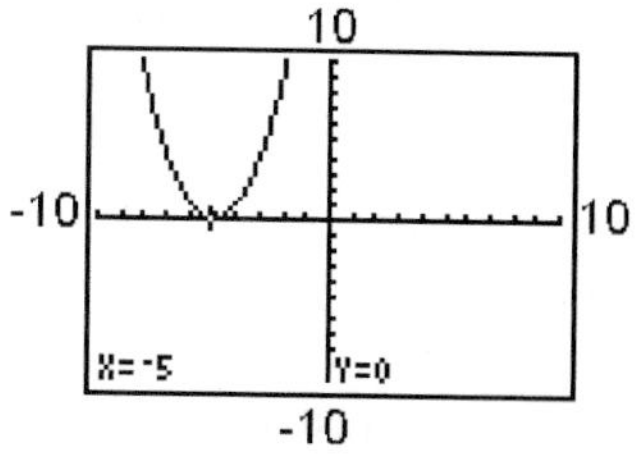

98. $\{5\}$

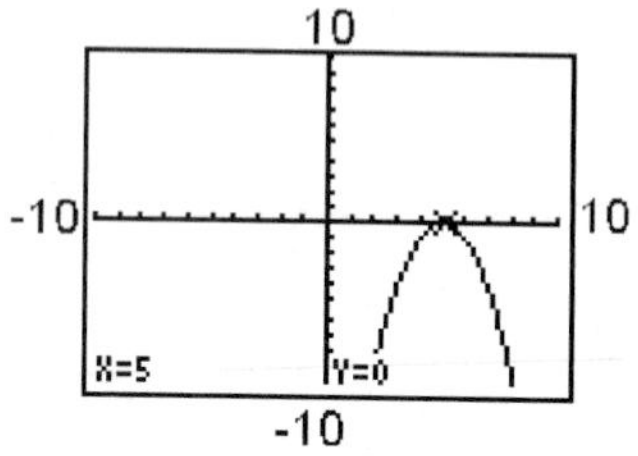

99. $\{\ \}$

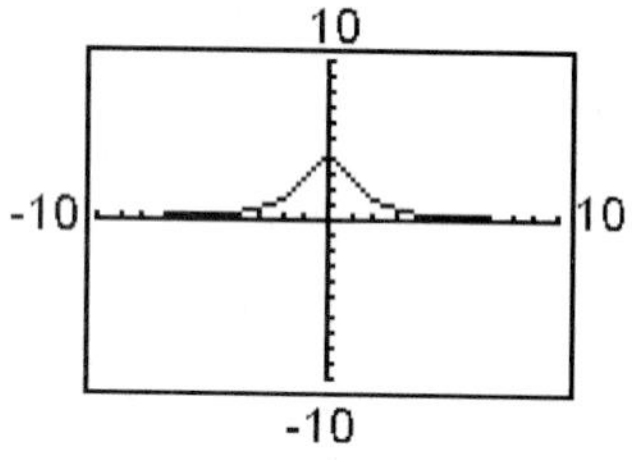

100. $\{\ \}$

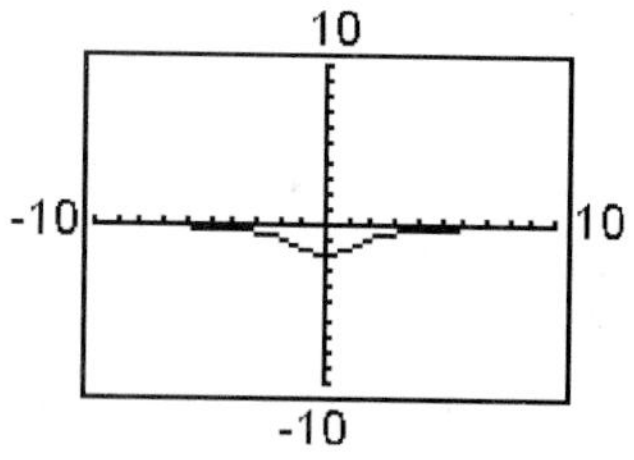

Section 9.3 Practice Exercises, pp. 654–655

1. a. absolute; $\{a, -a\}$ **b.** Subtract 5 from both sides. **c.** $y; -y$ **d.** $\{\ \}; \{-4\}$

3. $(-\infty, -1] \cup [1, \infty)$ **5.** $(-\infty, -1) \cup \left[\frac{1}{2}, \infty\right)$

7. $\{7, -7\}$ **9.** $\{6, -6\}$ **11.** $\{\ \}$ **13.** $\{-2, 2\}$

15. $\{0\}$ **17.** $\left\{4, -\frac{4}{3}\right\}$ **19.** $\left\{\frac{9}{2}, -\frac{1}{2}\right\}$ **21.** $\left\{\frac{10}{7}, -\frac{8}{7}\right\}$

23. $\{\ \}$ **25.** $\{-12, 28\}$ **27.** $\left\{\frac{5}{2}, -\frac{7}{2}\right\}$ **29.** $\left\{\frac{7}{3}\right\}$

31. $\{\ \}$ **33.** $\left\{\frac{3}{2}\right\}$ **35.** $\left\{-4, \frac{16}{5}\right\}$ **37.** $\left\{-\frac{1}{2}, \frac{7}{6}\right\}$

39. $\left\{\frac{5}{2}, -\frac{3}{2}\right\}$ **41.** $\left\{-4, \frac{1}{3}\right\}$ **43.** $\left\{\frac{1}{2}\right\}$ **45.** $\left\{-\frac{1}{16}\right\}$

47. $\left\{\frac{1}{4}\right\}$ **49.** $\{-1.44, -0.4\}$ **51.** $\{\ \}$

53. $\{w \mid w \text{ is a real number}\}$ **55.** $\{\ \}$ **57.** $|x| = 6$

59. $|x| = \frac{4}{3}$

Section 9.3 Graphing Calculator Exercises, p. 655

61. $\left\{2, -\frac{1}{2}\right\}$

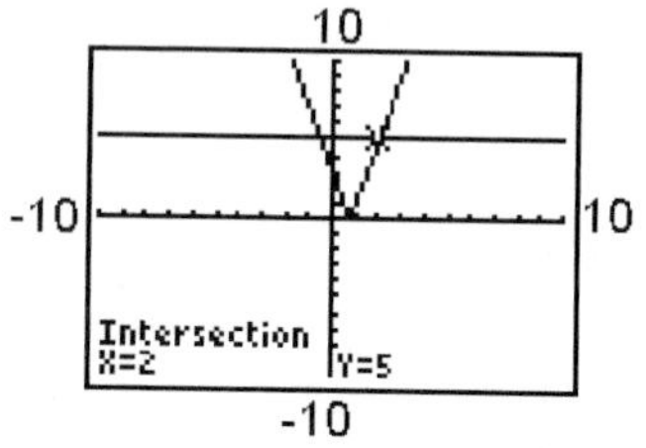

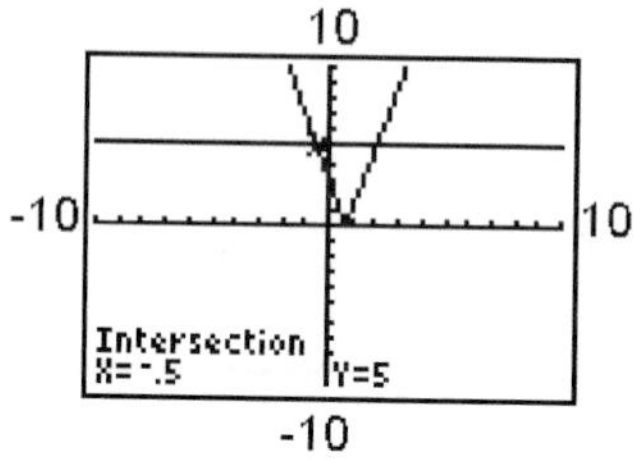

62. $\{7, 1\}$

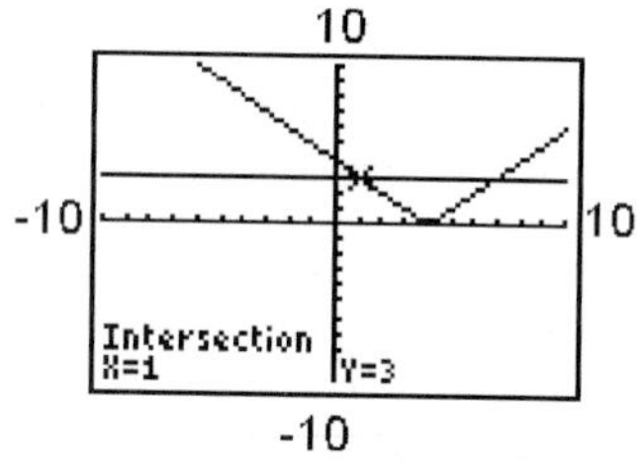

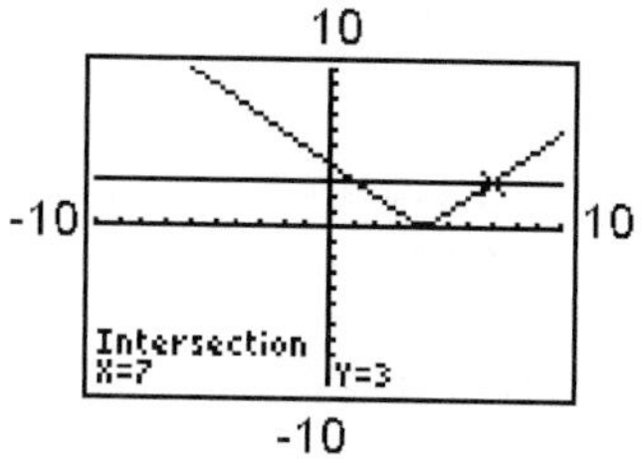

63. $\{\ \}$

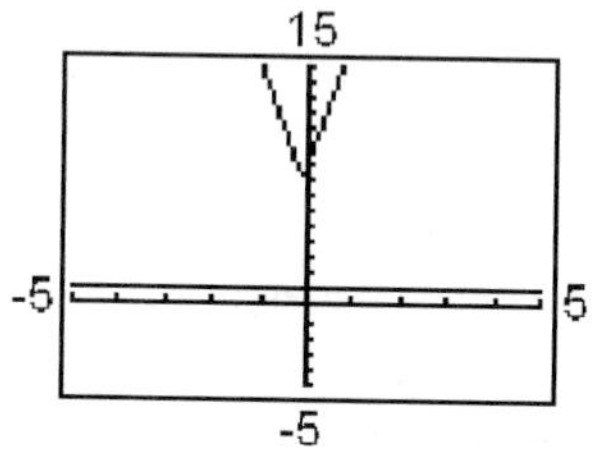

64. $\{\ \}$

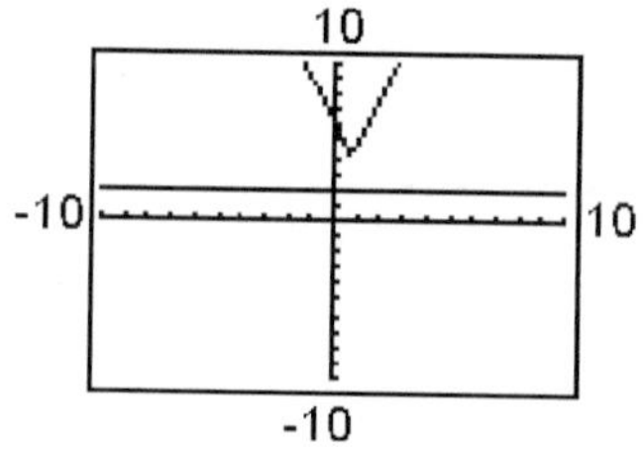

65. $\left\{\frac{1}{2}\right\}$

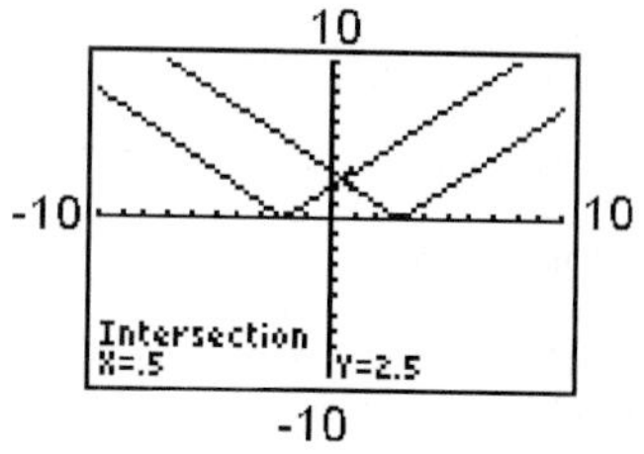

66. $\{-1\}$

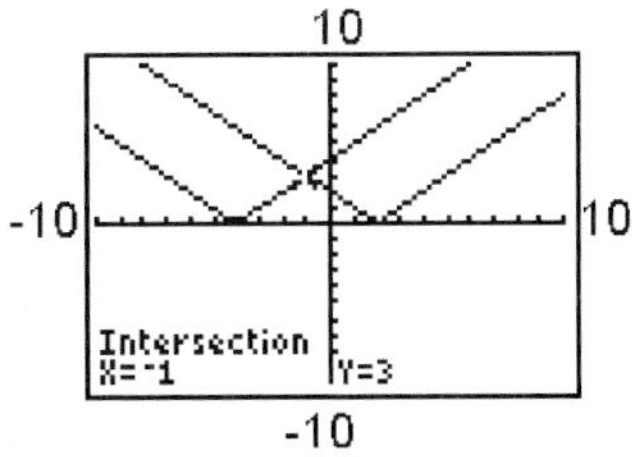

Section 9.4 Practice Exercises, pp. 663–665

1. a. $-a$; a **b.** $-a$; $>$ **c.** $\{\ \}$; $(-\infty, \infty)$ **d.** includes; excludes

3. $\left\{\frac{4}{7}, \frac{6}{7}\right\}$ **5.** $(-3, -1]$

7. $(-\infty, \infty)$

9. a. $\{-5, 5\}$

b. $(-\infty, -5) \cup (5, \infty)$

c. $(-5, 5)$

11. a. $\{10, -4\}$

b. $(-\infty, -4) \cup (10, \infty)$

c. $(-4, 10)$

13. a. $\{\ \}$ **b.** $(-\infty, \infty)$

c. $\{\ \}$ **15. a.** $\{\ \}$

b. $(-\infty, \infty)$

c. $\{\ \}$

17. a. $\{0\}$ **b.** $(-\infty, 0) \cup (0, \infty)$

c. $\{\ \}$ **19. a.** $\{7\}$

b. $(-\infty, 7) \cup (7, \infty)$

c. $\{\ \}$

21. $(-\infty, -6) \cup (6, \infty)$

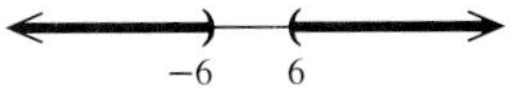

23. $[-3, 3]$

25. $(-\infty, \infty)$

27. $(-\infty, -2] \cup [3, \infty)$

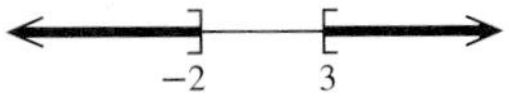

29. $\{\ \}$ **31.** $[-10, 14]$

33. $\left(-\infty, -\frac{5}{4}\right] \cup \left[\frac{23}{4}, \infty\right)$

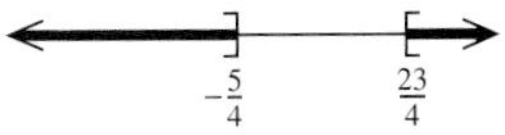

35. $\left(-\frac{21}{2}, \frac{19}{2}\right)$

37. $(-\infty, \infty)$

39. $\{\ \}$ **41.** $\{-5\}$

43. $(-\infty, 6) \cup (6, \infty)$

45. $(-\infty, 2] \cup [4, \infty)$

47. $(4, 8)$

49. $(-10.5, 4.5)$

51. $|x| > 7$ **53.** $|x - 2| \le 13$ **55.** $|x - 32| \le 0.05$

57. $\left|x - 6\frac{3}{4}\right| \le \frac{1}{8}$

59. The solution set is $\{w \mid 1.99 \le w \le 2.01\}$ or, equivalently in interval notation, $[1.99, 2.01]$. This means that the actual width of the bolt could be between 1.99 cm and 2.01 cm, inclusive. **61.** b **63.** a

Section 9.4 Graphing Calculator Exercises, p. 666

65. $(-\infty, -6) \cup (2, \infty)$

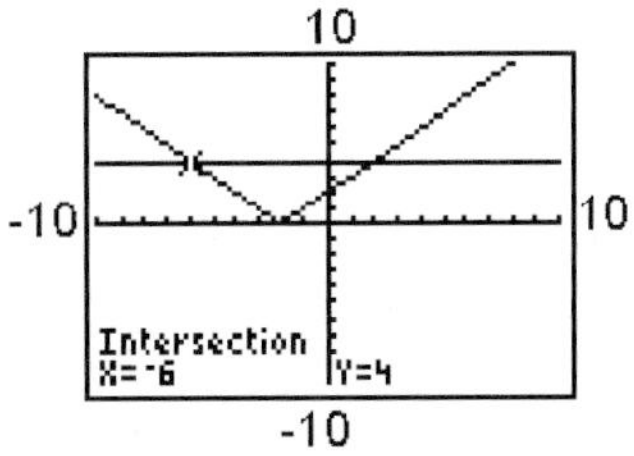

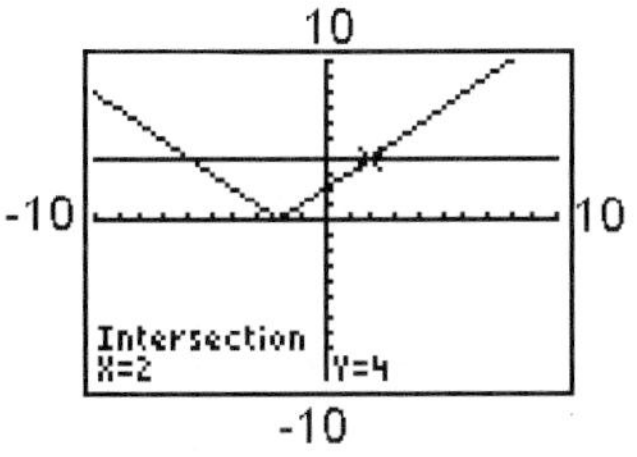

66. $(-\infty, -3) \cup (9, \infty)$

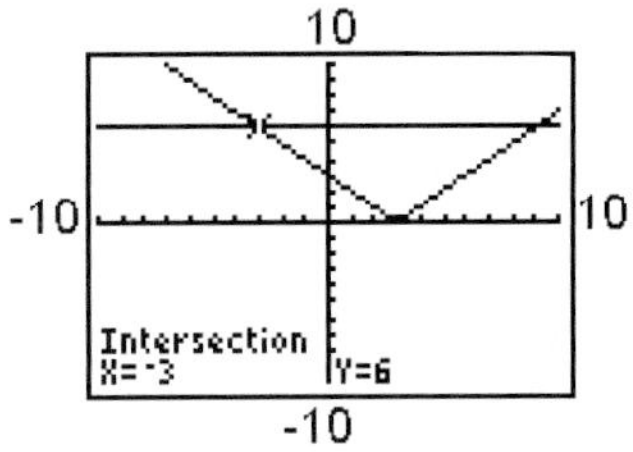

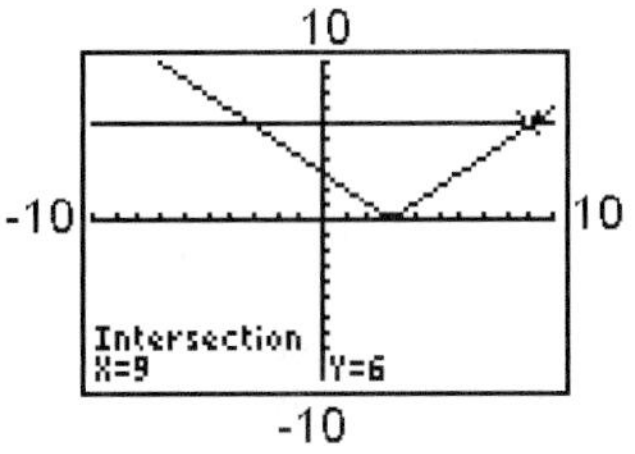

67. $(-7, 5)$

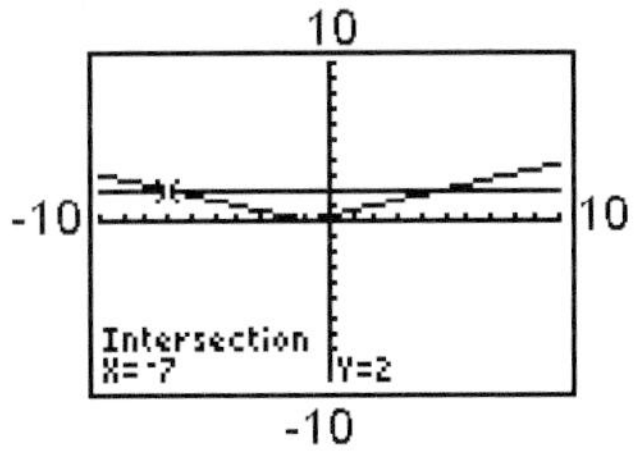

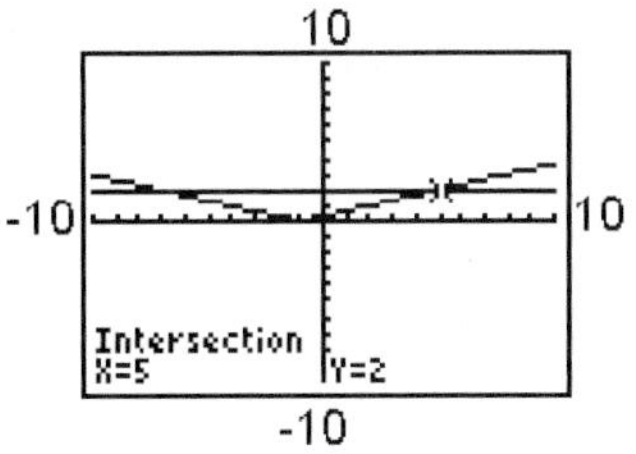

68. $(-3, 5)$

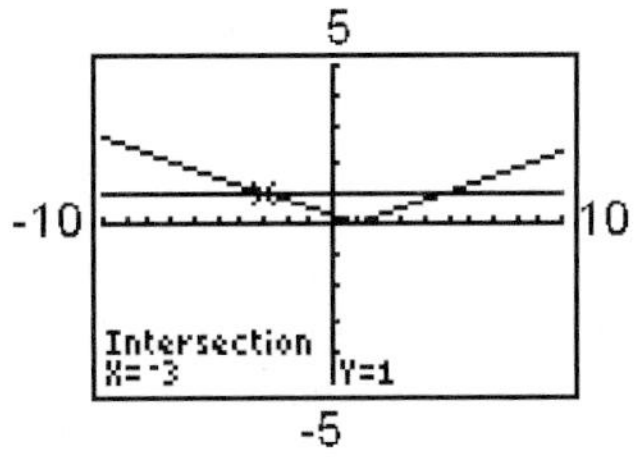

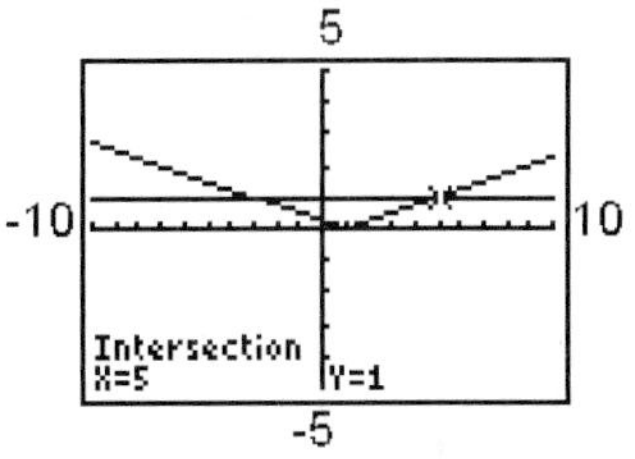

69. $\{\ \}$

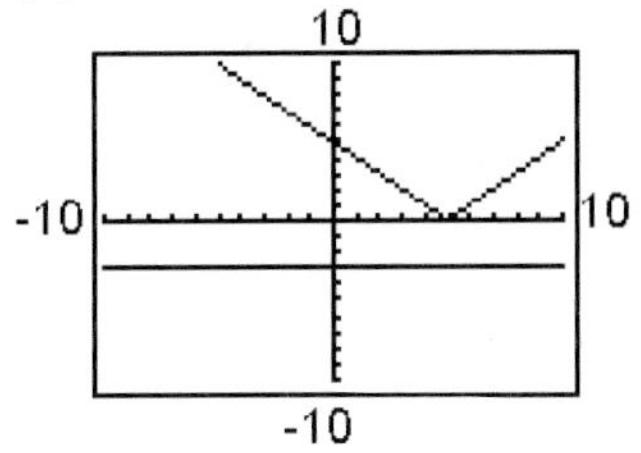

70. $\{\ \}$

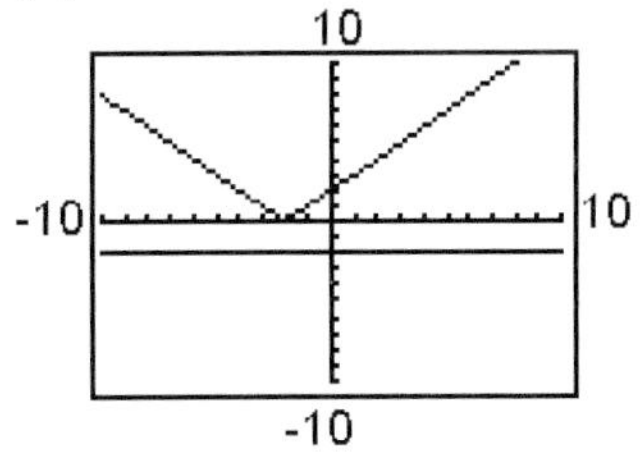

71. $(-\infty, \infty)$

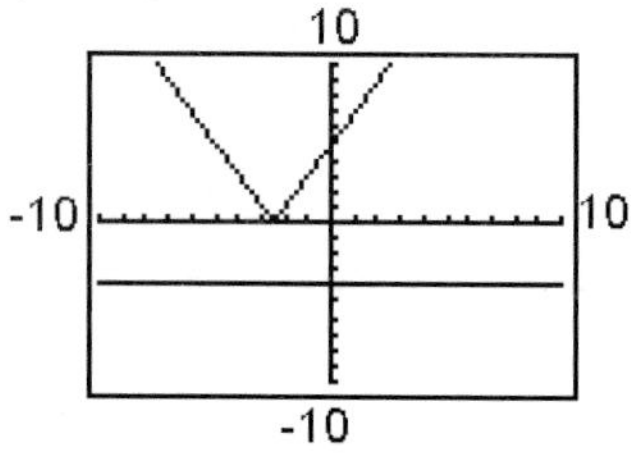

72. $(-\infty, \infty)$

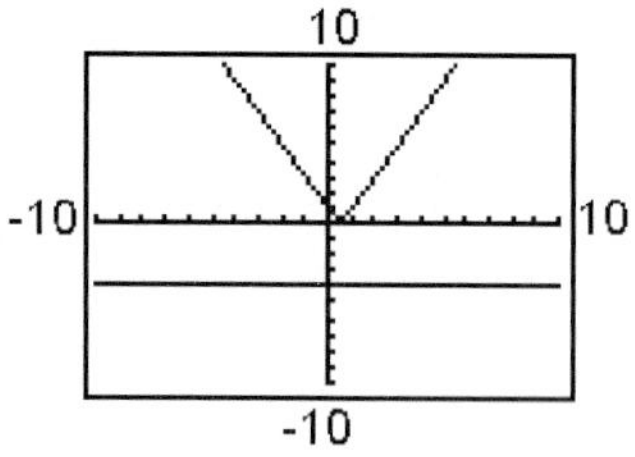

73. $\left\{-\frac{1}{6}\right\}$

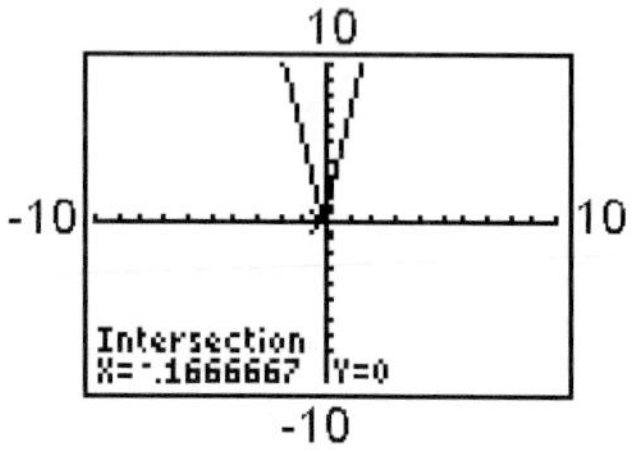

74. $\left\{\frac{4}{3}\right\}$

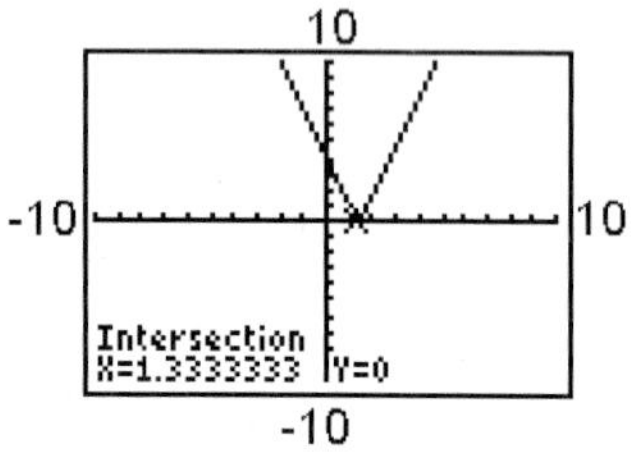

Chapter 9 Problem Recognition Exercises, p. 666

1. Quadratic; $(-\infty, -9) \cup (-1, \infty)$ **2.** Linear; $\{-26\}$
3. Rational; $[-8, -2)$ **4.** Quadratic; $\{-\frac{1}{4}, 2\}$
5. Absolute value; $(-\frac{1}{3}, 1)$ **6.** Quadratic; $\{\ \}$
7. Linear; $(-\infty, -10)$ **8.** Quadratic; $[-4, 1]$
9. Quadratic; $(-\infty, -1] \cup [\frac{2}{3}, \infty)$ **10.** Rational; $\{-\frac{11}{3}\}$
11. Linear; $\left[\frac{16}{7}, \infty\right)$ **12.** Absolute value; $\{\ \}$
13. Polynomial; $[-5, -\frac{1}{2}] \cup [3, \infty)$ **14.** Quadratic; $(-\infty, \infty)$
15. Rational; $(-\infty, -1) \cup (2, \infty)$ **16.** Quadratic; $\{-1, 5\}$
17. Absolute value; $(-\infty, -8) \cup (-8, \infty)$
18. Quadratic; $(-6, 6)$ **19.** Polynomial; $\{2, -2, -\frac{5}{3}\}$
20. Absolute value; $\{12, -4\}$ **21.** Linear; $\{0\}$
22. Rational; $(-\infty, 0] \cup (5, \infty)$ **23.** Absolute value; $\{-\frac{1}{2}\}$
24. Polynomial; $(-\frac{3}{2}, 0)$

Section 9.5 Practice Exercises, pp. 674–679

1. **a.** linear **b.** is not; is **c.** dashed; is not **d.** solid; is
3. $[1, 3)$ **5.** $(-\infty, -4] \cup (-2, \infty)$ **7. a.** No **b.** No **c.** Yes **d.** Yes **9. a.** No **b.** Yes **c.** Yes **d.** No
11. $>$ **13.** $\geq$ **15.** $\geq, \leq$

17.

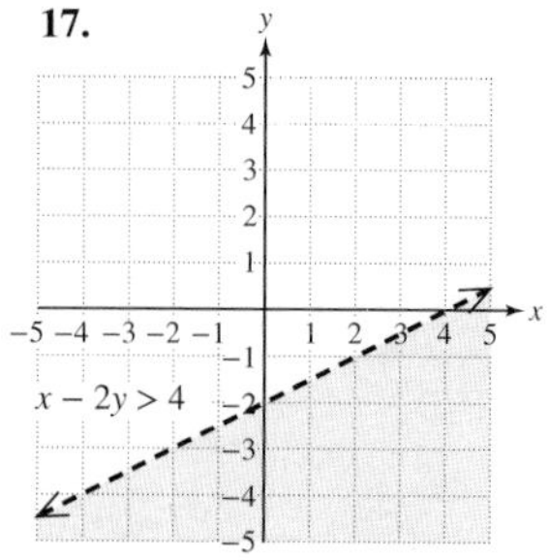

19.

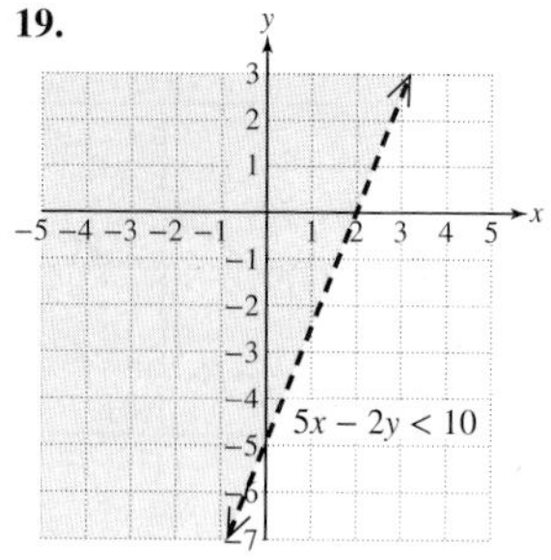

21.

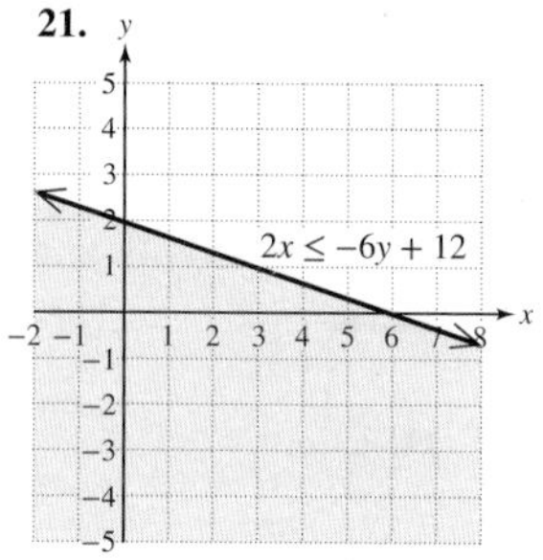

23.

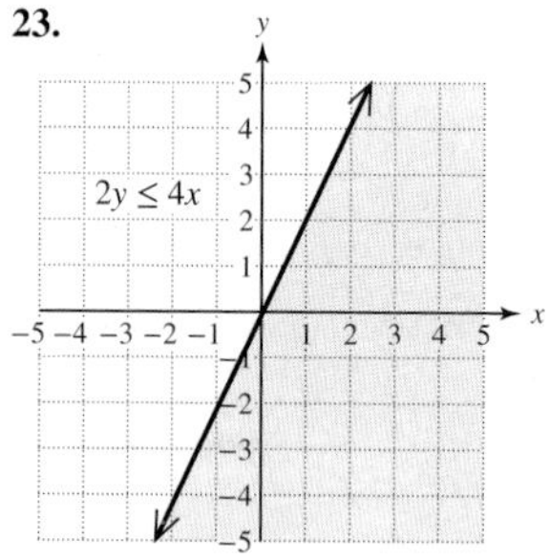

25.

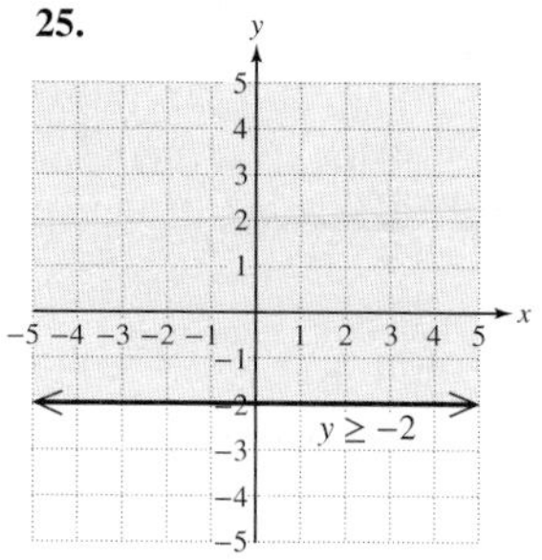

27.

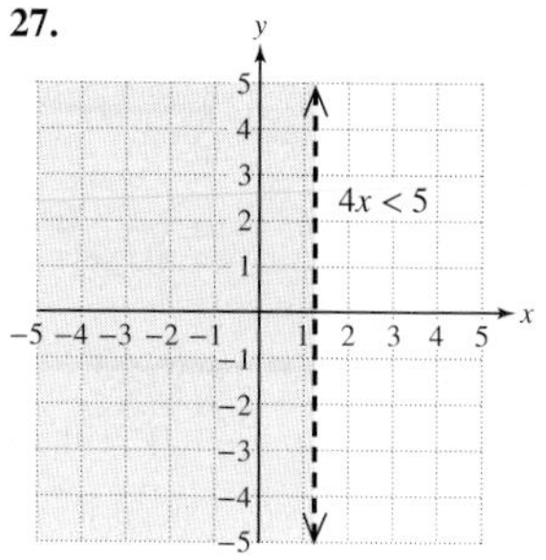

29.

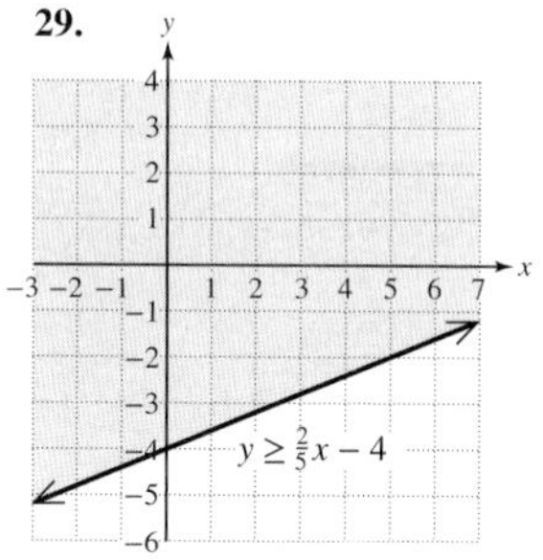

31.

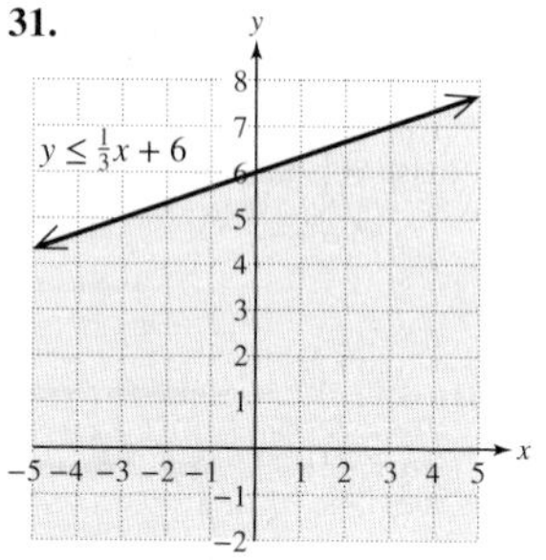

33.

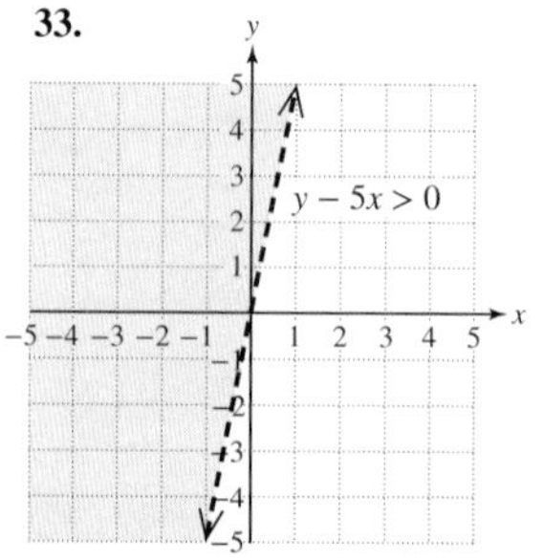

35.

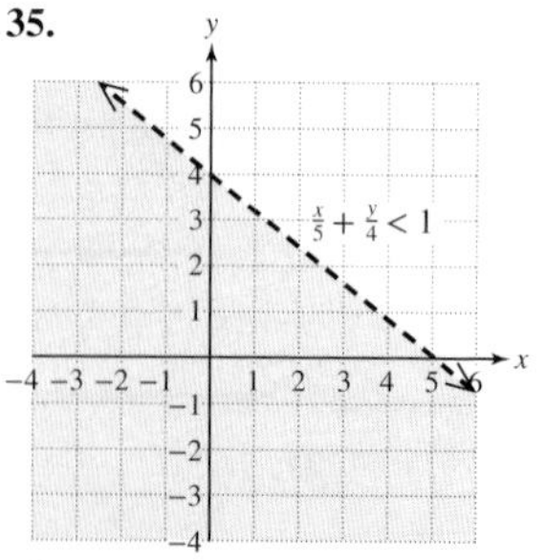

37.

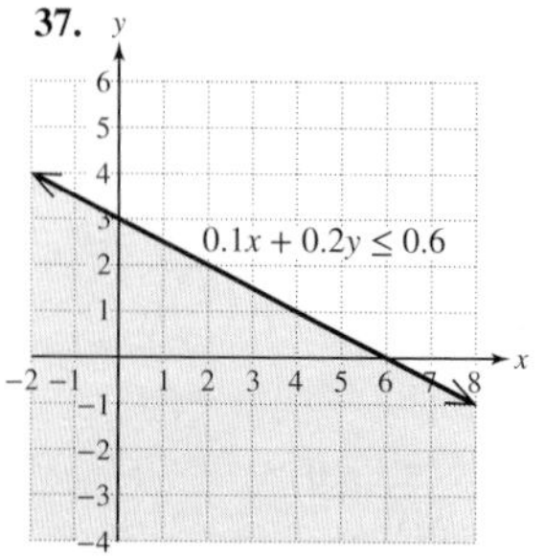

39.

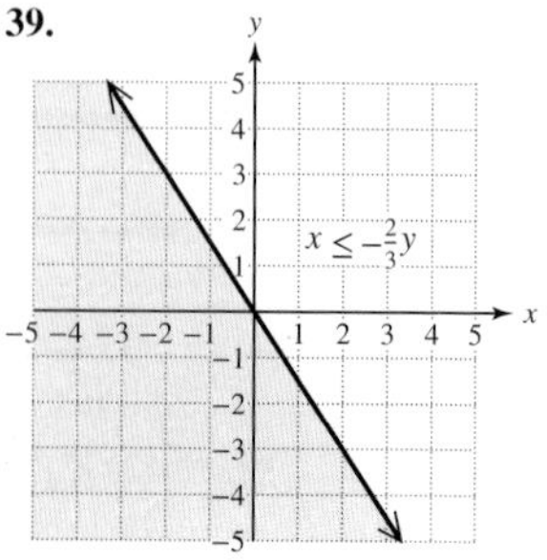

41.

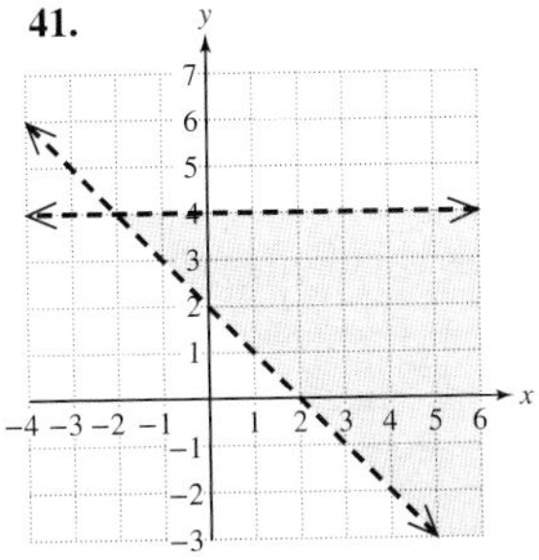

43.

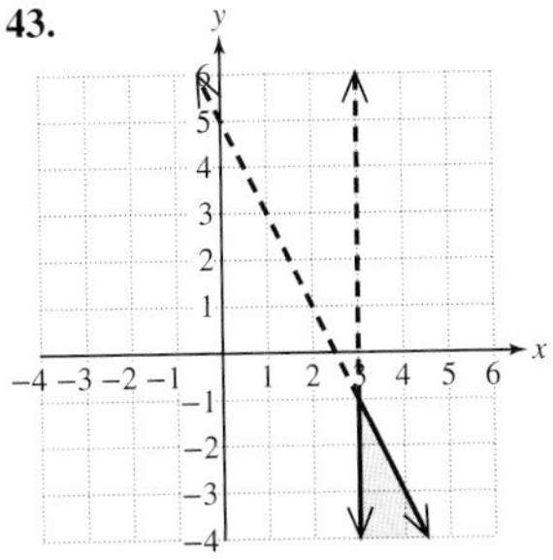

45.

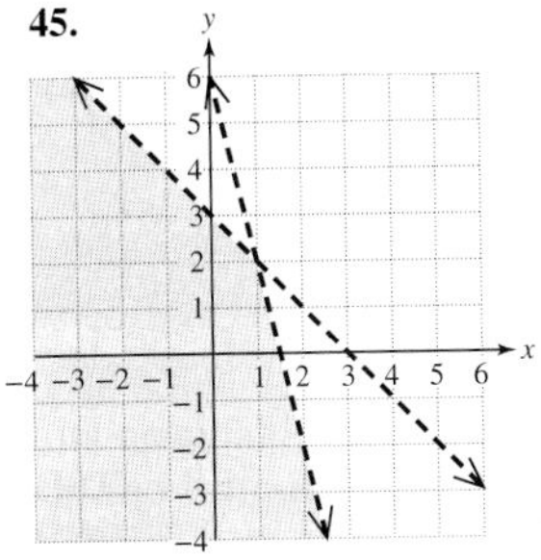

47.

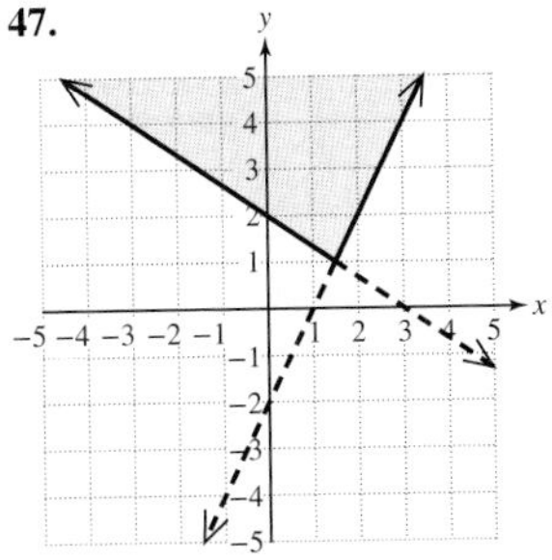

49.

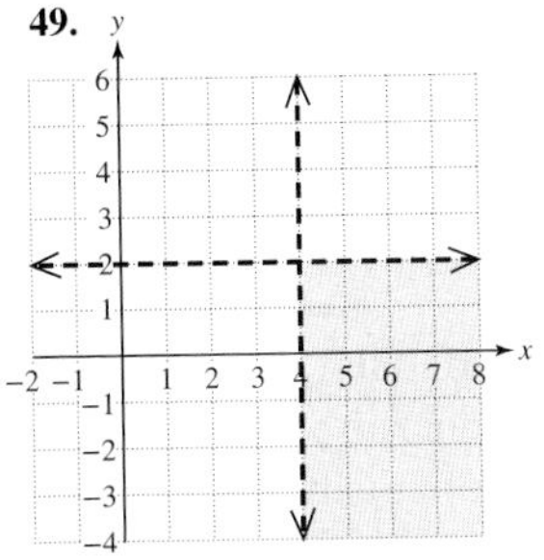

51.

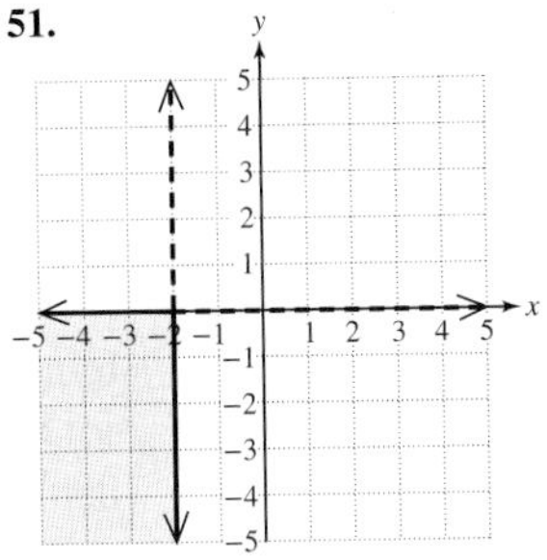

53.

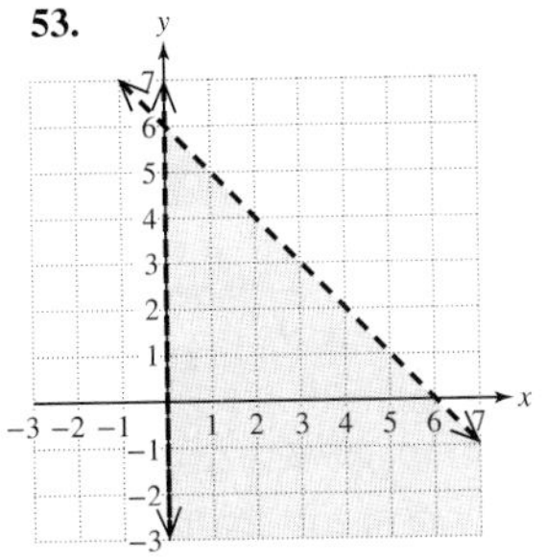

55.

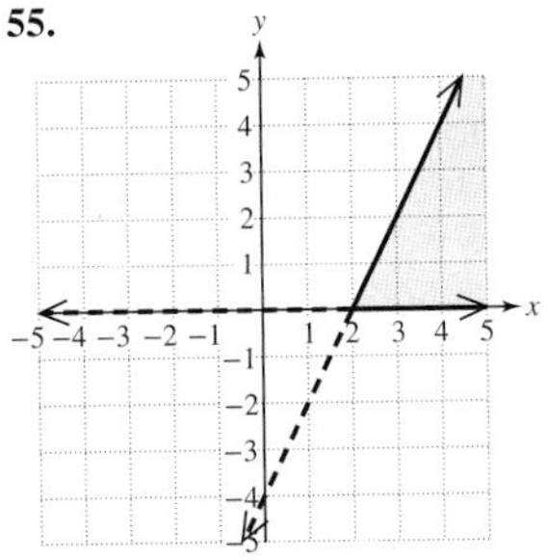

57.

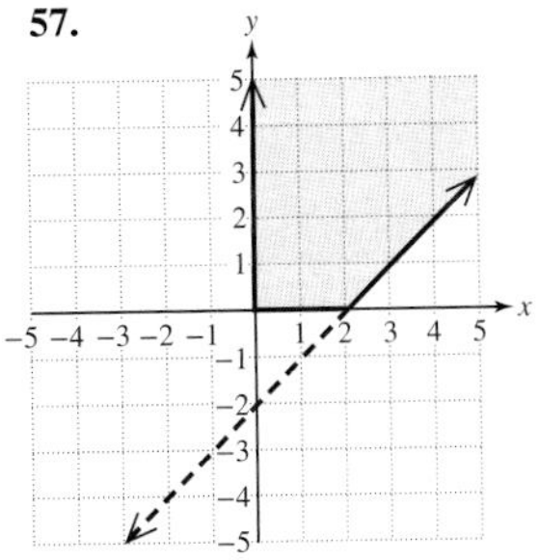

59.

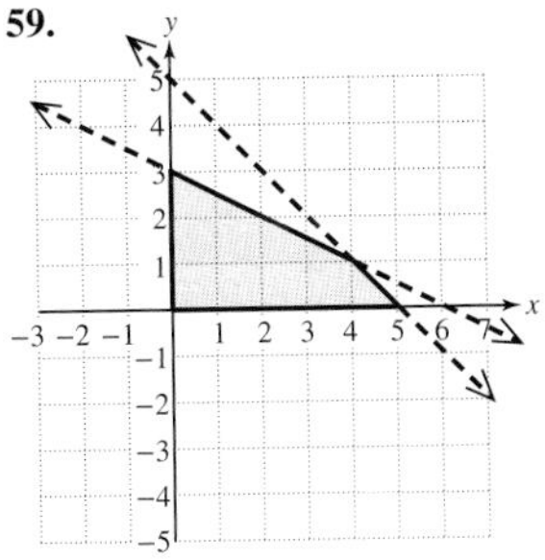

61. a. $2x + 2y \le 40$

b.

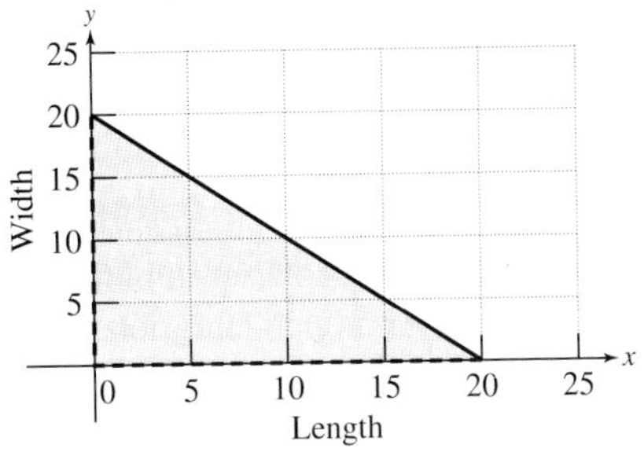

63. a. $x \ge 0, y \ge 0$ **b.** $x \le 40, y \le 40$ **c.** $x + y \ge 65$

d.

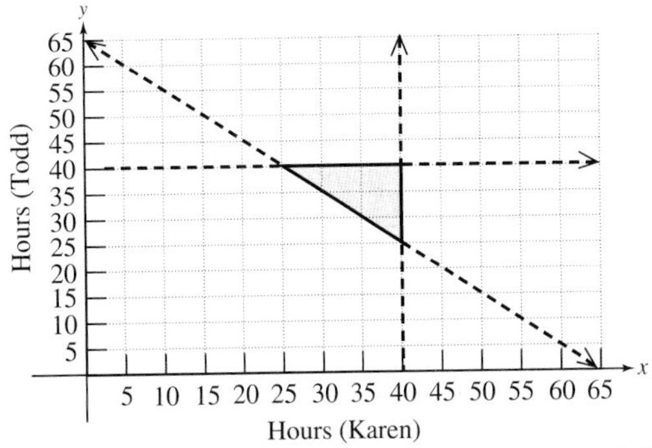

e. Yes; The point (35, 40) means that Karen works 35 hr and Todd works 40 hr. **f.** No; The point (20, 40) means that Karen works 20 hr and Todd works 40 hr. This does not satisfy the constraint that there must be at least 65 hr total.

Chapter 9 Review Exercises, pp. 686–689

1. $C \cap D$ is the set of elements common to both sets C and D.

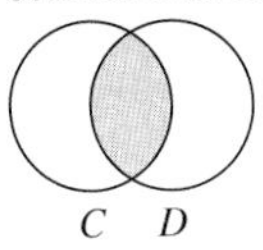

$C \cup D$ is the set of elements in either set C, set D, or both sets.

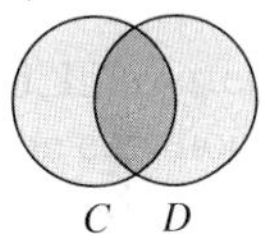

2. $[-10, 1)$ **3.** $(-\infty, \infty)$ **4.** $(-\infty, \infty)$ **5.** $(-1, 1)$

6. $(-\infty, -3] \cup (-1, \infty)$ **7.** $\{\ \}$ **8.** $\left(-\frac{11}{4}, 4\right]$

9. $[-5, 2)$ **10.** $(-\infty, 6] \cup (12, \infty)$

11. $(-\infty, -2) \cup [2, \infty)$ **12.** $\left[0, \frac{4}{3}\right]$ **13.** $[-7, -2)$

14. a. $140 \le x \le 225$ **b.** $x < 140$ or $x > 225$

15. a. $125 \le x \le 200$ **b.** $x < 125$ or $x > 200$

16. a. $(-2, 0)$ and $(2, 0)$ are the x-intercepts. **b.** On the interval $(-2, 2)$ the graph is below the x-axis. **c.** On the intervals $(-\infty, -2)$ and $(2, \infty)$ the graph is above the x-axis.

17. a. $x = 0$; $(0, 0)$ is the x-intercept. **b.** $x = 2$ is the vertical asymptote. **c.** On the intervals $(-\infty, 0]$ and $(2, \infty)$ the graph is on or above the x-axis. **d.** On the interval $[0, 2)$ the graph is on or below the x-axis. **18.** $(-2, 6)$ **19.** $(-\infty, \infty)$ **20.** $(-\infty, -2) \cup [0, \infty)$

21. $(-\infty, -1] \cup (1, \infty)$ **22.** $(-2, 0) \cup (5, \infty)$

23. $(-2, 0) \cup \left(\frac{5}{2}, \infty\right)$ **24.** $[-3, -1]$

25. $(-\infty, -5) \cup (1, \infty)$ **26.** $(3, \infty)$ **27.** $(-3, \infty)$

28. $\{-5\}$ **29.** $(-\infty, -2) \cup (-2, \infty)$ **30.** $\{10, -10\}$

31. $\{17, -17\}$ **32.** $\{1.3, 7.4\}$ **33.** $\{-0.44, 2.54\}$

34. $\{5, -9\}$ **35.** $\{3, 1\}$ **36.** $\{\ \}$

37. $\{\ \}$ **38.** $\left\{\frac{3}{7}\right\}$ **39.** $\left\{-\frac{5}{4}\right\}$ **40.** $\left\{6, \frac{4}{5}\right\}$

41. $\left\{-\frac{1}{2}\right\}$ **42.** Both expressions give the distance between 3 and −2. **43.** $|x| > 5$ **44.** $|x| < 4$

45. $|x| < 6$ **46.** $|x| > \frac{2}{3}$

47. $(-\infty, -14] \cup [2, \infty)$

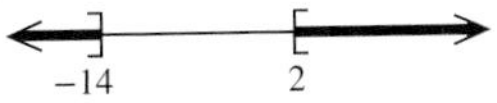

48. $[-11, -5]$

49. $\left(-\infty, \frac{1}{7}\right) \cup \left(\frac{1}{7}, \infty\right)$

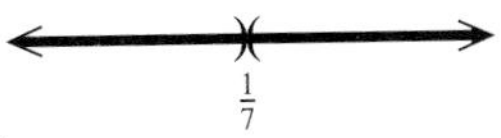

50. $\left(-\infty, -\frac{1}{5}\right) \cup \left(-\frac{1}{5}, \infty\right)$

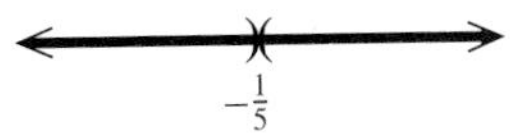

51. $\left[-2, -\frac{2}{3}\right]$ 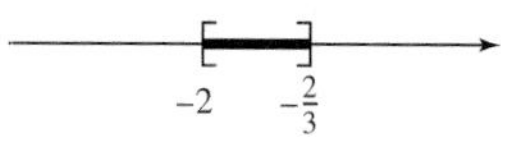

52. $\left[0, \frac{6}{5}\right]$ 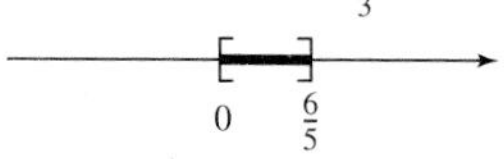

53. (2, 22) 

54. (−12, 0) 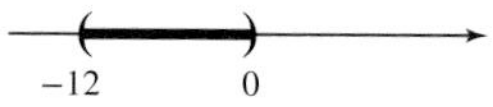

55. $(-\infty, \infty)$ 
56. $(-\infty, \infty)$ 
57. $(-\infty, \infty)$ 
58. $(-\infty, \infty)$ 

59. { } **60.** { } **61.** If an absolute value is less than a negative number, there will be no solution. **62.** If an absolute value is greater than a negative number, then all real numbers are solutions. **63.** $0.17 \le p \le 0.23$ or, equivalently in interval notation, [0.17, 0.23]. This means that the actual percentage of viewers is estimated to be between 17% and 23%, inclusive.
64. $3\frac{1}{8} \le L \le 3\frac{5}{8}$ or, equivalently in interval notation, $[3\frac{1}{8}, 3\frac{5}{8}]$. This means that the actual length of the screw may be between $3\frac{1}{8}$ in. and $3\frac{5}{8}$ in., inclusive.

65.
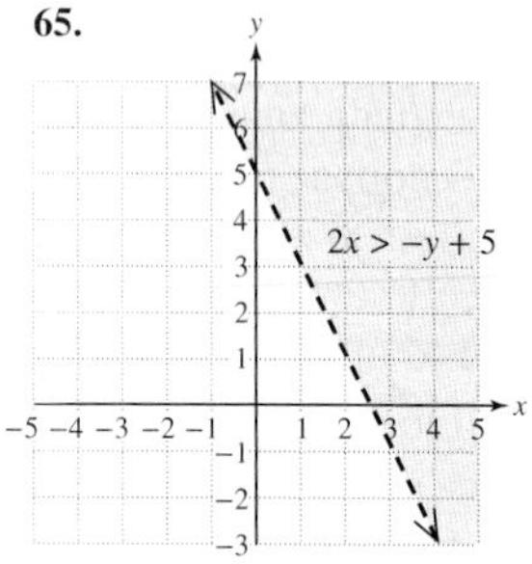

66.
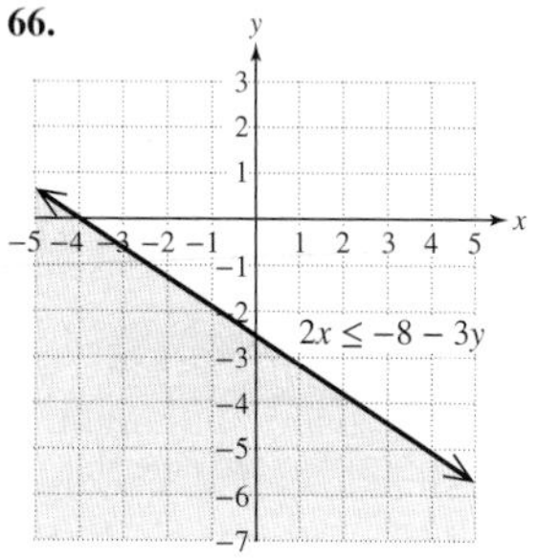

67.
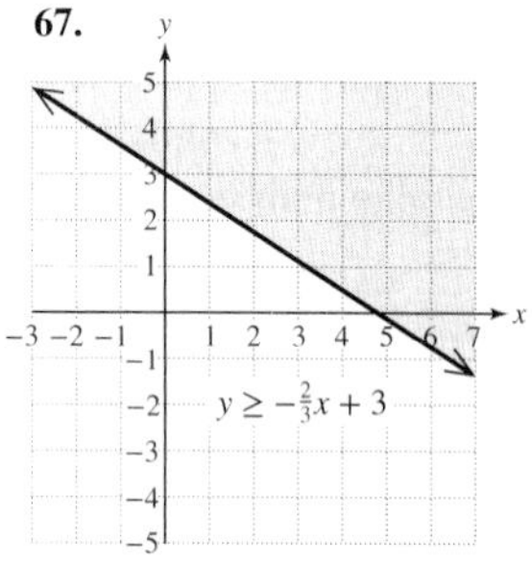

68.
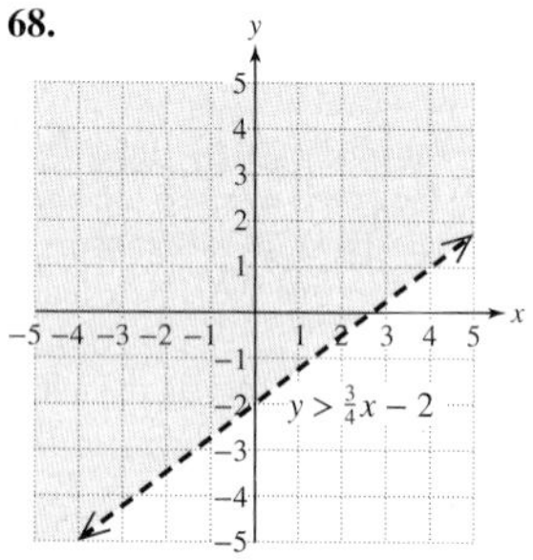

69.
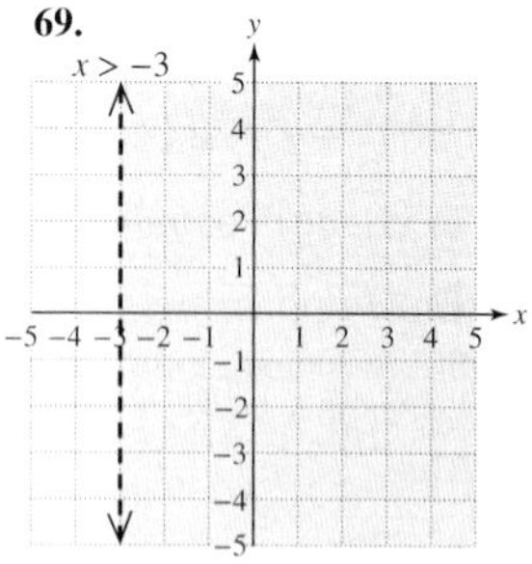

70.
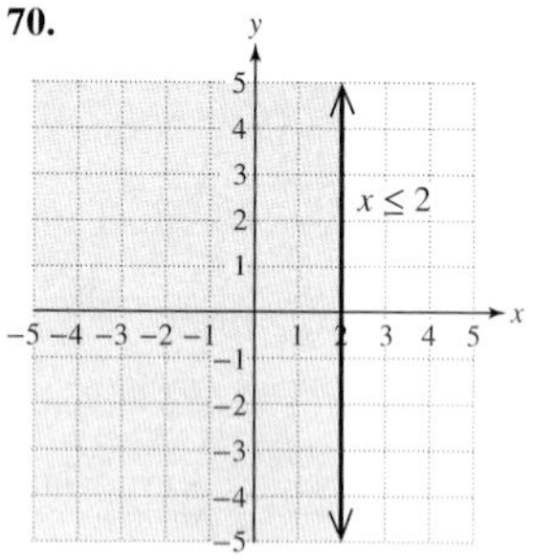

71.
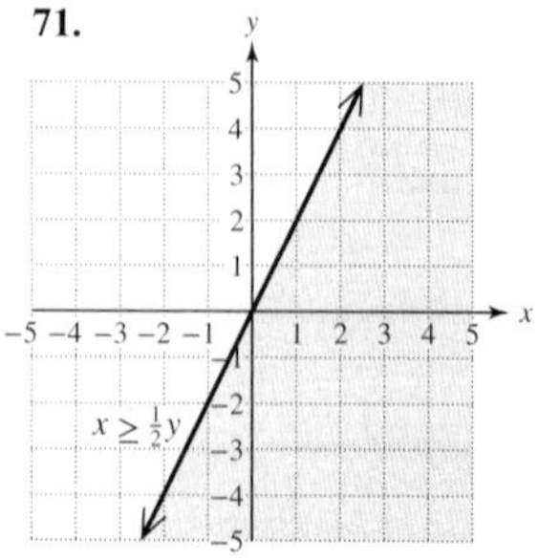

72.
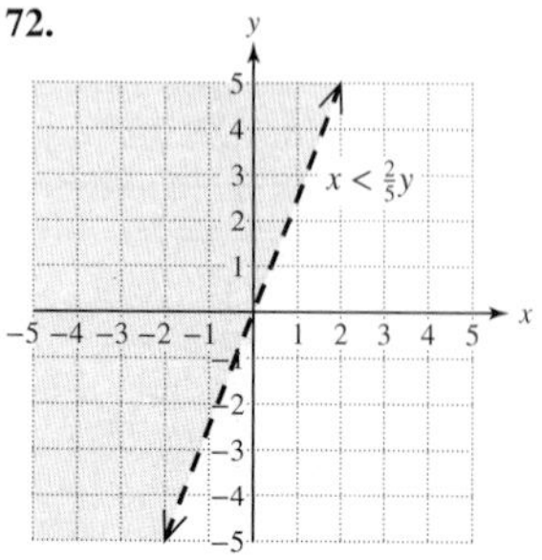

73.
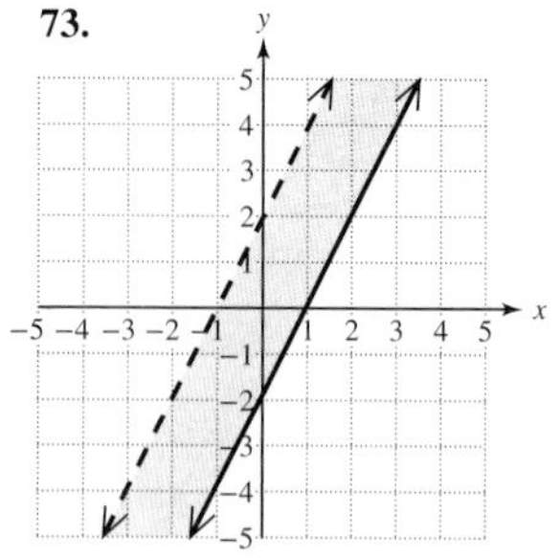

74.
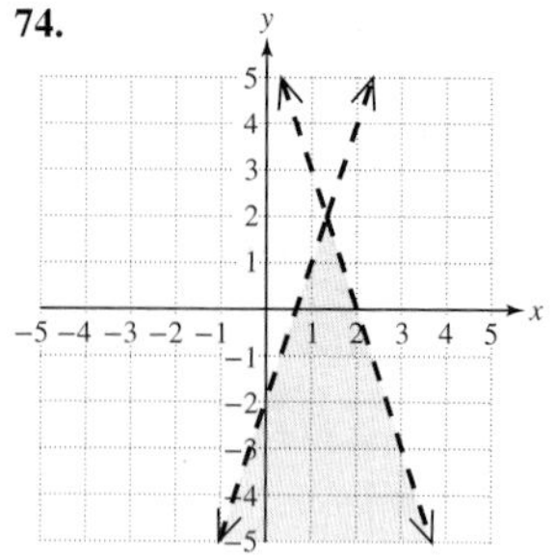

75.
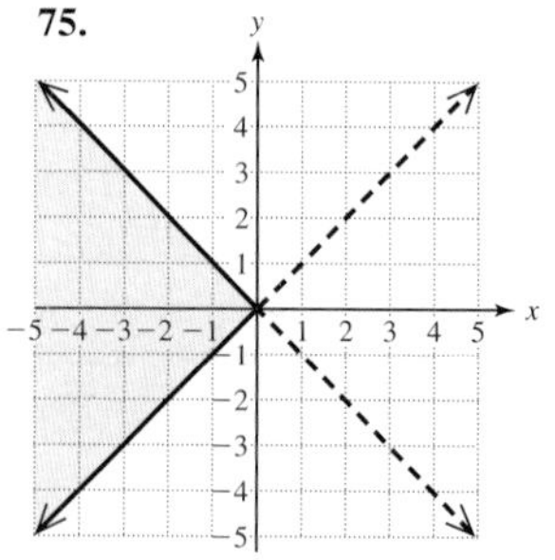

76.
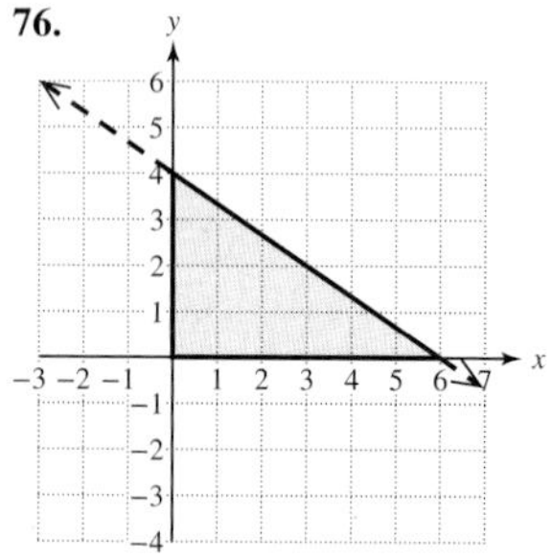

77. a. $x \ge 0, y \ge 0$ **b.** $x + y \le 100$ **c.** $x \ge 4y$
d.
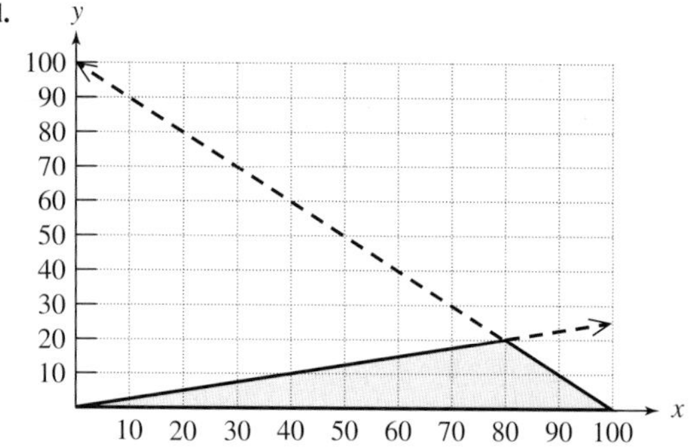

Chapter 9 Test, pp. 689–690

1. $\left[-\frac{1}{3}, 2\right]$ **2.** $(-\infty, -24] \cup [-15, \infty)$ **3.** $[-3, 0)$
4. $(-\infty, \infty)$ **5.** { } **6. a.** $9 \le x \le 33$
b. $x < 9$ or $x > 33$ **7.** $(-5, 5)$ **8.** $(-\infty, -3) \cup (-2, 2)$
9. { } **10.** {−11} **11.** $\left[\frac{1}{2}, 6\right)$ **12.** $\left(-3, -\frac{3}{2}\right)$
13. {10, −22} **14.** {−8, 2} **15.** { }
16. $\left(-\infty, -\frac{1}{3}\right) \cup \left(\frac{17}{3}, \infty\right)$ **17.** (−18.75, 17.25)
18. $(-\infty, \infty)$ **19.** $|x - 15.41| \le 0.01$
20.
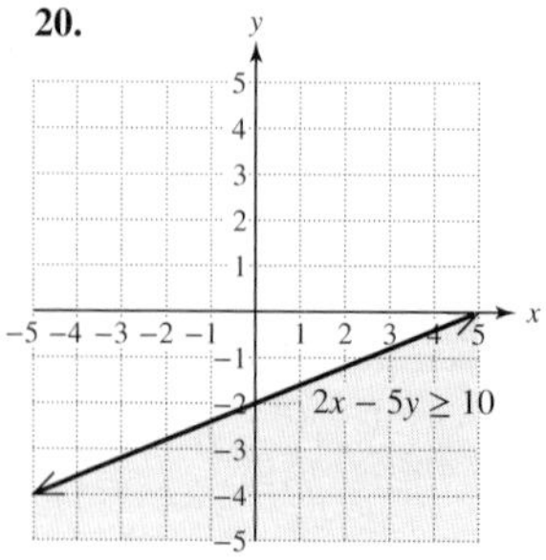

21.
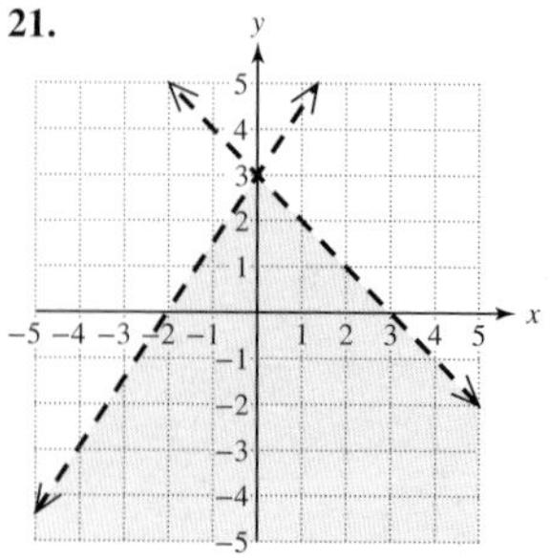

22.

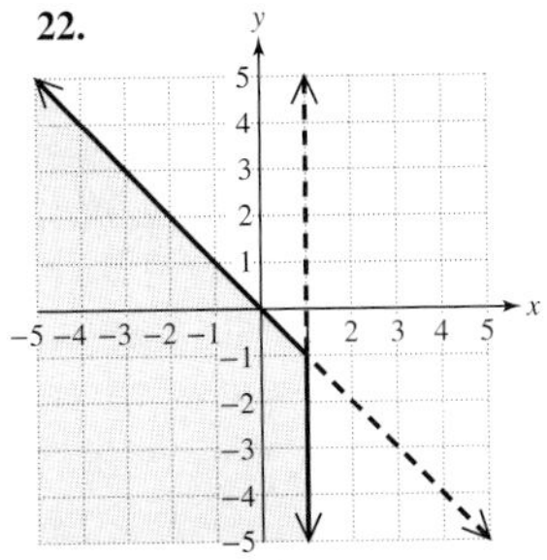

23. a. $x \geq 0, y \geq 0$ **b.** $300x + 400y \geq 1200$

c.

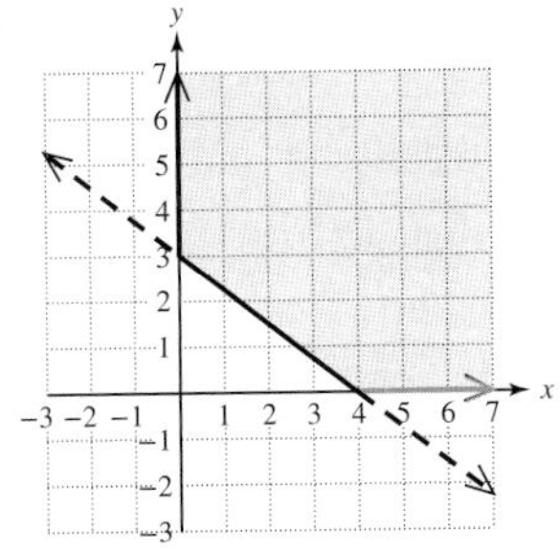

16. a. x-intercept $(1, 0)$; no y-intercept; undefined slope **b.** x-intercept $(8, 0)$; y-intercept $(0, 4)$; slope $-\frac{1}{2}$

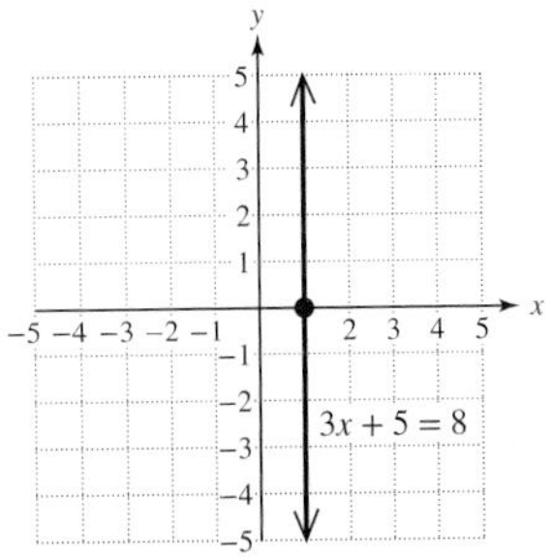

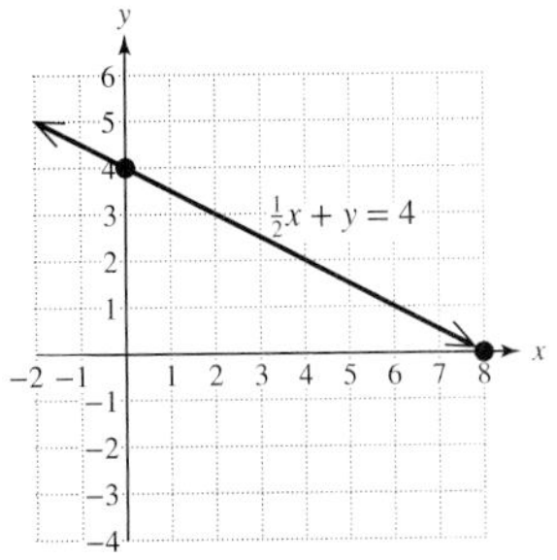

17. $y = -\dfrac{2}{3}x - \dfrac{13}{3}$ **18.** $\{(-1, 3, -2)\}$ **19.** $\dfrac{6}{x^4y^5}$

20. Plane: 500 mph; wind: 20 mph **21. a.** Quadratic **b.** $P(0) = -2600$. The company will lose \$2600 if no desks are produced. **c.** $P(x) = 0$ for $x = 20$ and $x = 650$. The company will break even (\$0 profit) when 20 desks or 650 desks are produced.
22. $3(x - 2)^2(x + 2)$

23. $-\dfrac{xy}{x + y}$ **24.** $-\dfrac{a + 1}{a}$ **25.** $\dfrac{2x + 5}{(x - 5)(x - 2)(x + 10)}$

Chapters 1–9 Cumulative Review Exercises, pp. 690–692

1. $x^2 - x - 13$ **2.** $\left\{-\dfrac{3}{2}, 1\right\}$

3. a. $\{0, 6\}$ **b.** $(0, 6)$ **c.** $(-\infty, 0) \cup (6, \infty)$
4. a. $\{14, -10\}$ **b.** $(-10, 14)$ **c.** $(-\infty, -10) \cup (14, \infty)$
5.

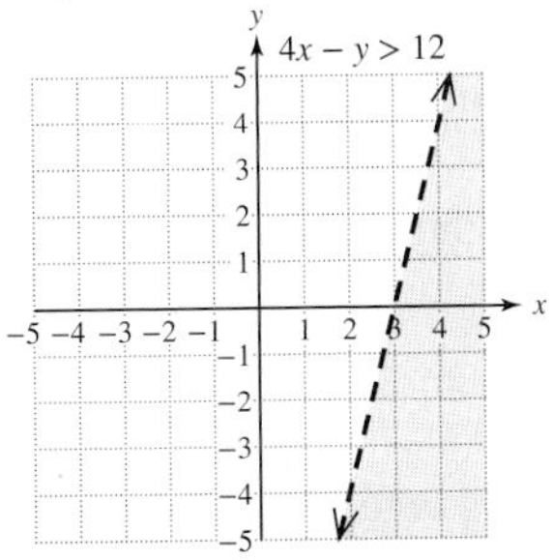

6. a. $t(1) = 9$. After one trial the rat requires 9 min to complete the maze. $t(50) = 3.24$. After 50 trials the rat requires 3.24 min to complete the maze. $t(500) = 3.02$. After 500 trials the rat requires 3.02 min to complete the maze. **b.** The limiting time is 3 min. **c.** More than 5 trials

7. a. $\left(-\infty, -\dfrac{5}{2}\right] \cup [2, \infty)$ **b.** On these intervals the graph is on or above the x-axis.

8.

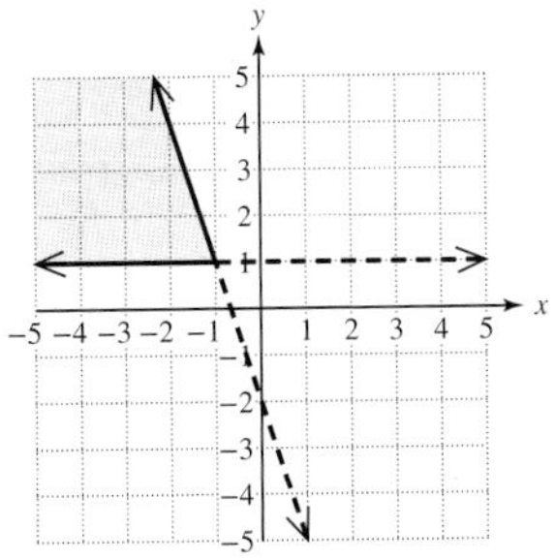

9. $-7x + 13$

10. a. Quotient: $2x^2 - 5x + 12$; remainder: $-24x + 5$

11. a. $b_1 = \dfrac{2A - hb_2}{h}$ or $b_1 = \dfrac{2A}{h} - b_2$ **b.** 10 cm

12. 75 mph **13.** 57°, 123° **14.** \$8000 in the 6.5% account; \$5000 in the 5% account **15.** Neither

Chapter 10

Section 10.1 Practice Exercises, pp. 702–705

1. a. b; a **b.** principal **c.** b^n; a **d.** index; radicand **e.** cube **f.** is not; is **g.** even; odd **h.** Pythagorean; c^2 **i.** $[0, \infty)$; $(-\infty, \infty)$ **j.** -5 and -4

3. a. 8, −8 **b.** 8 **c.** There are two square roots for every positive number. $\sqrt{64}$ identifies the positive square root.

5. a. 9 **b.** −9 **7.** There is no real number b such that $b^2 = -36$. **9.** 7 **11.** −7 **13.** Not a real number

15. $\dfrac{8}{3}$ **17.** 0.9 **19.** −0.4 **21. a.** 8 **b.** 4 **c.** −8 **d.** −4 **e.** Not a real number **f.** −4

23. −3 **25.** $\dfrac{1}{2}$ **27.** 2 **29.** $-\dfrac{5}{4}$ **31.** Not a real number **33.** 10 **35.** −0.2 **37.** 0.5 **39.** $|a|$

41. a **43.** $|a|$ **45.** $|x + 1|$ **47.** $|x|y^2$ **49.** $-\dfrac{x}{y}$

51. $\dfrac{2}{|x|}$ **53.** −92 **55.** 2 **57.** −923 **59.** y^4

61. $\dfrac{a^3}{b}$ **63.** $-\dfrac{5}{q}$ **65.** $3xy^2z$ **67.** $\dfrac{hk^2}{4}$ **69.** $-\dfrac{t}{3}$

71. $2y^2$ **73.** $2p^2q^3$ **75.** 9 cm **77.** 13 ft

79. They were 5 mi apart. **81.** They are 25 mi apart.

83. a. Not a real number **b.** Not a real number **c.** 0 **d.** 1 **e.** 2; Domain: $[2, \infty)$ **85. a.** −2 **b.** −1 **c.** 0 **d.** 1; Domain: $(-\infty, \infty)$ **87.** $\left(-\infty, \dfrac{5}{2}\right]$

89. $(-\infty, \infty)$ **91.** $[5, \infty)$ **93.** $(-\infty, \infty)$

95. a. $(-\infty, 1]$ **b.**

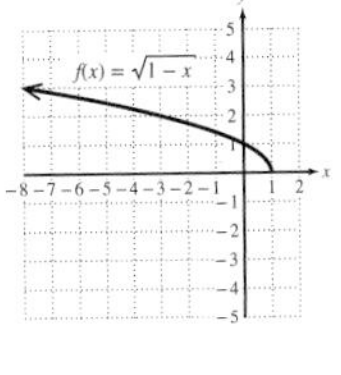

97. a. $[-3, \infty)$ **b.**

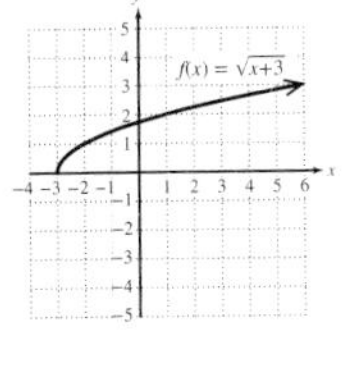

99. a. $[0, \infty)$ **b.**

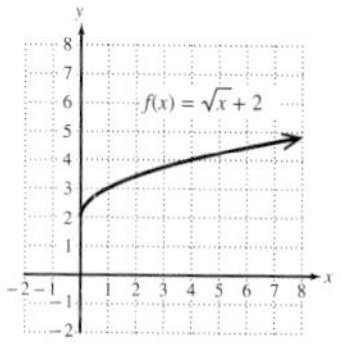

101. a. $(-\infty, \infty)$ **b.**

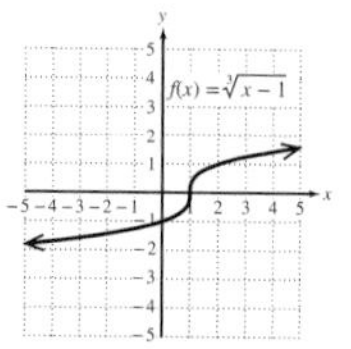

103. $q + p^2$ **105.** $\frac{6}{\sqrt[3]{x}}$ **107.** 8 in.

Section 10.1 Graphing Calculator Exercises, p. 705

109. 8.3066 **110.** 76.1446 **111.** 3.7100
112. −0.5566 **113.** 15.6525 **114.** −6.2403
115. −0.1235 **116.** 1.0622

117.

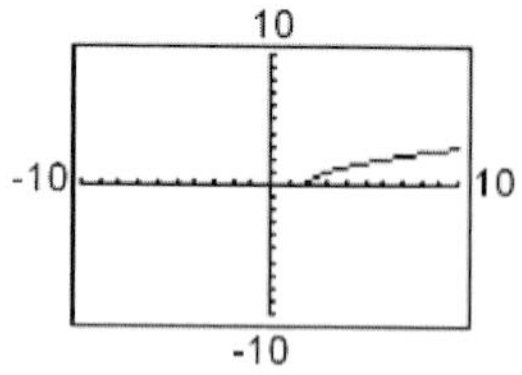

118.

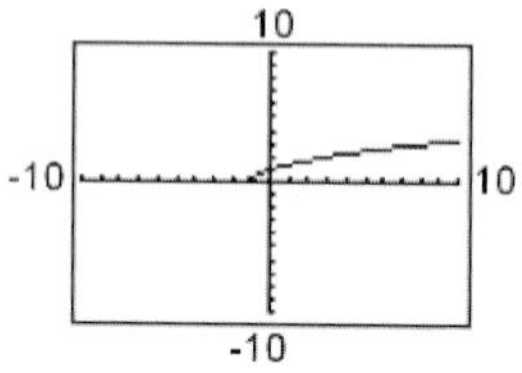

119.

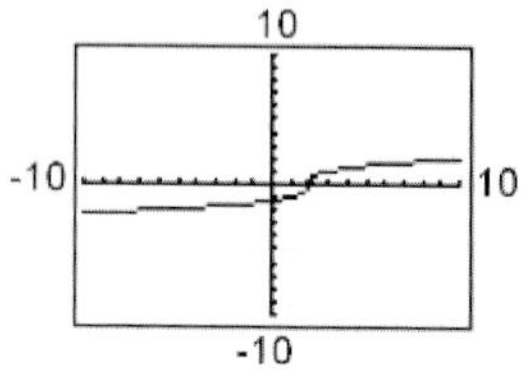

120.

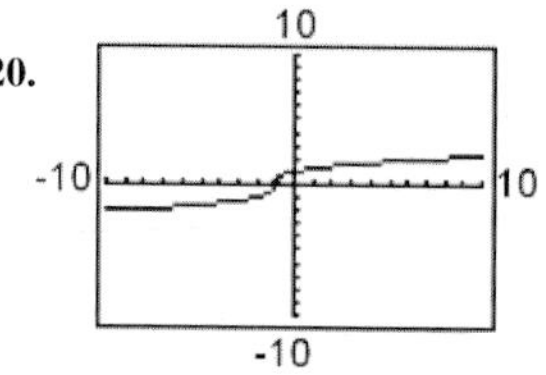

Section 10.2 Practice Exercises, pp. 710–713

1. a. $\sqrt[n]{a}$ **b.** $(\sqrt[n]{a})^m$ or $\sqrt[n]{a^m}$ **c.** $\frac{1}{\sqrt[n]{x}}$ **d.** 2; $\frac{1}{2}$

3. 5 **5.** 3 **7.** 12 **9.** −12 **11.** Not a real number

13. −4 **15.** $\frac{1}{5}$ **17.** $-\frac{1}{7}$

19. $a^{m/n} = \sqrt[n]{a^m}$; The numerator of the exponent represents the power of the base. The denominator of the exponent represents the index of the radical. **21. a.** 8 **b.** −8 **c.** Not a real number **d.** $\frac{1}{8}$ **e.** $-\frac{1}{8}$ **f.** Not a real number

23. a. 125 **b.** −125 **c.** Not a real number **d.** $\frac{1}{125}$ **e.** $-\frac{1}{125}$ **f.** Not a real number **25.** $\frac{1}{512}$ **27.** 27

29. $-\frac{1}{81}$ **31.** $\frac{27}{1000}$ **33.** Not a real number **35.** −2

37. −2 **39.** 6 **41.** 10 **43.** $\frac{3}{4}$ **45.** 1 **47.** $\frac{9}{2}$

49. $\sqrt[3]{q^2}$ **51.** $6\sqrt[4]{y^3}$ **53.** $\sqrt[3]{x^2y}$ **55.** $\frac{6}{\sqrt[5]{r^2}}$

57. $x^{1/3}$ **59.** $10b^{1/2}$ **61.** $y^{2/3}$ **63.** $(a^2b^3)^{1/4}$

65. $\frac{1}{x}$ **67.** p **69.** y^2 **71.** $6^{2/5}$ **73.** $\frac{4}{t^{5/3}}$

75. a^7 **77.** $\frac{25a^4d}{c}$ **79.** $\frac{y^9}{x^8}$ **81.** $\frac{2z^3}{w}$ **83.** $5xy^2z^3$

85. $x^{13}z^{4/3}$ **87.** $\frac{x^3y^2}{z^5}$ **89. a.** 10.9% **b.** 8.8% **c.** The account in part (a). **91.** 2.7 in. **93.** $\sqrt{y}$

95. $\sqrt[4]{z}$ **97.** $\sqrt[3]{x^2}$ **99.** $y\sqrt{x}$ **101.** $4x^4y^3$
103. $2x\sqrt[3]{y^2z}$ **105.** $\sqrt[6]{x}$ **107.** $\sqrt[15]{w}$ **109.** 3
111. 0.3761 **113.** 2.9240 **115.** 31.6228

Section 10.3 Practice Exercises, pp. 718–720

1. a. $\sqrt[n]{a}$; $\sqrt[n]{b}$ **b.** The exponent within the radicand is greater than the index. **c.** is not **d.** 3 **e.** t^{12} **f.** No. $\sqrt{2}$ is an irrational number and the decimal form is a nonterminating, nonrepeating decimal.

3. $\frac{p}{q^5}$ **5.** $\sqrt[7]{x^4}$ **7.** $y^{9/2}$ **9.** $x^2\sqrt{x}$ **11.** $q^2\sqrt[3]{q}$

13. $a^2b^2\sqrt{a}$ **15.** $-x^2y^3\sqrt[4]{y}$ **17.** $2\sqrt{7}$ **19.** $2\sqrt{5}$
21. $15\sqrt{2}$ **23.** $3\sqrt[3]{2}$ **25.** $5b\sqrt{ab}$ **27.** $2x^2\sqrt[3]{5x}$
29. $-2x^2z\sqrt[3]{2y}$ **31.** $2wz\sqrt[4]{5z^3}$ **33.** x **35.** p^2

37. 5 **39.** $\frac{1}{2}$ **41.** $\frac{5\sqrt[3]{2}}{3}$ **43.** $\frac{5\sqrt[3]{9}}{6}$ **45.** $4\sqrt{5}$

47. $-30\sqrt{3}$ **49.** $5x^2y\sqrt{y}$ **51.** $3yz\sqrt[3]{x^2z}$ **53.** $2w^2$

55. $\frac{1}{10y^6}$ **57.** $\frac{2}{b}$ **59.** $2a^7b^4c^{15}d^{11}\sqrt{2c}$

61. $3a^2b\sqrt[3]{2b}$ **63.** $-10a^2b^2\sqrt{3ac}$ **65.** $x\sqrt[4]{7xy}$

67. $3a^2b\sqrt{6}$ **69.** $2\sqrt{3}$ **71.** $\frac{3\sqrt{5}}{4}$

73. $\frac{1}{\sqrt[3]{w^6}}$ simplifies to $\frac{1}{w^2}$ **75.** $\sqrt{k^3}$ simplifies to $k\sqrt{k}$

77. $2\sqrt{41}$ ft **79.** $6\sqrt{5}$ m **81.** The distance is $90\sqrt{2}$ ft or approximately 127.3 ft. **83.** The path from A to B and B to C is faster.

Section 10.4 Practice Exercises, pp. 723–725

1. a. index; radicand **b.** $2\sqrt{3x}$ **c.** cannot; can **d.** $4\sqrt{2}$

3. $-xy\sqrt[4]{x^3}$ **5.** $\frac{b^2}{2}$ **7.** $(x^3y)^{1/4}$ **9.** $y^{11/12}$

11. a. Not *like* radicals **b.** *Like* radicals **c.** Not *like* radicals **13. a.** Both expressions can be simplified by using the distributive property. **b.** Neither expression can be simplified because the terms do not contain *like* radicals or *like* terms. **15.** $9\sqrt{5}$ **17.** $2\sqrt[3]{tw}$

19. $5\sqrt{10}$ **21.** $8\sqrt[4]{3} - \sqrt[4]{14}$ **23.** $2\sqrt{x} + 2\sqrt{y}$
25. Cannot be simplified further

27. Cannot be simplified further **29.** $\frac{29}{18}z\sqrt[3]{6}$

31. $0.7x\sqrt{y}$ **33.** Simplify each radical: $3\sqrt{2} + 35\sqrt{2}$. Then add *like* radicals: $38\sqrt{2}$ **35.** 15 **37.** $8\sqrt{3}$
39. $3\sqrt{7}$ **41.** $-5\sqrt{2} + 3\sqrt{3}$ **43.** $\sqrt[3]{3}$ **45.** $-5\sqrt{2a}$
47. $8s^2t^2\sqrt[3]{s^2}$ **49.** $6x\sqrt[3]{x}$ **51.** $14p^2\sqrt{5}$
53. $-\sqrt[3]{a^2b}$ **55.** $(5x + 6)\sqrt{x}$ **57.** $(5x - 6)\sqrt{2}$
59. $33d\sqrt[3]{2c}$ **61.** $2a^2b\sqrt{6a}$ **63.** $5x\sqrt[3]{2} - 6\sqrt[3]{x}$
65. False; $\sqrt{9} + \sqrt{16} \neq \sqrt{9 + 16}$; $7 \neq 5$ **67.** True
69. False; $\sqrt{y} + \sqrt{y} = 2\sqrt{y} \neq \sqrt{2y}$
71. False; $2w\sqrt{5} + 4w\sqrt{5} = 6w\sqrt{5} \neq 6w^2\sqrt{5}$
73. $\sqrt{48} + \sqrt{12}$ simplifies to $6\sqrt{3}$
75. $5\sqrt[3]{x^6} - x^2$ simplifies to $4x^2$ **77.** The difference of the principal square root of 18 and the square of 5
79. The sum of the principal fourth root of x and the cube of y
81. $9\sqrt{6}$ cm $\approx$ 22.0 cm **83.** $x = 2\sqrt{2}$ ft
85. a. $10\sqrt{5}$ yd **b.** 22.36 yd **c.** \$105.95

Section 10.5 Practice Exercises, pp. 731–733

1. a. $\sqrt[n]{ab}$ **b.** x **c.** a **d.** conjugates **e.** $m - n$ **f.** $c + 8\sqrt{c} + 16$ **3.** $-2ab\sqrt{5bc}$ **5.** $x^{1/6}y^{7/12}$ **7.** $2\sqrt[3]{7}$
9. $\sqrt[3]{21}$ **11.** $2\sqrt{5}$ **13.** $4\sqrt[4]{4}$ **15.** $8\sqrt[3]{20}$
17. $-24ab\sqrt{a}$ **19.** $6\sqrt{10}$ **21.** $6x\sqrt{2}$ **23.** $10a^3b^2\sqrt{b}$
25. $-24x^2y^2\sqrt{2y}$ **27.** $6ab\sqrt[3]{2a^2b^2}$ **29.** $12 - 6\sqrt{3}$

31. $2\sqrt{3} - \sqrt{6}$ **33.** $-2x - \frac{7}{3}\sqrt{x}$ **35.** $-8 + 7\sqrt{30}$

37. $x-5\sqrt{x}-36$ **39.** $\sqrt[3]{y^2}-\sqrt[3]{y}-6$
41. $9a-28\sqrt{ab}+3b$ **43.** $8\sqrt{p}+3p+5\sqrt{pq}+16\sqrt{q}-2q$
45. 15 **47.** $3y$ **49.** 6 **51.** 709 **53. a.** x^2-y^2 **b.** x^2-25 **55.** $29+8\sqrt{13}$ **57.** $p-2\sqrt{7p}+7$
59. $2a-6\sqrt{2ab}+9b$ **61.** $3-x^2$ **63.** 4
65. $\frac{4}{9}x-\frac{1}{4}y$ **67. a.** $3-x$ **b.** $3+2\sqrt{3x}+x$ **c.** $3-2\sqrt{3x}+x$ **69.** True **71.** False; $(x-\sqrt{5})^2=x^2-2x\sqrt{5}+5$ **73.** False; 5 is multiplied by 3 only.
75. True **77.** $6x$ **79.** $3x+1$
81. $x+19-8\sqrt{x+3}$ **83.** $2t+10\sqrt{2t-3}+22$
85. $12\sqrt{5}$ ft^2 **87.** $18\sqrt{15}$ in.^{2} **89.** $\sqrt[4]{x^3}$
91. $\sqrt[15]{(2z)^8}$ **93.** $p^2\sqrt[6]{p}$ **95.** $u\sqrt[6]{u}$
97. $\sqrt[6]{x^2y}$ **99.** $\sqrt[4]{2^3\cdot 3^2}$ or $\sqrt[4]{72}$ **101.** $\sqrt[12]{2^4 5^3 x^7 y^7}$
103. $2m\sqrt[6]{3^3 2mn^5}$ **105.** $a+b$

Chapter 10 Problem Recognition Exercises, p. 734

1. a. $2\sqrt{6}$ **b.** $2\sqrt[3]{3}$ **2. a.** $3\sqrt{6}$ **b.** $3\sqrt[3]{2}$
3. a. $10y^3\sqrt{2}$ **b.** $2y^2\sqrt[3]{25}$ **4. a.** $4z^7\sqrt{2z}$ **b.** $2z^5\sqrt[3]{4}$
5. a. $4\sqrt{5}$ **b.** $2\sqrt[3]{10}$ **c.** $2\sqrt[4]{5}$ **6. a.** $4\sqrt{3}$ **b.** $2\sqrt[3]{6}$ **c.** $2\sqrt[4]{3}$
7. a. $x^2y^3\sqrt{x}$ **b.** $xy^2\sqrt[3]{x^2}$ **c.** $xy\sqrt[4]{xy^2}$
8. a. $a^5b^4\sqrt{b}$ **b.** $a^3b^3\sqrt[3]{a}$ **c.** $a^2b^2\sqrt[4]{a^2b}$ **9. a.** $2st^2\sqrt[3]{4s^2}$ **b.** $2st\sqrt[4]{2st^2}$ **c.** $2st\sqrt[5]{t}$ **10. a.** $2v^2w^6\sqrt[3]{12vw^2}$ **b.** $2vw^5\sqrt[4]{6v^3}$ **c.** $2vw^4\sqrt[5]{3v^2}$ **11. a.** $2\sqrt{5}$ **b.** 5
12. a. $2\sqrt{10}$ **b.** 10 **13. a.** $-3\sqrt{6}$ **b.** 60
14. a. $-7\sqrt{7}$ **b.** 210 **15. a.** $3\sqrt{2}$ **b.** 4
16. a. $3\sqrt{3}$ **b.** 6 **17. a.** $7\sqrt{2}$ **b.** 240
18. a. $-\sqrt{2}$ **b.** 60 **19. a.** $14\sqrt[3]{3}$ **b.** $48\sqrt[3]{9}$
20. a. $\sqrt[3]{2}$ **b.** $30\sqrt[3]{4}$

Section 10.6 Practice Exercises, pp. 741–744

1. a. radical **b.** $\frac{\sqrt[n]{a}}{\sqrt[n]{b}}$ **c.** $\frac{4}{x^2}$ **d.** rationalizing **e.** is; is not **f.** denominator **3.** $12y\sqrt{5}$ **5.** $-18y+3\sqrt{y}+3$
7. $64-16\sqrt{t}+t$ **9.** -5 **11.** $\frac{7x^2}{y^3}$ **13.** $\frac{2a\sqrt{2}}{x^3}$
15. $\frac{-2j\sqrt[3]{2}}{k}$ **17.** $3b^2$ **19.** $\frac{1}{2b^2}$ **21.** $\frac{z\sqrt{3y}}{w^2}$ **23.** $\frac{\sqrt{5}}{\sqrt{5}}$
25. $\frac{\sqrt[3]{x^2}}{\sqrt[3]{x^2}}$ **27.** $\frac{\sqrt{3z}}{\sqrt{3z}}$ **29.** $\frac{\sqrt[4]{2a^2}}{\sqrt[4]{2a^2}}$ **31.** $\frac{\sqrt{3}}{3}$
33. $\frac{\sqrt{x}}{x}$ **35.** $\frac{3\sqrt{2y}}{y}$ **37.** $\frac{a\sqrt{2a}}{2}$ **39.** $\frac{3\sqrt{2}}{2}$
41. $\frac{3\sqrt[3]{4}}{2}$ **43.** $\frac{-6\sqrt[4]{x^3}}{x}$ **45.** $\frac{7\sqrt[3]{2}}{2}$ **47.** $\frac{\sqrt[3]{4w}}{w}$
49. $\frac{2\sqrt[4]{27}}{3}$ **51.** $\frac{\sqrt[3]{2x}}{x}$ **53.** $\frac{2\sqrt{6}}{21}$ **55.** $\frac{\sqrt{x}}{x^4}$
57. $\frac{\sqrt{2x}}{2x^3}$ **59.** $\sqrt{2}+\sqrt{6}$ **61.** $\sqrt{x}-23$
63. $\frac{4\sqrt{2}-12}{-7}$ or $\frac{-4\sqrt{2}+12}{7}$ **65.** $4\sqrt{6}+8$
67. $-\sqrt{21}+2\sqrt{7}$ **69.** $\frac{-\sqrt{p}+\sqrt{q}}{p-q}$ **71.** $\sqrt{x}-\sqrt{5}$
73. $\frac{w+11\sqrt{w}+18}{81-w}$ **75.** $\frac{4\sqrt{xy}-3x-y}{y-x}$
77. $5-\sqrt{10}$ **79.** $\frac{5+\sqrt{21}}{4}$ **81.** $-6\sqrt{5}-13$
83. $\frac{16}{\sqrt[3]{4}}$ simplifies to $8\sqrt[3]{2}$
85. $\frac{4}{x-\sqrt{2}}$ simplifies to $\frac{4x+4\sqrt{2}}{x^2-2}$

87. $\frac{\pi\sqrt{2}}{4}$ sec $\approx$ 1.11 sec **89. a.** $\frac{\sqrt{2}}{2}$ **b.** $\frac{\sqrt[3]{4}}{2}$
91. a. $\frac{\sqrt{5a}}{5a}$ **b.** $\frac{\sqrt{5}-a}{5-a^2}$ **93.** $\frac{2\sqrt{6}}{3}$ **95.** $\frac{17\sqrt{15}}{15}$
97. $\frac{8\sqrt[3]{25}}{5}$ **99.** $\frac{-33}{2\sqrt{3}-12}$ **101.** $\frac{a-b}{a+2\sqrt{ab}+b}$
103. $\frac{3}{\sqrt{5+3h}+\sqrt{5}}$ **105.** $\frac{5}{\sqrt{4+5h}+2}$

Section 10.7 Practice Exercises, pp. 751–754

1. a. radical **b.** isolate; 7 **c.** extraneous **d.** third
3. $\frac{3w\sqrt{w}}{4}$ **5.** $3c\sqrt[3]{2c}$ **7.** $4x-6$ **9.** $9p+7$
11. $\{100\}$ **13.** $\{4\}$ **15.** $\{3\}$ **17.** $\{42\}$ **19.** $\{2\}$
21. $\{29\}$ **23.** $\{140\}$ **25.** $\{\ \}$ (The value 25 does not check.)
27. $\{7\}$ (The value -1 does not check.)
29. $\{\ \}$ (The value 3 does not check.)
31. $V=\frac{4\pi r^3}{3}$ **33.** $h^2=\frac{r^2-\pi^2r^2}{\pi^2}$ or $h^2=\frac{r^2}{\pi^2}-r^2$
35. $a^2+10a+25$ **37.** $5a-6\sqrt{5a}+9$
39. $r+22+10\sqrt{r-3}$ **41.** $\{-3\}$
43. $\{\ \}$ (The value $\frac{1}{2}$ does not check.)
45. $\{2\}$ (The value 18 does not check.) **47.** $\{9\}$
49. $\{-4\}$ **51.** $\left\{\frac{9}{5}\right\}$ **53.** $\{2\}$
55. $\{\ \}$ (The value 9 does not check.)
57. $\left\{-\frac{11}{4}\right\}$ **59.** $\{\ \}$ (The value $\frac{8}{3}$ does not check.)
61. $\{-1\}$ (The value 3 does not check.) **63.** $\left\{\frac{1}{3}, -1\right\}$
65. $\{\ \}$ (The values 3 and 23 do not check.)
67. $\{6\}$ **69.** $\{2\}$ (The value 18 does not check.)
71. a. 30.25 ft **b.** 34.5 m **73. a.** \$2 million **b.** \$1.2 million **c.** 50,000 passengers **75. a.** 12 lb **b.** $t(18)=5.1$. An 18-lb turkey will take about 5.1 hr to cook.
77. $b=\sqrt{25-h^2}$ **79.** $a=\sqrt{k^2-196}$

Section 10.7 Graphing Calculator Exercises, p. 754

80. The x-coordinate of the point of intersection is the solution to the equation.

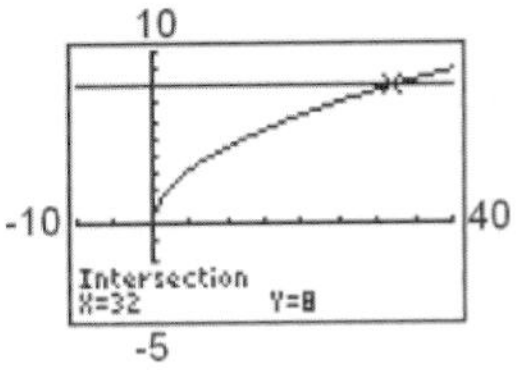

81. The x-coordinate of the point of intersection is the solution to the equation.

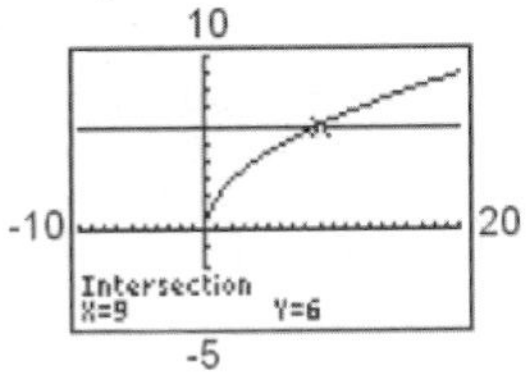

82.

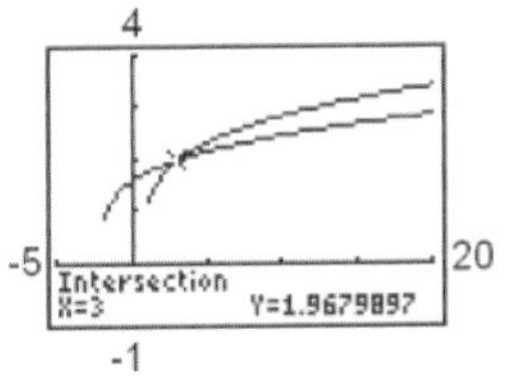

83.

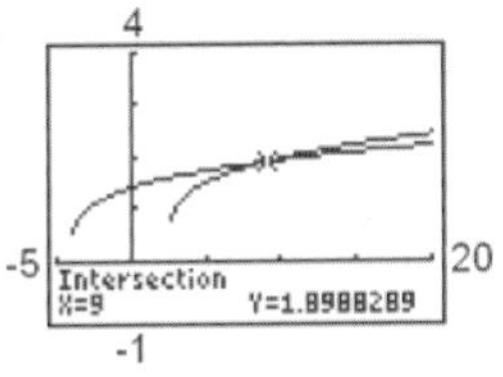

Section 10.8 Practice Exercises, pp. 762–764

1. a. imaginary **b.** $\sqrt{-1}$; -1 **c.** $i\sqrt{b}$ **d.** $a+bi$; $\sqrt{-1}$ **e.** real; b **f.** $a+bi$ **g.** True **h.** True
3. $9-x$ **5.** $\{-8\}$ **7.** $\left\{\frac{1}{25}\right\}$ **9.** $\sqrt{-1}=i$ and $-\sqrt{1}=-1$ **11.** $12i$ **13.** $i\sqrt{3}$ **15.** $-2i\sqrt{5}$

17. -60 **19.** $13i\sqrt{7}$ **21.** -7 **23.** -12
25. $-3\sqrt{10}$ **27.** $i\sqrt{2}$ **29.** 3 **31.** $-i$ **33.** 1
35. i **37.** 1 **39.** $-i$ **41.** -1 **43.** $a - bi$
45. Real: -5; imaginary: 12 **47.** Real: 0; imaginary: -6
49. Real: 35; imaginary: 0 **51.** Real: $\frac{3}{5}$; imaginary: 1
53. $7 + 6i$ **55.** $\frac{3}{10} + \frac{3}{2}i$ **57.** $5i\sqrt{2}$
59. $-1 + 10i$ **61.** $-24 + 0i$ **63.** $18 + 6i$
65. $26 - 26i$ **67.** $-29 + 0i$ **69.** $-9 + 40i$
71. $35 + 20i$ **73.** $-20 + 48i$ **75.** $\frac{13}{16} + 0i$
77. $\frac{1}{5} - \frac{3}{5}i$ **79.** $\frac{3}{25} - \frac{4}{25}i$ **81.** $\frac{21}{29} + \frac{20}{29}i$
83. $-\frac{17}{10} - \frac{1}{10}i$ **85.** $-\frac{1}{2} - \frac{5}{2}i$ **87.** $\frac{1}{2} - \frac{1}{3}i$
89. $1 + 10i$ **91.** $\frac{1}{4} + \frac{1}{2}i$ **93.** $-1 + i\sqrt{2}$
95. $-2 - i\sqrt{3}$ **97.** $-\frac{1}{2} + \frac{\sqrt{2}}{2}i$ **99.** Yes **101.** Yes

Chapter 10 Review Exercises, pp. 772–774

1. a. False; $\sqrt{0} = 0$ is not positive. **b.** False; $\sqrt[3]{-8} = -2$
2. $\sqrt{(-3)^2} = \sqrt{9} = 3$ **3. a.** False **b.** True
4. $\frac{5}{4}$ **5.** 5 **6.** 6 **7. a.** 3 **b.** 0 **c.** $\sqrt{7}$
d. $[1, \infty)$ **8. a.** 0 **b.** 1 **c.** 3 **d.** $[-5, \infty)$
9. $\frac{\sqrt[3]{2x}}{\sqrt[4]{2x}} + 4$ **10. a.** $|x|$ **b.** x **c.** $|x|$ **d.** $x + 1$
11. a. $2|y|$ **b.** $3y$ **c.** $|y|$ **d.** y **12.** 8 cm
13. Yes, provided the expressions are defined. For example: $x^5 \cdot x^3 = x^8$ and $x^{1/5} \cdot x^{2/5} = x^{3/5}$ **14.** n represents the root.
15. Take the reciprocal of the base and change the exponent to positive. **16.** -5 **17.** $\frac{1}{2}$ **18.** 4
19. b^{10} **20.** $\frac{16y^{12}}{xz^9}$ **21.** $\frac{a^3c}{b^2}$ **22.** $x^{3/4}$
23. $(2y^2)^{1/3}$ **24.** 2.1544 **25.** 6.8173 **26.** 54.1819
27. a. The radicand has no factor raised to a power greater than or equal to the index. **b.** The radicand does not contain a fraction. **c.** There are no radicals in the denominator of a fraction.
28. $6\sqrt{3}$ **29.** $xz\sqrt[4]{xy}$
30. $-10ab^3\sqrt[3]{2b}$ **31.** $-\frac{2a}{b}$
32. a. The principal square root of the quotient of 2 and x **b.** The cube of the sum of x and 1 **33.** 31 ft
34. They are *like* radicals. **35.** Cannot be combined; the indices are different. **36.** Cannot be combined; one term has a radical, but the other does not. **37.** Can be combined: $3\sqrt[4]{3xy}$ **38.** Can be added after simplifying: $19\sqrt{2}$
39. $5\sqrt{7}$ **40.** $9\sqrt[3]{2} - 8$ **41.** $10\sqrt{2}$ **42.** $13x\sqrt[3]{2x^2}$
43. False; 5 and $3\sqrt{x}$ are not *like* radicals.
44. False; $\sqrt{y} + \sqrt{y} = 2\sqrt{y}$ (add the coefficients).
45. 6 **46.** $2\sqrt[4]{2}$ **47.** $-2\sqrt{21} + 6\sqrt{33}$
48. $-6\sqrt{15} + 15$ **49.** $4x - 9$ **50.** $y - 16$
51. $7y - 2\sqrt{21xy} + 3x$ **52.** $12w + 20\sqrt{3w} + 25$
53. $-2z - 9\sqrt{6z} - 42$ **54.** $3a + 5\sqrt{5a} - 10$
55. $u^2\sqrt[6]{u^5}$ **56.** $\sqrt[4]{4w^3}$ **57.** $\frac{y^2\sqrt{3y}}{5x^3}$
58. $\frac{-2x^2y^2\sqrt[3]{2x}}{z^3}$ **59.** $9w^2$ **60.** $\frac{t^4}{4}$ **61.** $\frac{\sqrt{14y}}{2y}$
62. $\frac{\sqrt{15w}}{3w}$ **63.** $\frac{4\sqrt[3]{3p}}{3p}$ **64.** $-\frac{\sqrt[3]{4x^2}}{x}$
65. $\sqrt{10} - \sqrt{15}$ **66.** $3\sqrt{5} - 3\sqrt{7}$ **67.** $\sqrt{t} + \sqrt{3}$
68. $\sqrt{w} + \sqrt{7}$ **69.** The quotient of the principal square root of 2 and the square of x
70. $\left\{\frac{49}{2}\right\}$ **71.** $\{31\}$ **72.** $\{-12\}$ **73.** $\{7\}$
74. $\{9\}$ **75.** { } (The value -2 does not check.)
76. $\left\{\frac{1}{2}, 4\right\}$ **77.** $\{-2\}$ (The value 2 does not check.)
78. $6\sqrt{5}$ m $\approx$ 13.4 m **79. a.** $v(20) \approx 25.3$ ft/sec. When the water depth is 20 ft, a wave travels about 25.3 ft/sec. **b.** 8 ft **80.** $a + bi$, where a and b are real numbers and $i = \sqrt{-1}$
81. $a + bi$, where $b \neq 0$
82. Multiply the numerator and denominator by $4 - 6i$, which is the complex conjugate of the denominator.
83. $4i$ **84.** $-i\sqrt{5}$ **85.** -15 **86.** $-2i$ **87.** -1
88. i **89.** $-i$ **90.** 0 **91.** $-5 + 5i$ **92.** $9 + 17i$
93. $25 + 0i$ **94.** $24 - 10i$
95. $-\frac{17}{4} + i$; real part: $-\frac{17}{4}$; imaginary part: 1
96. $-2 - i$; real part: -2; imaginary part: -1
97. $\frac{4}{13} - \frac{7}{13}i$ **98.** $3 + 4i$ **99.** $-\frac{3}{2} + \frac{5}{2}i$
100. $-\frac{4}{17} + \frac{16}{17}i$ **101.** $-\frac{2}{3} + \frac{\sqrt{10}}{6}i$ **102.** $2 - 4i$

Chapter 10 Test, pp. 775–776

1. a. 6 **b.** -6 **2. a.** Real **b.** Not real **c.** Real
d. Real **3. a.** y **b.** $|y|$ **4.** 3 **5.** $\frac{4}{3}$ **6.** $2\sqrt[3]{4}$
7. $a^2bc^2\sqrt{bc}$ **8.** $3x^2yz^2\sqrt{2xy}$ **9.** $4w^2\sqrt{w}$ **10.** $\frac{x^2}{5y}$
11. $\frac{3\sqrt{2}}{2}$ **12. a.** $f(-8) = 2\sqrt{3}$; $f(-6) = 2\sqrt{2}$; $f(-4) = 2$; $f(-2) = 0$ **b.** $(-\infty, -2]$ **13.** -0.3080
14. -3 **15.** $\frac{20x^2y^3}{z}$ **16.** $\sqrt[6]{7y^3}$ **17.** $\sqrt[12]{10}$
18. $3\sqrt{5}$ **19.** $3\sqrt{2x} - 3\sqrt{5x}$ **20.** $40 - 10\sqrt{5x} - 3x$
21. $\frac{-2\sqrt[3]{x^2}}{x}$ **22.** $\frac{x + 6 + 5\sqrt{x}}{9 - x}$ **23. a.** $2i\sqrt{2}$ **b.** $8i$
c. $\frac{1}{2} + \frac{\sqrt{2}}{2}i$ **24.** $1 - 11i$ **25.** $30 + 16i$ **26.** -28
27. $-33 - 56i$ **28.** 104 **29.** $\frac{17}{25} + \frac{6}{25}i$
30. $-\frac{15}{17} + \frac{9}{17}i$ **31.** $r(10) \approx 1.34$; the radius of a sphere of volume 10 cubic units is approximately 1.34 units.
32. 21 ft **33.** $\{-16\}$ **34.** $\left\{\frac{17}{5}\right\}$
35. $\{2\}$ (The value 42 does not check.)

Chapters 1–10 Cumulative Review Exercises, pp. 776–777

1. 54 **2.** $15x - 5y - 5$ **3.** $\{-3\}$ **4.** $(-\infty, -5)$
5. $[-9, -3)$ **6.** { } **7.** $y = -2x + 5$ **8.** $x = -5$
9. $\left\{\left(\frac{1}{2}, \frac{1}{3}\right)\right\}$ **10.** $\left(2, -2, \frac{1}{2}\right)$ is not a solution.
11. Together it will take them $1\frac{7}{8}$ hr.

12. a. $f(-2) = -10$; $f(0) = -2$; $f(4) = 14$; $f\left(\frac{1}{2}\right) = 0$
b. $(-2, -10), (0, -2), (4, 14), \left(\frac{1}{2}, 0\right)$
c.

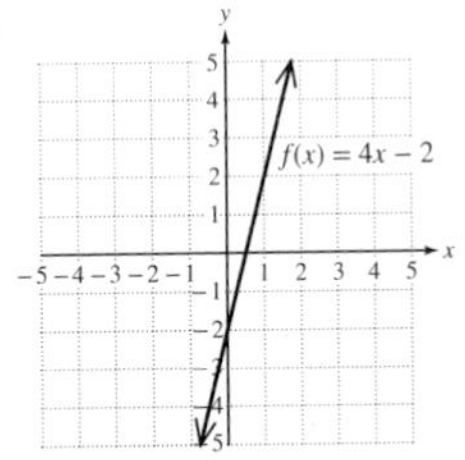

13. $a^6b^{12}c^4$ **14. a.** 1.4×10^{-4} **b.** 3.14×10^9
15. $2x^2 - x - 15$; 2nd degree **16.** $\sqrt{15} + 3\sqrt{2} + 3$
17. $x - 4$ **18.** $-\frac{1}{6}$ **19.** $\frac{3c\sqrt[3]{2}}{d}$ **20.** $32b\sqrt{5b}$
21. $2 + 3i$ **22.** $\{10\}$ **23.** $\frac{x - 15}{x(x+5)(x-5)}$
24. $\frac{-1}{(2a+1)(a+2)}$ **25.** $-14x^2 + 26x - 17$
26. $2\sqrt{3} + 2\sqrt{5}$ **27.** $\frac{6}{17} + \frac{10}{17}i$ **28.** $\left\{\frac{7}{6}, -\frac{3}{2}\right\}$
29. $(x + 3 - y)(x + 3 + y)$ **30.** $(x^2 + 2)(x^4 - 2x^2 + 4)$

Chapter 11

Section 11.1 Practice Exercises, pp. 786–789

1. a. 0; 0 **b.** 0 **c.** $\sqrt{k}; -\sqrt{k}$ **d.** 2; $\{3, -3\}$ **e.** completing **f.** 100 **g.** 4; 1 **h.** 8
3. $\{\pm 2\}$ **5.** $\{\pm\sqrt{7}\}$ **7.** $\left\{\frac{11}{6}, -\frac{11}{6}\right\}$ **9.** $\{\pm 5i\}$
11. $\{-1, -5\}$ **13.** $\left\{\frac{-3 \pm \sqrt{7}}{2}\right\}$ **15.** $\{-5 \pm 3i\sqrt{2}\}$
17. $\left\{\pm\frac{\sqrt{33}}{3}\right\}$ **19.** $\left\{-\frac{4}{5} \pm \frac{\sqrt{3}}{5}i\right\}$ **21.** $\{4i, -4i\}$
23. 1. Factoring and applying the zero product rule. 2. Applying the square root property. $\{\pm 6\}$ **25. a.** $\{16\}$ **b.** $\{2, -2\}$
27. $n = 9$; $(x - 3)^2$ **29.** $n = 16$; $(t + 4)^2$
31. $n = \frac{1}{4}$; $\left(c - \frac{1}{2}\right)^2$ **33.** $n = \frac{25}{4}$; $\left(y + \frac{5}{2}\right)^2$
35. $n = \frac{1}{25}$; $\left(b + \frac{1}{5}\right)^2$ **37.** $n = \frac{1}{9}$; $\left(p - \frac{1}{3}\right)^2$
39. 1. Divide both sides by a to make the leading coefficient 1. 2. Isolate the variable terms on one side of the equation. 3. Complete the square. 4. Apply the square root property and solve for x.
41. $\{-3, -5\}$ **43.** $\{-3 \pm i\sqrt{7}\}$ **45.** $\{-2 \pm i\sqrt{2}\}$
47. $\{5, -2\}$ **49.** $\left\{-1 \pm \frac{\sqrt{6}}{2}i\right\}$ **51.** $\left\{2 \pm \frac{2}{3}i\right\}$
53. $\left\{\frac{1}{5} \pm \frac{\sqrt{3}}{5}\right\}$ **55.** $\left\{-\frac{3}{4} \pm \frac{\sqrt{65}}{4}\right\}$ **57.** $\{2 \pm \sqrt{11}\}$
59. $\{1, -7\}$ **61. a.** $t = \frac{\sqrt{d}}{4}$ **b.** 8 sec
63. $r = \sqrt{\frac{A}{\pi}}$ or $r = \frac{\sqrt{A\pi}}{\pi}$ **65.** $a = \sqrt{d^2 - b^2 - c^2}$
67. $r = \sqrt{\frac{3V}{\pi h}}$ or $r = \frac{\sqrt{3V\pi h}}{\pi h}$ **69.** The shelf extends 4.2 ft.
71. The sides are 7.1 in. **73. a.** 4.5 thousand textbooks or 35.5 thousand textbooks **b.** Profit increases to a point as more books are produced. Beyond that point, the market is "flooded," and profit decreases. There are two points at which the profit is \$20,000. Producing 4.5 thousand books makes the same profit using fewer resources as producing 35.5 thousand books.

Section 11.2 Practice Exercises, pp. 800–803

1. a. quadratic; $\frac{-b \pm \sqrt{b^2 - 4ac}}{2a}$ **b.** $ax^2 + bx + c = 0$
c. 8; −42; −27 **d.** 7; 97 **e.** $b^2 - 4ac$; discriminant **f.** imaginary **g.** real **h.** less than
3. $4 - 2\sqrt{5}$ **5.** $2 - i\sqrt{3}$ **7.** linear **9.** $\{-12, 1\}$
11. $\left\{\frac{1}{9} \pm \frac{2\sqrt{11}}{9}i\right\}$ **13.** $\left\{\frac{1}{6} \pm \frac{\sqrt{14}}{6}i\right\}$ **15.** $\{7, -5\}$
17. $\left\{\frac{-3 \pm \sqrt{41}}{2}\right\}$ **19.** $\left\{\frac{2}{5}\right\}$ **21.** $\{3 \pm i\sqrt{5}\}$
23. $\left\{\frac{1 \pm \sqrt{29}}{2}\right\}$ **25.** $\left\{\frac{-1 \pm \sqrt{13}}{4}\right\}$
27. $\left\{-\frac{2}{3} \pm \frac{2\sqrt{2}}{3}i\right\}$ **29.** $\left\{\frac{-5 \pm \sqrt{13}}{2}\right\}$
31. $\{-2, -4\}$ **33.** $\left\{\frac{-7 \pm \sqrt{109}}{6}\right\}$
35. a. $(x - 3)(x^2 + 3x + 9)$ **b.** $\left\{3, -\frac{3}{2} \pm \frac{3\sqrt{3}}{2}i\right\}$
37. a. $3x(x^2 - 2x + 2)$ **b.** $\{0, 1 \pm i\}$ **39.** The length of each side is 3 ft. **41.** The legs are approximately 1.6 in. and 3.6 in.
43. The legs are approximately 8.2 m and 6.1 m.
45. a. Approximately 4.5 fatalities per 100 million miles driven
b. Approximately 1 fatality per 100 million miles driven
c. Approximately 4.2 fatalities per 100 million miles driven
d. For drivers 26 yr old and 71 yr old
47. The times are $\frac{3 + \sqrt{5}}{2}$ sec ≈ 2.62 sec or $\frac{3 - \sqrt{5}}{2}$ sec ≈ 0.38 sec. **49. a.** $x^2 + 2x + 1 = 0$
b. 0 **c.** 1 rational solution **51. a.** $19m^2 - 8m + 0 = 0$ **b.** 64
c. 2 rational solutions **53. a.** $5p^2 + 0p - 21 = 0$ **b.** 420
c. 2 irrational solutions **55. a.** $n^2 + 3n + 4 = 0$ **b.** −7
c. 2 imaginary solutions **57.** Discriminant: 16; two x-intercepts
59. Discriminant: 0; one x-intercept
61. Discriminant: −39; no x-intercepts
63. x-intercepts: $\left(\frac{5 + \sqrt{13}}{2}, 0\right), \left(\frac{5 - \sqrt{13}}{2}, 0\right)$; y-intercept: (0, 3) **65.** x-intercepts: none; y-intercept: (0, −1)
67. x-intercepts: $\left(\frac{-5 - \sqrt{41}}{4}, 0\right), \left(\frac{-5 + \sqrt{41}}{4}, 0\right)$; y-intercept: (0, −2) **69.** $\{-1 \pm 3i\}$
71. $\left\{-\frac{1}{3}, 6\right\}$ **73.** $\left\{\frac{5}{2} \pm \frac{3\sqrt{2}}{2}i\right\}$ **75.** $\left\{-\frac{1}{2} \pm 2i\right\}$
77. $\left\{\frac{3 \pm \sqrt{7}}{2}\right\}$ **79.** $\{1 \pm 3i\sqrt{2}\}$ **81.** $\{2 \pm \sqrt{2}\}$
83. $\left\{-\frac{1}{8}, \frac{3}{4}\right\}$ **85.** $\left\{\pm\frac{\sqrt{21}}{2}\right\}$
87. a. $\{-3 \pm \sqrt{14}\}$ **b.** $\{-3 \pm \sqrt{14}\}$ **c.** Answers will vary

Section 11.2 Graphing Calculator Exercises, p. 803

89.

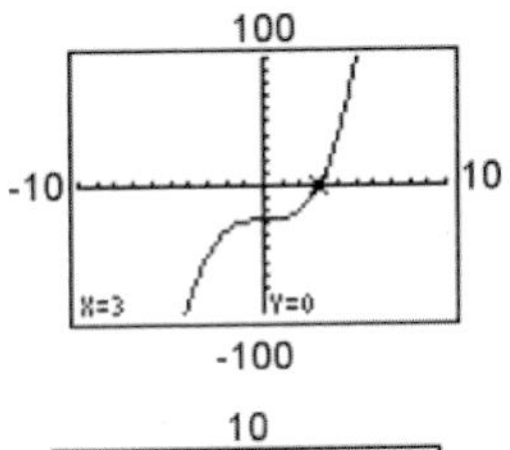

90.

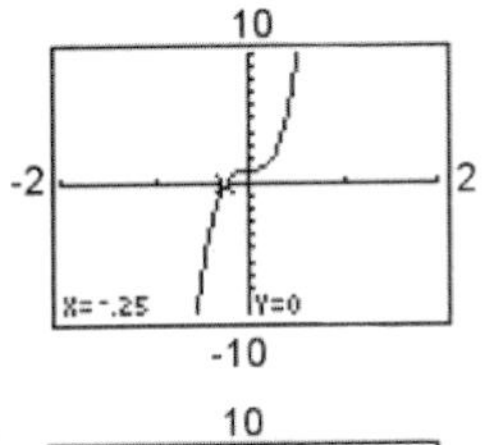

91.

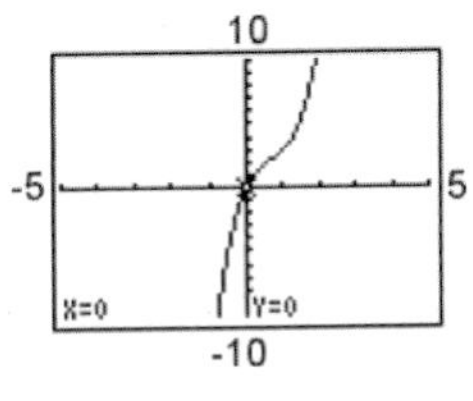

92.

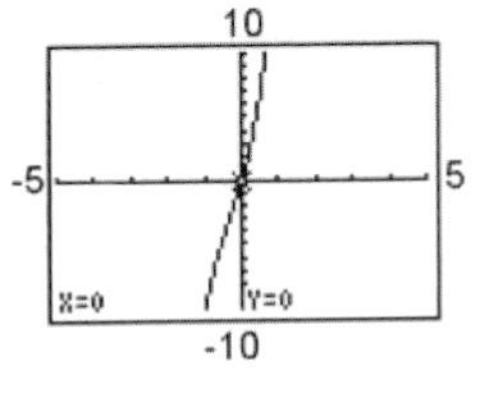

Section 11.3 Practice Exercises, pp. 807–809

1. a. quadratic **b.** $3x - 1$ **c.** $p^{1/3}$
3. $\left\{\frac{3}{2} \pm \frac{\sqrt{7}}{2}\right\}$ **5.** $\{-4\}$ **7.** $\{2 \pm \sqrt{26}\}$
9. a. $\{-4, -6\}$ **b.** $\{-4, -1, -2, -3\}$
11. $\{1 \pm i\sqrt{2}, 1 \pm \sqrt{2}\}$ **13.** $\{5, -1, 2\}$ **15.** $\{27, -8\}$
17. $\left\{-\frac{1}{32}, -243\right\}$ **19.** $\{4\}$ (The value 64 does not check.)
21. $\left\{\frac{1}{4}\right\}$ (The value 4 does not check.)
23. $\{-7\}$ **25.** $\{16\}$; yes **27.** $\{\pm 3i, \pm\sqrt{5}\}$
29. $\left\{\pm\frac{\sqrt{3}}{2}, \pm i\sqrt{5}\right\}$ **31.** $\left\{\frac{-5 \pm \sqrt{13}}{2}\right\}$
33. $\left\{\frac{9 \pm \sqrt{73}}{4}\right\}$ **35.** $\{2 \pm \sqrt{3}\}$ **37.** $\{\pm 2, \pm 2i\}$
39. $\left\{-\frac{7}{4}, -\frac{3}{2}\right\}$ **41.** $\left\{\frac{1}{2}, -\frac{1}{2}, \sqrt{2}, -\sqrt{2}\right\}$
43. $\left\{2, 1, -1 \pm i\sqrt{3}, -\frac{1}{2} \pm \frac{\sqrt{3}}{2}i\right\}$ **45.** $\{5, 4\}$ **47.** $\{0, 2\}$
49. $\left\{1, \frac{17}{2}\right\}$ **51.** $\{64, -125\}$ **53.** $\{\pm\sqrt{2}, \pm 2i\}$
55. $\{\pm 4i, 1\}$ **57.** $\{4, \pm i\sqrt{5}\}$ **59.** $\left\{\frac{8}{3}, 2\right\}$

Section 11.3 Graphing Calculator Exercises, p. 809

61. a. $\{\pm i\sqrt{2}\}$ **b.** Two imaginary solutions; no real solutions
c. No x-intercepts
d.
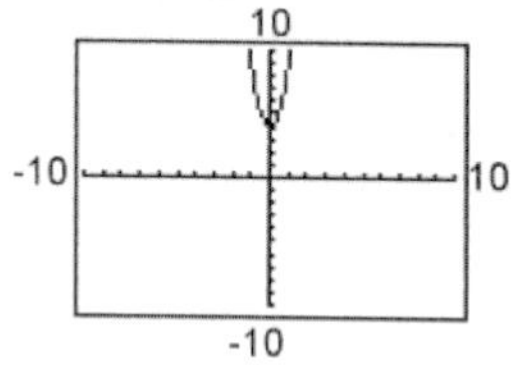

62. a. $\{1, -1\}$ **b.** Two real solutions; no imaginary solutions
c. Two x-intercepts
d.
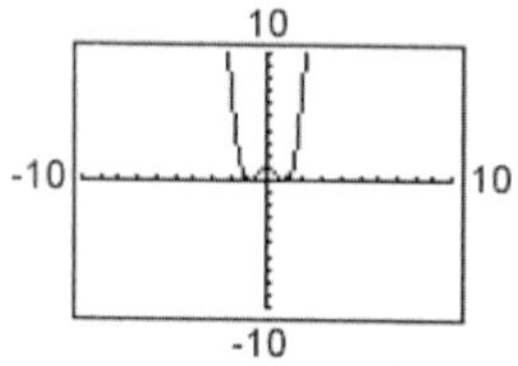

63. a. $\{0, 3, -2\}$ **b.** Three real solutions; no imaginary solutions
c. Three x-intercepts
d.
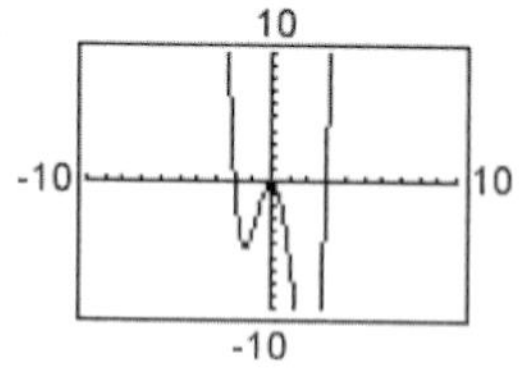

64. a. $\{\pm 1, \pm 3\}$ **b.** Four real solutions; no imaginary solutions
c. Four x-intercepts
d.
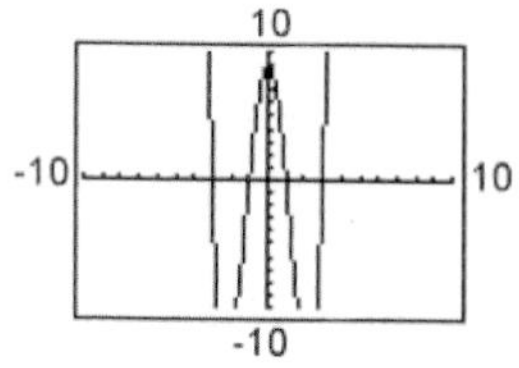

Chapter 11 Problem Recognition Exercises, pp. 809–810

1. $\{-5 \pm \sqrt{22}\}$ **2.** $\{8 \pm \sqrt{59}\}$ **3.** $\left\{-\frac{1}{6} \pm \frac{\sqrt{47}}{6}i\right\}$
4. $\left\{-\frac{3}{8} \pm \frac{\sqrt{71}}{8}i\right\}$ **5. a.** Quadratic **b.** $\{2, -7\}$
6. a. Quadratic **b.** $\{4, 5\}$ **7. a.** Quadratic form **b.** $\{-3, -1, 1, 3\}$ **8. a.** Quadratic form **b.** $\{2, -2, i, -i\}$
9. a. Quadratic form (or radical) **b.** $\{16\}$ (The value 1 does not check.) **10. a.** Quadratic **b.** $\left\{\frac{9 \pm \sqrt{89}}{2}\right\}$
11. a. Linear **b.** $\{4\}$ **12. a.** Linear **b.** $\{-1\}$
13. a. Quadratic **b.** $\{\pm i\sqrt{2}\}$ **14. a.** Quadratic **b.** $\{\pm i\sqrt{6}\}$ **15. a.** Rational **b.** $\{2, -1\}$
16. a. Rational **b.** $\{-2, 4\}$
17. a. Quadratic **b.** $\{10 \pm \sqrt{101}\}$
18. a. Quadratic **b.** $\{-9 \pm \sqrt{77}\}$
19. a. Quadratic **b.** $\left\{\frac{1 \pm \sqrt{17}}{2}\right\}$
20. a. Quadratic **b.** $\left\{\frac{1 \pm \sqrt{13}}{2}\right\}$
21. a. Radical **b.** $\{3\}$ (The value -1 does not check.)
22. a. Radical **b.** $\{6\}$ (The value -1 does not check.)
23. a. Quadratic form (or radical) **b.** $\{-125, 27\}$
24. a. Quadratic form (or radical) **b.** $\{-64, -1\}$

Section 11.4 Practice Exercises, pp. 819–823

1. a. parabola **b.** $>$; $<$ **c.** lowest; highest **d.** (h, k); upward; downward **e.** vertex; $x = h$
3. $\{3 \pm 2i\}$
5. $\left\{\frac{5 \pm \sqrt{10}}{5}\right\}$
7. $\{-27, -8\}$
9. The value of k shifts the graph of $f(x) = x^2$ vertically.

11.
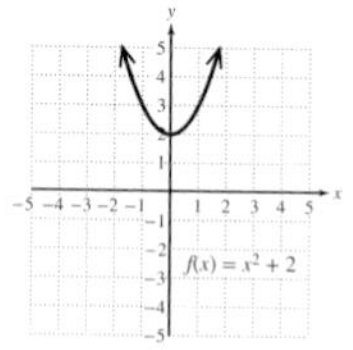

13.
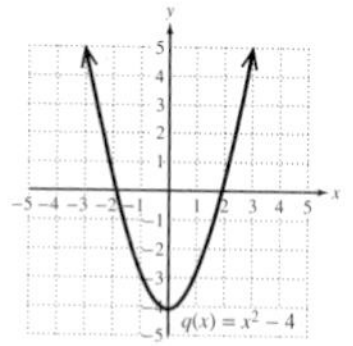

15.
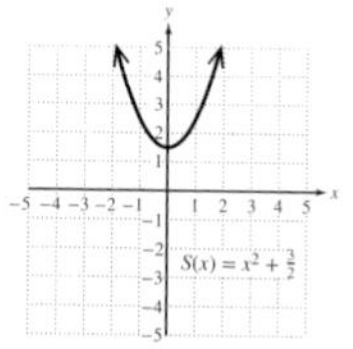

17.
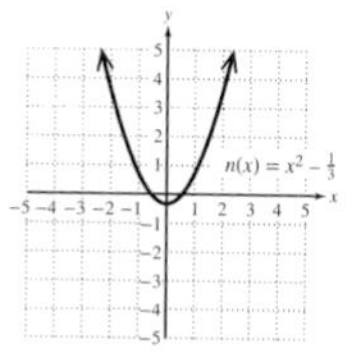

19.
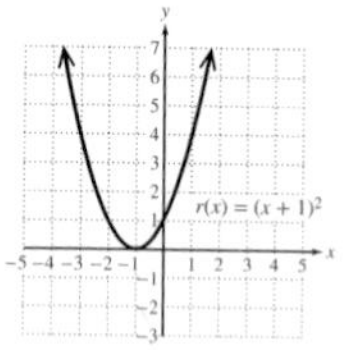

21.
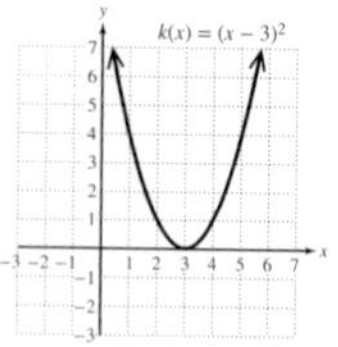

23.
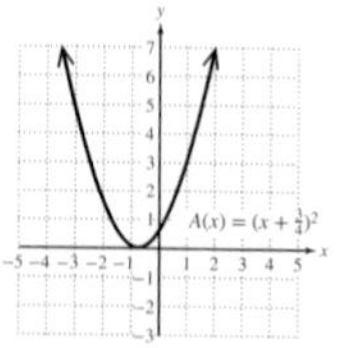

25.
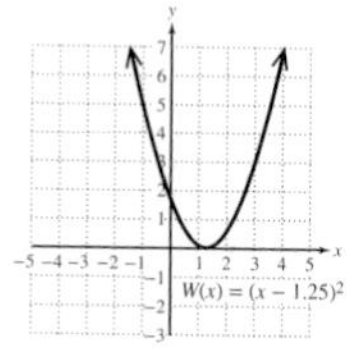

27. The value of a vertically stretches or shrinks the graph of $f(x) = x^2$.

29.
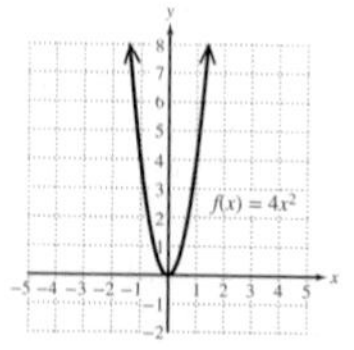

31.
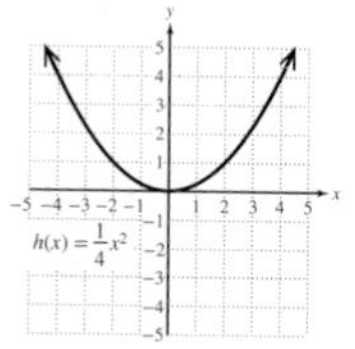

33.

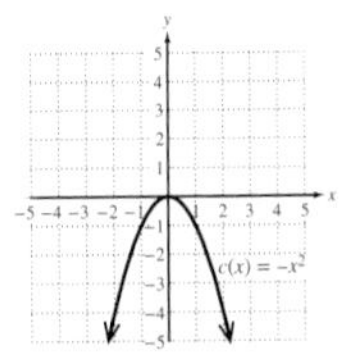

35.

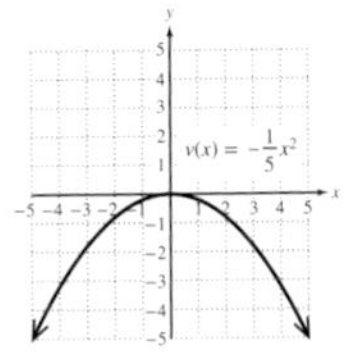

37. d **39.** g **41.** a **43.** e

45.

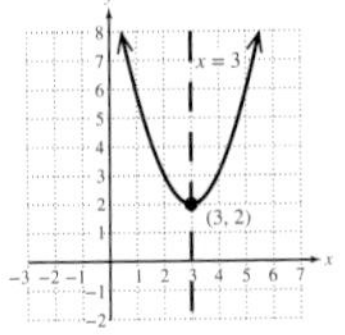

Domain: $(-\infty, \infty)$; range: $[2, \infty)$

47.

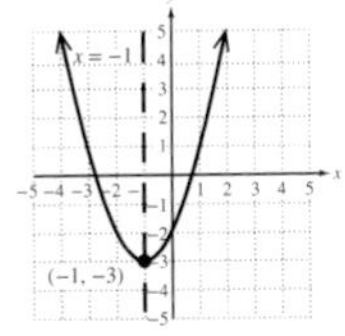

Domain: $(-\infty, \infty)$; range: $[-3, \infty)$

49.

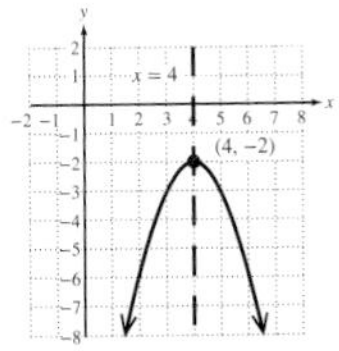

Domain: $(-\infty, \infty)$; range: $(-\infty, -2]$

51.

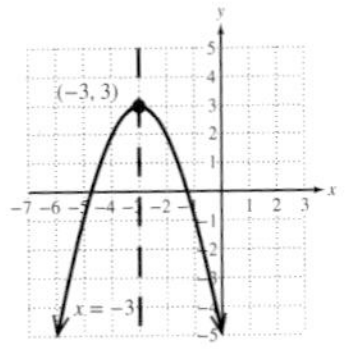

Domain: $(-\infty, \infty)$; range: $(-\infty, 3]$

53.

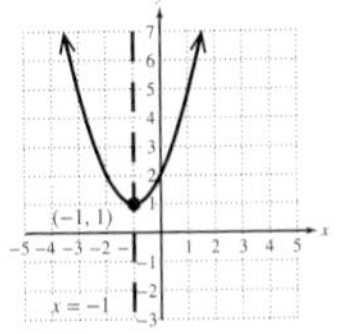

Domain: $(-\infty, \infty)$; range: $[1, \infty)$

55.

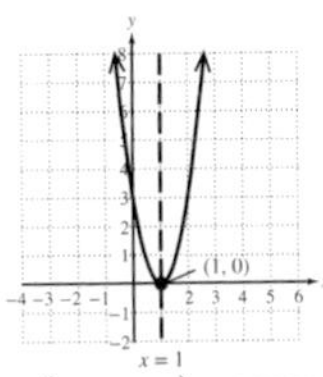

Domain: $(-\infty, \infty)$; range: $[0, \infty)$

57.

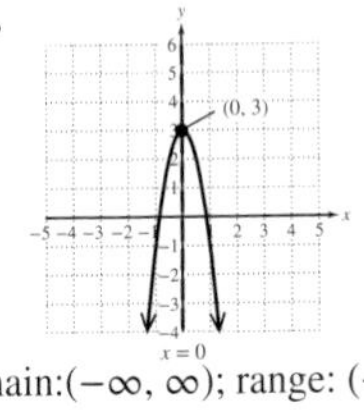

Domain: $(-\infty, \infty)$; range: $(-\infty, 3]$

59.

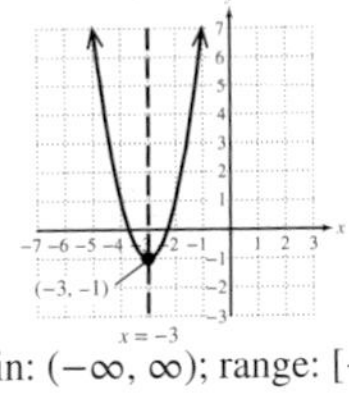

Domain: $(-\infty, \infty)$; range: $[-1, \infty)$

61.

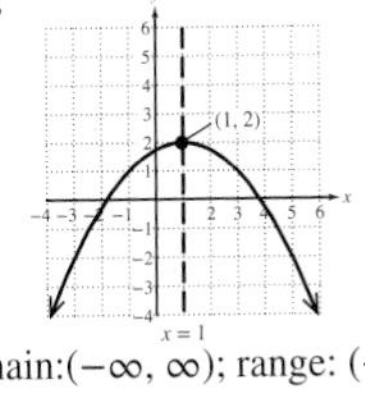

Domain: $(-\infty, \infty)$; range: $(-\infty, 2]$

63.

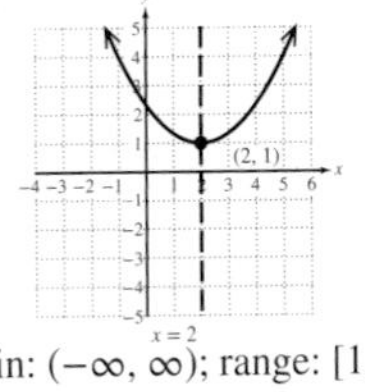

Domain: $(-\infty, \infty)$; range: $[1, \infty)$

65. a. $y = x^2 + 3$ is $y = x^2$ shifted up 3 units.
b. $y = (x + 3)^2$ is $y = x^2$ shifted left 3 units.
c. $y = 3x^2$ is $y = x^2$ with a vertical stretch.

67. Vertex $(6, -9)$; minimum point; minimum value: -9

69. Vertex $(2, 5)$; maximum point; maximum value: 5

71. Vertex $(-8, 0)$; minimum point; minimum value: 0

73. Vertex $\left(0, \frac{21}{4}\right)$; maximum point; maximum value: $\frac{21}{4}$

75. Vertex $\left(7, -\frac{3}{2}\right)$; minimum point; minimum value: $-\frac{3}{2}$

77. Vertex $(0, 0)$; minimum point; minimum value: 0

79. True **81.** False **83. a.** $(60, 30)$ **b.** 30 ft **c.** 70 ft

85. a. The fireworks will explode at a height of 150 ft.
b. Yes, because the ordered pair $(3, 150)$ is the vertex.

Section 11.5 Practice Exercises, pp. 830–834

1. a. $\frac{-b}{2a}; \frac{-b}{2a}$ **b.** True **c.** True **d.** True **e.** False

3. The graph of p is the graph of $y = x^2$ shrunk vertically by a factor of $\frac{1}{4}$.

5. The graph of r is the graph of $y = x^2$ shifted up 7 units.

7. The graph of t is the graph of $y = x^2$ shifted to the left 10 units.

9. $16; (x - 4)^2$ **11.** $\frac{49}{4}; \left(y + \frac{7}{2}\right)^2$

13. $\frac{1}{81}; \left(b + \frac{1}{9}\right)^2$ **15.** $\frac{1}{36}; \left(t - \frac{1}{6}\right)^2$

17. $g(x) = (x - 4)^2 - 11; (4, -11)$

19. $n(x) = 2(x + 3)^2 - 5; (-3, -5)$

21. $p(x) = -3(x - 1)^2 - 2; (1, -2)$

23. $k(x) = \left(x + \frac{7}{2}\right)^2 - \frac{89}{4}; \left(-\frac{7}{2}, -\frac{89}{4}\right)$

25. $F(x) = 5(x + 1)^2 - 4; (-1, -4)$

27. $P(x) = -2\left(x - \frac{1}{4}\right)^2 + \frac{1}{8}; \left(\frac{1}{4}, \frac{1}{8}\right)$ **29.** $(2, 3)$

31. $(-1, -2)$ **33.** $(-4, -15)$ **35.** $(-1, 2)$ **37.** $(1, 3)$

39. $\left(\frac{3}{2}, \frac{3}{4}\right)$ **41.** $(-4, -15)$ **43.** $(-1, 4)$

45. a. $(-1, -4)$ **b.** $(0, -3)$
c. $(1, 0), (-3, 0)$
d.

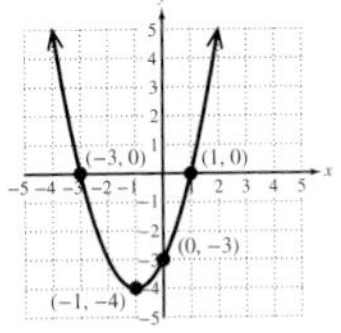

47. a. $\left(\frac{1}{2}, \frac{7}{2}\right)$ **b.** $(0, 4)$
c. No x-intercepts
d.

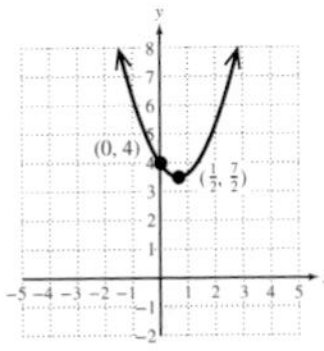

49. a. $\left(\frac{3}{2}, 0\right)$ **b.** $\left(0, -\frac{9}{4}\right)$
c. $\left(\frac{3}{2}, 0\right)$
d.

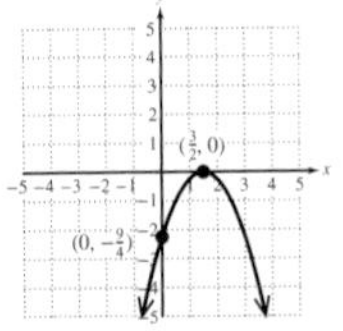

51. a. $(-1, 4)$ **b.** $(0, 3)$
c. $(1, 0), (-3, 0)$
d.

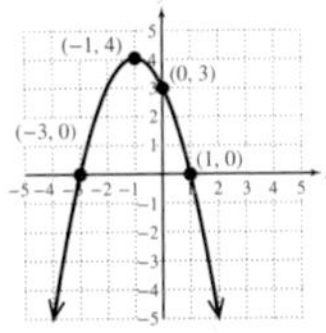

53. a. 164.25 ft **b.** 3.125 sec **55. a.** 45 mph **b.** 32 mpg

57. a. 48 hr **b.** 2 g **59.** $a = -9, b = 5, c = 4; y = -9x^2 + 5x + 4$

61. $a = 2, b = -1, c = -5; y = 2x^2 - x - 5$

63. $a = -3, b = 4, c = 0; y = -3x^2 + 4x$

65. a. The sum of the sides must equal the total amount of fencing.
b. $A = x(200 - 2x)$ **c.** 50 ft by 100 ft

Section 11.5 Graphing Calculator Exercises, p. 834

67.

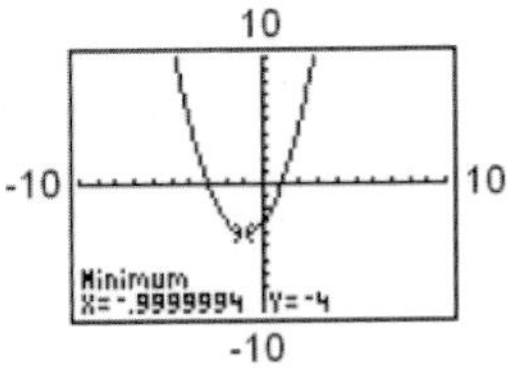

68.

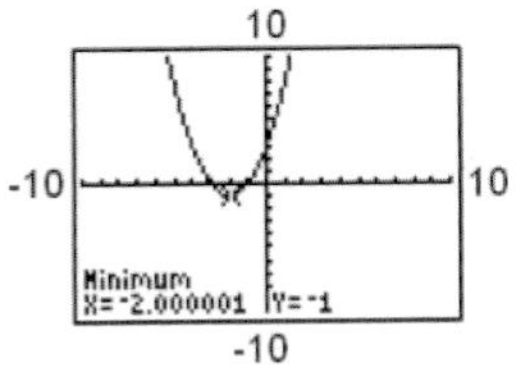

69.

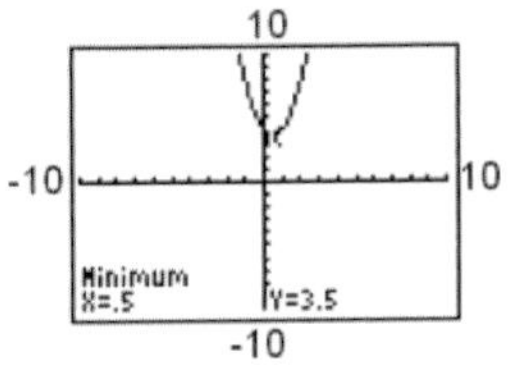

70.

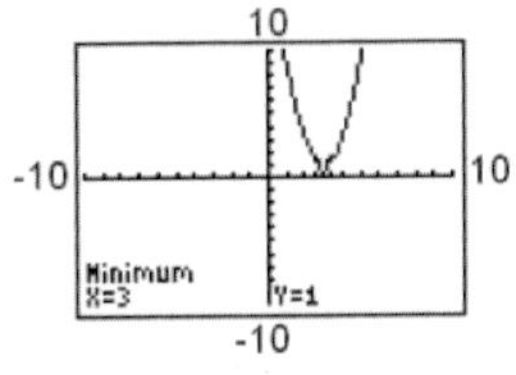

71.

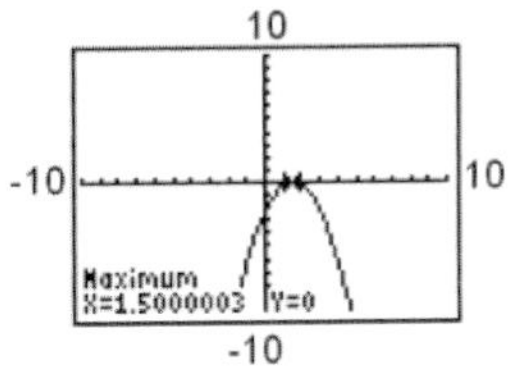

72.

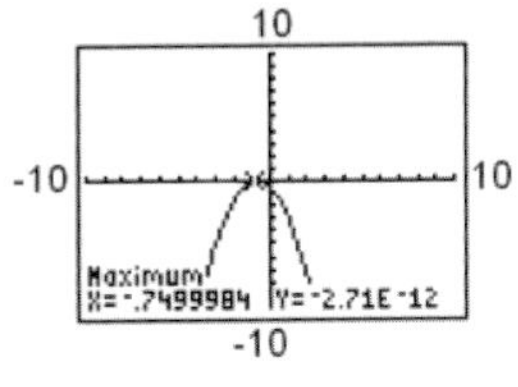

Chapter 11 Review Exercises, pp. 840–843

1. $\{\pm\sqrt{5}\}$ **2.** $\{\pm 2i\}$ **3.** $\{\pm 9\}$ **4.** $\left\{\pm\frac{\sqrt{57}}{3}i\right\}$

5. $\{2 \pm 6\sqrt{2}\}$ **6.** $\left\{\frac{5}{2} \pm \frac{3}{2}i\right\}$ **7.** $\left\{\frac{1 \pm \sqrt{3}}{3}\right\}$

8. $\{4 \pm \sqrt{5}\}$ **9.** $5\sqrt{3}$ in. ≈ 8.7 in. **10.** 9 in.
11. $5\sqrt{6}$ in. ≈ 12.2 in. **12.** $n = 64$; $(x + 8)^2$

13. $n = \frac{81}{4}$; $\left(x - \frac{9}{2}\right)^2$ **14.** $n = \frac{1}{16}$; $\left(y + \frac{1}{4}\right)^2$

15. $n = \frac{1}{25}$; $\left(z - \frac{1}{5}\right)^2$ **16.** $\{-2 \pm 3i\}$ **17.** $\{1 \pm \sqrt{6}\}$

18. $\{3 \pm 2\sqrt{3}\}$ **19.** $\{4 \pm 3i\}$ **20.** $\left\{\frac{1}{3}, -1\right\}$

21. $\left\{\frac{1}{2}, -4\right\}$ **22.** $r = \sqrt{\frac{V}{\pi h}}$ or $r = \frac{\sqrt{V\pi h}}{\pi h}$

23. $s = \sqrt{\frac{A}{6}}$ or $s = \frac{\sqrt{6A}}{6}$

24. There will be two imaginary solutions.
25. Two rational solutions **26.** Two rational solutions
27. Two irrational solutions **28.** Two imaginary solutions
29. One rational solution **30.** Two imaginary solutions

31. $\{2 \pm \sqrt{3}\}$ **32.** $\left\{\frac{5}{2} \pm \frac{5\sqrt{3}}{2}i\right\}$ **33.** $\left\{2, -\frac{5}{6}\right\}$

34. $\left\{2, \frac{4}{3}\right\}$ **35.** $\left\{\frac{4}{5}, -\frac{1}{5}\right\}$ **36.** $\left\{\frac{1}{10}, -\frac{1}{2}\right\}$

37. $\{2 \pm 2i\sqrt{7}\}$ **38.** $\{4 \pm \sqrt{6}\}$ **39.** $\left\{\frac{2 \pm \sqrt{22}}{3}\right\}$

40. $\{8, -2\}$ **41.** $\{-7 \pm \sqrt{3}\}$ **42.** $\{-1 \pm \sqrt{11}\}$
43. a. 1822 ft **b.** 115 ft/sec **44. a.** $\approx 53{,}939$ thousand **b.** 2021 **45.** The dimensions are approximately 3.1 ft by 7.2 ft. **46.** The distance between Lincoln and Omaha is approximately 50 mi. **47.** $\{49\}$ (The value 9 does not check.)

48. $\{4, 16\}$ **49.** $\{\pm 3, \pm\sqrt{2}\}$ **50.** $\left\{\pm\frac{\sqrt{6}}{2}, \pm i\right\}$

51. $\{-243, 32\}$ **52.** $\{32, 1\}$ **53.** $\{3 \pm \sqrt{10}\}$

54. $\left\{\frac{1 \pm \sqrt{181}}{6}\right\}$ **55.** $\{\pm 3i, \pm i\sqrt{3}\}$ **56.** $\{\pm\sqrt{7}, \pm 2\}$

57.

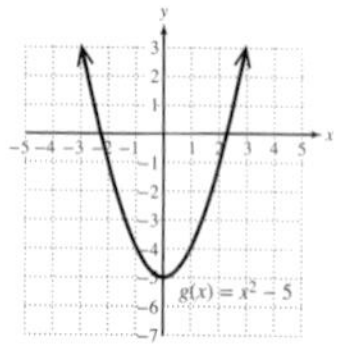

Domain: $(-\infty, \infty)$; range: $[-5, \infty)$

58.

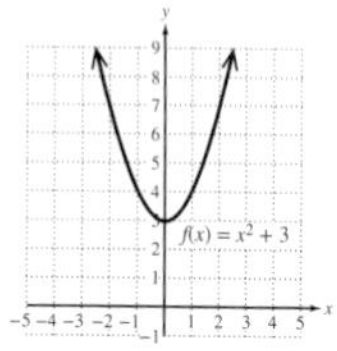

Domain: $(-\infty, \infty)$; range: $[3, \infty)$

59.

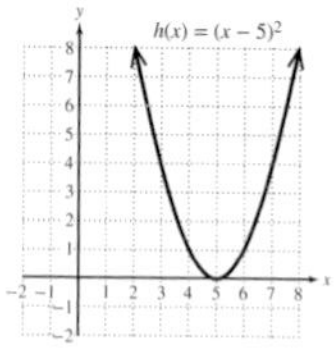

Domain: $(-\infty, \infty)$; range: $[0, \infty)$

60.

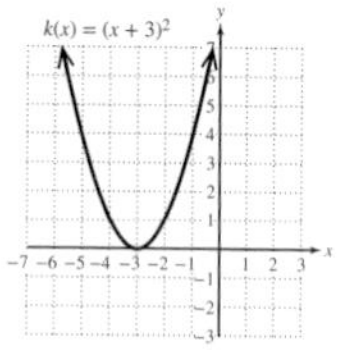

Domain: $(-\infty, \infty)$; range: $[0, \infty)$

61.

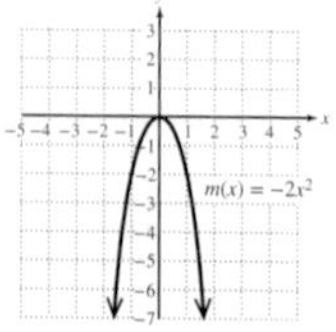

Domain: $(-\infty, \infty)$; range: $(-\infty, 0]$

62.

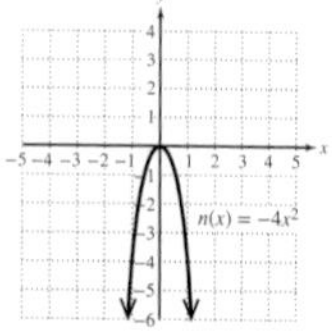

Domain: $(-\infty, \infty)$; range: $(-\infty, 0]$

63.

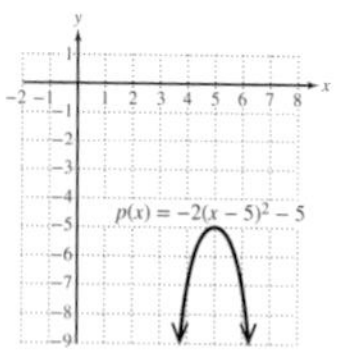

Domain: $(-\infty, \infty)$; range: $(-\infty, -5]$

64.

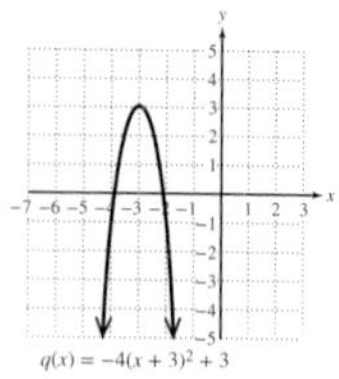

Domain: $(-\infty, \infty)$; range: $(-\infty, 3]$

65. $\left(4, \frac{5}{3}\right)$ is the minimum point. The minimum value is $\frac{5}{3}$.

66. $\left(1, -\frac{1}{7}\right)$ is the maximum point. The maximum value is $-\frac{1}{7}$.

67. $x = -\frac{2}{11}$ **68.** $x = \frac{3}{16}$

69. $z(x) = (x - 3)^2 - 2$; $(3, -2)$
70. $b(x) = (x - 2)^2 - 48$; $(2, -48)$
71. $p(x) = -5(x + 1)^2 - 8$; $(-1, -8)$
72. $q(x) = -3(x + 4)^2 - 6$; $(-4, -6)$ **73.** $(1, -15)$

74. $(-1, 7)$ **75.** $\left(\frac{1}{2}, \frac{41}{4}\right)$ **76.** $\left(-\frac{1}{3}, -\frac{22}{3}\right)$

77. a. $(2, -3)$ **b.** $(0, 0)$, $(4, 0)$
c.

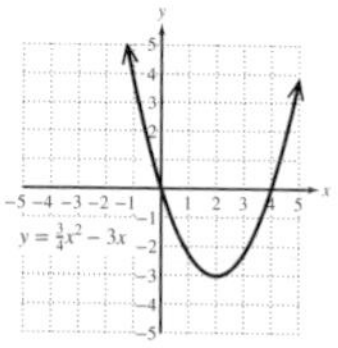

78. a. $(-2, 4)$ **b.** $(0, 0)$, $(-4, 0)$
c.

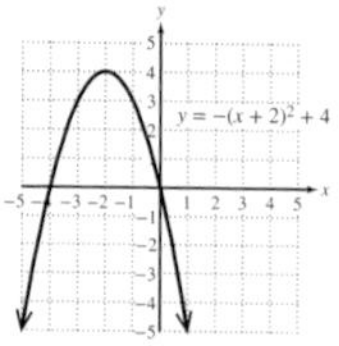

79. a. 3 sec **b.** 144 ft **80. a.** 150 meals **b.** \$1200
81. $a = 1, b = 4, c = -1$; $y = x^2 + 4x - 1$
82. $a = 1, b = -1, c = 6$; $y = x^2 - x + 6$

Chapter 11 Test, pp. 843–844

1. $\{2, -8\}$ **2.** $\{2 \pm 2\sqrt{3}\}$ **3.** $\{-1 \pm i\}$

4. $n = \frac{121}{4}$; $\left(d + \frac{11}{2}\right)^2$ **5.** $\{-3 \pm 3\sqrt{3}\}$

6. $\left\{\frac{3}{4} \pm \frac{\sqrt{47}}{4}i\right\}$ **7. a.** $x^2 - 3x + 12 = 0$
b. $a = 1, b = -3, c = 12$ **c.** -39 **d.** Two imaginary solutions
8. a. $y^2 - 2y + 1 = 0$ **b.** $a = 1, b = -2, c = 1$ **c.** 0 **d.** One rational solution

9. $\left\{1, \frac{1}{3}\right\}$ **10.** $\left\{\frac{-7 \pm \sqrt{5}}{2}\right\}$ **11.** The height is approximately 4.6 ft and the base is 6.2 ft. **12.** The radius is approximately 12.0 ft. **13.** $\{9\}$ (The value 4 does not check.) **14.** $\{8, -64\}$ **15.** $\left\{\frac{11}{3}, 6\right\}$

16. $\{\pm\sqrt{6}, \pm 3\}$ **17.** $\left\{\frac{5 \pm \sqrt{57}}{2}\right\}$ **18.** $\left\{5, -\frac{1}{2}\right\}$

19. $\{4 \pm \sqrt{15}\}$ **20.** $\{-7 \pm 2i\sqrt{6}\}$ **21.** $\{6 \pm \sqrt{23}\}$
22. The vertex is $(3, -17)$.

23.

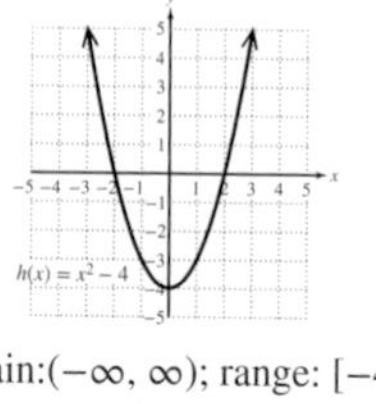

Domain: $(-\infty, \infty)$; range: $[-4, \infty)$

24.

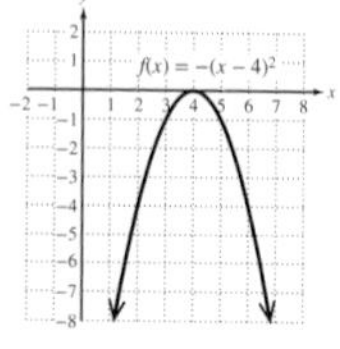

Domain: $(-\infty, \infty)$; range: $(-\infty, 0]$

25.

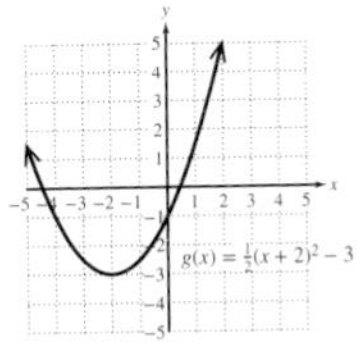

Domain: $(-\infty, \infty)$; range: $[-3, \infty)$

26. The rocket will hit the ground 256 ft away. **27. a.** 1320 million **b.** 1999 **28.** The graph of $y = x^2 - 2$ is the graph of $y = x^2$ shifted down 2 units. **29.** The graph of $y = (x + 3)^2$ is the graph of $y = x^2$ shifted 3 units to the left. **30.** The graph of $y = -4x^2$ is the graph of $y = 4x^2$ opening downward instead of upward. **31. a.** $(4, 2)$ **b.** Downward **c.** Maximum point **d.** The maximum value is 2. **e.** $x = 4$ **32. a.** $g(x) = 2(x - 5)^2 + 1$; $(5, 1)$ **b.** $(5, 1)$ **33. a.** $f(x) = (x + 2)^2 - 16$. **b.** Vertex: $(-2, -16)$ **c.** x-intercepts: $(-6, 0)$ and $(2, 0)$; y-intercept: $(0, -12)$ **d.** The minimum value is -16. **e.** $x = -2$

34. a. 200 ft **b.** 20,000 ft^2

Chapters 1–11 Cumulative Review Exercises, pp. 844–846

1. a. $\{2, 4, 6, 8, 10, 12, 16\}$ **b.** $\{2, 8\}$ **2.** $-3x^2 - 13x + 1$ **3.** -16 **4.** 1.8×10^{10} **5. a.** $(x + 2)(x + 3)(x - 3)$ **b.** Quotient: $x^2 + 5x + 6$; remainder: 0 **6.** $x - 2$

7. $\dfrac{2\sqrt{2x}}{x}$ **8.** \$8000 in 12% account; \$2000 in 3% account

9. $\{(8, 7)\}$ **10. a.** 720 ft **b.** 720 ft **c.** 12 sec

11. $\{3 \pm 4i\}$ **12.** $\left\{\dfrac{-5 \pm \sqrt{33}}{4}\right\}$ **13.** $n = 25$; $(x + 5)^2$

14. $2(x + 5)(x^2 - 5x + 25)$

15.

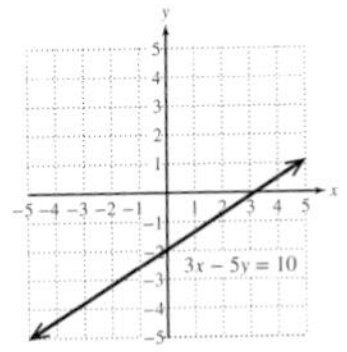

16. a. $\left(\frac{5}{2}, 0\right)$, $(2, 0)$ **b.** $(0, 10)$ **17.** The domain element 3 has more than one corresponding range element.

18.

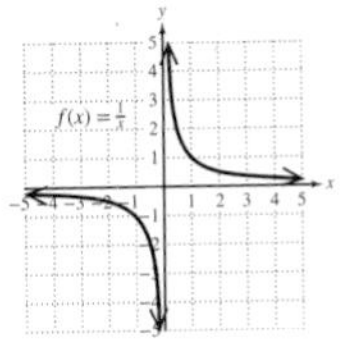

19. $y = 39$ **20. a.** Linear **b.** $(0, 300{,}000)$. If there are no passengers, the airport runs 300,000 flights per year. (These flights are cargo flights only.) **c.** $m = 0.008$ or $m = \frac{8}{1000}$. There are eight additional flights per 1000 passengers.

21. a. $[-4, \infty)$ **b.** $(-\infty, \infty)$

22. a. $(-\infty, 2]$ **b.** $(-\infty, 4]$ **c.** 4 **d.** 3 **e.** $x = -1$

23. $\left\{\dfrac{1}{18}, \dfrac{1}{2}\right\}$ **24.** $f = \dfrac{pq}{p + q}$ **25.** $\{7\}$

26. $\dfrac{y + 1}{y - 3}$ **27. a.** $(3, 1)$ **b.** Upward **c.** $(0, 19)$ **d.** No x-intercept

e.

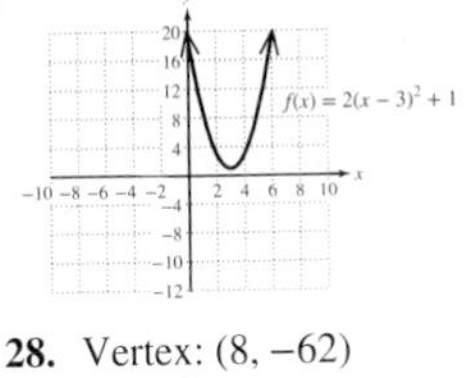

28. Vertex: $(8, -62)$

Chapter 12

Section 12.1 Practice Exercises, pp. 854–857

1. a. $\{(2, 1), (3, 2), (4, 3)\}$ **b.** one-to-one; y **c.** is not **d.** is **e.** $y = x$ **f.** x; x **g.** f^{-1} **h.** (b, a) **3.** Yes **5.** No **7.** Yes **9.** $g^{-1} = \{(5, 3), (1, 8), (9, -3), (2, 0)\}$ **11.** $r^{-1} = \{(3, a), (6, b), (9, c)\}$ **13.** The function is not one-to-one. **15.** Yes **17.** No **19.** Yes

21. a. $(f \circ g)(x) = 6\left(\dfrac{x - 1}{6}\right) + 1 = x$

b. $(g \circ f)(x) = \dfrac{(6x + 1) - 1}{6} = x$

23. a. $(f \circ g)(x) = \dfrac{\sqrt[3]{8x^3}}{2} = x$ **b.** $(g \circ f)(x) = 8\left(\dfrac{\sqrt[3]{x}}{2}\right)^3 = x$

25. a. $(f \circ g)(x) = (\sqrt{x - 1})^2 + 1 = x$ **b.** $(g \circ f)(x) = \sqrt{(x^2 + 1) - 1} = x$ **27.** $h^{-1}(x) = x - 4$ **29.** $m^{-1}(x) = 3(x + 2)$ **31.** $p^{-1}(x) = -x + 10$

33. $n^{-1}(x) = \dfrac{5x - 2}{3}$ **35.** $h^{-1}(x) = \dfrac{3x + 1}{4}$

37. $f^{-1}(x) = \sqrt[3]{x - 1}$ **39.** $g^{-1}(x) = \dfrac{x^3 + 1}{2}$

41. $g^{-1}(x) = \sqrt{x - 9}$

43. a. 1.2192 m, 15.24 m **b.** $f^{-1}(x) = \dfrac{x}{0.3048}$ **c.** 4921.3 ft

45. False **47.** True **49.** False **51.** True **53.** $(b, 0)$

55. a. Domain: $[1, \infty)$, range: $[0, \infty)$ **b.** Domain: $[0, \infty)$, range: $[1, \infty)$ **57. a.** $[-4, 0]$ **b.** $[0, 2]$ **c.** $[0, 2]$ **d.** $[-4, 0]$

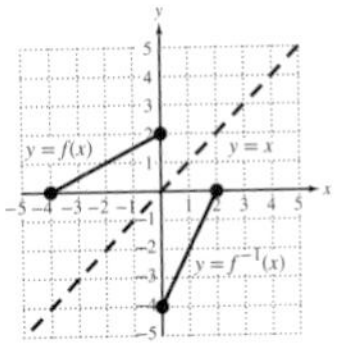

59. a. $[0, 2]$ **b.** $[0, 4]$ **c.** $[0, 4]$ **d.** $[0, 2]$

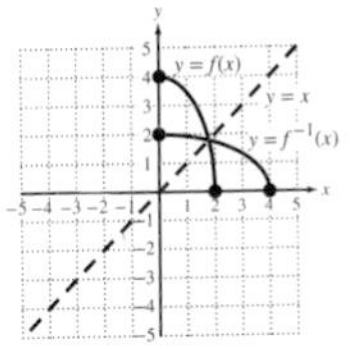

61. $q^{-1}(x) = x^2 - 4, x \geq 0$ **63.** $z^{-1}(x) = x^2 - 4, x \leq 0$

65. $f^{-1}(x) = \dfrac{x + 1}{1 - x}$ **67.** $t^{-1}(x) = \dfrac{x + 2}{x}$

69. $n^{-1}(x) = -\sqrt{x - 9}$

Section 12.1 Graphing Calculator Exercises, p. 857

71. $f^{-1}(x) = x^3 - 5$

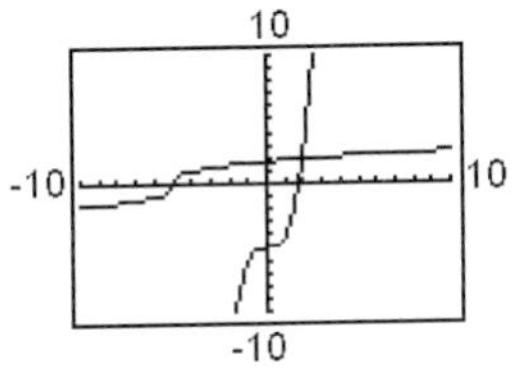

72. $k^{-1}(x) = \sqrt[3]{x + 4}$

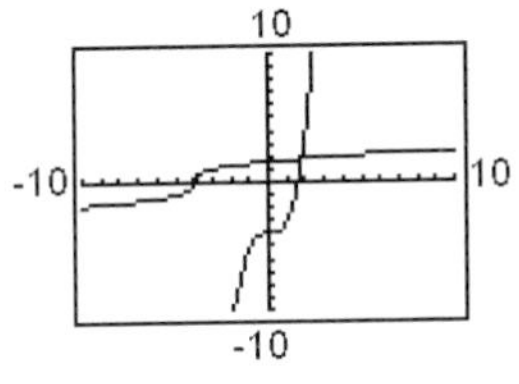

73. $g^{-1}(x) = \sqrt[3]{2x + 4}$

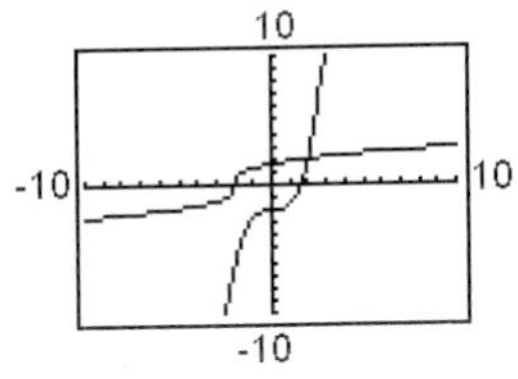

74. $m^{-1}(x) = \dfrac{x + 4}{3}$

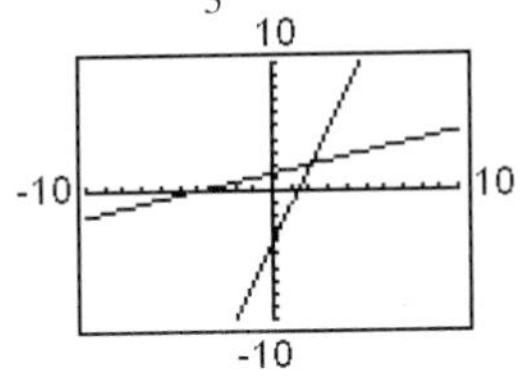

Section 12.2 Practice Exercises, pp. 863–866

1. a. b^x **b.** is not; is **c.** increasing **d.** decreasing **e.** $(-\infty, \infty)$; $(0, \infty)$ **f.** $(0, 1)$ **g.** $y = 0$ **h.** is not

3. $-2x^2 + 2x - 3$ **5.** $\dfrac{3x-1}{2x^2+x+2}$ **7.** $6x^2 + 3x + 5$

9. 25 **11.** $\dfrac{1}{1000}$ **13.** 6 **15.** 8 **17.** 5.8731

19. 1385.4557 **21.** 0.0063 **23.** 0.8950

25. a. $x = 2$ **b.** $x = 3$ **c.** Between 2 and 3

27. a. $x = 4$ **b.** $x = 5$ **c.** Between 4 and 5

29. $f(0) = 1, f(1) = \frac{1}{5}, f(2) = \frac{1}{25}, f(-1) = 5, f(-2) = 25$

31. $h(0) = 1, h(1) = 3, h(-1) = \frac{1}{3}, h(\sqrt{2}) \approx 4.73, h(\pi) \approx 31.54$

33. If $b > 1$, the graph is increasing. If $0 < b < 1$, the graph is decreasing.

35.

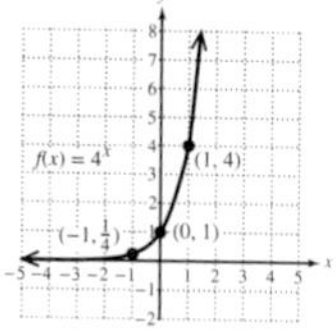

37.

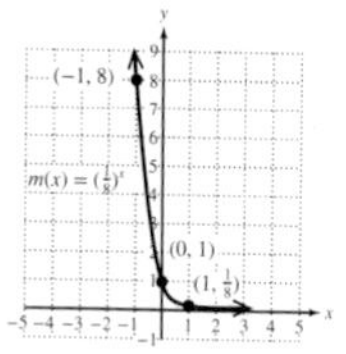

39.

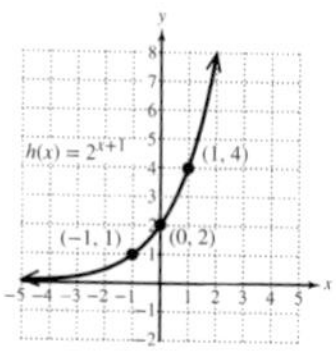

41.

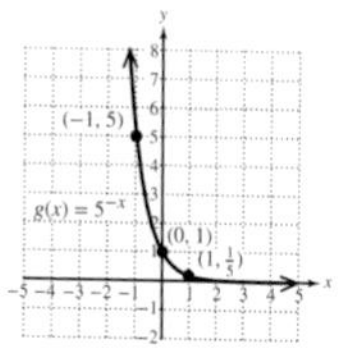

43. a. 0.25 g **b.** ≈ 0.16 g **45. a.** 758,000 **b.** 379,000 **c.** 144,000 **47. a.** $P(t) = 153{,}000{,}000(1.0125)^t$ **b.** $P(41) \approx 255{,}000{,}000$ **49. a.** \$1640.67 **b.** \$2691.80 **c.** $A(0) = 1000$. The initial amount of the investment is \$1000. $A(7) = 2000$. The amount of the investment doubles in 7 yr.

Section 12.2 Graphing Calculator Exercises, p. 866

51.

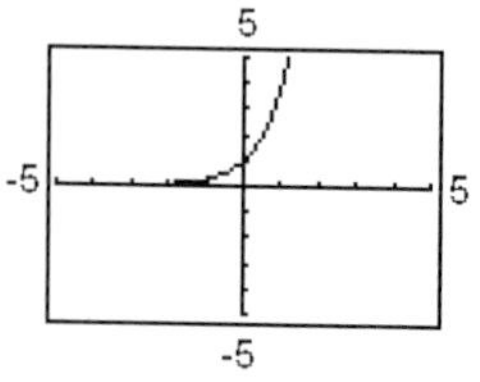

52.

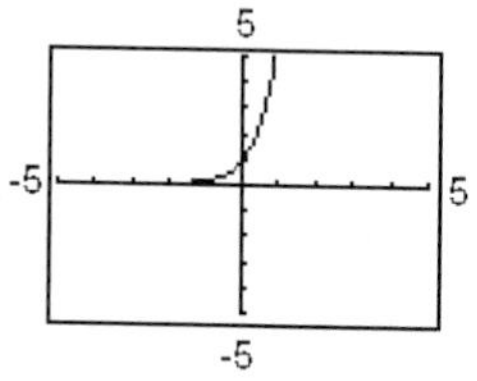

53.

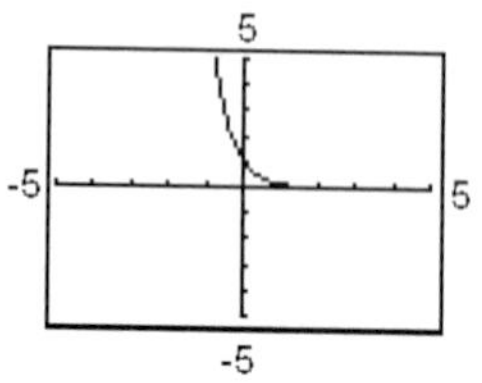

54.

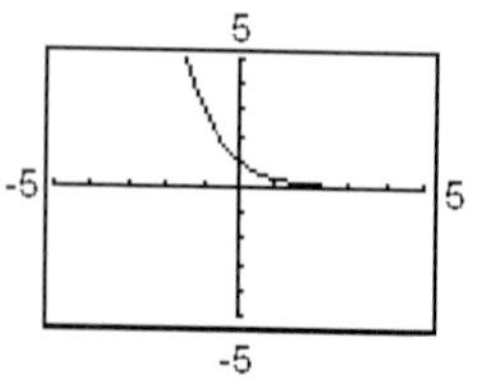

55.

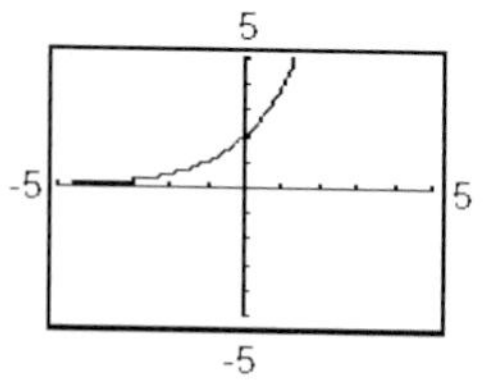

56.

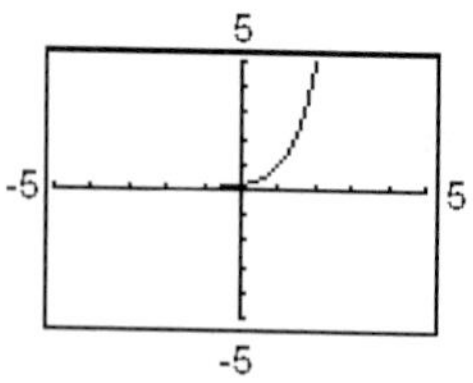

57.

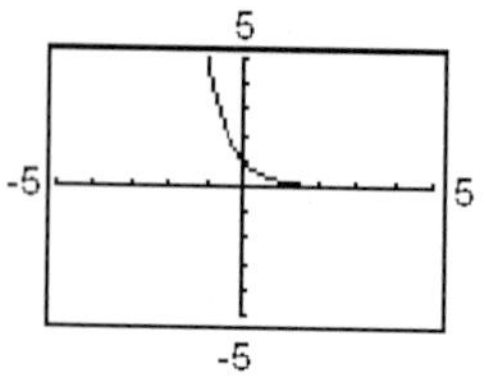

58.

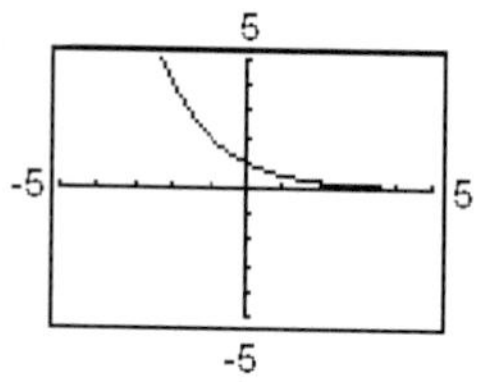

Section 12.3 Practice Exercises, pp. 875–879

1. a. logarithmic; b **b.** logarithm; base; argument **c.** $(0, \infty)$; $(-\infty, \infty)$ **d.** exponential **e.** common **f.** increasing; decreasing **g.** 2, 3, and 4 **h.** $y = x$ **3.** i

5. a. $s(-2) = \frac{25}{4}, s(-1) = \frac{5}{2}, s(0) = 1, s(1) = \frac{2}{5}, s(2) = \frac{4}{25}$

b.

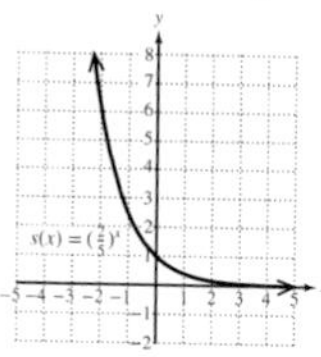

7. $g(-2) = \frac{1}{9}, g(-1) = \frac{1}{3}, g(0) = 1, g(1) = 3, g(2) = 9$

9. $b^y = x$ **11.** $5^4 = 625$ **13.** $10^{-4} = 0.0001$ **15.** $6^2 = 36$

17. $b^x = 15$ **19.** $3^x = 5$ **21.** $\left(\frac{1}{4}\right)^{10} = x$ **23.** $\log_3 81 = x$

25. $\log_5 25 = 2$ **27.** $\log_7\left(\frac{1}{7}\right) = -1$ **29.** $\log_b y = x$

31. $\log_e y = x$ **33.** $\log_{1/3} 9 = -2$ **35.** 2 **37.** −1 **39.** $\frac{1}{2}$

41. 0 **43.** 5 **45.** 1 **47.** 3 **49.** $\frac{1}{2}$ **51.** 1 **53.** 3

55. 6 **57.** −2 **59.** 0.7782 **61.** 0.4971 **63.** −1.5051

65. −2.2676 **67.** 5.5315 **69.** −7.4202

71. a. Slightly less than 2 **b.** Slightly more than 1 **c.** $\log 93 \approx 1.9685$, $\log 12 \approx 1.0792$

73. a. $f\left(\frac{1}{64}\right) = -3, f\left(\frac{1}{16}\right) = -2, f\left(\frac{1}{4}\right) = -1, f(1) = 0,$ $f(4) = 1, f(16) = 2, f(64) = 3$

b.

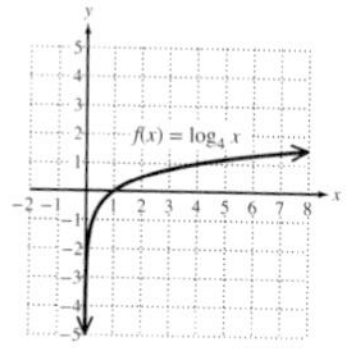

75. $3^y = x$

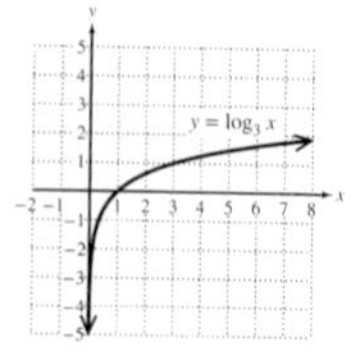

x	y
$\frac{1}{9}$	−2
$\frac{1}{3}$	−1
1	0
3	1
9	2

77. $\left(\frac{1}{2}\right)^y = x$

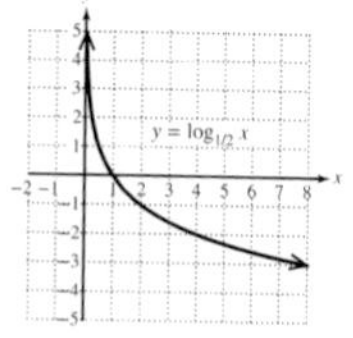

x	y
4	−2
2	−1
1	0
$\frac{1}{2}$	1
$\frac{1}{4}$	2

79. $(5, \infty)$ **81.** $(-\infty, 2)$ **83.** $\left(\frac{1}{3}, \infty\right)$ **85.** $(-1.2, \infty)$

87. $(-\infty, 2)$ **89.** $(-\infty, 0) \cup (0, \infty)$ **91.** ≈ 7.35

93. a.

t (months)	0	1	2	6	12	24
$S_1(t)$	91	82.0	76.7	65.6	57.6	49.1
$S_2(t)$	88	83.5	80.8	75.3	71.3	67.0

b. Group 1: 91; Group 2: 88 **c.** Method II

Section 12.3 Graphing Calculator Exercises, p. 879

95. Domain: $(-6, \infty)$; asymptote: $x = -6$

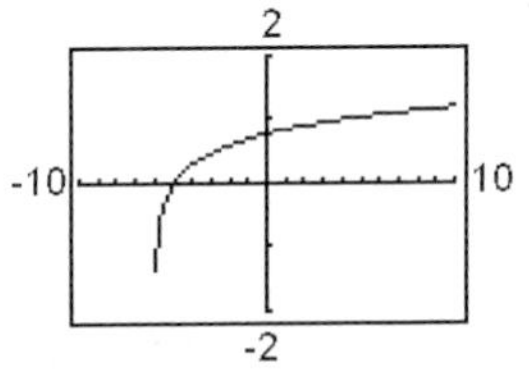

96. Domain: $(-2, \infty)$; asymptote: $x = -2$

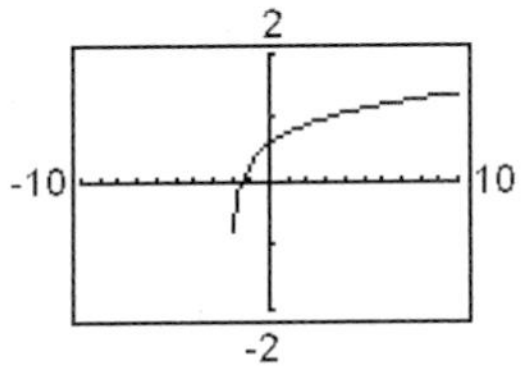

97. Domain: $(2, \infty)$; asymptote: $x = 2$

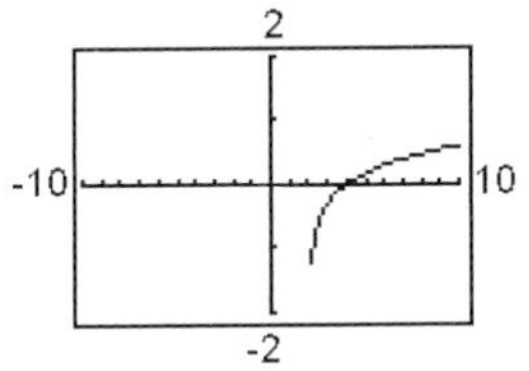

98. Domain: $(-8, \infty)$; asymptote: $x = -8$

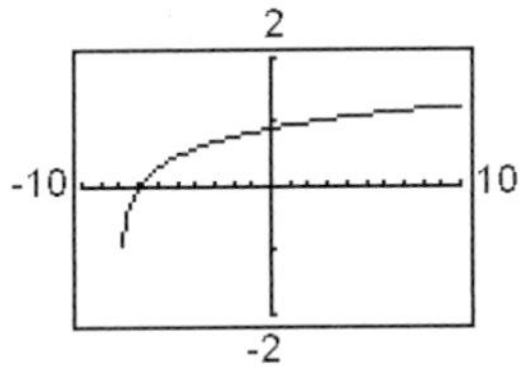

99. Domain: $(-\infty, 2)$; asymptote: $x = 2$

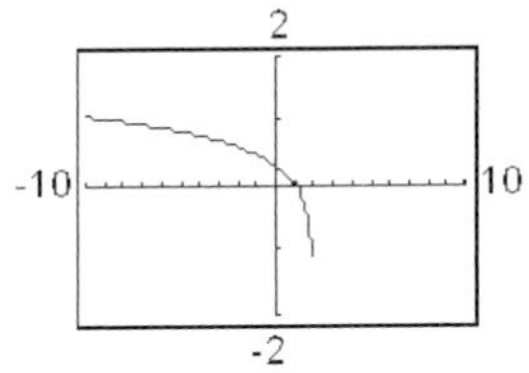

100. Domain: $(-\infty, 3)$; asymptote: $x = 3$

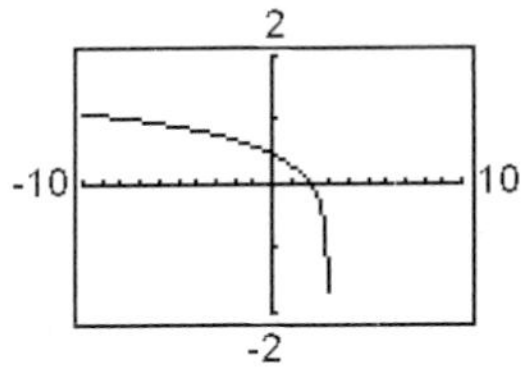

Chapter 12 Problem Recognition Exercises, p. 880

1. e **2.** l **3.** j **4.** g **5.** c **6.** a
7. k **8.** b **9.** i **10.** h **11.** f **12.** d

Section 12.4 Practice Exercises, pp. 886–889

1. a. 1; 0; x; x **b.** $\log_b x + \log_b y$; $\log_b x - \log_b y$ **c.** $p \log_b x$ **d.** False **e.** False **f.** False

3. 4 **5.** $\frac{1}{6}$ **7.** 0.9031 **9.** 5.0475 **11.** a **13.** c

15. a, b, c **17.** 1 **19.** 4 **21.** 11 **23.** 3 **25.** 0

27. 9 **29.** 0 **31.** 3 **33.** 1 **35.** $2x$ **37.** 4 **39.** 0

41. Expressions a and c are equivalent.

43. Expressions a and c are equivalent.

45. $\log_3 x - \log_3 5$ **47.** $\log 2 + \log x$ **49.** $4 \log_5 x$

51. $\log_4 a + \log_4 b - \log_4 c$

53. $\frac{1}{2}\log_b x + \log_b y - 3\log_b z - \log_b w$

55. $\log_2(x+1) - 2\log_2 y - \frac{1}{2}\log_2 z$

57. $\frac{1}{3}\log a + \frac{2}{3}\log b - \frac{1}{3}\log c$ **59.** $-5 \log w$

61. $\frac{1}{2}\log_b a - 3 - \log_b c$ **63.** 3 **65.** 2 **67.** $\log_3\left(\frac{x^2 z}{y^3}\right)$

69. $\log_3\left(\frac{a^2 c}{\sqrt[4]{b}}\right)$ **71.** $\log_b x^2$ **73.** $\log_8(8a^5)$ or $\log_8 a^5 + 1$

75. $\log\left[\frac{(x+6)^2\sqrt[3]{y}}{z^5}\right]$ **77.** $\log_b\left(\frac{1}{x-1}\right)$ **79.** 1.792

81. 2.485 **83.** 4.396 **85.** 0.916 **87.** 13.812 **89.** 16.09

91. a. $B = 10\log I - 10\log I_0$ **b.** $10\log I + 160$

Section 12.4 Graphing Calculator Exercises, p. 889

93. a. Domain: $(-\infty, 0) \cup (0, \infty)$ **b.** Domain: $(0, \infty)$

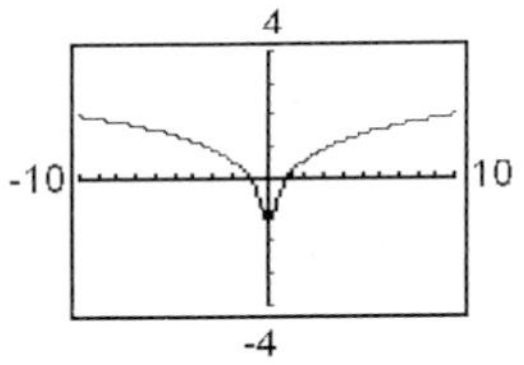

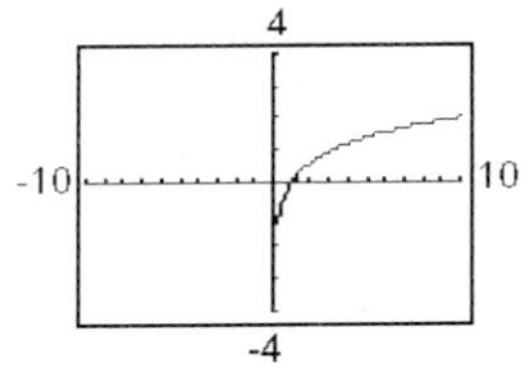

c. They are equivalent for all x in the intersection of their domains, $(0, \infty)$.

94. a. Domain: $(-\infty, 1) \cup (1, \infty)$ **b.** Domain: $(1, \infty)$

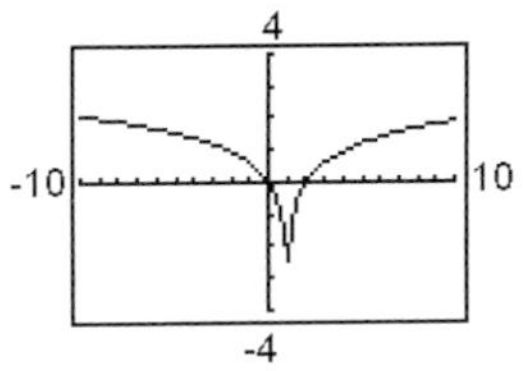

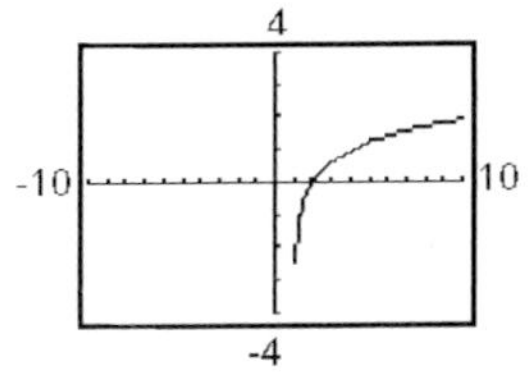

c. They are equivalent for all x in the intersection of their domains, $(1, \infty)$.

Section 12.5 Practice Exercises, pp. 897–901

1. a. e **b.** e **c.** natural; $\ln x$ **d.** 0; 1; p, x **e.** $\ln x + \ln y$; $\ln x - \ln y$ **f.** $p \ln x$ **g.** $\log_a b$

3. $\log_3\left(\frac{a\sqrt{d}}{c^5}\right)$ **5.** $\frac{1}{4}\log_6 x + \frac{1}{2}\log_6 y - \frac{3}{4}\log_6 z$

7.

x	y
−4	0.05
−3	0.14
−2	0.37
−1	1
0	2.72
1	7.39

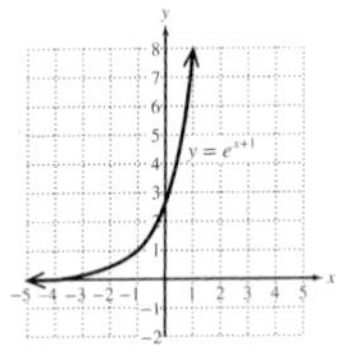

Domain: $(-\infty, \infty)$

9.

x	y
−2	2.14
−1	2.37
0	3
1	4.72
2	9.39
3	22.09

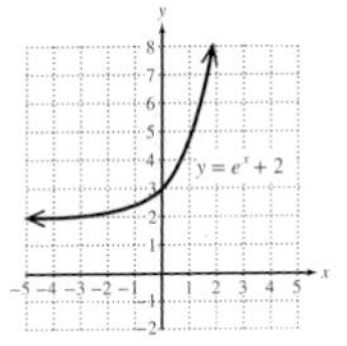

Domain: $(-\infty, \infty)$

11. a. \$12,209.97 **b.** \$13,488.50 **c.** \$14,898.46 **d.** \$16,050.09 An investment grows more rapidly at higher interest rates.

13. a. \$12,423.76 **b.** \$12,515.01 **c.** \$12,535.94 **d.** \$12,546.15 **e.** \$12,546.50 More money is earned at a greater number of compounding periods per year. **15. a.** \$6920.15 **b.** \$9577.70 **c.** \$13,255.84 **d.** \$18,346.48 **e.** \$35,143.44 More money is earned over a longer period of time.

17.

x	y
2.25	−1.39
2.50	−0.69
2.75	−0.29
3	0
4	0.69
5	1.10
6	1.39

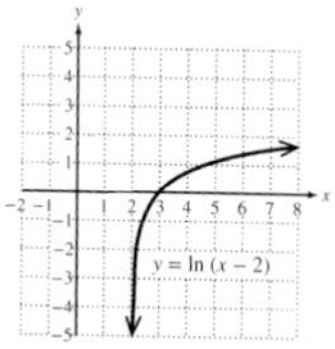

Domain: $(2, \infty)$

19.

x	y
0.25	−2.39
0.5	−1.69
0.75	−1.29
1	−1.00
2	−0.31
3	0.10
4	0.39

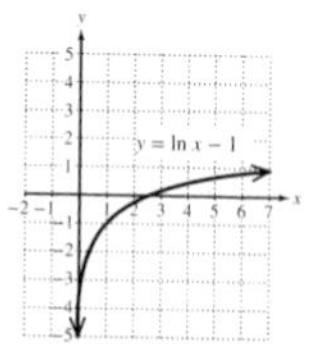

Domain: $(0, \infty)$

21. a.

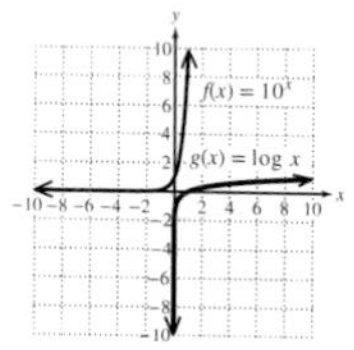

b. Domain: $(-\infty, \infty)$; range: $(0, \infty)$
c. Domain:$(0, \infty)$; range: $(-\infty, \infty)$

23. 1 **25.** 0 **27.** −6 **29.** $2x+3$ **31.** $\ln(p^6\sqrt[3]{q})$

33. $\ln\sqrt{\dfrac{x}{y^3}}$ **35.** $\ln\left(\dfrac{a^2}{b\sqrt[3]{c}}\right)$ **37.** $\ln\left(\dfrac{x^4}{y^3z}\right)$

39. $2\ln a - 2\ln b$ **41.** $2\ln b + 1$ **43.** $4\ln a + \frac{1}{2}\ln b - \ln c$

45. $\frac{1}{5}\ln a + \frac{1}{5}\ln b - \frac{2}{5}\ln c$ **47. a.** 2.9570 **b.** 2.9570

c. They are the same. **49.** 2.8074 **51.** 1.5283

53. −2.1269 **55.** 0 **57.** −3.3219 **59.** −3.8124

61. a. 15.4 yr **b.** 6.9 yr **c.** 13.8 yr **63. a.** 19.8 yr **b.** 13.9 yr **c.** 27.8 yr

Section 12.5 Graphing Calculator Exercises, pp. 901–902

65. a–b

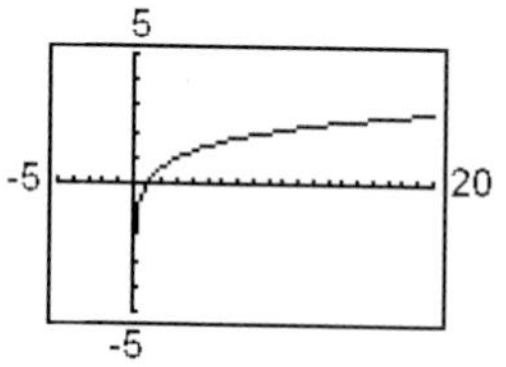

c. They appear to be the same.

66. a–b

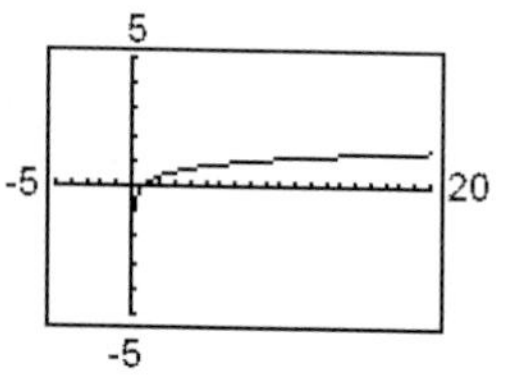

c. They appear to be the same.

67.

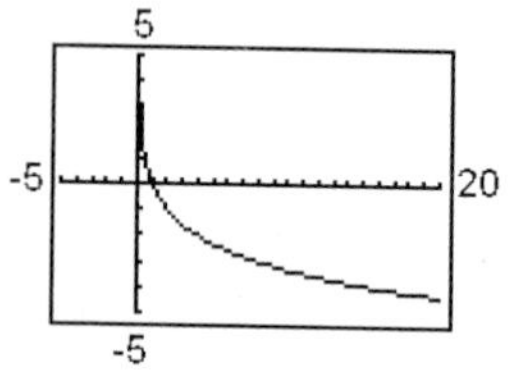

68.

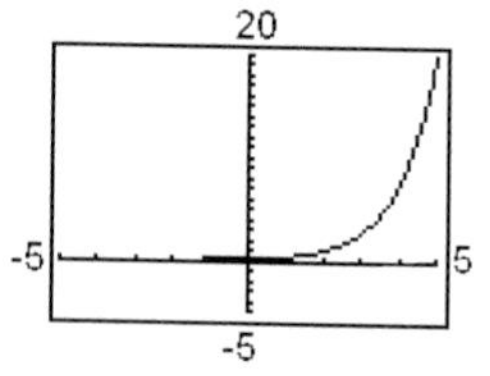

69.

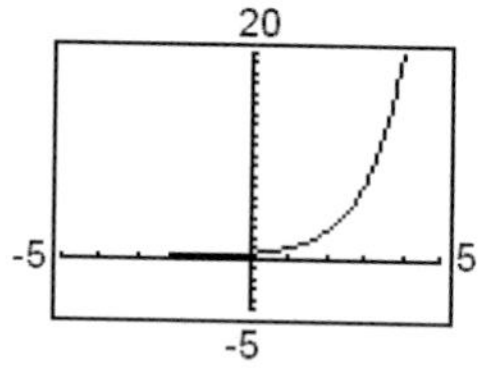

Chapter 12 Problem Recognition Exercises, p. 902

	Exponential Form	Logarithmic Form
1.	$2^5 = 32$	$\log_2 32 = 5$
2.	$3^4 = 81$	$\log_3 81 = 4$
3.	$z^y = x$	$\log_z x = y$
4.	$b^c = a$	$\log_b a = c$
5.	$10^3 = 1000$	$\log 1000 = 3$
6.	$10^1 = 10$	$\log 10 = 1$
7.	$e^a = b$	$\ln b = a$
8.	$e^q = p$	$\ln p = q$
9.	$(\frac{1}{2})^2 = \frac{1}{4}$	$\log_{1/2}(\frac{1}{4}) = 2$
10.	$(\frac{1}{3})^{-2} = 9$	$\log_{1/3} 9 = -2$
11.	$10^{-2} = 0.01$	$\log 0.01 = -2$
12.	$10^x = 4$	$\log 4 = x$
13.	$e^0 = 1$	$\ln 1 = 0$
14.	$e^1 = e$	$\ln e = 1$
15.	$25^{1/2} = 5$	$\log_{25} 5 = \frac{1}{2}$
16.	$16^{1/4} = 2$	$\log_{16} 2 = \frac{1}{4}$
17.	$e^t = s$	$\ln s = t$
18.	$e^r = w$	$\ln w = r$
19.	$15^{-2} = \frac{1}{225}$	$\log_{15}(\frac{1}{225}) = -2$
20.	$3^{-1} = p$	$\log_3 p = -1$

Section 12.6 Practice Exercises, pp. 911–915

1. a. $x = y$ **b.** $x = y$ **3.** $\log_b[x(2x+3)]$

5. $\log_b\left(\dfrac{x+2}{3x-5}\right)$ **7.** $\{9\}$ **9.** $\{10^{42}\}$ **11.** $\{e^{0.08}\}$

13. $\{10^{-9.2} - 40\}$ **15.** $\{5\}$ **17.** $\{10\}$ **19.** $\{25\}$ **21.** $\{59\}$

23. $\{1\}$ **25.** $\{0\}$ **27.** $\left\{-\dfrac{37}{9}\right\}$

29. $\{3\}$ (The value −3 does not check.) **31.** $\{4\}$ **33.** $\{3\}$

35. $\{2\}$ **37.** $\{\ \}$ (The value −3 does not check.) **39.** $\{4\}$

41. $\{-6\}$ **43.** $\left\{\dfrac{1}{2}\right\}$ **45.** $\{2\}$ **47.** $\left\{\dfrac{11}{12}\right\}$ **49.** $\{1\}$

51. $\left\{\dfrac{4}{19}\right\}$ **53.** $\{-2, 1\}$ **55.** $\left\{\dfrac{\ln 21}{\ln 8}\right\}$ **57.** $\{\ln 8.1254\}$

59. $\{\log 0.0138\}$ **61.** $\left\{\dfrac{\ln 15}{0.07}\right\}$ **63.** $\left\{\dfrac{\ln 3}{1.2}\right\}$

65. $\left\{\dfrac{\ln 3}{\ln 5 - \ln 3}\right\}$ **67.** $\left\{\dfrac{2\ln 2}{\ln 6 - \ln 2}\right\}$ **69.** $\left\{\dfrac{\ln 4}{0.04}\right\}$

71. $\left\{3 \ln\left(\frac{125}{6}\right)\right\}$ **73.** $\left\{\frac{\ln 20}{\ln 5} + 2\right\}$

75. a. $\approx$ 1285 million (or 1,285,000,000) people **b.** $\approx$ 1466.5 million (or 1,466,500,000) people **c.** The year 2049 ($t \approx 50.8$)
77. a. 500 bacteria **b.** $\approx$ 660 bacteria **c.** $\approx$ 25 min
79. It will take 9.9 yr for the investment to double. **81.** 5 yr
83. a. 7.8 g **b.** 18.5 days **85.** The intensity of sound of heavy traffic is $10^{-3.07}$ W/m^2. **87.** It will take 38.4 yr. **89. a.** 1.42 kg **b.** No **91.** $\{10^5, 10^{-3}\}$ **93.** $\left\{\frac{1}{27}, \frac{1}{9}\right\}$

Section 12.6 Graphing Calculator Exercises, p. 915

95.

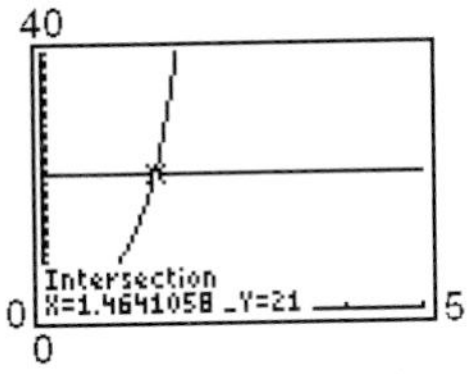

96.

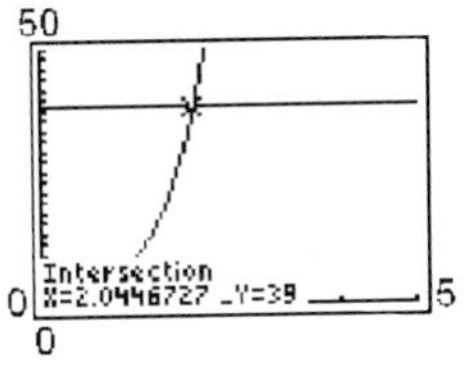

Chapter 12 Review Exercises, pp. 921–924

1. No **2.** Yes **3.** $\{(5, 3), (9, 2), (-1, 0), (1, 4)\}$

4. $q^{-1}(x) = \frac{4}{3}(x + 2)$ **5.** $g^{-1}(x) = (x - 3)^5$

6. $f^{-1}(x) = \sqrt[3]{x} + 1$ **7.** $n^{-1}(x) = \frac{2x + 4}{x}$

8. $(f \circ g)(x) = 5\left(\frac{1}{5}x + \frac{2}{5}\right) - 2 = x + 2 - 2 = x$

$(g \circ f)(x) = \frac{1}{5}(5x - 2) + \frac{2}{5} = x - \frac{2}{5} + \frac{2}{5} = x$

9. The graphs are symmetric about the line $y = x$.

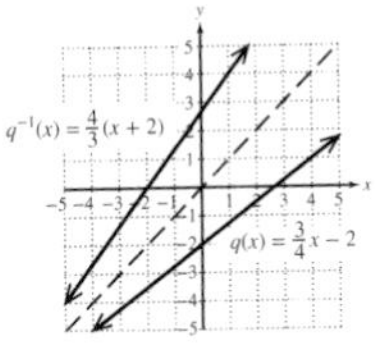

10. a. Domain: $[-1, \infty)$; range: $[0, \infty)$ **b.** Domain: $[0, \infty)$; range: $[-1, \infty)$ **11.** $p^{-1}(x) = (x - 2)^2, x \geq 2$

12. 1024 **13.** $\frac{1}{36} \approx 0.028$ **14.** 2 **15.** 10

16. 8.825 **17.** 16.242 **18.** 1.627 **19.** 0.681

20.

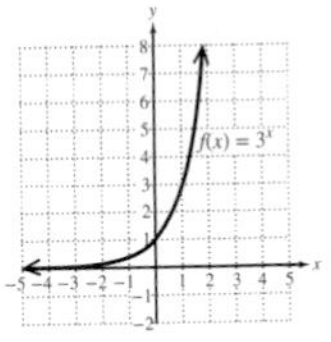

21.

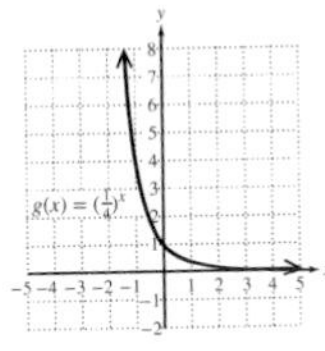

22.

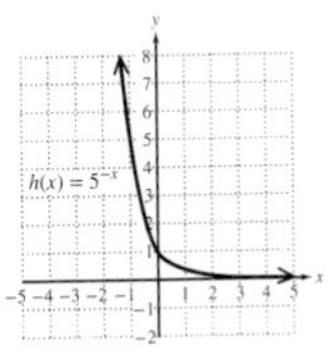

23.

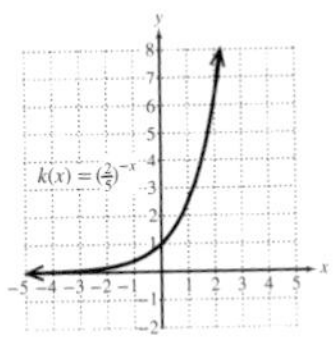

24. a. Horizontal **b.** $y = 0$ **25. a.** 15,000 mrem **b.** 3750 mrem **c.** Yes **26.** -3 **27.** 0 **28.** 1
29. 8 **30.** 4 **31.** 4 **32.** 5 **33.** -1

34.

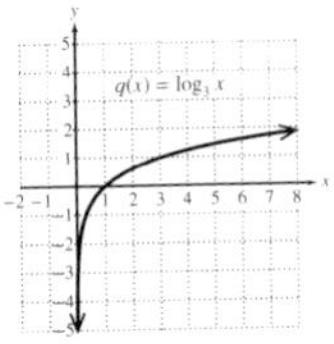

35.

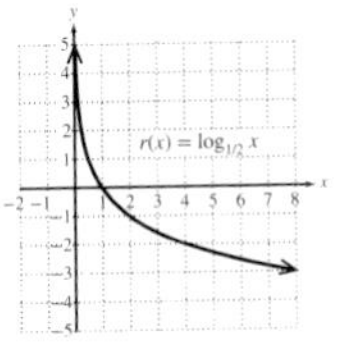

36. a. Vertical asymptote **b.** $x = 0$ **37. a.** 2.5 **b.** 9.5
38. 1 **39.** 6 **40.** 0 **41.** 7

42. a. $\log_b x + \log_b y$ **b.** $\log_b\left(\frac{x}{y}\right)$ **c.** $p \log_b x$

43. $\log_b\left(\frac{\sqrt[4]{x^3 y}}{z}\right)$ **44.** $\log_3\left(\frac{\sqrt{ab}}{c^2 d^4}\right)$ **45.** log 5

46. 0 **47.** b **48.** a **49.** 148.4132 **50.** 14.0940
51. 32.2570 **52.** 57.2795 **53.** 1.7918 **54.** -2.1972
55. 1.3424 **56.** 1.3029 **57.** 3.3219 **58.** 1.9943
59. -0.8370 **60.** -3.6668 **61. a.** \$33,361.92 **b.** \$33,693.90 **c.** \$33,770.48 **d.** \$33,809.18
62. a. $S(0) = 95$; the student's score is 95 at the end of the course. **b.** $S(6) \approx 23.7$; the student's score is 23.7 after 6 months. **c.** $S(12) \approx 20.2$; the student's score is 20.2 after 1 yr.
63. $(-\infty, \infty)$ **64.** $(-\infty, \infty)$ **65.** $(-\infty, \infty)$

66. $(0, \infty)$ **67.** $(-5, \infty)$ **68.** $(7, \infty)$ **69.** $\left(\frac{4}{3}, \infty\right)$

70. $(-\infty, 5)$ **71.** $\{125\}$ **72.** $\left\{\frac{1}{49}\right\}$ **73.** $\{216\}$

74. $\{3^{1/12}\}$ **75.** $\left\{\frac{1001}{2}\right\}$ **76.** $\{9\}$

77. $\{5\}$ (The value -2 does not check.) **78.** $\left\{\frac{190}{321}\right\}$

79. $\{-1\}$ **80.** $\left\{\frac{4}{7}\right\}$ **81.** $\left\{\frac{\ln 21}{\ln 4}\right\}$ **82.** $\left\{\frac{\ln 18}{\ln 5}\right\}$

83. $\{-\ln 0.1\}$ **84.** $\left\{-\frac{\ln 0.06}{2}\right\}$ **85.** $\left\{\frac{\log 1512}{2}\right\}$

86. $\left\{\frac{\log 821}{3}\right\}$ **87.** $\left\{\frac{3 \ln 2}{\ln 7 - \ln 2}\right\}$

88. $\left\{\frac{5 \ln 14}{\ln 14 - \ln 6}\right\}$ **89. a.** 1.09 μg **b.** 0.15 μg **c.** 16.08 days **90. a.** 150 bacteria **b.** $\approx$ 185 bacteria **c.** $\approx$ 99 min **91. a.** $V(0) = 15{,}000$; the initial value of the car is \$15,000. **b.** $V(10) = 3347$; the value of the car after 10 years is \$3347. **c.** 7.3 yr

Chapter 12 Test, pp. 924–926

1. A function is one-to-one if it passes the horizontal line test.
2. b **3.** $f^{-1}(x) = 4x - 12$ **4.** $g^{-1}(x) = \sqrt{x} + 1$
5.

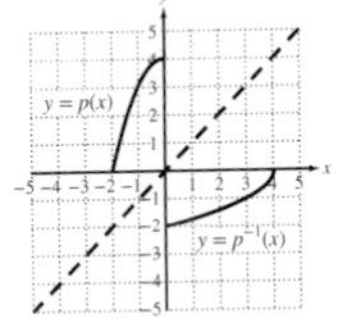

6. a. 4.6416 **b.** 32.2693 **c.** 687.2913
7.

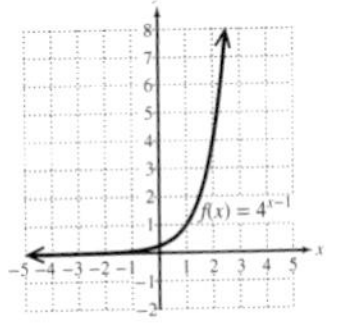

8. a. $\log_{16} 8 = \frac{3}{4}$ **b.** $x^5 = 31$

9.

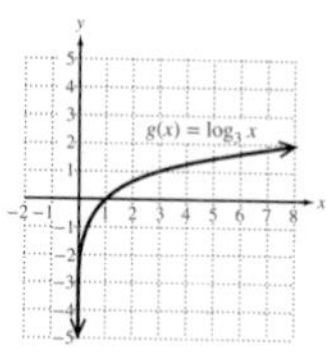

10. $\dfrac{\log_a n}{\log_a b}$ **11. a.** 1.3222 **b.** 1.8502 **c.** −2.5850

12. a. $1 + \log_3 x$ **b.** −5 **13. a.** $\log_b(\sqrt{x}y^3)$

b. $\log\left(\dfrac{1}{a^3}\right)$ or $-\log a^3$ **14. a.** 1.6487 **b.** 0.0498

c. −1.0986 **d.** 1 **15. a.** $y = \ln x$ **b.** $y = e^x$

16. a. $p(4) \approx 59.8$; 59.8% of the material is retained after 4 months. **b.** $p(12) \approx 40.7$; 40.7% of the material is retained after 1 yr. **c.** $p(0) = 92$; 92% of the material is retained at the end of the course. **17. a.** 9762 thousand (or 9,762,000) people **b.** The year 2020 ($t \approx 20.4$)

18. a. $P(0) = 300$; there are 300 bacteria initially. **b.** 35,588 bacteria **c.** 1,120,537 bacteria **d.** 1,495,831 bacteria

19. {25} (The value −4 does not check.)

20. {32} **21.** $\{e^{2.4} - 7\}$ **22.** {−7} **23.** $\left\{\dfrac{\ln 50}{\ln 4}\right\}$

24. $\left\{\dfrac{\ln 250}{2.4}\right\}$ **25.** $\left\{\dfrac{\ln 58}{\ln 2} + 3\right\}$ **26.** $\left\{\dfrac{7\ln 4}{\ln 5 - \ln 4}\right\}$

27. a. $P(2500) = 560.2$; at 2500 m the atmospheric pressure is 560.2 mm Hg. **b.** 760 mm Hg **c.** 1498.8 m

28. a. \$2909.98 **b.** 9.24 yr to double

Chapters 1–12 Cumulative Review Exercises, pp. 926–928

1. $-\dfrac{5}{4}$ **2.** $-1 + \dfrac{p}{2} + \dfrac{3p^3}{4}$

3. Quotient: $t^3 + 2t^2 - 9t - 18$; remainder: 0 **4.** $|x - 3|$

5. $\dfrac{2\sqrt[3]{25}}{5}$ **6.** $2\sqrt{7}$ in. **7.** $\dfrac{4d^{1/10}}{c}$

8. $(\sqrt{15} - \sqrt{6} + \sqrt{30} - 2\sqrt{3})$ m^2 **9.** $-\dfrac{7}{29} - \dfrac{26}{29}i$

10. $\left\{6, \dfrac{3}{2}\right\}$ **11.** 4.8 L **12.** 24 min **13.** {(7, −1)}

14. $\left\{-\dfrac{23}{11}\right\}$ **15.** $x = \dfrac{c + d}{a - b}$ **16.** $t = \dfrac{\sqrt{2sg}}{g}$

17. $\left\{\dfrac{4 \pm \sqrt{34}}{3}\right\}$ **18.** (7, 0), (3, 0)

19. a. $-30t$ **b.** $-10t^2$ **c.** $2t^2 + 5t$ **20.** {0}

21. a. $x = 2$ **b.** $y = 6$ **c.** $y = \dfrac{1}{2}x + 5$

22. 40°, 80°, 60° **23.** Infinitely many solutions; $\{(x, y) \mid -2x + y = -4\}$; dependent equations

24. $\left[\dfrac{1}{2}, \infty\right)$ **25.** $f^{-1}(x) = \dfrac{1}{5}x + \dfrac{2}{15}$ **26.** 40 m^3

27. $\dfrac{-x^2 + 5x - 25}{(2x + 1)(x - 2)}$ **28.** $1 + x$ **29. a.** Yes; $x \neq 4, x \neq -2$

b. {8} **c.** $(-\infty, -2) \cup (4, 8]$

30. The numbers are $-\dfrac{3}{4}$, 4. **31.** {−4} (The value −9 does not check.) **32.** $(-\infty, \infty)$

33. a. $P(6) = 2{,}000{,}000$, $P(12) = 1{,}000{,}000$, $P(18) = 500{,}000$, $P(24) = 250{,}000$, $P(30) = 125{,}000$ **b.** 48 hr

34. a. 2 **b.** −3 **c.** 6 **d.** 3 **35. a.** 217.0723 **b.** 23.1407 **c.** 0.1768 **d.** 3.7293 **e.** −0.4005 **f.** 2.6047

36. $\left\{\dfrac{2}{3}\right\}$ **37.** {ln 100} **38.** {3} (The value −9 does not check.) **39.** $\log\left(\dfrac{\sqrt{z}}{x^2y^3}\right)$ **40.** $\dfrac{2}{3}\ln x - \dfrac{1}{3}\ln y$

Chapter 13

Section 13.1 Practice Exercises, pp. 936–940

1. a. $\sqrt{(x_2 - x_1)^2 + (y_2 - y_1)^2}$ **b.** circle; center **c.** radius **d.** $(x - h)^2 + (y - k)^2 = r^2$ **e.** $\left(\dfrac{x_1 + x_2}{2}, \dfrac{y_1 + y_2}{2}\right)$

3. $3\sqrt{5}$ **5.** $\sqrt{34}$ **7.** $\dfrac{\sqrt{73}}{8}$ **9.** 4 **11.** 8

13. $4\sqrt{2}$ **15.** $\sqrt{42}$ **17.** Subtract 5 and −7. This becomes $5 - (-7) = 12$. **19.** $y = 13, y = 1$

21. $x = 0, x = 8$ **23.** Yes **25.** No

27. Center (4, −2); $r = 3$

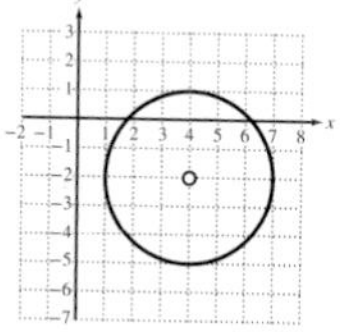

29. Center (−1, −1); $r = 1$

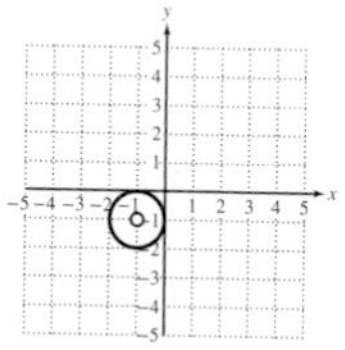

31. Center (0, 2); $r = 2$

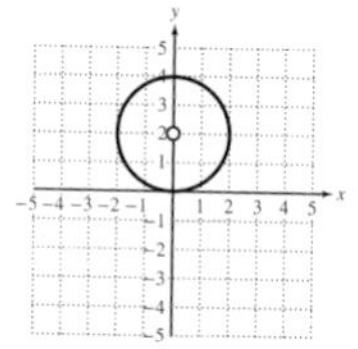

33. Center (3, 0); $r = 2\sqrt{2}$

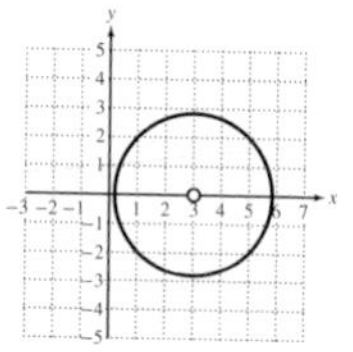

35. Center (0, 0); $r = \sqrt{6}$

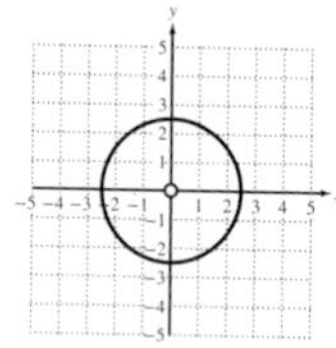

37. Center $\left(-\dfrac{4}{5}, 0\right)$; $r = \dfrac{8}{5}$

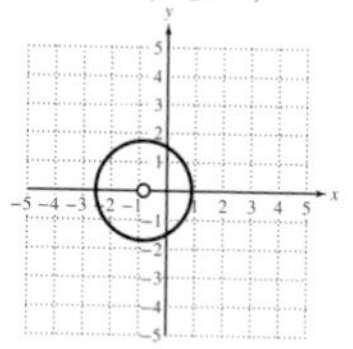

39. Center (1, 3); $r = 6$

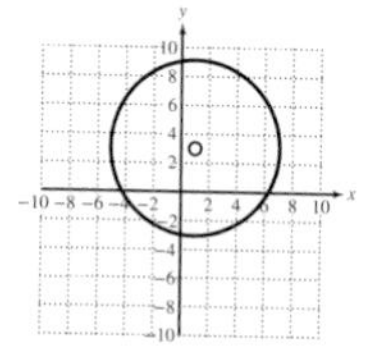

41. Center: (0, 3); $r = 2$

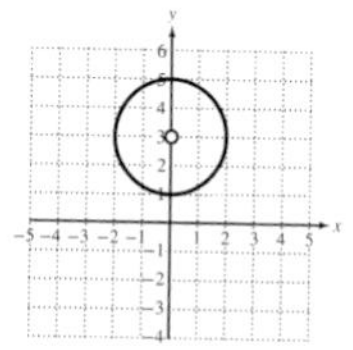

43. Center (0, −3); $r = \dfrac{4}{3}$

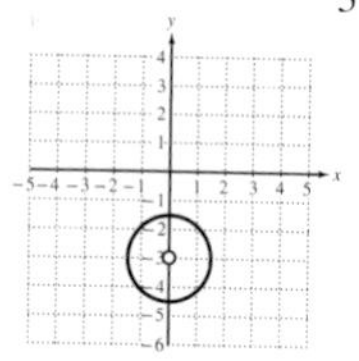

45. Center: (−1, −2); $r = 3$

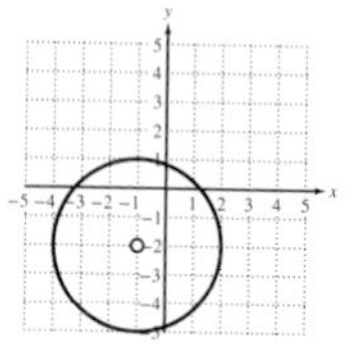

47. Center (0, 0); $r = 1$

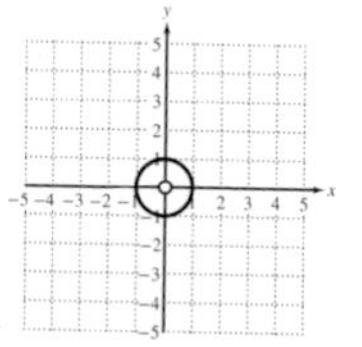

49. $x^2 + y^2 = 4$ **51.** $x^2 + (y - 2)^2 = 4$
53. $(x + 2)^2 + (y - 2)^2 = 9$ **55.** $x^2 + y^2 = 49$
57. $(x + 3)^2 + (y + 4)^2 = 36$ **59.** $(x - 5)^2 + (y - 3)^2 = 2.25$
61. $(1, 2)$ **63.** $(-1, 0)$ **65.** $(-1, 6)$
67. $(0, 3)$ **69.** $\left(-\frac{1}{2}, \frac{3}{2}\right)$ **71.** $(-0.4, -1)$
73. $(40, 7\frac{1}{2})$; they should meet 40 mi east, $7\frac{1}{2}$ mi north of the warehouse. **75. a.** $(1, 3)$ **b.** $(x - 1)^2 + (y - 3)^2 = 5$
77. a. $(0, 3)$ **b.** $x^2 + (y - 3)^2 = 4$
79. $(x - 4)^2 + (y - 4)^2 = 16$

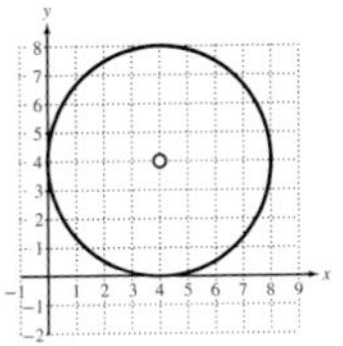

81. $(x - 1)^2 + (y - 1)^2 = 29$

Section 13.1 Graphing Calculator Exercises, p. 940

83.

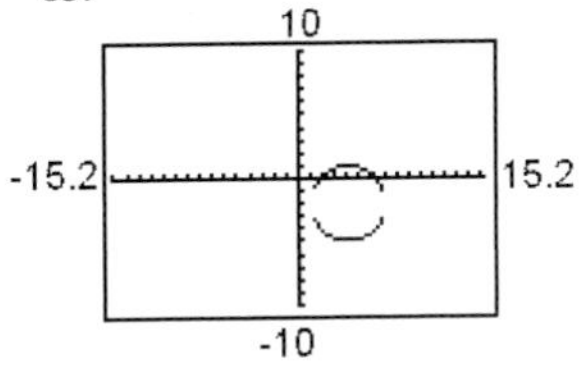

84.

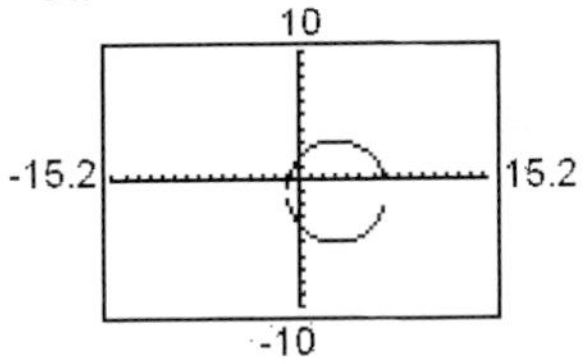

85.

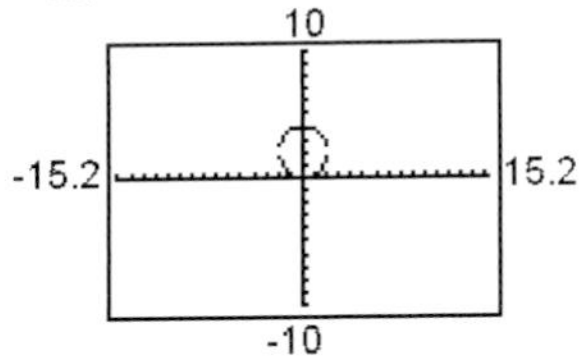

86.

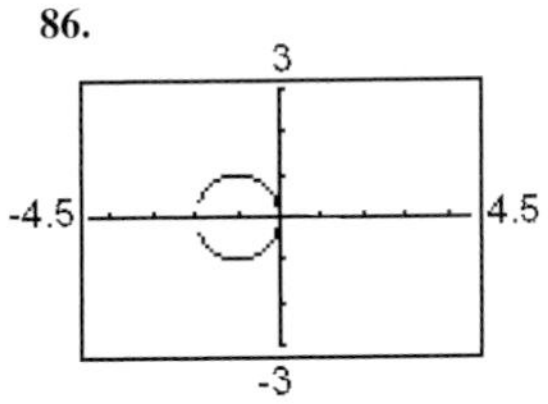

87.

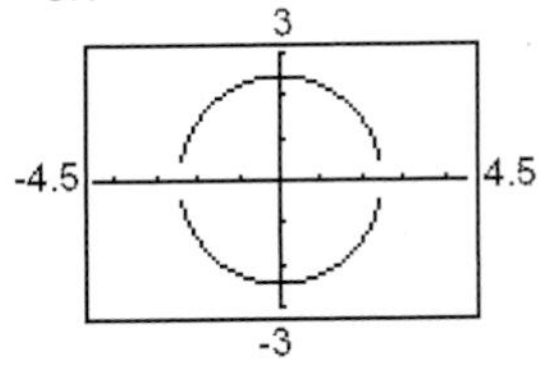

88.

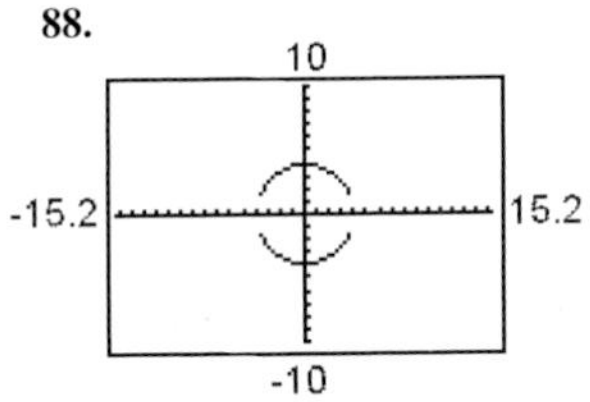

Section 13.2 Practice Exercises, pp. 947–950

1. a. conic; plane **b.** parabola; directrix; focus **c.** vertex; symmetry **d.** $y = k$
3. 5
5. Center: $(0, -1)$; radius: 4

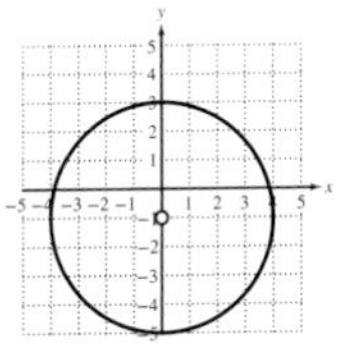

7. $\left(\frac{11}{2}, 1\right)$

9.

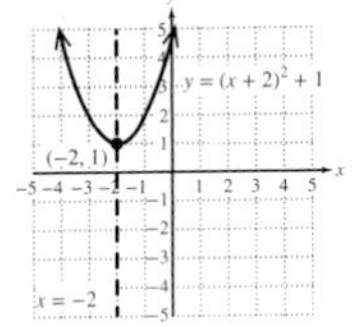

11.

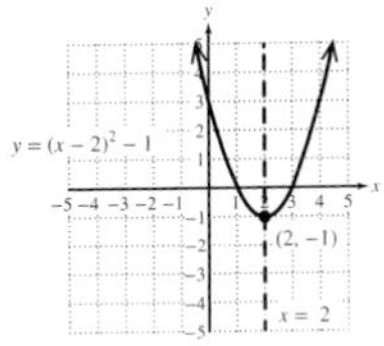

13.

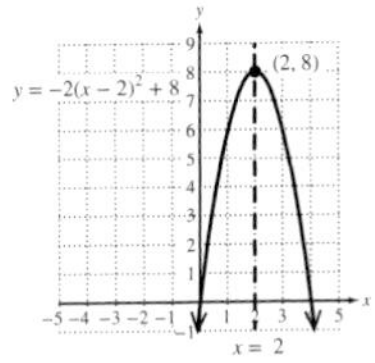

15.

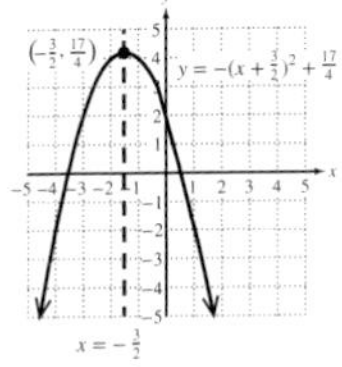

17.

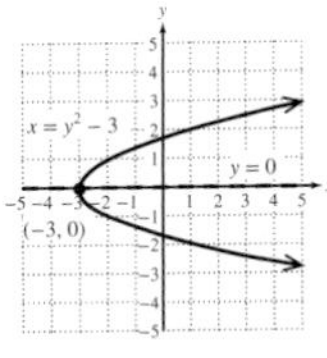

19.

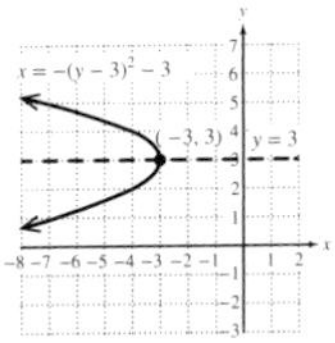

21.

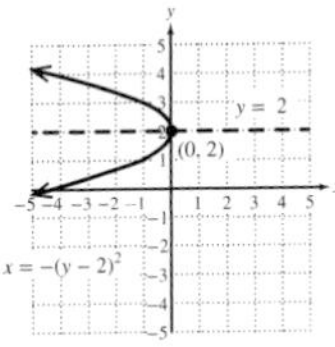

23.

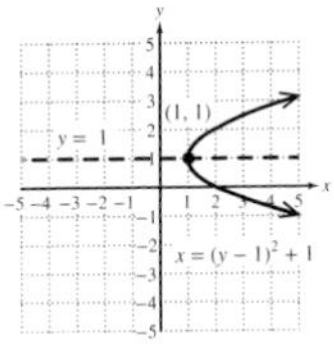

25. $(2, -1)$ **27.** $(5, -1)$ **29.** $\left(2, \frac{7}{4}\right)$ **31.** $\left(\frac{3}{2}, -\frac{1}{4}\right)$
33. $(10, -1)$ **35.** The maximum height of the water is 22 ft.
37. A parabola whose equation is in the form $y = a(x - h)^2 + k$ has a vertical axis of symmetry. A parabola whose equation is in the form $x = a(y - k)^2 + h$ has a horizontal axis of symmetry.
39. Vertical axis of symmetry; opens upward
41. Vertical axis of symmetry; opens downward
43. Horizontal axis of symmetry; opens right
45. Horizontal axis of symmetry; opens left
47. Vertical axis of symmetry; opens downward
49. Horizontal axis of symmetry; opens right

Section 13.3 Practice Exercises, pp. 955–959

1. a. ellipse; foci **b.** ellipse **c.** hyperbola; foci **d.** transverse
e. $\frac{x^2}{a^2} - \frac{y^2}{b^2} = 1$ **f.** $\frac{y^2}{b^2} - \frac{x^2}{a^2} = 1$
3. Center: $(8, -6)$; radius: 10
5. Vertex: $(-3, -1)$; $x = -3$
7. $\left(x - \frac{1}{2}\right)^2 + \left(y - \frac{5}{2}\right)^2 = \frac{1}{4}$

9.

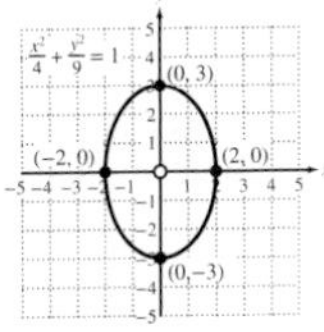

11.

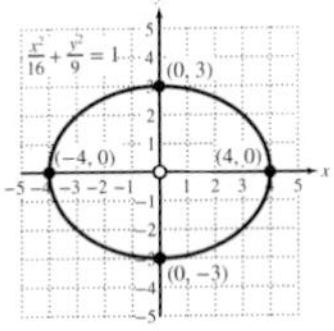

13.

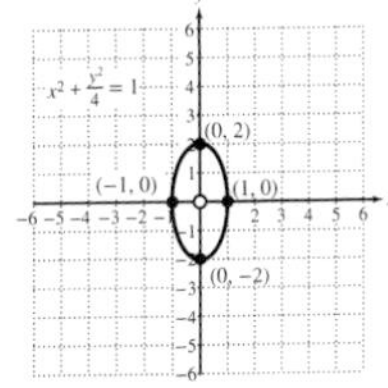

15.

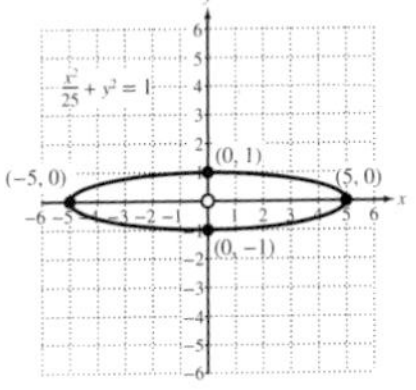

17. Center: $(4, 5)$

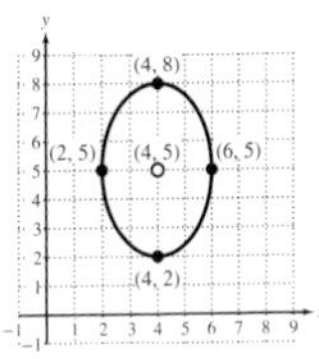

19. Center: $(-1, 2)$

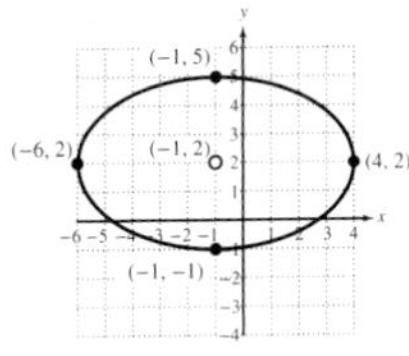

21. Center: (2, −3)

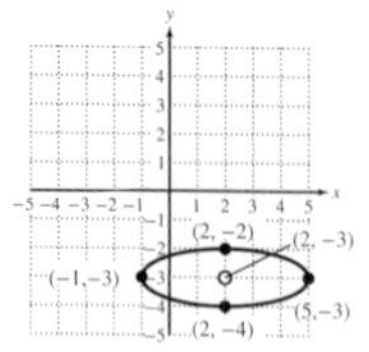

23. Center: (0, 1)

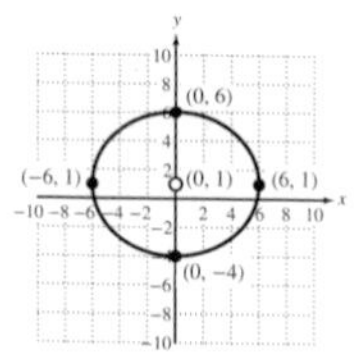

25. Vertical **27.** Horizontal **29.** Horizontal
31. Vertical

33.

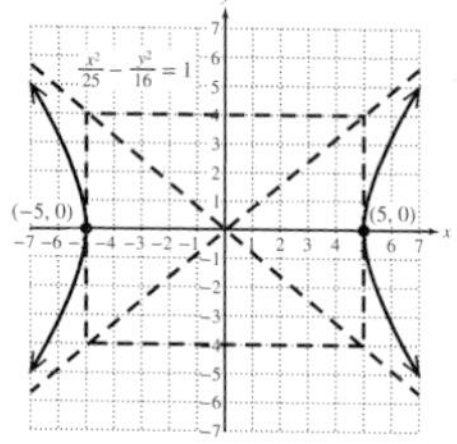

35.

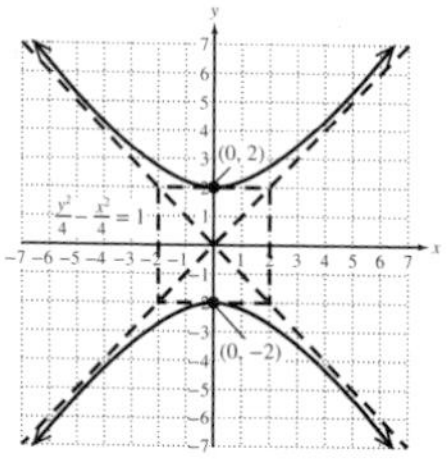

37.

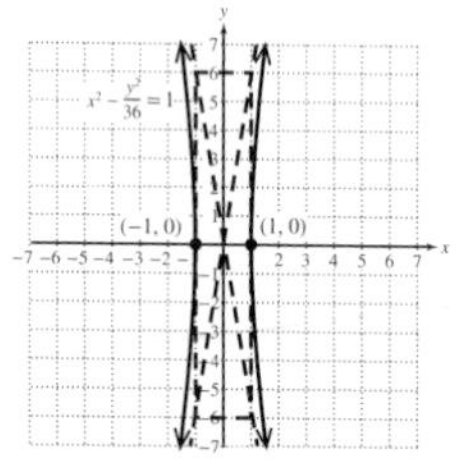

39.

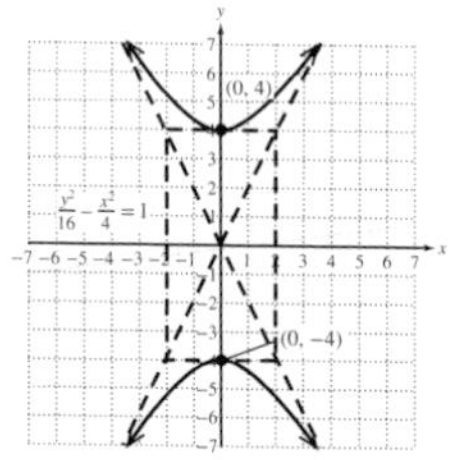

41. Hyperbola **43.** Ellipse
45. Ellipse **47.** Hyperbola
49. Ellipse **51.** Hyperbola
53. The height 10 ft from the center is approximately 49 ft.

55.

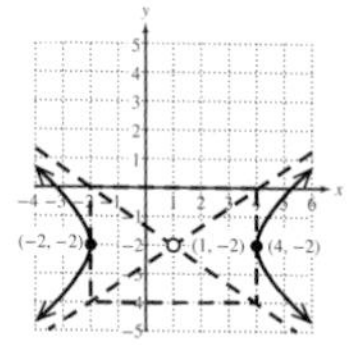

57.

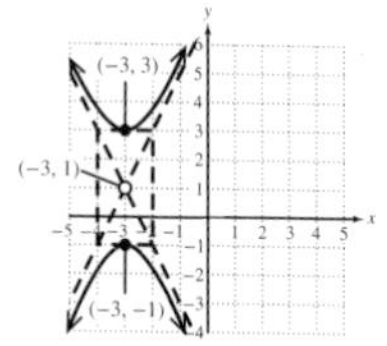

Section 13.3 Problem Recognition Exercises, pp. 959–960

1. Standard equation of a circle **2.** Ellipse centered at the origin **3.** Distance between two points
4. Midpoint between two points **5.** Parabola with vertical axis of symmetry **6.** Hyperbola with horizontal transverse axis
7. Hyperbola with vertical transverse axis
8. Parabola with horizontal axis of symmetry
9. Parabola **10.** Hyperbola **11.** Circle **12.** Circle
13. Hyperbola **14.** Ellipse **15.** None of these
16. Circle **17.** Parabola **18.** Hyperbola **19.** Parabola
20. Circle **21.** None of these **22.** Parabola
23. Ellipse **24.** Circle **25.** Parabola **26.** Ellipse
27. Hyperbola **28.** Circle **29.** Ellipse **30.** Parabola

Section 13.4 Practice Exercises, pp. 964–967

1. a. nonlinear **b.** intersection

3. $7\sqrt{2}$ **5.** $(x+5)^2+(y-3)^2=64$ **7.** $\left(-\frac{1}{2}, -\frac{7}{2}\right)$

9. Zero, one, or two **11.** Zero, one, or two
13. Zero, one, two, three, or four **15.** Zero, one, two, three, or four

17. $\{(-3, 0), (2, 5)\}$

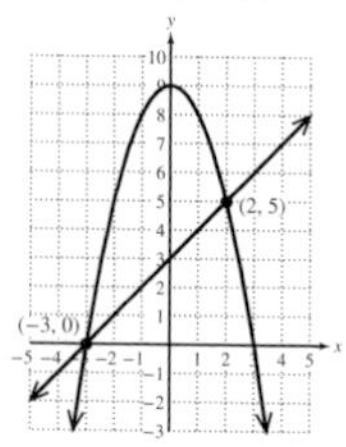

19. $\{(0, 1), (-1, 0)\}$

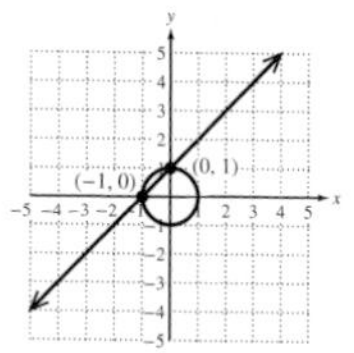

21. $\{(\sqrt{2}, 2), (-\sqrt{2}, 2)\}$

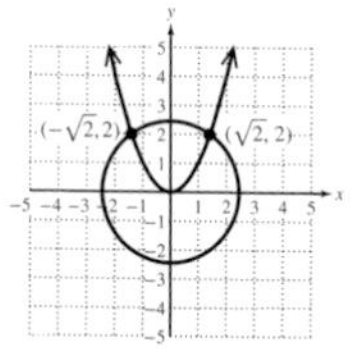

23. $\{(1, 1)\}$ **25.** $\{(0, 0)\}$ **27.** $\left\{\left(\frac{3}{2}, \frac{9}{4}\right)\right\}$

29. $\{(0, 0), (-2, -8)\}$ **31.** $\{(1, 4)\}$
33. $\{(1, 0), (-1, 0)\}$ **35.** $\{(2, 0), (-2, 0)\}$
37. $\{(3, 2), (-3, 2), (3, -2), (-3, -2)\}$
39. $\{(8, 6), (-8, -6)\}$ **41.** $\{(0, -2), (0, 2)\}$
43. $\{(2, 0), (0, 1)\}$ **45.** $\{(4, 5), (-4, -5)\}$

47. $\left\{\left(-\sqrt{2}, \frac{\sqrt{2}}{2}\right), \left(\sqrt{2}, -\frac{\sqrt{2}}{2}\right)\right\}$

49. The numbers are 3 and 4.
51. The numbers are 5 and $\sqrt{7}$, −5 and $\sqrt{7}$, 5 and $-\sqrt{7}$, or −5 and $-\sqrt{7}$.

Section 13.4 Graphing Calculator Exercises, p. 967

53.

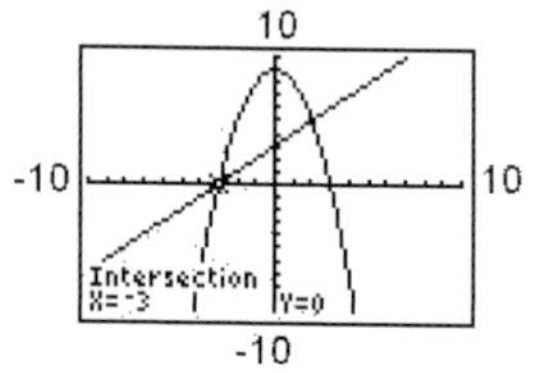

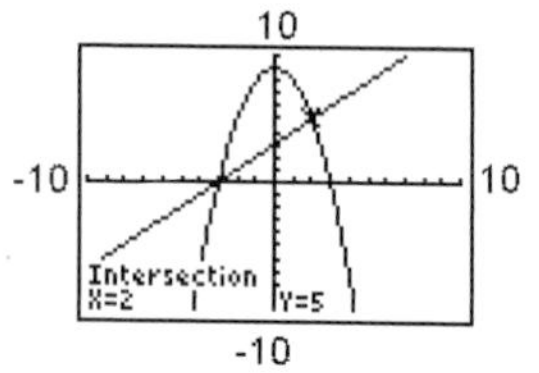

54.

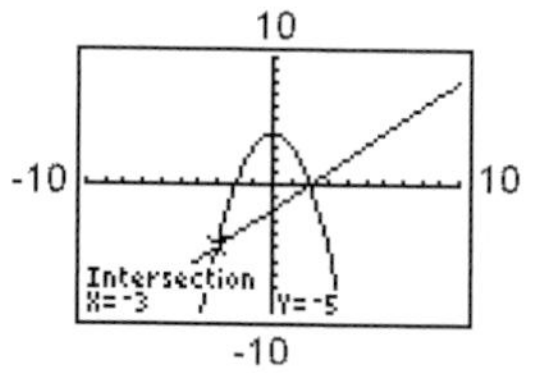

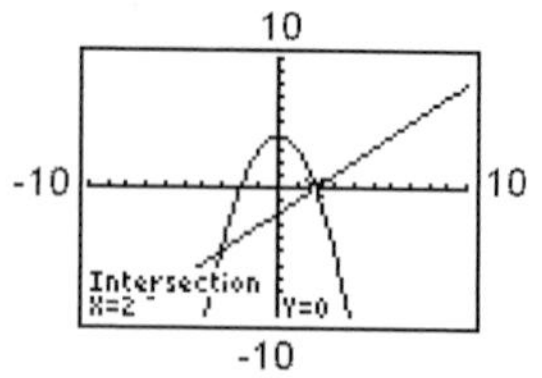

55.

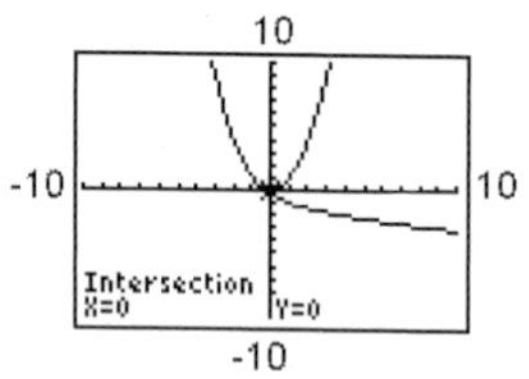

56.

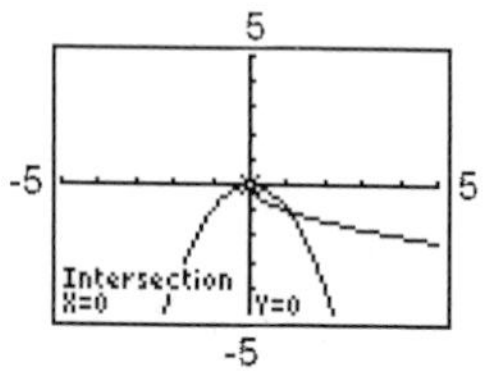

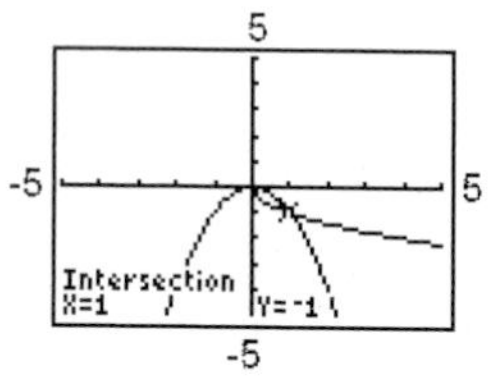

57. { }

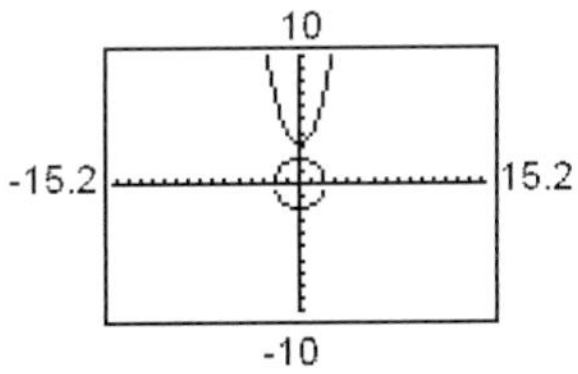

58. { }

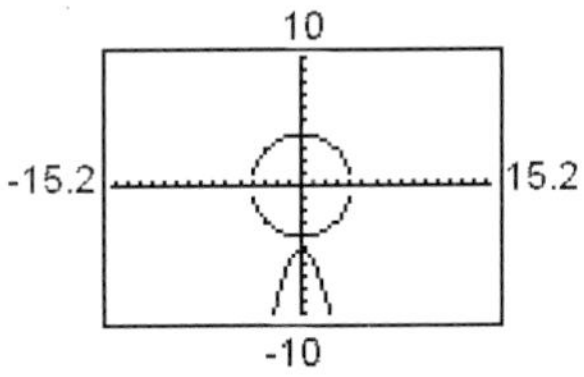

Section 13.5 Practice Exercises, pp. 971–975

1. k **3.** e **5.** i **7.** j **9.** a **11.** d
13. True **15.** False
17. a.

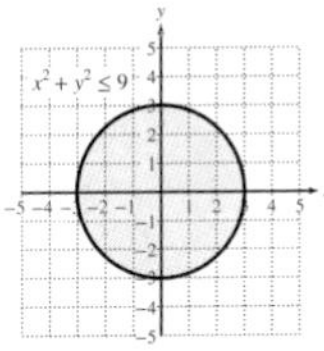

b. The set of points on and "outside" the circle $x^2 + y^2 = 9$
c. The set of points on the circle $x^2 + y^2 = 9$

19. a.

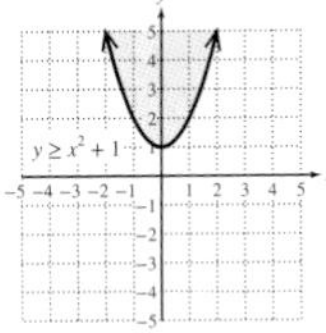

b. The parabola $y = x^2 + 1$ would be drawn as a dashed curve.

21. $(x-3)^2 + (y+4)^2 \le 625$

23.

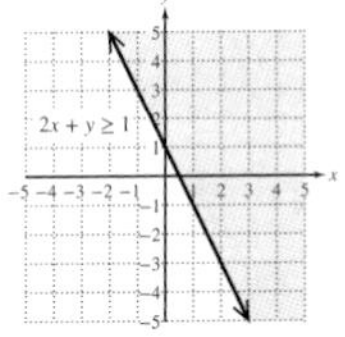

25.

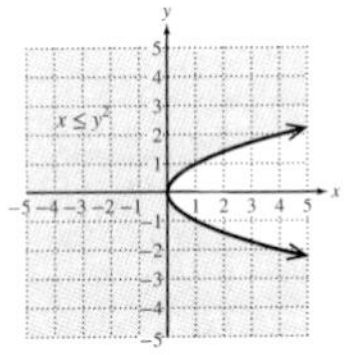

27.

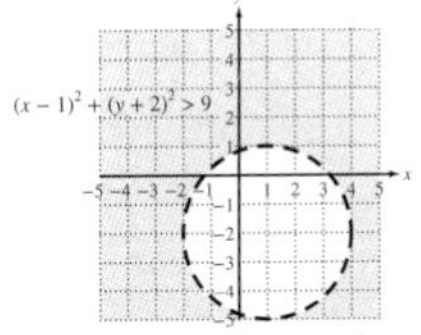

29.

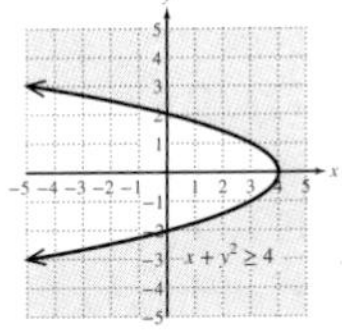

31.

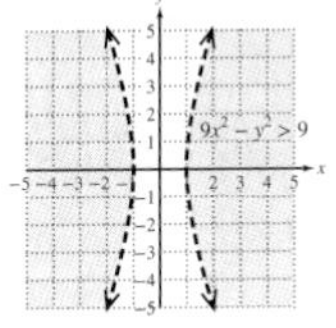

33.

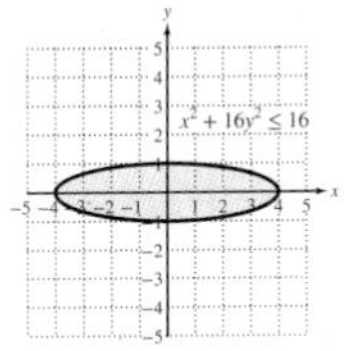

35.

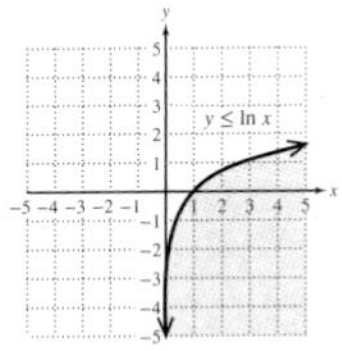

37.

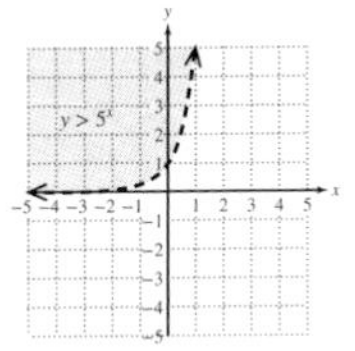

39.

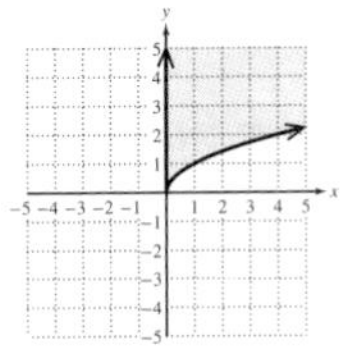

41.

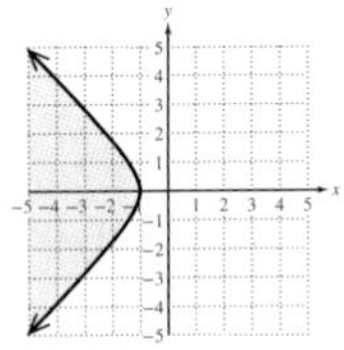

43.

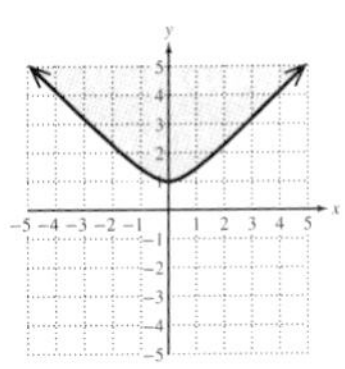

45.

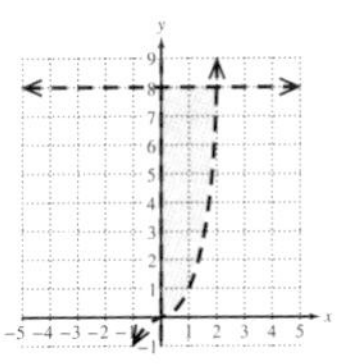

47. { }

49.

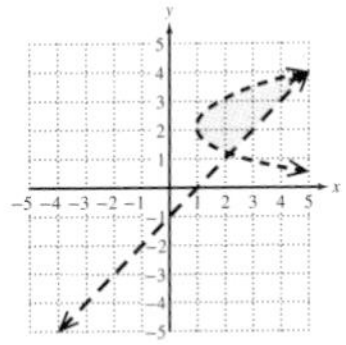

51.

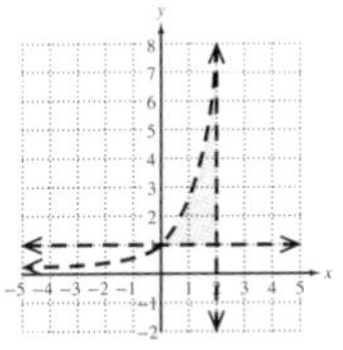

53.

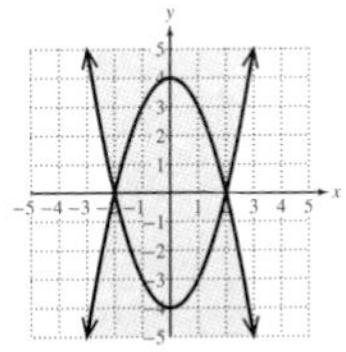

55.

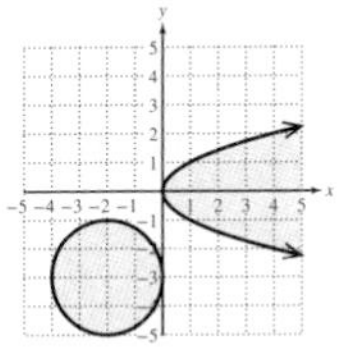

Chapter 13 Review Exercises, pp. 982–985

1. $2\sqrt{10}$ **2.** $\sqrt{89}$ **3.** $x = 5$ or $x = -1$
4. $x = -3$ **5.** Center (12, 3); $r = 4$
6. Center (−7, 5); $r = 9$ **7.** Center (−3, −8); $r = 2\sqrt{5}$
8. Center (1, −6); $r = 4\sqrt{2}$ **9. a.** $x^2 + y^2 = 64$
b. $(x-8)^2 + (y-8)^2 = 64$ **10.** $(x+6)^2 + (y-5)^2 = 10$
11. $(x+2)^2 + (y+8)^2 = 8$

12. $\left(x - \frac{1}{2}\right)^2 + (y-2)^2 = 4$

13. $(x-3)^2 + \left(y - \frac{1}{3}\right)^2 = 9$ **14.** $x^2 + y^2 = \frac{49}{4}$

15. $x^2 + (y-2)^2 = 9$ **16.** (−4, −2) **17.** (−1, 8)
18. Vertical axis of symmetry; parabola opens downward
19. Horizontal axis of symmetry; parabola opens right
20. Horizontal axis of symmetry; parabola opens left
21. Vertical axis of symmetry; parabola opens upward

22.

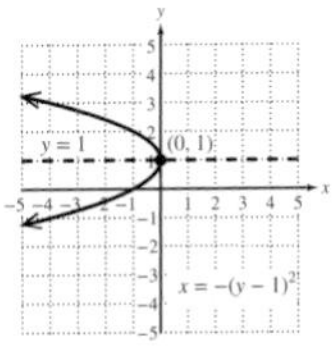

23.

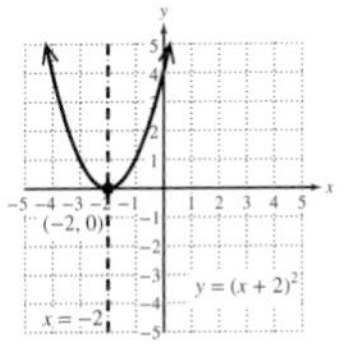

24.

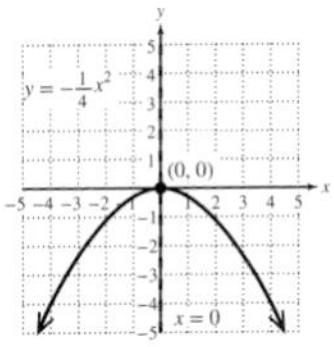

25.

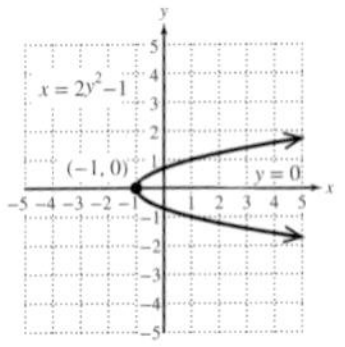

26. $y = (x-3)^2 - 4$; vertex: (3, −4); axis of symmetry: $x = 3$

27. $x = (y+2)^2 - 2$; vertex: (−2, −2); axis of symmetry: $y = -2$

28. $x = -4\left(y - \frac{1}{2}\right)^2 + 1$; vertex: $\left(1, \frac{1}{2}\right)$; axis of symmetry: $y = \frac{1}{2}$

29. $y = -2\left(x + \frac{1}{2}\right)^2 + \frac{1}{2}$; vertex: $\left(-\frac{1}{2}, \frac{1}{2}\right)$; axis of symmetry: $x = -\frac{1}{2}$

30.

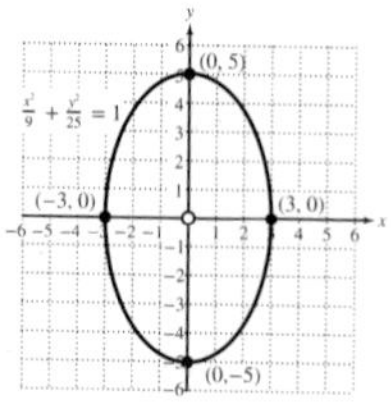

31.

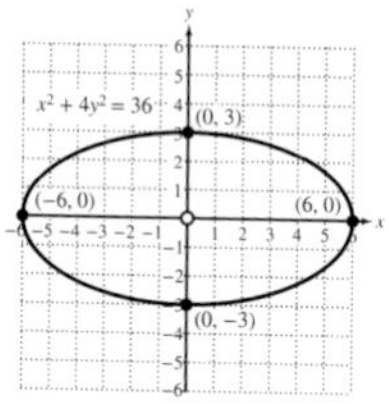

32. Center: (5, −3)

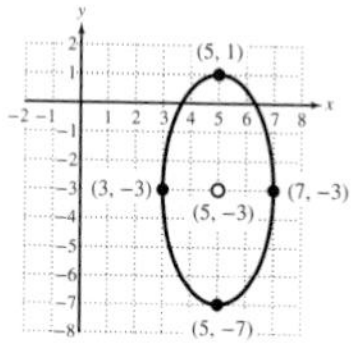

33. Center: (0, 2)

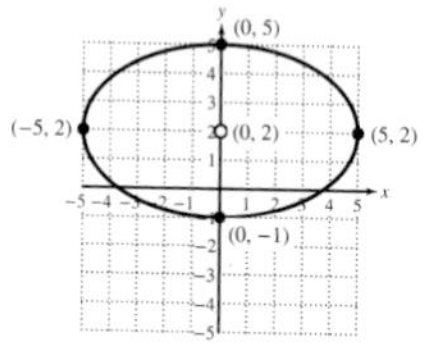

34. Horizontal **35.** Vertical
36. Vertical **37.** Horizontal

38.

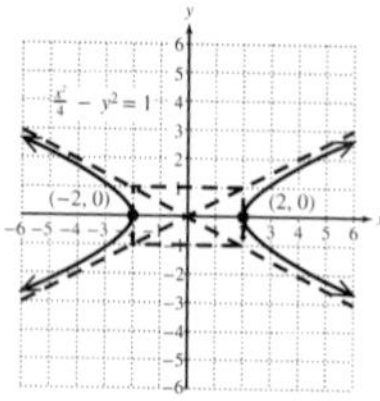

39.

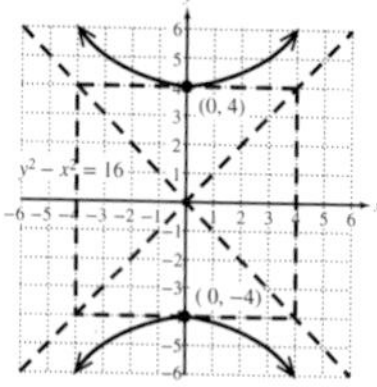

40. Hyperbola **41.** Ellipse
42. Ellipse **43.** Hyperbola

44. a. Line and parabola
b.

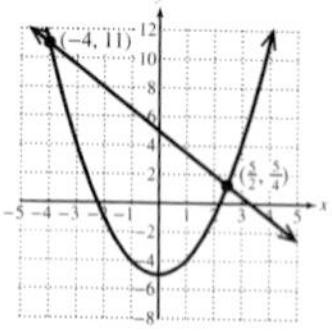

c. $\left\{\left(\frac{5}{2}, \frac{5}{4}\right), (-4, 11)\right\}$

45. a. Line and parabola
b.

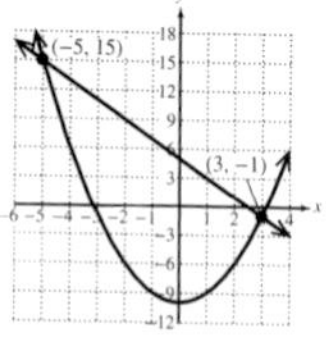

c. $\{(-5, 15), (3, -1)\}$

46. a. Circle and line
b.

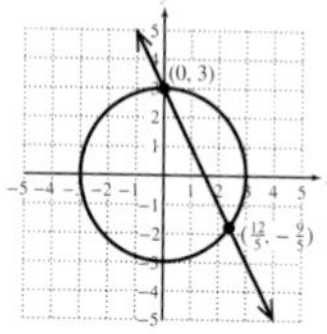

c. $\left\{(0, 3), \left(\frac{12}{5}, -\frac{9}{5}\right)\right\}$

47. a. Circle and line
b.

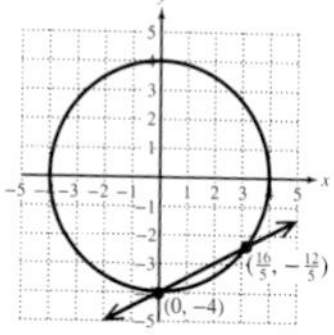

c. $\left\{(0, -4), \left(\frac{16}{5}, -\frac{12}{5}\right)\right\}$

48. $\left\{(0, -2), \left(\frac{16}{9}, \frac{14}{9}\right)\right\}$ **49.** $\left\{\left(-\frac{7}{5}, \frac{13}{5}\right), (-5, -1)\right\}$

50. $\{(8, 4), (2, -2)\}$ **51.** $\{(2, 4), (-2, 4), (\sqrt{2}, 2), (-\sqrt{2}, 2)\}$
52. $\{(3, 1), (3, -1), (-3, 1), (-3, -1)\}$
53. $\{(6, 5), (-6, 5), (6, -5), (-6, -5)\}$

54.

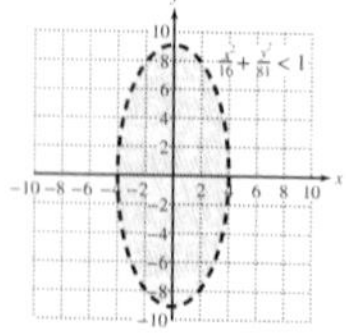

55.

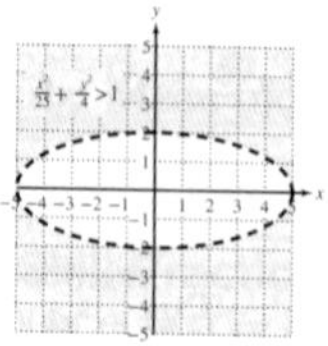

56.

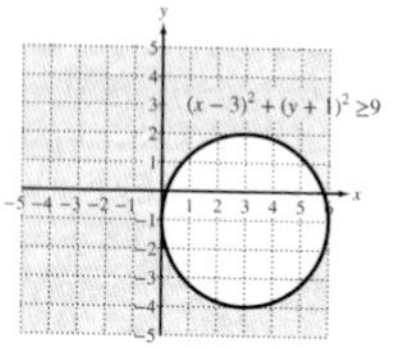

57.

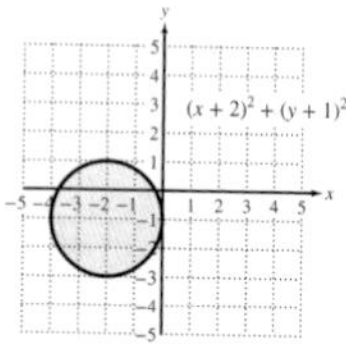

58.

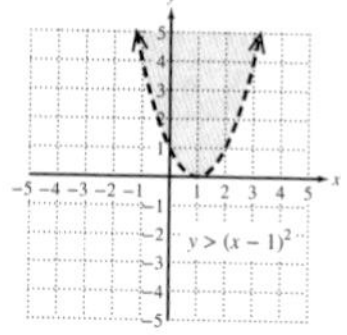

59.

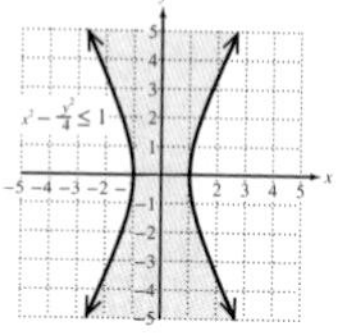

60.

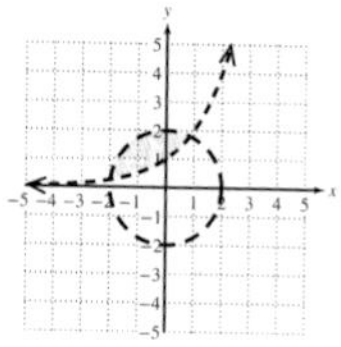

61.

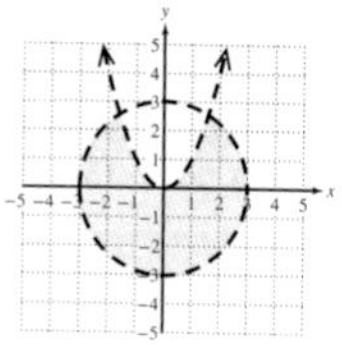

Chapter 13 Test, pp. 985–986

1. $4\sqrt{2}$ **2.** Center: $\left(\frac{5}{6}, -\frac{1}{3}\right)$; $r=\frac{5}{7}$
3. Center: (0, 2); $r = 3$ **4. a.** $\sqrt{5}$ **b.** $x^2+(y-4)^2=5$
5. The center is the midpoint (3.8, 1.95).

6.

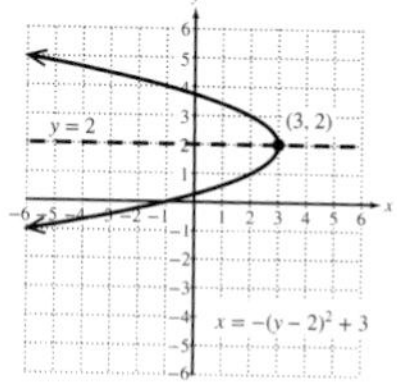

7.

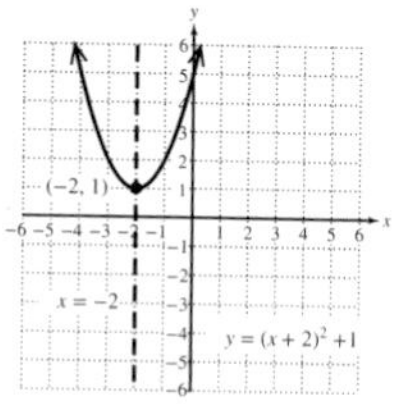

8.

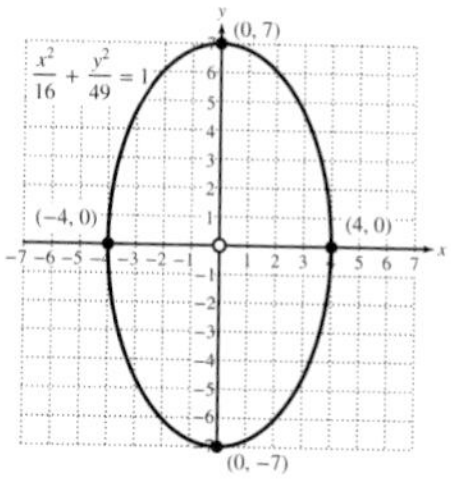

9.

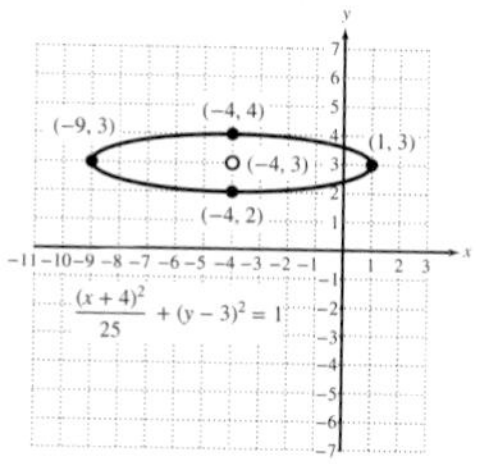

10.

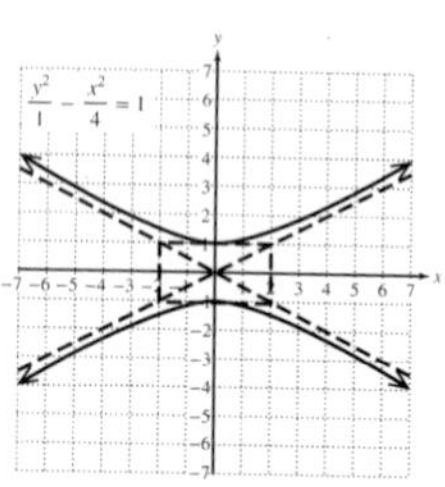

11. $\{(-3, 0), (0, 4)\}$; graph b **12.** { }; graph a
13. The addition method can be used if the equations have corresponding *like* terms. **14.** $\{(2, 0), (-2, 0)\}$

15.

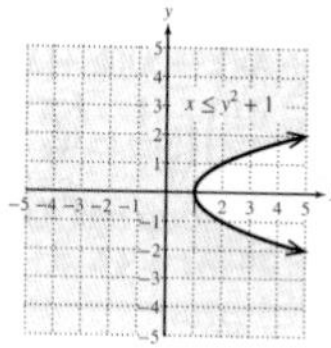

16.

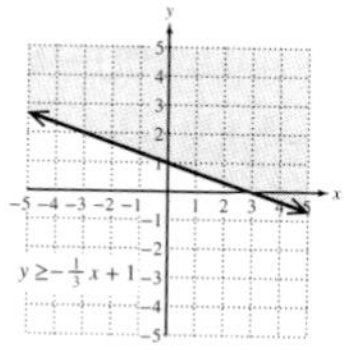

17.

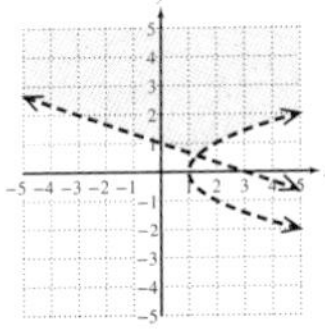

18.

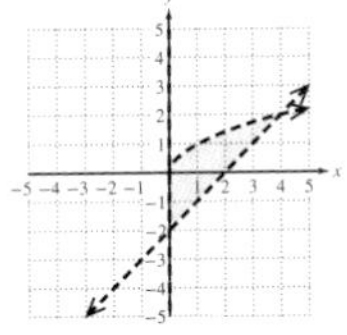

Chapters 1–13 Cumulative Review Exercises, pp. 987–988

1. $\{x \mid x \text{ is a real number}\}$

2. $\left(\frac{10}{3}, \infty\right)$

3. The integers are 10 and 15. **4. a.** $(-5, 0), (0, 3)$ **b.** $m = \frac{3}{5}$

c.

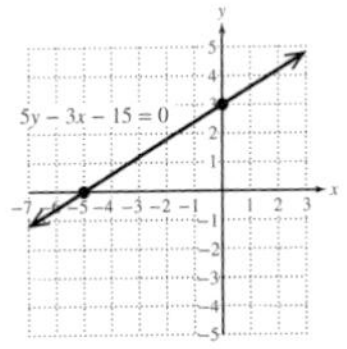

5. slope: $\frac{3}{4}$; y-intercept: $\left(0, -\frac{3}{2}\right)$

6. There are 12 dimes and 5 quarters.

7. $\{(2, -3, 1)\}$ **8.** $\left\{\left(\frac{5}{2}, \frac{3}{2}\right)\right\}$ **9.** $\{(6, 3)\}$

10. $f(0) = -12; f(-1) = -16; f(2) = -10; f(4) = -16$

11. $(-4, -2)$ **12.** $z = 32$ **13.** $(g \circ f)(x) = x + 7$; $x \geq -1$ **14. a.** -5 **b.** $(x + 1)(x^2 + 1)$; -5

c. They are the same. **15.** $(x + y)(x - y - 6)$

16. $x^3 - 2x^2 - 7x - 4$ **17.** $\left\{6, \frac{3}{2}\right\}$ **18.** $\frac{a - 1}{a + 2}$

19. $\frac{-x^2 - x - 4}{(x + 3)(x - 2)}$ **20.** $\{0, -1\}$ **21. a.** $\{\ \}$

b. $\{-11\}$ **22.** $-30 + 24i$ **23.** $\frac{12}{41} + \frac{15}{41}i$

24. $2\sqrt{7}$ m **25. a.** 17.6 ft; 39.6 ft; 70.4 ft **b.** 8 sec

26. $\left\{-\frac{1}{5}, \frac{1}{10} \pm \frac{\sqrt{3}}{10}i\right\}$ **27.** $\{2 \pm \sqrt{11}\}$

28. $(-5, -36)$

29. a. $(-3, 0), (1, 0)$ **b.** $(0, 3)$ **c** $(-1, 4)$

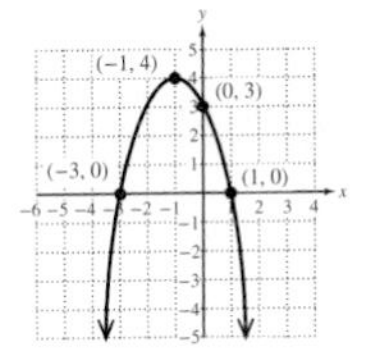

30. $(-1, 19)$ **31.** $\left(-\infty, \frac{1}{2}\right] \cup \left[\frac{9}{2}, \infty\right)$ **32.** $\log_8 32 = \frac{5}{3}$

33. $\left\{\frac{2}{3}\right\}$ **34.** $h^{-1}(x) = \sqrt[3]{x + 1}$

35. $x^2 + (y - 5)^2 = 16$

36.

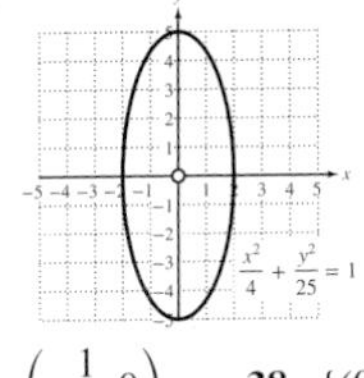

37. $\left(-\frac{1}{2}, 0\right)$ **38.** $\{(0, -4)\}$

39.

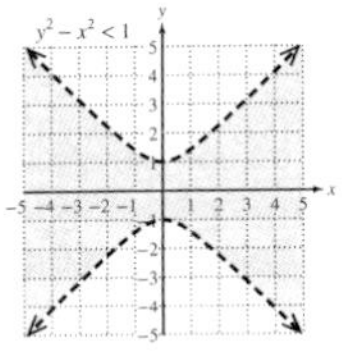

40.

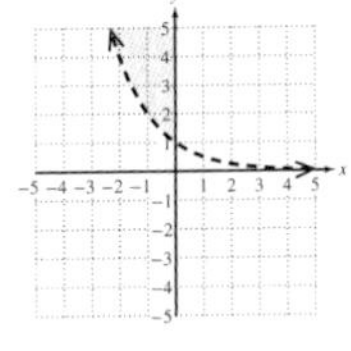

Chapter 14

Section 14.1 Practice Exercises, pp. 995–996

1. a. $a^2 + 2ab + b^2$; $a^3 + 3a^2b + 3ab^2 + b^3$; binomial **b.** $n(n - 1)(n - 2) \cdots (2)(1)$; factorial **c.** 6; 2; 1; 1 **d.** binomial **e.** Pascal's **3.** $a^3 + 3a^2b + 3ab^2 + b^3$

5. $1 + 4g + 6g^2 + 4g^3 + g^4$

7. $p^7 + 7p^6q^2 + 21p^5q^4 + 35p^4q^6 + 35p^3q^8 + 21p^2q^{10} + 7pq^{12} + q^{14}$

9. $s^5 - 5s^4t + 10s^3t^2 - 10s^2t^3 + 5st^4 - t^5$

11. $625 - 500u^3 + 150u^6 - 20u^9 + u^{12}$

13. $x^6 - 12x^4 + 48x^2 - 64$ **15.** 120 **17.** 1 **19.** False

21. True **23.** $6! = 6 \cdot (5 \cdot 4 \cdot 3 \cdot 2 \cdot 1) = 6 \cdot 5!$ **25.** 1680

27. 6 **29.** 56 **31.** 1 **33.** $m^{11} + 11m^{10}n + 55m^9n^2$

35. $u^{24} - 12u^{22}v + 66u^{20}v^2$ **37.** 9 terms

39. $s^6 + 6s^5t + 15s^4t^2 + 20s^3t^3 + 15s^2t^4 + 6st^5 + t^6$

41. $b^3 - 9b^2 + 27b - 27$ **43.** $16x^4 + 32x^3y + 24x^2y^2 + 8xy^3 + y^4$

45. $c^{14} - 7c^{12}d + 21c^{10}d^2 - 35c^8d^3 + 35c^6d^4 - 21c^4d^5 + 7c^2d^6 - d^7$

47. $\frac{1}{32}a^5 - \frac{5}{16}a^4b + \frac{5}{4}a^3b^2 - \frac{5}{2}a^2b^3 + \frac{5}{2}ab^4 - b^5$

49. $x^4 + 16x^3y + 96x^2y^2 + 256xy^3 + 256y^4$

51. $-462m^6n^5$ **53.** $495u^{16}v^4$ **55.** g^9

Section 14.2 Practice Exercises, pp. 1002–1004

1. a. infinite; finite **b.** terms; nth **c.** alternating **d.** series **e.** summation **f.** index; $(3)^2 + (4)^2 + (5)^2$

3. 28 **5.** $16x^4 + 32x^3z + 24x^2z^2 + 8xz^3 + z^4$

7. 4, 7, 10, 13, 16 **9.** $\sqrt{3}, 2, \sqrt{5}, \sqrt{6}$ **11.** $-\frac{2}{3}, \frac{3}{4}, -\frac{4}{5}, \frac{5}{6}$

13. 0, −3, 8 **15.** 0, 2, 6, 12, 20, 30 **17.** −3, 9, −27, 81

19. When n is odd, the term is negative. When n is even, the term is positive. **21.** $a_n = 2n$ **23.** $a_n = 2n - 1$

25. $a_n = \frac{1}{n^2}$ **27.** $a_n = (-1)^{n+1}$ **29.** $a_n = (-1)^n 2^n$

31. $a_n = \frac{3}{5^n}$ **33.** \$60, \$58.80, \$57.62, \$56.47

35. 25,000; 50,000; 100,000; 200,000; 400,000; 800,000; 1,600,000

37. A sequence is an ordered list of terms. A series is the sum of the terms of a sequence.

39. 90 **41.** $\frac{31}{16}$ **43.** 30 **45.** 10 **47.** $\frac{73}{12}$ **49.** 38

51. −1 **53.** 55 **55.** $\sum_{n=1}^{6} n$ **57.** $\sum_{i=1}^{5} 4$ **59.** $\sum_{j=1}^{5} 4j$

61. $\sum_{k=1}^{4} (-1)^{k+1}\frac{1}{3^k}$ **63.** $\sum_{i=1}^{6} \frac{i + 4}{11i}$ **65.** $\sum_{n=1}^{5} x^n$

67. −3, 2, 7, 12, 17 **69.** 5, 21, 85, 341, 1365

71. 1, 1, 2, 3, 5, 8, 13, 21, 34, 55

Section 14.3 Practice Exercises, pp. 1009–1010

1. a. arithmetic **b.** difference **c.** $a_1 + (n - 1)d$; d **d.** series **e.** $\frac{n}{2}(a_1 + a_n)$

3. −1, 1, −1, 1 **5.** −55 **7.** 3, 11, 19, 27, 35

9. 80, 60, 40, 20, 0 **11.** $3, \frac{15}{4}, \frac{9}{2}, \frac{21}{4}, 6$ **13.** 2 **15.** −3

17. −2 **19.** 3, 8, 13, 18, 23 **21.** $2, \frac{5}{2}, 3, \frac{7}{2}, 4$

23. 2, −2, −6, −10, −14 **25.** $a_n = -5 + 5n$

27. $a_n = -2n$ **29.** $a_n = \frac{3}{2} + \frac{1}{2}n$ **31.** $a_n = 25 - 4n$

33. $a_n = -14 + 6n$ **35.** $a_6 = 17$ **37.** $a_9 = 47$

39. $a_7 = -30$ **41.** $a_{11} = -48$ **43.** 19 **45.** 22

47. 23 **49.** 11 **51.** $a_1 = -2, a_2 = -5$ **53.** 670

55. 290 **57.** −15 **59.** 95 **61.** 924 **63.** 300

65. −210 **67.** 5050 **69.** 980 seats; \$14,700

Section 14.4 Practice Exercises, pp. 1016–1019

1. a. geometric **b.** ratio **c.** a_1r^{n-1} **d.** $\frac{a_1(1-r^n)}{1-r}$ **e.** $\frac{a_1}{1-r}$; 1 **3.** $a_n = 4n - 8$ **5.** 25 **7.** 1, 10, 100, 1000

9. 64, 32, 16, 8 **11.** $8, -2, \frac{1}{2}, -\frac{1}{8}$ **13.** 2 **15.** $-\frac{1}{4}$

17. −2 **19.** −3, 6, −12, 24, −48 **21.** $6, 3, \frac{3}{2}, \frac{3}{4}, \frac{3}{8}$

23. −1, −6, −36, −216, −1296 **25.** $a_n = 3(4)^{n-1}$

27. $a_n = -5(-3)^{n-1}$ **29.** $a_n = \frac{1}{2}(4)^{n-1}$ **31.** $\frac{1}{64}$

33. $-\frac{243}{8}$ **35.** −48 **37.** −9 **39.** $\frac{1}{8}$ **41.** 4

43. A geometric sequence is an ordered list of numbers in which the ratio between each term and its predecessor is constant. A geometric series is the sum of the terms of such a sequence.

45. a. 3 + 12 + 48 + 192 **b.** 255

47. $\frac{1562}{125}$ **49.** $-\frac{11}{8}$ **51.** $\frac{3124}{27}$ **53.** $\frac{665}{243}$

55. −172 **57. a.** \$1050.00, \$1102.50, \$1157.63, \$1215.51 **b.** $a_{10} = \$1628.89$; $a_{20} = \$2653.30$; $a_{40} = \$7039.99$

59. $r = \frac{1}{6}$; sum is $\frac{6}{5}$ **61.** $r = -\frac{1}{4}$; sum is $\frac{4}{5}$

63. $r = -\frac{3}{2}$; sum does not exist **65.** The sum is \$800 million.

67. The total vertical distance traveled is 28 ft.

69. a. $\frac{7}{10}$ **b.** $\frac{1}{10}$ **c.** $\frac{7}{9}$ **71. a.** \$1,429,348 **b.** \$1,505,828 **c.** \$76,480

Section 14.4 Problem Recognition Exercises, p. 1019

1. Geometric, $r = -\frac{1}{2}$ **2.** Arithmetic, $d = \frac{1}{2}$

3. Geometric, $r = 2$ **4.** Neither **5.** Arithmetic, $d = \frac{2}{3}$

6. Geometric, $r = -\frac{3}{2}$ **7.** Neither **8.** Geometric, $r = -1$

9. Arithmetic, $d = -2$ **10.** Neither **11.** Neither

12. Arithmetic, $d = 4$ **13.** Arithmetic, $d = \frac{1}{4}\pi$

14. Geometric, $r = -1$ **15.** Neither

16. Arithmetic, $d = \frac{1}{3}e$ **17.** Neither **18.** Geometric, $r = 3$

Chapter 14 Review Exercises, pp. 1024–1025

1. 40,320 **2.** 120 **3.** 66 **4.** 84
5. $x^{10} + 20x^8 + 160x^6 + 640x^4 + 1280x^2 + 1024$
6. $c^4 - 12c^3d + 54c^2d^2 - 108cd^3 + 81d^4$
7. $a^{11} - 22a^{10}b + 220a^9b^2$ **8.** $1512x^{10}y^3$
9. $-15{,}000x^3y^{21}$ **10.** $160a^3b^3$ **11.** 1, −2, −5, −8, −11

12. −2, −16, −54 **13.** $\frac{1}{3}, -\frac{1}{2}, \frac{3}{5}, -\frac{2}{3}$ **14.** $-\frac{2}{3}, \frac{4}{9}, -\frac{8}{27}, \frac{16}{81}$

15. $a_n = \frac{n}{n+1}$ **16.** $a_n = (-1)^n \cdot \frac{3}{2^n}$ **17.** k **18.** 5

19. 5 **20.** −22 **21.** $\sum_{i=1}^{7} \frac{i+3}{i}$ **22.** $a_n = n^2 + \left(\frac{n}{2}\right)h$

23. −12, −10.5, −9, −7.5, −6 **24.** $\frac{2}{3}, 1, \frac{4}{3}, \frac{5}{3}, 2$

25. $a_n = 10n - 9$ **26.** $a_n = -14n + 20$ **27.** $a_{17} = \frac{9}{2}$

28. $a_{25} = -155$ **29.** 24 terms **30.** 19 terms
31. $d = 10$ **32.** $a_n = -5n + 19$ **33.** −620
34. 92.5 **35.** 294 **36.** 5989 **37.** $r = 3$

38. $r = 1.2$ **39.** $-1, \frac{1}{4}, -\frac{1}{16}, \frac{1}{64}$ **40.** 10, 20, 40, 80

41. $a_n = -4(2)^{n-1}$ **42.** $a_n = 6\left(-\frac{1}{3}\right)^{n-1}$ **43.** $a_6 = \frac{128}{243}$

44. $a_4 = 270$ **45.** $a_1 = 4$ **46.** $a_1 = 1$ **47.** 1275

48. $-\frac{182}{3}$ **49.** 18 **50.** $\frac{25}{2}$

51. a. \$10,700, \$11,449, \$12,250.43 **b.** The account is worth \$12,250.43 after 3 yr. **c.** \$19,671.51

Chapter 14 Test, pp. 1025–1026

1. 1 **2.** 210 **3.** $a^4 + 4a^3b + 6a^2b^2 + 4ab^3 + b^4$
4. $81y^4 - 216y^3x^2 + 216y^2x^4 - 96yx^6 + 16x^8$

5. $-56a^3c^{15}$ **6.** $-1, -\frac{3}{4}, -\frac{3}{5}, -\frac{1}{2}$ **7.** 65

8. a. 8, 9.5, 11, 12.5, 14 **b.** $a_n = 1.5n + 6.5$ **9.** $\sum_{n=1}^{4} x^{3n}$

10. $d = \frac{1}{4}$ **11.** $r = \frac{1}{3}$ **12. a.** −15, −18, −21, −24 **b.** $a_n = -3n - 12$ **c.** $a_{40} = -132$ **13. a.** 4, −8, 16, −32

b. $a_n = 4(-2)^{n-1}$ **c.** −2048 **14.** $a_n = \frac{3}{5} \cdot \left(\frac{1}{2}\right)^{n-1}$

15. $a_n = -2n + 22$ **16.** 31 terms **17.** 7 terms

18. 10,900 **19.** $\frac{1023}{64}$ **20.** 8 **21.** $a_1 = \frac{1}{27}$

22. $a_{18} = -202$ **23. a.** \$2007.50 **b.** \$2087.80 **c.** \$6260.69 **d.** \$112,590.51

Chapters 1–14 Cumulative Review Exercises, pp. 1027–1028

1. $x^2 - x - 13$ **2.** $\frac{20a^6}{b^{10}}$ **3.** $\frac{1}{16}$ **4.** $\frac{\sqrt{10}}{2}$

5. $\frac{2c+5}{2(c+4)}$ **6.** $-\frac{xy}{x+y}$ **7.** 4 **8.** $3xy^4\sqrt[3]{2x^2z^2}$

9. $-\frac{a+1}{a}$ **10.** $\frac{2x+5}{(x-5)(x-2)(x+10)}$ **11.** $7x^2\sqrt{2x}$

12. $x - 9y$ **13.** $2x^3 + 3x^2 + 6x + 17 + \frac{27}{x-2}$

14. $(2a - 7)(3a + 2)$ **15.** $3c(5c - 2)(5c + 2)$
16. $(3x + 4y^2)(9x^2 - 12xy^2 + 16y^4)$
17. $(w + 9)(w - 2)(w + 2)$ **18.** {4} **19.** {0}

20. $\left\{\frac{5}{4}\right\}$ **21.** $\left\{\frac{2}{5} \pm \frac{\sqrt{3}}{5}i\right\}$ **22.** {4, −4, 1, −1}

23. $\left\{\frac{7}{2}, -\frac{3}{4}\right\}$ **24.** {1} **25.** {2} (The value −5 does not check.) **26.** $\ln\left(\frac{x\sqrt{z}}{y^5}\right)$ **27.** 3.4929

28. [−2, 5) **29.** [−5, 0] ∪ [1, ∞) **30.** {5}
31. (−∞, −4) ∪ [−1, ∞) **32.** (−∞, 1) ∪ (3, ∞)

33.

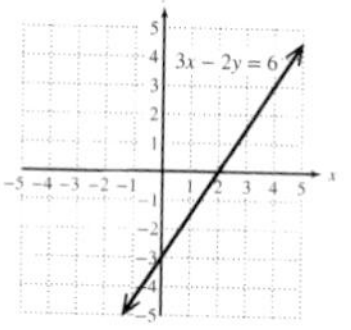

34.

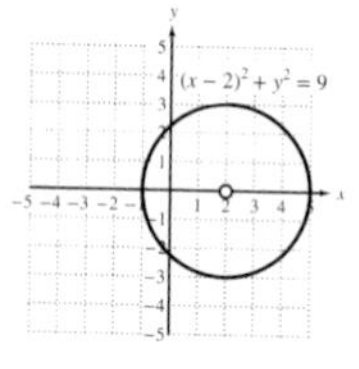

35.

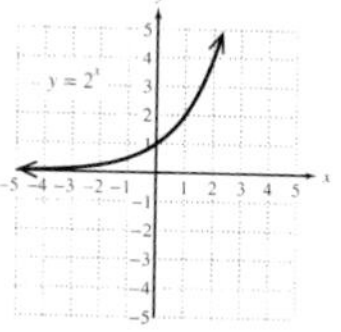

36.

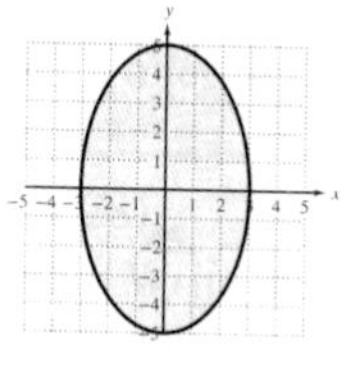

37. a. (−1, 0), (−5, 0) **b.** (0, 5) **c.** (−3, −4)
38. slope −4; y-intercept (0, 6) **39.** $y = -5x + 18$
40. a. 2 **b.** undefined **c.** $x = 2$ **d.** (−∞, 4) **e.** (−∞, 3]

41. $(-\infty, 5]$ **42.** $\{(3, -1)\}$ **43.** $\{(1, 2, 3)\}$

44. a. $2\sqrt{13}$ **b.** $(6, -2)$ **45.** $b_1 = \dfrac{2A - hb_2}{h}$

46. $t(9) = 4.2$; This means that it will take the rat 4.2 min if the rat has practiced 9 times. **47.** The car is moving 75 mph. **48.** The angles are 57° and 123°. **49.** She invested \$8000 at 6.5% and \$5000 at 5%. **50.** The plane travels 500 mph in still air. The wind speed is 50 mph.

Additional Topics Appendix

Section A.1 Practice Exercises, pp. A-4–A-6

1. Let $u = 3x - 2$. **3.** Factor the first three terms as $(x - 2)^2$. **5.** $2(4t + 3)(2t - 1)$ **7.** $(2w - 3)(w - 5)$ **9.** $(5x + 20 - y)(5x + 20 + y)$ **11.** $(15a - 7)(15a - 11)$ **13.** $-1(t + 3)(3t - 1)$ **15.** $(a + b + c)(a^2 + 2ab + b^2 - ac - bc + c^2)$ **17.** $(3c - d - 2)(9c^2 + 3cd + 6c + d^2 + 4d + 4)$ **19.** $(2x + 14y + 7)^2$ **21.** $(x - 5 - y)(x - 5 + y)$ **23.** $(a - x - 9y)(a + x + 9y)$ **25.** $(5a + 2b - 10c)(5a + 2b + 10c)$ **27.** $(8w - 3t + 4p)(8w + 3t - 4p)$ **29.** $(x + 2y)(x - 2y - 1)$ **31.** $(w + 2)(w^2 - 2w + 4)(w^2 + 1)(w - 1)(w + 1)$ **33.** $(y - 4)(x + 2z - 2)$ **35.** $(x - y)(x + 2y + 1)$ **37.** $(n - 4)(n^2 + 4n + 16)(n + 1)(n^2 - n + 1)$ **39.** $(a + b - 3c + 3d)^2$ **41.** $2x(2x - 5)(x + 3)(x - 3)$ **43.** $(a + b)(a + b - 1)$ **45.** $(x - y)(x + y)^2$ **47.** $(a + 3)^3(a + 9)$ **49.** $18(3x + 5)^2(4x + 5)$

51. $\left(\frac{1}{10}x + \frac{1}{7}\right)^2$ **53.** $5x^2(5x^2 - 6)$

55. $(4p^2 + q^2)(2p - q)(2p + q)$ **57.** $\left(y + \frac{1}{4}\right)\left(y^2 - \frac{1}{4}y + \frac{1}{16}\right)$

59. $(a + b)(a - b)(6a + b)$ **61.** $\left(\frac{1}{3}t + \frac{1}{4}\right)^2$

63. $(3a + b)(2x - y)$ **65.** $(x^4 + 1)(x^2 + 1)(x + 1)(x - 1)$ **67.** $(5c - 3d)(5c + 3d + 1)$

Section A.2 Practice Exercises, pp. A-11–A-15

1. 88 **3.** 5 **5.** 6 **7.** −15.8 **9.** 5.8 hr **11. a.** 397 Cal **b.** 386 Cal **c.** There is only an 11-Cal difference in the means. **13. a.** 86.5% **b.** 81% **c.** The low score of 59% decreased Zach's average by 5.5%. **15.** 17 **17.** 110.5 **19.** −52.5 **21.** 3.93 deaths per 1000 **23.** 0 **25.** 51.7 million passengers **27.** 4 **29.** −21 and −24 **31.** No mode **33.** 3.66 in. **35.** 5.2% and 5.8% **37.** Mean: 85.5%; median: 94.5%; The median gives Jonathan a better overall score. **39.** Mean: \$250; median: \$256; mode: There is no mode. **41.** Mean: \$942,500; median: \$848,500; mode: \$850,000 **43.** 2.38 **45.** 2.77 **47.** 3.3; Elmer's GPA improved from 2.5 to 3.3.

49.

Number of Residents in Each House	Number of Houses	Product
1	3	3
2	9	18
3	10	30
4	9	36
5	6	30
Total:	37	117

The mean number of residents is approximately 3.2.

Section A.3 Practice Exercises, pp. A-25–A-31

1. Perimeter **3.** 32 m **5.** 17.2 mi **7.** $11\frac{1}{2}$ in.

9. 31.4 ft **11.** a, f, g **13.** 33 cm^2 **15.** 16.81 m^2 **17.** 84 $in.^2$ **19.** 10.12 km^2 **21.** 13.8474 ft^2 **23.** 66 $in.^2$ **25.** 31.5 ft^2 **27.** c, d, h **29.** 307.72 cm^3 **31.** 39 $in.^3$ **33.** 113.04 cm^3 **35.** 1695.6 cm^3 **37.** 3052.08 $in.^3$ **39.** 113.04 cm^3 **41. a.** \$0.25/ft^2 **b.** \$104 **43.** Perimeter **45.** 54 ft **47. a.** 57,600 ft^2 **b.** 19,200 pieces **49. a.** 50.24 $in.^2$ **b.** 113.04 $in.^2$ **c.** One 12-in. pizza **51.** 289.3824 cm^3 **53.** True **55.** True **57.** True **59.** Not possible **61.** For example: 100°, 80° **63.** 45° **65. a.** $\angle 1$ and $\angle 3$, $\angle 2$ and $\angle 4$ **b.** $\angle 1$ and $\angle 2$, $\angle 2$ and $\angle 3$, $\angle 3$ and $\angle 4$, $\angle 1$ and $\angle 4$ **c.** $m(\angle 1) = 100°$, $m(\angle 2) = 80°$, $m(\angle 3) = 100°$ **67.** 57° **69.** 78° **71.** 147° **73.** 58° **75.** 7 **77.** 1 **79.** 1 **81.** 5 **83.** $m(\angle a) = 45°$, $m(\angle b) = 135°$, $m(\angle c) = 45°$, $m(\angle d) = 135°$, $m(\angle e) = 45°$, $m(\angle f) = 135°$, $m(\angle g) = 45°$ **85.** Scalene **87.** Isosceles **89.** True **91.** No, a 90° angle plus an angle greater than 90° would make the sum of the angles greater than 180°. **93.** 40° **95.** 37° **97.** $m(\angle a) = 80°$, $m(\angle b) = 80°$, $m(\angle c) = 100°$, $m(\angle d) = 100°$, $m(\angle e) = 65°$, $m(\angle f) = 115°$, $m(\angle g) = 115°$, $m(\angle h) = 35°$, $m(\angle i) = 145°$, $m(\angle j) = 145°$ **99.** $m(\angle a) = 70°$, $m(\angle b) = 65°$, $m(\angle c) = 65°$, $m(\angle d) = 110°$, $m(\angle e) = 70°$, $m(\angle f) = 110°$, $m(\angle g) = 115°$, $m(\angle h) = 115°$, $m(\angle i) = 65°$, $m(\angle j) = 70°$, $m(\angle k) = 65°$ **101.** 82 ft **103.** 36 $in.^2$ **105.** 15.2464 cm^2

Section A.4 Practice Exercises, pp. A-38–A-40

1. a. matrix; rows; columns **b.** column; one; square **c.** coefficient; augmented **d.** row echelon

3. $\left\{\left(12, \frac{1}{2}\right)\right\}$ **5.** $\{(1, 3, -3)\}$ **7. a.** 3×1 **b.** column matrix

9. a. 2×2 **b.** square matrix **11. a.** 1×4 **b.** row matrix **13. a.** 2×3 **b.** none of these

15. $\left[\begin{array}{cc|c} 1 & -2 & -1 \\ 2 & 1 & -7 \end{array}\right]$ **17.** $\left[\begin{array}{ccc|c} 1 & -2 & 1 & 5 \\ 2 & 6 & 3 & -2 \\ 3 & -1 & -2 & 1 \end{array}\right]$

19. $4x + 3y = 6$
$12x + 5y = -6$ **21.** $x = 4, y = -1, z = 7$

23. a. 7 **b.** −2 **25.** $\left[\begin{array}{cc|c} 1 & \frac{1}{2} & \frac{11}{2} \\ 2 & -1 & 1 \end{array}\right]$

27. $\left[\begin{array}{cc|c} 1 & -4 & 3 \\ 5 & 2 & 1 \end{array}\right]$ **29.** $\left[\begin{array}{cc|c} 1 & 5 & 2 \\ 0 & 11 & 5 \end{array}\right]$

31. a. $\left[\begin{array}{ccc|c} 1 & 3 & 0 & -1 \\ 0 & -11 & -5 & 10 \\ -2 & 0 & -3 & 10 \end{array}\right]$ **b.** $\left[\begin{array}{ccc|c} 1 & 3 & 0 & -1 \\ 0 & -11 & -5 & 10 \\ 0 & 6 & -3 & 8 \end{array}\right]$

33. True **35.** True **37.** Interchange rows 1 and 2. **39.** Multiply row 1 by −3 and add to row 2. Replace row 2 with the result. **41.** $\{(-3, -1)\}$ **43.** $\{(-21, 9)\}$ **45.** Infinitely many solutions; $\{(x, y) \mid x + 3y = 3\}$; dependent equations **47.** $\{(3, -1)\}$ **49.** $\{(-10, 3)\}$ **51.** No solution; { }; inconsistent system **53.** $\{(1, 2, 3)\}$ **55.** $\{(1, -2, 0)\}$

Section A.4 Graphing Calculator Exercises, p. A-40

57.

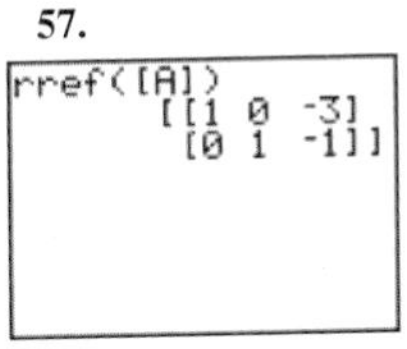

58.

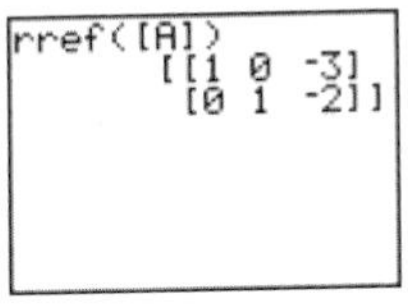

59.

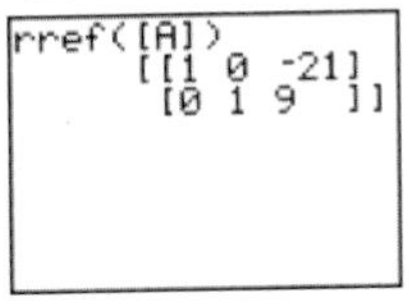

60.

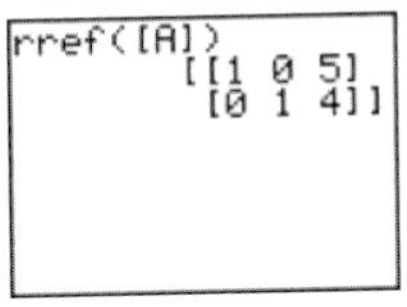

61.

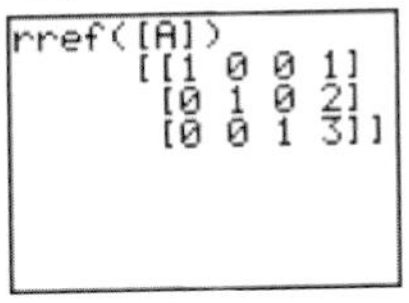

62.

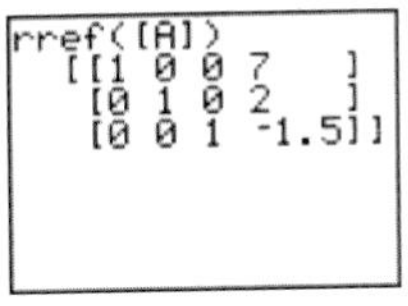

Section A.5 Practice Exercises, pp. A-49–A-52

1. **a.** determinant; $ad - bc$ **b.** minor **c.** a_2; $\begin{vmatrix} b_1 & c_1 \\ b_2 & c_2 \end{vmatrix}$

3. 16 **5.** 1 **7.** 4 **9.** 6 **11.** 26 **13.** 6
15. 46 **17.** **a.** 30 **b.** 30 **19.** Choosing the row or column with the most zero elements simplifies the arithmetic when evaluating a determinant.
21. 12 **23.** -15 **25.** 0 **27.** $8a - 2b$
29. $4x - 3y + 6z$ **31.** 0
33. $\mathbf{D} = 16$; $\mathbf{D}_x = -63$; $\mathbf{D}_y = 66$ **35.** $\{(2, -1)\}$ **37.** $\{(4, -1)\}$
39. $\left\{\left(\frac{23}{13}, \frac{9}{13}\right)\right\}$ **41.** $x = 1$ **43.** $z = \frac{1}{2}$ **45.** $y = \frac{16}{41}$
47. Cramer's rule does not apply when the determinant $\mathbf{D} = 0$.
49. No solution; { }; inconsistent system **51.** $\{(0, 0)\}$
53. Infinitely many solutions; $\{(x, y) \mid x + 5y = 3\}$; dependent equations **55.** $\{(3, 2, 1)\}$
57. No solution; { }; inconsistent system **59.** $x = -19$
61. $w = 1$ **63.** 36 **65.** **a.** 2 **b.** -2 **c.** $x = -1$
67. The measures are 37.5° and 52.5°.
69. 900 tickets in section A, 1500 tickets in section B, and 600 tickets in section C were sold.
71. There were 560 women and 440 men in the survey.

Application Index

Note: Page numbers preceded by the letter *A* or *B* indicate Appendix pages.

Biology/Health/Life Sciences

Business/Economics

Chemistry

Construction/Design

Consumer Applications

Distance/Speed/Time

Education/School

Environment/Earth Science/Geography

Gardening/Landscaping

Geometry

Investments

Politics/Public Policy

Science/Technology

Sports/Exercise/Entertainment

Statistics/Demographics

Subject Index

Note: Page numbers preceded by the letter *A* or *B* indicate Appendix pages.

A

F

G

H

I

J

L

M

N

O

P

Q

R

S

T

U

V

W

X

Y

Z

imeter and Circumference

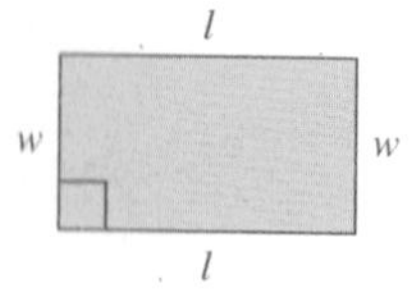

Rectangle

$P = 2l + 2w$

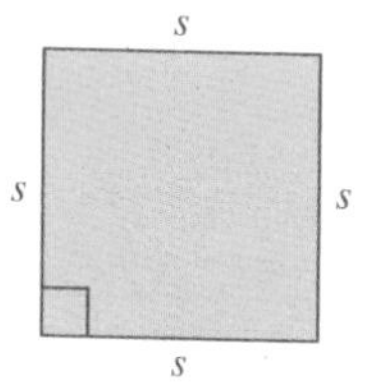

Square

$P = 4s$

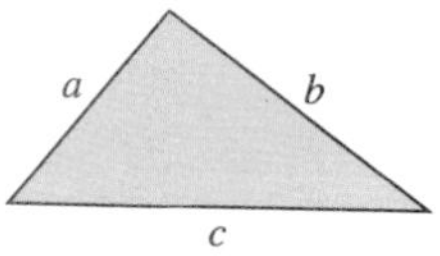

Triangle

$P = a + b + c$

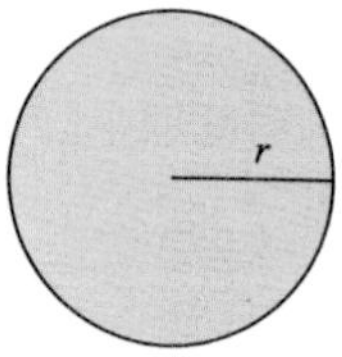

Circle

Circumference: $C = 2\pi r$

Area

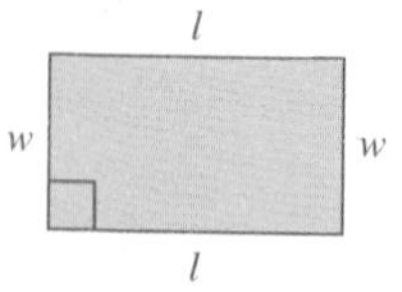

Rectangle

$A = lw$

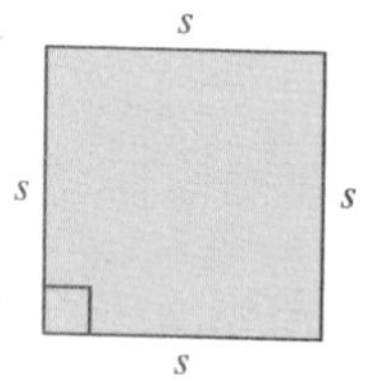

Square

$A = s^2$

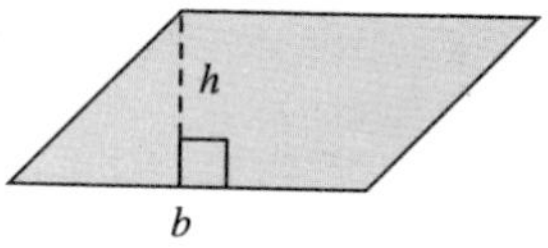

Parallelogram

$A = bh$

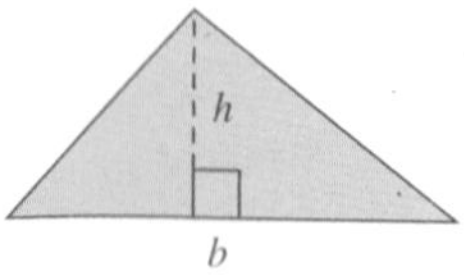

Triangle

$A = \frac{1}{2}bh$

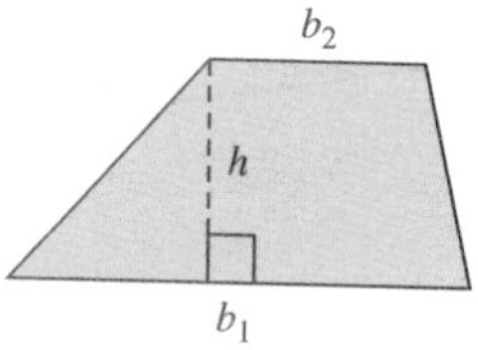

Trapezoid

$A = \frac{1}{2}(b_1 + b_2)h$

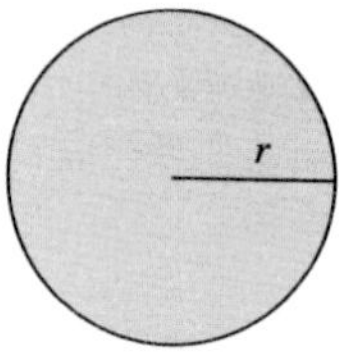

Circle

$A = \pi r^2$

Volume

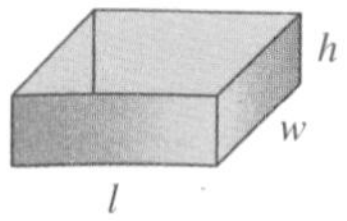

Rectangular Solid

$V = lwh$

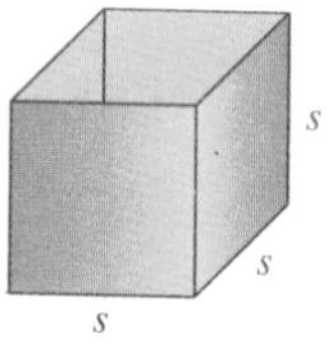

Cube

$V = s^3$

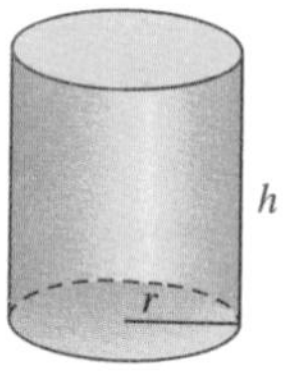

Right Circular Cylinder

$V = \pi r^2 h$

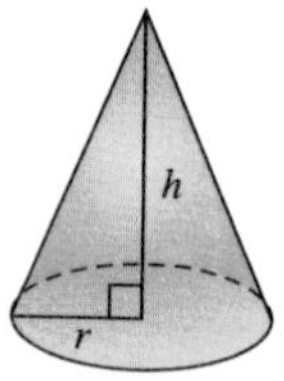

Right Circular Cone

$V = \frac{1}{3}\pi r^2 h$

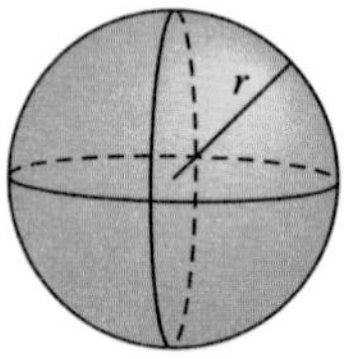

Sphere

$V = \frac{4}{3}\pi r^3$

Angles

- Two angles are **complementary** if the sum of their measures is 90°.

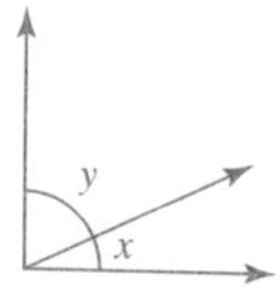

- Two angles are **supplementary** if the sum of their measures is 180°.

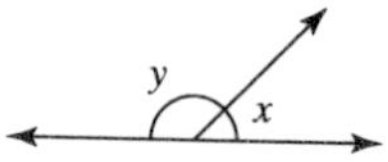

- $\angle a$ and $\angle c$ are vertical angles, and $\angle b$ and $\angle d$ are vertical angles. The measures of vertical angles are equal.

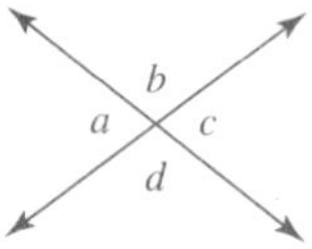

- The sum of the measures of the angles of a triangle is 180°.

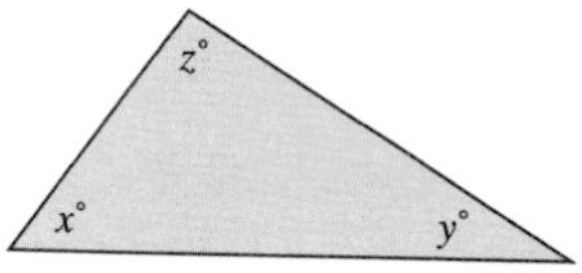

$x^\circ + y^\circ + z^\circ = 180^\circ$